C000156156

# HOTELS AND RESTAURANTS
*in*
# BRITAIN
# AND IRELAND
# 1992

# DISCOUNT SCHEME

Produced by the Publishing Division of The Automobile Association

All establishments in the Guide are regularly inspected by the AA's hotel and restaurant inspectors. The directory is compiled by the AA's Hotel and Touring Information Services Department and generated by the AA's Establishment Database.

The atlas and town plans are prepared by the Cartographic Department of The Automobile Association

**Cover Design:** The Paul Hampson Partnership
Props supplied by Hingstons Antiques, Southampton and Parkhouse & Wyatt, Southampton
**Photographs:** Halmpstone Manor –
Tom Teegan
Feature: Hotel at Work – Eric Meacher
**Features:** Tony Truscott Designs
**Feature:** *RSVP* written by Penny Hicks
**Illustrations:** Image Box

**Head of Advertisement Sales:** Christopher Heard, tel (0256) 20123. **Advertisement Production:** Karen Weeks, tel (0256) 20123

**Typeset, printed and bound in Great Britain by** William Clowes Limited, Beccles and London

**Colour produced by** JB Shears and Sons Ltd, Basingstoke, Hampshire

Every effort is made to ensure accuracy, but the Publishers do not hold themselves responsible for any consequences that may arise from errors or omissions. Whilst the contents are believed correct at the time of going to press, changes may have occurred since that time or will occur during the currency of this book. The up-to-date position may be checked through Hotel Services, The Automobile Association, Fanum House, Basingstoke

A CIP catalogue record for this book is available from the British Library.

Published by The Automobile Association, Fanum House, Basingstoke, Hampshire RG21 2EA.

ISBN 0 7495 0421 8

Owners of the 1992 edition of the Hotels and Restaurants Guide may claim a 10 per cent discount off their room bill at more than 1,100 hotels listed in the directory. The hotels which have agreed to participate in this scheme display the £ symbol at the end of their directory entry.

In order to take advantage of the discount, guests *must* remember to present their copy of the 1992 Hotels and Restaurants Guide at reception when *checking in*. If you do not do so, the hotel may legitimately refuse to give you the discount when you check out. This is very important, because many hotel accounts are now computerised and it may cause difficulties and delays if the account has to be adjusted at the last minute.

The discount only applies to the full-tariff room rate, and does not apply if you are already benefiting from any other form of discount or a special bargain rate, including weekly terms that work out at less per night than the full tariff for a single night's stay.

The discount is off the room rate and may not be claimed for restaurant or bar meals or drinks. In the case of a joint booking for a group of individuals, the discount would only apply to the person who presents the guide on checking in, *not* to the entire party.

If two persons are sharing a double room, however, at the full tariff rate, the discount would apply to the double room.

Please note that the discount may *only* be claimed at the hotels which display the £ symbol at the end of their directory entry, and that the bill must be settled before you leave the hotel. The discount is not applicable to company accounts.

This offer is only valid from the date of publication of this edition to 31 December 1992.

# CONTENTS

# EVERYWHERE YOU GO, YOU CAN BE SURE OF SHELL...

EVERYWHERE YOU GO
YOU CAN BE SURE OF SHELL

ST. IVES HUNTINGDON BY DUNCAN GRANT

This slogan first appeared on some of the most famous advertising posters of yesteryear – and the promise still holds good today.

It was partly through a concern for the environment in which it operates that in the twenties and thirties, the Company commissioned up-and-coming young artists such as Nash, Piper and Sutherland, to paint pictures extolling the beauty of the countryside.

The main aim of this was to catch the emerging breed of motorists who appreciated the freedom and the pleasure of touring, and encourage them to explore the highways and byways. Helping to point them in the right direction were the well-known Shell County Guides which also made their first appearance in the 1930s, and have remained popular throughout many editions up to the present day.

A long tradition of service to the motorist is something that Shell has very much in common with the AA. Once again it brings both organisations together through

sponsorship of the Hotels and Restaurants Guide, now in its 26th edition.

Today's driver – whether travelling on business or holiday or simply going out for a meal – will put quality and choice uppermost in the criteria for selecting a hotel or restaurant. An establishment that looks attractive, well maintained, and which offers friendly service with a hospitable welcome will always find favour. The same is true when it comes to choosing a service station.

In this guide we have identified for the motorist those Shell service stations which are open throughout the year between 7 am and 11pm, many of them for the full 24 hours. They all have unleaded and leaded petrol available, along with diesel. So it's a service which is helpful for the hotel guest who arrives late or leaves early and needs to fill up.

Explore MELBOURNE in rural DERBYSHIRE

DISCOVER UNKNOWN BRITAIN. FREE MAPS WITH SHELL PETROL.

Towns which have Shell service stations providing these services are identified in the directory by the Shell symbol following the town name and pinpointed on the featured town maps.

Around two million motorists drive onto Shell forecourts every day. As the country's leading marketer of oil products the Company supplies 2,700 service stations across the country with a family of advanced fuels and lubricants which it is constantly improving through world-wide research and development.

Shell led the way in ensuring the widespread availability of unleaded petrol and diesel to serve the growing number of cars which are able to use these fuels. It is also investing heavily in developing a new generation of service stations – working hard to ensure that motorists will be greeted by clean, well-maintained forecourts, with pumps that are lightweight and easy to use.

Other facilities, such as car wash, vacuum, and free air and water, are widely available, along with assisted service. In addition, many shops offer a range of goods, including groceries and fast foods such as sandwiches and burgers as well as the more traditional items you would expect: lubricants, car accessories, confectionery, tobacco and gifts. Many stations also have facilities for the disabled; telephones are often located outside the shop for use 24 hours a day – a particular boon for the business driver. And, of course, there are clean toilets.

Finally, if you have any queries about Shell products, services or facilities – or anything connected with Shell – please don't hesitate to ring the Shell Customer Service Centre on Freephone 0800 010 100. It is the only oil company which offers such a service to its customers and will always be pleased to take your call.

So not only can you be sure of Shell, today – **'You can tell when it's Shell.'**

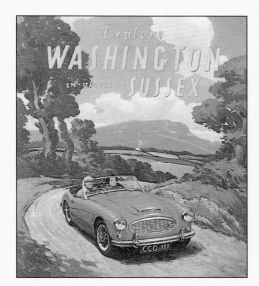

## What colour is your car?

There are so many things that flash through the mind whilst we are at the wheel – and green issues are claiming ever more of our thoughts.

Very few of us can claim to be environmentally friendly – we are all engaged in activities which have an impact on our environment, either now or in the future.

However, we can all reduce the impact of what we do. So whilst contemplating your trip, or relaxing when you are there, consider what we can do together:

– Shell can keep working to produce cleaner fuels which make cars go better

– The AA can keep improving its traffic information services to keep us on the move

– Motorists can keep their car well serviced

Jointly we reduce the amount of fuel wasted and the level of harmful emissions; motorists get better value and more enjoyment from their motoring.

# Disaster Prevention

Don't let your business trip or holiday be spoilt for the want of a little planning. These checklists will help ensure that a successful and enjoyable trip is the only thing on your mind.

## On business ?

- [ ] Fill up with Shell Advanced Fuel
- [ ] Spare petrol can
- [ ] Check oil and water
- [ ] Warning triangle
- [ ] Spare plastic screen
- [ ] Check serviceable spare tyre
- [ ] Car handbook
- [ ] Fire extinguisher
- [ ] *Wet start*
- [ ] *De-icer*
- [ ] *Scraper*
- [ ] *Waterproof coat*
- [ ] *Gloves (old)*
- [ ] *Shovel*
- [ ] *Old sacks*
- [ ] *Snow chains*

- [ ] AA Members Handbook
- [ ] AA road map
- [ ] Guidebooks
- [ ] Passport
- [ ] Driving licence / International Driving Permit
- [ ] Green card
- [ ] Hotel reservations
- [ ] E111 (for EC countries)
- [ ] Vaccination certificates
- [ ] Health precautions
- [ ] Briefcase
- [ ] Itinerary
- [ ] Diary
- [ ] Dictaphone
- [ ] Computer
- [ ] Emergency telephone numbers

*Items printed in italic type apply to winter journeys.*

## • *have a safe and enjoyable trip* •

## On a family trip?

- [ ] Fill up with Shell Advanced Fuel
- [ ] Spare petrol can
- [ ] Check oil and water
- [ ] Warning triangle
- [ ] Spare plastic screen
- [ ] Check serviceable spare tyre
- [ ] Car handbook
- [ ] Fire extinguisher
- [ ] Tow rope
- [ ] *Wet start*
- [ ] *De-icer*
- [ ] *Scraper*
- [ ] *Waterproof coat*
- [ ] *Gloves (old)*
- [ ] *Shovel*
- [ ] *Old sacks*
- [ ] *Snow chains*

- [ ] AA Members Handbook
- [ ] AA road map
- [ ] Guidebooks
- [ ] Passports
- [ ] Driving licence / International Driving Permit
- [ ] Green card
- [ ] Accommodation reservations
- [ ] E111 (for EC countries)
- [ ] Vaccination certificates
- [ ] First aid kit
- [ ] Rubbish bag
- [ ] Wet wipes / kitchen roll
- [ ] Sunglasses
- [ ] Coolbag with drinks / fruit
- [ ] Picnic kit
- [ ] Emergency telephone numbers

## For children

- [ ] Travel sweets and snacks
- [ ] Games
- [ ] Cassettes
- [ ] Personal stereos
- [ ] Toys
- [ ] Books

# GRANADA
## Hotels & Lodges

**Located on major motorways and trunk roads in Britain Granada Hotels and Lodges offer a high standard of accommodation at budget prices.**

### GRANADA Hotels

**M5** Exeter
**A38/A61** Alfreton
**A500/A34** Stoke-on-Trent
**A630/A6102** Sheffield

### GRANADA Lodges

**M1** Leicester (Markfield)
**M1** Toddington
**M1** Woolley Edge
**M25** Thurrock open Spring '92
**M4** Heston
**M4** Leigh Delamere
**M4** Magor open Summer '92
**M5** Frankley
**M62** Birch
**M62/A1** Ferrybridge
**M6** Southwaite
**M90** Kinross
**M9/M80** Stirling
**A1** Grantham (Colsterworth)
**A1** Edinburgh (Musselburgh)
**A1(M)** Washington
**A1(M)** Blyth
**A38** Saltash
**A36** Warminster
**M42/A5** Tamworth

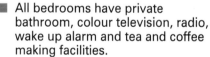

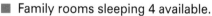

■ All bedrooms have private bathroom, colour television, radio, wake up alarm and tea and coffee making facilities.

■ Family rooms sleeping 4 available.

■ Bedroom especially adapted for use by disabled people.

■ Ample free parking.

■ At Granada Lodges meals may be taken in adjacent Country Kitchen Restaurant.

■ Granada Hotels have their own licenced restaurant and bar.

■ Meeting rooms available at Granada Hotels and selected Granada Lodges.

**FOR FURTHER INFORMATION OR RESERVATIONS CALL:**
**CENTRAL RESERVATIONS 0800 555 300 FAX: 052 555 602**

# PREFACE

As a mark of our commitment to fostering high standards throughout the catering industry, this 1992 edition of the *AA Guide to Hotels and Restaurants in Britain and Ireland* places considerably more emphasis on the assessment of food quality.

Our rosette award scheme has been completely revised so that there are now five levels of assessment rather than three. This has enabled our hotel and restaurant inspectors to provide a more comprehensive list of establishments considered noteworthy for their culinary skills.

It does not however mean that our rosette awards have been devalued. In fact it is, if anything, even more difficult for a hotel or restaurant to gain three, four or five rosettes in the new scheme than it was to achieve one, two or three rosettes in its predecessor. Nevertheless adding a further two levels of assessment has enabled us to highlight more than 750 places where the standard of food can be especially recommended. Within the directory of this guide you will find the rosette symbol immediately after the hotel star rating and before the restaurant knife and fork classification.

The introduction of this new system of food assessment is part of our commitment to providing the very best information on establishment quality. Our quality rating for hotels, expressed as a percentage score and introduced over the past two years, adequately assesses the hospitality, service, cleanliness and bedroom facilities of a hotel. Rosette awards for food quality complement this information on hotels and are an excellent way of identifying standards of cuisine in the many restaurants we feature.

It is our aim to constantly improve the information we publish about hotels and restaurants in the interests of both business and leisure users of this guide. In this context we have for 1992 included details of AA inspected and appointed hotels throughout the whole of Ireland. For your convenience we have listed these hotels in a separate directory.

The requirements of European travellers were a major factor in our decision to feature Irish hotels. They were equally important to our research article on the preparedness of British hoteliers to answer enquiries from French and German tourists seeking to take advantage of the 'Single Market' from 1992.

We wrote to 250 hotels in German and 250 hotels in French, despatching the letters from a suitable address in Germany and France and asking about the availability of accommodation. It is an indictment of the British hotel industry that a massive 30 per cent of the hotels contacted did not even bother to respond. A further 30 per cent replied solely in English: hardly the sort of care and attention potential European visitors might expect. However, some hotels tried very hard to respond effectively. Our researchers praised Browns, London for its French and the Holiday Inn, Telford was singled out for excellent German.

Coincidentally Holiday Inns have also featured this year in the AA's awards for 'Courtesy and Care', with the Holiday Inn, Leeds amongst 17 new award winners. We believe that high levels of customer care should be provided by all hotels at every level. The traditional view that hospitable, friendly service can only be found at small independently owned and managed hotels must not be accepted. We are pleased therefore to report that our inspectors have noted that larger group-owned hotels are increasingly rising to the challenge of providing better levels of customer care. It is therefore no surprise to find the Swallow Hotel, Birmingham and the Portman Inter-Continental, London have also been selected for the high level of 'Courtesy and Care' they show their guests.

Selecting establishments worthy of one of the AA's prestigious awards is a prime task for our inspectors. The main purpose of the inspection team is however to ensure that appointed establishments continue to meet the exacting standards we set at each level of classification. We do not though consider this to be merely a fault finding exercise. The inspectors use their professionalism and considerable experience to encourage proprietors to improve the facilities and services they provide in the interests of all guests.

All the establishments featured in this guide are inspected at least once every year and, as it is our policy to experience the hotel or restaurant as any guest would, our visits are unannounced. The inspectors remain incognito until the task is completed at which point they declare their presence to the proprietor or manager. They then highlight their findings, make recommendations on improvements and outline the recommendation they will give to the Association's Hotel and Restaurant Appointment Committees.

Visiting so many hotels and restaurants in the course of a year puts our inspectors in a unique position of being able to identify establishments worthy of special mention. They have, as you will find, selected seven hotels throught the UK and Ireland that are new to the AA's classification scheme, and singled out Hanbury Manor, Ware in Hertfordshire as the best newcomer nationally.

With so much additional emphasis on food it is no surprise to find some excellent restaurants featured for the first time. Again, we have especially featured our seven best newcomers amongst which is Roscoff's in Belfast where Paul and Jeanne Rankin, winners of the hotel industry's sought after Catey Award for 1991, run what is considered to be the number one restaurant.

Another Catey Award winner for 1991, the Old Course Hotel, St Andrews was previously identified by our inspection force as worthy of special merit and awarded red stars, a distinction given to just 84 of the 3831 hotels appointed by the AA. Amongst these are a number of 'old friends' welcomed back to the red star list this year such as the Dorchester, London, back after extensive refurbishment, and the Castle Hotel, Taunton. In fact no less than 15 of the total of 84 are new for this 1992 edition of our guide.

As usual you will find that this guide features handy quick reference lists for red star hotels, country house hotels and AA lodges. Symbols used are explained in French, German, Italian and Spanish as well as in English on a handy new bookmark. Features such as 'Hotel at Work', a behind-the-scenes look at the Goring Hotel in London and 'RSVP: British Hotels, ready for 1992?' make the guide interesting to read and act as a perfect accompaniment to a most comprehensive directory.

We in the AA fully appreciate the importance of selecting the right hotel in which to stay and the most appropriate restaurant in which to eat during an important business trip or whilst on holiday. We are confident that the comprehensive information available in this guide will provide you with the essential information you need to make a successful choice. With Europe in mind it only remains for me to wish you *'Bon Voyage'* and *'Guten Apetit'*.

Albert Hampson
Manager Hotel and Touring Information Services

# British Hospitality Association

As the lead body representing proprietors in the hotel and catering industry, the British Hospitality Association welcomes the greater emphasis now being given by the AA to quality assessments within its grading structure. With more detailed information at their fingertips, prospective customers can more readily choose the hotel or restaurant that best meets their requirements at the time.

Our members are part of the UK hospitality industry. Every day of the week, throughout the year, hoteliers and restaurateurs meet, greet, and host their customers. They and their staff must match the expectations of an ever more discerning public, choosing their establishment for varied social, leisure or business occasions. Which is why the BHA works closely with the AA, to ensure that the views and expectations of customers are reflected in the classification requirements used in the guide. A recent example is the introduction, last year, of percentage assessments for quality. Additional information which does, I am sure, help members of the public to pinpoint the hotel which matches their criteria.

Latterly, the BHA has worked with the AA to expand the rosette awards so that many more hotels and restaurants can be singled out for the quality of their cuisine, irrespective of their classification. The scheme it replaces, limited to three rosettes, inevitably concentrated awards at the luxury end of the market. There was, for example, little scope to highlight those small establishments, many with just one or two stars, which attract a loyal following through their dedicated approach to cooking or their nurturing of young talent. Eating out is now one of our most popular leisure activities.

The past few years have seen a revolution in the culinary standards and styles offered by the country's hotels and restaurants. Our leading chefs have become superstars, thanks in part to television programmes which have introduced their viewers to the professional's creative skills.

I welcome the AA's timely response, in meeting consumer requirements for a broader range of information, to guide them towards making their choice of hotel or restaurant.

Robin Lees
Chief Executive
**British Hospitality Association
(formerly BHRCA)**

# HIGHER STANDARDS.
# OUTSTANDING VALUE FOR MONEY.

For £31 per night – single, double or family room – Travel Inn sets new standards for budget hotels, offering outstanding value for money, and the opportunity to make more of your stay, whenever you're away from home.

Complete with a double bed, en-suite bathroom, colour TV, and complimentary coffee and tea-making facilities, our superb bedrooms couldn't be more comfortable.

Alongside each Travel Inn, there's a friendly restaurant, where children are welcome. Here you can breakfast, dine in the evening, or enjoy delicious food from the bar – all at sensible prices.

Conveniently located, you'll find Travel Inns welcoming, informal and very accommodating – an ideal base for a weekend break. A break you can make as exciting or relaxing as you like.

With Travel Inn you really have the choice.

## Make more of your stay.

The AA has for many years made awards to hotels and restaurants which we consider to be outstanding – red stars; rosettes, which this year have expanded from three to five to cover a wider range of establishments; and more recently, high percentage ratings. Naturally, these awards, made for exceptionally high standards of accommodation, food and hospitality, reflect the degree of dedication, professionalism and effort on the part of the owners, management and staff.

Last year, we felt that the time was right for us to make a new award on a more personal level and linked, appropriately, to the AA's motto – 'Courtesy and Care'. There are a number

of hotels which may not have attained the dizzy height of red stars, but whose courtesy towards, and care of guests is of an exceptionally high level. Red star hotels may feature in the award list, but only where 'Courtesy and Care' are particularly to the forefront of an already top quality hotel.

This year's award winners are featured below and we think that from their stories and their comments you will get a good idea of why they have been chosen. We are sure that a stay at the hotels will confirm our choice. Also listed below are the winners of our first 'Courtesy and Care' awards in 1990/1991.

# COURTESY AND CARE
## ──────AWARDS──────

**AA**

## 1991/1992

### SOUTH WEST

### Hurstone Country Hotel and Restaurant ,
*Waterrow, Somerset*

When John Bone first came to Hurstone as a teenager 26 years ago, his parents ran it as a working farm.

'I suppose it was in the late 60s that my mother first started to do bed and breakfast, taking one family at a time,' explained John.

'When I grew up and had a family of my own we simply took my mother's B & B a stage further; gradually we started to take more guests, opened the restaurant to non-residents, added more facilities like en suite bath-

rooms, full central heating and so on until eventually we had a full-blown hotel.'

The Bones found they enjoyed the hotel business more than farming so that's what they concentrate on now.

'We don't aim to be pretentious or have a lot of rules,' continued John, 'just to make people feel at home and relaxed in a lovely atmosphere. Our food may not be the best in the West – but it's good quality and interesting – and we even make our own Hurstone cheese and cider.

'Of course we're lucky in that the hotel is in a lovely situation, overlooking a wooded valley, so there's always something to look at, even if it's only the weather!'

### White House,
*Charmouth, Dorset*

John and Mollie Balfour decided to take early retirement from Shell International where they'd

worked for many years and try something entirely different.

'We thought we'd like to start a vineyard,' explained John, 'but when we started to look for a suitable place, either we didn't like the house or we didn't like the grounds, so we began to explore the possibility of buying a hotel instead. We found this beautiful Regency hotel in Charmouth and fell in love with it. Somehow, even though it was very run down it had a lovely warm atmosphere about it.'

That was nine years ago and since then the Balfours have lovingly restored the décor of the place to its Regency original and have created for their guests the sort of establishment that they themselves would want to stay in.

'Of course, we try and ensure that every aspect of the hotel is of a high standard,' John went on, 'but above all we want people to feel at home here.

'We're very keen on our food here and are particularly interested in regional fare. And wines, well, as you can imagine we're pretty keen on those too, with about 40 different varieties in our cellar for guests to try.

'Many of our guests come back, so we get really involved with them. In fact, they often become such good friends that it seems a shame to charge them!'

## SOUTH

### Sarum Hotel,
*St Helier, Jersey*

Italian-born Joseph Arena has lived in Jersey for the last 27 years and met and married his British-born wife Barbara there 17 years ago. They've both been in the hotel industry just about all of their working lives.

The Arenas came to manage the Sarum Hotel four years ago, with Barbara looking after public relations, reception and housekeeping and Joseph doing the accounts and supervising.

'We work really well together,' said Barbara, 'and that's because we each have our own slots, so we don't tread on each other's toes. What I say in my part goes and what he says in his part goes – although at the end of the day it's Joseph who's the boss.'

The Arenas believe that a good and happy staff is the essential ingredient in a successful hotel.

'Many of our staff have followed us from hotel to hotel,' continued Jospeph. 'They're part of the family. I've worked up from the bottom of the hotel industry so I know what it's like to be badly treated. I make sure that our staff are really well looked after. Because the staff are happy it reflects on the guests. They see the happy smiling faces of the people who work here and they feel happy too.

'We love to be with people – you couldn't do this job if you didn't – and many of our guests make return visits. When they return, we send them a box of chocolates to say 'thank you' – it's nothing, but they really appreciate it.'

Barbara is equally enthusiastic about their life. 'Every day is different and we meet such lovely and amusing people. When we close for the season we really miss our guests. I can't wait to get going again.'

### Blunsdon House,
*Swindon, Wiltshire*

Last year Peter and Zan Clifford celebrated 30 years as proprietors of Blunsdon House as a

Staff at the Sarum Hotel.

hotel. The house was originally the farmhouse of a pig and poultry farm, and the Cliffords began by taking bed and breakfast guests. The business has expanded somewhat since then, as has the hotel which is now much extended and grand with its 89 bedrooms (including a number of suites), eight conference rooms, two restaurants and a ballroom.

Son John Clifford and his wife Carrie are now also involved, along with the staff who count themselves as part of a big, friendly family. Carrie's Carvery is a very popular option, with help yourself hors d'oeuvres, three roasts or a choice of 'specials', and a selection from the sweet trolley; while the more formal Ridge Restaurant offers an à la carte menu at lunch and dinner.

The hotel is constantly refurbished and redecorated, and the management and staff pride themselves on their friendly service. The conference facilities attract business clients during the week, and there is a busy weekend break trade. Antiques, ballooning and Cheltenham special interest weekends have been a great success, and the hotel caters for many weddings and other functions including the Mayor's Ball.

## LONDON

### Stafford Hotel,
London SW1

There is something about the Stafford Hotel's friendly, clublike atmosphere that draws guests to stay over and over again. In fact, 70 per cent of this unusual, small, London hotel's custom is repeat business.

Terry Holmes, Vice President and Managing Director of Cunard Hotels, has an association with the Stafford that goes back over 17 years.

'I started as assistant manager and when Cunard bought the Stafford, they bought me with it,' explained Terry Holmes. 'Although my office is in the Ritz Hotel now, I still spend more time in the Stafford than anywhere else.

'The Stafford doesn't advertise and you don't read much about it, but it runs on one of the highest occupancy levels in London.

'It used to be a private house and we've tried to take it back to that, so it's not at all a grand hotel. Nor does it have the most luxurious bedrooms in London – in fact, we have nothing to sell but service.' However our inspector found the bedrooms very comfortable.

'The four heads of department here have between them notched up 120 years. It's nice for returning guests to see a familiar face, it gives them a high level of comfort. Many of the people who come here have been visiting us for years, their children come here now and even their children's children.

'We have a very high client involvement in what we do here too. If we want to make a change to the hotel, we talk to our guests about it. They soon let us know whether or not they approve.'

### Portman Inter-Continental,
London W1

The Portman is a hotel that prides itself on its service, and from day one each member of the workforce is trained to provide the highest level of customer care.

'When staff first come to work for us we book them and their partner into the hotel for a weekend' explained Public Relations Manager Dee Cayhill. 'That way they can sample all the hotel facilities as a guest.

'A couple of years ago we started a 'Customers come first' scheme in which front line staff throughout the hotel were trained and encouraged to sort out guests' enquiries and problems rather than referring these problems to higher management.

'Seventy per cent of the Portman's clientèle is repeat business so everyone seems to know everyone else and the hotel has a strong club atmosphere about it. We've built on this and started a guest history database so that any likes or dislikes of customers are known about. There's nothing nicer than being able to ask a returning guest whether, for example, they would like the same room or whether they still like hot milk with their cornflakes.'

## WALES

### West Arms,
*Llanarmon Dyffryn Ceiriog, Clwyd*

Geoffrey Hughes, Manager of West Arms, started his career as a student of geology, but soon decided that it wasn't for him and moved into the hotel business instead. After many years working his way through the hotel ranks, Geoffrey started his own catering agency.

Two and a half years ago he received a cry for help from the owner of West Arms.

'I came to help out running the hotel for a couple of weeks and here I am still here two and a half years later.'

Geoffrey describes West Arms as the sort of place that people never forget. 'It's an informal country inn, full of history (the original house is over 400 years old) with lots of exposed beams, flagged floors, deep sofas and so on. Although the atmosphere is very relaxed we try and provide enough attention make each visitor's stay something of an occasion. Our aim is to make them feel like house guests. The rooms of the hotel are not packed full of gadgets, but if there's anything anyone wants, then we'll do our utmost to provide it.

'Every day here I feel is like going on stage – ie we're only as good as our last performance. We're not competing with the bed factories but on giving care and attention to our guests and getting to know them.'

### Lake,
*Llangammarch Wells, Powys*

Up until nine years ago Jean-Pierre Mifsud was a hotel

inspector himself, but then his wife died and he was left with two small children to look after.

'I had to make a change of career,' explained Jean-Pierre. 'I tried an office job for a while, but it wasn't really what I wanted to do, so as I had always wanted to run my own hotel and had quite a lot of knowledge of being a customer myself, I decided to take the plunge and buy a place.'

By this time Jean-Pierre had married again and he and his second wife Jan started looking for a centrally located hotel to buy. But when his friends told them about the Lake Hotel at Llangammarch Wells, with its 50 acres of lovely grounds, four and a half miles of river and three acre lake, even though it was really isolated, against their better judgement they went to look at it.

'We fell in love with the place immediately and decided to buy it,' went on Jean-Pierre.

The Mifsuds didn't want the Lake to be in the true country house hotel mode. 'We didn't want guests to feel they were making a once only visit to a stately home that would cost them an arm and a leg. We

wanted them to feel they were coming to a comfortable home – the sort of place that they'd like to come to, and could afford to come to over and over again.

'We think good food is important and much of the produce is from local sources; we make all our own chocolates, biscuits and marmalade too. But more important is hospitality – the time given to guests and the manner in which they are treated.'

## MIDLANDS/EAST ANGLIA

### The Swallow Hotel,
*Birmingham, West Midlands*

The Swallow is a new hotel that opened its doors for the first time in March 1990. Its staff are looking to make it the best in Birmingham.

'All the staff are carefully chosen and trained using a standard performance manual as their bible,' explained Bill Adam, junior assistant manager. 'That doesn't mean that we're all clones or robots, just that we know how to talk to, and deal with all the different guests who come to stay here – whether they're business people, families or homeymoon couples.

'We try always to be friendly and hospitable and create a home-from-home feel in the hotel. Everyone gets the five–star treatment, and guests that make return visits are always recognised and made to feel especially welcome.

'I love it here and I know my colleagues do too, even though the hours are long and the pay not that wonderful. The hotel itself is gorgeous and we get to meet so many people from all over the world and have such

Mrs Karen King, Sales Manager with a member of the concierge staff *(The Swallow Hotel)*

interesting conversations – each day is different.'

## The Mill at Harvington,
*Evesham, Hereford & Worcester*

Simon and Jane Greenhalgh met at school and even then knew that they both wanted to go into the hotel industry. They both took training courses, worked in different hotels, got married and then bought an old village school in Gloucestershire which they converted and ran as a hotel.

In 1989 they wanted to go on to bigger and better things and bought the Mill at Harvington, a Georgian house with a derelict bakery mill, complete with cast iron oven doors, attached.

'Our philosophy has always been that a hotel doesn't have to be expensive to be good,' explained Simon. 'We've always

believed too that people value friendliness more than frills and that they don't want to pay a lot of money for a hotel where they may have every creature comfort but they can't relax. We always talk a lot to our guests and would rather be criticised for being over-familiar than for creating a barrier of aloofness which we think makes people feel awkward. Our staff too are chosen to be of the same mind as ourselves.

'We meet people at the door when they arrive and do what we can to satisfy their wants. We find they take a couple of days to defrost when they first arrive, it's almost as if they're waiting for a catch. Once they see that the friendliness and helpfulness is lasting and for real they relax.'

## Lords of the Manor,
*Upper Slaughter, Gloucestershire*

In 1985 businessman James Gulliver bought a rather run down 17th-century rectory and in the following year he was joined by Manager Richard Young to establish the Lords of the Manor as we know it today.

'The term Country House has been much abused in recent

years, but we do run the place as a country home. The service is very personal, and although it's a 30-bed establishment we know our guests, and whether they have been here before. We work long hours, and for us the client does come first.'

Richard has noticed that guests often comment on the friendliness of the staff, whom he describes as, 'a terrific team of people, very carefully chosen. At times when we've been short staffed we've all joined in and got things done, but you have to search for the right people, not just anyone will do. You can teach most things, but personality and character are paramount. The stiff old-school professionals are all very well, but we look for really friendly, caring people and professional ability.'

## NORTHERN ENGLAND

## Mill House,
*Mungrisdale, Cumbria*

Richard Quinlan has been in the hotel business all his working life, managing hotels in London and elsewhere before he and his

Staff at Lords of the Manor.

wife Eleanor took the plunge and bought a place of their own.

'I was trained in hotel kitchens, but my wife is the better cook. She had been in the business for 12 or 13 years, but for her cooking began as a hobby. We also have a trained chef in the kitchen, and our staff are local people who have been with us since we opened six years ago.

'We offer a home from home and half our bookings are repeat business. We make copious notes on our guests, remembering their birthdays and anniversaries so we can make a cake and help to make it a special occasion for them.

'This is what we have always wanted, a place we could put our own stamp on. It is hard work but it is rewarding, particularly when we can welcome returning guests as friends.'

## Holiday Inn,
*Leeds, West Yorkshire*

It isn't by chance that the Holiday Inn Leeds has become such a fine example of friendliness, hospitality and good service. General Manager Robert Kirby is very keen on staff training. Every member of staff goes through an 'Excellence Through People' programme put together by an outside consultant. The tenets of the hotel's philosophy are enshrined in a series of 'bullet points' which are carried by staff: give guests everything they require; keep the hotel clean and well presented; keep it a friendly place; make it a fun place to visit.

Management too have a four-point philosophy: care for your people and they will care for your guests; listen to your people and they will listen to you; praising your people lifts morale and encourages improved performance; guest satisfaction is the key to job satisfaction.

Members of staff, on their own initiative, have set up a forum of 'challenges', meeting monthly with a representative from each department to look at any areas that could be improved upon, and raising these with management if necessary. Clearly, management and staff are working very effectively together under this regime, with commendable dedication to customer care.

## SCOTLAND

### Haven Hotel,
*Plockton, Highland*

Marjorie Nichol and her husband bought the Haven 10 years ago, and following the death of Mr Nichol five years later, Commander John Graham joined Mrs Nichol as partner in the business.

Manager Alisdair Mackay is from the village and first came to the hotel as a student eight years ago. He returned later to help Mrs Nichol and has been with the hotel for six years now, the last four in his current role. He describes the staff as a good team, mostly village people with a good mix of ages who get on well together. About 80 per cent of their bookings is repeat business, customers whom they get to know well, returning annually to their favourite rooms.

## Kildrummy Castle,

*Kildrummy, Grampian*

Tom Hanna took on Kildrummy Castle 14 years ago, since when it has been upgraded to become the comfortable country house hotel we see today. With around 24 years' experience in the industry, he enjoys his role as host, restaurant manager and head waiter in his own establishment, and his friendly relations with guests. He and his wife are much involved in the day-to-day running of the hotel, Mary Hanna does the flowers and makes the sweets, while Tom looks after the office.

The Hannas' aim is to achieve the high standard of a quality establishment with none of the associated stuffiness. Tom prides himself on his local staff and their local knowledge, emphatic that this is a Scottish country house and as such should be distinct from a similar establishment anywhere else in the country: 'It's what our guests expect.'

## NORTHERN IRELAND

### Londonderry Arms,

*Carnlough, Co Antrim*

Frank and Moira O'Neill bought this old coaching inn in 1947 and it has been in the family every since. Mr O'Neill is now retired but Mrs O'Neill is still actively involved in the hotel, which is now under the management of their son, Frank O'Neill, along with his sister Siobhan Drummond.

Commenting on the friendliness of the establishment, Mrs Drummond explained that they have friendly customers: 'We have a wide range of customers, many farmers who are warm, friendly people; tourists on their way up the Antrim coast, and foreign tourists too – it's wonderful to see them in Northern Ireland again – and they came back on their own without the tour operators.

'We grew up in the business and it's like sharing your home - many of the customers are personal friends. We are a large family and although most of us have other occupations and professions there is always someone around for a chat or a drink.'

One member of staff, Lena Patterson, who is a great one for remembering the customers and what they like to drink, has been at the hotel nearly as long as the family. She joined them in 1948, and now has nieces and nephews working alongside her.

## EIRE

### Newport House Hotel,

*Newport, Co Mayo*

Guests come from all over the world to this lovely country house, and Reservations Manager Catherine Flynn says she often exchanges two or three letters with prospective visitors, so that by the time they book in she is really looking forward to meeting them. It is characteristic of the hotel's personal approach that she doesn't think it is enough to simply put a brochure in the post.

'The guests are a delight,' she explains. 'We seem to be particularly fortunate in the people we attract.'

Many come for the fishing, along with the beautiful countryside; and children are made most welcome so the hotel is popular with families. But one suspects it is the warmth of the welcome and the personal service that accounts for the high proportion of returning guests.

Proprietors Kieran and Thelma Thompson took over the hotel at the end of 1985, resolving to keep a sense of continuity, maintaining the natural ambience by changing as little as possible. All key members of staff were retained, many very long serving, such as General Manager Owen Mullins who came to the hotel in 1946. He is now semi-retired, but still manages the fishery, and remains a very influential member of staff.

The Thompsons have worked hard at improving the hotel in every area, but for them customer care is a priority, and in this they are ably assisted by dedicated staff who really enjoy their contact with guests.

### Winners of last year's 'Courtesy and Care' awards

BURY ST EDMUNDS, Angel Hotel
BLACKHEATH, LONDON SE3, Bardon Lodge
LLANDUDNO, Empire Hotel
DUNOON, Enmore Hotel
STOW ON THE WOLD, Grapevine Hotel
WINDERMERE, Holbeck Ghyll Country House Hotel
BLAIRGOWRIE, Kinloch House Hotel
RINGWOOD, Moortown Lodge Hotel
ABERSOCH, Neigwl Hotel
HOWTOWN, Sharrow Bay Country House Hotel
SALCOMBE, Tides Reach Hotel
ROTHERWICK, Tylney Hall Hotel
LONDON W2, Whites Hotel
WHIMPLE, Woodhayes Country House Hotel

# R.S.V.P.

# British hotels ready for

# 1992?

'The single market' and '1992' are terms which have been bandied about a lot recently, with the assumption that we all know exactly what it will mean. In fact, to most of us it has been a vague notion of easier movement across frontiers, a question over the future of duty-free allowances and an uneasy feeling that we will soon be expected to become proper Europeans.

The single market was one of the original aims of the Treaty of Rome which established the European Community in 1957. But it wasn't until 1985 that the heads of government of the 12 member countries actually committed themselves to completing the single market progressively by the end of 1992.

The elimination of trade restrictions involves the standardisation of many European regulations, the removal of restrictions on movement of capital, standardisation of national laws on patents and trade marks and the universal recognition of professional qualifications. Most of the red tape on road haulage will go, shipping services between member countries should be provided on equal terms and increased competition on air routes should bring the fares down. Government and other public body contracts will be opened up to all Community contractors on an equal basis and products approved in any one Community country can be freely marketed throughout the Community. It should become as easy for a Birmingham company to trade with Munich as it is with Manchester – and vice versa.

While our own business fraternity is preparing itself for the onslaught into Europe, Continental counterparts will have their sights set on Britain. One of the barriers that won't be so easily removed is that of language, and although language training must be fairly high on any company's list of priorities, it is still likely that many travellers will set off with a few basic phrases and a hope that someone at their destination will be able to communicate with them in their native tongue.

Hotels will frequently be the first point of contact for European business travellers to Britain, but how will our hotels cope with those guests who do not have a grasp of our language? In view of the number who claim to employ European – particularly French – staff, we assumed that problems would be few. Nevertheless, we decided to put a selection of British hotels to the test.

We invented two prospective hotel guests, each planning to bring his wife and nine-month-old child on a trip to Britain. 'Monsieur Moreau' wrote to 250 hotels at the three, four and five star levels, in French, asking for specific information about facilities for the baby; 'Herr Mayer' did the same in German, but, with one or two exceptions, to a different set of hotels. The responses we got were very interesting.

Of the 250 letters sent in French, 84 hotels did not reply at all, 56 replied in English (some simply sent their brochure, in English) and 110 replied in French of varying standards. From the German enquiries, 64 did not reply, 97 replied in English (again some just sent an English brochure) and 89 were in German. The standards again varied considerably, from excellent to unintelligible.

One of the strangest factors we found was that a substantial number of the hotels which replied in English assured Monsieur Moreau and/or Herr Mayer that they had French or German members of staff, or staff who could speak French or German fluently – some mentioned them by name and said where in the hotel they could be found if needed. One or two of the people who replied even claimed to speak the language themselves! Would it not have been

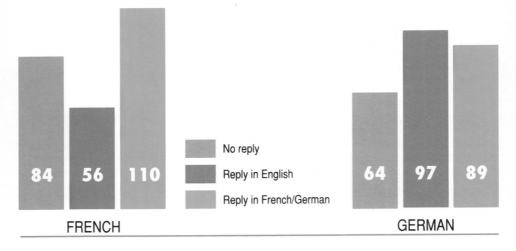

| | |
|---|---|
| 84 | 56 | 110 |
| **FRENCH** | |

No reply
Reply in English
Reply in French/German

| | |
|---|---|
| 64 | 97 | 89 |
| **GERMAN** | |

easy, and more courteous, to have asked one of the bi-lingual staff to translate the replies? We would particularly have expected more of an effort from the Dorchester.

From five star hotels we naturally expected a high standard of reply in the language of the original enquiry, but were surprised by the careless errors we found. Many letters, which would otherwise have been good, were let down by the inexcusable omission of French accents, poor grammar and spelling mistakes. The standard of French we got from the Ritz was frankly shocking, with careless grammar and barely adequate replies to specific questions; though their

German reply was excellent – correct, friendly and thorough. We were also somewhat surprised that only one five star hotel in London – Le Meridien – was able to supply a brochure in French. The standard of their letter was also good, and their German reply reasonably good, if a little brief. The Hilton's reply to Herr Mayer was obviously written by a German and so was correct, but it was a bit lacking in information and untidily handwritten – not quite the degree of professionalism one would expect from a hotel of this calibre.

From hotels outside London, we were impressed by the letter sent to Monsieur Moreau from the Bath Spa Hotel, which was correct, nicely personal and with comprehensive details about facilities for children. Their German reply was fluent, but the spelling appalling! Cliveden, the famous stately home hotel at Taplow, certainly knew the language and also included a brochure in French, but the tone of their reply was over-formal, to the extent of being considered curt by our translator. The Royal Bath Hotel at Bournemouth was more welcoming and offered an unusual facility – a 'room with private bathroom and one on the sea'. Hopefully they meant 'a sea view', otherwise the resort's Blue Flag Beach will be seriously threatened. North of the border, Gleneagles gets our top marks for perception and sense of humour – they obviously guessed the real purpose of our letters and we received two multi-lingual replies!

We expected the standard of French and German at the five star hotels to be immaculate,

but it was not. All answered the questions asked, but few volunteered any extra information and only one (Royal Garden, Kensington) actually said it 'looks forward to welcoming you, your wife and your baby'.

The standard of French and German varied considerably at four star level, but these hotels did seem to have put more personal effort into being helpful than the five star hotels, whose efficiency often seemed mechanical. However, the same degree of carelessness prevailed and even typing errors were allowed to pass uncorrected. The letter to Monsieur Moreau from the Shakespeare Hotel in Stratford-upon-Avon certainly lost something in the translation: among its many typing errors was one so bad that it could have changed *nourrisson* – (not quite the right word for baby) into *hérisson* – just the right word for hedgehog! And we wondered if

Cambridge's University Arms really meant to say 'nobody in our hotel likes to speak German, unfortunately, but if you do some people will definitely understand you.'

The Wessex Hotel in Winchester, however, demonstrates its true understanding of the priorities of a French baby, promising a high chair 'which will permit your child to enjoy his meals in total comfort'. No mention at all of a cot, but perhaps to a French baby mealtimes are far more important than a good night's sleep. Ashford's Aztec Hotel has a native German speaker on its staff, but he obviously had a problem with letter-writing – his brief, almost illegible letter suggested that Herr Mayer should telephone him instead.

In general, when the replies were written by German members of staff they were of an excellent standard, with all questions answered efficiently. One or two replies were written in very good German by English staff, but not many. Others were apparently written for the hotel by people not employed there – if that means a translation agency, we believe that the hotels should be getting a better service for their money.

The three star hotels produced some very good replies in both French and German – and some bad ones, with a range of brave attempts in between. But the overall impression was that, of all the replies received, this category was the most favourable and welcoming. One or two seemed so very keen to welcome Monsieur Moreau and his family that we felt some remorse at raising their hopes of accommodating this exciting international clientèle. Those with poor, or non-existent German had clearly made every effort to answer the main question about a cot – sometimes half in German and half in English – and one can't help warming to the people who would go to so much trouble. Those with only school standard French were quick to admit their shortcomings and apologise for them, although the writer from the Grange at York apologised for his French when it was, in fact, good.

Some of the translations seemed a little suspect at times. If the Trades Descriptions Act is one of those earmarked to become Europe-wide, the Swallow Hotel in Dundee might be in for

some trouble – they promised baby Moreau a high pulpit, or throne, or university chair, or Bishop's chair! At the Alexandra Hotel in Oban half board at £47 a night will entitle you to a free child, but sadly for Herr Mayer (or possibly a blessing), children are 'not available' at the Butterfly Hotel in King's Lynn. The Grand Atlantic at Weston-super-Mare can 'listen out for the baby and tell you if it's raining'. We assume they confused *s'il pleut* (raining) with *s'il pleure* (crying), but to any parent it's pretty well one and the same thing!

The chart overleaf shows the results of our survey, which assessed the replies in French and German on four separate points: prompt reply, standard of language, answers to specific questions and extra information volunteered. The number of hotels which replied in French or German varies between star ratings and so the chart represents each classification as a percentage of the total response for its star rating. In that way we can see how the star ratings compare. For instance, 18 per cent of four star hotels sent a good response in French, while only 17 per cent of five star responses were rated good, and only 12 per cent of three star hotels. We can also see that in many cases the standard of German was higher than that of French.

When it comes to the question of whether French or German is spoken by any of the hotel staff, many of those claiming to speak the language have not produced particularly good letters – but writing in a foreign language is always

more difficult than speaking it. A number of hotels admitted that no one spoke the language in question, but suggested that sign language and a phrase book will always get you by.

If we expected greater things from five star hotels than we actually got, we probably got better results than we expected from the three star hotels; much seemed to depend upon whether or not they employ foreign nationals. The results of our test do seem to endorse the widely held view that the British are extremely reticent when it comes to learning languages. With the single market practically upon us, this will have to change if we are to compete with the rest of Europe on an equal footing. Already some of our conference trade is slipping away as companies find it cheaper to transport all their delegates to France than to hold the event at a British hotel. If language barriers present a problem here, we may see an increase in the number of European-owned hotels in Britain competing for this growing business.

Concentrating bi-lingual staff at ports and air-ports will no longer suffice when all of our main business and industrial centres become frequented by European business travellers. Nor should

% OF REPLIES PER STAR RATING

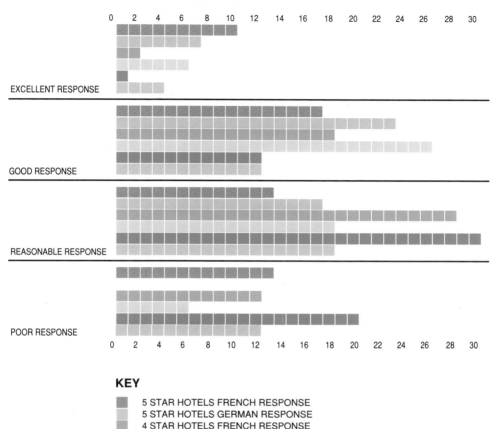

EXCELLENT RESPONSE

GOOD RESPONSE

REASONABLE RESPONSE

POOR RESPONSE

## KEY

- 5 STAR HOTELS FRENCH RESPONSE
- 5 STAR HOTELS GERMAN RESPONSE
- 4 STAR HOTELS FRENCH RESPONSE
- 4 STAR HOTELS GERMAN RESPONSE
- 3 STAR HOTELS FRENCH RESPONSE
- 3 STAR HOTELS GERMAN RESPONSE

we simply assume that all these new customers from the Community are bound to speak good English. Maybe they can, but won't they feel more welcome, and therefore more likely to return to a hotel where they are greeted in their own language and their needs are readily understood?

To end on a positive note, our top marks for the French replies go to Browns, that most English of London hotels. Their French was the most correct and elegant, their reply was prompt, efficient and helpful, they have French-speaking staff and they even sent a free street plan of London. From the German replies, the honours go to the Holiday Inn in Telford for excellent German, thorough answers to questions asked, a brochure in German, details of special breaks in German and a general eagerness to help.

The worst? Well, we could cite all those who failed to reply at all – certainly worse than those whose language skills might be appalling, but who really tried hard. However, the one that really stands out is the reply to Herr Mayer from the Copthorne Tara in London – turning him down for a job!

BY APPOINTMENT TO
HER MAJESTY QUEEN ELIZABETH II
MOTOR CAR MANUFACTURERS
ROLLS-ROYCE MOTOR CARS LIMITED

*For driving yourself.*

Rolls-Royce Motor Cars Limited
A Vickers Company

# Hotel at Work

*Twenty-four hours behind the scenes the Goring Hotel SW1*

> The Goring Hotel holds the AA's four red star award, denoting a hotel that offers not only the very best in accommodation, services and food, but which, with flair and individuality recognises its customers and gives them the personal attention that makes them feel welcome and comfortable.

It may not be everyone's choice to work all night for five nights a week but that is what a hotel Night Manager's job requires.

At the Goring Hotel, Abby Sourroukh find this is an arrangement that fits happily with his family life, enabling him to see his young children in the daytime. Dressed smartly in a dinner jacket, he sees in late-nighters and makes sure that the bills are made out for early leavers. However, there are moments in those dark hours when he has to don a chef's jacket and descend to the kitchen to prepare a midnight feast of steak sandwich and cup of cocoa for a guest (it must be that hotel inspector again) or to roll up his sleeves and deal with a leaking tap.

By 6am Breakfast Chef Manuele – who arrived in England from Portugal fifteen years ago – has already been in the kitchen for an hour preparing the breakfast menu. Porridge bubbles, poached

eggs are at the ready and grills are hot by the time service starts at 7.15. By this time, Mary Davin, the Head Housekeeper, and her band of maids are already in action. In the lounge and the bar the tables are being polished and dusted, carpets vacuumed and an air of intense yet discreet activity exists. David, who has been with the Goring for 11 years, is engaged in maintaining the high gloss on the marble hall floor, and in the background an elderly

American couple wearing trainers are asking directions from Ernest de Blasi, the Head Hall Porter who has just arrived for work and taken over from the Night Manager. In his 17 years working at the Goring he has become a fount of knowledge on the area. He thinks the main change in London over that period is that buildings tend to disappear – a remark substantiated later by a porter who had gone for a fitting of his new uniform only to return

*Mary Davin in charge of the daily domestic routine*

to the hotel to announce that he'd been unsuccessful as 'the building had gone!'

At 7.45am down in the kitchen Manuele is dealing with a steady stream of breakfast orders, some for the restaurant and others for bedroom service. Upstairs the maids are starting work on the 'departures' bedrooms. Lynne Cooper and Jackie Stanley are from Sheffield and reckon they've found a good way to live, as they want to be in London. They live in at the hotel's building just round the corner – 'nice accommodation,' they say and their reasonable rent leaves them both with about £100 a week to see London. Work starts at 7am and finishes at 3pm in the afternoon and then their time is their own. They're quite a comic turn together. It's hard work they say, changing bed linen on between 10 and 14 beds a day – hospital corners as well. Then they have to clean the bathrooms and completely clean the whole room. An untidy room can take a girl an hour to get shipshape. Then there are the little holdups – the residents who never alter their DO NOT DISTURB signs or double lock their doors inside. The maids have to be discreet in these cases; to knock on the door and walk straight in can be disastrous. And that late departure, leaving at 2pm, means a maid has to come back specially to clear one room – but it's all in a day's work.

By 8am things are beginning to happen in the kitchen. A hotel kitchen is divided into

*Chef John Elliott draws breath after a busy lunchtime*

separate sections or *parties*. So you have the larder – a large cool room where the hors d'oeuvres, salads, sandwiches, are prepared and the meat is cut, then there are the pastry, veg, sauce, roast sections and so on. From their homes in Battersea, Putney and Crystal Palace and round the corner the chefs start arriving, white jackets and cotton check trousers on and each goes to his place and starts work on his list which Chef has given him the day before. A young French trainee opens an impressive wooden box, lined with green baize, which reveals an array of wicked and beautiful knives which he proceeds to sharpen. This week he's working in the vegetable section. It's like a stage set with all the players assembling, Manuele calmly continues preparing breakfasts and then the Chef de Cuisine arrives.

Lunchtime at the Goring Hotel is the main business of the day. Not only is it when their five banqueting rooms are in use, but also when the restaurant is booked with its regular customers from outside

ordering from a table d'hôte and à la carte menu. The restaurant in particular is the hotel's showpiece – customers coming in for a meal who enjoy their food, their wine and personal attention they receive, may be the hotel residents of the future. Profit percentage on menus is seen as less important than the hope that a satisfied customer will return: – guests first, profits second.

Back to the kitchen where Chef de Cuisine John Elliott has just arrived and the pace increases. It's still only just after 8am; vegetables have been delivered and are checked off – something missing means an immediate telephone call as these are required for lunchtime; beautiful ruby red live crayfish have been delivered, only it was 2 lbs the hotel wanted not the 11 lbs delivered. The Chef de Cuisine is above all a manager and is constantly guarding against waste. Each chef is then consulted about his list and anything he needs to prepare the items on it. This is all gone through at a great rate as Chef then goes up to

*Careful planning and preparation precede a busy mealtime*

banqueting menus are the first away. Today a great side of roast pork is picked up by one of eight waiters on duty at lunchtime.

As a waiter brings down his order from the restaurant Chef makes sure he can read it and turns to shout to the kitchen *'Ça marche'* – are you ready – and reads out the items. Each chef recognises what he has prepared from his own list and responds to the shout with a grunt of acknowledgement. Chef listens for the response he does not hear and asks for affirmation. 'How do you manage with perhaps 60 orders coming down, often in a great bunch?' John Elliott just taps his ear and winks. His job is now like the conductor of an orchestra bringing in each player on time. He and his sous chefs, Jo and Gary garnish the dishes and check that orders are as ordered and send them on their way. His check board of flashing lights that signal between the kitchen and the restaurant flashes red, green, purple and yellow as orders are 'away' and more are due.

talk over the day's banqueting menu and the table d'hôte menus for the following day with the General Manager. Special instructions, changes in guest numbers are finalised and then it's back to the kitchen to check the stores and ring through the day's orders. Lunchtime could see 180 meals being prepared and in a week the Goring might order 270 lbs of lamb, 100 lbs of fresh salmon and 70 lbs of Dover Sole whilst up in the restaurant 1,000 bottles of wine are sold over the same period. Owner George Goring, 1990 'Hotelier of the Year' award winner of this family run hotel, is keen on having a good wine list, stocking good vintages and laying down stocks for 10 years' time. While he likes others to share his wine collection he cannot however, help a feeling of sorrow when he sees a customer order a favourite claret; 'you're not selling that to guests are you?' he mutters to the wine waiter.

At 10am John Elliott has his last meal of the working day – a bowl of Manuele's porridge. From then until midday the

kitchen concentrates: massive stock pots simmer as broccoli is cooked and dunked in ice cold water to preserve, parsley is chopped, hake cut into four-inch rounds, soup tasted, pastry cases made, puddings turned out, while in the larder open sandwiches are prepared, the hors d'oeuvres assembled – terrine of guinea fowl, gravlax, goat's cheese salad – and the finger buffets for the banqueting rooms.

By 12.30pm everything is in place, the grills are full on and the great stainles steel heated counter is ready for the first orders to be placed on it. The

*Diners with Restaurant Manager David Morgan-Hewitt*

The Restaurant Manager appears. 'What about the VIP order – they seem to be waiting longer than anyone?' But there's nothing that can be done as their order takes time and the number of people for lunch has doubled over those booked. A tray is returned and a frown appears on Jo's face. It turns out that a customer's 'well done' wasn't enough for him, and a few minutes' later the John Dory goes back up 'cremated' as John says. Tempers may fray, we're told, in the heat of the moment but by 2pm the lights on the check board are gradually switched off and the *plongeurs* continue their clatter which has been non-stop for over an hour.

As people leave after lunch, Peter and Fred at the main door collect customers' cars from the garage and there is an exchange of farewells. One gets a strong feeling that cutomers know and are known by the hotel staff as one asks after Peter's daughter as he is seen into his car.

In the restaurant and other dining rooms things had gone smoothly. David Morgan-Hewitt, a major-domo figure, as Restaurant Manager had soothed the VIPs and ensured

*David Morgan-Hewitt, Restaurant Manager.*

that regular customers were seated at their 'usual' tables. He aims to strike a balance between formality and a genially unassuming approach towards his guests. The Englishness of the table d'hôte menu continues to underline the very English

nature of the hotel. The sight of roast loin of pork and jam roly poly amongst the items on the menu strikes a feeling of home to many.

The blend of the formal and the unassuming is part of the style that typifies the Goring, together with a theory that happy staff make guests happy. Owner George Goring and his General Manager William Cowpe, have worked together for over 20 years to ensure that staff and guests are both well looked after. Regular meetings between management and heads of departments are held during which an Action Sheet is drawn up of staff's wants or dislikes and each item has a decision made on it by George Goring and William Cowpe. This is part of the day-to-day running of the hotel for William Cowpe, who will also be vetting the menus, dealing with any complaint (something unavoidable in a service industry, always taken seriously, and sometimes involving a tense meeting to resolve), ordering wine, sorting

*Fred chats to a guest outside the hotel*

*William Cowpe, General Manager checking the well stocked wine cellar*

out the problem of the bath water that had trickled off the lounge chandelier as the guest sat happily watching snooker, ordering replacement glass table tops, making sure the builders are not disturbing the guests, deciding on the expenditure on next year's hotel improvements and so on and so on, and of course, talking to his guests.

Afternoon tea, with scones and some Goring fruit cake, drifts into a quiet lull before residents start appearing in the lounge for pre-dinner drinks in the bar overlooking the garden. Jo, another Goring employee who has been there absolutely years although he is only 30, prepares for the evening. While lunchtimes are mainly for business people, in the evening the bar is used mainly by residents. Regular guests scarcely need to ask for their drinks as Jo knows most of their preferences. He also has to know how to mix Manhattans and Negronis and to indulge the Americans' passion for ice, 'Scotch on the rocks, with ice!' being a frequent request. On the other hand he is equally at home preparing a freshly squeezed orange drink or popping Champagne corks.

Tonight in the restaurant is the beginning of the new à la carte menu which is changed every four months to reflect the seasonal changes. In the kitchen preparation will take a little longer as chefs adapt their skills to the new menus to be ready for the evening customers who are, in the main, the residents. While the guests eat, the evening maids

*Jo mixes a cocktail; below, guests relax in the gracious lounge*

turn down the beds for the guests. Eleven o'clock when the theatres close sees a busy last rush for drinks, sandwiches and hot chocolate, by which time the Night Manager has come on duty again, and Jo goes back to Putney.

Maintaining the status quo is no mean feat in today's challenging business climate, and getting things even better really is an achievement. Opened on 1 March 1910 by Mr O R Goring, the Goring Hotel is now three generations on and one of the highest

rated hotels in London. The complete freedom that a family run hotel has in managing its affairs is not necessarily a recipe for success. However in the case of the Goring, the professionalism of a true hotelier ensures that the idiosyncrasies of his style of managing what is a relatively small hotel, together with an established and interested staff, creates an environment that one Scotsman admits he 'raves about' and which makes him feel very, very at home. Can one say better?

# BEST NEW
# HOTELS

## NATIONAL WINNER AND REGIONAL WINNERS

E very year we have great pleasure in making our regional awards to those hotels which have just entered our guide and which we consider deserve special pride of place. This year we have for the first time, a hotel chosen from our new entries from Ireland. Against increasing difficulties in the current financial climate, there are those hotels which have flourished; each one offering its own high standards combining attractive and well cared for buildings, excellent food, not to mention owners and staff who enjoy looking after their guests. The choice of national winner is never easy, but this year the hotel which we felt has given not only the comfort of its facilities but also that added touch of attention and atmosphere is Hanbury Manor, Ware in Hertfordshire.

Congratulations to all those involved: we are very happy to welcome you to the guide and to introduce you to our readers.

## NATIONAL WINNER AND REGIONAL WINNER
### SOUTH EAST OF ENGLAND

## HANBURY MANOR
### WARE, HERTFORDSHIRE

Hanbury Manor, owned by Poles Ltd and operated by Rockresorts Inc of the USA, opened as a hotel in August 1990. The house was origi- nally designed for the Hanbury family in 1890, in a Jacobean style by Sir Ernest George of Claridges Hotel fame. It had most recently been a girls' convent and boarding school. The building and the surrounding 200 acres of golf course, parkland and formal gardens have been faith-

fully restored, with the addition of extensive sports and health facilities. The original nine-hole golf course, designed by Harry Vardon in the 1920s, has been renovated and expanded to an 18-hole championship course by Jack Nicklaus II.

Richmond Inston Design Co, a leading British firm of country house hotel architects, supervised the restoration and refurbishment of the hotel which comprises 98 luxurious bedrooms, 71 in the main house and a further 27 overlooking the walled garden. There are three restaurants under the guidance of Albert Roux of the top London restaurant, Le Gavroche, as well as banqueting facilities in the refurbished chapel, and 10 separate meeting and function rooms for up to 100 people.

The country hotel, conveniently located just 22 miles from North London and 48 miles from Heathrow Airport, is aimed predominantly at the top end of the corporate sector and has already established itself as a major retreat for the executive and social market.

Michael Neary, who managed the development phase at Hanbury, has returned to Rockresort's corporate headquarters in Florida. Eugene Wagner, appointed General Manager in April 1991, is no stranger to prestigious new enterprises: he oversaw the opening of London's The Inn on the Park in 1970 and stayed at the helm there for a decade. As Vice President of Four Seasons Hotels Ltd he was out of the country for some years, followed by a period pursuing his own activities in the industry. He says 'I am delighted to return to England, especially to take over the management of a project of the stature of Hanbury Manor'.

Hanbury Manor is the first country hotel that Albert Roux has put his name to, and he was instrumental in the selection of Rory Kennedy as Executive Chef. Rory defines his cooking style as 'cuisine for the palate'.

'Good food shouldn't need to be pigeon-holed with labels,' he explains. 'The final consideration is – is it mouthwatering or isn't it? No gimmick can beat that.'

# GORDLETON MILL

SWAY, HAMPSHIRE

This creeper-clad, 17th-century former millhouse is beautifully situated in pretty landscaped grounds around the mill pond, with ducks, plants and picturesque bridges. The hotel has been in the ownership of Bill Stone for some eight years, but closed recently for a 15-month period while a major refurbishment programme was underway. The new-look hotel opened in April 1991 with a brand new kitchen and restaurant.

The restaurant, Le Provence, created in Provence style, extends out into the garden and overlooks the water. It provides the perfect setting for Chef/Manager Jean-Christophe Novelli's superb cuisine. Formerly of Geddes, Southampton, and Keith Floyd's establishment, the Maltsters Arms in Devon, Jean-Christophe's food is a happy mix of classic, modern and regional French.

Low ceilinged public rooms retain some original brickwork, and the décor enhances the rustic effect.

There are two lounges, one no-smoking, where the mill mechanism is on display. The seven bedrooms are traditionally furnished in a French style, and the white-tiled bathrooms are fitted with jacuzzi baths.

Only 10 minutes from the New Forest and just outside Lymington, the hotel attracts a wide range of guests: holidaymakers, locals, business people and Londoners who come down for a good meal and an overnight stay.

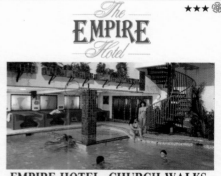

# PEN-Y-BRYN HOUSE

DEVAUDEN, GWENT

Anita and Richard Wallace had already been running a hotel in Chepstow for seven years when they identified the need for a really first class hotel and restaurant in the district, rather different from anything already in existence. They bought Pen-y-Bryn in May 1990, then a private house on the Tredean Estate five miles out of Chepstow. The conversion and renovation began in August that year, a job which Anita cheerfully describes as 'very big and very expensive', and just eight months later the hotel opened.

Their object was to create an informal atmosphere, with the feel of a dinner party in a private house, and relaxing surroundings with warm and subdued colours, like the dusky pinks and blues of the dining room. They chose antique furniture for a long-established look, and searched out just the right lightshade or painting to complete the picture. Bedrooms are individually designed and furnished with French antiques.

The Wallaces have lived 'all over the place', and been in the hotel business for the past 12 years, but once they moved to Chepstow they loved it so much they knew it was where they wanted to stay. It is a lovely area, just over the Severn Bridge between the rivers Wye and Usk, much of it officially designated 'of outstanding natural beauty'. Many guests come for the walking, there are a number of good routes, and others for the fishing where the rivers are renowned for their salmon. Golf is a popular pursuit too as there are several courses within reach, and the proximity of Chepstow Racecourse, just three miles away, is a great attraction.

# ON THE PARK

CHELTENHAM, GLOUCESTERSHIRE

Late of Charingworth Manor, where he was in partnership with his brother, Darryl Gregory has gone for the same country house atmosphere but this time in a charming Regency villa, with all the town's amenities at hand. And 'on the park' as the name describes, the hotel offers lovely views of Pittville Park opposite.

Formerly a guesthouse, the Gregorys ran it until existing bookings ran out, and then they gutted the place. They did the rounds of the auctions choosing just the right furniture, and Lesley-Anne Gregory is responsible for the hand-stencilling in the bedrooms which has been much admired, but her great labour of love was in the restoration of the grapevine cornice in the restaurant. She hired a scaffold and laid on her back every day for four weeks to paint each grape and leaf.

The Epicurean restaurant, moved from Stow-on-the-Wold where it was one of our 'Best New Restaurants' last year, is part of the hotel but run as a separate business by Chef Patrick MacDonald. Patrick was head chef at Charingworth Manor and at Ettington Park, and has gained experience at the Dorchester and Grosvenor House in London. He describes his style as 'eccentric modern British', while to Darryl Gregory words like 'rugged' and 'honest' spring to mind; he says he has known Patrick MacDonald for some time and his cooking just gets better and better.

The hotel opened in April 1991, but the Gregorys are not content to leave it as it is. At the time of writing they had just received long-awaited planning permission to extend the premises. They intend to increase the mass of the building by about two thirds. This will result in 12 bedrooms against an existing 10, but they will all be large.

# HALEY'S HOTEL

LEEDS, WEST YORKSHIRE

This hotel was the brainchild of John Appleyard. From the motor industry and with no experience in the hotel and catering field, he felt that Leeds was in need of a top quality individual hotel. Something different from the large company hotels, to cater for a sophisticated client from the new wave of business developing in the city. He found an existing hotel, a turreted building of York stone, ripe for transformation, and having no interest in being operationally involved brought General Manager Stephen Beaumont in to what he describes as a very exciting project, to be involved 'from scratch'.

In October 1989, the building was completely gutted, then began the long process of restoring it to its Victorian splendour. They wanted to avoid a squeaky clean, brand new appearance, and hope to achieve the feeling the hotel had always been there, and to set people wondering how they had managed to miss such a gem.

Interior designer Jean Schofield from Ilkley is responsible for the décor. She had previously worked on private houses and a few restaurants, but this was her first hotel and certainly her biggest job to date. She is justifiably proud of the results. She has gone for a rich, authentic Victorian look: neutral walls, dragged paintwork and lavish drapes. She has put together a fine collection of period furniture and interesting light fittings from all over the country, and had carpets specially woven with an oak leaf motif. There are pictures everywhere, in the bedrooms, bathrooms and corridors, with cricket and county themes predominating.

The hotel opened in July 1990 and it is clear that Mr Appleyard had done some careful preparatory work. The hotel, town-house style, is very conveniently located in a quiet cul-de-sac with easy access to the airport, and it combines every modern convenience with its period style.

The restaurant, open to non-residents is a very important part of the operation. Chef Andrew Foster returned from France to be involved at an early stage, helping to plan his kitchen and to recruit staff. Lunch is a club-like affair, with copper-domed carving trolleys and traditional steamed puddings. The evening menu – in French with an English translation – is rather different and, if pushed, Andrew would describe his cooking as modern English, with a classical base, using fresh ingredients. The dramatic décor is more modern in style than the rest of the hotel, with striking brown on white linen and huge 14-inch plates.

# KINNAIRD HOUSE

DUNKELD, TAYSIDE

Kinnaird House has been in the Ward family since the 1930s, and was mainly used for entertaining. It had been unused for some time when Chef/Manager John Webber came across it while honeymooning with his Scottish wife Caroline. It was the welcoming aura of the house that struck him before its appearance. He had been looking for a new position but hadn't thought of Scotland – and the rest is history.

The restaurant opened first, to be one of our 'Best Newcomers' last year, and the hotel opened in July 1990. John says it is the 'fantastic geography' of the location that

makes it so attractive, the stunning views over the Tay and the shooting and fishing. The house didn't need a great deal doing to it. The interior décor was designed by the current owner, Constance Ward, and is as close to the original as possible. A particular feature of the house is the painted panelling in the dining room, a detail of which has been picked out for the menu cover. The paintings date from the mid-1800s but remain very fresh as the building was always shuttered during summer.

John Webber has found local people's perception of food rather different from where he had been working in the south of England, so now he includes some more robust dishes, such as braised boned oxtail and sausage of guinea-fowl or pigeon, with a trend towards provincial styles and flavours. The hotel is as 'uncommercial' as they can make it, the aim being to create the feeling of being a guest in a private house while providing excellent levels of service.

# LOUGH INAGH HOUSE

RECESS, CO GALWAY

When John and Maire O'Connor bought this 19th-century shooting lodge it was in a state of dereliction, but over a period of three months they restored the place and extended it, in sympathy with the existing building, to be three times the original size. John O'Connor explains that they could have crammed in a lot more bedrooms, but decided on fewer larger rooms. They aim to provide the best quality accommodation and service throughout the hotel, but with the comfort and informality of a private house. Lounges too are spacious, and there is a cosy oak-panelled bar, all beautifully furnished with effective use of antiques and blazing log fires.

The hotel is in a lovely setting, looking out onto a lake and mountain scenery; the area around is zoned for conservation. The range of sporting and leisure activities, including fishing, golfing and walking are an added attraction to guests, and the hotel offers a seven-day sampling programme including all the various activities.

Martina Mannion does the cooking, and Connemara lamb and local seafood are specialities of the house. John describes the predominant styles as traditional Irish and French. Food is simply prepared out of respect for the excellent fresh produce, and sauces are not permitted to dominate.

John has always been in the hotel industry, working in England, Germany, Switzerland and the USA. The Lough Inagh opened in June 1990 and, while he still manages the nearby Bally Nahinch Hotel – the two buildings were once part of the same estate – he says it is great to have a place of their own although 'it has been a long road'.

# BEST NEW
# RESTAURANTS

Each year we welcome to our guide a number of new restaurants, and here we feature the five which most impressed our inspectors. *(For full details see directory).* We wish them every success for the future and would also like to welcome them to our new publication, *The Restaurant Guide.*

### DORKING, SURREY
### PARTNERS

Partners Tim McEntire and Andrew Thomason have been in business 12 years, 11 of those at Partners 23 in Sutton. In the autumn of 1990 they moved to bigger and better premises. 'We finally got our dream restaurant in Dorking, and there's a recession and it's not fair,' is Andrew's rueful comment

They still have the same ideals they started out with. Andrew believes the personal touch is important, 'to be on the shop floor selling Tim's cooking'. Consistency is their first priority; customers must have a first class meal every visit. And while the restaurant is at the top of the market the atmosphere is relaxed: 'We don't expect our customers to eat in hallowed silence.'

The menu is an amalgam of styles reflecting their joint careers, including Tim's period at the Savoy, and 'the best of food from the last 10 to 15 years thrown into the melting pot'.

### BLACKWATER, CORNWALL
### LONG'S

Ann and Ian Long have been in the business for 30 years, running places of their own for the last 15 of them. They have always loved Cornwall, and although not natives of the county feel it has a certain magic. They ran a very successful restau-

rant, the Count House at Botallack, right on the cliffs, then took on a hotel at Oakhill, near Bath, again to great acclaim. But Ann's great interest is in food, and so they have returned to restaurant-keeping and to Cornwall, opening Long's in March 1989. Ian, who is in charge front of house, describes his wife's cooking as modern British. 'She is an artist: colour and texture are perfectly balanced and the food is beautifully presented.

### SWANSEA, WEST GLAMORGAN
### KEENANS

Chef/Proprietor Chris Keenan is Swansea born and bred. After 11 years gaining experience in London he returned to find that there was no requirement for his particular skills,

and realised that his only option was to open a place of his own.

'It felt very lonely at first, but my wife Lynda was a great support, she's been fantastic. And it was Lynda who designed the restaurant's interior.' He is also relieved to have established a good team: Manageress Michelle Turner and Sous Chef Ian Harvey. 'People who really care about the restaurant and really care about me.'

Keenans opened to great critical acclaim, and two and a half years later Chris says the challenge is to maintain standards. He prides himself on his exclusive dishes, apart from a few classics. And his objective? Quite simple – perfection.

### MORETON-IN-MARSH, GLOUCESTERSHIRE
### THE MARSH GOOSE

Our inspector describes the cooking of chef Sonya Kidney as 'a revelation' at this new Cotswolds restaurant. The Marsh Goose opened in November 1990 by partners Gordon Campbell-Grey, who brought the Feathers at Woodstock to such acclaim, and former members of staff Lee Brooke-Little and Sonya Kidney. Sonya, who has worked with Francis Coulson at Sharrow Bay in Cumbria, cooks imaginatively from a classical English base, and the partners aim to provide first class food in a relaxed and accessible atmosphere: smartly laid tables are placed in unusual seating arrangements which mean you can sit in a private little area of your own. Most customers are from the surrounding villages, others from Stratford, Oxford and further afield as the restaurant's reputation spreads.

### HETTON, NORTH YORKS
### ANGEL INN

There was no doubt in our inspector's mind that the Angel Inn would be our 1991/1992 Best Newcomer – North Region. Chef / Proprietors Denis Watkins and John Topham have been running this popular Dales restaurant/pub for eight years now. Six miles from the nearest shop in the beautiful rural location of the Airedale moors, the Angel is only an hour from an urban population of some four million people in Leeds, Bradford, Liverpool and Manchester. Roads from the built up areas continue to improve and Denis Watkins says, 'they all lead here'. About 70/80 per cent of cus-

tomers are individual rather than corporate, and the fixed price menu is carefully cost-controlled to provide good value for money. Denis describes the food as 'eclectic British', cooked to concentrate and preserve strong flavours.

### GLASGOW, STRATHCLYDE
### MITCHELLS

The partnership of chefs Angus Boyd and Robin Grey is proving to be very effective at this split level bistro, bar and restaurant, attracting a lot of media attention in recent months. Robin was apprenticed to Angus many years ago, but now Robin is in charge of the kitchen while Angus runs things front of house. Angus has given up a number of similar concerns to concentrate on the success of his 'jewel in the crown'. Much of the produce is supplied by Robin's smallholding on the Isle of Arran, organically grown herbs, duck and

free range chickens. The atmosphere is friendly and informal, with a rood range of food and prices.

### BELFAST, CO BELFAST
### ROSCOFF

The Roscoff opened July 1989 and our inspector has already described it as 'the best restaurant in Northern Ireland'. There is absolutely no pretentiousness about the place, one can simply relax and enjoy the wonderful food. Chef/Proprietor Paul Rankin spent three years at London's Le Gavroche, and some time in Canada and California, and his food is in the modern style. Flavours are well defined and particularly well balanced, and the cooking is careful but exciting and accomplished. The double-fronted restaurant, in a parade of shops, attracts a large business clientèle at lunch time, while at dinner people have been known to travel from Dublin to eat here.

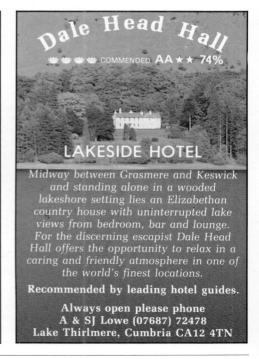

# *Britain's*
# *TOP HOTELS*

The award of red stars to an hotel is the most prestigious that the AA can give, indicating consistent all-round excellence. The 84 hotels listed below are those which have been judged by our inspectors to be the very best in their star classification: the best hotels in Britain (see p781 for Ireland).

Fifteen new awards are made this year to: Farleyer House, **Aberfeldy**; Lucknam Park, **Colerne**; One Devonshire Gardens, **Glasgow**; Greywalls, **Gullane**; Langshott Manor, **Horley**; Dunain Park, **Inverness**; The Marsh Country House, **Leominster**; The Dorchester, **London W1**; Ladyburn, **Maybole**; Stapleford Park, **Melton Mowbray**; The Old Course Hotel, **St Andrews**; The Castle, **Taunton**; 'Courtesy and Care' award winners last year: Woodhayes, **Whimple** and Holbeck Ghyll Country House Hotel, **Windermere**; The Grange Hotel, **York**.

## ENGLAND
### AVON
### HUNSTRETE
#### ★★★ ♨Hunstrete House
Set in gardens and parkland bordering the Mendip Hills, Hunstrete House continues to provide the solidity and comfort of a country house that is attractively decorated and has some notable antiques and objets d'art. English food, cooked expertly, complements that English country house feel.

### THORNBURY
#### ★★★ ♨Thornbury Castle
Thornbury Castle has just what you'd expect of a castle—mullioned windows, tapestries, tower bedrooms, yet also all the modern amenities, plus the accomplished and delicious cooking of Derek Hamlen; traditional dishes of Angus beef, treacle tart and many regional cheeses are amongst many tempting items on the restaurant menu.

### BUCKINGHAMSHIRE
### ASTON CLINTON
#### ★★★ Bell Inn
Under the ownership of Patsy and Michael Harris the Bell has, over several years, become the very model of a traditional English inn, with cobbled courtyard, flagged smoking room and panelled drawing room.

### AYLESBURY
#### ★★★ ♨Hartwell House
Vastly spacious bedrooms, rich furnishings and luxurious bathrooms delight the visitor to this superbly grand house, host in its time to several crowned heads, the most notorious being the exiled Louis XVIII.

### TAPLOW
#### ★★★★★ ♨Cliveden
At this celebrated and historic house, now owned by the National Trust, guests can enjoy the gracious building and also a choice of two good restaurants, the Terrace and Waldo's, with cooking by Ron Maxfield.

### CHANNEL ISLANDS, JERSEY
### ST SAVIOUR
#### ★★★★ ♨Longueville Manor
A rambling old manor of great charm which has belonged to the Lewis family for 3 generations and is set in spacious grounds on the edge of St Helier.

### CHESHIRE
### CHESTER
#### ★★★★ Chester Grosvenor
A Victorian building—with the black and white timbered look that is typical of the region—in the centre of Chester, the Chester Grosvenor is luxuriously and impressively fitted and decorated; marble floors in bathrooms, mirrors and panelling, an opulently furnished restaurant, the Arkle, and also an informal Brasserie, under the skilful direction of chef Paul Reed. Willing and enthusiastic staff are a strong presence here.

### CORNWALL
### LISKEARD
#### ★★ ♨Well House
Small (10 bedrooms), individualistic and in wonderful countryside, Well House has the added attraction of an elegant restaurant where the cooking of David Woolfall has put it firmly on the map as a restaurant that should be visited. Owner Nick Wainford has made this an extremely desirable place in which to get away and relax.

# BRITAIN'S TOP HOTELS

## CUMBRIA

### BRAMPTON

#### ★★♨Farlam Hall
'A mark of bygone days' is one description of the service and hospitality here. The Quinion and Stevenson families continue to unobtrusively pamper their guests with their foresight in offering not only a graceful and immaculately kept house but also the attention to details, like the presence of books, magazines and games that make one feel at home.

### GRASMERE

#### ★★★♨Michael's Nook
An altogether delightful Lakeland hideaway, a country house filled with antiques, with rich décor and courteous service in lovely surroundings.

### GRASMERE

#### ★White Moss House
A warm welcome is guaranteed at this charming hotel in an idyllic location overlooking Rydal Water.

### HOWTOWN

#### ★★★♨Sharrow Bay Hotel
At the forefront of Lake District country house hotels, Sharrow Bay's warm, elegant décor, exceptional views over the Ullswater Lake, traditional and modern cooking, and wide-ranging wine list contribute to the overall atmosphere of wellbeing, although owners, Brian Sack and Francis Coulson, after 43 years, now delegate some of the work.

### WATERMILLOCK

#### ★★♨Old Church Hotel
A cosy hotel in a lovely setting on Lake Ullswater, where hospitality and service are of the highest standard.

### WINDERMERE

#### ★★♨Holbeck Ghyll Country House Hotel
Genuinely friendly and extremely competent staff ensure standards for courtesy and care, while chef Leslie Anderson's wide-ranging dinners complete a visit here.

### WINDERMERE

#### ★★Miller Howe
A friendly hotel in a lovely position, with views of Lake Windermere from a new conservatory extension. John Tovey's team continue to maintain the high standards now expected.

### WITHERSLACK

#### ★♨Old Vicarage
A charming house in an idyllic setting run by a 2-family partnership, offering good food, fine wine and a warm welcome.

## DERBYSHIRE

### BASLOW

#### ★★★Cavendish
Eric Marsh's professional management makes for an excellent stay: fresh flowers, blazing log fires and paintings give an aura of comfort, with a smart restaurant or informal Garden Room for eating in. The Chatsworth estate sets off the house admirably.

## DEVON

### BARNSTAPLE

#### ★♨Halmpstone Manor
Approached by a remote lane in lovely Devonshire countryside, it is impossible to imagine the delights which await you at Halmpstone Manor, which is part of a working farm. The hotel exemplifies old-fashioned standards of hospitality and service.

### CHAGFORD

#### ★★★♨Gidleigh Park
Forty acres of grounds and gardens within Dartmoor National Park surround this luxurious hotel owned by Paul and Kay Henderson. Noted both for the tranquility of the setting and the superb cooking of its renowned chef Shaun Hill.

### LEWDOWN

#### ★★♨Lewtrenchard Manor
The former home of Sabine Baring Gould, rooms here are named after hymn tunes. And while the surroundings are splendidly ornate, the atmosphere is very relaxed.

### NORTH HUISH

#### ★★♨Brookdale House
Good food and a warm, friendly welcome from Charles and Carol Trevor-Roper and their staff are what draws guests to this secluded former rectory in its lovely woodland setting.

### SOUTH MOLTON

#### ★★♨Whitechapel Manor
Charming hosts John and Patricia Shapland have created an atmosphere of professional informality at this beautifully restored Elizabethan house. Attractive surroundings and fine cuisine ensure a pleasant stay.

### WHIMPLE

#### ★★♨Woodhayes
The combination of charming Georgian house, apple orchards, croquet, and of being well looked after will draw you to Woodhayes. The

Rendle family have chosen décor that fits the style of building and their high standards of housekeeping and cooking make this a very welcome and deserving re-entry to our red star list.

## DORSET
### EVERSHOT
★★**Summer Lodge**
Extremely comfortable bedrooms and luxurious bathrooms are an appealing feature of this village based country house hotel.

### GILLINGHAM
★★♨**Stock Hill House**
Peaceful Dorset with a hint of Austria combine well in this delightful Victorian manor house, where the meals are the highlight of a relaxing stay.

## EAST SUSSEX
### BATTLE
★★★♨**Netherfield Place**
A charming country house hotel set in 30 acres of parkland and gardens, owned and run in friendly style by Michael and Helen Collier.

### UCKFIELD
★★★♨**Horsted Place**
Recently converted from a private home, this immense Victorian house is now a very comfortable hotel. Its hand-carved oak staircase is a central feature, and the grounds were designed by Geoffrey Jellico with a heated swimming pool, croquet lawn and tennis court. Cooking is excellent and uncomplicated under the skilful direction of chef Allan Garth.

## ESSEX
### DEDHAM
★★★♨**Maison Talbooth**
A beautifully proportioned Victorian house where luxury abounds. At its restaurant, *Le Talbooth*, the arrival of chef Steven Blake has signalled new heights of creative cooking; exceptionally good raw materials and the chef's imaginative skills produce truly memorable meals.

## GLOUCESTERSHIRE
### BUCKLAND
★★★♨**Buckland Manor**
The pretty names of the rooms, such as Green, Floral, Oak and Fountain, evoke the charming surroundings of this lovely Cotswold manor.

### CHELTENHAM
★★★♨**Greenway Hotel**
Willing and unobtrusive service, and attention to small but important details such as good beds, quality linen and fine fabrics, show hotelkeeping at its best here at the Greenaway.

## TETBURY
★★★♨**Calcot Manor**
The silver-grey Cotswold stone of Calcot Manor blends happily with the surrounding countryside. Hospitality is unobtrusive yet always there to meet the guests' needs and in the dining room, you can be sure of a sound and imaginative meal which bears the individual touch of chef Ramon Farthing.

## HAMPSHIRE
### NEW MILTON
★★★★♨**Chewton Glen**
Martin Skan presides over what has become a world-class hotel, with the ultimate in standards and comfort. Recent enhancements include a superb leisure centre.

## HEREFORD & WORCESTER
### BROADWAY
★★★★**Lygon Arms**
This old Cotswold inn is full of character. Its Great Hall makes a splendid restaurant, and there is a choice of comfortable period or modern bedrooms.

### LEOMINSTER
★♨**The Marsh Country House**
Hardworking hosts Martin and Jacqueline Gilleland give guests a warm welcome and fine food amid gracious country surroundings—a worthy red star hotel.

### ROSS ON WYE
★★**Wharton Lodge**
The Gough family offer good old fashioned levels of service at their lovely Georgian house just outside Ross-on-Wye.

## KENT
### ASHFORD
★★★★♨**Eastwell Manor**
Set in a 3,000-acre estate in the Kentish countryside, this impressive manor house exudes grandeur, with carved wood-panelling, elaborate plasterworked ceilings, luxurious sofas and antiques. Bathrooms, furnishings and colour schemes are all top quality: a splendid place in which to stay and also a good stopping off point for the continent.

★NEW★ AWARD

### LEICESTER
### MELTON MOWBRAY
#### ★★★♨Stapleford Park
Former home of the Earls of Harborough with 500 acres of grounds designed by Capability Brown, Stapleford Park is now run in unique style by American Bob Payton. Much money and devotion has been lavished on the house to make it into the luxury house it now is, with traditional English country sports available to guests.

### OAKHAM
#### ★★★♨Hambleton Hall
High standards have been set by Tim Hart and his wife Stefa who have converted this Victorian house to the elegant hotel we now know. Peaceful countryside and views over Rutland Water combined with the excellent service and hospitality allows you to unwind in comfort.

### LONDON
### SW1
#### ★★★★★Berkeley
Extensive refurbishment has been completed and the Berkeley provides accommodation of a very high standard, along with good leisure facilities and sound French cuisine.

### SW1
#### ★★★★Goring Hotel
Highly acclaimed as the family-run hotel *par excellence*, the Goring Hotel's owner and his General Manager William Cowpe have this year been joined by chef John Elliott, formerly of the Connaught Hotel and more recently Les Ambassadeurs Club. Good service and good food are the order of the day here.

### SW1
#### ★Ebury Court
Ebury court remains an outstanding small hotel, centrally situated and individualistically run. Dubbed 'legendary' for its longstanding high reputation, it is now run by the former owner's daughter and son-in-law.

### SW3
#### ★★★★Capital
Highly professional service and a warm atmosphere are the distinctive characteristics of this charming hotel.

### W1
#### ★★★★★Claridges
Legendary standards at Claridges have been nurtured by the respected Director and General Manager Ronald Jones. Continual

improvements to bedrooms and suites maintain the hotel's pristine condition, and the restaurant continues its reputation as one of London's most dignified and elegant.

### W1
#### ★★★★★Connaught
Traditional values of hospitality and service are upheld by this legendary London hotel, and loyal and long-serving staff ensure consistently high standards. Recent refurbishments have enhanced the luxurious surroundings.

★NEW★ AWARD

### W1
#### ★★★★★Dorchester
Luxury abounds in the newly re-opened Park Lane hotel: Cantonese cooking can be savoured in the sumptuously decorated new Oriental restaurant while the familiar Grill Room and Terrace Restaurant reflects the French modern style of Chef Willi Elsener.

### W1
#### ★★★★Athenaeum
Continuing high standards, elegance and comfort bring praise from all quarters and in the attractive restaurant, with its pink colour motif, the cooking is in the deft hands of chef David Marshall.

### W1
#### ★★★★Brown's
Traditionalists will love this splendid old hotel for the style of its public rooms and the formality of its service.

### WC2
#### ★★★★★Savoy
Director Herbert Striessnig ensures that the Savoy maintains the incomparable standards of hotelkeeping with which its name is synonymous, while chef Anton Edelman reigns in the Savoy Restaurant, where guests can enjoy both the fine French cuisine and riverside views.

### NORFOLK
### GRIMSTON
#### ★★★♨Congham Hall
A most appealing hotel, run by Trevor and Christine Forecast, offering high standards of comfort in the north Norfolk countryside close to Sandringham.

### NORTH YORKSHIRE
### BILBROUGH
#### ★★★♨Bilbrough Manor
Five miles from the centre of York this comfortable, peaceful manor house, with its

deep sofas, oil paintings and extensive library, offers the service and hospitality that we have come to know.

## YORK

### ★★★Grange Hotel
Right in the centre of York is this Grade II listing building: Jeremy Cassel's elegant hotel. Its visual appeal is matched by excellent cooking and first rate service from a professional staff.

## YORK

### ★★★Middlethorpe Hall
A William III period house overlooking York racecourse, Middlethorpe Hall is full of character, from the fine furniture and impressive fitings, to the bedrooms in converted stables—all beautifully fitted out.

## OXFORDSHIRE

### GREAT MILTON

### ★★★★≜Le Manoir aux Quat' Saisons
Raymond Blanc's superb restaurant has gradually grown into a most comfortable hotel, its magnificent setting providing a relaxing atmosphere, large bedrooms, decorated with immense charm, and all the traditional hotel services to a very high standard under the management of Nicholas Dickinson.

## SOMERSET

### DULVERTON

### ★★★≜Ashwick House
Peace and relaxation high on Exmoor in comfortable and hospitable surroundings.

### STON EASTON

### ★★★★≜Ston Easton Park
The public rooms are of breathtaking proportions in this Palladian mansion set amid Humphrey Repton-designed grounds and gardens. Activities here include hot air ballooning.

### TAUNTON

### ★★★The Castle
A delightful blend of old and new greets visitors here—the castle keep and garden date from medieval times; inside sympathetic furnishings

and décor combine well with modern comforts and peaceful atmosphere.

## WIVELISCOMBE

### ★★Langley House
A small, exceptionally pretty hotel set in lovely countryside, where caring hosts, Peter and Anne Wilson, provide charming accommodation and good food.

## SUFFOLK

## HINTLESHAM

### ★★★★≜Hintlesham Hall
A charming country house hotel with a thriving restaurant, set in 23 acres of grounds, maintaining high standards of quality and comfort.

## SURREY

## HORLEY

### ★Langshott Manor
A delightful Elizabethan manor in a quiet corner in Surrey is the ideal setting for a stay in surroundings of luxury and comfort, complemented by the friendly hospitality of the Noble family.

## WARWICKSHIRE

## LEAMINGTON SPA (ROYAL)

### ★★★★≜Mallory Court
Set in 10 acres of mature grounds and gardens, this richly furnished, mellow stone manor house boasts a particularly comfortable restaurant.

## LEAMINGTON SPA (ROYAL)

### ★Lansdowne Hotel
A recently extended Regency building is the setting for this relaxing and comfortable hotel; interesting home-cooked meals complement an enjoyable stay.

## WEST SUSSEX

## EAST GRINSTEAD

### ★★★★≜Gravetye Manor
Storms may have ravaged the spectacular gardens of Elizabethan Gravetye Manor, but owner Peter Herbert has put as much effort into their restoration as he has into maintaining the high standards of hospitality, service and cuisine of this highly acclaimed hotel.

## WEST YORKSHIRE

## WETHERBY

### ★★★★≜Wood Hall
An elegant Georgian mansion, in the beautiful

Yorkshire setting of Wharfedale, which is a peaceful country house retreat furnished with every luxury.

## WILTSHIRE
### COLERNE
★★★★**Lucknam Park**
Lovely Wiltshire countryside is the setting for this elegant Georgian country house. General Manager Robert Carter ensures the highest standards of service, and guests enjoy Michael Wormesley's fine cuisine in the splendid dining room.

## WALES
### GWYNEDD
### LLANDUDNO
★★★**Bodysgallen Hall**
A choice of comfortable bedrooms or self-contained cottages is offered at this most popular of country house hotels, along with outstanding views of Snowdonia.

### LLANDUDNO
★★**St Tudno**
One of the nicest resort hotels in the country, the hospitality of Martin and Janette Bland being one of its strongest features.

### TALSARNAU
★★**Maes-y-Neuadd**
The gracious hospitality of the Slatter and Horsyall families, the imaginative cooking of chef Andrew Taylor, and comfortable surroundings in a wonderfully scenic setting combine to promise an ideal stay.

### TAL-Y-LLYN
★**Minffordd Hotel**
The unhurried pace and relaxing atmosphere at the Minffordd are reminiscent of the hotel's earlier existence as a 17th-century drover's inn.

## SCOTLAND
### CENTRAL
### DUNBLANE
★★★★**Cromlix House**
Now under the management of Edward Eden, with Chef Ian Corkhill in charge of the kitchen, Cromlix House continues to delight those who seek peace and relaxation.

### DUMFRIES & GALLOWAY
### PORTPATRICK
★★★**Knockinaam Lodge**
'An experience not to be missed', reported our inspector following a visit to this lovely retreat.

## FIFE
### ST ANDREWS
★★★★**St Andrews Old Course Hotel**
Recently extended and totally refurbished, this hotel maintains its long-standing reputation for dignity and luxury, and the restaurant is renowned for a high standard of cuisine.

## GRAMPIAN
### BANCHORY
★★★**Banchory Lodge**
This wonderful fishing lodge is popular and busy throughout the year—an ideal holiday retreat. Set on the banks of the Dee, this hotel is attractively appointed, and the chef, not surprisingly, makes good use of the fresh Dee salmon.

## HIGHLAND
### ARISAIG
★★★**Arisaig House**
A fine stone house of timeless beauty, with woodland paths down to the shore and views of many islands out to sea.

### FORT WILLIAM
★★★★**Inverlochy Castle**
Elegance and hospitality in a superb setting are the basis for Inverlochy Castle's international reputation. Although the cuisine remains basically British, new chef David Whiffen has brought his own style to fine meals in the restaurant.

### FORT WILLIAM
★**The Factor's House**
Described by our inspectors as 'a little gem', this lovely small hotel in the shadow of Ben Nevis is renowned for its friendliness.

### INVERNESS
★★★**Dunain Park**
Edward and Ann Nicoll preside over this charming lodge, offering guests a relaxing stay in gracious surroundings, and a sincerely friendly atmosphere.

### WHITEBRIDGE
★★★**Knockie Lodge**
Tucked away high in the mountains by Loch Nan, with distant views of Loch Ness far below,

the Milwards have created a lovely home from home.

## LOTHIAN

### GULLANE
★★★♨Greywalls

An outstanding Lutyens country house is the setting for this gracious hotel, and the Weaver family maintain the highest standards making this one of Scotland's top establishments.

## STRATHCLYDE

### ERISKA
★★★♨Isle of Eriska Hotel

A unique baronial mansion standing on its own 250-acre island of beautiful scenery and abundant wildlife.

## GLASGOW

★★★One Devonshire Gardens

Colour and confidence are the hallmarks of this Scottish hotel. Ken McCulloch eases his guests into its opulent style and chef Andrew Fleming's cooking attracts customers from the city with his modern cooking of excellent Scottish produce.

## MAYBOLE

★★♨Ladyburn

The hospitality offered by David and Jane Hepburn when guests visit 'their home' is second to none, and comfortable and attractive surroundings and a superb setting make for an ideal stay.

## PORT APPIN

★★★Airds

Eric Allen, resplendent in kilt, is a fine host in this very Scottish hotel, where fresh fish is a highlight of the fine meals; a superb setting and relaxing atmosphere complete this excellent hotel.

## TAYSIDE

### ABERFELDY
★★♨Farleyer House

A stay in this handsome Scottish country mansion, set in its own grounds near the river Tay is made doubly pleasurable by the hospitality of owners Bill and Frances Atkins. They are partnered by Chef Tony Heath who specialises in country dishes.

### AUCHTERARDER
★★★★★Gleneagles

A luxury hotel with the highest standards of professional but friendly service, with what are probably the best hotel leisure facilities in the country.

# Britain's
# *TOP RESTAURANTS*

This year we have extended our rosette scheme and awards now range from five rosettes at the top down to a single rosette. We can now include a much wider range of restaurants and give recognition to the efforts and expertise of many chefs and restaurants whose cooking and presentation of dishes and service reach exceptionally high standards. We list below those restaurants in the three highest categories: please consult the directory for full details. Some restaurants have been awarded rosettes for their dinner menu only.

**ENGLAND**

✸✸✸✸✸
**LONDON**
**SW17**
✸✸✸✸✸ ✕✕ Harvey's
**W1**
✸✸✸✸✸ ✕✕ **Chez Nico**
✸✸✸✸✸ ✕✕✕✕ **Le Gavroche**

**OXFORDSHIRE**
**Great Milton**
✸✸✸✸✸ ★★★ Le Manoir Aux Quat' Saisons

✸✸✸✸
**BERKSHIRE**
**Bray**
✸✸✸✸ ✕✕✕✕ Waterside Restaurant
**Shinfield**
✸✸✸✸ ✕✕✕ L'Ortolan

**HERTFORDSHIRE**
**Ware**
✸✸✸✸ ★★★★ Hanbury Manor

**LONDON**
**SW3**
✸✸✸✸ ★★★★ Capital Hotel
✸✸✸✸ ✕✕ Tante Claire
**SW8**
✸✸✸✸ ✕✕ Cavalier's
✸✸✸✸ ✕✕ L'Arlequin

✸✸✸
**AVON**
**Bristol**
✸✸✸ ✕✕ Restaurant Lettonie

**BEDFORDSHIRE**
**Flitwick**
✸✸✸ ★★★ Flitwick Manor

**CORNWALL AND ISLES OF SCILLY**
**Liskeard**
✸✸✸ ★★ Well House Hotel
**Padstow**
✸✸✸ ✕✕ Seafood Restaurant

**CUMBRIA**
**Cartmel**
✸✸✸ ✕✕ Uplands
**Howtown** (near Pooley Bridge)
✸✸✸ ★★★ Sharrow Bay Country House
**Windermere**
✸✸✸ ★★ Miller Howe

**DERBYSHIRE**
**Baslow**
✸✸✸ ★★ Fischers Hotel
**Ridgeway**
✸✸✸ ✕✕✕ Old Vicarage

**DEVON**
**Chagford**
✸✸✸ ★★★ Gidleigh Park Hotel
**Dartmouth**
✸✸✸ ✕✕ Carved Angel
**Gulworthy**
✸✸✸ ✕✕✕ Horn of Plenty
**North Huish**
✸✸✸ ★★ Brookdale House
**South Molton**
✸✸✸ ★★ Whitechapel Manor
**Torquay**
✸✸✸ ✕✕ The Table Restaurant

**EAST SUSSEX**
**Hastings & St Leonards**
✸✸✸ ✕ Roser's

**ESSEX**
**Dedham**
✸✸✸ ✕✕✕ Le Talbooth

**GLOUCESTERSHIRE**
**Cleeve Hill**
✸✸✸ ✕✕ Redmond's
**Stroud**
✸✸✸ ✕ Oakes
**Tetbury**
✸✸✸ ★★★ Calcot Manor

**GREATER MANCHESTER**
**Bury**
✸✸✸ ★★★ Normandie Hotel

**HAMPSHIRE**
**Brockenhurst**
❀❀❀ ✕✕ Le Poussin
**New Milton**
❀❀❀ ★★★★ Chewton Glen Hotel
**Romsey**
❀❀❀ ✕✕ Old Manor House
**Sway**
❀❀❀ ★★ Gordleton Mill Hotel

**HEREFORD & WORCESTER**
**Ledbury**
❀❀❀ ★★ Hope End Country House

**HUMBERSIDE**
**Winteringham**
❀❀❀ ✕✕✕ Winteringham Fields

**KENT**
**Faversham**
❀❀❀ ✕✕ Read's Restaurant
**Tunbridge Wells (Royal)**
❀❀❀ ✕✕ Thackeray's House

**LEICESTERSHIRE**
**Oakham**
❀❀❀ ★★★ Hambleton Hall

**LONDON**
**EC2**
❀❀❀ ✕✕✕ Le Poulbot
**SW3**
❀❀❀ ✕✕ Bibendum
❀❀❀ ✕✕ Turners
**SW7**
❀❀❀ ✕✕ Hilaire
**W1**
❀❀❀ ✕ Alastair Little
❀❀❀ ★★★★ Athenaeum
❀❀❀ ★★★★★ Connaught
❀❀❀ ★★★★★ Dorchester
❀❀❀ ★★★★★ Inn on the Park
❀❀❀ ★★★★★ Inter-Continental
❀❀❀ ★★★★★ Le Meridien London
❀❀❀ ✕✕✕ Rue St Jacques
❀❀❀ ✕✕ Sutherlands
❀❀❀ ✕✕✕ The Greenhouse
**W8**
❀❀❀ ✕✕ Clarke's
**W11**
❀❀❀ ✕✕✕ Leith's
**W14**
❀❀❀ ✕ Chinon
**WC2**
❀❀❀ ★★★★★ The Savoy

**NORFOLK**
**Norwich**
❀❀❀ ✕✕ Adlard's

**SURREY**
**Bagshot**
❀❀❀ ★★★★ Pennyhill Park
**Haslemere**
❀❀❀ ✕✕ Morels

**WARWICKSHIRE**
**Billesley**
❀❀❀ ★★★ Billesley Manor

**Leamington Spa (Royal)**
❀❀❀ ★★★ Mallory Court

**WEST MIDLANDS**
**Birmingham**
❀❀❀ ✕✕✕ Sloan's
❀❀❀ ★★★★ Swallow
**Hockley Heath**
❀❀❀ ★★★ Nuthurst Grange Country House

**WEST SUSSEX**
**Storrington**
❀❀❀ ✕✕✕ Manley's

**WEST YORKSHIRE**
**Ilkley**
❀❀❀ ✕✕✕ Box Tree
**Pool-in-Wharfedale**
❀❀❀ ✕✕✕ Pool Court

**WILTSHIRE**
**Colerne**
❀❀❀ ★★★★ Lucknam Park

**NORTHERN IRELAND**

**CO BELFAST**
**Belfast**
❀❀❀ ✕✕ Roscoff

**SCOTLAND**

**CENTRAL**
**Aberfoyle**
❀❀❀ ✕✕ Braeval Mill

**DUMFRIES & GALLOWAY**
**Portpatrick**
❀❀❀ ★★ Knockinaam Lodge

**FIFE**
**Cupar**
❀❀❀ ✕ Ostlers Close
**Peat Inn**
❀❀❀ ✕✕ The Peat Inn

**HIGHLAND**
**Ullapool**
❀❀❀ ✕✕ Altnaharrie Inn

**LOTHIAN**
**Gullane**
❀❀❀ ✕ La Potinière
**Linlithgow**
❀❀❀ ✕✕✕ Champany

**STRATHCLYDE**
**Port Appin**
❀❀❀ ★★★ Airds

**WALES**

**GWENT**
**Llanddewi Skyrrid**
❀❀❀ ✕ Walnut Tree Inn

**GWYNEDD**
**Pwllheli**
❀❀❀ ★★ Plas Bodegroes Restaurant

# How We Classify
# HOTELS AND RESTAURANTS

This 1992 edition incorporates for the first time AA-inspected hotels and restaurants in Ireland. These will appear as a separate section to those in Britain (see page 781).

## CLASSIFICATIONS

Hotels: classified with black stars, with additional quality percentage assessments.

AA lodges: simple accommodation of fairly standard quality near main roads.

Restaurants: classified with knives and forks. In addition to their classifications, hotels and restaurants can both receive awards for special merit.

Every establishment is inspected annually and classified according to specific criteria.

## THE INSPECTORS

Much of the inspectors' work consists of regular and detailed examination of premises. Inspectors either have a background in the hotel and catering industries, or training and work experience and they also undertake regular training courses to ensure consistent nationwide standards in their assessments. A balance is therefore achieved between their specialist expertise and awareness of market needs.

## HOTELS

Hotels are inspected anonymously. Having stayed a night and settled the bill in the morning, the inspector introduces herself or himself and makes a thorough inspection of the entire premises. Once granted recognition and given a rating, the hotel is inspected annually. Change of ownership means the hotel automatically loses its AA recognition and must be re-assessed under the new ownership before being re-appointed. A fee is levied for registration and appointment.

## RATINGS

Black stars range from one ★ to five ★★★★★. They denote a universally accepted standard ranging from the simplest to the most luxurious hotel. In addition all hotels are awarded percentage assessments to highlight quality differences between establishments within the same star classification.

★ Hotels generally of a small scale with good but often simple furnishing, facilities and food. This category sometimes includes private hotels where requirements for public access and full lunch service may be relaxed. Not all bedrooms will necessarily have en suite facilities. These hotels are often managed by the proprietor and there may well be a more personal atmosphere than in larger establishments.

★★ Small to medium sized hotels offering more in the way of facilities such as telephones and televisions in bedrooms. Like one star hotels, this category can also include private hotels. At least half the bedrooms will have full en suite facilities. These can be proprietor managed or group owned.

★★★ Medium sized hotels offering more spacious accommodation and a greater range of facilities and services. Generally these will include a full reception service as well as more formal restaurant and bar arrangements. You can expect all rooms to provide en suite facilities, most of which will include a bath. Though often individually owned, this category encompasses a greater number of company owned properties.

★★★★ Generally large hotels with spacious accommodation including availability of private suites. This category of hotel normally provides a full range of formal services including room service, reception and porterage and may well offer more than one dining operation. En suite facilities in all rooms should include both bath and shower. High standards of comfort and food are expected at this level.

★★★★★ Large luxury hotels offering the highest international standards of accommodation, facilities, services and cuisine.

## LODGES ⬆

Lodges offer reasonably priced accommodation catering for overnight stops and offering good, functional bedrooms with private facilities. They are usually situated adjacent to a motorway/roadside restaurant. They are of fairly standard quality and are not star rated.

# MERIT AWARDS

## PERCENTAGES

These are in addition to black star ratings. They represent the difference in quality between hotels within a particular star rating, reflecting the inspectors' experiences at the time of inspection.

## PERCENTAGE ASSESSMENT

**50% – 59%** A sound hotel which meets all the minimum standards for AA star rating and which overall provides modest but acceptable levels of accommodation, facilities and service.

**60% – 69%** A particularly sound hotel which exceeds the minimum requirements for its star rating by offering higher standards in certain areas.

**70% – 85%** Overall a very good hotel which can be strongly recommended for providing a high level of service, food and accommodation often with excellent standards in certain areas of its operation.

## RED STARS

Red stars range from one ★ to five ★★★★★. The AA recognises hotels which consistently provide outstanding levels of hospitality, service, food and comfort through its prestigious red star award scheme. These awards are given annually to a select group of hotels considered to be the very best within their star rating. In such cases, a percentage score for quality is considered unnecessary.

In the whole of Great Britain there are only 84 red star hotels (see list on page 41). They are highlighted in the directory by a pink tinted panel containing a full description and photograph. (See p 781 for Ireland.)

## COUNTRY HOUSE HOTEL 🏚

An AA Country House hotel with a relaxed informal atmosphere and offering a personal welcome. Often secluded, they are not always rurally situated but are quiet. See list on page 801.

Hotels attracting frequent conferences or functions are not normally granted this symbol.

## RESTAURANTS

Restaurants have their own classification scheme. As with hotels, this has five levels. However instead of 'stars', you will find from one to five 'knives and forks'. The level of amenities increases with the number of knives and forks awarded. Thus a modest bistro style restaurant may be classified as one knife and fork whereas an international top class restaurant may gain five knives and forks.

Restaurants are inspected anonymously. No fee is charged for a restaurant to be included in the guide.

Accommodation at restaurants is not AA inspected and is not included in the classifications.

## KNIVES AND FORKS

Comfort, facilities, cuisine, service and atmosphere are all assessed in determining the appropriate knife and fork classification, which can be described as follows:

✕ Simplicity is generally the keynote: this will be evident in both cuisine and décor. One knife and fork restaurants can be found in a variety of guises ranging from country inns and city taverns to French bistros, Italian trattorias and the smaller oriental restaurants.

✕✕ Generally, a higher standard of service, décor, furnishings and amenities will be found. A small lounge/cocktail bar may well be available.

✕✕✕ Often of a type where it is usual to sit in a bar lounge or alcove for an apéritif and order your meal in advance. You will expect to find a much higher standard of comfort and décor in restaurants with three knives and forks. A number of small country inns with well appointed dining rooms might fall into this category as well as good London and provincial restaurants.

✕✕✕✕ Normally found only in London and the larger cities, although country establishments with exceptionally well appointed rooms can be considered for this classification.

✕✕✕✕✕ A five knife and fork restaurant should reflect the height of luxury and good living and be comparable in décor, service and cuisine with the best London five star hotels. There will normally be much more seating than other types, possibly approaching 100.

## ROSETTES

This year the AA has expanded the rosette award scheme: the maximum number of rosettes that can now be awarded for food quality has increased from three to five. Recognition can now be given to the efforts of chefs across a wide range of establishments that are really noteworthy. Restaurants and hotel restaurants can be awarded rosettes to denote the quality of the food they serve, although only those establishments offering the highest international standards of cuisine will merit the AA's top awards of four and five rosettes.

Establishments with rosette awards have their names and addresses highlighted in pink in the directory.

❀ Enjoyable food, carefully prepared that reflects a high level of culinary skills.

❀❀ A high standard of food that demonstrates a serious, dedicated approach to cooking.

❀❀❀ Very fine food prepared with considerable flair, imagination and originality.

❀❀❀❀ Excellent standards of cuisine, service and wine consistently achieved.

❀❀❀❀❀ Outstanding cuisine, service and wine that reaches the highest international standards.

# USING THE GUIDE

## Sample
## *DIRECTORY ENTRY*

This entry is fictitious

| | |
|---|---|
| BEESTON Derbyshire Map **15** NJ90 ⊚ | } **1. Town name** |
| ★★★ 65% **Red Lion** | } **2. Hotel name** |
| The Square AB00 XY1 (GB Hotels) ☎(0685) 8276 Telex no 739619 Fax (0685) 6728 | |
| RS Nov–Mar | } **3. Restricted service** |
| *Attractive old coaching inn with comfortable, pretty bedrooms.* | |
| 19rm(14⇆5↖) Annexe5rm(8fb)3▥↙in 5 bedrooms CTV in all bedrooms®✗ **T** sB&B⇆↖£16.50–£24.50 dB&B⇆↖£31–£49 ⊟ | } **4. Accommodation details** |
| Lift ⊄ CTV 100P 3🅿⧉ CFA ▱ ♪ nc 3yrs | } **5. Hotel facilities** |
| ♀English & French **V** ♡⊡✗ Lunch £3–£4.50 Tea 85p–£1.40 High Tea £2.75–£6 Dinner £8.25–£11 &alc Last dinner 9pm | } **6. Meals** |
| Credit Cards [1][2][3][4][5] ⓔ | } **7. Payment details** |

**1. Town name** listed in directory in alphabetical order. This is followed by the county or region, which is the administrative county or region, and not necessarily part of the correct postal address. Towns on islands (not connected to the mainland by a bridge) are listed under the island name. Scottish regions or islands are followed by the old county name in italics. The **map reference** which follows denotes the map-page number and grid reference. Read 1st figure across, 2nd figure vertically, within the appropriate square.

**2. Hotel name,** address (including postcode) and telephone number with classification and percentage (see p 50 for details). When establishments' names are shown in *italics* the particulars have not been confirmed by the management. Within towns hotels are listed in descending order of star rating, with red stars first then descending order of percentage ratings, except for hotels in the Republic of Ireland. Hotels precede restaurants. London hotels are listed under London postal districts. *Company owned hotels* and marketing consortia are shown using abbreviations (key on page 858). Before its name is shown in the guide a company must own at least five AA-appointed hotels, or a hotel must be affiliated to one of the following marketing consortia: Best Western, Consort, Exec Hotels, Guestaccom, Inter-Hotels, Minotel, Prestige, Relais et Châteaux, Pride of Britain and Welsh Rarebits. The *telephone exchange* is that of the town heading, unless the name of the exchange is given after the ☎ symbol and before the dialling code and number. In some areas, numbers are likely to be changed during the currency of this book. In case of difficulty check with the operator. When making a reservation by *telex* it is advisable to specify which hotel you wish to book with as some hotels (particularly those in groups) use a central telex service. The same applies to *fax* messages.

**3. Restricted service.** Some hotels, while remaining open, operate a restricted service during the less busy months. This may take the form of a reduction in meals served, accommodation or facilities available, or in some cases both.

**4. Accommodation details.** The first figure shows the number of letting bedrooms. Where rooms have en suite bath or shower and WC, the number precedes the appropriate symbol.

Annexe bedrooms available in an annexe are noted only if they are at least of the same standard as those in the rest of the hotel. Facilities may not be the same as in the main building however, and it is advisable to check the nature of the accommodation and the tariff before making a reservation. In some hotels, accommodation is available only in an annexe.

🛏     number of bedrooms and/or area of the restaurant set aside for non-smokers.

fb     family bedrooms.

CTV/TV can mean colour or black and white television in lounge or available in bedrooms. Check when making reservations.

🐕     no dogs allowed into bedrooms. Some hotels may restrict the type of dogs permitted and the rooms into which they may be taken. Hotels which do not normally accept dogs may accept guide dogs. Generally dogs are not allowed in the dining room. Check when booking, the conditions under which pets are accepted.

T     automatic direct-dial telephone facilities available from bedrooms. Many hotels impose a surcharge for calls made from bedrooms, so check before making the call. A public telephone is usually available in the hotel hallway or foyer.

Prices     prices given have been provided by hoteliers and restaurateurs in good faith and are indications rather than firm quotations. Unless otherwise stated, they include full cooked breakfast. Some hotels offer free accommodation to children provided they share the parents' room. Check current prices before booking. Prices for the Republic of Ireland are shown in Irish Punts. At the time of going to press the exchange rate is 1.07 Punts = £1. See also page 781.

**5. Hotel facilities.** For key to symbols see bookmark (for French, German, Italian, Spanish see pp 56–57).

(     All hotels employing a night porter are shown thus. 4 and 5 star hotels all have night porters on duty.

🚌     No coaches. This information is published in good faith from information supplied by the establishments concerned. Inns, however, have well-defined legal obligations towards travellers, and it is for the customer to take up any queries with the proprietor or the local licensing authority.

♫     Live entertainment should be available at least once a week throughout the year.

Some hotels without this symbol will provide entertainment during high season or at certain other specified times only. You are advised to check this information before booking.

🐚     Shell filling station, open 7am–11pm (some 24 hours) throughout the year with leaded and unleaded petrol, and diesel.

nc     No children. Where this abbreviation does not appear, the hotels listed will accommodate children, but may not provide any special facilities. A minimum age (e.g. nc4yrs — no children under four years old) may be specified. For very young children, check before booking about such provisions as cots and high chairs and any reductions made.

🛝     establishments with special facilities for children, which will include baby-sitting service or baby intercom system, playroom or playground, laundry facilities, drying and ironing facilities, cots, high chairs and special meals.

CFA     hotels which offer conference facilities. Many other hotels offer facilities of this nature but may not be indicated as such. It is therefore advisable to check with the hotel's management.

Suitable for the disabled     Full details for disabled people will be found in AA *Guide for the Disabled Traveller* on sale at AA shops, free to members. Intending guests with any form of disability should notify proprietors so that arrangements can be made to minimise difficulties, particularly in the event of an emergency.

**6. Meals.** Details of the style of food served, last dinner orders and likely price ranges are given. Where the *table d'hôte* prices are given, the abbreviation '& alc' indicates that there is also an *à la carte* menu, which may be considerably dearer than the set menu.

V     a choice of vegetarian dishes available (but check before booking).

☕     morning coffee or afternoon tea are served to chance callers. All 4 and 5 star hotels serve morning coffee and, normally, afternoon tea to residents.

Prices     See page 55.

**7. Payment details** (but check current position when booking)
| 1 | — Access/Eurocard/Mastercard |
| 2 | — American Express |
| 3 | — Barclaycard/Visa |
| 4 | — Carte Blanche |
| 5 | — Diners |
| £ | — Hotel may offer a discount. See p 2 for details. |

# Useful Information
# (BRITAIN)

Note: see p 781 for information specifically relating to Northern Ireland and the Republic of Ireland

## BOOKING

Book as early as possible, particularly if accommodation is required during a holiday period (beginning of June to end of September, public holidays and, in some parts of Scotland, during the skiing season). Some hotels ask for a deposit, and some also ask for full payment in advance, especially for one-night bookings taken from chance callers. Not all hotels take advance bookings for bed and breakfast for overnight or short stays, and will not accept reservations from mid-week.

## CANCELLATION

Once the booking has been confirmed, notify the hotel straight away if you are in any doubt about whether you can keep to your arrangements. If the hotel cannot re-let your accommodation, you may be liable to pay about two-thirds of the price you would have paid had you stayed there (your deposit will count towards this payment).

In Britain it is accepted that a legally binding contract has been made as soon as an intending guest accepts an offer of accommodation, either in writing or on the telephone. Illness is not accepted as a release from this contract. For these reasons you are advised to effect insurance cover, eg AA Travelsure, against a possible cancellation.

## COMPLAINTS

Guests who wish to complain about food, services or facilities are urged to do so promptly and on the spot. This should provide an opportunity for the hotelier or restaurateur to correct matters. If a personal approach fails, members should inform AA Hotel Services, Fanum House, Basingstoke, Hampshire RG21 2EA.

## FIRE PRECAUTIONS

As far as we can discover, every hotel in Great Britain listed in this book has applied for, and not been refused, a fire certificate. The Fire Precautions Act does not apply to the Channel Islands, or the Isle of Man, which exercise their own rules regarding fire precautions for hotels.

## LICENSE TO SELL ALCOHOL

*Hotel and Restaurants.* All establishments in this guide are licensed unless otherwise stated. Basically, hotel residents can obtain alcoholic drinks at all times, if the owner is prepared to serve them. Restaurant customers can obtain drinks with their meals.

The sale of alcoholic drinks is controlled by separate licensing laws in England, Wales, Scotland, Isle of Man, the Isles of Scilly and each of the islands forming the Channel Islands.

*Licensing hours in public houses* are generally from mid morning to early afternoon and from mid evening to an hour or two before midnight. Some will remain open throughout the afternoon.

*Club Licence.* Drinks can be served only to club members, but an interval of 48 hours must elapse after joining.

*Children under 14* (18 in Scotland) may be excluded from bars, except areas intended for the service of food. Those under 18 may not be allowed to purchase or consume alcoholic drinks.

## MEALS

Unless otherwise stated, the terms quoted in the directory section of this book include full cooked breakfast.

In some parts of Britain, particularly in Scotland, *high tea* (ie a savoury dish followed by bread and butter, scones, cakes, etc) is sometimes served instead of dinner, which may, however, be available on request. The last time at which high tea or dinner may be ordered on weekdays is shown, but this may be varied at weekends.

On Sundays, some hotels serve the main meal at midday, and provide only a cold supper in the evening.

## PAYMENT

Most hotels will only accept cheques in payment of accounts if notice is given and some form of identification (usually a cheque card) is produced.

Travellers' cheques issued by the leading banks and agencies are accepted by many hotels but not all. If a hotel accepts leading credit or cheque cards, this is shown in the directory entry (see pages 52–53 for details).

## PRICES

The Hotel Industry Voluntary Code of Booking Practice was revised in 1986, and the AA encourages its use in appropriate establishments. Its prime object is to ensure that the customer is clear about the precise services and facilities he is buying, and what price he will have to pay, before he commits himself to a contractually binding agreement. If the price has not been previously confirmed in writing, the guest should be handed a card at the time of registration, stipulating the total obligatory charge.

The Tourism (Sleeping Accommodation Price Display) Order 1977 compels hotels, motels, guesthouses, farmhouses, inns and self-catering accommodation with four or more letting bedrooms to display in entrance halls the minimum and maximum prices charged for each category of room. This order complements the voluntary Code of Booking Practice.

The tariffs quoted in the directory of this book may be affected by inflation, variations in the rate of VAT and many other factors. You should always ascertain the current prices before making a booking. Those given in this book have been provided by hoteliers and restaurateurs in good faith and must be accepted as indications rather than firm quotations. Where information about 1992 prices is not given, you are requested to make enquiries direct.

Prices quoted show minimum and maximum for one or two persons and include a full breakfast unless otherwise stated. Where a Continental breakfast is included in the price, this is stated in the directory. However, some prices may vary for the following reasons:

a  weekday/weekend terms offered

b  season of the year

c  if double room is used for single occupancy

d  dinner is normally charged for separately, but in some areas an inclusive dinner, bed and breakfast option may be offered at a cheaper rate.

Some hotels charge for bed, breakfast and dinner, whether dinner is taken or not. Many hotels, particularly in short-season holiday areas, accept booking only at full-board rate.

For main meals served in hotels and restaurants, minimum and maximum *table d'hôte* (set menu) prices are given. Where an *à la carte* menu is available, the price of a three-course dinner and lunch is shown. Where establishments offer both types of menu, *table d'hôte* prices are the only ones shown but the abbreviation (&alc) is used to indicate that an *à la carte* menu is also available.

VAT is payable, in the United Kingdom and in the Isle of Man, on both basic prices and any service. VAT does not apply in the Channel Islands. With this exception, prices quoted in this guide are inclusive of VAT (and service where this is included on the bill).

# Symbols and Abbreviations
## FRENCH AND GERMAN

(see bookmark for English)

## FRANÇAIS

Classement des hôtels (voir p 50)
Classement d'hôtels supplémentaire
Hôtels qui doivent ouvrir prochainement
Hôtel de Campagne
% Pourcentage (voir p. 51)
Classement des Restaurants
Rosettes

prix 1991
téléphone
salle de bain privée avec WC particulier
Douche privée avec WC particulier
**Lits à quatre montants**
**Possibilité de faire le thé/le café dans les chambres**
Défense de garder des chiens pendant la nuit dans les chambres
Ce symbole indique que l'hôtel offre des week-ends à prix réduit hors saison
Concierge de nuit
Conditionnement d'air intégral
Chambres et/ou section de restaurant réservée(s) aux non-fumeurs
Stationnement à ciel ouvert pour voitures
Garage ou bien lieu de stationnement couvert
Pas de stationnement sur place
Les groupes en car ne seront pas admis
Jardin de plus de 0.20 ha
Piscine à l'intérieur
Piscine à l'extérieur
▶9▶18 Terrain de golf à 9 trous ou 18 trous
Court(s) de tennis
Pêche
Ecuries d'équitation sur les lieux
Facilités speciales pour enfants
disco, dance etc.
Categorie de cuisine. Si ce symbole ne figure pas, la cuisine est anglaise, écossaise, galloise ou l'Irlandais, selon la région ou l'hôtel se trouve
Café le matin
Thé l'après-midi
S% Le service est compris dans le prix
alc *à la carte*

sB&B Chambre à un lit et petit déjeuner par personne et par nuit
sB&B Chambre à un lit avec bain et WC particuliers, et petit déjeuner par personne et par nuit
sB&B Chambre à un lit avec douche privée et WC particulier et le petit déjeuner par personne la nuit
dB&B Chambre à deux lits (2 personnes à une chambre) avec petit déjeuner
dB&B Chambre à deux lits (2 personnes à une chambre) avec bain et WC particuliers, et petit déjeuner
dB&B Chambre à deux (deux personnes à une chambre) avec douche privée et WC particuliers et le petit déjeuner
CFA Facilities de conférence disponibles
CTV TV en couleurs
BH Jours fériés
Etr Pâques
fb Chambre de famille
fr à partir de
Map Repère du quadrillage de carte national
mdnt Minuit
nc Enfants pas admis, par ex. enfants audessous de ... ans pas admis
Plan Le numéro indique l'emplacement de l'hôtel ou du restaurant sur le plan de la ville
rm Location de chambres dans le bâtiment principal
RS Service limité
T Téléphone dans la chambre, direct avec l'extérieur
TV TV en noir et blanc
V Menu végétarien offert
£ Voir p. 53
*xmas* Programme spécial de Noël pour les clients
→ Suite au verso
① Carte de crédit

**Pour de plus amples renseignements sur les symboles, voir les pages 50–53**

## DEUTSCH

Hotelklassifikation (Siehe Seite 50)
Zusätzliche Hotelklassifizierung
Hotel wird während der Laufzeit dieses Führers eröffnet
Landgut-Hotel
% Prozentsatz (Siehe Seite 51)
Restaurantklassifikation
Rosetten

1991 Preise
Telefon
Privatbadezimmer mit eigenem WC
Privatdusche mit eigenem WC
**Himmelbett**
Tee/Kaffeemöglichkeiten im Zimmer
Hundeverbot im Zimmer während der Nacht

Betrieb gibt Wochenendermässigung für Vor-und Nachsaison
Nachtportier
Klimaanlage überall
Zimmer bzw. Restaurantabschnitt für Nichtraucher
P Parken im Freien
Garagen bzw. überdachtes Parken
Parken an Ortund Stelle
Reisebusgesellschaften nicht aufgenommen
Garten grösser als 0.20 ha
Hallenbad
Freibad
▶9▶18 Golfplatz mit 9 oder 18 Löchern
Tennisplatz (Plätze)
Angeln
Reitstall an Ort und Stelle
Sonderdienstleistungen für Kinder
Disco, Tanzen. usw
Küche, wenn dieses Zeichen nicht aufgeführt wird, ist die Küche englisch, schottisch, walisisch oder irrisch, je nach der Gegend, wo das Hotel sich befindet
Kaffee vormittags
Nachmittagstee
S% Bedienungsgeld im Preis inbegriffen
alc *à la carte*

sB&B Ubernachtung in einem Einzelzimmer mit Frühstück pro Person
sB&B Einzelzimmer mit Privatbad und WC und Frühstück pro Person pro Nacht
sB&B Einzelzimmer mit Privatdusche und WC und Frühstück pro Person pro Nacht
dB&B Doppelzimmer (2 Personen in einem Zimmer) mit Frühstück
dB&B Doppelzimmer (2 Personen in einem Zimmer) mit Privatbad und WC mit Frühstück
dB&B Doppelzimmer (2 Personen in einem Zimmer) mit Privatdusche und WC und Frühstück
CFA Tagungseinrichtungen vorhanden
CTV Farbfernsehen
BH Bankfeiertage
Etr Ostern
fb Familienzimmer
fr von
Map Planquadratangabe
mdnt Mitternacht
nc Kinder nicht aufgenommen z.B. Kinder unter ... Jahren nicht aufgenommen
Plan Nummer gibt die Lage des Hotels am Stadtplan an
rm Zimmeranzahl im Hauptgebäude
RS Beschränkte Dienstleistungen
T Zimmertelefon mit Aussenverbindung über Telefonzentrale
TV Schwarzweissfernsehen
V Vegetarische Kost vorhanden
£ Siehe Seite 53
*xmas* Sonderweihnachtsprogramm für Gäste
→ Fortsetzung siehe umseitig
① Kreditkarte

**Für weitere Informationen über die Zeichen, siehe Seiten 50–53**

# Symbols and Abbreviations
# ITALIAN AND SPANISH

(see bookmark for English)

## ITALIANO

★ Classificazione de gli alberghi (vedere p 50)
⇧ Classificazione supplementare hotel AA
○ Alberghi che saranno aperti durante il periodo di validità della guida
⚑ Alberghi in dimore di campagne
% Percentuale (vedere p 51)
✗ Classificazione dei Ristoranti
❀ Rosette

✳ Prezzi dei 1991
☎ Telefono
🛁 Bagno e servizi privati
🚿 Doccia e servizi privati
🛏 Letti a quattro colonne
® Attrezzatura per fare il té o il caffé nelle camere
✕ E proibito tenere i cani nelle camere di notte

🅑 Questo simbolo indica che l'albergo offre fine settimana economici fuori stagione
( Portiere notturno
⊞ Aria condizionata
✍ Camere e/o zona di ristorante per non fumatori

P Parcheggio macchine all'aperto
🅶 Garage o spazio coperto
✗ Vietato il pacheggio sul posto
🚐 Non si accettano comitive in gita turistica
✿ Giardino di più di 0.20 ha
▭ Piscina coperta
◠ Piscina scoperta
▶9▶18 Campo da golf a 9 o 18 buche
🎾 Campo(i) da tennis
𝅘 Pesca
∪ Scuola d'equitazionne sul posto
⚁ Attrezzature speciali per i bambini
♫ disco, danza etc
🍽 Tipo di cucina. Se manca questo simbolo, la cucina é inglese, scozzese, gallese o irlandese, a seconda di dove si trova l'albergo in oggetto
☕ Caffé mattutino
🍵 Té pomeridiano
S% Servizio imposto e compreso nel prezzo
alc Alla carta

sB&B Prezzo di una camera singola con la colazione compresa (per notte)
sB&B🚿 Prezzo di una camera singola con bagno e servizi e la colazione compresa (per notte)
sB&B🛀 Prezzo di una camera singola con doccia e servizie colazione compresa (per notte)
dB&B Prezzo di una camera doppia (2 persone per camera) con la colazione compresa
dB&B🚿 Prezzo di una camera doppia (2 persone per camera) con bagno e servizie colazione compresa
dB&B🛀 Prezzo di una camera doppia (2 persone per camera) con doccia e servizie colazione compresa
CFA Attrezzature per conferenze
CTV Televisione a colori
BH Festività nazionale
Etr Pasqua
fb Camera familiare
fr Da
Map Riferimento della cartina
mdnt Mezzanotte
nc Proibito ai bambini. E sempio: nc sottoi... anni

Plan Il numero indica la posizione dell'albergo o del ristorante sulla cartina della città
rm Numero di camere nell'edificio principale
RS Servizio limitato
T Telefono in camera comunicante direttamente con l'esterno
TV Televisione in bianco e nero
V Si offrono pasti vegetarini
ⓔ Vedere p 53
xmas Programma speciale di Natale per i clienti
→ La lista delle voci continua a tergo
⊡ Carte di credito

**Per ulteriori informazioni riguardanti la simbologie, vedere pp 50–53**

## ESPAÑOL

★ Hoteles a ser inaugurados (véase la pagina 50)
⇧ Clasificación adicional de hoteles
○ Hoteles a ser inaugur ados durante la vigencia de estaguía
⚑ Hoteles en casas de campo
% Porcentaje (véase la página 51)
✗ Clasificación de restaurantes
❀ Rosetas

✳ Precios de 1991
☎ Teléfono
🛁 Baño y servicios en cada habitación
🚿 Ducha y servicios en cada habitación
🛏 Camas de columnas
® Facilidades para hacer el té o el café en las habitaciones
✕ Se prohibe hacer pasar la noche a los perros en las habitaciones del hotel

🅑 Este simbolo indica que el hotel ofrece fines de semana económicos en l estación fuera de la temporada
( Conserje nocturno
⊞ Aire acondicionado en todo establecimiento
✍ Habitaciones y/o área del restaurante reservados para los no fumadores

P Aparcamiento descubierto
🅶 Garaje o espacio cubierto
✗ Establecimiento sin aparcamiento
🚐 No se aceptan los grupos de viajeros en coches de linea
✿ Jardín de más de 0.20 ha
▭ Piscina cubierta
◠ Piscina descubierta
▶9▶18 Campo de golf de 9 o 18 hoyos
🎾 Campo(s) de tenis
𝅘 Pesca
∪ Escuela hipica
⚁ Facilidades especiales para los niños
♫ Discoteca/baile
🍽 Tipo de cocina. Si no figura este simbolo, la cocina es inglés, escocés, galés o irlandés, según la ubicación del hotel
☕ Café de la mañana
🍵 Té de la tarde
S% Servicio impuesto e incluido en precio
alc A la carta

sB&B Precio por noche de una habitación individual con desayuno incluido
sB&B🚿 Precio por noche de una habitación individual con bañoy servicios (desayuno incluido)
sB&B🛀 Precio por noche de una habitación individual con ducha servicios (desayuno incluido)
dB&B Habitación para dos personas (compartiendo una habitación) con desayuno incluido
dB&B🚿 Habitación para dos personas (compartiendo una habitación) con bañoy servicios (desayuno incluido)
dB&B🛀 Habitación para dos personas (compartiendo una habitación) con duchay servicios (desayuno incluido)
CFA Facilidades para conferencias
CTV Televisión de color
BH Dia festivo para los bancos y el comercio en general
Etr Pascua de Resurrección
fb Habitación familiar
fr De
Map Referencia del mapa
mdnt Medianoche
nc Se prohibe la entrada a los niños, p.ej: nc de menos de... años

Plan El número indica la ubicación del hotel o del restaurante en el plano de la ciudad
rm Número de habitaciones del edificio principal
RS Servicio limitado
T Teléfono en la habitación, comunicando con el exterior
TV Televisión en blanco y negro
V Se ofrecen comidas vegetarianas
ⓔ Véase la página 53
xmas Programa especial de Navidad para los huéspedes
→ La lista de simbolos continúa a la vuelta
⊡ Tarjeta de crédito

**Para más información sobe los símbolos, véase las páginas 50–53**

# CALENDAR 1992

## JANUARY

| S | M | T | W | T | F | S |
|---|---|---|---|---|---|---|
|   |   |   | 1 | 2 | 3 | 4 |
| 5 | 6 | 7 | 8 | 9 | 10 | 11 |
| 12 | 13 | 14 | 15 | 16 | 17 | 18 |
| 19 | 20 | 21 | 22 | 23 | 24 | 25 |
| 26 | 27 | 28 | 29 | 30 | 31 |   |

## FEBRUARY

| S | M | T | W | T | F | S |
|---|---|---|---|---|---|---|
|   |   |   |   |   |   | 1 |
| 2 | 3 | 4 | 5 | 6 | 7 | 8 |
| 9 | 10 | 11 | 12 | 13 | 14 | 15 |
| 16 | 17 | 18 | 19 | 20 | 21 | 22 |
| 23 | 24 | 25 | 26 | 27 | 28 | 29 |

## MARCH

| S | M | T | W | T | F | S |
|---|---|---|---|---|---|---|
| 1 | 2 | 3 | 4 | 5 | 6 | 7 |
| 8 | 9 | 10 | 11 | 12 | 13 | 14 |
| 15 | 16 | 17 | 18 | 19 | 20 | 21 |
| 22 | 23 | 24 | 25 | 26 | 27 | 28 |
| 29 | 30 | 31 |   |   |   |   |

## APRIL

| S | M | T | W | T | F | S |
|---|---|---|---|---|---|---|
|   |   |   | 1 | 2 | 3 | 4 |
| 5 | 6 | 7 | 8 | 9 | 10 | 11 |
| 12 | 13 | 14 | 15 | 16 | 17 | 18 |
| 19 | 20 | 21 | 22 | 23 | 24 | 25 |
| 26 | 27 | 28 | 29 | 30 |   |   |

## MAY

| S | M | T | W | T | F | S |
|---|---|---|---|---|---|---|
|   |   |   |   |   | 1 | 2 |
| 3 | 4 | 5 | 6 | 7 | 8 | 9 |
| 10 | 11 | 12 | 13 | 14 | 15 | 16 |
| 17 | 18 | 19 | 20 | 21 | 22 | 23 |
| 24 | 25 | 26 | 27 | 28 | 29 | 30 |
| 31 |   |   |   |   |   |   |

## JUNE

| S | M | T | W | T | F | S |
|---|---|---|---|---|---|---|
|   | 1 | 2 | 3 | 4 | 5 | 6 |
| 7 | 8 | 9 | 10 | 11 | 12 | 13 |
| 14 | 15 | 16 | 17 | 18 | 19 | 20 |
| 21 | 22 | 23 | 24 | 25 | 26 | 27 |
| 28 | 29 | 30 |   |   |   |   |

## JULY

| S | M | T | W | T | F | S |
|---|---|---|---|---|---|---|
|   |   |   | 1 | 2 | 3 | 4 |
| 5 | 6 | 7 | 8 | 9 | 10 | 11 |
| 12 | 13 | 14 | 15 | 16 | 17 | 18 |
| 19 | 20 | 21 | 22 | 23 | 24 | 25 |
| 26 | 27 | 28 | 29 | 30 | 31 |   |

## AUGUST

| S | M | T | W | T | F | S |
|---|---|---|---|---|---|---|
|   |   |   |   |   |   | 1 |
| 2 | 3 | 4 | 5 | 6 | 7 | 8 |
| 9 | 10 | 11 | 12 | 13 | 14 | 15 |
| 16 | 17 | 18 | 19 | 20 | 21 | 22 |
| 23 | 24 | 25 | 26 | 27 | 28 | 29 |
| 30 | 31 |   |   |   |   |   |

## SEPTEMBER

| S | M | T | W | T | F | S |
|---|---|---|---|---|---|---|
|   |   | 1 | 2 | 3 | 4 | 5 |
| 6 | 7 | 8 | 9 | 10 | 11 | 12 |
| 13 | 14 | 15 | 16 | 17 | 18 | 19 |
| 20 | 21 | 22 | 23 | 24 | 25 | 26 |
| 27 | 28 | 29 | 30 |   |   |   |

## OCTOBER

| S | M | T | W | T | F | S |
|---|---|---|---|---|---|---|
|   |   |   |   | 1 | 2 | 3 |
| 4 | 5 | 6 | 7 | 8 | 9 | 10 |
| 11 | 12 | 13 | 14 | 15 | 16 | 17 |
| 18 | 19 | 20 | 21 | 22 | 23 | 24 |
| 25 | 26 | 27 | 28 | 29 | 30 | 31 |

## NOVEMBER

| S | M | T | W | T | F | S |
|---|---|---|---|---|---|---|
| 1 | 2 | 3 | 4 | 5 | 6 | 7 |
| 8 | 9 | 10 | 11 | 12 | 13 | 14 |
| 15 | 16 | 17 | 18 | 19 | 20 | 21 |
| 22 | 23 | 24 | 25 | 26 | 27 | 28 |
| 29 | 30 |   |   |   |   |   |

## DECEMBER

| S | M | T | W | T | F | S |
|---|---|---|---|---|---|---|
|   |   | 1 | 2 | 3 | 4 | 5 |
| 6 | 7 | 8 | 9 | 10 | 11 | 12 |
| 13 | 14 | 15 | 16 | 17 | 18 | 19 |
| 20 | 21 | 22 | 23 | 24 | 25 | 26 |
| 27 | 28 | 29 | 30 | 31 |   |   |

## HOLIDAY DATES

| | |
|---|---|
| Jan 1 | UK, Republic of Ireland |
| Jan 2 | Scotland |
| Mar 17 | Northern Ireland. Republic of Ireland |
| Apr 17 | (Good Fri) UK, Republic of Ireland |
| Apr 20 | (Easter Mon) UK (not Scotland), Republic of Ireland |
| May 4 | UK |
| May 25 | UK |
| Jun 1 | Republic of Ireland |
| Jun 13 | Northern Ireland |
| Aug 3 | Scotland, Republic of Ireland |
| Aug 31 | UK (not Scotland) |
| Oct 26 | Republic of Ireland |
| Dec 25 | (Christmas Day) UK, Republic of Ireland |
| Dec 26 | (Boxing Day)* UK, Republic of Ireland |
| | (*Dec 28 may be taken in lieu) |

# IT'S NICE TO KNOW YOU CAN RELAX
## ALL OVER THE UK

*Everything is possible at a*
*Queens Moat Houses hotel.*

*Whether it is a traditional inn,*
*country manor, modern airport*
*hotel or a city centre location,*
*every one of more than 100*
*Queens Moat Houses hotels*
*throughout the UK offer the same*
*warm friendly service, excellent*
*cuisine, and a range of conference*
*and leisure facilities which are*
*second to none. Yet every hotel is*
*as individual as you are.*

**Queens Moat Houses PLC**

INTERNATIONAL HOTELIERS

FOR A FAST EFFICIENT SERVICE
CALL QUEENS MOAT HOUSES RESERVATIONS
Tel: 0708 766677  Fax: 0708 761033  Telex: 929751

Queens Moat Houses Reservations, Queens Court, 9 - 17 Eastern Road, Romford, Essex, RM1 3NG.

# Directory — Britain

---

## ABBERLEY Hereford & Worcester Map 07 SO76

### ★★★ ❀🏊 77% Elms

WR6 6AT (on A443) (Queens Moat)(Small Luxury Hotels)
☎Great Witley(0299)896666 Telex no 337105
FAX (0299) 896804

*A beautiful Queen Anne mansion in well kept grounds midway between Worcester and Tenbury Wells on the A443. Gracious public rooms are furnished with antique pieces and deep, comfortable seating, with log fires in cool weather. The Regency Brooke Room restaurant provides a lovely setting for chef Michael Gaunt's competently prepared meals. Bedrooms are mostly spacious, attractive and comfortable, with some thoughtful touches, but those in the Coach House are somewhat functional. While it is a company operated hotel, Celia Rydström and her team have managed to retain the atmosphere of a country home.*

16⇌🏠Annexe9⇌🏠1🛏 CTV in all bedrooms T
🏋 (ex guide dogs) ✱ S% sB&B⇌🏠£82-£105 dB&B⇌🏠£97-£150 🍴
⟨ 60P 1🚗 ✿ CFA ♪ (hard) croquet putting *xmas*
♡ English & French V ♡ ♨ ✱ Lunch £11.95-£14.95&alc Dinner £22&alc Last dinner 9.30pm
Credit Cards ①②③④⑤ ⓔ

### ★★ 62% Manor Arms at Abberley

WR6 6BN ☎Great Witley(0299)896507 Telex no 335672
FAX (0562) 747488

*A pleasant village inn, some 300 years old, with well equipped bedrooms.*

7⇌Annexe3⇌ CTV in all bedrooms ⓡ T
40P ✿
V ♡ ♨ Last dinner 9.30pm
Credit Cards ①③

---

## ABBOTSBURY Dorset Map 03 SY58

### ★★ 63% Ilchester Arms

9 Market St DT3 4JR ☎(0305)871243

*On the main street of the picturesque village, this inn offers extensive menus of standard bar meals and grills as well as less usual daily specials, served in its characterful public bars and conservatory restaurant. Bedrooms, though rather small, are attractively decorated and well furnished.*

8⇌🏠Annexe2⇌(2fb)3🛏 CTV in all bedrooms ⓡ T 🍴
40P *xmas*
♡ English & Continental V ♡ ♨ ✄ ✱ Dinner £10.10&alc Last dinner 9pm
Credit Cards ①③

---

## ABBOT'S SALFORD Warwickshire Map 04 SP05

### ★★★ ❀74% Salford Hall

WR11 5UT (Best Western) ☎Evesham(0386)871300
Telex no 336682 FAX (0386) 871301

*This fine Tudor manor house, eight miles from Stratford-on-Avon on the A439 Evesham road, has been carefully restored to provide modern facilities while retaining much of its original charm. Bedrooms, including those in the tastefully converted former stable block, are fitted with quality furnishings and thoughtful extras, and guests can enjoy the imaginative, well cooked dishes of chef Scott Chance in the panelled dining room.*

15⇌🏠Annexe19⇌🏠8🛏 CTV in all bedrooms ⓡ T
🏋 (ex guide dogs) 🍴
51P 🚗 ✿ CFA ♪ (hard) snooker sauna solarium croquet *xmas*
V ♡ ♨ ✄ ✱ Lunch £15 Dinner £22.50 Last dinner 10pm
Credit Cards ①②③⑤ ⓔ

See advertisement under STRATFORD-UPON-AVON

---

## ABERDARON Gwynedd Map 06 SH12

### ★★ 62% Ty Newydd

LL53 8BE ☎(075886)207
Closed Dec-Feb

*Friendly and family-run, the hotel gives direct access to the sea shore, all but two of its bedrooms enjoying panoramic views of the bay.*

17rm(8⇌1🏠)(3fb) CTV in 12 bedrooms TV in 5 bedrooms ⓡ
🏋 (ex guide dogs) sB&Bfr£23.70 sB&B⇌🏠fr£29.50 dB&Bfr£47.40 dB&B⇌🏠fr£57
CTV
♡ Mainly grills V ♡ ✱ Bar Lunch fr£8.50
Credit Cards ①③ ⓔ

---

## ABERDEEN Grampian *Aberdeenshire* Map 15 NJ90 ◉

### See Town Plan Section
See also Aberdeen Airport & Westhill

### ★★★★ 51% Skean Dhu Altens

Souter Head Rd, Altens AB1 4LF (3m S off A956) (Mount Charlotte (TS)) ☎(0224)877000 Telex no 739631
FAX (0224) 896964
RS Xmas wk

*A large modern, multi-storey hotel which stands just off the A956 south of the city has recently refurbished its public areas. Bedrooms are functional, though dated, while service is friendly and helpful.*

221⇌🏠(70fb)✄in 6 bedrooms CTV in all bedrooms ⓡ T (room only)
Lift ⟨ ⊞ 300P ✿ ⌓ (heated) *xmas*
♡ International V ♡ ♨
Credit Cards ①②③④⑤

### ★★★ 72% Ardoe House

Blairs, South Deeside Rd AB1 5YP (Consort) ☎(0224)867355
Telex no 739413 FAX (0224) 861283

*This popular and efficiently run business, conference and function hotel stands in 17 acres of grounds on the South Deeside road just a short drive west of the city. It is an impressive, turreted, Scottish baronial mansion house, sympathetically converted and extended. Elegant day rooms reflect much of the original Victorian charm and character of the house. Bedrooms, though variable in size, have been tastefully furbished. Current developments include the provision of additional bedrooms, conference and function facilities which were not operational at the time of our visit.*

71⇌🏠(7fb)1🛏✄in 15 bedrooms CTV in all bedrooms ⓡ T
🏋 (ex guide dogs) ✱ sB&B⇌🏠£75-£106 dB&B⇌🏠£86.50-£120 (room only) 🍴
Lift ⟨ 200P ✿ CFA putting petanque *xmas*
♡ International V ♡ ♨ ✱ Lunch £7.50-£15 Dinner £19.50&alc Last dinner 9.30pm
Credit Cards ①②③⑤ ⓔ

### ★★★ 68% Caledonian Thistle

10 Union Ter AB9 1HE (Mount Charlotte (TS)) ☎(0224)640233
Telex no 73758 FAX (0224) 641627

*A comfortable, modern, city centre hotel which is popular with businessmen and small conference groups. It offers a choice of bars and a restaurant, while bedrooms range from the generally compact Club rooms to the more spacious Executive rooms which have additional facilities.*

80⇌🏠(4fb)🛏✄in 2 bedrooms CTV in all bedrooms ⓡ T (room only) 🍴
Lift ⟨ 25P sauna solarium
♡ International ♡ ♨ ✄
Credit Cards ①②③④⑤

See advertisement on page 63

**A**

### ★★★67% *Copthorne*
122 Huntly St AB1 1SU ☎(0224)630404 Telex no 739707
FAX (0224) 640573
*A former grain store has been converted and extended to create
this busy West- End business and function hotel. Public rooms are
comfortably furnished in the modern style, though the lounge is
rather small. Bedrooms are mostly spacious and well equipped.
The new Connoisseur rooms on the top floor have superior
appointments.*
89⇨🛏in 12 bedrooms CTV in all bedrooms ® T
Lift ( 20🛏 ♫
♀ Scottish & French V ♥ ⚖ Last dinner 10pm
Credit Cards ① ② ③ ④ ⑤

### ★★★62% New Marcliffe
51-53 Queen's Rd AB9 2PE ☎(0224)321371 Telex no 73225
FAX (0224) 311162
*An efficiently run business hotel which provides convenient access
to both city centre and ring route from its position in the West-End
is also a popular venue for local functions. Well equipped bedrooms
in a variety of sizes offer practical modern appointments, while
public areas have a club-like atmosphere.*
27⇨🛏(3fb) CTV in all bedrooms ® T 🐾 (ex guide dogs)
sB&B⇨🛏£37.50-£75 dB&B⇨🛏£42.50-£85 🏠
( 74P 🚗 CFA
♀ Scottish & French V ♥ ⚖ Lunch £12.50-£18.50alc Dinner
£16.50-£23.50alc Last dinner 9.45pm
Credit Cards ① ② ③ ⑤

---

ABERDEEN AIRPORT Grampian *Aberdeenshire*
Map **15** NJ81

### ★★★★67% Holiday Inn
Riverview Dr, Farburn AB2 0AZ (Holiday Inns)
☎Aberdeen(0224)770011 Telex no 739651 FAX (0224) 722347
*This comfortable purpose-built hotel on the outskirts of the city
appeals to the business traveller and the leisure user alike, as well
as being a popular venue for meetings and functions. Public rooms
are tastefully appointed in the modern style, and the extensive
leisure facilities are much in demand. The spacious bedrooms are
well furnished and thoughtfully equipped. Service is efficient and
the atmosphere friendly.*
154⇨🛏(71fb)⚥in 16 bedrooms CTV in all bedrooms ® T ✳
sB⇨🛏£84.60-£94 dB⇨🛏£84.60-£108.50 (room only) 🏠
( ⊞ 300P CFA ⬛ (heated) sauna solarium gymnasium
whirlpool ♨ *xmas*
♀ International V ♥ ⚖ ⚥ ✳ Lunch £16.95 Dinner £15.95&alc
Last dinner 10.30pm
Credit Cards ① ② ③ ④ ⑤ ⓕ

### ★★★★58% Skean Dhu
Argyll Rd AB2 0DU (adjacent to main entrance 1m N of A96)
(Mount Charlotte (TS)) ☎Aberdeen(0224)725252
Telex no 739239 FAX (0224) 723745
*Many spacious bedrooms are available at this modern 2-storey
hotel which is built around an enclosed central courtyard with
outdoor swimming pool ; set northwest of the city, off the A96, it
offers easy access to the airport terminal building.*
148⇨🛏(6fb)⚥in 6 bedrooms CTV in all bedrooms ® T 🏠
( ⊞ 450P ✳ ⬛ (heated) *xmas*
♀ Scottish & French V ♥ ⚖
Credit Cards ① ② ③ ⑤

### ★★★63% Skean Dhu Dyce
Farburn Ter AB2 0DW (off A947) (Mount Charlotte (TS))
☎Aberdeen(0224)723101 Telex no 73473 FAX (0224) 722965
*A friendly and well managed hotel with modern bedrooms, a coffee
shop, restaurant, and very good conference facilities.*
Annexe219⇨🛏(80fb)⚥in 12 bedrooms CTV in all bedrooms
® T 🏠

---

( 250P squash sauna solarium gymnasium pool table table
tennis *xmas*
♀ Scottish & French V ♥ ⚖
Credit Cards ① ② ③ ⑤

---

ABERDOUR Fife Map **11** NT18

### ★★66% Woodside
High St KY3 0SW ☎(0383)860328 FAX (0383) 860920
*The public areas of this beautifully renovated hotel feature the
ornately decorated captain's cabin from RMS Orontes. Bedrooms
are all attractive and well equipped, though some are on the small
side. Attentive service is provided by the hotel staff.*
21⇨🛏3🛏 CTV in all bedrooms ® T ✳ sB&B⇨🛏£31-£49.50
dB&B⇨🛏£47.50-£77
( 40P 🚗 sauna *xmas*
♀ Scottish & French V ♥ ⚖ ✳ Lunch fr£9.50&alc Dinner
fr£14.50&alc Last dinner 9.30pm
Credit Cards ① ② ③ ⑤

See advertisement in colour section

### ★64% *Fairways*
17 Manse St KY3 0TT ☎(0383)860478
*Friendly resident proprietors have created a cosy hotel with a
homely atmosphere where guests can enjoy home-cooked meals, its
lunch and dinner menus featuring a delightful selection of pies,
both sweet and savoury.*
10rm(2⇨)(2fb) CTV in all bedrooms ®
CTV 12P 🚗
♥ ⚖ ⚥ Last dinner 8.45pm
Credit Cards ① ③

---

ABERDOVEY Gwynedd Map **06** SN69

### ★★★♨65% Plas Penhelig Country House
LL35 0NA (Welsh Rarebits) ☎(0654)767676 FAX (0654) 767783
Closed Jan & Feb
*A delightful Edwardian country house set in 14 acres of grounds
and gardens, with fine views of the Dovey estuary. Plas Penhelig is
personally run with friendly informality and provides comfortable
accommodation and a relaxing atmosphere. Public rooms feature
oak panelling, stained glass windows and log fires, while facilities
include a tennis court, croquet lawn and putting green.*
12⇨🛏(3fb) CTV in all bedrooms T 🐾 ✳ sB&B⇨🛏£59-£63
dB&B⇨🛏£98-£106 (incl dinner) 🏠
48P 🚗 ✳ ♟ (hard) croquet putting
♀ English & French V ♥ ⚖ ✳ Lunch £8.95 Dinner fr£14.95
Last dinner 8.45pm
Credit Cards ① ③

### ★★★65% Trefeddian
LL35 0SB ☎(0654)767213 FAX (0654) 767777
Closed 2 Jan-20 Mar
*A well furnished hotel in traditional style offers good all-round
comforts and commands outstanding sea views from dining room,
lounge and several bedrooms.*
46rm(37⇨5🛏)(4fb) CTV in all bedrooms T sB&B⇨🛏£35-£54
dB&B⇨🛏£70-£108 (incl dinner) 🏠
Lift CTV 50P 18🛏 (£1.00 per night) 🚗 ✳ ⬛ (heated) ♟
(hard) snooker solarium pool table table tennis pitch & putt ♨
*xmas*
♀ English & French ♥ ⚖ ⚥ ✳ Lunch £7.50 Dinner £14.50
Last dinner 8.45pm
Credit Cards ① ③

See advertisement on page 65

### ★★♨68% Penhelig Arms Hotel & Restaurant
LL35 0LT ☎(0654)767215 FAX (0654) 767690
Closed 25 & 26 Dec
*This hospitable privately run hotel overlooking the estuary partly
dates back to the early 19th century and has well equipped modern
bedrooms, most with sea views, a cosy lounge and bars. Sally*

A

*Hughes' culinary talents have earned the restaurant a good reputation, dishes enjoyed on inspection having included dressed local crab; grilled breast of duck served with a ginger and orange sauce, followed by sticky toffee pudding with butterscotch sauce.*
11⇨↱ CTV in all bedrooms ® **T** sB&B⇨↱fr£35 dB&B⇨↱fr£60 ⊟
12P ⊞
**V** ♁ ☖ Bar Lunch £1.60-£8.50 Dinner £15.50 Last dinner 9.30pm
Credit Cards 1 3 £

**★★66% Harbour**
LL35 0EB ☏(0654)767250 & 767792 Telex no 35746
FAX (0654) 767418
RS Nov-Mar
*This privately owned and personally run establishment overlooking the Dyfi estuary from a position near the harbour has no car park of its own but stands opposite a large public one. A family restaurant/coffee shop supplements the hotel's main restaurant and bar, and there is also a very pleasant Victorian- style wine bar. Bedrooms vary in size, shape and quality, but they are all quite well equipped and have en suite facilities.*
12⇨↱(4fb)⊬in 3 bedrooms CTV in all bedrooms ® ✻ sB&B⇨↱£45-£55 dB&B⇨↱£55-£75 ⊟
CTV ₱
♉ English & French **V** ♁ ☖ ⊬ ✻ Lunch £5-£15alc High tea £5-£15alc Dinner £5-£15alc Last dinner 9pm
Credit Cards 1 2 3 5 £

**★❀68% Maybank Hotel & Restaurant**
4 Penhelig Rd, Penhelig LL35 0PT ☏(0654)767500
Closed 9 Jan-10 Feb RS 2 Nov-15 Dec & 1-9 Jan
*There are lovely views of the Dovey estuary from the windows of this small hotel, one of a row of houses and cottages on the outskirts of the picturesque village. The simple, pine-furnished dining room, warmed in cold weather by an open fire, is a pleasant setting for reasonably priced dinners cooked by Elizabeth Dinsdale.*
6rm(4↱)(1fb) CTV in all bedrooms ® sB&B↱£26.95-£37.95 dB&B£43.95-£57 ⊟
CTV ₱ ⊞ ✼ *xmas*
♉ English, Continental & Far Eastern **V** ♁ Dinner £17-£30alc Last dinner 10pm
Credit Cards 1 3 £

**ABERFELDY** Tayside *Perthshire* Map **14** NN84

★★

**★★❀ ♔ FARLEYER HOUSE**
PH15 2JE (Pride of Britain)
☏(0887)20332
FAX (0887) 29430

*Set in its own grounds on the northern side of the River Tay, 1.5 miles west of the town, Farleyer House commands fine views across the valley. Bought as a private dwelling in 1989, and initially operated as a restaurant, it has now developed into a delightful country house hotel offering accommodation in a variety of thoughtfully equipped bedrooms with particularly nice bathrooms. The first floor drawing room and library, both ideal for peaceful relaxation, provide an abundance of reading material and are warmed by log fires in winter; the library also contains a dispenser bar. Meals are made the highlight of one's stay here with quality food served in the attractively appointed ground floor restaurant, the emphasis being on the skilful blending of flavours in country dishes prepared in modern style and based on excellent raw materials.*
11rm(9⇨↱)(2fb) CTV in all bedrooms **T** ✖ ✻ sB&B£85-£90 sB&B⇨↱£85-£90 dB&B£150-£200 dB&B⇨↱£150-£200 (incl dinner)
CTV 20P ⊞ ✼ CFA ⚑ rough shooting ♫ nc10yrs *xmas*
✻ Lunch £17.50 Dinner £27.50 Last dinner 8.30pm
Credit Cards 1 2 3 £
**See advertisement under PERTH**

**★★61% Weem**
Weem PH15 2LD (1m NW B846) ☏(0887)20381
*A friendly roadside inn, full of character and with an interesting history. A popular base for touring holidaymakers, the hotel offers traditional comforts in practical, well-equipped bedrooms.*
14⇨↱(4fb)⊬in 4 bedrooms CTV in all bedrooms ® **T** sB&B⇨↱£22-£30 dB&B⇨↱£44-£60 ⊟
20P ✼ ♩ shooting loch fishing *xmas*
♉ European **V** ♁ ☖ ⊬ Lunch £8-£20alc High tea £5-£15alc Dinner £12.95-£15.95&alc Last dinner 8.30pm
Credit Cards 1 2 3 5 £

**★❀❀ ♔73% Guinach House**
"By The Birks", Urlar Rd PH15 2ET ☏(0887)20251
*Chef/proprietor Bert Mackay and his wife Marianne bought this fine Edwardian house in 1990, he deciding to opt out of a career in 4-star city hotels. Already they have established a deserved reputation, not only for the quality of Mr Mackay's cooking but for the friendly and relaxed atmosphere of their small country house hotel. The cosy lounge – there is no bar – and the pretty dining room both look out onto the gardens. Bedrooms vary in size and all are thoughtfully equipped. Guinach, with delightful views up the valley and across town, is reached from the A826 by way of a quiet driveway.*
7⇨↱ CTV in all bedrooms ® ✻ sB&B⇨↱fr£32.50 dB&B⇨↱fr£65
12P ⊞ ✼ ♩ *xmas*
♉ British, French & Italian **V** ♁ ☖ ⊬ ✻ Lunch £12.50 Dinner £17.50 Last dinner 9.30pm
Credit Cards 1 3

**ABERFOYLE** Central *Perthshire* Map **11** NN50

**★★64% Altskeith**
Kinlochard FK8 3TL ☏Kinlochard(08777)266 FAX (08777) 223
*This friendly family-run hotel enjoys an attractive setting in its own gardens, fronted by lawns and only divided by a narrow road from the shores of Loch Ard, 3.75 miles west of the town.*
6⇨↱(1fb)⊬in all bedrooms CTV in all bedrooms ® **T** ✖ (ex guide dogs) ✻ sB&B⇨↱£31-£39.50 dB&B⇨↱£36-£59 ⊟
20P ⊞ ✼ ♩ boats for hire shooting *xmas*
**V** ♁ ☖ ⊬ ✻ Lunch £11.35-£22alc Dinner £13-£13.95&alc Last dinner 8.30pm
Credit Cards 1 2 3

**❀❀❀ ✕✕Braeval Mill**
Braeval FK8 3UY ☏(08772)711
*Nick Nairn has established a deserved reputation at his country restaurant, a converted mill with flagstone floors and natural stone walls, on the eastern outskirts of the village. What makes Braeval stand out is the sheer quality of the basic cooking, in the sauces for example. The skill of marrying ingredients and flavours to bring out the best in dishes, exemplified in a parfait of duck liver and foie gras with Cumberland sauce, followed by deliciously sweet and succulent saddle of Scottish spring lamb with caramelised onions on a bed of spinach leaves with rosemary sauce. The chocolate marquise was beautifully textured, and the cinnamon flavoured crême Anglaise the perfect accompaniment. The quality and condition of the French farmhouse cheeses, specially imported*

weekly, are exceptional. Nick's charming wife Fiona is the perfect hostess, aided by friendly and attentive staff. The mill is on the A81 just east of its junction with the A821, and is now open for lunches every day except Monday.

Closed Mon, 2 wks Feb, 1 wk May/Jun & 2 wks Nov

Dinner not served Sun

♀ Scottish & French 32 seats Lunch £15-£17 Dinner £29-£32 Last lunch 1.30pm Last dinner 9.30pm 18 P nc10yrs

Credit Cards ①②③

---

## ABERGAVENNY Gwent Map 03 SO21

### ★★★58% The Angel

Cross St NP7 5EW (Forte Hotels) ☎(0873)7121 due to change to 857121 FAX (0873) 78059 due to change to 878059

*A town-centre hotel dating from the 17th century, its good function/conference facilities, comfortable public areas and friendly staff making it a popular venue for local activities. There are currently plans in hand to refurbish its bedrooms.*

29⇄ᏁᎦ(2fb)1⌨✕in 6 bedrooms CTV in all bedrooms ⓇT✳ S%sB⇄ᏁᎦfr£60 dB⇄ᏁᎦfr£75 (room only) 🍴

⊄ 35P CFA *xmas*

V ♥ ♨ ✕✳ S% Lunch £7.95-£9.95&alc Dinner £13.30&alc Last dinner 9.30pm

Credit Cards ①②③⑤

### ★★⏚70% Llanwenarth Arms

Brecon Rd NP8 1EP ☎Crickhowell(0873)810550 FAX (0873) 811880

*A very comfortable hotel, beside the A40 midway between Abergavenny and Crickhowell, offering well furnished bedrooms with views of the Sugar Loaf or the River Usk. The restaurant provides a range of simple but carefully cooked food and is a popular choice with local families. Our inspector enjoyed a meal which included salmon, poached and served with hollandaise sauce, and a home-made chocolate and cream cheese mousse.*

18⇄ᏁᎦ CTV in all bedrooms ⓇT⋈✳ sB&B⇄ᏁᎦ£49 dB&B⇄ᏁᎦ£59 🍴

60P⌨ ♪

♀ International V ♥ ✳ Lunch £10-£20alc Dinner £10-£20alc Last dinner 10pm

Credit Cards ①②③⑤

---

## ABERGELE Clwyd Map 06 SH97 ◎

### ★★63% Kinmel Manor

St Georges Rd LL22 9AS ☎(0745)832014

*This privately owned hotel stands in open countryside a mile east of the town. Once a country house, it has undergone considerable restructuring to provide modern and very well appointed accommodation which includes a room specially designed to meet the needs of disabled guests. Extensive conference and function facilities are available, together with a good quality leisure centre containing an indoor swimming pool and well equipped gymnasium.*

42⇄ᏁᎦ(3fb) CTV in all bedrooms ⓇT✳ sB&B⇄ᏁᎦ£44 dB&B⇄ᏁᎦ£62 🍴

CTV 120P ❊ CFA ▣ (heated) sauna solarium gymnasium spa bath steam room *xmas*

♀ English & French V ♥ ♨ ✕✳ Lunch £8.50&alc High tea £3.50-£5.95 Dinner £13&alc Last dinner 9.30pm

Credit Cards ①②③④⑤ ⓔ

---

## ABERLADY Lothian *East Lothian* Map 12 NT47

### ★★64% Kilspindie House

Main St EH32 0RE ☎(08757)682

*A friendly family owned hotel, popular with both business guests and golfers. Improvements continue to be made, and include a wing of comfortable bedrooms, but the characterful Golf Addict's Bar remains unchanged.*

26⇄ᏁᎦ1⌨ CTV in all bedrooms ⓇT sB&B⇄ᏁᎦ£34-£43 dB&B⇄ᏁᎦ£60-£66 🍴

30P⌨ CFA ♫

V ♥ ♨ ✳ Sunday Lunch fr£9 High tea £6.50-£8 Dinner fr£11.50&alc Last dinner 8.30pm

Credit Cards ①③ⓔ

---

## ABERLOUR

See **Archiestown**

---

## ABERPORTH Dyfed Map 02 SN25

### ★★★64% Hotel Penrallt

SA43 2BS ☎(0239)810227 FAX (0239) 811375

Closed 23-31 Dec

*Set among a complex of good quality self-catering units and enjoying leisure facilities which now include a small golf course, this large country house provides accommodation in well equipped bedrooms which are for the most part spacious; the restaurant features interesting ceiling timbers and wall panelling.*

16⇄ᏁᎦ(2fb) CTV in all bedrooms ⓇT✳ sB&B⇄ᏁᎦfr£44 dB&B⇄ᏁᎦfr£68 🍴

CTV 100P⌨ ❊ CFA ⌿ (heated) ♪ (hard) sauna solarium gymnasium pitch & putt ♋

♥ ♨ ✳ Sunday Lunch fr£7.95 Dinner fr£13.50&alc Last dinner 9pm

Credit Cards ①②③⑤ⓔ

### ★★68% Penbontbren Farm

Glynarthen SA44 6PE (3.5m SE off A487) (Welsh Rarebits) ☎(0239)810248 FAX (0239) 811129

*This small hotel, situated along a narrow road east of the A487 and run by local staff under the direction of friendly owners, complements well equipped pine-furnished annexe bedrooms by a central complex containing the spacious lounge, attractive restaurant and bar.*

→

Annexe10⇨🛏(6fb) CTV in all bedrooms ® T ✳
sB&B⇨🛏£30-£35 dB&B⇨🛏£52-£58 🛢
35P ⇖ ✿ CFA ✐ *xmas*
V ♥ ♨ ✗ Dinner fr£10alc Last dinner 8.15pm
Credit Cards ①③

### ★★ 55% Highcliffe
SA43 2DA (Minotels) ☎(0239)810534
*Conveniently situated above the town and a short walk from two sandy beaches, is this friendly, family-run hotel. Bedrooms, although modestly furnished, are well equipped with modern facilities and are gradually being upgraded.*
9rm(6⇨)Annexe4⇨(4fb) CTV in all bedrooms ® T
sB&B⇨£29 dB&B⇨£49.50 🛢
CTV 18P *xmas*
♀ International V ♥ ♨ ✗ Lunch £3.95-£15&alc Dinner fr£12.50&alc Last dinner 8.30pm
Credit Cards ①②③⑤ⓔ

### ★ 73% Glandwr Manor
Tresaith SA43 2JH ☎(0239)810197
Closed Nov-Feb
*Set in 5 acres of pleasant woodland, this very friendly small hotel is situated north of Aberporth, along the coast at Tresaith. Everything is sparkling clean, and there is a choice of 3 lounge areas, some with cheerful log fires. Bedrooms are neat and cosy, and the hotel offers a table d'hôte or larger à la carte menu.*
7rm(2⇨3🛏)(2fb) ® ✖ sB&Bfr£19 sB&B⇨🛏fr£20 dB&Bfr£38 dB&B⇨🛏fr£40
CTV 14P ⇖ ✿
♥ ♨ ✗

---

Gwynedd Map **06** SH32

### ★★★🍴 65% Porth Tocyn
Bwlch Tocyn LL53 7BU ☎(075881)3303 FAX (075881) 3538
Closed end Nov-21 Mar
*This delightfully situated hotel stands in 25 acres of farmland with superb views over Cardigan Bay. Owned by the same family since the 1940's it offers a relaxing informal atmosphere in the excellent lounges and dining room. The cuisine has a good reputation and bedrooms are attractively furnished.*
17⇨🛏(1fb) CTV in all bedrooms T S% sB&B⇨🛏£40-£53 dB&B⇨🛏£61-£96 🛢
CTV 50P ⇖ ✿ ⌇ (heated) ⚲ (hard) windsurfing
♥ ♨ S% Sunday Lunch fr£13.75 High tea £6 Dinner £17.25-£23 Last dinner 9.30pm
Credit Cards ①

### ★★★ 65% Riverside
LL53 7HW (Exec Hotel) ☎(075881)2419 & 2818
Closed Dec-Feb
*A comfortable hotel on the banks of the river, as its name suggests, and close to both harbour and town centre. It is very popular with holidaymakers, but equally suitable for business people, and the owners ensure that both will feel welcome.*
12⇨🛏(4fb) CTV in all bedrooms ® T ✖ sB&B⇨🛏£35-£38.75 dB&B⇨🛏£70-£77.50 🛢
25P ⇖ ✿ ▣ (heated) sailing windsurfing
♀ European ♥ ♨ ✳ Bar Lunch fr£2.50 High tea fr£4.50 Dinner £19.50 Last dinner 9pm
Credit Cards ①②③⑤

### ★★★ 63% Abersoch Harbour
LL53 7HR ☎(075881)2406 & 3632
RS Jan & Feb
*The hotel is situated alongside the River Soch and commands good views of the harbour. A change of ownership in 1991 has been followed by considerable modernisation and refurbishment to provide good quality, well equipped accommodation.*
9⇨🛏Annexe5⇨🛏(2fb)1⇔ CTV in all bedrooms ® T ✳
sB&B⇨🛏£25-£61 dB&B⇨🛏£50-£120 🛢

---

50P ✿ *xmas*
♀ English & French V ♥ ♨ ✳ Lunch fr£7.95 Dinner fr£12&alc Last dinner 10pm
Credit Cards ①③

### ★★ 76% Neigwl
Lon Sarn Bach LL53 7DY ☎(075881)2363
*A combination of good friendly hospitality, attentive service, well equipped bedrooms and enjoyable, imaginative food make this impeccably maintained family-run hotel special. It is situated close to a good sandy beach and enjoys excellent views across Cardigan Bay to the Cambrian Mountains.*
7rm(1⇨4🛏)Annexe2⇨(2fb) CTV in all bedrooms ®
✖ (ex guide dogs) sB&B£37 sB&B⇨🛏£37 dB&B£62 dB&B⇨🛏£62 🛢
CTV 30P ⇖ ✿ ✿ *xmas*
♥ ♨ Lunch £9.25 Dinner £16-£18.50 Last dinner 8.30pm
Credit Cards ①③⑤ⓔ

### ★★ 64% White House
LL53 7AG ☎(075881)3427 & 3428
*A large house set in attractive gardens with abundant car parking space. It is on the A499 to the north of Abersoch, commanding panoramic views of the harbour, St Tudwals Islands and Cardigan Bay. The hotel is enthusiastically run by young proprietors, David and Jayne Smith, who acquired it at the beginning of 1991 and embarked on a programme of extensive improvements.*
10rm(9⇨🛏)(1fb) CTV in all bedrooms ® T ✳ sB&B£22.50 dB&B£35 dB&B⇨🛏£45
100P ✿ *xmas*
♀ English & French V ♥ ♨ ✗ ✳ Sunday Lunch £10 Dinner £14.95&alc Last dinner 9.30pm
Credit Cards ①③

### ★★ 61% Deucoch
LL53 7LD ☎(075881)2680
*A friendly, family-run hotel in an elevated position on the outskirts of the town commands panoramic views across Cardigan Bay from Snowdonia to mid-Wales. Its accommodation is equally suitable for holidaymakers or business travellers, rooms being quite well furnished and having en suite facilities in the majority of cases.*
10rm(3⇨5🛏)(2fb) CTV in all bedrooms ® ✳
sB&B⇨🛏£20.50-£22.50 dB&B⇨🛏£41-£45 🛢
CTV 30P ✿ *xmas*
V ♥ ♨ ✳ Bar Lunch £2.50-£4alc Dinner fr£11 Last dinner 8pm
Credit Cards ①③ⓔ

---

Dyfed Map **06** SN58

### ★★★ 🍴🍴 66% Conrah
Ffosrhydygaled, Chancery SY23 4DF (Welsh Rarebits)
☎(0970)617941 Telex no 35892 FAX (0970) 624546
Closed 24-31 Dec
*This fine Georgian country mansion, set in 20 acres of woodland off the A487 south of the town, offers typically Welsh hospitality and service as well as good meals soundly based on produce from the hotel's own garden. Bedroom modernisation is planned, public areas are particularly elegant, and there is a small leisure centre.*
11rm(9⇨🛏) CTV in all bedrooms ® T ✖ ✳
sB&Bfr£47.50 sB&B⇨🛏£54 dB&Bfr£66 dB&B⇨🛏£66-£86.50 🛢
Lift 60P ⇖ ✿ CFA ▣ (heated) sauna table tennis croquet nc5yrs
♀ International V ♥ ♨ ✗ ✳ Lunch fr£12.75&alc Dinner fr£18.50&alc Last dinner 9.30pm
Credit Cards ①②③⑤

A rosette means exceptional standards of cuisine.

★★64% **Belle Vue Royal**
Marine Ter SY23 2BA ☎(0970)617558 FAX (0970) 612190
Closed 24-26 Dec
*Right on the seafront, this very well run Victorian hotel provides friendly service. Bedrooms are being upgraded to a high standard and the recently opened grill room adds to the choice of dishes in the restaurant. Residents can benefit from free golf on the local course.*
37rm(30⇔🏠)(6fb) CTV in all bedrooms ® T
✕ (ex guide dogs) sB&B£29-£32 sB&B⇔🏠£35-£38 dB&B£49.50-£54.50 dB&B⇔🏠fr£55.50 🖪
《 CTV 6P 9🐎
♀ Continental V ♥ ♨ ✱ Lunch fr£8.50 Dinner fr£13.50&alc
Last dinner 9pm
Credit Cards ①②③⑤ ⓔ

★★63% **Four Seasons**
50-54 Portland St SY23 2DX ☎(0970)612120
Closed 25 Dec-2 Jan
*This small friendly hotel close to the town centre has comfortable bedrooms with modern amenities, a cosy residents' lounge and small bar. A good choice of food is offered and a private dining room for small functions has recently been added.*
14rm(11⇔🏠)(1fb) CTV in all bedrooms ® T ✱ sB&B£29-£34 sB&B⇔🏠£34-£45 dB&B£45 dB&B⇔🏠£56 🖪
CTV 10P CFA
♀ English & Continental V ♥ ♨ ✂ ✱ Sunday Lunch £8.75
Dinner £12-£12.75 Last dinner 8.30pm
Credit Cards ①③

★★61% **Groves**
44-46 North Pde SY23 2NF (Minotels) ☎(0970)617623
Closed Xmas
*A pleasant little town centre hotel, run by the same friendly family for many years and popular with business people as well as leisure guests, offers modern bedrooms, a cosy bar and lounge, a dining room featuring a 'Taste of Wales' menu and a small meeting room.*
11⇔🏠✂in 1 bedroom CTV in all bedrooms ® T
✕ (ex guide dogs) ✱ sB&B⇔🏠fr£33 dB&B⇔🏠fr£55 🖪
8P CFA nc3yrs
♀ International V ♥ ✱ Sunday Lunch fr£7.95 Dinner fr£12.75
Last dinner 8.30pm
Credit Cards ①②③⑤

★★59% **Bay**
35-37 Marine Ter SY23 2BX ☎(0970)617356 FAX (0970) 612198
Closed 24 Dec-1 Jan
*This modernised hotel is situated on the seafront, with some rooms having good sea views. There is an innovative menu each night as well as the roast of the day.*
32rm(7⇔13🏠)(3fb) CTV in all bedrooms ® T ✱ sB&B£20-£32 sB&B⇔🏠fr£32 dB&B⇔🏠£50-£55 🖪
20P CFA pool table skittle alley
V ♥ ♨ ✂ ✱ Sunday Lunch fr£8 Dinner fr£12&alc Last dinner 8.30pm
Credit Cards ①②③⑤ ⓔ

★★57% **Queensbridge**
Promenade, Victoria Ter SY23 2BX ☎(0970)612343 & 615025
FAX (0970) 617452
Closed 1wk Xmas
*Right on the seafront, this small family hotel is a popular venue for both holidaymakers and business travellers. Bedrooms, although modestly furnished, are clean and bright. There is a comfortable lounge with an adjoining bar, and a basement dining room.*
15⇔🏠(6fb) CTV in all bedrooms ® T ✕ (ex guide dogs)
sB&B⇔🏠£30-£32 dB&B⇔🏠£43-£46 🖪
Lift CTV ♪
♥ ✱ Bar Lunch £5.10-£10 Dinner £10-£13.50 Last dinner 8pm
Credit Cards ①②③⑤ ⓔ

★★56% **Cambrian**

Alexandra Rd SY23 1LG ☎(0970)612446

Closed 25 Dec

*This mock Tudor hotel opposite the railway station, notable for its very interesting collection of old household and agricultural implements, offers neat bedrooms equipped with modern facilities. Its ground floor bar is much used by the town's student population.*

12rm(2⇔5♠)(3fb) CTV in all bedrooms ® ✱ sB&B£28 sB&B⇔♠£30 dB&B£45 dB&B⇔♠£50 ₽

✘

♡ Welsh, English & Continental V ✧ ℒ ✱ Lunch £8-£10 High tea £5.50-£7.50 Dinner £10-£12&alc Last dinner 9.30pm

Credit Cards ①③⑤

---

**ABINGDON** Oxfordshire Map **04** SU49

★★★62% **Abingdon Lodge**

Marcham Rd OX14 1TZ (Consort) ☎(0235)553456

Telex no 837750 FAX (0235) 554117

Closed 25-26 Dec

*A modern, purpose-built hotel, its convenient situation at the A34/A415 junction offering easy access to the M4 and many major routes, provides a range of functionally designed but comfortable and well equipped bedrooms which are all similar in size and decor. Modern, bright and airy public areas include an à la carte restaurant, and a carvery-style operation is also available at weekends. Friendly young staff give helpful service, and the hotel is ideal for either commercial traveller or short-stay guest.*

63⇔♠ ⅄ in 8 bedrooms CTV in all bedrooms ® T

✖ (ex guide dogs) ✱ sB&B⇔♠£45-£75 dB&B⇔♠£55-£85 Continental breakfast ₽

⟨ 85P CFA

♡ English & French V ✧ ℒ ⅄ ✱ S10% Lunch £7.75-£9.95 Dinner £10.50&alc Last dinner 10pm

Credit Cards ①②③⑤ⓔ

★★★60% **Upper Reaches**

Thames St OX14 3JA (Forte Hotels) ☎(0235)522311

FAX (0235) 555182

*Beautifully situated on the edge of the historic town, with the River Thames on one side and an old mill stream on the other, this former abbey cornmill has been converted to provide cosy public rooms and well furnished bedrooms with modern facilities. The Millwheel restaurant provides a good standard of cooking.*

26⇔♠⅄ in 10 bedrooms CTV in all bedrooms ® T ✱ sB⇔♠fr£75 dB⇔♠fr£95 (room only) ₽

80P ✿ CFA *xmas*

V ✧ ℒ ⅄ ✱ S% Lunch £8.95-£11.20 Dinner £17.20 Last dinner 9.30pm

Credit Cards ①②③④⑤

★★61% **Crown & Thistle**

Bridge St OX14 3HS (Chef & Brewer) ☎(0235)522556

FAX (0235) 553281

*This popular hotel is conveniently sited for commercial users, being close to major motorway and main road links. Prettily decorated bedrooms with co- ordinating Laura Ashley prints offer good modern facilities, and guests can take meals in an informal Berni Grill restaurant.*

21rm(16⇔♠)(3fb)1₮ CTV in all bedrooms ® T

✖ (ex guide dogs) sB&B£45-£51 sB&B⇔♠£51-£56 dB&B£73 dB&B⇔♠£79 ₽

⟨ 36P

♡ English & Continental V ✧ ℒ ⅄ Bar Lunch £2.95-£5.50alc

Credit Cards ①②③⑤

---

Red star hotels are each
highlighted by a pink
tinted panel.

---

**ABOYNE** Grampian *Aberdeenshire* Map **15** NO59

★★66% *Birse Lodge*

Charleston Rd AB3 5EL ☎(03398)86253 & 86254

*Considerable improvements have been made at this popular fishing and tourist hotel close to the River Dee. Public areas have been enhanced and main house bedrooms now have excellent modern décor and fabrics.*

11⇔♠ Annexe4⇔♠(2fb) CTV in all bedrooms ® T

CTV 80P ☞ ✿ putting green

♡ International V ✧ ℒ Last dinner 8.30pm

Credit Cards ①②③

---

**ACCRINGTON** Lancashire Map **07** SD72 ◎

★★★61% **Dunkenhalgh**

Blackburn Rd, Clayton le Moors BB5 5JP (adj to M65, junct 7) (Rank) ☎Blackburn(0254)398021 Telex no 63282

FAX (0254) 872230

*An impressive country house with modern bedrooms, attractive public rooms and extensive leisure facilities.*

29⇔♠ Annexe51⇔♠(14fb)1₮ CTV in all bedrooms ® T ✱ sB&B⇔♠£51-£74 dB&B⇔♠£72-£89 ₽

⟨ CTV 400P ✿ CFA ⌸ (heated) snooker sauna solarium gymnasium ♪ *xmas*

♡ International V ✧ ℒ ✱ Lunch £7-£9.75 High tea £3.95-£7.50 Dinner £16-£16.50&alc Last dinner 9.45pm

Credit Cards ①②③⑤

---

**ACHNASHEEN** Highland *Ross & Cromarty* Map **14** NH15

★★♨70% **Ledgowan Lodge**

IV22 2EJ (Best Western) ☎(044588)252 Telex no 75431

FAX (044588) 240

Closed 22 Oct-10 Apr

*Just south of the village, this former shooting lodge has been converted to create a welcoming and efficiently run Highland hotel. The original character of the house has been retained, with inviting open fires in the day rooms, and the well equipped bedrooms are comfortable.*

13⇔♠(1fb) CTV in all bedrooms ® T ✖ sB&B⇔♠£39.95-£45 dB&B⇔♠£59-£95

25P ✿

✧ ℒ Lunch £5-£12.50 Dinner £15-£25 Last dinner 8.30pm

Credit Cards ①②③⑤

★★69% *Loch Maree*

IV22 2HL ☎Kinlochewe(044584)288 FAX (044584) 241

Closed Nov-11 Apr

*Major refurbishment has completely transformed this welcoming Victorian hotel on the picturesque loch shore. Public rooms invite relaxation and the bedrooms, though compact, are well equipped and tastefully furnished.*

18⇔♠(1fb) CTV in all bedrooms ® T

50P ✿ ♩

V ✧ ℒ Last dinner 9pm

Credit Cards ①③

---

**ACLE** Norfolk Map **09** TG41

⬦**Forte Travelodge**

(junc A47 & Acle Bypass) (Forte)

☎(0493)751970 Central Res (0800) 850950

*Midway between Norwich and Great Yarmouth on the A47, this Travelodge is set in the pretty village of Acle, next to a Little Chef (open 7am-10pm) with a service station and shop. Well sited for the Broads and within easy reach of the city or coast.*

40⇔♠(40fb) CTV in all bedrooms ® sB⇔♠£29.95 dB⇔♠£29.95 (room only)

⟨ 40P ☞

Credit Cards ①②③

## ADDERBURY Oxfordshire Map **04** SP43

### ★★68% *Red Lion*

The Green, Oxford Rd OX17 3LU ☎(0295)810269
FAX (0295) 811906

*A stone-built 16th-century coaching inn which overlooks the village green from a position beside the A423 3 miles south of Banbury Cross. Friendly and informal in style, the hotel looks after the guests' comfort and offers a high level of hospitality. Bedrooms are individually furnished to a good standard, while recent refurbishment in keeping with the hotel's period façade has made lavish use of fabrics in highlighting the stone chimneys and linen fold panelling of bars and dining room as well as providing modern facilities.*

9rm(6⇌🟊)1🛏 CTV in all bedrooms ® T 🏃 (ex guide dogs)
24P

♥ English & Continental V ♥ ⬚ ⤬ Last dinner 10pm
Credit Cards 1 3

## ADLINGTON Cheshire Map **07** SJ98

### 🏠Forte Travelodge

London Rd South SK12 4NA (on A523) (Forte)
☎(0625)875292 Central Res (0800) 850950

*A modern Lodge on the A523 midway between Stockport and Macclesfield, within easy reach of Manchester Airport. There is a Little Chef restaurant adjacent.*

32⇌🟊 (32fb) CTV in all bedrooms ® sB⇌🟊£29.95
dB⇌🟊£29.95 (room only)

《 32P ♿

Credit Cards 1 2 3

## ADLINGTON Lancashire Map **07** SD61

### ★★64% *Gladmar*

Railway Rd PR6 9RG ☎(0257)480398 FAX (0257) 482681
Closed 25 Dec & 1 Jan

*Privately owned, and set in its own secluded grounds and gardens just off the A6 near the town's railway station, a spotlessly clean and carefully maintained hotel with a congenial atmosphere. Particularly well equipped bedrooms complement a comfortable lounge, cosy bar and attractively appointed dining room.*

20⇌🟊 (1fb)⤬in 2 bedrooms CTV in all bedrooms ® T
🏃 (ex guide dogs) ✻ S% sB&B⇌🟊£37-£49 dB&B⇌🟊£59 🍴
CTV 30P ✻ CFA

V ♥ ⬚ ⤬ ✻ Dinner £9.80&alc Last dinner 8.30pm
Credit Cards 1 3 5

## AIRDRIE Strathclyde *Lanarkshire* Map **11** NS76

### ★64% *The Staging Post*

8/10 Anderson St ML6 0AA ☎(0236)67525 & 52211
FAX (0236) 62742
Closed 26 Dec & 1-2 Jan RS 24-25 Dec & 31 Dec

*A small, friendly, town centre hotel which has recently been refurbished. Bedrooms have good facilities, and an extensive choice of dishes is available in the pleasantly furnished restaurant.*

9rm(7⇌1🟊) CTV in all bedrooms ® T 🏃 ✻ sB&B⇌🟊fr£31
dB&B⇌🟊fr£46 🍴

《 🅿 ♿

♥ French V ✻ Lunch fr£6.50&alc Dinner £10.75-£27.60alc
Last dinner 9.30pm
Credit Cards 1 2 3 5

## ALCESTER Warwickshire Map **04** SP05 ◎

### ★★★64% *Kings Court*

Kings Coughton B49 5QQ ☎(0789)763111 FAX (0789) 400242
Closed 24-30 Dec

*A mile north of Alcester on the A435 at Kings Coughton, this hotel offers comfortable modern accommodation. It was completely refurbished during the summer of 1990 but public areas still retain*

*the character of the original Tudor farmhouse building with many oak-beamed walls and ceilings. The bar has a typical village pub atmosphere and there is a quiet foyer/lounge. While bedrooms are well appointed some of the singles are rather compact.*

4⇌🟊Annexe15⇌🟊(1fb) CTV in all bedrooms ® T ✻
sB&B⇌🟊£47 dB&B⇌🟊£58-£65 🍴
120P ✻

V ♥ ⬚ ✻ Sunday Lunch £8.95-£9.40
Credit Cards 1 2 3

### ★★56% *Cherrytrees*

Stratford Rd B49 6LN ☎(0789)762505
RS 25-26 Dec

*This motel-style establishment, set beside the A422 Stratford road one mile east of the town, offers open-plan public areas which include a restaurant serving popular simple dishes; bedrooms are contained in chalet blocks outside the main building.*

2⇌🟊Annexe22⇌🟊(2fb) CTV in all bedrooms ® T ✻
sB&B⇌🟊£45 dB&B⇌🟊£55 🍴
CTV 80P ✻ CFA

♥ International V ♥ ✻ Lunch £9 Dinner £11 Last dinner
9.30pm
Credit Cards 1 2 3 £

## ALCONBURY Cambridgeshire Map **04** TL17

### ★★64% *Alconbury House*

Alconbury Weston PE17 5JG (1.5m N on A1)
☎Huntingdon(0480)890807 FAX (0480) 891259

*An attractive Georgian house set in its own grounds adjacent to the A1 (northbound). Attentive staff ensure an hospitable welcome and a good range of dishes is served in both the bar and restaurant.*

24🟊(2fb) CTV in all bedrooms ® T ✻ sB&B🟊£25-£45
dB&B🟊£40-£55 🍴
80P ✻ squash snooker sauna solarium

→

### Aboyne, Royal Deeside AB34 5EL
### Telephone: (03398) 86253

This privately owned Country House Hotel is set in its own grounds. Popular with fishers and shooters also golfing enthusiasts who have a choice of 5 Golf Courses all within a few miles of the hotel.

♀ European **V** ⌖ ᵇ _♫_ ⅍ Lunch fr£13&alc High tea £8.50
Dinner £13 Last dinner 9.30pm
Credit Cards ①②③⑤ ⓔ

---

## ALDBOURNE Wiltshire Map **04** SU27

### ❀ ✕ ✕ Raffles

The Green SN8 2BW ☎Marlborough(0672)40700

*An intimate and traditionally furnished little restaurant in a
picturesque village setting offers at both lunch and dinner times a
short but interesting menu with an international flavour which
features fish, game, red and white meats. Gnocchi with Citrus
Cream Sauce would make a tasty beginning to your meal, and this
could be followed by Noissetes of Venison in a delicious gamey
sauce or Monkfish and Scallops on a warmed Tomato, Basil and
Olive Oil Vinaigrette ; classic desserts are equally enjoyable, the
cuisine is complemented by an uncomplicated list of the more
popular wines, and service is both relaxed and attentive.*
Closed Sun, last 2 wks Aug & 25-30 Dec Lunch not served Mon
& Sat

♀ French 36 seats ✱ Lunch £12.20-£18.85alc Dinner £12.50-
£18.85alc Last lunch 2.15pm Last dinner 10.30pm 2 P nc3yrs
Credit Cards ①②③⑤

---

## ALDEBURGH Suffolk Map **05** TM45

### ★★★68% White Lion

Market Cross Place IP15 5BJ (Best Western) ☎(0728)452720
FAX (0728) 452986

*An above average, family owned and managed hotel in prime
position on the seafront successfully attracts both leisure and
commercial users. Modern bedrooms are light and comfortable,
while public areas include a Buttery bar serving informal meals
and snacks as well as the popular, good value restaurant.*
38⇨♠(1fb)2🚪 CTV in all bedrooms ® **T** sB&B⇨♠£55-£65
dB&B⇨♠£70-£95 ⊞

15P 🚭 CFA *xmas*

♀ English & French **V** ⌖ _♫_ Sunday Lunch £10.95-£12.95
Dinner £14.95-£15.95alc Last dinner 8.45pm
Credit Cards ①②③⑤

---

### ★★★65% Wentworth

Wentworth Rd IP15 5BD (Consort) ☎(0728)452312
Closed 28 Dec-11 Jan

*Situated on the seafront, this hotel provides a relaxing atmosphere.
The spacious well furnished lounges are delightful, and a well
chosen menu, which uses fresh local produce, is offered in the
restaurant. A small team of staff provide an efficient and personal
service. The accommodation is well furnished with the majority of
rooms having en suite facilities.*
31rm(24⇨4♠) CTV in all bedrooms **T** ✱ sB&B£34.50-£40
sB&B⇨♠£40-£49 dB&B⇨♠£72.50-£100 ⊞

16P 🚭 *xmas*

♀ English & French **V** ⌖ _♫_ ✱ Lunch £12.50-£14.75 Dinner
£15.95&alc Last dinner 9pm
Credit Cards ①②③⑤

---

### ★★★58% Brudenell

The Parade IP15 5BU (Forte Hotels) ☎(0728)452071
FAX (0728) 454082

*Comfortable, inviting public areas and good service from a
particularly friendly team of staff are among the attractive
features of a seafront hotel which offers excellent views from many
of its rooms ; accommodation is, for the most part, quite spacious
and well equipped.*
47⇨♠(4fb)⅍in 11 bedrooms CTV in all bedrooms ® **T** ✱ S%
sB⇨♠fr£55 dB⇨♠fr£70 (room only) ⊞

Lift ℂ 14P 8🚗 CFA games room *xmas*

**V** ⌖ _♫_ ⅍ ✱ S% Lunch £8.95-£9.95&alc Dinner £14.50&alc
Last dinner 9pm
Credit Cards ①②③⑤

---

### ★★65% Uplands

Victoria Rd IP15 5DX ☎(0728)452420
Closed 23-30 Dec

*This small hotel with a beautifully maintained walled garden
stands on the approach to the town and within easy walking
distance of it ; furnished on country house lines, it also offers some
more modestly appointed but comfortable chalet-style
accommodation with attractive soft furnishings.*
12rm(8⇨)Annexe8⇨♠(2fb) CTV in 17 bedrooms TV in 3
bedrooms ® **T** ✱ (ex guide dogs) sB&Bfr£26 sB&B⇨♠£42
dB&B⇨♠£56-£60 ⊞

CTV 22P 🚭 ❀ nc12yrs

**V** Dinner fr£14 Last dinner 8.30pm
Credit Cards ①②③⑤

---

## ALDERLEY EDGE Cheshire Map **07** SJ87

### ★★★❀73% Alderley Edge

Macclesfield Rd SK9 7BJ ☎(0625)583033 FAX (0625) 586343

*This completely refurbished bustling hotel in a peaceful residential
area has comfortable attractive public areas and well equipped
bedrooms. The increasingly popular restaurant offers a variety of
menus featuring the skilful cooking of chef Brian Joy.*
32⇨♠2🚪 CTV in all bedrooms ® **T** ✱ sB⇨♠£35-£87
dB⇨♠£50-£99.50 (room only) ⊞

ℂ 90P ❀ CFA *xmas*

**V** ⌖ _♫_ ✱ Lunch £15.50&alc Dinner £20.50&alc Last dinner
10pm
Credit Cards ①②③④⑤ ⓔ

---

## ALDERMINSTER Warwickshire Map **04** SP24

### ★★★★75% Ettington Park

CV37 8BS ☎Stratford-upon-Avon(0789)740740
FAX (0789) 450472

*A Victorian mansion in Gothic style, glimpsed through the mature
trees of 40 acres of parkland, now offers standards of comfort
unprecedented in the many years that it has operated as an hotel.
The new wing's modern accommodation, though plainer and more
uniform than the spacious, ornate and individually styled bedrooms
of the main house, is equally comfortable ; the restaurant enjoys a
well-earned reputation for good food, a small but attractive leisure
centre is available for guests' use.*
48⇨1🚪⅍in 5 bedrooms CTV in all bedrooms **T**
✖ (ex guide dogs) ✱ sB&B⇨♠£110-£145 dB&B⇨♠£140-£165 ⊞

Lift ℂ 85P ❀ CFA ⌖ (heated) 🅿 (hard) 🏌 U sauna solarium
croquet clay pigeon shooting archery *xmas*

♀ English & French **V** ⌖ _♫_ ⅍ ✱ Lunch fr£15.75&alc Dinner
fr£28&alc Last dinner 9.30pm
Credit Cards ①②③⑤ ⓔ

**See advertisement under STRATFORD-UPON-AVON**

---

## ALDERNEY

See Channel Islands

---

## ALDWARK North Yorkshire Map **08** SE46

### ★★★⚐78% Aldwark Manor

YO6 2NF (Best Western) ☎(03473)8146 FAX (03473) 8867

*This delightfully furnished 19th-century mansion is set in 180
acres of parkland, with its own 9-hole golf course. The luxurious
bedrooms are individually designed, lounge areas are comfortable
and relaxing and the elegant restaurant provides an interesting
menu.*
17⇨♠Annexe3⇨♠(2fb)2🚪⅍in 2 bedrooms CTV in 18
bedrooms ® **T** ✱ sB&B⇨♠£65-£88 dB&B⇨♠£99.50-£132
⊞

ℂ 52P ❀ CFA ⚑ 9 🏌 course fishing

♀ European **V** ⌖ _♫_ ✱ Sunday Lunch fr£9.95 Dinner fr£16.90
Last dinner 9pm
Credit Cards ①②③⑤ ⓔ

**ALFORD** Lincolnshire Map **09** TF47

★ 64% **White Horse**
29 West St LN13 9DG ☎(0507)462218
*A cheerful roadside inn on the main street where the proprietors work hard to meet the needs of guests and bar customers, and keep all in good condition. Accommodation is modestly furnished, attractively decorated, clean and comfortable, mostly with en suite facilities.*
9rm(7⇨)(2fb) CTV in all bedrooms ® sB&Bfr£20
sB&B⇨ͨfr£24 dB&Bfr£30 dB&B⇨ͨfr£34
10P 3🐾
♀ English & Continental ♥ ✱ Lunch £7-£15alc Dinner £7-£15alc Last dinner 10pm
Credit Cards ① ③

**ALFRETON** Derbyshire Map **08** SK45

★★★ 61% **Granada Lodge**
DE55 1HJ (junc A38/A61) (Granada) ☎(0773)520040
FAX (0773) 521087
*A modern, purpose-built hotel that also provides a good service to passing motorists stands where the A38 and A61 meet 3 miles from junction 28 of the M1 motorway. Bedrooms are identical to those in the Granada Lodges, all having private bathrooms and a good range of facilities, with provision for both disabled and non-smoking guests. The flexible Platters Restaurant offers an all-day snack service and a balanced grill-style menu with daily choices at both lunch and dinner.*
61⇨ͨ®(10fb)⤶in 13 bedrooms CTV in all bedrooms ® T
✖ (ex guide dogs) S% sB⇨ͨ✿fr£37 dB⇨ͨ✿fr£41 (room only)
🅿
⑩ 105P CFA
V ♥ ⚏ ⤶ ✱ S% Sunday Lunch fr£9.25 Dinner fr£12.50 Last dinner 9.30pm
Credit Cards ① ② ③ ⑤

**ALFRISTON** East Sussex Map **05** TQ50

★★★ 65% **The Star**
BN26 5TA (Forte Hotels) ☎(0323)870495 FAX (0323) 870922
*Dating from the 13th century, and claiming to be one of the oldest inns in the country, the Star retains the charm of its origins in cosy beamed lounges where inglenook fires burn in winter. Bedrooms come in a variety of styles, some being housed in a modern annexe, but all are well equipped, and friendly staff are courteous and eager to please.*
34⇨ͨ✿ ⤶in 10 bedrooms CTV in all bedrooms ® T ✱
sB⇨ͨ✿fr£65 dB⇨ͨ✿fr£85 (room only) 🅿
⑩ 36P CFA *xmas*
V ♥ ⚏ ⤶ ✱ Lunch £11.75-£12.50&alc Dinner fr£14.95&alc
Last dinner 9.30pm
Credit Cards ① ② ③ ④ ⑤

❀✖ **Moonraker's**
High St BN26 5TD ☎(0323)870472
*Delightful small 14th-century cottage restaurant featuring inglenook log fire and a homely lounge. Chef Elaine Wilkinson's cooking is very reliable, wholesome and interesting. A good wine selection is available, particularly Estate and Domaine bottled wines. All is complemented by friendly supervision and service.*
Closed Sun, Mon & 13 Jan-13 Feb Lunch not served
♀ French **V** 32 seats ✱ Dinner £19.90 Last dinner 9.15pm
♪ nc5yrs

The AA's star rating scheme is the
market leader in hotel
classification.

**ALLENDALE** Northumberland Map **12** NY85

★★❀ ♨70% **Bishopfield Country House**
NE47 9EJ ☎(0434)683248 FAX (0434) 683830
Closed 24-26 Dec
*Once a working farm, outbuildings and barns have been skilfully converted to create a delightful hotel. Bedrooms are modern and offer good facilities, and the charming lounges provide comfort and tranquillity. Carefully cooked food is served in the country-style restaurant, and Keith and Kathy Fairless are fine hosts.*
13⇨🅟(3fb) CTV in all bedrooms ® T S% sB&B⇨🅟£38-£48 dB&B⇨🅟fr£76
20P ⇔ ❀ CFA ✎
🍴 English & French V ✿ ⚏ ⅍ S% Dinner fr£14 Last dinner 8.30pm
Credit Cards ①③

**ALLOA** Central *Clackmannanshire* Map **11** NS89

★★★❀❀ ♨79% **The Gean House**
Gean Park, Tullibody Rd FK10 2HS ☎(0259)219275
FAX (0259) 213827
*Built at the end of the art nouveau period, Gean House (gean: Scots for wild cherry) is an elegant turn-of-the-century hotel, fully restored and luxuriously furnished, with all the comforts of the 1990s. The panelled dining rooms overlooks the formal scented rose garden and Antony Mifsud's stylish menus are entirely appropriate to the surroundings. Dishes include mousseline of smoked Finnan Haddock with a delicate leek sauce, or poached fillet of Highland lamb. Terraces outside enable guests to enjoy views of the nearby Ochil Hills, and wide doors and a ground floor free of steps are helpful to people with disabilities.*
7⇨🅟 CTV in all bedrooms T ✠ (ex guide dogs) ✱
sB⇨🅟fr£70 dB⇨🅟£120-£140 (room only) 🍴
《 30P ⇔ ❀ ♫ (hard) nc12yrs xmas
🍴 French V ⅍ ✱ Lunch fr£15 Dinner fr£27.50 Last dinner 9pm
Credit Cards ①②③⑤

**ALLOWAY** Strathclyde *Ayrshire* Map **10** NS31

★★67% **Burns Monument**
KA7 4PQ (2m S on B7024) ☎Ayr(0292)42466 FAX (0292) 43174
*This comfortable hotel takes its name from the nearby Burns Monument and the Auld Brig O' Doon. Its own setting, in the midst of landscaped gardens overlooking the River Doon, is spectacular, and the recent refurbishment of its rooms makes a bright and welcoming impression. Snacks and light meals are provided in the Alloway Lounge, which has lovely views of the river, and the Poet's Restaurant serves an imaginative range of dishes. The Brig O'Doon public bar is busy and full of character.*
9⇨🅟(2fb)1🚻 CTV in all bedrooms ® T S% sB&B⇨🅟£40-£45 dB&B⇨🅟£70-£80 🍴
《 CTV 20P ❀ CFA ✎ ♫ ♫♫ xmas
🍴 British & French V ✿ ⚏ ⅍ Lunch £5-£12.50&alc High tea £5.50-£7.50 Dinner £15.50-£18.50&alc Last dinner 10.30pm
Credit Cards ①②③⑤ £

**ALMONDSBURY** Avon Map **03** ST68

★★★★64% **Aztec**
Aztec West Business Park BS12 4TS (Shire) ☎(0454)201090
FAX (0454) 201593
*Easily reached via junction 16 of the M5, this completely new hotel provides extensive leisure and conference facilities. Public areas are comfortable and attractive, especially the galleried lounge, and the hotel also features its own 'Black Sheep' public house. Bedrooms are all furnished and equipped to high standards.*
88⇨🅟(13fb)2🚻⅍in 12 bedrooms CTV in all bedrooms ® T ✱ S% sB&B⇨🅟£92-£122.50 dB&B⇨🅟£106.50-£132.50 🍴

Lift 《 240P ❀ CFA ▭ (heated) squash snooker sauna solarium gymnasium spa bath steam room *xmas*
🍴 International V ✿ ⚏
Credit Cards ①②③⑤

**ALNWICK** Northumberland Map **12** NU11 ⊙

★★★63% **White Swan**
Bondgate Within NE66 1TD ☎(0665)602109
FAX (0665) 510400
*A traditional town-centre hotel offering friendly service and well equipped bedrooms which are gradually being upgraded. A feature is the oak-panelled Olympic Suite, taken from the SS Olympic, sister ship of the Titanic.*
43⇨🅟(2fb)⅍in 4 bedrooms CTV in all bedrooms ® T sB&B⇨🅟£63-£70 dB&B⇨🅟£75-£95 🍴
《 30P ❀ CFA ♨ xmas
🍴 English & French V ✿ ⚏ Lunch £8.50-£12.50 High tea fr£4.95 Dinner £14.95-£21.95&alc Last dinner 9pm
Credit Cards ①②③ £

★★74% *The Oaks*
South Rd NE66 2PN ☎(0665)510014
*A delightful small and friendly hotel formed from two 18th-century stone-built houses. Bedrooms are very well furnished and equipped, and the attractive restaurant serves a good range of well produced dishes.*
4⇨🅟Annexe4⇨ CTV in all bedrooms ®
▦ 32P
V ✿ Last dinner 9pm
Credit Cards ①③

★★54% *Hotspur*
Bondgate Without NE66 1PR ☎(0665)510101
Closed 24-26 Dec & 1 Jan
*An old coaching inn on the edge of the town centre which is personally owned and run and offers friendly service.*
28rm(17⇨1🅟)(2fb) CTV in all bedrooms ®
CTV 25P
V ✿ ⚏ Last dinner 9pm
Credit Cards ①③

**ALRESFORD** Hampshire Map **04** SU53

❀❀ ✕✕**Old School House**
60 West St SO24 9AU ☎(096273)2134
*This restaurant could justifiably claim to serve the best school dinners in Hampshire! Meals of excellent quality, selected from two fixed-price menus, are based on good-quality ingredients, well seasoned and individually cooked; there is a separate pudding menu and a popular wine list. Service is efficient, attentive and friendly.*
Closed Mon, 1st wk Jan & last wk Oct
Dinner not served Sun
🍴 English & French V 36 seats ✱ Lunch £6.65-£8.75alc Dinner £16.95-£22.95 Last lunch 2pm Last dinner 10pm ₽ ⅍
Credit Cards ①③

**ALSAGER** Cheshire Map **07** SJ75

★★★66% **Manor House**
Audley Rd ST7 2QQ ☎Crewe(0270)884000 FAX (0270) 882483
RS 25-30 Dec
*The large modern extension to this friendly, commercial-style hotel incorporates a swimming pool, function suite and spacious reception area as well as bedrooms; by contrast, the exposed beams of the original farmhouse are a feature of the bars and of the restaurant, with its good local reputation.*
57⇨🅟(5fb)1🚻 CTV in all bedrooms ® T ✱ sB&B⇨🅟£55-£75 dB&B⇨🅟£70-£92 🍴
《 CTV 178P ❀ CFA ▭ (heated) snooker pool table ♫

♥ English & French **V** ♦ ♨ ✳ Lunch £9.50-£12&alc High tea £4-£8 Dinner £14-£16&alc Last dinner 9.30pm
Credit Cards ①②③⑤ⓔ

---

**ALSTON** Cumbria Map **12** NY74

★★♨78% **Lovelady Shield Country House**
CA9 3LF ☎(0434)381203 FAX (0434) 381515
Closed 3 Jan-21 Feb

*Attractively set off the A689 2.5 miles east of Alston, beside the River Nent, and approached by a long drive through well tended gardens with a croquet lawn, this charming, unpretentious country house hotel dating back to 1830 offers complete peace and relaxation. Cosy lounges with open fires and plenty of reading material retain a traditional atmosphere, though bedrooms boast every modern facility. The 4-course dinner menu (changed daily and accompanied by a carefully chosen wine list) generally provides a choice of three starters, a home-made soup and two main courses as well as delicious sweets, and breakfasts are memorable.*
12⇨🏾(1fb)1🏾 CTV in all bedrooms **T** sB&B⇨🏾£31.50 dB&B⇨🏾£60-£80 🛏
20P 🚗 ✿ ♟ (hard) croquet *xmas*
♥ English & French ♦ ♨ ✂ Sunday Lunch £9-£12.50 High tea £4-£10 Dinner £18.50-£21.50 Last dinner 8.30pm
Credit Cards ①②③⑤ⓔ

★★67% **Lowbyer Manor Country House**
CA9 3JX ☎(0434)381230

*This interesting period house on the A686, 1 mile north of the town centre, has a cosy bar, attractive dining room and comfortable lounge.*
7⇨🏾Annexe4⇨ CTV in all bedrooms ⓡ **T** sB&B⇨🏾£30 dB&B⇨🏾£55-£75 🛏
14P ✿ *xmas*
**V** ♦ ♨ ✳ Sunday Lunch £7.50 High tea £5 Dinner £13.60-£18.50alc Last dinner 9pm
Credit Cards ①②③⑤ⓔ

★★64% **Nent Hall Country House**
CA9 3LQ ☎(0434)381584

*This recently refurbished and extended hotel beside the A689 3 miles east of the town now features very well appointed bedrooms which include one with a 4-poster bed and sunken bath.*
10rm(9⇨)(1fb)1🏾 CTV in 9 bedrooms ⓡ **T** sB&B£36-£46 sB&B⇨🏾£36-£46 dB&B£50-£60 dB&B⇨🏾£50-£60 🛏
CTV 48P ✿ CFA ⚊ *xmas*
**V** ♦ ♨ S% Sunday Lunch £7-£9 High tea £1.50-£7alc Dinner £13.50-£15 Last dinner 8.30pm
Credit Cards ①②③ⓔ

★63% *Hillcrest*
Townfoot CA9 3RN ☎(0434)381251 & 381444

*This friendly hotel is situated on the A680, as it aproaches the town from the west, and looks out over the south Tyne and the hills beyond. Some bedrooms are basic but improvements are underway. Present owners Jane and Martin Stephenson have improved the public rooms which now include a coffee shop as well as a comfortable lounge and lounge bar.*
11rm(2fb) ✈ (ex guide dogs)
CTV 16P 3🛏 ✿ ♨
**V** ♦ ♨ ✂ Last dinner 9pm
Credit Cards ①③

---

**ALTARNUN** Cornwall & Isles of Scilly Map **02** SX28

★★69% *Penhallow Manor Country House*
PL15 7SJ ☎Pipers Pool(0566)86206

*The former vicarage of this pretty village on the edge of Bodmin Moor stands adjacent to the historic church, still retaining its own gate to the churchyard. Featured by Daphne du Maurier in Jamaica Inn as the house of the Vicar of Altarnun, the elegant Georgian-style listed property has since 1975 been run as a country*

*house hotel. It now offers 7 tastefully decorated and well equipped bedrooms featuring some individual styles and colour schemes; comfortable lounges and bar invite relaxation in a warm, welcoming, atmosphere and an intimate dining room provides table d'hôte and à la carte menus.*
7⇨🏾 CTV in all bedrooms ⓡ **T**
10P 🚗 ✿ nc8yrs
**V** ♦ ♨ Last dinner 9.30pm
Credit Cards ①③

---

**ALTHORPE** Humberside Map **08** SE81

See also Scunthorpe
★★64% *Lansdowne House*
Main St DN17 3HJ ☎Scunthorpe(0724)783369

*A very well maintained Victorian house set in 2 acres of attractive gardens. Bedrooms and public rooms are spacious with many original fireplaces. The cocktail bar, also serving as a lounge, has a cheerful open fire. There is a pretty restaurant and this can be extended for wedding parties and other functions.*
7⇨🏾 Annexe3⇨🏾(5fb) CTV in all bedrooms ⓡ **T**
✈ (ex guide dogs)
CTV 40P ✿
♥ English & French **V** ♦ ♨ Last dinner 10pm
Credit Cards ①②③⑤

---

**ALTON** Hampshire Map **04** SU73

★★★62% *Swan*
High St GU34 1AT (Forte Hotels) ☎(0420)83777
Telex no 859916 FAX (0420) 87975

*A town centre hotel with good car parking at the rear, this former coaching inn has been refurbished to a good standard while its original character has been retained. There is a spacious lounge with co-ordinated furnishings, and the bedrooms are currently* →

★★ 75%

**NENTHEAD ROAD, NEAR ALSTON, CUMBRIA CA9 3LF**
**Tel: Alston (0434) 381203 Fax: (0434) 381515**

Comfortable Georgian style house nestling in own grounds in a secluded wooded valley. Good walking country all around, central for lakes, dales and lowlands.

12 well furnished and equipped bedrooms all with en suite facilities, most have superb views.

Widely acclaimed cuisine, only fresh food being used. Many good wines available. The comfort and satisfaction of guests is our prime consideration and the number of them who return again is our main recommendation.

**Write or telephone for brochure**
*Egon Ronay, Johansen, Ashley Courtenay recommended*

**A**

*being upgraded. Refurbishment in the attractive restaurant and cocktail bar is complete. Conference and meeting rooms are available.*

38⇄🛏(2fb)1🛏⚊in 15 bedrooms CTV in all bedrooms Ⓡ T ✶ S5% sB⇄🛏£45-£65 dB⇄🛏£55-£85 (room only) 🗦
《 70P *xmas*

V ✿ ♨ ⚊ S5% Lunch £8.95-£10.95&alc High tea £4.50-£12.50 Dinner £13.95-£15&alc Last dinner 9.30pm
Credit Cards ① ② ③ ④ ⑤

★★★61% **Alton House**
Normandy St GU34 1DW ☎(0420)80033 FAX (0420) 89222
*On the eastern side of town with good car parking, Alton House offers a range of facilities, a pool and tennis courts for the use of residents and club members, a full sized billiard table in the Old Town Bar, and various sizes of conference rooms. Bedrooms are comfortable and well furnished, including 13 rooms in a new wing approached through the Fountain Lounge. The O'Connors restaurant serves a short table d'hôte menu which offers excellent value for money, and the innovative à la carte menu is extensive.*
38⇄🛏(2fb)1🛏 CTV in all bedrooms Ⓡ T ✶ sB&B⇄🛏£38-£50 dB&B⇄🛏£48-£60 🗦
《 80P 6🚗 ❈ CFA ⚊ (heated) 🎿 (hard) snooker
♥ English & Continental V ✿ ♨ ⚊ Lunch £8.50-£12.50alc Dinner fr£11.25&alc Last dinner 9.45pm
Credit Cards ① ② ③ ⑤

★★64% *Grange*
17 London Rd, Holybourne GU34 4EG ☎(0420)86565
FAX (0420) 541346
Closed Xmas-30 Dec
*Twenty new, well co-ordinated bedrooms have been added to a personally run hotel with attractive rear gardens and good car parking which stands on the eastern outskirts of the town. The no-smoking restaurant serves soundly cooked meals from both table d'hôte and à la carte menus, and a friendly atmosphere encourages relaxation.*
27rm(23⇄🛏)Annexe6⇄🛏(2fb)1🛏⚊in 2 bedrooms CTV in all bedrooms Ⓡ T
CTV 48P 🚗 ❈ ⚊ (heated) croquet putting nc3yrs
♥ English & French V ✿ ♨ ⚊ Last dinner 9pm
Credit Cards ① ② ③ ⑤

---

ALTON Staffordshire Map **07** SK04

★★61% **Bull's Head Inn**
High St ST10 4AQ ☎Oakamoor(0538)702307
*Residents happily mingle with the locals in the cheerful bar of this friendly inn, located in the heart of the village. Prior booking is essential during the school holidays due to the close proximity of Alton Towers leisure park.*
6rm(5🛏) CTV in all bedrooms Ⓡ ✶ sB&B£25-£35 sB&B🛏£25-£35 dB&B£30-£50 dB&B🛏£30-£50
CTV 15P 🚗
V ✿ Lunch £6-£11.25alc Dinner £6-£11.25alc Last dinner 9.15pm
Credit Cards ① ③

---

ALTRINCHAM Greater Manchester Map **07** SJ78

★★★66% **Bowdon**
Langham Rd, Bowdon WA14 2HT ☎061-928 7121
Telex no 668208 FAX 061-927 7560
RS 25 Dec
*Conveniently situated for the motorway network, this extended Victorian building has been refurbished to a high standard and offers comfortable, well equipped modern accommodation, with lounge areas, bars and conference facilities. Smartly dressed staff provide efficient service.*
82⇄🛏(1fb) CTV in all bedrooms Ⓡ T sB&B⇄🛏£33-£58 dB&B⇄🛏£49-£76 🗦
《 168P CFA ♫

♥ English & French V ✿ ♨ ⚊ Sunday Lunch £7.95 Dinner £12.95&alc Last dinner 10pm
Credit Cards ① ② ③ ⑤

★★★66% *Woodland Park*
Wellington Rd, Timperley WA15 7RG (Inter-Hotels)
☎061-928 8631 Telex no 635091 FAX 061-941 2821
*Family-owned and particularly friendly, this hotel is set in a quiet residential area between A560 and A56 at Timperely. Continual improvements are resulting in some very pleasant bedrooms with smart modern bathrooms, and public areas have been enhanced by the addition of a striking conservatory lounge.*
44⇄🛏(6fb)5🛏 CTV in all bedrooms Ⓡ T ✖ (ex guide dogs)
《 150P 1🚗 (charged)
♥ International V ✿ ♨ Last dinner 9.45pm
Credit Cards ① ② ③ ⑤
See advertisement under MANCHESTER AIRPORT

★★★65% **Cresta Court**
Church St WA14 4DP ☎061-927 7272 Telex no 667242
FAX 061-926 9194
*This well managed hotel has been refurbished and now offers well equipped bedrooms and a choice of two air-conditioned restaurants and three bars. It also has extensive conference and function facilities.*
139⇄🛏(5fb) CTV in all bedrooms Ⓡ T sB&B⇄🛏£32.50-£59.50 dB&B⇄🛏£50.50-£72 🗦
Lift 《 200P CFA
♥ English & French V ✿ ♨ ✶ Lunch £5.75-£10.50 Dinner £5.75-£12.50 Last dinner 11pm
Credit Cards ① ② ③ ⑤ ⓔ

★★★61% **The Swan**
WA16 6RD (De Vere) ☎Bucklow Hill(0565)830295
FAX (0565) 830614
(For full entry see Bucklow Hill)

★★★58% **Ashley**
Ashley Rd, Hale WA15 9SF (De Vere) ☎061-928 3794
FAX 061-926 9046
Closed 26 Dec RS 27-31 Dec
*Near the railway station on the south side of Hale village centre, this popular commercial hotel with friendly hospitable staff is part of a modern shopping complex, with public rooms on the first floor and bedrooms with modern facilities on two floors above them.*
47⇄🛏 CTV in all bedrooms Ⓡ T S% sB&B⇄🛏£60-£70 dB&B⇄🛏£65-£75 🗦
Lift 《 100P CFA bowling green
♥ English & French V ✿ ♨ ✶ Lunch £7.50-£10&alc Dinner fr£12&alc Last dinner 9.45pm
Credit Cards ① ② ③ ⑤ ⓔ

★★58% **Grove Park**
Park Rd, Bowdon WA14 3JE ☎061-928 6191
*A friendly informally run hotel beside the A5162, convenient for both the airport and the M56. Bedrooms have recently been redecorated to a good standard and the pleasant restaurants remain popular both at lunch and dinner. The two bar areas provide limited lounge facilities.*
14⇄🛏 CTV in all bedrooms Ⓡ T ✖ ✶ sB&B⇄🛏£15-£39 dB&B⇄🛏£20-£48 🗦
《 CTV 28P
♥ International V ✿ ✶ Sunday Lunch £6.95&alc Dinner £9.95-£12&alc Last dinner 11.30pm
Credit Cards ① ③ ⓔ

★63% **The Unicorn**
Hale Rd, Halebarns WA15 8SS ☎061-980 4347
*This pleasant public house is in the centre of Hale Barns, on the A538, less than a mile west of the M56. It is about 2.5 miles south east of Altrincham, and convenient for Manchester Airport. There are 5 nicely appointed bedrooms, all with modern en suite bath or*

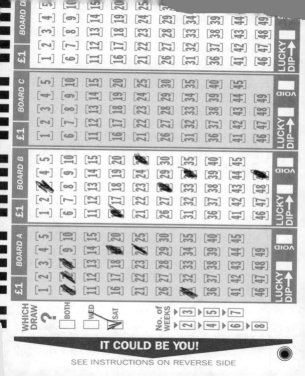

...nber prize...

...y 5 or 4 numbers from the first 6 main numbers drawn in any order, you win the Match 5 or Match 4 prize respectively.
- matches any 3 numbers from the first 6 main numbers drawn, you win the Match 3 prize.

## ALLOCATION OF PRIZE MONEY

- The game promoter determines a prize structure, the text of which may be obtained from The National Lottery and at points of sale, and allocates for that purpose a sum not less than 45% of all amounts played for each draw. The amount of each prize as a result of a draw is calculated in accordance with the prize structure then in force.

## HOW TO CLAIM YOUR PRIZE

- Prizes must be claimed within 180 days after the relevant draw date on the ticket.
- Prizes must be claimed in the manner stated on the back of the ticket.

## THE NATIONAL LOTTERY GAME RULES

- The Rules and Procedures of The National Lottery game, as amended from time to time, govern this game and the sale of the ticket to you. Prize winnings and all aspects of the game are subject to these Rules and Procedures. You may inspect a copy at every National Lottery Game retailer, or obtain a copy by telephoning the National Lottery Line on 0645 100000.
- The ticket issued is the only valid proof of your number selection and is the only valid receipt for claiming a prize. **THE PLAYSLIP IS NOT A VALID RECEIPT.**
- The promoter accepts no responsibility for tickets cancelled in error or for the entries on the face of the ticket differing from the central computer entries.
- Tickets shall not be sold to nor prizes claimed by, persons under the age of 16.
- **The National Lottery game is run and promoted by Camelot Group plc under licences granted by the Director General of The National Lottery.**

**stralfors** 7M04983F

*shower facilities. On the ground floor is an attractive Victorian style open plan lounge bar and adjoining dining area.*

5➪🛏 CTV in all bedrooms ® 🛏 (ex guide dogs) ✳
sB&B➪🛏£20-£35 dB&B➪🛏£30-£50
25P 🚗
V ⚘ ✳ Lunch £4-£7.10 Dinner £8-£12 Last dinner 8.45pm
Credit Cards ①

---

★58% *Greystone*
305 Manchester Rd, West Timperley WA14 5PH ☎061-905 2233
*A former private residence situated beside the A56 has been converted into a small hotel offering pleasant, well equipped modern bedrooms, a fairly limited range of catering and a friendly relaxed atmosphere.*
12🛏 CTV in all bedrooms ® T
⟨ CTV 12P 🚗 sauna
V ⚘ ⬚ Last dinner 10.30pm
Credit Cards ① ② ③

---

ALVESTON Avon Map 03 ST68

★★★72% *Alveston House*
BS12 2LJ ☎Thornbury(0454)415050 Telex no 449212
FAX (0454) 415425
*Situated on the A38, between junctions 14 and 16 of the M5 and convenient for access to the M4, a well maintained hotel which is equally suitable for tourists or businessmen – including delegates using the conference facilities – complements fully equipped modern accommodation by friendly and attentive service.*
30➪🛏(1fb) CTV in all bedrooms ® T sB&B➪🛏£68.50-£74.50 dB&B➪🛏£79.50-£89.50 🛏
CTV 75P ✳
🍴 English & French V ⚘ ⬚ Lunch £10.75-£15&alc Dinner £14.25-£16&alc Last dinner 9.30pm
Credit Cards ① ② ③ ⑤ ⓔ

**See advertisement under BRISTOL**

★★★★61% *Forte Posthouse*
Thornbury Rd BS12 2LL (Forte Hotels)
☎Thornbury(0454)412521 Telex no 444753
FAX (0454) 413920
*An extension to the original Ship Inn, the hotel combines character with modern facilities for the businessman. Bedrooms vary in style but are all well equipped and comparable in quality, while a wide range of efficient services includes a range of eating options which ensures that guests can obtain a meal at any time of day.*
75➪🛏(13fb)⚋in 23 bedrooms CTV in all bedrooms ® T ✳
S% dB➪🛏£49.50 (room only) 🛏
⟨ 150P ✳ CFA ⬚ (heated) mini golf pitch & putt ♫ *xmas*
V ⚘ ⬚ ⚋ ✳ Lunch £9.50-£10.50 Dinner fr£13.95&alc Last dinner 10.30pm
Credit Cards ① ② ③ ④ ⑤

---

ALWALTON Cambridgeshire Map 04 TL19

★★★★62% *Swallow*
Lynchwood PE2 0GB (Swallow) ☎Peterborough(0733)371111
Telex no 32422 FAX (0733) 236725
*A modern purpose-built hotel with an extensive range of facilities aimed at the commercial user. There is a choice of restaurants, a leisure centre and conference facilities offering the latest equipment. Bedrooms are mostly spacious and the staff efficient and friendly.*
163➪🛏(10fb)⚋in 89 bedrooms CTV in all bedrooms ® T ✳
sB&B➪🛏fr£83 dB&B➪🛏fr£99 🛏
⟨ CTV 200P ✳ CFA 🏊 (heated) sauna solarium gymnasium steam room spa bath beauty therapist ♫ *xmas*
🍴 English & French V ⚘ ⬚ ⚋ ✳ Lunch £11.75-£13.80&alc Dinner £14.30-£17.90&alc Last dinner 10.30pm
Credit Cards ① ② ③ ④ ⑤ ⓔ

**See advertisement under PETERBOROUGH**

---

⌂**Forte Travelodge**
Great North Rd PE7 3UR (on A1, southbound) (Forte)
☎Peterborough(0733)231109 Central Res (0800) 850950
*Still popular with a loyal clientele despite obvious signs of wear and tear to its well equipped bedrooms, this lodge with adjacent Little Chef stands on the southbound carriageway of the A1 southwest of Peterborough.*
32➪🛏(32fb) CTV in all bedrooms ® sB➪🛏£29.95
dB➪🛏£29.95 (room only)
32P 🚗
Credit Cards ① ② ③

---

ALYTH Tayside *Perthshire* Map 15 NO24

★★🎗62% *Lands of Loyal*
Loyal Rd PH11 8JQ ☎(08283)3151
*Considerable improvements are taking place at this lovely Victorian mansion house, set in 9 acres of well tended grounds. The panelled hall with domed ceiling and marble fireplace invites relaxation and there is a cosy bar and refurbished restaurant serving imaginative food. Bedrooms vary in size and are quite modest, though improvements are planned.*
11➪🛏(2fb) 🖥 CTV in 3 bedrooms ® T
CTV 20P 6🚗 🚗 ❄ snooker shooting
🍴 Scottish & Continental V ⚘ ⬚ Last dinner 10pm
Credit Cards ① ② ③

---

AMBERLEY Gloucestershire Map 03 SO80

★★67% *Amberley Inn*
GL5 5AF (Best Western) ☎(0453)872565 Telex no 94012242
FAX (0453) 812738
*This large stone-built inn was constructed at the turn of the century but its style is of a much earlier period. From its elevated position in the village it offers good views of Minchinhampton Common and the Woodchester Valley. Public rooms are full of charm and* →

character enhanced by period furnishings and log fires. The well equipped bedrooms include 4 in a cottage annexe to the rear of the hotel.

10rm(9⇨) Annexe4⇨(1fb) CTV in all bedrooms ® T
30P ⇔ ❀
♦ Last dinner 9.30pm
Credit Cards ① ② ③

---

**AMBERLEY** West Sussex Map **04** TQ01

### ★★★ ❀❀❀♨♨ 77% **Amberley Castle**
BN18 9ND (Small Luxury Hotels) ☎Bury(0798)831992 FAX (0798) 831998

This ancient castle, half ruin half discreetly restored, lies in a fold of the Downs. Resident owners Martin and Joy Cummings have created a most comfortable, civilised and friendly hotel. Within the walls are neatly planted grounds and in the castle are 3 delightful lounges, all in a different mood. The decoration is not all historic, but there are suits of armour, halberds, panelled walls and roaring fires. The bedrooms are in various staircases; they vary in size and splendour with 4-poster and canopied beds, attractive furniture and excellent modern bathrooms – all with jacuzzis and fine showers. This is a unique setting and it is in dedicated hands. The largest public room is the first floor dining room, with vaulted ceilings and a celebrated mural of Charles II and his wife. Dinner guests can take aperitifs in one of 2 lounges or in the garden in summer. Chef Boschetti prepares imaginative menus in the modern vein, with dishes such as lobster and filo pastry with a truffle and sesame seed vinaigrette; chicken and mushroom timbale with leeks, quails eggs and red wine; turbot with brioche and almond crumbs, orange and chives; lamb with sweetbreads and bayleaf. The imagination of the kitchen sometimes confuses the presentation and the palate, but meat dishes enjoy sound saucing. Service is amiable; but for the prices charged a little fine tuning is needed.

12⇨ 2⇨ CTV in all bedrooms T ✳ sB⇨↑£100-£175
dB⇨↑£130-£225 (room only) ☴
50P ⇔ ❀ ♪ (grass) xmas
♀ French V ♦ ♌ ✳ Lunch £17.50-£25.50 Dinner £23.50-£37 Last dinner 10.30pm
Credit Cards ① ② ③ ⑤ ⓔ

---

**AMBLESIDE** Cumbria Map **07** NY30

See also **Elterwater**

### ★★★ ❀ 73% **Rothay Manor**
Rothay Bridge LA22 0EH ☎(05394)33605 FAX (05394) 33607 Closed 2 Jan-6 Feb

An elegant, Regency-style house set in its own well tended lawns and gardens, just outside Ambleside, on the Coniston road. Family run, comfortable and relaxing, service is unobtrusive, and there are many nice touches in bedrooms, such as iced water, fruit and small floral arrangements. Fresh flowers are also displayed throughout the hotel. Dinner is a much acclaimed and imaginative five-course meal. Although set, the menu offers an adequate choice of dishes for each course. Afternoon tea is also highly recommended, taken in the lounge, or on the lawns in summer. A charming hotel in every respect.

15⇨ Annexe3⇨(6fb) CTV in all bedrooms ® T
✈ (ex guide dogs) sB&B⇨£63-£70 dB&B⇨£98-£110 ☴
30P ⇔ ❀ xmas
♀ English & Continental V ♦ ♌ ⅀ Sunday Lunch £13.20 High tea £3-£6 Last high tea 7pm
Credit Cards ① ② ③ ⑤

### ★★★ 61% **Regent**
Waterhead Bay LA22 0ES (1m S A591) ☎(05394)32254

An attractive courtyard and a small indoor swimming pool are features of this hotel, which is situated close to Waterhead Bay and the steamer pier. Accommodation is cosy and comfortable and dinner in the restaurant is the highlight of the evening.

21⇨(2fb)3⊞ CTV in all bedrooms ® T ✳ sB&B⇨↑£45-£60 dB&B⇨↑£80-£100 ☴

---

30P ⇔ ☐ (heated) xmas
♀ English & French V ♦ ♌ ⅀ ✳ Bar Lunch £3-£10alc High tea £1.95-£6alc Dinner £16.95-£20 Last dinner 8.30pm
Credit Cards ① ③ ⓔ

### ★★★ 60% **The Salutation**
Lake Rd LA22 9BX ☎(05394)32244 FAX (05394) 34157
29⇨↑(5fb) CTV in all bedrooms ® T sB&B⇨↑£34-£47 dB&B⇨↑£68-£94 (incl dinner)
41P CFA xmas
♀ English & French V ♦ ♌ ⅀ Bar Lunch £3-£10.50 Dinner £13.50-£15.50 Last dinner 9pm
Credit Cards ① ③

### ★★★ 54% *Waterhead*
Lake Rd LA22 0ER (Best Western) ☎(05394)32566 Telex no 65273 FAX (05394) 34157

Attractively located overlooking Lake Windermere at the southern end of the town, this friendly hotel has plans to improve its mainly small bedrooms with compact en suite facilities. Larger more comfortable rooms include some of high standard.

27⇨↑(6fb) CTV in all bedrooms ® T
50P ❀
♀ English & French V ♦ ♌ ⅀ Last dinner 8.30pm
Credit Cards ① ② ③ ⑤

### ★★ ❀ 76% *Wateredge*
Borrans Rd, Waterhead LA22 0EP ☎(05394)32332
Closed mid Dec-early Feb
(Rosette awarded for dinner only)

This delightful hotel with gardens leading down to the shore of Lake Windermere has been skilfully extended from two 17th-century fishermen's cottages. Comfortable lounges with open fires give lovely views, all bedrooms have private facilities and dinner in the oak-beamed dining room is a special occasion with 6-courses of creatively prepared mainly English fare served by friendly staff.

18⇨ Annexe5⇨↑(1fb) CTV in all bedrooms ® T ✳ sB&B⇨↑£53-£65 dB&B⇨↑£96-£140 (incl dinner) ☴
CTV 25P ⇔ ❀ rowing boat nc7yrs
♦ ♌ ⅀ Bar Lunch £6.50-£12alc Dinner £21.50-£23.50 Last dinner 8.30pm
Credit Cards ① ② ③

### ★★♨ 72% *Nanny Brow Country House*
Clappersgate LA22 9NF ☎(05394)32036 Telex no 265871

A delightful and relaxing country house hotel set in 5 acres of beautiful gardens and woodland enjoys an elevated position above the A593 one mile west of Ambleside. Built in 1908 as a family home, it retains many original features, and a recently added garden wing was designed so as not to detract from its charm and character. Many of the attractive and comfortable en suite bedrooms offer fine views towards Langdale Pikes, log fires in the drawing room are welcoming on cooler days and dinner in the attractive dining room is something of an occasion.

19rm(16⇨1↑)(3fb)4⊞ CTV in all bedrooms ® T
20P ⇔ ❀ ♪ solarium croquet spa bath
♀ English & French V ♦ ♌ ⅀ Last dinner 9pm
Credit Cards ① ② ③

### ★★ 72% **Skelwith Bridge**
Skelwith Bridge LA22 9NJ (2.5m W A593) ☎(05394)32115 FAX (05394) 34254

Recent extension and modernisation have enhanced this hotel without spoiling its character, oak-beamed ceilings and traditional hospitality still being very much in evidence despite the addition of 5 bedrooms, a residents' bar and spacious public bar; set in congenial surroundings on the A592 2.5 miles west of Ambleside, it is popular for its fine ales and wholesome meals.

23⇨↑ Annexe6⇨↑(3fb)2⊞ ⅄in 6 bedrooms CTV in all bedrooms ® T sB&B⇨↑£30-£40 dB&B⇨↑£58-£75 ☴
60P ⇔ CFA ♪

→

♀ English & French **V** ✿ ⚲ ⅄ Sunday Lunch £8.45-£9.25
Dinner £16.35-£17.50 Last dinner 9pm
Credit Cards 1 3 £

---

★★70% **Kirkstone Foot Country House**
Kirkstone Pass Rd LA22 9EH ☎(05394)32232
FAX (05394) 31110
Closed 8-22 Dec & 3 Jan-early Feb

*A charming 17th-century manor house with well appointed
bedrooms, comfortable lounges and an attractive dining room.
Within easy walking distance of the town centre, it is situated in
secluded grounds just off the Kirkstone pass road. Loyal guests
return year after year to enjoy the renowned hospitality and good
food.*

15⇌♠(2fb) CTV in all bedrooms ® **T** ✖ sB&B⇌♠£37.50-
£49.50 dB&B⇌♠£75-£99 (incl dinner) 閂
35P 邙 ✿ *xmas*
**V** ✿ ⚲ ⅄ ✖ High tea £5 Dinner £17.50-£18.25 Last dinner
8.30pm
Credit Cards 1 2 3 5 £

---

★★69% **Fisherbeck**
Lake Rd LA22 0DH ☎(05394)33215
Closed 25 Dec-13 Jan

*Comfortable, tastefully furnished and decorated, and very well
maintained, the hotel is run under the personal supervision of the
resident proprietors. Bedrooms are particularly well equipped, and
most have en suite facilities. There is a comfortable lounge with
views over the fells, and meals are available in the attractive
restaurant or in the Tannery Bar. The Fisherbeck is situated on
the A591 as it approaches the town from the south.*

20rm(17⇌♠)(3fb) CTV in all bedrooms ® **T** ✖ sB&B£32-
£41.50 sB&B⇌♠£42.70-£53.50 dB&B£55-£76 dB&B⇌♠£64-
£85 閂
CTV 24P 邙
**V** ✿ ⚲ Bar Lunch £4-£10alc Dinner £15.50-£16.95alc Last
dinner 8pm
Credit Cards 1 3

---

★★69% **Riverside**
Under Loughrigg, Rothay Bridge LA22 9LJ ☎(05394)32395
Closed Dec-Jan

*Standing amid its own well tended gardens in a country lane, and
looking across the River Rothay to Loughrigg Fell, the hotel offers
attractive, comfortable public rooms – its peaceful setting and
relaxing ambience belying the fact that the town is only ten
minutes' walk away.*

10⇌♠(2fb)1珝 CTV in all bedrooms ® **T** ✖ (ex guide dogs)
✶ dB&B⇌♠£72-£86 (incl dinner) 閂
CTV 20P 邙 ✿ ♩ nc8yrs
♀ Continental **V** ✿ ⚲ ⅄ Bar Lunch £5-£6 Dinner £18&alc
Last dinner 8pm
Credit Cards 1 3

---

★★❀68% **Borrans Park**
Borrans Rd LA22 0EN ☎(05394)33454
Closed 21-31 Dec

*This fine Georgian house is set in its own landscaped gardens on
the southern outskirts of the town. It has been extended to provide
comfortable public rooms and some very attractive bedrooms. A 4-
course dinner is served at about 7pm and breakfasts, too, are
enjoyable. The hotel offers good value for money and pleasantly
relaxed service.*

12⇌♠(1fb)7珝 CTV in all bedrooms ® **T** ✖ sB&B⇌♠£30-
£60 dB&B⇌♠£60-£72 閂
20P 邙 ✿ nc7yrs
**V** ⅄ Dinner £14 Last dinner 7pm
Credit Cards 1 3

---

For key to symbols in English see the bookmark.

★★⚏66% **Crow How**
Rydal Rd LA22 9PN ☎(05394)32193
Closed 2 Dec-Jan RS 2 Nov-1 Dec & Feb-9 Apr

*Beautifully located in attractive gardens three-quarters of a mile
north of Ambleside, the hotel provides comfortable, well decorated
bedrooms, a relaxing lounge and a cosy bar.*

9rm(7⇌1♠)(2fb) CTV in all bedrooms ® sB&B£22.50-£23.50
sB&B⇌♠£49-£51 dB&B£45-£47 dB&B⇌♠£54-£56 閂
9P 邙 ✿
♀ English & French **V** ✿ Dinner £11 Last dinner 7.30pm
£

---

★★63% **Elder Grove**
Lake Rd LA22 0DB (on A591 .5m S) ☎(05394)32504
Closed Nov-mid Feb

*This friendly and relaxing small hotel just south of the town centre
offers pleasant en suite bedrooms, 2 very comfortable lounges and a
cosy bar.*

12⇌♠(1fb)1珝 CTV in all bedrooms ® sB&B⇌♠fr£25
dB&B⇌♠fr£50 閂
CTV 12P 邙
**V** ✿ ⚲ ⅄ Bar Lunch £2-£5 Dinner £13.50&alc Last dinner
8.15pm
Credit Cards 1 3

---

★★60% **Glen Rothay**
Rydal LA22 9LR ☎(05394)32524 FAX (05394) 31079

*A quaint, historical hotel, close to the road yet set back in the
rockside and surrounded by its own gardens. Bedrooms vary
considerably in size.*

11⇌♠(2fb)4珝 CTV in all bedrooms ® **T** sB&B⇌♠£32-£37
dB&B⇌♠£64-£130 閂
35P 邙 ✿ ♩ *xmas*

→

V ✿ ⅀ Bar Lunch £6.70-£14.50 Dinner £17.50-£18.95 Last
dinner 8pm
Credit Cards ①②③ ⓔ

### ★★59% Horseshoe
Rothay Rd LA22 0EE ☎(05394)32000
*Recent upgrading of the older bedrooms and provision of more en
suite facilities has enhanced an hotel which enjoys views of the
surrounding fells and mountains from its convenient setting near
the town centre. Car parking facilities are available.*
19⇔🛏(5fb)1🎬 CTV in all bedrooms ® S%
sB&B⇔🛏fr£29.75 dB&B⇔🛏fr£54 🍴
CTV 19P 🎄 *xmas*
♀ Continental V ✿ ⅁ ⅀ S% High tea fr£3.50 Dinner fr£10.75
Last dinner 9pm
Credit Cards ①②③ ⓔ

## AMERSHAM Buckinghamshire Map 04 SU99

### ★★62% The Crown
High St HP7 0DH (Forte Hotels) ☎(0494)721541
FAX (0494) 431283
*A character inn with exposed beams and an original Jacobean
mural, set around a cobbled courtyard in the centre of the town.
Most of the bedrooms have been recently refurbished and all
provide good facilities for both business and holiday visitors. The
attractive lounge and bar are popular with locals, and the intimate
restaurant, overlooking the courtyard and garden, offers a choice
of menus.*
23rm(13⇔1🛏) CTV in all bedrooms ® T ✳ S% sB⇔🛏£75
dB⇔🛏£90 (room only) 🍴
51P CFA *xmas*
V ✿ ⅁ ⅀ ✳ S% Lunch £9.75 Dinner £14.95&alc Last dinner
9.30pm
Credit Cards ①②③⑤

## AMESBURY Wiltshire Map 04 SU14

### ⌂Forte Travelodge
SP4 7AS (junc A345 & A303 eastbound) (Forte)
☎(0980)624966 Central Res (0800) 850950
*On the A303 between Stonehenge and Salisbury, this well
managed motorists' lodge adjacent to a Little Chef restaurant
provides functional good value accommodation, with clean mostly
spacious bedrooms with modern facilities.*
32⇔🛏(32fb) CTV in all bedrooms ® sB⇔🛏£29.95
dB⇔🛏£29.95 (room only)
☾32P 🎄

Credit Cards ①②③

## AMLWCH Gwynedd Map 06 SH49

### ★★59% Trecastell
Bull Bay LL68 9SA (Frederic Robinson) ☎(0407)830651
FAX (0407) 832114
*Overlooking the bay, this privately run detached hotel provides
simple but sound accommodation with several bedrooms giving sea
views.*
12rm(8⇔3🛏)(3fb) CTV in 10 bedrooms ® T ✳ sB&B⇔🛏£25
dB&B⇔🛏£40 🍴
CTV 60P 🎄 ❊
✿ Bar Lunch £1.25-£6 Dinner £9-£12&alc Last dinner 8.30pm
Credit Cards ①②③

## AMMANFORD Dyfed Map 02 SN61

### ★★67% Mill at Glynhir
Glyn-Hir, Llandybie SA18 2TE (3m NE off A483) (Exec Hotel)
☎(0269)850672
RS 24 Dec-4 Jan
*At least 250 years old, this old flour mill, 3 miles from Ammanford,
has an attractive split-level format with lovely gardens and*

*terraces. The well equipped bedrooms are all en suite and most
have spa baths. There is a cosy lounge with dispenser bar, and an
indoor swimming pool. Free golfing is provided for residents on the
adjacent course, and trout fishing is also available.*
9⇔Annexe2⇔🛏 CTV in all bedrooms ® T sB&B⇔🛏£31
dB&B⇔🛏£62 🍴
20P 🎄 ❊ ▣ (heated) ► 18 ✦ nc11yrs
♀ Welsh & French V ✿ ✳ Dinner £13.50 Last dinner 8.30pm
Credit Cards ①③

## AMPFIELD Hampshire Map 04 SU32

### ★★★64% Potters Heron
SO51 9ZF (Lansbury) ☎Southampton(0703)266611
Telex no 47459 FAX (0703) 251359
*At first sight an attractive thatched period property, this hotel in
fact incorporates a large block of comfortable and well equipped
modern bedrooms at its rear. 'The Pub at the Potters' – popular
locally – offers value-for-money meals as an alternative to the table
d'hôte and à la carte menus served in the more formal atmosphere
of the Garden Restaurant with its cocktail bar. Limited leisure
amenities include snooker, sauna and trimnasium; secretarial
facilities are available, and wedding receptions are well catered
for.*
60⇔(3fb)1🎬⅀in 12 bedrooms CTV in all bedrooms ® ✖
sB&B⇔🛏fr£83 dB&B⇔🛏fr£96 🍴
Lift ☾200P sauna gymnasium *xmas*
♀ English & French V ✿ ⅁ ✳ Lunch fr£12&alc Dinner
fr£12&alc Last dinner 10pm
Credit Cards ①②③⑤

## ANDOVER Hampshire Map 04 SU34

### ★★★63% Ashley Court
Micheldever Rd SP11 6LA ☎(0264)357344 FAX (0264) 356755
*This quietly located business/conference hotel provides well
equipped bedrooms, most of them built in 1989, and conference
rooms of various sizes, with equipment supplied if needed. The
Rendez-vous Restaurant has a fairly extensive à la carte lunch and
dinner menu, served by smartly uniformed, friendly young staff,
with bar meals also available at lunchtime.*
9⇔🛏Annexe26⇔🛏⅀in 7 bedrooms CTV in all bedrooms ®
T sB&B⇔🛏£66-£72 dB&B⇔🛏£86-£92 Continental breakfast
🍴
☾ CTV 120P CFA snooker gymnasium croquet petanque *xmas*
♀ English & Continental V ✿ ⅁ Sunday Lunch £8-£15&alc
Dinner £10-£15&alc Last dinner 9.30pm
Credit Cards ①②③ ⓔ

### ★★54% Danebury
High St SP10 1NX (Lansbury) ☎(0264)323332 Telex no 47587
FAX (0264) 334021
*Parts of this commercial hotel in the centre of town date back to
the sixteenth century, but its comfortable bedrooms provide all the
modern facilities expected by today's business user. A varied à la
carte menu is available in the informal dining room, and public
bars are popular with local trade.*
24⇔🛏1🎬 CTV in all bedrooms ® T ✖ (ex guide dogs)
☾40P CFA
♀ European V ✿ ⅁ Last dinner 10.30pm
Credit Cards ①②③⑤

## ANGLESEY, ISLE OF

See Amlwch, Beaumaris, Benllech Bay, Llanfair P.G.,
Llangefni, Menai Bridge, Red Wharf Bay & Treaddur Bay.

*A rosette means exceptional standards of cuisine.*

## ANNAN Dumfries & Galloway *Dumfriesshire* Map **11** NY16

### ★★65% **Queensberry Arms**

DG12 6AD (Consort) ☎(0461)202024 FAX (0461) 205998

*Recently refurbished, this high street hotel offers inviting lounges, modern well appointed bedrooms and a good value Steakhouse Restaurant.*

24⇔🅵🄼(3fb) CTV in all bedrooms Ⓡ T sB&B⇔🄼£32-£42 dB&B⇔🄼£42-£55 🄱

₡ 50P ❀ CFA ♫ *xmas*

🄥 Cosmopolitan V ♉ ⚅ Lunch £12.75alc Dinner £12.75alc Last dinner 9.30pm

Credit Cards ①②③⑤

### ★★65% **Warmanbie Hotel & Restaurant**

DG12 5LL ☎(0461)204015

*A modernised country house on the outskirts of town which is informally run. Bedrooms are well appointed and reflect some thoughtful touches; some of the bedrooms are spacious and traditionally furnished, while others are more compact and modern in style. With its own stretch of water, this compact Georgian house is very popular with fishermen.*

7⇔🄼(1fb)📺 CTV in all bedrooms Ⓡ T ✱ sB&B⇔🄼£42.50-£47 dB&B⇔🄼£59-£67 🄱

25P 1❀ ❀ ♪ clay pigeon shooting *xmas*

V ♉ ⚅ ✱ Sunday Lunch fr£7.45alc Dinner fr£6.75alc Last dinner 9.30pm

Credit Cards ①②③

## ANSTRUTHER Fife Map **12** NO50

### ★★★60% **Craws Nest**

Bankwell Rd KY10 3DA ☎(0333)310691 FAX (0333) 312216

*A traditional tourist hotel managed by friendly owners. Bedrooms are generally compact though neat and well appointed.*

31⇔🄼Annexe19⇔🄼(4fb)📺 CTV in all bedrooms Ⓡ T 🏵 (ex guide dogs) ✱ sB&B⇔🄼£33-£47 dB&B⇔🄼£56-£82 🄱

CTV 150P ❀ CFA solarium games room ♫ *xmas*

V ♉ ⚅ Lunch £6.10-£8.95&alc High tea £5.75&alc Dinner £12.50-£14&alc Last dinner 9pm

Credit Cards ①②③④⑤

### ★★62% **Smugglers Inn**

High St KY10 3DQ ☎(0333)310506

*A former inn, set in the main street but having views of the Firth of Forth to the rear, offers accommodation in bedrooms that are for the most part compact.*

8⇔🄼 CTV in all bedrooms T sB&B⇔🄼£25-£27 dB&B⇔🄼£50-£54

CTV 12P

🄥 Scottish, French & Italian V ♉

Credit Cards ①②③⑤

### ❀❀ ✕✕*Cellar*

24 East Green KY10 3AA ☎(0333)310378

*Tucked away through an attractive small courtyard, this characterful restaurant, with its tiled floor and exposed stone walls and beamed ceilings offers a warm welcome and superb cuisine. Chef Peter Jukes produces simple but effective dishes based largely on startlingly fresh, top-quality fish, accompanied by light sauces which never dominate. The menu is not extensive, but well balanced, accurately cooked and reliable – a delightful place to dine. A good wine list complements the menus.*

Closed Sun, 24 Dec-4 Jan & 1 wk May Lunch not served Mon 🄥 French 32 seats Last lunch 1.30pm Last dinner 9.30pm P nc5yrs ✂

Credit Cards ①②③

A rosette means exceptional standards of cuisine.

## ANSTY Warwickshire Map **04** SP38

### ★★★70% **Ansty Hall**

CV7 9HZ ☎Coventry(0203)612222 FAX (0203) 602155

*An impressive Caroline house dating from the 17th century and set on the edge of the village is only a couple of minutes' drive from the M69 and junction 2 of the M6. Accommodation is in spacious, well equipped rooms, each of which is individually decorated.*

25⇔🄼Annexe6⇔🄼✂in 8 bedrooms CTV in all bedrooms T 🏵 (ex guide dogs) ✱ sB⇔🄼fr£80 dB⇔🄼fr£100 (room only) 🄱

50P ♨ ❀ CFA *xmas*

V ♉ ⚅ ✂ ✱ S10% Lunch fr£17.50 Dinner fr£17.50 Last dinner 9.30pm

Credit Cards ①②③⑤⑥

**See advertisement under COVENTRY**

## APPIN Strathclyde *Argyllshire* Map **14** NN04

### ★★★❀ 🄿73% **Invercreran Country House**

Glen Creran PA38 4BJ ☎(063173)414 & 456 FAX (063173) 532 Closed Dec-Feb

*The Kersleys continue to be dedicated hosts at their imposing country house, built as a private residence by the previous owners in the 70s. In its own grounds, its hillside position is perfect for appreciating the grandeur of Glen Creran. The spacious lounge, with comfortable settees and a log-burning fire, has french windows leading out into a balcony. Drinks are served in the lounge as there is no bar. The small semi-circular dining room has a marble floor and a unique circular painting on the ceiling. Tony Kersley's 4-course dinners offer a small choice, but the emphasis is on providing the best quality Scottish seafood, meats and game, all cooked in the modern style. Accommodation comprises some very spacious studio-style rooms providing a high degree of comfort, and 2 attractive new bedrooms were added in 1991. The hotel lies three*

→

*quarters of a mile into Glen Creran, some 14 miles north of Connel Bridge off the A828.*

9⇄🅵(3fb)⊬in 1 bedroom CTV in all bedrooms **T**
✖ (ex guide dogs) sB&B⇄🅵£72.50-£77.50 dB&B⇄🅵£120-£140 (incl dinner) 🍴
18P 🚗 ✿ sauna nc5yrs *xmas*
V 🕙 ⚏ ⊬ Lunch £12-£25alc Dinner £27 Last dinner 8pm
Credit Cards 1 3 £

---

## APPLEBY-IN-WESTMORLAND Cumbria Map **12** NY62

### ★★★🏚✿70% **Appleby Manor Country House**
Roman Rd CA16 6JD (Best Western) ☎Appleby(07683)51571
FAX (07683) 52888
Closed 24-26 Dec

*A mid-Victorian country house built of red sandstone with more modern, though sympathetically extended extensions, set in its own grounds in an elevated position overlooking the town. This is a friendly family-run hotel with comfortable, well equipped bedrooms, delightful lounges and a small leisure centre. Food in the elegant restaurant is of a high standard, with 4 fixed price menus starting at £14.50, offering mostly British dishes from Manor House beefsteak and oyster pudding to Garden of Eden salmon. Home-made sweets are delicious and there is a selection of local cheeses.*

23⇄🅵Annexe7⇄🅵(8fb)2🛏 CTV in all bedrooms ® **T**
sB&B⇄🅵£47.25-£57 dB&B⇄🅵£72.50-£92 🍴
40P 3🚗 (£1) ✿ CFA 🏊 (heated) sauna solarium gymnasium croquet jacuzzi pool table steam room
V 🕙 ⚏ ⊬ Lunch £14.50-£16&alc Dinner £14.50-£16&alc Last dinner 9pm
Credit Cards 1 2 3 5

### ★★★67% *Tufton Arms*
Market Square CA16 6XA (Consort) ☎Appleby(07683)51593
FAX (07683) 52761

*This elegantly restored hotel is situated in the town centre. The comfortable drawing room with its open fire, the half panelled bar with interesting photographs, and the luxurious conservatory restaurant are all in a tasteful Victorian style, and a high standard of cuisine is offered from the extensive à la carte menu. Bedrooms have been individually furnished and decorated, two have their own sitting rooms, and there are also six simpler rooms, designed more for the business client.*

19⇄🅵(2fb) CTV in all bedrooms ® **T**
CTV 15P 2🚗 🚗 ✈ shooting
V 🕙 ⚏ Last dinner 9.30pm
Credit Cards 1 3

### ★★61% **Royal Oak Inn**
Bongate CA16 6UN (Exec Hotel) ☎Appleby(07683)51463
Closed 25 Dec

*An historic coaching inn in traditional style, standing beside the main street at the southern end of the town and providing accommodation in pleasant – though for the most part compact – rooms, is extremely popular for bar meals (service of which extends into the dining room). Both the busy little bars offer real ale and a characteristic atmosphere, whilst the upstairs residents' lounge offers a peaceful haven for those who prefer it.*

8rm(3⇄3🅵)(1fb) CTV in all bedrooms ® **T** sB&B£24
sB&B⇄🅵£36.50 dB&B⇄🅵£55 🍴
9P ✈ U
🍷 International V 🕙 ✿ Lunch £9.75-£16.75alc Dinner £9.75-£16.75alc Last dinner 9pm
Credit Cards 1 2 3

### ★★59% **White Hart**
Boroughgate CA16 6XG ☎Appleby(07683)51598
*This 18th-century, small, modernised hotel is situated in the town centre.*

---

15rm(7⇄3🅵)(4fb)⊬in all bedrooms CTV in all bedrooms ® **T**
✳ sB&B£25-£35 sB&B⇄🅵£30-£40 dB&B£40-£45
dB&B⇄🅵£45-£50 🍴
CTV 6P CFA hairdresser beauty consultant
🍷 International V 🕙 ⚏ ✳ Sunday Lunch £5.95 Dinner fr9.25&alc Last dinner 9.30pm
Credit Cards 1 2 3 5 £

### ★58% *Courtfield*
Bongate CA16 6UP ☎Appleby(07683)51394

*Standing in three acres of gardens on the approach road into the town from the direction of Brough, this one-time vicarage offers wholesome meals, generously served, and the opportunity to relax in comfortable public rooms where log fires blaze during the colder months.*

6rm(2⇄2🅵)Annexe5rm(1⇄)(1fb) CTV in 6 bedrooms TV in 2 bedrooms ®
CTV 20P 2🚗 🚗 ✿ ♨
V 🕙 ⚏ Last dinner 8pm

---

## APPLETON-LE-MOORS North Yorkshire Map **08** SE78

### ★★🏚73% **Dweldapilton Hall**
YO6 6TF ☎Lastingham(07515)227 & 452 FAX (07515) 540
Closed Jan

*Set in well tended gardens in the centre of the charming moorland village, this impressive hall provides a relaxing atmosphere and attentive service from its resident owners. Furnished in period style, public rooms are comfortable and bedrooms feature many thoughtful extras. The six-course home-cooked dinner can be recommended.*

12⇄🅵1🛏 CTV in all bedrooms ® **T** S% sB&B⇄🅵£39.50
dB&B⇄🅵£79-£88 🍴
Lift CTV 30P 🚗 ✿ croquet nc14yrs *xmas*
🍷 English & Continental 🕙 ⚏ S% Bar Lunch £2.50-£7.50
Dinner £19.50-£23 Last dinner 8.15pm
Credit Cards 1 2 3 £

---

## ARBROATH Tayside *Angus* Map **12** NO64

### ★★★65% *Letham Grange*
Colliston DD11 4RL ☎Gowanbank(024189)373
FAX (024189) 414

*Set in extensive wooded grounds, this splendid Victorian mansion has elegant public rooms with oak panelling, carved fireplaces and ornate ceilings. Comfortable bedrooms range from spacious master rooms with lovely period furniture to more modest standard rooms and leisure facilities include an 18-hole championship golf course and a 4-sheet curling rink.*

19⇄(4fb)1🛏 CTV in all bedrooms ® ✖ (ex guide dogs)
《100P 🚗 ▶ 18 ♟ (hard & grass) U croquet putting pool tables
🍷 International V 🕙 ⚏ Last dinner 9.30pm
Credit Cards 1 2 3 5

### ★★59% **Hotel Seaforth**
Dundee Rd DD11 1QF ☎(0241)72232 FAX (0241) 77473

*A family-run commercial hotel on the western edge of the town also provides a popular venue for local functions and meetings. Public areas have been substantially refurbished, accommodation is gradually being improved, and leisure facilities are available.*

20⇄🅵(2fb) CTV in all bedrooms ® **T** sB&B⇄£36-£38
dB&B⇄🅵£47-£49
100P ✿ CFA 🏊 (heated) snooker sauna solarium gymnasium jacuzzi *xmas*
V 🕙 ⚏ Lunch fr£8 Dinner fr£9.50&alc Last dinner 9.30pm
Credit Cards 1 2 3 5 £

---

For key to symbols in English see the bookmark.

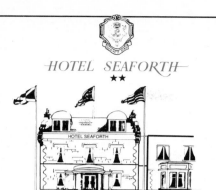

### ARCHIESTOWN Grampian *Morayshire* Map **15** NJ24

★★ ❀❀71% **Archiestown**

AB38 7QX ☎Carron(03406)218 FAX (03406) 239

Closed mid Dec-1 Mar

(Rosettes awarded for dinner only)

*This striking Victorian hotel stands beside the well-kept square of this attractive village and provides an ideal base for anglers fishing on the River Spey, holidaymakers and business people. Its new owners, Judith and Michael Bulger have come here from Dunain Park near Inverness where they achieved AA Red Star status and a Rosette for their restaurant. They have completely refurbished this hotel, but in keeping with its character, and it now offers three cosy lounges (one of which can be used for pre-dinner drinks). Judith Bulger takes care of the cooking, which is refreshingly uncomplicated and free of gimmickry, relying on good local produce to create interesting dishes. Bedrooms have a bright, cared-for feel and many extra touches have been provided to make guests feel at home.*

8rm(6⇨) TV available ® **T** ✳ sB&B£20.50-£30.50 dB&B⇨frf51

CTV 20P ✿ ⏛

♀ International **V** ♱ ♨ Sunday Lunch fr£12.50 Dinner fr£17.50 Last dinner 8.30pm

Credit Cards 1 3

### ARCHIRONDEL

See **Jersey under Channel Islands**

### ARDELVE Highland *Ross & Cromarty* Map **14** NG82

★ 76% *Loch Duich*

IV40 8DY ☎Dornie(059985)213

Closed Nov-Etr

*This whitewashed hotel, conveniently positioned for those travelling to and from Skye, enjoys spectacular views of mountains, lochs and the much-photographed Eilean Donan Castle. Deservedly popular, it has a relaxed, friendly atmosphere and bedrooms which, though modestly equipped, are bright and fresh; inviting public areas include a choice of lounges and bars, together with an attractive dining room featuring a daily-changed dinner menu which makes good use of fresh produce. Cheerful service is provided throughout by friendly local staff.*

18rm(2⇨♠)(1fb)⊁in 2 bedrooms

CTV 40P 1🐎 ✿ ✿ fishing shooting

**V** ♱ ⊁ Last dinner 9pm

Credit Cards 1 3

### ARDENTINNY Strathclyde *Argyllshire* Map **10** NS18

★★ 67% **Ardentinny**

PA23 8TR ☎(036981)209 & 275 FAX (036981) 345

Closed Nov-15 Mar

*Friendly roadside inn full of character and delightfully situated with gardens leading down to the sea. Popular with yachtsmen and those who enjoy good food.*

11rm(5⇨5♠)(1fb) CTV in all bedrooms ® ✳ sB&B⇨♠£26-£39 dB&B⇨♠£50-£80 🅱

CTV 30P ✿ CFA boating

♀ Scottish, French & German **V** ♱ ♨ ⊁ S% Sunday Lunch £5-£15alc High tea £5-£10alc Dinner £17-£20 Last dinner 9.30pm

Credit Cards 1 2 3 5

### ARDUAINE Strathclyde *Argyllshire* Map **10** NM80

★★★ ❀69% **Loch Melfort**

PA34 4XG ☎Kilmelford(08522)233 FAX (08522) 214

Closed 3 Jan-Feb

*Boldly claiming to be 'The finest location on the west coast', this family-owned hotel lives up to expectations, with superb views southwards of the sea and islands, which, on fine days, has few*

*equals. Many improvements have been made by Philip and Rosalind Lewis, particularly to the 20 bedroomed Cedar Wing, where rooms either have balconies or patios from which to enjoy the view. The table d'hôte menu, with supplements, makes good use of local seafood and meats, as well as quality imported items. The Chart Room Bar serves food for most of the day, and is popular with families and the yachting fraternity.*

6⇨♠Annexe20⇨ CTV in all bedrooms ® **T** sB&B⇨♠£35-£53 dB&B⇨♠£60-£91 🅱

65P ✿ CFA *xmas*

**V** ♱ ♨ ⊁ Bar Lunch £2-£20&alc High tea £3-£5 Dinner fr£20.50 Last dinner 9pm

Credit Cards 1 3

**See advertisement under OBAN**

### ARDVASAR

See **Skye**, Isle of

### ARISAIG Highland *Inverness-shire* Map **13** NM68

★★★

★★★❀♨♨ **ARISAIG HOUSE**

Beasdale PH39 4NR (3m E A830) (Relais et Châteaux) ☎(06875)622

Telex no 777279

FAX (06875) 626

Closed 11 Nov-8 Mar

*The Road to the Isles may pass closely by but this splendid stone house on the Fort William to Mallaig road is well hidden from view behind towering trees including redwoods that would be more at home in the western States rather than the Western Isles. There are formal gardens and deeply wooded areas with footpaths to walk off excesses of food, the shore is just a few minutes away and as can be expected, local sea food does figure prominently on the menu, none better than the really succulent Arisaig scallops, briefly pan fried and served with a tarragon and tomato butter sauce. Produce is virtually all from the prolific Scottish larder and, with the exception of Stilton, all the cheeses are Scottish too. During a visit in 1991 a combination of minor setbacks resulted in some serious delays but the actual quality never suffered and young chef Matthew Burns no doubt learned well from the experience.*

15rm(13⇨) CTV in all bedrooms **T** ✖ (ex guide dogs) sB&B⇨£83.50-£90 dB&B⇨£203-£260 (incl dinner) 🅱

16P ✿ ✿ snooker croquet nc10yrs

♀ British & French **V** ♱ ♨ ⊁ Lunch £12.50-£20alc Dinner fr£35 Last dinner 8.30pm

Credit Cards 1 3

★★ 64% **Arisaig**

PH39 4NH ☎(06875)210

*A family-run Highland holiday hotel delightfully situated by the shore of Loch Nan Ceal with some fine island views. It has a welcoming atmosphere and there is a choice of traditional lounges together with comfortably furnished bedrooms. The dining room, with an inviting open fire, offers wholesome Taste of Scotland dishes with the emphasis on local seafood. A recent addition to the menu is smoked alligator.*

15rm(6⇨)(4fb) ® **T** sB&B£25-£34.50 dB&B£50-£69 dB&B⇨£62-£85

CTV 60P 🚗

**V** ♱ ♨ ⊁ Bar Lunch £2-£15alc High tea £2-£15alc Dinner £23.50 Last dinner 8.15pm

Credit Cards 1 3

## ARNCLIFFE North Yorkshire Map **07** SD97

★★⚜ 74% **Amerdale House**

BD23 5QE ☎(075677)250 due to change to (0756) 770250
Closed mid Nov-mid Mar

*Amerdale is a former manor house said to date back to the Elizabethan era, set in idyllic rural surroundings just off the main tourist routes. It is managed by friendly resident proprietors who continue to improve its already comfortable accommodation. Traditional bedrooms with substantial furniture, hand crafted locally, contain many thoughtful little extras, while the lounge, restaurant and busy bar are all tastefully styled and inviting. A short table d'hôte menu offers carefully prepared dishes based on fresh local produce.*

10➪↑Annexe1➪(3fb)1⌷ CTV in all bedrooms ®
✠ (ex guide dogs) ✱ sB&B➪↑£56-£60.50 dB&B➪↑£95-£101 (incl dinner)
30P ⇄ ✻
V ✠ ✱ Dinner fr£17 Last dinner 8.30pm
Credit Cards ①③

## ARRAN, ISLE OF Strathclyde *Bute* Map **10**

## BRODICK Map **10** NS03

★★★ 72% **Auchrannie Country House**

KA27 8BZ ☎(0770)2234 & 2235 FAX (0770) 2812

*Built in 1860, and formerly the home of the Dowager Duchess of Hamilton, this pleasant country house set amid Scots Pine and mature woodland on the northern outskirts of Brodick has been converted into a small, tastefully decorated hotel which will eventually become the centrepiece of a time share leisure complex. Bedrooms vary in size, but most are spacious, and all are well equipped and appointed, having views over the rose garden or lawns. Public areas, though not extensive, are comfortable and welcoming, with an open fire in the relaxing cocktail lounge where drinks are served. The standard of cuisine is high, and service throughout the hotel friendly and attentive.*

28➪↑(3fb) CTV in all bedrooms ® T ✠ (ex guide dogs)
sB&B➪↑£22.50-£45 dB&B➪↑£45-£75 ⊟
⟨ 30P ⇄ ✻ CFA ▱ (heated) snooker sauna solarium gymnasium turkish steam room hair & beauty salon *xmas*
♥ Scottish & French V ♥ ⊮ Lunch £7.35-£9.45alc High tea fr£7.50alc Dinner £15.50&alc Last dinner 10pm
Credit Cards ①③ⓔ

## LAGG Map **10** NR92

★★ 65% **Lagg**

Kilmory KA27 8PQ ☎Sliddery(077087)255

*This picturesque, 18th-century coaching inn stands amid 10 acres of woodland, its well kept gardens extending to the Lagg Burn. Welcoming log fires burn in the relaxing lounge and bar areas, while bedrooms, though they vary in size and are fairly modestly equipped, are comfortable. Enjoyable home-cooked meals are based on fresh local produce and helpful service is provided by friendly young staff.*

15➪↑(3fb) ® sB&B➪↑£28-£40 dB&B➪↑£56-£80 (incl dinner)
CTV 40P ⇄ ✻ CFA ♪ *xmas*
♥ Scottish & French V ♥ ⊮ ✱ Lunch £8-£12&alc High tea £5-£8 Dinner £14-£16&alc Last dinner 9pm

## LAMLASH Map **10** NS03

★★ 66% **Glenisle**

KA27 8LS ☎(07706)559 & 258
Closed Nov-15 Mar

*Set on the seafront, overlooking Holy Isle, a small, personally run hotel has been completely refurbished to offer comfortable, well appointed and equipped bedrooms complemented by attractive public areas which include a compact lounge and cocktail bar. Enjoyable meals featuring fresh local produce are served in a*

*popular restaurant whose pleasant view takes in both the carefully tended garden and the sea.*

13➪↑ CTV in all bedrooms ® T ✱ sB&B➪↑£25-£35
dB&B➪↑£50-£70
⟨ 10P ⇄ ✻
♥ Scottish & French V ♥ S% Lunch £3-£4.50alc Dinner £10.50-£13.50alc Last dinner 9pm
Credit Cards ①③

## WHITING BAY Map **10** NS02

★ 57% **Cameronia**

Shore Rd KA27 8PZ ☎(07707)254
RS Nov-Mar

*A small, homely, family-run hotel looking out across the sea to the mainland.*

5↑(2fb) ® ✠ sB&B↑£15-£25 dB&B↑£39-£43 ⊟
CTV 6P ⇄ ♒
V ♥ ✠ ✱ Sunday Lunch £7.50-£9.50 Dinner £7.50-£11.50&alc
Last dinner 9pm
Credit Cards ②ⓔ

## ARUNDEL West Sussex Map **04** TQ00

★★★ 67% **Norfolk Arms**

High St BN18 9AD (Forestdale) ☎(0903)882101
FAX (0903) 884275

*An historic hotel, built by the Duke of Norfolk as a coaching inn 200 years ago and skilfully modernised to retain an atmosphere of traditional permanence, offers a choice of accommodation, the tastefully furnished and well equipped rooms in the main building being supplemented by those in a modern annexe. Public areas include a comfortable traditional lounge combined with the very popular public bar, another small bar, the Arun Restaurant and a breakfast room. Well managed service is both friendly and*

→

*attentive and there are good car parking facilities (some under cover).*

21⇄Annexe13⇄(1fb)6🛏⚼in 3 bedrooms CTV in all bedrooms ® **T** ✳ sB&B⇄fr£57.50 dB&B⇄fr£72.50-£82.50 ₧ ⊄ 15P 15🎱 CFA *xmas*

♀ International **V** ✿ ⚫ ⚼ ✳ Lunch £8.95-£12.50 High tea £3.95 Dinner £12.50-£15.50 Last dinner 10pm

Credit Cards ①②③④⑤ ⓔ

### ★▲♨62% **Burpham Country**

Old Down, Burpham BN18 9RJ (3m NE off A27)
☎(0903)882160

*This long established, old fashioned, family-run hotel in a quiet location is slowly being upgraded by the provision of individually furnished en suite bedrooms, and there are plans to extend. Resident proprietors offer a very warm welcome and the opportunity to enjoy a peaceful, relaxing stay in typical country house surroundings.*

10⇄🏠 CTV in all bedrooms ® ✈ sB&B⇄🏠fr£40 dB&B⇄🏠£64-£73 ₧

12P 🛏 ✿ nc12yrs *xmas*

**V** ✿ ⚫ ⚼ Lunch fr£9 Dinner £13.50-£16 Last dinner 8pm

Credit Cards ①③ⓔ

---

### ★★★★57% **Berystede**

Bagshot Rd, Sunninghill SL5 9JH (Forte Hotels) ☎(0344)23311 Telex no 847707 FAX (0344) 872301

*A well established hotel set in wooded grounds with ample car parking has recently been considerably improved – this much needed upgrading being set to continue until all rooms reach a high standard of quality and comfort. For the time being the best accommodation is contained in the main building, and regular visitors will be impressed by the transformation of public rooms which now include a second bar and pleasing library lounge ; the refurbished restaurant offers a choice of attractively presented menus, and helpful staff provide willing service.*

91⇄🏠(6fb)2🛏⚼in 30 bedrooms CTV in all bedrooms ® **T** ✳ sB&B⇄🏠fr£85 dB&B⇄🏠fr£100 (room only) ₧

Lift ⊄ 240P 1🎱 ✿ CFA ⌐ (heated) games room ♫ *xmas*

♀ European **V** ✿ ⚫ ⚼ ✳ ✳ S% Lunch £15.50-£19.50&alc Dinner £20&alc Last dinner 9.45pm

Credit Cards ①②③④⑤

### ★★67% **Brockenhurst**

Brockenhurst Rd SL5 9HA ☎(0344)21912 FAX (0344) 873252

*A detached Edwardian house with its own grounds in south Ascot has been totally refurbished to provide a good all-round standard of accommodation, with well equipped attractive bedrooms, some with whirlpool spa baths. The restaurant, due to be extended, has an à la carte menu and service is friendly and informal.*

11⇄🏠(2fb) CTV in all bedrooms ® **T** ✈ ✳ sB&B⇄🏠£65-£85 dB&B⇄🏠£75-£100 Continental breakfast ₧

15P 🛏 ✿ CFA *xmas*

♀ French ✿ ⚫ ⚼ Lunch £8.50-£15&alc Dinner £10-£15&alc Last dinner 9.30pm

Credit Cards ①②③⑤ⓔ

### ★★65% **Highclere**

19 Kings Rd, Sunninghill SL5 9AD ☎(0344)25220 FAX (0344) 872528

*This attractive detached hotel, originally an Edwardian family home, stands opposite Sunninghill Post Office, within a mile of Ascot race course and offering easy access to both the M3 and M4. A recently completed refurbishment programme has resulted in the provision of 11 well equipped en suite bedrooms with tastefully co-ordinated colour schemes, while public areas include an informal restaurant serving a table d'hôte menu and a popular lounge with an ambience of warmth.*

12⇄🏠(2fb)⚼in 3 bedrooms CTV in 11 bedrooms ® **T** ✈ (ex guide dogs) ✳ sB&B⇄🏠£38-£65 dB&B⇄🏠£50-£78

CTV 14P 🛏 *xmas*

♀ European **V** ✿ ⚫ ⚼ ✳ Lunch £4.80-£15.50&alc Dinner £8-£18.50&alc Last dinner 10pm

Credit Cards ①②③

---

### ★★★69% **Ashbourne Oaks Lodge**

Derby Rd DE6 1XH ☎(0335)46666 FAX (0335) 46549

*Set high above the town on the A52, this modern hotel provides a good range and standard of services, with a choice of formal restaurant and all-day brasserie, and conference and function facilities. Clean, well equipped bedrooms vary from spacious to quite compact, with suites and non-smokers rooms available.*

50⇄🏠(5fb)⚼in 11 bedrooms CTV in all bedrooms ® **T** ✈ (ex guide dogs) ✳ sB&B⇄🏠fr£65 dB&B⇄🏠fr£75 ₧

Lift ⊄ 200P ✿ *xmas*

**V** ✿ ⚫ ⚼ ✳ Lunch £12.50&alc High tea £2.45-£4.95 Dinner £17.50&alc Last dinner 10pm

Credit Cards ①③

### ★★★60% **Beresford Arms**

Station Rd DE6 1AA ☎(0335)300035 FAX (0335) 300065

*Comfortable surroundings and the polite and courteous service provided by resident proprietors and their small team of staff combine to make this hotel increasingly popular with residents and local customers alike. Most of its well equipped bedrooms are of a good size, and all have en suite facilities.*

12⇄🏠(1fb) CTV in all bedrooms ® **T** ✈ (ex guide dogs)

30P 🛏

♀ English & French **V** ✿ ⚫ Last dinner 9.30pm

Credit Cards ①②③

### ★★🏵♨74% **Callow Hall**

Mappleton Rd DE6 2AA ☎(0335)43403 & 43164 FAX (0335) 43624

Closed 25-26 Dec & 2 wks Feb

*The home of David and Dorothy Spencer, Callow Hall is set in beautiful countryside just five minutes from Ashbourne and has been lovingly restored to provide superior accommodation. David has long had a local reputation for the interesting dishes he creates from the fresh quality produce.*

12⇄🏠(2fb)1🛏 CTV in all bedrooms ® **T** ✈ (ex guide dogs) sB&B⇄🏠£63-£78 dB&B⇄🏠£85-£115 ₧

20P 1🎱 🛏 ✿ ♪

♀ English & French **V** ⚼ Sunday Lunch fr£11.50 Dinner fr£23.50&alc Last dinner 9.15pm

Credit Cards ①②③⑤ⓔ

---

### ★★🏵♨73% **Holne Chase**

TQ13 7NS (Inter-Hotels) ☎Poundsgate(03643)471 FAX (03643) 453

*This secluded country house is in a peaceful setting, on the southern edge of Dartmoor off the A38 between Exeter and Plymouth. Bedrooms have been tastefully modernised and offer excellent facilities, and log fires blaze in the attractive lounges in the cooler months. The spacious, airy restaurant is a popular choice for smart but relaxed meals with set-price menus at both lunch and dinner. The productive kitchen garden provides many of the vegetables used in the cooking. Chef David Beazley, whose previous experience included a spell in Joyce Molyneux's acclaimed Carved Angel restaurant, cooks in an unshowy, traditional style, with a particular fondness for fish : a starter might be of pan-fried slices of huss, served in a light creamy curried sauce with a garnish of grapes. Simple bar lunches are also available. Salmon fishing is available in the grounds.*

12rm(9⇄2🏠)1🛏 CTV in all bedrooms ® **T** sB&B⇄🏠£59-£63.50 dB&B⇄🏠£82-£120 ₧

30P 🛏 ✿ ♪ croquet putting *xmas*

☺ English & French **V** ♻ ⚿ ✗ ✳ Lunch fr£13.75 Dinner fr£21.50 Last dinner 9pm
Credit Cards ①②③⑤ⓔ

★★67% **Tugela House**

68-70 East St TQ13 7AX ☎(0364)52206

*The atmosphere and style of this pleasant little hotel are those of a country residence, despite its setting at the heart of the moorland town. Antique furnishings are complemented by a compatable modern range in comfortable, individually decorated and nicely appointed bedrooms which are warm, homely and spotlessly clean. Public rooms rich in mahogany and pine boast similar standards, the elegant residents' lounge on the first floor and the twin cosy, Victorian-style dining rooms sharing an intimate atmosphere. Meals are commendable, and prompt, hospitable service is provided in a pleasantly informal manner.*

7rm(6⇨🅙)(1fb) CTV in all bedrooms sB&B⇨🅙£30-£45 dB&B⇨🅙£45-£60

10P 2🚗 🚭 ❀

☺ English & French **V** ♻ ✗ Lunch £12-£15alc Dinner £12-£15alc Last dinner 9pm
ⓔ

★★63% **Dartmoor Lodge**

Peartree Cross TQ13 7JW (Exec Hotel) ☎(0364)52232
FAX (0364) 53990

*Beams and exposed stone walls create a warm atmosphere at the Dartmoor Lodge. Bedrooms are well equipped and vary in size and style. The well presented Dart Inn serves food all day, and an à la carte menu at night offers more substantial dishes. The hotel is easily accessible from the A38 and convenient for Dartmoor and South Devon.*

30⇨🅙(6fb)2🛏 CTV in all bedrooms ® **T** sB⇨🅙fr£28.50 dB⇨🅙fr£32.50 (room only) 🛏

Lift ⟨ CTV 50P🚗 (charged) ❀ CFA *xmas*

☺ English & French **V** ♻ ⚿ ✗ Lunch fr£8.85 Dinner fr£12alc Last dinner 9.30 pm
Credit Cards ①②③

---

**ASHBY-DE-LA-ZOUCH** Leicestershire Map **08** SK31

★★★57% *Royal Osprey*

Station Rd LE6 5GP (Toby) ☎(0530)412833 Telex no 341629
RS 24 Dec-1 Jan

*Built in 1826 this Regency-style hotel provides modern accommodation and a choice of bars. Situated on the busy A453 just outside town.*

31⇨🅙(3fb)✗in 3 bedrooms CTV in all bedrooms ® **T**
⟨ 100P ❀ 🎵

☺ English & French **V** ♻ ⚿ ✗ Last dinner 9.45pm
Credit Cards ①②③④⑤

---

**ASHFORD** Kent Map **05** TR04

★★★★❀⚙
**EASTWELL MANOR**

Eastwell Park, Boughton Lees TN25 4HR (Queens Moat)(Small Luxury Hotels)
☎(0233)635751
Telex no 966281
FAX (0233) 635530

(Rosette awarded for dinner only)

*This impressive manor house, set amid a 3000-acre estate some 3 miles from the town, exudes grandeur from the moment you cross its attractive courtyard and enter the roomy*

→

# The
## Dartmoor Lodge
(Formerly Dartmoor Motel)

PEARTREE CROSS, ASHBURTON, DEVON TQ13 7JW
Telephone: 0364 52232

**AA** ★★

Attractive, comfortable hotel, in a rural setting near historic Ashburton, bordering Dartmoor National Park. Ideal touring stop (midway Plymouth & Exeter). The restaurant and beamed lounge bar offer a complete range of barsnacks, beverages and full meals all day. A la carte dinner is served every evening. Bedrooms all have private bathrooms, colour TV/radio, telephone and tea making (some ground floor rooms). Two four poster rooms available, one with jacuzzi bath!
*Colour brochure upon request.*

---

★★★★
# The Berystede
# Ascot

BAGSHOT ROAD, SUNNINGHILL, ASCOT, BERKSHIRE, SL5 9JH
TELEPHONE: ASCOT (0344) 23311
TELEX: 847707 FAX: (0344) 872301

The Berystede, situated on the south side of Ascot and set in 9 acres of formally landscaped gardens and natural woodlands, enjoys a seclusion and tranquillity away from the outside world and yet is only 5 minutes from the M3 motorway and 20 minutes from Heathrow Airport. The main routes of the M4 and M25 are close-by and the West End of London is less than one hour by train or car.

*stone-flagged reception hall where open log fires create a particularly welcoming atmosphere in winter. The traditional wood-panelled lounge and separate cocktail bar are complemented by bedrooms and bathrooms which are well up to 5-star standards in size, comfort and quality. À la carte and table d'hôte menus combine English and French dishes in uncomplicated style (sauces being chef Mark Clayton's strength), and a fine wine list is available. Tranquillity, spaciousness and service which combines professionalism with friendliness all help to make this an attractive stopping place for those travelling to and from the Continent.*

23⇨🏲 CTV in all bedrooms T ✳ sB&B⇨🏲£98-£135 dB&B⇨🏲£160-£160 🖪

Lift ( 50P 10🚗 🕸 ❄ CFA ♪ (hard) ♪ ∪ snooker croquet *xmas*

♀ English & French V ♥ ⚏ ✳ Lunch fr£17.50&alc Dinner fr£26&alc Last dinner 10pm

Credit Cards 1 2 3 5

---

### ★★★★67% Ashford International

Simone Weil Av TN24 8UX (Queens Moat) ☎(0233)611444
Telex no 96498 FAX (0233) 627708
Closed 24-28 Dec

*This modern hotel close to junction 9 of the M20 features a glazed roofed 'boulevard' with an airy lounge area, select shops and access to a small leisure centre. Bedrooms are comfortable and well equipped, each with a bright functional bathroom. The brasserie is open all day, while the Alhambra restaurant serves more sophisticated cuisine.*

200⇨🏲(4fb)⤬in 57 bedrooms CTV in all bedrooms ® T sB&B⇨🏲£98.50-£176.50 dB&B⇨🏲£116-£265 🖪

Lift ( 400P CFA 🖾 (heated) sauna solarium gymnasium spa bath

♀ English & French V ♥ ⚏ ⤬ ✳ Lunch £11-£16.50&alc Dinner £15&alc Last dinner 10.30pm

Credit Cards 1 2 3 5 £

---

### ★★★62% Forte Posthouse

Canterbury Rd TN24 8QQ (Forte Hotels) ☎(0233)625790
Telex no 966685 FAX (0233) 43176

*Skilfully converted from a 15th-century manor house, this hotel offers modern, comfortable accommodation with a choice of bedrooms, and friendly service.*

60⇨🏲(2fb)⤬in 30 bedrooms CTV in all bedrooms ® T ✳ sB⇨🏲£39.50-£49.50 dB⇨🏲£39.50-£49.50 (room only) 🖪

( 120P ❄ CFA 🐾 *xmas*

V ♥ ⚏ ⤬ ✳ S% Lunch £9.50-£10.95&alc Dinner £13.95&alc Last dinner 11.30pm

Credit Cards 1 2 3 5

---

### ★★★57% Master Spearpoint

Canterbury Rd., Kennington TN24 9QR (Best Western) ☎(0233)636863 Telex no 965978 FAX (0233) 610119

*Set beside the A28 in 5 acres of award-winning parkland gardens with a pleasant summer terrace and good car parking facilities, the hotel offers a choice of comfortable, well equipped and modern bedrooms, some of which are contained in a new extension. The Parkland Restaurant and bar lounge provide generally acceptable levels of service and cooking, while a first-floor residents' lounge is usually available and there are popular conference, wedding reception and dinner dance facilities.*

36⇨🏲(1fb) CTV in all bedrooms ® T sB&B⇨🏲£46-£70 dB&B⇨🏲£77-£95

60P ❄ CFA

♀ International V ♥ ⚏ ✳ Lunch £4.50-£10alc Dinner fr£15&alc Last dinner 9.45pm

Credit Cards 1 2 3 5

---

## ASHFORD-IN-THE-WATER Derbyshire Map 07 SK17

### ★★★♨69% Riverside Country House

Fennel St DE4 1QF ☎Bakewell(0629)814275
FAX (0629) 812873

*This charming ivy-clad Georgian country house stands in lovely gardens in the centre of this delightful Peak District village. The public rooms are cosy and peaceful, and, like the well equipped bedrooms, are decorated and furnished in a style sympathetic with the character of the house. A five-course fixed-price menu provides an imaginative selection of dishes and takes full advantage of seasonally available fresh produce. It is complemented by a comprehensive wine list and good, attentive service.*

15⇨🏲in all bedrooms CTV in all bedrooms ® T sB&B⇨🏲£77 dB&B⇨🏲£80-£92.50 🖪

CTV 30P 🕸 ❄ CFA *xmas*

♀ English & French V ♥ ⚏ ⤬ ✳ Lunch fr£13.95 Dinner £28-£31.60 Last dinner 9.30pm

Credit Cards 1 2 3 £

### ★★73% Ashford

Church St DE4 1QB ☎Bakewell(0629)812725

*This little inn is popular for its cheerful, informal atmosphere and its food, particularly bar meals in the summer months. The comfortable accommodation is very well equipped and decorated in an appealing rustic style, with good use of co-ordinated fabrics to set off the oak-beamed ceilings.*

7⇨🏲2🏲 CTV in all bedrooms ® T

CTV 50P 🕸 ❄

♀ French V ♥ ⚏ ⤬ Last dinner 10pm

Credit Cards 1 3

---

## ASHINGTON West Sussex Map 04 TQ11

### ★★68% Mill House

Mill Ln RH20 3BZ ☎(0903)892426 FAX (0903) 892855

*This 18th-century farm mill house has been lovingly restored and is now a comfortable and welcoming hotel. The friendly proprietors are busy completing work on the bedrooms, which are individually decorated and have modern facilities. The restaurant is cosy and relaxed and offers a choice of menus, and there is a new conference room.*

10rm(7⇨2🏲)(1fb)2🕸 CTV in all bedrooms ® T sB&B£40.60 sB&B⇨🏲£44.80-£47 dB&B⇨🏲£73.80-£90 🖪

CTV 12P 🕸 ❄ CFA 🐾 *xmas*

♀ English & French V ♥ ⚏ ✳ Lunch fr£9.55&alc Dinner fr£13.45&alc Last dinner 9.30pm

Credit Cards 1 2 3 4 5 £

### ⊛ ✕✕The Willows

London Rd RH20 3JR ☎(0903)892575

(Rosette awarded for dinner only) *Chef/Patron Carl Illes has spent most of his career in some famous hotel kitchens, and his professional skill is demonstrated in such dishes as mignon of veal with madeira sauce and a shallot and cream sauce; rack of lamb roasted with garlic and garnished with lentils; fillet steak with red wine and mushroom sauce, and supreme of salmon with duxelle (chopped mushroom) and citrus butter sauce. After the complimentary appetiser, try the delicious French onion soup, among the choice of simply constructed starters. Puddings can be a little disappointing, but the very attentive service provided and supervised by partner Julie Holdnall is both efficient and helpful. There is a good wine list with some half bottles. Ample car parking is available but access from the busy A24 can be difficult.*

Closed Mon Lunch not served Sat

Dinner not served Sun

♀ International 30 seats ✳ Lunch £14.95 Dinner £16.95 Last lunch 2pm Last dinner 10pm 25 P

Credit Cards 1 2 3

**ASHTON-UNDER-LYNE** Greater Manchester
Map **07** SJ99 ⊖

★★70% **York House**
York Place, Richmond St OL6 7TT ☎061-330 5899
FAX 061-343 1613
Closed Bank Hols
*Situated in a peaceful tree-lined cul-de-sac close to the A635/
A6017 junction, this very well maintained family-owned hotel has
been developed from several Victorian properties. Bedrooms are all
well equipped, with those in the annexe particularly comfortable,
and the restaurant features an interesting monthly-changing menu.*
24⇔ℵAnnexe10⇔(2fb)1⊞ CTV in all bedrooms ® T ✱
S10% sB&B⇔ℵ£46-£58.50 dB&B⇔ℵ£66-£71 ℞
⟨ 34P ✿ CFA
♀ English & French V ♥ ⫴ ✱ S10% Lunch fr£9.50&alc
Dinner fr£10alc Last dinner 9.30pm
Credit Cards ①②③④⑤

**ASKRIGG** North Yorkshire Map **07** SD99

★★70% **King's Arms**
Market Place DL8 3HQ (Minotels) ☎Wensleydale(0969)50258
FAX (0969) 50635
*This interesting old village inn is currently undergoing vast
alterations to improve already comfortable facilities without
sacrificing its original character.*
11⇔ℵ(1fb)6⊞ CTV in all bedrooms ® T ✱ sB&B⇔ℵ£35-
£50 dB&B⇔ℵ£55-£80 ℞
17P nc6yrs *xmas*
♀ English & French V ♥ ⫴ ✱ Lunch £17.25&alc Dinner
£17.25&alc Last dinner 10pm
Credit Cards ①③⑥

**ASPLEY GUISE** Bedfordshire Map **04** SP93

★★★71% **Moore Place**
The Square MK17 8DW ☎Milton Keynes(0908)282000
FAX (0908) 281888
RS 26-28 Dec
*An elegant red-brick country mansion, dating from 1786 and
looking out proudly over the village square, has recently been
landscaped and carefully extended to offer a range of
accommodation covering the needs of both business and leisure
guests. Well appointed rooms feature smart contemporary
furniture, high quality fabrics and good bathrooms, while
comfortable public areas retain many period features. The
restaurant, an attractive conservatory overlooking the rock garden
and cascade, provides an interesting menu based on freshly
prepared ingredients, though results can be variable.*
39⇔Annexe15⇔ CTV in all bedrooms ® T ✱ sB&B⇔£85-
£90 dB&B⇔£92-£112 ℞
⟨ 60P ✿ CFA ♪
V ♥ ⫴ ✱ Lunch £15.50 Dinner £19.95&alc Last dinner 10pm
Credit Cards ①②③⑤

**ASTON CLINTON** Buckinghamshire Map **04** SP81

★★★

★★★✸✸ **BELL INN**
HP22 5HP (Relais et
Châteaux)
☎Aylesbury(0296)630252
FAX (0296) 631250
RS Sun eve & Mon
*The Bell has been
transformed by owners Mr
and Mrs Harris into the very model of an English coaching*

*inn, complete with 'old world' courtyard, flag-floored smoking
room, and elegant panelled drawing room. Its attractive
bedrooms are in the converted building around the flower-
filled courtyard, and thus separate from the original inn, which
now concentrates on its restaurant. Here the walls are covered
with murals of food, flora and fauna across the seasons, and
guests sit at polished wooden tables. Menus are extensive and
in French with translations; the food is elaborate and rich, the
ingredients coming with many flavourings and garnishes, and
elaborate constructions presented under cloches in the old-
fashioned way. Service is formal but cheerful, and personally
supervised by the owner, Mr Harris. There are both à la carte
and set menus, the Menu Fraicheur, (derived from seasonal
produce) being particularly good value. The wine list is
noteworthy.*
6⇔ℵAnnexe15⇔ℵ2⊞ CTV in all bedrooms T ✱ S%
sB&B⇔ℵ£92-£160 dB&B⇔ℵ£107-£133 Continental
breakfast ℞
150P ⇐⇒ ✿ CFA croquet *xmas*
♀ English & French V ♥ ⫴ ✱ Lunch fr£17.35 Dinner
£17.35-£36 Last dinner 9.45pm
Credit Cards ①②③⑥

**ATHERSTONE** Warwickshire Map **04** SP39

★★70% *Old Red Lion*
Lone St CV9 1BB ☎(0827)713156 FAX (0827) 711404
*This 17th-century coaching inn has recently been totally
refurbished to offer particularly well equipped en suite bedrooms
and comfortable, modern public areas which include a restaurant
whose à la carte and table d'hôte menus – including both flambé
and vegetarian selections – are popular with resident and local
alike.*
22⇔ℵ(1fb)2⊞ CTV in all bedrooms ® T ✤ (ex guide dogs)
⟨ 22P
♀ English & French V ♥ ⫴ ✔ Last dinner 9.45pm
Credit Cards ①②③⑤

★71% **Chapel House**
Friar's Gate CV9 1EY ☎(0827)718949
Closed Xmas wk
*A former dower house, nestling in the shadows of the church, with
its own well tended garden. Owners Pat and David Roberts
provide attractive accommodation combining the original charm of
the building with modern comforts. Traditional public areas
include a comfortable lounge with conservatory extension, and the
dining room where imaginative meals are served.*
13rm(11⇔ℵ) CTV in all bedrooms T ✤ ✱ sB&Bfr£29.50
sB&B⇔ℵ£37.50-£45 dB&B£49.50-£55 dB&B⇔ℵfr£55
⇐⇒
Credit Cards ①③⑤

**ATTLEBOROUGH** Norfolk Map **05** TM09

★★60% **Sherbourne Country House**
Norwich Rd NR17 2JX ☎(0953)454363 FAX (0953) 453509
*Standing 5 minutes' walk from the town, in an acre of mature
grounds next to the old turnpike, this well maintained 17th-century
house offers comfortable rooms (most having en suite facilities), an
attractive bar and lounge, and good standards of hospitality.*
8rm(4⇔1ℵ)3⊞ CTV in all bedrooms ® T sB&B£27.50-£32.50
sB&B⇔ℵ£38-£50 dB&B£37-£44 dB&B⇔ℵ£47-£70 ℞
35P ✿ *xmas*
♥ ⫴ ✔ Lunch £10.95 High tea £4.95 Dinner £12.95-£14.95
Last dinner 9pm
Credit Cards ①②③⑥

A rosette means exceptional standards of cuisine.

**AUCHENCAIRN** Dumfries & Galloway *Kirkcudbright* Map **11** NX75

### ★★★⚑70% Balcary Bay
DG7 1QZ ☎(055664)217 & 311
Closed Dec-Feb

*A delightful hotel, in a charming coastal situation, whose grounds run down to the water's edge. Bedrooms are bright and airy and public areas comfortable and tastefully appointed.*

17⇨♠(1fb) CTV in all bedrooms ® T sB&B⇨♠£55-£63 (incl dinner) 🏳
50P ⇶ ❋ CFA snooker ♨ *xmas*
♀ English & French V ♦ ℒ Lunch £10-£15 Dinner £17&alc Last dinner 9pm
Credit Cards ①③

### ★★★61% Solwayside House
25 Main St DG7 1QU ☎(055664)280 FAX (055664) 283

*Managed by the resident proprietors, this small hotel offers unpretentious accommodation and good value menus.*

10rm(8⇨♠)(3fb) CTV in all bedrooms ® T sB&B£16-£17 sB&B⇨♠£20.50-£24.50 dB&B⇨♠£32-£36 🏳
CTV 10P CFA games room pool table putting *xmas*
V ♦ ℒ ⤳ Lunch £6.50&alc Dinner £10.50-£12.50&alc Last dinner 8.30pm
ⓔ

---

**AUCHTERARDER** Tayside *Perthshire* Map **11** NN91

★★★★★⊛⊛
**THE GLENEAGLES HOTEL**
PH3 1NF ☎(0764)62231
Telex no 76105
FAX (0764) 62134

*A visit to Gleneagles is an experience not to be missed, particularly if you are a golfing enthusiast or a health fiend. The leisure facilities are probably the best, for a hotel, in the country. In keeping with the trend, the atmosphere is professional but not stuffy, and that is clear from the moment you arrive to be greeted by Colonel Smith, the friendly guest relations manager. Charm, quality and comfort pervade the whole hotel, the relaxing sitting rooms, the cosy bar and the spacious restaurant with its conservatory extension. Bedrooms vary in size, some are compact, but they are thoughtfully decorated and furnished, and equipped with all the modern facilities. Restaurant staff are traditionally dressed and well supervised by Ahmed Yurdakol, the maître d' hôtel at Gleneagles for some 20 years. Head chef Alan Hill together with head sous chef Colin Bussey have devised interesting set price and à la carte menus, complemented by an impressive wine list. Some of their specialities are marbled vegetable terrine with onion sauce, and potted oxtails with garden herbs, vegetables and grated horseradish. Main dishes include supreme of halibut with woodland mushrooms and smoked venison. A range of hot and cold puddings is available ; a fine example is ginger soufflé with apricot brandy.*

236⇨♠10🚪 CTV in all bedrooms T ❋ sB&B⇨♠£125 dB&B⇨♠£185-£235 🏳
Lift ⟨ 200P ⇶ ❋ CFA ▣ (heated) ▶ 18 ♪ (hard & grass )✚ squash ∪ snooker sauna solarium gymnasium croquet bowls putting shooting ♫ *xmas*
♀ International V ⤳ ❉ Lunch £17-£21.50 Dinner £34-£46&alc Last dinner 10pm
Credit Cards ①②③④⑤

---

### ★★★⊛⊛⚑76% Auchterarder House
PH3 1DZ (Small Luxury Hotels) ☎(0764)63646 & 63647 FAX (0764) 62939

*A careful refurbishment programme is nearing completion at this impressive baronial mansion which is set in 17 acres of grounds amid the gently rolling Perthshire Hills. Elegant and tranquil public areas feature magnificent panelling, open fires, fine antique furniture and an abundance of fresh flowers, while bedrooms – which include two new annexe rooms on the other side of the courtyard – are very individual in style and character. The atmosphere throughout is that of an informal houseparty, with someone always on hand to make your stay enjoyable, and the owner's son demonstrates his natural flair and talent in the kitchen by producing imaginative dishes which are honest in flavour. A typical dinner might include a lobster mousse with a delicate Champagne sauce, chilled strawberry soup and pan-fried medallions of hare served with peppercorn and juniperberry sauce and garnished with black grapes and wild mushrooms, the menus being complemented by an extensive and well chosen wine list which should satisfy the most discerning palate.*

12⇨Annexe2⇨ CTV in all bedrooms T sB&B⇨£80-£100 dB&B⇨£125-£185 🏳
⟨ 40P ⇶ ❋ CFA ✚ croquet lawn pitch & putting green nc11yrs *xmas*
♀ Scottish & French V ♦ ℒ ⤳ Lunch £15-£25 Dinner £28.50-£50 Last dinner 10pm
Credit Cards ①②③④⑤ⓔ

### ★★★⚑68% Duchally House
PH3 1PN ☎(0764)63071 FAX (0764) 62464

*Major improvements are taking place at this fine Victorian manor house, set in 27 acres of peaceful grounds 2 miles south of the town. Guests can relax in comfortable lounges with open fires and dine in the elegant restaurant or more informal bar bistro. Refurbished, mostly spacious bedrooms provide modern comforts and facilities. Additional rooms are planned plus new conference and leisure amenities.*

15⇨♠(3fb)1🚪 CTV in all bedrooms ® T 🏳
30P ❋ ♪ (hard) snooker ♨ *xmas*
V ♦ ℒ ⤳
Credit Cards ①②③⑤

---

**AUCHTERHOUSE** Tayside *Forfarshire* Map **11** NO33

### ★★★⊛⚑71% Old Mansion House
DD3 0QN ☎(082626)366 FAX (082626) 400
Closed 25 Dec-3 Jan

*A 16th-century baronial home set in 10 acres of wooded grounds and gardens just 7 miles from Dundee, has been converted by its dedicated owners into a charming little country house hotel with a reputation for both warm hospitality and fine food. Individually decorated and furnished, bedrooms provide all the expected comforts and facilities, while public areas, decked with fresh flowers, reflect the charm and character of a former age, in their ornate Jacobean plasterwork ceilings ; the elegant dining room's à la carte menu features a range of imaginative and well prepared dishes based on the best fresh produce available.*

6⇨♠(2fb)1🚪 CTV in all bedrooms ® T ❋ sB&B⇨♠£65-£70 dB&B⇨♠£85-£100 🏳
50P 1⇶ ⇶ ❋ ⤳ (heated) ♪ (grass) squash croquet
♀ Scottish & French V ♦ ℒ ⤳ ❉ Lunch £14-£15&alc Dinner £20-£28alc Last dinner 9.30pm
Credit Cards ①②③⑤

---

**AULTBEA** Highland *Ross & Cromarty* Map **14** NG88

### ★★68% Aultbea
IV22 2HX ☎(0445)731201 FAX (0445) 731214

*A warmly welcoming holiday hotel, delightfully situated by the shore of Loch Ewe, has been substantially refurbished by its caring owners ; the Waterside Bistro now provides an informal alternative to the main restaurant, the lounge bar has been considerably upgraded, and bedrooms are all comfortably appointed and well equipped though limited in size.*

8⇨🎔(1fb) CTV in all bedrooms ℝ **T** sB&B⇨🎔£22.50-£36 dB&B⇨🎔£45-£72 🅡

CTV 40P ✿ pool table ♫ ๛ *xmas*

♀ International **V** ✢ ◿ Sunday Lunch £7.50 Dinner £18.50-£20&alc Last dinner 9.30pm

Credit Cards ① ③

---

## AUST MOTORWAY SERVICE AREA (M4) Avon
Map **03** ST58

### ⌂Rank Motor Lodge
M4 Motorway (junc 21) BS12 3BJ (Rank) ☎Pilning(04545)3313 FAX (04545) 3819

*Situated on the English side of the Severn Bridge, and only opened in 1990, this lodge offers well equipped en suite bedrooms of which some have been adapted for the less mobile. The service block contains both a good choice of popular eating options and a well stocked shop.*

51⇨🎔(21fb)✁in 8 bedrooms CTV in all bedrooms ℝ ✱ sB&B⇨🎔£29.75 dB&B⇨🎔£37.75 Continental breakfast 60P ✿

**V** ✢ ◿ ✱ Lunch £1.35-£5.35alc High tea £3-£6.05alc Dinner £3-£6.05alc

Credit Cards ① ② ③ ⑤

---

## AUSTWICK North Yorkshire Map **07** SD76

### ★68% The Traddock
LA2 8BY ☎Clapham(04685)224

*This Georgian country house is a friendly, family-run hotel, set within the Yorkshire Dales National Park, and located on the edge of the picturesque village. Bedrooms are modest but comfortable. There are cosy lounges, one with an open fire. A home-cooked dinner is the highlight of the stay here with the set meal freshly prepared from local produce.*

12rm(11⇨🎔)(3fb) CTV in 11 bedrooms ℝ **T** ✖ (ex guide dogs) ✱ sB&B£29-£39 dB&B£42-£58 dB&B⇨🎔£46-£66 🅡

15P ✿ *xmas*

♀ International **V** ✢ ◿ ✁ ✱ Lunch £9.95-£12.50 High tea £4.50-£10alc Dinner £12.50-£14.50&alc Last dinner 8.45pm

Credit Cards ① ③ Ⓔ

---

## AVIEMORE Highland *Inverness-shire* Map **14** NH81

### ★★★★58% Stakis Four Seasons
Aviemore Centre PH22 1PF (Stakis) ☎(0479)810681 Telex no 75213 FAX (0479) 810862

*This hotel with a distinctive castle keep, modern style, occupies a prominent position, commanding particularly fine views of the Spey Valley and surrounding mountains from many of its bedrooms. Boasting a pleasantly situated swimming pool and associated leisure activities, it enjoys a good reputation for package holidays.*

88⇨🎔(6fb)✁in 54 bedrooms CTV in all bedrooms ℝ **T** sB⇨🎔£84-£94.50 dB⇨🎔£111.30-£121.80 (room only) 🅡

Lift ℂ 100P ✿ CFA 🏊 (heated) sauna solarium gymnasium turkish bath whirlpool *xmas*

♀ Scottish, English & French ✢ ◿ ✱

Credit Cards ① ② ③ ⑤

### ★★★65% Red McGregor
Main Rd PH22 1RH ☎(0479)810256 FAX (0479) 810685

*Modern and purpose built, this tourist hotel offers convenient access to central activities from its position in the main street. Well equipped bedrooms are comfortably appointed in the modern style, public areas include a coffee house, a grill restaurant and a choice of bars, and there is a good range of leisure facilities.*

30⇨🎔(8fb) CTV in all bedrooms ℝ **T** ✖ (ex guide dogs) ✱ sB&B⇨🎔£52 (incl dinner) 🅡

---

( 65P CFA 🏊 (heated) sauna solarium gymnasium beauty salon steam room *xmas*

♀ English, French & Italian **V** ✢ ◿ Dinner £10-£15alc Last dinner 10pm

Credit Cards ① ② ③ ⑤

### ★★★55% *Aviemore Highlands*
Aviemore Centre PH22 1PJ ☎(0479)810771 Telex no 75597 FAX (0479) 811473

*This hotel at the heart of the Aviemore Centre offers fine views of the varied landscape that surrounds it. Bedrooms are basically furnished in modern style and equipped with compact bathrooms, while public areas include a choice of bars, the contemporary Ben Macdui Restaurant, a coffee shop and good function amenities; a games room and solarium are provided for guests' use, and facilities can be arranged for children.*

103⇨🎔(34fb) in 27 bedrooms CTV in all bedrooms ℝ **T** Lift ℂ 140P ✿ solarium games room ♫ ๛

♀ English & French **V** ✢ ◿ Last dinner 9pm

Credit Cards ① ② ③ ④ ⑤

### ★★64% Cairngorm
Grampian Rd PH22 1PE ☎(0479)810233 FAX (0479) 810791

*This tour hotel is on the main road right in the centre of Aviemore. In addition to the restaurant, bar meals are served throughout the day and evening, and there is a small coffee shop. Bedrooms vary in size and comfort but are all well equipped.*

30⇨🎔(4fb) CTV in all bedrooms ℝ **T** ✖ (ex guide dogs) ✱ sB&B⇨🎔frf39 dB&B⇨🎔frf58 🅡

( 40P *xmas*

**V** ✢ ◿ ✱ Bar Lunch £1.75-£7.75 High tea £4.45-£7.75 Dinner £12.50-£16.50 Last dinner 9pm

Credit Cards ① ② ③

---

**AXBRIDGE** Somerset Map **03** ST45

**★★ 63% Oak House**
The Square BS26 2AP ☎(0934)732444 FAX (0934) 733112
*Oak House is situated within the town square overlooking the*
*medieval St John's Hunting Lodge with parking available nearby.*
*Beamed public areas are pleasantly decorated and bedrooms are*
*individually styled. The dining room is well equipped, and food is*
*carefully prepared and cooked in the modern style.*
11rm(10⇔ℕ)(2fb) CTV in all bedrooms ® T ✱ S%
sB&Bfr£25 sB&B⇔ℕfr£35 dB&B⇔ℕfr£55 🅟
⚬ *xmas*
☻ French **V** ⚬ ⚖ ✱ S% Lunch £11.95 Dinner £14.95&alc Last
dinner 10pm
Credit Cards ①③④⑤
**See advertisement under CHEDDAR**

---

**AXMINSTER** Map **03** SY29

See Hawkchurch

---

**AYLESBURY** Buckinghamshire Map **04** SP81 ☺

**★★★★ 65% Forte Crest**
Aston Clinton Rd HP22 5AA (Forte Hotels) ☎(0296)393388
Telex no 838820 FAX (0296) 392211
*Opened in 1988 on the outskirts of the town, this is a modern*
*purpose-built hotel. Spacious public areas are comfortable and well*
*co-ordinated. The Club House Restaurant serves two fixed price*
*menus and an à la carte. Bedrooms are comfortable and well*
*equipped and the health and fitness club is a popular venue with*
*residents and members alike.*
94⇔ℕ(6fb)⚡in 22 bedrooms CTV in all bedrooms ® T ✱ S%
sB⇔ℕ£85 dB⇔ℕ£95 (room only) 🅟
Lift ( ⊞ 150P ✿ CFA ▱ (heated) sauna solarium gymnasium
*xmas*
☻ International **V** ⚬ ⚖ ✱ S% Lunch £12.95 Dinner
£15.90&alc Last dinner 9.30pm
Credit Cards ①②③⑤

**★★★**

**HARTWELL HOUSE**
Oxford Rd HP17 8NL (Small
Luxury Hotels)
☎(0296)747444
Telex no 837108
FAX (0296) 747450
*Recipient of our Southern*
*Region Best Newcomer*

*Award for 1990-91, Hartwell House, under the enthusiastic*
*Directorship of Johnathan Thompson, goes from strength to*
*strength. This elegant Grade 1 listed building with both*
*Jacobean and Georgian façades is owned by the small group*
*Historic House Hotels. Décor and furnishings throughout are*
*in keeping with the distinguished history of the house.*
*Beautifully proportioned reception rooms comprise 3 graceful*
*lounges, a stylish wood-panelled cocktail bar and 3 equally*
*glorious dining rooms. Bedrooms, especially those on the first*
*floor, are vastly spacious and very comfortable with an*
*abundance of modern facilities. Second-floor rooms are*
*smaller but equally rich in décor, furnishings and personal*
*touches, set off by the luxurious en suites. Chef Aidan*
*McCormack appears to have redressed the occasional*
*tendency to an over-complicated style, with quality dishes*
*making good use of fresh products with honest flavours and*
*textures. Praiseworthy are his duck foie gras and vegetable*
*terrine with toasted brioche, and loin of lamb with rosemary*
*gravy; and more unusual offerings such as smoked Lunesdale*
*duck with sherry and walnut dressing, and Ferndale quail*

*with clementine flavoured jus. Simply cooked vegetables and*
*rich home-made puddings complete the picture. At the time of*
*our last visit we were pleased to report the construction of new*
*luxury suites, function rooms, an additional restaurant and an*
*indoor leisure complex. Completion is anticipated by autumn*
*1991.*
32⇔ℕ5🖃 CTV in all bedrooms T ✖ (ex guide dogs)
S10% sB⇔ℕ£90-£128 dB⇔ℕ£135-£299 (room only) 🅟
Lift ( 60P ⇋ ✿ CFA ♪ croquet ♫ nc8yrs *xmas*
**V** ⚬ ⚖ S10% Lunch £19.50-£24&alc Dinner £33.50-
£38&alc Last dinner 9.45pm
Credit Cards ①②③⑤

---

**⊛⊛✖Pebbles**
1 Pebbles Ln HP20 2JH ☎(0296)86622
*The provincial English appearance of this little restaurant – two*
*small rooms in a beamed terrace cottage with stencilled*
*furnishings, set on a cobbled road leading to the church – contrasts*
*dramatically with the exuberance of the food served. Lunch menus*
*of different lengths include vegetarian options, the à la carte*
*selection exhibiting some robust and confident flavours while the*
*Menu Gastronomique concentrates on dishes in the light modern*
*style. Winter menus feature particularly good game dishes, 'pot*
*roasted fallow deer with braised red cabbage and poivrade sauce'*
*winning praise from our inspector. Home-made pasta and other*
*Italian ideas make occasional appearances while scallop mousse,*
*served hot in a jacket of smoked salmon with a champagne butter*
*sauce, and Confit of Challons Duckling with ginger sauce exhibit a*
*Continental influence. Desserts include both light and richer*
*options; fruit pastries and such traditional favourites as steamed*
*treacle pudding. Coffee is accompanied by excellent though pricey*
*petits fours, and the wine list is extensive.*
Closed Mon, 26 Dec & 1-3 Jan
Dinner not served Sun
☻ English & French V 32 seats ✱ Lunch £17.50 Dinner
fr£33alc Last lunch 2.15pm Last dinner 10pm ⚬
Credit Cards ①②③

---

**AYR** Strathclyde *Ayrshire* Map **10** NS32

See also Maybole

**★★★ 64% Caledonian**
Dalblair Rd KA7 1UG (Jarvis) ☎(0292)269331 Telex no 776611
FAX (0292) 610722
*The bright, spacious public areas of this centrally located, modern*
*hotel include a terrace café which is open from 7am to 11pm.*
*Many of the comfortable bedrooms have sea views and all are*
*attractively presented, with pastel décor and light wood furniture.*
114⇔ℕ in 22 bedrooms CTV in all bedrooms ® T
sB⇔ℕ£73.50 dB⇔ℕ£97 (room only) 🅟
Lift ( 70P CFA ▱ (heated) snooker sauna solarium
gymnasium jacuzzi *xmas*
☻ Scottish & French **V** ⚬ ⚖ ⚡ Lunch £6.50-£9.50&alc High
tea fr£6.50 Dinner £15.95&alc Last dinner 10pm
Credit Cards ①②③⑤ £

**★★★ 60% Pickwick**
19 Racecourse Rd KA7 2TD ☎(0292)260111 FAX (0292) 43174
*This Victorian business and tourist hotel set in its own grounds on*
*the south side of town, has comfortable well equipped bedrooms of*
*varying size. There is a small lounge and popular restaurant and*
*bar with an extensive bar menu.*
15⇔ℕ(3fb)🖃 CTV in all bedrooms ® T sB&B⇔ℕ£45-£50
dB&B⇔ℕ£80-£90 🅟
( 100P ⇋ ✿ CFA ♪ putting green ⚬ *xmas*
☻ Scottish & French **V** ⚬ ⚖ ✱ Lunch £8.50-£9.50 High tea
£5.95-£6.95&alc Dinner £14.95-£16.50&alc Last dinner 9.45pm
Credit Cards ①②③⑤ £

★★★ **53% Savoy Park**
16 Racecourse Rd KA7 2UT ☎(0292)266112
FAX (0292) 611488
*Old-established and family-run, this hotel remains a bastion of traditionalism; once a substantial mansion, it has country-house style rooms and some smaller, more functional ones.*
16⇨♠(4fb) CTV in all bedrooms ® T sB&B⇨♠£30-£45 dB&B⇨♠£45-£70 ♬
《 CTV 80P ❄ ᴔ *xmas*
♀ Scottish & French V ✧ ⚏ Bar Lunch fr£2.50alc High tea £5.65-£6.75 Dinner £12.50-£19 Last dinner 9pm
Credit Cards 1 2 3

★★ **69% Carrick Lodge**
46 Carrick Rd KA7 2RE ☎(0292)262846
*Bright, well equipped bedrooms, popular bar meals and a nicely appointed restaurant are features of this well maintained hotel situated on the south side of town.*
8⇨♠(2fb) CTV in all bedrooms ® T ✖ sB&B⇨♠£35-£37.50 dB&B⇨♠£55-£60 ♬
《 25P
V ✧ ⚏ ✳ Lunch £6.95-£7.25 High tea £5-£8 Dinner £14.50-£15&alc Last dinner 9.45pm
Credit Cards 1 2 3

★★ **67% Annfield**
49 Maybole Rd KA7 4SF ☎(0292)41986 FAX (0292) 43174
*Purpose-built in roadhouse style, this hotel on the south side of the town offers well equipped bedrooms and caters mainly for business guests.*
7⇨♠(1fb) CTV in all bedrooms ® T sB&B⇨♠£30-£35 dB&B⇨♠£50-£60 ♬
《 CTV 80P ❄ ✳ ᴖ games room ♪ *xmas*
♀ English & French V ✧ ⚏ Lunch £7.50-£8.95 High tea £5.50-£7.50alc Dinner £13.95-£15.05&alc Last dinner 10pm
Credit Cards 1 2 3 5 £

★★ **66% Elms Court**
21 Miller Rd KA7 2AX ☎(0292)264191 & 282332
FAX (0292) 610254
*Centrally situated between the town and seafront this is a family-run hotel with modest accommodation and friendly, professional service. Enjoyable bar meals are served in the recently refurbished lounge bar which is popular with locals at lunchtime.*
20⇨♠(4fb) CTV in all bedrooms ® T ✳ sB&B⇨♠£29.50 dB&B⇨♠£59
《 40P CFA *xmas*
♀ Scottish & French V ✧ ⚏ ✳ Lunch £4.95-£7alc High tea £5.15-£8.25alc Dinner £10.50&alc Last dinner 9.30pm
Credit Cards 1 2 3

★ **65% The Almont Hotel**
39 Charlotte St KA7 1EA ☎(0292)263814
*Compact, well maintained and friendly, this commercial/tourist hotel set between promenade and town centre serves simple, reasonably priced bar-style food in the dining room as well as the bar.*
14rm(1⇨6♠)(7fb)✕in 2 bedrooms CTV in all bedrooms ® ✳ sB&B£21 sB&B⇨♠£21 dB&B£42 dB&B⇨♠£42
CTV 12P snooker ♪
V ✧ ⚏ ✳ High tea fr£4.95 Dinner fr£11.95 Last dinner 9pm

★ **62% Aftongrange**
37 Carrick Rd KA7 2RD ☎(0292)265679
*Though this small, family-run, commercial hotel on the south side of the town can offer no lounge facilities other than its large bar, it is popular for the generous portions served in the dining room.*
8rm(1⇨4♠)(2fb) CTV in all bedrooms ® T ✳ sB&Bfr£20 sB&B⇨♠£25 dB&Bfr£36 dB&B⇨♠fr£42 ♬
30P pool table
V ✧ ⚏ ✳ Lunch £7.50 High tea £5-£7.75 Dinner £13 Last dinner 9pm

❀✖ **Fouters Bistro**
2A Academy St KA7 1HS ☎(0292)261391
Closed Mon, 25-27 Dec & 1-3 Jan Lunch not served Sun
♀ English & French V 38 seats Lunch £8.50&alc Dinner £15.50-£21.50alc Last lunch 2pm Last dinner 10.30pm ✗
Credit Cards 1 2 3 4 5

**AYTON, GREAT** North Yorkshire Map **08** NZ51

★★★ ❀♨ **74% Ayton Hall**
Low Green TS9 6BW ☎Middlesbrough(0642)723595
FAX (0642) 722149
*A Grade II listed building set in well tended grounds and claiming connections with Captain Cook has been personally converted by resident proprietors to retain its original character whilst providing luxurious bedrooms and relaxing public areas. The intimate restaurant offers interesting and imaginative menus following home-made soups, pâtés and starters like home-smoked chicken breast with such main courses as Beef cooked over Black Beer or a range of fresh fish dishes; Meringue Swan on a Lake of Blue Curacao remains an outstanding sweet choice, while the proprietor's real interest in wine is reflected in a superb list.*
9⇨♠(2fb)3☷✕in 1 bedroom CTV in all bedrooms T ✖ ✳ sB&B⇨♠£75-£105 dB&B⇨♠£105-£130 ♬
《 35P ❄ ♪ (hard) croquet archery nc11yrs *xmas*
♀ International V ✧ ⚏
Credit Cards 1 2 3 5 £

**BABBACOMBE**

See **Torquay**

**BAGINTON** Warwickshire Map **04** SP37

★★ **63% Old Mill**
Mill Hill CV8 3AH (Chef & Brewer) ☎Coventry(0203)303588
FAX (0203) 307070
*Many points of interest – notably an 18ft grinding wheel in the popular restaurant – are retained in the public areas of this village-centre hotel which was a working mill until the 1920s; spacious, well equipped bedrooms are provided with en suite facilities.*
20⇨(4fb)1☷ CTV in all bedrooms ® T ✖ (ex guide dogs) sB&B⇨£61 dB&B⇨£74 ♬
《 200P ❄ CFA ᴖ ᴔ
♀ International V ✧ ⚏ ✕ Bar Lunch £2.95-£5.50alc
Credit Cards 1 2 3 5

**BAGSHOT** Surrey Map **04** SU96 ❂

★★★★ ❀❀❀♨ **72% Pennyhill Park**
London Rd GU19 5ET (Small Luxury Hotels) ☎(0276)71774
FAX (0276) 73217
*Set in spacious, well kept gardens, this imposing country house has been extended to include unique designer accommodation connected to the main house by long covered walkways. Most bedrooms are very spacious with good quality furnishings, some have unusual open style bathrooms, and additional facilities set many bedrooms apart from the rest. The Latymer Restaurant and bar is rather confined, but recently improved with better seating, and there are 2 lounges and a garden terrace. A friendly atmosphere is engendered by the dedicated hotel management, and the standard of cooking is commendable. Chef David Richards continues to produce innovative and carefully prepared dishes.*
22⇨♠Annexe54⇨♠4☷✕in 31 bedrooms CTV in 56 bedrooms T ✖ (ex guide dogs) ✳ sB&B⇨♠£115-£184 dB&B⇨♠£135-£255 (room only) ♬
《 250P ❄ CFA ⌿ (heated) ► 9 ♪ (hard) ✈ ᴖ sauna solarium clay pigeon shooting croquet *xmas*
♀ English & French V ✧ ⚏ ✳ Lunch fr£21.50&alc Dinner fr£35alc Last dinner 10.30pm
Credit Cards 1 2 3 4 5

**See advertisement on page 95**

B

BAINBRIDGE North Yorkshire Map **07** SD99

**★★68% Rose & Crown**
Village Green DL8 3EE ☎Wensleydale(0969)50225
*Set in the heart of 'Herriot' country this 15th-century hotel has attractive, well-cared-for bedrooms, three bars and a comfortable lounge. The intimate restaurant provides enjoyable meals, using fresh local produce, the trout from the local fish farm can be especially recommended. Enthusiastic staff provide old-fashioned hospitality.*
12⇌↱(1fb)3⊟ CTV in all bedrooms ® sB&B⇌↱fr£43 dB&B⇌↱fr£68 ⊟
65P ✲ ♪
V ♢ ⊒ ✱ Sunday Lunch £7-£9.50alc Dinner £12.50-£15.50alc Last dinner 9.30pm
Credit Cards [1] [3]

BAKEWELL Derbyshire Map **08** SK26

During the currency of this publication some telephone numbers are liable to change.

**★★★70% Hassop Hall**
Hassop DE4 1NS ☎Great Longstone(062987)488
FAX (062987) 577
RS 24-26 Dec
*Quietly situated in a lovely parkland setting, close to the steeply wooded slopes of the Arboretum and surrounded by beautiful Peak District scenery, this hotel offers accommodation in rooms ranging from the somewhat compact to the positively huge. Hospitality is its strong point, the proprietor and his conscientious team providing friendly, attentive service.*
12⇌↱(2fb)2⊟ CTV in all bedrooms T ✱ sB⇌↱£59-£89 dB⇌↱£69-£99 (room only) ⊟
Lift 80P ✲ ⚲ (hard) croquet ♫
V ✱ Lunch £11.75 Dinner £19.95 Last dinner 9pm
Credit Cards [1] [2] [3] [5]

**★★★60% Rutland Arms**
The Square DE4 1BT (Best Western) ☎(0629)812812
FAX (0629) 812309
*Centrally situated in this small market town in the heart of the beautiful Peak District, this hotel is gradually being upgraded. It has a lively atmosphere by day and is a popular meeting place with locals. The accommodation is much used by tourists and the conference trade. Bedrooms vary in size and standard, there are some good examples while others are dated and more modest in comparison.*
19⇌↱Annexe17⇌(2fb) CTV in all bedrooms ® T sB&B⇌↱£42-£51 dB&B⇌↱£59-£69 ⊟
☾ 30P 2🚗 CFA ♫ *xmas*
☋ English & French V ♢ ⊒ Lunch £7.75-£9.50 High tea £6-£8 Dinner £16.95&alc Last dinner 9.45pm
Credit Cards [1] [2] [3] [5] £

**★★77% Croft Country House**
Great Longstone DE4 1TF ☎Great Longstone(062987)278 due to change to (0629) 640278
Closed 5 Jan-Feb
*This gem of a country house has warm, stylish rooms, very comfortable lounges, charming gardens and extremely hospitable hosts, who really make their guests feel welcome and relaxed.*
9rm(4⇌3↱) CTV in all bedrooms ® ✗ (ex guide dogs) sB&B£50-£55 sB&B⇌↱£50-£55 dB&B£62-£70 dB&B⇌↱£73-£81 ⊟
Lift CTV 30P ⊠ ✲ *xmas*
☋ English & French V ⊁ Dinner £18.50 Last dinner 6.30pm
Credit Cards [1] [3] £

For key to symbols in English see the bookmark.

**★★66% Milford House**
Mill St DE4 1DA ☎(0629)812130
Closed Jan & Feb RS Nov, Dec & Mar
*This old Georgian residence is peacefully set it its own attractive gardens, some 300 yards from the town centre. The Hunt family have owned and run the hotel for many years, and offer a high level of old-fashioned hospitality, making it a favourite with regular guests.*
12⇌↱ CTV in all bedrooms ® ✗ ✱ sB&B⇌↱£29.38-£31.73 dB&B⇌↱£56.40-£63.46
10P 7🚗 ⊠ ✲ nc10yrs
V ✱ Sunday Lunch £11.75-£12.34 Dinner £14.10-£15.28 Last dinner 7.30pm

BALA Gwynedd Map **06** SH93

**★★63% Bala Lake**
LL23 7YF (1m S on B4403) ☎(0678)520344 FAX (0678) 521193
*This former 18th-century hunting lodge is delightfully situated in spacious grounds, which stretch to the east shore of the lake. The hotel is approximately 1 mile south of the town. The accommodation is modest but well equipped, and all bedrooms have en suite facilities. The hotel has its own 9- hole golf course and outdoor swimming pool.*
1⇌Annexe12↱(2fb) CTV in all bedrooms ® T ⊟
40P 10🚗 ⊠ ⩫ (heated) ⚑ 9
♢ ⊒
Credit Cards [1] [3] [5]

**★★60% White Lion Royal**
61 High St LL23 7AE (Consort) ☎(0678)520314
Closed 25-26 Dec
*This large, imposing inn stands in the High Street and has an ample car park to the rear. It is privately owned and personally run by Mrs June Prescott. Many improvements have been undertaken in the last 12 months.*
26rm(22⇌↱)(3fb) CTV in all bedrooms ® T ✱ sB&B£18.65-£20.50 sB&B⇌↱£36-£40 dB&B£38-£42 dB&B⇌↱£61-£67.25 ⊟
CTV 30P CFA
V ♢ ⊒ ✱ Lunch £8.20-£9.25 Dinner £10.50-£13.50 Last dinner 8.30pm
Credit Cards [1] [2] [3] [5] £

**★★57% Plas Coch**
High St LL23 7AB ☎(0678)520309 FAX (0678) 521135
Closed 25 Dec
*This former 18th-century coaching inn is situated in the High Street and has its own rear car park. Accommodation is modest but fairly well equipped.*
10⇌↱(4fb) CTV in all bedrooms ® T sB&B⇌↱£32-£45 dB&B⇌↱£51 ⊟
20P ⊠ windsurfing canoeing sailing
V ♢ ⊒ ⊁ ✱ Lunch £7.50 Dinner £8.75-£9.75&alc Last dinner 8.30pm
Credit Cards [1] [2] [3] [5] £

BALDOCK Hertfordshire Map **04** TL23

**⌂Forte Travelodge**
Great North Rd, Hinxworth SG7 5EX (on A1, southbound) (Forte) ☎Hinxworth(0462)835329 Central Res (0800) 850950
*This lodge situated between junction 10 and 11 of the A1(M) offers well- equipped value-for-money accommodation and the facilities of an adjacent Happy Eater Restaurant.*
40⇌↱(40fb) CTV in all bedrooms ® sB⇌↱£29.95 dB⇌↱£29.95 (room only)
☾ 40P ⊠
Credit Cards [1] [2] [3]

## THE CROFT
## COUNTRY HOUSE HOTEL ★ ★
### & Restaurant
**Great Longstone, Bakewell,**
**Derbyshire DE4 1TF**
**Tel: (0629) 640278**

An interesting and secluded country house set in 4 acres, ideally situated for exploring the Peak National Park, Bakewell, Chatsworth and many other attractions. All 9 bedrooms are Victorian style and radiate from the featured galleried landing off the main hall. Fresh food, fine wine and good value with traditional hospitality are provided with Mini Breaks available throughout most of the year. The Restaurant is open to non residents throughout the week. Dinner served at 7.30pm. An ideal venue for a private party or family gathering.

*Ashley Courtenay recommended*

# PENNYHILL PARK PLAYS HOST TO THOSE WHO TREASURE PRIVACY AND QUIET

SURROUNDED by peace and tranquillity Pennyhill Park Hotel stands in 112 acres of legendary parkland and landscaped gardens to be enjoyed whatever the season.

Forty-eight bedrooms and suites, all beautifully furnished and retaining the original charm and character of a country manor. The Latymer Restaurant provides the elegance and quiet dignity expected from its surroundings. The food and service – known to many, is complemented by an oustanding selection of fine wines.

The Pennyhill Park Country Club's tempting pastimes are a nine-hole golf course, tennis courts, outdoor heated, Roman style swimming pool, horse-riding and clay pigeon shooting.

Whatever the occasion, Pennyhill Park offers a unique setting be it business or pleasure – *slip away now and enjoy us.*

*The Elegant Hayward Suite*

*Pennyhill Park*
HOTEL & COUNTRY CLUB

AA ★★★★

**B**

BALLACHULISH Highland *Argyllshire* Map **14** NN05

See also North Ballachulish

★★★59% **Ballachulish**

PA39 4JY (Inter-Hotels) ☎(08552)606 Telex no 94013696
FAX (08552) 629

*Set amid beautiful loch and mountain scenery, this is a family-run holiday hotel. Refurbished public areas are spacious and comfortable, and staff are friendly and willing, though room service at the time of our visit was uncharacteristically poor. Bedrooms vary in size but are comfortably furnished in sturdy pine, and well equipped. It is advisable to check the single occupancy supplement of a double or twin, the rate varies according to demand and at peak times may not be to everyone's liking!*

30⇥↖(3fb)1🛏 CTV in all bedrooms ® T ✱
sB&B⇥↖£44.50-£55.50 dB&B⇥↖£57-£98 🏳
《 50P 4🚗 ✿ CFA *xmas*
🍴 International V ✧ ⬛ ✱ Lunch £8-£25&alc High tea £5-£10&alc Dinner £19.50&alc Last dinner 10pm
Credit Cards ① ③ ⑤

**See advertisement under FORT WILLIAM**

○**The Isles of Glencoe**

PA39 ☎(08552)603
Due to open Apr 1992
39⇥↖

BALLATER Grampian *Aberdeenshire* Map **15** NO39

★★★★❀❀68% **Craigendarroch Hotel & Country Club**

Braemar Rd AB3 5XA ☎(03397)55858 Telex no 739952
FAX (0338) 55447

*Set in its own extensive grounds overlooking beautiful Deeside country, this popular leisure and conference hotel forms part of an extensive time-share and country club complex. The original mansion house has been sympathetically extended to provide the comforts and facilities required by the modern traveller. It has a friendly atmosphere and the young staff are helpful and willing to please. Brightly decorated bedrooms are furbished with attractive modern fabrics, leisure facilites are extensive and much in demand, and there is a choice of bars and restaurants. Scottish cuisine in the deft hands of Chef Ralph Porciani is very popular, with a Scottish evening with its set-priced menu being a major attraction on Thursday evenings.*

50⇥↖(6fb)1🛏✂in 10 bedrooms CTV in all bedrooms ® T ✈
✱ sB&B⇥↖£87-£170 dB&B⇥↖£118-£170 🏳
Lift 《 100P ✿ CFA ⌧ (heated) ℘ (hard) squash snooker sauna solarium gymnasium games room beauty salon creche ♫
♨ *xmas*
🍴 International V ✧ ⬛ ✂ ✱ Lunch £15.50&alc Dinner £17.50-£28.50&alc Last dinner 10pm
Credit Cards ① ② ③ ⑤

★★68% **Darroch Learg**

Braemar Rd AB35 5UX ☎(03397)55443
Closed Dec

*Set in 5 acres of grounds overlooking the golf course and the River Dee to the hills beyond, this comfortable family-run hotel is an ideal base from which to explore Royal Deeside. It offers a choice of relaxing lounges and enjoyable food is served in the attractive restaurant and new conservatory extension. Well equipped bedrooms are individually decorated, with a mixture of modern and traditional furnishings.*

15⇥↖Annexe6⇥↖1🛏✂in 4 bedrooms CTV in all bedrooms
® T S% sB&B⇥↖£30-£35 dB&B⇥↖£60-£80 🏳
25P ⇦ ✿ CFA
✧ ✂ S% Sunday Lunch £8.50-£10.50 Dinner fr£17 Last dinner 8.30pm
Credit Cards ① ③

★★59%, **Monaltrie**

5 Bridge Square AB35 5QJ (Inter-Hotels) ☎(03397)55417
FAX (03397) 55180

*This modernised Victorian hotel on the edge of the town is a popular base for tour groups, many of its well equipped and practically appointed bedrooms offering pleasant views of the River Dee, beside which it stands. Gradual improvements are being made, and a new development is the introduction of a secondary restaurant specialising in Thai cuisine.*

23rm(18⇥3↖)(3fb)1🛏 CTV in all bedrooms ® T ✱ S%
sB&B⇥↖£38.30-£40.85 dB&B⇥↖£56.20-£61.30 🏳
45P ✿ CFA *xmas*
🍴 Scottish & Thai V ✧ ⬛ ✂ ✱ S% Bar Lunch £3.50-£8.50alc
High tea £5.25 Dinner £15.95 Last dinner 8.30pm
Credit Cards ① ② ③ ⑤ ⑥

BALLOCH Strathclyde *Dunbartonshire* Map **10** NS38

★★★★❀❀❀74% **Cameron House Hotel and Country Estate**

G83 8QZ ☎(0389)55565 FAX (0389) 59522

*Opened in summer 1990, this international standard hotel, designed around a splendid turreted mansion set in extensive parkland on the banks of Loch Lomond, is aimed at the business and leisure market, with the emphasis on quality throughout. Bedrooms are beautifully furnished and very well equipped, and elegant lounges have the character of a fine country house. Facilities include a superb leisure centre, a marina and golf course. There is a choice of restaurants, with imaginative cuisine of a high standard that makes full use of fresh ingredients and local produce.*

68⇥↖(9fb)3🛏✂in 19 bedrooms CTV in all bedrooms ® T
✈ (ex guide dogs) ✱ sB&B⇥↖£110-£120 dB&B⇥↖£140-£150
Lift 《 150P ✿ CFA ⌧ (heated) ▶ 9 ℘ (hard) ✦ squash snooker sauna solarium gymnasium steamroom jacuzzi badminton ♫
V ✧ ⬛ ✂ Lunch fr£17&alc Dinner fr£22&alc Last dinner 10pm
Credit Cards ① ② ③ ⑤

BALSALL COMMON West Midlands Map **04** SP27 ⊙

★★❀68% **Haigs**

Kenilworth Rd CV7 7EL ☎Berkswell(0676)33004
FAX (0676) 34572
Closed 26 Dec-3 Jan

*A privately owned commercial hotel on the A452, convenient for the motorway network and within easy driving distance of the NEC and airport. Bedrooms are modest but well equipped for the business traveller, the atmosphere is friendly and caring, and the popular dining room serves a choice of well prepared food.*

13rm(12⇥5↖) CTV in all bedrooms ® T S% sB&B£25.25-£36.95 sB&B⇥↖£33.25-£49.95 dB&B£44.25-£64.95
dB&B⇥↖£49.25-£69.95
CTV 22P ⇦ ✿ nc4yrs
🍴 French V ✧ S% Sunday Lunch £9.75-£10.50 Dinner £15.25-£16&alc Last dinner 9pm
Credit Cards ① ③

**See advertisement under BIRMINGHAM (NATIONAL EXHIBITION CENTRE)**

BAMBURGH Northumberland Map **12** NU13

★★69% **Lord Crewe Arms**

Front St NE69 7BL ☎(06684)243
Closed Dec-Mar

*This attractive hotel, situated at the centre of the quaint village and managed by friendly resident proprietors, features pretty bedrooms, comfortable lounges and a good-value five-course dinner.*

25rm(14⇥6↖)(1fb) CTV in all bedrooms ® ✱ sB&B£32-£34
sB&B⇥↖£40-£43 dB&B£44-£46 dB&B⇥↖£58-£60 🏳

34P ⚑ nc5yrs
♀ English & French ✿ ✄ Lunch £3.50-£8alc Dinner £16.50-£17.50 Last dinner 9pm
Credit Cards ① ③

### ★★57% Victoria
Front St NE69 7BP ☎(06684)431
*A comfortable family-owned hotel in the centre of the village, with well equipped bedrooms.*
23rm(15⇨1♜)(3fb)1⊟ CTV in all bedrooms ® T sB&B£25-£30 sB&B⇨♜£30-£35 dB&B£40-£55 dB&B⇨♜£50-£70 ▤
7P CFA snooker games room *xmas*
V ✿ ✄ Lunch £7.50-£8 Dinner £16.50-£17.50&alc Last dinner 8.30pm
Credit Cards ① ② ③ ⑤

### ★59% Sunningdale
21-23 Lucker Rd NE69 7BS ☎(06684)334
*This family-managed hotel offers comfortable accommodation, and friendly service is assured. Bedroom accommodation is basic with some compact rooms.*
19rm(6⇨)(4fb)✄ in 2 bedrooms ® sB&B£18-£27 sB&B⇨♜£18-£32 dB&B£32-£44 dB&B⇨♜£36-£51.50 ▤
CTV 16P games room *xmas*
V ✿ Lunch £5 Dinner £12.50 Last dinner 7.30pm
Credit Cards ① ③ ⑤

---

**BAMFORD** Derbyshire Map **08** SK 28

### ★★59% *Rising Sun*
Castleton Rd S30 2AL (on main A625 rd)
☎Hope Valley(0433)51323
*Located on the A625 between Bamford and Castleton this attractive half- timbered hotel has a panelled à la carte restaurant and a separate bar/restaurant which serves hot dishes throughout the day. Conference and banqueting facilities are also available.*
11⇨♜(1fb) CTV in all bedrooms ® T ✖ (ex guide dogs)
70P ✿
V ✿ ⚏
Credit Cards ① ③

### ★★56% *Marquis of Granby*
Hathersage Rd S30 2BH ☎Hope Valley(0433)51206
*Standing in the beautiful Peak District, this friendly hotel is situated alongside the A625, and looks out on to pleasant lawns and gardens. Panelling from the SS Olympic is much in evidence, and the bedrooms, many of which are beamed, are spacious and well equipped. There is a choice of bars and a good range of restaurant and bar meals. Please note that the restaurant is closed on Mondays.*
7⇨♜(2fb)1⊟ CTV in all bedrooms ®
CTV 100P ✿ ♪
V ✿ ⚏
Credit Cards ① ② ③ ⑤

---

**BAMPTON** Devon Map **03** SS92

### ★★⊛69% *Bark House*
Oakford Bridge EX16 9HZ (2.5m W A396)
☎Oakford(03985)236
Closed 21 Dec-1 Mar
*Situated beside the A396 in the hamlet of Oakfordbridge near the River Exe. The hotel is a stone building, formerly a tannery. The well kept garden is terraced on the hillside of this Devonshire valley to picturesque effect. The bedrooms are comfortable and well-decorated, and the public rooms promote a cottage atmosphere. A warm welcome and good home cooking are offered.*
6rm(2⇨2♜)(1fb) CTV in 5 bedrooms T
12P 2🚗 (£1) ⚑ ✿ nc5yrs
♀ English, French & American ✿ ⚏ Last dinner 8.30pm
Credit Cards ① ③

**B**

---

### BANBURY Oxfordshire Map **04** SP44

#### ★★★ 67% Whately Hall

Banbury Cross OX16 0AN (Forte Hotels) ☎(0295)263451
Telex no 837149 FAX (0295) 271736

*Set back from the main road with well kept gardens and car
parking to the rear, this part 17th-century hotel has a welcoming
cosy atmosphere. Bedrooms, some in a modern wing, are
attractively decorated, with good modern facilities. Comfortable
public areas with wood panelling and open fires include a
restaurant offering a choice of menus.*

74⇔🎇✦in 15 bedrooms CTV in all bedrooms ® T ✱ S%
sB⇔🎇£75 dB⇔🎇£85 (room only) 🅟
Lift ( ▦ 60P 20🚣 ❀ CFA croquet & games room 🏊
♀ International V ❖ ⚏ ✦ ✱ S% Lunch £11.75&alc Dinner
£15.85 Last dinner 9.15pm
Credit Cards ①②③④⑤

#### ★★★ 64% Banbury Moat House

27-29 Oxford Rd OX16 9AH (Queens Moat) ☎(0295)259361
Telex no 838967 FAX (0295) 270954
Closed 26 Dec-1 Jan

*This busy hotel, situated on the main road into the town and
catering predominantly for commercial clients and conference
delegates, features bedrooms which have now been refurbished to a
good standard and well equipped with modern amenities;
attractive public areas include a pretty restaurant and traditional-
style Cellar Bar, and a selection of conference rooms in various
sizes is available. An enthusiastic, helpful and, for the most part,
young staff helps to create a pleasant, welcoming atmosphere.*

50⇔🎇(2fb)1🅟✦in 10 bedrooms CTV in all bedrooms ® T
sB&B⇔🎇£69 dB&B⇔🎇£79 🅟
( 48P
♀ International V ❖ ⚏ ✦ ✱ Lunch fr£11.50&alc Dinner
fr£13.50&alc Last dinner 9.45pm
Credit Cards ①②③⑤ⓔ

#### ★★ 62% Cromwell Lodge

North Bar OX16 0TB ☎(0295)259781
FAX (0295) 276619
Closed 1 wk Xmas & New Year

*Pleasant, professionally run hotel with pleasant staff. Modern, well
equipped bedrooms and attractive restaurant.*

32⇔🎇(1fb) CTV in all bedrooms ® T
( CTV 25P 🏊
♀ International V ❖ ⚏ Last dinner 9.30pm
Credit Cards ①②③④⑤

#### ★★ 61% Lismore Hotel & Restaurant

61 Oxford Rd OX16 9AJ ☎(0295)267661
Closed 24 Dec-3 Jan

*This 100-year-old hotel on the main Oxford to Banbury road offers
a homely and informal atmosphere which is popular with travelling
businessmen. Comfortable bedrooms are reasonably appointed
(though those in the annexe are somewhat limited in size) while
attractive public areas include a recently redecorated restaurant
serving an enjoyable evening meal. Friendly, relaxed staff and
management provide helpful service throughout.*

14rm(11⇔🎇)Annexe7⇔🎇(4fb)1🅟 CTV in all bedrooms ® T
✱ sB&B£30-£35 sB&B⇔🎇£45-£50 dB&B⇔🎇£60-£65 🅟
CTV 19P
♀ English & French V ❖ ⚏ Lunch £5.95-£14.50 Dinner
£12.50-£14.50 Last dinner 9.30pm
Credit Cards ①②③ⓔ

---

### BANCHORY Grampian *Kincardineshire* Map **15** NO69

#### ★★★★ ❀♨ 71% Invery House

Bridge of Feugh AB3 3NJ (Small Luxury Hotels) ☎(03302)4782
Telex no 73737 FAX (03302) 4712
Closed 5-25 Jan

*Set in 47 acres of woodland beside the west bank of the River
Feugh, this privately owned small hotel is an elegant haven of*

*peace. The stone-flagged entrance hall is adorned with fishing
trophies, though the hotel's appeal is by no means only to
sportsmen. The house has been tastefully and comfortably
furnished throughout and most of the spacious bedrooms, all
named after Walter Scott novels, have luxurious bathrooms and
thoughtful extras. The kitchen makes good use of fresh local
produce and dishes are rich and plentiful. Pleasant, helpful service
is provided by young staff under the personal supervision of the
resident proprietors.*

14⇔🎇1🅟 CTV in all bedrooms T ✖ (ex guide dogs)
sB&B⇔🎇£85-£135 dB&B⇔🎇£105-£165 🅟
( 20P 2🚣 ❀ CFA ♪ (grass) ✐ snooker croquet lawn
putting green nc8yrs *xmas*
♀ Scottish & French V ❖ ⚏ ✦ Lunch £16.50-£18.50 Dinner
£31.50-£34.50 Last dinner 9.45pm
Credit Cards ①②③⑤

---

★★★

#### ★★★ ❀♨ BANCHORY LODGE

AB3 3HS ☎(03302)2625
FAX (03302) 5019

Closed 13 Dec-Jan

*One of the most unpretentious
and honest of all our top-
rated hotels, this tremendous
fishing lodge is busy from one end of the year to the other. The
pleasant grounds run down to the banks of the River Dee,
where it is joined by the Feugh, and many an hour can idle by
watching the salmon as they leap upstream. Under the same
ownership for over 25 years now, the Lodge has been extended
by the Jaffreys in a sympathetic manner. The key to its
success remains the Jaffrey family involvement, although they
are ably assisted by a team of staff, some of whom have been
with them for many years. One such individual is the cook,
Rosemary Shiach, who not surprisingly makes much of the
fresh Dee salmon that makes the short journey from water to
table. The hotel's public rooms are comfortable and peaceful,
with a choice of lounges, a bar, and a traditionally styled
dining room. Breakfast is served in a separate oak panelled
room. Bedrooms are subject to ongoing upgrading and those in
the newer wings are particularly spacious, and all are well
equipped. A lovely holiday retreat for fishers and non-fishers
alike, and close enough to Aberdeen to entice the selective
business person for a stay.*

23⇔🎇(11fb)2🅟 CTV in all bedrooms ®
CTV 50P 🚣 ❀ ✐ sauna pool table 🏊
♀ English & French V ❖ ⚏ Last dinner 9.30pm
Credit Cards ①②③④⑤

---

#### ★★★ ❀♨ 75% Raemoir

AB3 4ED ☎(03302)4884 Telex no 73315 FAX (03302) 2171
Closed 12-24 Jan

*An eighteenth-century manor house set in extensive wooded
grounds offers a unique blend of natural charm and traditional
values which will appeal to conference groups, visiting
holidaymakers, businessmen and sporting enthusiasts alike. Day
rooms with well worn antiques, an abundance of fresh flowers and
welcoming open fires have a comfortably 'lived-in' atmosphere,
while bedrooms are very individual, ranging from Master rooms
with tapestried walls and fine antiques to the more compact
standard rooms with their homely appointments. A young chef
makes excellent use of fresh raw produce in creating the interesting
range of dishes served in the attractive Georgian restaurant, and
the proprietors continue to provide their own special brand of
hospitality.*

**B**

18➪ Annexe6➪ (1fb)1⊞ CTV in all bedrooms ® T ✷
sB&B➪£65-£85 dB&B➪£105-£125 ⊟
CTV 200P ⊞ ❈ CFA ♪ (hard) ✔ sauna solarium gymnasium
croquet mini golf shooting stalking ♣ xmas
♥ International V ♦ ⬛ ✗ ✷ Bar Lunch £2.50-£12alc Dinner
£24-£25&alc Last dinner 9pm
Credit Cards ① ② ③ ⑤ ⑥

**★★★66% Tor-na-Coille**
AB31 4AB ☎(03302)2242 FAX (03302) 4012
Closed 3-31 Jan
*The enthusiastic owner of this lovely Victorian hotel – which
stands among mature pine trees at the west end of the town –
continues to make good progress with her ambitious improvement
programme. Tastefully appointed day rooms with welcoming open
fires invite relaxation, while comfortable bedrooms individually
furnished with Victorian and Edwardian pieces are thoughtfully
equipped.*
24➪ (4fb) CTV in all bedrooms ® T sB&B➪£55-£81
dB&B➪£76-£97 ⊟
Lift 130P ❈ squash croquet lawn xmas
♥ Scottish & French V ♦ ⬛ ✗ Lunch £14&alc Dinner
£20&alc Last dinner 9.30pm
Credit Cards ① ② ③ ⑤

**See advertisement on page 101**

**★★61% Burnett Arms**
25 High St AB3 3TD (Consort) ☎(03302)4944 Telex no 739925
*This modernised old coaching inn on the main street close to the
town centre amenities offers traditional comforts in the public
rooms, including two popular bars, a lounge and dining room, while
the rather compact bedrooms are well equipped and functional.*
16➪ (2fb)1⊞ CTV in all bedrooms ® T sB&B➪£32-£36
dB&B➪£45-£49 ⊟
40P CFA ♫ xmas

→

**B**

V ✿ ⌐ Lunch £5.50-£15alc High tea £5-£12alc Dinner £13-£16
Last dinner 9pm
Credit Cards ① ② ③ ④ ⑤ ⓔ

---

### BANFF Grampian *Banffshire* Map **15** NJ66

**★★★56% Banff Springs**
Golden Knowes Rd AB45 2JE (Consort) ☎(02612)2881 due to
change to (0261) 812881 FAX (02612) 5546
*A popular venue for local functions, this modern, purpose-built
hotel stands on the edge of the town overlooking the Moray Firth.
Bedrooms, though practical in style, are comfortable and well
equipped.*
30⇨↑(4fb) CTV in all bedrooms ® T ✱ sB&B⇨↑£38.50
dB&B⇨↑£55 ⊟
( 120P CFA *xmas*
♀ French V ✿ ⌐ ✱ Lunch £8.50 Dinner £12.75&alc Last
dinner 9pm
Credit Cards ① ② ③ ④ ⑤ ⓔ

---

### BANGOR Gwynedd Map **06** SH57

**★★73% Menai Court**
Craig y Don Rd LL57 2BG ☎(0248)354200
Closed 27 Dec-7 Jan
*This delightful privately owned and personally run hotel is situated
conveniently close to the town centre and railway station. It
provides good quality, very well equipped accommodation, warm
and friendly service, and has earned a deservedly high reputation
for its imaginative cuisine.*
12⇨↑(2fb) CTV in all bedrooms ® T ✱ sB&B⇨↑£44-£48
dB&B⇨↑£81 ⊟
22P ⇱ *xmas*
♀ British & French V ✿ Lunch £11.50-£12.50 Dinner £15-
£20alc Last dinner 9.30pm
Credit Cards ① ③

**★★65% Ty Uchaf**
Tal-y-Bont LL57 3UR ☎(0248)352219
Closed 24 Dec-2 Jan
*A pleasant inn 2 miles east of Bangor in the small village of Tal-y-
Bont, run in friendly informal style. Meals are served in both the
restaurant and bar, next to the cosy lounge, and the comfortable
well equipped bedrooms are suitable for tourists or business people.*
9⇨↑ CTV in all bedrooms ® ✈ (ex guide dogs) ✱
sB&B⇨↑£25-£30 dB&B⇨↑£45-£50 ⊟
40P ❀ nc10yrs
V ✿ ⌐ ✱ Bar Lunch £7-£12 Dinner £9.50-£12.50&alc Last
dinner 8.30pm
Credit Cards ① ③

**★★63% Telford**
Holyhead Rd LL57 2HX ☎(0248)352543
*Once a private house, built in the late eighteenth-century for the
Devies family whose shipping company was the inspiration behind
the Onedin Line saga, an hotel in two acres of terraced gardens
commands spectacular views from its position beside the famous
suspension bridge, right on the edge of the Menai Straights; its
position also makes it popular with travellers to and from the Irish
Ferry Terminal at Holyhead. Family-run, it has a well deserved
reputation for friendliness and hospitality.*
10rm(4↑)(2fb)⊱in 2 bedrooms CTV in 9 bedrooms TV in 1
bedroom ✈ (ex guide dogs) ✱ ⊟
( ⊞ CTV 15P ❀ CFA ♪
V ✿ ⌐ ✱ ✱ Lunch £6.50-£8.50 Dinner £12.50-£19.50alc Last
dinner 9pm
Credit Cards ① ③

---

A rosette means exceptional standards of cuisine.

---

### BARDON MILL Northumberland Map **12** NY76

**★67% Vallum Lodge**
Military Rd, Twice Brewed NE47 7AN
☎Haltwhistle(0434)344248
Closed Dec-Feb RS Nov-Mar
*A small, friendly hotel, peacefully set beside the B6318 in open
countryside close to Hadrian's Wall, offers warm, comfortable
bedrooms, a cosy lounge and a separate small bar; resident owners
make sure that their guests are well cared for, and good home
cooking is provided.*
7rm(2⇨↑) ® sB&B£18.50-£21 dB&B£35-£38 dB&B⇨↑£42-
£45 ⊟
CTV 30P ⇱ ❀
V ✿ ⌐ ✔ Bar Lunch £2.75-£5.50alc Dinner £12 Last dinner
8pm

---

### BARFORD Warwickshire Map **04** SP26

**★★★66% The Glebe at Barford**
Church St CV35 8BS ☎Warwick(0926)624218
FAX (0926) 624625
*Off the A429 on the edge of the peaceful village, this hotel was
totally refurbished in 1990 to provide excellent facilities for
business and leisure guests in the 90s. En suite bedrooms of varying
size are all well furnished with quality fabrics and the latest
facilities, and comfortable public areas include a choice of bars and
a conservatory restaurant.*
36⇨↑(3fb)5⊞ CTV in all bedrooms ® T ✱ sB&B⇨↑£85-
£95 dB&B⇨↑£99.50-£115 ⊟
Lift ( 56P ❀ CFA ▣ (heated) sauna gymnasium jacuzzi steam
room croquet lawn *xmas*
♀ English & Continental V ✿ ⌐ ✱ Lunch £6.15-£15.15alc
Dinner fr£16.50&alc Last dinner 9.45pm
Credit Cards ① ② ③ ⑤ ⓔ

---

### BAR HILL Cambridgeshire Map **05** TL36

**★★★62% Cambridgeshire Moat House**
CB3 8EU (Queens Moat) ☎Crafts Hill(0954)780555
Telex no 817141 FAX (0954) 780010
Closed 24-26 Dec
*Ideally situated just off the A604 5.5 miles north of the city centre,
this modern hotel is surrounded by 134-acre grounds; excellent
leisure facilities include an 18-hole golf course, indoor swimming
pool, mini-gym, solarium and steam room, tennis and squash
courts. Identically furnished and equipped bedrooms offer a high
standard of comfort, there is a choice of bars, and a good range of
meeting rooms is available.*
100⇨↑(8fb) CTV in all bedrooms ® T ✱ sB&B⇨↑£51.50-
£71.50 dB&B⇨↑£78-£88.90 ⊟
( 200P ❀ CFA ▣ (heated) ▶ 18 ♪ (hard) squash sauna
solarium gymnasium putting green ♪
♀ English & French V ✿ ⌐ ✱ Lunch £15.50&alc Dinner
£15.50&alc Last dinner 10pm
Credit Cards ① ② ③ ⑤

---

### BARKSTON Lincolnshire Map **08** SK94

**❀ ✕ ✕ Barkston House**
NG32 2NH ☎Loveden(0400)50555
*Sound British dishes with fresh produce treated in a light, modern
style, form the basis of the short but imaginative menu here, where
the quality of food is matched by charming attentive service. The
dining room – originally the kitchen of the pleasant eighteenth-
century house – has stripped beams, complete with servants' bells,
and open fireplace. The warm, country atmosphere carries through
to an attractive sitting room and a large, comfortable bar. Two fine
bedrooms are available for overnight guests.*
Closed Sun, Mon, 25-30 Dec & 2 wks Jun Lunch not served Sat

---

28 seats ✻ Lunch £11 Dinner fr£16.85alc Last lunch 1.30pm
Last dinner 9.15pm 16 P
Credit Cards 1 2 3 5

---

**BARMOUTH** Gwynedd Map **06** SH61

★★65% **Ty'r Graig**
Llanaber Rd LL42 1YN ☎(0341)280470
Closed Nov-Feb
*This large detached late Victorian house, of unusual architecture,
is located approximately half a mile from the town centre. It
stands in its own attractive gardens and wooded grounds in an
elevated position overlooking the beach and Cardigan Bay. The
public areas are elegant, and tastefully furnished and decorated,
and have a wealth of carved pitch pine woodwork and stained glass
leaded windows. The bedrooms are well equipped, all with en suite
facilities.*
12⇨♪2✍🍴in 1 bedroom CTV in all bedrooms ® T
✖ (ex guide dogs) sB&B⇨♪£36-£40 dB&B⇨♪£52-£68 ▤
15P ⇔ ❄ windsurfing yachting sea fishing
♡ Welsh, English & French V ✧ ⬛ 🍴 ✻ Sunday Lunch £8.50
Dinner £14&alc Last dinner 8.30pm
Credit Cards 1 3

---

★★62% **Panorama**
Panorama Rd LL42 1DQ ☎(0341)280550 FAX (0341) 280346
*This large stone built Victorian hotel is aptly named as it does,
indeed, enjoy panoramic views from its elevated position. Family-
run in an informal manner the hotel provides comfortable
accommodation suitable for both holidaymakers and business
people alike.*
19rm(15⇨♪)(4fb) CTV in all bedrooms ® T ✻ sB&B£19
sB&B⇨♪£28-£33 dB&B£38 dB&B⇨♪£50-£55 ▤
CTV 40P ❄ CFA putting green nc2yrs

→

B

♈ English & French **V** ♧ 🎜 ✱ Sunday Lunch £7.50 Dinner
£11.25&alc Last dinner 9.30pm
Credit Cards 1 3 £

★63% **Bryn Melyn**
Panorama Rd LL42 1DQ ☎(0341)280556 FAX (0341) 280276
Closed Dec-Feb
*A small family run hotel in an elevated position east of the town,
commanding splendid views across the Mawddach Estuary to the
Cader Mountains. The bedrooms are quite well equipped, the
majority have en suite showers and toilets.*
10rm(8♟)(2fb) CTV in 9 bedrooms ® T sB&Bℝfr£28.50
dB&Bℝfr£48 🏳
10P 🚗 ❀
**V** ♧ ✱ Bar Lunch fr£3.50 Dinner fr£11.50 Last dinner 8.30pm
Credit Cards 1 3 £

★60% *Marwyn*
21 Marine Pde LL42 1NA ☎(0341)280185
*A small, seafront hotel enjoying views of the beach, Cardigan Bay
and the Mawddach Estuary. The majority of the well equipped
bedrooms have en suite facilities.*
7⇔ℝ(1fb)1🛏 CTV in all bedrooms ®
CTV 🚗 nc7yrs
**V** ♧ 🎜 Last dinner 11pm
Credit Cards 1 3

★★★60% *Ye Olde Bell*
DN22 8QS ☎Retford(0777)705121 FAX (0777) 860424
*This traditional English hotel has maintained its character despite
modernisation, and offers open fires during the winter, comfortable
bedrooms and various conference/function rooms.*
55⇔ℝ(4fb)1🛏⅍in 18 bedrooms CTV in all bedrooms ® T
《 250P ❀ putting green ⚙
**V** ♧ 🎜 ⅍ Last dinner 9.45pm
Credit Cards 1 2 3 5

❀✕**Mims**
63 East Barnet Rd EN4 8RN ☎081-449 2974 & 081-447 1825
Lunch not served Sat
♈ Continental 50 seats ✱ Lunch £12.50 Dinner £20.50 Last
lunch 3pm Last dinner 11pm 6 P nc8yrs
Credit Cards 1 3

★★★65% **Barnham Broom Hotel Conference & Leisure**
Centre NR9 4DD (Best Western) ☎(060545)393
FAX (060545) 8224
*An hotel 10 miles outside Norwich, easily located from the A47
and set amid 250 acres which include a championship golf course,
provides excellent sporting facilities, recently refurbished public
areas and well equipped bedrooms which should be similarly
upgraded by the end of 1991.*
52⇔ℝ CTV in all bedrooms ® T 🐕 (ex guide dogs) ✱
sB&B⇔ℝ£59.50-£65 dB&B⇔ℝ£79.50-£85 🏳
《 200P CFA ▱ (heated) ▶ 36 ♟ (hard) squash snooker sauna
solarium gymnasium hairdressing salon beautician *xmas*
♈ English & Continental **V** ♧ 🎜 ⅍ S% Lunch £8-£9 Dinner
£13-£13.50&alc Last dinner 9.30pm
Credit Cards 1 2 3 5 £

**See advertisement under NORWICH**

Hotels with red star ratings are
especially high quality.

⌂**Forte Travelodge**
Wentbridge WF8 3JB (on A1, southbound) (Forte)
☎Pontefract(0977)620711 Central Res (0800) 850950
Telex no 557457
*Located on the south-bound carriageway of the A1 just 8 miles
north of Doncaster, the lodge stands adjacent to a Little Chef
restaurant and shop in a busy service area.*
56⇔ℝ(56fb) CTV in all bedrooms ® sB⇔ℝ£29.95
dB⇔ℝ£29.95 (room only)
《 56P 🚗
Credit Cards 1 2 3

★★★66% **Ardsley Moat House**
Doncaster Rd, Ardsley S71 5EH (Queens Moat) ☎(0226)289401
Telex no 547762 FAX (0226) 205374
Closed 25 Dec
*This converted 18th-century mansion with popular conference
facilities has recently been upgraded to provide good
accommodation and modern public areas. The Allendale
restaurant serves a varied selection of dishes and guests can choose
between the cocktail bar and more lively Joplins Pub.*
73⇔ℝ(3fb)3🛏⅍in 6 bedrooms CTV in all bedrooms ® T
sB⇔ℝ£61-£64 dB⇔ℝ£74-£77 (room only) 🏳
《 300P ❀ snooker 🎜
♈ English & French **V** ♧ 🎜 ✱ Lunch fr£10.75&alc Dinner
fr£14.50&alc Last dinner 10.30pm
Credit Cards 1 2 3 5 £

⌂**Forte Travelodge**
(at Stairfoot roundabout A633/A635) (Forte)
☎(0226)298799 Central Res (0800) 850950
*On the south-east of the town off the (Stairfoot) roundabout
junction of the A633 and A635, with access only from the A633
approaching the roundabout. It is set back from the road next to a
little Chef restaurant.*
32⇔ℝ(32fb) CTV in all bedrooms ® sB⇔ℝ£29.95
dB⇔ℝ£29.95 (room only)
《 32P 🚗
Credit Cards 1 2 3

★★★62% **Park**
Taw Vale EX32 8NJ (Brend) ☎(0271)72166 Telex no 42551
FAX (0271) 78558
*Situated by Rock Park overlooking the river, this popular family
run hotel offers friendly service and a relaxing atmosphere. A new
bedroom annexe provides good modern standards of
accommodation, while other bedrooms and en suites are being
further upgraded.*
25⇔ℝAnnexe17⇔ℝ(7fb) CTV in all bedrooms ® T
sB&B⇔ℝ£49.50-£55 dB&B⇔ℝ£75-£88 🏳
《 80P 🎜 *xmas*
♈ English & French **V** ♧ 🎜 Lunch £7.50&alc Dinner £11.50-
£16.50&alc Last dinner 9pm
Credit Cards 1 2 3 5 £

★★❀♨69% **Downrew House**
Bishops Tawton EX32 0DY ☎(0271)42497 & 46673
FAX (0271) 23947
*Good levels of hospitality in a relaxed environment are enhanced
here by the worthy food standards promoted by Chef Paul Bending
who produces well presented dishes such as crab and mango
mousse, game terrine in a spring onion sauce, venison with a rich
Port wine and bacon sauce, saddle of rabbit with a sherry and
green pepper sauce, and a range of tempting home-made puddings.
The house itself, originally built in 1640, stands in 12 acres of
meadow and amid attractive countryside just a few miles outside
Barnstaple and now easily accessible from the new link road.*

Compact but attractively appointed public areas offer cosy comfort, while bedrooms are for the most part charming and personally furnished, only those in the adjoining lodge tending to be more functional ; recent improvements include the installation of satellite TV and restaurant refurbishment. The hotel also boasts a 5-hole pitch and putt and outdoor swimming pool neatly tucked away in the gardens.

6⇨📞Annexe6⇨📞(2fb) CTV in all bedrooms ® T ✱ sB&B⇨📞£52.25-£67.50 dB&B⇨📞£80.80-£107 🛏
20P 🚗 ❀ CFA ⌕ (heated) ♟ (hard) snooker solarium golf (5 hole approach & putt) croquet nc7yrs *xmas*
♡ English & Continental V ✂ ✱ Lunch £15.30-£24.35alc Dinner £15&alc Last dinner 9.15pm
Credit Cards ① ③

★★ 66% **Royal & Fortescue**
Boutport St EX31 1HG (Brend) ☎(0271)42289 Telex no 42551 FAX (0271) 78558
*A choice of dining room and all-day coffee shop are available at this bustling town-centre commercial hotel. Management is efficient and service friendly, whilst the bedrooms are all well equipped, though they vary in style.*
62rm(35⇨📞)(4fb) CTV in all bedrooms ® T sB&B£22 sB&B⇨📞£33-£45 dB&B£38 dB&B⇨📞£49-£66 🛏
Lift ( CTV 20P 6🛆 ♫ *xmas*
♡ English & French V ✌ ⌑ Lunch £7-£8&alc Dinner £11.50&alc Last dinner 9pm
Credit Cards ① ② ③ ⑤ ⑥

**See advertisement on page 105**

**B**

★❀♨

**HALMPSTONE MANOR**

Bishop's Tawton EX32 0EA
☎(0271)830321
FAX (0271) 830826

*Jane and Charles Stanbury
have been much praised for
their small hotel which, rather
unusually, forms part of a
working farm just south of Barnstaple, in lovely rolling
countryside. Guests are warmly greeted by friendly hosts
whose hospitality and care are a consistent feature of a stay
here. Guest rooms are carefully planned with beautiful soft
furnishings, and offer a good degree of comfort, particularly
the 2 4-poster rooms. A decanter of sherry and fresh fruit and
flowers are welcoming touches. The cosy lounge is particularly
inviting when the open fire is blazing, and here guests may
enjoy an aperitif while perusing Jane Stanbury's menus. Good
local produce is prepared with skill, and enjoyable dinners are
served in the wood-panelled dining room where service is well
paced and thoughtful. For old-fashioned standards of service,
excellent accommodation and good food, Halmpstone Manor
is hard to beat.*

5⇄🛏2🖺 CTV in all bedrooms ® T ✱ sB&B⇄🛏£48-£60
dB&B⇄🛏£64-£100 🖩

12P 🚗 ❀ nc10yrs *xmas*

♡ English & French ✱ Lunch £20&alc Dinner £20&alc
Last dinner 9.30pm
Credit Cards ①②③ⓔ

○**Forte Travelodge**
South Molton(Forte) ☎Central Res (0800) 850950
Due to have opened Winter 1991
31⇄🛏

❀ ✕✕✕**Lynwood House**
Bishops Tawton EX32 9DZ ☎(0271)43695
FAX (0271) 79340

*This stylish but not too formal restaurant with rooms, a detached
villa in a residential area, retains the atmosphere of a private
residence at the hands of the Roberts family who have run it for
some considerable time. In the relaxing atmosphere of the
personally furnished dining room, fresh, imaginative dishes based
on quality produce are served. Seafood features strongly in creamy
fish soups, well made terrines and pâtés, grilled scallops, Dover
sole and brill, but there is also a selection of meat options like
crispy duck or English lamb; rich and tempting home-made
puddings include a light meringue with butterscotch sauce and a
chocolate cup with complementary white chocolate sauce. Prompt,
hospitable service is professional without being pretentious.
Lunch not served Sun*

♡ British & Continental V 50 seats ✱ Lunch £15-£25alc
Dinner £15-£25alc Last lunch 2pm Last dinner 9.30pm 35 P ✂
Credit Cards ①③

**BARRA, ISLE OF** Western Isles *Inverness-shire* Map **13**

**TANGUSDALE** Map **13** NF60

★★62% **Isle of Barra**
Tangusdale Beach PA80 5XW (Consort) ☎Castlebay(08714)383
FAX (08714) 385
Closed Nov-Mar RS Apr
*Situated beside one of the island's most attractive sandy beaches,
to which there is easy access, this purpose-built, modern hotel offers
pleasant, comfortable public areas, and functional bedrooms, some
of which enjoy fine views of the sea. Service is friendly and helpful.*

30⇄🛏(2fb) CTV in all bedrooms ® sB&B⇄🛏£35-£39
dB&B⇄🛏£59.50-£65 🖩
CTV 🅿 ❀ CFA ♪
V ♡ 🕮 ✱ Dinner £13.50-£15 Last dinner 8.30pm
Credit Cards ①③ⓔ

**BARR, GREAT** West Midlands Map **07** SP09

★★★62% **Forte Posthouse Birmingham**
Chapel Ln B43 7BG (at junction M6/A34) (Forte Hotels)
☎021-357 7444 Telex no 338497 FAX 021-357 7503
*Bedrooms are currently being refurbished to a good standard at
this hotel, which has extensive leisure and conference facilities and
a choice of eating options, with a restaurant and coffee shop. Staff
provide helpful and attentive service.*

204⇄🛏(42fb)⚥in 100 bedrooms CTV in all bedrooms ® T ✱
sB⇄🛏£39.50-£49.50 dB⇄🛏£39.50-£49.50 (room only) 🖩
《 300P CFA ☐ (heated) ⊇ (heated) sauna solarium
gymnasium *xmas*
V ♡ 🕮 ✕✱ S% Bar Lunch fr£1.50
Credit Cards ①②③④⑤

★★★60% **Great Barr Hotel & Conference Centre**
Pear Tree Dr, off Newton Rd B43 6HS (1m W of junc A34/
A4041) ☎021-357 1141 Telex no 336406 FAX 021-357 7557
*This busy, conference-orientated hotel, set close to junction 7 of the
M6 and offering easy access to both Birmingham and Walsall,
provides bedrooms which, though compact, have good facilities and
are geared to the needs of the business traveller.*

114⇄🛏(1fb) CTV in all bedrooms ® T ✱ (ex guide dogs) ✱
S% sB&B⇄🛏£30-£62 dB&B⇄🛏£40-£72 🖩
《 175P ❀ CFA
♡ English & Continental V ♡ 🕮 ✱ Lunch £9&alc Dinner
fr£12.50&alc Last dinner 9.45pm
Credit Cards ①②③④⑤ⓔ

**BARRHEAD** Strathclyde *Renfrewshire* Map **11** NS45

★★62% **Dalmeny Park**
Lochlibo Rd G78 1LG ☎041-881 9211
*On the A376 on the southern side of town, this business and
function hotel in a 19th-century house with gardens has a popular
lounge bar serving a wide range of bar meals as well as a
restaurant and cocktail lounge.*

18rm(3⇄🛏10🛏)(2fb) CTV in all bedrooms ® T ✱ sB&B£30-
£43 sB&B⇄🛏£40-£56 dB&B£50-£62 dB&B⇄🛏£52-£87 🖩
《 150P ❀ CFA
V ♡ 🕮 ✱
Credit Cards ①②③④⑤ⓔ

**BARROW-IN-FURNESS** Cumbria Map **07** SD16 ◎

★★66% *Lisdoonie*
307/309 Abbey Rd LA14 5LF ☎(0229)27312
Closed Xmas & New Year
*A friendly, homely atmosphere pervades this long-established and
family-run private hotel which stands on the main approach road to
Barrow. Bedrooms vary in size but are all well equipped, and
popular function facilities are available.*

12⇄🛏(2fb) CTV in all bedrooms ® T
CTV 30P
♡ English & French ♡ 🕮 Last dinner 7.30pm
Credit Cards ①②③

★★65% **Majestic**
Duke St LA14 1HP ☎(0229)870448
*Total refurbishment has considerably enhanced this Edwardian
hotel in the town centre. Bedrooms, all with en suite facilities, are
particularly well equipped and service is friendly and helpful.*

34⇄🛏🛏(2fb)1🖺 CTV in all bedrooms ® T ✱ (ex guide dogs)
✱ sB&B⇄🛏£27-£40 dB&B⇄🛏£40-£52.50 🖩
Lift 《 CTV 26P CFA pool tables *xmas*

V ✿ ⬛ ✻ Lunch £5.55-£9 Dinner £9.85-£15.70 Last dinner 9.30pm
Credit Cards 1 2 3 £

---

BARRY South Glamorgan Map **03** ST16

★★★⬛ ⬛76% **Egerton Grey Country House**
Porthkerry CF6 9BZ (Welsh Rarebits) ☎(0446)711666
FAX (0446) 711690
*This 19th-century former rectory, converted to hotel use in 1988, stands at the head of a steep wooded valley which ends in a golf course and shingled beach ; its view of the sea is framed by a listed viaduct across which trains occasionally pass. Several comfortable lounges and even more comfortable bedrooms are equipped with furniture appropriate to the house's early days, and the original names of rooms are still kept – 'The Nursery ;, for example, or 'Uncle Fred's'. The restaurant, which attracts a wide-ranging and discerning clientèle, bases its dishes on only the freshest of ingredients, deliberately keeping the menu short to concentrate on the local Welsh produce which is so popular ; vegetarian dishes are always available, and the wine list should suit every taste and pocket.*
10⟶🛏(4fb)2🛏 CTV in all bedrooms ® T sB&B⟶🛏£55-£95 dB&B⟶🛏£75-£110 Continental breakfast 🅿
30P ⬛ ✿ ▶ 9 ♪ (hard) croquet ⬛ *xmas*
V ✿ ⬛ ⬛ ✻ Lunch £14.75-£19.50alc High tea £5-£10alc Dinner £19.50-£22.50alc Last dinner 9.45pm
Credit Cards 1 2 3 £

**See advertisement under CARDIFF**

★★★57% **Mount Sorrell**
Porthkerry Rd CF6 8AY (Consort) ☎(0446)740069
FAX (0446) 746600
*This purpose-built commercial hotel overlooking the Bristol Channel features an excellent new leisure complex and quite good function facilities. Many bedrooms have been completely modernised and upgrading is planned for all of them.*
45⟶🛏 Annexe4⟶🛏(3fb) CTV in all bedrooms ® T sB&B⟶🛏£53-£63 dB&B⟶🛏£65-£80 🅿
⟨ 17P CFA ⬛ (heated) sauna gymnasium *xmas*
♀ Continental V ✿ ⬛ ⬛ S% Lunch £9.50-£13.50 Dinner £12.80-£14.25&alc Last dinner 10pm
Credit Cards 1 2 3 4 5 £

---

BARTON Lancashire Map **07** SD53

★★★62% **Barton Grange**
Garstang Rd PR3 5AA (Best Western)
☎Broughton(0772)862551 Telex no 67392 FAX (0722) 861267
*Barton Grange is situated 6 miles north of Preston, on the A6, next to a large garden centre. Bedrooms are well equipped but many are dated, although upgrading is planned during 1991. The 14 executive bedrooms are of a very good standard. There are flexible banqueting and conference facilities, gardens, swimming pool, and a coffee shop as well as the main restaurant.*
56⟶🛏 Annexe10⟶🛏(10fb)1🛏 CTV in all bedrooms ® T 🐕 (ex guide dogs) ✻ sB&B⟶🛏£64-£70 dB&B⟶🛏£74-£82 🅿
Lift ⟨ CTV 250P ✿ CFA ⬛ (heated) *xmas*
♀ English & French V ✿ ⬛ ⬛ ✻ Lunch £9-£10.50&alc Dinner £16-£18&alc Last dinner 10pm
Credit Cards 1 2 3 5 £

---

BARTON MILLS Suffolk Map **05** TL77

⬛Forte Travelodge
IP28 6AE (on A11) (Forte)
☎(0638)717675 Central Res (0800) 850950
*Situated on the roundabout juction of the A1065, A11 and A1101 at Barton Mills, accessible off the A1101. There is a Little Chef restaurant adjacent to the lodge.*

---

32⟶🛏🛏(32fb) CTV in all bedrooms ® sB⟶🛏🛏£29.95 dB⟶🛏🛏£29.95 (room only)
⟨ 32P ⬛
Credit Cards 1 2 3

---

BARTON-ON-SEA Hampshire Map **04** SZ29

★★68% **The Cliff House**
Marine Dr West BH25 7QL ☎New Milton(0425)619333
FAX (0425) 612462
*A personally run hotel set in three-quarter-acre grounds at the top of fossil- studded cliffs overlooking Christchurch Bay features a restaurant which is very popular with locals, its extensive wine list, table d'hôte and à la carte menus representing excellent value for money. The comfortable lounge is furnished in attractive chintz fabrics and bedrooms in a variety of sizes are all well equipped ; smoking is not permitted in bedrooms or restaurant.*
9rm(4⟶🛏4🛏)(1fb)⬛in all bedrooms CTV in all bedrooms ® T 🐕 sB&B⟶🛏£42-£48 dB&B⟶🛏£66-£80 🅿
50P ⬛ ✿ *xmas*
V ✿ ⬛ Lunch £8.95-£10.50&alc Dinner £13.50&alc Last dinner 9pm
Credit Cards 1 2 3 5

---

BARTON STACEY Hampshire Map **04** SU44

⬛Forte Travelodge
SO21 3NP (on A303) (Forte)
☎Andover(0264)72260 Central Res (0800) 850950
*Single storey purpose-built bedroom block set back from the west bound A303, behind a Little Chef, offering excellent budget accommodation.*

→

B

**B**

20⇌🌂(20fb) CTV in all bedrooms ® sB⇌🌂£29.95
dB⇌🌂£29.95 (room only)
《 20P 🚗
Credit Cards ① ② ③

---

⇧**Forte Travelodge (Northbound)**
DE13 0ED (on A38, northbound) (Forte)
☎(0283)716343 Central Res (0800) 850950
*One of the original lodges situated on the northbound carriageway
of the A38 close to Burton on Trent, offers warm modern
accommodation; meals and snacks are available in the Little Chef
restaurant next door.*
20⇌🌂(20fb) CTV in all bedrooms ® sB⇌🌂£29.95
dB⇌🌂£29.95 (room only)
《 20P 🚗
Credit Cards ① ② ③

⇧**Forte Travelodge (Southbound)**
Rykneld St DE13 8EH (on A38, southbound) (Forte)
☎(0283)716784 Central Res (0800) 850950
*A lodge beside the southbound carriageway of the A38 near
Burton-on-Trent provides warm, well equipped bedrooms which
are equally suitable for business or leisure users; refreshments are
available in the Happy Eater Restaurant next door.*
40⇌🌂(40fb) CTV in all bedrooms ® sB⇌🌂£29.95
dB⇌🌂£29.95 (room only)
《 40P 🚗
Credit Cards ① ② ③

---

★★★66% **Forte Crest**
Cranes Farm Rd SS14 3DG (Forte Hotels) ☎(0268)533955
Telex no 995141 FAX (0268) 530119
*Set in its own grounds away from the main road, this modern
purpose-built hotel looks functional but the interior is smart and
comfortable, from the open-plan entrance foyer and bar-lounge, to
the first-floor restaurant and the well designed, well equipped
bedrooms. Compact modern bathrooms have excellent showers
over the baths.*
110⇌🌂⚡in 35 bedrooms CTV in all bedrooms ® T ✳ S%
sB⇌🌂£77 dB⇌🌂£88 (room only) 🚩
Lift 《 200P ✿ CFA snooker putting green
♀ International V ✿ ⚓ ⚡ ✳ S% Lunch £13.25 High tea £4.75
Dinner £16.30 Last dinner 11pm
Credit Cards ① ② ③ ⑤

★★★63% **Chichester**
Old London Rd, Wickford SS11 8UE ☎(0268)560555
FAX (0268) 560580
*Quietly situated on the A129 2 miles west of Wickford, this
modern hotel and freehouse in Tudor style features spacious, well
equipped bedrooms set around a garden courtyard. Several eating
options are provided at weekends – including popular dinner
dances.*
2⇌Annexe32⇌ CTV in all bedrooms ® T ✖ (ex guide dogs)
sB&B⇌£49-£59 dB&B⇌£59-£69
《 150P ♫ nc5yrs
♀ English & French V Lunch £10.50-£12.50&alc Dinner
£13.50-£17.50alc Last dinner 9.30pm
Credit Cards ① ② ③ ⑤

⇧**Campanile**
Miles Grey Rd, Pipps Hill Industrial Estate, Southend Arterial
Rd SS14 3AE (A127) (Campanile) ☎(0268)530810
Telex no 995068 FAX (0268) 286710
*Simple, well designed bedrooms at a fair tariff, with a cheerful
reception, bar and restaurant facilities in a separate building.*
Annexe100⇌🌂 CTV in all bedrooms ® T sB⇌🌂fr£36
dB⇌🌂fr£36 (room only) 🚩

---

63P
♀ English & French
Credit Cards ① ③ ⓔ

---

⇧**Watermill Travel Inn**
Felmores, East Mayne SS13 1BW ☎(0268)522227
FAX (0268) 530092
Closed 25 & 26 Dec
*This attractively landscaped travel lodge offers comfortable, well
equipped and good value accommodation. Bar and restaurant
facilities are available at the nearby Watermill Steak House where
the reception is open 7 am to 11 pm.*
Annexe32⇌🌂✖⚡in 5 bedrooms CTV in all bedrooms ®
✖ (ex guide dogs)
160P
♀ Mainly grills V ⚡ Last dinner 10.30pm
Credit Cards ① ② ③ ⑤

---

See also Odiham, Sherfield on Loddon & Stratfield Turgis

★★★★🏆80% **Tylney Hall**
RG27 9AJ (Small Luxury Hotels) ☎(0256)764881
Telex no 859864 FAX (0256) 768141
(For full entry see Rotherwick)

★★★★70% **Audleys Wood Thistle**
Alton Rd RG25 2JT (Mount Charlotte (TS)) ☎(0256)817555
Telex no 858273 FAX (0256) 817500
*Though this Victorian country house has been extended, the two
modern wings echo the design of the main building and blend well
into the gardens and woodland that surround it. Spacious and
attractively furnished bedrooms use co-ordinated soft fabrics, and
there are 7 individually styled suites. The restaurant – formerly a
conservatory – has a minstrels' gallery where Henry the
Hampshire Hog oversees proceedings; dishes presented in modern
style make up table d'hôte and à la carte menus, and an extensive
wine list features over 300.*
71⇌🌂(6fb)2🏨⚡in 12 bedrooms CTV in all bedrooms ® T
(room only) 🚩
《 100P ✿ croquet putting bicycles *xmas*
♀ British & French V ✿ ⚓
Credit Cards ① ② ③ ④ ⑤

★★★69% **Centre Court**
Centre Dr, Chineham RG24 0FY ☎(0256)816664
FAX (0256) 816727
*An hotel tucked away behind Chineham shopping centre, offers
both professional tennis coaching and some of the country's finest
facilities in its combination of indoor and extensive, floodlit, all-
weather courts. The comprehensive range of leisure amenities also
includes a well supervised gymnasium, attractive indoor pool, spa
bath, sauna and solarium; a crèche is available for the under 4's.
Executive and standard bedrooms feature a variety of pleasantly
co-ordinated colour schemes, and the à la carte and table d'hôte/
carvery Garden Restaurant and Bar is complemented by the more
informal eating style of the Pavilion Bar and Pantry.*
50⇌🌂(6fb)⚡in 25 bedrooms CTV in all bedrooms ® T
sB&B⇌🌂£97-£110 dB&B⇌🌂£110-£114 🚩
Lift 《 CTV 120P CFA 🏊 (heated) 🎾 (hard) sauna solarium
gymnasium steam room spa bath *xmas*
V ✿ ⚓ ⚡ Lunch £13.75&alc High tea £3-£6.30alc Dinner
£16.50&alc Last dinner 10pm
Credit Cards ① ② ③ ⑤ ⓔ

★★★67% **Basingstoke Country**
Nately Scures, Hook RG27 9JS ☎(0256)764161 Telex no 859981
FAX (0256) 768341
*The hotel predominantly aimed at a business clientele, set in 4.5
acres of landscaped garden and woodland on the A30 London-
Basingstoke road, boasts an impressive conservatory with a
walkway leading through to the inviting indoor pool, fitness area
and café-style Garden Restaurant. The Winchester Restaurant,*

*which is smart and traditional in style, supplements an imaginative
à la carte menu with a table d'hôte choice; your meal could include
a strongly flavoured Stilton and Guinness mousse followed by
tender chicken breast filled with cheese and garlic wrapped in a
light, flavoursome pastry and served with mustard sauce.
Accommodation is fairly spacious, comfortable and well equipped,
a selection of executive rooms and suites being available, and
conference facilities in a variety of sizes are well utilised.*
70⇨🛏️(8fb)1🛏️⚄in 14 bedrooms CTV in all bedrooms ® T ✳
sB⇨🛏️£32.50-£99.50 dB⇨🛏️£65-£165 (room only) 🍴
Lift ( 200P ⇔ CFA ▭ (heated) sauna solarium gymnasium
V ✧ ⚌ ✳ Lunch £14.50-£17.50&alc Dinner £19.50&alc Last
dinner 9.45pm
Credit Cards 1 2 3 4 5

**★★★61% Forte Posthouse**
Grove Rd RG21 3EE (Forte Hotels) ☎(0256)468181
Telex no 858501 FAX (0256) 840081
*A purpose-built hotel on the southern boundary of the town.
Bedrooms vary from Executive rooms, Study and Lady Crest
rooms to the standard item. The Fox and Duck is the hotel's fully
licensed pub bar, which also serves food. The restaurant is
attractively furnished and offers table d'hôte and à la carte menus.
Several conference and function rooms are available.*
84⇨🛏️⚄in 42 bedrooms CTV in all bedrooms ® T ✳
sB⇨🛏️£39.50-£49.50 dB⇨🛏️£39.50-£49.50 (room only) 🍴
( 150P CFA snooker pool table *xmas*
V ✧ ⚌ ⚄ ✳ Lunch £15-£25alc Dinner £15-£25alc Last dinner
10.30pm
Credit Cards 1 2 3 4 5

**★★63% Wheatsheaf**
RG25 2BB (Lansbury) ☎Dummer(0256)398282 Telex no 859775
FAX (0256) 398253
(For full entry see North Waltham)

### ⬆Forte Travelodge

Stag and Hounds, Winchester Rd RG22 6HN (off A30) (Forte)
☎(0256)843566 Central Res (0800) 850950

*This lodge stands to the rear of the Stag and Hounds pub and
Harvesters – a themed restaurant featuring a vast collection of
fascinating farming memorabilia and serving bar food and meals
(including breakfast). Positioned just off the Brighton Hill
roundabout A30/Ring Road, it is in fact reached from the old
Winchester road.*

32⇨🅵(32fb) CTV in all bedrooms Ⓡ sB⇨🅵£29.95
dB⇨🅵£29.95 (room only)

《 32P 🚗

Credit Cards ①②③

---

**BASLOW** Derbyshire Map **08** SK27

★★★★ ⚘ CAVENDISH

DE4 1SP ☎(0246)582311
FAX (0246) 582312

*Guests are assured of a warm
welcome at this pleasant
hotel, enthusiastically run by
owner Eric Marsh and his
team of long serving staff. Although situated beside the A619,
all bedrooms have uninterrupted views over the Chatsworth
estate, and the atmosphere is tranquil and relaxed.
Particularly so in the elegant, inviting lounge with its beamed
ceiling, deep cushioned chairs, fresh flowers and blazing fire.
Bedrooms, in contrast, are simpler in style but are comfortably
furnished with 2 deep armchairs and many thoughtful extras.
Larger rooms have antique pieces, some from Chatsworth
itself. Throughout the hotel the walls are hung with a varied
and interesting collection of paintings, a particular interest of
the owner. Guests have a choice of eating formally in the
stylish restaurant or more casually in the Garden Room,
where food and drink are available throughout the day and in
the evening.*

24⇨🅵1🛏 CTV in all bedrooms Ⓡ T ✖ (ex guide dogs) ✳
sB⇨🅵£70-£80 dB⇨🅵£85-£95 (room only) 🅿

《 50P 🚗 ✣ ✦ putting green *xmas*

🍴 European V ✧ ⚟ ✄ ✳ Lunch fr£22&alc High tea
fr£15&alc Dinner fr£22&alc Last dinner 11pm

Credit Cards ①②③⑤

---

### ★★ ⚘⚘⚘73% Fischer's

Baslow Hall, Calver Rd DE4 1RR ☎(0246)583259
Closed 25-26 Dec

*Max and Susan Fischer are now well established in this delightful
small hotel, where Max Fischer has earned a high reputation for
his cooking. The set 4 and 5 course menus show his enjoyment of
fish cookery – but not to the exclusion of meat. The inspection meal
began with a light but full-flavoured crab mousseline with ravioli,
followed by a surprise course of baby courgette stuffed with
ratatouille set on a basil sauce. An unusual combination of
monkfish and calves liver formed the main course, and the desserts
were of an equally high standard. Service is smooth and efficient.*

6⇨🅵1🛏 CTV in all bedrooms T ✖ (ex guide dogs) ✳
sB&B⇨🅵£62.50-£77.50 dB&B⇨🅵£88.50-£107.50
Continental breakfast 🅿

40P 🚗 ✣

🍴 European ✄ ✳ Lunch £7.50-£18.50 Dinner fr£28.50&alc
Last dinner 10pm

Credit Cards ①②③

---

**BASSENTHWAITE** Cumbria Map **11** NY23

### ★★★★ ♨60% Armathwaite Hall

CA12 4RE ☎Keswick(07687)76551 Telex no 64319
FAX (07687) 76220

*Set amidst extensive grounds on the lakeside and offering good
sporting facilities, this country house dating to 1872 retains many
original features. Public areas comprise elegant lounges, an oak-
panelled hall with log fire, cocktail bar and restaurant with
magnificent lake views. Bedrooms are mostly spacious and
comfortable; some smaller rooms await refurbishment.*

42⇨🅵(4fb)1🛏 CTV in all bedrooms Ⓡ T ✳ sB&B⇨🅵£50-
£95 dB&B⇨🅵£100-£180 🅿

Lift 《 100P ✣ CFA ▱ (heated) ♪ (hard) ✦ ∪ snooker sauna
solarium gymnasium croquet games room pitch & putt *xmas*

🍴 English & French V ✧ ⚟ ✳ Lunch fr£12.95 Dinner
fr£25.95&alc Last dinner 9.30pm

Credit Cards ①②③⑤£

### ★★★63% Castle Inn

CA12 4RG (Best Western) ☎Keswick(07687)76401
FAX (07687) 76604

*A well known hotel, very conveniently situated on the A591 a few
minutes' walk from the head of Bassenthwaite Lake, has been
considerably upgraded in recent years to provide spacious,
comfortable accommodation. Guests can enjoy the carefully
tended lawns and gardens or make use of a range of leisure
facilities which include a large swimming pool, fitness room,
badminton court and outdoor tennis court.*

36⇨🅵(8fb)1🛏 CTV in all bedrooms Ⓡ T sB&B⇨🅵£48-£64
dB&B⇨🅵£77-£95 🅿

150P ✣ CFA ▱ (heated) ♪ (grass) snooker sauna solarium
gymnasium badminton table tennis *xmas*

🍴 English & French V ✧ ⚟ ✳ S% Lunch £8.95&alc Dinner
£13.95&alc Last dinner 9.30pm

Credit Cards ①②③⑤£

See advertisement under KESWICK

### ★★72% Pheasant Inn

CA13 9YE ☎Keswick(07687)76234
Closed 25 Dec

*Peacefully set between Bassenthwaite Lake and Thornthwaite
Forest, this delightful traditional country inn provides comfortable,
well furnished bedrooms and attractive public areas which are full
of character and atmosphere. Well prepared fresh produce features
on the table d'hôte dinner menu, and the wide choice of freshly-
prepared dishes makes this a popular lunchtime venue.*

17⇨🅵Annexe3⇨🅵 Ⓡ ✖

80P 🚗 ✣

V ✧ ⚟ ✄ Last dinner 8.30pm

### ★★ ⚘♨69% Overwater Hall

Ireby CA5 1HH ☎Keswick(07687)76566
Closed 24 Dec-21 Feb

*This family-run hotel is situated in unspoilt countryside, in a
secluded location. Many of the well appointed bedrooms have
superb views. There are very comfortable lounges and a bar
featuring a grand piano. A varied and interesting choice of mainly
British dishes is offered at dinner.*

13⇨🅵(4fb)3🛏 CTV in all bedrooms Ⓡ ✳ sB&B⇨🅵fr£35
dB&B⇨🅵fr£60 🅿

25P 🚗 ✣

🍴 English & French ✧ ⚟ Dinner fr£16 Last dinner 8.30pm

Credit Cards ①③

BATH Avon Map **03** ST76

See **Town Plan Section.**
See also Colerne, Hinton Charterhouse & Limpley Stoke

★★★★★66% **Bath Spa**
Sydney Rd BA2 6JF (Forte Hotels) ☎(0225)444424
Telex no 449729 FAX (0225) 444006

*Once a boys' home, and more recently a nurses' home, this beautifully positioned hotel opened to a blaze of publicity in 1990 following a £20 million renovation. Designed by Olga Polizzi, the accommodation provides high quality comfort. Elegant public areas include a smart drawing room, the delightful Colonnade Lounge and the restaurant, once the ballroom, where Chef Alec Howard is beginning to stamp his authority. Two bars, virtually self-contained function suites and a super sports and leisure centre complete the picture. Bedrooms are practically equipped and furnished, but individually decorated, and include a number of spacious suites.*

103⇔⬄♠7⬄↙in 31 bedrooms CTV in all bedrooms T ✱ S%
sB⇔♠£115 dB⇔♠£150 (room only) ⊟
Lift ⦅ 156P ⬆ ✿ CFA ▦ (heated) ♪ (hard) sauna solarium gymnasium croquet *xmas*
♈ International V ♥ ☑ ↙ ✱ S% Lunch £16 Dinner £32&alc Last dinner 10pm
Credit Cards ①②③⑤

★★★★✿✿66% **Royal Crescent**
16 Royal Crescent BA1 2LS (Queens Moat)(Small Luxury Hotels) ☎(0225)319090 Telex no 444251 FAX (0225) 339401

*A change of management has brought Simon Coombe from Eastwell Manor to this hotel which is formed from two of the largest houses in Bath's magnificent Royal Crescent built by John Wood in the 18th century. A noticeable improvement in standards is the immediate result and a programme of refurbishment is being carried out, already evident in the comfortable lounges and (mostly) spacious bedrooms. Michael Croft's cooking continues to be praiseworthy, although our inspectors have noted some inconsistency on occasions.*

27⇔♠Annexe17⇔♠(8fb)4⬄ CTV in all bedrooms T
✖ (ex guide dogs) ✱ sB⇔♠fr£90 dB⇔♠£118-£175 (room only) ⊟
Lift ⦅ 12⬆ ✿ CFA croquet plunge pool *xmas*
♈ English & French V ♥ ☑ ✱ Lunch £18-£22&alc Dinner £25-£30&alc Last dinner 9.30pm
Credit Cards ①②③⑤ⓔ

★★★✿79% **The Priory**
Weston Rd BA1 2XT (Select) ☎(0225)331922 Telex no 44612
FAX (0225) 448276

*An impressive Gothic-style Victorian house on the west side of the city centre, close to Victoria Park and Royal Crescent, has been carefully converted to provide an hotel which still retains much of its original charm whilst geared to meet present-day requirements. Bedrooms named after English flowers offer tasteful colour schemes, elegantly comfortable furnishings and such extras as fresh fruit and flowers. Spacious public rooms include three cosy dining areas and a drawing room from which French windows open onto the large and immaculately tended walled garden. Long-serving staff provide willing, friendly and attentive service.*

21⇔♠1⬄ CTV in all bedrooms T ✖ (ex guide dogs)
24P 1⬆ ⬄ ✿ ⌒ (heated) croquet
♈ French V ♥ ☑ ↙ Last dinner 9.15pm
Credit Cards ①②③⑤

★★★73% **Combe Grove Manor Hotel & Country Club**
Brassknocker Hill, Monkton Combe BA2 2HS (2m SE)
☎(0225)834644 FAX (0225) 834961

*Superbly situated in 68 acres of garden and woodland at Brassknocker Hill, southeast of the town, this 18th century manor house has been very carefully converted and modernised. Elegant public areas are complemented by spacious bedrooms, some contained in a recently added block adjoining the leisure centre*

→

**B**

# Bath

*with its tennis and squash facilities and golf driving range. Staff are friendly, and high levels of service are provided throughout.*
10⇨🏠 Annexe31⇨🏠(11fb)1🏢⧖in 8 bedrooms CTV in all bedrooms ® T ✖ ✱ sB&B⇨🏠£80 dB&B⇨🏠£85-£215 Continental breakfast 🅿

《 150P ♨ ♣ ❀ (heated) ⌲ (heated) ♪ (hard) squash sauna solarium gymnasium croquet spa baths steam room ♿ *xmas*
V ✆ 🅩 ⧖ ✱ Bar Lunch £9-£12alc Dinner £23-£28alc Last dinner 9.30pm
Credit Cards ①②③⑤

### ★★★68% Lansdown Grove
BA1 5EH (Best Western) ☎(0225)315891 Telex no 444850 FAX (0225) 448092
*This hotel – owned by the same family for over a century and run in traditional style to provide good levels of service and hospitality – enjoys fine views across the city from its elevated setting. Accommodation is well equipped, rooms being tastefully and individually decorated.*
45⇨🏠(3fb)⧖in 9 bedrooms CTV in all bedrooms ® T ✱ sB&B⇨🏠£60-£70 dB&B⇨🏠£85-£105 🅿
Lift 《 38P 6🚗 ❀ CFA
🍴 English & French V ✆ 🅩
Credit Cards ①②③④⑤

### ★★★66% Compass
North Pde BA1 1LG ☎(0225)461603 Telex no 44812 FAX (0225) 447758
*Centrally located in a handsome Georgian terrace near the Abbey, this completely refurbished hotel has bedrooms on five floors (there is a lift), which vary in size and views but are all smartly decorated and well equipped. Attractive public areas include a comfortable bar lounge, coffee shop and restaurant.*
54⇨🏠(4fb) CTV in all bedrooms ® T
Lift 《 ♪
🍴 British & French V ✆ 🅩 ⧖ Last dinner 9.30pm
Credit Cards ①②③⑤

### ★★★62% Francis
Queen Square BA1 2HH (Forte Hotels) ☎(0225)424257 Telex no 449162 FAX (0225) 319715
*This characterful building – an hotel for a hundred years – enjoys a superb situation 3 miles from the city centre, occupying one side of Queens Square. Many improvements have recently been made, public areas now providing comfortable and relaxing facilities, and bedroom refurbishment is almost complete.*
94⇨🏠⧖in 30 bedrooms CTV in all bedrooms ® T ✱ sB⇨🏠£75 dB⇨🏠£95 (room only) 🅿
Lift 《 30P CFA *xmas*
🍴 English & French V ✆ 🅩 ⧖ ✱ Lunch £15.50&alc Dinner £15.50&alc Last dinner 10pm
Credit Cards ①②③⑤

### ★★★61% Pratts
South Pde BA2 4AB (Forestdale) ☎(0225)460441 Telex no 444827 FAX (0225) 448807
*An hotel which forms part of South Parade, a fine Regency terrace close to the Abbey, retains such original features as fireplaces and moulded cornices. Comfortable, well equipped bedrooms are complemented by a choice of lounges.*
48rm(46⇨🏠)(5fb)1🏢⧖in 2 bedrooms CTV in 46 bedrooms ® T ✱ sB&Bfr£35 sB&B⇨🏠£60-£67.50 dB&B⇨🏠£70-£95 🅿
Lift 《 ♪ CFA *xmas*
🍴 English & French V ✆ 🅩 ✱ S% Sunday Lunch £9.25-£15.75 High tea £7.25 Dinner £14.25-£18.50&alc Last dinner 9.30pm
Credit Cards ①②③⑤

### ★★★59% Bath
Widcombe Basin BA2 4JP ☎(0225)338855 Telex no 445876 FAX (0225) 428941

*Situated beside Widcombe Basin, close to the city centre, this hotel offers bright, attractive open-plan public areas including the carvery restaurant which overlooks the canal. The bedrooms are modern and well equipped, with en suite facilities.*
96⇨🏠 CTV in all bedrooms ® T S% sB⇨🏠fr£78 dB⇨🏠fr£93 (room only) 🅿
Lift 《 102P CFA *xmas*
V ✆ 🅩 Lunch £10-£15&alc Dinner £15.50&alc Last dinner 9.30pm
Credit Cards ①②③④⑤

### ★★69% Duke's
Great Pulteney St BA2 4DN ☎(0225)463512 Telex no 449227
*This welcoming owner-run hotel in a Grade I listed Georgian parade has many period features, including a handsome staircase. Bedrooms are attractive and well equipped, there is a restful sitting room, cosy bar and a restaurant with an inviting menu.*
21⇨🏠(4fb) CTV in all bedrooms ® T sB&B⇨🏠£40-£65 dB&B⇨🏠£60-£80 🅿
1🚗 🚗 *xmas*
V ✆ 🅩 ⧖ Bar Lunch £4-£7alc Dinner £11-£16 Last dinner 8.30pm
Credit Cards ①②③ⓔ

### ★★64% Bailbrook Lodge
35/37 London Rd West BA1 7HZ ☎(0225)859090
*Situated 200 yards east of junction A46 on the A4, this imposing double-fronted Georgian house has been carefully modernised to provide elegant and comfortable public areas and various sized bedrooms, all with good en suite facilities.*
13⇨🏠(2fb)4🏢 CTV in all bedrooms ® ✖ (ex guide dogs) sB&B⇨🏠£30.75-£41 dB&B⇨🏠£41-£61.50
CTV 14P 🚗 ❀
V ✆ 🅩 ⧖ ✱ Sunday Lunch £10.50-£12.50 Dinner £12.50-£14.50 Last dinner 8.30pm
Credit Cards ①②③⑤

### ★★62% Haringtons
9/10 Queen St BA1 1HE ☎(0225)461728
*Set on a cobbled street behind Queen's Square, within walking distance of the city's historical attractions, an hotel created from four 18th-century town houses offers particularly good value for money – the restaurant which takes up the majority of the public areas being very popular locally. Visitors are advised to request the hotel's detailed car parking location map before arrival.*
12rm(8⇨🏠)(4fb) CTV in all bedrooms ® ✖ (ex guide dogs) sB&B£26-£30 sB&B⇨🏠£30-£42 dB&Bfr£36 dB&B⇨🏠£42-£53 🅿
♪ CFA
🍴 English & French 🅩 S% Lunch fr£3.50alc Dinner £5.95-£18.95alc Last dinner 10pm
Credit Cards ①②③

**See advertisement on page 113**

### ★68% Berni Royal
Manvers St BA1 1JP (Chef & Brewer) ☎(0225)463134 FAX (0225) 442931
*The cheerful friendliness of the staff is undoubtedly this hotel's main attribute. It is conveniently situated opposite the railway station, just a few minutes walk from a public car park. The bedrooms, while a little dated, are well equipped.*
30⇨🏠(4fb) CTV in all bedrooms ® T ✖ (ex guide dogs) sB&B⇨🏠£56-£66 dB&B⇨🏠£73 🅿
《 ♪
🍴 International V ✆ 🅩 ⧖ Bar Lunch £2.95-£5.50alc
Credit Cards ①②③⑤

### ❀✖✖✖Popjoys
Beau Nash House, Sawclose BA1 1EU ☎(0225)460494 FAX (0225) 446319
*In this fine Regency house next to the Theatre Royal, home of Beau Nash's mistress Juliana Popjoy, you can relax over aperitifs*

*in the elegant first- floor drawing room before moving downstairs to the equally beautifully proportioned dining room, decorated in yellow and hung with gilt-framed portraits. Chef John Headley's interesting menu offers a choice of mainly classical dishes, with firm flavours and good portions. Recent examples include a succulent duck terrine wrapped in pastry with a spiced apple chutney, and a deliciously light salmon and hake panaché served with a creamy sauce infused with ginger and green peppercorns. Vegetables have shown the same combination of careful cooking and restrained use of flavours. Desserts continue the traditional theme with dishes such as bread and butter pudding, served with a whisky and honey crème anglaise, or 'Eton mess' a mixture of cream, yogurt, marinated strawberries and piece of meringue under a crisp caramel top. Service is friendly, slightly formal and competent.*

Closed Sun & Mon Lunch not served Sat

♀ English & International **V** 32 seats ✳ Lunch fr£12 Dinner £22.50-£27.75 Last lunch 2pm Last dinner 10.30pm ♪ nc6yrs ¼

Credit Cards ①②③④

**❀ ✕ Garlands**

7 Edgar Buildings, George St BA1 2EE ☎(0225)442283

*This intimate restaurant, situated in an elevated terrace to the north of Milsom Street, occupies part of the house featured as the lodging of Isabella Thorpe in Jane Austen's Northanger Abbey. Meals are prepared from good, fresh ingredients, with a strong emphasis on fish and vegetarian dishes which are accompanied by light, delicate sauces; particularly worthy of note is the imaginative, value-for-money, fixed-price luncheon menu.*

Closed 1st 2 wks Jan Lunch not served Mon

♀ English & French **V** 30 seats ✳ Lunch £15&alc Last lunch 2.15pm Last dinner 10.30pm ♪

Credit Cards ①②③

---

**BATLEY** West Yorkshire Map **08** SE22

**★★66% Alder House**

Towngate Rd, off Healey Ln WF17 7HR ☎(0924)444777
Telex no 51363 FAX (0924) 442644

*This attractive Georgian house in a quiet road close to the town centre has recently been extended to provide comfortable well furnished accommodation. The cosy restaurant serves well prepared food and the atmosphere is very hospitable.*

22rm(21⇔♠)(1fb) CTV in all bedrooms ® **T** sB&B£37-£46 sB&B⇔♠£43-£52 dB&B⇔♠£62-£65 ☐

CTV 50P 2❀ ✿ CFA

♀ English & Continental **V** ✿ ♨ Lunch £7.50-£8 Dinner £11.50-£12.95&alc Last dinner 9.30pm

Credit Cards ①②③

---

**BATTLE** East Sussex Map **05** TQ71

★★★

**★★★❀ ⚐**
**NETHERFIELD PLACE**

Netherfield TN33 9PP (3m NW B2096) (Pride of Britain) ☎(04246)4455 FAX (04246) 4024

Closed 2 wks Xmas, New Year & 2wks Jan

*Michael and Helen Collier, ably assisted by a team of young staff, continue to run this pleasant hotel with flair and charm. All its rooms are attractively furnished, with views over the 30 acres of park and garden to the pretty countryside that surrounds the hotel. Bedrooms are well equipped with comforts and are being*

*gradually refurbished. In addition to the public rooms, there is accommodation – a small meeting room and dining room – for conferences or private functions. The Chef, Matthew Whalley devises menus which show considerable imagination, making much of the produce of the kitchen garden. The wine list includes some classic clarets from the 1961 and 1966 vintages, as well as good Burgundies and interesting New World wines.*

14⇔♠(1fb) ☐ CTV in all bedrooms **T** ✖ (ex guide dogs) ✳ sB&B⇔♠£48-£60 dB&B⇔♠£80-£110 ☐

30P 2❀ ⚐ ✿ CFA ♪ (hard) croquet clay pigeon shooting archery

♀ French **V** ✿ ♨ ✳ Bar Lunch fr£3.50 High tea fr£3.50 Dinner fr£20 Last dinner 9.30pm

Credit Cards ①②③⑤ⓔ

**See advertisement under HASTINGS & ST LEONARDS**

---

**★★❀67% La Vieille Auberge**

27 High St TN33 0EA (Minotels) ☎(04246)5171
FAX (04246) 4015

*A high-street inn built in 1688 from the stones of Battle Abbey, and retaining much of its original charm is at present undergoing a major refurbishment programme to create a comfortable new lounge and more spacious bar; bedrooms are also being upgraded with coordinated Laura Ashley furnishings – each to its own scheme. The cosy restaurant with inglenook fireplace now offers a shortened menu with an interesting choice of 5 dishes at each course, prices being set according to how many courses you select; symbols denote alcohol- free, non-dairy and vegetarian dishes. A typical meal might include Sausage of Smoked Haddock with Asparagus Cream, Crispy Confit of Duckling served on a bed of mixed lentils with a mustard sauce, and a classic dessert such as the popular Assiette de Chocolat, Crème Brûlée or Snow Eggs with caramel and toasted almonds. An extensive and reasonably priced list contains a good range of Bordeaux and Burgundy wines with some fine vintages. Young staff (though sometimes lacking finesse) provide friendly service, and the proprietors maintain good standards of hospitality.*

7rm(6⇔♠)(1fb) ☐ CTV in all bedrooms ® **T** ✖ (ex guide dogs) sB&B£39 sB&B⇔♠£49-£59 dB&B£49 dB&B⇔♠£59-£74 ☐

♪ ⚐ xmas

♀ French **V** ✿ ♨ Lunch £14.75 Dinner £16-£27&alc Last dinner 10pm

Credit Cards ①②③

**★★59% The George**

23 High St TN33 0EA (Resort) ☎(04246)4466 FAX (04246) 4853

*This old coaching inn is a listed building, and offers rooms of various shapes and sizes, all equipped with every modern convenience. Service is friendly and well managed and there are plans to refurbish the public areas.*

22rm(19⇔2♠)(4fb) ☐ CTV in all bedrooms ® **T** sB&B⇔♠fr£41 dB&B⇔♠fr£56 ☐

30P CFA xmas

♀ English & French **V** ✿ ♨ ✳ Lunch fr£8.50&alc High tea fr£2.75 Dinner fr£10.50&alc Last dinner 9.45pm

Credit Cards ①②③④⑤

---

**BAWTRY** South Yorkshire Map **08** SK69

**★★★66% The Crown**

High St DN10 6JW (Forte Hotels) ☎Doncaster(0302)710341
Telex no 547089 FAX (0302) 711798

*This charming inn, centrally situated on the High Street, has a history dating back over 300 years. Sympathetic refurbishment continues, providing modern amenities and comfort in both bedrooms and public areas.*

57⇔♠ ☐ ¼ in 12 bedrooms CTV in all bedrooms ® **T** ✳ S% sB⇔♠fr£65 dB⇔♠fr£85 (room only) ☐

《 80P CFA xmas

V ✿ ⚏ ✂ ✳ S% Lunch £8.50&alc Dinner £13.95&alc Last dinner 9.30pm
Credit Cards ① ② ③ ④ ⑤

---

**BEACONSFIELD** Buckinghamshire Map **04** SU99

**★★★68%, Bellhouse**
Oxford Rd HP9 2XE (2m E A40) (De Vere)
☎Gerrards Cross(0753)887211 Telex no 848719
FAX (0753) 888231
*An imposing modern white building on the A40 between Beaconsfield and Gerrards Cross affords easy access to the major motorways and London. Comfortable, well equipped bedrooms – some of which are now due for refurbishment – are complemented by public areas where cool brick walls and terracota flooring create a Mediterranean atmosphere; the recent addition of a comprehensive leisure complex and many conference rooms has increased the hotel's popularity with both tourist and holiday guests. The restaurant's table d'hôte and à la carte menus offer a range of interesting dishes, and professional services are provided by a well dressed, competent team of staff.*
136⇌(5fb)✂in 40 bedrooms CTV in all bedrooms ® T ✳
sB&B⇌£120-£135 dB&B⇌£160-£180 ⌸
Lift ⟨ 405P ✿ CFA ▱ (heated) squash snooker sauna solarium gymnasium pool table beauty therapy room *xmas*
♀ English & Continental V ✿ ⚏ ✳ Lunch £18 Dinner £19
Last dinner 10pm
Credit Cards ① ② ③ ④ ⑤

**★★55%, White Hart Toby**
Aylesbury End HP9 1LW (Toby) ☎(0494)671211
Telex no 837882
*A spacious bar and Toby Restaurant form the public areas of this lively inn, which dates back to the 16th century; accommodation is for the most part in a modern annexe, though there are a few characterful bedrooms in the main building.*
6🌂Annexe28🌂1⌸ CTV in all bedrooms ®
⟨ 80P
V ✿ ✂
Credit Cards ① ② ③ ⑤

---

**BEAMINSTER** Dorset Map **03** ST40

**★★❀❀70%, Bridge House**
3 Prout Bridge DT8 3AY (Minotels) ☎(0308)862200
RS 24-29 Dec
*An historic stone building near the village centre, Bridge House makes a charming small hotel run in friendly, informal style. Its bedrooms look delightful, with their fresh flowers and little personal touches, like home- made biscuits, abound. The hotel's most noteworthy feature, however, is the gracious, panelled restaurant, where the set 4-course menu (with choices), offers really good value. Cooking is done by an enthusiastic staff who, although not formally trained, take great care over their work, with notable success. Fresh fish from Newquay and game dishes are their strengths. The wine list, though short, is well chosen and not overpriced.*
9⇌🌂Annexe4⇌🌂(1fb) CTV in 14 bedrooms ® T
sB&B⇌🌂£34-£53.25 dB&B⇌🌂£61.50-£83.50 ⌸
22P 🐾 ✿ *xmas*
♀ International ✿ ⚏ Lunch £9.50-£17.50alc Dinner £24.75&alc Last dinner 9pm
Credit Cards ① ② ③ ⓔ

---

**BEARSDEN** Strathclyde *Dunbartonshire* Map **11** NS57

**❀❀ ✕ ✕October Restaurant**
128 Drymen Rd G61 3RB ☎041-942 7272 FAX 041-942 9650
*This sophisticated restaurant, which stands just west of Glasgow, enjoys ever- increasing popularity for an artistically-presented but unpretentious modern cuisine based on the best of Scottish produce, though, flavours can err on the side of over-subtlety and vegetables*
→

B

are sometimes overcooked. Menus include Lobster and Orkney Cheese Soufflé, Best End of Lamb, Chicken Mousseline, Tarragon and Mushroom Sauce and a delicious Chocolate Terrine with Expresso Creme Anglaise which will tempt any dessert-lover, all served in friendly fashion by a personable young team. Aperitifs are served in a separate small area and cloakrooms are immaculately maintained.
Closed Sun, Mon, BH's, 1 wk Etr & 1st 2 wks Aug
♀ International **V** 48 seats ✳ Lunch £9.95-£11.95 Dinner £20.20-£27.65alc Last lunch 2pm Last dinner 10pm ✗
Credit Cards [1] [3]

---

**BEATTOCK** Dumfries & Galloway *Dumfriesshire* Map **11** NT00

See also Moffat
**★★★ 67% Auchen Castle**
DG10 9SH (Inter-Hotels) ☎(06833)407 FAX (06833) 667
Closed 3 wks Xmas-New Year
*Set in 50 acres of attractive grounds in an elevated position a mile north of the village, this fine Victorian country house has relaxing public rooms and comfortable bedrooms of varying size, with some stylish rooms with spacious showers in the main house and more functional rooms with private showers in the adjacent lodge.*
15⇨♠Annexe10♠(1fb) CTV in all bedrooms ® T sB&B⇨♠£43 dB&B⇨♠£46-£64 🏳
35P ✿ CFA ✔
**V** ♥ ⚘ ✳ Bar Lunch fr£1alc Dinner £11-£14alc Last dinner 9pm
Credit Cards [1] [2] [3] [4] [5] £

**★★ 62% Beattock House**
DG10 9QB ☎(06833)403 & 402
*A converted Victorian house – still retaining some of its original features – is family run to provide guests with traditional comforts and service. Part of its six-acre grounds form a small caravan park, and its setting offers convenient access to the A74.*
7rm(3♠)(2fb) CTV in 4 bedrooms ® ✳ sB&B£27.50-£32 dB&Bfr£50 dB&B♠£52-£55 🏳
CTV 30P ✿ ✔ putting
**V** ♥ ⚘ ✳ Lunch fr£8.50 High tea fr£5.50 Dinner fr£15 Last dinner 9.30pm
Credit Cards [1] [2] [3] [5]

---

**BEAULIEU** Hampshire Map **04** SU30

**★★★ ✸72% Montagu Arms**
SO42 7ZL ☎(0590)612324
*A listed, creeper-clad building backed by terraced gardens and set in the picturesque New Forest village famed for its Motor Museum offers suites as well as standard and four poster accommodation, most rooms being attractively co-ordinated. The restaurant's excellent, artistically presented dishes are supplemented by the wide range of meals available in the Wine Press Bar, and dedicated staff provide attentive service throughout. The hotel has recently also taken over the village shop, post office and bakery.*
24⇨♠(3fb)4🖾 CTV in all bedrooms T ✳ sB&B⇨♠£67.90 dB&B⇨♠£95.90-£165.90 🏳
《 80P 6🚗 ✿ CFA xmas
**V** ♥ ⚘ ✔ ✳ Lunch £9.95-£14.95 Dinner fr£21.90&alc Last dinner 9.30pm
Credit Cards [1] [2] [3] [5]

**★★★ 61% Beaulieu**
Beaulieu Rd SO42 7YQ ☎Southampton(0703)293344
FAX (0703) 283719
*Providing the venue for 4 pony sales a year, and set in an isolated forest location at the Beaulieu Road rail station (between Beaulieu and Lyndhurst), this hotel offers comfortable, well equipped accommodation and a choice of eating options – the Hungry Horse Restaurant, with its table d'hôte and à la carte menus, and the*

popular Carvery operated by the Beaulieu Road pub across the attractive gravelled courtyard.
18⇨♠(2fb) CTV in all bedrooms ® T sB&B⇨♠£39-£55 dB&B⇨♠£68-£84 🏳
Lift CTV 100P ✿ xmas
♀ English & French **V** ♥ ⚘ ✗ ✳ Lunch £11 High tea fr£5.50 Dinner £11 Last dinner 8.45pm
Credit Cards [1] [2] [3] [5] £

---

**BEAULY** Highland *Inverness-shire* Map **14** NH54

**★★ 63% Priory**
The Square IV4 7BX (Inter-Hotels) ☎(0463)782309
FAX (0463) 782531
*A major transformation is taking place at this friendly family-run hotel, conveniently situated on the village square. The public areas are being considerably altered and upgraded, and new bedrooms with modern appointments are gradually being phased in. Later on, existing bedrooms are to be extended and completely refurbished.*
12⇨♠(2fb) CTV in all bedrooms ® T ✳ sB&B⇨♠£27.95-£34.95 dB&B⇨♠£47.50-£59.50 🏳
Lift ✗ CFA
**V** ♥ ⚘ ✗ Lunch £4-£8.50alc High tea £3.75-£8.95alc Dinner £7.75-£17.50alc Last dinner 9pm
Credit Cards [1] [2] [3] [5] £

**★★ 59% The Lovat Arms**
IV4 9EG ☎Inverness(0463)782313
*A friendly family-run hotel on the High Street close to the village square offering traditional comforts in the public areas and modern amenities in the practical comfortable bedrooms.*
22⇨♠(4fb) CTV in all bedrooms ® T ✳ sB&B⇨♠£27-£35 dB&B⇨♠£44-£55 🏳
CTV P CFA xmas
**V** ♥ ⚘ ✗ ✳ Dinner fr£13.50 Last dinner 9pm
Credit Cards [1] [3]

---

**BEAUMARIS** Gwynedd Map **06** SH67

**★★ ✸✸75% Ye Olde Bulls Head Inn**
Castle St LL58 8AP (Welsh Rarebits) ☎(0248)810329
FAX (0248) 811294
Closed 25-26 Dec
*Charles Dickens and Dr Johnson are numbered among the famous guests of this historic 15th-century posting house with its character beamed bars, elegant lounge with log fire and bedrooms furnished to a high standard. Skilful and imaginative preparation of local seafood, game and meats provides a range of dishes that will delight even the most serious gastronome.*
10⇨♠Annexe1⇨♠ CTV in all bedrooms ® T ✗ (ex guide dogs) sB&B⇨♠£40-£47 dB&B⇨♠fr£68 🏳
12P 🚲
♀ English & French **V** ♥ ✳ Sunday Lunch fr£13.75 Dinner £20-£26alc Last dinner 9.30pm
Credit Cards [1] [3]

**★★ 66% Bishopsgate House**
54 Castle St LL58 8AB ☎(0248)810302
Closed 22 Dec-12 Feb
*This beautifully preserved mid 18th-century house, now a privately owned hotel, is situated close to the town centre and just a few yards from the seafront. The house has been sympathetically decorated and furnished in keeping with the building's character.*
10⇨♠1🖾 CTV in all bedrooms ® T sB&B⇨♠£27.50-£33 dB&B⇨♠£48-£54 🏳
10P 🚲 nc5yrs
♀ English & French **V** ♥ ✗ ✳ Sunday Lunch £7.95 Dinner £12.50&alc Last dinner 9pm
Credit Cards [1] [3] £

B

## BEAUMONT

See Jersey **under** Channel Islands

## BEBINGTON Merseyside Map 07 SJ38

★★65% *Bridge Inn*
Bolton Rd, Port Sunlight L62 4UQ ☎051-645 8441
*Situated beside the church in the centre of the picturesque village of Port Sunlight, this old-world style coaching inn dates from 1905 and offers comfortable modern accommodation, with two popular bars and a beamed restaurant.*
16⇌♠(2fb)1 CTV in all bedrooms ® ✠
50P
♀ English & Continental V ✇ ⚏
Credit Cards ① ② ③ ⑤

⇧Forte Travelodge
New Chester Rd L62 9AQ (on A41, northbound) (Forte)
☎051-327 2489 Central Res (0800) 850950
*Set back from the A41 just off junction 5 of the M63, this Lodge offers good value accommodation with meals available in the adjacent Little Chef restaurant.*
31⇌♠(31fb) CTV in all bedrooms ® sB⇌♠£29.95
dB⇌♠£29.95 (room only)
《 31P ⚗
Credit Cards ① ② ③

## BECCLES Suffolk Map 05 TM49

★★63% *Kings Head*
New Market NR34 9HA ☎(0502)712147
*Once a coaching inn, this town-centre hotel with its own car park at the rear now offers a good base for the leisure user because of its setting in the Waveney Valley and for the businessman because of having easy access to the A143 and A146. Bedrooms are homely and well equipped, bars and lounge/foyer enjoy a convival atmosphere, and the restaurant features a popular steak menu augmented by daily blackboard specials.*
12rm(8⇌3♠) CTV in all bedrooms ® T ✠ (ex guide dogs)
18P
V ✇ ⚏ ✂ Last dinner 9.30pm
Credit Cards ① ② ③ ⑤

★★61% *Waveney House*
Puddingmoor NR34 9PL ☎(0502)712270
*This hotel enjoys a riverside setting and is a popular mooring place during the season. Equally suited to the needs of leisure and commercial users, it provides well cared for, traditionally furnished accommodation and maintains a good standard of cleanliness.*
13⇌♠(2fb)1 CTV in all bedrooms ®
CTV 100P ✿ ✍
♀ English & French V ✇ ⚏ Last dinner 9.30pm
Credit Cards ① ② ③ ④ ⑤

## BECKINGHAM Lincolnshire Map 08 SK85

❀❀ ✕✕ Black Swan
Hillside LN5 0RF ☎Newark(0636)626474
*This family-run restaurant nestles on the banks of the River Witham. A lounge with an open fire provides an inviting setting in which to study the 6-course menu. The fine style of cuisine, concentrating on quality not quantity, uses subtle blends of herbs and natural flavours to delicately enhance dishes such as Duck Soup with fine herb quenelles or a Seafood Casserole with Saffron. Service is courteous and attentive.*
Closed Sun & Mon
♀ English & French V 35 seats ✳ Lunch £15.50-£23.75alc
Dinner £15.50-£23.75alc Last lunch 2pm Last dinner 10pm 9 P
✂
Credit Cards ① ③

# The Famous Olde Bridge Inn Hotel

*Bolton Road,*
*Port Sunlight Village,*
*Bebington, Wirral,*
*Merseyside L62 4UQ*
Telephone: 051-645 8441

★★★

# Montague Arms Hotel

**Beaulieu,**
**Brockenhurst,**
**Hampshire SO42 7ZL**
Telephone: (0590) 612324

---

### BEDALE North Yorkshire Map **08** SE28

### ★★63% **Motel Leeming**
Great North Rd DL8 1DT (1m NE junc A1/A684)
☎(0677)423611 FAX (0677) 424507

*Situated within the service area on the northbound carriageway of the A1 near the town, this hotel offers functional but well equipped accommodation which represents good value for money ; cafeteria and à la carte restaurant provide a choice of eating styles, and there is a comfortable bar lounge.*

40⇨🔔2🖼⚊in 8 bedrooms CTV in all bedrooms ® T ✱
sB&B⇨🔔£29.50-£39.50 dB&B⇨🔔£42 🛏
《 100P 14🚗 (£2 per night) ✿ CFA
♀ English & Continental V ✧ ⚊ ⚊ ✱ Lunch £3-£7alc High tea £4-£6alc Dinner £8.95&alc Last dinner 10pm
Credit Cards 1 2 3 5 £

### ★★61% **White Rose**
DL7 9AY ☎(0677)422707 & 424941 FAX (0677) 425123
(For full entry see Leeming Bar)

---

### BEDDGELERT Gwynedd Map **06** SH54

### ★★★66% **Royal Goat**
LL55 4YE ☎(076686)224 & 343 FAX (076686) 422

*Set in the village centre amidst the spectacular scenery of Snowdonia, this privately owned hotel was built in 1800 to accommodate climbers and remains popular with sporting enthusiasts as well as tourists. Bedrooms are modern and very well equipped and there is a choice of bars and restaurants, plus conference facilities.*

32⇨🔔(4fb)1🖼⚊in 5 bedrooms CTV in all bedrooms ® T
sB&B⇨🔔£42-£60 dB&B⇨🔔£66-£90 🛏
Lift 《 150P ♪ games room *xmas*
♀ Welsh & French V ✧ ⚊ ⚊ Lunch £9&alc High tea £3-£6&alc Dinner £16&alc Last dinner 10pm
Credit Cards 1 2 3 5 £

### ★★♨64% *Bryn Eglwys Country House*
LL55 4NB ☎(076686)210

*Surrounded by spectacular mountain scenery, this much extended country house is set in spacious grounds on the outskirts of the village and has a large attractive restaurant, comfortable lounges and modern bedrooms, most of them with en suite facilities.*

16rm(12⇨)(3fb) CTV in 12 bedrooms ®
30P 🚗 ✿
♀ English & French V ✧ ⚊ ⚊
Credit Cards 1 3 5

### ★★♨69% **Sygun Fawr Country House**
LL55 4NE ☎(076686)258

*This stone-built manor house dates back at least to the 17th century, and some parts are reputed to be even older. In a secluded location, surrounded by magnificent mountain scenery, about a mile northeast of the village, it is reached by way of a steep, narrow lane from the A498. The hotel has been considerably renovated in recent times, and it is particularly popular with walkers being within easy reach of many Snowdon footpaths.*

7⇨🔔(1fb) ® sB&B⇨🔔£24.50-£25 dB&B⇨🔔£42-£43 🛏
CTV 30P 🚗 ✿ sauna *xmas*
V ✧ Dinner £10-£11 Last dinner 8.30pm
£

### ★59% **Tanronen**
LL55 4YB (Frederic Robinson) ☎(076686)347

*This magnificent scenery of the Snowdonia National Park surrounds this small, cosy hotel in the centre of the village, its setting making it understandably popular with tourists – particularly walkers and climbers.*

8rm CTV in all bedrooms ® ✈ ✱ sB&B£18 dB&B£36 🛏
CTV 12P 3🚗 *xmas*
V ✧ ✱ Lunch £7.25 Dinner £12.50 Last dinner 9pm
Credit Cards 1 3 5

---

### BEDFORD Bedfordshire Map **04** TL04

### ★★★78% **Woodlands Manor**
Green Ln, Clapham MK41 6EP (2m N A6) ☎(0234)363281
Telex no 825007 FAX (0234) 272390

*A handsome Victorian mansion set back in its own tree-lined grounds from the A6 north of Bedford greets guests warmly in a welcoming, half-panelled entrance hall with an open fire and leather Chesterfields. Public areas also include a dining room with an appetising menu – some of its ambitious dishes being more successful than others. The best bedrooms are those which have recently been added, for they are very spacious and attractively decorated, while the original ones vary in both size and style ; all rooms are well equipped, however, many have luxurious marble bathrooms ; three further rooms are contained in a cottage in the grounds. Owners and staff provide high standards of service, including 24-hour room service and such old fashioned luxuries as shoe cleaning, a hot water bottle and early morning tea.*

22⇨Annexe3⇨ CTV in all bedrooms T ✈ (ex guide dogs)
sB&B⇨£50-£79 dB&B⇨£69-£89 🛏
《 100P ✿ CFA croquet nc7yrs
♀ English & French V ✧ ⚊ ⚊ Lunch £11.95-£16 Dinner £23-£25 Last dinner 9.45pm
Credit Cards 1 2 3 £

### ★★★68% **Bedford Moat House**
2 Saint Mary's St MK42 0AR (Queens Moat) ☎(0234)355131
Telex no 825243 FAX (0234) 340447
Closed Xmas RS Bank hols

*This busy, modern, commercial hotel makes good use of its riverside setting, offering fine views from the tow-path Mallards Coffee Shop, lounge bar, Terrace Restaurant and many bedrooms up to the 6th floor. All bedrooms are of a good size, tastefully appointed in relaxing colours, and fully equipped.*

100⇨🔔(20fb)⚊in 22 bedrooms CTV in all bedrooms ® T
sB&B⇨🔔fr£70 dB&B⇨🔔fr£85 🛏
Lift 《 CTV 72P CFA sauna jacuzzi mini-gym
♀ English & Continental ✧ ⚊ Lunch fr£14.50 Dinner fr£14.50 Last dinner 9.45pm
Credit Cards 1 2 3 5 £

### ★★★66% **The Barns**
Cardington Rd, Fenlake MK44 3SA (Lansbury) ☎(0234)270044
Telex no 827748 FAX (0234) 273102

49⇨🔔(1fb)1🖼⚊in 11 bedrooms CTV in all bedrooms ® T
✈ (ex guide dogs) sB&B⇨🔔fr£75 dB&B⇨🔔fr£88 🛏
《 120P ✿ CFA ♪ sauna solarium gymnasium *xmas*
♀ English & Continental V ✧ ⚊ Lunch fr£10&alc Dinner fr£13.85&alc Last dinner 10pm
Credit Cards 1 2 3 5

---

### BEER Devon Map **03** SY28

### ★★60% **Anchor Inn**
EX12 3ET ☎Seaton(0297)20386
Closed 1 wk Xmas

*A traditional-looking business hotel, which faces the slipway to the beach is popular for its successful combination of original character and completely refurbished interior . Bedrooms – though not over-large – are warm, cosy and attractively decorated, while the character bars and adjacent restaurant offer a good choice of wholesome fare with the emphasis on seafood. Service is informally friendly, and in summer the cliff-top beer garden serving real ale is an attraction.*

9rm(2⇨2🔔)(1fb) CTV in all bedrooms ® ✈ ✱ sB&B£20-£39
sB&B⇨🔔£26-£39 dB&B£40-£45 dB&B⇨🔔£52-£58 🛏
CTV ⚊ nc10yrs
V ✧ ✱ Lunch £1.95-£11.95alc Dinner £10.70-£25alc Last dinner 9.30pm
Credit Cards 1 3

---

**BEETHAM** Cumbria Map **07** SD47

**★62% Wheatsheaf**
LA7 7AL ☎Milnthorpe(05395)62123
*An attractive, oak-beamed village inn close to Lakeland, noted for
its bar food. Bedrooms are compact but cosy.*
6➪♠ CTV in all bedrooms ® ✳ sB&B➪♠£30-£32
dB&B➪♠£40-£42 ➡
CTV 50P
♡ ✳ Lunch £6.65&alc Dinner £7.70-£12 Last dinner 8.30pm
Credit Cards ①③

---

**BELFORD** Northumberland Map **12** NU13

**★★★63% Blue Bell**
Market Place NE70 7NE (Consort) ☎(0668)213543
FAX (0668) 213787
RS 13 Jan-21 Feb
*This attractive coaching inn at the centre of the village offers a
good standard of accommodation and service, with home-grown
produce featuring in the good-value bar meals and dinners.*
17➪♠(1fb)1➡⁀in 4 bedrooms CTV in 15 bedrooms ®
10P 2🐎 (£3 per night) ✿ putting green nc6yrs
V ♡ ⁀ Last dinner 8.45pm
Credit Cards ①②③⑤

**★★⚑77% Waren House**
Waren Mill NE70 7EE ☎Bamburgh(06684)581
FAX (06684) 484
Closed 16 Dec-12 Jan
*A lovely country house, set in 6 acres of grounds close to Budle
Bay and only a short distance from the impressive Bamburgh
Castle, offers accommodation in individually designed and
particularly well furnished bedrooms with good facilities.
Comfortable lounges are warmed by open log fires during the
colder months, and resident owners provide friendly, attentive
service.*
7➪♠1➡⁀in all bedrooms CTV in all bedrooms ® T
✈ (ex guide dogs) dB&B➪♠£140-£180 (incl dinner) ➡
20P 🚫 ✿ croquet nc16yrs
♀ European V ⁀ Dinner £19.50-£23 Last dinner 8.30pm
Credit Cards ①②③⑤

---

**BELLINGHAM** Northumberland Map **12** NY88

**★★66% Riverdale Hall**
NE48 2JT (Exec Hotel) ☎(0434)220254 FAX (0434) 220457
*Overlooking its own cricket pitch and the River Tyne beyond, this
pleasantly furnished hotel is situated on the edge of the charming
village. Friendly and attentive service is provided and the resident
owners are always in attendance.*
20➪♠(6fb)3➡ CTV in all bedrooms ® T sB&B➪♠£32-
£37.50 dB&B➪♠£54-£65 ➡
CTV 60P ✿ CFA 🏊 (heated) ♫ sauna cricket field putting
green *xmas*
♀ English & Danish V ♡ ⚓ ✳ Lunch £6-£9&alc High tea £6-
£10 Dinner £15.50-£16.50 Last dinner 9.30pm
Credit Cards ①②③⑤ⓔ

---

**BELPER** Derbyshire Map **08** SK34 ⊙

**⊛ ✕ ✕ Eighty Four Bridge Street**
84 Bridge St DE5 1AZ ☎(0773)822246
*This small first-floor restaurant, situated on the A6, offers, rather
surprisingly for this area, ethnic and regional dishes from the USA
including Mexican, Chinese, and Cuban and South American
cuisine from Southern Florida's Hispanic communities. The 4-
course evening meal might start with Crawfish Pie, with an
interlude of salad served with sour dough rolls, to be followed by
Cajun Catfish. There is a choice of six or so desserts and, finally,
coffee.*
Closed Mon Lunch not served Sat

---

Dinner not served Sun
♀ English & American V 35 seats Lunch £8-£12alc Dinner
£12-£25alc Last lunch 2pm Last dinner 10pm ✗ nc5yrs
Credit Cards ①③

---

**BELTON** Lincolnshire Map **04** SK93

**★★★★65% Belton Woods Hotel & Country Club**
NG32 2LN ☎Grantham(0476)593200 Telex no 378508
FAX (0476) 74547
*This mellow yellow-brick conference and leisure hotel, built in the
style of a Georgian country mansion and set in 475 acres of
parkland complete with golf course, offers easy access to the A1
from its position on the A607 a couple of miles north of Grantham
(almost opposite Belton House). Opened in January 1991, it has
been carefully designed to keep conference and leisure facilities
separate from public areas offering a choice of bars and
restaurants. Bedrooms in pastel shades, pleasantly furnished in
maple, enjoy good views over the countryside, and a well trained
and fully informed staff provides efficient service.*
96➪♠ CTV in all bedrooms ® T ✳ sB&B➪♠£55-£92
dB&B➪♠£110-£122 (incl dinner) ➡
Lift ⓒ 340P ✿ 🏊 (heated) ➤ 18 ♟ (hard) ♩ squash snooker
sauna solarium gymnasium archery croquet putting spa bath
♫ ♒ *xmas*
V ♡ ⚓ ⁀ ✳ Lunch fr£14.50&alc Dinner fr£18.50&alc Last
dinner 10pm
Credit Cards ①②③⑤

---

⛽ Shell filling station, open 7am–11pm
(some 24 hours) throughout the year with leaded
and unleaded petrol, and diesel.

---

## BEMBRIDGE

See **Wight, Isle of**

## BENLLECH BAY Gwynedd Map **06** SH58

★★59% **Bay Court**
Beach Rd LL74 8SW ☎Tynygongl(0248)852573
*This privately owned hotel, situated within 200yds of the beach,
offers modern accommodation and is popular with holidaymakers.*
15rm(2⇌4♠)Annexe4⇌(5fb) CTV in 15 bedrooms ®
CTV 65P 🚘
🖵 English & French **V** ✿ 🖵 Last dinner 9pm
Credit Cards ①②③£

## BERKELEY Gloucestershire Map **03** ST69

★★63% *Old Schoolhouse*
Canonbury St GL13 9BG ☎Dursley(0453)811711
Closed 22 Dec-7 Jan
*Situated adjacent to the castle entrance, this Victorian house,
which was used as the village school until 1963, has been carefully
converted into a small hotel of quality with good modern facilities.
Bedrooms are spacious and well equipped, and the open-plan
public areas retain much of their original character.*
7⇌♠(1fb) CTV in all bedrooms ® **T** ✖
15P 🚘
🖵 International **V** Last dinner 8.45pm
Credit Cards ①③

★★59% **Berkeley Arms**
Canonbury St GL13 9BG ☎Dursley(0453)810291
FAX (0453) 511334
*This 18th-century former coaching inn at the heart of the historic
little town has characterful public areas and modest but well-
equipped bedrooms. The Whiteside family and their staff provide
friendly services.*
10⇌(1fb) CTV in all bedrooms ® **T** ✳ sB&B⇌fr£35
dB&B⇌fr£48 🎏
50P ✿ CFA
🖵 English & French **V** ✿ 🖵 ✳ Lunch £5-£14alc Dinner £5-
£18alc Last dinner 9.30pm
Credit Cards ①③

## BERKELEY ROAD Gloucestershire Map **03** ST79

★★62% *Prince of Wales*
GL13 9HD ☎Dursley(0453)810474 Telex no 437464
*Recent improvements by the new owners of this hotel have resulted
in bright, comfortable, modern accommodation and good facilities
which are complemented by attentive, friendly service. Its pleasant
location near the historic village of Berkeley, yet only a few miles
from the business centres of Bristol, Cheltenham and Gloucester,
makes it attractive to both tourist and businessman.*
8⇌♠(1fb) CTV in all bedrooms ® **T**
150P ✿
🖵 English & French **V** ✿ 🖵 Last dinner 9pm
Credit Cards ①②③

## BERRIEW Powys Map **07** SJ10

★★67% **Lion**
SY21 8PQ ☎(0686)640452 & 640844
*A charming 17th-century inn, with beamed ceilings and a stone
fireplace, offering comfortable bedrooms and cosy bars. The food is
good with a choice of bar meals or an à la carte menu.*
7⇌♠(1fb)1🖵 CTV in all bedrooms ® **T** ✖ sB&B⇌♠£40-£45
dB&B⇌♠£65-£70 🎏
6P ⭑

For key to symbols in English see the bookmark.

🖵 Welsh, English & Continental **V** ✿ ✳ Sunday Lunch
fr£7.20alc Dinner £12.50-£15&alc Last dinner 9pm
Credit Cards ①③£

## BERWICK-UPON-TWEED Northumberland
Map **12** NT95 ⊖

★★★63% **Turret House**
Etal Rd, Tweedmouth TD15 2EG (Inter-Hotels) ☎(0289)330808
FAX (0289) 330467
*Elegant hotel in its own grounds with tastefully decorated open-
plan bar, dining room and lounge.*
13⇌♠(1fb) CTV in all bedrooms ® **T** sB&B⇌♠fr£55
dB&B⇌♠fr£70 🎏
100P ✿
**V** ✿ 🖵 ✳ Lunch fr£5.75 Dinner fr£15.50 Last dinner 8.45pm
Credit Cards ①②③⑤

★60% **Queens Head**
Sandgate TD15 1EP ☎(0289)307852
*This is a small, well furnished inn situated in the centre of the town.
Bedrooms have good facilities and a good range of food is
available.*
6⇌♠(5fb) CTV in all bedrooms ® **T** sB&B⇌♠fr£25
dB&B⇌♠fr£49.50
CTV 🅿
**V** ✿ ✖ Lunch £7.50-£9.50 High tea fr£5.50 Dinner fr£11 Last
dinner 8.30pm
Credit Cards ①③£

## BETWS GARMON Gwynedd Map **06** SH55

★★64% *Castell Cidwm*
LL54 7YT ☎(028685)243
RS Jan-Feb
*A former Victorian fishing lodge now operated as a small,
personally run and very friendly hotel stands amid mountain
scenery on the shore of Loch Cwellyn, halfway between Beddgelert
and Caernarfon. Some of its 8 bedrooms offer fine views, the dining
room also overlooks the lake, and a cosy little lounge welcomes
guests with an open fire in cooler weather. Fishing and boating can
both be arranged, as half the lake belongs to the hotel.*
8rm(6⇌3♠)(2fb)1🖵 ✖in all bedrooms ® ✖
25P 🚘 ✿ ⭑ sauna solarium watersports
**V** ✿ 🖵 ✖ Last dinner 9.30pm
Credit Cards ①③

## BETWS-Y-COED Gwynedd Map **06** SH75

★★★69% **Waterloo**
LL24 0AR (Consort) ☎(0690)710411 FAX (0690) 710666
Closed Xmas
*This privately owned modern hotel complex on the town's southern
outskirts provides a range of facilities including a well equipped
leisure centre with an indoor pool and gymnasium. Spacious
modern bedrooms are suited to both tourists and business people
and there is a choice of bars, a coffee shop and an attractive
restaurant.*
9⇌Annexe30⇌(2fb) CTV in all bedrooms ® **T**
sB&B⇌£43.50-£49.50 dB&B⇌£69-£75 🎏
200P ✿ 🏊 (heated) ⭑ sauna solarium gymnasium Jaccuzi
steam room *xmas*
🖵 International **V** ✿ 🖵 ✳ Sunday Lunch £7.75-£8.75 Dinner
£16-£16.50&alc Last dinner 9.30pm
Credit Cards ①②③⑤£

★★★⭑64% **Craig-y-Dderwen Country House**
LL24 0AS (Minotels) ☎(0690)710293 FAX (0690) 710362
*This attractive house was built in 1890 as a country retreat by a
Midlands industrialist and became a hotel in the 1920s. Set in 5
acres of secluded grounds on the bank of the River Conwy, it is*

*located on the edge of the village, close to the famous Waterloo Bridge. Bedrooms and public rooms are pleasant and attractive.*
17⇨🟊(3fb)3🛏 CTV in all bedrooms ® T ✷ sB&B⇨🟊fr£45 dB&B⇨🟊fr£60 🏳
60P ✿ CFA ⏶ xmas
♀ International V ↻ ⎘ ⵖ ✷ Lunch fr£8.95alc High tea fr£4.50alc Dinner fr£16.50 Last dinner 8.30pm
Credit Cards ①②③£

★★★🛁 64% **Plas Hall**
Pont-y-Pant, Dolwyddelan LL25 0PJ (3m SW A470)
☎Dolwyddelan(06906)206 FAX (06906) 526
*This privately owned stone-built hotel, once a country house, stands beside the A470 to the south of the town in attractive grounds and gardens which stretch down to the bank of the River Lledr. Its well equipped accommodation is understandably popular with tourists but would be equally suitable for business people – and well worth the short diversion from the A5.*
17⇨🟊(4fb)2🛏 CTV in all bedrooms ® T ✷
sB&B⇨🟊£45.50-£58.50 dB&B⇨🟊£70-£90 🏳
36P ✿ CFA ⚓ games room xmas
♀ Welsh & French V ↻ ⎘ ⵖ ✷ Lunch fr£5.95 Dinner fr£14.95&alc Last dinner 8.30pm
Credit Cards ①③£

See advertisement on page 121

★★★ 62% **Royal Oak**
Holyhead Rd LL24 0AY ☎(0690)710219 FAX (0690) 710603
Closed 25-26 Dec
*A privately owned hotel which was once a coaching inn, standing beside the A5 in the village centre, complements a choice of restaurants and bars with accommodation which is equally suited to the needs of tourists or business clients.*
27⇨🟊(5fb) CTV in all bedrooms T ✘ sB&B⇨🟊£36-£50 dB&B⇨🟊£50-£70 🏳
⟪ 60P CFA

→

**B**

English, French & Italian **V** ♦ 🍸 Lunch £9-£12&alc High tea £4-£8alc Dinner £12-£18&alc Last dinner 9pm
Credit Cards ⓵ ⓶ ⓷ ⓹

### ★★68% Park Hill
Llanrwst Rd LL24 0HD ☎(0690)710540
*This friendly little hotel boasts facilities surprisingly good for its size, including an indoor swimming pool ; privately owned and run, it provides well equipped modern accommodation equally suited to the needs of holidaymakers or business people. An elevated position on the A470, north of the town, provides good views across the Conwy River and its valley.*
11rm(6⇨3♠)(2fb)1🏠 CTV in all bedrooms ®
🏋 (ex guide dogs) ✳ sB&B£17-£18 dB&B⇨♠£23-£28 🅟
CTV 14P 🚲 ❀ ▢ (heated) sauna nc6yrs *xmas*
Welsh, English & French **V** ♦ 🍸 ✂ ✳ Lunch £5.50-£7.50 Dinner £12.50-£13.50 Last dinner 7.45pm
Credit Cards ⓵ ⓶ ⓷ ⓹

### ★★67% Ty Gwyn
LL24 0SG ☎(0690)710383 & 710787
*This ancient stone-built hotel – once a coaching inn – standing beside the A5 on the outskirts of the village retains a wealth of charm and character, many of its individually and tastefully styled bedrooms being furnished with antique pieces though the majority also boast modern en suite facilities.*
13rm(2⇨7♠)(1fb)4🏠 CTV in 8 bedrooms ® sB&B£19 dB&B£36 dB&B⇨♠£55-£80 🅟
CTV 12P *xmas*
English & French **V** ♦ Lunch £9-£17alc Dinner £14.50&alc Last dinner 9.30pm
Credit Cards ⓵ ⓷ ⓺

### ★62% Fairy Glen
LL24 0SH ☎(0690)710269
Closed Dec & Jan
*A small and friendly hotel, personally run by its resident owners, stands beside the river in a wooded area close to the village.*
10rm(5⇨2♠)(3fb) CTV in all bedrooms ® sB&B£16-£20 dB&B£30-£40 dB&B⇨♠£32-£40 🅟
⟮ CTV 10P 🚲 ❀
**V** ♦ 🍸 ✂ Bar Lunch fr£5 Dinner fr£10.50 Last dinner 7.30pm
Credit Cards ⓵ ⓷ ⓹

---

## BEVERLEY Humberside Map **08** TA03

### ★★★67% Beverley Arms
North Bar Within HU17 8DD (Forte Hotels)
☎Hull(0482)869241 Telex no 597568 FAX (0482) 870907
*A modernised coaching inn offers sound accommodation in functional, up-to-date bedrooms complemented by public areas whose traditional features have been highlighted to good effect.*
57⇨♠(4fb)✂in 9 bedrooms CTV in all bedrooms ® **T** ✳
sB⇨♠fr£65 dB⇨♠fr£89 (room only) 🅟
Lift ⟮ 70P CFA 🎵 *xmas*
**V** ♦ 🍸 ✂ ✳ Lunch £9.95 Dinner £14.95 Last dinner 9.45pm
Credit Cards ⓵ ⓶ ⓷ ⓸ ⓹

### ★★★66% Tickton Grange
Tickton HU17 9SH (3m NE on A1035) ☎Hornsea(0964)543666
FAX (0964) 542556
RS 25-29 Dec
*Two miles out of Beverley on the A1035 to Hornsea, this friendly, family-owned Georgian hotel is run in country-house style, and has been carefully renovated, retaining many original features, to provide comfortable and modern accommodation.*
16⇨♠(1fb)1🏠 CTV in all bedrooms ® **T** sB&B⇨♠£59.50 dB&B⇨♠£69.50 🅟
65P ❀
**V** ♦ 🍸 ✳ Lunch fr£11.95alc Dinner fr£14.95alc Last dinner 9.30pm
Credit Cards ⓵ ⓶ ⓷ ⓹ ⓺

### ★★71% *Lairgate*
30-34 Lairgate HU17 8EP ☎Hull(0482)882141
Closed 24-27 Dec
*This privately owned, town centre hotel provides a friendly and relaxed environment, created by polite and conscientious staff. Continual upgrading of facilities means modern accommodation with a good range of facilities, and the restaurant offers interesting menus that are popular with both residents and locals alike.*
23rm(9⇨10♠)(2fb)1🏠 CTV in all bedrooms ® **T**
⟮ CTV 18P
English & Continental **V** ♦ 🍸 Last dinner 9.30pm
Credit Cards ⓵ ⓷

---

## BEWDLEY Hereford & Worcester Map **07** SO77

### ★★53% *Black Boy*
Kidderminster Rd DY12 1AG ☎(0299)402119
Closed 25 Dec
*An 18th-century inn, standing on the A456 close to both the River Severn and the centre of this lovely old town, offers accommodation that is equally suitable for business people and tourists, with simple but comfortable bedrooms, pleasant bar facilities and a small, cosy restaurant.*
17rm(5⇨♠)Annexe8rm(2⇨♠)(2fb) CTV in 15 bedrooms ® **T**
CTV 28P 🚲 ❀
English and French **V** ♦ Last dinner 8.45pm
Credit Cards ⓵ ⓶ ⓷

---

## BEXHILL-ON-SEA East Sussex Map **05** TV70

See also **Cooden Beach**
### ★★★64% Granville
Sea Rd TN40 1EE ☎Bexhill(0424)215437 FAX (0424) 225028
*This elegant hotel, situated close to both seafront and town centre, is renowned for its friendly service ; all the well equipped bedrooms have recently been refurbished to provide a good standard of comfort.*
50⇨♠(1fb) CTV in all bedrooms ® **T** ✳ sB&B⇨♠£34.75-£49.75 dB&B⇨♠£55.50-£69.50 🅟
Lift ⟮ 🅿 CFA *xmas*
**V** ♦ 🍸 ✳ Lunch £8.50 Dinner £13&alc Last dinner 9pm
Credit Cards ⓵ ⓶ ⓷ ⓹

---

## BEXLEY Greater London Map **05** TQ47

### ★★★70% Forte Crest
Black Prince Interchange, Southwold Rd DA5 1ND (Forte Hotels) ☎(0322)526900 Telex no 8956539 FAX (0322) 526113
*This efficiently managed commercial hotel offers a good standard of well equipped accommodation – and the new bedroom wing will add executive studios, rooms for lady executives and spa rooms. Attractive public areas include a separate lounge bar for residents and a business centre.*
102⇨♠✂in 60 bedrooms CTV in all bedrooms ® **T** ✳
sB⇨♠fr£85 dB⇨♠fr£95 (room only) 🅟
Lift ⟮ 200P ❀ CFA games room
**V** ♦ 🍸 ✳ S% Lunch £16.50&alc Dinner £16.50&alc Last dinner 11pm
Credit Cards ⓵ ⓶ ⓷ ⓸ ⓹

### ○Swallow
1 Broadway, Bexleyheath DA6 7JZ (Swallow)
☎Central Res 091-529 4666
Due to open early 1992
122⇨♠

Red star hotels are each highlighted by a pink tinted panel.

**BIBURY** Gloucestershire Map **04** SP10

★★🏨67% **Bibury Court**
GL7 5NT ☎(028574)337 & 324 FAX (028574) 660
Closed 24-30 Dec
*Set within landscaped walled grounds this fine period building is now a hotel of charm and character. Spacious public areas retain many original features and the well equipped bedrooms are comfortable. The new Coach House restaurant, 50 yards from the main building, serves imaginative food in intimate surroundings.*
18⇄(1fb)10🛏 CTV in all bedrooms ® T ✳ sB&B⇄£41-£50 dB&B⇄£62-£68 Continental breakfast 🍴
CTV 100P 🚗 ❀ CFA ⚓ squash ᴕ croquet shooting
♥ English & French V ♥ 🍷 ✳ Lunch £11.50-£12.50 Dinner £15-£20alc Last dinner 9pm
Credit Cards 1 3

---

**BICKLEIGH** Devon Map **03** SS90

★★62% **Fisherman's Cot**
EX16 8RW ☎(0884)855237 & 855289 FAX (0884) 855241
23⇄🟢(5fb)1🛏⚡in 6 bedrooms CTV in all bedrooms ® T ✳
sB&B⇄🟢£44.50-£54.50 dB&B⇄🟢£54.50-£64.50 🍴
CTV 147P ❀ ⚓ xmas
V ♥ 🍷 ✳ Lunch £9.95&alc High tea £1.95-£3.25 Dinner £9.95&alc Last dinner 10pm
Credit Cards 1 3

---

All black star hotels are given a
percentage grading within their star bands.
See 'Using the Guide' at the front of the book
for full details.

**B**

---

See also Landcross & Westward Ho!

★★★ 66% **Royal**

Barnstaple St EX39 4AE (Brend) ☎(0237)472005 Telex no 42551
FAX (0237) 478957

*This extensively refurbished traditional hotel overlooking the historic port provides bright spotlessly clean bedrooms with good modern facilities and a wide range of room services. Stylish public rooms include the lounge bar with wood panelling and ornate ceiling. Staff are friendly and helpful.*

30⇌⋔(3fb) CTV in all bedrooms ® T sB&B⇌⋔£50-£56 dB&B⇌⋔£77-£90 ☐

( 70P ♫ *xmas*

♡ English & French V ⊕ ⊒ Lunch £8&alc Dinner £11-£13&alc Last dinner 9pm
Credit Cards ① ② ③ ⑤ ⓔ

★★★ 63% **Durrant House**

Heywood Rd, Northam EX39 3QB (Consort) ☎(0237)472361
FAX (0237) 421709
Closed 1st two weeks Jan

*This bright, attractive, family-run hotel, conveniently positioned for access to major link roads, creates a friendly atmosphere which attracts both commercial and holiday trade. A top-floor extension offers 30 comfortable, stylishly furnished and well equipped executive bedrooms with marble-floored en suite bathrooms, while more modestly appointed accommodation is in process of varying degrees of upgrading. Public areas are spacious and brightly decorated, guests taking meals either in a traditional dining room or the more intimate Bridge Steak Bar.*

120⇌⋔(6fb) CTV in all bedrooms ® T ☐
Lift 150P ✿ CFA ⊿ sauna solarium *xmas*
♡ English & French ✱ Lunch fr£5.95 Dinner £15&alc Last dinner 9.30pm
Credit Cards ① ② ③ ⑤ ⓔ

★★ 69% **Sonnenheim**

Heywood Rd EX39 2QA ☎(0237)474989
Closed Nov-Feb

*The personally-run country-house-style hotel provides pleasant bedrooms, comfortable public areas, and a friendly atmosphere throughout. A table d'hôte menu of honest cooking, using fresh garden produce whenever possible, offers an interesting choice of dishes.*

9rm(6⇌2⋔)(1fb) CTV in all bedrooms ® sB&B⇌⋔£23-£28 dB&B⇌⋔£36-£46 ☐
10P 1🚗 (£2 per night) 🚭 ✿
♡ English & Continental V Dinner £11-£14 Last dinner 8pm
Credit Cards ① ③ ⓔ

★★ 67% **Orchard Hill Hotel & Restaurant**

Orchard Hill, Northam EX39 2QY ☎(0237)472872

*An hotel looking down on town and river from its elevated position provides comfortable accommodation to suit both businessman and holidaymaker ; a relaxed atmosphere prevails in the public lounges and bar, while the refurbished restaurant serves an à la carte menu and resident proprietors give personal service throughout.*

9⇌⋔ CTV in all bedrooms ® 🐕 (ex guide dogs) ✱
sB&B⇌⋔£33 dB&B⇌⋔£45 ☐
15P 🚭 nc8 yrs *xmas*
♡ English & French V ⊕ ⊒ ⊁
Credit Cards ① ③

★★ 60% *Riversford*

Limers Ln EX39 2RG (Inter-Hotels) ☎(0237)474239
FAX (0237) 421661

*A family-managed hotel standing about a mile from the centre of the town, provides comfortable bedrooms (most with en suite facilities) and informal public rooms which include a restaurant offering a table d'hôte menu.*

16⇌⋔(3fb)2🛏 CTV in all bedrooms ® T

---

( CTV 20P 2🚗 ✿ solarium badminton putting ⚿
♡ English & Continental V ⊕ ⊒ ⊁ Last dinner 9pm
Credit Cards ① ② ③ ⑤

---

★★ 65% *White Lion*

High St B50 4BQ ☎(0789)773309 & 773218 FAX (0789)490058

*An attractive little hotel by the river in the village centre, offering friendly service and characterful public areas, including a separate bar which is popular with the locals. Bedrooms are comfortable and well furnished, with good modern facilities.*

10⇌⋔ CTV in all bedrooms ® T
18P ♪
♡ English & French ⊕ ⊒ ⊁ Last dinner 9.30pm
Credit Cards ① ② ③ ⑤

---

★ 69% **Henley**

TQ7 4AR ☎(0548)810240

*Charles and Louvain Beer have achieved commendable results at their cosy hotel. Perched above Bigbury Bay and with dramatic sea and countryside views, it has a private cliff path to the beach and gardens. Recent extensive refurbishment promotes a cottage atmosphere, with comfortable public rooms including an attractive small dining room. Compact bedrooms are pleasantly redecorated with colour co-ordinated fabrics and modern facilities. Home-cooked food is prepared from fresh produce varying the table d'hôte menu daily. There is a no smoking policy throughout the hotel.*

8⇌⋔(2fb)⊁in all bedrooms CTV in all bedrooms ® T
sB&B⇌⋔£21.50-£25.50 dB&B⇌⋔£43-£51 ☐
9P 🚭 ✿ ⚿ *xmas*
♡ English & French ⊕ ⊒ ⊁ Lunch £6.95 High tea £2.40
Dinner £12.75 Last dinner 8pm
Credit Cards ① ② ③

---

★★★ ⊛⊮ 75% **Shieldhill**

Quothquan ML12 6NA ☎(0899)20035 Telex no 777308
FAX (0899) 21092
RS Fri-Sun

*This lovely old country house hotel, set in open countryside about 3.5 miles from Biggar and completely refurbished in 1988 by the present owners, offers a warm welcome and very comfortable public areas adorned with antiques. Individually designed bedrooms are of an outstanding quality, and the elegant restaurant provides a good standard of home cooking.*

11⇌⋔4🛏⊁in all bedrooms CTV in all bedrooms T
🐕 (ex guide dogs) sB&B⇌⋔£88-£120 dB&B⇌⋔£98-£150 ☐
25P 🚭 ✿ CFA croquet bowls nc12yrs
V ⊕ ⊒ ⊁ Lunch £18-£22alc Dinner £20-£25alc Last dinner 9.30pm
Credit Cards ① ② ③ ④ ⑤ ⓔ

★★★ 67% **Tinto**

Symington ML12 6PQ ☎Tinto(08993)454 FAX (08993) 520

*Set in its own gardens on the A72 3 miles southwest of Biggar, this hotel appeals to both business and holiday users, and attracts local custom to its 2 restaurants and function room. The comfortable bedrooms, including 2 suites, are well presented and spotlessly maintained. In addition to the main lounge and cosy bar there is an attractive residents' lounge on the first floor.*

38⇌⋔(2fb)2🛏 CTV in all bedrooms ® T sB&B⇌⋔£39-£42 dB&B⇌⋔£58-£60 ☐
( CTV 100P 🚭 ✿ CFA solarium pool table *xmas*
♡ Continental V ⊕ ⊒ ✱ Lunch £7.50-£12.50alc High tea £6.15-£11.30alc Dinner £11-£16alc Last dinner 10pm
Credit Cards ① ② ③ ⑤ ⓔ

**B**

★★�’68% **Wyndales House**

Symington ML12 6JU (3m W off A72) ☎Tinto(08993)207 & 555

*In the hands of its new owners this former mansion is undergoing a phased programme of improvements designed to restore the original charm and character of the Edwardian building. The panelled public rooms, especially the lounge, are comfortable and the bedrooms, individually decorated, are well equipped. The hotel stands in 19 acres of wooded grounds at the foot of Tinto Hill.*

14⇨🏠(3fb)1⚃ CTV in all bedrooms ® T S%
sB&B⇨🏠£39.50-£41.50 dB&B⇨🏠£52-£55 ⊟

( 60P ❈ ♬ (grass) *xmas*

♡ International **V** ♧ ♨ S% Lunch £9-£9.50 Dinner £15-£16&alc Last dinner 9.30pm

Credit Cards 1 2 3 ⓔ

---

BILBROOK Somerset Map **03** ST04

★68% **Bilbrook Lawns**

TA24 6HE ☎Washford(0984)40331

Closed Nov-Feb (ex Xmas)

*A small Georgian house with elegant, well proportioned rooms stands back from the road in its own gardens. Bedrooms in country style contain some antique furnishings, while the restaurant serves enjoyable meals in which fresh ingredients have been used to create some interesting and well-flavoured – but not over-elaborate – European dishes; resident proprietors provide good-natured hospitality.*

7rm(1⇨3🏠)(1fb) CTV in all bedrooms ® sB&Bfr£21.50 sB&B⇨🏠fr£25 dB&Bfr£33 dB&B⇨🏠£38-£44 ⊟

8P 🚗 ❈ 👶 *xmas*

♡ English & French **V** ♧ ♨ ⊁ Lunch fr£6.50 Dinner fr£10.50 Last dinner 7.30pm

Credit Cards 2

---

BILBROUGH North Yorkshire Map **08** SE54

★★★

★★★⚄
**BILBROUGH MANOR COUNTRY HOUSE**

YO2 3PH
☎Tadcaster(0937)834002
FAX (0937) 834724

Closed 25-29 Dec

*A tranquilly peaceful and comfortable country manor house at the edge of this conservation village, just 5 miles from the centre of York, has been carefully restored by its current owners to provide accommodation in bedrooms which are all strikingly decorated and well equipped although they vary in shape and size. Wood panelling is a feature of both the pleasant dining room and a most inviting drawing room with large open fireplace, comfortable chairs and sofas, fine oil paintings and an extensive library; from this room, as from the bedrooms, guests enjoy delightful views of the gardens and surrounding countryside. Though the past year has seen some changes in personnel – the saddest caused by the death of Hyde, the butler who looked after guests so attentively – the style of service is expected to remain unchanged; new chef Andrew Pressley as yet lacks the skill and flair of his predecessor, but it seems likely that he will soon be providing meals of the quality associated with this hotel.*

12⇨🏠1⚃ CTV in all bedrooms T ⊁ ❋ sB&B⇨🏠£60-£77 dB&B⇨🏠£65-£145 ⊟

( CTV 50P 🚗 ❈ croquet nc12yrs *xmas*

---

♡ French **V** ♧ ♨ ⊁ ❋ Lunch £10-£14.50&alc Dinner £18.50&alc Last dinner 9.30pm

Credit Cards 1 2 3 5 ⓔ

---

○**Forte Travelodge**

(A63 eastbound) (Forte) ☎Central Res (0800) 850950

Due to have opened Jul 1991

36⇨🏠

---

BILLESLEY Warwickshire Map **04** SP15

★★★❀❀❀⚄76% **Billesley Manor**

B49 6NF (Queens Moat)(Small Luxury Hotels)
☎Stratford-upon-Avon(0789)400888 Telex no 312599 FAX (0789) 764145

*Panelled walls and leather chairs create a comfortable, traditional atmosphere where meals are served with friendliness and professionalism. A short daily menu and a seasonal à la carte menu are on offer, with simple dishes such as whole Dover sole available alongside more modern ideas such as chicken with paprika and caraway. The sauces were highly praised by our Inspector, as were the carefully chosen garnishes that allow the main ingredient to speak for itself. Some serious wine growers feature on the wine list.*

41⇨🏠(6fb)3⚃ CTV in all bedrooms ® T ⊁ sB&B⇨🏠£99 dB&B⇨🏠£128-£160 ⊟

( 100P ❈ CFA ▣ (heated) ♬ (hard) croquet pitch & putt *xmas*

♡ English & French **V** ♧ ♨ Lunch £17&alc Dinner £25&alc Last dinner 9.30pm

Credit Cards 1 2 3 5 ⓔ

**See advertisement under STRATFORD-UPON-AVON**

---

BILLINGHAM

See Stockton-on-Tees

---

BILLINGTON Lancashire Map **07** SD73

★★★★69% **Foxfields Country Hotel & Restaurant**

Whalley Rd BB6 9HY ☎Blackburn(0254)822556
FAX (0254) 824613

*Set in rural surroundings yet offering convenient access to a number of business centres, this hotel is said to be the only one outside London providing totally suited accommodation – its 28 bedrooms all having luxury bathrooms and large sitting rooms. This accommodation was added as recently as 1990, the original restaurant (which already had an excellent reputation) and cocktail bar also being extended to provide very well appointed public areas.*

28⇨🏠1⚃ CTV in all bedrooms ® T ⊁ (ex guide dogs) ❋ sB&B⇨🏠£45-£75 dB&B⇨🏠£60-£85 ⊟

( 175P ❈ CFA *xmas*

♡ English & French **V** ♧ ♨ ⊁ ❋ Lunch £8.95-£11.95&alc Dinner £14.50-£18.95&alc Last dinner 9.45pm

Credit Cards 1 2 3 5 ⓔ

---

BINGLEY West Yorkshire Map **07** SE13

★★★64% **Bankfield**

Bradford Rd BD16 1TU (Jarvis) ☎Bradford(0274)567123 FAX (0274) 551331

*Modern bedrooms and conference rooms have been built around this stone country house set in its own grounds, providing comfortable accommodation with good facilities.*

103⇨🏠(5fb)⊁in 6 bedrooms CTV in all bedrooms ® T ❋ S10% sB⇨🏠£76-£88 dB⇨🏠£89.50-£98 (room only) ⊟

Lift ( 250P 20🚗 ❈ CFA ♫ *xmas*

V ⏱ ⬛ ⚊ ✳ S10% Lunch fr£13.50&alc Dinner fr£13.50&alc
Last dinner 9.15pm
Credit Cards ①②③⑤

★★★63% **Oakwood Hall**
Lady Ln BD16 4AW ☎Bradford(0274)564123 & 563569
FAX (0274) 561477
Closed 25-28 Dec
*A mansion dating from the Victorian era and set in a peaceful
residential area on the northern edge of the town is now a family-
owned and run hotel providing generally spacious, attractively
decorated and comfortably furnished accommodation with modern
facilities.*
16⇔🎝(1fb)2🛏 CTV in all bedrooms ⓇT ✳ sB&B⇔🎝£55-
£75 dB&B⇔🎝£75-£95
⌞ 100P ✿
♡ English & French V ⏱ ✳ Lunch fr£10.75&alc Dinner
£17&alc Last dinner 9.30pm
Credit Cards ①②③④⑤ⓔ

---

BIRCHGROVE West Glamorgan Map **03** SS79

★★★62% **Oak Tree Parc**
Birchgrove Rd SA7 9JR (300yds from M4 junc 44)
☎Skewen(0792)817781 FAX (0792) 814542
Closed 25-31 Dec
*A small commercial hotel run by the friendly Tilbrook family
providing comfortable, well equipped accommodation and well
cooked food.*
10⇔🎝(2fb) CTV in all bedrooms ⓇT ✳ sB&B⇔🎝fr£41
dB&B⇔🎝fr£57 🛏
⌞ 40P ✿ CFA
♡ Welsh, English, French & Italian V ⏱ ⬛ ⚊ Lunch £7.95-
£10&alc High tea £5-£10 Dinner fr£12&alc Last dinner 10pm
Credit Cards ①②③⑤ⓔ

---

BIRCH MOTORWAY SERVICE AREA (M62) Greater
Manchester Map **07** SD80

⛺**Granada Lodge**
M62 Service Area OL10 2HQ (Granada) ☎061-655 3403
FAX 061-655 3358
*This lodge between junctions 18 and 19 of the M62 – located on
the eastbound carriageway but accessible from both sides –
provides clean, well maintained accommodation at budget prices;
meals are available in the adjacent Country Kitchen, which is open
24 hours a day.*
37⇔🎝(5fb)⚊in 5 bedrooms CTV in all bedrooms Ⓡ
✕ (ex guide dogs) S% sB⇔🎝fr£31 dB⇔🎝fr£34 (room only) 🛏
⌞ 322P
V ⏱ ⬛ ⚊
Credit Cards ①②③⑤

**See advertisement under Manchester**

---

BIRDLIP Gloucestershire Map **03** SO91

★★★59% **Royal George**
GL4 8JH (Lansbury) ☎Gloucester(0452)862506
Telex no 437238 FAX (0452) 862277
*The hotel stands in rural surroundings on the edge of the village,
and guests can expect to enjoy a much more peaceful stay now that
the completed bypass has diverted the majority of the traffic. For a
drink in surroundings full of atmosphere, visit the Applecart Pub,
converted from a 17th-century chapel.*
34⇔🎝Annexe2⇔🎝(4fb)1🛏⚊in 6 bedrooms CTV in all
bedrooms ⓇT ✕ (ex guide dogs) ✳ sB&B⇔🎝£68
dB&B⇔🎝£80 🛏
⌞ 120P ✿ CFA sauna solarium 9 hole putting green ♋ *xmas*
V ⏱ ⬛ ⚊ Lunch fr£8.95 Dinner fr£14&alc Last dinner 10pm
Credit Cards ①②③⑤

---

⊛ ✕**Kingshead House**
GL4 8JH ☎Gloucester(0452)862299
*A cosy, intimate restaurant situated opposite the Royal George
Hotel is operated by Warren and Judy Knock, who use local
produce – including organically grown vegetables – to provide
imaginative meals ; worthy of particular note are the range of fresh
soups and the steak and mushroom pie. The wine list, which
includes some 70 bins, offers wide coverage, individual descriptions
and good value for money.*
Closed Mon, 10 days holiday, 25-26 Dec & 1 Jan Lunch not
served Sat
Dinner not served Sun
♡ English & French V 30 seats Lunch £15.50 Dinner £23 Last
lunch 2pm Last dinner 9.45pm 12 P
Credit Cards ①②③⑤

---

BIRKENHEAD Merseyside Map **07** SJ38 ◒

★★★62% **Bowler Hat**
2 Talbot Rd, Oxton L43 2HH ☎051-652 4931 Telex no 628761
FAX 051-653 8127
*In a quiet residential area, less than 2 miles from junction 3 of the
M63, this period gabled house offers well equipped bedrooms, most
of which are in a modern extension to the rear of the building.*
29⇔🎝 CTV in all bedrooms ⓇT ✳ sB&B⇔🎝£33-£54.50
dB&B⇔🎝£48-£69 🛏
⌞ 40P ✿ CFA
♡ International V ⏱ ⬛ ✳ Lunch £7.50-£9.95&alc Dinner £10-
£13.50&alc Last dinner 10pm
Credit Cards ①②③⑤ⓔ

---

A rosette means exceptional standards of cuisine.

**B**

## ★★64% **Riverhill**

Talbot Rd, Oxton L43 2HJ ☎051-653 3773 FAX 051-653 7162

*This hospitable, privately owned hotel standing in its own grounds has well equipped bedrooms, an attractive cocktail bar and a popular restaurant, in elegant Victorian style, featuring both classical and Italian dishes.*

16⇦♪ (1fb)2⊞ CTV in all bedrooms ® T ⋈
sB&B⇦♪£29.95-£44.95 dB&B⇦♪£43.95-£54.95
CTV 30P ⊞ ❖

♀ English, French & Italian V ✱ Lunch £7.95-£9.95&alc
Dinner frf11.90&alc Last dinner 9.30pm

Credit Cards 1 2 3 5

## ❀ ✗ **Beadles**

15 Rosemount, Oxton L43 5SG ☎051-653 9010

*This small, shop-fronted restaurant on the main street of Oxton Village has a pleasant, relaxed atmosphere ; enthusiastic proprietor Roy Gott is happy to explain any item on the reasonably priced menu and wine list, and it is his wife who produces the simple, honest and reliably cooked dishes from sound, fresh ingredients. A monthly changing à la carte selection offers 5 items at each course, usually including some European-inspired items such as Escalibada or Tiramisu, and the courteous service is unhurried.*

Closed Sun, Mon & Aug Lunch not served Tue-Sat
32 seats Dinner £14-£16alc Last dinner 9pm ⨇

Credit Cards 1 3

---

**BIRMINGHAM** West Midlands Map **07** SP08 ◉

### See Town Plan Section

See also Barr, Great, Birmingham Airport, Birmingham (National Exhibition Centre), Bromsgrove & Lea Marston

## ★★★★❀❀❀72% **Swallow**

12 Hagley Rd, Five Ways B16 8SJ (Swallow) ☎021-452 1144
Telex no 333806 FAX 021-456 3442

*At Fiveways, in the centre of Edgbaston, this Edwardian building has been cleverly converted to create a luxury hotel. Guest rooms are elegantly appointed and include a good range of modern facilities and some thoughtful extras. Afternoon tea is served in the drawing room, and there is a small library with a large range of books and newspapers. A comprehensive leisure centre includes a swimming pool and a state of the art gymnasium. Chef Idris Caldora continues to impress with the quality of his menus and his cooking in the new classical style, served in the Edward Elgar Restaurant, while traditional and regional dishes are available in Langtrys. We are delighted to award one of our 1991/1992 'Courtesy and Care' awards to this well run hotel. (See colour feature on p17.)*

98⇦♪ in 54 bedrooms CTV in all bedrooms ® T S%
sB&B⇦♪frf£97.50 dB&B⇦♪frf£120 ₪
Lift ⦅ ⊞ 70P ⊞ CFA ⊠ (heated) sauna solarium gymnasium
♫ xmas

♀ English & French V ❖ ⬚ ⅓ ✱ Lunch £23.50&alc Dinner
£23.50-£30&alc Last dinner 10.30pm

Credit Cards 1 2 3 5

## ★★★★❀62% **Plough & Harrow**

Hagley Rd, Edgbaston B16 8LS (Forte Hotels) ☎021-454 4111
Telex no 338074 FAX 021-454 1868

*History records that there has been an inn on the site of this hotel since 1612. Today's guests appreciate its position on the A456 not far from the city centre, the well equipped and almost club-like – though rather dark and dated – bedrooms provided in an annexe at the rear, and the restaurant which has gained a good local reputation for classical cuisine.*

44⇦♪ in 6 bedrooms CTV in all bedrooms T ✱
sB⇦♪frf£75 dB⇦♪frf£85 (room only) ₪
Lift ⦅ 80P ⊞ CFA sauna xmas

♀ English & French V ❖ ⬚ ✱ S% Lunch £17&alc Dinner
£18&alc Last dinner 10.15pm

Credit Cards 1 2 3 4 5

---

## ★★★★54% **Holiday Inn**

Holliday St B1 1HH (Holiday Inns Inc) ☎021-631 2000
Telex 337272 FAX 021-643 9018

*This busy hotel, close to the city centre with adjacent car parking, has updated its public areas. A new leisure centre and the new-look Prinneys Bar have proved popular. Bedrooms are well equipped, though the décor in some looked rather tired on our inspection.*

288⇦(210fb)⅓ in 102 bedrooms CTV in all bedrooms ® T
sB⇦£96-£111 dB⇦£105-£120 (room only) ₪
Lift ⦅ ⊞ ⨇ CFA ⊠ (heated) sauna solarium gymnasium
steam room spa bath ♫

♀ International V ❖ ⬚ Lunch £12.50&alc Dinner £14.95&alc
Last dinner 11pm

Credit Cards 1 2 3 4 5 £

## ★★★★51% **Forte Crest**

Smallbrook Queensway B5 4EW (Forte Hotels) ☎021-643 8171
Telex no 337031 FAX 021-631 2528

*An impressive, modern, 13-storey building with extensive views over the city.*

254⇦♪⅓ in 160 bedrooms CTV in all bedrooms ® T ✱ S%
sB⇦♪frf80 dB⇦♪frf90 (room only) ₪
Lift ⦅ ⊞ ⨇ CFA ⊠ (heated) squash sauna solarium
gymnasium health & fitness club

♀ European V ❖ ⬚ ⅓ ✱ Lunch £12.50&alc Dinner
£12.50&alc Last dinner 10.30pm

Credit Cards 1 2 3 4 5

## ★★★❀❀79% **Norton Place**

180 Lifford Ln, Kings Norton B30 3NT ☎021-433 5656
FAX 021-433 3048

*Just 15 minutes' drive from the city centre, this Victorian paper mill has been converted and much extended to create a unique complex including a museum, a large conference centre, a good restaurant and, latterly, a hotel. Small and exclusive, the hotel has only 10 guest rooms, each individually styled, with the highest standards of décor and furnishings, luxuriously appointed and offering an excellent range of facilities. Guests have their own sitting room with a conservatory extension, and the building is set in formal gardens. There are few hotels which could match the consistency achieved at Norton Place, managed with admirable professionalism by Antony Davis, the young staff are impeccably mannered and standards of service are quite remarkable. The Lombard Room Restaurant, which predates the hotel, has built up a good reputation. Chef Andrew Morgan and his team provide interesting menus and food is prepared with skill and care.*

10⇦♪2⊞⅓ in 5 bedrooms CTV in all bedrooms T
⋈ (ex guide dogs) S% sB&B⇦♪frf90 dB&B⇦♪frf99
Continental breakfast ₪
⦅ 300P ⊞ ❖ gymnasium clay pigeon shooting nc xmas

♀ English & French V ❖ ⬚ ⅓ ✱ Lunch £12-£15&alc Dinner
£18-£19&alc Last dinner 10pm

Credit Cards 1 2 3 5 £

## ★★★68% **Westley Arms**

80-90 Westley Rd, Acocks Green B27 7UJ ☎021-706 4312
FAX 021-706 2824

*Just off the A41 (Warwick road) and 3 miles from the city centre at Acocks Green, this hotel was extensively refurbished in 1989 and offers very well equipped bedrooms, including 10 in the adjacent Victorian town house. Public areas are attractively furnished and include an intimate restaurant with cocktail bar and a popular bar and brasserie.*

27⇦♪Annexe10⇦♪(1fb)⊞ CTV in all bedrooms ® T
⋈ (ex guide dogs) sB&B⇦♪£65 dB&B⇦♪£70-£85 ₪
⦅ CTV 100P CFA

♀ English & French V ❖ ⬚
Credit Cards 1 3 £

For key to symbols in English see the bookmark.

★★★ 65% **Strathallan Thistle**
225 Hagley Rd, Edgbaston B16 9RY (Mount Charlotte (TS))
☎021-455 9777 Telex no 336680 FAX 021-454 9432
*This striking modern hotel situated on the A456 just a short drive*
*from the city centre offers a good range of services, including an*
*extensive room service menu. Well appointed public areas include*
*the Mange-Tout Restaurant, which also serves a wide range of*
*meals, while accommodation is comprehensively equipped though*
*rooms are compact.*
167⇱♪(5fb)✂in 18 bedrooms CTV in all bedrooms ® T
(room only) ⊟
Lift ( ⊞ 250P 150🕿
♥ International ⊹ ⏛ ✂
Credit Cards ①②③④⑤

See advertisement on page 129

★★★ 64% **Royal Angus Thistle**
St Chads, Queensway B4 6HY (Mount Charlotte (TS))
☎021-236 4211 Telex no 336889 FAX 021-233 2195
*A well run city centre hotel with an adjoining National Car Park.*
*The attractive bedrooms offer a good range of modern facilities*
*and are particularly suitable for business travellers. 24-hour room*
*service is available.*
135⇱♪(4fb)✂in 8 bedrooms CTV in all bedrooms ® T (room
only) ⊟
Lift ( 600🕿 (charged)
♥ International ⊹ ⏛ ✂
Credit Cards ①②③④⑤

See advertisement on page 133

★★★ 62% **Forte Posthouse Birmingham**
Chapel Ln B43 7BG (Forte Hotels) ☎021-357 7444
Telex no 338497 FAX 021-357 7503
(For full entry see Barr, Great)

# Birmingham

**★★★62% Westmead Hotel & Restaurant**
Redditch Rd, Hopwood B48 7AL (Lansbury) ☎021-445 1202
Telex no 335956 FAX 021-445 6163
*The hotel stands near to junction 2 of the M42 in a peaceful rural location, but convenient for access to Birmingham. Accommodation is spacious and well equipped, ideally suited for the business traveller. Conference facilities are extensive.*
60⇨🛏(4fb)2🛏½in 4 bedrooms CTV in all bedrooms ® T
✖ (ex guide dogs) ✱ sB&B⇨🛏£72 dB&B⇨🛏£84 🅿
《 250P ✿ CFA *xmas*
♀ English & French V ☙ ⚌ ½ ✱ Lunch £8.50-£13.95&alc
Dinner fr£13.95&alc Last dinner 10pm
Credit Cards ⑴⑵⑶⑸£

**★★★61% *Novotel Birmingham***
70 Broad St B1 2HT ☎021-643 2000 Telex no 335556
FAX 021-643 9796
*A modern hotel, opened in 1990, in a convenient location close to the city centre. Rooms are well equipped but the furnishings and décor are quite simple. Le Grill restaurant opens from 6am to midnight, and there is a fitness centre with gym, jacuzzi and sauna.*
148⇨🛏(148fb) CTV in all bedrooms ® T
Lift ⊞ 65🛎 🚗 sauna gymnasium jacuzzi
V ☙ ⚌ Last dinner mdnt
Credit Cards ⑴⑵⑶⑸

**★★★60% Great Barr Hotel & Conference Centre**
Pear Tree Dr, off Newton Rd B43 6HS ☎021-357 1141
Telex no 336406 FAX 021-357 7557
(For full entry see Barr, Great)

**★★★56% Grand**
Colmore Row B3 2DA (Queens Moat) ☎021-236 7951
Telex no 338174 FAX 021-233 1465
Closed 4 days Xmas
*Extensive refurbishment has recently been undertaken at what was a rather dated city centre hotel ; accommodation offers excellent modern facilities, whilst two bars, a carvery and the Penny Black Restaurant provide a range of eating options. The nearest NCP car park is a few minutes' walk away.*
173⇨🛏(7fb) CTV in all bedrooms ® T S10% sB&B⇨🛏£40-£80 dB&B⇨🛏£60-£100 🅿
Lift 《 ✔ CFA
♀ English & French V ☙ ⚌ ½ ✱ Lunch £8.95-£10.95&alc
Dinner £12.95&alc Last dinner 9.45pm
Credit Cards ⑴⑵⑶⑸£

**★★★53% Apollo**
243-247 Hagley Rd, Edgbaston B16 9RA (Mount Charlotte (TS))
☎021-455 0271 Telex no 336759 FAX 021-456 2394
*A modern motel-style operation on the A456 with easy access to the city centre. Some bedrooms are of a good standard, whilst others are rather dated and less comfortable. There is a choice of eating options.*
128⇨🛏(9fb)½in 22 bedrooms CTV in all bedrooms ® T
(room only) 🅿
Lift 《 CTV 130P *xmas*
♀ English & French V ☙ ⚌ ½
Credit Cards ⑴⑵⑶⑸

**★★67% Wheatsheaf**
Coventry Rd, Sheldon B26 3EH (Porterhouse) ☎021-742 6201 &
021-743 2021 FAX 021-722 2703
Closed 25 & 26 Dec
*This busy hotel, conveniently situated on the A45 close to the NEC and airport, has attractively decorated rooms equipped with all modern facilities. The popular restaurant offers a good choice of meals, served by friendly, helpful staff.*
86⇨🛏½in 10 bedrooms CTV in all bedrooms ® T
✖ (ex guide dogs) ✱ sB&B⇨🛏£58 dB&B⇨🛏£74 🅿
《 100P CFA *xmas*

♀ English, French & Italian V ½ ✱ Lunch £8.95-£15alc
Dinner fr£15alc Last dinner 10pm
Credit Cards ⑴⑵⑶⑸

**★★66% Portland**
313 Hagley Rd, Edgbaston B16 9LQ ☎021-455 0535
Telex no 334200 FAX 021-456 1841
*Located on the A456 Hagley Road convenient for the city centre, this friendly hotel continues to be popular with business people for its well-maintained accommodation that provides a good range of facilities.*
63⇨🛏 CTV in all bedrooms ® T ✖ (ex guide dogs)
sB&B⇨🛏£50.50-£51.50 dB&B⇨🛏£67.35-£68.90 🅿
Lift 《 CTV 80P CFA
♀ English & French V ⚌ Lunch £11.25-£11.95&alc Dinner
£11.25-£11.95&alc Last dinner 10pm
Credit Cards ⑴⑵⑶⑸£

**★★64% Hagley Court**
229 Hagley Rd, Edgbaston B16 9RP ☎021-454 6514
FAX 021-456 2722
Closed Xmas
*On the western route out of the city centre on the A456, this privately owned hotel has well equipped rooms and a hospitable atmosphere.*
28⇨🛏(1fb) CTV in all bedrooms ® T ✖ (ex guide dogs) ✱
sB&B⇨🛏£26-£48 dB&B⇨🛏£36-£62 🅿
《 28P 🚗 CFA
♀ English & Continental ☙ ⚌ ✱ Bar Lunch £4.10-£8.50alc
Dinner £14&alc Last dinner 9.30pm
Credit Cards ⑴⑵⑶⑸£

**★★64% Norwood**
87-89 Bunbury Rd, Northfield B31 2ET ☎021-411 2202
*A welcoming owner-run hotel with a pleasant garden to the southwest of the city close to the M5, M6 and M42. Bedrooms can be compact but all are well equipped and ideal for commercial visitors.*
15⇨🛏 CTV in all bedrooms ® T ✱ sB&B⇨🛏£49.75-£59.75
dB&B⇨🛏£59.75-£69.75 🅿
11P ✿ CFA
♀ English & French V ☙ ⚌ ✱ Dinner £15.50-£16.50 Last dinner 9.30pm
Credit Cards ⑴⑵⑶

**★★64% Westbourne Lodge**
27/29 Fountain Rd, Edgbaston B17 8NJ ☎021-429 1003
FAX 021-429 7436
*A family-run private hotel located just off the A456 at Edgbaston provides a friendly, informal atmosphere and value-for-money accommodation in well equipped, efficiently maintained rooms.*
18⇨🛏(4fb) CTV in all bedrooms ® T sB&B⇨🛏fr£40
dB&B⇨🛏fr£56
CTV 12P
♀ English, French & Italian V ☙ ⚌ ½ Lunch £8-£13.50 High
tea fr£3.60 Dinner £14.50 Last dinner 7.45pm
Credit Cards ⑴⑶

**★★63% Meadow Court**
397 Hagley Rd, Edgbaston B17 8BL ☎021-429 2377
FAX 021-434 3140
*Small and privately owned, this hotel has recently been extensively refurbished to provide well equipped modern accommodation which, together with a convenient location on the A456 about 1.5 miles west of the city centre and within easy reach of the M5, makes it particularly popular with commercial visitors. Some conferences can be accommodated.*
14⇨🛏 CTV in all bedrooms ® T ✖ sB&B⇨🛏£43.75-£47
dB&B⇨🛏£58
CTV 16P 🚗 CFA

♀ English & French **V** Bar Lunch £4.50-£6.50 Dinner £12.95
Last dinner 8.30pm
Credit Cards ① ② ③ ⑤ ⓔ

**★★62%** *Copperfield House*
60 Upland Rd, Selly Park B29 7JS ☎021-472 8344
Closed 24 Dec-2 Jan RS 30 Jul & 14 Aug
*Comfortable, well equipped accommodation, a friendly atmosphere and a setting in a pleasant residential area are the attractions of this small, personally owned and run hotel.*
14⇄(1fb) CTV in all bedrooms ⓡ **T**
12P 🚗
**V** ✽ Last dinner 7.30pm
Credit Cards ① ③

**★★60%** *Beechwood*
201 Bristol Rd, Edgbaston B5 7UB ☎021-440-2133
FAX 021-446 4549
*A small, efficiently managed hotel on the A38, a mile from the city centre, provides accommodation in simply furnished, well kept rooms and features extensive rear gardens with a trout lake.*
18rm(6⇄10♪)(4fb) CTV in all bedrooms ⓡ
⊞ CTV 30P ❋ trout lake ♨
**V** ✿ ♨ Last dinner 10pm
Credit Cards ① ③ ⑤

**★★60%** **Edgbaston Palace**
198 Hagley Rd B16 9PQ ☎021-452 1577
*A personally run family hotel, converted from 2 large houses, on one of the busy routes into the city. A planned extension will increase the number of bedrooms and provide a larger restaurant for guests.*
17rm(16⇄♪)(1fb) CTV in all bedrooms ⓡ **T ✳** S10%
sB&Bfr£35 sB&B⇄♪fr£40 dB&B⇄♪£55-£80 ♬
《 CTV 20P 3🚗 ❋
♀ Continental **V** ✿ ♨ ✳ S10% Lunch fr£5 Dinner £9.50-£14.50 Last dinner 9.30pm
Credit Cards ① ② ③ ⑤

**★★56%** **Sheriden House**
82 Handsworth Wood Rd, Handsworth Wood B20 2PL
☎021-554 2185 & 021-523 5960 FAX 021-551 4761
*Popular with its mainly commercial guests, this small privately owned hotel is convenient for the city centre and West Bromwich. Some bedrooms have been refurbished to a good standard whilst others remain more modest. There is a very small lounge, a bar and dining room.*
11rm(9⇄♪)1🚗 CTV in all bedrooms ⓡ **T ✳** sB&B£31-£32
sB&B⇄♪£48-£50 dB&B£48-£50 dB&B⇄♪£68.50-£71 ♬
《 CTV 30P
♀ English & French **V** ✿ ♨ S% Lunch £10.95-£11.25 Dinner £11.75-£12.25&alc Last dinner 9.30pm
Credit Cards ① ② ③ ⓔ

**⇧Campanile**
55 Irving St, Lee Bank B1 1DH (Campanile) ☎021-622 4925
Telex no 333701 FAX 021-622 4195
*Popular for its proximity to the city centre and for the value-for-money accommodation it provides in standard rooms with good modern facilities, this busy hotel is run by a friendly management couple.*
Annexe50⇄♪ CTV in all bedrooms ⓡ
50P
♀ English & French Last dinner 10pm
Credit Cards ① ③ ⓔ

**See advertisement on page 131**

A rosette means exceptional standards of cuisine.

**B**

※※※×××**Sloan's**
27-29 Chad Square, Hawthorne Rd, Edgbaston B15 3TQ
☎021-455 6697 FAX 021-454 4335
*A small modern shopping precinct in a Birmingham suburb is an unlikely spot for an award winning restaurant such as this, though it does nothing to diminish its popularity. Sloan's has received much acclaim over the years, and Chef Roger Narbett is well known for his competition cookery – Young Chef of the Year 1985 and Chef of the Year 1990. The menu combines classical and modern French dishes; there is a good balance of ingredients and no gimmicks. The preparation and presentation of fish dishes is a particular strength, such as panache of John Dorey and plump scallops with fried summer vegetables and saffron sauce. The dessert enjoyed by our Inspector, prune and armagnac tart with praline mousse and vanilla sauce, was a triumph.*
Closed Sun, 26-31 Dec & BH's Lunch not served Sat
♀ French V 60 seats Lunch fr£15.50&alc Dinner £26-£33.45alc Last lunch 2pm Last dinner 10pm 40 P nc10yrs ✻
Credit Cards ①②③

---

## BIRMINGHAM AIRPORT West Midlands Map 07 SP18

★★★61% **Forte Posthouse**
Coventry Rd, Elmdon B26 3QW (Forte Hotels) ☎021-782 8141
Telex no 338005 FAX 021-782 2476
*Situated on the A45 close to the NEC. The majority of the bedrooms have now been refurbished and similar treatment is planned for public areas.*
136⇨↑✻in 70 bedrooms CTV in all bedrooms ® T ✳
sB⇨↑£39.50-£49.50 dB⇨↑£39.50-£49.50 (room only) 🍴
℄ 250P CFA snooker ⌀ xmas
♀ European V ♥ ⏛ ✻ ✳ Lunch £10.50&alc Dinner £13.95&alc Last dinner 10.30pm
Credit Cards ①②③⑤

★★★61% **Novotel Birmingham Airport**
B26 3QL ☎021-782 7000 Telex no 338158 FAX 021-782 0445
*Opened in June 1991, this hotel is opposite the main passenger terminal and linked by monorail to the railway station and NEC. Functional bedrooms are triple glazed and public areas include a bar, foyer lounge and Le Grill restaurant, open from 6am to midnight.*
195⇨↑✻in 64 bedrooms CTV in all bedrooms ® T ✳
sB⇨↑fr£64 dB⇨↑fr£74 (room only)
Lift ℄ ⊞ ♪
V ♥ ✻ ✳
Credit Cards ①②③⑤

---

## BIRMINGHAM (NATIONAL EXHIBITION CENTRE)
West Midlands Map 07 SP18

★★★58% **Arden Hotel & Leisure Club**
Coventry Rd, Bickenhill B92 0EH (A45)
☎Hampton-in-Arden(06755)3221 Telex no 334913
FAX (06755) 3225
*Located on the A45, next to the NEC, this hotel has its own leisure centre and extensive conference facilities. The bedrooms are modestly decorated and furnished, although some are being refurbished.*
76⇨↑(2fb) CTV in all bedrooms ® T ✳ sB⇨↑£65
dB⇨↑£72.50 (room only) 🍴
Lift ℄ 150P ✿ CFA ▣ (heated) snooker sauna solarium gymnasium jacuzzi
♀ French V ♥ ⏛ ✳ Lunch £11.45&alc Dinner £11.45&alc Last dinner 10pm
Credit Cards ①②③⑤

---

🐚 Shell filling stations (7am–11pm) are marked on the town plans.

---

## BISHOP AUCKLAND Co Durham Map 08 NZ22

★★68% *Park Head*
New Coundon DL14 8QT (1m N on A688) ☎(0388)661727
*A popular, well appointed hotel on the A688 just north east of the town offers spaciously comfortable bedrooms, traditional menus based on local produce in its restaurant and an equally high standard of cuisine in the congenial surroundings of its carvery and function room.*
8⇨↑Annexe7⇨↑(3fb)1🛏 CTV in all bedrooms ®
℄ 96P ✿ ♪ ⌀
♀ English, French & Italian V ♥ ⏛ ✻ Last dinner 9.45pm
Credit Cards ①②③④⑤

★★61% *The Postchaise*
36 Market Pl DL14 7NX ☎(0388)661296
*An abundance of original oak beams characterises the bars and public areas of a market-square hotel whose functional bedrooms offer colour TV, telephones and en suite facilities.*
12⇨↑↑(1fb)2🛏 CTV in all bedrooms ® ✻
♪ 🍴 ♪
✻
Credit Cards ①③⑤

---

## BISHOP'S STORTFORD Hertfordshire Map 05 TL42

★★★★66% **Down Hall Country House**
Hatfield Heath CM22 7AS ☎(0279)731441 Telex no 81609
FAX (0279) 730416
103⇨↑1🛏 CTV in all bedrooms ® T S15% sB&B⇨↑£90-£101 dB&B⇨↑£123-£138 🍴
Lift ℄ ⊞ 200P ✿ CFA ▣ (heated) ♪ (hard) snooker sauna croquet petanque lawn chess ♪ xmas

→

B

♡ International **V** ✿ ☑ S15% Lunch £15.50&alc High tea £8
Dinner £17&alc Last dinner 9.45pm
Credit Cards ①②③⑤

**❀❀❀ ✕ ✕ The Mill**
Hallingbury Mill, Old Mill Lane, Gaston Green, Little
Hallingbury CM22 7QS ☎(0279)726554
*Hallingbury Mill, dating back to 1874, was converted by the
present owners to house 2 restaurants. Keen to preserve the
atmosphere of the mill, the proprietors have retained much of the
machinery, which diners can watch turning as they sip their
aperitifs. Those who come for the peaceful surroundings will not be
disappointed, and for those in search of gastronomic satisfaction
the Mill's well served choice of food should prove rewarding.*
Closed Mon Lunch not served Sat
Dinner not served Sun
♡ English & Continental **V** 45 seats ✳ Lunch fr£20alc Dinner
fr£20alc Last lunch 2pm Last dinner 10pm 50 P ✂
Credit Cards ①②③

---

**BISHOPSTEIGNTON** Devon Map **03** SX87

**★★58% *Cockhaven Manor***
Cockhaven Rd TQ14 9RF ☎Teignmouth(0626)775252
*Full of the character and charm of a village inn, this hotel situated
in a small village just a short drive from Teignmouth, offers a
friendly atmosphere under the personal supervision of its owners.
Bars are convivial, the restaurant serves an à la carte menu on
which both fish and steak dishes are featured daily, and delightful
surroundings are combined with modern facilities in cosy bedrooms
which are well furnished and equipped.*
12rm(4⇦7🏠)4🏠✂in 2 bedrooms CTV in all bedrooms ® **T**
50P games room
**V** ✿ ☑ Last dinner 9.30pm
Credit Cards ①③

---

**BLACKBURN** Lancashire Map **07** SD62

See also **Langho**
**★★★60% Blackburn Moat House**
Preston New Rd BB2 7BE (Queens Moat) ☎(0254)264441
Telex no 63271 FAX (0254) 682435
*A modern hotel situated in rural surroundings at the junction of the
A677 and A6119 west of the town. Bedrooms are well equipped
though becoming a little dated. Public areas have recently been
upgraded and there are good banqueting and conference facilities.*
98⇦🏠(2fb)✂in 12 bedrooms CTV in all bedrooms ® **T** ✳ S%
sB&B⇦🏠£49-£69 dB&B⇦🏠£64-£82 🛒
Lift ℂ CTV 350P ❀ CFA pool table ♫
♡ English & French **V** ✿ ☑ ✳ S% Lunch £6.65-£8.65&alc
Dinner £12.45-£12.95&alc Last dinner 10pm
Credit Cards ①②③④⑤ⓔ

**★★76% Millstone**
Church Ln, Mellor BB2 7JR (3m NW) (Shire)
☎Mellor(0254)813333 FAX (0254) 812628
*Good, interesting food is available in the attractive, wood-panelled
dining room of this charming country village inn with its pleasant
atmosphere. The attractive bedrooms are well furnished, there is
an open-plan bar/lounge area, management is attentive and service
willing.*
20⇦🏠(1fb)✂in 4 bedrooms CTV in all bedrooms ® **T** ✳ S%
sB&B⇦🏠£53.50-£73.50 dB&B⇦🏠£81-£89 🛒
40P CFA *xmas*
**V** ✿ ☑ ✳
Credit Cards ①②③⑤

---

**BLACKPOOL** Lancashire Map **07** SD33 ◎

**★★★64% *Savoy***
Queens Promenade, North Shore FY2 9SJ (Consort)
☎(0253)52561 FAX (0253) 500735
*The recent refurbishment of this large hotel on the seafront has
been sympathetic to its Edwardian origins, particularly in the case
of the elegantly panelled Gilbert Restaurant. Well equipped
bedrooms – most of which have sea views – are all similarly
furnished and decorated, but those on the fourth floor cannot be
reached by lift.*
147⇦🏠✂in 18 bedrooms CTV in all bedrooms ® **T**
Lift ℂ 40P
♡ International **V** ✿ ☑ Last dinner 10.30pm
Credit Cards ①②③⑤

**★★★63% Clifton**
Talbot Square FY1 1ND ☎(0253)21481 FAX (0253) 27345
*A fine building situated close to town and pier has been refurbished
to provide well appointed and equipped bedrooms. Lavishly
decorated public areas include a restaurant, large bar and lively
lounge bars, with a quieter residents' lounge and cocktail bar on the
first floor. Visitors arriving by car should note that parking outside
the hotel can be difficult.*
80⇦🏠(2fb) CTV in all bedrooms ® **T** ✳ sB&B⇦🏠£25-£55
dB&B⇦🏠£50-£85 🛒
Lift ℂ CTV ♪ CFA pool table *xmas*
♡ English, French & Italian **V** ✿ ☑ ✳ Lunch fr£5 High tea
fr£5.50 Dinner fr£9.50 Last dinner 9.30pm
Credit Cards ①②③⑤ⓔ

**★★68% Brabyns**
Shaftesbury Av, North Shore FY2 9QQ (Exec Hotel)
☎(0253)54263 FAX (0253) 52915
*This very friendly hotel just off Queens Promenade in the north
shore area, has comfortable, very well equipped bedrooms and an
attractive panelled restaurant and spacious lounge bar, all
spotlessly maintained by the caring proprietors.*
22⇦🏠Annexe3⇦🏠(10fb) CTV in all bedrooms ® **T**
sB&B⇦🏠£30-£34 dB&B⇦🏠£54-£62 🛒
CTV 12P *xmas*
**V** ✿ ☑ Lunch £6-£7 Dinner £10-£11 Last dinner 7.30pm
Credit Cards ①③⑤ⓔ

**★★67% Headlands**
611-613 South Prom FY4 1NJ ☎(0253)41179
Closed 2-13 Jan
*A reasonably priced, long-established hotel at the southern end of
the Promenade is very popular with holidaymakers, many of whom
return year after year. Accommodation has been refurbished to
create comfortable, well equipped en suite bedrooms and service
throughout is hospitable and friendly.*
43⇦🏠(11fb) CTV in all bedrooms ®
Lift CTV 40P 8🏓 snooker solarium ♫
**V** ✿ ☑ ✂ Last dinner 7.30pm
Credit Cards ①③

See advertisement on page 135

**★★65% *Ruskin***
55-61 Albert Rd FY1 4PW ☎(0253)24063 FAX (0253) 23571
*Situated close to the town centre, this attractive hotel is suited to
both business and pleasure purposes. Public rooms are spacious
and comfortable and staff smartly dressed and helpful.*
80⇦🏠(14fb)1🖳 CTV in all bedrooms ® **T**
Lift ℂ CTV 16🏓 (£5 for 24hrs) pool table
**V** ✿ ☑ ✂ Last dinner 8.30pm
Credit Cards ①③

---

Hotels with red star ratings are
especially high quality.

For key to symbols in English see the bookmark.

133

**B**

**★★65% Hotel Sheraton**

54-62 Queens Promenade FY2 9RP ☎(0253)52723

*The friendly, well run hotel, overlooking the sea on the north shore, offers good all-round value and is ideal for family holidays.*

119⇨🅜(37fb) CTV in all bedrooms ® ✳ sB&B⇨🅜£31-£33 dB&B⇨🅜£62-£66 🏠

Lift ( CFA ⌧ (heated) sauna solarium *xmas*

V ✿ ⚌ ✳ Bar Lunch £1-£5 Dinner £10 Last dinner 7.45pm

Credit Cards ①③

**★★62% Warwick**

603-609 New South Promenade FY4 1NG (Best Western)

☎(0253)42192 Telex no 677334 FAX (0253) 405776

*Overlooking the new South Promenade and close to the Pleasure Beach, this friendly hotel has simply decorated but well equipped bedrooms all with en suite facilities, an attractive restaurant and comfortable popular bar, plus a heated indoor pool.*

52⇨🅜(10fb) CTV in all bedrooms ® T sB&B⇨🅜£34.20-£42 dB&B⇨🅜£57.70-£71.50 🏠

( 30P CFA ⌧ (heated) solarium ♫ *xmas*

🅖 International V ✿ ⚌ ✳ Bar Lunch £3-£7alc Dinner £12-£13.50 Last dinner 8.30pm

Credit Cards ①②③⑤ⓔ

**★★61% Cliffs**

Queens Promenade FY2 9SG ☎(0253)52388 FAX (0253) 500394

*On the seafront to the north of the town, this large hotel caters equally well to business and leisure users, with well equipped bedrooms (though some of them have not yet been fully upgraded) and a comprehensive leisure complex. Staff are friendly and helpful and the 5-course dinner is good value.*

162⇨🅜(28fb)1🔟 CTV in all bedrooms ® T ✖ (ex guide dogs) ✳ sB&B⇨🅜£30.25-£80 dB&B⇨🅜£61-£113.50 🏠

Lift ( 70P CFA ⌧ (heated) squash snooker sauna gymnasium jacuzzi *xmas*

🅖 English & French V ✿ ⚌ ⚌ ✳ Bar Lunch £5-£9 Dinner £11.25 Last dinner 8.30pm

Credit Cards ①②③

**★★60% Revill's**

190-4 North Promenade FY1 1RJ ☎(0253)25768 & 24736

*Improvements continue at this family-owned hotel, situated on the sea front near the North Pier. All bedrooms now have en suite facilities, and the attractive, comfortable public areas feature the colourul new Bobbins bar and bistro.*

47⇨🅜(10fb) CTV in all bedrooms ® T ✖ ✳ sB&B⇨🅜£24.75-£28 dB&B⇨🅜£42.35-£49.50

Lift ( CTV 23P snooker *xmas*

V ✿ ⚌ ✳ Bar Lunch £1.50-£3 Dinner £6.50-£7.50 Last dinner 7.30pm

Credit Cards ①③

**★★54% Claremont**

270 North Prom FY1 1SA ☎(0253)293122 FAX (0253) 752409

*Refurbishment continues at this large seafront hotel, and those bedrooms which have been upgraded are of a good standard. The Claremont is convenient for the town centre and central areas of entertainment.*

143⇨🅜Annexe25⇨🅜(51fb) CTV in all bedrooms ® T ✖ (ex guide dogs) ✳ sB&B⇨🅜£28-£37 dB&B⇨🅜£46-£74 🏠

Lift ( 60P CFA ⌧ (heated) sauna gymnasium ♨ *xmas*

V ✿ ⚌ ✂ S15% Lunch £5.50-£7 High tea £5.50-£9 Dinner £11-£12.50 Last dinner 8.30pm

Credit Cards ①②③ⓔ

See advertisement on page 137
**See advertisement on page 137**

**★65% Kimberley**

New South Promenade FY4 1NQ ☎(0253)41184

FAX (0253) 408737

Closed 3-13 Jan

*A friendly, informal hotel, standing in a crescent off the seafront and managed by its resident proprietors, offers a choice of eating*

*styles, the light snacks offered throughout the day by the Coffee Shop complementing restaurant menus.*

54rm(36⇨🅜)(8fb) CTV in all bedrooms ® sB&Bfr£24.55 sB&B⇨🅜fr£29.50 dB&Bfr£43.20 dB&B⇨🅜fr£59 🏠

Lift ( CTV 26P 🚲 CFA table tennis *xmas*

🅖 English & Continental ✿ ⚌ Lunch fr£5.95 Dinner fr£9.95 Last dinner 7.30pm

Credit Cards ①③ⓔ

**❀❀ ✕✕ Long's**

TR4 8HH ☎Truro(0872)561111

Closed Mon, Tue & mid Jan-mid Feb Lunch not served Wed-Sat

Dinner not served Sun

V 35 seats Sunday Lunch £11.75 Dinner £23.50-£25.75alc Last dinner 9.30pm 20 P nc12yrs

Credit Cards ①②③

**❀ ✕✕ Pennypots**

TR4 8EY ☎St Day(0209)820347

*It is easy to forget the traffic rumbling past as you enjoy your meal in this period cottage on the A30. Surroundings are simple, the atmosphere relaxing and the cuisine from the short à la carte menu and fish menu is light in style. Of particular delight are Mr Peter's own bresoala and the boned quail stuffed with mushrooms and cashew nuts. The small carefully-chosen wine list represents excellent value for money.*

Closed 3 wks winter Lunch not served

Dinner not served Sun (Oct-mid Jun) & Mon

V 30 seats Dinner £20-£25alc Last dinner 10pm 10 P nc5yrs

Credit Cards ①②③⑤

**★★★56% Maes Manor**

NP2 0AG ☎(0495)224551 & 220011

*An old manor house set in several acres of woodland near the local golf course is very popular locally for functions and meetings, providing spaciously comfortable bar areas, an attractive restaurant and bright, neat bedrooms.*

8⇨🅜Annexe14⇨🅜(2fb)2🔟 CTV in all bedrooms ® T ✳ sB&B⇨🅜£43-£49 dB&B⇨🅜£57-£67

( 100P ❀ CFA

🅖 Welsh, English & French V ✿ ⚌ ✳ Lunch £7.50-£13&alc Dinner £12-£20alc Last dinner 9.30pm

Credit Cards ①②③⑤

**★★65% Tilt**

Bridge of Tilt PH18 5SU ☎(079681)333 FAX (079681) 335

*An hospitable hotel at the southern end of the village offers accommodation in 7 good-sized chalet rooms; public areas include a cosy dining room, a comfortable lounge and a bar where log fires burn during the colder months.*

28⇨🅜(4fb) CTV in all bedrooms ® T ✳ sB&B⇨🅜£22.50-£32.50 dB&B⇨🅜£45-£75 🏠

40P ❀ CFA ✈ gamesroom *xmas*

V ✿ ⚌ Lunch £6.75-£9.25 Dinner fr£12.50&alc Last dinner 8.30pm

Credit Cards ①③ⓔ

**★★60% Atholl Arms**

PH18 5SG (Minotels) ☎Blairatholl(079681)205

FAX (0796) 81550

*Situated opposite Blair Castle this long established village hotel is popular with tour groups, holidaymakers and sporting enthusiasts.*

*It offers traditional comforts and has a splendid dining room with a minstrel gallery.*

30⇄🅟(3fb) CTV in all bedrooms ® T ✱ sB&B⇄🅟£28.50-£39.50 dB&B⇄🅟£45-£70 🅡
100P 3🏖 ❄ CFA ♪ rough shooting *xmas*
V ♡ ⚏
Credit Cards ①③④

BLAIR DRUMMOND Central *Stirlingshire* Map **11** NS79

❀❀✗**Broughton's Restaurant**
Burnbank Cottages FK9 4XE (1m W on A873)
☎Doune(0786)841897
*Chef/proprietor Helen Broughton's little cottage restaurant, situated only 5 miles from Stirling, provides the very best of Cordon Bleu country cooking; everything is home-made from fresh produce – vegetables and herbs being grown in the garden. Local game in season appears in robust dishes such as pot-roast shoulder of venison, rabbit casseroled with bacon, and potted pigeon. The 3-course set dinner menu offers a choice of 5 starters, half a dozen main courses which always include a vegetarian option, a selection of desserts, and coffee and petits fours. Excellent bread, a large home-made wheaten bap, is left on the table, with a cutting knife to help yourself. A rich, bittersweet chocolate mousse was one of a range of good, traditional home-made desserts tried by our inspector. A choice of simpler dishes and snacks is available at lunchtime, and the good-value 3-course Sunday lunch menu always includes roast beef and a vegetarian main course. House wine is £7.25 a litre.*
Closed Mon & 2-3 wks Feb
Dinner not served Sun

A rosette means exceptional standards of cuisine.

→

♀ International **V** 42 seats Lunch £12&alc Dinner £20 Last lunch 2.30pm Last dinner 10pm 22 P nc10yrs ✠
Credit Cards [1] [3]

## BLAIRGOWRIE Tayside *Perthshire* Map **15** NO14

### ★★★⚑77% **Kinloch House**
PH10 6SG (3m W on A923) ☎Essendy(025084)237
FAX (025084) 333
Closed 20-29 Dec

*It is now 10 years since David and Sarah Shentall took over this 19th-century house. Their original intention of making it a sporting venue was quickly and successfully met, but now it attracts many tourists and business people as well as hunstmen, fishermen and golfers, all of whom can relax in its dependable comfort. The cosseting guests receive makes for loyal customers. Bedrooms vary in size, most look out onto a paddock of shaggy Highland cattle to the Marble Loch and the Sidlaw Hills, and acres of raspberry fields. There is a recent addition of 8 lovely big bedrooms incorporating every comfort including warm bathrooms and huge beds. Also in this wing is the Sportsman's Room equipped with gun safe, rod racks, deep freeze, game larder, cleaning and drying facilities, even dog bowls. Dinner, Scottish food at its best, is very good value.*

21⇨🌙(1fb)8🛏 CTV in all bedrooms ® **T** sB&B⇨🌙£69.75 dB&B⇨🌙£132 (incl dinner)
CTV 40P 🚼 ❀ ✎
**V** ✠ ✻ Lunch £13.25 Dinner £20.90 Last dinner 9.15pm
Credit Cards [1] [2] [3] [5]

### ★★⚑65% *Altamount House*
Coupar Angus Rd PH10 6JN ☎(0250)3512 & 3814
Closed 4 Jan-14 Feb

*Set in 6 acres of peaceful grounds, this charming Georgian house is a good base for the touring holidaymaker. It offers traditional services and comforts, with well equipped bedrooms.*

7⇨🌙(2fb) CTV in all bedrooms ® **T**
40P 3🏆 ❀
♕ ⚗ Last dinner 9pm
Credit Cards [1] [3]

### ★★62% **Angus**
46 Wellmeadow PH10 6NQ (Consort) ☎(0250)2838
Telex no 76526 FAX (0250) 5289

*A popular base for visiting tour groups as well as holidaymakers and businesspeople, this town centre hotel has a good range of leisure facilities. Public rooms are bright and modern and about half of the bedrooms have been substantially refurbished.*

86⇨🌙(4fb) CTV in all bedrooms ® **T** sB&B⇨🌙£28.50-£35 dB&B⇨🌙£57-£70 🛏
Lift 60P CFA ▱ (heated) squash snooker sauna solarium *xmas*
♀ British & French **V** ✧ ⚗ Bar Lunch £3-£6 High tea £3-£6 Dinner £12.75-£13.75&alc Last dinner 8.30pm
Credit Cards [1] [2] [3]

### ★★62% *Rosemount Golf*
Golf Course Rd, Rosemount PH10 6LJ ☎(0250)2604

*Set in its own grounds close to the golf course, this welcoming family-run hotel appeals to golfers and holidaymakers alike. Public areas offer traditional comforts, while well equipped bedrooms provide practical modern facilities.*

8⇨🌙Annexe4🌙(2fb) CTV in all bedrooms ® **T**
✈ (ex guide dogs)
70P 🚼 ❀
**V** ✧ Last dinner 9pm
Credit Cards [1] [3]

Remember to book early for holiday
and bank holiday times.

## BLAKENEY Norfolk Map **09** TG04

### ★★★65% **Blakeney**
The Quay NR25 7NE ☎Cley(0263)740797 FAX (0263) 740795
*Situated on the quay overlooking the point, this hotel offers comfortable accommodation and attractive public areas. The well appointed restaurant serves an interesting and freshly prepared table d'hôte menu. The service is efficient, and the attractive setting is enhanced by well tended gardens.*

42⇨🌙Annexe10⇨🌙(4fb)2🛏 CTV in 51 bedrooms ® **T** ✱
sB&B⇨🌙£43-£68 dB&B⇨🌙£86-£176 🛏
⟨ 75P 🚼 ❀ CFA ▱ (heated) snooker sauna gymnasium table tennis pool *xmas*
♀ English & Continental **V** ✧ ⚗ Lunch £9-£12alc Dinner fr£15&alc Last dinner 9.30pm
Credit Cards [1] [2] [3] [5]

### ★★61% **Manor**
NR25 7ND ☎Cley(0263)740376 FAX (0263) 741116
Closed 2-27 Dec

*Dating back to the 16th century the Manor Hotel overlooks Blakeney Quay and Point. The main flintstone building houses comfortable public areas and well equipped warm bedrooms, courtyard rooms provide similar comfort on ground level. Good, fresh food features on the menu.*

8⇨🌙Annexe27⇨🌙(2fb)1🛏 CTV in all bedrooms ® **T**
60P ❀ bowling green nc10yrs
♀ English & Continental **V** ✧ ⚗ ✠ Last dinner 8.30pm

## BLANCHLAND Northumberland Map **12** NY95

### ★★❀67% **Lord Crewe Arms**
DH8 9SP ☎Hexham(0434675)251 FAX (0434675) 337
*An integral part of the somewhat remote but most attractive village, this old inn with flagstone floors and vaulted ceilings which dates from medieval times is gradually being improved; bedrooms – half of which are contained in a separate house opposite the main building – come in various shapes, sizes and styles, but all have modern amenities and most offer smart, clean, en suite bathrooms. The character of the public areas is epitomised in the striking restaurant, with its blazing fires, candle-lit tables, gleaming silver and sparkling crystal, where guests can enjoy an interesting range of straightforward but honestly flavoured dishes which might include medallions of venison, complemented by a cream and chestnut sauce and accompanied by vivid-tasting fresh vegetables – broccoli, cauliflower, courgettes and boiled potatoes. Staff provide friendly, attentive service throughout.*

8⇨🌙Annexe10⇨🌙(3fb)1🛏 CTV in all bedrooms ® **T**
✈ 🚼 ❀
**V** ✧ ⚗ ✻ Sunday Lunch fr£11.50 Dinner £17.50-£21alc Last dinner 9.15pm
Credit Cards [1] [2] [3] [5]

## BLANDFORD FORUM Dorset Map **03** ST80

### ★★★66% **Crown**
8 West St DT11 7AJ (Consort) ☎(0258)456626 Telex no 418292 FAX (0258) 451084
Closed 25-28 Dec

*Close to the town centre yet overlooking open countryside the Crown has majestic panelled public rooms and spacious bedrooms. The main features of the hotel are the friendly staff and the skilfully cooked reasonably priced food.*

32⇨🌙(1fb)2🛏 CTV in all bedrooms ® **T** sB&B⇨🌙£56-£58 dB&B⇨🌙£66-£68 🛏
80P 4🏆 (£3) ❀ CFA ✎
♀ English & French **V** ✧ ⚗ ✻ Lunch £6.75-£11.50&alc High tea £2.50 Dinner £6.75-£11.50&alc Last dinner 9.15pm
Credit Cards [1] [2] [3] [5] (£)

**B**

### ★★61% The Anvil Hotel & Restaurant
Salisbury Rd, Pimperne DT11 8UQ ☎Blandford(0258)453431 & 480182
*A small, thatched hotel where the bedrooms are well furnished and equipped, if a little small. There is often live entertainment in the bar at night, and the beamed dining room offers an extensive à la carte menu.*
9⇌♠(1fb) CTV in all bedrooms ® T ✱ sB&B⇌♠£40-£42.50 dB&B⇌♠£58-£62.50 ➡
25P ♫
V ☆ ⚏ Lunch £9.50-£18alc Dinner £9.50-£18alc Last dinner 9.45pm
Credit Cards ① ② ③ ⑤ ⓔ

### ❀✕✕La Belle Alliance
Whitecliff Mill St DT11 7BP ☎(0258)452842 FAX (0258) 480053
*A small restaurant with rooms which stands on the Sherbourne/Shaftsbury edge of town complements its cool, well appointed dining room with a comfortable lounge where an unhurried and hospitable young staff provides table service of pre-dinner drinks. The fixed-price menu features a range of freshly produced dishes, including fish, which are light in style and accompanied by good, flavoursome sauces; bread, canapes and petit four are home-made, and a well chosen wine list includes some 60 items.*
Closed Mon & 1st 3 wks Jan Lunch not served Tue-Sat (ex by arrangement only)
Dinner not served Sun
♀ British & French 32 seats Sunday Lunch £12.50 Dinner £16-£23 Last dinner 9.30pm 13 P ✄
Credit Cards ① ② ③

### BLOCKLEY Gloucestershire Map **04** SP13

### ★★★64% Crown Inn
High St GL56 9EX ☎(0386)700245 FAX (0386) 700247
*This 16th-century village inn, now tastefully modernised, offers well equipped, comfortable bedrooms and character public areas including à la carte and grill restaurants. Friendly, attentive services are provided by the Champion family.*
13⇌♠Annexe8⇌♠(2fb)4➡ CTV in all bedrooms ® T ✱ sB&B⇌♠£49.50 dB&B⇌♠£66.50-£106 ➡
50P CFA *xmas*
♀ English & Continental V ☆ ⚏ ✄ ✱ Lunch £3.95-£12.95alc Dinner £6.96-£11.95alc Last dinner 9.30pm
Credit Cards ① ② ③

### BLUNDELLSANDS Merseyside Map **07** SJ39

### ★★★62% Blundellsands
Serpentine L23 6TN (Lansbury) ☎051-924 6515
Telex no 626270 FAX 051-931 5364
*Improvements continue to be made to this Edwardian property in a residential area of Crosby. Though some bedrooms remain compact, all are attractive and well equipped. The restaurant is modelled on a ship liner, with friendly service provided by appropriately dressed staff, and there are extensive and pleasant function facilities.*
41⇌♠(6fb)✄in 7 bedrooms CTV in all bedrooms ® T sB&B⇌♠£60-£64 dB&B⇌♠£72-£76 ➡
Lift ⓒ CTV 350P ♫
♀ English & French V ☆ ⚏ Lunch £8-£9&alc Dinner £12.50-£13&alc Last dinner 9.30pm
Credit Cards ① ② ③ ⑤

### BLYTH Nottinghamshire Map **08** SK68

### ★★★63% Charnwood
Sheffield Rd S81 8HF ☎(0909)591610 FAX (0909) 591429
*A friendly business hotel, a mile from the A1 yet in a peaceful rural location. There is a conference room, banqueting suite, and a very popular lounge bar where substantial snacks are served. An à la*

*carte menu is available in the Lantern Restaurant overlooking the landscaped gardens.*
20⇌♠(1fb) CTV in all bedrooms ® T ✖ (ex guide dogs) sB&B⇌♠£30-£55 dB&B⇌♠£40-£60 ➡
70P ⌖ ❀ CFA *xmas*
♀ English & French V ☆ ⚏ Lunch £8.60&alc Dinner £13.75&alc Last dinner 9.45pm
Credit Cards ① ② ③ ⑤ ⓔ

### ⇪Forte Travelodge
(on A1, southbound) (Forte)
☎(0909)591775 Central Res (0800) 850950
*This modern establishment on the southbound carriageway of the A1, situated to the rear of a Little Chef restaurant, provides accommodation which is both warm and well equipped.*
32⇌♠(32fb) CTV in all bedrooms ® sB⇌♠£29.95 dB⇌♠£29.95 (room only)
ⓒ 32P ⌖
Credit Cards ① ② ③

### ⇪Granada Lodge
Hilltop Roundabout S81 8HG (junct. A1M/A614) (Granada)
☎(0909)591836 FAX (0909) 591831
*This modern establishment is easily accessible from both north and southbound carriageways. A Country Kitchen Restaurant is adjacent for meals, although some room service is available.*
39⇌♠(6fb)✄in 8 bedrooms CTV in all bedrooms ®
✖ (ex guide dogs) S% sB⇌♠fr£29.50 dB⇌♠fr£32 (room only) ➡
ⓒ 174P
Credit Cards ① ② ③ ⑤

### BOAT OF GARTEN Highland *Inverness-shire* Map **14** NH91

### ★★★63% Boat
PH24 3BH (Best Western) ☎(047983)258 FAX (047983) 414
*Situated beside the Strathspey Steam Railway in the centre of the village, this friendly hotel is a popular base for holidaymakers, numbering golfers, fishermen and water-skiing enthusiasts among its guests. A relaxed atmosphere prevails in the comfortably furnished day rooms; and bedrooms, which are gradually being improved, provide the expected comforts and facilities.*
32⇌♠(1fb) CTV in all bedrooms ® T sB&B⇌♠£44-£49.50 dB&B⇌♠£76-£83 ➡
36P ⌖ ❀ ⚬ *xmas*
♀ Scottish, English & French V ☆ ⚏ ✄ ✱ Lunch £12-£13 High tea £5.50-£6.50 Dinner £17.50-£18.50&alc Last dinner 9.30pm
Credit Cards ① ② ③ ⑤ ⓔ

### ★★63% *Craigard Country House*
Kinchurdy Rd PH24 3BP ☎(047983)206
Closed Nov
*Once a hunting lodge, and still retaining its Victorian style, a comfortable and warmly welcoming hotel which is well furnished throughout looks across the Strathspey Railway and the golf course to the Cairngorms beyond from the setting of its own grounds.*
20⇌♠(1fb) CTV in all bedrooms ®
20P 4➡ (£1) ⌖ ❀
♀ International ☆ ⚏ ✄ Last dinner 8.45pm
Credit Cards ① ② ③

### BODINNICK Cornwall & Isles of Scilly Map **02** SX15

### ★71% Old Ferry Inn
PL23 1LX ☎Polruan(0726)870237
RS Nov-Feb
*For almost 400 years this inn has stood on the edge of the Fowey estuary overlooking the ferry service to Bodinnick. Six of the bedrooms in its oldest part are now being upgraded and improved, and public areas comprise a feature lounge with river terrace, two*

*very popular 'locals' bars with flagstone floors and real ale, and a small restaurant generously furnished with antiques which includes home-made pasties and local fish and seafood among its range of well cooked dishes.*
12rm(7⇨1👁)(1fb)1🛏 CTV in 10 bedrooms ® sB&B£30-£40 sB&B⇨👁£35-£45 dB&B£60-£80 dB&B⇨👁£80
8P 2🚗 🍴
♀ English & French ♥ Bar Lunch £1-£4 Dinner £16 Last dinner 8.15pm
Credit Cards ①③

---

BODMIN Cornwall & Isles of Scilly Map **02** SX06

★★55% **Westberry**
Rhind St PL31 2EL ☎(0208)72772 FAX (0208) 72212
Closed 5 days Xmas/New Year
*Situated close to the town centre, within easy reach of major road routes, this hotel is privately owned and offers simply furnished bedrooms with modern facilities, mainly for commercial users. Public areas are spacious and comfortable.*
15rm(5⇨4👁)Annexe8⇨👁(3fb) CTV in 20 bedrooms ® T ✱
S% sB&B£24 sB&B⇨👁£40 dB&B£35 dB&B⇨👁£45 🛏
CTV 30P 🍴 CFA snooker gymnasium
V ♥ ⚲ ✱ Sunday Lunch £6 Dinner £11&alc Last dinner 8.45pm
Credit Cards ①③⑤

---

BOGNOR REGIS West Sussex Map **04** SZ99

★62% **Black Mill House**
Princess Av, Aldwick PO21 2QU (Minotels) ☎(0243)821945 & 865596 FAX (0243) 821316
*This is a traditional and long established family-run hotel offering a friendly atmosphere and conventional style services. Bedrooms vary in size but all are neat and well equipped.*
22rm(18⇨👁)Annexe4rm(6fb) CTV in all bedrooms ® T
sB&B£27-£31 sB&B⇨👁£32-£38.50 dB&B£46-£56 dB&B⇨👁£54-£68 🛏
CTV 13P 🍴 CFA table tennis putting 👶 xmas
♀ English & French V ♥ ⚲ ✂ ✱ Lunch fr£7.50 Dinner fr£9.60 Last dinner 8pm
Credit Cards ①②③⑤ⓔ

---

BOLDON Tyne & Wear Map **12** NZ36

★★★63% **Friendly**
Witney Way, Boldon Business Park NE35 9PE ☎091-519 1999
FAX 091-519 0655
*A newly built hotel set round a courtyard features a leisure centre and spacious, well appointed bedrooms. Its location on the edge of a business park near the A1/A19 junction attracts a predominantly business clientele.*
84⇨👁(12fb)1🛏✂in 25 bedrooms CTV in all bedrooms ® T
sB⇨👁£53.25-£63.50 dB⇨👁£70.50-£80.75 (room only) 🛏
《150P CFA 🏊 (heated) sauna solarium gymnasium jacuzzi
♀ English & French V ♥ ⚲ ✂ Lunch fr£8.50 Dinner fr£12.75 Last dinner 9.45pm
Credit Cards ①②③⑤ⓔ

❀❀ ✗✗ **Forsters**
2 St Bedes, Station Rd NE36 0LE ☎091-519 0929
*Barry Forster has brought the wide experience gained at such prestigious hotels as Longuerville Manor, Jersey, and the Ritz in London to the establishment he opened in 1990 in this little known part of the north-east. His restaurant provides a standard of cuisine that will delight those in search of fine food, worked with flair and beautifully presented and served. The carte offers 5 or 6 alternatives at each course ; typical dishes are swiss soufflé, made with ham and gruyère cheese, as a first course, followed by grilled breast of duck with chorizo sausage and a red-wine jus, or peppered fillet steak with a cream and brandy sauce served with exquisitely cooked vegetables. Crème brûleé, mille feuille of fresh*
→

*raspberries or home-made chocolate ice cream are favourite choices for dessert.*
Closed Sun & Mon Lunch not served
♀ English & French 28 seats Dinner £20-£30alc Last dinner 10.30pm 7 P nc10yrs
Credit Cards ①②③⑤

---

**BOLLINGTON** Cheshire Map **07** SJ97

★★★57% **Lukic-Belgrade**
Jackson Ln, Kerridge SK10 5BG ☎(0625)573246
Telex no 667554 FAX (0625) 574791
*This Gothic-style Victorian house, which overlooks the village, is reached via a winding shrub-lined drive. There is a modern rear bedroom wing, and two comfortable lounges, one of which is a conservatory.*
54⇨↑ CTV in all bedrooms ® T ✖ (ex guide dogs)
sB&B⇨↑£55-£62 dB&B⇨↑£62-£70 ➡
《 200P ✿ CFA *xmas*
♀ English & French V ♥ ♨ ✱ Lunch £6-£9.95&alc Dinner fr£13.25&alc Last dinner 10pm
Credit Cards ①②③⑤ ⓔ

✿ ✕ ✕ **Mauro's**
88 Palmerston St SK10 5PW ☎(0625)573898
*Vicenzo Mauro and his wife Gillian have run their authentic Italian trattoria (no pizzas here) with great success for the past 4 years. Housed in what was once the village co-op, the décor is predominantly white, giving a spacious atmosphere and forming a good background for the pictures of Capri, Vicenzo's birthplace, and their collection of pottery. The reasonably priced à la carte menu features Italian favourites like Saltimbocca alta Romana, Pollo Sorpresa, home-made Gnocchi and Ravioli, but the most popular features are the Antipasti alla Caprese – a trolley laden with daily specials – and the wide selection of excellent fresh fish, which on the evening of the inspection visit included fresh sardines, fine Dublin Bay prawns, monkfish, salmon, sea bream, and merlin. the all-Italian wine list included a fine Brunello di Montalcino and A Sassicaia.*
Closed Mon, 25-26 Dec & 3 wks Aug/Sep Lunch not served Sat Dinner not served Sun
♀ Italian V 50 seats ✱ Lunch £7.70-£18.50alc Dinner £9-£20alc Last lunch 2pm Last dinner 10pm ✍
Credit Cards ①②③

---

**BOLNEY** West Sussex Map **04** TQ22

★★★63% **Hickstead Resort**
Jobs Ln RH17 5PA (Resort) ☎Burgess Hill(0444)248023
Telex no 877247 FAX (0444) 245280
*A tile-hung Victorian house set amid green fields offers accommodation in a modern block where well equipped ground and first-floor bedrooms are identical in décor and furnishings. The enlarged Gate Restaurant now serves imaginative table d'hôte and à la carte menus while the Grange Bar, though compact, provides good service; a well designed Health Club proves popular with hotel residents and club members alike, and a selection of conference rooms is available. Young staff operate under the direction of a management totally involved with the day-to-day running of the hotel.*
49⇨↑(8fb)⊬in 5 bedrooms CTV in all bedrooms ® T ✱
S10% sB⇨↑fr£62 dB⇨↑fr£77 (room only) ➡
《 150P ✿ CFA ⊠ (heated) ➴ sauna solarium gymnasium *xmas*
♀ English & French V ♥ ♨ ⊬ ✱ S10% Lunch fr£10.50&alc Dinner fr£15&alc Last dinner 9.15pm
Credit Cards ①②③⑤

*A rosette means exceptional standards of cuisine.*

---

★★★64% **Egerton House**
Blackburn Rd, Egerton BL7 9PL (3m N A666) (Rank)
☎(0204)57171 Telex no 635322 FAX (0204) 593030
*An 18th-century residence peacefully situated in over four acres of ground just off the A666 has been sympathetically extended to offer comfortable and well equipped accommodation while retaining something of its original character. Public areas, though not over extensive, include two cosy, chintzy lounges and a small dining room overlooking the grounds, while bedrooms featuring attractive fabrics are provided with smart modern bathrooms.*
32⇨↑(8fb) CTV in all bedrooms ® T ✖ (ex guide dogs) ✱
sB&B⇨↑£52-£76 dB&B⇨↑£72-£91 ➡
《 100P ✿
♀ English & French V ♥ ♨ ✱ Lunch £15.10-£25alc Dinner £15.10-£25alc Last dinner 9.30pm
Credit Cards ①②③⑤

★★★64% **Last Drop**
Hospital Rd, Bromley Cross BL7 9PZ (3m N off B6472) (Rank)
☎(0204)591131 Telex no 635322 FAX (0204) 54122
*Imaginatively created from a group of derelict 18th-century farm buildings set on the moorland at Bromley Cross, high above the town, this 'living village' has become a noted tourist attraction. Its many facilities include a choice of restaurant bars, gift shops, a traditional tea shop and a good modern leisure centre. Bedrooms – located throughout the village – vary in style and comfort, but all are well equipped.*
73⇨↑Annexe10⇨↑(35fb)4⊞ CTV in all bedrooms ® T ✱
sB&B⇨↑£56-£90 dB&B⇨↑£77-£105 ➡
《 400P ✿ CFA ⊠ (heated) squash snooker sauna solarium gymnasium jacuzzi beauty therapist ♫ *xmas*
♀ International V ♥ ♨ ✱ Lunch £10.25 Dinner £15.50&alc Last dinner 10pm
Credit Cards ①②③⑤

★★★62% **Forte Posthouse**
Beaumont Rd BL3 4TA (Forte Hotels) ☎(0204)651511
FAX (0204) 61064
*A purpose-built hotel on the A58 to the west of the town, conveniently situated for junction 5 of the M61, offers functional, well equipped bedrooms in modern style.*
96⇨↑(10fb)⊬in 30 bedrooms CTV in all bedrooms ® T ✱
sB⇨↑£39.50-£49.50 dB⇨↑£39.50-£49.50 (room only) ➡
《 CTV 150P ✿ CFA games room *xmas*
V ♥ ♨ ⊬ ✱ Lunch £10.85-£21.85alc High tea £5-£6.05 Dinner £10.85-£21.85alc Last dinner 9.45pm
Credit Cards ①②③④⑤

★★★61% **Pack Horse**
Bradshawgate, Nelson Square BL1 1DP (De Vere)
☎(0204)27261 Telex no 635168 FAX (0204) 364352
*Attractively located to overlook a small, tree-lined square in the centre of town, this Georgian-fronted hotel offers well proportioned and traditionally styled public rooms; bedrooms are generally rather small, but many have recently been refurbished to a good, modern standard. A public car park is situated to the rear of the hotel.*
72⇨↑(4fb)⊬in 13 bedrooms CTV in all bedrooms ® T ✱ S%
sB&B⇨↑£30-£70 dB&B⇨↑£60-£86 ➡
Lift 《 ✍ CFA
♀ English & Continental V ♥ ♨ ✱ Lunch fr£7.50&alc Dinner fr£13&alc Last dinner 9.45pm
Credit Cards ①②③⑤ ⓔ

★57% **Broomfield**
33-35 Wigan Rd, Deane BL3 5PX ☎(0204)61570
RS Jul-Aug
*This small, friendly, family-run hotel stands on the A58 just over a mile from the town centre. Constantly being improved, it now offers bedrooms with en suite facilities, a comfortable lounge bar, an attractive restaurant and a cosy lounge.*

---

15🛏🏠(1fb) CTV in all bedrooms ® ✖ (ex guide dogs)
sB🛏🏠£28-£30 dB🛏🏠£40-£42 (room only) 🅿
CTV 20P 🚗
✾ Dinner £8.65-£12.90alc Last dinner 9pm
Credit Cards ⬜1⬜3 £

○**Moat House**
1 Higher Bridge St BL21 2EW (Queens Moat) ☎(0204)383338
Due to have opened Aug 1991
128🛏🏠

---

**BOLTON ABBEY** North Yorkshire Map **07** SE05

★★★ ֍78% **Devonshire Arms Country House**
BD23 6AJ (Best Western) ☎(075671)441 Telex no 51218
FAX (075671) 564
*This charming country house hotel is situated at the A59/B6160
junction on the beautiful Bolton Abbey estate, only a short walk
from the Abbey itself. Restored in recent years, under the watchful
eye of the Duchess of Devonshire, its relaxing lounges now provide
an elegant character setting for many antiques and paintings
brought from Chatsworth, while the log-burning fire in the entrance
hall is a welcome sight on colder days. The interesting
accommodation in the older part of the hotel is augmented by
compact but comfortable bedrooms contained in a new wing.*
40🛏8⊞🛏✂in 6 bedrooms CTV in all bedrooms ® T S10%
sB&B🛏£85-£90 dB&B🛏£110-£125 🅿
《 CTV 150P ✽ CFA ⏴ clay pigeon shooting ballooning ๑
xmas
🍴 French V ✾ 🍴 ✂ S10% Lunch £15.95-£17.95 Dinner
£25.50-£28.50&alc Last dinner 10pm
Credit Cards ⬜1⬜2⬜3⬜5 £

---

**BONCHURCH**

See Wight, Isle of

---

**BONTDDU** Gwynedd Map **06** SH61

★★★66% **Bontddu Hall**
LL40 2SU ☎(034149)661 FAX (034149) 284
Closed Nov-Etr
*Standing in 14 acres of wooded grounds, including 3 acres of
beautiful landscaped gardens, this very impressive house was built
in 1873. It is situated on the A496 between Dolgellau and
Barmouth. From its elevated position, it commands superb views
across the Mawddach Estuary to the Cader Idris Mountains. The
bedrooms, all of which have en suite facilities, are individual in
style and are well equipped. Public rooms are spacious, attractive
and comfortable and include two quiet and relaxing lounges.*
16🛏🏠Annexe4🛏🏠(6fb)⊞🏷 CTV in all bedrooms ® T
sB&B🛏🏠£52.50-£62.50 dB&B🛏🏠£80-£105 🅿
50P 🚗 ✾ nc3yrs
🍴 British & French V ✾ 🍴 ✂ Lunch fr£9.75 Dinner fr£19.50
Last dinner 9.30pm
Credit Cards ⬜1⬜2⬜3⬜5

---

**BOREHAMWOOD** Greater London Map **04** TQ19

○**Elstree Moat House**
Barnet Bypass WD6 5PU (Queens Moat) ☎081-953 1622
Telex no 928581 FAX 081-207 3194
Due to have opened Oct 1991
140🛏🏠

---

**BOROUGHBRIDGE** North Yorkshire Map **08** SE36

★★★64% *Crown*
Horsefair YO5 9LB ☎Harrogate(0423)322328 Telex no 57906
*Once a very busy coaching inn, this town-centre hotel is still
popular with modern-day coach parties touring the area. The well
equipped bedrooms are equally suitable for both tourists and
business travellers.*

42🛏🏠(6fb) CTV in all bedrooms ® T
Lift 《 ⊞ 60P
V ✾ 🍴 Last dinner 9.15pm
Credit Cards ⬜1⬜2⬜3⬜5

★★★58% **Three Arrows**
Horsefair YO5 9LL ☎Harrogate(0423)322245
Closed 27-30 Dec
*Set in 26 acres of grounds on the edge of the town, not far from the
A1, this country house provides mainly spacious bedrooms, a
traditional lounge and a bright modern restaurant and bar where
set dinner and bar menus are available.*
17🛏🏠(4fb) CTV in all bedrooms ® ✳ S% sB🛏🏠fr£56.38
dB🛏🏠fr£61.50 (room only) 🅿
50P ✽ CFA xmas
V ✾ 🍴 ✳ Lunch £4-£8.20 Dinner £15 Last dinner 9pm
Credit Cards ⬜1⬜2⬜3⬜5

---

**BORROWDALE** Cumbria Map **11** NY21

See also Keswick & Rosthwaite

★★★★65% **Lodore Swiss**
CA12 5UX (Stakis) ☎(07687)77285 Telex no 64305
FAX (07687) 77343
Closed 4 Jan-14 Feb
*Set at the head of the Borrowdale valley, commanding views
across the lake from its public areas and some bedrooms, this
typically Cumbrian slate-built hotel has recently been refurbished
to provide tasteful furnishings and décor in both public areas and
bedrooms, though some of the latter are very compact. The
restaurant offers a simple but imaginative table d'hôte menu,
and the wide range of leisure facilities available includes
both indoor and outdoor pools.*
70🛏🏠(13fb) CTV in all bedrooms ® T ✖ ✳ sB🛏🏠£81.90
dB🛏🏠£113.40 (room only) 🅿                                    →

B

Lift ☾ 55P 24🚗 (£3.50) ⚘ ✲ ⛶ (heated) ⛆ (heated) ℘ (hard) squash sauna solarium gymnasium ⌂ *xmas*
☋ British, French & Swiss V ♁ ⚲ ⚟
Credit Cards [1] [2] [3] [5]

**★★★ ⚜67% Borrowdale**
CA12 5UY ☎(07687)77224 FAX (07687) 77338
*A friendly, family-run hotel, traditional in style, situated in the beautiful Borrowdale Valley. A feature of the hotel is the 6-course dinner menu which offers Continental dishes and English roasts, plus traditional Cumbrian cheeses and delicious sweets. The bar meals, available in the newly refurbished bar, are popular at lunchtimes.*
34⇌↱(8fb)6⊟ CTV in all bedrooms ® T sB&B⇌↱fr£56.25 dB&B⇌↱£112.50-£123 (incl dinner) ⊟
100P ⚘ ✲ *xmas*
☋ English & Continental V ♁ ⚲
Credit Cards [1] [3]

**★★★ 66% Borrowdale Gates Country House**
CA12 5UQ ☎(07687)77204
*Set amid beautiful Lakeland scenery and surrounded by almost 2 acres of wooded gardens, this delightful hotel offers comfortable, well equipped bedrooms with lovely views. Relaxing lounges are warmed by log fires, an attractive dining room provides meals of a good standard, and personal service is given by friendly owners.*
23⇌↱(2fb) CTV in all bedrooms ® T ✗ (ex guide dogs) sB&B⇌↱£31-£46 dB&B⇌↱£57.50-£86 ⊟
35P ⚘ ✲ ⌂ *xmas*
☋ English & French V ♁ ⚲ ✱ Sunday Lunch £8.95-£9.75 Dinner £16.50-£18 Last dinner 8.45pm
Credit Cards [1] [3]

## BOSCASTLE Cornwall & Isles of Scilly Map 02 SX09

**★★ 65% Bottreaux House**
PL35 0BG ☎(0840)250231
Closed Dec-Feb (ex Xmas)
*Standing on a hill overlooking the picturesque harbour village, the personally-run hotel offers a friendly atmosphere and accommodation in bright, clean bedrooms equipped to modern standards. There is a pleasant lounge (with separate bar) and also an attractive dining room providing a good choice of imaginative dishes.*
7⇌↱ CTV in all bedrooms ® sB&B⇌↱fr£29 dB&B⇌↱£50-£52 ⊟
10P nc10yrs *xmas*
☋ English, French & Italian V ♁ ⚟ ✱ Lunch fr£8 Dinner fr£12.50alc Last dinner 9.30pm
Credit Cards [1] [3] £

**★★ 62% The Wellington Hotel**
The Harbour PL35 0AQ ☎(0840)250202 FAX (0840) 250621
Closed 5 Jan-13 Feb
*Next to an Elizabethan harbour in National Trust countryside, this turreted 16th-century stone coaching inn with 10 acres of private woodland walks provides comfortable well modernised bedrooms and cheerful personal service. The locally popular Long Bar serves a good range of bar meals, while the Anglo-French La Belle Alliance restaurant has an imaginative fixed prive menu.*
21rm(10⇌6↱)1⊟ CTV in all bedrooms ® T sB&B£18-£20 sB&B⇌↱£28-£31 dB&B⇌↱£52-£58 ⊟
20P ✲ nc10yrs *xmas*
☋ French V ♁ ⚟ Bar Lunch £1.25-£15alc Dinner £13-£15.60&alc Last dinner 9.30pm
Credit Cards [1] [2] [3] [5] £

Shell filling stations (7am–11pm) are marked on the town plans.

## BOSHAM West Sussex Map 04 SU80

**★★ 73% The Millstream**
Bosham Ln PO18 8HL (Best Western) ☎(0243)573234
FAX (0243) 573459
*This delightful hotel, situated in a picturesque village on the shores of Chichester harbour, offers tastefully and individually decorated bedrooms which are particularly well equipped, many of them having been refurbished recently; public areas include a small cocktail bar and an elegant lounge where afternoon tea and pre-dinner drinks can be enjoyed. High standards of service are continually improving, the natural warmth of the staff ensuring a relaxing and enjoyable stay for guests.*
29⇌↱(2fb)1⊟ CTV in all bedrooms ® T sB&B⇌↱£57-£67 dB&B⇌↱£89-£109 ⊟
☾ CTV 40P ✲ CFA *xmas*
☋ English & French ♁ ⚲ ⚟ ✱ Lunch £15.25-£16.25 High tea £5-£10 Dinner fr£16.25 Last dinner 9.30pm
Credit Cards [1] [2] [3] [5]

## BOSTON Lincolnshire Map 08 TF34

**★★ 64% White Hart**
1-5 High St, Bridge Foot PE21 8SH ☎(0205) 364877
*An attractive Regency building by the River Wytham at the edge of the town centre has been well modernised to provide comfortable bedrooms and pleasant public areas including bars and a Berni restaurant.*
23rm(8⇌10↱)(2fb) CTV in all bedrooms ® T ✗ (ex guide dogs) ✱ sB&Bfr£32 sB&B⇌↱fr£40 dB&Bfr£48.50 dB&B⇌↱fr£56.50 ⊟
☾ 35P CFA
☋ Mainly grills V ♁ ⚟ Lunch £8 Dinner £9 Last dinner 10.30pm
Credit Cards [1] [2] [3] [5]

**★★ 61% New England**
49 Wide Bargate PE21 6SH (Forte Hotels) ☎(0205)365255
FAX (0205) 310597
*A town centre company-owned hotel which, despite first impressions, offers good, friendly service in all departments. Bedrooms are well equipped and comfortable and a good standard of cleanliness is maintained throughout.*
25⇌⚟in 5 bedrooms CTV in all bedrooms ® ✱ S% sB⇌fr£50 dB⇌fr£60 (room only) ⊟
☾ P̸ CFA *xmas*
☋ Mainly grills V ♁ ⚲ ⚟ ✱ S% Lunch £8.50 Dinner £12.95&alc Last dinner 10pm
Credit Cards [1] [2] [3] [4] [5]

## BOSTON SPA West Yorkshire Map 08 SE44

**⚜ ✕ La Jardiniere**
174 High St LS23 6BN ☎Wetherby(0937)845625
*An attractive little village-centre restaurant, housed in a 400-year-old building which has been decorated and furnished to preserve its original character, offers a good choice on its set-price menu of 3 or 4 courses. Adequately prepared and attractively presented dishes are served by a friendly, attentive staff ably supervised by the owners, and a good wine list is available.*
Closed Mon, 25-26 Dec & 1-7 Jan Lunch not served Tue-Sat
Dinner not served Sun
V 47 seats Sunday Lunch £12.50 Dinner £11.50-£12.50&alc Last dinner 10pm P nc10yrs ⚟
Credit Cards [1] [3]

The AA's star rating scheme is the market leader in hotel classification.

## BOTHWELL Strathclyde *Lanarkshire* Map **11** NS75

### ★★★60% *Bothwell Bridge*
89 Main St G71 8LN ☎(0698)852246 Telex no 776838
*All the bedrooms at this business hotel, most of which are contained in a modern extension, are well equipped, and some are extremely spacious and comfortable ; meals demonstrate the influence of its Italian owners.*
41⇨🛏(5fb)1🚻 CTV in all bedrooms ® T 🐾 (ex guide dogs)
《 90P ❀ ♫
🍴 Continental V ♨ Last dinner 10.45pm
Credit Cards 1 2 3 5

**See advertisement under HAMILTON**

### ★★58% *Silvertrees*
Silverwells Crescent G71 8DP ☎(0698)852311
*In a quiet residential area, this sandstone house with an ornate foyer ceiling operates as a business and function hotel, with many of the bedrooms in two well furnished annexes, a Victorian house and former coach house, within the spacious grounds.*
7⇨🛏Annexe19⇨🛏(1fb)1🚻 CTV in all bedrooms ® T
sB&B⇨🛏£53.50 dB&B⇨🛏£62
100P 🚗 ❀ CFA
V ♨ Lunch £10.50&alc High tea £7.50 Dinner £13.50&alc Last dinner 8.45pm
Credit Cards 1 2 3 5

## BOTLEY Hampshire Map **04** SU51

### ★★★★❀68% *Botley Park Hotel & Country Club*
Winchester Rd, Boorley Green SO3 2UA (Rank)
☎(0489)780888 FAX (0489) 789242
*Set in its own landscaped parkland and thoughtfully appointed to provide comfortable, well equipped accommodation, this modern hotel features excellent leisure and conference facilities. An attractive restaurant with a choice of menus offers a high standard of cuisine, while service is friendly and attentive throughout.*
100⇨🛏½in 17 bedrooms CTV in all bedrooms ® T ✱
sB&B⇨🛏£57-£87 dB&B⇨🛏£67-£102 🍴
《 CTV 250P ❀ CFA ▱ (heated) ▶ 18 ♟ (hard) squash snooker sauna solarium gymnasium croquet petanque hairdressing salon ♫ *xmas*
🍴 English & French V ♨ ⚓ ✱ Lunch £14&alc Dinner £17.25 Last dinner 10pm
Credit Cards 1 2 3 5

### ❀ ✕ ✕ *Cobbett's*
15 The Square SO3 2EA ☎(0489)782068
*A restaurant in cottage style, dating back to the 16th century and situated in the village square, exhibits a distinct French bias under the personal management of Mrs Lucie Skipworth and her husband Charles. In its relaxed and friendly atmosphere, served by cheerful staff, guests enjoy a range of honest, simply flavoured dishes with a regional French theme – chef Peter Hayes, though a Yorkshireman, having travelled and worked extensively in France. Choices include Aiguilettes de Canard (sliced breast of duck with a sauce of pink, green and black peppercorns) and Mille Feuilles aux Fruits Rouges, which is as delightful to look at as it is to eat.*
Closed Sun, 2 wks summer & BH's Lunch not served Sat & Mon
🍴 French V 45 seats Last lunch 1.45pm Last dinner 9.45pm 20 P nc11yrs
Credit Cards 1 2 3

## BOURNE Lincolnshire Map **08** TF02

### ★★53% *Angel*
Market Place PE10 9AE ☎(0778)422346 FAX (0778) 393990
*An attractive former coaching inn situated in the town centre features a lively public bar, separate lounge bar, and restaurant. The imaginative menu is supplemented by a range of bar meals.*
→

B

13⇌🏠(1fb)2🛏 CTV in all bedrooms ® T 🚫 (ex guide dogs) sB&B⇌🏠£20-£37.50 dB&B⇌🏠£36-£54 🏠

CFA

♀ English & French V ♧ ♨ ✻ Lunch £6-£12alc Dinner £15&alc Last dinner 9.30pm

Credit Cards ⨯1⨯ ⨯2⨯ ⨯3⨯ ⨯£⨯

---

## BOURNEMOUTH Dorset Map **04** SZ09

**See Town Plan Section**

See also Christchurch, Longham & Poole

### ★★★★★❀64% Royal Bath

Bath Rd BH1 2EW (De Vere) ☎(0202)555555 Telex no 41375 FAX (0202) 554158

*A popular resort hotel retaining many Victorian features, where hospitable staff ensure a warm welcome. Some of the spacious public rooms are in the process of refurbishment. There is a comfortable little cocktail bar and a restaurant serving residents, with Oscars as the smart alternative offering a more adventurous style of cooking. Bedrooms vary in size, some are quite spacious and all have been refurbished to a good standard.*

131⇌2🛏 CTV in all bedrooms T 🚫 (ex guide dogs) S% sB&B⇌🏠£100.65-£115.50 dB&B⇌🏠£154-£308 🏠

Lift ⓒ 120🅿 (£3.50 per day) 🚗 ✿ 🏊 (heated) sauna solarium gymnasium beauty salon putting green croquet ♧ xmas

♀ English & French V ♧ ♨ ✻ S% Lunch £16.50 Dinner £25 Last dinner 10.30pm

Credit Cards ⨯1⨯ ⨯2⨯ ⨯3⨯ ⨯4⨯ ⨯5⨯ ⨯£⨯

### ★★★★69% Norfolk Royale

Richmond Hill BH2 6EN ☎(0202)551521 FAX (0202) 299729

*Cast iron filigree and lots of plants give this Edwardian town centre hotel an impressive façade. Bedrooms vary in size but all are well equipped with modern facilities, and there is a choice of eating options. Staff are particularly friendly and helpful.*

95⇌🏠(9fb)⅔in 14 bedrooms CTV in all bedrooms ® T 🚫 (ex guide dogs) sB⇌🏠£85-£95 dB⇌🏠£115-£125 (room only) 🏠

Lift ⓒ 85🅿 ✿ CFA 🏊 (heated) sauna steamroom whirlpool ♫ xmas

♀ English & French V ♧ ♨ ⅔ Lunch £10-£15&alc Dinner £15-£18.50&alc Last dinner 10.30pm

Credit Cards ⨯1⨯ ⨯2⨯ ⨯3⨯ ⨯4⨯ ⨯5⨯ ⨯£⨯

### ★★★★61% Bournemouth Highcliff

St Michaels Rd, West Cliff BH2 5DU ☎(0202)557702 Telex no 417153 FAX (0202) 292734

*In a cliff top position with sea views this hotel has refurbished bedrooms, including 50 new rooms, and a new conference room with adjoining syndicate rooms. The totally refurbished Hop Inn offers a second food operation with a popular menu and friendly service.*

146⇌🏠Annexe14⇌(30fb) CTV in all bedrooms ® T 🚫 (ex guide dogs) sB&B⇌🏠fr£87 dB&B⇌🏠fr£120 🏠

Lift ⓒ 150P ✿ CFA 🏊 (hard) snooker sauna solarium croquet putting ♧ xmas

♀ English & French V ♧ ♨ ⅔ ✻ Lunch £9.50-£12.50&alc Dinner fr£15&alc Last dinner 9pm

Credit Cards ⨯1⨯ ⨯2⨯ ⨯3⨯ ⨯5⨯ ⨯£⨯

### ★★★68% Chine

Boscombe Spa Rd BH5 1AX ☎(0202)396234 FAX (0202) 391737

*A well managed hotel with much to commend it, offers comfortable, well furnished public areas which include a quiet lounge and a candlelit dining room where the short dinner menu of interesting dishes is professionally served (though lunch is a more informal meal). Attractive but practical bedrooms have all been upgraded to good modern standards, and both indoor and outdoor swimming pools feature among the extensive leisure facilities, the latter being set in a sheltered garden. A popular conference venue, the hotel is also ideal for holidaymakers.*

97⇌🏠(15fb) CTV in all bedrooms ® T 🚫 (ex guide dogs) ✻ sB&B⇌🏠£40-£50 dB&B⇌🏠£80-£100 🏠

Lift ⓒ 40P 3🚗 (£2) ✿ 🏊 (heated) 🏊 (heated) sauna solarium gymnasium ♧ xmas

♀ English & French V ♧ ♨ ✻ Lunch £11 High tea £2.75 Dinner £16 Last dinner 8.30pm

Credit Cards ⨯1⨯ ⨯2⨯ ⨯3⨯ ⨯5⨯ ⨯£⨯

**See advertisement under POOLE**

### ★★★68% East Anglia

6 Poole Rd BH2 5OX ☎(0202)765163 FAX (0202) 752949

*The attractive and well decorated public areas of this popular, efficiently managed hotel include comfortable lounges and a restaurant where the dinner menu offers straightforward British food ; though bedrooms vary in size and furnishings, the majority combine modern fitted furniture with a fresh, light décor, and service is friendly throughout.*

49⇌🏠Annexe24⇌🏠(12fb) CTV in all bedrooms ® T 🚫 (ex guide dogs) sB&B⇌🏠£43-£51.50 dB&B⇌🏠£80-£103 (incl dinner) 🏠

Lift ⓒ 73P CFA 🏊 (heated) sauna solarium gymnasium jacuzzi games room xmas

♀ English & French ♧ ♨ ⅔ ✻ Sunday Lunch fr£7.75 Dinner fr£14 Last dinner 8.30pm

Credit Cards ⨯1⨯ ⨯2⨯ ⨯3⨯ ⨯5⨯

### ★★★67% The Connaught

West Hill Rd, West Cliff BH2 5PH ☎(0202)298020 FAX (0202) 298028

*The Connaught has recently been completely upgraded to a good modern standard, with extensive leisure facilities including large indoor and outdoor swimming pools. The attractive bar/lounge is comfortably furnished, and there is entertainment in the ballroom at times. The 4-course menu is competently cooked and served, and staff are genuinely helpful, making this a popular conference and meeting venue.*

60⇌🏠(15fb)⅔in 12 bedrooms CTV in all bedrooms ® T ✻ sB&B⇌🏠£38-£56 dB&B⇌🏠£76-£98 🏠

Lift ⓒ 45P ✿ CFA 🏊 (heated) 🏊 (heated) snooker sauna solarium gymnasium table tennis pool table steam room ♫ xmas

♀ English, French, Italian & Oriental V ♧ ♨ ⅔ ✻ Lunch £7.95-£8.95 High tea £3.95-£5.95 Dinner £18.50-£20.50&alc Last dinner 10pm

Credit Cards ⨯1⨯ ⨯2⨯ ⨯3⨯ ⨯5⨯ ⨯£⨯

### ★★★67% Piccadilly

Bath Rd BH1 2NN ☎(0202)552559 FAX (0202) 298235

*This popular central hotel, efficiently run by friendly staff, has well furnished modernised bedrooms and a very attractive restaurant serving table d'hôte and à la carte (mainly grills) menus. There is also a large ballroom and conference facilities.*

45⇌🏠(2fb)1🛏 CTV in all bedrooms ® T 🚫 (ex guide dogs) ✻ sB&B⇌🏠£39-£43 dB&B⇌🏠£57-£66 🏠

Lift ⓒ 30P CFA ♫ xmas

♀ English & French V ♧ ⅔ ✻ Sunday Lunch £7.50 Dinner £13.50&alc Last dinner 9pm

Credit Cards ⨯1⨯ ⨯2⨯ ⨯3⨯ ⨯5⨯ ⨯£⨯

### ★★★66% East Cliff Court

East Overcliff Dr BH1 3NA ☎(0202)554545 FAX (0202) 557456

*This seafront hotel has virtually been completely refurbished in the last year, and offers comfortable modern accommodation.*

70⇌🏠(10fb)2🛏 CTV in all bedrooms ® T 🚫 S% sB&B⇌🏠£45-£65 dB&B⇌🏠£80-£132 🏠

Lift ⓒ CTV 100P CFA 🏊 (heated) sauna solarium ♫ xmas

♀ English & French V ♧ ♨ S% Lunch £6.50-£8.50 High tea £6 Dinner £14.50 Last dinner 9pm

Credit Cards ⨯1⨯ ⨯2⨯ ⨯3⨯ ⨯4⨯ ⨯5⨯ ⨯£⨯

★★★66% **Langtry Manor**
26 Derby Rd, East Cliff BH1 3QB (Consort) ☎(0202)553887
FAX (0202) 290115
*Once the loveliest of Lillie Langtry and Edward VII, this is now a cosy, romantic hotel specialising in Edwardian weekends complete with appropriate costumes, banquet and Son et Lumière. Attractive bedrooms feature many with four-poster beds and corner baths, and staff are friendly and welcoming.*
14⇌🛏Annexe13⇌🛏(6fb)8🛏⊱in 2 bedrooms CTV in all bedrooms ® T sB&B⇌🛏£49.50-£79.50 dB&B⇌🛏£79-£159
30P 🚗 ❁ CFA *xmas*
♀ International V ✿ ⌓ ⊱ ✳ Dinner £19.75&alc Last dinner 9pm
Credit Cards 1 2 3 5 ⓔ

★★★65% **Durlston Court**
Gervis Rd, East Cliff BH1 3DD ☎(0202)291488
FAX (0202) 290335
*A well equipped hotel near the centre and BIC provides accommodation decorated in modern style ; public rooms consist of various comfortably furnished lounge areas and a restaurant in whose relaxed atmosphere genial staff serve a simple table d'hôte menu.*
54⇌🛏Annexe4⇌🛏(16fb) CTV in all bedrooms ® T sB&B⇌🛏£43-£49 dB&B⇌🛏£86-£98 (incl dinner) 🍴
Lift ℂ 50P CFA ⌿ (heated) sauna solarium gymnasium ♫ *xmas*
♀ English & French V ✿ ⌓ ⊱ Bar Lunch £4-£10alc Dinner £12-£15 Last dinner 8.30pm
Credit Cards 1 3 ⓔ

★★★64% **Bay View Court**
35 East Overcliff Dr BH1 3AH ☎(0202)294449
FAX (0202) 292883
*On the East Overcliff Drive, with 2 entrances, one of which is sea-facing, this hotel has recently been completely refurbished to a good overall standard. Bedrooms vary in size, one or 2 being a little compact, but all nicely furnished, smartly presented and well equipped. Public areas are spacious and comfortably furnished. An indoor pool was being completed at the time of going to print.*
64⇌🛏(11fb) CTV in all bedrooms ® T ✳ sB&B⇌🛏£24-£41 dB&B⇌🛏£48-£82 (incl dinner) 🍴
Lift CTV 58P snooker jacuzzi ♫ *xmas*
♀ International V ✿ ⌓ ⊱ ✳ Sunday Lunch £6 High tea £3 Dinner £8&alc Last dinner 8.30pm
Credit Cards 1 2 3

★★★64% **Cadogan**
8 Poole Rd BH2 5QU ☎(0202)763006 FAX (0202) 763006
*In a central position, close to the town, the sea and the resort's attractions, the hotel has recently undergone a complete renovation. Bedrooms are smartly decorated and furnished, and well equipped with modern facilities. Public areas, though not spacious, are comfortable and well presented ; and there is a conference room complemented by syndicate bedrooms of various sizes. A simple table d'hôte menu is offered in the basement restaurant.*
54⇌🛏(3fb)2🛏 CTV in all bedrooms ® T ✳ S%
sB&B⇌🛏£35-£42 dB&B⇌🛏£50-£70 (incl dinner) 🍴
Lift ℂ 55P ❁ ⚬ *xmas*
♀ English & French V ⌓ ⊱ ✳ S% Lunch £3.50-£6.50 Dinner fr£11 Last dinner 8.45pm
Credit Cards 1 2 3 5

★★★64% **Elstead**
12-14 Knyveton Rd BH1 3QP ☎(0202)293071
FAX (0202) 293827
Closed Oct-Mar (ex weekends)
*This hotel, in a quiet situation, has undergone complete renovation. Facilities include two bedrooms designed specifically for disabled guests, extensive conference rooms and full-size snooker table and pool table.*

51rm(39⇌11🛏)(4fb)⊱in 5 bedrooms CTV in all bedrooms ®
T sB&B⇌🛏£26.50-£30 dB&B⇌🛏£53-£60 🍴
Lift ℂ 32P CFA snooker ♫
V ✿ ⌓ Lunch fr£6.10 Dinner fr£12.95&alc Last dinner 8.30pm
Credit Cards 1 3

★★★64% **Hinton Firs**
Manor Rd, East Cliff BH1 3HB (Exec Hotel) ☎(0202)555409
FAX (0202) 299607
*Attractively set in a corner position amidst well kept gardens and car park areas, this hotel has both an indoor and an outdoor swimming pool with whirlpool sauna. Bedrooms are all neatly furnished and very comfortable. Personally owned and managed, the Hinton Firs Hotel has been in the Waters family since 1946. The staff are friendly and smartly uniformed. In addition to the table d'hôte dinner menu, a short à la carte is also available, accompanied with a sound, popular wine list.*
46⇌🛏Annexe6⇌(19fb) CTV in all bedrooms ® T ✗ ✳
sB&B⇌🛏£38.75-£50 dB&B⇌🛏£73.40-£95.90 (incl dinner) 🍴
Lift ℂ CTV 40P 🚗 ▣ (heated) ⌿ (heated) sauna games room ♫ *xmas*
♀ English & French V ✿ ⌓ ⊱ ✳ Sunday Lunch £6.75 Dinner £10.50&alc Last dinner 8.30pm
Credit Cards 1 3

See advertisement on page 147

★★★64% **Marsham Court**
Russell Cotes Rd BH1 3AB ☎(0202)552111 FAX (0202) 294744
*This large seafront hotel with extensive conference facilities offers comfortable well furnished accommodation, with freshly decorated public areas and bedrooms, most of them spacious. A sheltered terrace garden includes a swimming pool. Helpful service is provided by smartly dressed staff.*
→

# Bournemouth

86⇨🏠(16fb) CTV in all bedrooms ® T ✹ (ex guide dogs) sB&B⇨🏠fr£60 dB&B⇨🏠fr£100 (incl dinner)
Lift ℄ 80P 20🚗 CFA ⌒ (heated) snooker *xmas*
♀ English & French V ✤ ⏛ S% Lunch £9.50 High tea £5
Dinner £14.50&alc Last dinner 9pm
Credit Cards 1 2 3 5 £

## ★★★64% Moat House
Knyveton Rd BH1 3QQ (Queens Moat) ☎(0202)293311
Telex no 417226 FAX (0202) 292221
*This large conference and holiday hotel has extensive lounges and leisure facilities. Many bedrooms have recently been upgraded to a high modern standard; those not yet upgraded are offered at a reduced rate. Staff are friendly and helpful, and the restaurant provides both à la carte and table d'hôte menus.*
146⇨🏠(20fb) CTV in all bedrooms ® T ✱ sB&B⇨🏠£55-£66 dB&B⇨🏠£75-£85 🍴
Lift ℄ 100P 🖵 (heated) ⌒ snooker sauna gymnasium table tennis *xmas*
♀ English & French V ✤ ⏛ Lunch £10.50 Dinner £15 Last dinner 9.30pm
Credit Cards 1 2 3 5 £

## ★★★64% New Durley Dean
Westcliff Rd BH2 5HE ☎(0202)557711 FAX (0202) 292815
*A vast Victorian hotel near to sea and shops popular for holidays and conferences, was completely refurbished during 1988/89 to provide accommodation in bedrooms which are all freshly decorated and fitted with light oak furniture though they vary in size, some singles being rather small. In addition to the usual lounges and bars, public areas include a small leisure suite and a night spot with entertainment every evening; the largely self-service carvery dining room offers a limited range of meals, and staff are friendly and helpful.*
112⇨🏠(27fb)5🖵 CTV in all bedrooms ® T ✹ (ex guide dogs) ✱ sB&B⇨🏠£29.50-£51 dB&B⇨🏠£59-£105 (incl dinner) 🍴
Lift ℄ 40P CFA 🖵 (heated) snooker sauna solarium gymnasium jacuzzi table tennis steam room ♫ *xmas*
♀ English & Continental V ✤ ⏛ ✱ Sunday Lunch £4.95-£8.95alc High tea £4.50-£5.95alc Dinner £7.50-£13.95alc Last dinner 8.30pm
Credit Cards 1 2 3

## ★★★63% Belvedere
Bath Rd BH1 2EU ☎(0202)297556 FAX (0202) 294699
*Though bedrooms vary in size at this centrally located hotel they are all maintained to a high standard; spacious and newly decorated public areas include a restaurant in soothing pastel shades offering a choice of freshly prepared dishes on both its à la carte and table d'hôte menus. Staff are helpful and obliging. On some evenings there is live music.*
63⇨🏠(8fb)1🖵 CTV in all bedrooms ® T ✹ (ex guide dogs) ✱ sB&B⇨🏠£39-£42 dB&B⇨🏠£62-£66 🍴
Lift ℄ 50P CFA ♫ *xmas*
♀ English & Continental V ✤ ✱ Lunch £7.95&alc Dinner £11.50&alc Last dinner 9pm
Credit Cards 1 2 3 5 £

## ★★★63% Chesterwood
East Overcliff Dr BH1 3AR (Inter-Hotels) ☎(0202)558057 FAX (0202) 556285
*The comfortable public areas of this seafront hotel include a ballroom where guests can dance to live music some evenings, together with a sheltered terrace and outdoor pool which are popular during the summer months. Bedrooms vary in style but are generally light and modern.*
49⇨🏠Annexe3⇨🏠(13fb)2🖵 CTV in all bedrooms ® T ✹ (ex guide dogs)
Lift ℄ CTV 39P 8🚗 ✽ ⌒ (heated) ♫ ⌀
V ✤ ⏛ ✂ Last dinner 8.30pm
Credit Cards 1 2 3 5

## ★★★63% Hotel Courtlands
16 Boscombe Spa Rd, East Cliff BH5 1BB (Best Western) ☎(0202)302442 Telex no 41344 FAX (0202) 309880
*A holiday and conference hotel with a range of modern, well furnished bedrooms and extensive public rooms. There is a lighthearted atmosphere, and the dinner menu offers both English and Continental dishes together with a tempting table of sumptuous puddings.*
60⇨🏠(15fb) CTV in all bedrooms ® T sB&B⇨🏠£39-£45 dB&B⇨🏠£72-£80 🍴
Lift ℄ 50P 🚗 ✽ CFA ⌒ (heated) sauna solarium spa bath *xmas*
♀ English & French V ✤ ⏛ ✂ Sunday Lunch £7.25 High tea £4.50 Dinner £14 Last dinner 8.30pm
Credit Cards 1 2 3 5

## ★★★63% Durley Hall
Durley Chine Rd, West Cliff BH2 5JS (Consort) ☎(0202)766886 FAX (0202) 762236
*This recently extended hotel offers bedrooms both in executive style and more modest. A formal dining room is augmented by a coffee shop, and there are new indoor sports facilities and a sun lounge.*
70⇨🏠Annexe11⇨🏠(28fb)1🖵 CTV in all bedrooms ® T sB&B⇨🏠£35-£65 dB&B⇨🏠£70-£130 🍴
Lift ℄ 150P ✽ CFA ⌒ (heated) ⌒ (heated) sauna solarium gymnasium steam room table tennis hairdresser ✤ *xmas*
♀ English & Continental V ✤ ⏛ ✱ Sunday Lunch £6.90-£7.50 High tea £3.75-£6 Dinner £15.50-£16.50 Last dinner 8.45pm
Credit Cards 1 2 3 5 £

## ★★★63% Suncliff
29 East Overcliff Dr BH1 3AG ☎(0202)291711 Telex no 41363 FAX (0202) 299182
*This large seafront hotel with extensive leisure facilities and evening entertainment is popular for both holidays and conferences; bedrooms vary in size and price, but all are well equipped with every modern facility, and a cheerful young staff offers informal service.*
95⇨🏠(30fb)6🖵 CTV in all bedrooms ® T sB&B⇨🏠£31-£65 dB&B⇨🏠£62-£130 (incl dinner) 🍴
Lift ℄ 55P CFA 🖵 (heated) squash sauna solarium spa bath ♫ *xmas*
♀ English & French V ✤ ⏛ ✂ Sunday Lunch £6.50-£12 Dinner £14-£20 Last dinner 8.30pm
Credit Cards 1 2 3 5

## ★★★62% Burley Court
Bath Rd BH1 2NP ☎(0202)552824 FAX (0202) 298514
Closed 29 Dec-14 Jan
*A fairly small, proprietor-run hotel with a relaxing holiday atmosphere offers friendly, professional service, drinks and light refreshments being available beside the pool as well as in the lounge. Many bedrooms are now freshly decorated and furnished in the modern style.*
38rm(36⇨🏠)(8fb)1🖵 CTV in 34 bedrooms TV in 5 bedrooms ® T sB&B⇨🏠£29.50-£41 dB&B⇨🏠£57-£80 🍴
Lift ℄ CTV 35P 🚗 ⌒ (heated) solarium games room *xmas*
♀ English & French ✤ ⏛ ✱ S5% Dinner £10-£10.50 Last dinner 8.30pm
Credit Cards 1 3 £

## ★★★62% Cumberland
East Overcliff Dr BH1 3AF ☎(0202)290722 Telex no 418297 FAX (0202) 294810
*Holidaymakers and business/conference guests are equally well catered for at this 1930s cliff-top hotel with its pleasantly informal atmosphere. A bedroom refurbishment programme is well under way, providing accommodation of a high standard, and public areas include a small but comfortable lounge with chandeliers and a majestic panelled dining room where the table d'hôte menu of well prepared fresh dishes features excellent home-made puddings.*

→

B

147

# Bournemouth

102⇨🖐(12fb)3🛏 CTV in all bedrooms Ⓡ T ✱
sB&B⇨🖐£36.50-£42 dB&B⇨🖐£73-£84 🖨

Lift ℂ 65P CFA ⌿ (heated) games room table tennis pool ♫ ♨ *xmas*

♀ British & Continental V ♥ ⚗ ✱ Lunch £8.25-£11.50 High tea £4.50-£5.50 Dinner £15.50-£19.95 Last dinner 8.30pm
Credit Cards ①③£

★★★62% **Wessex**
West Cliff Rd BH2 5EU (Forestdale) ☎(0202)551911
FAX (0202) 297354
*This large professionally run Victorian hotel on the West Cliff, not far from the Conference Centre, offers a range of indoor sports as well as conference facilities. The modern bedrooms are all very well equipped, though furnishings tend to vary in quality, and public rooms include a spacious lounge and two restaurants.*
84rm(73⇨9🖐)(15fb)⚹in 3 bedrooms CTV in all bedrooms Ⓡ T sB&B⇨🖐£45-£57.50 dB&B⇨🖐£57.50-£77.50 🖨

Lift ℂ 250P CFA ▣ (heated) ⌿ (heated) snooker sauna solarium gymnasium table tennis *xmas*

♀ International V ♥ ⚗ ✂ ✱ Lunch £8.50-£11 High tea £3.45-£5.45 Dinner £14-£16 Last dinner 9.15pm
Credit Cards ①②③⑤£

★★★61% **Bournemouth Heathlands**
12 Grove Rd, East Cliff BH1 3AY ☎(0202)553336
Telex no 8954665 FAX (0202) 555937
*A very large hotel, busy with parties of conference delegates and individual guests on holiday. The 4-course dinner menu offers a choice of English dishes, and a wide selection of puddings is temptingly displayed and guests can help themselves. Bedrooms vary, the smaller rooms tend to have more modern furniture, but all are well equipped.*
116⇨🖐(17fb) CTV in all bedrooms Ⓡ T ✱ sB&B⇨🖐£59-£63 dB&B⇨🖐£98-£105 (incl dinner) 🖨

Lift ℂ 80P ❋ CFA ⌿ (heated) sauna solarium gymnasium health club *xmas*

♀ English & French V ♥ ⚗ ✱ Lunch £9-£11 Dinner £14-£16 Last dinner 8.30pm
Credit Cards ①③£

★★★61% **Cliffeside**
East Overcliff Dr BH1 3AQ ☎(0202)555724 Telex no 418297
FAX (0202) 294810
*A seafront hotel popular for family holidays in summer and conferences during the winter offers friendly, helpful service and an informal atmosphere. Bedrooms generally have good soft furnishings and are being upgraded during 1991, while both lounge and bar are modern and comfortable. Meals are for the most part freshly prepared on the premises, sweets and puddings being professionally made, and the table d'hôte menu at dinner provides some additional dishes.*
62⇨🖐(10fb) CTV in all bedrooms Ⓡ T ✱ sB&B⇨🖐£30-£45 dB&B⇨🖐£60-£90 🖨

Lift ℂ CTV 45P CFA ⌿ (heated) snooker table tennis pool table ♫ *xmas*

♀ French & Italian V ♥ ⚗ ✱ Lunch fr£8.25
Credit Cards ①③£

★★★61% *Grosvenor*
Bath Rd, East Cliff BH1 2EX ☎(0202)558858 Telex no 417200
*Friendly, helpful service and an effort to provide fresh, home-cooked food at reasonable prices number among the attractions of this family holiday hotel. Public rooms are ornately decorated, and attractive indoor leisure facilities are available for guests' use.*
40rm(33⇨5🖐)(10fb)2🛏 CTV in 38 bedrooms Ⓡ T

Lift ℂ CTV 40P ▣ (heated) sauna solarium gymnasium spa exercise area ♫

♀ English & French V ♥ ⚗ ✂ Last dinner 8.45pm
Credit Cards ①③

★★★60% **Embassy**
Meyrick Rd, East Cliff BH1 3DW ☎(0202)290751
FAX (0202) 557459
*Quietly located in a tree-lined avenue convenient for the town and the East Cliff, this friendly hotel offers garden annexe bedrooms of a good standard and comfortable lounge areas.*
39⇨🖐Annexe33⇨🖐(12fb)1🛏 CTV in all bedrooms Ⓡ T ✱
sB&B⇨🖐£31-£42 dB&B⇨🖐£62-£84 🖨

Lift ℂ CTV 75P CFA ⌿ (heated) games room *xmas*

♀ British & Italian ♥ ⚗
Credit Cards ①②③⑤£

★★★60% **Queens**
Meyrick Rd, East Cliff BH1 3DL ☎(0202)554415
Telex no 418297 FAX (0202) 294810
*A large conference and holiday hotel with a mixture of bedrooms, some in older traditional style and others purpose-built and modern. The restaurant offers a 5-course dinner menu of freshly prepared dishes.*
114⇨🖐(15fb)1🛏 CTV in all bedrooms Ⓡ T sB&B⇨🖐£42.50-£46 dB&B⇨🖐£85-£92 🖨

Lift ℂ 80P 12🅿 (£3) ❋ CFA snooker beauty salon games room *xmas*

♀ English & French V ♥ ⚗ ✱ Lunch £8.50-£10 High tea £4.25-£4.95 Dinner £15.95-£16.95 Last dinner 9pm
Credit Cards ①③£

★★★60% **Trouville**
Priory Rd BH2 5DH ☎(0202)552262 FAX (0202) 293324
*A large holiday and conference hotel close to the International Centre, Winter Gardens and shops. Attractive bedrooms have modern co-ordinated furnishings, though bathrooms tend to be more dated, and there are spacious lounge areas and a dining room offering fresh competently cooked food.*
80⇨🖐(22fb) CTV in all bedrooms Ⓡ T sB&B⇨🖐£35-£49.50 dB&B⇨🖐£70-£99 (incl dinner) 🖨

Lift ℂ 55P 5🅿 (£3.50 per night) sauna solarium gymnasium jacuzzi *xmas*

♀ English & French V ♥ ⚗ Lunch £7.50-£8.95 Dinner £13.95-£15.95 Last dinner 8.30pm
Credit Cards ①③£

★★★58% **Pavilion**
22 Bath Rd BH1 2NS ☎(0202)291266 Telex no 418253
FAX (0202) 559264
*A popular commercial hotel close to the town centre, with good conference facilities and modern recently refurbished public areas. Bedrooms are rather compact but attractively decorated and well equipped. The relaxed dining room serves a simple nightly changing table d'hôte menu.*
44⇨🖐(4fb)2🛏 CTV in all bedrooms Ⓡ T ✱ sB&B⇨🖐£38-£39 dB&B⇨🖐£64-£77 🖨

Lift ℂ CTV 40P CFA ♫ ♨ *xmas*

♀ English, French & Italian V ♥ ⚗ ✂ ✱ Lunch £5-£7.50 High tea fr£3 Dinner £15 Last dinner 8.30pm
Credit Cards ①②③⑤£

★★★55% **Forte Posthouse**
Lansdowne BH1 2PR (Forte Hotels) ☎(0202)553262
FAX (0202) 527698
*This modern hotel, circular in shape, offers good, well equipped accommodation of a uniform standard close to sea and shops; Lady Crest and no smoking rooms are available if preferred. The restaurant serves an ambitious à la carte menu with vegetarian and diabetic alternatives, whilst other public areas are now ready for refurbishment.*
98⇨🖐(11fb)⚹in 49 bedrooms CTV in all bedrooms Ⓡ T ✱ dB⇨🖐£39.50-£49.50 (room only) 🖨

Lift ℂ 50🅿 CFA snooker table tennis darts games room skittles ♨ *xmas*

**B**

V ✿ ⬛ ✂ ✳ Lunch £9.50-£10.95&alc Dinner fr£13.95&alc
Last dinner 10pm
Credit Cards ① ② ③ ⑤

★★68% **Boltons**
9 Durley Chine Rd South, West Cliff BH2 5JT
☎(0202)760907 & 751517 FAX (0202) 751629
*This long-established, family-owned and run hotel is set in a quiet
residential area and yet is very central. Originally built in 1876,
the hotel was recently refurbished : bedrooms are particularly well
appointed and comfortable. Freshly cooked meals are available,
and the service is friendly and relaxed.*
12⇩🏠(2fb) CTV in all bedrooms ® T ✳ sB&B⇩🏠£23.50-
£35.25 dB&B⇩🏠£47-£70.50 ❚
10P 🚙 ⊑ (heated) nc5yrs *xmas*
♀ English & French ✿ ⬛ ✳ Lunch fr£6.75 Dinner
fr£11.75&alc Last dinner 8.30pm
Credit Cards ① ② ③ ⑤

★★66% **Arlington**
Exeter Park Rd BH2 5BD ☎(0202)552879 & 553012
RS Jan-Mar
*Very centrally positioned with the bar and terrace overlooking the
Pleasure Gardens, this well kept hotel has a warm friendly
atmosphere created by the genuinely caring staff and owner.
Though bedrooms tend to be small, they are very clean and
attractively furnished.*
28⇩🏠Annexe1🏠(6fb) CTV in 28 bedrooms ® T ✂
sB&B⇩🏠£29-£37 dB&B⇩🏠£58-£74 (incl dinner) ❚
Lift CTV 21P ❀ nc2yrs *xmas*
♀ English & French V ✿ ⬛ ✂ Sunday Lunch £6.25 Dinner
£9.75 Last dinner 8pm
Credit Cards ① ③

# Bournemouth

**★★66% Chinehurst**
18-20 Studland Rd, Westbourne BH4 8JA ☎(0202)764583
FAX (0202) 762854
*A well run family-owned hotel close to the beach on the Poole/*
*Bournemouth border, popular with both business people and*
*holidaymakers. The restaurant offers a choice of menus, table*
*d'hôte and grill type dishes. Bedrooms are well equipped but vary*
*in size.*
31➪🛏(4fb)1🏠 CTV in all bedrooms ® T sB&B➪🛏£25.50-
£28 dB&B➪🛏£50-£56 🍴
14P 2🏛 (£2.50 per night) games room *xmas*
♀ Continental V ❖ ⚿ ✻ Lunch £6.50 Dinner £12.50&alc Last
dinner 8.30pm
Credit Cards 1 2 3 5 £

*See advertisement under POOLE*

**★★65% *Durley Grange***
6 Durley Rd, West Cliff BH2 5JL ☎(0202)554473 & 290743
FAX (0202) 293774
*This friendly owner-run hotel has attractive bedrooms with modern*
*fitted furniture. Public areas include a large plush bar with live*
*entertainment on some evenings and there is a new indoor*
*swimming pool and sauna.*
50➪🛏(6fb) CTV in all bedrooms ® T
Lift ℭ CTV 25P 🔲 (heated) sauna solarium ♫ nc5yrs
♀ English, French & German ❖ ✻ Last dinner 8pm
Credit Cards 1 3

**★★65% Hartford Court**
48 Christchurch Rd BH1 3PE ☎(0202)551712 & 293682
*This small, friendly hotel is popular with business people and*
*holidaymakers alike. Resident proprietors make guests feel most*
*welcome. The hotel is neat and freshly decorated, and though the*
*dinner menu offers a limited choice, food is well presented.*
34rm(6➪20🛏)Annexe6➪🛏(6fb) CTV in all bedrooms ® T
S5% sB&B£21-£23 sB&B➪🛏£23-£27 dB&B£42-£46
dB&B➪🛏£46-£54 🍴
Lift CTV 40P 🔅 nc10yrs *xmas*
❖ ⚿ S5% Bar Lunch £1.20-£3.50 Dinner £8.50-£9.50 Last
dinner 7.30pm
Credit Cards 1 2 3 5 £

**★★65% Mansfield**
West Cliff Gardens BH2 5HL ☎(0202)552659
Closed 28 Dec-17 Jan
*A small, personally run hotel where proprietor Brian Oakley is*
*much in evidence. Bedrooms have modern furnishings and all the*
*usual facilities. Freshly decorated public rooms are neat and tidy,*
*if a little regimented. A short dinner menu of simple, well cooked*
*dishes includes a wonderful display of home-made puddings*
*including fresh fruit gâteau and profiteroles.*
30➪🛏(7fb)1🏠 CTV in all bedrooms ® T ✻ sB&B➪🛏£25-
£33 dB&B➪🛏£50-£60 (incl dinner) 🍴
12P ♯ ♫ *xmas*
♀ English & French ❖ ⚿ ✻ Sunday Lunch £7-£8 Dinner £9-
£10 Last dinner 8pm
Credit Cards 1 3

**★★64% Durley Chine**
Chine Crescent, West Cliff BH2 5LB ☎(0202)551926
*A warm friendly hotel where resident proprietors have created a*
*cheerful and relaxing atmosphere. Bedrooms are in two types, all*
*are clean and have modern facilities.*
22rm(6➪9🛏)Annexe14rm(8➪2🛏)(5fb) CTV in all bedrooms
® T sB&B➪🛏£28.50-£36.50 dB&B➪🛏£57-£73 (incl dinner)
🍴
40P 🔅 ⛶ (heated) ♫ nc5yrs *xmas*
♀ English & Continental V ❖ ⚿ ✻ Bar Lunch £4.50-£8
Dinner fr£14 Last dinner 7.30pm
Credit Cards 1 2 3 £

**★★63% Chinehead**
31 Alumhurst Rd, Westbourne BH4 8EN ☎(0202)752777
*Situated between Poole and Bournemouth with easy access to the*
*amenities of both resorts, this friendly family-run hotel offers well*
*equipped bedrooms suited to both holiday and business guests.*
*Comfortable public areas include an informal dining room serving*
*a good choice of dishes.*
21➪🛏(2fb) CTV in all bedrooms ® T ✖ (ex guide dogs) ✻
sB&B➪🛏£26.50-£28.50 dB&B➪🛏£50-£57 🍴
20P CFA *xmas*
♀ English & Continental V ❖ ⚿ ✖ ✻ Lunch £6.25-£7.30
Dinner £8.75-£10&alc Last dinner 8.30pm
Credit Cards 1 3 £

**★★63% *Gresham Court***
4 Grove Rd, East Cliff BH1 3AX ☎(0202)551732
*This detached hotel, with its own garden, offers spacious public*
*areas including a ballroom with live entertainment on some nights.*
*Bedrooms have many modern facilities, and although the hotel*
*specialises in coach parties, this does not detract from the warm*
*hospitality provided by resident proprietors John and Pauline*
*Moore.*
34➪🛏(12fb) CTV in all bedrooms ®
Lift CTV 35P 🔅
❖ ⚿ Last dinner 7.30pm
Credit Cards 1 2 3 5

**★★63% Royal Exeter**
Exeter Rd BH2 5AG (Chef & Brewer) ☎(0202)290566 & 290567
*Spacious, well furnished accommodation is provided by an hotel*
*which is very well placed for BIC, pleasure gardens, shops and sea ;*
*good value meals are served in its very popular Berni-style*
*restaurants.*
36➪🛏(10fb) CTV in all bedrooms ® T ✖ (ex guide dogs)
sB&B➪🛏£48-£55 dB&B➪🛏£64 🍴
Lift ℭ 56P CFA
♀ International V ❖ ⚿ ✖ Bar Lunch £2.95-£5.50alc
Credit Cards 1 2 3 5

**★★63% Ullswater**
West Cliff Gardens BH2 5HW ☎(0202)555181
*This friendly hotel, at present being upgraded, has a very*
*comfortable lounge and bar, and some well furnished bedrooms. It*
*is suitable for both holiday and commercial guests.*
42➪🛏(7fb) CTV in all bedrooms ® T ✖ (ex guide dogs)
sB&B➪🛏£23-£36 dB&B➪🛏£46-£72 (incl dinner) 🍴
Lift 10P CFA table tennis snooker room ♫ *xmas*
♀ English & French ❖ ⚿ Sunday Lunch £6.75 Dinner £9.75
Last dinner 8pm
Credit Cards 1 2 3

**★★63% Whitehall**
Exeter Park Rd BH2 5AX ☎(0202)554682 FAX (0202) 554682
Closed 6 Nov-Feb
*This quiet hotel, overlooking the Central Gardens from a position*
*close to the shops and catering mainly for individual guests, offers*
*clean, well kept bedrooms and comfortable lounges.*
49rm(44➪🛏)(5fb) CTV in all bedrooms ® T ✻
sB&B➪🛏£26-£27 dB&B➪🛏£52-£54 🍴
Lift ℭ 25P 🔅 CFA
❖ ⚿ Dinner £10 Last dinner 8pm
Credit Cards 1 2 3 5

**★★62% Fircroft**
4 Owls Rd, Boscombe BH5 1AE ☎(0202)309771
FAX (0202) 302542
*Slightly compact but very well equipped bedrooms with mainly*
*modern furnishings, ample lounge space, a ballroom and facilities*
*for squash are available at this hotel.*
49➪🛏(18fb) CTV in all bedrooms ® T ✻ sB&B➪🛏£22.50-
£26.50 dB&B➪🛏£45-£53 🍴

Lift ℂ CTV 50P CFA squash ♪ *xmas*
V ✤ ⬛ ✳ Bar Lunch £2-£5 Dinner fr£12 Last dinner 8pm
Credit Cards ① ② ③ ⓔ

### ★★ 62% Winterbourne

Priory Rd BH2 5DJ (Inter-Hotels) ☎(0202)296366
FAX (0202) 780073
Closed 1-14 Jan
*With excellent views of the town and sea, this friendly hotel with
an informal atmosphere has modern bedrooms, a bar and games
room. It is suitable for business people and holidaymakers alike.*
41⇒🛏(12fb) CTV in all bedrooms ® T sB&B⇒🛏£34-£45
dB&B⇒🛏£60-£81 🍴
Lift 32P 1🏎 ❋ CFA ⌸ (heated) pool table ♨ *xmas*
V ✤ ⬛ Bar Lunch £5.50-£8 High tea £3 Dinner fr£11.50&alc
Last dinner 8pm
Credit Cards ① ② ③ ⑤ ⓔ

### ★★ 61% Cottonwood

Grove Rd, East Cliff BH1 3AP (Minotels) ☎(0202)553183
*In a seafront location with fine views, this family holiday hotel
offers a variety of bedrooms, some spacious and well furnished and
some rather more modest, but all have modern facilities. A
cheerful, relaxing atmosphere is created by the young staff.*
32⇒🛏(8fb) CTV in all bedrooms ® T ✳ S%
sB&B⇒🛏£38.50-£44.50 dB&B⇒🛏£62-£74 🍴
Lift 50P ❋ CFA snooker ♪ *xmas*
♀ English & French V ✤ ⬛ ⤧ ✳ S% Bar Lunch £1.50-£4
Dinner £9.50 Last dinner 8pm
Credit Cards ① ② ③ ⑤

### ★★ 61% St George

West Cliff Gardens BH2 5HL ☎(0202)556075
Closed 27 Dec-3rd wk Mar
*A restful hotel with a warm atmosphere, personally run by resident
proprietors and set in a quiet position overlooking gardens and the
sea, offers simply furnished but well equipped bedrooms and a very
comfortable lounge.*
22rm(20⇒🛏)(5fb) CTV in all bedrooms ® T sB&B⇒🛏£23-
£28.50 dB&B⇒🛏£46-£60 🍴
Lift 12P 🚲 CFA pool table *xmas*
♀ English, French & Italian ✤ ⬛ ⤧ Sunday Lunch £4.95-
£5.95 Dinner fr£6.99 Last dinner 7.30pm
**See advertisement on page 153**

### ★★ 60% Riviera

Burnaby Rd, Alum Chine BH4 8JF ☎(0202)763653
Telex no 41363 FAX (0202) 299182
Closed 2-31 Jan
*A popular resort hotel near the Promenade specialising in family
holidays. Bedrooms tend to be compact but have all the usual
modern facilities. Leisure amenities include indoor and outdoor
pools, two snooker tables and a ball room with regular
entertainments. A menu of mainly British dishes is offered at
dinner, with a buffet at lunchtime.*
70⇒🛏 Annexe9⇒🛏(24fb) CTV in all bedrooms ® T
sB&B⇒🛏£27.50-£53 dB&B⇒🛏£55-£106 (incl dinner)
Lift 79P 🛏 (heated) snooker sauna solarium 2
games rooms ♪ *xmas*
♀ French & English V ✤ ⬛ Lunch £6.50-£7.50 Dinner £14-
£16.50 Last dinner 8.30pm
Credit Cards ① ③
**See advertisement on page 153**

### ★★ 60% Hotel Riviera

West Cliff Gardens BH2 5HL ☎(0202)552845
Closed Dec-Mar
*A friendly hotel which has been under the same ownership for 30
years and has acquired a loyal clientele who appreciate its
generally pretty fitted bedrooms and the cosy, comfortable public
rooms.*
34⇒🛏(5fb) CTV in all bedrooms ® ✳ sB&B⇒🛏£24-£28
dB&B⇒🛏£48-£56 🍴

→

Lift ( CTV 24P 🚗 *xmas*
✿ ⚸ Dinner £9 Last dinner 7.30pm
Credit Cards 1 3

**★★60% Russell Court**
Bath Rd BH1 2EP (Inter-Hotels) ☎(0202)295819
FAX (0202) 293457
*A busy hotel whose public areas include a well decorated dining room, bar and ballroom, well placed for shops, sea and entertainment, caters mainly for coach parties.*
62rm(46⇨10↟)(6fb) CTV in all bedrooms ® T
✹ (ex guide dogs) S% sB&B£28-£36 sB&B⇨↟£25-£32 dB&B£48-£78 dB&B⇨↟£56-£86 (incl dinner) 🅿
Lift ( CTV 60P CFA *xmas*
V ✿ ⚸ Sunday Lunch £5.50-£9.50 High tea £5-£7.50 Dinner £8.90-£15.90 Last dinner 8pm
Credit Cards 1 2 3 5 £

**★★60% Woodcroft Tower**
Gervis Rd, East Cliff BH1 3DE (Consort) ☎(0202)558202
FAX (0202) 551807
*A detached hotel with neat gardens, in a pleasant location not far from the sea. Bedrooms vary a little but most have modern fitted furniture and the usual range of facilities. The spacious lounge is comfortable, and the bar and restaurant have been recently refurbished and are now bright and attractive.*
42rm(22⇨17↟)(4fb) CTV in all bedrooms ® T
✹ (ex guide dogs) ✱ sB&B£30-£40 sB&B⇨↟£30-£40 dB&B⇨↟£50-£60 🅿
Lift ( 60P (charged) ✿ CFA *xmas*
♺ English & French ✿ ⚸ Bar Lunch £3-£7 Dinner £12-£14 Last dinner 8.30pm
Credit Cards 1 3 £

**★★58% West Cliff Hall**
14 Priory Rd BH2 5DN ☎(0202)299715
*Well placed for the Conference Centre, this busy hotel offers good value holiday accommodation with clean rooms and modern facilities. Public areas are spacious and a simple menu of mainly British dishes is available at dinner.*
49⇨↟(9fb) CTV in all bedrooms ® T
Lift CTV 36P ♫
V ✿ ⚸ Last dinner 8pm
Credit Cards 1 2 3 5

**★★57% Sun Court**
West Hill Rd, West Cliff BH2 5PH ☎(0202)551343
*This modern family holiday and commercial hotel with an outdoor pool and attractive bar lounge offers a range of very well equipped bedrooms, the small rooms let at a reduced rate.*
36⇨↟(4fb) CTV in all bedrooms ® T sB&B⇨↟£37.50-£42.50 dB&B⇨↟£58-£89 (incl dinner) 🅿
Lift ( CTV 50P 1🐾 CFA ⌁ (heated) solarium gymnasium *xmas*
♺ English & Italian ✿ ⚸ ✂ Sunday Lunch £6.25&alc Dinner £14&alc Last dinner 8.30pm
Credit Cards 1 2 3 5 £

**★★53% County**
Westover Rd BH1 2BT ☎(0202)552385 FAX (0202) 297255
*Well placed close to the pier, gardens and shops, this hotel offers the usual modern bedroom facilities and a lively disco.*
51rm(37⇨9↟)(11fb) CTV in all bedrooms ® T sB&Bfr£20 sB&B⇨↟fr£35 dB&Bfr£40 dB&B⇨↟fr£60 🅿
Lift ( ✂ *xmas*
✿ ✱
Credit Cards 1 2 3 £

For key to symbols in English see the bookmark.

**★67% Lynden Court**
8 Durley Rd, West Cliff BH2 5JL ☎(0202)553894
Closed Nov-Mar (ex Xmas & New Year)
*Small and personally run, the hotel offers comfortable bedrooms equipped with all modern facilities. Meals are sound, with a good choice of dishes at dinner, and during the season entertainment is provided in the open-plan lounge and bar.*
32⇨↟(7fb) CTV in 31 bedrooms ®
Lift 20P ♫
Last dinner 7.15pm
Credit Cards 1 2 3 5

**★60% Silver How**
West Cliff Gardens, West Cliff BH2 5HN ☎(0202)551537
Closed Jan
*A small, family-managed hotel within easy reach of both sea and shops offers pleasant public rooms that include a bar with dance floor, dining room and conservatory-style lounge. Bedrooms are traditional in design, and meals comprise simple, home-cooked fare.*
22rm(9⇨9↟)(11fb) CTV in all bedrooms ® T ✹ sB&B£21-£25 dB&B⇨↟£46-£54 🅿
12P *xmas*
✱ Dinner £7.50 Last dinner 7pm
Credit Cards 1 3 £

**★59% Taurus Park**
16 Knyveton Rd BH1 3QN ☎(0202)557374
*Quietly located in a tree-lined avenue close to the town centre and East Cliff, this cheerful family-run hotel offers good value accommodation, with simply furnished bedrooms of varying size, spacious public areas and home-cooked food.*
46rm(7⇨24↟)(4fb) CTV in all bedrooms ® ✹ sB&B£17.50-£22 sB&B⇨↟£19-£25 dB&B£35-£42 dB&B⇨↟£38-£50 (incl dinner)
Lift CTV 25P games room nc3yrs *xmas*
Bar Lunch £1.20-£4.25 Dinner £5-£6 Last dinner 7.30pm

**❀✕✕Sophisticats**
43 Charminster Rd BH8 8UE ☎(0202)291019
*In a street of shops about 1.5 miles from the centre of Bournemouth. Booth seating and friendly service create an intimate atmosphere. The à la carte menu has sensibly been extended and is supplemented by daily additions. Local fish and game are delicious, as are some imaginative dishes from the Far East. The menu includes pheasant in red wine with bacon and chipolata, grilled halibut with tarragon and chevril hollandaise and Javanese fillet steak. The vegetables are cooked al dente to retain their colour and flavour.*
Closed Sun, Mon, 2 wks Feb, 1 wk Jun & 2 wks Nov Lunch not served
♺ International V 34 seats ✱ Dinner £20-£25alc Last dinner 9.30pm ✈

---

**BOURTON-ON-THE-WATER** Gloucestershire Map **04** SP12

**★★69%   Dial House**
The Chestnuts, High St GL54 2AN ☎(0451)22244
*Originally a farmhouse dating from 1698 this small, privately run hotel offers well equipped accommodation and cosy public areas. Well prepared dishes are served in the intimate dining rooms and there is a secluded rear garden where guests can relax and enjoy a game of croquet.*
10⇨↟3🛏✂in 2 bedrooms CTV in all bedrooms ® T
✹ (ex guide dogs) sB&B⇨↟fr£35.75 dB&B⇨↟fr£66 🅿
20P 🚗 ✿ croquet lawn putting green nc8yrs *xmas*
♺ English & French V ✿ ⚸ ✂ ✱ Sunday Lunch fr£10.50 Dinner £8-£21alc Last dinner 9.15pm
Credit Cards 1 3 £

**See advertisement on page 155**

B

### ★★66% **Finden Lodge**
Whiteshoots Hill, Cirencester Rd GL54 2LE (Inter-Hotels)
☎Cotswold(0451)20387 FAX (0451) 21635
*Close to Bourton-on-the-Water on the A429, this hotel is an ideal base for touring the Cotswolds. Accommodation is comfortable and attractive and all rooms are equipped with good modern facilities. It is family-owned and run, hence the friendly and relaxed atmosphere.*
12⇨🖰(2fb)1🛏✂in 3 bedrooms CTV in all bedrooms ® T ✱
sB&B⇨🖰£37-£47 dB&B⇨🖰£58-£92 🗗
38P ✱ *xmas*
♀ English & Continental V ✿ ⚲ ✂ ✱ Lunch £12.75&alc
Dinner £12.75&alc Last dinner 9.30pm
Credit Cards ①②③£

### ★★66% *Old Manse*
Victoria St GL54 2BX ☎Cotswold(0451)20082 & 20642
*The Old Manse was built in the 18th century and was the home of the village pastor. It has recently been refurbished to a good standard, tourists will enjoy the relaxing atmosphere whilst business guests will appreciate the modern facilities. Management and staff offer genuine hospitality.*
12⇨🖰(2fb)1🛏 CTV in all bedrooms ® T ✖ (ex guide dogs)
12P
♀ English & French V ✿ ⚲ Last dinner 9.30pm
Credit Cards ①③

### ★★64% **Chester House Hotel & Motel**
Victoria St GL54 2BS (Minotels) ☎Cotswold(0451)20286
FAX (0451) 20471
Closed mid Dec-mid Feb
*This friendly and very well maintained hotel in a delightful Cotswold village offers spacious, well equipped and comfortable bedrooms, a bar and lounge for residents and an attractive restaurant providing a good choice of food.*
13⇨🖰Annexe10⇨🖰(5fb)2🛏 CTV in all bedrooms ® T
sB&B⇨🖰£40-£44.25 dB&B⇨🖰£61-£77 Continental
breakfast 🗗
23P
V ✿ Lunch fr£8 Dinner fr£16.80&alc Last dinner 9.30pm
Credit Cards ①②③④⑤

### ★★63% **Old New Inn**
High St GL54 2AF ☎Cotswold(0451)20467 FAX (0451) 810236
Closed 25 Dec
*An inn on the edge of this charming Cotswold village, managed by the same family for the past 50 years and maintaining old-fashioned standards of comfort and hospitality, provides relaxed, attentive service throughout – even the parrot offering a friendly greeting!*
17rm(6⇨2🖰)Annexe5rm1🛏 CTV in 14 bedrooms ® S10%
sB&B⇨🖰£28-£34 sB&B⇨🖰£34-£36 dB&B£56-£68
dB&B⇨🖰£68-£72 🗗
CTV 25P 6🐾 (£2) 🚗 ✱
V ✿ S10% Lunch £10-£14 Dinner fr£16 Last dinner 8.30pm
Credit Cards ①③

---

### BOVEY TRACEY Devon Map 03 SX87

### ★★★63% **Edgemoor**
Haytor Rd TQ13 9LE ☎(0626)832466 FAX (0626) 834760
*A fairly recent change of ownership has not changed the atmosphere of a friendly hotel run on country house lines, popular with both business travellers and tourists, which offers easy access to the adjacent moors. Brightly appointed accommodation features a pleasing, co-ordinated décor, all rooms offering modern comforts and some having four poster or half tester beds. Public areas include a pretty little restaurant where good fresh food standards prevail, a spacious, galleried residents' lounge and a cosy bar. Informal service is provided by the family management and local staff.*

---

12⇨🖰(1fb)2🛏 CTV in all bedrooms ® T sB&B⇨🖰£42.50-
£50 dB&B⇨🖰£78.50-£85 🗗
45P 🚗 ✱
♀ English & French V ✿ ⚲ Lunch £8.50-£10.50 High tea
£1.75-£3.50 Dinner £16.95-£19.95 Last dinner 9pm
Credit Cards ①②③⑤

### ★★60% **Coombe Cross**
Coombe Cross TQ13 9EY (Inter-Hotels) ☎(0626)832476
*In a quiet position on the edge of town in its own small garden, this small country-house style hotel has commanding views over Dartmoor. Personally run with informal friendly services, it offers bright traditional bedrooms, all well equipped with modern facilities. There are comfortable lounges and a pleasant dining room where traditional cooking is available from a table d'hôte menu.*
26rm(23⇨1🖰)(2fb) CTV in all bedrooms ® T sB&B⇨🖰£36
dB&B⇨🖰£55 🗗
( CTV 26P ✱ CFA
V ✿ ⚲ ✂ ✱ Bar Lunch £3.50-£7.50 High tea £4.50 Dinner
£16.95 Last dinner 8pm
Credit Cards ①②③⑤

---

### BOWMORE
See Islay, Isle of

---

### BOWNESS ON WINDERMERE
See Windermere

---

### BOX Wiltshire Map 03 ST86

### ❀❀✖✖✖**Clos du Roy**
Box House SN14 9NR ☎Bath(0225)744447 Telex no 831476
FAX (0225) 743971
*An elegant Georgian mansion in village setting, surrounded by its own grounds, provides the ideal setting for a relaxing lunch or dinner. Food is carefully prepared by chef/proprietor Philippe Roy, and guests can choose between a set meal 'surprise' and an interesting à la carte menu, these being supplemented by an 8-course Menu Dégustation in the evenings. There is a preponderance of game and fish, the terrine of turbot and courgette served with aïoli and ratatouille being particularly noteworthy. Main courses include roast fillet of sea bass with a truffle fumet and a crepinette of lamb in a light mustard sauce, while, among the desserts, a rich chocolate torte also deserves mention. Menus are complemented by an extensive, though expensive, list of fine wines, and the all-French staff are unfailingly attentive and professional. A selection of individually furnished bedrooms is also available for overnight guests.*
Closed Mon
Dinner not served Sun
♀ French V 55 seats Lunch £12.50-£15.50 Dinner £29.50-£38
Last lunch 2.30pm Last dinner 10pm 35 P ✂
Credit Cards ①②③④⑤

---

### BRACKLESHAM West Sussex Map 04 SZ89

### ❀✖**Cliffords Cottage**
Bracklesham Ln PO20 8JA ☎(0243)670250
*Small 17th-century cottage restaurant with a cosy atmosphere, serving good, honest cooking of a very good standard.*
Closed Tue (winter only) Lunch not served Mon-Sat
Dinner not served Tue & Sun
♀ French V 28 seats ✱ Sunday Lunch £10.50 Dinner
£15.50&alc Last dinner 9pm 16 P nc3yrs
Credit Cards ①②③⑤

---

A rosette means exceptional standards of cuisine.

BRACKNELL Berkshire Map **04** SU86 ☺

★★★62% *Stirrups Country House*
Maidens Green RG12 6LD (Best Western)
☎Winkfield(0344)882284 FAX (0344) 882300
*A popular, mainly commercial hotel with attractive Tudor-style exterior, set in a rural location outside the town, offers accommodation in well equipped modernised bedrooms which include 5 larger executive rooms. Local racecourses provide the theme for public areas, and the congenial beamed bar is warmed by an open fire.*
24⇨(6fb) CTV in all bedrooms ® T
Lift ( 150P ❀
♀ English & Continental V ❖
Credit Cards [1] [2] [3] [5]

BRADFORD West Yorkshire Map **07** SE13 ☺

★★★60% **Tong Village**
Tong Ln, Tong BD4 0RP (Lansbury) ☎Leeds(0532)854646
FAX (0532) 853661
*This mainly modern hotel in open countryside, conveniently situated off the A450 within 10 miles of Bradford and only a short distance from junction 27 of the M62, is ideal for both business and leisure guests. En suite bedrooms are all well equipped, and the elegant restaurant offers table d'hôte and à la carte menus which include local specialities.*
60⇨🏠(6fb)1 🛏🔓in 22 bedrooms CTV in all bedrooms ® T ✱
sB&B⇨🏠£30-£68 dB&B⇨🏠£60-£80 🍴
Lift ( CTV ❀ sauna solarium gymnasium ♫ *xmas*
♀ English & French V ❖ ⚟ 🔓 ✱ Lunch £3-£20alc Dinner £15.50&alc Last dinner 10.30pm
Credit Cards [1] [2] [3] [4] [5]

Enjoy the Edgemoor

Take a midweek or weekend bargain break in this delightful country house set in beautiful gardens.

Designer bedrooms equipped to highest standards for the 1990's.

Some 12 miles south of Exeter on A38
then 2 miles in direction of Bovey Tracey

AA ★★★ **THE EDGEMOOR** ★★★ AA
HAYTOR ROAD, BOVEY TRACEY, SOUTH DEVON TQ13 9LE
TEL: (0626) 832466 FAX: (0626) 834760

★★

# CHESTER HOUSE HOTEL&MOTEL

**Bourton-on-the-Water, Cheltenham, Gloucestershire, GL54 2BU**
**Telephone: Cotswold (0451) 20286**
**Fax: 0451 20471**

Under personal supervision of the proprietors, Mr & Mrs Julian Davies. 23 rooms all with private bath or shower, central heating, colour TV, radio, telephone and tea & coffee making facilities. Four posters. Comfortable Lounge and Dining Room. Parking for 21 cars.

Ideal centre for touring picturesque Cotswold villages. Dogs are accepted at the discretion of the management. Licensed restaurant open daily to residents and non-residents.

★★

# Dial House Hotel

**The Chestnuts, High Street, Bourton on the Water, Gloucestershire GL54 2AN**
**Telephone: (0451) 22244**

A 17th century country house hotel in a secluded situation within 1½ acres of walled garden yet within village centre. Beautifully converted in 1989, 10 ensuite bedrooms all with colour TV, teamaker, telephone and some rooms with four posters. Beautiful candlelit restaurant where the à la carte menu uses freshly cooked local produce.

**Bargain Break. Ample car parking.**
**Egon Ronay recommended.**

Colour brochure with pleasure
Resident proprietors: Lynn and Peter Boxall

155

### ★★★57% *Novotel Bradford*

Merrydale Rd BD4 6SA (3m S adjacent to M606)
☎(0274)683683 Telex no 517312 FAX (0274) 651342
*This purpose-built hotel, situated on the Europa Trading Estate just off the M606 between Bradford city and the M62, provides modern comforts, sound accommodation and friendly, helpful service from a well trained staff.*
132⇨🛏(132fb) CTV in all bedrooms ® T
Lift ( ▦ 180P ❀ ⌿ (heated) ๘
♀ English & French **V** ❖ ⚴ Last dinner mdnt
Credit Cards ①②③④⑤

### ★★★51% *The Victoria*

Bridge St BD1 1JX (Forte Hotels) ☎(0274)728706
Telex no 517456 FAX (0274) 736358
*Spacious public areas, including a Carvery Restaurant with fixed-price menu, are an attractive feature of this traditional-style hotel which stands at the centre of the city, next to St George's Hall.*
59⇨🛏(1fb)⌿in 12 bedrooms CTV in all bedrooms ® ✱
sB⇨🛏fr£65 dB⇨🛏fr£85 (room only) 🅟
Lift ( 40P CFA *xmas*
♀ Mainly grills **V** ❖ ⚴ ⌿ ✱ S% Lunch fr£1 Dinner £12.25
Last dinner 10pm
Credit Cards ①②③⑤

### ★★63% *Dubrovnik*

3 Oak Av, Manningham BD8 7AQ ☎(0274)543511
FAX (0274) 480407
*This warm, family-owned and run hotel, set in a quiet side road just off the Keighley road about 1.5 miles from the city, offers comfortable bedrooms and a restaurant serving a good range of dishes. The new extension at present under construction and due to open in late 1991 will provide function areas and further accommodation.*
20⇨🛏(6fb) CTV in all bedrooms ® ✖
( 60P
♀ English & Yugoslavian **V** ❖ ⚴
Credit Cards ①③

### ★★62% *Park Drive*

12 Park Dr BD9 4DR ☎(0274)480194
*Just a mile from the town centre near Lister Park, this unpretentious hotel enjoys a peaceful setting in its own well tended gardens. Modern bedrooms are well appointed and service, by the resident proprietors, is friendly but unobtrusive.*
11⇨🛏(1fb) CTV in all bedrooms ® T ✱ sB&B⇨🛏£36-£44
dB&B⇨🛏£46-£54 🅟
9P ⏦ ๘
✱ Dinner £10.75 Last dinner 7.30pm
Credit Cards ①②③

### ❀❀ ✖ ✖ Restaurant Nineteen

19 North Park Rd, Heaton BD9 4NT ☎(0274)492559
*This elegantly furnished restaurant in a quiet residential area of the town provides a particularly high standard of cuisine, making good use of the best produce to create such dishes as Sautéed Monkfish on Chive Pasta with Saffron Sauce, Beef Fillet with Fine Grain Mustard Sauce, and delicious home-made ice creams. A fine wine list accompanies the menu, and friendly staff provide efficient service.*
Closed Sun, Mon, 1 wk after Xmas, 1 wk Jun & 2 wks Aug/Sep
Lunch not served (ex by arrangement only)
♀ English & French 40 seats Dinner £27-£28.50 Last dinner
9.30pm 15 P nc8yrs ⌿
Credit Cards ①②③

Restaurants and hotel restaurants
with rosettes have their names and addresses
tinted pink in the directory.

---

**BRADFORD ON AVON** Wiltshire Map **03** ST86

### ★★★❀❀ ⚑⚑75% *Woolley Grange*

Woolley Green BA15 1TX (Pride of Britain) ☎(02216)4705
FAX (02216) 4059
*The Chapman family's fabulous stone manor house, converted to a hotel in 1989, continues to improve. It is one of the few hotels in the country that provides the highest levels of accommodation and cuisine, together with good standards of service, and welcomes children, providing several excellent facilities. Bedrooms are beautifully appointed with quality fabrics and antique furnishings – not always very practical – and the comfortable public areas are being supplemented by a terrace. Staff are pleasant and relaxed and cooking is now under the management of chef Ian Mansfield.*
14⇨🛏Annexe6⇨🛏(6fb) CTV in all bedrooms T S%
sB&B⇨🛏£85-£152 dB&B⇨🛏£95-£169 🅟
CTV 40P ⏦ ❀ CFA ⌿ (heated) ℘ (grass) badminton croquet
games room ๘ *xmas*
**V** ❖ ⚴ S% Lunch £10-£25 High tea fr£6 Dinner £26.50&alc
Last dinner 10pm
Credit Cards ①②③⑤£

### ★★❀65% *Swan*

1 Church St BA15 1LN ☎(02216)7666 FAX (0225) 868060
Closed 1 Jan
*This well managed and centrally located coaching inn, dating from 1500, features friendly bars offering a good range of food as well as the smart little dining room with its interesting fixed-price menu based on organically farmed meats; this menu changes every 4-6 weeks and is supplemented by fresh fish dishes which are varied daily. Chef Steve Breese's passion for fish spurs him on to more adventurous specialities such as Monkfish and Mushroom Curry, or Fillet of Brill with Wild Mushrooms and Truffle Sauce. Guests can also enjoy roast fillet of Welsh lamb served on a bed of spiced lentils with tomato sauce, or escalope of salmon with olive, lemon, garlic and coriander sauce – quality fresh ingredients being enhanced by sauces which are good, though simple. Staff are friendly, and bedrooms are modern and well equipped though they vary slightly in size and comfort.*
12⇨🛏(1fb)1⚑ CTV in all bedrooms ® T ✖ (ex guide dogs)
24P
♀ English & French **V** ❖ Last dinner 9.45pm
Credit Cards ①②③⑤

---

**BRADLEY STOKE** Avon Map **03** ST68

### ★★★70% *Stakis Leisure Lodge*

Woodlands Ln, Patchway BS12 4JF (Stakis)
☎Almondsbury(0454)201144 Telex no 445774
FAX (0454) 612022
*On the A38 just south of junction 16 of the M5, this complex sucessfully combines modern hotel facilities with an indoor leisure club. Accommodation is comfortable and quite spacious with a good range of facilities.*
112⇨🛏(35fb)⌿in 28 bedrooms CTV in all bedrooms ® T (room only) 🅟
( ▦ 132P ⌑ (heated) sauna solarium gymnasium *xmas*
**V** ❖ ⚴ ⌿
Credit Cards ①②③⑤

---

**BRAE**

See **Shetland**

---

**BRAEMAR** Grampian *Aberdeenshire* Map **15** NO19

### ★★★67% *Invercauld Arms*

AB3 5YR (Mount Charlotte (TS)) ☎(03397)41605
FAX (03397) 41428
*This well established, traditional hotel has now been fully renovated. Set in the heart of Royal Deeside the hotel is popular all year round, in winter because of its proximity to the Glenshee ski*

*slopes and attractively priced packages. Bedrooms are mostly spacious, comfortable and well equipped. There is a foyer lounge, and a cocktail bar conceding to its Highland heritage only by the tartan fabric of the comfortable chairs. Both the main lounge and restaurant are elegant, the latter spoilt only by the utilitarian chairs which are entirely out of character.*

68⇨♠(11fb) CTV in all bedrooms ℝ **T**
Lift ( 80P ♫
**V** ♁ ⬚ Last dinner 8.45pm
Credit Cards [1] [2] [3] [5]

---

★★⊛69% **Braemar Lodge**
Glenshee Rd AB35 5YQ ☎(03397)41627
Closed Dec & Apr
*The conversion of an attractive granite house into a small hotel of distinction over the past 3 years has fulfilled the ambitions of involved proprietors who bring their own philosophy of hospitality to its running. Meals are of a high standard, and the limited number of tables available in the elegant dining room makes booking essential for non-residents. A cosy cocktail lounge complete with wood panelling and a log fire has been created in the style of Charles Rennie Mackintosh, the famous Scottish architect, and an attractive lounge provides an abundance of books and games for guests' amusement; pretty, individually styled bedrooms (most of which have en suite shower facilities) offer pleasant personal touches.*
8rm(6♠) CTV in all bedrooms ℝ S% sB&B£27.50 sB&B♠£40 dB&B£55 dB&B♠£70 ➡
20P 1♠ ⇨ ✿
**V** ♁ ⬚ ⅃ S% Dinner £15-£25 Last dinner 8.30pm
Credit Cards [1] [3]

---

**BRAINTREE** Essex Map **05** TL72 ⊙

★★68% **White Hart**
Bocking End CM7 6AB (Lansbury) ☎(0376)21401
Telex no 988835 FAX (0376) 552628
*This former coaching inn in the centre of town has been extended to provide good modern accommodation. The original building houses 2 timbered bars, a Beefeater restaurant with extended menu, and a few beamed bedrooms. Most rooms are in a modern wing over the car park; these are more spacious, comfortable and well equipped.*
35⇨♠(4fb)1⌨⅄in 6 bedrooms CTV in all bedrooms ℝ **T** ✗ (ex guide dogs) sB&B⇨♠fr£62 dB&B⇨♠fr£75 ➡
( 40P CFA
☺ Mainly grills **V** ♁ ⅄ Bar Lunch 65p-£3.95
Credit Cards [1] [2] [3] [5]

---

**BRAITHWAITE** Cumbria Map **11** NY22

★★65% **Middle Ruddings**
CA12 5RY ☎(07687)78436 Telex no 934999 FAX (07687) 78438
RS mid Nov-Mar (ex New Year)
*After extensive refurbishment, this is now a very comfortable and well appointed hotel, quality being the keynote throughout.*
13⇨♠1⌨ CTV in all bedrooms ℝ **T** ✗ sB&B⇨♠fr£39 dB&B⇨♠fr£70-£76 ➡
20P 2♠ (£1) ⇨ ✿ CFA bowls
☺ English & French **V** ♁ ⬚ ⅄ Bar Lunch £1.95-£6.50 Dinner fr£15.50 Last dinner 8.45pm
Credit Cards [1] [3]

---

**BRAMBER** West Sussex Map **04** TQ11

★★★63% **The Old Tollgate**
The Street BN44 3WE ☎Steyning(0903)879494
FAX (0903) 813399
*Attractive, purpose-built bedrooms with every modern facility are provided by this recently extended and completely refurbished hotel; the large and very popular restaurant offers a carvery-style*

*à la carte menu which is mainly self service though assisted by helpful staff.*
11⇨♠ Annexe20⇨♠(5fb)2⌨ CTV in all bedrooms ℝ **T** ✗ (ex guide dogs) ✳ sB&B⇨♠£65-£85 dB&B⇨♠£75-£95 Lift ( 60P ✿ xmas
**V** ✳ Lunch £10.45-£13.25 Dinner £14.45-£15.25 Last dinner 9.45pm
Credit Cards [1] [2] [3] [5]

---

**BRAMHALL** Greater Manchester Map **07** SJ88

★★★67% **Bramhall Moat House**
Bramhall Ln South SK7 2EB (Queens Moat) ☎061-439 8116
Telex no 668464 FAX 061-440 8071
*Set back from the A5102 within easy reach of the M56 and M63, this pristine modern hotel offers stylish public areas and well equipped and furnished bedrooms, the newer of which are more spacious. Extensive conference facilities make it popular with business people.*
65⇨♠(3fb) CTV in all bedrooms ℝ **T** ✗ (ex guide dogs) sB&B⇨♠£77 dB&B⇨♠£88 ➡
Lift ( 132P CFA sauna gymnasium
☺ English & French **V** ♁ ⬚ ✳ Lunch fr£9&alc Dinner fr£13.50&alc Last dinner 9.45pm
Credit Cards [1] [2] [3] [5]

---

**BRAMHOPE** West Yorkshire Map **08** SE24 ⊙

★★★67% **Forte Crest Leeds/Bradford**
Otley Rd LS16 9JJ (Forte Hotels) ☎Leeds(0532)842911
Telex no 556367 FAX (0532) 843451
*This large, modern and well furnished hotel enjoys a position in open countryside with convenient access to the airport; comfortable bedrooms offer good facilities and a choice of dining styles is available.*

→

126⇌⅟↙in 90 bedrooms CTV in all bedrooms ® T ✱ S%
sB⇌£80 dB⇌£86 (room only) ⊟
Lift ℂ 220P ❖ CFA ▨ (heated) sauna solarium gymnasium
health and fitness club *xmas*
♀ French V ♻ ♨ ⅟↙ Lunch £13.75 Dinner £16.10&alc Last
dinner 10.30pm
Credit Cards ①②③⑤

---

### BRAMLEY Surrey Map **04** TQ04

#### ※※ ✕ Le Berger
4a High St GU5 0HB ☎Guildford(0483)894037
*A modest shopfront conceals a smart interior and some equally
smart cooking. Tables are attractively laid in 2 small rooms, with
crisp linen and silver cruets. The menu is short and inviting, and
ingredients are good. Delicious rabbit was finished with cream and
vinegar, a pungent chicken mousse was moistened with a stock and
madeira jus, and various fish were carefully cooked in a seafood
symphony. Good bread and vegetables, but the wine list needs
some attention.*
Closed Sun, Mon & 1st 2 wks Jan
♀ French 24 seats ✱ Lunch £16.50&alc Dinner £16.50&alc
Last lunch 2pm Last dinner 9.30pm ⅌⅟↙
Credit Cards ①②③⑤

---

### BRAMPTON Cambridgeshire Map **04** TL27

#### ★★59% *Grange*
115 High St PE18 8TG ☎Huntingdon(0480)459516
*Built in about 1773, and once a girls' school, this friendly and
comfortable family-owned hotel offers good food and facilities.*
9rm(1⇌7↑)(1fb) CTV in all bedrooms ® ✖ ✱ sB&B£25
sB&B⇌↑£35.50-£39.50 dB&B⇌↑£45-£49.50
CTV 40P ❖
♀ English & Continental V ♻ ✱ Sunday Lunch £7.40-£9.25
Dinner £11.65-£25.30alc Last dinner 10pm
Credit Cards ①③

---

### BRAMPTON Cumbria Map **12** NY56

★★

#### ★★※※♨ FARLAM HALL
Hallbankgate CA8 2NG
(2.75m SE A689) (Relais et
Châteaux) ☎Hallbankgate
(06977)46234
FAX (06977) 46683
Closed Feb
(Rosettes awarded for
dinner only)

*A part 17th, part 19th-century house set in well maintained
grounds and peaceful rural surroundings, thoughtfully
converted into a charming country house hotel. Owned and
personally run by the Quinion and Stevenson families with the
help of attentive staff, the hospitality and service have a mark
of bygone days, and guests are assured of a warm, friendly
welcome. The public rooms offer comfort of a high standard
together with a relaxing atmosphere. Dinner is served at 8pm
in the elegantly appointed dining room. A 4-course menu is
offered, of a predominantly British style : honest and
uncomplicated. Chef Barry Quinion makes good use of
quality fresh produce.*
13⇌1↑ CTV in all bedrooms T sB&B⇌↑£90-£95
dB&B⇌↑£150-£180 (incl dinner) ⊟
35P ⇎ ❖ croquet nc5yrs

---

V ♻ ♨ Dinner £26-£27.50 Last dinner 8pm
Credit Cards ①③

---

### ★★※69% *Tarn End*
Talkin Tarn CA8 1LS (2m S off B6413) ☎(06977)2340
Closed Feb RS Oct-Jan
*A friendly family-run hotel on the edge of the renowned Talkin
Tarn. An ideal base for touring the area or to relax amid unspoilt
countryside. In addition to the excellent dinners served in the
traditional dining room overlooking the lake, bar lunches can also
be recommended.*
6⇌↑(1fb) CTV in all bedrooms ® ✖ (ex guide dogs) ✱
sB&B⇌↑fr£38.50 dB&B⇌↑fr£59 ⊟
70P ⇎ ♪ rowing *xmas*
♀ French V ♻ ♨ ✱ Sunday Lunch £10 Dinner £14-£20alc
Last dinner 9pm
Credit Cards ①②③⑤ ⓔ

---

### ★60% *Howard Arms*
Front St CA8 1NG ☎(06977)2357
*This 16th-century former coaching inn in the town centre is
friendly and unpretentious, providing en suite bedrooms with
modern facilities.*
9rm(2⇌6↑)(1fb) CTV in 8 bedrooms ® ✖
⊞P
♻ ♨ Last dinner 9pm
Credit Cards ①③

---

### BRANDESBURTON Humberside Map **08** TA14

#### ★★67% *Burton Lodge*
YO25 8RU ☎Hornsea(0964)542847
*The owners of this small private hotel make every effort to ensure
the comfort of their guests, providing a cosily relaxed home-from-
home environment in its compact public areas. Bedrooms, though
limited in number, are well appointed, equipped with en suite
facilities and spotlessly clean, while the quality and flavour of the
range of traditional dishes available in the dining room more than
compensates for a restricted menu choice.*
8⇌↑(1fb) CTV in all bedrooms ® T ✱ sB⇌↑£25-£28
dB⇌↑£40-£45 (room only) ⊟
12P 1🚗 ⇎ ❖ ⚑ 18
♻ ♨ Dinner £10-£12 Last dinner 9.15pm
Credit Cards ①③ ⓔ

---

### BRANDON Suffolk Map **05** TL78

#### ★★★68% *Brandon House*
High St IP27 0AX (Minotels) ☎Thetford(0842)810171
FAX (0842) 814859
*This establishment in country house style, set back from the main
road on the outskirts of the town centre, is a first venture into hotel
ownership for its current proprietors, but they are successfully
maintaining the good standards set by their predecessors and are
perfect hosts. Bedrooms, though plain, are comfortable, sensibly
laid out and equipped with facilities that will appeal to the
commercial user.*
15⇌↑ CTV in all bedrooms ® T ✱ sB&B⇌↑£39.50-£49.50
dB&B⇌↑£54.50-£64.50 ⊟
40P ⇎ ❖
♀ English & French V ♻ ♨ ⅟↙
Credit Cards ①②③ⓔ

---

⬤ Shell filling station, open 7am–11pm
(some 24 hours) throughout the year with leaded
and unleaded petrol, and diesel.

## BRANDON Warwickshire Map **04** SP47

★★★63% **Brandon Hall**

Main St CV8 3FW (Forte Hotels) ☎Coventry(0203)542571
Telex no 31472 FAX (0203) 544909

*This hotel set in landscaped gardens beside the A428 began life as a shooting lodge to Brandon Manor ; in the early 18th century it was extended to become the estate's principle house, and public areas still retain many original features. Bedrooms are comfortable and well equipped, whilst leisure facilities include six indoor squash courts and a pitch and putt course.*

60⇄🛏(6fb)⅙in 20 bedrooms CTV in all bedrooms ® T ✻
sB⇄🛏fr£70 dB⇄🛏£80-£120 (room only) 🖪

《 250P ❀ CFA squash pitch & putt ♫ ♨ *xmas*

V ♥ ⏛ ⅙ ✻ Lunch fr£9.55&alc Dinner £15.30-£16.50&alc
Last dinner 9.30pm

Credit Cards 1 2 3 4 5

## BRANDS HATCH Kent Map **05** TQ56

★★★★63% **Brands Hatch Thistle**

DA3 8PE (Mount Charlotte (TS))
☎West Kingsdown(0474)854900 Telex no 966449
FAX (0474) 853220

*Situated at the entrance to the famous motor race track, this modern commercial and conference hotel offers various styles of bedrooms which vary in size. Some are non-smoking, and all are comfortable and well equipped. Two eating options are available with a Brasserie and a more formal restaurant. Service is attentive with pleasant and helpful staff.*

140⇄🛏(7fb)1🖾⅙in 12 bedrooms CTV in all bedrooms ® T (room only) 🖪

《 180P ❀ *xmas*

♡ English & French V ♥ ⏛
Credit Cards 1 2 3 4 5

## BRANKSOME

See **Poole**

## BRANSFORD Hereford & Worcester Map **03** SO75

★★★64% *Bank House*

Hereford Rd WR6 5JD ☎Leigh Sinton(0886)33551
FAX (0886) 32461

*Built orignally in 1680 and recently completely redeveloped, an hotel on the A4103 just outside the city is ideal both for business travellers and for visitors wishing to explore the beautiful Worcestershire countryside. Spacious, well equipped and functional accommodation is complemented by extensive conference facilities as well as the Barclay Restaurant and two bars.*

20⇄🛏(14fb) CTV in all bedrooms ® T ✖

《 150P ❀

♡ English & French V ♥ ⏛ Last dinner 9.30pm
Credit Cards 1 2 3

**See advertisement under WORCESTER**

## BRANSTON Lincolnshire Map **08** TF06

★★★54% *Moor Lodge*

LN4 1HU (Consort) ☎Lincoln(0522)791366 FAX (0522) 794389

*An hotel located on the B1188 at the centre of the village has a close association with the nearby RAF bases which is reflected in the naming of the individually styled and comfortable Lancaster Bar and Arnhem Room Restaurant. Accommodation is varied, some rooms being old-fashioned and more serviceable in appearance, but the Carvery Restaurant serves healthy portions of mainly fresh produce, and service is professionally efficient.*

25⇄🛏(3fb)1🖾 CTV in all bedrooms ® T

CTV 150P ♫

♡ English & French V ♥ ⏛ Last dinner 9.30pm
Credit Cards 1 2 3 5

## BRAUNTON Devon Map **02** SS43

★★64% *Poyers Hotel & Restaurant*

Wrafton EX33 2DV ☎(0271)812149
Closed 23 Dec-4 Jan

*A pretty thatched hotel run on friendly and informal lines provides a warm, relaxing atmosphere throughout the small bar lounge, the homely quiet lounge and a popular cottagey restaurant offering worthy standards of cuisine. En suite bedrooms – set around a pleasant little courtyard at the rear – are furnished on simple yet comfortable lines in bamboo and cane, their style softened by attractive fabrics and thoughtful personal touches, and are all well equipped with modern facilities.*

Annexe10⇄🛏 CTV in all bedrooms ® T

20P 🚲 ❀

♡ English, French, German & Italian Last dinner 9.30pm
Credit Cards 1 2 3

## BRAY Berkshire Map **04** SU97

❀❀❀❀✕✕✕✕ **WATERSIDE**

River Cottage, Ferry Rd SL6 2AT (Relais et Châteaux)
☎Maidenhead(0628)20691 & 22941 FAX (0628) 784710

*Michel Roux has made this delightful riverside restaurant synonymous with the highest levels of French cuisine in this country. Books by the Roux brothers and literature about their enterprises, generously distributed around the lounge and entrance hall, provide a pleasant distraction for guests waiting for their tables, and an appetiser for the à la carte menu which reflects a balance between classical dishes, modern interpretations and signature dishes such as the delightful starter of a Petit Flan d'Escargots frais en habit vert. High praise also from our inspector for a perfectly cooked Tournedos with a delicate little Feuilleté of creamed wild mushrooms and an intensely flavoured sauce Périgourdine. A glorious caramelised Tarte Tatin with a globe of apple sorbet and a very good custard of eggs, milk and cream*

→

*completed the meal. Service is highly professional and a knowledgeable sommelier presides over a distinguished wine list that includes such rarities as Château Grillet.*

Closed Mon & 7 wks fr 26 Dec Lunch not served Tue Dinner not served Sun (3rd wknd Oct-2nd wknd Apr)

♀ French **V** 70 seats ✳ Lunch £25.50-£52.50&alc Dinner £52.50&alc Last lunch 2pm Last dinner 10pm 25 P nc12yrs

Credit Cards [1] [3] [4] [5]

---

## BREADSALL Derbyshire Map 08 SK 33

### ★★★ 75% **Breadsall Priory**

Moor Rd DE7 6DL (0.5m N) ☎Derby(0332)832235
Telex no 37409 FAX (0332) 833509

*Set in 200 acres of quiet parkland on the outskirts of town, this hotel has been thoughtfully refurbished to provide comfortable, well equipped bedrooms both in the old priory and the modern extension. Facilities include conference and function rooms, and extensive indoor and outdoor leisure activities.*

14⇔🏠 Annexe77⇔🏠1 🏠 ⚹ in 11 bedrooms CTV in all bedrooms ® **T** ✻ (ex guide dogs) ✳ sB&B⇔🏠£80-£88 dB&B⇔🏠£90-£98 🏴

《 300P ✿ CFA 🖼 (heated) ➤ 18 ♪ (hard) squash snooker sauna solarium gymnasium health & beauty salon steam room *xmas*

**V** ⭗ ⚏ ✳ Lunch £11.25 Dinner £17.50&alc Last dinner 9.45pm

Credit Cards [1] [2] [3] [5] ⓔ

---

## BRECHFA Dyfed Map 02 SN53

### ★★ ✿71% **Ty Mawr**

SA32 7RA ☎(0267)202332 FAX (0267) 202437

*Situated in the heart of the village, this delightful 16th century stone-built house offers the kind of peaceful atmosphere one normally only expects from a country-house hotel. The lounge and the bedrooms are all attractively furnished and meals, with local Welsh and classical French influences to the fore, are most enjoyable. The hotel also has its own bakery specialising in organic and wholefood products.*

5rm(4⇔3🏠)(1fb) ® sB&B⇔🏠£42 dB&B⇔🏠£64 🏴
45P 🚗 ✿ ♪ *xmas*

♀ Welsh & French **V** ⭗ ⚏ Lunch £13.50-£15 Dinner £16.50-£18 Last dinner 9.30pm

Credit Cards [1] [2] [3] ⓔ

---

## BRECHIN Tayside *Angus* Map 15 NO56

### ★★56% **Northern**

Clerk St DD9 6AE ☎(03562)2156 & 5505 FAX (03562) 2714
RS 1 & 2 Jan

*This family-run former coaching inn is conveniently situated in the town centre. Public rooms are being considerably altered and upgraded, while the well equipped bedrooms continue to offer good value, practical commercial accommodation.*

17rm(4⇔11🏠) CTV in all bedrooms ® **T** sB&B£15-£28 sB&B⇔🏠fr£28 dB&B£30-£44 dB&B⇔🏠fr£44
20P CFA

**V** ⭗ ⚏ ✳ Lunch fr£5 High tea £4-£5 Last high tea 6.30pm
Credit Cards [1] [2] [3] ⓔ

---

## BRECON Powys Map 03 SO02

### ★★62% **Wellington**

The Bulwark LD3 7AD (Inter-Hotels) ☎(0874)625225

*Set in the centre of town this hotel has a very popular public bar, and a coffee bar/bistro and wine bar for diners. The bedrooms are well equipped and generally spacious.*

21⇔🏠(1fb) CTV in all bedrooms ® **T** ✻ (ex guide dogs) ✳ sB&B⇔🏠fr£39 dB&B⇔🏠fr£59 🏴
♪ CFA *xmas*

♀ Welsh, English & French **V** ⭗ ⚏ ⚹ ✳ Lunch £2.50-£10alc High tea £2.75-£4alc Dinner fr£14.95&alc Last dinner 10pm
Credit Cards [1] [2] [3] [5] ⓔ

---

### ★★61% **Castle of Brecon**

Castle Square LD3 9DB (Consort) ☎(0874)624611
Telex no 57515 FAX (0874) 623737

*This modern commercial and tourist hotel near the town centre has been developed from the remains of Brecknock Castle and has a comfortable lounge, modern bars serving bar meals, an à la carte restaurant and good function facilities. The recently improved bedrooms have the usual modern facilities.*

34⇔🏠Annexe12🏠(3fb)1 🏠 CTV in all bedrooms ® **T** S%
sB&B⇔🏠£35-£55 dB&B⇔🏠£55-£69 🏴
30P CFA

♀ Welsh, English & French **V** ⭗ ✳ Sunday Lunch fr£6.95 Dinner fr£13.90&alc Last dinner 9pm
Credit Cards [1] [2] [3] [4] [5] ⓔ

---

### ★★61% *Nant Ddu Lodge Country House*

Cwm Taf CF48 2HY (Minotels) ☎Merthyr Tydfil(0685)79111
FAX (0685) 77088
(For full entry see Nant-Ddu)

---

### ★65% **Lansdowne**

39 The Watton LD3 7EG ☎(0874)623321 FAX (0874) 624384

*This pleasant, friendly, family-run hotel just off the town centre is in process of upgrading its bedrooms and equipping them with modern facilities. Public areas include 2 comfortable lounges and a popular restaurant offering a wide choice of food.*

10rm(3⇔5🏠)(2fb) CTV in all bedrooms ® **T**
✻ (ex guide dogs) sB&Bfr£22 sB&B⇔🏠fr£25 dB&Bfr£37 dB&B⇔🏠fr£43 🏴
CTV 4P 🚗 ✿ nc5yrs

♀ English & French **V** ⭗ ⚏ ⚹ ✳ Lunch £8.75&alc Dinner £8.75&alc Last dinner 9.30pm
Credit Cards [1] [2] [3] [5] ⓔ

---

## BRENT KNOLL Somerset Map 03 ST35

### ★★64% **Shrub Farm Country**

Burton Row TA9 4BX ☎(0278)760479 FAX (0278) 760513

*This recently refurbished and extended 15th-century farmhouse on the Somerset Levels – 15 feet below sea level, in fact – is operated as a small hotel under the ownership of one-time National Hunt Jockey Richard Robinson, whose former profession is reflected in the pictures and other memorabilia scattered around the ground floor. Bedrooms are attractive, comfortable and well equipped, while the restaurant offers an à la carte menu of dishes where originality has been brought to bear on good fresh ingredient; a relaxed, friendly atmosphere prevails throughout – but beware of low doorways!*

10⇔🏠(3fb)1 🏠 CTV in all bedrooms ® **T** ✳ sB&B⇔🏠£35 dB&B⇔🏠£45 🏴
CTV 25P ✿ CFA 🐕 *xmas*

♀ French **V** ⭗ ⚏ ✳ Sunday Lunch £8.95 Dinner £9.50&alc Last dinner 9.30pm
Credit Cards [1] [3] ⓔ

---

### ★★62% **Battleborough Grange Country**

Bristol Rd TA9 4HJ (Exec Hotel) ☎(0278)760208

*This attractive, detached hotel is set in its own grounds overlooking the Somerset countryside. Décor is pleasant throughout and the hotel provides modern bedrooms and attentive service.*

18rm(8⇔6🏠)4 🏠 CTV in all bedrooms ® **T** ✻ ✳ sB&B⇔🏠£44.50-£49 dB&B£40 dB&B⇔🏠£55-£63 🏴
CTV 60P ✿ CFA nc8yrs *xmas*

♀ English & French **V** ⭗ ⚏ ✳ Lunch £8.50-£21 Dinner £10.50&alc Last dinner 9pm
Credit Cards [1] [2] [3] [5]

**BRENTWOOD** Essex Map **05** TQ59

★★★★65% **Brentwood Moat House**
London Rd CM14 4NR (Queens Moat) ☎(0277)225252
Telex no 995182 FAX (0277) 262809

*Though most of the modern, well furnished bedrooms of this small hotel are contained in garden annexes, the main building retains some interesting architectural evidence of its Tudor origin. A dining room with stained glass windows and twisted pillars offers a long à la carte menu which combines classical and modern styles and includes some flambé dishes; this is accompanied by an extensive wine list with some good vintages. This is very much a business persons' hotel, having few leisure or recreational facilities, but pleasant, friendly staff provide a high level of service.*

33⇖🐾 Annexe 30⇖🐾2🛏 CTV in all bedrooms **T** ✳
sB⇖🐾£85-£97 dB⇖🐾£107-£112 (room only) 🍴
《 CTV 80P 🏧 CFA
♙ International **V** ❖ ⚌ ✔ Lunch £17.50&alc Dinner £18.50-£38.50alc Last dinner 10.15pm
Credit Cards ①②③④⑤ⓔ

★★★66% **Forte Posthouse**
Brook St CM14 5NF (Forte Hotels) ☎(0277)260260
Telex no 995379 FAX (0277) 264264

*A modern hotel, its position at the southern end of the town offering convenient access to the M25, is currently undergoing substantial refurbishment. All its smartly decorated, well equipped and very spacious bedrooms have modern bathrooms with good showers, while extensive public areas incorporate two bars, a coffee shop and a leisure complex.*

120⇖🐾in 30 bedrooms CTV in all bedrooms ⑧ ✳ **S**%
sB⇖£39.50-£49.50 dB⇖£39.50-£49.50 (room only) 🍴
Lift 《 148P ✿ CFA ▣ (heated) sauna solarium gymnasium health & fitness club *xmas*

→

**B**

♀ International **V** ♦ ♨ ✂ ✳ S% Lunch £12.50 Dinner £16.50&alc Last dinner 10pm
Credit Cards 1 2 3 4 5

---

### BRETBY Derbyshire Map **08** SK22

#### ★★★65% **Stanhope**
Ashby Rd East DE15 0PU (Lansbury)
☎Burton upon Trent(0283)217954 Telex no 347185
FAX (0283) 226199
*Located on the busy A50 (cross with care if approaching from the car park opposite), this hotel provides helpful service, comfortable well equipped bedrooms and a pleasantly furnished restaurant overlooking the terraced gardens at the rear.*
28⇌↑(1fb)1 ⊞ ✂in 5 bedrooms CTV in all bedrooms ® T
✗ (ex guide dogs) ✳ sB&B⇌↑frf60 dB&B⇌↑frf72 ◪
《 150P ✿ CFA sauna solarium gymnasium *xmas*
♀ Continental **V** ♦ ✂ ✳ Lunch £7-£8.95 Dinner fr£13.50&alc
Last dinner 10pm
Credit Cards 1 2 3 5 £

---

### BRIDGEND

See Islay, Isle of

---

### BRIDGEND Mid Glamorgan Map **03** SS97 ◉

#### ★★★❀71% **Coed-y-Mwstwr**
Coychurch CF35 6AF (Welsh Rarebits) ☎(0656)860621
FAX (0656) 863122
*This 19th-century country mansion, whose name means 'Whispering Trees', stands in 17 acres of woodland gardens. Comfortably appointed bedrooms are complemented by recently refurbished public areas which include a dining room offering a well chosen fixed-price menu of good food and an excellent wine list; a friendly staff operates under the personal supervision of the hotel's proprietors.*
24⇌↑ CTV in all bedrooms T ✗ (ex guide dogs)
sB&B⇌↑£85-£135 dB&B⇌↑£95-£160 Continental breakfast ◪
Lift 《 100P ✿ CFA ⌫ (heated) ♪ (hard) snooker croquet petanque table tennis ♫
♀ British & French **V** ♦ ♨ ✳ Lunch £14.95-£20.95&alc
Dinner £21.95-£25.95&alc Last dinner 10pm
Credit Cards 1 2 3 5 £

#### ★★★65% **Heronston**
Ewenny CF35 5AW (2m S B4265) ☎(0656)668811
Telex no 498232 FAX (0656) 767391
Closed 25-26 Dec & 1 Jan
*This large, well run commercial hotel, situated south of the A48 some 1.5 miles from the town centre, provides well equipped bedrooms, comfortably furnished public areas and excellent function and conference facilities; a leisure centre and snooker room are also available.*
76⇌↑(4fb) CTV in all bedrooms ® T S% sB&B⇌↑£60-£88
dB&B⇌↑£80-£100 ◪
Lift 《 CTV 175P ⇗ ▣ (heated) ⌫ (heated) snooker sauna solarium jacuzzi steamroom
♀ Welsh & French **V** ♦ ♨ S% Lunch fr£15alc Dinner fr£12.75&alc Last dinner 10pm
Credit Cards 1 2 3 4 5 £

#### ★★60% **Court Colman**
Pen-y-Fai CF31 4NG ☎Aberkenfig(0656)720212
*This imposing house, originally a gentleman's country residence, is set amidst woodland and lawns. Inside, there are panelled walls and several beautiful fireplaces. Bedrooms are spacious, public rooms are comfortable and elegant.*
32rm(14⇌12↑)(7fb)2⊞ CTV in 26 bedrooms ®
150P ✿ solarium
♦ ♨ Last dinner 9.45pm
Credit Cards 1 2 3 5

---

#### ★★57% **Wyndham**
Dunraven Place CF31 1JE ☎(0656)652080 & 657431
FAX (0656) 766438
*A busy town-centre hotel, parts of which date back to the 17th century, provides neat, clean bedrooms and an additional small bar for residents and diners where a good range of food is served. Car parking is available nearby.*
28rm(25⇌)1 ⊞ CTV in all bedrooms ®
《 CTV ♨
♀ English & French **V** ♦ ✂ Last dinner 10pm
Credit Cards 1 2 3 5

#### ⌂Forte Travelodge
Sarn Park Motorway Services CF32 9RW (Forte)
☎(0656)659218 Central Res (0800) 850950
(For full entry see Sarn Park Motorway Service Area (M4))

---

### BRIDGE OF ALLAN Central *Stirlingshire* Map **11** NS79

#### ★★★❀65% **Royal**
Henderson St FK9 4HG ☎(0786)832284 FAX (0786) 834377
*A popular business hotel situated in the town centre yet only 2.5 miles from Stirling offers attentive service and an intimate period restaurant featuring competitively priced menus of innovative dishes cooked in the modern style.*
32⇌↑(2fb) CTV in all bedrooms ® T ✳ sB&B⇌↑£35-£57.50 dB&B⇌↑£50-£76.50 ◪
Lift 《 60P CFA *xmas*
♀ Scottish & French **V** ♦ ♨ ✳ Lunch £8.80-£11 Dinner £17.50-£20.50 Last dinner 9.30pm
Credit Cards 1 2 3 5 £
See advertisement under STIRLING

#### ❀✕✕ *Kipling's Restaurant*
Mine Rd FK9 4DT ☎Stirling(0786)833617
*This former hotel, off the old A9 in the centre of Bridge of Allan, and now functioning simply as a restaurant and cocktail bar, stands high above the town centre in a quiet residential area. Chef/ proprietor Peter Bannister compiles his menus according to the daily availability of game and seafood as well as the traditional meats and fish and finds inspiration in several traditions to make effective use of a variety of good ingredients. Cooking has a provincial air about it, honest, robust flavours being enhanced by the good use of herbs. A well trained young staff provides polite, attentive service. In the evening, a menu offers a choice of some ten starters and main courses, and a handful of desserts, but there's nothing for vegetarians. You might try grouse and wild duck en croûte, or grilled crayfish with dill sauce. Vegetables – perhaps salsify, courgettes and potatoes – are carefully and simply cooked, and, for dessert, no surprises with 'Death by chocolate gateau' or fresh pineapple. House wine is £8.50.*
Closed Sun, Mon, 24 Dec-3 Jan & 1st 2 wks Aug
V 68 seats Last lunch 2pm Last dinner 9.30pm 20 P
Credit Cards 1 2 3

---

### BRIDGE OF CALLY Tayside *Perthshire* Map **15** NO15

#### ★65% **Bridge of Cally**
PH10 7JJ ☎(025086)231
Closed Nov & 1st 2 wks Dec
*Set in its own well tended garden beside the River Ardle, this small, family-run holiday hotel is also a popular base for the sporting and ski enthusiasts. It has a friendly atmosphere, and enjoyable food is served on candlelit tables in the neatly appointed dining room. Bedrooms, though compact, are cheery and comfortable.*
9rm(3⇌3↑) ® ✗ (ex guide dogs) sB&Bfr£27 dB&Bfr£46
dB&B⇌↑fr£50 ◪
CTV 40P ⇗ ✿ ♩
V ♦ ♨ ✳ Lunch £1.55-£7 Dinner £14-£15 Last dinner 9pm
Credit Cards 1 3 5

BRIDGNORTH Shropshire Map **07** SO79

★★**69%** **Parlors Hall**
Mill St WV15 5AL ☎(0746)761931 FAX (0746) 767058
*This fully modernised hotel in a fine mainly Georgian building in
Lowtown has maintained traditional standards of service.
Bedrooms are well equipped and the attractive bar and restaurant
feature fine oak-carved panelling and fireplaces.*
15⇨🛏(2fb)2🛏 CTV in all bedrooms ® T ✖ (ex guide dogs)
sB&B⇨🛏£43.50 dB&B⇨🛏£52
24P CFA *xmas*
♀ European **V** ✆ ⏛ Lunch £7&alc Dinner £6.95-£7.25&alc
Last dinner 10pm
Credit Cards ①③

★★**65%** **Croft**
Saint Mary's St WV16 6DW (Minotels) ☎(0746)762416
*Friendly, hospitable service and satisfying home cooking are the
hallmarks of this family-run hotel which stands in a road off High
Town's main street.*
12rm(4⇨6🛏)(3fb) CTV in all bedrooms **T** ✳ sB&B£23.50
sB&B⇨🛏£39.50 dB&B⇨🛏£48 🛏
CTV ✗ ♨ 🛏
**V** ✆ ⏛ ✳ Lunch £7.50&alc Dinner fr£9.95&alc Last dinner
9pm
Credit Cards ①②③

★★**61%** **Falcon**
Saint John St, Lowtown WV15 6AG (Consort) ☎(0746)763134
FAX (0746) 765401
*Close to the bridge over the Severn in Low Town, this old inn has
comfortable bedrooms and public areas with much historic
character.*
15rm(5⇨7🛏)(3fb) CTV in all bedrooms ® **T** sB&Bfr£35
sB&B⇨🛏£43 dB&B⇨🛏£50-£55 🛏
CTV 200P CFA
♀ English & French **V** ✆ ⏛ Lunch £6.50-£9.50alc Dinner
£10.50-£12.50alc Last dinner 9.30pm
Credit Cards ①②③ⓔ

See advertisement on page 165

★**65%** **Whitburn Grange**
35 Salop St WV16 5BH ☎(0746)766786 & 732188
FAX (0746) 766037
*A well run small hotel close to the town centre, on Low Town
Road, with its own courtyard car park. The public areas have been
refurbished and the bedrooms offer a choice of styles.*
8rm(2⇨1🛏)Annexe7rm(2⇨)(2fb)1🛏 CTV in all bedrooms ®
**T**
CTV 9P CFA *xmas*
✆ ⏛ ✳ Lunch £3.95-£20alc Dinner £3.95-£20alc Last dinner
9.30pm
Credit Cards ①②③

BRIDGWATER Somerset Map **03** ST33

★★★**68%** **Walnut Tree Inn**
North Petherton TA6 6QA (3m S A38) (Best Western)
☎North Petherton(0278)662255 Telex no 46529
FAX (0278) 663946
*A former coaching inn, now a friendly commercial hotel on the
busy High Street of North Petherton, on the A38 south of
Bridgewater. Executive or standard bedrooms are available, each
individually decorated and furnished. Guests can choose between
the realistically priced à la carte menu and the budget priced
cottage restaurant. The hotel has good conference facilities.*
28⇨(2fb)1🛏 CTV in all bedrooms ® **T** ✖ (ex guide dogs)
sB&B⇨£48-£66 dB&B⇨£68-£86 🛏
（ 70P CFA solarium *xmas*
→

**B**

V ⌖ ⚏ Lunch £4.60-£12.90alc Dinner £4.60-£12.90alc Last dinner 10pm
Credit Cards ①②③⑤ ⓔ

### ★★64% Friarn Court

37 St Mary St TA6 3LX ☎(0278)452859 FAX (0278) 452988

*Close to the town centre and recently converted to provide quality bedrooms with modern facilities – all is new and in good order, though the public rooms are small. The proprietor runs the hotel personally with warm hospitality. An all day menu is served in the restaurant.*

12⇨ᔑ(2fb)1🛏 CTV in all bedrooms ® T 🐾 (ex guide dogs)
S% sB&B⇨ᔑ£44.50-£69.50 dB&B⇨ᔑ£59.50-£69.50
Continental breakfast 🖪
(12P CFA
V English & French V ⌖ ⚏ S% Sunday Lunch £8.50 High tea £5.50 Dinner £8.50&alc Last dinner 9.30pm
Credit Cards ①②③⑤ ⓔ

---

### BRIDLINGTON Humberside Map 08 TA16

### ★★★66% Expanse

North Marine Dr YO15 2LS ☎(0262)675347 FAX (0262) 604928

*Comfortable, well appointed bedrooms, a wealth of cosy lounges and particularly friendly service are the attractions of this large seafront hotel.*

48⇨ᔑ(4fb) CTV in all bedrooms ® T 🐾 (ex guide dogs)
sB&B⇨ᔑ£45.75-£43.75 dB&B⇨ᔑ£65.50-£71.50 🖪
Lift ( 15P 15🅿 (£1.50) 🚼 CFA *xmas*
V English & French V ⌖ ⚏ Lunch £6.75-£8 Dinner £12-£12.75&alc Last dinner 9pm
Credit Cards ①②③⑤

### ★★67% Monarch

South Marine Dr YO15 3JJ (Consort) ☎(0262)674447
Telex no 57515 FAX (0262) 604928
Closed 18 Dec-7 Jan

*A comfortable friendly seafront hotel offering very good value menus.*

40rm(36⇨ᔑ)(5fb) CTV in all bedrooms ® T
🐾 (ex guide dogs) ❋ sB&B£30.75-£38.75 sB&B⇨ᔑ£30.75-£38.75 dB&B£51.50 dB&B⇨ᔑ£54-£61.50 🖪
Lift ( CTV 10P CFA ⚗
V English & French V ⌖ ⚐ ❋ Sunday Lunch £6-£10 Dinner £12-£20&alc Last dinner 8.30pm
Credit Cards ①②③⑤

### ★★66% New Revelstoke

1-3 Flamborough Rd YO15 2HU ☎(0262)672362

*The bedrooms of this hotel are, for the most part, well equipped and of a good size; resident proprietors and their keen young staff will make every effort to ensure that your stay is comfortable and pleasant, providing polite, attentive service.*

26rm(17⇨ᔑ)(5fb) CTV in all bedrooms ® T 🐾 ❋
sB&B⇨ᔑ£33-£45 dB&B⇨ᔑ£52-£65 🖪
14P CFA *xmas*
V English & French V ⌖ ⚏ ❋ Dinner £11&alc Last dinner 8.30pm
Credit Cards ①②③⑤ ⓔ

---

### BRIDPORT Dorset Map 03 SY49

### ★★★61% Haddon House

West Bay DT6 4EL (2m S off B3157 Weymouth rd)
☎(0308)23626 & 25323

*The spacious public areas of this Regency-style hotel include a comfortable lounge and a beamed dining room serving a good range of dishes (many with cream sauces). Bedrooms are of a good size, rather simply furnished but newly decorated.*

13⇨ᔑ CTV in all bedrooms ® T sB&B⇨ᔑ£39.50-£45
dB&B⇨ᔑ£50-£62 🖪
CTV 70P 4🅿 ❀ CFA *xmas*

V English & French V ⌖ ❋ Lunch £10.95 Dinner £16.50 Last dinner 9pm
Credit Cards ①②③⑤

### ★★❀68% Roundham House

Roundham Gardens, West Bay Rd DT6 4BD (Exec Hotel)
☎(0308)22753 & 25779 Telex no 417182 FAX (0308) 421145
Closed mid Nov-Jan

*Resident proprietors offer a welcoming cup of tea to guests arriving at their home, a substantial turn-of-the-century house set in an elevated position with views both across the river valley and out to sea. Recently redecorated and refurnished rooms are neat and clean, the larger providing comfortable armchairs. A substantial, home-cooked 3-course dinner of mainly British dishes is based on fresh local ingredients wherever possible, and individual diets can be catered for if sufficient notice is given. Informal and aimiable service creates a relaxed holiday atmosphere which is particularly popular with older guests.*

8rm(4⇨3ᔑ)(2fb) CTV in all bedrooms ® T 🐾
sB&B⇨ᔑ£29.50-£35 dB&B⇨ᔑ£45-£55 🖪
12P 1🅿 ❀ ⚗
V ⌖ ⚏ 🍴 Bar Lunch £1.35-£6.25 Dinner £12.50-£14 Last dinner 8.15pm
Credit Cards ①②③⑤ ⓔ

### ★★66% Eype's Mouth Country

Eype DT6 6AL (2m SW) ☎(0308)23300

*Set in rural surroundings just five minutes from the sea and coastal footpath this is a friendly hotel with very clean, well equipped bedrooms. Dinner dances are held in the large dining room.*

18⇨ᔑ1🛏 CTV in all bedrooms ® T ❋ sB&B⇨ᔑ£38.50-£49
dB&B⇨ᔑ£53.25-£74.75 🖪
55P 🎵 *xmas*
V English & French V ⌖ ⚏ ❋ Lunch £5.99-£7.75&alc Dinner £9.95&alc Last dinner 9pm
Credit Cards ①③

### ★★62% Bull

34 East St DT6 3LF ☎(0308)22878
Closed 24-26 Dec

*This main street coaching inn continues to improve. Most bedrooms now have fresh décor and modern furniture, and the attractively furnished restaurant offers a short, interesting menu. Resident proprietors have created an informal atmosphere in the busy bar.*

22rm(5⇨3ᔑ)(1fb) CTV in 16 bedrooms ® 🐾
40P 2🅿 🚼 snooker
V French ⌖
Credit Cards ①③

### ★59% Bridport Arms

West Bay DT6 4EN (2m S off B3157 Weymouth rd)
☎(0308)22994

*An unusual thatched inn situated on the beach by the quay. Bedrooms are comfortable and simply furnished, but those in the main house are better equipped than those in the annexe. There is a TV lounge and family room in addition to the 2 bars and restaurant.*

8rm(1⇨5ᔑ)Annexe5rm(3fb) CTV in 8 bedrooms ®
sB&B£19-£21.50 sB&B⇨ᔑ£26-29.50 dB&B£38-£43
dB&B⇨ᔑ£49-£55 🖪
CTV 4🅿
V ⌖ 🍴 Sunday Lunch £7.75-£9.50 Dinner £10.95-£16.95alc Last dinner 8.45pm
Credit Cards ①③ ⓔ

### ❀ ✕ Riverside Cafe & Restaurant

West Bay DT6 4EZ ☎(0308)22011

*This café serves everything from mugs of coffee to full breakfasts and hamburgers, but it is famous for its fish, which is excellent, very fresh and skilfully cooked; your Dover sole, lobster, skate, scallops and mullet being served with simple sauces and plain fresh vegetables. The atmosphere is distinctly informal, with counter or* →

165

*table service and as everything is cooked to order, delays are inevitable at peak times. The selection of fish varies according to what is available on a daily basis, but there is plenty of choice, and it is definitely worth leaving room for a pudding (plum crumble, sticky toffee pudding or treacle tart with clotted cream are among the favourites).*

Closed Mon (ex Jul-Aug) Dec-1 Mar ex 2 wks after Xmas
Dinner not served Wed in winter
V 80 seats ✳ Lunch £10-£25alc Dinner £10-£25alc Last lunch 3.30pm Last dinner 8.30pm ✗
Credit Cards 1 3

---

**BRIGG** Humberside Map **08** TA00

★★★67% **Briggate Lodge Inn**
Ermine St, Broughton DN20 0NQ (3m NW) ☎(0652)650770
FAX (0652) 650495
*This large modern hotel, purpose-built and privately owned, stands amid spacious wooded grounds close to the M189 motorway on the north side of junction 4. Understandably popular with both tourists and business people, it offers well equipped bedrooms of good quality and a choice of bars and eating options. The needs of disabled guests are catered for in two specially adapted ground-floor bedrooms.*
21 ⇨ CTV in all bedrooms ® T ✖ (ex guide dogs) ✳
sB&B ⇨ £40-£57 dB&B ⇨ £50-£68 ❚
130P ✿ ♫
♀ International V ♥ ♨ ✖ ✳ Lunch fr£10.30&alc High tea £1.45-£9.95alc Dinner fr£10.30&alc Last dinner 10pm
Credit Cards 1 2 3

---

**BRIGHOUSE** West Yorkshire Map **07** SE12

★★★★62% **Forte Crest**
Clifton Village HD6 4HW (Forte Hotels) ☎(0484)400400
Telex no 518204 FAX (0484) 400068
*Conveniently located close to junction 25 of the M62, this modern hotel is in an elevated position overlooking the Calder Valley. Spacious, comfortable public areas and well equipped bedrooms are provided along with a leisure centre.*
94 ⇨ (20fb) ✗ in 62 bedrooms CTV in all bedrooms ® T ✳
sB ⇨ fr£85 dB ⇨ fr£95 (room only) ❚
( 155P ❀ ✿ CFA ☒ (heated) sauna solarium gymnasium croquet *xmas*
♀ British & French V ♥ ♨ ✖ ✳ Lunch £10.95-£11.50&alc Dinner fr£16.50&alc Last dinner 10.15pm
Credit Cards 1 2 3 4 5

---

**BRIGHTON & HOVE** East Sussex Map **04** TQ30 ◉

See **Town Plan Section**
See also **Rottingdean**

★★★64% **Sackville**
Kingsway BN3 4GU ☎Brighton(0273)736292 Telex no 877830 FAX (0273) 205759
*This imposing hotel, set in a prime position overlooking the sea, has benefited from extensive refurbishment, all rooms now being equipped with modern conveniences though varying in size and décor; public areas include a cosy bar and restaurant and a bright sun lounge. Services are extensive, a friendly management and staff ensuring an enjoyable stay for both commercial or leisure guests.*
45rm

★★★62% **Norfolk Resort**
149 Kings Rd BN1 2PP (Resort) ☎Brighton(0273)738201 FAX (0273) 821752
*The bedrooms of this extensively refurbished seaside hotel vary from front-facing executive to standard, but all are fully equipped and very comfortable, with modern furniture and co-ordinating soft furnishings. Drakes Restaurant, though fairly compact for the size of the establishment, offers a carefully balanced table d'hôte menu*

*supplemented by a very limited à la carte choice, and there are 2 bars – the America, which is open to residents both throughout the day and into the evening, and the well presented Brunel, where guests can enjoy an imaginative selection of bar meals. An extensive range of conference/function rooms is available, together with a leisure complex and beauty salon.*
121 ⇨ (5fb) ✗ in 7 bedrooms CTV in all bedrooms ® T
sB ⇨ £51-£66 dB ⇨ £72-£82 (room only) ❚
Lift ( 10P 30 (£1) ☒ (heated) sauna solarium jacuzzi hair salon exercise equipment *xmas*
♀ International V ♥ ♨ ✳ Sunday Lunch £9.95-£12.50 Dinner £16.50-£18&alc Last dinner 9.45pm
Credit Cards 1 2 3 5

★★★58% **Old Ship**
King's Rd BN1 1NR (Best Western) ☎(0273)29001
Telex no 877101 FAX (0273) 820718
*This former inn, one of the oldest hotels in the town, has been undergoing extensive refurbishment. The most luxurious bedrooms are in the east wing, though all rooms provide adequate comfort. There are quiet lounges, an elegant wood-panelled bar and extensive conference facilities, plus the asset of a covered garage.*
152 ⇨ (19fb) CTV in all bedrooms ® T ✳ sB&B ⇨ £85-£95 dB&B ⇨ £100-£110 ❚
Lift ( 80 (£6 per 24hrs) CFA ♫ ♨ *xmas*
♀ English & French V ♥ ♨ ✳ Lunch fr£14 Dinner fr£18 Last dinner 9.30pm
Credit Cards 1 2 3 5

★★★56% **Courtlands**
19-27 The Drive BN3 3JE ☎Brighton(0273)731055
Telex no 87574 FAX (0273) 28295
*Situated in a quiet tree-lined avenue within easy walking distance of the seafront and town, this hotel has a variety of bedrooms, some rather dated but all equipped with modern facilities. There is a cosy bar and a restaurant with a choice of menus. Leisure facilities include an indoor swimming pool, solarium and spa bath.*
53 ⇨ Annexe5 ⇨ (3fb) CTV in all bedrooms ® T ✳ sB&B ⇨ fr£60 dB&B ⇨ fr£78 ❚
Lift ( CTV 26P ✿ CFA ☒ (heated) solarium *xmas*
♀ International V ♥ ♨ ✖ ✳ Lunch fr£9.75 Dinner fr£12.75 Last dinner 9.30pm
Credit Cards 1 2 3 5

★★ ❀75% **Topps**
17 Regency Square BN1 2FG (Exec Hotel)
☎Brighton(0273)729334 FAX (0273) 203679
*A town house hotel converted from 2 terraced houses, furnished with style and individuality. Bedrooms are spacious, some with gas flame fires, and most with very good levels of comfort. The particularly well appointed bathrooms have every conceivable little extra, and the standard of housekeeping throughout is commendable. Paul Collins supervises the very helpful and extensive service, while Pauline Collins does the cooking for Bottoms Restaurant. The restaurant is closed Sunday and Wednesday but a restricted room service menu is available.*
14 ⇨ (2fb)2 CTV in all bedrooms ® T ✖ (ex guide dogs) ✳ sB&B ⇨ £32-£45 dB&B ⇨ £59-£99 ❚
Lift ✗ ✿
V ✳ Dinner fr£17.95&alc Last dinner 9.30pm
Credit Cards 1 2 3 4 5

★★64% **Whitehaven**
34 Wilbury Rd BN3 3JP ☎Brighton(0273)778355
Telex no 877159 FAX (0273) 731177
*In a peaceful residential area, not too far from the seafront and local amenities, this small hotel offers a range of comfortable bedrooms, functionally furnished but particularly well equipped. There is a charming lounge and cosy bar and pre-dinner drinks. The Rolling Clock restaurant is elegantly appointed and offers a selection of menus to suit every pocket.*
17 ⇨ (2fb)1 CTV in all bedrooms ® T ✖ sB&B ⇨ £46.50-£52.50 dB&B ⇨ £61.50-£70 ❚

🎢 🛋 solarium nc8yrs
🍴 French V 🕭 ⚡ Lunch £13.50-£20alc Dinner £13.50-£20alc
Last dinner 9.30pm
Credit Cards ① ② ③ ⑤ ⑥

### ★★60% St Catherines Lodge

Seafront, Kingsway BN3 2RZ (Inter-Hotels)
☎Brighton(0273)778181 Telex no 877073 FAX (0273) 774949
*The public areas of this Regency-style hotel, which stands opposite*
*Hove Leisure Centre on the seafront, include an elegant restaurant*
*serving both set and à la carte meals, a comfortable lounge, small*
*bar and games room. Bedrooms vary in style and size, but most are*
*en suite and equipped with modern facilities.*
50rm(40⊸🛏)(4fb)2🏠 CTV in all bedrooms T S10%
sB&Bfr£36 sB&B⊸🛏fr£45 dB&B£54-£60 dB&B⊸🛏£65-£80
🚭

Lift 《 CTV 5P 4🏐 (£4) CFA games room *xmas*
🍴 European V 🕭 ⚡ S10% Lunch £5-£8.25&alc Dinner
fr£13.50&alc Last dinner 9pm
Credit Cards ① ② ③ ⑤ ⑥

### ◯Oak

West St BN21 2DX ☎Brighton(0273)220033
Due to have opened Sep 1991
138⊸🛏

### ❀ ✕ Le Grandgousier

15 Western St BN1 2PG ☎Brighton(0273)772005
*Remarkable value for money in its 6-course fixed price menu*
*(£11.95 including half a bottle of wine), is the secret of Lewis*
*Harris's well established restaurant. The first 3 could start with a*
*basket of vegetables for crudités, served with good garlic*
*mayonnaise and a lentil salad, then a home-made pâté and, to*
*complete Act One, a basket of salamis – as ideal for those who like*
*to nibble, as for those who like to eat a lot. Main courses include a*
*range of steaks (but there is a supplement to pay) as well as the*
*chef's special which changes daily.*

Closed Sun & 23 Dec-3 Jan Lunch not served Sat
🍴 French V 36 seats Last lunch 1.30pm Last dinner 9.30pm
🎢 nc5yrs
Credit Cards ① ② ③

### ❀ ✕ Whyte's

33 Western St BN1 2PG ☎Brighton(0273)776618
*Chef/patron Ian, and Jane Whyte co-ordinate their skills in*
*personally running this small, cosy and attractively furnished*
*restaurant. It features a chef's Fish of the Day as well as a choice*
*of prix fix courses which might include scallops in white wine au*
*gratin, coarse duck liver pâté, roast rack of lamb with cassis,*
*supreme of wild salmon and a good selection of desserts and*
*cheeses. Service is particularly attentive and helpful, under the*
*supervision of Jane Whyte. Some interesting wines are available to*
*accompany a meal which represents good value for money.*
Closed Sun (ex by prior arrangement) Lunch not served (ex by
prior arrangement)
Lunch by arrangement
🍴 English & French 36 seats ✳ Dinner £13.95-£15.95 Last
dinner 10pm 🎢
Credit Cards ① ② ③

---

### BRIMFIELD Hereford & Worcester Map **07** SO56

### ❀❀ ✕ Poppies

Roebuck Inn SY8 4LN ☎(058472)230
*The Roebuck Inn stands in the centre of the village – at the rear is*
*Poppies Restaurant, where Carole Evans, a self-taught cook,*
*continues to improve the interest and quality of her menu. The*
*menu is a tempting range of dishes, making good use of the best*
*local produce. Choices include starters such as spinach soufflé with*
*anchovy hollandaise and fresh pear with stilton and walnut sauce.*
*For the main course, diners enjoy brill with scallops on a bed of*
*sorrel and salmon with ginger in a cream, vermouth and chive*
*sauce. Desserts are a treat not to be missed – poppyseed parfait*
→

*with a ragout of dates, or old favourites such as bread and butter pudding.*
Closed Sun, Mon, 1 wk Oct & 2 wks Feb
V 40 seats ✳ Lunch £21.50-£27alc Dinner £21.50-£27alc Last lunch 2pm Last dinner 10pm 30 P ✂
Credit Cards ①③

---

**BRISTOL** Avon Map **03** ST57 ⊖
See **Town Plan Section**
★★★★61% **Bristol Moat House**
Victoria St BS1 6HY (Queens Moat) ☎(0272)255010
FAX ℂ (0272) 255040
Closed 26-30 Dec RS 25 & 31 Dec
*Opened in September 1990, this modern hotel close to Temple Meads station offers attractive and comfortable open-plan public areas and very well equipped bedrooms. Additional benefits include a private car park and up-to-date air-conditioned conference facilities.*
132⇨🛏(6fb)✂in 37 bedrooms CTV in all bedrooms ® T ✳
sB⇨🛏fr£88 dB⇨🛏fr£100 (room only) 🛏
Lift ℂ 150🍴 CFA solarium gymnasium
♡ International V ✧ ⯑ ✂ ✳ Lunch £12.95-£14.50&alc Dinner fr£18.95&alc Last dinner 10pm
Credit Cards ①②③⑤£

★★★★59% **Holiday Inn**
Lower Castle St BS1 3AD (Holiday Inns) ☎(0272)294281
Telex no 449720 FAX (0272) 225838
*A conveniently positioned modern high-rise hotel with car parking in the adjacent multi-storey. This large and busy hotel is in the process of major refurbishment, and the accommodation so far has seen significant upgrading to provide modern facilities and comforts. At the time of our last visit a new multi-complex conference centre was under construction, and on completion it is hoped that similar good work will encompass the hotel's restaurant and public rooms.*
284⇨🛏(138fb)✂in 78 bedrooms CTV in all bedrooms ® T
sB⇨🛏£36-£107 dB⇨🛏£72-£122 (room only) 🛏
Lift ℂ ▦ 20🍴 ⌧ (heated) sauna solarium gymnasium *xmas*
♡ International V ✧ ⯑ ✂ ✳ Lunch £11.50-£16.50 High tea fr£3 Dinner £13.50-£17.75&alc Last dinner 10.45pm
Credit Cards ①②③④⑤£

★★★69% **Redwood Lodge & Country Club**
Beggar Bush Ln, Failand BS8 3TG (2m W of Clifton Bridge on B3129) ☎(0275)393901 Telex no 444348 FAX (0275) 392104
*Situated just west of the Avon Gorge, in a peaceful setting beside the B3129, this purpose-built hotel offers guests the use of substantial leisure and conference facilities which are accessed by central entrances. The main building contains comfortable open-plan public areas and spacious, well equipped bedrooms, most of which have now been refurbished, and willing staff create a friendly atmosphere throughout the busy establishment.*
112⇨🛏(4fb)✂in 20 bedrooms CTV in all bedrooms ® T
✖ (ex guide dogs) ✳ sB&B⇨🛏fr£70 dB&B⇨🛏fr£90 🛏
ℂ 1000P ✿ CFA ⌧ (heated) ⌑ ♪ (hard) squash snooker sauna solarium gymnasium badminton cinema (wknds only) steam room 🐴 *xmas*
♡ English & French V ✧ ⯑ ✂ ✳ Lunch £12 Dinner £18 Last dinner 10pm
Credit Cards ①②③⑤£

★★★68% **Berkeley Square**
15 Berkeley Square, Clifton BS8 1HB ☎(0272)254000
FAX (0272) 252970
*This completely modern hotel, set in the seclusion of a wooded Georgian square within walking distance of the city centre, offers very well furnished bedrooms, lounge facilities which are comfortable though limited in size, and a choice of two restaurants; friendly staff provide helpful service throughout. The hotel is not easy to find – guests should turn off Queens Road*
→

# Bristol

*almost opposite the City Museum – and parking is difficult at present, though it is hoped that the situation will be remedied soon.*
43➪🍴in 9 bedrooms CTV in all bedrooms ® **T** s℟➪🍴£49-£76 d℟➪🍴£69-£99 (room only) 🅿
Lift ( 🅰 (£2 per night) *xmas*
♀ European **V** ✿ ♨ ✂ ✱ Lunch £12.50-£15.50&alc Dinner £17.95-£19.95&alc Last dinner 9.30pm
Credit Cards ①②③⑤

## ★★★68% Forte Crest
Filton Rd, Hambrook BS16 1QX (6m NE off A4174) (Forte Hotels) ☎(0272)564242 Telex no 449376 FAX (0272) 569735
*Close to junction 1 of the M32 with easy access to the M4 and M5, this purpose-built hotel set in 16 acres of woodland has well equipped bedrooms including a luxury executive wing, a good leisure club and a business centre. Attractive open-plan public areas include comfortable bars and a restaurant serving a wide choice of dishes.*
197➪🍴(14fb)✂in 60 bedrooms CTV in all bedrooms ® **T** ✱ s℟➪🍴fr£87 d℟➪🍴fr£100 (room only) 🅿
Lift ( ⊞ 400P ✿ ▣ (heated) snooker sauna solarium gymnasium ♫ ℴ *xmas*
**V** ✿ ♨ ✂
Credit Cards ①②③⑤

## ★★★65% Avon Gorge
Sion Hill, Clifton BS8 4LD (Mount Charlotte (TS)) ☎(0272)738955 Telex no 444237 FAX (0272) 238125
*An hotel well run on traditional lines to provide good standards of service offers warm, smart and well equipped bedrooms, those at the rear of the building commanding spectacular views of the Gorge and Suspension Bridge.*
76➪🍴(6fb)2🛏✂in 2 bedrooms CTV in all bedrooms ® **T** (room only) 🅿
Lift ( 20P ✿ *xmas*
♀ English & French **V** ✿ ♨
Credit Cards ①②③⑤

## ★★★62% Henbury Lodge
Station Rd, Henbury BS10 7QQ (4.5m NW of City centre off B4055) ☎(0272)502615 FAX (0272) 509532
*A Georgian country-style hotel situated north of the city close to the M5, and run by the Pearce family. Bedrooms are spacious and well equipped and the food is imaginative and well prepared.*
10➪🍴Annexe6➪🍴(4fb)✂in 6 bedrooms CTV in all bedrooms ® **T** ✱ s℟➪B➪🍴£29.50-£64.50 d℟B&B➪🍴£44-£74.50 🅿
24P ⊞ ✿ sauna solarium gymnasium *xmas*
♀ English & Continental **V** ✿ ♨ ✂ ✱ Lunch £4.50-£16.20 Dinner £16.20 Last dinner 9pm
Credit Cards ①②③⑤

## ★★★54% Unicorn
Prince St BS1 4QF (Rank) ☎(0272)230333 Telex no 44315 FAX (0272) 230300
*Situated on the waterfront, this large city centre hotel, with adjacent multi-storey car park, is currently undergoing an extensive programme to refurbish its compact and dated bedrooms. The new rooms are a great improvement, providing good quality, well equipped accommodation. Public areas include a choice of restaurants and bars.*
247➪🍴(29fb)✂in 8 bedrooms CTV in all bedrooms ® **T** ✱ s℟B&B➪🍴£41-£95 d℟B&B➪🍴£62-£101 🅿
Lift ( 400🅰 (charged) CFA ♫ *xmas*
♀ International **V** ✿ ♨ ✱ Lunch £12.95 Dinner £14.95&alc Last dinner 10.30pm
Credit Cards ①②③④⑤

For key to symbols in English see the bookmark.

## ★★★50% St Vincent Rocks
Sion Hill, Clifton BS8 4BB (Forte Hotels) ☎(0272)739251 FAX (0272) 238139
*Some of the rooms of this hotel afford good views of the Avon Gorge and the Clifton Suspension Bridge, near which it stands. Much of the accommodation has been refurbished to a good standard, though there is still work to be done, and the friendly, helpful service provided throughout contributes to its popularity.*
46➪🍴(2fb)1🛏✂in 10 bedrooms CTV in all bedrooms ® **T** ✱ s℟➪🍴fr70 d℟➪🍴£90-£115 (room only) 🅿
( 18P CFA *xmas*
♀ International **V** ✿ ♨ ✂ ✱ Lunch fr£10.95&alc Dinner fr£14.95&alc Last dinner 9.30pm
Credit Cards ①②③④⑤

## ★★★✸69% Rodney Hotel
Rodney Place, Clifton BS8 4HY ☎(0272)735422 Telex no 449075 FAX (0272) 741082
*This hotel has smart and clean stonework, and renovation which has taken place provides comfortable and attractive accommodation. Rooms are well equipped and cuisine is of a high standard and the menu includes a range of vegetarian dishes.*
31➪🍴✂in 2 bedrooms CTV in all bedrooms ® **T** ✱ s℟➪🍴£49-£55 d℟➪🍴£78-£82 (room only) 🅿
( ✂
♀ English & French **V** ✿ ♨ ✱ Sunday Lunch fr£12 Dinner fr£12.95 Last dinner 10pm
Credit Cards ①②③⑤ ④

## ★★★64% Parkside
470 Bath Rd, Brislington BS4 3HQ ☎(0272)711461 FAX (0272) 711507
*This neo-gothic stone building on the busy A4 a mile from the city centre has spacious public areas that include two bars, a conservatory restaurant, a snooker room and a night club. Bedrooms are attractive and of reasonable size, some situated across the courtyard and the best in the main building.*
30rm(9➪1🍴)1🛏 CTV in all bedrooms ® **T**
( ⊞ 250P ✿ snooker
**V** ✿ ♨ Last dinner 10.30pm
Credit Cards ① ③

## ★★62% Glenroy
Victoria Square, Clifton BS8 4EW ☎(0272)739058
Closed 22 Dec-1 Jan
*This busy commercial hotel facing a small park in a residential area is formed from two houses, with the main house containing the reception, lounge bar and dining room, where a carvery menu is offered in the evening.*
26➪🍴Annexe24➪🍴(9fb) CTV in all bedrooms ® **T** ✱ s℟B&B➪🍴£35-£43 d℟B&B➪🍴£44-£63
( 16P
**V** ✿ ♨ Sunday Lunch fr£8.95alc Dinner fr£9.95alc Last dinner 9.30pm
Credit Cards ① ③

## ★★58% Clifton
St Pauls Rd, Clifton BS8 1LX ☎(0272)736882 Telex no 449075 FAX (0272) 741082
*An hotel situated off Whiteladies Road, close to the city centre, provides modestly priced accommodation in compact but reasonably equipped bedrooms; breakfast and dinner are taken in the basement bistro restaurant.*
63rm(4➪41🍴)(4fb)✂in 8 bedrooms CTV in all bedrooms ® **T** s℟B&B£26-£28 s℟B&B➪🍴£36-£45 d℟B&B£37-£45 d℟B&B➪🍴£49-£64 🅿
Lift ( 12P
♀ English & French **V** ✿ ♨ ✱ Lunch £5-£12 High tea £2 Dinner £9.75-£11.50&alc Last dinner 10.30pm
Credit Cards ①②③⑤ ④

○**Swallow Royal**
College Green BS1 5TE (Swallow) ☎(0272)255100
Due to have opened Sep 1991
242⇌♠

❀❀❀✕✕**Restaurant Lettonie**
9 Druid Hill, Stoke Bishop BS9 1EW (2m NW) ☎(0272)686456
*This discreet, predominantly French restaurant in a residential
area to the northwest of the city centre offers exciting dishes
cooked and presented with confidence and flair by Martin Blunos,
whose wife Sian provides a friendly welcome at the front of house.
Ingredients with strong flavours are beautifully handled: lambs'
tongues with basil jelly; pike and dill ravioli; pig's trotter with
sweetbreads. Technical refinement is shown, for example, in clear
soups such as rabbit and celeriac or scallop and coriander. Main
courses provide equally excellent contrasts of texture, taste and
colour. Our inspector particularly enjoyed a pink fillet of lamb
topped with a lentil puree and ringed by imaginative combinations
of flavoursome vegetables, accompanied by a thyme sauce. Leave
room for desserts, which might include pear and ginger mousse
with caramelised pear or biscuit praline topped with spun sugar.
Delicate petits fours served with the coffee make a perfect ending.*
Closed Sun, Mon, Xmas, BH's & last 2 wks Aug
♥ French 24 seats ✳ Lunch £13.95-£23.95 Dinner £23.95 Last
lunch 2pm Last dinner 10pm P
Credit Cards [1] [2] [3]

❀❀❀✕✕**Markwicks**
43 Corn St BS1 1HT ☎(0272)262658
*There is a French bias to the cooking here, but Steven Markwick's
culinary skill and flair contribute a degree of innovation and
imagination. There is a small à la carte menu which changes to
allow for seasonal specialities and is always supplemented by fresh
fish. Worthy of special note is the scallop ravioli with a delicate
beurre blanc, an outstanding leek tart, bacon-wrapped lamb
tournedos placed on a courgette gratin and an iced nougat with*
→

*honey sauce. Décor is in soft shades of yellow and service is charming and attentive.*

Closed Sat, Sun & BH Mons 10 days Xmas & Etr; 2 wks Aug
♡ English & French **V** 40 seats ✳ Lunch £15.75&alc Dinner £23.25-£27.75alc Last lunch 2pm Last dinner 10.30pm 🍴

Credit Cards 1 3

### ❀ ✕ ✕ Orient Rendezvous

95 Queens Rd, Clifton BS8 1LW ☎(0272)745202 & 745231

*An oriental garden leads to this friendly family-run restaurant on the outskirts of Clifton, consisting of several interconnecting rooms decorated with Chinese fans and drawings. The menu is a well-chosen blend of Cantonese, Peking and Szechuan dishes. Carefully cooked seafood might be served with a piquant black bean sauce or steamed with Chinese mushrooms. Special dishes include pork with a spicy ginger and garlic sauce.*

Closed 25-26 Dec
♡ Chinese **V** 150 seats Last lunch 2.25pm Last dinner 11.30pm 25 P 🍴

Credit Cards 1 2 3 5

### ❀❀ ✕ Bistro Twenty One

21 Cotham Rd South, Kingsdown BS6 5TZ ☎(0272)421744

*Situated in a quaint little shopping area to the south of the Cotham district, an intimate restaurant which is decorated to a French theme, its tables covered by oil cloth, complements imaginative food with relaxed yet attentive service. Lightly cooked dishes are enhanced by well chosen sauces, and fish now features more prominently on chef/patron Alain Dubois' menus. A wine list of some 70 bins offers good coverage and value for money.*

Closed Sun & Xmas-New Year Lunch not served Sat
♡ French **V** 40 seats Last lunch 2.30pm Last dinner 11.30pm 🍴

Credit Cards 1 3

### ❀ ✕ Howard's

1A-2A Avon Crescent, Hotwells BS1 6XQ ☎(0272)262921

*This friendly bistro on the edge of the town is a sister establishment to the one of the same name in Nailsea, taking the same honest value-for-money approach with distinctive personal style. The bustling bistro atmosphere is stronger in the ground floor room, with its church pews, half panelling, pictures and plants, and service is competent and informal. A daily 2-course fixed-price menu supplements the short à la carte selection, both offering good fresh flavours and reliable cooking. Medallions of beef with Port and Stilton sauce, and a crème brûlée accompanied by Cointreau-marinated fresh strawberries, or a good praline iced parfait with a bitter chocolate sauce, are particularly noteworthy. A well chosen wine list of some 30 items is augmented by some sensibly priced bin ends.*

Closed Sun Lunch not served Sat
♡ English & French **V** 65 seats Lunch £12-£15&alc Dinner fr£15&alc Last lunch 2.30pm Last dinner 11pm 🍴 ✂

Credit Cards 1 3

### BRIXHAM Devon Map 03 SX95

★★★60% **Quayside**
King St TQ5 9TJ (Inter-Hotels) ☎(0803)855751 Telex no 336682 FAX (0803) 882733

*A rambling, character property, commanding views across to Torbay from its enviable position directly overlooking Brixham's picturesque harbour, offers good amenities and bedrooms which, though compact, are well equipped. Public areas are similarly limited in size, but they are cosy and pleasantly furnished, and the popular restaurant provides a range of freshly prepared meals which make good use of local fish. Service is conducted in an informally friendly manner that suits the style and location of the establishment, and car parking facilities are provided 500 yards away from the main entrance.*

29⇨🛏(4fb)2🔔 CTV in all bedrooms ® **T** ✳ sB&B⇨🛏£34-£38 dB&B⇨🛏£63-£80 🏠

37P CFA 🎵 *xmas*

---

♡ English & French **V** 🕏 ⬙ ✳ Lunch £5.90-£7.95 High tea 95p-£2.95 Dinner £15.45&alc Last dinner 9.45pm

Credit Cards 1 2 3 5 £

★55% **Smugglers Haunt**
Church St TQ5 8HH ☎(0803)853050 & 859416

*A stone-built inn that has stood near the old world harbour for four centuries is a popular venue for tourists and locals alike. Age and architectural features place obvious restrictions on accommodation, so that bedrooms, though soundly equipped are very compact and thus more suited to the needs of transient rather than long-stay guests, but friendly family ownership ensures a relaxing informal atmosphere, and local car parking facilities are conveniently close at hand. The small character public bar and adjacent cottage restaurant serve an extensive range of dishes and bar food featuring the best local fish available, last dinner orders being as late as 10pm.*

14rm(4⇨🛏)Annexe2rm(2fb) CTV in all bedrooms ® ✳ sB&B£30-£35 sB&B⇨🛏£34-£39 dB&B£44-£54 dB&B⇨🛏£48-£58
《 CTV 🍴 *xmas*
♡ English & French **V** 🕏 ⬙ Lunch £7-£9 Dinner £10-£24alc Last dinner 10pm

Credit Cards 1 2 3 5

### BROADFORD

See Skye, Isle of

### BROADSTAIRS Kent Map 05 TR36

★★★52% *Castle Keep*
Joss Gap Rd, Kingsgate CT10 3PQ (Best Western) ☎Thanet(0843)65222 FAX (0843) 65225

*Set on a cliff top overlooking the sea this hotel has a popular bar which extends into an attractive, comfortable lounge and a restaurant where dinner dances are held on Saturday evenings. Some bedrooms have recently been refurbished and conference facilities are available.*

29⇨🛏(3fb) CTV in all bedrooms ®
《 🎛 CTV 100P ✿ ⌂ (heated) 🎵
♡ English, French & Italian 🕏 ⬙ Last dinner 10pm

Credit Cards 1 2 3 4 5

★★67% **Royal Albion**
Albion St CT10 1LU (Consort) ☎Thanet(0843)68071 FAX (0843) 61509

*A long established and soundly managed family-run hotel which continues to improve, with bedroom upgrading and extensive levels of service. Bedrooms are particularly well equipped and have full en suite facilities. Except for breakfasts, the restaurant is separate from the hotel, located next door but one in Marchesi's. Chef Stephen Watson offers an enterprising à la carte and table d'hôte menu, and the wine list is commendable. There are facilities for meetings and private dining, and car parking provided nearby.*

19⇨🛏(3fb)1🔔 CTV in all bedrooms ® **T** 🐾 (ex guide dogs) S% sB&B⇨🛏£62-£65 dB&B⇨🛏£75-£80 🏠
《 CTV 20P 2🚗 CFA *xmas*
♡ French **V** 🕏 ⬙ ✳ Lunch £13-£20 Dinner £15-£20 Last dinner 9.30pm

Credit Cards 1 2 3 5

★★65% **Castlemere**
Western Esplanade CT10 1TD ☎Thanet(0843)61566 FAX (0843) 866379
Closed 29 Dec-5 Jan

*This long-established, family-run hotel facing the sea has been completely refurbished in recent years. Accommodation now comprises a choice of traditionally furnished modern bedrooms, an attractive, well appointed restaurant and good bar and lounge facilities.*

36rm(24⇨6🛏)(5fb)2🔔 CTV in all bedrooms ® **T** S% sB&B⇨🛏£35-£38.50 dB&B⇨🛏£66-£79 🏠
《 CTV 30P ✿ CFA *xmas*

---

♀ English & French ✆ ♨ S% Dinner £11.80 Last dinner 7.45pm

Credit Cards 1 3 £

---

## BROADWAY Hereford & Worcester Map **04** SP03

See also **Buckland**

★★★★ LYGON ARMS

WR12 7DU (Small Luxury Hotels) ☎(0386)852255
Telex no 338260
FAX (0386) 858611

*Friendly staff ensure a warm welcome and willing service at this famous old Cotswolds inn. The original building has great character and offers delightful period bedrooms, while comfortable modern accommodation is available in the garden wings. All the bedrooms are very well equipped and have beautiful soft furnishings. The Great Hall is the splendid setting for Clive Howe's British cuisine. A sensible seasonal à la carte menu is presented along with a daily changing set price menu at lunch and dinner. Straightforward starters include a well balanced creamed smoked haddock soup, or a pressed terrine of English asparagus, salmon and sole, marred only by a rather harsh tomato relish. Plain grills are good – excellent calves liver for instance. Puddings are firmly English, such as a satisfying baked apple and raisin turnover.*

61⇨🛏5🛁 CTV in all bedrooms T Continental breakfast
《 CTV 100P 4🚗 (£7.50 per night) 🏋 ❈ ♪ (hard)

♀ International ✆ ♨ Lunch fr£17.50 Dinner fr£27.50 Last dinner 9.45pm

Credit Cards 1 2 3 5

---

★★★❀70% **Dormy House**
Willersey Hill WR12 7LF (2m E off A44 in Gloucestershire)
☎(0386)852711 Telex no 338275 FAX (0386) 858636
Closed 25 & 26 Dec

*Beautifully located on Broadway's steep wooded escarpment overlooking the Vale of Evesham, this appealing 17th-century converted farmhouse retains such original features as exposed timbers and Cotswold stone. Bedrooms, in the main house and surrounding annexes, are all well equipped with modern facilities, though some are quite compact. Charming public areas with log fires and fresh flowers include a recently extended restaurant serving a choice of interesting dishes.*

26⇨🛏Annexe23⇨🛏(3fb)2🛁 CTV in all bedrooms ® T
sB&B⇨🛏£54-£70 dB&B⇨🛏£108-£130 🍴
《 80P 🏋 ❈ CFA
♀ English & French V ✆ ♨ ✂ Lunch £14.25-£16.50&alc
Dinner £24.95&alc Last dinner 10pm
Credit Cards 1 2 3 5

See advertisement on page 175

★★★61% **Broadway**
The Green WR12 7AB (Inter-Hotels) ☎(0386)852401
FAX (0386) 853879
*This converted 16th-century house in the heart of the village, formerly used by the Abbots of Pershore, provides comfortable characterful accommodation, with an attractive galleried lounge full of exposed beams. Many bedrooms have recently been refurbished though older rooms are rather functional and tired-looking.*

20⇨🛏🛁🛁✂in 4 bedrooms CTV in all bedrooms ® T ✗ ✱
sB&B⇨🛏£56-£58.50 dB&B⇨🛏£81-£87 🍴
30P 🏋 ❈ CFA *xmas*

---

♀ English & French V ✆ ♨ ✂ ✱ Sunday Lunch £12.50
Dinner £16.95 Last dinner 9.30pm
Credit Cards 1 2 3 5

See advertisement on page 175

★★★❀♨71%, **Collin House**
Collin Ln WR12 7PB ☎(0386)858354 & 852544
Closed 24-27 Dec

*Set in 8 acres of grounds just off the A44 to the northwest of the village, this charming 16th-century Cotswold stone house offers peace, comfort and hospitality, with a relaxing lounge and generally spacious bedrooms with antique furnishings. But outstanding is the food in the small cosy restaurant where chef Mark Brookes provides a menu of skilfully prepared dishes using the best fresh ingredients and featuring daily specialities.*

7rm(5⇨🛏1🛁)2🛁 ® 🛏 sB&B⇨🛏fr£44 dB&B⇨🛏£85-£98 🍴
CTV 35P 🏋 ❈ ▭ croquet *xmas*

V Lunch £12.50-£15.50alc Dinner £17.50-£23&alc Last dinner 9pm
Credit Cards 1 3

---

❀ ✗ ✗ ✗ *Hunter's Lodge*
High St WR12 7DT ☎(0386)853247

*A fine Cotswold house where friendly and attentive services are provided by Dotti Friedli and her staff whilst husband Kurt presides over a kitchen which produces imaginative food. His Swiss origin is very much in evidence with mouth-watering pastry work and delicate sauces.*

Closed Mon, 1st 2 wks Feb & 1st 2 wks Aug
Dinner not served Sun
♀ English & French V 50 seats Last lunch 2pm Last dinner 9.45pm 20 P nc8yrs
Credit Cards 1 2 3 5

B

**BROCKENHURST** Hampshire Map **04** SU20

**★★★ 70% New Park Manor**
Lyndhurst Rd SO42 7QH ☎Lymington(0590)23467
FAX (0590) 22268
*Dating from 1890, set at the end of an ornamental drive and fronted by attractive formal gardens, this hotel offers well designed and equipped accommodation in a modern block sympathetically styled to blend in with the original house. The fully panelled Armada Restaurant, refurbished for 1991, serves imaginative menus, whilst teas, coffees and light lunches can be enjoyed in the conservatory and there is a spacious, comfortable bar lounge. Time-share apartments are available, a selection of conference/function rooms includes the splendid Great Hall, and former cellars in the basement are now occupied by the Atlantis Leisure Club. Grounds in which small herds of deer can often be seen contain an attractive outdoor swimming pool, and a children's play area is under construction.*
26⇌↱(2fb)2⊞⊬in 10 bedrooms CTV in all bedrooms ® T ✱
S8% sB&B⇌↱fr£62 dB&B⇌↱fr£104 ⊟
60P 1⌂ ✲ CFA ⌓ (heated) ℘ (hard) U solarium croquet *xmas*
⊖ English & French V ✪ ☕ ✱ S8% Sunday Lunch £11.50
High tea £4.95 Dinner £18.50&alc Last dinner 9.30pm
Credit Cards [1] [2] [3] [5] £

**See advertisement on page 177**

**★★★ 69% Careys Manor**
Lyndhurst Rd SO4 7RH ☎Lymington(0590)23551
FAX (0590) 22799
*This hotel has well kept gardens and ample car parking, the Manor offers simply furnished bedrooms in the main building, with the new wing containing two styles of bedroom, Deluxe and Knightwood; smoking is prohibited in about 30 rooms. A truly Gallic atmosphere prevails in Le Blaireau, a separate French café/bar near the hotel entrance. The Carat Club is an extensive, professionally run health and fitness centre, and both touring and mountain bicycles are available for hire.*
80⇌↱6⊞⊬in 30 bedrooms CTV in all bedrooms ® T
sB&B⇌↱£74-£80 dB&B⇌↱£100-£128 ⊟
☾ CTV 180P ⊞ ✲ CFA ⊡ (heated) sauna solarium gymnasium jacuzzi steam room beauty therapist ♧ *xmas*
⊖ English & French V ✪ ☕ ⊬ ✱ Lunch fr£10.95 High tea fr£5 Dinner fr£19.95 Last dinner 10pm
Credit Cards [1] [2] [3]

**★★★ 66% Rhinefield House**
Rhinefield Rd SO42 7QB ☎Lymington(0590)22922
Telex no 477617 FAX (0590) 22800
*This magnificent country house is set in formal gardens in a peaceful and attractive area of the New Forest by the Ornamental Drive. Part time-share, part hotel, there are extensive leisure facilities including indoor and outdoor swimming pools. Public rooms include a splendid galleried main hall, panelled dining room and the unusual Alhambra Room. The restaurant provides imaginative menus in the modern British style.*
34⇌↱(2fb)1⊞⊬in 6 bedrooms CTV in all bedrooms ® T
⋈ (ex guide dogs) ✱ sB&B⇌↱£82.50 dB&B⇌↱£107.80 ⊟
☾ 80P ✲ CFA ⊡ (heated) ⌓ (heated) ℘ (hard) sauna solarium gymnasium jacuzzi table tennis pool table croquet *xmas*
V ✪ ☕ ✱ Lunch £14.50 Dinner £19.50 Last dinner 10pm
Credit Cards [1] [2] [3] [5]

**★★★ 62% Balmer Lawn**
Lyndhurst Rd SO42 7ZB ☎Lymington(0590)23116
Telex no 477649 FAX (0590) 23864
*A former coaching inn dating from the mid 1800s, set back from the Brockenhurst to Lyndhurst road, overlooking a cricket pitch and the forest. Good leisure facilities are offered to residents and local members, and there is a good range of conference rooms. Bedrooms are comfortable, well equipped and dramatically co-ordinated. The spacious restaurant serves imaginative dishes as well as traditional favourites. Service at breakfast is particularly noteworthy for its friendliness and efficiency: an extensive array of cereals, fruits and yoghurts is available, buffet style, followed by a freshly cooked choice of dishes.*
58⇌↱(8fb)⊬in 26 bedrooms CTV in all bedrooms ® T ✱
sB&B⇌↱£55-£86 dB&B⇌↱£86-£118 ⊟
Lift ☾ 90P ✲ CFA ⊡ (heated) ⌓ (heated) ℘ (hard) squash sauna gymnasium *xmas*
V ✪ ☕ ⊬ ✱ Lunch £9.25-£10 Dinner £15-£20 Last dinner 9.30pm
Credit Cards [1] [2] [3] [4] [5]

**★★★ 60% Forest Park**
Rhinefield Rd SO4 7ZG (Forestdale) ☎Lymington(0590)22844
FAX (0590) 23948
*A pretty roadside hotel on the outskirts of Brockenhurst. Most bedrooms have recently been refurbished and are ideally equipped to suit both leisure and business guests. Cuisine is straightforward and the service is relaxed.*
38⇌↱(5fb)3⊞⊬in 3 bedrooms CTV in all bedrooms ® T ✱
S% sB&B⇌↱£39.50-£49.50 dB&B⇌↱£79-£99 (incl dinner) ⊟
☾ 80P ✲ CFA ⌓ (heated) ℘ (hard) U sauna pool table ♫ *xmas*
⊖ English & French V ✪ ☕ ⊬ ✱ Lunch £9.25 High tea £4.25
Dinner £13.25-£16.25&alc Last dinner 10pm
Credit Cards [1] [2] [3] [5] £

**★★♛ 70% Whitley Ridge Country House**
Beaulieu Rd SO4 7QL ☎Lymington(0590)22354
FAX (0590) 22856
*A delightful country house, surrounded by the forest, built in the 18th century as a royal hunting lodge, and now a charming hotel. Bedrooms are attractively co-ordinated with some strikingly bold décor. Standards of housekeeping are good, the usual facilities are provided along with fresh milk and herbal teas available on the landing. The restaurant is popular with both residents and locals. Owners Rennie and Sue Law are happy to assist with routes and advise on expeditions and tourist attractions.*
11⇌↱1⊞ CTV in all bedrooms ® T ✱ sB&B⇌↱£48-£52
dB&B⇌↱£80-£88 ⊟
CTV 30P ✲ ℘ (hard) *xmas*
⊖ English & French V ✪ ☕ ✱ Lunch £9.50-£10&alc Dinner £16-£17&alc Last dinner 9pm
Credit Cards [1] [2] [3] [5] £

**★★ 64% The Cottage Hotel & Restaurant**
Sway Rd SO42 7SH ☎Lymington(0590)22296
*A cosy cottage hotel run personally by the resident proprietors. There is a small restaurant, a beamed open-plan lounge and a choice of modern bedrooms, some of which have excellent bathrooms. Service is friendly and helpful and there is good car parking.*
6⇌↱ CTV in all bedrooms ® ⋈ ✱ sB&B⇌↱£38-£40
dB&B⇌↱£56-£64 ⊟
11P ✲ nc16yrs *xmas*
⊖ English & French V ✪ ☕ ⊬ ✱ Dinner £12&alc Last dinner 9.30pm
Credit Cards [1] [3] £

**★★ 62% Watersplash**
The Rise SO42 7ZP ☎Lymington(0590)22344
*A detached Victorian house with well tended gardens in a residential area of the town. The hotel has been run by the Foster family for over 30 years. Robert Foster is now at the helm, and a loyal team of friendly staff attend to guests' comfort. The traditional table d'hôte menu remains popular with guests, and honest home cooking is served in generous portions. Improvements continue to be made to the well equipped bedrooms.*
23⇌↱(6fb)1⊞ CTV in all bedrooms ® T ✱ sB&B⇌↱£55-£58 dB&B⇌↱£60-£80 ⊟
CTV 25P 4⌂ (£1.50 per night) ✲ CFA ⌓ (heated) *xmas*

→

175

♡ English & Continental **V** ✿ ⚏ ⅍ ✻ Lunch £8-£12 High tea £2.50-£5 Dinner £12-£18 Last dinner 8.30pm
Credit Cards ① ③ ⑥

★65% *Cloud*
Meerut Rd SO4 7DJ ☎Lymington(0590)22165 & 22254
Closed 29 Dec-14 Jan
*The Owton family have created a relaxed and friendly atmosphere at this hotel for over 20 years. It offers comfortable bedrooms, well-cooked fresh food and four cosy lounge areas all overlooking open forest heathland.*
19rm(5fb)
CTV 20P 2⇴ (£1.25 per night) ⌨
**V** ✿ ⚏ Last dinner 8pm

❀❀❀ ✕ ✕ **Le Poussin**
The Courtyard, 49-55 Brookley Rd SO42 7RB
☎Lymington(0590)23063 FAX (0590) 22912
*Pictures of hens and cockerels decorate the walls of this small but assured French restaurant. The regularly changing à la carte and gourmet menus offer dishes such as seabass and skate with an olive oil sauce, a trio of meats with a red wine and shallot sauce and caramelised apple tart with cinnamon ice cream. Local produce is used whenever possible, and seasonal specialities are usually excellent. The wine list concentrates on French growers, and there is a good choice of half bottles.*
Closed Mon , 1st wk Sep & 1st 2wks Jan
Dinner not served Sun
♡ British & French 28 seats ✻ Lunch £10-£13&alc Dinner £20-£25alc Last lunch 2pm Last dinner 10pm 6 P ⅍
Credit Cards ① ③ ④

## BRODICK

See Arran, Isle of

## BROMBOROUGH Merseyside Map **07** SJ38

★★★67% **Cromwell**
High St L62 7HZ (Lansbury) ☎051-334 2917 Telex no 628225 FAX 051-346 1175
*A friendly, well managed hotel beside the A41, offering comfortable well equipped bedrooms, efficiently heated in winter. The popular restaurant serves carefully prepared food with a good range of Italian specialities.*
31⇨🛏(3fb)1🔔⅍in 2 bedrooms CTV in all bedrooms ® **T**
sB&B⇨🛏£60-£66 dB&B⇨🛏£76-£83 🅿
⚓110P CFA sauna solarium gymnasium
♡ International **V** ✿ ⚏ ⅍ Lunch £8.75&alc High tea £4.50 Dinner £14-£15.95&alc Last dinner 10pm
Credit Cards ① ② ③ ⑤

★★64% **Dibbinsdale**
Dibbinsdale Rd L63 0HJ ☎051-334 5171
19⇨🛏1🔔 CTV in all bedrooms ® **T** ✖ (ex guide dogs) ✻
sB&B⇨🛏£32-£40 dB&B⇨🛏£45-£55 🅿
60P ⌨
♡ International **V** ✿ ⚏ ⅍ ✻ Dinner £6-£15alc Last dinner 9.30pm
Credit Cards ① ② ③ ⑤ ⑥

## BROME Suffolk Map **05** TM17

★★★62% **Oaksmere**
IP23 8AJ ☎Eye(0379)870326 FAX (0379) 870051
*Parts of this country hotel, in its setting of well tended gardens and topiary, date back to the middle of the 16th century. Now restored and recently refurbished, it provides comfortable, well equipped en suite bedrooms and a beautiful restaurant with adjoining vine-clad conservatory. The more informal bar – popular locally for an interesting range of bar meals – makes up for any lack of comfort by its real character and friendly atmosphere.*

11⇨🛏(3fb)4🔔 CTV in all bedrooms ® **T** sB&B⇨🛏fr£55 dB&B⇨🛏fr£75 🅿
90P ⌨ ❀ *xmas*
♡ English & French **V** ✿ ⚏ S10% Lunch £11.95-£17.50alc Dinner fr£17.50alc Last dinner 9.30pm
Credit Cards ① ② ③ ⑤ ⑥

**See advertisement on page 60**

★★★61% *Brome Grange*
IP23 8AP (on A140 ) ☎Eye(0379)870456 FAX (0379) 870921
*Services are offered in a warm, friendly manner at this inn on the A143 just outside Diss, well equipped motel-style accommodation being provided in a block at the rear.*
Annexe22⇨🛏 CTV in all bedrooms ® **T**
CTV 100P ❀
♡ English & French **V** ✿ ⚏
Credit Cards ① ② ③ ⑤

**See advertisement on page 60**

## BROMLEY Greater London

See **LONDON plan 1***F2*(page 435)
★★★58% **Bromley Court**
Bromley Hill BR1 4JD (Consort) ☎081-464 5011
Telex no 896310 FAX 081-460 0899
*This stylish mansion with modern extensions, stands in a quiet area in its own grounds. Bedrooms vary in size and half overlook the attractive gardens. There is a cocktail bar, a spacious foyer/lounge and a conservatory restaurant.*
122⇨🛏(5fb)⅍in 7 bedrooms CTV in all bedrooms ® **T**
✖ (ex guide dogs) S% sB&B⇨🛏£78-£80 dB&B⇨🛏£100-£105 🅿
Lift ⚓CTV 100P ❀ CFA putting green ♫ *xmas*
♡ English & French **V** ✿ ⚏ ⅍ Lunch £13.95-£14.50 Dinner £13.95-£14.50 Last dinner 9.45pm
Credit Cards ① ② ③ ⑤ ⑥

## BROMSGROVE Hereford & Worcester Map **07** SO97

★★★★65% **Country Court**
Birmingham Rd B61 0JB (Stakis) ☎021-447 7888
Telex no 336976 FAX 021-447 7273
*This modern hotel on the A38 offers convenient access to Birmingham and is close to both junction 1 of the M42 and junction 4 of the M5. Comfortable, well equipped accommodation, striking public areas and a leisure centre including gymnasium, swimming pool and jacuzzi make it popular with business and leisure users alike.*
141⇨🛏(39fb)⅍in 73 bedrooms CTV in all bedrooms ® **T**
sB&B⇨🛏£84 dB&B⇨🛏£94.50 (room only) 🅿
⚓160P CFA ⌷ (heated) sauna solarium gymnasium *xmas*
**V** ✿ ⚏ ⅍
Credit Cards ① ② ③ ④ ⑤

★★★62% **Perry Hall**
Kidderminster Rd B61 7JN (Jarvis) ☎(0527)579976
Telex no 8813387 FAX (0527) 575998
*Once the family home of A E Houseman, the original building has latticed windows and ivy-clad walls. Inside is an open plan reception lounge and bar, recently refurbished. Bedrooms are in a purpose-built wing, all well equipped, some larger than others, and with some en suites shower only.*
55⇨🛏 CTV in all bedrooms ® **T** ✻ sB&B⇨🛏£68.50-£78.50 dB&B⇨🛏£76.50-£87 (room only) 🅿
⚓120P ❀ *xmas*
♡ English & French **V** ✿ ⚏ ⅍ ✻ Lunch fr£10.95&alc Dinner fr£13.25&alc Last dinner 9.45pm
Credit Cards ① ② ③ ④ ⑤

❀ ✗ ✗ ✗ **Grafton Manor**
Grafton Ln B61 7HA ☎(0527)579007 FAX (0527) 575221
*This elegant manor house dates back to the 16th century, though it was substantially rebuilt following extensive fire damage in 1710. The well appointed dining room provides a splendid setting in which to enjoy an imaginative and skilfully prepared range of dishes based on the finest of ingredients, their flavours enhanced by fresh herbs from the hotel's own garden.*
Lunch not served Sat
V 45 seats ✳ Lunch £14.95-£20.50 Dinner £28.50 Last lunch 1.45pm Last dinner 9pm 50 P
Credit Cards 1 2 3 5

---

**BROOK (NEAR CADNAM)** Hampshire Map **04** SU21

★★★68% **Bell Inn**
SO43 7HE ☎Southampton(0703)812214 FAX (0703) 813958
*Under the same ownership and control as Bramshaw Golf Club, with its 2 courses, The Manor and The Forest, this handsome red brick, listed hotel has recently undergone a total refurbishment. Period features have been retained, and public rooms comprise a comfortable bar, an attractive lounge, and a beamed restaurant offering well balanced menus. Bedrooms vary in size but they are all comfortable, pleasantly co-ordinated and well equipped. The power showers are particularly noteworthy.*
22➪🝌(3fb) CTV in all bedrooms ® T ✳ S%
sB&B➪🝌£48.25-£53.65 dB&B➪🝌£69-£76.70 🝩
150P ✿ ▶ 36 *xmas*
♡ English & French ✿ ⌂ ✳ S% Lunch £9-£15 Dinner £16&alc Last dinner 9.30pm
Credit Cards 1 2 3 5

A rosette means exceptional standards of cuisine.

---

**BRORA** Highland *Sutherland* Map **14** NC90

★★★59% **Links**
Golf Rd KW9 6QS (Best Western) ☎(0408)21225 due to change to 621225 FAX (0408) 621383
Closed 25 Dec-2 Jan
*A personally run holiday, golfing and fishing hotel, situated beside the golf course and with fine sea views. The Links has a relaxed atmosphere and offers a choice of lounges. Bedrooms are well equipped, mostly with modest traditional furnishings.*
21➪🝌(2fb) CTV in all bedrooms ® T S% sB&B➪🝌£44-£49 dB&B➪🝌£82-£90 🝩
55P ✿ CFA ▶ 18
♡ International V ✿ ⌂ ✖ S% Bar Lunch £7-£12alc Dinner £17.50-£19.50 Last dinner 9pm
Credit Cards 1 2 3 5 £

★★62% *Royal Marine*
Golf Rd KW9 6QS ☎(0408)21252 Telex no 76165
*Conveniently situated for the golf course, this friendly hotel caters for the sporting enthusiast. The Royal Marine offers a good range of leisure facilities together with traditional services and comforts.*
11rm(9➪1🝌)(1fb)1🝩 CTV in all bedrooms ® T
CTV 40P 6🝩 🝩 ✿ 🗔 (heated) ▶ 18 ♪ (hard) ♪ snooker sauna ice curling rink in season
♡ Scottish & French ✿ ⌂ Last dinner 9pm
Credit Cards 1 2 3 5

---

**BROUGH** Cumbria Map **12** NY71

★★60% **Castle**
Main St CA17 4AX ☎(07683)41252
*An hotel with attractive dining room, lounge and cosy lounge bar offers bedrooms ranging from the spacious and traditional to the more modern and compact.*
→

---

★ ★ ★
**70%**

**COMMENDED**
♕ ♕ ♕ ♕

NEW PARK MANOR

# BROCKENHURST, HAMPSHIRE SO42 7QH
## Telephone: (0590) 23467　　　　Fax: (0590) 22268

Previously a royal hunting lodge, now a country house of real character in a peaceful New Forest setting. Tastefully decorated, reflecting the high standard of accommodation, all the 26 bedrooms are individually designed with comfort in mind and have private facilities. The restaurant overlooking the park, offers discreet and efficient service, and a menu that combines good English food with French style. A friendly bar and lounge is the perfect place for relaxation or to meet fellow guests.
A self-contained Business Centre provides conference and seminar rooms. There is much to do and see locally. Activities from sailing, golf or riding, from the hotel's own stables, can be easily arranged.

177

**B**

14⇄♪(2fb) CTV in all bedrooms ® T ✕ (ex guide dogs)
sB&B⇄♪£28.50 dB&B⇄♪£40 ☎
60P CFA *xmas*
♡ Mainly grills **V** ♧ ☑
Credit Cards ①②③

---

### BROUGHTON IN FURNESS Cumbria Map 07 SD28

#### ★★61% *Eccle Riggs*
Foxfield Rd LA20 6BN ☎(0229)716398 & 716780
*This Victorian mansion sits in parkland 1 mile south of the village.
Popular with commercial and business travellers it has very well
equipped bedrooms of varying size and standard.*
12⇄♪(6fb) CTV in all bedrooms ® T ✕ (ex guide dogs)
120P ✿ ▢ (heated) ▶ 9 sauna solarium clay pigeon shooting
♡ English & French **V** ♧ ☑ Last dinner 9pm
Credit Cards ①②③⑤

#### ★59% *Old King's Head*
Station Rd LA20 6HJ ☎(0229)716293
*Beamed bars, old photographs, horse brasses and other bric a brac
add much character to the interior of an old-world inn whose bars
and cosy dining room are renowned for the provision of excellent
food. Bedrooms are all well equipped, though only one offers en
suite facilities, and there are carefully tended gardens at the rear
of the hotel where guests can enjoy refreshments in summer.*
5rm(1♪)(1fb) CTV in all bedrooms ®
50P ✿
♧ Last dinner 9pm

---

### BROXTED Essex Map 05 TL52

#### ★★★❀❀80% Whitehall
Church End CM6 2BZ (Pride of Britain)
☎Bishops Stortford(0279)850603 FAX (0279) 850385
Closed 26-30 Dec
*This attractive black and white Elizabethan manor house stands in
hedged and walled gardens at the eastern edge of the village by the
church. Excellent food is served with imagination in the charming
beamed restaurant. Guests can enjoy pre-dinner drinks on the
terrace, in the pastel-coloured lounge or in the lively bar while
choosing from the à la carte menu or a 6-course dinner menu.
Modern dishes maintain a fine balance of colour, texture, and
flavour, and are complemented by a good wine list. Run by the
Keane family for 6 years, service is efficient and friendly.*
25⇄♪ CTV in all bedrooms ✕ (ex guide dogs)
sB&B⇄♪£75-£95 dB&B⇄♪£105-£155 ☎
35P 2❀❀ ✿ CFA ⌑ ♪ (hard) nc5yrs
♡ French **V** ✳ Sunday Lunch fr£19 Dinner fr£31.50 Last
dinner 9.30pm
Credit Cards ①②③⑤

---

### BROXTON Cheshire Map 07 SJ45

#### ★★★67% Frogg Manor
Fullersmoor, Nantwich Rd CH3 9JH ☎(0829)782629 & 782280
*A delightful Georgian house set in 8 acres of grounds and beautiful
gardens which include a tennis court, situated on the A534 about
three quarters of a mile east of its junction with the A41.
Proprietor John Sykes has tastefully refurbished the house to
create this small, personally run hotel with well equipped
accommodation.*
6⇄♪1❀ CTV in all bedrooms ® T ✳ sB⇄♪£40-£75
dB⇄♪£46.30-£95.50 (room only) ☎
37P ✿ ♪ (hard) nc4yrs
♡ English & French **V** ♧ ☑ ⅍ ✳ Lunch £11-£12.50 Dinner
£21&alc Last dinner 10pm
Credit Cards ①②③④⑤

---

#### ★★★62% Broxton Hall Country House
Whitchurch Rd CH3 9JS ☎(0829)782321 FAX (0829)782330
RS BH Mon
*This comfortable and welcoming half-timbered country house set
in 3 acres of gardens has relaxing lounges with log fires, well
equipped bedrooms and an attractive popular restaurant.*
12⇄♪(1fb)1❀⅍in 1 bedroom CTV in all bedrooms ® T ✳
sB&B⇄♪£55-£60 dB&B⇄♪£65-£85 ☎
30P ❀ ✿ nc12yrs
♡ English & French **V** ♧ ☑ ⅍
Credit Cards ①②③⑤ⓔ

**See advertisement under CHESTER**

---

### BRUTON Somerset Map 03 ST63

#### ❀ ✕Truffles
95 High St BA10 0AR ☎(0749)812255
*All the ingredients of a popular little restaurant are here: an
inviting cottage exterior, a warm welcome from Denise Bottrill, a
pretty dining room and an interesting monthly changing menu.
There is also a keenly arranged wine list, reflecting the Botrill's
interest. But most important of all is the sound cooking of Martin
Botrill, deftly marrying his classical French training with a modern
lightness, eschewing overuse of cream, sugar and flour. Not
suprisingly, chocolate truffles are served with coffee.*
Closed Mon Lunch not served Tue
Dinner not served Sun
♡ French **V** 20 seats ✳ Lunch £12.95 Dinner £17.95 Last lunch
2pm Last dinner 10.30pm ♪ nc5yrs

---

### BUCKDEN North Yorkshire Map 07 SD97

#### ★★65% Buck Inn
BD23 5JA ☎Kettlewell(075676)228 FAX (075676) 227
*This charming Georgian coaching inn, set amid the captivating
scenery of Upper Wharfedale and full of character, with cosy
beamed bars still warmed by open fires, provides an ideal base
from which to explore the area. Its recently created Courtyard
Restaurant is worth a visit, offering – as do the bars – extensive
menus and real ale hand-pulled from the stone cellar. Compact but
attractive en suite bedrooms with pine furniture and co-ordinated
colours include one with a 4-poster bed.*
15⇄♪(2fb)1❀ CTV in all bedrooms ® T ✳
sB&B⇄♪£30.30-£34.85 dB&B⇄♪£60.60-£69.70 ☎
36P CFA *xmas*
♡ International **V** ♧ ☑ ⅍ ✳ Lunch £6-£13alc Dinner £16&alc
Last dinner 9pm
Credit Cards ①③

---

### BUCKHURST HILL Essex London plan 1 F5 (page 435)

#### ★★59% The Roebuck
North End IG9 5QY (Forte Hotels) ☎081-505 4636
FAX 081-504 7826
*This creeper-clad Victorian hotel stands away from the main road
facing common land at the edge of Epping Forest. Bedrooms are
on several different floors, and are comfortable and well equipped.
Public space contains a popular locals bar with open fire.*
29⇄♪⅍in 12 bedrooms CTV in all bedrooms ® T ✳
sB⇄♪£70-£76 dB⇄♪£85-£91 (room only) ☎
45P CFA *xmas*
**V** ♧ ☑ ⅍ ✳ Lunch fr£11.20&alc High tea fr£1.25 Dinner
fr£14.80&alc Last dinner 10pm
Credit Cards ①②③⑤

Red star hotels are each
highlighted by a pink
tinted panel.

**BUCKIE** Grampian *Banffshire* Map **15** NJ46

★★57% **Cluny**
2 High St AB5 1AL ☎(0542)32922
Closed 1-2 Jan

*Conveniently situated by the town centre square, this long-established commercial hotel has a friendly atmosphere and offers good-value practical accommodation. It is also a popular venue for local functions.*
10⇄↟Annexe4rm(1fb) CTV in all bedrooms ® T
sB&B⇄↟£19-£23 dB&B⇄↟£34-£39 🛏
16P CFA
♡ Scottish & French ♦ ⬙ ✻ Bar Lunch £5.50-£7alc High tea £4.50-£7alc Dinner £8.50-£17alc Last dinner 8pm
Credit Cards ①②③⑤£

---

**BUCKINGHAM** Buckinghamshire Map **04** SP63

★★★66% **Buckingham Lodge**
Ring Rd South MK18 1RY (Consort) ☎(0280)822622
FAX (0280) 823074

*Well equipped, modern bedrooms are provided by this new and privately owned hotel beside the Buckingham ring road. Airy, open-plan public areas include a restaurant featuring some interesting dishes on its table d'hôte and à la carte menus, a range of meeting rooms is available, and the extensive leisure complex containing an indoor pool. Staff and management offer a warm welcome to guests and strive to ensure that their stay is enjoyable.*
70⇄↟(6fb)⬥in 8 bedrooms CTV in all bedrooms ® T ✻ S%
sB&B⇄↟£35-£68 dB&B⇄↟£50-£82 Continental breakfast
🛏
⟮ 120P CFA ▣ (heated) snooker sauna solarium gymnasium jacuzzi *xmas*
♡ English & French V ♦ ⬙ ⑂ ✻ Lunch £7.75-£9.75 High tea £3.20 Dinner £8.75-£9.75 Last dinner 10pm
Credit Cards ①②③£
**See advertisement under STRATFORD-UPON-AVON**

---

**BUCKLAND (NEAR BROADWAY)** Gloucestershire Map **04** SP03

★★★⊛⊛🚹
**BUCKLAND MANOR**

WR12 7LY
☎Broadway(0386)852626
FAX (0386) 853557

*This lovely Cotswold manor house is in a peaceful location just off the B4362 (formerly A46), 2 miles south of Broadway on the Cheltenham road, set against a backdrop of woods and green fields, and surrounded by 10 acres of gardens. Converted from a private house into a highly acclaimed hotel in the early 80s, it changed hands at the end of 1990, but we are happy to confirm that the staff, under the direction of Manager Nigel Power, have maintained the high standards we have come to expect. Bedrooms are mostly spacious and all are well equipped. Their names reflect their decorative schemes: Green, Floral or Oak, for example, the latter having oak panelling and a 4-poster bed. Others are named after the view, and have luxurious bathrooms with walnut veneers and exotic drapes like that in Fountain. Lounges are comfortable with log fires in winter, and the dining room has had a facelift; tables are a little close together, but there is the atmosphere of a special occasion. Staff are attentive and Chef Martyn Pearn's cooking maintains a consistently high standard.*
→

# 𝕿he
# 𝕺ld Kings Head ★

### Broughton in Furness, Cumbria LA20 6HJ
### Telephone: (0229) 716293

Claimed to be one of the oldest inns within the district, with recorded history spanning at least 300 years. Inside is full of character, the upstairs was once the town theatre and downstairs interesting reminders of the famous Broughton family of clockmakers. A traditional country town pub with an eye for modern day comforts. All the bedrooms are well equipped with central heating throughout. The restaurant has an enviable reputation and offers a full bar menu equally highly praised. Situated in the centre just a couple of hundred yards in any direction to the edge of town and the open countryside.

---

# Eccle Riggs Manor
## Hotel ★★

### Foxfield Road, Broughton in Furness, Cumbria LA20 6BN
### Telephone: (0229) 716398 & 716780

Set in 35 acres of gardens and woodlands this splendid hotel, built in 1865, has been tastefully refurbished and offers every modern amenity. Twelve bedrooms have private facilities and all have colour TV with remote control plus in house video system, radio, coffee/tea making facilities, hair dryer, trouser press and direct dial telephone. The Restaurant overlooks the lawns and Duddon Estuary. A heated indoor swimming pool with adjoining patio is open all year. The hotel is an ideal base for the golfing enthusiast with a 9 hole golf course or those who enjoy the outdoor life.

10⇨🅟(2fb)2🗗 CTV in 11 bedrooms T 🏕
sB&B⇨🅟£135-£230 dB&B⇨🅟£145-£240 🄴
30P 🚗 ❋ ⤚ (heated) ♪ (hard) croquet lawn putting
green nc12yrs *xmas*
🍴 International V ♥ ⚖ ✻ Lunch £17.50&alc Dinner
£24.80-£32.45alc Last dinner 8.45pm
Credit Cards 1️⃣ 2️⃣ 3️⃣ £

---

**BUCKLERS HARD** Hampshire Map **04** SU40

★★★64% *Master Builders House*
SO4 7XB ☎(0590)616253 FAX (0590) 612624
*Set in an original period village which is part of the Beaulieu
Estate, this hotel was the home of the 18th-century shipbuilder
Henry Adams, and has superb estuary views. The Yachtsman Bar
with its huge log fire has great character. A self service buffet is a
popular food operation, and the formal restaurant offers an
excellent value-for-money table d'hôte menu in addition to the à la
carte selection. Bedrooms in the original building and in the
modern wing are individually decorated and furnished and are
quite charming. Staff are smartly uniformed and professional.*
6⇨🅟Annexe17⇨(1fb)3🗗 CTV in all bedrooms Ⓡ
80P 🚗 ❋ ♪ clay pigeon shooting boating
🍴 English & French V ♥ ⚖ ✂ Last dinner 9.45pm
Credit Cards 1️⃣ 2️⃣ 3️⃣ 5️⃣

---

**BUCKLOW HILL** Cheshire Map **07** SJ78

★★★61% **The Swan**
WA16 6RD (De Vere) ☎(0565)830295 FAX (0565) 830614
*Originally an inn and now a busy hotel with comfortable bedrooms
and a popular restaurant, the Swan is well situated for Manchester
Airport and offers travellers a value for money package – 'Before
you Fly'.*
70⇨🄴(11fb)3🗗✂in 14 bedrooms CTV in all bedrooms Ⓡ T
✻ S10%, sB&B⇨🅟£69-£95 dB&B⇨🅟£75-£95 🄴
《 200P ❋ CFA
🍴 French & English V ♥ ⚖ ✻ S10% Lunch fr£9 High tea fr£4
Dinner fr£14.75 Last dinner 10pm
Credit Cards 1️⃣ 2️⃣ 3️⃣ 5️⃣ £

---

**BUDE** Cornwall & Isles of Scilly Map **02** SS20

★★★64% **Hartland**
Hartland Ter EX23 8JY (Exec Hotel) ☎(0288)355661
Closed Dec-Feb (ex Xmas)
*Friendly, attentive service will enhance your stay at this family-run
hotel with its fine views over town and sea. Modestly furnished
bedrooms are comfortable and well equipped, entertainment is
provided nightly, and an outdoor swimming pool with good
sunbathing facilities is an additional attraction during the summer
months.*
29⇨🅟(2fb)3🗗 CTV in all bedrooms T sB&B⇨🅟£37.60-
£41.10 dB&B⇨🅟£58.75-£70.50 🄴
Lift 30P ❋ CFA ⤚ (heated) *xmas*
🍴 International ♥ ⚖ Lunch £14.10 Dinner £16.45-£18.80 Last
dinner 8.30pm

★★65% **Bude Haven**
Flexbury Av EX23 8NS ☎(0288)352305
*This is a well kept detached Edwardian house. Freshly cooked
meals are served in the new dining room and bedrooms are well
equipped and decorated.*
13⇨🅟(1fb) CTV in all bedrooms Ⓡ 🏕 S% sB&B⇨🅟£20-£21
dB&B⇨🅟£40-£42 🄴
CTV 8P 🚗
V ♥ ⚖ S% Bar Lunch £2.50-£5.50 Dinner £7-£8 Last dinner
7.30pm
Credit Cards 1️⃣ 2️⃣ 3️⃣ £

---

★★64% **Camelot**
Downs View EX23 8RE ☎(0288)352361 FAX (0288) 355470
*Well kept and proprietor run, a hotel with strong ties to the golf
course across the road offers well equipped bedrooms and a genial
atmosphere.*
21⇨🅟(3fb) CTV in all bedrooms Ⓡ T 🏕 (ex guide dogs) ✻
sB&B⇨🅟£20.50-£25.50 dB&B⇨🅟£41-£51 🄴
21P 🚗 solarium *xmas*
V ✂ ✻ Dinner £14&alc Last dinner 8.30pm
Credit Cards 1️⃣ 3️⃣ £

★★62% **St Margaret's**
Killerton Rd EX23 8EN ☎(0288)352252 & 352401
FAX (0288) 355995
*Quietly situated a short walk from the town centre, this is a small
well run hotel with friendly staff. Bedrooms are being upgraded
and home cooked meals are available, with vegetables being
imaginatively cooked.*
10⇨🅟(3fb) CTV in all bedrooms Ⓡ T sB&B⇨🅟£26-£30
dB&B⇨🅟£51-£55 🄴
CTV 4P 🚗 ❋ CFA games room *xmas*
🍴 English & Continental V ♥ ⚖ Lunch £6.50 Dinner £9&alc
Last dinner 8.30pm
Credit Cards 1️⃣ 3️⃣ £

★★61% **Penarvor**
Crooklets Beach EX23 8NE ☎(0288)352036 FAX (0288) 355027
Closed Nov-Feb
*With fine views of the bay and the golf course, this detached house
is professionally run by resident proprietors Leighton and Mair
Davies, with the help of their friendly staff. The bedrooms are all
well equipped and the spacious dining room is well appointed.*
16⇨🅟(3fb) CTV in all bedrooms Ⓡ T sB&B⇨🅟£23-£26
dB&B⇨🅟£46-£52 🄴
20P ❋ solarium gymnasium pool table games room
🍴 English & French V ✂ Bar Lunch £2-£4.50 Dinner
fr£12.50&alc Last dinner 8pm
Credit Cards 1️⃣ 2️⃣ 3️⃣ £

★★60% **Florida**
17-18 Summerleaze Crescent EX23 8HJ ☎(0288)352451
Closed 10 Nov-Feb
*A personally-run small hotel with a friendly atmosphere, offering
well-organised activity holidays which are especially suitable for
adventurous children. Brightly decorated bedrooms, though not
very large, are well equipped and there is also a small selection of
student/teenager rooms. Public areas include a choice of
comfortable lounges and a pleasant dining room where the short
table d'hôte menu includes some interesting dishes. Set in a row of
terraced properties near to both the town centre and Summerleaze
Beach, the hotel commands good views over the river estuary and
out to sea.*
19rm(12⇨🅟)(4fb) CTV in all bedrooms Ⓡ 🏕 (ex guide dogs)
sB&B£26.90-£28.60 sB&B⇨🅟£29.68-£33 dB&B⇨🅟£59.36-
£66 (incl dinner) 🄴
10P games room
V ♥ ✻ Bar Lunch £1.50-£4.65 Dinner £10.50 Last dinner
7.30pm
£

★63% **Maer Lodge**
Crooklets Beach EX23 8NG ☎(0288)353306
*A small detached hotel, run for the last 32 years by Bill and Beryl
Stanley, overlooking the Downs and a short walk from Crooklets
Beach. Service by Mr Stanley and his son Ashley is friendly and
relaxed, assisted in the main season by part time staff. Mrs
Stanley's hot puddings are worthy of note.*
19rm(15⇨🅟)(3fb)✂in all bedrooms CTV in all bedrooms Ⓡ
S% sB&B£21.50-£25.50 sB&B⇨🅟£24-£28 dB&B£39-£47
dB&B⇨🅟£44-£52 🄴
CTV 20P ❋ CFA pool table mini-golf 🛷 *xmas*

♀ English & Continental **V** ✿ ⚌ ⅍ S% Dinner fr£8.50 Last dinner 7.30pm
Credit Cards 1 3 £

★60% **Meva Gwin**
Upton EX23 0LY ☎(0288)352347
Closed 5 Oct-17 Apr
*This hotel has glorious coastal and country views. Simple traditional fare is served in the dining room. Bedrooms are mostly en suite, light and airy and are simply furnished. The Surf-Rider bar is a popular venue for residents of the hotel.*
11rm(4⇨6♠)(4fb) CTV in all bedrooms ® ✕ sB&B£14-£18 sB&B⇨♠£16-£20 dB&B⇨♠£32-£40
CTV 44P ✿
✿ ⚌ ⅍ ✳ Dinner £7.95 Last dinner 7.30pm

★59% **Edgcumbe**
Summerleaze Crescent EX23 8HJ ☎(0288)353846
*Personally run hotel specialising in family holidays.*
15rm(8♠)(5fb) CTV in all bedrooms ® sB&B£16-£18.25 sB&B♠£19-£21.50 dB&B£32-£36.50 dB&B♠£38-£43 ▤
CTV 7P pool table *xmas*
**V** ✿ ⚌ Bar Lunch £3-£10alc Dinner fr£8.50 Last dinner 7.30pm
Credit Cards 1 2 3

---

**BUILTH WELLS** Powys Map 03 SO05

★★★⚌64% **Caer Beris Manor**
LD2 3NP (Inter-Hotels) ☎(0982)552601 FAX (0982) 552586
*Set in 27 acres of parkland, rich in bird life, and alongside the River Irfon, this comfortably appointed country hotel features spacious public rooms including the Elizabethan panelled dining room. Bedrooms are all tastefully decorated and staff are particularly friendly and helpful.*
21⇨(1fb)4▤ CTV in all bedrooms ® **T**
30P 2🏇 ✿ CFA ✎ ♁ clay pigeon shooting
♀ International **V** ✿ ⚌ ✳ Lunch £14.50 High tea £6.50-£7.50 Dinner £15.50&alc Last dinner 10pm
Credit Cards 1 3 5

★★64% **Pencerrig Country House**
LD2 3TF (Consort) ☎(0982)553226 FAX (0982) 552347
*This country mansion just off the A483 between Builth and Llandindrod Wells caters well for functions and conferences as well as providing bedrooms equipped with modern comforts and public areas which include comfortable lounges and bars.*
20⇨♠(1fb)1▤ CTV in all bedrooms ® **T** ✳
sB&B⇨♠fr£43.50 dB&B⇨♠fr£64 ▤
⟨ 40P ✿ CFA *xmas*
♀ English & French **V** ✿ ⚌ ✳ Lunch fr£8.50 Dinner fr£13.50 Last dinner 9pm
Credit Cards 1 2 3 5

★★59% **Lion**
2 Broad St LD2 3DT ☎(0982)553670 FAX (0982) 553999
*At the heart of the mid-Wales market town close to the River Wye, this historic hotel has two cosy bars and a traditional lounge. The modestly furnished bedrooms were, at the time of inspection, being improved.*
20rm(12⇨2♠)(4fb)1▤ CTV in all bedrooms ® **T**
sB&B£26.75-£32.50 sB&B⇨♠£32.50 dB&B£43 dB&B⇨♠£54 ▤
CTV 12P CFA *xmas*
♀ English, French & Italian **V** ✿ ⚌ ✳ Lunch £6.50-£6.90&alc High tea fr£4 Dinner fr£10.25&alc Last dinner 9.30pm
Credit Cards 1 3 £

**BUNWELL** Norfolk Map 05 TM19

★★⚌64% **Bunwell Manor**
Bunwell St NR16 1QU ☎(0953)788304
*Set back from the village road in its own grounds, this modestly furnished country house dates from the 16th-century but has all modern amenities. The welcoming resident owners Bob and Maggie Nylk ensure the comfort of their guests, and there is an attractive restaurant and separate bar.*
10⇨♠(2fb) CTV in all bedrooms ® **T** sB&B⇨♠£40-£44 dB&B⇨♠£55-£60 ▤
30P ✿ *xmas*
**V** ✿ Lunch £11.25&alc Dinner £11.25&alc Last dinner 9.30pm
Credit Cards 1 3 £

---

**BURBAGE** Wiltshire Map 04 SU26

★★55% *Savernake Forest*
Savernake SN8 3AY (1m NE off A346)
☎Marlborough(0672)810206
*A hotel in a rural setting on the edge of the forest, beside the Kennet and Avon Canal, offers well equipped bedrooms (about half of which have been refurbished), a Buttery lunch and dinner menu in the bar which is augmented by the restaurant's evening table d'hôte and à la carte choice, and informal service from a friendly local staff.*
10⇨♠Annexe6⇨♠(2fb)1▤ CTV in all bedrooms ® **T**
CTV 80P ✿ ✎
♀ English & French **V** ✿ Last dinner 9.15pm
Credit Cards 1 2 3 5
**See advertisement under MARLBOROUGH**

---

**BURFORD** Oxfordshire Map 04 SP21

★★★61% *The Bay Tree*
Sheep St OX8 4LW (Select) ☎(099382)2791
*In the centre of the village of Burford, the Bay Tree makes an ideal base for touring the Cotswolds. The hotel dates back to the 16th century, and has been carefully restored, refurbished and tastefully decorated, yet still retains the original oak beams, fireplaces and flag-stone floors, all enhanced with the unique furnishings.*
23rm

★★★59% *Inn For All Seasons*
Little Barrington OX8 4TN (3m W on A40)
☎Windrush(04514)324 FAX (04514) 508
*On the A40 3 miles west of Burford, this 16th-century former coaching inn with beams, stone walls and open fires has comfortable bedrooms well equipped with modern facilities. Attractive public areas include a cosy lounge near the main restaurant, and a popular conservatory restaurant overlooking the gardens.*
9⇨♠(1fb) CTV in all bedrooms ® **T** ✕
30P ✿ Shooting nc10yrs
**V** ✿ ⚌ Last dinner 9.30pm
Credit Cards 1 3

★★67% *Cotswold Gateway*
Cheltenham Rd OX8 4HX ☎(099382)2695 FAX (099382) 3600
*On the crown of the hill leading into the picturesque village, this old Coltswold stone building has been attractively refurbished to provide comfortable bedrooms of varying sizes, all equipped with modern facilities. The pretty restaurant offers enjoyable dishes served by friendly attentive staff.*
13⇨Annexe4⇨(4fb) CTV in all bedrooms ® **T**
60P 🚲
♀ English & French **V** ✿ ⚌ Last dinner 9.45pm
Credit Cards 1 2 3 5

---

For key to symbols in English see the bookmark.

A rosette means exceptional standards of cuisine.

### ★★ ❀64% **Golden Pheasant**
High St OX8 4RJ ☎(099382)3223 & 3417 Telex no 849041
FAX (099382) 2621
*This attractive hotel, dating back in part to the 14th-century but predominantly 15th-century, is situated centrally in the town's pretty High Street. Recently refurbished front-facing public areas are very comfortable and cosy, particularly in winter when the open-plan lounge boasts a roaring fire. Bedrooms (including 2 located in the courtyard) are pleasantly furnished with co-ordinating fabrics and antiques which include an impressive 17th-century bed in one of the 2 four-poster rooms. A friendly young management and staff, though professionally efficient, create a relaxed atmosphere.*
12⇅🛏(2fb)2🛏 CTV in all bedrooms ® T sB&B⇅🛏£55-£60
dB&B⇅🛏£75-£85 🅿
CTV 18P 🚗 CFA *xmas*
♥ English & French V ♦ ♨ ✂ Lunch £6.95-£12.95 High tea £2.50-£8 Dinner £12.95-£20.95 Last dinner 9.30pm
Credit Cards [1][2][3] ⓔ

---

### BURGH HEATH Surrey Map **04** TQ25 ⊘

### ★★ 62% **Heathside**
Brighton Rd KT20 6BW ☎(0737)353355 FAX (0737) 370857
*At the time of inspection a new block of bedrooms, a 'plunge pool' a mini gym and sauna were planned and the original bedrooms were to be upgraded. By publication of this guide, the Heathside Hotel will have been completely renovated and upgraded.*
73⇅🛏(32fb)✂in 11 bedrooms CTV in all bedrooms ® T
sB&B⇅🛏£65-£75 dB&B⇅🛏£75-£85 🅿
⟨ 150P ✿ CFA ⊠ (heated) sauna gymnasium *xmas*
♥ English & French ♦ ♨ ✂ Lunch fr£12 Dinner fr£14 Last dinner 10pm
Credit Cards [1][2][3][5]

---

### BURLEY Hampshire Map **04** SU20

### ★★★ 62% **Moorhill House**
BH24 4AG ☎(04253)3285 FAX (0703) 283719
*Set in 3 acres of lawns and gardens and surrounded by the New Forest, the hotel offers comfortable lounges with leather chairs and sofas. Bedrooms are all furnished and equipped to a similar standard. There is a choice of menus in the restaurant and service is friendly, relaxed, yet professional. The small leisure complex is popular with residents.*
24⇅🛏(7fb) CTV in all bedrooms ® T sB&B⇅🛏£44-£66
dB&B⇅🛏£73-£95 🅿
CTV 40P 🚗 ✿ CFA ⊠ (heated) sauna jacuzzi spa bath ♨
*xmas*
V ♦ ♨ ✂ Sunday Lunch £11 High tea fr£5.50 Dinner £11&alc
Last dinner 9pm
Credit Cards [1][2][3][5] ⓔ

### ★★★ 58% **Burley Manor**
Ringwood Rd BH24 4BS (Forestdale) ☎(04253)3522
Telex no 41565 FAX (04253) 3227
*This 19th-century manor house is set in 54 acres of parkland, within the New Forest, with skilfully extended ground floor accommodation. There is a large meeting room and open style country house bar, lounge and restaurant. Riding stables are nearby, and a separate conference and banqueting suite adjoins the main house. Service is relaxed and friendly and particularly well managed by Miss Sally Whittle, the general manager. An interesting and reliable standard of cooking is available, along with a good wine list.*
20⇅🛏Annexe10⇅🛏(3fb)4🛏✂in 4 bedrooms CTV in all
bedrooms ® T sB&B⇅🛏£40-£62.50 dB&B⇅🛏£50-£87.50 🅿
60P ✿ CFA ⊇ (heated) ♪ ∪ croquet *xmas*
V ♦ ♨ ✿ Sunday Lunch fr£10.95 High tea fr£5.45 Dinner fr£12.50&alc Last dinner 10pm
Credit Cards [1][2][3][5] ⓔ

---

### BURNHAM Buckinghamshire Map **04** SU98

### ★★★ ❀65% **Burnham Beeches Moat House**
Grove Rd SL1 8DP (Queens Moat) ☎(0628)603333
FAX (0628) 603994
*A splendid Georgian house set in its own grounds, with modern bedroom extensions containing some spacious and attractive rooms. Public areas have a certain style with moulded ceilings and oil paintings, and there is a fine panelled restaurant where guests can enjoy a wide variety of dishes created by Lawrence Bryant.*
75⇅2🛏✂in 8 bedrooms CTV in all bedrooms ® T ✱
sB&B⇅🛏£86-£91 dB&B⇅🛏£98-£103 🅿
Lift ⟨ 150P ✿ CFA ⊠ (heated) ♪ (hard) sauna solarium gymnasium croquet *xmas*
♥ French V ♦ ♨ ✱ Lunch fr£16&alc Dinner fr£19&alc Last dinner 10pm
Credit Cards [1][2][3][4][5] ⓔ

### ★★ 58% **Grovefield**
Taplow Common Rd SL1 8LP ☎(0628)603131 Telex no 846873
Closed 1 wk Xmas
*This late Victorian country house, set in 7.5 acres of gardens in the heart of the Thames Valley, has been extended and modernised to offer well equipped comfortable bedrooms, with some more spacious rooms in the original house. An extensive choice of dishes is available in the restaurant and there are various conference facilities.*
42⇅🛏 CTV in all bedrooms ®
Lift ⟨ 100P 🚗 🚗 ✿ ♨
♥ International V ♦ Last dinner 10.30pm
Credit Cards [1][2][3][4][5]

---

### BURNHAM MARKET Norfolk Map **09** TF84

### ★★ 69% **Hoste Arms**
The Green PE31 8HE ☎(0328)738257 FAX (0328) 730103
*Fully restored and modernised, with elegant furnishings designed to enhance its original features, this lovely 17th-century coaching inn stands on the green of a peaceful Georgian village ; fresh, good value bar meals provide an alternative to restaurant menus featuring local fish and game.*
8⇅🛏(1fb)2🛏✂in 2 bedrooms CTV in all bedrooms ® T
sB&B⇅🛏£38-£48 dB&B⇅🛏£60-£80 🅿
30P 🚗 ✿ CFA ⊠ (heated) sauna ♪ *xmas*
♥ English & French V ♦ ♨ ✂ Lunch £5.50-£12.50alc Dinner £10-£16alc Last dinner 9.30pm
Credit Cards [1][3] ⓔ

---

### BURNHAM-ON-CROUCH Essex Map **05** TQ99

### ❀✕✕**Contented Sole**
80 High St CM0 8AA ☎Maldon(0621)782139
Closed Sun, Mon, last 2 wks Jul & 4 wks Sat prior 25 Dec
♥ English & French V 65 seats ✱ Lunch £10&alc Dinner £17.50-£27.50alc Last lunch 2pm Last dinner 9.30pm 🅿

---

### BURNHAM-ON-SEA Somerset Map **03** ST34

### ★★ 61% **Royal Clarence**
31 The Esplanade TA8 1BQ (Minotels) ☎(0278)783138
FAX (0278) 792965
*Situated on the seafront, this family-run hotel has recently been upgraded throughout. The accommodation is comfortable and bedrooms are well equipped. Comprehensive table d'hote and à la carte menus are offered in the dining room, and dishes are well prepared. Guests can also sample the real ale made on the premises.*
16rm(14⇅🛏)Annexe2⇅🛏(2fb) CTV in all bedrooms ® T ✱
sB&B⇅🛏£28 dB&B⇅🛏£43 🅿
CTV 20P 🚗 CFA

V ✿ ⬛ ✱ Lunch £5.95 Dinner £10.50&alc Last dinner 8.30pm
Credit Cards ①②③⑤
See advertisement under **BRIDGWATER**

---

**BURNLEY** Lancashire Map **07** SD83 ◉

**★★★71% Oaks**
Colne Rd, Reedley BB10 2LF (Shire) ☎(0282)414141
FAX (0282) 33401
*A country house has been sympathetically converted to offer comfortable, tastefully modernised bedrooms and fine public rooms which retain its original character.*
58⇨🛏(10fb)2🛏✁in 28 bedrooms CTV in all bedrooms ® **T**
✱ S% sB&B⇨🛏£75.50-£85.50 dB&B⇨🛏£94-£104 🅿
《 100P ✿ CFA ⬛ (heated) squash snooker sauna solarium gymnasium spa pool *xmas*
🍴 English & French V ✿ ⬛ ✁
Credit Cards ①②③④⑤

**★★★63% Keirby**
Keirby Walk BB11 2DH (Consort) ☎(0282)27611
Telex no 63119 FAX (0282) 36370
Closed 24-26 Dec
*Staff are friendly and helpful at this purpose-built commercial hotel in the town centre; all the well equipped bedrooms are maintained to a good standard, though some are fairly compact.*
49⇨🛏(12fb)✁in 12 bedrooms CTV in all bedrooms ® **T**
sB⇨🛏£50-£60.25 dB⇨🛏£59.75-£70 (room only) 🅿
Lift 《 CTV 100P 20🚗 CFA mini-gym
🍴 English & French V ✿ ⬛ ✁ Lunch fr£8.50 Dinner fr£12.75
Last dinner 10pm
Credit Cards ①②③⑤ⓔ

**★★65% Rosehill House**
Rosehill Av B11 2PW ☎(0282)53931 FAX (0282) 55628
*A tastefully converted country house offers comfortable accommodation and interesting menus.*
20⇨🛏(1fb)1🛏 CTV in all bedrooms ® **T** ✱ sB&B⇨🛏£28-£38.50 dB&B⇨🛏£39-£56 🅿
CTV 70P 1🚗 🚲 ✿
V ✿ ⬛ ✱ Lunch £9.75-£11.50 Dinner £9.75-£11.50 Last dinner 9.30pm
Credit Cards ①③⑤ⓔ

**⛫Forte Travelodge**
Cavalry Barracks, Barracks Rd BB11 4AS (junc A671/A679)
(Forte) ☎(0282)416039 Central Res (0800) 850950
*Conveniently situated just off junction 10 of the M65, this small unit offers good value comfortable modern accommodation. Meals are available at the Happy Eater in the adjacent car parking area.*
32⇨🛏(32fb) CTV in all bedrooms ® sB⇨🛏£29.95
dB⇨🛏£29.95 (room only)
《 32P 🚲
Credit Cards ①②③

---

**BURNSALL** North Yorkshire Map **07** SE06

**★★69% *Fell***
BD23 6BT ☎(075672)209
*Beautifully situated with spectacular views of the surrounding fells and River Wharfe, this is a family run hotel providing warm Yorkshire hospitality. Many of the cosy bedrooms have recently been refurbished and guests can relax in two lounges.*
14rm(10⇨1🛏)(4fb) ®
CTV 60P ✿ 🐾
V ✿ ⬛
Credit Cards ①②③

---

For key to symbols in English see the bookmark.

---

**★★★66% Red Lion**
BD23 6BU ☎(075672)204
*Situated in the heart of the picturesque Dales village of Burnsall, overlooking the River Wharfe, this charming hotel offers comfortable accommodation. Bedrooms are located in the main hotel and in an adjacent annexe. A good selection of food is available either from the attractive restaurant or from the cosy public bar, and all food is cooked to a high standard. Guests can relax in the comfortable lounge.*
8rm(2⇨)Annexe4⇨🛏(2fb) CTV in 4 bedrooms ® ✈ ✱
sB&Bfr£24 dB&Bfr£38 dB&B⇨🛏fr£48
CTV 40P CFA ⚓
✿

---

**BURNTISLAND** Fife Map **11** NT28

**★★69% Inchview Hotel**
69 Kinghorn Rd KY3 9EB ☎Kirkcaldy(0592)872239
*A pleasant, friendly hotel managed by the resident proprietors. The traditional bedrooms are spacious and well appointed and the food is imaginative and well prepared.*
12⇨🛏(3fb)🛏 CTV in all bedrooms ® **T** sB&B⇨🛏£42.50
dB&B⇨🛏£55 🅿
15P *xmas*
🍴 International V ✿ ⬛ Lunch £8.95&alc High tea £8.50-£12
Dinner £16.95-£19.50&alc Last dinner 9.45pm
Credit Cards ①②③ⓔ

---

**BURNT YATES** North Yorkshire Map **08** SE26

**★★68% Bay Horse Inn & Motel**
HG3 3EJ ☎Harrogate(0423)770230
*Originally an eighteenth-century coaching inn, the Bay Horse retains its original atmosphere with low beams, log fires and a traditionally friendly welcome. Meals are of a particularly good standard – the bar food's local popularity making for brisk trade* →

**B**

*while bedrooms are prettily decorated and well equipped, some being situated in an adjacent house of later date.*
5🜚Annexe10🜚 CTV in all bedrooms ® T ✱ sB&Bℕ£36-£39 dB&Bℕ£49-£55 🔒
100P CFA *xmas*
♀ English & French V ✧ ⚖ Lunch £8.95 High tea fr£8.95 Dinner £13.95-£15.95&alc Last dinner 9.30pm
Credit Cards 1️⃣ 2️⃣ 3️⃣ ⓔ

---

### BURRINGTON Devon Map **02** SS61

#### ★★★🏵🔱69% **Northcote Manor**
EX37 9LZ (2m NW of village towards Station & A377) (Best Western) ☎High Bickington(0769)60501 FAX (0769) 60770
Closed Nov-Feb
*Once the home of the local squire, this small relaxed and informal country house is set in 12 acres of sweeping lawns and landscaped gardens. Under the personal ownership of Peter and Glenda Brown the hotel has benefited from refurbishment to the public areas and the majority of the bedrooms (the remaining bedrooms are due for identical treatment). Enjoyable country house cooking uses fresh produce and homegrown organic vegetables.*
11⇄🜚🄝🛏 CTV in all bedrooms ® T sB&B⇄🜚fr£51 dB&B⇄🜚fr£100 🔒
20P 🚗 ✿ ℛ (hard) croquet nc12yrs
♀ English & French ✧ ⚖ ✂ Lunch £10-£15 Dinner £17.50-£18.50 Last dinner 8.30pm
Credit Cards 1️⃣ 2️⃣ 3️⃣ 5️⃣ ⓔ

---

### BURTON UPON TRENT Staffordshire Map **08** SK22 ☺

#### ★★★63% **Riverside Inn**
Riverside Dr, Branston DE14 3EP ☎(0283)511234
FAX (0283) 511441
Closed 30 Dec RS 24-26 & 31 Dec
*Set in gardens reaching down to the Trent, the original inn is the heart of this hotel, with a modern bedroom wing at one end of the building and a function suite at the other. The popular restaurant offers a varied choice of meals served by professional but friendly staff. Last year the company acquired the adjacent golf course, available to guests at certain times.*
22⇄ CTV in all bedrooms ® T ✱ sB&B⇄£58 dB&B⇄£68 🔒
《 130P ✿ CFA ⚓
♀ English & French V ✧ ⚖ ✱ Lunch £9.95-£14.40&alc Dinner £14.95-£17.45&alc Last dinner 10pm
Credit Cards 1️⃣ 2️⃣ 3️⃣

---

### BURTONWOOD MOTORWAY SERVICE AREA (M62) Cheshire Map **07** SJ59

#### ⛫Forte Travelodge
WA5 3AX (between junc 7 & 9 M62 westbound) (Forte)
☎Central Res (0800) 850950
40⇄🜚(40fb) CTV in all bedrooms ® sB⇄🜚£29.95 dB⇄🜚£29.95 (room only)
40P 🚗

---

### BURY Greater Manchester Map **07** SD81 ☺

#### ★★★🏵🏵🏵72% **Normandie**
Elbut Ln, Birtle BL9 6UT ☎061-764 3869 & 061-764 1170
Telex no 635091 FAX 061-764 4866
Closed 26 Dec-8 Jan RS Sun
*Originally a small country inn, but now enlarged and extended in a variety of architectural styles, this hotel enjoys panoramic views over the Manchester plain from its setting on a hillside at Birtle, one mile off the B6222. The restaurant is very much the heart of the operation, and a dedicated chef's flair, sound technique and real understanding of how to combine flavours and textures is brought to bear on the best of ingredients. Though all bedrooms are equipped to modern standards the superior ones, with their spotless and brightly lit bathrooms, are particularly attractive and*

*comfortable. Attentive service under the personal supervision of the proprietor includes such extras as comprehensive evening room service and excellent shoe cleaning.*
21⇄🜚Annexe3⇄🜚 CTV in all bedrooms ® T
✘ (ex guide dogs) sB&B⇄🜚£59-£69 dB&B⇄🜚£69-£79 Continental breakfast
Lift 《 60P 🚗 ✿
♀ French V ✂ ✱ Lunch £12.50-£15&alc Dinner £18.95&alc Last dinner 9.30pm
Credit Cards 1️⃣ 2️⃣ 3️⃣ 5️⃣

#### ★★64% **Bolholt**
Walshaw Rd BL8 1PU ☎061-764 5239 & 061-764 3888
FAX 061-763 1789
*Set in grounds reclaimed from industrial land, this former mill-owner's residence a mile northwest of the town centre has gradually been extended to provide comfortable well equipped bedrooms, with small conference and leisure facilities. Service is friendly and informal.*
47rm(43⇄3🜚)(2fb)2🛏 CTV in 38 bedrooms ® T
✘ (ex guide dogs) sB&B⇄🜚£48 dB&B⇄🜚£58 🔒
CTV 200P ✿ ℛ (hard) ⚓ sauna gymnasium bowling pool table table tennis darts
♀ International V ✧ ⚖ Lunch £8&alc Dinner £10-£14&alc Last dinner 9pm
Credit Cards 1️⃣ 2️⃣ 3️⃣ 5️⃣

#### ★60% **Woolfield House**
Wash Ln BL9 6BJ ☎061-797 9775
*This family-run commercial hotel conveniently situated between the M66 and the town centre offers compact but well equipped bedrooms, the best of which are in a modern wing to the rear.*
16rm(3⇄7🜚)1🛏 CTV in 11 bedrooms TV in 5 bedrooms ® T
✘ (ex guide dogs) ✱ sB&B£22-£23 sB&B⇄🜚£32-£34 dB&B£39 dB&B⇄🜚£45-£47
40P nc3yrs
✧ ⚖ ✱ Bar Lunch fr£3.25alc Dinner £9-£15alc Last dinner 8.30pm
Credit Cards 1️⃣ 3️⃣

---

### BURY ST EDMUNDS Suffolk Map **05** TL86 ☺

See also Lawshall

#### ★★★🏵76% **Angel**
Angel Hill IP33 1LT ☎(0284)753926 Telex no 81630
FAX (0284) 750092
*Situated at the Abbey, this 15th century, ivy-clad building is of long standing repute. It is a hotel where hospitality and good personal services are readily provided, and since January 1991 has been under the experienced guidance of the new General Manager John Robson. Rooms are individually fashioned and furnished, and share the same range of facilities, levelled at quality and comfort. The large lounge is comfortably furnished with plump cushioned sofas and armchairs. The Regency Restaurant in the Angel is an elegant room – fine paintings are on the walls, and good silver and china adorn the tables. Menus concentrate on classical English dishes such as the roast, which is moist and succulent and carved at the table. Accompanying vegetables are uncomplicated and firm. The home-made desserts are in a quite straightforward style.*
41⇄🜚 CTV in all bedrooms T ✱ sB⇄🜚£70-£80 dB⇄🜚£100-£155 (room only) 🔒
《 50P 12🚗 CFA
♀ English & French V ✧ ⚖ ✱ Lunch £12.95 Dinner £19.75&alc Last dinner 9.45pm
Credit Cards 1️⃣ 2️⃣ 3️⃣ 5️⃣

#### ★★★🏵🔱75% **Ravenwood Hall**
Rougham IP30 9JA (3m E off A45) ☎Beyton(0359)70345
FAX (0359) 70788
*Situated by the A45 just east of the town, this personally run Tudor country house, set in secluded grounds and woodlands, offers warm hospitality. The comfortable accommodation is*

furnished to a high standard and the restaurant comes up with some interesting dishes which follow the seasons of the year : light asparagus and yogurt timbale as a starter ; crispy Gressingham Duck cooked in the Aga, already boned and rolled with a delightfully crispy outer layer, followed by steamed treacle suet pudding and a good selection of hand made cheeses are some of the choices. The wine list is predominantly French.

14⇨Annexe 6rm1🛏 CTV in 14 bedrooms ® sB&B⇨£72-£82.50 dB&B⇨£93.50-£100 🍴

100P 3🏊 🛁 ❀ CFA ⌷ (heated) ♪ (hard) ◡ croquet shooting parties *xmas*

V ♥ ⌷ Lunch £18&alc High tea £5.25 Dinner £18&alc Last dinner 9.30pm

Credit Cards ①②③⑤

### ★★★ 70% The Priory

Tollgate IP32 6EH (Best Western) ☎(0284)766181 FAX (0284) 767604

*An 18th-century house behind a high brick and flint wall, with mature trees and lovely lawns, in a residential area quite close to the town centre. A relaxed country house atmosphere prevails despite its proximity to main roads. All bedrooms are spacious and well equipped, many of them garden rooms of a bungalow appearance with an attractive courtyard and extensive lawns in front. To find the Priory from the town, follow the signs to Thetford.*

9⇨🏠Annexe18⇨🏠(2fb)⌿in 2 bedrooms CTV in all bedrooms ® T sB&B⇨🏠£49-£57 dB&B⇨🏠£63-£75 🍴

70P 2🏊 ❀ CFA ⌷

♡ English & French V ♥ ⌷ ✳ Lunch £16.50&alc Dinner £16.50&alc Last dinner 9.45pm

Credit Cards ①②③⑤ ⓔ

### ★★★ 64% Butterfly

Symonds Rd, Moreton Hall IP32 7BW (Consort) ☎(0284)760884 FAX (0284) 755476

*A friendly well kept hotel at the junction of the A45 eastbound and A134 features attractive cottage-style restaurant/bar and lounge seating. Double bedrooms tend to be compact, but the singles are particularly comfortable, and a determined effort is made to maintain the relaxed atmosphere which is appreciated by both commercial and leisure users.*

66⇨🏠(2fb) CTV in all bedrooms ® T ✻ (ex guide dogs) S% sB⇨🏠£56.50-£58.50 dB⇨🏠£56.50-£58.50 (room only) 🍴 ℄85P

♡ European V ♥ ⌷ ⅄ S% Lunch £9.50-£10.50&alc Dinner £10.50-£11.50&alc Last dinner 10pm

Credit Cards ①②③⑤

### ★★ 77% *Kingshotts Hotel & Restaurant*

12 Angel Hill IP33 1UZ ☎(0284)704088 FAX (0284) 763133

*This delightful hotel can, perhaps, best be described as a country house in the town. Resident proprietors, Gary and Dianne Kingshott have sympathetically converted a small 18th-century town house to provide generally spacious bedrooms, each with its own character and style. Public areas are compact but of good quality and the well appointed restaurant has gained a good local reputation.*

6⇨🏠1🛏 CTV in all bedrooms T ✻ (ex guide dogs) 3P 🚗

V ♥ Last dinner 9pm

Credit Cards ①③

### ★★ 64% The Suffolk

38 The Buttermarket IP33 1DC (Forte Hotels) ☎(0284)753995 FAX (0284) 750973

*Ample parking space is available at the rear of an hotel which remains a popular meeting place for locals and visitors alike. The accommodation is generally well furnished and equipped, while staff offer ready smiles as well as efficient service.*

33⇨🏠(4fb)⌿in 15 bedrooms CTV in all bedrooms ® T ✳ sB⇨🏠fr£70 dB⇨🏠fr£90 (room only) 🍴

℄ 20P 16🚗 *xmas*

→

**B**

V ✿ ☑ ✂ ✱ Lunch fr£9.95&alc Dinner fr£14.95&alc Last dinner 9.30pm
Credit Cards ① ② ③ ⑤

### ✹ ✕ Mortimer's Seafood
31 Churchgate St IP33 1RG ☎(0284)760623

*Former shop premises, situated at the centre of the town in a building dating back to the 15th century, have for the past 6 or 7 years housed a fish restaurant. Wine merchant Michael Gooding and his partner Ken Ambler present fresh fish in a straightforward manner, the advertised sauces being interchangeable, included only as a suggestion to clients. Main courses follow a fairly consistent repertoire of North Sea fish, allowing for seasonal changes; competently cooked dishes are accompanied only by buttered new potatoes and a token salad, while starters remain simple and desserts light. House wine and mineral water seem the popular drinks, but there is also a short list of white Burgundies including Puligny Montrachet for the more adventurous.*

Closed Sun, BH's & following Tue, 2 wks Aug & 23 Dec-3 Jan Lunch not served Sat
♀ British & French 60 seats Lunch £10-£25alc Dinner £10-£25alc Last lunch 2pm Last dinner 8.15-9pm ✍ ✂
Credit Cards ① ② ③ ⑤

---

### BUTE, ISLE OF Strathclyde *Buteshire* Map **10**

### ROTHESAY Map **10** NS06

#### ★60% St Ebba
37 Mountstuart Rd, Craigmore PA20 9EB ☎(0700)502683
*Modest, homely hotel on the south bay looking across to the Cowal Peninsula. The dinner menu, though limited, offers honest home cooking.*
11⇨➚(3fb) CTV in all bedrooms ® ✱ sB&B⇨➚£22 dB&B⇨➚£44
CTV 7P ⇱ *xmas*
V ✿ ☑ ✱ Dinner fr£7 Last dinner 7pm

---

### BUTTERMERE Cumbria Map **11** NY11

#### ★★66% Bridge
CA13 9UZ ☎(059685)252 & 266
*This hotel stands at the heart of Lakeland walking country, surrounded by fells and between Lake Buttermere and Crummock Water; featuring a bar serving well-kept real ales and a very comfortable lounge, it is the hub of the local community.*
22⇨➚2▨ ® T sB&B⇨➚£39.50-£57.50 dB&B⇨➚£64-£98 (incl dinner) ▤
50P ⇱ CFA *xmas*
♀ English & French V ✿ ✂ Bar Lunch £3-£16alc High tea £3.50-£5 Dinner £16.50 Last dinner 8.30pm

---

### BUXTON Derbyshire Map **07** SK07

#### ★★★68% Lee Wood
13 Manchester Rd SK17 6TQ (Best Western) ☎(0298)23002 & 70421 Telex no 669848 FAX (0298) 23228
Closed 24-29 Dec
*Known locally for its friendly efficient service, and just a short walk from the town centre, the hotel is popular with tourists and business guests alike – particularly for small conferences. Nearly all the bedrooms have been refurbished over the last year and now offer well equipped and comfortable facilities, with just 3 more modest rooms remaining. Public rooms include a conservatory restaurant with pleasant views over the garden.*
36⇨➚(2fb)✂in 4 bedrooms CTV in all bedrooms ® T sB&B⇨➚£59-£72 dB&B⇨➚£74-£92 ▤
Lift ( CTV 50P ✿ CFA
♀ English & French V ✿ ☑ Lunch £9.25-£18alc Dinner £16-£17.50&alc Last dinner 9.30pm
Credit Cards ① ② ③ ⑤ ⓔ

---

#### ★★★60% Palace
Palace Rd SK17 6AG (Forte Hotels) ☎(0298)22001 Telex no 668169 FAX (0298) 72131

*This impressive Victorian building overlooking the spa town provides recently upgraded bedrooms and elegant public areas. Guests can also enjoy the gymnasium, swimming pool and well laid out gardens.*
122⇨➚(12fb)✂in 33 bedrooms CTV in all bedrooms ® T ✱ S% sB⇨➚£70 dB⇨➚£80-£135 (room only) ▤
Lift ( 100P ✿ CFA ⊠ (heated) snooker sauna solarium gymnasium croquet & putting green *xmas*
♀ English, French & Spanish V ✿ ☑ ✂ ✱ S% Lunch £8.50 High tea fr£5 Dinner £14.50&alc Last dinner 9.30pm
Credit Cards ① ② ③ ⑤

#### ★★64% Portland
32 St John's Rd SK17 6XQ ☎(0298)71493 FAX (0298) 27464
*In a pleasant location opposite the Pavilion and gardens on the A53, a base from which to explore the surrounding Peak District, this welcoming family-run hotel has ever-improving standards. Freshly prepared meals are served in a conservatory restaurant, a comfortable lounge invites relaxation, and there is a small conference room.*
25⇨➚(3fb)▨✂in 1 bedroom CTV in all bedrooms ® T ✱ sB&B⇨➚fr£48 dB&B⇨➚fr£56 ▤
18P CFA *xmas*
♀ English & French V ✿ ☑ ✱ Lunch fr£9 High tea fr£4.65 Dinner fr£15&alc Last dinner 9pm
Credit Cards ① ② ③ ⑤ ⓔ

#### ★63% Hartington
18 Broad Walk SK17 6JR ☎(0298)22638
RS Nov-Mar
*Set in a quiet residential area, with attractive views over the lake at the Pavilion Gardens, this family-run hotel is reached via Hartington Road, as Broad Walk is closed to traffic.*
17rm(3⇨4➚)(3fb) CTV in 7 bedrooms ® ✈ (ex guide dogs) sB&B£20-£28 sB&B⇨➚£35-£40 dB&B£38-£42 dB&B⇨➚£48-£52 ▤
CTV 15P
✂ ✱ Dinner fr£9.90 Last dinner 8pm
Credit Cards ① ③ ⓔ

---

### CADNAM Hampshire Map **04** SU21

#### ★★★63% Bartley Lodge
Lyndhurst Rd SO4 2NR ☎Southampton(0703)812248 FAX (0703) 812075
*This red brick hotel, first built as a hunting lodge in 1759, still commands views over forest and fields. Bedrooms are comfortable and well co-ordinated, an attractive galleried and panelled reception lounge is an original feature, various conference rooms are available and two new hard-surface all-weather tennis courts have been installed. Guests have a choice of eating options, the varied menus offered in the Crystal Restaurant being supplemented by the bar meals served in the cosy Hunters Bar.*
19⇨➚(3fb)✂ CTV in all bedrooms ® sB&B⇨➚£44-£66 dB&B⇨➚£73-£95 ▤
CTV 50P ✿ ≏ (heated) ♪ (hard) ⋇ *xmas*
V ✿ ☑ ✂ Lunch £11 High tea fr£5.50 Dinner £11&alc Last dinner 8.45pm
Credit Cards ① ② ③ ⑤ ⓔ

---

### CAERNARFON Gwynedd Map **06** SH46

#### ★★★75% Seiont Manor
Llanrug LL55 2AQ ☎(0286)673366 FAX (0286) 2840
*This purpose-built luxury hotel complex is situated within 150 acres of grounds adjacent to the lovely manor house. It is in easy reach of both the Snowdonia National Park and the Isle of Anglesey, to the east of Caernarfon via the A4086. The bedrooms are extremely well equipped and public rooms are delightful. The*

*hotel is well suited for leisure guests, as a good indoor swimming pool, a solarium, sauna and mini gymnasium are all part of the hotel's amenities.*

28⇨📶(7fb)1🔟 CTV in all bedrooms ® T 🏃 (ex guide dogs) ❋ sB&B⇨📶£71.50-£86.50 dB&B⇨📶£97.50-£150 🚩 🕯 50P ❄ CFA 🖵 (heated) ♪ sauna solarium gymnasium *xmas* ♇ French V ♥ ♨ ✂ ❋ Lunch £9.50 Dinner £15.50&alc Last dinner 10pm
Credit Cards ①②③⑤ⓔ

★★65% **Stables**
LL54 5SD (Minotels) ☎Llanwnda(0286)830711 & 830935
FAX (0286) 830413
(For full entry see Llanwnda)

★64% **Menai Bank**
North Rd LL55 1BD ☎(0286)673297
*As suggested by its name, the family-run hotel stands just north of the town centre overlooking the Menai Straits; the comfortable and well maintained accommodation it provides is equally suitable for tourist or business user.*

15rm(4⇨5📶)(3fb) CTV in all bedrooms ® sB&B£17-£19 sB&B⇨📶£24.50-£38 dB&B£30-£34 dB&B⇨📶£38-£42 🚩 CTV 10P pool table
♥ ❋ Dinner £10.50-£11.50 Last dinner 7.30pm
Credit Cards ①③

★63% *Chocolate House*
Plas Treflan, Caeathro LL55 2SE ☎(0286)672542 & 4872
Closed 2 Jan-13 Feb
*A former farmhouse with spacious gardens on the outskirts of Caernarfon, on the A4085 with easy access to the coast and the Snowdonia National park. Most of the well equipped bedrooms are located in cottage-style units converted from farm buildings. The unusual name comes from the dessert menu which features numerous chocolate dishes.*

3⇨📶Annexe7📶(1fb)1🔟✂in 1 bedroom CTV in all bedrooms ®
15P 🚗 ❄ solarium putting softball pool table badminton nc7yrs
V ♥ ♨ ✂ Last dinner 8.30pm
Credit Cards ①③

CAERPHILLY Mid Glamorgan Map **03** ST18

★★66% **Griffin Inn Motel**
Rudry CF8 3EA ☎(0222)869735 FAX (0222) 863681
Closed Xmas
*In a rural setting alongside Rudry church, this professionally run hotel, extended from a characterful inn, offers a choice of bars, a spacious restaurant serving a range of food and a comfortable foyer lounge. Bedrooms are all modern and well equipped.*
Annexe32⇨📶 CTV in all bedrooms ® T ❋ sB&B⇨📶£32-£51 dB&B⇨📶£45-£59
🕯 100P ❄ CFA
♇ English & French V ❋ Bar Lunch £1.20-£5.50alc Dinner £10.95&alc Last dinner 10pm
Credit Cards ①②③⑤

CALLANDER Central *Perthshire* Map **11** NN60

★★★ ❋🛁Roman Camp
FK17 8BG ☎(0877)30003 Telex no 9312132123
FAX (0877) 31533
(instructions from JRC)
*Reminiscent of a small French château, this delightful hotel is set in 20 acres of grounds and is now under the personal direction of the Brown family, who also own Auchterarder House. Public areas are elegant and comfortable, with a choice of period-style lounges, and of particular interest is the tiny turret chapel. Bedrooms are individual in shape, size and style, but all are comfortable and well equipped.*

14rm(13⇨📶)(3fb)1🔟 CTV in all bedrooms ® T sB&B⇨📶£60-£80 dB&B⇨📶£70-£125 🚩
30P ❄ CFA ♪ croquet *xmas*
♇ Scottish & French ♥ ♨ ✂ Lunch £17-£18.50 Dinner £30-£34 Last dinner 9pm
Credit Cards ①②③⑤

★★68% **Bridgend House**
Bridgend FK17 8AH ☎(0877)30130
*On the Glasgow road just outside the town centre, this small family-run hotel overlooking the River Teith has the character of a friendly inn, with a comfortable lounge, a cosy bar serving a wide range of bar meals and an attractive dining room where good country cooking brings out the best of flavours from seasonal game, meat and seafood.*
7rm(5⇨📶)(1fb)2🔟 CTV in all bedrooms ® T sB&B£25-£30 sB&B⇨📶£35-£40 dB&B£30-£40 dB&B⇨📶£50-£60 🚩 CTV 30P ❄ *xmas*
♇ Scottish & French V ♥ Bar Lunch £1.50-£11alc Dinner £12-£22alc Last dinner 9pm
Credit Cards ①②③ⓔ

★★❋68% **Lubnaig**
Leny Feus FK17 8AS (off A84) ☎(0877)30376
Closed Nov-Etr
*A detached Victorian house set in its own gardens in a residential area some 30yds from the main road. Family-run, catering for residents only, the Lubnaig offers a friendly and relaxed environment. Crawford Low is a cheerful and fully involved host, while his wife Sue is responsible for the excellent home cooking. The 4-course dinner menu offers a small choice but invariably everything is fresh and cooked to order. A typical meal may start with broccoli and cheese soufflé with a home-made soup to follow. The main course might be duck breast with morello cherry sauce, quail with madeira sauce or a simple lasagne. Puddings are old favourites such as lemon meringue pie, bread and butter pudding or*

→

**C**

187

*cheesecake. There is no bar but the hotel is licensed, and there are 3 lounges. Bedrooms, like the rest of the house, are attractively decorated and well maintained. Two are in a small coach house at the rear and are ideal as a family unit.*

6♠Annexe4♠ CTV in all bedrooms ® sB&B♠£35.50-£42.50 dB&B♠£71-£85 (incl dinner) 🏋

CTV 14P (charged) ⊞ ✿ croquet nc7yrs ✔

---

## CALNE Wiltshire Map 03 ST97

**★★63% Lansdowne Strand Hotel & Restaurant**

The Strand SN11 0JR ☎(0249)812488 FAX (0249) 815323

*This former coaching inn, dating back to the 16th century and standing beside the main road into the town, offers spacious bedrooms – many of which have been refurbished over the past 2 years to provide comfortable, well equipped accommodation – and public areas which are being smartened up by redecoration whilst awaiting upgrading; its 3 bar areas prove popular with residents and locals alike. Car parking is available in the courtyard behind the hotel, close to some of the yard annexe bedrooms.*

21⇨♠Annexe5⇨(2fb)1⊞ CTV in all bedrooms ® T ✱ sB&B⇨♠£48 dB&B⇨♠£54 🏋

21P CFA

♥ English & French V ♿ ⚖ Lunch £7.50&alc Dinner £10.50&alc Last dinner 10pm

Credit Cards [1][2][3][5]

---

## CAMBERLEY Surrey Map 04 SU86

**★★★66% Frimley Hall**

Portsmouth Rd GU15 2BG (Forte Hotels) ☎(0276)28321 Telex no 858446 FAX (0276) 691253

*Dating back to 1864, this elegant manor house retains much of the charm of its era. The original section of the building houses the individually decorated rooms of great character whilst the extension offers a more uniform choice of comfortable and well equipped rooms. A well appointed restaurant has an adjoining cocktail bar/lounge.*

66⇨♠(2fb)1⊞✔in 8 bedrooms CTV in all bedrooms ® T ✱ sB⇨♠fr£80 dB⇨♠fr£90 (room only) 🏋

( 200P ✿ CFA xmas

♥ English & French V ♿ ⚖ ✔ ✱ Lunch fr£14.75&alc Dinner fr£18.75&alc Last dinner 10pm

Credit Cards [1][2][3][4][5]

**★★★58% Lakeside International**

Wharf Rd, Frimley Green GU16 6JR ☎Deepcut(0252)838000 Telex no 858095 FAX (0252) 837857

*An attractively situated purpose-built hotel offering pleasantly appointed bedrooms equipped to a modern standard. Several rooms have their own balconies and overlook the lake at the centre of a complex which includes a night club and leisure centre. Regrettably, standards of food and service can be disappointing.*

97⇨♠ CTV in all bedrooms ® T 🐕 (ex guide dogs) ✱ sB&B⇨♠£45-£78 dB&B⇨♠£65-£96

Lift ( 250P ✿ CFA squash snooker

♥ English & French V ♿ ⚖ ✱ Lunch fr£15&alc Dinner fr£15&alc Last dinner 10.30pm

Credit Cards [1][2][3][5]

---

## CAMBRIDGE Cambridgeshire Map 05 TL45 ⊖

**★★★64% Garden House**

Granta Place, Mill Ln CB2 1RT (Queens Moat) ☎(0223)63421 Telex no 81463 FAX (0223) 316605

*This large, pleasant and attractively furnished hotel, professionally run by a team of attentive and willing staff, stands near the city centre, on the bank of the river. An extensive improvement programme has recently been completed, providing good quality public areas and very well equipped bedrooms, the majority of*

*which have garden and river views. The hotel is not easy to find, but a location plan is sent with reservation confirmations.*

118⇨♠(4fb)✔in 15 bedrooms CTV in all bedrooms ® T 🐕 (ex guide dogs) ✱ sB&B⇨♠£82-£135 dB&B⇨♠£115-£160 Continental breakfast 🏋

Lift ( 180P ✿ CFA ✔ punting xmas

♥ International V ♿ ⚖ Lunch £17.45-£19.85&alc High tea £5.25-£24.20alc Dinner £20.75-£30.50&alc Last dinner 9.45pm

Credit Cards [1][2][3][5] £

**★★★★57% Forte Posthouse**

Lakeview, Bridge Rd, Impington CB4 4PH (2.5m N, on N side of rdbt jct A45/B1049) (Forte Hotels) ☎(0223)237000 Telex no 817123 FAX (0223) 233426

*A busy purpose-built hotel situated at the A45/B1049 junction 1.5 miles north of the city is particularly popular with business people (including delegates using the conference facilities). Family visitors will appreciate the gymnasium and heated swimming pool.*

115⇨♠(14fb)✔in 60 bedrooms CTV in all bedrooms ® T ✱ sB⇨♠£39.50-£49.50 dB⇨♠£39.50-£49.50 (room only) 🏋

( 200P ✿ ⊠ (heated) sauna solarium gymnasium xmas

♥ International V ♿ ⚖ ✱ Lunch £10.95-£13 Dinner £13.95&alc Last dinner 10.30pm

Credit Cards [1][2][3][4][5]

**★★★★53% University Arms**

Regent St CB2 1AD (De Vere) ☎(0223)351241 Telex no 817311 FAX (0223) 315256

*On the edge of the city centre by Parkers Piece, this famous hotel has undergone substantial refurbishment to provide more pleasing accommodation. There is a choice of bars and a comfortable lounge serving a traditional English tea, plus extensive banqueting and conference facilities.*

117⇨♠(5fb)✔in 12 bedrooms CTV in all bedrooms ® T S10% sB&B⇨♠fr£90 dB&B⇨♠fr£105 🏋

Lift ( 80P CFA

♥ English & French V ♿ ⚖ ✱ S12.5% Lunch fr£11.50&alc High tea £6-£10 Dinner fr£16&alc Last dinner 9.45pm

Credit Cards [1][2][3][5]

**★★★64% Gonville**

Gonville Place CB1 1LY ☎(0223)66611

Closed 4 days at Xmas

*Well positioned overlooking Parker's Green in the centre, this traditional, popular hotel provides good service, with comfortable public areas and bedrooms equipped with modern facilities.*

62⇨♠(6fb) CTV in all bedrooms ® T ✱ sB&B⇨♠fr£68 dB&B⇨♠fr£84 🏋

Lift ( CTV 100P CFA

♥ English & French V ♿ ⚖ ✱ Lunch £10.50&alc Dinner £12.65&alc Last dinner 9.45pm

Credit Cards [1][2][3][4]

**★★★62% Cambridgeshire Moat House**

CB3 8EU (Queens Moat) ☎Crafts Hill(0954)780555 Telex no 817141 FAX (0954) 780010

(For full entry see Bar Hill)

**★★70% Cambridge Lodge**

Huntingdon Rd CB3 0DQ ☎(0223)352833 FAX (0223) 355166

Closed Xmas RS Sat

*A detached Edwardian house, located one mile north of the town centre on the A1207. The accommodation is well furnished and comfortable and the good table d'hôte and à la carte menus in the restaurant offer an interesting range of dishes, prepared from fresh ingredients.*

11⇨♠ CTV in all bedrooms ® T S% sB&B⇨♠£45-£70 dB&B⇨♠£67-£100 🏋

20P ⊞ ✿

♥ English & Continental V S% Lunch £14.95-£17&alc Dinner £19.95-£21.50&alc Last dinner 9.30pm

Credit Cards [1][2][3][5]

**★★69% Centennial**
63-71 Hills Rd CB2 1PG ☎(0223)314652 FAX (0223) 315443
Closed 23 Dec-2 Jan
39⇨➚♠(1fb) CTV in all bedrooms ⓡ T ✕ ✳ sB&B⇨➚♠£50-
£58 dB&B⇨➚♠£65-£73 ♬
《 32P
♀ English & French V ♥ ⚲ ⅍ ✳ Lunch £10-£15&alc High tea
£2.50-£6 Dinner fr£13 Last dinner 9.30pm
Credit Cards ① ② ③ ⑤

**★★67% Arundel House**
53 Chesterton Rd CB4 3AN ☎(0223)67701 FAX (0223) 67721
Closed 25-26 Dec
*Situated on the edge of Jesus Green and close to the city centre,
this hotel has grown in both size and quality. Some rooms are
above average for this classification whilst others, although more
dated and modestly furnished, are comfortable and well equipped.
A good range of well prepared dishes is served in both the bar and
restaurant.*
66rm(56⇨➚♠)Annexe22⇨➚♠(7fb) CTV in all bedrooms ⓡ T
✕ sB&B£28-£37.50 sB&B⇨➚♠£38-£52.50 dB&B£41.50
dB&B⇨➚♠£53.50-£72 Continental breakfast ♬
《 70P CFA
♀ English, French & Italian V ♥ ⚲ ⅍ Lunch £6.95-£7.75&alc
High tea £1.45-£5.85 Dinner £12.50&alc Last dinner 9.30pm
Credit Cards ① ② ③ ⑤

**○Holiday Inn**
Downing St CB2 3DT (Holiday Inns Inc) ☎(0223)464466
Open
199⇨➚♠

**❀❀ ✕✕ Midsummer House**
Midsummer Common CB4 1HA ☎(0223)69299
*Situated on the edge of Midsummer Common this restaurant
comprises a series of small dining areas, elegantly furnished and
distinctly decorated. Chef/Patron Hans Schweitzer continues to
produce skilful, imaginative dishes using good quality fresh
ingredients. A warm winter salad could be followed by roast
pheasant garnished with truffle, red cabbage and dauphin potatoes.
An extensive and fine wine list accompanies the frequently
charming menu.*
 Lunch not served Sat
Dinner not served Sun
♀ International V 55 seats ✳ Lunch £15-£34 Dinner £23-£35
Last lunch 2pm Last dinner 9.30pm ⅌
Credit Cards ① ② ③ ⑤

**❀ ✕ Chato Singapore**
2-4 Lensfield Rd CB2 1EG ☎(0223)63129 & 64115
*Reservation is necessary for this very popular city-centre
restaurant on the edge of Parker's Piece, at the junction of
Lensfield Road and Regent Street. Simply and comfortably
furnished, it features a menu which, though limited in length, offers
a wide range of fish, meat and vegetarian options, making good use
of fresh spices and herbs; the spicy dishes of lamb and chicken are
particularly noteworthy, as are the Lobak – a selection of fish and
meat. The smart cocktail bar provides a pleasant setting in which
to enjoy a drink before your meal, and there is a short, reasonably
priced wine list.*
Closed Sun & 25-26 Dec Lunch not served Mon
♀ Malaysian & Singapore V 80 seats ⅌ nc7yrs
Credit Cards ②

**CAMPBELTOWN** Strathclyde *Argyllshire* Map **10** NR72

**★★64%** *Royal*
Main St PA28 6AG ☎(0586)52017
*A popular commercial hotel in the town centre, overlooking the
waterfront, with an attractive new bar and restaurant on the first
floor and plain practical bedrooms, some of which are compact.*
16rm(8⇨➚4♠)(2fb) CTV in all bedrooms ⓡ T

→

Lift CTV 4P ♫
♡ English & French **V** ᕁ ⌘ ⌣ Last dinner 9pm
Credit Cards ⬚1⬚ ⬚3⬚

★ 65% *Seafield*
Kilkerran Rd PA28 6JL ☎(0586)54385
*A small, homely family-run hotel with a cosy little lounge bar. Most of the well equipped bedrooms are contained in a modern bungalow at the rear.*
3♠Annexe6♠ CTV in all bedrooms ® **T**
11P
**V** ᕁ Last dinner 9pm
Credit Cards ⬚1⬚ ⬚3⬚

CANNICH Highland *Inverness-shire* Map **14** NH33

★★ ❀⊶ 69% **Cozac Lodge**
Glen Cannich IV4 7LX (8m W on unclass Glen Cannich rd)
☎(04565)263
*This charming and hospitable country house hotel is situated beside Loch Sealbanach at the top of a rugged and remote Highland glen, amid spectacular scenery where wildlife is abundant. Bedrooms are comfortably appointed and well equipped with useful extras, and the elegant public rooms have a tranquil atmosphere.*
7⇨♠(1fb) CTV in all bedrooms ® ✳ sB&B⇨♠£33.50-£41.50 dB&B⇨♠£49-£65 🄟
CTV 12P ⊟ ❀ ♪
♡ International ᕁ ⌘
Credit Cards ⬚1⬚ ⬚2⬚ ⬚3⬚

CANNOCK Staffordshire Map **07** SJ91 ⊖

★★★ 64% *Roman Way*
Watling St, Hatherton WS11 1SH (on A5) (Crown & Raven)
☎(0543)572121 FAX (0543) 502749
*A complete re-modelling programme has been carried out at this hotel. New rooms have been added and a spacious Roman theme reception/lounge area created. The lounge bar has increased in size and, subsequently, in popularity.*
56⇨♠ CTV in all bedrooms ® **T**
( 200P ♫
♡ English & French **V** ᕁ ⌘ Last dinner 10pm
Credit Cards ⬚1⬚ ⬚2⬚ ⬚3⬚ ⬚5⬚

⏏ **Longford House Travel Inn**
Watling St, Longford WS11 1SJ ☎(0543)572721
FAX (0543) 466130
*Modern accommodation, equipped to meet the needs either of families or of business travellers, is provided by this attractive chalet-style lodge at the rear of the Longford House Beefeater.*
38⇨♠(2fb)⌣in 14 bedrooms CTV in all bedrooms ®
✈ (ex guide dogs)
⊟
ᕁ

CANTERBURY Kent Map **05** TR15

★★★ 62% **Falstaff**
St Dunstans St CT2 8AF (Lansbury) ☎(0227)462138
Telex no 96394 FAX (0227) 463525
*A coaching inn dating back at least to the 16th century has been tastefully furnished and well equipped whilst retaining its exposed timbers and such original features as the Turret Rooms. The Two Seasons Restaurant, which overlooks a very pretty flagstoned courtyard, offers a recommendable Chef's Daily Speciality. The very popular bar is supplemented by the Falstaff Tap, there is a beamed lounge, and conference facilities are available ; service throughout is friendly, helpful and well managed.*
24⇨♠(2fb)2⊟⌣in 6 bedrooms CTV in all bedrooms ®
✈ (ex guide dogs) sB&B⇨♠fr£75 dB&B⇨♠fr£88 🄟
( 50P *xmas*

♡ English & Continental **V** ᕁ ⌘ ✳ Lunch fr£12&alc Dinner fr£12&alc Last dinner 10pm
Credit Cards ⬚1⬚ ⬚2⬚ ⬚5⬚

★★★ 57% **The Chaucer**
Ivy Ln CT1 1TT (Forte Hotels) ☎(0227)464427 Telex no 965096 FAX (0227) 450397
*This sizeable hotel near the city centre, largely rebuilt after the Second World War, has embarked on a programme of modernisation and improvement which will result in accommodation equally suitable for tourist or business user, though bedrooms are compact.*
43⇨♠⌣in 17 bedrooms CTV in all bedrooms ® **T** ✳
sB⇨♠fr£65 dB⇨♠fr£80 (room only) 🄟
( 45P CFA *xmas*
♡ English & French **V** ᕁ ⌘ ⌣ ✳ Lunch fr£9.10&alc Dinner fr£13.10&alc Last dinner 9.45pm
Credit Cards ⬚1⬚ ⬚2⬚ ⬚3⬚ ⬚4⬚ ⬚5⬚

★★ 63% **Canterbury**
71 New Dover Rd CT1 3DZ ☎(0227)450551 Telex no 965809 FAX (0227) 450873
*In a very convenient location and with good car parking, this hotel offers a choice of bedrooms, a combined reception/bar and a comfortable restaurant. A small meeting room and conference facilities are also available.*
27⇨♠(4fb) CTV in all bedrooms ® **T** ✳ sB&B⇨♠£40-£45 dB&B⇨♠£55-£58 🄟
Lift CTV 40P CFA
♡ English & French ᕁ ⌘ ✳ Lunch fr£6.50 Dinner fr£11.50&alc Last dinner 10pm
Credit Cards ⬚1⬚ ⬚2⬚ ⬚3⬚ ⬚5⬚ ⬚£⬚

❀✕ **Ristorante Tuo e Mio**
16 The Borough CT1 2DR ☎(0227)761471
*Close to the cathedral, this well established Italian restaurant has been run by proprietors Mr and Mrs Greggio for the last 16 years. The large menu is very traditional, but is supplemented by 'Rafael's Suggestions' and daily specialities, usually several fish/seafood dishes. Desserts are mostly fruit based and are displayed at the front of the restaurant. There are also profiteroles with hot chocolate sauce or tiramisu. Beware the cover charge, and although there is a 10% service charge, for service which is prompt and attentive, it may be found to be abrupt. The short list of Italian wines is inexpensive and the house wine is particularly good value.*
Closed Mon, last 2 wks Feb & last 2 wks Aug Lunch not served Tue
♡ Italian **V** 40 seats ✳ Lunch £14-£20alc Last lunch 2.30pm
Last dinner 10.45pm ♪
Credit Cards ⬚1⬚ ⬚2⬚ ⬚3⬚ ⬚5⬚

CAPEL CURIG Gwynedd Map **06** SH75

★★ 63% **Cobdens**
LL24 0EE (on A5) ☎(06904)243 & 308
*This 200-year-old stone-built property stands beside the A5 at the foot of Moel Siabod in the Snowdonia National Park – one of its unusual features being the natural rock face that forms the wall of one of the bars. Family-run, it provides well equipped accommodation which is equally suitable for tourists or businessmen and is understandably popular with climbers.*
17rm(10⇨6♠)(2fb) CTV in all bedrooms ® **T** ✳ sB&B£16.50-£18.15 sB&B⇨♠£22-£25 dB&B⇨♠£44-£50
60P ❀ ⊡ ♪
**V** ᕁ ⌘ ✳ Lunch £12-£15alc High tea 50p-£1.50alc Dinner £12-£15alc Last dinner 9.30pm
Credit Cards ⬚1⬚ ⬚2⬚ ⬚3⬚ ⬚£⬚

Hotels with red star ratings are especially high quality.

## CARBIS BAY

See St Ives

## CARCROFT South Yorkshire Map 08 SE50

⭐Forte Travelodge
Great North Rd(Forte)
☎(0302)330841 Central Res (0800) 850950
*On the busy A1, northbound, about 6 miles north of Doncaster with
a Happy Eater restaurant and a Texaco petrol station adjacent.*
40⇨🏠(40fb) CTV in all bedrooms Ⓡ sB⇨🏠£29.95
dB⇨🏠£29.95 (room only)
《40P ⇑
Credit Cards ①②③

## CARDIFF South Glamorgan Map 03 ST17 ◎

See **Town Plan Section**
★★★★64% **Holiday Inn**
Mill Ln CF1 1EZ (Holiday Inns) ☎(0222)399944
Telex no 497365 FAX (0222) 395578
*A very efficiently run hotel at the heart of the city complements
well equipped bedrooms and a popular carvery featuring an à la
carte menu by excellent conference/function facilities, a good
quality leisure centre and friendly service.*
182⇨🏠(78fb)⤫in 36 bedrooms CTV in all bedrooms Ⓡ T ✳
S10% sB⇨🏠£90-£225 dB⇨🏠£105-£225 (room only) 🍴
Lift 《⊞ 90P CFA 🏊 (heated) squash sauna solarium
gymnasium turkish bath beauty therapist *xmas*
♡ French & Welsh V ✿ ⤳ ⤫ ✳ S10% Lunch
fr£12.75 Dinner fr£14.50 Last dinner 10.30pm
Credit Cards ①②③④⑤

★★★★54% **Park**
Park Place CF1 3UD (Mount Charlotte (TS)) ☎(0222)383471
Telex no 497195 FAX (0222) 399309
*A busy, city-centre hotel, well equipped to handle both conferences
and private functions. Renovation and refurbishment of all rooms
is well under way, and the management hopes to completely
redesign the public areas in the near future.*
119⇨🏠(7fb)⤫in 30 bedrooms CTV in all bedrooms Ⓡ T
(room only) 🍴
Lift 《80P *xmas*
♡ English & French V ✿ ⤳
Credit Cards ①②③④⑤
**See advertisement on page 193**

★★★71% **Cardiff International**
Mary Ann St CF1 2EQ (Best Western) ☎(0222)341441
Telex no 498005 FAX (0222) 223742
*A fairly recent addition, the Cardiff International has quickly
established itself as a well managed, quality hotel. It is
strategically located in the city centre in an ideal position for the
Cardiff World Trade Centre, due to open in 1992. Bedrooms are
very well equipped and attractively decorated and furnished.
Public areas provide interest, set around an open plan foyer
designed to resemble a Victorian town square, in which there are 3
small shops and a central reception. The Gazebo Restaurant and a
large lounge and bar area are at either side. The hotel has a small
car park and there is a public multi-storey adjacent.*
143⇨🏠(8fb)⤫in 8 bedrooms CTV in all bedrooms Ⓡ T
🍴 (ex guide dogs) S10% sB⇨🏠fr£70 dB⇨🏠fr£85 (room
only) 🍴
Lift 《55🏊 CFA ♫ *xmas*
♡ International V ✿ ⤳ ⤫ Lunch fr£10&alc Dinner fr£15&alc
Last dinner 11.30pm
Credit Cards ①②③⑤ ⓔ

A rosette means exceptional standards of cuisine.

---

### ★★★70% **Manor Parc Country Hotel & Restaurant**
Thornhill Rd, Thornhill CF4 5UA ☎(0222)693723
FAX (0222) 614624
Closed 24-26 Dec
*Situated on the A469 at Thornhill, approximately 3 miles north of the city centre, this hotel is managed by two Italian families whose influence is discernable in both style and professional service. The comfortable bedrooms are very well equipped, and an intimate restaurant, where guests can enjoy well cooked dishes which include some Venetian specialities, contains some fine original old paintings.*
12⇄🟦(2fb) CTV in all bedrooms ® T ⊁ (ex guide dogs) ✱
sB&B⇄🟦£57.50 dB&B⇄🟦£85-£110 🏳
⊂ 70P ⇜ ❀ CFA ♗ (hard)
♀ International V ✱ Lunch £12-£20alc Dinner fr£22alc Last dinner 10pm
Credit Cards 1 2 3 ⓔ

### ★★★64% **Cardiff Moat House**
Circle Way East, Llanederyn CF3 7XF (Queens Moat)
☎(0222)732520 Telex no 497582 FAX (0222) 549092
Closed 23-30 Dec (ex lunch 25 Dec)
*A popular commercial hotel off the A48 (Eastern Avenue) provides good, extensive function and leisure facilities; a wide choice of food is available, and the complete refurbishment of bedrooms is due to be completed during 1991.*
137⇄🟦⊁in 8 bedrooms CTV in all bedrooms ® T
sB⇄🟦£35-£89 dB⇄🟦£50-£99 (room only) 🏳
Lift ⊂ 300P CFA ◩ (heated) sauna solarium gymnasium jacuzzi baby pool ♫
♀ English & Continental V ✧ ⍟ Lunch £9.95-£14.95&alc Dinner £15.60-£17.25&alc Last dinner 10pm
Credit Cards 1 2 3 5 ⓔ

### ★★★64% **Forte Crest**
Castle St CF71 2XB (Forte Hotels) ☎(0222)388681
Telex no 497258 CENTEL G FAX (0222) 371495
*This well run, city-centre hotel lies adjacent to the Cardiff Arms Park. Bedrooms are all well equipped and there is a good range of bars in the hotel. A modern business centre has been added, and the hotel benefits from good parking facilities.*
155⇄🟦⊁in 102 bedrooms CTV in all bedrooms ® T ✱
sB⇄🟦fr£78 dB⇄🟦£90-£115 (room only) 🏳
Lift ⊂ 120P CFA snooker *xmas*
♀ European V ✧ ⍟ ⊁ ✱ Lunch fr£10 Dinner fr£15.45&alc Last dinner 11pm
Credit Cards 1 2 3 4 5

### ★★★63% **Forte Posthouse**
Pentwyn Rd, Pentwyn CF2 7XA (Forte Hotels) ☎(0222)731212
Telex no 497633 FAX (0222) 549147
*This modern purpose-built hotel is situated alongside the city's Eastern Avenue bypass, 4 miles from the city centre and a short drive from junction 29 of the M4 motorway. Refurbishment has continued over the last year to provide comfortable, well equipped accommodation. The hotel has extensive conference facilities and a popular health and fitness centre.*
136⇄🟦(50fb)⊁in 42 bedrooms CTV in all bedrooms ® T ✱
sB&B⇄🟦£39.50-£49.50 dB&B⇄🟦£39.50-£49.50 🏳
Lift ⊂ 300P ❀ CFA ◩ (heated) sauna solarium gymnasium *xmas*
♀ International V ✧ ⍟ ⊁ ✱ Lunch £3-£8alc Dinner fr£13.95&alc Last dinner 10pm
Credit Cards 1 2 3 4 5

### ★★★56% **Royal**
Saint Mary's St CF1 1LL (Jarvis) ☎(0222)383321
Telex no 498062 FAX (0222) 222238
*A period hotel occupying a corner site in the bustling town centre features public areas which include three bars which are very popular locally; spacious bedrooms await planned refurbishment.*

63rm(39⇄8🟦)(3fb)⊁in 6 bedrooms CTV in all bedrooms ® T
sB£40-£45 sB⇄🟦£72.50-£87.50 dB£50-£60 dB⇄🟦£85-£120 (room only) 🏳
Lift ⊂ CTV ♗ CFA snooker *xmas*
♀ British & French V ✧ ⍟ Sunday Lunch £8.50 High tea fr£6.50 Dinner fr£15&alc Last dinner 10pm
Credit Cards 1 2 3 4 5

### ★★65% **Riverside Hotel**
Taff Embankent, Riverside CF1 8RG ☎(0222)378866
FAX (0222) 388306
*A popular hotel alongside the River Taff directly opposite the home of Welsh Rugby. Bedrooms are all modern and well equipped, and there is a comfortable residents' lounge bar in addition to the public facilities. Steaks and a carvery feature in the attractive restaurant, and there is an adjacent night spot.*
36⇄🟦(3fb)1⊟ CTV in all bedrooms ® T sB&B⇄🟦£39.50 dB&B⇄🟦£58.50 🏳
⊂ 22P CFA sauna *xmas*
V ✧ ⍟ ✱ Sunday Lunch £6.50 Dinner £5.50-£7.50&alc Last dinner 9.30pm
Credit Cards 1 2 3 5 ⓔ

### ★★64% **Sandringham**
21 Saint Mary St CF1 2PL ☎(0222)232161 FAX (0222) 383998
*This city centre hotel with concessionary local parking provides well equipped modern bedrooms. Sandy's Bar and Restaurant, next door and reached by the street, is open all day.*
28⇄🟦(1fb) CTV in all bedrooms ® T ⊁ (ex guide dogs)
⊂ CFA
V ✧ ⍟ ⊁ ✱ Lunch £2.95-£9.75&alc
Credit Cards 1 2 3 5 ⓔ

**See advertisement on page 195**

C

**C**

### ★★61% **The Phoenix**
199 Fidlas Rd, Llanishen CF4 5NA ☎(0222)764615
FAX (0222) 747812
*This popular hotel in the northern suburbs of the city provides well equipped, compact bedrooms. There are good facilities, and the public areas are well maintained and comfortable.*
24rm(5⇨16♠)(2fb) CTV in all bedrooms ® T sB&B⇨♠£20-£39.95 dB&B£30-£36.75 dB&B⇨♠£36.75-£62.95
Lift ℂ CTV 30P CFA ♫
♡ English & French V ♦ ♨ ✳ Lunch £6.95-£7.95&alc Dinner £7.95&alc Last dinner 10pm
Credit Cards ① ③ ④ ⓔ

### ★★60% *Lincoln*
118 Cathedral Rd CF1 9LQ ☎(0222)395558 FAX (0222) 230537
*This modern hotel is situated near the National Sports Centre and Sophia Gardens. It is popular with business travellers and has comfortable bedrooms and a small residents' bar.*
18⇨♠(1fb) CTV in all bedrooms ® ✈ (ex guide dogs)
ℂ 18P
V ♦ ♨ Last dinner 9.30pm
Credit Cards ① ② ③ ⑤

### ⚑Campanile
Caxton Place, Pentwyn CF2 7HA (Campanile) ☎(0222)549044
Telex no 497553 FAX (0222) 549900
*This complex near the Pentwyn junction of the Cardiff and Eastern Avenue Bypass provides a modern block of bedrooms and a separate restaurant and bar offering a wide selection of food.*
Annexe50⇨♠ CTV in all bedrooms ® T sB⇨♠fr£36 dB⇨♠fr£36 (room only) ♪
50P *xmas*
♡ English & French Lunch £3.75-£8.90 Dinner £6.80-£8.90
Last dinner 10pm
Credit Cards ① ③ ⓔ

### ⚑Forte Travelodge
Circle Way East, Off A48 (M), Llanederyn CF3 7ND (4m NE of city centre, off A48(M)) (Forte)
☎(0222)549564 Central Res (0800) 850950
*This modern bedroom block is just off the Cardiff Eastern Avenue bypass, reached by the Llanedeyrn Interchange. The adjacent Harvesters Restaurant serves breakfast and other meals as needed.*
32⇨♠(32fb) CTV in all bedrooms ® sB⇨♠£29.95 dB⇨♠£29.95 (room only)
ℂ 32P ⚘
Credit Cards ① ② ③

### ⚑Rank Motor Lodge
Cardiff West CF7 8SB (M4, junct 33) (Rank) ☎(0222)892255
FAX (0222) 892497
*This modern unit, situated within the service area off junction 33 of the M4, offers particularly well equipped accommodation with Continental breakfast included in the room rate ; full meals are available in the adjoining service area restaurant.*
50⇨♠(25fb)✂in 7 bedrooms CTV in all bedrooms ®
Continental breakfast
ℂ 50P
Credit Cards ① ② ③ ⑤

### ⊛⊛ ✕ Le Cassoulet
5 Romilly Crescent, Canton CF1 9NP ☎(0222)221905
*Claire and Gilbert Viader originate from Toulouse and have named their restaurant after one of the town's most famous dishes. The region's strong flavours feature prominently on the menu, which is changed daily, and there is a small but well chosen wine list.*
Closed Sun, Mon & 4 weeks in summer.(Ring for details)
Lunch not served Sat
♡ French 36 seats Last lunch 2pm Last dinner 10pm ✗
Credit Cards ① ③

---

### CARDIGAN Dyfed Map **02** SN14

### ★★63% *Black Lion*
30 High St SA43 1HJ ☎(0239)612532
*Originally a one-room 'grogg shoppe' the Black Lion is probably one of the oldest coaching inns in Wales. Established in 1105 and upgraded by a local squire in the 17th century, it now offers friendly service, a character bar and simple, compact modern bedrooms.*
11⇨♠ CTV in all bedrooms ®
CTV ✗
♡ French ♦ ♨ Last dinner 8.45pm
Credit Cards ① ② ③ ⑤

---

### CARFRAEMILL Borders *Berwickshire* Map **12** NT55

### ★★58% *Carfraemill*
Oxton TD2 6RA ☎Oxton(05785)200 Telex no 336587
FAX (05785) 640
*A warm welcome is extended to both residents and diners by this comfortable hotel at the A697/A68 juction. Interesting menus represent good value for money, and a friendly atmosphere prevails throughout.*
8rm(2⇨)(2fb) CTV in all bedrooms ®
100P 3⚑
♡ International V ♦ ♨
Credit Cards ① ② ③ ⑤

---

### CARLISLE Cumbria Map **11** NY45 ⊙
See also **Hayton**

### ★★★68% **Cumbrian**
Court Square CA1 1QY (Best Western) ☎(0228)31951
Telex no 64287 FAX (0228) 47799
*An elegant Victorian building, recently modernised, situated next to the main railway station in the centre of the town. Spacious public rooms and well appointed bedrooms are features, together with the stylish Balmoral Restaurant and the Cumbrian Kitchen which serves a variety of snacks and meals throughout the day.*
70⇨♠(3fb)✂in 4 bedrooms CTV in all bedrooms ® T sB⇨♠£35-£79.50 dB⇨♠£60-£95 (room only) ♪
Lift ℂ 15P 30⚑ CFA ♫ *xmas*
♡ Continental V ♦ ♨ ✂ Lunch fr£10.50 Dinner fr£15.50 Last dinner 10pm
Credit Cards ① ② ③ ⑤ ⓔ

### ★★★63% **The Central Plaza**
Victoria Viaduct CA3 8AL (Consort) ☎(0228)20256
FAX (0228) 514657
*Recently refurbished city centre hotel with a comfortable lounge bar.*
84⇨♠(2fb)1⚑ CTV in all bedrooms ® T sB&B⇨♠£62-£73 dB&B⇨♠£72-£83 ♪
Lift ℂ CTV 20⚑ CFA *xmas*
♡ English & French V ♦ ♨ Bar Lunch £5-£7 Dinner fr£14.50&alc Last dinner 9pm
Credit Cards ① ② ③ ⑤ ⓔ

### ★★★62% **Forte Posthouse**
Parkhouse Rd, Kingstown CA3 0HR (junc 44/M6) (Forte Hotels)
☎(0228)31201 FAX (0228) 43178
*An hotel conveniently situated on the A7, just off junction 44 of the M6, now has the added attraction of a well equipped leisure centre. Staff are friendly and helpful, while accommodation offers every modern amenity – executive and Lady Crest rooms providing superior furnishings and décor as to standard ones.*
93⇨♠(12fb)✂in 46 bedrooms CTV in all bedrooms ® T sB⇨♠£39.50-£49.50 dB⇨♠£39.50-£49.50 (room only) ♪
ℂ CTV 250P ✲ CFA ▣ (heated) snooker sauna solarium gymnasium spa bath & steam room ♫ ⚘ *xmas*

International **V** ✆ ⎙ ⊬ ✳ Lunch £9.50-£20alc Dinner £9.50-£20alc Last dinner 10.30pm
Credit Cards ① ② ③ ④ ⑤

★★★ 62% **Swallow Hilltop**
London Rd CA1 2PQ (Swallow) ☎(0228)29255 Telex no 64292 FAX (0228) 25238
*Large modern hotel with very good facilities and new leisure complex.*
92⇆🛏(10fb)⊬in 13 bedrooms CTV in all bedrooms ® **T** S% sB&B⇆🛏fr£70 dB&B⇆🛏fr£80 🚭
Lift ℂ 350P ✿ CFA 🖾 (heated) sauna solarium gymnasium table tennis massage putting green ♫ ♨ *xmas*
✆ English & French **V** ✆ ⎙ ⊬ ✳ Lunch £9.50&alc Dinner £15.60&alc Last dinner 10pm
Credit Cards ① ② ③ ⑤ ⓔ

★★ 59% **Pinegrove**
262 London Rd CA1 2QS ☎(0228)24828 FAX (0228) 810941
Closed 25 & 31 Dec
*Conveniently situated on a main road on the south side of the city, a commercial hotel offers a range of bedroom styles.*
28rm(8⇆13🛏)Annexe4rm(1⇆2🛏)(8fb) CTV in all bedrooms ® **T** sB&B£27 sB&B⇆🛏£37 dB&B£39 dB&B⇆🛏£49 CTV 32P ✿
**V** ✆ ⎙ ⊬ ✳ Bar Lunch fr£6&alc Dinner fr£11&alc Last dinner 9pm
Credit Cards ① ③

★★ 57% **Woodlands**
264/266 London Rd CA1 2QS (Minotels) ☎(0228)45643
Closed 24 Dec-8 Jan
*Situated on the A6, 2 miles from junction 42 of the M6, this red sandstone hotel has a friendly atmosphere and features an attractive L-shaped dining room and comfortable lounge bar.* →

**C**

15rm(6⇨1♠)(1fb) CTV in all bedrooms ® T ✱ sB&B£25
sB&B⇨♠£35 dB&B£42 dB&B⇨♠£50 ₽
20P 🚗 CFA
V ✧ Lunch £6.95 High tea £4.85-£6.45 Dinner £11.75-£17 Last
dinner 9pm
Credit Cards ①②③⑤ €

★58% **Vallum House Garden**
Burgh Rd CA2 7NB ☎(0228)21860
Closed 25 & 26 Dec
*This family run, mainly commercial hotel, is situated on the
western edge of town on the road to Burgh by Sands. Bedrooms
vary in size, some singles are very compact, staff are helpful and
the bar meals popular.*
9rm(1⇨4♠)(1fb) CTV in all bedrooms ® T sB&B£25-£30
sB&B⇨♠£30-£35 dB&B£40-£45 dB&B⇨♠£40-£50
CTV 30P ❀ CFA
♥ English, French & Italian V ✧ ⚊ ✱ Lunch £5.50-£6.50&alc
High tea fr£6.50 Dinner £9.50-£11.50 Last dinner 9pm
Credit Cards ①③ €

---

CARMARTHEN Dyfed Map **02** SN42

★★★63% **Ivy Bush Royal**
Spilman St SA31 1LG (Forte Hotels) ☎(0267)235111
Telex no 48520 FAX (0267) 234914
*Within walking distance of the town centre and an ideal base for
touring West Wales, this popular hotel which was once a retreat
for Lord Nelson and Lady Hamilton provides attractive modern
accommodation plus good conference and function facilities. Fixed
price and à la carte menus offer a wide selection of dishes.*
78⇨♠(4fb)✂in 21 bedrooms CTV in all bedrooms ® T ✱
sB⇨♠fr£60 dB⇨♠fr£75 (room only) ₽
Lift 《 75P 3🚗 CFA sauna *xmas*
V ✧ ⚊ ✂ ✱ Lunch fr£9.95&alc Dinner fr£14&alc Last dinner
9.30pm
Credit Cards ①②③④⑤

★★62% **Falcon**
Lammas St SA31 3AP ☎(0267)234959 & 237152
Closed 25-26 Dec RS Sun
*A privately owned and run hotel in the town centre offers modern
quite well equipped accommodation which is understandably
popular with travelling business people ; adjacent car parking
facilities are available.*
14rm(4⇨7♠)(1fb)1♨ CTV in all bedrooms ® T ✱
sB&B⇨♠fr£39 dB&B⇨♠fr£49
30P CFA
V ✧ ⚊ ✱ Lunch fr£3.35 Dinner fr£6.50 Last dinner 9.30pm
Credit Cards ①②③④⑤

---

CARNFORTH Lancashire Map **07** SD47

★★63% **Royal Station**
Market St LA5 9BT ☎(0524)732033 & 733636
FAX (0524) 733636
*This popular commercial hotel beside the railway station in the
town centre, has a friendly atmosphere and offers a choice of bars
and comfortable well- equipped bedrooms, plus conference and
function facilities.*
12⇨♠(1fb) CTV in all bedrooms ® T sB&B⇨♠£28-£30
dB&B⇨♠fr£45 ₽
8P 10🚗 CFA
♥ English, French & Italian V ✧ ⚊ ✱ Lunch fr£5.95alc
Dinner £7.50-£13alc Last dinner 8.30pm
Credit Cards ①②③⑤ €
**See advertisement under MORECAMBE**

For key to symbols in English see the bookmark.

---

CARNOUSTIE Tayside *Angus* Map **12** NO53

★★60% **Carlogie House**
Carlogie Rd DD7 6LD ☎(0241)53185
Closed 1-3 Jan
*Set in its own grounds just north of the town, this friendly
commercial and tourist hotel offers practical but well equipped
bedrooms and public areas with traditional comforts. It also caters
for local functions.*
11⇨♠(1fb) CTV in all bedrooms ® T ✖ (ex guide dogs) ✱
sB&B⇨♠£35 dB&B⇨♠£50
CTV 150P 4🚗 ❀
♥ Scottish & French V ✧ ⚊ ✱ Lunch fr£12.50 High tea
fr£5.30 Dinner fr£12.50 Last dinner 9.30pm
Credit Cards ①②③⑤

★★59% **Glencoe**
Links Pde DD7 7JF ☎(0241)53273
Closed 1 Jan
*Homely, family hotel overlooking the golf course, offering very
good value meals.*
11rm(3⇨5♠)(2fb) CTV in all bedrooms T S10% sB&B£19.50
dB&B⇨♠£50
CTV 10P 🚗
♥ Scottish & French V ✧ ⚊ ✱ S% Bar Lunch £1-£7.50alc
Dinner £10.50-£16.50 Last dinner 9pm
Credit Cards ①②③⑤ €

★59% *Station*
DD7 6AR ☎(0241)52447
*This traditional village inn with log fires, oak beams and a friendly
atmosphere provides well equipped bedrooms, most with en suite
facilities, and a charming restaurant serving a good choice of
mainly British dishes.*
9rm(6♠)(1fb) CTV in 3 bedrooms ®
CTV 10P pool 🎵
V ✧ ⚊ Last dinner 9pm
Credit Cards ①③

---

CARPERBY North Yorkshire Map **07** SE08

★★64% **Wheatsheaf**
DL8 4DF ☎Wensleydale(0969)663216
*Run in an informal, friendly manner by the Mackay family the
hotel has prettily decorated bedrooms, a character bar and cosy
lounge. It was here that James Herriot and his wife Helen spent
their honeymoon in 1941.*
8⇨♠(1fb)2♨ CTV in all bedrooms ® ✱ sB&B⇨♠£24-£26
dB&B⇨♠£46-£56 ₽
50P 🚗 ncl2yrs
V ✧ ⚊ ✱ Lunch £4.95-£6.75 Dinner £12.50-£14.50 Last dinner
9.30pm
Credit Cards ①②③⑤ €

---

CARRADALE Strathclyde *Argyllshire* Map **10** NR83

★★65% **Carradale**
PA28 6RY ☎(05833)223 FAX (05833) 638
RS 31 Oct-15 Mar
*Standing in its own grounds overlooking Kilbrannan Sound and
the Isle of Arran, this pleasant holiday hotel offers modest
bedrooms and public rooms and a small leisure centre. The golf
course is conveniently situated next to the hotel.*
12rm(10⇨♠)Annexe5⇨♠(2fb) CTV in all bedrooms ®
✖ (ex guide dogs) S% sB&B£29-£40 dB&B⇨♠£58-£70 ₽
20P 🚗 ❀ squash sauna solarium
V ✧ ⚊ ✱ Lunch £6.50-£10 High tea fr£6.50&alc Dinner £16-
£20 Last dinner 8.45pm
Credit Cards ①③ €

CARRBRIDGE Highland *Inverness-shire* Map **14** NH92

★★69% **Dalrachney Lodge**
PH23 3AT ☎(047984)252 FAX (047984) 382
*This former shooting lodge stands in its own gardens on the edge of*
*the village overlooking the River Dulnain. In traditional country-*
*house style, it has a comfortable lounge and cosy bar with open*
*fires, an attractive dining room and many well proportioned*
*bedrooms.*
11rm(8⇔1↟)(3fb) CTV in all bedrooms ® T sB&B£23-£33
sB&B⇔↟£23-£33 dB&B£46-£66 dB&B⇔↟£46-£66 ☒
40P ∰ ✿ ♪
♡ Scottish & French V ♥ ✔ ✳ Sunday Lunch £6.95-£7.95
Dinner £16-£17.95&alc Last dinner 9pm
Credit Cards ①②③ⓔ

CARRUTHERSTOWN Dumfries & Galloway *Dumfriesshire*
Map **11** NY17

★★★65% **Hetland Hall**
DG1 4JX (Best Western) ☎Dumfries(0387)84201
Telex no 776819 FAX (0387) 84211
*An attractive and comfortably furnished hotel in extensive grounds*
*with access from the A75 road. Service is very friendly and helpful*
*and the lounges are very good.*
27⇔↟(3fb)✔in 3 bedrooms CTV in all bedrooms ® T S%
sB&B⇔↟£50-£60 dB&B⇔↟£75-£90 ☒
⊄ CTV 60P ✿ CFA ♪ snooker sauna solarium gymnasium
Indoor badminton *xmas*
♡ International V ♥ ⚲ ✳ Lunch fr£10.50&alc Dinner £15.50-
£20&alc Last dinner 9.30pm
Credit Cards ①②③⑤ⓔ
**See advertisement under DUMFRIES**

CARTMEL Cumbria Map **07** SD37

★★69% **Aynsome Manor**
LA11 6HH (1m N on unclass rd) ☎(05395)36653
Closed 2-28 Jan
*This charming, friendly hotel, family-run to create a relaxing*
*atmosphere, stands in open countryside about a quarter of a mile*
*northeast of the village. All its well equipped, traditionally styled*
*bedrooms have private facilities, and there is a spacious beamed*
*family room as well as two cottage annexe rooms across the*
*courtyard.*
11rm(9⇔1↟)Annexe2⇔(2fb)1☒ CTV in all bedrooms ® T
sB&B⇔↟£45-£55 dB&B£84-£92 dB&B⇔↟£90-£98 (incl
dinner) ☒
20P ∰ ✿ *xmas*
♡ English & French V ♥ ✔ Sunday Lunch £9.50 Dinner £17
Last dinner 8.15pm
Credit Cards ①②③

★★67% **Priory**
The Square LA11 6QB ☎(05395)36267
Closed Jan
*A small, creeper-clad, family-run hotel offering traditional style*
*bedrooms, a comfortable lounge, cosy bar, tea room and an*
*attractive first-floor dining room. Alcoholic drinks are served to*
*residents and diners only.*
9rm(5⇔)(2fb)1☒ ®
CTV 8P
♡ French V ♥ ⚲ ✔ Last dinner 8.45pm
Credit Cards ①③

⊛⊛⊛ ✕✕ **Uplands**
Haggs Ln LA11 6HD ☎(05395)36248
(Rosettes awarded for dinner only)
*Tom and Diana Peter have, over the past 7 years, established*
*Uplands as one of Cumbria's leading restaurants. Tom Peter is a*
*fine chef and continually produces some real culinary delights, for*
*example his puff pastry slice with asparagus, smoked salmon and*

*Hollandaise sauce. A main course of grilled Dover sole with a chive*
*and Noilly Prat sauce also earned high praise from our Inspector.*
Closed Mon & 1 Jan-25 Feb
30 seats Lunch £14.40 Dinner £23.50 Last lunch 1pm Last
dinner 8pm 14 P nc8yrs ✔
Credit Cards ①②③

CASTERTON Cumbria Map **07** SD67

★★⊛69% **Pheasant Inn**
LA6 2RX ☎Kirkby Lonsdale(05242)71230
Closed 3 wks in Jan
(Rosette awarded for dinner only)
*Comfortable village inn, popular for its restaurant dinners and bar*
*lunches. Annexe bedrooms are contained in a modernised coach*
*house.*
10⇔↟(1fb)☒ CTV in all bedrooms ® T sB&B⇔↟£40
dB&B⇔↟£60
CTV 60P ✿
V ♥ ✔ Sunday Lunch £12.50 Dinner £8-£15alc Last dinner
9pm
Credit Cards ①③

CASTLE ASHBY Northamptonshire Map **04** SP85

★★65% **Falcon**
NN7 1LF (Best Western) ☎Yardley Hastings(060129)200
FAX (060129) 673
*This pleasant hotel is set in a picturesque rural village. Bedrooms*
*in the main hotel are beautifully decorated and furnished, while*
*those in the cottage annexe are simpler. Attractive public areas*
*include a well appointed restaurant and a cosy bar.*
6rm(5⇔)Annexe8⇔↟2☒ CTV in all bedrooms ® T ✳
sB&B⇔↟£60 dB&B⇔↟£75 ☒
CTV 75P ✿ ⚙

→

**C**

♡ English & French **V** ⋄ ᴊ ✳ Lunch £17.50&alc Dinner £17.50&alc Last dinner 9.30pm
Credit Cards ① ② ③ ④

---

CASTLE COMBE Wiltshire Map **03** ST87

★★★★ ❀❀ ⚑ 76% **Manor House**
SN14 7HR ☎(0249)782206 Telex no 449931 FAX (0249) 782159
*An old manor house delightfully positioned in a wooded valley with 26 acres of parkland, lawns, a romantic Italian garden and the River Bybrook flowing through. Public rooms are elegant, the drawing room fresh in yellow, while other rooms are panelled, with log fires in winter. Leisure facilities include an outdoor pool and tennis court, together with croquet and trout fishing. Bedrooms in the main house have been completely refurbished to a high standard achieving a more distinctive character than some in the mews cottages. Chef Nicholas Evenden produces a menu of modern British cuisine, with its roots in the classical traditions. Wherever possible fresh local produce is used.*
12⇔ᐢAnnexe24⇔ᐢ6⇔ CTV in all bedrooms **T**
sB⇔ᐢ£100-£250 dB⇔ᐢ£100-£250 (room only) ⏚
《 100P ❀ CFA ⌑ (heated) ᵠ (hard) ᴗ croquet lawn jogging track *xmas*
♡ English & French **V** ⋄ ᴊ Lunch fr£16.95&alc Dinner £28-£45.45alc Last dinner 10pm
Credit Cards ① ② ③ ⑤

---

CASTLE DONINGTON Leicestershire Map **08** SK42

★★★66% **Donington Thistle**
East Midlands Airport DE7 2SH (Mount Charlotte (TS))
☎Derby(0332)850700 Telex no 377632 FAX (0332) 850823
*A location on the perimeter of the East Midlands Airport, proximity to Donington Park racing circuit and the local reputation of the Sherwood Restaurant with its good food and friendly, attentive service combine to make this hotel a popular venue. Modern leisure facilities – well used by guests – are constantly updated, and meeting rooms are to be refurbished during 1991.*
110⇔ᐢ(4fb)⚞in 15 bedrooms CTV in all bedrooms ® **T** (room only) ⏚
《 180P ❀ ⌑ (heated) sauna solarium gymnasium
♡ International **V** ⋄ ᴊ
Credit Cards ① ② ③ ⑤

★★★64% **Priest House**
Kings Mills DE7 2RR ☎Derby(0332)810649
FAX (0332) 811141
25⇔ᐢAnnexe18⇔ᐢ(2fb)7⇪ CTV in all bedrooms ® **T** ✳
sB&B⇔ᐢ£57.50-£67.50 dB&B⇔ᐢ£67.50-£87.50 ⏚
150P ❀ ᴗ clay pigeon shooting *xmas*
♡ English & French **V** ⋄ ᴊ ✳ High tea £4-£6alc Dinner fr£13.95&alc Last dinner 9.30pm
Credit Cards ① ② ③ ④ ⑤

★★★60% **Donington Manor**
High St DE7 2PP ☎Derby(0332)810253 FAX (0332) 850330
Closed 27-30 Dec
*This former coaching inn, dating from Regency days, retains a wealth of charm and character; bedrooms – though furnished in a variety of styles and equipped with modern facilities – are all in keeping with the original building, while compact public areas have been restored to their former elegance. A further meeting room now in operation extends the hotel's conference facilities, while a convenient location close to the M1 motorway and East Midlands Airport also adds to its popularity.*
35rm(33⇔)Annexe3rm(1⇔)(3fb)5⇪ CTV in all bedrooms ® **T** ✘ (ex guide dogs) S% sB&B⇔£56-£62 dB&B⇔£63-£73 ⏚
《 60P CFA
♡ English & French ⋄ ᴊ ✳ S10% Lunch £6.75-£8.75&alc Dinner £8.75&alc Last dinner 9.30pm
Credit Cards ① ② ③ ⑤

---

CASTLE DOUGLAS Dumfries & Galloway
*Kirkcudbrightshire* Map **11** NX76

★★70% **Douglas Arms**
King St DG7 1DB ☎(0556)2231
*Managed by the friendly resident proprietors, this comfortable high street hotel offers attentive service, cosy bedrooms and inviting lounges and bars. The menus at both lunch and dinner are good value.*
22rm(15⇔ᐢ)(2fb) CTV in all bedrooms ® **T** sB&Bfr£22 sB&B⇔ᐢfr£27 dB&Bfr£40 dB&B⇔ᐢfr£48 ⏚
《 6P 8🚗 CFA *xmas*
**V** ⋄ ᴊ Bar Lunch £2-£8 Dinner fr£11.50&alc Last dinner 9pm
Credit Cards ① ③ ④

★★63% **Urr Valley Country House**
Ernespie Rd DG7 3JG ☎(0556)2188 FAX (0556) 4055
*Convenient for the A75, being situated in 14 acres of wooded grounds on the eastern outskirts of the town, this privately owned hotel is being refurbished by its new owners to provide well equipped and pleasant public areas.*
16rm(14⇔ᐢ)(4fb) CTV in all bedrooms ® **T** sB&B⇔ᐢ£20-£30 dB&B⇔ᐢ£40-£60 ⏚
200P ❀ CFA ᴗ *xmas*
♡ Scottish & French **V** ⋄ ᴊ Lunch £4-£8 High tea £6.50-£7.50 Dinner £13-£15&alc Last dinner 9.30pm
Credit Cards ① ③ ④

★★62% **Imperial**
King St DG7 1AA ☎(0556)2086 & 3009
RS 25-26 Dec & 1-2 Jan
*Situated in the main street and easily distinguished by its striking black-painted exterior, this former coaching inn is a favourite meeting place with locals, which means that its lounge bar is often very busy. Quiet relaxation is possible, however, in a comfortable first-floor lounge, and the whole hotel is well equipped and very clean; those bedrooms having private bathrooms are the most comfortable, but all are gradually being improved.*
13rm(11⇔ᐢ)⚞in 2 bedrooms CTV in all bedrooms ® **T** sB&B£22-£25 sB&B⇔ᐢ£28-£30 dB&B£40-£44 dB&B⇔ᐢ£50-£54 ⏚
20P 9🚗 CFA
**V** ⋄ ᴊ Lunch £5-£8.50 Dinner £7.50-£10.50&alc Last dinner 8pm
Credit Cards ① ③ ④

---

CASTLETON Gwent Map **03** ST28

★★★59% **Wentloog Resort**
CF3 8UQ (Resort) ☎(0633)680591 FAX (0633) 681287
55⇔ᐢ⚞in 12 bedrooms CTV in all bedrooms ® **T** ✳
sB⇔ᐢfr£52 dB⇔ᐢfr£62 (room only) ⏚
《 100P CFA
♡ English & French **V** ⋄ ⚞ ✳ Sunday Lunch £8.50 Dinner £13.95&alc Last dinner 10pm
Credit Cards ① ② ③ ⑤ ④

---

CASTLETOWN

See **Man, Isle of**

---

CATEL (CASTEL)

See Guernsey **under** Channel Islands

---

CATTERICK BRIDGE North Yorkshire Map **08** SE29

★★55% **Bridge House**
DL10 7PE ☎Richmond(0748)818331
*An historic roadside coaching inn overlooking Catterick racecourse from its attractive setting beside the River Swale offers informal service by local staff and modest accommodation.*
15rm(4⇔9ᐢ)(2fb) CTV in all bedrooms ® **T** S%
sB&B⇔ᐢ£36-£42 dB&B£45-£50 dB&B⇔ᐢ£54-£62 ⏚

CTV 70P CFA ♪
♡ English & French V ♧ ✳ Lunch £7.95-£10.95alc Dinner
£10.50-£16.50alc Last dinner 10pm
Credit Cards ① ② ③ ⑤ ⓔ

---

CAWSTON Norfolk Map **09** TG12

★❀ ♨66% **Grey Gables**
Norwich Rd NR10 4EY ☎Norwich(0603)871259
Closed 24-26 Dec
6rm(4⇄1♠)(1fb) CTV in all bedrooms ® T sB&B⇄♠£42-
£43 dB&B⇄♠£44-£54 ➡
20P ⇔ ✿ ♪ (grass)
♡ English & French ✱ Dinner £15-£21 Last dinner 8.30pm
Credit Cards ① ③ ⓔ

---

CHADDESLEY CORBETT Hereford & Worcester
Map **07** SO87

★★★❀❀ ♨75% **Brockencote Hall Country House**
DY10 4PY (0.50 m W, off A448) ☎(0562)777876
FAX (0562) 777872
Closed 26 Dec-3rd wk Jan
*This impressive country house is a haven of peace and tranquillity,*
*commanding some delightful rural views from a setting in its own*
*70-acre estate on the A448 between Kidderminster and*
*Bromsgrove. Generally spacious guest rooms, all individually*
*decorated and furnished, offer a good level of comfort and some*
*thoughtful extras such as fresh fruit, flowers and sherry, while the*
*recently extended restaurant provides an elegant setting in which*
*to enjoy the imaginative French cuisine of chef Didier Philipot ;*
*attentive personal service is closely supervised by the owners.*
8⇄♠(2fb)1⊞ CTV in all bedrooms T ✖ ✳ sB&B⇄♠£62-
£105 dB&B⇄♠£99-£126 ➡
45P ⇔ ✿

→

# Chaddesley Corbett - Channel Islands, Alderney

♀ French ⍟ ⚗ ✳ Lunch £15.50-£33.50 Dinner £19.50-£33.50
Last dinner 9.30pm
Credit Cards 1 2 3 5 £

---

**CHADLINGTON** Oxfordshire Map **04** SP32

### ★★❀ ♨79% The Manor
OX7 3LX ☎(060876)711
*David Grant has created a comfortable country house of
international standard in this small Cotswold stone building behind
the village church. Bedrooms are attractively decorated and
furnished with antiques, while the public areas are elegant and
welcoming. Chris Grant produces a 4-course dinner of fresh
English fare.*
7⇨ CTV in all bedrooms **T** ✷ (ex guide dogs) S% sB&B⇨£65-
£75 dB&B⇨£100-£130
20P ⇔ ❀ xmas
S% Dinner £26.50-£28.50 Last dinner 9pm
Credit Cards 1 3

### ★★66% *Chadlington House*
OX7 3LZ ☎(060876)437 Telex no 83138
Closed Jan & Feb
*A stay at Chadlington House will be memorable for the genuine
welcome and homely atmosphere created by the natural warmth of
resident proprietors Rita and Peter Oxford. It is an attractive
property, part 16th-century, on the edge of the village. The
extensive grounds are well cared for and the house enjoys glorious
views of open Cotswold countryside. Bedrooms are comfortable, as
are the lounges where log fires blaze in winter months. Home-
cooked English fare is featured on the table d'hôte menu offered in
the recently refurbished dining room.*
11rm(5⇨5↑)(2fb)1⊞ CTV in all bedrooms ⓡ
✷ (ex guide dogs)
CTV 20P 2🐾 ❀
♀ English & French **V** ⍟ ⚗ ⅄ Last dinner 8.30pm
Credit Cards 1 3

---

**CHAGFORD** Devon Map **03** SX78

★★★

★★★❀❀❀♨
**GIDLEIGH PARK**

TQ13 8HH (Relais et
Châteaux)
☎(0647)432367 & 432225
Telex no 42643
FAX (0647) 432574
*Gidleigh Park was opened as
an hotel in 1977 and goes
from strength to strength as the years roll by. It is a fine 1920s
house in mock Tudor style, hidden away in the Dartmoor
National Park and surrounded by 40 acres of delightful
grounds watered by the River Teign. Owners Paul and Kay
Henderson have created an atmosphere of luxury in which
guests are enveloped in every comfort and looked after by a
courteous and attentive staff. Bedrooms are beautifully
furnished, whether in the main house, in the annexe wing or in
the thatched cottage near by. Their renowned chef and
managing director, Shaun Hill, has lately turned best-selling
author as well as continuing to inspire his kitchen brigade of
young and enthusiastic staff, with his unique brand of cooking
which draws imaginatively on the traditions of European,
Asian and American cuisine. The wine list is extensive,
offering not only a good selection of classic French wines, but
also an excellent range of American, Australian, New
Zealand and English wines.*

---

12⇨Annexe2⇨ CTV in all bedrooms **T** ✳ S%
sB&B⇨£190-£325 dB&B⇨£225-£360 Continental
breakfast (incl dinner)
25P ⇔ ❀ ♗ (hard) ♪ croquet
⍟ ⚗ ✳ S% Lunch £33-£43 Dinner £43-£50 Last dinner
9pm
Credit Cards 1 3

### ★★★❀ ♨75% Mill End
Sandy Park TQ13 8JN (2m N on A382) ☎(0647)432282
FAX (0647) 433106
Closed 13-23 Dec & 12-22 Jan RS Nov-12 Dec & 23 Jan-Mar
*A former flour mill, dating back to the 17th century and converted
into an hotel in 1929, stands beside the River Teign in its own well-
kept gardens just 1.5 miles from the stannary town of Chagford.
Interesting features include the waterwheel, retained to enhance
the public rooms. Comfortable bedrooms offer every facility for
both business client and holidaymaker. Varied and interesting
menus are complemented by personal service, and the excellence of
the food – all freshly prepared on the day that it is to be eaten –
ensures that guests return again and again.*
17rm(15⇨↑)(2fb) CTV in all bedrooms ⓡ **T** sB£30-£55
sB⇨↑£47.50 dBfr£65 dB⇨↑£65-£75 (room only) 🍽
CTV 17P 2🐾 (£2.50) ⇔ ❀ ♪ shooting xmas
♀ English & French **V** ⍟ ⚗ Lunch £15.50-£20 Dinner £20-£26
Last dinner 9pm
Credit Cards 1 2 3 5

### ★★62% Easton Court
Easton Cross TQ13 8JL (1.5m E A382) ☎(0647)433469
Closed Jan
*This part thatched hotel is run in a friendly and informal manner
by owners Graham and Sally Kidson. Public areas are cosy, with
open fires during the cooler months, and bedrooms offer a variety
of styles. Evelyn Waugh's 'Brideshead Revisited' was written here.*
8⇨↑2🅗 CTV in all bedrooms ⓡ **T** sB&B⇨↑£50-£60
dB&B⇨↑£85-£110 (incl dinner) 🍽
CTV 20P ⇔ nc12yrs xmas
♀ English & Continental **V** ⍟ ⚗ ✳ Dinner £19.50-£22.50 Last
dinner 8.30pm
Credit Cards 1 2 3 £

---

**CHALE**

See Wight, Isle of

---

**CHANNEL ISLANDS** Map **16**

---

**ALDERNEY**

### ★★57% *Inchalla*
St Anne ☎(048182)3220
*A comfortable, modern hotel commanding delightful sea views
from its position on the outskirts of St Anne, the only AA-
recommended establishment on this charming little island, offers
pleasant, particularly well equipped bedrooms, limited public
areas, good home cooking and friendly, informal service.*
11rm(8⇨)(2fb) CTV in all bedrooms ⓡ ✷
8P ⇔ ❀ sauna solarium jacuzzi
♀ English & French **V** ⍟ ⚗ Last dinner 8.30pm
Credit Cards 2 3

If you have booked a
restaurant meal and cannot get there,
remember you have a contractual obligation
to cancel your booking.

## GUERNSEY

### CATEL (CASTEL)

**★★62% Hotel Hougue du Pommier**
Hougue Du Pommier Rd ☎Guernsey(0481)56531
Telex no 4191664 FAX (0481) 56260

*Facilities for swimming and pitch and putt are provided in the attractive grounds of this establishment, and there is plenty of outdoor seating available for fine days. Lounge facilities within the hotel are more limited, however, and the bar can become quite crowded at its busiest times. A table d'hôte meal is served in the early evening only, a more enterprising à la carte menu being in operation thereafter. Accommodation is well equipped for the holidaymaker (with extensive refurbishment planned) and service is pleasant throughout – reception staff being particularly helpful.*
39⇔♠(12fb) CTV in all bedrooms ® T ✗ (ex guide dogs) ✱
sB&B⇔♠£25-£39 dB&B⇔♠£50-£78 (incl dinner)
《 CTV 87P ✿ CFA ⌒ (heated) ▶ 18 solarium gymnasium games room *xmas*
♡ English & Continental V ✆ ⌴ ✱ Sunday Lunch £5.65-£11.30alc Dinner £9.90&alc Last dinner 9.45pm
Credit Cards①②③④⑤

### FERMAIN BAY

**★★★64% Le Chalet**
(Consort) ☎Guernsey(0481)35716 Telex no 4191342
FAX (0481) 35718
Closed mid Oct-mid Apr

*In one of the finest positions on the island, Le Chalet is on a quiet road leading to the bay and has its own extensive woodland. Most of the bedrooms have been refurbished and the bright, attractive restaurant, lounge and bar have commanding sea and woodland views. Friendly and attentive service is provided by British and Austrian staff, many of whom wear national costume.*
47⇔♠ CTV in all bedrooms ® T sB&B⇔♠£34-£64
dB&B⇔♠£55-£76
35P ⇖ ✿
♡ English, Austrian & French V ✆ ⌴ Sunday Lunch £10
Dinner £12.50&alc Last dinner 9.30pm
Credit Cards①②③④⑤

**★★★63% La Favorita**
☎Guernsey(0481)35666 FAX (0481) 35413
Closed 21 Dec-7 Feb RS 1-20 Dec & 8-28 Feb

*This privately owned hotel overlooking the bay has been upgraded to a good standard, with some particularly fine public rooms and comfortable bedrooms. The restaurant offers a reasonably priced table d'hôte menu and the coffee shop is open throughout the day.*
29⇔♠(6fb) CTV in all bedrooms ® T ✗ ✱ sB&B⇔♠£30-£39 dB&B⇔♠£54-£72 ☒
40P ⇖ ✿
♡ English & French V ✆ ⌴ ✂ ✱ Sunday Lunch £8.75 Dinner
£9.75 Last dinner 9pm
Credit Cards①②③ⓕ

### PERELLE

**★★★66% L'Atlantique**
Perelle Bay ☎Guernsey(0481)64056 FAX (0481) 63800

*In a prime location on the coast road, overlooking the bay, this modern hotel provides well equipped bedrooms and smart public areas. Eating options include bar snacks, carvery, carte du jour and an extensive à la carte menu, with some imaginative dishes offered.*
23⇔♠(4fb) CTV in all bedrooms ® T ✗ (ex guide dogs)
sB&B⇔♠£24.50-£31 dB&B⇔♠£49-£62 (incl car hire) ☒
80P ✿ CFA ⌒ *xmas*
♡ International V ✆ S% Sunday Lunch £7.50-£9.50 Dinner
£9.50-£13&alc Last dinner 9.30pm
Credit Cards①②③⑤

**Hotel Hougue du Pommier ★★**

### CÂTEL, GUERNSEY
### Tel: (0481) 56531 & 53904 Telex: 4191664
### Fax: (0481) 56260

This 1712 Farmhouse now transformed into an elegant 2 star Hotel, which stands in its own 10 acres of ground, with a solar heated swimming pool, 18 hole putting green, 9 hole pitch and putt golf course offers you pleasure and relaxation. Enjoy our famous Carvery luncheons in our Tudor Bar or superb Dining Room. An à la carte candlelit dinner in this renowned Farm House Restaurant with its extensive wine menu is a must. We are looking forward to welcoming you here to the Hougue du Pommier.

*Mill End* HOTEL ★★★

### Sandy Park, Chagford, Devon TQ13 8JN
### Tel: (0647) 432282 Fax: (0647) 433106

This old flour mill, with its wheel still turning in the peaceful courtyard, nestles in the Teign Valley on the edge of Dartmoor about one and a half hours drive from Bristol and three and a half hours from London.

The whole atmosphere is one of a rather comfortable private house, with lots of nooks and corners. Tea by the fire in Winter, drinks on the lawn in Summer – it is a most relaxing place.

The restaurant is open every day for all meals; prior booking strongly recommended.

# Channel Islands, Guernsey

## ST MARTIN

### ★★★62% Green Acres

Les Hubits ☎Guernsey(0481)35711 FAX (0481) 35978

*This comfortable hotel is set in some attractive gardens, and features a heated swimming pool and a spacious lounge. The bedrooms are nicely appointed and well equipped, whilst the restaurant offers a reasonably priced set menu.*

48⇨↑(3fb) CTV in all bedrooms ® T ✗ (ex guide dogs) ✹
sB&B⇨↑£40-£72 dB&B⇨↑£60-£94 (incl dinner)
75P ⇔ ✿ ⌒ (heated) solarium *xmas*
♡ English & French V ♦ ⌒ ✄ ✱ Dinner £10.50&alc Last dinner 8.30pm
Credit Cards 1 2 3

### ★★★62% St Margaret's Lodge

Forest Rd ☎Guernsey(0481)35757 Telex no 4191664
FAX (0481) 37594

*This hotel has undergone extensive refurbishment over the last 18 months. Public areas are now smartly presented and bedrooms are comfortable and attractively furnished, providing good facilities, although one or two are more compact than others. The restaurant has a choice of table d'hôte and à la carte menus, using fresh local fish. The table d'hôte menu especially offers interesting value-for-money dishes. The hotel is conveniently sited for the airport.*

47⇨ CTV in all bedrooms ® T ✗ (incl dinner)
Lift ( 100P ⇔ ✿ ⌒ (heated) sauna solarium *xmas*
♡ English & French V ♦ ⌒
Credit Cards 1 2 3

### ★★★61% Hotel Bella Luce

La Fosse ☎Guernsey(0481)38764

*Quietly situated in a peaceful lane not far from Moulin Huet Bay, a manor house dating from the 12th-century, though extended and converted to hotel use, remains one of the island's original Norman residences. Now under new directorship, it is the subject of considerable improvement and upgrading; bedrooms, in particular, are being refurbished to a good modern standard and provided with the facilities expected by today's guests. Charming, characterful public areas include a cosy, popular bar area where diners can browse through the restaurant's extensive à la carte and simpler table d'hôte menus together with the wide-ranging wine list that complements them; during the summer months cream teas are served in the attractive and well tended gardens. For more energetic guests there is an outdoor pool and a small health room complete with sauna, solarium and mini gym.*

31⇨↑(9fb) CTV in all bedrooms ® T sB&B⇨↑£22-£42 dB&B⇨↑£40-£80 ⋣
( 50P ⇔ ✿ ⌒ (heated) sauna solarium ✿ *xmas*
♡ English & Continental V ♦ ⌒ Lunch fr£9 High tea fr£2.50 Dinner fr£9.50&alc Last dinner 10pm
Credit Cards 1 3 £

### ★★★55% St Martin's Country

Les Merriennes ☎Guernsey(0481)35644 FAX (0481) 39356
Closed Nov-Feb

*A simple hotel situated in 15-acre grounds and attracting both young families and older guests (many of them travelling with an organised party) offers a range of bedrooms in various sizes, shapes and degrees of comfort, all simple in style but reasonably decorated and furnished. Relatively spacious public areas include a newly completed sun lounge on the third floor and a split-level dining room featuring table d'hôte and à la carte menus. Leisure amenities include a swimming pool, terrace and pitch and putt, and friendly staff provide pleasant service.*

60⇨(24fb) CTV in all bedrooms T sB&B⇨£25-£35 dB&B⇨£50-£70 ⋣
Lift ( CTV 250P 1⚐ ✿ CFA ⌒ ♪ (hard) putting green croquet table tennis ✿
♡ English & French V ♦ ⌒ ✄ ✱ Bar Lunch £3-£7.50alc Dinner fr£7.75&alc Last dinner 9pm
Credit Cards 1 2 3 4 5 £

### ★★68% Windmill

La Rue Poudreuse ☎Guernsey(0481)35383 Telex no 4191501
Closed Nov-Mar

*The Windmill, in a residential area of the parish of St Martin, has much to offer. Hospitality and a warm atmosphere are paramount, and both Mr Graham the proprietor and manageress Jan Nicholls are very involved in the day-to-day life of the hotel. The bedrooms have recently been completely refurbished and are now very smart and comfortable with pretty co-ordinated décor and good facilities. Public areas are well appointed and the dining room offers a table d'hôte menu of simple home-cooked food.*

18⇨↑(6fb) CTV in all bedrooms ® T sB&B⇨↑£30.50-£39 dB&B⇨↑£55-£72 (incl dinner) ⋣
CTV 18P ⇔ ✿ ⌒ (heated) pool table nc3yrs
♡ International ♦ ⌒ ✄ Lunch £9.50 Dinner £9.50 Last dinner 7.30pm
Credit Cards 1 2 3 5

### ★★65% Idlerocks

Jerbourg Point ☎Guernsey(0481)37711 FAX (0481) 35592

*Situated at Jerbourg Point enjoying breathtaking views across the bay, this family-owned hotel continues to improve under the ownership of Paul Hamill. Bedrooms vary in size, some being more compact than others. All are well equipped with smart en suites and fresh décor; many enjoy lovely views out to sea. The public areas have received attention in recent months and a good standard of comfort is now offered throughout the hotel.*

23⇨↑(4fb)2⚐ CTV in all bedrooms ® T sB&B⇨↑£23-£42 dB&B⇨↑£42-£90 (incl dinner) ⋣
( 100P ✿ ⌒ (heated) ✿ *xmas*
♡ English & French V ♦ ⌒ ✄ ✱ Lunch fr£10.50 High tea fr£4.50 Dinner fr£11.50&alc Last dinner 10pm
Credit Cards 1 2 3 4 5

## ST PETER PORT

### ★★★★67% St Pierre Park

Rohais ☎Guernsey(0481)28282 Telex no 4191662
FAX (0481) 712041

*Set in parkland with a 9-hole golf course, this modern well furnished hotel has extensive leisure facilities including a shopping arcade and hairdressing and beauty salons. The balconied bedrooms are comfortable and well equipped; 24-hour room service is provided and there are two quality restaurants with enterprising menus featuring seafood, plus a brasserie and bar in live entertainment in season.*

135⇨↑(1fb) CTV in all bedrooms ® T ✗ (ex guide dogs)
sB&B⇨↑£93 dB&B⇨↑£125 ⋣
Lift ( CTV 350P ✿ ◱ (heated) ▶ 9 ♪ (hard) snooker sauna solarium gymnasium croquet childrens playground ♫ ✿ *xmas*
♡ English & French V ♦ ⌒ ✄ Sunday Lunch £8.50-£12.50 High tea £5-£10alc Dinner £12-£25alc Last dinner 10pm
Credit Cards 1 2 3 5

### ★★★★60% Old Government House

Ann's Place JE2 3QA ☎Guernsey(0481)724921
Telex no 4191144 FAX (0481) 724429

*Affectionately known as OGH, this is the former official residence of the Governors of Guernsey. The hotel first opened in 1858 and has been considerably extended, but it retains much of its traditional atmosphere and style. Bedrooms are slowly being upgraded and refurbished to a generally acceptable standard. Levels of hospitality are very good and facilities include 2 bars, a compact, well managed restaurant, a large conference room, Scarletts Night Club, an outdoor swimming pool and terrace, and a small car park operated by the hotel's concierge.*

74⇨(8fb) CTV in all bedrooms T sB&B⇨£36-£61.50 dB&B⇨£72-£123
Lift ( 20P CFA ⌒ (heated) solarium ♫ ✿ *xmas*
♡ English, French & Italian V ♦ ⌒ ✱ Lunch fr£7.50&alc Dinner fr£12&alc Last dinner 9.15pm
Credit Cards 1 2 3 5 £

★★★ ®69% **La Fregate**

Les Cotils ☎Guernsey(0481)724624 FAX (0481) 720443

*This delightful 18th-century manor house is tucked away on a garden hillside overlooking the harbour. Bedrooms are in the modern style and are well equipped – 6 have balconies and all but 2 have stunning views. The restaurant has acquired a reputation for fresh seafood and home-grown vegetables and chef/manager Oswald Steinsdorfer continues to produce reliable and professional standards of cooking. Service is very attentive and is particularly well managed by Roberto Chiappa.*

13⇨↑ CTV in all bedrooms ® T ✖ sB⇨↑£50-£55 dB⇨↑£90-£97 (room only)

25P 🚗 ❋ nc14yrs

♀ Continental **V**

Credit Cards ① ② ③ ④ ⑤

★★★ ®68% **Hotel de Havelet**

Havelet(Consort) ☎Guernsey(0481)722199 Telex no 4191342 FAX (0481) 714057

*Occupying one of the most prized sites in the town, with panoramic views over Castle Cornet, this Georgian styled hotel offers comfortable well equipped bedrooms and traditional public areas. There is a smart new leisure complex comprising pool, sauna and jacuzzi. Eating options are the relaxed Havelet Grill or the more formal Wellington Boot Restaurant. Both have a good choice of reasonably priced dishes and a reasonable selection of wines.*

33⇨↑(4fb) CTV in all bedrooms ® T ✖

CTV 40P 🚗 ❋ ▤ (heated) sauna gymnasium

♀ English, Austrian & French **V** ♥ ☡ ✲ Lunch £8.50 Dinner £10.50&alc Last dinner 9.30pm

Credit Cards ① ② ③ ④ ⑤

A rosette means exceptional standards of cuisine.

*Saint Margaret's Lodge Hotel* ★★★

**Forest Road, St Martin, Guernsey, CI**
**Tel: Guernsey 35757 Telex: 4191664**

C

**★★★65% Moore's**

Pollet(Consort) ☎Guernsey(0481)724452 Telex no 4191342 FAX (0481) 714037

*A Georgian hotel situated in the attractive shopping street of Le Pollet. It has a smart pâtisserie serving lunches and mouthwatering home-made gâteaux, and the spacious Library Bar offers lunches and bar snacks, or guests may prefer to dine in the Conservatory Restaurant, with its extensive table d'hôte and à la carte menu – portions are generous. Bedrooms vary in size and design, but all are comfortable and have good facilities. The lounge area is newly refurbished and further upgrading is planned. The hotel has no parking facilities, although there is a public car park some distance away where overnight parking is permitted, loading and unloading luggage can be a problem.*

42⇔ฅAnnexe6⇔ฅ(8fb) CTV in all bedrooms ® T sB&B⇔ฅ£30-£68 dB&B⇔ฅ£40-£72 ⊟

Lift ( ⨿ ⇔ CFA *xmas*

♀ English & French V ⊕ ⌂ Lunch fr£9&alc Dinner £12&alc Last dinner 9pm

Credit Cards ⓵ ⓶ ⓷ ⓸ ⓹

**★★★60% La Collinette**

St Jacques ☎Guernsey(0481)710331 FAX (0481) 713516

*Quietly situated away from the centre of town, this privately owned hotel offers well equipped, simply furnished bedrooms and attractive, recently refurbished public areas. Overall, the atmosphere is informal and relaxed. Amenities include an outdoor solar-heated pool, sauna, jacuzzi and solarium. Seven self-catering cottages are also available.*

27⇔ฅ CTV in all bedrooms ® ✖ (ex guide dogs) ⊟

CTV 25P ⇔ ✿ CFA ⌇ (heated) sauna solarium spa bath ⚕

♀ English & Continental V ⊕ ⌂ ⌇

Credit Cards ⓵ ⓶ ⓷ ⓹

**★★65% Sunnycroft**

5 Constitution Steps ☎Guernsey(0481)723008

Closed Nov-Mar

*A small family owned holiday hotel, up Constitution Steps, high above the town with views far out across the rooftops. Bedrooms are pretty and simply furnished with modern facilities. Similarly, public areas are nicely appointed, with an attractive pastel colour scheme. Many of the rooms have patios and 2 have balconies.*

14⇔ฅ CTV in all bedrooms ® T ✖

CTV ✿ nc14yrs

⊕ ⌂ Last dinner 7.30pm

Credit Cards ⓵ ⓷

**✿✖✖Le Nautique**

Quay Steps ☎Guernsey(0481)721714

*Carlo Grazini extends a warm welcome at this long-established old-fashioned restaurant with an international clientèle. Chef V Garau's reliable and imaginative cooking features daily specialities often using fresh fish and local seafood, plus a separate dessert menu.*

Closed Sun & 1st 2 wks Jan

♀ French V 68 seats Lunch £14-£20alc Last lunch 2pm Last dinner 10pm ⨍ nc5yrs

Credit Cards ⓵ ⓶ ⓷ ⓹

**✿✖✖La Piazza Ristorante**

Under the Arch, Trinity Square ☎Guernsey(0481)725085

*Situated opposite Holy Trinity Church, this comfortable, intimate restaurant, in shades of pink and grey, spills onto its attractive walled courtyard in warmer months. The cooking style is very Italian, but great use is made of local fish – nine varieties at the time of our visit – and other fresh produce. Of particular note are the Scallops Brettona and the Veal Marsala, accompanied by an imaginative selection of vegetables. It is also a pleasure to find an Italian restaurant which will prepare a Zabaglione for one. The small wine list is carefully balanced and offers good value.*

Closed Sun & 24 Dec-23 Jan

♀ French & Italian 55 seats Lunch £15-£25alc Dinner £15-£25alc Last lunch 2pm Last dinner 10pm ⨍ nc6yrs

Credit Cards ⓵ ⓶ ⓷

**VALE**

**★★★65% Novotel Guernsey**

Les Dicqs ☎Guernsey(0481)48400 Telex no 4191306 FAX (0481) 48706

*Purpose-built, and overlooking the bay from its own grounds, the hotel is run with the needs of families in mind. Spacious bedrooms are well equipped, and the dinning room offers meals from noon until midnight (with set menus at lunch and dinner), while leisure facilities include a sun terrace, open-air swimming pool with adjacent children's pool and a gymnasium.*

99⇔(99fb) CTV in all bedrooms ✳ S% sB⇔£32-£62 dB⇔£38-£66 (room only)

Lift ( 120P ✿ ⌇ (heated) gymnasium *xmas*

♀ English & Continental V ⊕ ⌂

Credit Cards ⓵ ⓶ ⓷ ⓸ ⓹ £

**HERM**

**★★❀71% White House**

☎Guernsey(0481)722159 FAX (0481) 710066

Closed 16 Oct-Mar

*This hotel – the only one in the peaceful island retreat, 3 miles from Guernsey and accessible only by boat – can boast many visitors who return regularly, the main attraction being the natural, sincere and extremely friendly staff for whom nothing seems too much trouble. Simple, basic bedrooms with few modern facilities apart from en suite bathrooms are located for the most part in nearby cottages; those in the main building are slightly more comfortable, but all are adequate, clean and bright. Public areas which, by contrast, are cosy, traditional and full of character, offer a choice of both eating options and lounge areas, the latter including an airy conservatory sun lounge. Frequently changing menus offer a wide variety of enjoyable, well presented dishes based on fresh, quality, local produce. Home-made chicken liver parfait in a Cumberland sauce is worthy of note, as are the fresh fish dishes and very tempting puddings. A well balanced, reasonably priced wine list accompanies the meal.*

10⇔Annexe22⇔ ® ✖ dB&B⇔£95-£108 (incl dinner)

⨍ ⇔ ✿ CFA ⌇ (heated) ⨗ (hard)

♀ English & French V ⊕ ⌂ ⌇ Lunch £9.25 High tea £4-£6 Last high tea 5pm

Credit Cards ⓵ ⓷

**JERSEY**

**ARCHIRONDEL**

**★★67% Les Arches**

Archirondel Bay ☎Jersey(0534)53839 Telex no 4192085 FAX (0534) 56660

*A popular and lively hotel with nig.ttclub offers a choice of modern bedrooms with views of sea, pool or rear garden. Public areas include a well-run dining room and a residents' bar and lounge, there are extensive leisure facilities, and the Bar Papillon and Les Arches Nightclub feature nightly musical entertainment.*

54⇔ฅ CTV in all bedrooms ® T S% sB&B⇔ฅ£27.50-£43 dB&B⇔ฅ£55-£86 ⊟

( CTV 120P ⇔ ✿ ⌇ (heated) ⨗ (hard) sauna gymnasium ⚕ *xmas*

♀ English & Continental V ⊕ ⌂ ✳ Lunch £10.50-£17.50 Dinner £12.50-£25 Last dinner 8.45pm

Credit Cards ⓵ ⓷ ⓸ £

For key to symbols in English see the bookmark.

## BEAUMONT

### ★★60% Hotel L'Hermitage
☎Jersey(0534)33314 Telex no 4192170 FAX (0534) 21207
Closed Nov-mid Mar

*A traditional family-run hotel convenient for the airport and
popular with holidaymakers, with well kept grounds, indoor and
outdoor leisure facilities and an informal, friendly atmosphere.
Most bedrooms are arranged chalet style around the swimming
pool. A large, busy dining room provides live entertainment most
evenings.*

43⇌🛏Annexe66⇌🛏 CTV in all bedrooms ® 🗙
sB&B⇌🛏£23.20-£34.80 dB&B⇌🛏£44.30-£67.60 (incl
dinner)
《 100P 🚗 ✿ ▭ (heated) ⌣ (heated) sauna solarium spa bath
♫ nc14yrs
♀ English & French ♥ ⚗ Lunch £5.50 Dinner £7.50 Last
dinner 8pm

## GOREY

### ★★★63% Old Court House
JE3 9EX ☎Jersey(0534)54444 Telex no 4192032
FAX (0534) 53587
Closed Nov-Feb

*Set in its own grounds near the 'old village' and opposite the beach,
this hotel provides modern, functional bedrooms, the best with
balconies overlooking the pool and garden. The spacious bar and
adjoining dance floor feature live entertainment in season, and a
small, comfortable lounge supplements the patio and garden
facilities. Attentive service is provided in the extended restaurant
with its original beamed section.*

58⇌🛏(4fb) CTV in all bedrooms T 🗙
Lift 《 40P 🚗 ⌣ (heated) sauna solarium ♫
♀ English, French & Italian ♥ ⚗ Last dinner 9pm
Credit Cards ①②③⑤ⓔ

### ★★66% The Moorings
Gorey Pier ☎Jersey(0534)53633 Telex no 4192085
FAX (0534) 56660

*Sister hotel to Les Arches, this cosy little establishment is huddled
between the impressive walls of Mont Orgueil (Gorey Castle) and
the waterfront of Gorey harbour. Bedrooms, some a little compact,
are bright and well equipped. The popular restaurant is one of the
hotel's strengths, air conditioned and formal in style, it has the
standard of traditional skills normally associated with hotels of a
higher classification. A good range of menus caters for most tastes
and pockets. There is no car park on site, but there is unrestricted
overnight parking and limited day time parking opposite.*

16⇌🛏 CTV in all bedrooms ® T S% sB&B⇌🛏£32-£45
dB&B⇌🛏£64-£90 🍴
《 CTV ✗ 🚗 xmas
♀ English & Continental V ♥ S% Lunch £10.25-£23&alc
Dinner £14-£32 Last dinner 10.15pm
Credit Cards ①②③④ⓔ

## L'ETACQ

### ★★★66% Lobster Pot Hotel & Restaurant
☎Jersey(0534)82888 Telex no 4192605 FAX (0534) 81574

*A popular and long-established restaurant is the focal point of this
skilfully converted 18th century granite farmhouse with its coach
house bar and patio; comfortable bedrooms are particularly well
furnished and equipped, service is generally efficient and the
standard of cooking is reliable.*

13⇌🛏(1fb) CTV in all bedrooms ® T 🗙 (ex guide dogs) ✷
sB&B⇌🛏£45.50-£63.50 dB&B⇌🛏£71-£107
《 ⊞ 56P ✿ ♫ xmas
♀ English, Continental & North American V ♥ ⚗ ✷ Lunch
fr£9.75 Dinner fr£13.95 Last dinner 10.15pm
Credit Cards ①②③④⑤ⓔ

## ROZEL BAY

### ★★★✾👫75% Château la Chaire
Rozel Valley JE3 6AJ ☎Jersey(0534)63354 Telex no 437334
FAX (0534) 65137

*Quietly situated on a terraced hillside, this beautifully furnished
country house offers bedrooms ranging from the luxurious and
spacious to some rather more restricted 2nd floor rooms. There is a
splendid rococo lounge and wood-panelled bar and restaurant; and
the conservatory restaurant extension is ideal for breakfast,
catching the early sunlight. The standard of cooking under the
direction of Chef David Tilbury continues to impress, with home-
made breads, pâtisserie and hot puddings.*

13⇌🛏(1fb)1🛁 CTV in all bedrooms T 🗙 (ex guide dogs)
sB&B⇌🛏£52-£100 dB&B⇌🛏£74-£125 🍴
《 30P ✿ nc7yrs xmas
♀ French V ♥ ⚗ ✂ Lunch £10.25-£13.75&alc Dinner £19.95-
£22.50alc Last dinner 10pm
Credit Cards ①②③⑤

### ✾✾ 🗙 Granite Corner
Rozel Harbour ☎Jersey(0534)63590

*The French chef and proprietor Jean-Luc Robin with his wife
Louise offer regional French dishes at their delightful little
restaurant perched right at the water's edge in Rozel. Some
ingredients are specially imported to prepare dishes that include
home made terrine of goose foie gras, and ballotine of canard.
Sweets are deliciously fresh and brightly presented, there is
cinnamon parfait on fresh strawberry coulis or walnut gâteau
amongst others. Lunch is a more simple affair with a fixed-price
menu. The restaurant has a keen following, so booking is essential.*

Closed 15 Dec-10 Jan Lunch not served Mon
Dinner not served Sun
♀ French 24 seats Last dinner 9pm ✗ nc12yrs
Credit Cards ①②③⑤

C

## ST AUBIN

**★★★ 62% Somerville**
Mont du Boulevard ☏Jersey(0534)41226 Telex no 4192505
FAX (0534) 46621
Closed 2nd wk Nov-mid Mar
*A popular resort hotel situated on a hill overlooking St Aubin Bay, the Somerville has well appointed rooms, a spacious restaurant, good leisure facilities and entertainment in the evenings.*
59rm(58⇌⌒)(7fb) CTV in all bedrooms ® T ⋈ sB&Bfr£30 sB&B⇌⌒fr£30 dB&B⇌⌒fr£64
Lift ☾ CTV 40P ⛟ ✲ ⩳ (heated) games room ♫ nc4yrs
♡ English & French V ☧ ⌐ ⁄ Sunday Lunch £11&alc Dinner £10-£14&alc Last dinner 8.30pm
Credit Cards [1] [2] [3] [4] £

## ST BRELADE

**★★★★ ⊛71% Hotel L'Horizon**
St Brelade's Bay(Clipper) ☏Jersey(0534)43101
Telex no 4192281 FAX (0534) 46269
*In a prime position at the water's edge in St Brelades Bay, this well appointed holiday and conference hotel offers traditional services by an established staff and the conscientious management of R G Fletcher. Bedrooms, many with balconies, are in the final stages of upgrading to provide comfortable surroundings and a good range of modern facilities. There is a choice of 3 restaurants, the Star Grill, Crystal Room and Brasserie, the latter adjoining the new Club L'Horizon leisure complex. Good work by Chef Peter Marek has been rewarded with a Rosette for the Star Grill, with menus making good use of local produce.*
104⇌⌒(7fb)1⊟ CTV in all bedrooms T ⋈ (ex guide dogs) sB&B⇌⌒£75-£85 dB&B⇌⌒£150-£170 ⊟
Lift ☾ 125P ⛟ CFA ▭ (heated) sauna gymnasium windsurfing/water skiing spa steam baths ⌂ *xmas*
♡ English, French & Italian V ☧ ⌐ ⁄ Lunch £14&alc Dinner £23&alc Last dinner 10.45pm
Credit Cards [1] [3]

**★★★★ 66% *Atlantic***
La Moye ☏Jersey(0534)44101 Telex no 4192405
FAX (0534) 44102
Closed Jan-Feb
*There has been further upgrading at this well sited hotel to coincide with its 21st anniversary in 1991. Bedrooms, while not large, are comfortable, brightly styled and furnished, with co-ordinating fabrics and a good range of modern facilities. The majority of rooms have balconies with views of the golf course or over St Ouen's Bay; and the recent addition of the commendable garden studio and full suite bedrooms add a touch of luxury. The public rooms, which tend to suffer from 1970s architecture, are also rather small, but the new Palm Court leisure complex adds another dimension. One of the hotel's strengths is the consistent, well managed, professional service, including 24-hour room service.*
50⇌⌒ CTV in all bedrooms T ⋈ (ex guide dogs)
Lift ☾ 60P ⛟ ✲ ▭ (heated) ⩳ (heated) ℘ (hard) sauna solarium gymnasium spa pool
♡ International V ☧ ⌐ Last dinner 9.15pm
Credit Cards [1] [2] [3] [5]

**★★★ 67% St Brelade's Bay**
JE3 8EF ☏Jersey(0534)46141 FAX (0534) 47278
Closed 14 Oct-Apr RS 4-13 Oct
*Enjoying a fine location at the end of the bay, this family-run holiday hotel benefits from a regular clientele. The restaurant is particularly well managed and offers table d'hôte and à la carte menus, together with a very good wine list. Most bedrooms facing the sea have a balcony, whilst others overlook the terraced gardens. Room service is available, and all bedrooms are well equipped, furnished in the modern style with good quality coordinated fabrics and décor.*
72⇌⌒(50fb) CTV in all bedrooms T ⋈ (ex guide dogs) ✱ sB&B⇌⌒£41-£76 dB&B⇌⌒£62-£184
Lift ☾ 60P ⛟ ✲ ⩳ (heated) ℘ (hard) snooker sauna solarium croquet putting green petanque ♫ ⌂
♡ English & French V ☧ ⌐ ✱ Lunch fr£10&alc Dinner fr£17&alc Last dinner 9pm
Credit Cards [1] [2] [3] [5]

**★★★ 66% Château Valeuse**
Rue de Valeuse, St Brelade's Bay JE3 8EE ☏Jersey(0534)46281
FAX (0534) 47110
Closed Jan-Mar
*Set back from the bay with outdoor leisure facilities including a swimming pool in the gardens, this well managed hotel offers a choice of modern, bright bedrooms, the best of which have balconies with views. There is a comfortable lounge and bar, and chef Terry Bunting specialises in seafood, with a good range of dishes.*
33⇌⌒(1fb) CTV in all bedrooms T ⋈ ✱ S% sB&B⇌⌒£32-£38 dB&B⇌⌒£64-£76 ⊟
☾ 50P ⛟ ✲ ⩳ (heated) nc5yrs *xmas*
♡ French V ☧ ⌐ ✱ Lunch £9&alc High tea £3 Dinner £13.50&alc Last dinner 9.15pm
Credit Cards [1] [3]

**★★ 67% Beau Rivage**
St Brelades Bay JE3 8EF ☏Jersey(0534)45983
FAX (0534) 47127
Closed Nov-mid Mar
*Right on one of Jersey's most popular bays, this sunny hotel continues to improve. All bedrooms have been recently refurbished along with the restaurant and terraces. The Beau Bar, where live entertainment is featured most evenings, continues to attract the visitors. There is a laundry room and a limited 24-hour room service.*
27⇌⌒(9fb) CTV in all bedrooms ⋈ (ex guide dogs) dB&B⇌⌒£34-£93
Lift ☾ 14P sunbathing terrace video games ♫
♡ English, French & Italian V ☧ ⌐ Dinner £13.50 Last dinner 7.30pm
Credit Cards [1] [2] [3]

## ST HELIER

**★★★★ ⊛62% The Grand**
The Esplanade JE4 8WD (De Vere) ☏Jersey(0534)22301
Telex no 4192104 FAX (0534) 37815
*We found continued good work and upgrading at this centrally positioned, formal hotel. There are elegant new public lounges and a choice of restaurants, including Victoria's where professional service and cuisine combine well with the ornate surroundings. Bedrooms vary in size and many have fine views; at the time of our visit they were in the final stages of refurbishment to a bright modern standard. Other facilities are an indoor leisure complex, summer terrace, beauty salon and reasonable car parking.*
115⇌⌒ CTV in all bedrooms ® T ✱ sB&B⇌⌒£55-£75 dB&B⇌⌒£100-£145 ⊟
Lift ☾ 15P 25⌂ ⛟ CFA ▭ (heated) snooker sauna solarium gymnasium spa bath hairdresser massage parlour ♫ *xmas*
♡ English, French & Italian V ☧ ⌐ ⁄ ✱ Lunch £14-£25 High tea fr£7.25 Dinner £15.50-£18.50&alc Last dinner 10pm
Credit Cards [1] [2] [3] [5]

**★★★ 65% Pomme D'Or**
Liberation Square JE2 3QA ☏Jersey(0534)78644
Telex no 4192309 FAX (0534) 37781
*Situated in the heart of St Helier overlooking the harbour and marina, this conveniently located hotel has good access to all the shopping precincts. The bedrooms are modern and well equipped, and the public rooms are air conditioned and include the Coffee Shop, lobby bar, Tavern Carvery, the 'Wharf', and the first-floor cocktail bar and restaurant. The service is particularly well managed.*

150⊸🛏(3fb)⌿in 78 bedrooms CTV in all bedrooms ® T
✻ (ex guide dogs) S% sB&B⊸🛏£55-£57.50 dB&B⊸🛏£80-
£85 🅿

Lift ℂ 🎤 CFA *xmas*
♀ International V ⇪ ⚏ ⌿ ✳ Lunch £8-£14.50&alc Dinner £8-
£14.50&alc Last dinner 9pm
Credit Cards ①②③⑤

★★★63% **Beaufort**
Green St JE2 4UH ☎Jersey(0534)32471 Telex no 4192160
FAX (0534) 20371
*The provision of a good range of de luxe bedrooms is just part of
the upgrading which is in evidence throughout this centrally-
situated hotel. An indoor swimming pool and whirlpool spa is
another new addition and there are plans to further increase leisure
facilities. Nicely decorated throughout, the hotel has comfortable
public rooms and staff are efficient and friendly.*
54⊸🛏(2fb)1🛏 CTV in all bedrooms ® T ✻ sB&B⊸🛏£55-
£75 dB&B⊸🛏£85-£95 🅿
Lift ℂ 40P CFA ▨ (heated) jacuzzi spa bath ♫ *xmas*
♀ English & French V ⇪ ⚏ ⌿ Sunday Lunch fr£10 Dinner
fr£12 Last dinner 8.45pm
Credit Cards ①②③⑤

**See advertisement on page 209**

★★★62% **Apollo**
St Saviours Rd JE2 4LA ☎Jersey(0534)25441 Telex no 4192086
FAX (0534) 22120
*Situated right in the heart of St Helier, but built around its own
quiet courtyard, the Apollo has recently been significantly
renovated. Bedrooms are bright and comfortable and their modern
facilities include satellite TV and teletext. Public rooms have been
tastefully decorated, with lounges and a cocktail bar in modern
style. The attractive indoor leisure centre includes a stylish coffee
shop terrace which in the evening takes on a bistro atmosphere
amid the soft-lit waters of the adjacent pool.*

→

**C**

85⇨(5fb)1⊞ CTV in all bedrooms ® T ⋈ sB&B⇨£46-£66 dB&B⇨£76-£86 ⊟

Lift ☾ 50P CFA ⊡ (heated) sauna solarium gymnasium jacuzzi spa bath ♫ *xmas*

☋ English & French V ✿ ⊥ ⚟ Sunday Lunch fr£9 Dinner fr£11 Last dinner 8.45pm

Credit Cards [1] [2] [3] [5]

**★★★60% Hotel Savoy**

Rouge Bouillon ☎Jersey(0534)27521 FAX (0534) 68480

*This family-run holiday hotel offers a friendly informal atmosphere and comfortable accommodation with some well-equipped bedrooms. Traditional cooking is served in the spacious restaurant.*

61⇨↱(1fb) CTV in all bedrooms T ⋈ (ex guide dogs) sB&B⇨↱£35-£43 dB&B⇨↱£70-£86 (incl dinner) ⊟

Lift ☾ 55P ⊞ CFA ⩯ (heated) pool table *xmas*

☋ English, French, Italian & Spanish V ✿ ⊥ ⚟ Lunch fr£7 Dinner fr£9.50 Last dinner 8.30pm

Credit Cards [1] [2] [3] [£]

**★★69% Sarum Hotel**

19-21 New St John's Rd JE2 3LD ☎Jersey(0534)58163 FAX (0534) 31340

Closed Nov-mid Mar

*Already a winner of the 1990 Jersey 'Hospitality Care and Service' Cup, this hotel is a deserving winner of one of our 'Courtesy and Care' awards 1991/1992 for the Southern region. In a residential area within walking distance of the town centre, the hotel enjoys a good reputation for friendly, traditional service under very experienced management. Bedrooms are particularly bright and are equipped with an intercom system – there is a telephone for guests on each floor. The hotel has an in-house TV video channel, and live entertainment is featured 3 nights a week in season. Car parking is difficult, though there are some rear parking spaces and a local map has been prepared to assist guests arriving by car. (See colour feature on p15.)*

49⇨↱(6fb) CTV in all bedrooms sB&B⇨↱£18-£40.50 dB&B⇨↱£30-£75

Lift ☾ 6P games room

☋ English & Continental V Dinner fr£6.50 Last dinner 7.30pm

Credit Cards [1] [2] [3]

**★★63% Royal Yacht**

The Weighbridge ☎Jersey(0534)20511 FAX (0534) 67729

*Retaining much of its original Victorian style and atmosphere, the hotel nevertheless provides accommodation in consistently well equipped bedrooms, all furnished to the same high standard; guests can eat in either the London Grill or Victoria's Carvery, there is a choice of popular bars, and a fifth-floor sun lounge offers an excellent view of the harbour.*

45⇨↱ CTV in all bedrooms ® T S% sB&B⇨↱£32-£45 dB&B⇨↱£64-£90 ⊟

Lift ☾ CTV ℙ *xmas*

☋ English, French & Italian V ✿ ⊥ S% Lunch £5.25-£12.50&alc Dinner £12.50-£28 Last dinner 8.45pm

Credit Cards [1] [2] [3] [4] [£]

**★63% Graham**

60 Saint Saviours Rd JE2 4LA ☎Jersey(0534)30126 FAX (0534) 21246

Closed mid Nov-mid Mar

*An hotel near the centre of the town plans a complete refurbishment during the winter of 1991/2 which should result in better equipped bedrooms with modern facilities and comfortable quality public areas. An outdoor swimming pool and limited car parking are available, staff are friendly, and the cheerful manager is very involved in the day-to-day running of the establishment.*

27rm(17⇨↱)(6fb) CTV in 6 bedrooms ⋈ (ex guide dogs) ✱ sB&B£20.50-£36 sB&B⇨↱£25-£40.50 dB&B£27-£58 dB&B⇨↱£36-£67 (incl dinner)

CTV 11P ⩯ games room ♤

☋ English & Continental V ✱ High tea £4.50 Dinner £7 Last dinner 7.45pm

Credit Cards [1] [3]

## ST LAWRENCE

***★★★❀❀77% Little Grove***

Rue De Haut ☎Jersey(0534)25321 FAX (0534) 25325

(Rosettes awarded for dinner only)

*This small pink-granite hotel has great charm and is run with friendly informality by the attentive owners and staff. Public rooms are comfortable and attractive and the varying bedrooms are well equipped, though some of them are quite compact and cluttered. A wide choice of menus, including vegetarian, is offered in the restaurant where the skilful French/British cooking is by chef Thierry Billion.*

13⇨↱ CTV in all bedrooms T ⋈

☾ 30P ⊞ ✲ ⩯ (heated) croquet nc12yrs

☋ English & French V ✿ ⊥ Last dinner 9.30pm

Credit Cards [1] [2] [3] [5]

## ST PETER

**★★★63% Mermaid**

JE3 7BN ☎Jersey(0543)41255 Telex no 4192249 FAX (0534) 45826

*Set in 18 acres of grounds with a natural lake, this well managed hotel close to the airport has extensive leisure facilities and good conference rooms. All bedrooms are furnished to the same standard with balconies giving views of the gardens. Besides the formal restaurant, there is a grill room open at lunchtimes and an attractive public bar, the Mermaid Tavern. An outdoor swimming pool is planned to supplement the 45-foot-long indoor pool.*

68⇨1⊞ CTV in all bedrooms ® T ⋈ sB&B⇨£45-£55 dB&B⇨£73-£90 ⊟

☾ 250P ⊞ ✲ CFA ⊡ (heated) ⩯ ⚑ 18 ℘ (hard) sauna solarium gymnasium jacuzzi putting green ♫ *xmas*

☋ English & French V ✿ ⊥ ⚟ Dinner fr£12&alc Last dinner 9.30pm

Credit Cards [1] [2] [3] [5]

**See advertisement on page 211**

## ST SAVIOUR

★★★★

**★★★★❀❀ LONGUEVILLE MANOR**

JE2 7SA (off St Helier/ Grouville Rd A3) (Relais et Châteaux)

☎Jersey(0534)25501

Telex no 4192306

FAX (0534) 31613

*Dating back to the 13th century, Longueville Manor is a most delightful hotel, owned and run for the last 40 years by three generations of the Lewis family and now also by the Dufty family. The rambling old house is set in 16 acres of grounds, barely two miles from St Helier. Its rooms, bedrooms and public rooms alike, are furnished with taste and quality, with great attention paid to the comfort of guests, masses of fresh flowers and paintings providing that personal touch that makes a home-like atmosphere. There are two dining rooms, one (non-smoking) oak panelled and the other more spacious and air conditioned. At 24, the chef, Andrew Baird, is one of the youngest head chefs in Britain, and he offers three separate menus, ranging from the mainly French-inspired à la carte, to the menu dégustation and a very good vegetarian menu. The owners*

→

**C**

*take a very personal interest in the hotel and their staff are both courteous and professional.*

32⊸🛏1🛁 CTV in all bedrooms **T** ✱ dB&B⊸🛏£115-£191 🅿

Lift ℄ 40P 🚗 ❀ CFA ⌲ (heated) nc7yrs *xmas*
♀ English & French **V** ✿ 🎱 ✂ ✱ S10% Lunch £20 Dinner £28&alc Last dinner 9.30pm
Credit Cards ①②③⑤ ⓔ

---

**CHAPELTOWN** South Yorkshire Map **08** SK39

**★★★62% Staindrop Lodge**
Ln End S30 4UH ☎Sheffield(0742)846727 FAX (0742) 846783
Closed 25 & 26 Dec
*Situated about 2 miles from Junction 35 of the M1, this small privately owned hotel is set in its own grounds close to the parish church and provides comfortable accommodation with modern facilities. The restaurant has a good local reputation.*
13⊸🛏(1fb) CTV in all bedrooms ® **T** ✖ sB&B⊸🛏£55-£65 dB&B⊸🛏£70-£85 🅿
℄ 60P ❀
♀ English & French **V** ✿ Lunch £9-£12 Dinner £16-£24 Last dinner 9.30pm
Credit Cards ①②③⑤ ⓔ

**❀ ✖✖Greenhead House**
84 Buncross Rd S30 4SF ☎(0742)469004
*Neil and Anne Allen own this small restaurant in one of the outer suburbs of Sheffield, providing good food and service in the comfortable surroundings of a large stone built house looking out onto a walled garden. The 4-course menu changes every month, and offers a choice of starters, main course and dessert, with a set 'soup of the day'. Cooking is basically French, with Yorkshire overtones, and this has proved a popular and successful combination. Our inspector noted a full flavoured country pâté and langoustines with tomato jelly among the starters. Fish is much in request as a main course. The range includes elaborate lobster dishes as well as a simpler fresh salmon and asparagus with Hollandaise sauce. There is only a small choice of desserts, often based on seasonal fresh fruit, with a well balanced English cheeseboard as an alternative.*
Closed Sun, Mon, last 2 wks Apr & last 2 wks Aug Lunch not served Tue-Sat (ex by prior arrangement)
32 seats ✱ Dinner £22-£27 Last dinner 9pm 15 P ✂
Credit Cards ①②③

---

**CHARD** Somerset Map **03** ST30

**★★69% Lordleaze**
Lordleaze Ln, off Forton Rd TA20 2HW ☎(0460)61066
FAX (0460) 66468
*Tucked away behind a residential area, just 3 minutes from Chard centre, the Lordleaze achieves an old world atmosphere in a modern, purposely constructed building. Fourteen bedrooms are tastefully decorated and furnished, and equipped with every facility for either business or holiday guests. A new bar proves popular with locals, as does the conference room and conservatory-style restaurant, where an extensive choice of dishes is offered from a range of menus.*
14⊸🛏(1fb) CTV in all bedrooms ® **T** ✖ (ex guide dogs) ✱
sB&B⊸🛏£28-£35 dB&B⊸🛏£42-£58 🅿
60P ♨ *xmas*
♀ English & French **V** ✿ 🎱 ✂ Lunch £8.95-£10.95&alc High tea £4.50-£6&alc Dinner £12.95-£14.95&alc Last dinner 9.30pm
Credit Cards ①②③

---

A rosette means exceptional standards of cuisine.

---

**CHARDSTOCK** Devon Map **03** ST30

**★★★❀72% Tytherleigh Cot**
EX13 7BN ☎South Chard(0460)21170 FAX (0460) 21291
(Rosette awarded for dinner only)
*Frank and Pat Grudgings have added more individually styled cosy bedrooms, set around a courtyard, plus a new conservatory lounge and small conference suite, to their charming and hospitable thatched cottage hotel. Bedrooms have excellent modern facilities and the elegant Victorian-style restaurant serves popular dishes, nicely balanced between modern and traditional French, such as steamed breast of chicken with a herb stuffing or filet mignon with a light, rich Madeira and truffle sauce. Tempting puddings and good coffee accompanied by petits fours round off the meal.*
3⊸🛏Annexe16⊸🛏6🛁 CTV in all bedrooms ® **T** S10%
sB&B⊸🛏£51.25-£55.25 dB&B⊸🛏£87-£110.50 🅿
CTV 25P ❀ CFA ⌲ (heated) sauna solarium gymnasium nc12yrs *xmas*
**V** ✿ 🎱 ✂ Lunch £8.45-£11.95 High tea £2.95-£6.50&alc Dinner £14.95-£15.95&alc Last dinner 9.30pm
Credit Cards ①③ ⓔ

---

**CHARINGWORTH** Gloucestershire Map **04** SP13

**★★★★❀❀ ⚘79% Charingworth Manor**
GL55 6NS (on B4035 3m E of Chipping Campden) (Small Luxury Hotels) ☎Paxford(0386)78555 Telex no 333444 FAX (0386) 78353
*A tastefully restored 14th-century manor house with fine beams and some original medieval decoration. The dining room has been recently refurbished and named The John Greville Room. Chef Tony Robson-Burrell is building up a good reputation for his cooking, which is simple but interesting and makes good use of fresh local produce. He offers a reasonably priced set menu at lunch and dinner, and à la carte dishes are prepared to order. Starters include quail stuffed with morel mousse on black pudding with rare salad leaves. For main course perhaps pan-fried medallions of monkfish with fennel, roast shallots and red wine jus. A short selection of sweets includes delice of white and dark chocolate with mocha sauce.*
25⊸🛏2🛁 CTV in all bedrooms **T** ✱ sB&B⊸🛏£85-£180 dB&B⊸🛏£105-£200 🅿
℄ 50P 🚗 ❀ CFA ♟ (hard) croquet *xmas*
♀ English & French **V** ✿ 🎱 ✱ Lunch £12.50-£15.50&alc Dinner fr£25&alc Last dinner 10pm
Credit Cards ①②③⑤

---

**CHARLBURY** Oxfordshire Map **04** SP31

**★★❀65% The Bell**
Church St OX7 3PP (Best Western) ☎(0608)810278
FAX (0608) 811447
*This 17th-century coaching inn with beams and sloping floors has prettily decorated bedrooms equipped with modern facilities and an attractive restaurant offering interesting dishes. Helpful service is provided by the caring proprietor and his friendly young staff.*
10⊸🛏Annexe4⊸🛏(1fb) CTV in all bedrooms ® **T**
sB&B⊸🛏£50-£55 dB&B⊸🛏£75-£80 🅿
CTV 50P ❀ CFA clay pigeon shooting *xmas*
**V** ✿ 🎱
Credit Cards ①②③④⑤ ⓔ

---

**CHARLECOTE** Warwickshire Map **04** SP25

**★★★61% Charlecote Pheasant Country**
CV35 9EW (Queens Moat) ☎Stratford-upon-Avon(0789)470333
FAX (0789) 470222
*In the centre of the village, this hotel complex centres on an 18th-century farmhouse to which bedrooms have been added in converted farm buildings or purpose built blocks. All are well*

equipped although some are rather basic. The main building houses a popular carvery restaurant and good modern meeting rooms.
Annexe60⇥🏠(1fb)8🛏✗in 6 bedrooms CTV in all bedrooms ®T✗ (ex guide dogs) sB&B⇥🏠£69.50-£78.50 dB&B⇥🏠£85-£125 🍴
⟨ 120P ✿ CFA ⌇ (heated) 🎾 (hard) solarium gymnasium croquet lawn pool table
🍷 English & French V ♥ ⏁ Lunch £9.95-£10.95&alc Dinner fr£12.95&alc Last dinner 10pm
Credit Cards ①②③⑤ⓔ
**See advertisement under STRATFORD-UPON-AVON**

---

**CHARMOUTH** Dorset Map **03** SY39

★★72% **White House**
2 Hillside, The Street DT6 6PJ ☎(0297)60411
Closed Dec-Feb
*One of our 1991/1992 'Courtesy and Care' award winners of the South West region, this delightful hotel is a fine Regency building with well proportioned rooms and unusual curved doors. Bedrooms tend to be small but are well furnished with pretty coordinated fabrics and the best use is made of the space. Thoughtful extras such as sherry, shortbread and mineral water are provided. John and Mollie Balfour are amiable hosts, taking great care of their guests. The atmosphere is quiet and informal, and the 5-course meal will satisfy the heartiest of appetites. (See colour feature on p14.)*
7⇥🏠 CTV in all bedrooms ®T S2% sB&B⇥🏠£46-£48.50 dB&B⇥🏠£72-£77 🍴
15P 🚗 nc14yrs
♥ ⏁ S2% Lunch £12&alc Dinner £18.50&alc Last dinner 9pm
Credit Cards ①③ⓔ

---

★★61% **Queen's Armes**
The Street DT6 6QF ☎(0297)60339
Closed 2nd wk Nov-2nd wk Feb
*Nicely appointed hotel with low, beamed ceilings and comfortable rooms. Table d'hôte and à la carte menus are available at reasonable prices.*
11rm(5⇥5🏠)(1fb)1🛏✗in all bedrooms CTV in all bedrooms ® sB&B£24-£27 sB&B⇥🏠£24-£27 dB&B£48-£54 dB&B⇥🏠£48-£54 🍴
CTV 20P 🚗 ✿ nc5yrs
🍷 English & French V ♥ ✗ Bar Lunch £1.50-£6alc Dinner £10-£16alc Last dinner 8pm
Credit Cards ①③

---

★64% *Hensleigh*
Lower Sea Ln DT6 6LW ☎(0297)60830
Closed Nov-Feb
*Small, personally run hotel only a short walk from the sea, popular with walkers and older holidaymakers, offering comfortable but simply furnished bedrooms and cosy public areas which include a dining room serving mostly fresh home-made dishes.*
10⇥🏠(2fb) CTV in all bedrooms ®
15P 🚗 nc3yrs
Last dinner 7.30pm

---

**CHARNOCK RICHARD** Lancashire Map **07** SD51 ◎

★★★63% **Park Hall Hotel, Leisure & Conference Centre**
PR7 5LP (off A49 W of village) ☎Eccleston(0257)452090
FAX (0257) 451838
*This modern hotel adjoining Camelot Theme Park is part of a recently refurbished village complex ideal for family or business needs, offering well equipped bedrooms, a choice of restaurants and bars, excellent leisure amenities and extensive conference and banqueting facilities.*
→

55⤳🛏Annexe59⤳🛏(2fb)1⌷🛁✒in 13 bedrooms CTV in all bedrooms ⓇT🞨(ex guide dogs) dB⤳🛁£55 (room only) 🅿
Lift ⒸCTV 3500P CFA ▣(heated) ⌖squash snooker sauna solarium gymnasium ♫
V ⚲⚑✱✒Lunch £7.50-£8.95 High tea £1.50-£7.50 Dinner £12.50&alc Last dinner 10pm
Credit Cards ①②③⑤ⓔ

**See advertisement on inside back cover.**

---

## CHARNOCK RICHARD MOTORWAY SERVICE AREA
(M6) Lancashire Map **07** SD51 ⊙

### ★★58% **Welcome Lodge**
Mill Ln PR7 5LR (Forte Hotels) ☎Coppull(0257)791746
Telex no 67315

*Accessible from both carriageways of the M6, accommodation here includes the price of a full breakfast. Bedrooms are functional and well equipped, and there is a small restaurant and bar, besides facilities available in the service area complex.*

100⤳✒in 10 bedrooms CTV in all bedrooms Ⓡ🅿
ⒸCTV 120P ⇆
♱Mainly grills V ⚲⚑✒
Credit Cards ①②③④⑤

---

## CHATTERIS Cambridgeshire Map **05** TL38

### ★65% **Cross Keys**
16 Market Hill PE16 6BA ☎(03543)3036 & 2644

*This former coaching inn dating back to 1540 retains much of its original character while providing accommodation with every modern comfort. Bedrooms are individually furnished and service is efficient and caring.*

7rm(5🛏)(1fb)1⌷✒in all bedrooms CTV in all bedrooms ⓇT🞨(ex guide dogs) ✱S% sB&B£21-£35 sB&B🛏£35 dB&B🛏£32.50-£45 🅿
CTV 8P CFA
V ⚲⚑✒S% Lunch £7.25 Dinner £12-£15alc Last dinner 10pm
Credit Cards ①②③⑤ⓔ

---

## CHEDDAR Somerset Map **03** ST45

### ★57% **Gordons**
Cliff St BS27 3PT ☎(0934)742497
Closed 23 Dec-Jan

*At the foot of the famous Cheddar Gorge, opposite a municipal car park, bedrooms here are simply furnished and comfortable. A grill menu is served in the steak house restaurant, and there is a cosy lounge and bar. Service is informal and relaxed, and the garden has a covered pool for the use of hotel guests.*

10rm(2⤳1🛏)Annexe2⤳🛏(2fb) CTV in 6 bedrooms TV in 6 bedrooms Ⓡ✱sB&B£17-£19 sB&B⤳🛏£25-£30 dB&B£33-£35 dB&B⤳🛏£38.50-£43
CTV 10P ✿⌖(heated)
V ⚲⚑✱Dinner £7.50-£12alc Last dinner 9pm
Credit Cards ①③⑤ⓔ

---

## CHELMSFORD Essex Map **05** TL70

### ★★★★✤74% **Pontlands Park Country**
West Hanningfield Rd, Great Baddow CM2 8HR ☎(0245)76444
FAX (0245) 478393
Closed 27 Dec-4 Jan (ex 31 Dec) RS Sat/Mon lunch & Sun dinner

*Although it dates back to the mid 16th century, Pontlands Park was rebuilt as a Victorian mansion and subsequently converted into a country house hotel. It has a tastefully appointed lounge and an elegant restaurant offering interesting menus and a good wine list. Individually furnished bedrooms and suites are spacious and well equipped. Within the beautiful grounds is 'Trimmers' health and leisure centre.*

17⤳(1fb)3⌷CTV in all bedrooms T🞨(ex guide dogs) S10% sB⤳£78-£90 dB⤳£85-£115 (room only) 🅿
Ⓒ60P ⇆✿▣(heated) ⌖(heated) sauna solarium gymnasium beauty salon jacuzzi
♱English & French V ⚲⚑✱S10% Lunch £10.50-£19&alc Dinner £19&alc Last dinner 9.45pm
Credit Cards ①②③⑤ⓔ

### ★★★59% **South Lodge**
196 New London Rd CM2 0AR ☎(0245)264564 Telex no 99452 FAX (0245) 492827

*Set in its own grounds to the south of the town, this welcoming family-run hotel provides generally compact but well equipped bedrooms, those in the annexe having no direct natural light. There is an attractive sun lounge room and the dining room offers a varied menu using fresh ingredients.*

24⤳🛏Annexe17⤳(3fb)🛏in 8 bedrooms CTV in all bedrooms ⓇTS% sB&B⤳🛏£50-£70 dB&B⤳🛏£60-£85 Continental breakfast 🅿
Ⓒ50P ⇆CFA games room
♱International V ⚲⚑✱✒S10% Lunch £10-£15&alc Dinner £12-£16&alc Last dinner 9.30pm
Credit Cards ①②③⑤

### ★★60% **County**
Rainsford Rd CM1 2QA ☎(0245)491911 FAX (0245) 492762
Closed 27-30 Dec

*This busy commercial hotel continues to improve. It has a friendly informal atmosphere with pleasant attentive staff. Neatly arranged bedrooms are well equipped with modern facilities and adequate comfort.*

29rm(27⤳🛏)Annexe23rm(7⤳)(1fb) CTV in all bedrooms Ⓡ T sB&B£22.50-£31 sB&B⤳🛏£40-£56.50 dB&B£36-£49 dB&B⤳🛏£56.50-£77
Ⓒ80P CFA
♱English & French V ⚲⚑✱Lunch £7.75 Dinner £11-£12.50&alc Last dinner 9pm
Credit Cards ①②③⑤

---

## CHELTENHAM Gloucestershire

See also Cleeve Hill

### ★★★★56% **Golden Valley Thistle**
Gloucester Rd GL51 0TS (Mount Charlotte (TS))
☎(0242)232691 Telex no 43410 FAX (0242) 221846

*Popular with businessmen and offering good conference facilities, the hotel is easily accessible from junction 11 of the M5; modern bedrooms reflect the needs of a business clientele and the new Leisure Club will make a good range of activities available.*

124⤳🛏(24fb)✒in 9 bedrooms CTV in all bedrooms ⓇT (room only) 🅿
Lift Ⓒ275P ✿▣(heated) sauna solarium gymnasium hairdresser
♱International ⚲⚑✒
Credit Cards ①②③④⑤

### ★★★★50% **The Queen's**
Promenade GL50 1NN (Forte Hotels) ☎(0242)514724
Telex no 43381 FAX (0242) 224145

*This Regency hotel, standing majestically at the head of the town's tree-lined Promenade, is entering on a major bedroom refurbishment programme; lounge and bar facilities, though rather limited, are much used by locals, and several function/conference rooms are available.*

77⤳🛏(6fb)1⌷✒in 10 bedrooms CTV in all bedrooms ⓇT✱sB⤳🛏£75-£80 dB⤳🛏£95-£100 (room only) 🅿
Lift Ⓒ80P CFA xmas
V ⚲⚑✱✒Lunch £14.50&alc Dinner fr£19.50&alc Last dinner 9.45pm
Credit Cards ①②③④⑤

★★★ GREENWAY

Shurdington GL51 5UG
(Pride of Britain)
☎(0242)862352
FAX (0242) 862780

Closed 28 Dec-6 Jan RS Sat
& BH Mon

*The area bordering the A46
leading out of Cheltenham does not augur well for a well
known country house hotel. But perserverance is rewarded as
one approaches, up a long drive, the ivy clad 16th-century
manor house set amid attractive lawns and gardens. Inside the
spacious hall, with its comfortable seating and a blazing fire in
winter, one warms rapidly to the style and ambience of this
tastefully appointed hotel. There is a most appealing drawing
room with a cosy cocktail bar adjoining, while the 2 dining
rooms offer a choice between a modern conservatory and a
part wood-panelled room. Chef Edward Stephens presents
fixed price menus at both lunch and dinner, based on modern
British cuisine. Dishes could include Cotswold venison on a
bed of carrot and celeriac with a rich game jus, or poached
scallops and delicious Dublin Bay prawns in a butter pastry
case with a coriander sauce. Some of the flavour combinations
are less successful, but a starter that especially appealed was
the chilled timbale of fresh salmon filled with crab meat on a
gazpacho dressing. There is also an excellent, well chosen
wine list. Much of the charm and merit of the Greenway
depends on the proprietor Tony Elliott and his well trained
staff. Service is very willing but unobtrusive, and with the
attention to small but important detail, in the good beds,
quality linen and towels, decent hangers, hairdryers
intelligently located and so on, it is pleasing to experience and
acknowledge hotelkeeping at its best.*

11➪🖍Annexe7➪🖍 CTV in all bedrooms T ✂
sB&B➪🖍£94 dB&B➪🖍£130-£190 🍴

50P 🚗 ❀ CFA croquet nc7yrs *xmas*

V Lunch £15-£18 Dinner £31 Last dinner 9.30pm

Credit Cards 1 2 3 4 5

**★★★65% Carlton**
Parabola Rd GL50 3AQ ☎(0242)514453 Telex no 43310
FAX (0242) 226487

*Quietly situated in a tree-lined road within easy reach of the town
centre, this attractive hotel, behind its elegant Regency façade,
strives to offer modern comforts and facilities. Public rooms are
spacious and high ceilinged. Bedrooms in the 'modern' wing are the
most comfortable, though refurbishment is presently extending to
the older rooms and a new wing with a separate entrance.*

66➪🖍Annexe13➪🖍(3fb)3🛏 CTV in 68 bedrooms ® T
sB&B➪🖍£50-£61 dB&B➪🖍£65-£90 🍴

Lift ℭ 50P *xmas*

♨ Lunch £10.50-£15&alc Dinner £11.50&alc Last dinner
9.30pm

Credit Cards 1 2 3 5 £

**★★★64% *Hotel De La Bere***
Southam GL52 3NH (3m NE A46) (Forte Hotels)
☎(0242)237771 Telex no 43232 FAX (0242)236016

*On the road to Cleeve Hill, the de la Bere is a magnificent Tudor
manor house retaining many original features: oak panelling, open
fires and ornate plasterwork in the public rooms. Bedrooms vary in
size, shape and location, half are in the main house, many are full
of character, but inevitably several are along winding corridors or
up old staircases. The remainder are in a courtyard block a short
distance away, and these are equally varied in terms of access,* →

**C**

*though all are well equipped and mostly of good size. There are extensive leisure facilities and fine views.*

32⇨🛏Annexe25⇨(2fb)6🛏⅍in 14 bedrooms CTV in all bedrooms ® T

《 150P ❀ ⌒ (heated) ♪ (hard) squash snooker sauna solarium badminton

🖵 English & French V ৬ ♨ ⅍ Last dinner 10pm
Credit Cards ① ② ③ ④ ⑤

### ★★★64% Prestbury House
The Burgage, Prestbury GL52 3DN (2m NE A46)
☎(0242)529533 & 30106 FAX (0242) 227076

*This hotel is popular for its peaceful situation and friendly owners and staff. Bedrooms in the attractive new annexe have similar modern facilities to those in the main house, but are more compact in size.*

9⇨🛏Annexe9⇨🛏(3fb)1🛏 CTV in all bedrooms ® T
🗙 (ex guide dogs) S10% sB&B⇨🛏£62.50 dB&B⇨🛏£74.50 🛏

CTV 50P ❀ CFA ∪ clay pigeon shooting croquet ♫ xmas
🖵 English, French & Italian V ৬ ♨ ⅍ Lunch £16.50&alc High tea £5.50 Dinner £16.50&alc Last dinner 9pm
Credit Cards ① ② ③ ②

### ★★★63% White House
Gloucester Rd, Staverton GL51 0ST (3m W off B4063)
☎Gloucester(0452)713226 Telex no 437382
FAX (0452) 857590

*Situated two miles west of the town centre on the Staverton road, this modern hotel offers good sized comfortable and well equipped bedrooms and attractive public areas including a marble-floored lounge.*

50⇨(3fb)2🛏 CTV in all bedrooms ® T 🗙 (ex guide dogs) ✱ sB⇨£62-£70 dB⇨£74-£82 (room only) 🛏

《 100P ❀ CFA xmas
🖵 English & French V ৬ ♨ ✱ Lunch fr£6alc Dinner fr£13.50&alc Last dinner 9.30pm
Credit Cards ① ② ③ ⑤ ②

### ★★ ❀❀76% On the Park
38 Evesham Rd GL52 2AH ☎(0242)518898 FAX (0242) 511526
Closed 3rd wk Jan-2nd wk Feb RS Sun & Mon

*The Gregory's delightful townhouse overlooking Pittville Park now includes, as a separate business, chef Patrick McDonald's well-known restaurant. Those familiar with his Epicurean restaurant at Stow-on-the-Wold will feel at home immediately in the beautifully panelled dining room, tastefully furnished with lavish use of fabrics; tables though are rather large. The lounge is an added advantage, where diners and residents can peruse the innovative menus in comfort. The style of cooking is definitely modern. The mille feuilles of pigeon is a creative variation, the layers separating the tender slices of game are set off against caramelised shallots, which some may find sweet and overpowering, and a perfectly formed Madeira jus garnished with truffle. On The Park is the deserving winner of our 'Best Newcomer' award for Midlands and East Anglia (see colour feature on p36).*

10⇨🛏 CTV in all bedrooms ® T ✱ sB⇨🛏£45-£70 dB⇨🛏£55-£80 (room only) 🛏
8P 1🚗 (£5) 🚗 nc8yrs
V ৬ ♨ ✱ S% Lunch fr£17.50&alc Dinner fr£25&alc Last dinner 10.30pm
Credit Cards ① ② ③ ⑤

### ★★68% Charlton Kings
London Rd, Charlton Kings GL52 6UU ☎(0242)231061
FAX (0242) 241900

*A small modern purpose-built hotel on the A40, 2.5 miles southeast of the town centre. Privately owned and personally run, it offers good quality, well equipped accommodation.*

14⇨🛏(1fb)⅍in 6 bedrooms CTV in all bedrooms ® T
sB&B⇨🛏£35-£56 dB&B⇨🛏£50-£78 🛏

20P ❀ CFA xmas
V ৬ ♨ ⅍ Dinner fr£15 Last dinner 9pm
Credit Cards ① ③ ②

### ★★67% George Hotel
St Georges Rd GL50 3DZ ☎(0242)235751 FAX (0242) 224359
*Situated in a main side road, 100 yards from the Promenade, this hotel has been converted from 5 Georgian terraced houses. A recent refurbishment has created small public areas of quality and very well equipped modern bedrooms, all with good en suite facilites, while retaining many of the original features of the building.*

39⇨🛏(2fb)⅍in 2 bedrooms CTV in all bedrooms ® T ✱ sB&B⇨🛏£38-£55 dB&B⇨🛏£48-£65 🛏

《 30P CFA xmas
৬ ♨ ✱ Lunch £8.50-£12 Dinner £13-£15 Last dinner 9.15pm
Credit Cards ① ② ③ ⑤ ②

### ★★65% Wyastone
Parabola Rd GL50 3BG ☎(0242)516654 & 245549
FAX (0242) 522659
Closed 24 Dec-2 Jan

*In the elegant Montpellier part of town, this friendly small hotel provides well equipped modern bedrooms. There is a comfortable lounge, a small bar and an attractive restaurant offering a fixed price 2 or 3-course menu.*

13⇨🛏(2fb)1🛏 CTV in all bedrooms ® T 🗙 (ex guide dogs) ✱ sB&B⇨🛏£53 dB&B⇨🛏£75 🛏
17P 🚗

🖵 English & Continental V ৬ ♨ ⅍ ✱ Lunch £12.50-£18.95 Dinner £16.25-£18.95 Last dinner 9pm
Credit Cards ① ② ③ ⑤ ②

### ★★59% Cotswold Grange
Pittville Circus Rd GL52 2QH ☎(0242)515119
FAX (0242) 241537
Closed 24 Dec-1 Jan

*A family town hotel of mellow Cotswold stone situated in the Pittville area of town, close to the centre. Service is informal and relaxed and guests are made to feel very welcome.*

25⇨🛏(4fb) CTV in all bedrooms ® T sB&B⇨🛏fr£39 dB&B⇨🛏fr£50

CTV 20P ❀ CFA ♨
V ৬ ♨ ⅍ Lunch £3.50-£12.50alc Dinner £7-£17alc Last dinner 7.30pm
Credit Cards ① ② ③ ②

### ❀❀✕✕Le Champignon Sauvage
24 Suffolk Rd GL50 2AQ ☎(0242)573449

*Helen and David Everitt-Matthias preside over this friendly and well established town centre restaurant, offering a good standard of highly decorative French cuisine. The luncheon menu offers an option of 3 items at each course, and changes daily. Our inspector noted the roast leg of rabbit on a grain mustard sauce, accompanied by home-made parsleyed and oiled spaghetti with a light garnish of baby broad beans. For dessert an orange flavoured chocolate mousse was enhanced by chopped pistachio with a chocolate sauce and contained in a piped chocolate shape.*

Closed Sun, 2 wks in Jun, BH's & Xmas-New Year Lunch not served Sat

🖵 French V 32 seats Lunch £17.50 Dinner £22.50 Last lunch 1.30pm Last dinner 9.15pm ⅌
Credit Cards ① ② ③

### ❀✕✕Cleeveway House
Bishops Cleeve GL52 4SA (3m N A435)
☎Bishop's Cleeve(0242)672585

*Situated beside the A435 3 miles east of the town centre, dating from the early 18th-century and originally the home of the Bishop of Worcester, a Cotswold-stone house with lovely gardens has been transformed into a quality restaurant with a country house atmosphere. Chef/patron John Marfell's cooking skills can be seen as he prepares the meals in view of the diners. The à la carte menu*

*offers a wide selection of game and lamb dishes, and such daily extras as a range of fresh fish, while a wine list of some 80 bins achieves good coverage and represents value for money.*
Closed 1 wk Xmas & 2 wks annual hols Lunch not served Sun (ex by reservation) & Mon
Dinner not served Sun
♥ English & French V 38 seats Lunch £14.05-£26.85alc Dinner £14.05-£26.85alc Last lunch 1.45pm Last dinner 9.45pm 30 P
Credit Cards ①③

⊛ ✕ ✕ **Mayflower Chinese**
32-34 Clarence St GL50 3NX ☎(0242)522426 & 511580
FAX (0242) 251667
*This very comfortable, richly decorated Chinese restaurant specialises in Cantonese dishes, but the wide-ranging menu offers other regional specialities as well.*
Closed 25-28 Dec Lunch not served Sun
♥ Cantonese V 80 seats ✳ Lunch fr£7&alc Dinner £17-£35alc Last lunch 1.30pm Last dinner 10.30pm ₽

Credit Cards ①②③⑤

**See advertisement on page 217**

CHELWOOD Avon Map 03 ST66

★★⊛73% **Chelwood House**
BS18 4NH ☎Compton Dando(0761)490730
RS 24 Dec-15 Jan
*A charming, 300-year-old building, tastefully transformed to provide country house style accommodation, retains a tranquil ambience despite its setting on the A37; individually decorated rooms incorporate an excellent range of modern facilities and carefully prepared food is based on quality ingredients – the breakfast menu featuring some particularly appetising and unusual dishes.*

→

**C**

11⇄♠(1fb)3☷ CTV in all bedrooms ® T ✂ (ex guide dogs)
sB&B⇄♠fr£65 dB&B⇄♠£75-£99.50 ♬
15P ⌕ ✿ croquet nc10yrs
♡ English, French & German V ♥ ✂ Lunch fr£14.50 Dinner
£18-£26alc Last dinner 9pm
Credit Cards ① ② ③ ⑤ ⓔ

**See advertisement under BRISTOL**

---

**CHENIES** Buckinghamshire Map **04** TQ09

★★★69% **Bedford Arms Thistle**
WD3 6EQ (Mount Charlotte (TS)) ☎Chorleywood(0923)283301
Telex no 893939 FAX (0923) 284825
*This charming, historic, small hotel, set in rural surroundings, has
been well equipped and furnished in modern style; identical
bedrooms are complemented by a cocktail lounge with popular bar
and an oak-panelled restaurant offering an international à la carte
menu. Meeting room facilities are available, and friendly service is
well managed.*
10⇄♠(4fb)✂in 1 bedroom CTV in all bedrooms T (room
only) ♬
《 120P
♡ International ♥ ✂ ✂
Credit Cards ① ② ③ ④ ⑤

---

**CHEPSTOW** Gwent Map **03** ST59

★★★69% **St Pierre Hotel, Golf & Country Club**
St Pierre Park NP6 6YA (2.5m W off A48) ☎(0291)625261
Telex no 497562 FAX (02912) 79975
*Now carefully extended and modernised, this 14th-century
mansion with its own Norman church stands in 400 acres of
parkland which contain two famous golf courses as well as various
other leisure facilities. Food options include a poolside grill room, a
small à la carte restaurant and a carvery operation in the main
restaurant. Both lounge and bar are extremely spacious and
comfortable, while bedrooms are well furnished and equipped.*
106⇄♠Annexe41⇄♠(2fb)1☷✂in 23 bedrooms CTV in all
bedrooms ® T ✱ sB&B⇄♠£95-£105 dB&B⇄♠£110-£125 ♬
《 480P ✿ CFA ⊡ (heated) ✔ 18 ♪ (hard) squash snooker
sauna solarium gymnasium beauty salon badminton steam
room bowls ♧ xmas
♡ English & French V ♥ ✂ ✂ ✱ Lunch £12.50-£15.50 High
tea fr£3.75 Dinner £15.50&alc Last dinner 10pm
Credit Cards ① ② ③ ⑤ ⓔ

★★66% **Castle View**
16 Bridge St NP6 5EZ ☎(02912)70349 FAX (0291) 627397
*This ivy-clad hotel near the castle, dating back some 300 years,
offers well equipped bedrooms and attractive, comfortable lounge
and bar areas ; a good choice of food is available in the stone-
walled restaurant.*
9⇄♠Annexe2⇄♠(5fb) CTV in all bedrooms ® T ✱
sB&B⇄♠£39.50-£43.50 dB&B⇄♠£57.50-£61 ♬
CTV ✔ ⌕ ✿
V ♥ ✂ ✱ Lunch fr£9.35&alc Dinner £12.50-£18alc Last dinner
9pm
Credit Cards ① ② ③ ⑤ ⓔ

★★62% *Beaufort*
Beaufort Square, Saint Mary St NP6 5EP (Inter-Hotels)
☎(0291)625074 & 622497 Telex no 498280
*Originally a 16th-century coaching inn, this busy hotel with its
attractive panelled restaurant is near the town centre. Bedrooms
are modern and well equipped and a good choice of food is
available including bar meals.*
18rm(10⇄3♠)(2fb) CTV in all bedrooms ® T
12P ⌕
♡ International V ♥ ✂ Last dinner 9.30pm
Credit Cards ① ② ③

---

★★61% **First Hurdle**
9/10 Upper Church St NP6 5EX ☎(0291)622189
*Family-run and friendly, this small hotel just 5 minutes from the
M4 complements tastefully furnished bedrooms by an attractive
Edwardian restaurant and a cosy little lounge and bar.*
12rm(3⇄3♠)(1fb) CTV in all bedrooms ® sB&B£26-£38
sB&B⇄♠£38 dB&B£39-£44 dB&B⇄♠£52 ♬
✔ ♧
♡ English & French V ♥ ✂ Lunch £3.50-£8 High tea £4
Dinner £8.50-£9.95&alc Last dinner 9.30pm
Credit Cards ① ② ③

★★55% **The George**
Moor St NP6 5DB (Forte Hotels) ☎(0291)625363
FAX (0291) 627418
*Friendly, informal young staff provide a cheerful atmosphere at
this cosy little coaching inn. Set at the centre of a charming small
village, it complements comfortable, well equipped bedrooms in
rather rustic style with an interesting menu and carefully chosen
wine list.*
14⇄♠1☷✂in 7 bedrooms CTV in all bedrooms ® T ✱
sB⇄♠fr£50 dB⇄♠fr£65 (room only) ♬
25P ⌕ CFA xmas
♡ English & French V ♥ ✂ ✂ ✱ S% Lunch £6.50-£8.50
Dinner fr£13.95 Last dinner 9.30pm
Credit Cards ① ② ③ ⑤

---

**CHESTER** Cheshire Map **07** SJ46 ◎

★★★★ ✿✿
**THE CHESTER GROSVENOR**
Eastgate St CH1 1LT (Small
Luxury Hotels)
☎(0244)324024
Telex no 61240
FAX (0244) 313246
Closed 25-26 Dec
*This city centre Victorian
establishment has undergone an impressive transformation
into a luxurious modern hotel. The lounge facilities, though
limited, are elegant and comfortable. The bedrooms, which
vary in size, are tastefully furnished and equipped with
facilities of a high standard. A strong feature of the hotel is
the discreet and willing service. The informal Brasserie offers
light meals and snacks, or one can sample chef Paul Reed's
cooking in the opulent surrounding of the Arkle Restaurant.
Dishes, from the à la carte or chef's gourmet surprise menus,
are skilfully prepared and good use is made of fresh produce,
and there is an excellent wine list.*
86⇄♠2☷ CTV in all bedrooms T ✂ (ex guide dogs) ✱
sB⇄♠£115.15-£135.13 dB⇄♠£176.25-£199.75 (room
only) ♬
Lift 《 ▦ ♪ CFA sauna solarium gymnasium ♫
♡ British & French V ♥ ✂ ✂ ✱ Lunch fr£16.50 Dinner
fr£17.25 Last dinner 11pm
Credit Cards ① ② ③ ④ ⑤

---

★★★★71% **Chester International**
Trinity St CH1 2BD (Queens Moat) ☎(0244)322330
Telex no 61251 FAX (0244) 316118
Closed 24-29 Dec
*This new hotel sits within the city walls and enjoys views of Chester
Racecourse. Modern accommodation and friendly proficient staff
ensure a comfortable stay for both business and leisure guests.*
150⇄✂in 22 bedrooms CTV in all bedrooms ® T S%
sB&B⇄£52-£98.70 dB&B⇄£90-£145 ♬

Lift ℂ 70P CFA sauna solarium gymnasium jacuzzi steam bath ♫ *xmas*
♀ Continental **V** ✿ 🍷 Lunch £15-£20&alc Dinner £15-£22&alc Last dinner 10.30pm
Credit Cards ①②③④⑤ ⓔ

**★★★★65% Mollington Banastre**
Parkgate Rd CH1 6NN (A540) (Best Western) ☎(0244)851471 Telex no 61686 FAX (0244) 851165
*Large and privately owned, this hotel stands in the village of Mollington, on the A540 to the north of the city, providing convenient access to both the A55 (North Wales Coastal Expressway) and junction 16 of the M56. It is understandably popular with business people (including delegates using its extensive conference facilities) and tourists alike for its close proximity to Chester and excellent leisure facilities.*
64⇴(6fb)1📺⅍in 5 bedrooms CTV in all bedrooms ® **T** ✱
sB&B⇴£62-£82 dB&B⇴£95-£110 🏠
Lift ℂ 300P ❀ ⊟ (heated) ♪ (hard & grass)squash ∪ sauna solarium gymnasium hairdressing health & beauty salon ♋ *xmas*
♀ English & French **V** ✿ 🍷 ⅍ ✱ Lunch £10.25-£20&alc Dinner fr£19.50&alc Last dinner 10.30pm
Credit Cards ①②③⑤

**★★★❀❀♨78% Crabwall Manor**
Parkgate Rd, Mollington CH1 6NE (Small Luxury Hotels) ☎(0244)851666 Telex no 61220 FAX (0244) 851400
*Should you not wish to stay in the busy centre of Chester, a few minutes; drive along the A450 will bring you to this comfortable hotel where a courteous staff offers friendly yet professional service. Spacious, well equipped bedrooms with every amenity appeal equally to tourists or business clients, and the restaurant has recently been extended to accommodate the growing number of diners who come to sample the culinary delights prepared by Peter Mayoh and his band of experienced chefs. Before or after dinner it* →

C

*is pleasant to relax in one of the lounges – or, in summer, to retreat to the patio and look across landscaped grounds to the lights of the city.*

48⇌↑1🍴⚲in 2 bedrooms CTV in all bedrooms **T**
🐾 (ex guide dogs) ✳ sB⇌↑fr£95 dB⇌↑fr£125 (room only)
🍴

( 100P ✿ CFA snooker croquet lawn 🐴 *xmas*
🍴 English & French **V** 🌣 🎟 ✂ ✳ Lunch fr£13.50&alc Dinner fr£23&alc Last dinner 9.45pm
Credit Cards ①②③⑤ ⓔ

---

**★★★65% Hoole Hall**
Warrington Rd, Hoole Village CH2 3PD (Crown & Raven)
☎(0244)350011 Telex no 61292 FAX (0244) 320251
*This manor house with modern extensions is situated on the A56 ring road. Bedrooms are modern and comfortable, in keeping with the well designed public areas.*
99⇌(3fb)✂in 16 bedrooms CTV in all bedrooms ® **T**
Lift ( ⊞ 200P ✿
🍴 European **V** 🌣 🎟 ✂ Last dinner 9.45pm
Credit Cards ①②③

---

**★★★64% Forte Posthouse**
Wrexham Rd CH4 9DL (Forte Hotels) ☎(0244)680111
Telex no 61450 FAX (0244) 674100
*A modern hotel that stands adjacent to the junction of the A55 and A483 features a refurbished restaurant which offers a popular carvery operation as well as its à la carte menu.*
105⇌↑✳in 52 bedrooms CTV in all bedrooms ® **T** ✳
dB⇌↑£39.50-£49.50 (room only) 🍴
( 220P ✿ CFA ▣ (heated) sauna solarium gymnasium spa pool *xmas*
🍴 International **V** 🌣 🎟 ✂ ✳ Sunday Lunch £9.25-£10.50&alc Dinner fr£13.95&alc Last dinner 10pm
Credit Cards ①②③④⑤

---

**★★★62% Rowton Hall**
Whitchurch Road, Rowton CH3 6AD (2m SE A41) (Consort)
☎(0244)335262 Telex no 61172 FAX (0244) 335464
Closed 25-26 Dec
*Situated in a residential country lane just off the A49 this Georgian house has a busy leisure complex and conference/banqueting facilities.*
42⇌↑(4fb)3🍴 CTV in all bedrooms ® **T** ✳ sB&B⇌↑£68-£76 dB&B⇌↑£90-£98 🍴
( CTV 120P ✿ CFA ▣ (heated) sauna solarium gymnasium
🍴 English & French **V** 🌣 🎟 ✳ Lunch £11&alc Dinner £14.50-£16&alc Last dinner 9.30pm
Credit Cards ①②③⑤

---

**★★★61% Abbots Well**
Whitchurch Rd, Christleton CH3 5QL (Jarvis) ☎(0244)332121
Telex no 61561 FAX (0244) 335287
*Set in well kept grounds on the southern route out of town, this busy commercial hotel is also popular with tourists and offers comfortable modern bedrooms, conference and banqueting facilities and a new leisure centre.*
127⇌↑(5fb)✂in 6 bedrooms CTV in all bedrooms ® **T**
sB⇌↑£82.50-£98.50 dB⇌↑£98.50-£109.50 (room only) 🍴
( 160P ✿ CFA ▣ (heated) sauna solarium gymnasium jacuzzi pool table *xmas*
🍴 English & French **V** 🌣 🎟 Lunch £9.85-£10.50&alc Dinner £15.95&alc Last dinner 9.30pm
Credit Cards ①②③⑤ ⓔ

---

**★★★60% Royal Oak**
Warrington Rd, Mickle Trafford CH2 4EX (3m NE A56) (Toby)
☎(0244)301391 Telex no 61536
*A recently refurbished hotel on the outskirts of Chester, in the village of Mickle Trafford on the A56 Warrington road. There is a choice of bars and the carvery restaurant is proving to be very popular.*

→

36⇨♠(10fb) CTV in all bedrooms ®
☾150P ✲
V ♔ ☕
Credit Cards [1] [2] [3] [5]

**★★★59% Blossoms**
St John St CH1 1HL (Forte Hotels) ☎(0244)323186
Telex no 61113 FAX (0244) 346433
*Traditional in style and located at the centre of the city, this hotel offers a choice of conference rooms, accommodation which is on the whole both spacious and well decorated, and friendly service. Though it has no car parking facilities of its own, arrangements can be made.*
64⇨♠(2fb)1⊞ ⊁in 13 bedrooms CTV in all bedrooms ® T ✱
sB⇨♠£70-£80 dB⇨♠£90-£95 (room only) ⊟
Lift ☾ ⊁ CFA *xmas*
☋ English & French V ♔ ☕ ⊁ ✱ Lunch £8.95 Dinner fr£13.95&alc Last dinner 9.45pm
Credit Cards [1] [2] [3] [5]

**★★★55% Plantation Inn**
Liverpool Rd CH2 1AG ☎(0244)374100 Telex no 61263
FAX (0244) 379240
*Just off the A41 and close to the city centre, this friendly commercial hotel with good conference facilities offers some high quality executive rooms besides its more functional bedrooms. The restaurant serves international cuisine and the bars have a dance floor and stay open as a nightclub on several evenings a week.*
75⇨♠(4fb)⊁in 15 bedrooms CTV in all bedrooms ® T
sB⇨♠£47.50-£75 dB⇨♠£60-£95 (room only) ⊟
Lift ☾ ⊞ 150P CFA solarium *xmas*
☋ Continental V ♔ ☕ Lunch fr£7.50&alc High tea fr£6.50 Dinner fr£15&alc Last dinner 10.30pm
Credit Cards [1] [2] [3] [5] £

**★★69% Green Bough**
60 Hoole Rd CH2 3NL ☎(0244)326241 FAX (0244) 326265
Closed 21-28 Dec RS 29 Dec-6 Jan
*A spotlessly clean family-run hotel with very hospitable hosts. A new annexe has been opened next door which includes a boardroom as well as additional bedrooms. Meals are simply prepared and, afterwards, there is an elegant lounge in which to relax.*
14⇨♠Annexe6rm(4⇨♠)(5fb)1⊞ CTV in 18 bedrooms ® T
✱ sB&B⇨♠£39-£43 dB&B⇨♠£49-£54 ⊟
CTV 21P
V ✱ Lunch £6.50-£7.25 Dinner £10.10-£11.10 Last dinner 8.30pm
Credit Cards [1] [3] £

**★★63% Brookside**
Brook Ln CH2 2AN (Exec Hotel) ☎(0244)381943
FAX (0244) 379701
Closed 24 Dec-2 Jan
*This privately owned hotel, situated just north of the city centre and offering convenient access to most amenities, complements well equipped accommodation by nicely appointed, attractive public areas. Such facilities as its own small car park, a conference room and a pool room with sauna, solarium and fitness equipment make it equally popular with tourists and commercial visitors.*
26⇨♠(6fb) CTV in all bedrooms ® T ✱ sB&B⇨♠£29.50-£32 dB&B⇨♠£46-£76 (incl dinner) ⊟
13P sauna solarium gymnasium pool table
☋ French V ⊁ ✱ High tea £2.95-£4.95 Dinner £8.95-£10.50&alc Last dinner 9.30pm
Credit Cards [1] [3]

**★★63% Cavendish**
42-44 Hough Green CH4 8JQ ☎(0244)675100
FAX (0244) 679942
*An early Victorian property set beside the A549 just south of the city centre, now a privately owned and personally run business and holiday hotel, has been extensively refurbished during 1991 to offer modern, well equipped bedrooms and attractive public areas. A pleasant garden and ample car park are provided at the rear.*
21rm(7⇨9♠)(2fb)2⊞ CTV in all bedrooms ® T ✱
sB&B⇨♠£35-£39.50 dB&B⇨♠£49.50-£65 ⊟
☾ CTV 36P *xmas*
V ♔ ☕ ✱ Dinner £10.50 Last dinner 9pm
Credit Cards [1] [2] [3]

**★★62% Dene**
Hoole Rd CH2 3ND ☎(0244)321165 FAX (0244) 350277
*A fully extended commercial-style hotel, set in its own grounds adjacent to Alexandra Park on the city, is family owned and managed, creating a relaxed, informal atmosphere.*
41rm(39⇨♠)Annexe8⇨♠(4fb) CTV in all bedrooms ® T
sB&B£28-£30 sB&B⇨♠£39-£41 dB&B⇨♠£51-£53 ⊟
CTV 55P ✲ pool table
V ♔ ⊁ High tea £5-£8 Dinner fr£8&alc Last dinner 8.30pm
Credit Cards [1] [3] £

## CHESTERFIELD Derbyshire Map 08 SK37

**★★★64% Chesterfield**
Malkin St S41 7UA (Best Western) ☎(0246)271141
Telex no 547492 FAX (0246) 220719
*A modernised hotel with ample car parking and close to the railway station. Recent additions include good leisure club facilities, a new wing of bedrooms and an extra conference room.*
72⇨♠(10fb)⊁in 18 bedrooms CTV in all bedrooms ® T
sB&B⇨♠£58-£70 dB&B⇨♠£72-£82 ⊟
Lift ☾ 100P CFA ⊡ (heated) snooker sauna solarium gymnasium *xmas*
☋ International V ♔ ✱ Lunch £7-£12.45&alc Dinner £12.45&alc Last dinner 10pm
Credit Cards [1] [2] [3] £

**★★68% Sandpiper**
Sheffield Rd, Sheepbridge S41 9EH ☎(0246)450550
FAX (0246) 452805
*An established restaurant has been brought to hotel status by the provision of accommodation in a modern annexe block, all its well appointed rooms offer a good range of amenities and en suite bathroom facilities.*
Annexe28⇨♠(3fb)1⊞ ⊁in 4 bedrooms CTV in all bedrooms ® T ✱ sB⇨♠£46-£52 dB⇨♠£56-£62 (room only) ⊟
☾ 220P CFA
☋ French V ♔ ☕ ✱ Lunch £3-£8.50&alc Dinner £12.95-£13.95 Last dinner 10pm
Credit Cards [1] [2] [3] [5] £

**★★65% Ringwood Hall**
Brimington S43 1DQ (Consort) ☎(0246)280077
FAX (0246) 472241
*This large hotel, lying northeast of the town on the A619, has a very busy function and conference trade; both function facilities and residential accommodation have recently been upgraded.*
24⇨♠(2fb)2⊞ ⊁in 3 bedrooms CTV in all bedrooms ® T
sB&B⇨♠£50-£60 dB&B⇨♠£50-£87.50 ⊟
☾ CTV 170P ✲ CFA snooker bowling green ♫ *xmas*
☋ English & Continental V ♔ ☕ ✱ Lunch £6.95-£7.90 Dinner fr£14.95&alc Last dinner 10pm
Credit Cards [1] [2] [3] [5] £

**★★59% Portland**
West Bars S40 1AY ☎(0246)234502 & 234211
FAX (0246) 550915
*An hotel on the edge of the town centre (accessed from New Seetwell Street) offers a choice of restaurants, busy bar and banqueting facilities, simple accommodation and friendly service.*
26rm(19⇨♠)(4fb) CTV in all bedrooms ® T
✈ (ex guide dogs) ✱ sB&B£30-£35 sB&B⇨♠£35-£48
dB&B⇨♠£48-£63 ⊟
☾ CTV 30P CFA

♥ Mainly grills **V** ♦ Lunch £5-£7.50 Dinner £5-£10 Last dinner 10pm
Credit Cards 1 3

★67% **Abbeydale**
1 Cobden Rd s40 4TD (Minotels) ☎(0246)277849
FAX (0246) 558223
Closed Xmas week
*Conveniently situated in a quiet residential area behind the local football ground, this small family-run hotel is immaculately kept and provides very well equipped bedrooms, most of them with modern en suite facilities.*
11rm(9♠)(1fb) CTV in all bedrooms ® **T** ✻ ✻ sB&Bfr£28 sB&B♠fr£35.60 dB&B♠fr£54 ♬
CTV 15P ⇺
**V** ✄
Credit Cards 1 2 3 5

⇧**Forte Travelodge**
A61 Brimmington Rd, Inner Ring Rd(Forte)
☎(0246)455411 Central Res (0800) 850950
*On the northern outskirts of the town, on the roundabout junction of the A61/B6050/B6057/B6052, adjacent to a Little Chef restaurant. Access is only from the B6050 signed Brimmington.*
20⇔♠(20fb) CTV in all bedrooms ® sB⇔♠£29.95
dB⇔♠£29.95 (room only)
℄ 20P ⇺
Credit Cards 1 2 3

The AA's star rating scheme is the market leader in hotel classification.

**C**

---

## ★★55% The Crown House

CB10 1NY ☎Saffron Walden(0799)30515 FAX (0799) 30683

*The ground floor of this small, historic house on the outskirts of the village comprises an informal bar/lounge and dining rooms where a choice of menus offers a range of well prepared dishes. Bedrooms, though modestly furnished, are mostly of a good size, some being contained in an annexe conversion near the main house.*

8⇨Annexe10⇨♠4📺 CTV in all bedrooms ® T
✈ (ex guide dogs) ✷ sB&B⇨♠£26-£65 dB&B⇨♠£52-£85 ▯
CTV 30P ⇶ CFA *xmas*

♡ English & French V ❖ ⚏ ✁ ✷ Lunch £11-£16.50 Dinner fr£11&alc Last dinner 9.45pm

Credit Cards ①③ⓔ

---

## ★★★65% Goodwood Park

PO18 0QB ☎(0243)775537 FAX (0243) 533802
(For full entry see Goodwood)

## ★★★64% Chichester Resort

Westhampnett PO19 4UL (Resort) ☎(0243)786351
Telex no 86381 FAX (0243) 782371

*Situated east of Chichester on the A27 bypass, this hotel features modern, well equipped bedrooms, a split-level carvery-style restaurant, a bar and the White Swan pub. There are extensive conference and business facilities along with an indoor health and leisure club.*

76⇨♠(1fb)1⊞✁in 8 bedrooms CTV in all bedrooms ® T ✷
sB⇨♠£72 dB⇨♠£82 (room only) ▯
( 138P CFA ▣ (heated) sauna solarium gymnasium *xmas*
♡ English & Continental V ❖ ⚏ ✷ Lunch £9&alc Dinner £14&alc Last dinner 9.30pm

Credit Cards ①②③⑤

## ★★★61% The Dolphin & Anchor

West St PO19 1QE (Forte Hotels) ☎(0243)785121
FAX (0243) 533408

*A charming town centre hotel, originally two ancient inns, conveniently situated opposite the cathedral. Parking and access can be difficult, however, so guests would be well advised to ask for directions in advance. Bedrooms vary, though there is a continuing refurbishment programme, while public areas include a popular coffee shop, bar, attractively appointed restaurant and comfortable lounge.*

49⇨♠(5fb)✁in 25 bedrooms CTV in all bedrooms ® T ✷
sB⇨♠fr£70 dB⇨♠£85-£97 (room only) ▯
( 6P 20⇶ CFA *xmas*
V ❖ ⚏ ✁ ✷ Lunch fr£8.20&alc Dinner £14.85&alc Last dinner 9.30pm

Credit Cards ①②③⑤

## ★★62% Ship

North St PO19 1NH ☎(0243)782028 FAX (0243) 774254

*Situated in the centre of the town, this traditional-style hotel is undergoing gradual refurbishment. Work on the public areas is almost complete and has been carried out to a good standard, but a number of the bedrooms remain rather functional. Cheerful staff and straightforward cuisine ensure its popularity, particularly with business guests.*

37rm(31⇨♠)(4fb) CTV in all bedrooms ® T sB&B£47-£58
sB&B⇨♠£57-£69 dB&B£57-£81 dB&B⇨♠£78-£102 ▯
Lift ( 35P 3⇶ (£3 per night) CFA *xmas*
V ❖ ⚏ Lunch £9.20-£14&alc High tea £3.50-£7 Dinner £14.50-£17.50&alc Last dinner 9.30pm

Credit Cards ①③

---

For key to symbols in English see the bookmark.

---

## ★66% Bedford

Southgate PO19 1DP ☎(0243)785766 FAX (0243) 533175

*A popular and friendly hotel in a good central position with easy access to the town centre and railway station. Accommodation is neat and modern and a good standard of home cooking is served in the pleasant restaurant.*

24rm(4⇨8♠)(2fb) CTV in all bedrooms ® T ✷ sB&B£31
sB&B⇨♠£42 dB&B£48.50 dB&B⇨♠£58.50-£60 ▯
CTV 6P CFA
V ❖ ⚏ ✷ Bar Lunch £5.50-£7alc Dinner £11.50-£13.50alc Last dinner 9pm

Credit Cards ①②③⑤ⓔ

## ❋❋✕✕Comme Ça

Broyle Rd PO19 4BD ☎(0243)788724

*This one time English pub, situated on the outskirts of Chichester, has been cleverly adapted by the addition of hanging baskets, window boxes and shutters to look like a French country inn. Though this thoughtful little restaurant still features traditional French cuisine, its à la carte menu has now been extended to embrace such popular regional dishes as Coquilles St Jacques à la Chartreuse (scallops served cold with Chartreuse sauce), Moules au Gratin (giant mussels baked with garlic and herbs), Entrecôte Bordelaise (sirloin steak with red wine sauce) and Filet Dijon (beef topped with mustard caramelised and flambé). The wine list contains a fine selection of Beaujolais, while service is efficient and informal.*

Closed Mon, 25 Dec, 1 Jan & BH's
Dinner not served Sun
♡ French V 45 seats ✷ Lunch £15-£18alc Dinner £15-£18alc Last lunch 1.45pm Last dinner 10.45pm 45 P

Credit Cards ①③

## ❋✕Thompson's

30a Southgate PO19 1DR ☎(0243)528832

Closed Sun, 1st 2wks Jan, BH's (ex Good Friday) Lunch not served Mon
♡ English & French V 40 seats ✷ Lunch £11.50-£15.75alc Dinner £17-£24alc Last lunch 2pm Last dinner 11pm ✗

Credit Cards ①③

---

## ❋❋✕✕White Horse Inn

PO18 9HX ☎East Marden(024359)219 & 251 FAX (024359) 301

*This pretty bar and restaurant, set on the Downs, is well known both for the enduring hospitality of Barry and Dorothea Phillips and for the spectacular wine list with its wide spread of countries, vintages and growers and its honest pricing. A 'guarantee' is given that the wine you select will be available – the list is regularly updated and bin ends are available at reasonable prices to take away. Chef and joint owner Neil Rusbridger provides fittingly unpretentious, appealing and reasonably priced set menus, changed weekly, with 3 courses at lunchtime – some 6 or 7 choices in each, always with a vegetarian main dish. Local seafood and game appear in dishes such as Selsey Crab Tart, and Local Rabbit with Cider and Fresh Cèpes. A meal could well include Vichyssoise, a ballotine of duck and turbot in a champagne sauce, and simple vegetables full of flavour, followed by home-made ice cream.*

Closed Mon, 3 wks Feb & 1 wk Oct
Dinner not served Sun
♡ English & French V 60 seats Lunch fr£16.15 Dinner £24.20-£25.85 Last lunch 1.45pm Last dinner 9.30pm 200 P nc14yrs

Credit Cards ①③④⑤

---

All black star hotels are given a
percentage grading within their star bands.
See 'Using the Guide' at the front of the book
for full details.

**C**

## CHILLINGTON Devon Map 03 SX74

### ★★64% Oddicombe House
TQ7 2JD ☎Frogmore(0548)531234
Closed Nov-Etr

*Family-run hotel featuring comfortable bedrooms, good home cooking and an extensive garden with a swimming pool. The atmosphere is relaxed and informal and the hotel is well situated for touring the South Hams.*

8rm(6⇨)Annexe2rm(1⇨)(3fb) ® sB&B£25.50-£30
sB&B⇨£31.60-£34 dB&B£51-£60 dB&B⇨£57-£64
CTV 15P ∰ ❋ ⌂
🍴 European ⇔ ⚖ ⊁ Dinner £14 Last dinner 8.15pm

### ★69% White House
TQ7 2JX ☎Kingsbridge(0548)580580
Closed Nov-Etr (ex Xmas)

*Ideally situated for touring the South Hams coastline, this Georgian house in its own carefully tended gardens offers eight individually furnished, well equipped bedrooms (most with en suite facilities), the comfortably decorated Normandy Bar and a drawing room in elegant peaceful style where coffee can be enjoyed after a pleasant home-cooked meal which will have made use of local produce wherever possible.*

8rm(3⇨3🏠)(1fb) CTV in all bedrooms ® T dB&B£50-£57.80
dB&B⇨🏠£61-£79 🍴
CTV 8P ∰ ❋ croquet badminton nc5yrs *xmas*
🍴 English, French & Italian ⇔ ⚖ ⊁ ❋ Bar Lunch £1.40-£4.50
Dinner £12.50 Last dinner 8.05pm
Credit Cards ①③

## CHIPPENHAM Wiltshire Map 03 ST97

See also **Sutton Benger**

### ★★★61% Angel
Market Place SN15 3HD (Queens Moat) ☎(0249)652615
FAX (0249) 443210

*A centuries-old building, centrally situated, with good car parking at the rear. Bedrooms, in the original building, are comfortable, well equipped and attracatively co-ordinated, while courtyard bedrooms are functional. The panelled restaurant serves both fixed price and à la carte menus, and the 2 bars are popular with locals and residents alike.*

12⇨🏠Annexe32⇨(3fb)4∰⊁in 6 bedrooms CTV in all
bedrooms ® T sB&B⇨🏠£60-£75 dB&B⇨🏠£75-£100 🍴
℄ 75P CFA *xmas*
V ⇔ ⚖ ⊁ ❋ Lunch £5.75-£10 Dinner £12.75 Last dinner
9.30pm
Credit Cards ①②③⑤ⓔ

### ★58% The Bear
12 Market Place SN15 3HJ ☎(0249)653272
Closed 25 Dec

*This old inn dating from the 1600s now provides simple sound accommodation. Personally run by the friendly proprietors, it has a popular public bar and pleasant restaurant.*

9rm(2⇨)(1fb) CTV in all bedrooms ®
6P
🍴 Mainly grills V ⇔
Credit Cards ①③

## CHIPPERFIELD Hertfordshire Map 04 TL00

### ★★66% The Two Brewers Inn
The Common WD4 9BS (Forte Hotels)
☎King's Langley(0923)265266 FAX (0923) 261884

*You will find a welcoming atmosphere and a popular beamed bar at this charming and cosy 17th-century inn which overlooks the village green. Bedrooms offer well equipped, modern accommodation and there is a spacious and comfortable lounge.*

20⇨🏠⊁in 4 bedrooms CTV in all bedrooms ® T ❋ S%
sB⇨🏠£75 dB⇨🏠£90 (room only) 🍴

25P CFA *xmas*
🍴 English & French V ⇔ ⚖ ⊁ ❋ S% Lunch £15.55 Dinner
£16.95&alc Last dinner 9.30pm
Credit Cards ①②③⑤

## CHIPPING Lancashire Map 07 SD64

### ★68% *The Brickhouse*
PR3 2QH ☎(0995)61316
RS Mon & Sun eve

*A small, friendly hotel on the edge of this attractive village, overlooking pastureland and distant hills. This is a well maintained establishment with a pretty restaurant, cosy bar and well equipped bedrooms, ideal for touring the Forest of Bowland.*

5⇨🏠(2fb) CTV in all bedrooms ® ✈ (ex guide dogs)
100P ❋
🍴 English & Continental V ⇔ ⚖ Last dinner 9.30pm
Credit Cards ①③

## CHIPPING CAMPDEN Gloucestershire Map 04 SP13

### ★★★77% Cotswold House
The Square GL55 6AN ☎Evesham(0386)840330
FAX (0386) 840310
Closed 25-27 Dec

*This lovely house is a magnet for tourists. Decoration is elaborate, with numerous trompe l'oeil features around the spiral staircase and restaurant area, extending into the bedrooms to be complemented by unique interior design. Each bedroom is individually themed and offers a high level of comfort and facilities. There is an elegant dining room and lounge, and a popular bistro style operation, open all day for refreshments and meals.*

15⇨🏠1🏠 CTV in all bedrooms T ✈ sB&B⇨🏠£60-£75
dB&B⇨🏠£90-£146 🍴
12P ∰ ❋ nc8yrs ♫ *xmas*
V ⇔ ⚖ ⊁ Sunday Lunch £15.95&alc High tea £2.95-£4 Last
high tea 6.30pm
Credit Cards ①②③⑤ⓔ

**See advertisement on page 225**

### ★★★68% Seymour House
High St GL55 6AH ☎(0386)840429 Telex no 31626
FAX (0386) 804369

*At the heart of the striking town centre, this newly opened hotel combines several buildings dating to around 1700, including a malt house, and has been sensitively restored to take account of lovely original features – fine fireplaces, ornate staircases, ancient beams and stonework. The restaurant, with a grapevine reaching into the glazed cupola at its centre, offers international menus featuring Italian specialities. Bedrooms are spacious and very comfortable, with very good Italian reproduction furniture and some fine antique pieces.*

11⇨🏠Annexe4⇨🏠 CTV in all bedrooms ® T
✈ (ex guide dogs) sB⇨🏠£61.50-£67.50 dB⇨🏠£84.50-£145
(room only) 🍴
28P ❋ *xmas*
🍴 English, French & Italian V ⇔ ⚖ Lunch £11.50-£15&alc
High tea £3-£8&alc Dinner £14.95-£20&alc Last dinner
9.30pm
Credit Cards ①②③ⓔ

### ★★69% Noel Arms
High St GL55 6AT (Exec Hotel) ☎Evesham(0386)840317
FAX (0386) 841136

*An inn built in the 14th century to cater for visiting Continental wool merchants has been carefully refurbished over recent years to offer modern facilities though still preserving much of the original character. The comfortable carvery/à la carte restaurant with its attractive conservatory lounge forms an effective contrast to the original intimate bar and panelled lounge while bedrooms are clean and very well equipped. Friendly and attentive service is provided by the proprietor and his staff.*

→

26⇔🅝2🄴 CTV in all bedrooms Ⓡ T ✖ (ex guide dogs) sB&B⇔🅝£50-£60 dB&B⇔🅝£75-£100 🄻
40P *xmas*
V ♥ ⚏ ✻ Sunday Lunch fr£10.95 Dinner £12-£18 Last dinner 10pm
Credit Cards ①②③£

---

CHITTLEHAMHOLT Devon Map **02** SS62

★★★⚑**74% Highbullen**
EX37 9HD ☎(0769)540561 FAX (0769)540492
*A charming folly of a building, full of character and individual style, situated in a commanding position between the Mole and Taw valleys; and set in 60 acres of wooded parkland, mature grounds and gardens which include a 9-hole golf course and a herd of Manchurian sika deer. This busy leisure-centre hotel is a little different from the usual country house hotel, service is pleasant but more relaxed. Bedrooms are located in the main building and scattered around the various annexes in the grounds. Some are at quite a distance and are spacious but don't offer the same extent of room service. The cosy restaurant offers prompt service, a varied menu making good use of fresh local produce, and a fine wine list. Commendable breakfasts are served in the bright, recently refurbished breakfast room. However, the main attractions are the excellent leisure facilities and the hospitable service.*
12⇔Annexe23⇔ CTV in all bedrooms Ⓡ T ✖ S%
sB&B⇔£60-£65 dB&B⇔£100-£140 Continental breakfast (incl dinner)
60P ♨ ✻ CFA 🄴 (heated) ⌇ (heated) ♪ 9 ♬ (hard) ⤜
squash snooker sauna solarium gymnasium croquet putting table tennis nc 8yrs
♈ International V ♥ ⚏ ✂ S% Bar Lunch £2.50-£7alc Dinner £17.50 Last dinner 9pm

---

CHOLLERFORD Northumberland Map **12** NY97

★★★**71% George**
NE46 4EW (Swallow) ☎Humshaugh(0434)681611
FAX (0434) 681727
*A delightful riverside hotel with very comfortable and well appointed bedrooms complemented by inviting lounges and bars. The attractive restaurant looks over the well tended gardens to the river.*
50⇔(5fb)1🄴🗅✂in 19 bedrooms CTV in all bedrooms Ⓡ T ✻
S% sB&B⇔£63-£70 dB&B⇔£82-£90 🄻
〖 70P ✻ CFA 🄴 (heated) ⤜ sauna solarium putting *xmas*
♈ International V ♥ ⚏ ✻ S10% Bar Lunch £1.90-£2.50alc Dinner fr£16.50&alc Last dinner 9.30pm
Credit Cards ①②③⑤

---

CHORLEY Lancashire Map **07** SD51

★★★**63% Park Hall Hotel, Leisure & Conference Centre**
PR7 5LP ☎Eccleston(0257)452090 FAX (0257) 451838
(For full entry see Charnock Richard)

★★★*61% Shaw Hill Hotel Golf & Country Club*
Preston Rd, Whittle-le-Woods PR6 7PP (2m N A6)
☎(0257)269221 FAX (0257) 261223
*This converted Georgian mansion with a championship golf course offers comfortable accommodation, with opulent public rooms, business and leisure facilities and a very popular restaurant.*
22⇔🅝(1fb)🄴 CTV in all bedrooms Ⓡ T
〖 CTV 200P ✻ ▶ 18 ⤜ snooker sauna solarium
♈ International V ♥ ⚏
Credit Cards ①②③⑤

★★**66% Hartwood Hall**
Preston Rd PR6 7AX (Minotels) ☎(0257)269966
FAX (0257) 241678
Closed 25-30 Dec
*Conveniently situated 1 mile north of the town on the A6 close to its junction with the M61, this privately owned hotel has well*

---

*equipped bedrooms of varying size. The restaurant is open for lunch and dinner, with bar lunches also served on weekdays. Conference and function rooms are available.*
12rm(8⇔🅝)Annexe10⇔🅝(2fb)1🄴 CTV in all bedrooms Ⓡ
✻ sB&B£32.80-£41 sB&B⇔🅝£37.60-£47 dB&B£41.60-£52 dB&B⇔🅝£45.60-£57 🄻
CTV 150P CFA
♈ English & Continental V ♥ ⚏ Lunch £8.75&alc High tea £8.75&alc Dinner £12.50&alc Last dinner 9pm
Credit Cards ①②③⑤£

---

CHRISTCHURCH Dorset Map **04** SZ19 ◉

★★★**73% Waterford Lodge**
87 Bure Ln, Friars Cliff, Mudeford BH23 4DN (2m E off B3059) (Best Western) ☎Highcliffe(0425)272948 & 278801
FAX (0425) 279130
*A quiet family-run hotel where brothers Ian and David Badley are on hand to welcome guests. Bedrooms are pretty and comfortable with armchairs and many extra niceties. There is a pleasant lounge and small bar for pre-dinner drinks. The interesting dinner menu specialises in fresh fish from the nearby quay, and service at dinner is by friendly, professional staff.*
20⇔(3fb)1🄴 CTV in all bedrooms Ⓡ T sB&B⇔£60-£70 dB&B⇔£72-£90 🄻
38P ♨ ✻ *xmas*
♈ English & French V ♥ ⚏ ✻ Lunch £12.10-£20.70alc High tea £2.95-£12.55alc Dinner £17-£19 Last dinner 8.30pm
Credit Cards ①②③⑤

★★★**60% The Avonmouth**
Mudeford BH23 3NT (2m E off B3059) (Forte Hotels)
☎(0202)483434 FAX (0202) 479004
*Beautifully located on the harbour side with a garden leading to the water, this popular resort hotel has comfortable public areas with fine views from the dining room where a short menu offers a* →

C

**C**

*good range of mainly British dishes. Most of the bedrooms have recently been refurbished to a high standard.*
27⇄Annexe14⇄(3fb)⅟₄in 10 bedrooms CTV in all bedrooms ® T ✱ sB⇄frf80 dB⇄frf90 (room only) 🏴
《 100P 🚲 ✿ CFA ⌂ (heated) mini-golf ♫ ⚸ *xmas*
♀ English & French V ⌂ ⚌ ✱ Lunch £4.75-£9&alc Dinner £15.30 Last dinner 9pm
Credit Cards ① ② ③ ④ ⑤

### ★★62% Fisherman's Haunt
Salisbury Rd, Winkton BH23 7AS (2.5m N on B3347)
☎(0202)477283 & 484071 FAX (0202) 478883
Closed 25 Dec
*Many of the comfortable bedrooms at this small but very popular hotel are situated in surrounding cottages and stables. The dining room serves an inexpensive menu of classical dishes and real ale is available in the busy bar.*
5rm(1⇄2🛏)Annexe15rm(13⇄)(4fb)2🛏 CTV in all bedrooms ® T ✱ sB&B£30 sB&B⇄🛏£35 dB&B£52 dB&B⇄🛏£59 🏴
100P ✿
V ⌂ ⚌ ✱ Lunch £8.25-£8.50 Dinner £15-£20alc Last dinner 10pm
Credit Cards ① ② ③ ⑤

### CHUDLEIGH Devon Map 03 SX87

### ★★63% Old Coaching House
25 Fore St TQ13 0HX ☎Newton Abbot(0626)853270
14⇄🛏(2fb) CTV in all bedrooms ® sB&B⇄🛏£30-£45 dB&B⇄🛏£50-£65 🏴
90P CFA *xmas*
♀ English & French V ⌂ ⚌ ⅟₄ Sunday Lunch £6.95-£8.50 Dinner £9-£12.50&alc Last dinner 10pm
Credit Cards ① ③ ⓔ

### CHURCH STRETTON Shropshire Map 07 SO49

### ★★★60% *Stretton Hall*
All Stretton SY6 6HE ☎(0694)723224
*On the northern edge of the pleasant village, this small country house-style hotel with attractive gardens has a relaxing atmosphere and provides quite simple but well equipped accommodation, equally suitable for tourists and business guests.*
13⇄🛏(1fb) CTV in all bedrooms ®
CTV 60P ✿
♀ English & French ⌂ ⚌ ⅟₄ Last dinner 9pm
Credit Cards ① ② ③ ⑤

### ★★69% Mynd House
Little Stretton SY6 6RB (2m S B4370) (Exec Hotel)
☎(0694)722212 FAX (0694) 724180
Closed 24 Dec-Feb
*An Edwardian house at the foot of the Long Mynd is personally run by its proprietors in a professional yet welcoming manner ; a choice of menus includes vegetarian dishes, and an extensive list of quality wines complements the meals.*
8⇄🛏1🛏 CTV in all bedrooms ® T sB&B⇄🛏£35-£40 dB&B⇄🛏£50-£80 🏴
16P 🚲 ✿
♀ English, French & Italian V ⌂ ⚌ ⅟₄ Bar Lunch £3-£5.75alc High tea £7.50-£12.50alc Dinner £16-£17.50&alc Last dinner 9.15pm
Credit Cards ① ② ③ ⓔ

### CHURT Surrey Map 04 SU83

### ★★★65% *Frensham Pond*
GU10 2QB ☎Frensham(025125)3175 Telex no 858610
*An hotel in a peaceful, beautiful setting overlooking Frensham Great Pond is currently undergoing the second stage of an extensive refurbishment programme. Accommodation is modern, well equipped and spacious, chalet rooms outside the main building*

*providing a greater degree of privacy. The popular leisure centre offers relaxation in pleasant surroundings, friendly staff provide helpful service, and improved conference facilities are attracting a business clientele.*
7⇄🛏Annexe12🛏 CTV in all bedrooms ® ✈
《 100P 🚲 ✿ ⊡ (heated) squash sauna solarium gymnasium jacuzzi ♫
♀ English & French V ⌂
Credit Cards ① ② ③ ④ ⑤

### CIRENCESTER Gloucestershire Map 04 SP00

### ★★★68% Fleece
Market Place GL7 2NZ (Resort) ☎(0285)658507
Telex no 437287 FAX (0285) 651017
*Situated in the market place of the historic town, this Tudor coaching inn, with oak beams and open fireplaces, has been carefully modernised to provide comfortable accommodation. Bedrooms are well equipped and the attractive restaurant or less formal Shepherds Bistro serve a choice of interesting dishes.*
25rm(21⇄🛏)(4fb)2🛏 CTV in all bedrooms ® T ✱ sB⇄🛏£67-£77 dB⇄🛏£77-£97 (room only) 🏴
12P 🚲 CFA ♫ *xmas*
♀ English & French V ⌂ ⚌ ✱ Sunday Lunch £11.95 High tea fr£3.50 Dinner £16.50&alc Last dinner 9.30pm
Credit Cards ① ② ③ ⑤ ⓔ

### ★★★65% The Crown of Crucis
Ampney Crucis GL7 5RS ☎(0285)851806 FAX (0285) 851735
Closed 25 Dec
*A popular hostelry built of Cotswold stone and dating from the 16th-century stands beside the A417 in the village of Ampney Crucis, 3 miles east of the town. Accommodation is housed in a courtyard, most of the tastefully furnished rooms overlooking the Ampney Brook and cricket club, while public areas are limited to a restaurant, bar and conference facilities.*
26⇄🛏 CTV in all bedrooms ® T sB&B⇄🛏£47-£49 dB&B⇄🛏£58-£60 🏴
82P CFA *xmas*
V ⌂ ⚌ Lunch £3-£7alc Dinner £11-£14 Last dinner 10pm
Credit Cards ① ② ③ ⓔ

### ★★★65% Stratton House
Gloucester Rd GL7 2LE (Forestdale) ☎(0285)651761
FAX (0285) 640024
*The dining room and many of the older bedrooms of this hotel have recently undergone considerable improvement, and further upgrading is planned, as well as the building of an additional accommodation wing. A comfortable drawing room offers a pleasant, quiet area in which guests can relax.*
25⇄🛏 CTV in all bedrooms ® T
《 100P ✿ CFA
♀ English & French V ⌂ ⚌ Last dinner 9.45pm
Credit Cards ① ② ③ ⑤ ⓔ

### ★★★64% King's Head
Market Place GL7 2NR (Best Western) ☎(0285)653322
FAX (0285) 655103
Closed 27-30 Dec
*This former coaching inn with its own car park, situated in the market square, maintains good, old fashioned standards of service and hospitality ; accommodation varies, all rooms being well equipped though some bathrooms are very compact, while public areas include a choice of bars, two lounge areas and a traditional restaurant.*
70⇄🛏(4fb)2🛏 CTV in all bedrooms ® T
Lift 《 25P pool skittle alley darts table tennis
V ⌂ ⚌ ⅟₄ ✱ S% Lunch fr£10.50&alc Dinner fr£14&alc Last dinner 9pm
Credit Cards ① ② ③ ④ ⑤

## ★★58% **Corinium Court**
Gloucester St GL7 2DG ☎(0285)659711 FAX (0285) 885807

*Situated in the oldest part of town, this former 16th-century wool merchant's house is now a hotel with good modern facilities. Public areas have charm and character and the dining room offers imaginative food.*

16⇨🏠(1fb) CTV in all bedrooms **T**
40P 🚗

♨ English & Italian **V** ♦ 🗓 Lunch £7-£12.50 Dinner fr£10&alc Last dinner 9.30pm
Credit Cards ①②③⑤ ⑥

---

### CLACHAN-SEIL Strathclyde *Argyllshire* Map **10** NM71

## ★★65% **Willowburn**
PA34 4TJ (Guestaccom) ☎Balvicar(08523)276
Closed Nov-mid Apr

*A small, family-run hotel which looks deceptively like a private house is surrounded by open gardens whose lawns run down to the shore; the island on which it stands is joined to the mainland by a bridge – the only one to span the Atlantic! Fully-involved owners ensure that guests can rely on friendly service and good home-cooked meals featuring local seafood.*

6⇨🏠 CTV in all bedrooms ® sB&B⇨🏠£36-£40
dB&B⇨🏠£36-£40 (incl dinner) 🍴

36P 🚗 ✿

♦ 🗓 Bar Lunch £3-£10 Dinner £14-£15&alc Last dinner 8pm
Credit Cards ①③

---

### CLACTON-ON-SEA Essex Map **05** TM11

## ★★63% **King's Cliff**
King's Pde, Holland on Sea CO15 5JB ☎(0255)812343
Telex no 817589 FAX (0255) 812271

*A solid seafront hotel in Holland-on-Sea a few miles north of Clacton. There is a popular public bar and a residents' bar/lounge area. Bedrooms are all on the first floor, mostly of a reasonable size, cheerful and well kept.*

15⇨🏠(5fb)1🛏 CTV in all bedrooms ® **T** 🇽 🍴
⟪ CTV 80P 5🚗 (£2 per night) ✿ CFA *xmas*

♨ European **V** ♦ 🗓 ✂ ✱ Lunch £7.75&alc Dinner £9.25&alc
Last dinner 9pm
Credit Cards ①②③ ⑥

---

### CLANFIELD Oxfordshire Map **04** SP20

## ❀❀❀ ✕✕✕ *Plough at Clanfield*
Bourton Rd OX8 2RB ☎(036781)222 & 494 Telex no 449848
FAX (036781) 596

*This charming Elizabethan manor house in the Cotswolds, houses a renowned restaurant offering separate lunchtime and dinner menus supplemented by interesting 'specials' – meat, game, fish and vegetarian dishes all being represented. Roast Partridge with Red Wine Sauce or Salmon with a Chervil Cream Sauce could be followed by either Warmed Apple Flan with Pearls of Cinnamon Ice Cream or a savoury. Cuisine is refreshingly simple and honest, but the enthusiastic staff are happy to describe any dish, and the menu is complemented by a fine wine list. Six bedrooms are available for overnight guests.*

♨ English & French **V** 45 seats Last lunch 2pm Last dinner 10pm 30 P nc7yrs ✂
Credit Cards ①②③⑤

---

### CLARE Suffolk Map **05** TL74

## ★★70% **Bell**
Market Hill CO10 8NN (Minotels) ☎(0787)277741
FAX (0787) 278474

*Individually designed, well equipped bedrooms, characterful public areas which are warmed by open fires and offer a choice of bars and restaurants, and friendly, informal service are the attractions of this village-centre hotel.*

10rm(3⇨4🏠)Annexe11⇨(1fb)4🛏 CTV in all bedrooms ® **T**
✱ sB&B£38.50 sB&B⇨🏠£44.50-£66.50 dB&B£56.50
dB&B⇨🏠£61.50-£97.50 🍴
15P CFA 🐕 *xmas*

♨ English, French & Italian **V** ♦ 🗓 ✱ Lunch £14.50&alc
Dinner £6.50-£14.50&alc Last dinner 9.30pm
Credit Cards ①②③⑤ ⑥

---

## ★71% *The Seafarer*
Nethergate St CO10 8NP ☎(0787)277449

5rm(3🏠) CTV in all bedrooms ®
10P ✿

♨ English & French **V** ♦ 🗓 Last dinner 10pm
Credit Cards ①②③⑤

---

### CLARENCEFIELD Dumfries & Galloway *Dumfriesshire*
Map **11** NY06

## ★★⚲67% **Comlongen Castle**
DG1 4NA ☎(038787)283 FAX (038787) 266
Closed Jan-Feb

*Part of a castle dating from the mid 15th-century has recently been refurbished to provide spacious, well appointed bedrooms and impressive, lofty public areas – many of which are wood-panelled. The remaining part of the castle has been retained as a museum, and guests are invited to a wonderful candlelit tour before dinner. Tranquility is assured by the hotel's setting within its own 50 acres of parkland.*

9⇨🏠(1fb)3🛏 CTV in all bedrooms ® **T** 🇽 (ex guide dogs) ✱
sB&B⇨🏠frf£35 dB&B⇨🏠£60-£80 🍴
30P 2🚗 🚗 🍴 🌳 nature trail *xmas*

**V** ♦ 🗓 ✂ ✱ Lunch fr£4 Dinner £16-£18 Last dinner 9.30pm
Credit Cards ①③

---

### CLAWTON Devon Map **02** SX39

## ★★⚲70% **Court Barn Country House**
EX22 6PS (Exec Hotel) ☎North Tamerton(040927)219
Closed 1-7 Jan

*A lovely manor house, dating from the 14th century, rebuilt in 1853, personally run by Robert and Susan Wood. Since our last visit a pretty new restaurant has been added to complement the cosy, log-fired lounges. Bedrooms are individually furnished, many with William Morris wallpapers and fabrics, there are fresh flowers and reading material; many rooms have views of the garden and countryside beyond. Everywhere is spotlessly clean. Plentiful home-cooking is based on quality produce and there is an extensive, well balanced wine list; Mercier Prix d'Elite Award 1988. The hotel is an ideal venue for traditional afternoon tea.*

8rm(4⇨3🏠)(3fb)1🛏✂in all bedrooms CTV in all bedrooms ® **T** sB&B⇨🏠£53-£68 dB&B⇨🏠£98-£110 (incl dinner) 🍴
CTV 16P 2🚗 ✿ ☉ solarium gymnasium croquet putting outdoor badminton 🐕 *xmas*

♨ English & French **V** ♦ 🗓 ✂ Lunch £8.95-£10.50 High tea £3.50-£6 Dinner £15-£18 Last dinner 9.15pm
Credit Cards ①②③⑤ ⑥

---

### CLAYGATE Surrey
See LONDON plan 1*B1*(page 434)

## ❀❀ ✕✕ *Les Alouettes*
High St KT10 0JW ☎Esher(0372)64882 FAX (0372) 65337

*An attractive restaurant situated away from the hustle and bustle of the surrounding area offers an interesting and varied menu which features an extensive range of French dishes; this is supplemented by such 'dishes of the day' as Terrine of Languoustines with a lemon butter sauce flavoured with tarragon and a Rendezvous de Poissons with a Champagne butter sauce. The tastefully decorated restaurant and unobtrusive professional service combine to create a refined atmosphere, and chef Michel Perraud likes to visit tables and speak with guests when things are not too busy.*

Closed Sun, 25-30 Dec, 1-2 Jan, 12-29 Aug & BH's Lunch not served Sat
♀ French **V** 70 seats Last lunch 2.15pm Last dinner 9.30pm ⚡
Credit Cards 1 2 3 5

❀ ✕ **Le Petit Pierrot**
4 The Parade KT10 0NU ☎Esher(0372)465105
*An unpretentious town-centre restaurant specialising in good, reliable, provincial French cuisine, offers a short but interesting menu (changed every 6 weeks) at both lunchtime and dinner. The all-French team, headed by Madame Brichot in the restaurant and her husband Jean-Pierre in the kitchen, produces such notable starters as a terrine of fish and prawns with a basil-scented sauce, or a pastry 'pillow' of snails and mushrooms; these can be followed by tender calves' liver with raspberries, or corn-fed Chicken Niçoise. Service is courteous and professional without being intrusive.*
Closed Sun BH's & last wk Aug-1st wk Sep Lunch not served Sat
♀ French 28 seats ✳ Lunch £9.95-£16.85 Dinner £18.95 Last lunch 2.15pm Last dinner 10pm ⚡ nc10yrs
Credit Cards 1 2 3 5

## CLAYWORTH Nottinghamshire Map **08** SK78

★★★**67% Royston Manor**
St Peters Ln DN22 9AA ☎Retford(0777)817484
FAX (0777) 817155
*A delightful Elizabethan manor dating from 1588 and overlooking open countryside houses the bar, lounge and restaurant of this hotel, its well-furnished and comfortable bedrooms being peacefully set in the attractive gardens.*
Annexe22⇆🦃(3fb)3⬚ CTV in all bedrooms ® **T**
🦃 (ex guide dogs) ✳ sB&B⇆🦃£45-£54 dB&B⇆🦃£50-£60 ⊟
CTV 100P ⇗ ✿ *xmas*
♀ English & French **V** ☼ ⚖ ✳ Lunch £9.50&alc Dinner £13.50&alc Last dinner 9.30pm
Credit Cards 1 2 3 5

## CLEARWELL Gloucestershire Map **03** SO50

★★★**65% Clearwell Castle**
Church Rd GL16 8LG ☎Dean(0594)32320 due to change to 832320 FAX (0594) 35523 due to change to 835523
*Beautifully situated on the edge of a Forest of Dean village, this early 18th-century castle and private residence until 1980 retains its original grandeur, with imposing, comfortable public areas, antique furnishings and spacious bedrooms that feature four-poster and half-tester beds plus modern en suite facilities. The basement includes a chapel and the original servants' quarters, sometimes used for medieval banquets.*
14⇆ CTV in all bedrooms ® **T** 🦃 (ex guide dogs)
⟨ 100P 3☂ (£5) ✿ ⚘
♀ English & French **V** ☼ ⚖ Last dinner 9.30pm
Credit Cards 1 2 3

★★★**63% Wyndham Arms**
GL16 8JT ☎Dean(0594)33666 due to change to 833666
FAX (0594) 36450 due to change to 836450
*Situated in the village centre, this former 13th-century inn has been carefully modernised and extended by the proprietors Rosemary and John Stanford, to provide a hotel of character with good modern facilities.*
5⇆🦃Annexe12⇆🦃(3fb) CTV in all bedrooms ® **T** S10% sB&B⇆🦃£40-£62 dB&B⇆🦃£80 ⊟
52P 2☂ ⇗ ✿ *xmas*
♀ International **V** ☼ Lunch £12.75-£18.95&alc Dinner £16.50&alc Last dinner 9.30pm
Credit Cards 1 2 3 4 5 ⓔ

## CLEATOR MOOR Cumbria Map **11** NY02

★★★**61% Ennerdale Country House**
CA23 3DT (Consort) ☎(0946)813907 FAX (0946) 815260
*Guests are assured of good comforts and service at this hotel, a Grade II listed building situated on the west side of the Lake District between coast and hills. Attractively furnished bedrooms have good facilities, and a wide choice of meals is available in both restaurant and bar.*
20⇆🦃2🦃 CTV in all bedrooms ® **T** ✳ S% sB&B⇆🦃£60 dB&B⇆🦃£70
65P ✿ *xmas*
♀ International **V** ☼ ⚖ ✳ Lunch £6.95-£12 Dinner £15 Last dinner 10pm
Credit Cards 1 2 3 5

## CLEETHORPES Humberside Map **08** TA30

★★★**70% Kingsway**
Kingsway DN35 0AE ☎(0472)601122 Telex no 527920
FAX (0472) 601381
Closed 25-26 Dec
*This traditional hotel is managed by the owning family who, along with their staff, provide warm courteous service. Bedrooms are comfortable and well appointed and public rooms are tasteful.*
50⇆🦃 CTV in all bedrooms ® **T** 🦃 (ex guide dogs)
sB&B⇆🦃£54-£59 dB&B⇆🦃£80 ⊟
Lift ⟨ 30P 20☂ (£1.50) ⇗ nc5yrs
♀ English & French **V** ☼ ✳ Lunch £11&alc Dinner £14.50&alc Last dinner 9pm
Credit Cards 1 2 3 5

A rosette means exceptional standards of cuisine.

# The Bell Hotel ★★
## Clare, West Suffolk, England CO10 8NN
## Telephone Clare 277741
## Code 0787

20 bedrooms – private bathrooms – wine bar – conference rooms. Beamed Restaurant. 16th-century posting house within easy reach of LONDON (62 miles) and ferry ports of HARWICH (40 miles) and FELIXSTOWE (47 miles). Ideal centre for touring East Anglia all year round.

*Resident Proprietors:*
*Brian and Gloria Miles*

MINOTELS

## ★★ 64% **Wellow**

Kings Rd DN35 0AQ ☎(0472)695589

*Facing the sea and away from the bustle of the town centre, this popular modern hotel in its own grounds is orientated round its smart bars but also has a pleasant small restaurant and 10 well equipped modern bedrooms, although a few of them are compact.*

10⇨ ⋔(4fb) CTV in all bedrooms ® T ✖ (ex guide dogs) 60P *xmas*

♀ English & Continental V ♥ ⚏

Credit Cards ①③

## CLEEVE HILL Gloucestershire Map 03 SO92

### ★★★ 57% **Rising Sun**

GL52 3PX (Lansbury) ☎Bishops Cleeve(0242)676281 Telex no 437410 FAX (0242) 673069

*In a commanding position overlooking the Malvern Hills, 4 miles south of Cheltenham on the Broadway road, this hotel offers well equipped bedrooms of varying standards, and a popular restaurant operation.*

24⇨(3fb)1🛏✁in 6 bedrooms CTV in all bedrooms ® T ✱ sB&B⇨⋔fr£58 dB&B⇨⋔fr£70 🄱

⊄ 60P ✿ CFA sauna *xmas*

♀ English & French V ♥ ⚏ ✁ ✱ Lunch £8.95-£10.50&alc Dinner £15&alc Last dinner 10.30pm

Credit Cards ①②③⑤£

### ❀❀❀✕✕ **Redmond's**

GL52 3PR ☎Cheltenham(0242)672017

*Redmond and Pippa Hayward have been in charge here for over 2 years, and established a very professionally run and comfortable restaurant, with mouthwatering menus fully realised on the plate. From black olives in the bar to delicious petits fours, every course offers sound ingredients matched with imaginative and harmonious garnishes: for example a good shellfish broth infused with ginger and coriander, and a seafood ravioli. Clear distinctive flavours balanced in each dish are the hallmark here. The wine list encompasses a wide geographical spread with clear description, and prices to encourage drinking.*

Closed 1st wk Jan Lunch not served Sat & Mon

Dinner not served Sun

36 seats ✱ Lunch £17.50 Dinner £32 Last lunch 2pm Last dinner 10pm 16 P ✁

Credit Cards ①③

## CLEOBURY MORTIMER Shropshire Map 07 SO67

### ★★ 69% **Redfern**

DY14 8AA (Minotels) ☎(0299)270395 Telex no 335176 FAX (0299) 271011

*This busy village hotel has good quality bedrooms, and a friendly atmosphere prevails. Generous portions of well prepared food are served in the country-kitchen style restaurant.*

5⇨⋔Annexe6⇨⋔(4fb)1🛏 CTV in all bedrooms ® T S% sB&B⇨⋔£41-£55 dB&B⇨⋔£60-£75 🄱

20P 🚗 CFA clay pigeon shooting pheasant shooting *xmas*

♀ English & French V ♥ ⚏ S% Lunch £5-£7.50alc Dinner fr£15.25&alc Last dinner 9.30pm

Credit Cards ①②③⑤£

## CLEVEDON Avon Map 03 ST47

### ★★★ 61% **Walton Park**

Wellington Ter BS21 7BL ☎(0272)874253 FAX (0272) 343577

*A grey stone mansion standing on a cliff overlooking the Bristol Channel to the north of the town. After a lengthy refurbishment programme, the spacious bedrooms are now neatly decorated and well equipped, with bright bathrooms. Public rooms include a popular bar and airy lounge.*

38⇨⋔(3fb) CTV in all bedrooms ® T ✱ sB&B⇨⋔£32-£61.75 dB&B⇨⋔£54-£82 🄱

Lift ⊄ 37P ✿ CFA *xmas*

♀ English & French V ♥ ⚏ ✱ Lunch £7.95-£12.50alc Dinner £12.50&alc Last dinner 9.30pm

Credit Cards ①②③⑤£

## CLIMPING West Sussex Map 04 TQ00

### ★★★ ♨ 67% **Bailiffscourt**

BN17 5RW ☎Littlehampton(0903)723511 Telex no 877870 FAX (0903) 723107

*Situated in rural tranquillity and built only 50 years ago, this replica of a 13th-century courthouse has been furnished with sturdy antiques. Several bedrooms have open fireplaces and the thatched house can be reached by an underground passage. Chef Garry Leaf continues to impress with a menu which changes weekly and the levels of service can be extensive particularly during the summer months.*

18⇨Annexe2⇨(2fb)8🛏 CTV in all bedrooms T sB&B⇨£65-£80 dB&B⇨£85-£190 🄱

⊄ 50P 🚗 ✿ CFA ⌿ ℘ (hard) ◡ croquet nc 8yrs *xmas*

♀ English & French V ♥ ⚏ ✁ Lunch fr£15.50 Dinner £25-£30 Last dinner 10pm

Credit Cards ①②③⑤£

## CLITHEROE Lancashire Map 07 SD74

### ★★ 66% **Calfs Head**

Worston BB7 1QA ☎(0200)41218 FAX (0200) 41510

*A personally owned and run hotel set just off the A59 in the attractive village of Worston – under the lee of Pendle Hill, famous for its witches! – features recently upgraded bedrooms with good facilities; both the Tudor Room and bar serve an extensive range of food, and there is a delightful garden.*

6⇨⋔(1fb) CTV in all bedrooms ® T ✱ sB&B⇨⋔£36 dB&B⇨⋔£48 Continental breakfast 🄱

80P ✿ *xmas*

♀ English & French V ♥ ⚏ ✱ Lunch £15 Dinner £15 Last dinner 9.30pm

Credit Cards ①②③④⑤

## CLOVELLY Devon Map 02 SS32

### ★ 61% **Red Lion**

The Quay EX39 5TF ☎Bideford(0237)431237

*Right at the bottom of Clovelly's steep, cobbled street, at the harbour's edge, stands a cosy little pub which has recently benefited from significant and commendable upgrading. Many of the bright, cottagey en suite bedrooms boast fine sea views, while all are well furnished and equipped with a good range of modern facilities. Public rooms are slightly restrictive, but their size is in keeping with the nature of the establishment, and friendly services are provided on a suitably informal basis. Limited car parking is available, and there is also a Land Rover 'ferry' service for those reluctant to attempt the steep walk.*

12⇨⋔(1fb) CTV in all bedrooms ® ✖ ✱ sB&B⇨⋔£32 dB&B⇨⋔£51 🄱

20P *xmas*

V ♥ ⚏ ✱ S10% Lunch £5.25-£7.50alc Dinner fr£10.75alc Last dinner 9pm

Credit Cards ①③

## CLUN Shropshire Map 07 SO38

### ❀✕✕ **Old Post Office**

9 The Square SY7 8JA ☎(05884)687

*The building's original use is quite apparent, even without the name, but it can never have looked as inviting as it does now. Paintwork is smart and fresh, and sparkling windows offer a clear view into a light, airy dining room, through a conservatory extension, with a couple of tables on 'deck' for fine weather. Richard Arbuthnot, his Savoy training and Guide inspection days over, does the cooking, while his wife Anne, assisted by charming*

*local ladies, looks after the service. Much local produce is used and inventive dishes reflect the owner's tastes.*
Closed Mon (ex BH), Tue, 20 Jan-8 Mar & 23 Dec-3 Jan Lunch not served Wed
V 30 seats ✻ Lunch £12-£14 Dinner £10-£18&alc Last lunch 1.30pm Last dinner 9.30pm P
Credit Cards ① ② ③

CLYDEBANK Strathclyde *Dunbartonshire* Map **11** NS56

★★★66% **Patio**
1 South Av, Clydebank Business Park G81 2RW ☎041-951 1133
FAX 041-952 3713
80⇔♠↙in 16 bedrooms CTV in all bedrooms ® T S%
sB⇔♠£50 dB⇔♠£60 (room only)
Lift ⟨ 120P ✤ CFA *xmas*
♀ French V ♥ ♫ ✻ Lunch £10.50&alc Dinner £11.50&alc
Last dinner 10pm
Credit Cards ① ② ③ ⑤ ⓔ

COALVILLE Leicestershire Map **08** SK41

★★62% **Bardon Hall**
Beveridge Ln, Bardon Hill LE6 5BY ☎(0530)813644
FAX (0530) 815425
*A recently-built hotel (opened in the latter part of 1989) stands 2.5 miles east of the town, 9.5 miles west of Leicester and conveniently close to junction 22 of the M1. Public areas include a large, split-level lounge bar, an attractive restaurant with a conservatory for family groups and a self-contained function room which holds up to two hundred people. All the well-equipped bedrooms are contained in cottage-style annexes standing between 70 and 200 yards from the main building.*
35⇔♠↙in 4 bedrooms CTV in all bedrooms ® T
✖ (ex guide dogs) ✻ sB&B⇔♠fr£42 dB&B⇔♠fr£49.50 ⊟
150P ✤ CFA
♀ French V ♥ ♫ ✔ ✻ Lunch fr£7.95&alc Dinner fr£7.95&alc
Last dinner 10pm
Credit Cards ① ② ③ ⑤
**See advertisement under LEICESTER**

COCKERMOUTH Cumbria Map **11** NY13

★★★63% **Grecian Villas**
Crown St CA13 0EH ☎(0900)827575 FAX (0900) 827772
RS 25 Dec
*This attractive sandstone building, with Greek-style frontage, is situated in the centre of the town. The hotel is well furnished in all areas, and offers good comforts, service and food.*
13⇔♠(1fb)1⊞ CTV in all bedrooms ® T ✻ sB&B⇔♠£49
dB&B⇔♠£65 ⊟
⟨ 25P *xmas*
♀ International V ♥ ♫ ✻ Lunch fr£6.50 High tea fr£5 Dinner
fr£14.95&alc Last dinner 9.30pm
Credit Cards ① ② ③ ⑤ ⓔ

★★★63% **The Trout**
Crown St CA13 0EJ ☎(0900)823591 FAX (0900) 827514
*An attractive and friendly hotel surrounded by well tended gardens which stands on the banks of the River Derwent near Wordsworth's Birds Place. Fully equipped bedrooms have been enhanced by recent upgrading, there are cosy lounges in which to relax, and a well appointed dining room offers both table d'hôte and à la carte menus.*
23⇔♠(1fb) CTV in all bedrooms ® T ✻ sB&B⇔♠£55-£65
dB&B⇔♠£71-£77 ⊟
⟨ 80P 🚗 ✤ CFA ♪ *xmas*
♀ English, French & Italian V ♥ ✻ Lunch £8.50-£9.50 Dinner
£16-£18&alc Last dinner 9.30pm
Credit Cards ① ③

C

★★★61% **Broughton Craggs**
Great Broughton CA13 0XP ☎(0900)824400 FAX (0900) 825350
*A small country hotel and restaurant that is favoured by business clientele. It sits in its own gardens beside a vicarage 2 miles west of Cockermouth. To reach it you should turn off the A66 at the signpost for Great Broughton, cross a bridge and then bear right uphill towards Keith.*
14⇨↑(1fb)1⌷ CTV in all bedrooms ® T ✈ (ex guide dogs) ✻ sB&B⇨↑fr£41 dB&B⇨↑£51-£56 🅡
60P 🚗 ❀ ♪ *xmas*
♀ English & Continental V ↻ ⚏ ✻ Lunch £7.95-£15.50 Dinner fr£15.50&alc Last dinner 9.30pm
Credit Cards ①②③⑤

★★56% *Globe*
Main St CA13 9LE (Consort) ☎(0900)822126 Telex no 57515
FAX (0900) 823705
*Originally a coaching inn, this hotel is popular with the coach tour and commercial trade. Its practical bedrooms vary in size.*
30rm(20⇨↑)(3fb) CTV in all bedrooms ® T
CTV 12🚗
V ↻ ⚏ ✗ Last dinner 9.30pm
Credit Cards ①②③⑤

---

**COGGESHALL** Essex Map **05** TL82

★★★63% **White Hart**
Market End CO6 1NH ☎(0376)561654 FAX (0376) 561789
*An old hostelry of great character with magnificent roof timbers and a beamed bar lounge with copper tables and log fires in winter. The hotel has been tastefully restored and incorporates many original features. Bar snacks and room service supplement the well-appointed restaurant, which also has a dance floor. The young staff are friendly.*
18⇨↑(1fb) CTV in all bedrooms ® T ✈ (ex guide dogs) ✻ sB&B⇨↑£57.50-£76 dB&B⇨↑£76-£92 🅡
30P 3🚗 🚗 ❀ CFA
♀ French & Italian V ↻ ⚏ ✻ Lunch £12.50-£27.50alc Dinner £14.95&alc Last dinner 10pm
Credit Cards ①②③⑤ⓕ

---

**COLBOST**

See Skye, Isle of

---

**COLCHESTER** Essex Map **05** TL92

★★★62% **Red Lion**
High St CO1 1DJ (Best Western) ☎(0206)577986
FAX (0206) 578207
*This former inn, dating from the early 16th-century and hidden down an alley in the bustling centre of the town, retains many period features in a first floor bar, dining room and reception area which are reached by way of a wonderful Tudor stairwell and courtyard. Bedrooms vary in style, some having exposed beams and oak furniture while others (on the floor above), though more compact, are attractively furnished in pine. Light sleepers are advised to check their room requirements, and motorists should be aware that the nearest parking facilities are some distance away.*
24⇨↑1⌷ CTV in all bedrooms ® T S10% sB&B⇨↑£66-£80 dB&B⇨↑£72-£88 🅡
《 🚗 CFA
♀ English & French V ↻ ⚏ ✻ Lunch £6.10-£10.95&alc Dinner £12.80&alc Last dinner 9.30pm
Credit Cards ①②③⑤

★★★60% **George**
116 High St CO1 1TD (Queens Moat) ☎(0206)578494
FAX (0206) 761732
*The public areas of this historic former coaching inn in the town centre offer a choice of bars as well as a carvery restaurant and welcoming foyer lounge; bedrooms are modernised, but guests*

---

*should check at what floor level theirs is situated if stairs could be a problem.*
47⇨↑(3fb) CTV in all bedrooms ® T ✻ S% sB&B⇨↑fr£70 dB&B⇨↑fr£85 🅡
《 50P CFA sauna solarium gymnasium
V ↻ ⚏ ✗ ✻ S% Lunch fr£11.50 Dinner fr£11.50 Last dinner 10pm
Credit Cards ①②③⑤

★★65% **Kings Ford Park**
Layer Rd, Layer De La Haye CO2 0HS (2.5m S B1026)
☎(0206)34301 due to change to 734301 Telex no 987562
FAX (0206) 34512 due to change to 734512
*This comfortable regency mansion set in its own grounds has stylish, well equipped bedrooms, with a spacious hall, cosy bar and an extended garden room restaurant.*
13⇨↑(2fb)1⌷ CTV in all bedrooms ® T sB&B⇨↑fr£63 dB&B⇨↑fr£79 🅡
CTV 100P 3🚗 ❀ CFA pitch & putt 🐎 *xmas*
♀ International V ↻ ⚏ ✻ Lunch £8.50-£25alc Dinner £15-£25alc Last dinner 9.30pm
Credit Cards ①②③⑤ⓕ

○**Butterfly**
Old Ipswich Rd(A12/A120 Crown Interchange)
☎Central Res (0284) 705800
Due to open May 1992
50⇨↑

🌸✗**Martha's Vineyard**
18 High St, Nayland CO6 4JF ☎(0206)262888
*A bright, simple cottage restaurant in the high street of this attractive Suffolk village provides a warm, unassuming welcome and a short but regularly changed menu of dishes in modern style with Continental and Californian influences. Such specialities as pan-fried rabbit on mâche salad, cioppino California fish stew and Austrian plum torte are accompanied by a concise but well chosen wine list which, like the menu, is extremely fairly priced.*
Closed Sun, Mon, 2 wks Etr, 2 wks summer & 2wks Xmas
Lunch not served
♀ International V 41 seats ✻ Dinner £15.50-£17.50alc Last dinner 9pm ♪
Credit Cards ①③

---

**COLEFORD** Gloucestershire Map **03** SO51

★★69% *Lambsquay House*
GL16 8QB ☎Dean(0594)33127
RS Jan
*A small, attractive Georgian house set in peaceful surroundings on the outskirts of the town provides well equipped en suite bedrooms with a good range of facilities, home cooking of good quality and friendly, attentive service.*
9⇨↑(1fb) CTV in all bedrooms ® T
30P 🚗 ❀
♀ English & Continental ↻ ⚏ Last dinner 8.30pm
Credit Cards ①③⑤

★★63% **The Speech House**
Forest of Dean GL16 7EL (Forte Hotels) ☎Dean(0594)822607
FAX (0594) 823658
*In the heart of the Forest of Dean, well outside the town, this 17th-century house is signposted from all directions. Its historic Verderers Court Room – now a dining room – is still occasionally used for passing judgement on affairs unique to the forest. Some bedrooms contain massive four-poster beds and friendly caring staff have earned the hotel a reputation for good service.*
14⇨↑4⌷✗ in 3 bedrooms CTV in all bedrooms ® T ✻ sB⇨↑fr£60 dB⇨↑fr£75 (room only) 🅡
40P ❀ CFA *xmas*

English & French V Lunch £8.50 Dinner £13-£18.50 Last dinner 9pm
Credit Cards 1 2 3 4 5

**COLERNE** Wiltshire Map **03** ST87

★★★★

★★★★

**LUCKNAM PARK**

SN14 8AZ (Small Luxury Hotels) ☎(0225)742777
FAX (0225) 743536

*An elegant and stately Georgian country house a few miles from Bath, converted to hotel use in 1988 and sympathetically developed and extended since that time, stands in an attractive country estate which it shares with a racing stud. Spacious bedrooms with modern fabrics and antique furnishings have been discreetly provided with modern amenities, and there are many thoughtful touches such as fresh fruit, local spring water and home-made biscuits. Both private individuals and corporate business groups will appreciate the leisure spa and a range of opulent public areas which are tastefully appointed, decked with magnificient floral arrangements and crammed with period furnishings and carefully chosen antiques. Both the library lounge and comfortable drawing room overlook manicured grounds, and guests eating in the splendid dining room with its frescoed ceiling may be entertained by a harpist during the evening. Constantly evolving set-price menus on which one or two items attract supplements are kept to sensible proportions both at lunch and dinner; the fine, modern English cuisine which is impeccably served in professional style by a well groomed, mainly French staff includes such enjoyable dishes as Rosette of Lobster (a crisp herb crêpe packed with lobster and served on a very fine, intense lobster jus), perhaps followed by superbly flavoured, locally reared Wiltshire lamb with a competent Madeira sauce. Fish is equally prominent, with dishes such as Armadillo of Brill and crisp potato on a a red wine sauce. A fair selection of desserts includes some hot ones – a chocolate pudding with a rather clever licorice sauce being particularly worthy of note.*

24 Annexe18 9 CTV in all bedrooms T (ex guide dogs) sB&B fr£100 dB&B £140-£310 Continental breakfast

90P CFA (heated) (hard) snooker sauna solarium gymnasium whirlpool croquet beauty hair salon *xmas*

V Lunch fr£21alc Dinner fr£37.50alc Last dinner 10pm
Credit Cards 1 2 3 5 £

**COLESHILL** Warwickshire Map **04** SP28

★★★60% **Grimstock Country House**
Gilson Rd, Gilson B46 1AJ (off A446 W of Coleshill)
☎(0675)462369 & 462121 FAX (0675) 467646

*This attractive chalet-style hotel standing half a mile northwest of the town centre, in the village of Gilson, has been modernised to provide well equipped bedrooms and a good range of conference and function facilities.*

44 (1fb) CTV in all bedrooms ® T sB&B £60-£65 dB&B £70-£80

80P CFA

English & French V Lunch £12.90-£14 Dinner £12.90-£14 Last dinner 9.15pm
Credit Cards 1 2 3 5

★★63% **Coleshill**
152 High St B46 3BG (Lansbury) ☎(0675)465527
Telex no 333868 FAX (0675) 464013

*This modernised business hotel, set on the town's main street a mile and a half from the M6/M42 junction, offers a good self-contained conference/function complex and popular restaurant with a choice of bars. All the well equipped bedrooms have en suite facilities, the newer accommodation across in Fernley House being particularly spacious and comfortable.*

15 Annexe8 2 in 8 bedrooms CTV in all bedrooms ® T (ex guide dogs) sB&B £26.50-£67.50 dB&B £53-£81.50

48P

English & French V Lunch £8.50-£9.25&alc Dinner £15&alc Last dinner 10pm
Credit Cards 1 2 3 5 £

★★63% **Swan**
High St B46 3BL (Porterhouse) ☎(0675)462212
FAX (0675) 467493

*Fully modernised hotel popular with business people.*

32 CTV in all bedrooms ® T sB&B £48 dB&B £58

CTV 80P 8 CFA

V Lunch £8.20-£10alc Dinner fr£10alc Last dinner 10pm
Credit Cards 1 2 3 5

**COLN ST ALDWYNS** Gloucestershire Map **04** SP10

★★65% **New Inn 16th Century Country House**
Main St GL7 5AN ☎Cirencester(0285)750651
FAX (0285) 750657

*This historic inn, situated at the heart of the pretty Cotswold village, has been totally refurbished to meet modern standards whilst retaining much of its original charm. Public areas with*

→

C

*beams, scrubbed floors and open log fires create a warm and intimate atmosphere, while the main house bedrooms are comfortably furnished with quality and taste. Four rooms in the former coach house are equally well equipped though more simply furnished.*

8⇌♠Annexe4⇌♠(1fb)1⊞ CTV in all bedrooms ® T ✱ sB&B⇌♠£30-£50 dB&B⇌♠£50-£90 ⊟

30P ⍩ *xmas*

♀ English & French V ♦ ⚏ ⛌ ✱ Lunch £9-£12.50 Dinner £9-£12&alc Last dinner 9.30pm

Credit Cards ①②③

---

**COLONSAY, ISLE OF** Strathclyde *Argyllshire* Map **10**

---

**SCALASAIG** Map **10** NR39

★❀73% **Colonsay**

PA61 7YP ☎Colonsay(09512)316 FAX (09512) 353

Closed 6 Nov-27 Dec & 12 Jan-Feb

*This unique island hotel, around which most social activities are centred, is not for the casual visitor. Sometimes complex ferry timetables require careful forward planning and a minimum 2 nights stay, but the 2.5 hour crossing from Oban is well worthwhile for this is a haven of peace and tranquillity. The island, with its abundant wildlife and splendid beaches, is spoilt only one day a week, in summer, by day trippers. The hotel is friendly and comfortable with a lively bar and some lovely sea views over the pier. Kevin and Christa Byrne have been here 13 years, Kevin is a fountain of local knowledge and Christa provides the well balanced, no choice dinners. Don't come expecting slick service or hi-tech bedrooms, guests here simply enjoy themselves to exhaustion and achieve exceptional value for money.*

10rm(1⇌7♠)Annexe1rm(1fb) TV in 6 bedrooms ® sB&B£48-£60 dB&B⇌♠£96-£120 (incl dinner) ⊟

32P ⍩ ✿ bicycles sailing equipment

♀ European ♦ ⚏ ⛌ Bar Lunch £1-£5alc High tea £9 Dinner £17 Last dinner 7.30pm

Credit Cards ①②③⑤ ⓔ

---

**COLSTERWORTH** Lincolnshire Map **08** SK92

⌂ **Forte Travelodge**

NG33 5JJ (at roundabout of junc A1/A151) (Forte) ☎(0476)861181 Central Res (0800) 850950

*On the roundabout intersection of the A1 southbound, A151 and A607 with access off the A151. The adjacent Happy Eater is open 7am-10pm, and there is a children's play area.*

32⇌♠(32fb) CTV in all bedrooms ® sB⇌♠£29.95 dB⇌♠£29.95 (room only)

⓿ 32P ⍩

Credit Cards ①②③

⌂ **Granada Lodge**

A1 NG33 5JR (Granada) ☎Grantham(0476)860686 FAX (0476) 861078

*Conveniently situated on the A1 southbound at the roundabout junction with the A151 Bourne road and the B676 Melton Mowbray road, the Granada Lodge offers comfortable, well equipped and value-for-money accommodation. The Country Kitchen, which is open 24 hours a day, serves a range of hot and cold food and beverages. A high standard of cleanliness is maintained throughout.*

38⇌♠(9fb)⛌in 4 bedrooms CTV in all bedrooms ® ✗ (ex guide dogs) S% sB⇌♠fr£29.50 dB⇌♠fr£32 (room only) ⊟

⓿ 110P

Credit Cards ①②③⑤

**See advertisement under GRANTHAM**

---

**COLVEND** Dumfries & Galloway *Kirkcudbrightshire* Map **11** NX85

★★63% **Clonyard House**

DG5 4QW ☎Rockcliffe(055663)372 FAX (055663) 422

*Peacefully situated in seven acres of woodland this pleasant, family-run small hotel is an ideal base from which to explore the Solway coast, with several spacious modern ground floor bedrooms and a comfortable bar, popular for light meals both at lunchtime and during the evening.*

15⇌♠(2fb) CTV in all bedrooms ® T sB&B⇌♠£33-£35 dB&B⇌♠£55 ⊟

CTV 40P ⍩ ✿ ⚤

♀ British & French V ♦ ✱ Sunday Lunch £5-£10alc Dinner £10.50-£16alc Last dinner 9pm

Credit Cards ①③

---

**COLWYN BAY** Clwyd Map **06** SH87

★★★65% **Norfolk House**

Princes Dr LL29 8PF ☎(0492)531757 Telex no 61155

*This friendly privately owned hotel provides well equipped, comfortable accommodation and is equally popular with both holidaymakers and business people. It is conveniently situated for the town centre and the beach.*

25⇌♠(3fb) CTV in all bedrooms ® ✱ sB&B⇌♠£29.50-£42 dB&B⇌♠£58-£61 ⊟

Lift ⓿ 30P ✿ CFA

♀ English & French V ♦ ⚏ ⛌ Bar Lunch £1.75-£6alc Dinner fr£12.50 Last dinner 9pm

Credit Cards ①②③⑤ ⓔ

★★★57% **Hotel 70 Degrees**

Penmaenhead LL29 9LD (2m E A547) (Best Western) ☎(0492)516555 Telex no 61362 FAX (0492) 515565

*Purpose-built at 70-degree angles on a superb clifftop site east of the town, this large privately owned hotel enjoys panoramic sea views and has well equipped bedrooms which are particularly popular with business people. An extensive refurbishment programme to enhance quality and facilities should be completed by 1992.*

43⇌♠(7fb)1⊞ CTV in all bedrooms ® T

⓿ 200P ♫

♀ English & French V ♦ ⚏ Last dinner 9.30pm

Credit Cards ①②③④⑤

★★69% **Hopeside**

Princes Dr, West End LL29 8PW ☎(0492)533244

*Privately owned, personally run and very carefully maintained, this hotel provides well equipped accommodation which is equally suitable for holidaymakers and business people. Town centre, railway station and the seafront are all within easy reach, and it is also conveniently close to the A55 expressway.*

19⇌♠✗in 1 bedroom CTV in all bedrooms ® T ✱ sB&B⇌♠£27.50-£36 dB&B⇌♠£40-£70 ⊟

CTV 25P CFA solarium nc11yrs

♀ English & French V ♦ ⚏ ✱ Lunch £3-£20alc Dinner £13.95 Last dinner 9pm

Credit Cards ①②③⑤

★★65% **Ashmount**

18 College Av, Rhos-on-Sea LL28 4NT (Minotels) ☎(0492)545479 & 544582

*Privately owned and personally run, this hotel offers accommodation in modern, well equipped en suite rooms which include some designed for disabled guests. Set in a quiet road in Rhos-on-Sea, close to the seafront, it is equally suitable for holidaymakers or business users.*

18⇌♠(4fb) CTV in all bedrooms ® T sB&B⇌♠£31.43-£34.30 dB&B⇌♠£52.12-£58 ⊟

10P CFA *xmas*

♀ English & French **V** ♥ ♨ ✂ Lunch £5-£17.50&alc Dinner £9.50-£10.75&alc Last dinner 8pm
Credit Cards ⒈ ⒉ ⒊ ⒌ ⒠

★★64% **Edelweiss**
Lawson Rd LL29 8HD (Consort) ☎(0492)532314
FAX (0492) 534707
*Close to the town centre and seafront, this large Victorian house with an extensive garden and its own car park, offers warm hospitality and well equipped accommodation popular with both commercial guests and holidaymakers.*
25⇨🌥(3fb) CTV in all bedrooms ® **T** sB&B⇨🌥fr£30 dB&B⇨🌥fr£47 🏳
25P ♣ CFA sauna solarium children's play area games room *xmas*
♀ Welsh, English, French & Italian **V** ♥ ♨ ✂ Bar Lunch fr£3.25 Dinner fr£11.50&alc Last dinner 8.30pm
Credit Cards ⒈ ⒉ ⒊ ⒌ ⒠

★67% *West Point*
102 Conway Rd LL29 7LE ☎(0492)530331
Closed last 2 wks Dec & 1st 2 wks Jan
*This small privately owned hotel a short walk from the town centre and seafront, offers friendly service and well-equipped comfortable bedrooms, half of them with en suite facilities.*
10rm(2⇨3🌥)(3fb) CTV in all bedrooms ®
CTV 8P
♀ English & French **V** ♥ ✂ Last dinner 7pm
Credit Cards ⒈ ⒊

★65% **Whitehall**
Cayley Promenade, Rhos on Sea LL28 4EP ☎(0492)547296
Closed Nov-Etr
*A small, privately owned and personally run hotel, providing simple but quite well equipped accommodation equally suitable for either holidaymaker or business user, overlooks the sea from its setting on*

*the Promenade at Rhos-on-Sea. Car parking is available at the rear.*
13rm(1⇨6🌥)(2fb) CTV in all bedrooms ® ✳ sB&B£15.50-£16.50 sB&B⇨🌥£17.50-£19.50 dB&B£31-£33 dB&B⇨🌥£35-£37 🏳
CTV 5P ⊞
**V** ♥ ✂
Credit Cards ⒈ ⒊

★64% **Marine**
West Promenade LL28 4BP ☎(0492)530295
Closed Nov-Mar
*This well maintained, family-run hotel stands on the Promenade, offering good sea views from several rooms, and has the advantage of its own car park. The town centre and leisure centre are both within easy reach.*
14rm(11🌥)(4fb) CTV in 11 bedrooms TV in 3 bedrooms ® ✳ sB&B£16-£17 sB&B🌥£18.50-£19.50 dB&B£28-£30 dB&B🌥£33-£35 🏳
CTV 11P ⊞
**V** ♥ ♨ ✂ ✳ Bar Lunch £2-£5 Dinner fr£7 Last dinner 7.30pm
Credit Cards ⒉ ⒌ ⒠

COLYTON Devon Map **03** SY29

★★65% **White Cottage**
Dolphin St EX13 6NA ☎(0297)52401
Closed 23-28 Dec
*A cosy, Grade II listed thatched cottage on the edge of this historic little village. The hotel has recently changed ownership, but continues to provide a warm, hospitable atmosphere. The architecture obviously imposes some constraints and some rooms are small, but all are nicely decorated and well equipped with modern facilities. Many original features such as exposed beams and stonework have been retained in both bedrooms and public rooms. Honest, fresh cooking is served in the pretty little*

→

*restaurant. Car parking on site makes this a good touring base for South Devon and Dorset.*

6⇄🛏(1fb)1🛏 CTV in all bedrooms ® T ✈ (ex guide dogs) sB&B⇄🛏£29.90-£34.90 dB&B⇄🛏£49.80-£55.80 🛏

16P 🚗 ❄ nc7yrs

V 🕏 ⚏ ✾ Bar Lunch £2-£8

Credit Cards ① ③

---

### COMBE MARTIN Devon Map 02 SS54

#### ★★ 59% Rone House

King St EX34 0AD ☎(0271)883428

Closed Nov-Feb (ex 23-27 Dec)

*Small, family-run hotel in the centre of Combe Martin, providing comfortable accommodation, simple menus and a friendly atmosphere.*

11rm(4⇄4🛏)(4fb) CTV in all bedrooms ® sB&B£16.80-£19 sB&B⇄🛏£22-£25.60 dB&B£33.60-£38 dB&B⇄🛏£35.80-£40 🛏

CTV 15P 🚗 ❄ ⌣ (heated) *xmas*

Bar Lunch £4.95-£9&alc Dinner £11&alc Last dinner 9.30pm

Credit Cards ① ③

---

### COMRIE Tayside *Perthshire* Map 11 NN72

#### ★★ 64% Royal

Melville Square PH6 2DN ☎(0764)70200 Telex no 76277

RS Oct-Mar

*Tucked in a small square off the main street, this small family-run hotel with historic connections caters to both holidaymakers and business travellers, offering traditional services and comfort, with well equipped bedrooms.*

9rm(8⇄🛏)1🛏 CTV in all bedrooms ® T ✳ sB&B⇄£29.50-£31 dB&B⇄£47-£52

30P 2🚗 ♪ snooker 🕏 *xmas*

♉ Scottish & French V 🕏 ✳ Lunch £3.75-£12alc Dinner £16&alc Last dinner 9.30pm

Credit Cards ① ② ③ ⑤

#### ★★ 62% *Comrie*

Drummond St PH6 2DY ☎(0764)70239

RS Nov-Etr

*Situated at the east end of the village, the Comrie is a hospitable establishment providing good value for money. Pleasantly furnished and comfortable, several improvements have recently been carried out here.*

9⇄🛏Annexe2⇄ CTV in all bedrooms ® T

24P 🚗 nc5yrs

V 🕏 ⚏

Credit Cards ① ③

---

### CONGLETON Cheshire Map 07 SJ86

#### ★★★ 65% Lion & Swan

Swan Bank CW12 1JR ☎(0260)273115 FAX (0260) 299270

*A town centre inn dating from Tudor times, which has been thoughtfully and tastefully restored. Chef Vincent Valentine provides an interesting menu in the sophisticated restaurant.*

21⇄🛏(2fb)1🛏✾in 3 bedrooms CTV in all bedrooms ® T sB&B⇄🛏£45-£65 dB&B⇄🛏£55-£90 🛏

CTV 80P 6🚗 ❄ CFA *xmas*

♉ English & Continental V 🕏 ⚏ ✾ ✳ Lunch £7.50-£9.50&alc Dinner £13.95-£16.95&alc Last dinner 9.30pm

Credit Cards ① ② ③ ⑤ ⑥

---

### CONISTON Cumbria Map 07 SD39

#### ★★ 65% Coniston Sun

LA21 8HQ ☎(05394)41248

*Enjoyable Cordon Bleu meals are a feature of this spaciously comfortable family-run hotel which stands high above the village amid fine Lakeland scenery.*

11rm(7⇄3🛏)2🛏 CTV in all bedrooms ® T sB&B⇄🛏£27-£35 dB&B⇄🛏£54-£70 🛏

20P ❄

V 🕏 ⚏ ✾ ✳ Bar Lunch £5-£15alc Dinner £9-£18alc Last dinner 8.30pm

Credit Cards ① ③

#### ★★ 63% Yewdale

Yewdale Rd LA21 8LU ☎(05394)41280

*A small family-run hotel in the centre of Coniston. Most bedrooms have en suite facilities, all have colour TV and tea-making facilities. Part of the building was once a bank and the hotel bar is the former bank counter.*

12rm(2⇄8🛏)(4fb) CTV in all bedrooms ® S% dB&B⇄🛏£42-£60 🛏

6P

V 🕏 ⚏ ✾ Lunch £3.25-£7.95alc Dinner £10.95 Last dinner 8.30pm

Credit Cards ① ③ ⑥

#### ★⚭ 72% Old Rectory

Torver LA21 8AX ☎(05394)41353

Closed 2-3 wks Jan

*Standing in three acres of wooded grounds, this charming Victorian country house has been refurbished throughout to a very high standard. The atmosphere is warm and friendly and there are fine views over the surrounding meadowland and fells from most of the rooms. It is about 2.5 miles south of Coniston off the A593.*

7⇄🛏(1fb) CTV in all bedrooms ® ✈ (ex guide dogs) dB&B⇄🛏£60-£85 (incl dinner) 🛏

10P 🚗 ❄ *xmas*

♉ English & Continental ✾

#### ★ 66% Black Bull

Yewdale Rd LA21 8DU ☎(05394)41335 FAX (05394) 41168

*This attractive country inn at the centre of the village has now been enhanced by the extension of the bar and the provision of additional accommodation; all the well equipped rooms now have en suite facilities, though some are compact. Popular bars serve a wide range of meals in charming, characterful surroundings.*

10⇄🛏Annexe4🛏(3fb)1🛏✾in 1 bedroom CTV in all bedrooms ® T ✳ sB&B⇄🛏£28 dB&B⇄🛏£45-£50 🛏

CTV 12P 3🚗 ❄ CFA pony trekking sailing *xmas*

♉ English & French V 🕏 ⚏ ✳ Lunch fr£7 Dinner fr£10 Last dinner 9pm

Credit Cards ① ③

---

### CONNEL Strathclyde *Argyllshire* Map 10 NM93

#### ★★ 64% Falls of Lora

PA37 1PB (Inter-Hotels) ☎(063171)483 FAX (063171) 694

Closed 25 Dec & 1 Jan

*This spacious tourist hotel has lovely views of Loch Etive and a pleasant, relaxing atmosphere. Bedrooms in the main house are individual in style, those in the modern wing are more uniform, but all are well equipped. For meals there is a choice of the formal restaurant or the bistro bar.*

30⇄(4fb)1🛏 CTV in all bedrooms T sB&B⇄£27.50-£47.50 dB&B⇄£35-£95 🛏

CTV 40P 9🚗 🚗 ❄ CFA

♉ Scottish & French V 🕏 ⚏ ✾ Bar Lunch £4.75-£9.50alc High tea £5.50-£6.50alc Dinner fr£16.25 Last dinner 8pm

Credit Cards ① ② ③ ⑤ ⑥

CONSTANTINE BAY Cornwall & Isles of Scilly
Map **02** SW87

★★★ ⚜76% *Treglos*
PL28 8JH (Consort) ☎Padstow(0841)520727
FAX (0841) 521163
Closed 4 Nov-7 Mar
*A second generation has joined Ted and Barbara Barlow, who have run this country-house style hotel overlooking the rocky coastline for the last 25 years. Comfortable, spacious accommodation includes five lounges and a bridge room, with log fires and fresh flowers. The restaurant offers imaginative, well prepared dishes, caringly served.*
44⇄🏠(12fb) CTV in all bedrooms **T**
Lift ℂ 50P 8🏌 (90p) 🚕 ❋ 🏊 (heated) snooker croquet jacuzzi
🖵 English & French **V** 🖐 ⚲ ✕ Last dinner 9.30pm
Credit Cards 1

**See advertisement under PADSTOW**

CONWY Gwynedd Map **06** SH77

See also **Rowen**

★★★ 65% *Sychnant Pass*
Sychnant Pass Rd LL32 8BJ ☎Aberconwy(0492)596868 &
596869 Telex no 61155 FAX (0492) 70009
*This delightful house is situated at the foot of the Sychnant Pass amidst superb scenery. Tastefully extended and converted a few years ago it is now a pleasant, comfortable, personally run hotel with well equipped modern accommodation.*
13⇄🏠(2fb) CTV in all bedrooms ® **T**
CTV 30P ❋ sauna solarium jacuzzi spa bath
🖵 British & French 🖐 ⚲ Last dinner 9.30pm
Credit Cards 1 2 3 5

★★ ⚜72% *Castle Bank*
Mount Pleasant LL32 8NY ☎Aberconwy(0492)593888
Closed Jan RS Dec & Feb
*A large stone-built, detached Victorian house in an elevated position just outside the town walls. It is fronted by an attractive terraced garden and its own private car park. Owned and personally run by Sean and Marilyn Gilligan, it provides warm and friendly hospitality, good wholesome food and well equipped accommodation.*
9rm(8🏠)(3fb) CTV in all bedrooms ® ✈ sB&B🏠fr£25
dB&B🏠fr£50 🍴
CTV 12P 🚕
🖵 International **V** Sunday Lunch fr£8.25 Dinner fr£13 Last dinner 8pm
Credit Cards 1 3 £

★★ 63% *The Castle*
High St LL32 8DB (Forte Hotels) ☎Aberconwy(0492)592324
FAX (0492) 583351
*Parts of this former coaching inn date back to the 15th century. Situated in the centre of town it provides well equipped, traditional accommodation and has the distinct advantage of two car parks.*
29⇄🏠(1fb)1🛏✕in 2 bedrooms CTV in all bedrooms ® **T** ✱
sB⇄🏠fr£65 dB⇄🏠fr£75 (room only) 🍴
30P CFA *xmas*
**V** 🖐 ✕ ✱ Sunday Lunch fr£7.95 Dinner fr£12.50&alc Last dinner 8.45pm
Credit Cards 1 2 3 4 5

★★ 60% *The Park Hall*
Bangor Rd LL32 8DP ☎Aberconwy(0492)592279
*A privately owned and personally run hotel situated on the western outskirts of the town, commanding views of the Conwy Estuary and Great Orme from its enviable position. It offers simple but quite well equipped bedrooms which are particularly popular with commercial visitors.*
9⇄🏠(2fb) CTV in all bedrooms ® **T** ✱ sB&B⇄🏠£25-£30
dB&B⇄🏠£45-£50
→

40P ⌖ ♨ *xmas*

♀ English, French & Italian V ♥ ✳ Sunday Lunch fr£5.95
Dinner fr£12&alc Last dinner 9.30pm
Credit Cards ① ② ③ ⑤

---

## COODEN BEACH East Sussex Map **05** TQ70

★★★62% **Cooden Resort**
TN39 4TT (Resort) ☎Cooden(04243)2281 FAX (04243) 6142
*Magnificent views across Pevensey Bay, well equipped bedrooms*
*and leisure club and conference facilities make this hotel equally*
*suited to holidaymaker or business person. The recently*
*refurbished Ocean Restaurant offers a choice of menus, with*
*friendly service from the young staff.*
40⇔↑(6fb)✂in 3 bedrooms CTV in all bedrooms ® T ✳
sB&B⇔↑fr£63.50 dB&B⇔↑fr£81 ⊟
℄ 60P ✿ CFA ▭ (heated) ➾ (heated) sauna solarium jacuzzi
hair salon *xmas*
♀ English & French V ♥ ⬠ ✳ Lunch fr£12.25&alc Dinner
fr£17.25&alc Last dinner 9.30pm
Credit Cards ① ② ③ ⑤ ⓔ
**See advertisement under BEXHILL-ON-SEA**

---

## COOKHAM Berkshire Map **04** SU88

❀✕✕**Cookham Tandoori**
High St SL6 9SL ☎Bourne End(06285)22584
FAX (0628) 770520
*An untypical Indian restaurant in the High Street of this pretty*
*town offers delicious food in three intimate rooms with well*
*appointed tables and comfortable seating. The lengthy menu*
*presents an appetising variety of tender and tasty dishes (most*
*with helpful descriptions) based on good raw ingredients, the chef's*
*expertise with spicing imparting a unique character to each meal;*
*Chicken Chat (stirred chicken and potato) is flavoured with herbs,*
*while Lamb Hasina involves capsicum, onion and tomato, and*
*spinach is infused with garlic. Takeaways are also available.*
Closed 25-26 Dec
♀ Indian V 85 seats Lunch £11.95&alc Last lunch 2pm Last
dinner 10.30pm ⫤nc7yrs ✂
Credit Cards ① ② ③ ⑤

---

## COPTHORNE

See **Gatwick Airport**

---

## CORBRIDGE Northumberland Map **12** NY96

★★63% **The Lion of Corbridge**
Bridge End NE45 5AX ☎Hexham(0434)632504
FAX (0434) 632571
*A family-owned and run hotel located on the banks of the River*
*Tyne, close to the attractive bridge. The bedrooms are well*
*furnished and comfortable, meeting all the modern traveller's*
*needs. There are adequate lounges and a choice of dining styles is*
*available.*
14⇔↑⬚↑🛏 CTV in all bedrooms ® T ✂ (ex guide dogs) ✳
sB&B⇔↑£46 dB&B⇔↑£59.45 ⊟
30P ✿ CFA *xmas*
V ♥ ✂ ✳ Sunday Lunch £8.50&alc Dinner £12&alc Last
dinner 9.30pm
Credit Cards ① ② ③ ⑤ ⓔ

★★59% *Angel Inn*
Main St NE45 5LA ☎(0434)632119
*This small, creeper-clad hotel features an attractive split-level*
*restaurant, a wood-panelled foyer lounge where popular bar meals*
*are served, and modern bedroom accommodation.*
5⇔↑ CTV in all bedrooms ® T ✂
5P
♀ English, French & Italian V ♥ Last dinner 10pm
Credit Cards ① ② ③ ⑤

---

★66% *Riverside*
Main St NE45 5LE (Guestaccom) ☎(0434)632942
Closed Xmas & Jan
*A pleasant, friendly little hotel, family owned and run, it offers*
*good standards of accommodation in all areas and is well situated*
*overlooking the Tyne valley.*
11rm(3⇔4↑)(1fb) CTV in all bedrooms ®
10P ⌖
♀ English & French Last dinner 8pm

---

## CORBY Northamptonshire Map **04** SP88

See also **Cottingham**
★★★63% **Forte Posthouse**
Rockingham Rd NN17 1AE (Forte Hotels) ☎(0536)401348
Telex no 341752 FAX (0536) 66383
*On the outskirts of town close to picturesque Rockingham village,*
*this modern purpose-built hotel has spacious well equipped*
*bedrooms and extensive conference and banqueting facilities. The*
*restaurant has a carvery option as well as table d'hôte and à la*
*carte menus.*
70⇔↑2🛏✂in 34 bedrooms CTV in all bedrooms ® T ✳
sB⇔↑£39.50-£49.50 dB⇔↑£39.50-£49.50 (room only) ⊟
℄ 120P ✿ CFA *xmas*
♀ International V ♥ ⬠ ✂ ✳ Lunch fr£10.95&alc Dinner
fr£13.95&alc Last dinner 10.30pm
Credit Cards ① ② ③ ⑤

---

## CORFE CASTLE Dorset Map **03** SY98

★★★❀63% **Mortons House**
East St BH20 5EE ☎(0929)480988 FAX (0929) 480820
*A charming listed Elizabethan manor house in the midst of this*
*much visited, picturesque village. It has been extended in keeping*
*with the original building and provides delightful well equipped*
*bedrooms.*
14⇔↑Annexe3⇔↑(1fb)1🛏 CTV in all bedrooms ® T ✳
sB&B⇔↑£45-£55 dB&B⇔↑£70-£90 ⊟
40P ⌖ ✿ croquet *xmas*
V ♥ ⬠ ✂ ✳ Lunch fr£15 Dinner fr£19.50 Last dinner 9pm
Credit Cards ① ③

---

## CORNHILL-ON-TWEED Northumberland Map **12** NT83

★★★⚐62% **Tillmouth Park**
TD12 4UU ☎Coldstream(0890)2255
*This attractive country house near the Scottish border, built in*
*1882 with stones from nearby Twizel Castle, retains the*
*atmosphere of a bygone age in its attractive galleried lounge.*
*Bedrooms have good facilities, meals are enjoyable, and the hotel*
*has its own salmon fishing on the River Tweed.*
12⇔↑Annexe1⇔↑(1fb)1🛏 CTV in all bedrooms ® T ✳
sB&B⇔↑fr£58 dB&B⇔↑fr£86 ⊟
50P ✿ ✍
♀ International V ♥ ⬠ ✳ Lunch £3.50-£11alc Dinner
£16.50&alc Last dinner 9.30pm
Credit Cards ① ② ③ ⑤

---

## CORSE LAWN Hereford & Worcester Map **03** SO83

★★★❀❀70% **Corse Lawn House**
GL19 4LZ ☎Gloucester(0452)780479 & 780771
FAX (0452) 780840
*This elegant Queen Anne building, set back from the village green,*
*stands beside the B4211 6 miles southwest of Tewkesbury. Many*
*of its individually styled guest rooms are furnished with antiques,*
*but all include good modern facilities and such thoughtful extras as*
*home-made biscuits and fresh fruit. The restaurant remains the*
*focal point of the hotel, its reputation for providing interesting*
*menus of dishes based on the best possible ingredients being well*
*deserved, and meals served in the bar are also popular. Genial*

*hospitality and a relaxed, welcoming atmosphere attract both tourists and business travellers to this establishment.*
19⇌🛏️2🛁 CTV in all bedrooms ® T ✱ sB&B⇌🛏️fr£70 dB&B⇌🛏️fr£85 ⊟
50P 🅿️ ✿ CFA ⌂ (heated) ♫ (hard) croquet lawn *xmas*
🍴 English & French V ♥ ⚗️ ✱ Lunch £15.95-£17.95&alc Dinner fr£23.50&alc Last dinner 10pm
Credit Cards ①②③⑤

## CORSHAM Wiltshire Map **03** ST86

### ★★★★✦66% **Rudloe Park**
Leafy Ln SN13 0PA ☎️Bath(0225)810555 FAX (0225) 811412
*A Victorian country house in 4 acres of grounds with views down to Bath. Bedrooms are both spacious and comfortable. In the dining room, cuisine is classic in style and an award-winning wine list is available. The service is professional but never intrusive.*
11⇌🛏️(1fb)1🛏️ CTV in all bedrooms ® T sB&B⇌🛏️£55-£65 dB&B⇌🛏️£80-£100 ⊟
70P 🅿️ ✿ croquet nc10yrs *xmas*
🍴 International V ♥ ⚗️ ✂️ Lunch £14.50-£15.50&alc Dinner £17-£18&alc Last dinner 10pm
Credit Cards ①②③④⑤ⓔ

### ★★✦67% **Methuen Arms**
High St SN13 0HB (Exec Hotel) ☎️(0249)714867
FAX (0249) 712004
Closed 23-27 Dec RS Sun
*A cosy, character hotel, well sited in the town centre and only 8 miles from the city of Bath, has gradually been converted to combine the charm of ancient stonework, mullioned windows and heavy oak beams with the provision of present-day comforts and amenities – the 100-foot extent of the Long Bar, where comfortable, restaurant-style furnishings are set against rubblestone walls, being a good example of this. Bright, fully equipped, modern bedrooms with en suite facilities are decorated in pleasant pastel shades which are echoed in attractive duvet covers and fabrics. At mealtimes guests have a choice between the simple, modern-style classical dishes of the popular Winters Court Restaurant and the lighter meals and snacks served at the bar.*
19⇌🛏️Annexe6⇌🛏️(2fb) CTV in all bedrooms ® T ✖️ ✱ sB&B⇌🛏️£39-£45 dB&B⇌🛏️£56-£62 ⊟
60P 3🚗 (£12 per night) ✿ CFA skittle-alley ⚗️
🍴 English & French V ♥ ✱ Lunch £11.75-£16.25&alc Dinner £11.75-£16.25&alc Last dinner 9.30pm
Credit Cards ①③ⓔ

### ✽✖️✖️Copperfields
1 High St SN13 0ES ☎️(0249)713982
*The interior of this first-floor restaurant at the top of the High Street is more inspiring than its exterior would suggest, oak beams, an attractive décor and plenty of plants creating a pleasant setting in which to enjoy a meal. At the time of going to press we have learned of a change of hands at this restaurant – too late, unfortunately to report on new standards and menus.*
Lunch not served Sat
Dinner not served Sun
V 34 seats Lunch £10-£15alc Dinner £17.50-£24alc Last lunch 2pm Last dinner 9.30pm ♫ nc5yrs ✂️
Credit Cards ①③

## COSHAM Hampshire Map **04** SU60

### ✽✖️Barnards
109 High St PO6 3BB ☎️Portsmouth(0705)370226
*David and Sandie Barnard run this small, single fronted restaurant in Cosham High Street. The weekly changing luncheon menu, represents good value for money, and is supplemented by an à la carte menu in the evenings which changes every three weeks. On the inspection visit, the robust onion soup was commended, as was the salmon en croûte served with Hollandaise sauce and well*

*cooked vegetables. The wine list is short, with some wines available by the glass.*
Closed Sun, Mon, 2 wks Aug, BH's, Xmas & 1 Jan Lunch not served Sat
🍴 French 24 seats ✱ Lunch fr£12.95&alc Dinner fr£18.50&alc Last lunch 2pm Last dinner 9.30pm ♫
Credit Cards ①②③

## COTTINGHAM Northamptonshire Map **04** SP89

### ★★63% *Hunting Lodge*
High St LE16 8XN ☎️Rockingham(0536)771370
RS 25-26 Dec & 1 Jan
*New owners have made some effort to upgrade the hotel's bar and 2 restaurants, housed in a 16th-century building, and the introduction of Indian cuisine to supplement the traditional menu has proved very popular. Accommodation is in two annexes, that in the older, modular block – now showing its age – being modest in comparison with the good modern bedrooms of the purpose-built addition.*
Annexe23⇌🛏️ CTV in all bedrooms ®
CTV 120P ✿
🍴 English & French V ♥ ⚗️ Last dinner 10.30pm
Credit Cards ①③⑤

## COVENTRY West Midlands Map **04** SP37 ⊘

### ★★★★57% **De Vere**
Cathedral Square CV1 5RP (De Vere) ☎️(0203)633733
Telex no 31380 FAX (0203) 225299
*This large, busy, city-centre hotel with its own car park caters for a wide variety of visitors, including delegates using the conference facilities and tourists, to whom its proximity to the famous cathedral will appeal. Extensive improvements have recently provided a quiet, pleasant lounge and an attractive new restaurant* →

C

*which, together with the buttery and bar are also popular venues for non-resident guests.*
190⇌🏠(9fb) in 20 bedrooms CTV in all bedrooms ® T S%
sB&B⇌🏠£95 dB&B⇌🏠£150 🅿
Lift ( 130👜 ♫ *xmas*
♀ International **V** ✧ ⚏ ⅍
Credit Cards ① ② ③ ④ ⑤ ⓔ

★★★❀68% **Brooklands Grange Hotel & Restaurant**
Holyhead Rd CV5 8HX ☎(0203)601601 FAX (0203) 601277
*On the A4114 with easy access to the city centre and NEC, this extended Jacobean farmhouse has been converted into a comfortable friendly hotel, with individually decorated and well equipped bedrooms. Attractive public areas retain some original features and include a popular restaurant.*
30⇌🏠(1fb)⅍in 4 bedrooms CTV in all bedrooms ® T
🛪 (ex guide dogs) sB&B⇌🏠£82.50-£88 dB&B⇌🏠£99-£105
( 52P ❀ *xmas*
**V** ✧ ⅍ ✳ Lunch £14.95&alc Dinner £20.95-£30.45alc Last dinner 9.30pm
Credit Cards ① ② ③ ⑤ ⓔ

★★★64% **Leofric Regal**
Broadgate CV1 1LZ ☎(0203)221371 Telex no 311193
FAX (0203) 551352
*A large city centre hotel which has undergone extensive refurbishment to provide modern accommodation with a good range of facilities. Public areas include Frederic's à la carte restaurant, the Brasserie and a hair salon. It is best to ask for advice on parking when booking.*
94⇌🏠(5fb) CTV in all bedrooms ® T 🛪 (ex guide dogs) ✳
sB⇌🏠fr£79.50 dB⇌🏠£94.50-£135 (room only) 🅿
Lift ( ♫ *xmas*
♀ International **V** ✧ ⚏ ✳ Lunch fr£7.50&alc High tea £1.50-£6.50alc Dinner £11-£29alc Last dinner 9.45pm
Credit Cards ① ② ③ ⑤

★★★63% **Forte Crest**
Hinckley Rd, Walsgrave CV2 2HP (Forte Hotels)
☎(0203)613261 Telex no 311292 FAX (0203) 621736
RS Xmas
*Close to junction 6 of the M6 and convenient for the city centre and NEC, this large modern hotel has well equipped bedrooms plus extensive conference facilities and a leisure club with a wide range of amenities.*
147⇌🏠(6fb)⅍in 96 bedrooms CTV in all bedrooms ® T ✳
S% sB⇌🏠£79.50 dB⇌🏠£90 (room only) 🅿
Lift ( 450P ❀ CFA 🖼 (heated) sauna solarium gymnasium pool tables ♫ *xmas*
♀ English & French **V** ✧ ⚏ ⅍ ✳ S% Lunch fr£9.50 High tea fr£4.50 Dinner £16.75&alc Last dinner 9.45pm
Credit Cards ① ② ③ ⑤

★★★61% **The Chace**
London Rd, Willenhall CV3 4EQ (Forte Hotels) ☎(0203)303398
Telex no 311993 FAX (0203) 301816
*Situated beside the A423, with convenient access to the city centre, this hotel provides compact functional accommodation in a modern extension block; public areas are more distinctive in character, being housed in the older part of the hotel.*
67⇌🏠(2fb)1🗗⅍in 20 bedrooms CTV in all bedrooms ® T ✳
sB⇌🏠fr£75 dB⇌🏠£85-£106 (room only) 🅿
( 80P ❀ CFA pool table *xmas*
**V** ✧ ⚏ ⅍ ✳ Lunch fr£9.50 Dinner fr£15.35 Last dinner 9.45pm
Credit Cards ① ② ③ ⑤

★★★61% **Hylands**
Warwick Rd CV3 6AU (Best Western) ☎(0203)501600
Telex no 312388 FAX (0203) 501027
Closed 24-26 Dec

*Set beside the A444, overlooking parkland from a position close to the city centre and railway station, an hotel much used by business travellers and popular as a conference venue offers rooms with a good range of modern facilities.*
55rm(54⇌🏠)(4fb) CTV in all bedrooms ® ✳ sB&B⇌🏠£70-£75
dB&B⇌🏠£85-£90 🅿
( CTV 60P pool table
♀ English & Continental **V** ✧ ⚏ ⅍ ✳ Lunch £10-£12 Dinner £13.50-£15 Last dinner 9.45pm
Credit Cards ① ② ③ ⑤

★★★58% *Novotel Coventry*
Wilsons Ln CV6 6HL ☎(0203)365000 Telex no 31545
*A busy hotel to the north of the city centre close to junction 3 of the M6 providing functional bedrooms and a restaurant which is open from 6am until midnight.*
100⇌🏠(100fb) CTV in all bedrooms ®
Lift ( ▦ 160P ❀ ⟷ (heated) squash sauna solarium gymnasium pool table petanque putting table tennis ⚅
♀ British & French **V** ✧ ⚏
Credit Cards ① ② ③ ④ ⑤

★★★56% **Forte Posthouse**
Rye Hill, Allesley CV5 9PH (Forte Hotels) ☎(0203)402151
Telex no 31427 FAX (0203) 402235
*A busy hotel which offers easy access to the M42 and city centre from its position on the A45 provides accommodation in well equipped bedrooms which are nevertheless rather dated and lack-lustre (though a refurbishment programme is in progress). Public areas include a carvery restaurant which also serves a concise à la carte menu.*
184⇌🏠(19fb)⅍in 86 bedrooms CTV in all bedrooms ® T ✳
sB⇌🏠£39.50-£49.50 dB⇌🏠£39.50-£49.50 (room only) 🅿
Lift ( 250P CFA *xmas*
**V** ✧ ⚏
Credit Cards ① ② ③ ④ ⑤

★★63% **Old Mill**
Mill Hill CV8 3AH (Chef & Brewer) ☎(0203)303588
FAX (0203) 307070
(For full entry see Baginton)

★★60% **Beechwood**
Sandpits Ln, Keresley CV6 2FR (3m NW on B4098)
☎(0203)338662 FAX (0203) 337080
*In semi-rural surroundings just 2 miles from the city centre this hotel was formerly a farmhouse. Rooms are well kept and have modern facilities, although simple in terms of décor and furnishings.*
24⇌🏠(1fb) CTV in all bedrooms ® T ✳ sB&B⇌🏠fr£42
dB&B⇌🏠fr£55
( 62P ❀
**V** ✧ ⚏ ✳ Lunch £9-£12alc Dinner £10-£15alc Last dinner 9.30pm
Credit Cards ① ③ ⑤

⬆Campanile
4 Wigston Road/Hinkley Rd, Walsgrave CV2 2SD (Campanile)
☎(0203)622311 Telex no 317454 FAX (0203) 602362
*Well equipped value for money accommodation in a modern annexe building is provided by this Campanile, its situation beside the A46 close to both the M6 and city centre making it a popular stop-over for business travellers.*
Annexe50⇌🏠 CTV in 47 bedrooms ® T sB⇌🏠fr£36
dB⇌🏠fr£36 (room only) 🅿
50P ❀ CFA *xmas*
♀ English & French Lunch £3.75-£8.90 Dinner £6.80-£8.90 Last dinner 10pm
Credit Cards ① ③ ⓔ

C

**C**

## COWES

See **Wight, Isle of**

---

## CRAIGELLACHIE Grampian *Banffshire* Map **15** NJ24

★★★74% **Craigellachie**

AB38 9SR ☎Aberlour(0340)881204 FAX (0340) 881253

*This fine Victorian hotel at the junction of the A95 and A941 has been sympathetically altered to meet modern needs. Charming bedrooms of varying size and style provide all modern comforts and facilities, while elegant public rooms include a relaxing drawing room, cosy cocktail bar and less formal bar, popular with fishermen and locals. Young friendly staff provide willing service.*
30⇨ℕ(4fb)1🎬 CTV in all bedrooms ® T sB&B⇨ℕ£50-£75 dB&B⇨ℕ£85-£110 🏠
《 70P 🚗 ✿ CFA ✔ snooker sauna solarium gymnasium *xmas*
V ✿ ⚖ ✔ Lunch £7.50-£15.50 High tea fr£7.50&alc Dinner £22.50-£35&alc Last dinner 9.30pm
Credit Cards ①②③④⑤ ⓔ

---

## CRAIGNURE

See **Mull, Isle of**

---

## CRAIL Fife Map **12** NO60

★62% **Croma**

Nethergate KY10 3TU ☎(0333)50239

Closed Nov-Mar

*Located in an attractive, quiet area, yet very close to amenities, this small, friendly hotel is managed by resident proprietors who create a comfortable, homely atmosphere.*
8rm(4⇨ℕ)(2fb) CTV in all bedrooms ✳ sB&B£12-£16 sB&B⇨ℕ£14.50-£18.50 dB&B£24-£32 dB&B⇨ℕ£29-£37
10P 🚗 ✿
V ✿ ⚖ ✳ Dinner £10-£11.50 Last dinner 10pm
ⓔ

---

## CRAMLINGTON Northumberland Map **12** NZ27

○**Forte Travelodge**

(junc A1/A189) (Forte) ☎Central Res (0800) 850950

Due to have opened Winter 1991
40⇨ℕ

---

## CRANBROOK Kent Map **05** TQ73

★★👜69% **Kennel Holt Country House**

Goudhurst Rd TN17 2PT ☎(0580)712032 FAX (0580) 712931

*Set in 6 acres of gardens with a duck pond and paddock, this family-run Elizabethan manor has individually furnished bedrooms with many little extras, a cosy lounge with inglenook fireplace and an attractive restaurant offering a 5-course fixed-price menu of good quality. Service is very efficient and friendly.*
9⇨ℕAnnexe1ℕ2🎬 CTV in all bedrooms ® T ✳ S%
sB⇨ℕfr£50 dB⇨ℕfr£70 (room only) 🏠
CTV 35P ✿ croquet 9 hole mini golf putting green nc6yrs *xmas*
🍴 English & French V ✿ ⚖ ✔ ✳ S% Lunch £11.50-£16.75 Dinner £22.75&alc Last dinner 9pm
Credit Cards ①②③⑤ ⓔ

---

## CRANLEIGH Surrey Map **04** TQ03

✿✿✿✕**Bonnet**

High St GU6 8AE ☎(0483)273889

*The interior of this high street restaurant, with its beams, alcoves and copperware, provides a dramatic contrast to the cooking of proprietor Jean-Pierre Bonnet, where technical sophistication brings a modern lightness of touch to traditional French dishes. Choices from the short menu might include a robust chicken liver terrine, fresh brill with a delicious saffron sauce, and a warm apple*

*charlotte – flavours being clear, saucing accomplished and presentation unfussy.*
Closed Mon Lunch not served Sat
Dinner not served Sun
🍴 French 50 seats Lunch £12-£16 Dinner £23-£29 Last lunch 2pm Last dinner 10pm 🅿 🎵
Credit Cards ①②③

---

## CRANTOCK Cornwall & Isles of Scilly Map **02** SW76

★★65% **Crantock Bay**

West Pentire TR8 5SE (Minotels) ☎(0637)830229

FAX (0637) 831111

Closed late Nov-mid Mar

*An enviable position overlooking the beach and rolling surf of Crantock Bay, friendly service and a convivial atmosphere are the attractions of an hotel in established family ownership which is popular both as a family holiday retreat and as a touring base from which to explore Cornwall and the southwest peninsula. Though the bright, well equipped bedrooms vary in size all have en suite facilities, and five new rooms on the ground floor feature patio doors opening onto the garden. Public rooms whose large picture windows command unrestricted views complement a good choice of spacious, comfortable lounges with a new bar and bright, airy restaurant, while recent additions to leisure amenities have provided an indoor swimming pool complex with two saunas, a jacuzzi and a games room; pleasant grounds and gardens to the forefront of the headland include a children's adventure playground, an all-weather tennis court and a croquet lawn.*
36⇨ℕ(4fb) CTV in all bedrooms ® T ✳ sB&B⇨ℕ£33.50-£43 dB&B⇨ℕ£67-£90 (incl dinner) 🏠
35P 🚗 ✿ CFA 🏊(heated) ♙ (hard) sauna gymnasium putting croquet 🎵 ॐ
✿ ⚖ ✔ ✳ Bar Lunch fr£2.50 Dinner £9.75-£11.75 Last dinner 8pm
Credit Cards ①②③⑤ ⓔ

---

## CRATHORNE North Yorkshire Map **08** NZ40

★★★★👜63% **Crathorne Hall**

TS15 0AR ☎Stokesley(0642)700398 FAX (0642) 700814

*This fine Edwardian country house in splendidly kept grounds and peaceful rural surroundings is in the process of complete refurbishment, with much thought and skill being given to retaining original features. There are some fine public rooms with lovely panelling, particularly over the fireplace in the drawing room, and there is an impressive stone fireplace featured in the restaurant. Most bedrooms have been tastefully refurbished, they are comfortable and offer good facilities.*
37⇨ℕ(4fb)1🎬✔in 5 bedrooms CTV in all bedrooms ® T sB&B⇨ℕ£80-£95 dB&B⇨ℕ£95-£130 🏠
《 100P ✿ CFA ✔ croquet *xmas*
🍴 English & French V ✿ ⚖ Lunch £5.50-£18alc Dinner £17.50-£25alc Last dinner 10pm
Credit Cards ①②③⑤ ⓔ

---

## CRAWLEY

See **Gatwick Airport**

---

## CREWE Cheshire Map **07** SJ75

★★★57% **Crewe Arms**

Nantwich Rd CW1 1DW (Jarvis) ☎(0270)213204

FAX (0270) 588615

*An hotel set beside the A534 only yards from one of the country's main railway stations features an elegant façade and public areas decorated to a Victorian theme. Some bedrooms have recently been refurbished to offer a good standard of accommodation.*
53⇨ℕ(3fb)✔in 7 bedrooms CTV in all bedrooms ® S%
sB⇨ℕ£64-£78 dB⇨ℕ£78-£90 (room only) 🏠
《 150P CFA games room *xmas*

♀ English & French **V** ✿ ⚑ ✔ S% Lunch fr£10&alc Dinner
fr£14&alc Last dinner 9.30pm
Credit Cards [1] [2] [3] [4] [5]

★★67% **White Lion**
Weston CW2 5NA (2m S A5020) ☎(0270)587011 & 500303
Closed Xmas & New Year
*An attractive inn in the centre of the village of Weston offers a*
*choice of bars in the original building, which dates back to Tudor*
*times. At the rear there is a modern bedroom extension with warm*
*well equipped rooms. Linking these is an elegant restaurant and*
*cocktail bar where reservations are required, particularly at*
*weekends.*
16⇄🎇(2fb)✔in 2 bedrooms CTV in all bedrooms ® **T** ✳
sB&B⇄🎇£45 dB&B⇄🎇£55-£65 🅿
( 100P ✿ crown green bowling
♀ English & French **V** ✿ ⚑ ✳ Lunch £9.75
Credit Cards [1] [2] [3] [4] [5]

⬆**Forte Travelodge**
Alasager Rd, Barthomley CW2 5PT (5m E, at junc 16 M6/A500)
(Forte) ☎(0270)883157 Central Res (0800) 850950
*A very busy Lodge, virtually adjacent to junction 16 of the M6,*
*signposted to Alsager. The complex includes a Little Chef*
*restaurant and a petrol station.*
42⇄🎇(42fb) CTV in all bedrooms ® sB⇄🎇£29.95
dB⇄🎇£29.95 (room only)
( 42P ⇔
Credit Cards [1] [2] [3]

CRIANLARICH Central Map **10** NN32

⬆**Benmore Lodge**
FK20 8QS ☎(08383)210
RS Nov-14 Mar
*Standing beside the A85 on the edge of the village and providing a*
*convenient stop-over point for the touring holidaymaker this*
*family-run complex offers compact but well equipped*
*accommodation in pine-clad lodges, each bedroom unit having en*
*suite facilities and a canopied verandah. The adjacent main*
*building – which incorporates a craft shop – contains a bar and*
*restaurant appointed in practical style, but there is no lounge.*
Annexe8🎇(2fb) CTV in all bedrooms ® ✳ dB&B🎇£42-£48 🅿
50P ✿ ✈ canoeing *xmas*
♀ International **V** ✿ ⚑ Lunch £6-£11.50alc Dinner £10-£14alc
Last dinner 8.45pm
Credit Cards [1] [3] £

CRICCIETH Gwynedd Map **06** SH43

★★★⚑66% **Bron Eifion Country House**
LL52 0SA (Inter-Hotels) ☎(0766)522385 FAX (0766) 522003
*This large stone-built country house dating to the 1870s stands in*
*spacious well tended grounds and gardens on the edge of town. The*
*interior abounds with magnificent pine panelling, also featuring in*
*the delightful minstrels' gallery. Well equipped bedrooms and*
*caring service from the enthusiastic owners make this relaxing*
*hotel equally popular with holidaymakers and business people.*
19⇄🎇(4fb)5⬚ CTV in all bedrooms ® **T** sB&B⇄🎇£42-£48
dB&B⇄🎇£60-£78 🅿
CTV 80P ✿ CFA clock golf table tennis *xmas*
♀ International **V** ✿ ⚑ ✳ Lunch £8.25-£9.50 Dinner
£15.50&alc Last dinner 9.30pm
Credit Cards [1] [3]

★★66% **Gwyndy**
Llanystumdwy LL52 0SP ☎(0766)522720
Closed Dec & Jan
*Situated in the village of Llanystumdwy (famous for its Lloyd*
*George connections), the main house dates back to the 17th*
*century and contains the dining room and public areas. Bedrooms*
*are spacious and well furnished.*

Annexe10⇄🎇(5fb) CTV in all bedrooms ® sB&B⇄🎇£28-£30
dB&B⇄🎇£45-£47
CTV 20P ⇔ ✈
♀ British & French ✿ ⚑

★★66% **Parciau Mawr**
High St LL52 0RP ☎(0766)522368
Closed Nov-Feb
*A pleasant, family-run hotel in its own grounds at the edge of the*
*village offers warm, well furnished bedrooms, a delightful lounge*
*overlooking the gardens and a good standard of home cooking.*
6⇄🎇Annexe6🎇(1fb) CTV in all bedrooms ® ✳ S%
sB&B⇄🎇£26-£28 dB&B⇄🎇£44-£48 🅿
30P ⇔ ✿ nc5yrs
♀ English & French ✿ ⚑ ✔ ✳ S% Dinner fr£9 Last dinner
8pm
Credit Cards [1] [3]

★★⚑65% **Mynydd Ednyfed Country House**
Caernarfon Rd LL52 0PH ☎(0766)523269
Closed 25-26 Dec
*Set in 7 acres of wood, pastureland and gardens, this charming*
*little manor house offers well furnished and attractively decorated*
*accommodation, with well equipped bedrooms and a choice of*
*home-cooked meals in the restaurant.*
8rm(4⇄🎇2🎇)(1fb)2⬚ CTV in all bedrooms ® **T**
30P ✿
♀ English & Continental **V** Last dinner 8.45pm
Credit Cards [1] [2] [3] [5]

★★62% **Plas Isa**
Porthmadog Rd LL52 0HP ☎(0766)522443
Closed 24-28 Dec
*This personally run hotel east of the town centre commands views*
*of both the sea and the castle, and provides well equipped*
*accommodation suited to tourists or business people.*

→

14⇨🏱(3fb) CTV in all bedrooms ® sB&B⇨🏱£28-£35
dB&B⇨🏱£46-£50 🅿
CTV 14P
♀ Chinese, French, Indian & Italian V ✿ ✳ Dinner £10-£12&alc Last dinner 8.45pm
Credit Cards ① ③ ⑤ ⑤

### ★★58% Lion
Y Maes LL52 0AA ☎(0766)522460
RS Nov-Mar
*The resident owner of this old coaching inn offers a warm welcome to guests, and a stay in its adequately furnished accommodation represents good value for money.*
36rm(27⇨🏱)(4fb) CTV in all bedrooms ® ✳ sB&B£19.40
sB&B⇨🏱£22 dB&B£37.80 dB&B⇨🏱£41.90 🅿
Lift 20P 12🚗 ✿ ♫ *xmas*
♀ Welsh & French V ✿ 🖵 ✳ Lunch £5.75-£8.25 Dinner £11.75-£15.25 Last dinner 8.15pm
Credit Cards ① ② ③ ⑤ ⑤

### ★★62% Plas Gwyn
Pentrefelin LL52 0PT (1m NE A497) ☎(0766)522559
FAX (0766) 523200
*On the A497 a mile east of the town, this privately owned hotel has well equipped bedrooms all with en suite facilities and is particularly popular with commercial visitors.*
14⇨🏱(6fb) CTV in all bedrooms ® T sB&B⇨🏱£21.50-£23.50 dB&B⇨🏱£40-£44 🅿
CTV 50P CFA
♀ English, French & Italian V ✿ 🖵 Lunch £7.50-£9.50 High tea £4-£6 Dinner £11-£15&alc Last dinner 9pm
Credit Cards ① ② ③ ⑤

### ★66% Abereistedd
West Pde LL52 0EN ☎(0766)522710
Closed Nov-Feb
*Situated on the seafront, with views across Cardigan Bay, this is a small, well maintained family-run hotel offering well equipped bedrooms suitable for holidaymakers and commercial visitors alike.*
12rm(8🏱)(2fb) CTV in all bedrooms ® sB&B£16.50-£18.50
sB&B🏱£18.50-£20.50 dB&B£33-£37 dB&B🏱£37-£41 🅿
12P
♀ English & French V ✿ 🖵 ✳ Lunch £5.50-£8.50 Dinner £8.50 Last dinner 7.30pm
Credit Cards ① ⑤

### ★62% Caerwylan
LL52 0HW ☎(0766)522547
Closed Nov-Etr
*A well furnished and comfortable family-run hotel overlooking the sea.*
25rm(17⇨5🏱) CTV in all bedrooms ® sB&B⇨🏱fr£17.50
dB&B⇨🏱fr£35 🅿
Lift CTV 8P 8🚗 (£1.10) ✿
✿ 🖵 Lunch fr£7 Dinner fr£8.50 Last dinner 7.30pm

CRICK Northamptonshire Map 04 SP57

### ★★★66% Forte Posthouse Northampton/Rugby
NN6 7XR (Forte Hotels) ☎(0788)822101 FAX (0788) 823955
*Well equipped accommodation of the type ideal for business travellers is available at this very well managed hotel at junction 8 of the M1. Eating options span the informal Coffee Shop and the Mantons Restaurant, where a friendly staff gives caring and helpful service, and a supervised leisure centre is provided for guests' use.*
88⇨🏱(38fb)✍in 41 bedrooms CTV in all bedrooms ® T ✳
sB⇨🏱£39.50-£49.50 (room only) 🅿
《 200P ✿ 🖾 (heated) sauna solarium gymnasium *xmas*

V ✿ 🖵 ✳ ✳ Lunch £10.90-£27.10alc High tea £3.95-£5alc
Dinner £10.90-£27.10alc Last dinner 10pm
Credit Cards ① ② ③ ⑤

CRICKHOWELL Powys Map 03 SO21

### ★★★70% Gliffaes Country House
NP8 1RH ☎Bwlch(0874)730371 FAX (0874) 730463
Closed Jan-mid Mar
*Set in 29 acres of fine grounds overlooking the River Usk, this delightful mid-Victorian country house is popular both with anglers and holidaymakers seeking relaxation. Personally run with friendly informality, it offers comfortable accommodation with modern facilities and sound home cooking.*
19rm(15⇨3🏱)Annexe3⇨🏱(3fb) CTV in 3 bedrooms ® T
S10%sB&B⇨🏱£30-£53 dB&B⇨🏱£60-£82 🅿
CTV 34P ✿ ♪ (hard) ✦ snooker painting croquet putting
♀ European V ✿ 🖵 ✳ S10% Lunch £9.90 Dinner £15.90&alc
Last dinner 9.15pm
Credit Cards ① ② ③ ⑤

### ★★67% Ty Croeso
Dardy, Llangattock NP8 1PU (Minotels) ☎(0873)810573
*This small, privately owned hotel, personally run by extremely friendly and hospitable proprietors who go out of their way to ensure that guests feel at home, is aptly named, since 'Ty Croeso' means 'Welcome House'. Considerably modernised, it provides accommodation in well equipped (though in some cases rather compact) bedrooms, and its elevated position in the tiny village offers excellent views across the Usk Valley towards the Black Mountains.*
8rm(5⇨3🏱)(1fb) CTV in all bedrooms ® T ✳ sB&B£15-£17
sB&B⇨🏱£35-£45 dB&B⇨🏱£40-£55 🅿
20P 🚗 ✿ *xmas*
V ✿ 🖵 ✳ Sunday Lunch £7.50-£8.50 Dinner £10.50-£14.50&alc Last dinner 9.30pm
Credit Cards ① ② ③ ⑤

### ★★☆66% Bear
NP8 1BW (Welsh Rarebits) ☎(0873)810408 FAX (0873) 811696
*This 15th century coaching inn is the focal point of the bustling market town. Most bedrooms have now been upgraded to excellent standards, public areas are spacious and comfortable and the food imaginative and enjoyable.*
14rm(7⇨6🏱)Annexe13⇨🏱(6fb)1🛏 CTV in all bedrooms ® T
✳ sB&B⇨🏱£33-£49 dB&B⇨🏱£44-£70
CTV 38P CFA
♀ English & French V ✿ Lunch £16-£25alc Dinner £16-£25alc
Last dinner 9.30pm
Credit Cards ① ② ③

### ☆ × Glan-y-Dwr
Brecon Rd NP8 1BT ☎(0873)810756
*In this attractive restaurant in a quiet but central location, Chef/ Patron Jean Pierre Vermeire combines fresh local produce with the artistry of his native Belgian cuisine. He offers special interest nights on certain Fridays with Caribbean, Parisienne, Chinese or Italian food. Telephone for details.*
Closed Mon & 2nd & 3rd wks Jan
Dinner not served Sun
♀ French V 30 seats Last lunch 1pm Last dinner 9pm 12 P
Credit Cards ① ③

CRIEFF Tayside Perthshire Map 11 NN82

### ★★68% Murray Park
Connaught Ter PH7 3DJ (Inter-Hotels) ☎(0764)3731
FAX (0764) 5311
*Constant improvement is taking place at this warmly welcoming family hotel set in its own garden in a quiet residential area just north of the town centre. Well equipped bedrooms are comfortably appointed, while the atmosphere of the tastefully furnished public areas is relaxed and friendly. Highly original menus and*

*imaginative cooking which makes excellent use of fresh raw
produce guarantee that a meal here is a pleasurable experience.*
13⇨(1fb) CTV in all bedrooms ® **T ✱** sB&B⇨£39.50-£43
dB&B⇨£56-£61
50P ⇔ ✿ shooting stalking
♀ Scottish & French **V** ♦ ✱ Lunch £10.50 Dinner £18.50&alc
Last dinner 9.30pm
Credit Cards ①②③⑤ⓔ

**★★**63% **Crieff**
47-49 East High St PH7 3JA ☎(0764)2632 FAX (0764) 5019
*Many areas have recently been upgraded, and the Crieff Hotel
now offers very pleasant accommodation. A good range of food is
available, either in the cosy restaurant or the attractive bar.*
8⇨♠(2fb) CTV in all bedrooms ® **T ✱** sB&B⇨♠£26.50-
£27.50 dB&B⇨♠£49.50 ⊟
CTV 9P sauna solarium gymnasium hair & beauty salon
**V** ♦ ⬛ ✱ Dinner £10-£15alc Last dinner 9pm
Credit Cards ①②③ⓔ

**★★**58% **The Drummond Arms**
James Square PH7 3HX ☎(0764)2151
*Commanding a central position in the town, this traditional resort
hotel, which has a popular coach tour trade, offers reasonably
priced accommodation and meals.*
29rm(22⇨♠)Annexe7rm(3⇨2♠)(3fb) CTV in all bedrooms
® **T ✱** sB&B£20 sB&B⇨♠£25 dB&B£40 dB&B⇨♠£50 ⊟
Lift 30P ♫ *xmas*
**V** ♦ ⅄ ✱ Bar Lunch £4.75-£8.05alc High tea £5.50-£8.50
Dinner £7.40-£11.50alc Last dinner 8.30pm
Credit Cards ①③

**★**66% **Lockes Acre**
7 Comrie Rd PH7 4BP ☎(0764)2526
*Set in its own grounds on the western edge of the town overlooking
the Ochil Hills, the Kennedys' small and welcoming holiday hotel
offers comfortable well equipped bedrooms, though some are
compact.*
7rm(4♠)(2fb) CTV in all bedrooms ® ✱ sB&B£17.50-£20
sB&B♠£20-£22.50 dB&B£35-£40 dB&B♠£40.40-£45
CTV 35P ⇔ ✿
♀ International **V** ♦ ⬛ ⅄ ✱ Lunch £5-£10alc High tea £5.45-
£8.65alc Dinner £6.90-£13.20alc Last dinner 8.30pm
Credit Cards ①③

**★**60% **Gwydyr House**
Comrie Rd PH7 4BP ☎(0764)3277
Closed Nov-Etr
*Situated at the west end of town in its own gardens, this small
family owned and run hotel offers good value and friendly service.*
10rm(4fb) CTV in all bedrooms ® sB&B£13.25-£16
dB&B£26.50-£32 ⊟
15P ✿
♀ British & Continental **V** ♦ Bar Lunch £5-£9.50alc Dinner
£9.25&alc Last dinner 8pm
ⓔ

CROCKETFORD Dumfries & Galloway *Kirkcudbrightshire*
Map **11** NX87

**★**60% *Lochview Motel*
Crocketford Rd DG2 8RF ☎(055669)281
Closed 26 Dec & 1 Jan
*This simple roadside motel offers compact, but clean and freshly
decorated bedrooms. Public areas are rather limited, but there is a
popular lounge bar/restaurant with stunning views of Loch
Auchenreoch. Food can be obtained throughout the day and the
atmosphere is relaxed and friendly.*
7♠ CTV in all bedrooms ® ✖
80P ♪ ♫
♦ ⬛
Credit Cards ①③

---

### CROMARTY Highland *Ross & Cromarty* Map **14** NH76

#### ★★63% **Royal**
Marine Ter IV11 8YN (Exec Hotel) ☎(03817)217
*This small, family-run hotel is situated on the waterfront and offers comfortable and traditionally furnished accommodation. 'Taste of Scotland' dishes feature in the dining room and an extensive range of bar meals is also available.*
10rm(5⇨2♠)(2fb) CTV in all bedrooms ® ✱ sB&B⇨♠fr£25 dB&B⇨♠fr£48 ▤
CTV 20P 3🚗 ✿ ⚓
V ♥ ⚏ ✱ Lunch fr£10 High tea fr£6.50 Dinner fr£15 Last dinner 8pm
Credit Cards ①②③ⓔ

#### ✿ ✕ **Thistles**
30 Church St IV11 8XA ☎(03817)471
*A pleasant small restaurant set in this historic and colourful village at the tip of the Black Isle offers enjoyable, well cooked meals at reasonable prices, chef/proprietor David Wilkinson (formerly of Arisaig House) handling local produce with skill and his charming wife providing attentive service.*
Closed Mon (ex BH's), 2 wks Feb & 2 wks Oct
Dinner not served Sun
V 26 seats ✱ Lunch £13-£20.65alc Dinner £13-£20.65alc Last lunch 2pm Last dinner 9pm P ✄
Credit Cards ①③

---

### CROMER Norfolk Map **09** TG24

#### ★★68% **Red Lion**
Brooke St NR27 9HD ☎(0263)514964
Closed 24-26 Dec
12⇨♠(1fb) CTV in all bedrooms ® ✖ sB&B⇨♠£41-£45 dB&B⇨♠£76-£84 (incl dinner) ▤
CTV 8P CFA snooker sauna solarium gymnasium
♡ English & French V ♥ ⚏ Bar Lunch £1.50-£9 High tea £1.15-£2.70 Dinner £14.95-£16.95 Last dinner 9.30pm
Credit Cards ①②③ⓔ

#### ✿ ✕ *Church Barn*
Church St, Northrepps NR27 0LG ☎Overstrand(026378)691
*This attractive flint-exterior building, dating from 1854 and situated in a quiet, picturesque village 2 miles southeast of the town, was converted to restaurant use some years ago ; chef/ proprietors Tony and Sheila Salmon now offer à la carte and supper menus based on good quality fresh local produce and placing a strong emphasis on fish and game. Preparation is, in the main, simple, natural flavours being enhanced by the accompanying sauces. Service is friendly and informal.*
Closed Mon Lunch not served Tue-Sat
Dinner not served Sun
♡ English & French V 50 seats Last dinner 9.15pm 14 P
Credit Cards ①③

---

### CROOKLANDS Cumbria Map **07** SD58 ◯

#### ★★★✿67% **Crooklands**
LA7 7NW (Best Western) ☎(04487)432 due to change to (05395) 67432 Telex no 94017303 FAX (04487) 525 due to change to (05395) 67525
(Rosette awarded for dinner only)
*Beams and stone walls are features of this attractive ivy-clad hotel, a former 16th-century croft and ale house on the A65 1.5 miles from junction 36 of the M6 (follow Kirby Lonsdale signs then first left at roundabout). Bedrooms are well appointed and those in the new wing are of a particularly high standard. The beamed Hayloft Restaurant is especially recommended.*
30⇨♠✄in 2 bedrooms CTV in all bedrooms ® T
✖ (ex guide dogs) ▤
150P CFA *xmas*

♡ French V ♥ ✱ Lunch fr£7.50 Dinner fr£18.50&alc Last dinner 9.30pm
Credit Cards ①②③⑤ⓔ

---

### CROSBY-ON-EDEN Cumbria Map **12** NY45

#### ★★★✿▲70% **Crosby Lodge Country House**
High Crosby CA6 4QZ ☎(022873)618 due to change to (0228) 573618 FAX (022873) 428 due to change to (0228) 573428
Closed 24 Dec-mid Jan RS Sun evening
*A charming family-run country house set in extensive grounds and gardens just off the B6264, providing individually styled bedrooms with luxurious bathrooms, very comfortable lounges and an attractive restaurant serving dishes of a high standard.*
9⇨♠Annexe2⇨(3fb)2▤ CTV in all bedrooms T
sB&B⇨♠£65-£69 dB&B⇨♠£85-£90 ▤
40P ▥ ✿
♡ English & French V ♥ Lunch £15.50-£19.50&alc Dinner £24-£28&alc Last dinner 9pm
Credit Cards ①②③

#### ★★★56% *Newby Grange*
CA6 4RA ☎(022873)645 due to change to (0228) 573645 FAX (022873)420 due to change to (0228) 573420
*An attractive five acres of grounds is the setting for this hotel. A very popular venue for functions and weddings, Newby Grange offers efficient and friendly service. Bedrooms vary in size and style, but are all well equipped.*
20⇨♠(4fb)1▥ CTV in all bedrooms ® T
⟨ CTV 200P ✿ ✦
V ♥ ⚏ Last dinner 10.30pm
Credit Cards ①③

---

### CROSS HANDS Dyfed Map **02** SN51

#### ⌂ **Forte Travelodge**
SA14 6NW (on A48, eastbound) (Forte)
☎(0269)845700 Central Res (0800) 850950
*A modern bedroom complex standing alongside the Little Chef restaurant, just off the A40 3 miles west of the end of the M4.*
32⇨♠(32fb) CTV in all bedrooms ® sB⇨♠£29.95 dB⇨♠£29.95 (room only)
⟨ 32P ▥
Credit Cards ①②③

---

### CROSSMICHAEL Dumfries & Galloway *Kirkcudbrightshire* Map **11** NX76

#### ★★▲59% **Culgruff House**
DG7 3BB ☎(055667)230
RS Oct-Etr
*Genuine warmth and hospitality are foremost in this baronial mansion, furnished with many antiques. Overlooking the village and the Ken Valley, it is set in 35 acres of grounds in which peacocks roam. The lounges with log fires are particularly comfortable and electric blankets are provided on the beds.*
16rm(4⇨)(8fb) CTV in all bedrooms TV in 1 bedroom sB&B£15-£17 sB&B⇨♠£21.75 dB&B£25-£33.50 dB&B⇨♠£43.50 ▤
CTV 50P 8🚗 (70p) ✿ CFA
V ♥ ⚏ ✄ Lunch £7&alc High tea £5.20-£5.60&alc Dinner £12&alc Last dinner 7.30pm
Credit Cards ①②③⑤ⓔ

---

### CROWTHORNE Berkshire Map **04** SU86

#### ★★★55% **Waterloo**
Duke's Ride RG11 7NW (Forte Hotels) ☎(0344)777711 FAX (0344) 778913
*Modern facilities and friendly service are found in this basically Victorian building.*

58➪✿1🛏✂in 28 bedrooms CTV in all bedrooms ® T ✹
sB➪✿fr£75 dB➪✿£85-£120 (room only) 🅿
《120P CFA *xmas*
V ⊙ ☺ ✂ ✹ Lunch fr£10.95 Dinner fr£13.95&alc Last dinner
10pm
Credit Cards ①②③④⑤

---

CROYDE Devon Map 02 SS43

★★66% **Croyde Bay House**
Moor Ln, Croyde Bay EX33 1PA ☎(0271)890270
Closed mid Nov-Feb
*Beautifully situated overlooking the bay, this warmly welcoming
personally run hotel has a cottage atmosphere, with a choice of
lounges, well stocked bar and comfortable bedrooms. Meals are
home cooked and generous.*
7➪✿(2fb) CTV in all bedrooms ® sB&B➪✿£38.50-£56.50
dB&B➪✿£77-£96.50 (incl dinner) 🅿
8P 🚗
🍴 English & French ⊙ ☺ ✂
Credit Cards ①③

★★66% **Kittiwell House**
St Mary's Rd EX33 1PG ☎(0271)890247 FAX (0271) 890469
Closed mid Jan-mid Feb
*Over the years Jim and Yvonne Lang have painstakingly restored
this one-time Devon longhouse into a cosy and popular hotel and
restaurant, to which they are continually making improvements.
They have, however, kept the old beamed ceilings and panelled
walls which give such character to the hotel. Booking is advisable
for the restaurant, which maintains worthy food standards and has
a well chosen and realistically priced wine list. Guests are looked
after well, and the owners ensure a friendly, welcoming
atmosphere. The hotel is well sited for holidays, being within
walking distance of the sea, and convenient for golf, riding and
other leisure pursuits.*
→

Comfortable 7 bedroom hotel, situated at the edge of the beach near the village of Croyde on the beautiful north Devon coast and in an area of outstanding natural beauty. Many sporting facilities nearby including championship golf course and miles of National Trust walks on the doorstep. All rooms have bath or shower en suite, colour television, tea making facilities and with lovely views of the beach and sea. Good food in relaxing surroundings.

## *Croyde Bay House Hotel*
★ ★
### Croyde Bay, Braunton,
### N. Devon EX33 1PA
ETB ♨♨♨                    Ashley Courtenay
Commended                       recommended
*Please telephone Croyde
(0271) 890270 for brochure*

**C**

12⇪⬧♦(2fb)3⬚¥in 4 bedrooms CTV in all bedrooms ® T ✳
sB&B⇪♦£49-£56 dB&B⇪♦£84-£98 (incl dinner) ᕻ
CTV 21P ⬚ ❉ *xmas*
♀ English & French V ♥ ⚓ ✳ Sunday Lunch £9.25 Dinner
£14.70&alc Last dinner 9.30pm
Credit Cards ①②③

---

## CROYDON Greater London

See **LONDON plan 1***D1* (page 435)
★★★★62% **Selsdon Park**
Sanderstead CR2 8YA (3m SE off A2022) ☎081-657 8811
Telex no 945003 FAX 081-651 6171
*A mansion set in beautiful gardens amid 200-acre grounds has
been sympathetically upgraded to retain most of its original
character. An impressive entrance lobby features fine carved
woodwork and some good pieces of furniture, while the spacious
restaurant's light, airy surroundings provide an ideal setting in
which to enjoy your choice of dishes from table d'hôte or à la carte
menus. Most of the bedrooms have been refurbished to a high
standard and are well equipped. New conference facilities are
available, and good leisure amenities are provided both indoors
and out.*
170⇪♦(7fb)1⬚ CTV in all bedrooms ® T S10% sB⇪♦£108-
£123 dB⇪♦£132-£166 (room only) ᕻ
Lift ℂ 250P 15 (£1.50) ❉ CFA ▣ (heated) ⚲ (heated) ▶ 18
♪ (hard & grass )squash snooker sauna solarium gymnasium
croquet jacuzzi putting boules ♫ ⚓ *xmas*
♀ International V ¥ S% Lunch £20.50-£21.50&alc Dinner
£24-£30 Last dinner 9.30pm
Credit Cards ①②③⑤

★★★65% **Croydon Park**
7 Altyre Rd CR9 5AA ☎081-680 9200 Telex no 8956268
FAX 081-760 0426
*A large modern hotel, near the town centre but well set back from
the main road, features a spacious, marble lobby lounge as well
the gas-lit Whistlers Bar – which, being popular, can quickly
become overcrowded – and well appointed Oscar's Restaurant
where menus include a fixed-price buffet. Bedrooms are all of a
good size, well equipped, comfortable and air conditioned ; half of
them also boast queen size beds and sofa seating. Conference
rooms and leisure facilities are available, and an extensive range of
services includes 24-hour room service.*
214⇪♦(40fb)¥in 26 bedrooms CTV in all bedrooms ® T S%
sB⇪♦£97 dB⇪♦£109 (room only) ᕻ
Lift ℂ ▦ 118P ❉ CFA ▣ (heated) squash sauna solarium
gymnasium whirlpool bath *xmas*
♀ International V ♥ ⚓ ¥ ✳ Lunch £14.50 High tea £6.50
Dinner £15.50 Last dinner 10pm
Credit Cards ①②③④⑤ £

★★★63% **Forte Posthouse**
Purley Way CR9 4LT (Forte Hotels) ☎081-688 5185
Telex no 893814 FAX 081-681 6438
*Northbound access off the A23 is recommended although
southbound access is possible via the deliveries entrance. A new
wing offers modern accommodation whilst other bedrooms are
slowly being refurbished. Chef Victor Firth provides creative
international cuisine and service is particularly friendly.*
86⇪♦¥in 28 bedrooms CTV in all bedrooms ® T ✳ S%
sB⇪♦£39.50-£49.50 dB⇪♦£39.50-£49.50 (room only) ᕻ
ℂ 70P CFA *xmas*
♀ English & French V ♥ ⚓ ¥ ✳ S% Lunch £8.75-£10.95
Dinner £13.95&alc Last dinner 10.30pm
Credit Cards ①②③⑤

★★63% **Norfolk House**
587 London Rd CR7 6AY ☎081-689 8989 FAX 081-689 0335
*The attractively landscaped and canopied entrance to a
redeveloped series of large houses brings one into a busy
commercial hotel where the airy, open-plan areas include carvery,*

*lounge seating and bar ; en suite bedrooms on four floors are all
well equipped, although some are rather compact for two guests.*
78⇪♦(3fb) CTV in all bedrooms ® T ✘ (ex guide dogs) ✳
sB⇪♦£48-£72 dB⇪♦£61-£90 (room only) ᕻ
ℂ 150P 4⚲
V ♥ ⚓ ✳ Lunch £6-£15 Dinner £8.95-£15 Last dinner 10pm
Credit Cards ①②③④⑤

★★57% **Briarley**
8 Outram Rd CR0 6XE ☎081-654 1000 FAX 081-656 6084
*This privately run commercial hotel in a residential street promotes
an informal atmosphere in public areas which include a
comfortable bar with an unusual clock collection. Half its
accommodation is contained in the main building, and these rooms
vary in both size and comfort ; the rest, in a refurbished, converted
house, are larger and more attractively furnished, but the walk to
reach them is not an appealing one and you are advised to use your
car.*
18⇪♦Annexe20⇪♦(3fb)1⬚ CTV in all bedrooms ® T ✳
sB&B⇪♦fr£57.50 dB&B⇪♦fr£67.50 ᕻ
CTV 20P
♀ Mainly grills V ¥ Sunday Lunch £10.50 Dinner £10.50&alc
Last dinner 10pm
Credit Cards ①②③⑤

★65% **Central**
3-5 South Park Hill Rd, South Croydon CR2 7DY
☎081-688 0840 & 081-688 5644 FAX 081-760 0861
*Set in a quiet residential area half a mile south of the town centre,
a commercial hotel which is constantly being improved offers
modestly furnished but well equipped bedrooms and an attractive
garden-themed dining room.*
23rm(22⇪♦)(1fb)1⬚ CTV in all bedrooms ® T
✘ (ex guide dogs) ✳ sB&Bfr£38 sB&B⇪♦fr£52
dB&B⇪♦fr£64 ᕻ

→

## Kittiwell House Hotel & Restaurant

❀ ❀ ❀ ★★

Magnificent 16th Century thatched hotel with considerable
character, situated in one of Devon's prettiest villages
within walking distance from the sea. Beamed and panelled
ceilings and walls in all the public rooms creating a relaxing
atmosphere. 12 well appointed bedrooms all en-suite and colour TV, direct dial telephone, coffee & tea making facilities
in all bedrooms and a few "under the thatch" have 4 poster
beds. Restaurant offers high standard of cuisine with à la carte
and table d'Hote menus. Fresh vegetables a speciality. Wide
choice of local and international wines. Ideal venue for short
breaks and holidays as well as overnight stops for business
people. Golf, Saunton G.C. (2-18 hole courses), walking,
riding, clay pigeon shooting minutes away. Ashley Courtenay
and Derek Johansens recommended. Personally managed by
resident proprietors. Own car park. Open 11 months (closed
mid Jan/Feb).

*Croyde, N. Devon. Tel: (0271) 890247,
Fax: (0271) 890469*

248

★★★★

C

# Relax
## On a 200 acre country estate

No other hotel quite compares with Selsdon Park Hotel.

Set in over 200 acres of Surrey parkland it is uniquely situated to offer guests Championship golf, tennis and squash, putting, swimming, gymnastics, jogging, boules, snooker – even croquet.

While the less energetic can simply relax, dining and dancing in the first-class restaurant.

Or just indulge themselves in our Tropical Leisure Complex, complete with sauna, jacuzzi, steam room, solarium and swimming pool.

Reserve some time to enjoy yourself and relax amid the rolling countryside that is Selsdon Park Hotel.

Only 30 minutes from Central London and 10 minutes from junction 6 of the M25.

## SELSDON PARK HOTEL

**Sanderstead, South Croydon, Surrey CR2 8YA Tel: 081-657 8811 Fax: 081-651 6171 Telex: 945003**

MEMBER OF CONCORDE HOTELS GROUP

《 CTV 15P
V ✿ ⊡
Credit Cards 1 3

❀✕✕**Thirty Four Surrey Street**
34 Surrey St CR0 1RJ ☎081-686 0586 & 081-681 3316
*At first sight a typical American-theme 'eaterie', this converted
warehouse in fact houses a well run restaurant offering some
exciting and unusual dishes. Its speciality is American fish like
barracuda, blue marlin and tuna which, together with shellfish, are
appetisingly char-grilled on the outside whilst remaining moist and
succulent inside, but steaks, poultry and pasta are also available.
Starters might include seafood chowder, conch salad or mesquite
smoked sausage, and desserts are enjoyable though limited. The
décor is California seaboard, service is informal, knowledgeable
and obliging, and a meal here represents good value for money –
the owner being involved in the importation of fish and wine. A
basement wine bar serves lighter snacks.*
 Lunch not served Sat
Dinner not served Sun
♀ American V 60 seats Lunch £15-£25alc Dinner £15.50-
£25alc Last lunch 2.45pm Last dinner 10.45pm P
Credit Cards 1 2 3 5

❀✕*Le Saint Jacques*
1123 Whitgift Centre CR0 1UZ ☎081-760 0881
*A smart, simply decorated little French restaurant – run for the
last 6 years by the Rochebouet family and improbably located in a
modern shopping centre – provides a pleasant setting for the
enjoyment of honest cuisine, the sensible à la carte menu being
supplemented by daily suggestions proposed by the charming, well
managed French staff. Starters might include a tasty twice- baked
cheese soufflé with a bubbling cheese sauce, to be followed perhaps
by a moist, nicely browned breast of chicken sliced onto a bed of
spinach and served with a cream sauce, with a smooth créme brulée
or delicious apple tart to end the meal. A short but quite adequate
list concentrates mainly on French wines, and a full-bodied
Corbières, Château de Caraguilles 1988, is well worth drinking,
though house wines do tend to change.*
Closed Sun & 24 Dec-4 Jan & BH's Lunch not served Sat
Dinner not served Mon-Wed
♀ French 36 seats Last lunch 2.45pm Last dinner 10pm
✍ nc8yrs
Credit Cards 1 2 3 4 5

---

CRUDWELL Wiltshire Map **03** ST99

★★68% **Crudwell Court**
SN16 9EP ☎(06667)7194 & 7195 FAX (06667) 7853
*A 17th-century rectory set in 3 acres of well tended walled gardens
that include a swimming pool has been lovingly refurbished to
create a charming country house hotel with a warmly welcoming
atmosphere. Comfortable bedrooms vary in size, while relaxing
public rooms in pastel shades have log fires in winter. A daily
changing menu uses fresh quality produce.*
15⇋⇍↑(3fb) CTV in all bedrooms ® T ✳ sB&B⇋↑£40-£65
dB&B⇋↑£77-£100 ➡
20P ⇛ ✿ ⊇ (heated) croquet lawn *xmas*
V ✿ ⊡ ✗ ✳ Lunch fr£13 Dinner fr£17.50 Last dinner 9.30pm
Credit Cards 1 2 3 5 £

★★66% **Mayfield House**
SN16 9EW ☎(06667)409 & 7198 FAX (06667) 7977
*An hotel which was once a veterinary surgery offers easy access to
the M4 from a pretty village setting. Neatly presented bedrooms,
well equipped with modern facilities, are complemented by public
areas which contain a Continental-style lounge with low seating
and ceramic floor, an attractive split-level restaurant and a
spacious bar – and enthusiastic new owners plan to improve the
already high standards. An extensive bar menu supplements the
short but imaginative à la carte selection, while staff are both
friendly and polite.*

20⇋↑(1fb) CTV in all bedrooms ® T ✗ sB&B⇋↑£45-£55
dB&B⇋↑£58-£68 ➡
CTV 50P ✿ CFA *xmas*
♀ English & French ✿ ⊡ ✳ Sunday Lunch fr£9.75alc Dinner
£12-£20alc Last dinner 9.30pm
Credit Cards 1 2 3 £
                    **See advertisement under MALMESBURY**

---

CRUGYBAR Dyfed Map **03** SN63

★★♨70% **Glanrannell Park**
SA19 8SA (Welsh Rarebits) ☎Talley(0558)685230
FAX (0558) 685784
Closed Nov-Mar
*Set in 23 acres of beautiful grounds including a lake, this country
hotel lies off the B4302 between Llandeilo and Lampeter. There
are 2 very comfortable residents' lounges and a small cosy bar. All
bedrooms are now en suite or have a private bathroom. David and
Bronwen Davies have run the hotel for over 20 years and their
hospitality is warm and genuine. Fishing and other country sports
are available.*
8⇋(3fb) sB&B⇋£31-£36 dB&B⇋£52-£62 ➡
CTV 30P 3🚗 (£3) ⇛ ✿ ✍
♀ International ✿ ⊡ ✗ Bar Lunch £1.50-£5 Dinner £14-£16
Last dinner 8pm
Credit Cards 1

---

CUCKFIELD West Sussex Map **04** TQ32

★★★❀73% **Ockenden Manor**
Ockenden Ln RH17 5LD ☎Haywards Heath(0444)416111
FAX (0444) 415549
(Rosette awarded for dinner only)
*This delightful 16th-century manor house, commanding beautiful
views of the Sussex countryside from 5-acre gardens, provides
guests with a choice between its characterful original
accommodation and new rooms tastefully furnished to the highest
standards. Public areas include an elegantly comfortable lounge
where a log fire burns during the winter months, a cosy oak-
panelled bar and a well appointed restaurant whose ornate, painted
ceiling and stained glass windows make it the perfect setting for an
enjoyable meal. Interesting set menus for 3, 4 and 5-course meals
make good use of local produce and herbs from the hotel's own
garden, noteworthy dishes including a baked pheasant and pigeon
breasts with rosemary and garlic served with a flavoursome jus,
and the unusual combination of chicken, pistachio and prune
parfait with pinenut dressing; an impressive board of farmhouse
cheeses accompanies the selection of modern and classic desserts,
and an admirable – though, sometimes rather expensive – wine list
contains some fine vintages. Service throughout is attentively
professional without being obtrusive.*
22⇋↑4⇛ CTV in all bedrooms ® T ✗ sB&B⇋↑£70-£95
dB&B⇋↑£95-£165 Continental breakfast ➡
《 40P ⇛ ✿ CFA *xmas*
V ✿ ⊡ Lunch £17.95-£18.50 Dinner £26.50-£35 Last dinner
9.15pm
Credit Cards 1 2 3 5

❀❀✕*Jeremy's at the Kings Head*
South St RH17 5JY ☎Haywards Heath(0444)440386
*Jeremy's – named after its talented chef/patron – retains the
character of an English inn with its simple appointments, log-
burning fires and friendly service. Daily menus offer a good range
of dishes, professionally and skilfully cooked, including fresh fish
as available; popular choices include fish soup with coriander,
Stilton soufflé, wild salmon with samphire and Gressingham duck
with Madeira, while a tasty pudding provides a fitting end to an
enjoyable meal.*
Dinner not served Mon
V 38 seats 10 P
Credit Cards 1 2 3 5

## CULLERCOATS Tyne & Wear Map **12** NZ37

### ★★55% Bay

Front St NE30 4QB ☎091-252 3150

*This mainly commercial hotel commands fine views over Cullercoats Bay, from cocktail bar, restaurant and lounge as well as several bedrooms. Accommodation has, for the most part, been decorated and furnished to modern standards, though some rooms remain more modest.*

17rm(11⇨♠)(2fb)3🛏 CTV in all bedrooms ® T
✻ (ex guide dogs) ✱ sB&B£17-£25 sB&B⇨♠£25-£28 dB&B£32 dB&B⇨♠£45-£48

CTV 9P sailing sea fishing *xmas*

♡ English & French ✿ ♨ Lunch £2.95-£6.25 Dinner £5.50-£6.25&alc Last dinner 9pm

Credit Cards ①②③④⑤

**See advertisement under WHITLEY BAY**

## CULNACNOC

See Skye, Isle of

## CUMBERNAULD Strathclyde *Dumbartonshire* Map **11** NS77

### ★★★★⚜69% Westerwood Hotel Golf & Country Club

1 St Andrews Dr, Westerwood G68 0EW ☎(0236)457171 FAX (0236) 738478

*In an elevated position north of the new town with lovely views towards the Campsie Fells and across the testing 18-hole golf course designed by Seve Ballesteros, this modern hotel opened in early 1991 with an eye to the corporate market, offering relaxation as well as good business/seminar facilities. The clubhouse is well equipped with a spacious swimming pool which offers breathtaking views. Locals, too, are attracted to the Masters Restaurant and the attractive lounge and cocktail bars. Bedrooms are bright and modern, executive rooms being particularly comfortable. Bathrooms are well finished but some may find the low, shallow baths awkward. Staff try very hard to provide attentive, thorough and thoughtful service.*

47⇨♠⅟in 4 bedrooms CTV in all bedrooms T ✻ ✳
sB&B⇨♠£90-£105 dB&B⇨♠£105-£120 🛏

Lift ℂ ⊞ 200P ✿ ▱ (heated) ▶ 18 ♪ (hard) snooker solarium gymnasium steam room bowling green ♫ *xmas*

♡ International V ✿ ♨ ✳ Sunday Lunch £12.50-£15 Dinner £14-£20&alc Last dinner 10pm

Credit Cards ①②③⑤

## CUMNOCK Strathclyde *Ayrshire* Map **11** NS51

### ★★61% Royal

1 Glaisnock St KA18 1BP ☎(0290)20822

*This commercial hotel at the town centre, though somewhat traditional in style, is homely, comfortable and very clean; meals are simple and home-cooked, good afternoon/high teas being available.*

11rm(2⇨1♠)(1fb) CTV in all bedrooms ® S10% sB&B£23 sB&B⇨♠£35 dB&B£46 dB&B⇨♠£58 🛏

CTV 10P CFA

V ✿ ♨ S10% Lunch £6.50-£9 High tea £6-£10 Dinner £12.50-£14 Last dinner 9pm

Credit Cards ①③⓹

## CUPAR Fife Map **11** NO31

### ⊛⊛⊛ ✕ Ostlers Close

Bonnygate KY15 4BU ☎(0334)55574

*A friendly and cosily attractive little restaurant standing just off the main street, with its entrance in a narrow passageway at the side, offers good value for money in its short, constantly changing menus of skilfully cooked dishes which put great emphasis on local produce, particularly game and fish. A typical meal might include delicious leek soup, seafood ragout with a wide variety of ingredients and a delectable sticky toffee pudding with*

butterscotch sauce, while a list of about 50 wines features some competitively priced examples from the New World.

Closed Sun, Mon & 2 wks Jun

♡ French & Swiss 28 seats Lunch £11-£13alc Dinner £21-£25alc Last lunch 2pm Last dinner 9.30pm ⟋

Credit Cards ①③

## DALKEITH Lothian *Midlothian* Map **11** NT36

### ★★64% Eskbank Motor

29 Dalhousie Rd EH22 3AT ☎031-663 3234 FAX 031-660 4347

*Conveniently located close to the Edinburgh city bypass this family-owned hotel offers well appointed motel-style bedrooms, with service in keeping with a friendly, traditional hotel.*

16⇨♠(3fb)1🛏 CTV in all bedrooms ® T sB&B⇨♠£36-£45 dB&B⇨♠£50-£60 🛏

ℂ CTV 40P 6🚗 ✿ CFA

♡ International V ✿ ♨ Lunch £6-£8.50&alc High tea £6-£8.50&alc Dinner £6-£8.50&alc Last dinner 9pm

Credit Cards ①②③⑤ⓔ

**See advertisement under EDINBURGH**

## DALLINGTON East Sussex Map **05** TQ61

### ⊛⊛⊛ ✕✕ Little Byres

Christmas Farm TN21 9LE ☎(042482)230

*Skilful conversion of a 200-year-old barn has created an interesting setting for Chris Davis's inventive cooking. He and his wife Evelyn offer a fixed price menu with a choice of 5 alternatives at each of the 4 courses. They pride themselves on using only the finest ingredients, including herbs from the garden and delicious butter churned by Chris himself from cream from a local Jersey herd. Although our inspector thought that a rich sauce of chicken livers, whisky and tarragon somewhat overpowered the good, home-made fettucini, the tender fillet of lamb, served with a gratin*

*of aubergines, tomatoes basil and fennel seeds, was praised, as were the French farmhouse cheeses. Desserts may include caramelised apple tart, made to order, or roasted quince with cinammon parfait. There is a short but well chosen and reasonably priced list of young, predominantly French wines.*
Closed Sun Lunch not served all week (ex by prior arrangement)
♀ English & French 30 seats ✱ Dinner £23.50 Last dinner 9pm 20 P
Credit Cards [1][3]

---

DALWHINNIE Highland *Inverness-shire* Map **14** NN68

★★56% **Loch Ericht**
PH19 1AF (Inter-Hotels) ☎(05282)257 FAX (05282) 270
Closed Nov-27 Mar
*Amidst splendid scenery in the Highlands' highest village, this former lodge is conveniently placed for the A9. It has been extended to provide modern, functional accommodation. Meals are available all day in the split-level bar and restaurant.*
27⇨🏠(4fb) ® sB&B⇨🏠£26-£30 dB&B⇨🏠£45-£50 🍴
CTV 50P ✱ CFA ✔ shooting ski-ing ♫ *xmas*
V ☺ ⚏ Lunch £2.50-£7.50 High tea £3.50-£8 Dinner £5-£12
Last dinner 9pm
Credit Cards [1][2][3] £

---

DARESBURY Cheshire Map **07** SJ58

★★★68% **Lord Daresbury**
Chester Rd WA4 4BB (De Vere) ☎Warrington(0925)67331
Telex no 629330 FAX (0925) 65615
*This modern hotel is sited just off junction 11 of the M56. Various food operations are available here, the popular Looking Glass Restaurant and the Terrace, which specialises in Cuisine Moderne, are both supervised by chef David Chapman. Weekend breaks offer good value, especially when using the comprehensive leisure centre.*
141⇨🏠(7fb)✂in 27 bedrooms CTV in all bedrooms ® T ✱
sB&B⇨🏠£71.50-£137.50 dB&B⇨🏠£104.50-£159.50 🍴
Lift 《 400P CFA 🏊 (heated) squash snooker sauna solarium gymnasium jacuzzi
♀ English & French V ☺ ⚏ ✂ ✱ Lunch £16-£21&alc Dinner £16-£21&alc Last dinner 9.45pm
Credit Cards [1][2][3][5] £

---

DARLINGTON Co Durham Map **08** NZ21 ◉

See also Teeside Airport
★★★★61% **Blackwell Grange Moat House**
Blackwell Grange DL3 8QH (Queens Moat) ☎(0325)380888
Telex no 587272 FAX (0325) 380899
*Conveniently located south of the town and close to the motorway, this much extended 17th-century mansion is set amidst parkland which includes a golf course and offers high quality accommodation, with good conference facilities and a new small leisure centre. The pleasant Capability Brown restaurant features some local dishes.*
99⇨🏠(11fb)3🛏✂in 14 bedrooms CTV in all bedrooms ® T
sB&B⇨🏠£80-£125 dB&B⇨🏠£98-£140 🍴
Lift 《 🛏 250P 3🚗 ✱ CFA 🏊 (heated) ▶ 18 ♪ (hard) sauna solarium gymnasium boules croquet ♫ *xmas*
♀ International V ☺ ⚏ ✂ Lunch £11.25-£14&alc Dinner £15-£22.50&alc Last dinner 9.45pm
Credit Cards [1][2][3][5]

★★★71% **Hallgarth Country House**
Coatham Mandeville DL1 3LU (Consort)
☎Aycliffe(0325)300400 FAX (0325) 310083
*A handsome country house set in parkland only minutes from the A1(M) off the A167. Thoughtfully modernised it now offers inviting lounges, attractive and well appointed bedrooms, and an*

*intimate restaurant with interesting menus. Bar meals are available in the Stable Bar.*
29⇨🏠Annexe11⇨🏠(1fb)5🛏 CTV in all bedrooms ® T ✱
sB&B⇨🏠£45-£65 dB&B⇨🏠£60-£85
《 150P 🚗 ✱ ⊇ (heated) ♪ (grass) sauna solarium croquet lawn ⌀
V ☺ ⚏ ✂ ✱ Lunch £9.95 Dinner £12.95&alc Last dinner 9.45pm
Credit Cards [1][2][3][5]

★★★≛67% **Headlam Hall**
Headlam, Gainford DL2 3HA ☎(0325)730238
FAX (0325) 730790
Closed 25-26 Dec
*A splendid Jacobean mansion set in 3 acres of formal gardens in the tiny hamlet of Headlam, 2 miles north of the town. The atmosphere is peaceful and relaxing, bedrooms are individually furnished and decorated, and traditional English food is served in the panelled dining room. A swimming pool in a former coach house has recently been opened.*
17⇨🏠Annexe5⇨🏠(3fb)9🛏 CTV in all bedrooms ® T
✈ (ex guide dogs) ✱ S% sB&B⇨🏠£47-£60 dB&B⇨🏠£59-£72 🍴
60P ✱ CFA 🏊 (heated) ♪ (hard) ✔ snooker sauna gymnasium clay pigeon shooting croquet lawn *xmas*
♀ English & French V ☺ ✂ ✱ Lunch frf9 Dinner £12-£20&alc Last dinner 9.30pm
Credit Cards [1][2][3] £

★★★62% **White Horse**
DL1 3AD ☎(0325)382121 Telex no 778704 FAX (0325) 355953
*A Tudor-style building, on the A167 on the outskirts of town, with a modern bedroom extension of very well appointed and comfortable rooms. Public areas are limited to bars and a restaurant serving mainly grills and additional daily dishes.*
40⇨🏠(6fb)✂in 20 bedrooms CTV in all bedrooms ®
Lift 《 120P
♀ Mainly grills V ☺ ⚏ ✂ Last dinner 10pm
Credit Cards [1][2][3][5]

★★★61% **Swallow King's Head**
Priestgate DL1 1NW (Swallow) ☎(0325)380222 Telex no 587112 FAX (0325) 382006
*Victorian four-storey town centre hotel.*
60⇨🏠(1fb)✂in 25 bedrooms CTV in all bedrooms ® T 🍴
Lift 《 P *xmas*
♀ English, French & Italian V ☺ ⚏ ✱ Sunday Lunch £9.50 Dinner £13 Last dinner 9.30pm
Credit Cards [1][2][3][5] £

❀ ✗**Victor's**
84 Victoria Rd DL1 5JW ☎(0325)480818
*Housed in shop-fronted premises between the railway station and football ground, with a public car park close by, a tiny, unpretentious restaurant features lunch and dinner menus that represent exceedingly good value for money, cuisine being British in style and offering a varied choice of meat, poultry and fish dishes which are normally preceded by a home-made soup in the four-course evening meal.*
Closed Sun, Mon & one wk Xmas-New Year
V 30 seats Lunch £7.50 Dinner £18 Last lunch 2pm Last dinner 10.30pm ✗ ✂
Credit Cards [1][2][3][5]

---

DARTFORD Kent Map **05** TQ57

○**Stakis Country Court**
(Stakis) ☎Central Res (0800) 262626
Due to open Mar 1992
183⇨🏠

## DARTMOUTH Devon Map 03 SX85

### ★★★69% **Royal Castle**

11 The Quay TQ6 9PS ☎(0803)833033 FAX (0803) 835445

*Set alongside the inner harbour, with glorious views across to Kingswear, this former 17th-century hostelry has been sympathetically restored to retain its charm and character whilst providing modern day comforts. The elegant Adam Restaurant overlooks the river and is noted for its worthy food standards which feature local seafood and other produce. Parking is limited, but there are public car parks nearby.*

24⇌🛏6🛏 CTV in all bedrooms ® T sB&B⇌🛏£39-£48 dB&B⇌🛏£68-£98 🅿

《 7🛏 (£1.50) CFA ♫ *xmas*

♀ English & French **V** ♥ ⚏ ✳ Sunday Lunch £9.25 Dinner £15.75-£20.50 Last dinner 9.45pm

Credit Cards [1] [3]

### ★★★59% **Dart Marina**

Sandquay TQ6 9PH (Forte Hotels) ☎(0803)832580 FAX (0803) 835040

*Situated, as its name implies, in an unrivalled position, this well established, proprietor-managed hotel enjoys views up and down the river as well as across to Kingswear. Recently refurbished bedrooms are bright, comfortable and well equipped, and plans are in hand to extend the somewhat restricted public areas in the near future. Good car parking on site is an attraction in this busy, popular location.*

35⇌🛏in 10 bedrooms CTV in all bedrooms ® T ✳ S% sB⇌🛏£65-£70 dB⇌🛏£85-£115 (room only) 🅿

75P 🚗 *xmas*

**V** ♥ ⚏ ✳ S% Lunch £7.50-£15 Dinner £15.50 Last dinner 9pm

Credit Cards [1] [2] [3] [5]

### ★★★56% **Stoke Lodge**

Cinders Ln, Stoke Fleming TQ6 0RA (2m S A379) ☎Stoke Fleming(0803)770523

*A convenient base from which to tour South Devon, this small, friendly and family-owned holiday hotel commands good sea views from its position on the coast road at Stoke Fleming, about 3 miles from Dartmouth. Run as a country house, it offers informal service and a range of leisure facilities that includes both indoor and outdoor swimming pools, spa bath and tennis court. Bedrooms vary in size, but all are warm, bright and well equipped, while public areas comprise a choice of lounges and a simply appointed garden room restaurant.*

24⇌🛏(5fb)1🛏 CTV in all bedrooms ® T ✳ sB&B⇌🛏fr£38 dB&B⇌🛏fr£62 🅿

50P 4🛏 (£2.50) 🚗 ✿ CFA ☒ (heated) ⊇ (heated) ♟ (hard) sauna solarium gymnasium jacuzzi putting table tennis *xmas*

♀ English & Continental **V** ♥ ⚏ ✳ Lunch £8.50&alc Dinner fr£14.25&alc Last dinner 9pm

Credit Cards [1] [3]

### ★★63% **Royle House**

Mount Boone TQ6 9HZ ☎(0803)833649 RS Dec-Feb

*An attractive Georgian building in its own grounds and gardens, this small, personally run hotel with a country house atmosphere commands enviable views of Dartmouth College and the Estuary from an elevated position just outside the town. Soundly furnished bedrooms are equipped with modern facilities, while public areas include a cosy character lounge, dining room and bright breakfast room.*

10⇌🛏in 2 bedrooms CTV in all bedrooms ® T ✳ sB&B⇌🛏fr£49 dB&B⇌🛏£70-£78 🅿

CTV 15P 🚗 ✿ ☒ (heated) sauna solarium hairdressing salon nc9yrs

**V** ♥ ⚖ ✳ Dinner fr£12.95 Last dinner 8pm

Credit Cards [1] [3]

★**65% New Endsleigh**
New Rd, Stoke Fleming TQ6 0NR
☎Stoke Fleming(0803)770381
11rm(10⇨🛏🟊)Annexe1🟊(1fb) CTV in all bedrooms ®
✖ (ex guide dogs) ✳ sB&B⇨🟊£29-£33 dB&B£41.50-£49.50
dB&B⇨🟊£47.50-£60.50 🅿
CTV 16P 🎟 nc5yrs xmas
♀ English & French V ✿ ⚓ ✳ Sunday Lunch £7.50 High tea
£2-£2.95 Dinner £9&alc Last dinner 9pm
Credit Cards ① ③

---

❀❀❀✖ ✖ **Carved Angel**
2 South Embankment TQ6 9BH ☎(0803)832465

*A continuing and consistent high level of cooking is the hallmark of
this famous and utterly delightful waterfront restaurant. Joyce
Molyneux's flair is undimmed after 16 years and she and her head
chef Nick Boiley produce interesting menus both at lunch and
dinner, basing their dishes mainly, but not exclusively, on British
traditions. Although fish is one of their strongpoints, this is by no
means exclusively a fish restaurant ; meat and game are equally
good.*

Closed Mon, Xmas, Jan & beginning of Feb
Dinner not served Sun
♀ International 34 seats ✳ Lunch £25&alc Dinner £39.50 Last
lunch 1.45pm Last dinner 9.30pm ℘

---

❀❀❀✖ **Bistro Too**
☎(0803)835325

*At this cosy little bistro just off the harbour, Kevan Pester handles
the cooking with abundant use of first class fresh produce. The
twice baked soufflé is delightfully light yet well rounded ; and the
handsome poached salmon with a smooth dill hollandaise and
cucumber spaghetti was praiseworthy. Simple, flavoursome
vegetables accompany and rich home-made puddings follow.*

Closed Sun & Mon
♀ English, French & Italian V 50 seats ✳ Lunch fr£3.50&alc
Dinner fr£14alc Last lunch 2pm Last dinner 10pm ℘
Credit Cards ① ③

---

★★★**57%** *Whitehall*
Springbank, Whitehall BB3 2JU ☎(0254)701595
FAX (0254) 773426
Closed 25 & 26 Dec

*A friendly family-run hotel set in its own grounds off the A666
about a mile south of the town centre. Attractively decorated
bedrooms in the main house and more spacious rooms in the new
wing have good facilities, and conference and function rooms are
available.*

18rm(14⇨🟊) CTV in all bedrooms ® T
60P ✿ 🖵 (heated) snooker sauna solarium
♀ English & French V ✿ ⚓ Last dinner 10pm
Credit Cards ① ② ③ ④ ⑤

---

★★**55% The Manor**
The Village Green SL3 9EA (Consort) ☎Slough(0753)43442
Telex no 41363 FAX (0753) 45292

*This busy hotel overlooks the village green, standing between a
through road and the railway station. Double-glazed bedrooms are
well equipped, though some are rather compact, and there are two
popular bars and a beamed restaurant.*

30⇨🟊(2fb)1🛌 CTV in all bedrooms ® T sB&B⇨🟊£65
dB&B⇨🟊£86 🅿
⚓ CTV 30P CFA 🎵 xmas
♀ English, French, Italian & Spanish V ✿ ⚓ ✳ Lunch
£14.50&alc Dinner £15.50&alc Last dinner 10pm
Credit Cards ① ② ③ ⑤

**See advertisement under WINDSOR**

---

○**Holiday Inn**
Ashby Rd (A361) NN11 5NX (Holiday Inns Inc) ☎(0327)301777
Telex no 312513 FAX (0327) 706313
Open
138⇨🟊

---

★★★**58% Langstone Cliff**
Dawlish Warren EX7 0NA (1.5m NE off A379 Exeter rd)
(Consort) ☎(0626)865155 Telex no 57515 FAX (0626) 867166

*Set in 19 acres of wooded grounds overlooking the sea and Exe
estuary, this well established family-run hotel caters for family
holidays in summer while small conferences are a feature in
autumn and winter. Bedrooms are bright with modern facilities
and there is a choice of bars and both indoor and outdoor
swimming pools.*

64⇨🟊(52fb) CTV in all bedrooms ® T sB&B⇨🟊£45-£52
dB&B⇨🟊£78-£94 🅿
Lift ⚓ CTV 200P ✿ CFA 🖵 (heated) ⇌ (heated) ℘ (hard)
snooker solarium table tennis 🎵 ⚽ xmas
V ✿ ⚓ ✳ Lunch fr£9 High tea fr£3.50 Dinner fr£12.50 Last
dinner 9pm
Credit Cards ① ② ③ ⑤ ⓔ

---

★★**70% Holcombe Hotel & Restaurant**
High St OX15 0SL (Best Western) ☎(0869)38274 Telex no 83147
FAX (0869) 37167
Closed 1-10 Jan

*This charming 17th-century hotel in the quiet village centre has a
friendly relaxed atmosphere. Attractively refurbished bedrooms,
many with beams and low ceilings, are well equipped with modern
facilities and public areas are cosy and warm.*

17⇨🟊(3fb) CTV in all bedrooms ® T sB&B⇨🟊£59-£69
dB&B⇨🟊£78-£90 🅿
60P xmas
♀ English & French V ✿ ⚓ ⚖ S% Lunch £11.50-£17.95
Dinner £17.50-£22 Last dinner 10pm
Credit Cards ① ② ③ ⑤ ⓔ

---

★★★

★★★🏩 MAISON TALBOOTH
Stratford Rd CO7 6HN (Pride
of Britain)
☎Colchester(0206)322367
FAX (0206) 322752

*Gerald Milsom's long-
established hotel enjoys a
secluded position overlooking
the village and will most
easily be found by following signs from the A12 to Stratford
St Mary. Meals, apart from breakfast, are not served in the
hotel itself, but transport is available to take diners to Le
Talbooth, well known for its fine cuisine, or there is a
Rotisserie in nearby Dedham Vale or yet another Milsom
venture, the Pier Restaurant in Harwich. Guests who decide to
stay in the hotel can have a range of snacks and drinks
comfortably served in their room.*

10⇨🟊(1fb) CTV in all bedrooms T ✖ ✳
sB&B⇨🟊£82.50-£107.50 dB&B⇨🟊£102.50-£137.50
Continental breakfast 🅿
12P 🎟 ✿ croquet

V ✱ Lunch fr£20.35&alc Dinner £32.45-£37.12alc Last dinner 9.30pm
Credit Cards ⒈ ⒊

---

### ❊❊❊ ✕ ✕ ✕ Le Talbooth
CO7 6HP ☎Colchester(0206)323150 FAX (0206) 322752
*An ideal setting, this timber-framed house with its sympathetic extension offers a meal which is bound to please. Since the arrival of Steven Blake, the standard of imaginative and creative cooking have touched new heights. The dishes are prepared from good fresh produce and only the best is used ; his sauces are exceptionally good. Starter dishes include Gamba prawns with a light curry sauce, and sauté of livers, wood mushrooms and baby onions. Main- course items might be roast saddle of rabbit, or Lasagne of lobster in a shellfish butter ; tantalising desserts include our inspector's favourite – a strudel of apples. A well chosen wine list includes some good vintage first- growth clarets and fine Burgundies.*
♡ English & French V 70 seats ✱ Lunch fr£20.35&alc Dinner £32.45-£37.12alc Last lunch 2pm Last dinner 9pm 40 P
Credit Cards ⒈ ⒊

---

**DEGANWY** Gwynedd Map **06** SH77

### ★★66% *Bryn Cregin Garden*
Ty Mawr Rd LL31 9UR (Exec Hotel) ☎(0492)585266
Closed Jan
*A large, detached, late Victorian house, set in an elevated position with good views across the Conwy Estuary, has been converted into a privately owned and personally run hotel which is particularly popular with golfing parties as there are 3 courses within 2 miles. Well equipped bedrooms provide en suite facilities, while the public areas include both a very attractive restaurant and a spaciously comfortable lounge.*
16⇆♪1🛏 CTV in all bedrooms Ⓡ T ✖
30P 🛆 ✿
♡ International V ♧ ⚏ ↙ Last dinner 9pm
Credit Cards ⒈ ⒊

### ★★58% Deganwy Castle
Station Rd LL31 9DA ☎(0492)583555
RS Jan-Feb
*Commanding excellent views of the Conwy Estuary and Conwy Castle this large rambling house is situated on the A496. The bedrooms, although fairly simple in style, are quite well equipped and suitable for both holidaymakers and business people.*
32⇆♪(4fb)2🛏↙in 2 bedrooms CTV in all bedrooms ⓇT✱
sB&B⇆♪£35 dB&B⇆♪£54 🅿
70P ✿ CFA *xmas*
V ♧ ⚏ ✱ Bar Lunch £1-£6.50 High tea fr£5 Dinner fr£12.50 Last dinner 9.30pm
Credit Cards ⒈ ⒉ ⒊ ⒌ ⓔ

**See advertisement under CONWY**

---

**DERBY** Derbyshire Map **08** SK33 ◔

### ★★★68% Forte Posthouse
Pasture Hill, Littleover DE3 7BA (Forte Hotels) ☎(0332)514933
Telex no 377081 FAX (0332) 518668
RS Xmas & New Year
*Located adjacent to the junction of the A5250 and B5019 at Littleover on the southern edge of the city. Management and staff provide polite and friendly service to complement the consistently good accommodation.*
62⇆↙in 29 bedrooms CTV in all bedrooms ⓇT✱S%
sB⇆£39.50-£49.50 dB⇆£39.50-£49.50 (room only) 🅿
⒧200P ✿ CFA
♡ International V ♧ ⚏ ↙ ✱ S% Lunch fr£8.50 High tea fr£1.25 Dinner £13.95&alc Last dinner 10.30pm
Credit Cards ⒈ ⒉ ⒊ ⒋ ⒌

---

### ★★★68% Hotel Ristorante La Gondola
220 Osmaston Rd DE3 8JX ☎(0332)32895 FAX (0332) 384512
*For many years the restaurant here has been popular for its varied international cuisine and recently a wing of quality bedrooms has been built, offering warm well equipped accommodation. Close to the city on the A514, the whole complex offers friendly attentive service.*
20rm(19⇆♪)(7fb) CTV in all bedrooms ⓇT
✖ (ex guide dogs) sB&B⇆♪£41-£69 dB&B⇆♪£50-£79 🅿
⒧CTV 50P CFA *xmas*
♡ Continental V ♧ ⚏ ✱ Lunch fr£7.25 Dinner £9.25-£10.45 Last dinner 10pm
Credit Cards ⒈ ⒉ ⒊ ⒋ ⒌

### ★★★67% Midland
Midland Rd DE1 2SQ (Best Western) ☎(0332)45894
Telex no 378373 FAX (0332) 293522
Closed 25-26 Dec & 1 Jan
*An hotel conveniently situated beside the railway station now offers, at the end of stage one of a major alteration and refurbishment programme, 51 comfortably appointed rooms with a good range of facilities ; improved accommodation and the provision of additional meeting rooms make this a popular choice with businessmen during the week.*
49⇆♪1🛏 CTV in all bedrooms ⓇT✱ sB&B⇆♪£66-£71.50 dB&B⇆♪£86-£91.50 🅿
⒧95P 15☝ CFA 🎵
♡ English & French V ♧ ⚏ ✱ Lunch £10-£22alc Dinner £12.85-£20.10 Last dinner 10pm
Credit Cards ⒈ ⒉ ⒊ ⒌

Remember to book early for holiday
and bank holiday times.

**★★★59% International**

Burton Rd (A5250) DE3 6AD (Consort) ☎(0332)369321
Telex no 377759 FAX (0332) 294430

*An hotel on the A5250 Littleover road, popular with business guests during the week and kept busy at weekends by local people attending speciality evenings, offers extremely well equipped – if rather dull – accommodation; bedrooms vary considerably in both size and style, the lightest and most modern being located in an annexe.*

41⇆Annexe21⇆(2fb) CTV in all bedrooms ® T S%
sB&B⇆£25-£55 dB&B⇆£35-£70 ➤
Lift ( 75P CFA gymnasium ♫ xmas
♀ English & Continental V ♥ ⊉ Lunch £7.50-£8.50 Dinner
£8.50-£10.50&alc Last dinner 10.30pm
Credit Cards [1][2][3][5] ⓔ

**★★70% Kedleston Country House**

Kedleston Rd DE6 4JD (3m NW) ☎(0332)559202 & 556507
FAX (0332) 558822

*Set in open countryside this mid 18th-century house is continually being improved yet still retains its Georgian charm and character. Staff are friendly and attentive and the hotel is popular with businessmen and tourists alike.*

14⇆🛏1🖫 CTV in all bedrooms ® T 🍴 sB&B⇆🛏£44-£48
dB&B⇆🛏£62-£68
120P ⇜ CFA
♀ English & French V ♥ ⊉ Sunday Lunch £6.50-£10.50&alc
Dinner £13.50&alc Last dinner 9.15pm
Credit Cards [1][2][3][4][5] ⓔ

---

**DESBOROUGH** Northamptonshire Map **04** SP88

**⇪ Forte Travelodge**

Harborough Rd(on A6, southbound) (Forte)
☎(0536)762034 Central Res (0800) 850950

*Well equipped value-for-money accommodation is provided at this Travelodge on the A6 southbound, 4 miles southeast of Market Harborough and 5 miles northwest of Kettering. There is an adjacent Little Chef.*

32⇆🛏(32fb) CTV in all bedrooms ® sB⇆🛏£29.95
dB⇆🛏£29.95 (room only)
( 32P ⇜
Credit Cards [1][2][3]

---

**DEVAUDEN** Gwent Map **03** ST49

**★★⁂⁂⁂81% Pen-y-Bryn House**

NP6 6NN ☎Wolvesnenton(02915)707 & 708 FAX (02915) 777

*Richard and Anita Wallace moved from the The Valley of the Wye at Tintern to this smaller property on the top of Devauden Hill to realise an ambition to run a small hotel with a top class restaurant. And the result of their labours, the Pen-y-Bryn, is our 'Best Newcomer' for Wales this year. The Wallaces have put their hearts into creating just 6 lovely bedrooms, with all the little comforts the modern traveller requires. However, the restaurant, much larger than 6 bedrooms would usually dictate, is the centre of attraction with its restful atmosphere of comfortable opulence. They set out to appoint the best chef they could find – and Wayne Michael Leadon is a quite a find. He cooks with considerable skill and dedication, drawing from experience gained from his training at the Savoy and during his travels in France and Spain. Dishes are ambitious and carefully described, the menu never too large but always tempting, with a nice balance between meats and seafood. Good food is complemented by formal service and a wine list that offers examples from a wide range of producing countries, many under £12.*

6⇆🛏 1🖫 CTV in all bedrooms ® T 🍴 (ex guide dogs) ✳
sB&B⇆🛏£72-£85 dB&B⇆🛏£96-£120 ➤
20P ⇜ ✿ xmas
V ♥ ⊉ ⅙ ✳ Lunch fr£16.95 Dinner fr£22&alc Last dinner
10pm
Credit Cards [1][2][3][4]

---

**DEVIZES** Wiltshire Map **04** SU06

**★★★62% Bear**

Market Place SN10 1HS ☎(0380)722444 FAX (0380) 722450
Closed 25-26 Dec

*Dating from 1550, this friendly former coaching inn in the centre of town provides comfortable prettily decorated bedrooms of varying size but all well equipped. The traditional bar and supper rooms are very popular with locals and residents alike, and the restaurant offers table d'hôte and à la carte menus.*

24⇆🛏(5fb)3🖫 CTV in all bedrooms ® T sB&B⇆🛏fr£46
dB&B⇆🛏£64-£75 ➤
CTV 25P (50p) 🐾 (£1)
V ♥ ⊉ ⅙ ✳ Lunch fr£8.50&alc Dinner fr£14.75&alc Last
dinner 9.30pm
Credit Cards [1][3] ⓔ

**★★65% Castle**

New Park St SN10 1DS ☎(0380)729300 FAX (0380) 729155
Closed 26 Dec

*The cosy public areas of this 18th-century former coaching inn retain their traditional character, with a popular bar serving a wide range of bar food and a restaurant with table d'hôte and grill menus. An extensive refurbishment programme has provided comfortable bedrooms with modern facilities. Staff are friendly and helpful.*

18⇆🛏(2fb) CTV in all bedrooms ® T ✳ sB&B⇆🛏£40-£45
dB&B⇆🛏£55-£65
9🐾 CFA
V ♥ ⊉ ✳ Lunch fr£8 Dinner fr£10&alc Last dinner 9.45pm
Credit Cards [1][2][3][5] ⓔ

---

**DINAS MAWDDWY** Gwynedd Map **06** SH81

**★★64% Buckley Pines**

SY20 9LP ☎(06504)261 due to change to (0654) 531261

*A small 19th century inn set in the foothills of Snowdonia, with a spacious comfortable lounge and cosy bar with log fires, pretty bedrooms and a large restaurant with beautiful tranquil views.*

11rm(3⇆2🛏)(1fb) CTV in all bedrooms ® sB&B£25
sB&B⇆🛏£28 dB&B£40 dB&B⇆🛏£46 ➤
40P ⇜ 🚣 pool table xmas
♀ English & French V ♥ ⊉ Sunday Lunch £5.75-£6.25 Dinner
£9&alc Last dinner 9pm
Credit Cards [1][3] ⓔ

---

**DINNINGTON** South Yorkshire Map **08** SK58

**★★★67% Dinnington Hall**

Falcon Way S31 3NY ☎Worksop(0909)569661
FAX (0909)563441

*In a quiet residential area only 4 miles from junction 31 of the M1, this Georgian manor house of architectural and historical interest is set in 3 acres of grounds. Run on country house lines, it offers friendly personal service and interesting choices on the restaurant menu.*

10⇆🛏(2fb)1🖫 CTV in all bedrooms ® T ✳ sB⇆🛏£51.50-
£57.75 dB⇆🛏£57.75-£68.25 (room only) ➤
60P ⇜ ✿ xmas
♀ French V ♥ ⊉ ✳ Dinner fr£15.95&alc Last dinner 9.30pm
Credit Cards [1][2][3]

---

**DISLEY** Cheshire Map **07** SJ98

**★★★66% Moorside**

Mudhurst Ln, Higher Disley SK12 2AP ☎(0663)764151
Telex no 665170 FAX (0663) 762794

*Hidden behind this quiet moorland village, off Buxton Old Road in the village of Higher Disley, is an extensive hotel with a high quality leisure complex. It offers comfortable lounges and a choice of restaurants, and despite its size it retains a feeling of individuality.*

96rm(93⇆3🛏)(2fb)2🖫 CTV in all bedrooms ® T ✳ S%
sB⇆🛏£73-£88 dB⇆🛏£88-£98 (room only) ➤
( CTV 250P ✿ CFA ☒ (heated) ▶ 9 ♪ (hard) squash snooker
sauna solarium gymnasium aerobics studio clay pigeon
shooting ♫ xmas

♀ English & French **V** ♿ ⚗ Lunch fr£11.50 Dinner fr£17.50
Last dinner 10pm
Credit Cards 1 2 3 5 £

---

**DISS** Norfolk Map **05** TM18

⚘ ✗ ✗**Salisbury House**
84 Victoria Rd IP22 3JG ☎(0379)644738
*This detached and harmoniously furnished period house on the
outskirts of the town complements a two-part dining room
overlooking the gardens with two lovely lounges. Sue Davies is a
warm and attentive hostess, while her husband Barry provides a
well balanced selection of imaginative dishes which is changed
regularly to make full use of fresh seasonal produce. Mainly light
cuisine, its delicate flavours enhanced by skilfully prepared sauces,
includes red snapper mousseline on a refined bouillabaisse sauce, or
poached salmon with vermouth and lemon. Dinner offers 5 choices
at each course and the luncheon menu, though shorter, offers very
good value. The list of some 210 French wines that accompanies
the meal includes 40 or so half bottles.*
Closed Sun & Mon, 1wk Xmas & 2wks Summer Lunch not
served Sat (Tue-Fri by arrangement only)
♀ British & French 34 seats Lunch £19.25-£25alc Dinner
£19.25-£25alc Last lunch 1.45pm Last dinner 9.15pm 10 P ⚡
Credit Cards 1 3

---

**DOLGELLAU** Gwynedd Map **06** SH71

★★★⚘ ⚑70% **Dolmelynllyn Hall**
Ganllwyd LL40 2HP (5m N on A470) ☎Ganllwyd(034140)273
Closed Jan-Feb RS Dec
*Parts of this stone-built country house date back to the 16th
century, and it has a wealth of charm and character. It stands in
extensive grounds and delightful formal gardens, off the A410, 3
miles north of Dolgellau. Jonathan Barkwith and his daughter Jo,
who is also the chef, acquired the house in 1988, and have
painstakingly restored and converted it into a very pleasant
country house hotel, with well equipped accommodation, and
elegant, comfortable public rooms.*
11➪ꛯ1♨⚡in 2 bedrooms CTV in all bedrooms ® **T**
sB&B➪ꛯ£43.50-£54 dB&B➪ꛯ£87-£108 (incl dinner) 🛏
25P ⚘ ❋ CFA ♪ nc10yrs
♿ ⚗ ⚡ Bar Lunch £3.50-£6.50 Dinner £18.75 Last dinner 9pm
Credit Cards 1 2 3 £
**See advertisement on page 259**

★★66% **Dolserau Hall**
LL40 2AG (Minotels) ☎(0341)422522
*An attractive mid-Victorian country house set in its own grounds in
picturesque countryside approximately 2 miles east of Dolgellau.
With well equipped bedrooms and pleasant public areas it is
suitable for both tourists and business people alike.*
14rm(13➪ꛯ)(4fb) CTV in all bedrooms ® **T** sB&B➪ꛯ£39
dB&B➪ꛯ£70 🛏
Lift 70P ⚘ ❋ CFA ⚭ xmas
**V** ♿ ⚗ ⚡ Bar Lunch £2.50-£10alc High tea £3-£6alc Dinner
£15-£20 Last dinner 8.30pm
Credit Cards 1 3
**See advertisement on page 259**

★★64% **George III**
Penmaenpool LL40 1YD ☎(0341)422525 FAX (0341) 423565
Closed 25 Dec-6 Jan RS May Day
*The original part of the hotel dates back to 1650, and the public
areas retain much of their original character. The bedrooms are
well equipped, and the majority have an suite facilities. Some are
located in an adjacent lodge which was once the railway station
master's house ; it stands at the head of the Mawddach Estuary, 2
miles west of Dolgellau on the A493.*
6rm(4➪ꛯ)Annexe6➪ꛯ CTV in all bedrooms ® **T** ❋ S10%
dB&B£48-£52 dB&B➪ꛯ£85-£95 🛏
100P ⚘ ❋ ♪
♀ Welsh, English & French **V** ♿ ❋ S10% Lunch fr£8.80
Dinner fr£4alc Last dinner 8.45pm
Credit Cards 1 2 3

Opening doors to the World of books

Book Tokens

Book Tokens can be bought and exchanged at most bookshops

Visit the incomparable Derbyshire Dales
Magnificent countryside, so many places of interest to see and enjoy, from Stately Homes to Theme Parks. All within easy reach of the luxurious comforts of our modern★★★ family hotel..

DINNER DANCES Friday & Saturday

Send for FREE colour brochure

Prices fully inclusive of Dinner, Bed & Breakfast & Sunday Lunch where applicable

For Business Accommodation or for a short holiday break, you'll enjoy your stay at the

International
BURTON RD, DERBY Tel:0332-369321

### ★★ 63% **Royal Ship**

Queens Square LL40 1AR (Frederic Robinson) ☎(0341)422209

*As a result of recent refurbishment, the majority of rooms in this 19th-century former coaching inn in the town centre are attractively furnished and decorated, and are quite well equipped with modern en suite facilities.*

24rm(13⇌3↑) CTV in all bedrooms ® ₦ (ex guide dogs) ✱ sB&B£17.50 sB&B⇌↑£29-£34 dB&B£35 dB&B⇌↑£58-£68 ➡

Lift CTV 8P *xmas*

V ♥ ♨ ✱ Lunch £7.50 Dinner £12.50 Last dinner 9pm

Credit Cards ①③⑤

### ★ ❀65% **Clifton House**

Smithfield Square LL40 1ES ☎(0341)422554

*Sturdy and stone-built, a town-centre house dating back to 1813 is now operated as a privately owned hotel personally run by enthusiastic young proprietors. Bedrooms are well equipped (several having en suite facilities) and equally suited to the needs of holidaymakers or business people. A pleasant restaurant in the stone-walled, low-ceilinged basement – which dates from 1730 and was originally the County Gaol – provides a popular venue in which to enjoy a range of skilfully prepared dishes.*

7rm(4⇌↑) CTV in all bedrooms ® ₦ sB&B£21-£28 sB&B⇌↑£26-£33 dB&B£34-£40 dB&B⇌↑£44-£50 ➡ 3P ⇔

V ♥ Lunch £7.50-£8.50 Dinner £7.50-£14&alc Last dinner 9.30pm

Credit Cards ①③ £

---

## DOLPHINTON Strathclyde *Lanarkshire* Map 11 NT14

### ★★★ ⚑ 65%, **Dolphinton House**

EH46 7AB ☎(0968)82286 FAX (0899) 20456

*Set in extensive parkland, this fine converted country mansion retains much of its original Victorian character. Bedrooms and bathrooms are generally spacious and all are well equipped. There is a comfortable lounge, snug bar serving many malts and local beers, and attractive dining room featuring Scottish country cooking and hearty breakfasts.*

12⇌↑(2fb)2⊞ CTV in all bedrooms ® T ✱ sB&B⇌↑£48.25-£65 dB&B⇌↑£75-£119.50 ➡ 40P ⇔ ❀ croquet ♨ *xmas*

V ♥ ♨ ✂ ✱ Lunch £8-£15alc Dinner £19.50-£23.50&alc Last dinner 9.30pm

Credit Cards ①②③④⑤ £

---

## DOLWYDDELAN Gwynedd Map 06 SH75

### ★★ 63% **Elen's Castle**

LL25 0EJ ☎(06906)207

*This 18th-century former beer house and coaching inn is now a small, friendly, privately owned hotel with a wealth of charm and character. It is situated on the A470, 6 miles south of Betws-y-Coed.*

10rm(3⇌4↑)(2fb)1⊞ ® ✱ sB&B£17.50 sB&B⇌↑£19.50 dB&B£20 dB&B⇌↑£21.50 ➡

CTV 40P ⇔ ❀ CFA ✎ sauna *xmas*

♀ English & Welsh V ♥ ♨ ✂ ✱ Bar Lunch £1.20-£7.95alc High tea £5-£7alc Dinner £11.50 Last dinner 8.30pm

Credit Cards ①③

---

## DONCASTER South Yorkshire Map 08 SE50 ◎

### ★★★ 69% **Doncaster Moat House**

Warmsworth DN4 9UX (2.5m SW on A630 at junc with A1) (Queens Moat) ☎(0302)310331 Telex no 547963 FAX (0302) 310197

*Situated at Warmsworth on the A630, almost on the A1(M) junction and within easy access of the M18, this well managed modern hotel provides comfortable accommodation which at the time of inspection was being extended further with the addition of a leisure complex.*

100⇌↑(4fb)✂in 6 bedrooms CTV in all bedrooms ® T ✱ sB&B⇌↑£44-£75 dB&B⇌↑£64-£87 ➡

Lift ( 200P ❀ CFA ▣ (heated) sauna solarium gymnasium ♀ French V ♥ ♨ ✂ ✱ Lunch fr£8.50&alc Dinner fr£13.50&alc Last dinner 10pm

Credit Cards ①②③④⑤

### ★★★ 64% **Mount Pleasant**

Great North Rd DN11 0HP (Consort) ☎(0302)868696 & 868219 FAX (0302) 865130

(For full entry see Rossington)

### ★★★ 62% **Danum Swallow**

High St DN1 1DN (Swallow) ☎(0302)342261 Telex no 547533 FAX (0302) 329034

*Standards continue to rise at this conference-orientated hotel, the recent refurbishment of restaurant and cocktail bar completing the upgrading of all public rooms to provide bright and comfortable areas which are well frequented by local people. Bedrooms vary in size and style, but all offer a good range of facilities and have en suite bathrooms.*

66⇌↑(2fb)1⊞ ✂in 30 bedrooms CTV in all bedrooms ® T ✱ sB&B⇌↑£67 dB&B⇌↑£86 ➡

Lift ( 60P 25◉ CFA *xmas*

V ♥ ♨ ✱ Lunch £7-£8.25&alc Dinner £13.25&alc Last dinner 9.45pm

Credit Cards ①②③④⑤ £

### ★★★ 68%, **Regent**

Regent Square DN1 2DS ☎(0302)364180 & 364336 Telex no 54480 FAX (0302) 322331

Closed 25 Dec & 1 Jan RS Bank Hols

*Refurbishment and alteration of two of the three bars has now been completed. Returning guests list highly the 'comfortable and relaxed atmosphere' as an important asset.*

50⇌↑(2fb)3⊞ CTV in all bedrooms ® T sB&B⇌↑£49.50-£56.50 dB&B⇌↑£55-£60 ➡

Lift ( 20P CFA sauna

♀ English & French V ♥ ♨ Lunch £2.95-£12 High tea £3.50 Dinner £11.95&alc Last dinner 10pm

Credit Cards ①②③④⑤ £

### ⭫Campanile

Doncaster Leisure Park, Bawtry Rd DN4 7PD (Campanile) ☎(0302)370770 Telex no 547942 FAX (0302) 370813

*A hotel standing close to the racecourse in an extensive leisure park.*

50⇌↑ CTV in all bedrooms ® T sB⇌↑fr£36 dB⇌↑fr£36 (room only) ➡

56P CTV *xmas*

♀ English & French Lunch £3.75-£5 Dinner £6.80-£8.90 Last dinner 10pm

Credit Cards ①③ £

**See advertisement on page 261**

---

## DONNINGTON

See **Telford**

---

## DORCHESTER Dorset Map 03 SY69

### ★★★ 70% *King's Arms*

DT1 1HF (Exec Hotel) ☎(0305)65353 FAX (0305) 60269

*A large and busy hotel with much to commend it features 2 outrageously furnished suites with Tutankhamun and Lawrence of Arabia themes; bedroom décor and furnishings are attractively co-ordinated, and an extensive bar menu and bistro offer alternatives to the more formal meals served in the comfortable dining room. Polite and friendly staff provide efficient service throughout.*

31⇌↑(1fb) CTV in all bedrooms ®

Lift 36P ⇔

♥ ♨ ✂ Last dinner 8.30pm

Credit Cards ①②③

**See advertisement on page 261**

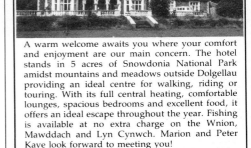

259

## DORCHESTER-ON-THAMES Oxfordshire Map **04** SU59

**★★★ ❀71% *White Hart***
High St OX9 8HN ☎Oxford(0865)340074 FAX (0865) 341082
(Rosette awarded for dinner only)
*This old coaching inn in the quiet village centre has individually styled comfortable bedrooms with many thoughtful extras. Public areas, with beams and log fires, have lots of character and the popular restaurant serves carefully prepared tempting dishes. Professional staff provide friendly service.*
20⇨♠(2fb)2⊞ CTV in all bedrooms ® **T** ✖ (ex guide dogs)
CTV 25P ⇎
♀ English & French **V** ♦ ⊬ Last dinner 9pm
Credit Cards 1 2 3 5

**★★ 65% *George***
High St OX9 8HH ☎Oxford(0865)340404 Telex no 83147
Closed 1 wk Xmas
*This cosy little coaching inn, set at the centre of the charming village, provides comfortable accommodation: more traditional in the main building including some four-poster beds, newer in the converted outbuildings. Friendly, informal young staff create a cheerful atmosphere in the character public areas. Meals are served in two attractive vaulted beamed dining rooms and the wide choice of dishes is accompanied by a carefully chosen wine list.*
9⇨♠Annexe8⇨♠2⊞ CTV in all bedrooms ®
CTV 60P ⇎ ✲
♀ English & French **V** ♦ ⊬ Last dinner 9.45pm
Credit Cards 1 2 3 5

## DORKING Surrey Map **04** TQ14

**★★★★ 57% The Burford Bridge**
Burford Bridge, Box Hill RH5 6BX (2m NE A24) (Forte Hotels) ☎(0306)884561 Telex no 859507 FAX (0306) 880386
*Set amidst beautiful gardens on the banks of the River Mole, this hotel was a fashionable rendezvous for country weekends as far back as the 18th century. It continues to offer a warm welcome and comfortable accommodation in well equipped bedrooms, many of which have been refurbished. Service is well executed by pleasant, courteous and friendly staff.*
48⇨♠⊬in 16 bedrooms CTV in all bedrooms ® **T** ✱
sB⇨♠fr£85 dB⇨♠£110 (room only) ⊟
☾ 100P ✲ CFA ⇒ (heated) ♧ *xmas*
**V** ♦ ⊈ ⊬ ✱ Lunch £15&alc Dinner £19.95 Last dinner 10pm
Credit Cards 1 2 3 4 5

**★★★ 53% The White Horse**
High St RH4 1BE (Forte Hotels) ☎(0306)881138
FAX (0306) 887241
*Conveniently situated in the town centre with a car park to the rear, this busy coaching inn is geared mainly to the commercial traveller. Bedrooms in the main building vary in size and shape, but those in the garden annexe offer a uniform standard of well equipped accommodation and have all recently benefited from the addition of new bathrooms. Public areas are limited and therefore often overcrowded.*
36⇨♠Annexe32⇨♠(2fb)1⊞⊬in 20 bedrooms CTV in all bedrooms ® **T** ✱ S% sB⇨♠£70 dB⇨♠£85-£93 (room only)
⊟
☾ 73P CFA ⇒ (heated) *xmas*
**V** ♦ ⊈ ⊬ ✱ Lunch £9.95-£10.95 High tea fr£3.75 Dinner £15.95&alc Last dinner 9.30pm
Credit Cards 1 2 3 4 5

**⌂ Forte Travelodge**
Reigate Rd RH4 1QB (0.5m E, on A25) (Forte)
☎(0306)740361 Central Res (0800) 850950
*A well maintained, purpose-built block of identical well equipped bedrooms offering excellent value for money. Meals are available at the adjacent Little Chef.*
29⇨♠(29fb) CTV in all bedrooms ® sB⇨♠£29.95
dB⇨♠£29.95 (room only)
☾ 29P ⇎
✱
Credit Cards 1 2 3

**❀❀✕✕ Partners West Street**
2, 3 & 4 West St RH4 1BL ☎(0306)882826
*One of our Best New Restaurants 1991/1992 to be included in our guide, this smart and tastefully decorated restaurant, newly opened near Dorking High Street after relocating from Sutton, aims to provide a short but interesting fixed-price menu of such imaginative dishes as red mullet served on a bed of aubergines and peppers, or calves' liver served with a delicately flavoured spring onion butter. Value-for-money meals can be accompanied by the excellent house wine, service is efficient, yet relaxed and friendly, and the atmosphere is lively. (See colour feature on p39.)*
Closed Mon Lunch not served Sat
Dinner not served Sun
♀ French 45 seats ✱ Lunch £13.25-£19.50 Dinner £16-£26.95 Last lunch 2pm Last dinner 9.30pm ⊅ nc8yrs ⊬
Credit Cards 1 2 3 5

## DORNIE Highland *Ross & Cormarty* Map **14** NG82

**★★ 64% Castle Inn**
IV40 8DT ☎(059985)205
RS Jan (ex New Year) & Feb
*This small family-run inn on 'the road to the isles' has been refurbished to provide the comforts and facilities required by the modern traveller. It is a friendly place, and consistently good food is served in the attractive west-facing restaurant.*
12rm(1⇨6♠)(1fb) CTV in all bedrooms ® sB&B£18.50-£22.50 sB&B⇨♠£22.50-£28.50 dB&B£37-£45 dB&B⇨♠£45-£57 ⊟
20P ⇎ *xmas*
♀ Scottish & French **V** ♦ ⊈ ✱ Bar Lunch £5-£12alc Dinner £16.50-£18.50 Last dinner 9pm
Credit Cards 1 3

**See advertisement on page 263**

## DORNOCH Highland *Sutherland* Map **14** NH78

**★★ 65% Dornoch Castle**
Castle St IV25 3SD (Inter-Hotels) ☎(0862)810216
FAX (0862) 810981
Closed Nov-mid Apr
*Parts of this privately owned hotel date back to the 15th century. Public rooms are comfortable and characterful. There are bedrooms in the older part of the building as well as in the newer wing, where some have direct access to the attractive well kept and sheltered garden.*
4⇨♠Annexe15rm(13⇨♠)(2fb) CTV in 4 bedrooms ® **T** ✱
sB&B⇨♠£32-£34 dB&B⇨♠£56-£72 ⊟
Lift CTV 16P ⇎ ✲
♀ Scottish & Continental **V** ♦ ⊈ ⊬ ✱ Lunch £6.50-£8 Dinner fr£15.50 Last dinner 8.30pm
Credit Cards 1 2 3

## DORRINGTON Shropshire Map **07** SJ40

**❀❀✕✕ Country Friends Restaurants**
SY5 7JD ☎(074373)707
*A half-timbered black and white house beside the A49 Shrewsbury-Leominster road at the heart of the village, offers very enjoyable meals which are prepared to order, making the fullest use of fresh produce and complementing main ingredients by light sauces and a wide variety of crisp vegetables. Overnight accommodation is available, including a 'special' breakfast.*
Closed Sun & Mon, 5 days Xmas, 1 wk Feb, 2 wks end Jul & 1 wk Oct

→

D

40 seats Lunch £16.50&alc Dinner £16&alc Last lunch 2pm
Last dinner 9pm 30 P
Credit Cards 1 3

## DOUGLAS

See Man, Isle of

## DOVER Kent Map 05 TR34

### ★★★63% Dover Moat House

Townwall St CT16 1SZ (Queens Moat) ☎(0304)203270
Telex no 96458 FAX (0304) 213230
*Spacious king-size and standard double bedrooms – all well
equipped and very comfortable – are currently being refurbished
and upgraded to match the standards of modern, attractively
furnished public areas which include a smart reception lobby and
the popular Braids Restaurant. Levels of service are generally
acceptable, room service being available all day and reception
operating throughout the night, and car parking facilities are
provided.*
79⇌♠(32fb)⊁in 5 bedrooms CTV in all bedrooms ® T ✳ S%
sB⇌♠£73-£77.50 dB⇌♠£84-£92 (room only) ☒
Lift ( 8P ⌷ (heated)
♀ English & French V ♥ ♨ ✳ S% Lunch £15-£17&alc Dinner
£15-£17&alc Last dinner 10.15pm
Credit Cards 1 2 3 5

### ★★★62% Forte Posthouse

Singledge Ln, Whitfield CT16 3LF (3m NW junc A2/A256)
(Forte Hotels) ☎(0304)821222 Telex no 965866
FAX (0304) 825576
*An hotel conveniently located on the A2 north of Dover has been
skilfully designed to meet every need in its generally spacious,
comfortable and very well equipped bedrooms. Le Jardin
Restaurant, which usually offers a choice of à la carte and carvery
menus, is augmented by a relaxing lobby lounge and an attractive
bar/conservatory. Conference facilities and good car parking
amenities are available. Provision is made for disabled guests and
service is friendly.*
67⇌♠(15fb)⊁in 30 bedrooms CTV in all bedrooms ® T ✳ S%
sB⇌£39.50-£49.50 dB⇌£39.50-£49.50 (room only) ☒
( 75P ✿ CFA *xmas*
V ♥ ♨ ⊁ ✳ S% Lunch £7.50 Dinner £13.95 Last dinner 10pm
Credit Cards 1 2 3 5

## DOWNHAM MARKET Norfolk Map 05 TF60

### ★★57% Castle

High St PE38 9HF ☎(0366)384311 FAX (0366) 384770
*A 300-year-old coaching inn, standing in the centre of this market
town, which is described as the gateway to Norfolk, offers rooms
which are well equipped though modestly decorated and furnished.
Meals are freshly prepared and enjoyable.*
11rm(4⇌5♠)2₤ CTV in all bedrooms ® T S% sB&B£34
sB⇌♠£36 dB&B£42 dB&B⇌♠£45 ☒
( 30P 1♠ CFA *xmas*
♀ English & Continental V ♥ ♨ ⊁ S% Lunch £9.50&alc High
tea £6.50 Dinner £10.50&alc Last dinner 9pm
Credit Cards 1 2 3 ④

### ★61% Crown

Bridge St PE38 9DH ☎(0366)382322
*Guests are assured of a warm welcome at this characterful town-
centre inn. The accommodation is fairly old-fashioned with good
facilities and the Buttery serves snacks and freshly cooked meals
throughout the day. There is a large rear car park.*
10rm(5⇌2♠) CTV in 7 bedrooms ® T sB&B£26
sB&B⇌♠£35 dB&B£36 dB&B⇌♠£45 ☒
CTV 30P
V ♥ S% Lunch £5.60-£6.75&alc Dinner £5.60-£6.75&alc Last
dinner 9pm
Credit Cards 1 2 3 5 ④

### ✱✕Swinton House

Stow Bridge PE34 3PP (3m N) ☎(0366)383151
*Situated just off the A10 on the outskirts of the village, 2 miles
north of Downham Market, this restaurant offers a small lounge
serving aperitifs and coffee as well as the dining room with its
outlook over a lovingly cared-for garden with floodlit pond. The
menu, though limited in range, is well composed and changes daily,
such dishes as lambs' liver in yoghurt and chicken breast with field
mushrooms being based on fresh, quality ingredients ; your meal
being completed by warm apple strudel or a selection of British
cheeses. A short wine list, like the menu, represents excellent value
for money, and an enthusiastic hostess provides warm hospitality.*
Closed Mon & 24-28 Dec Lunch not served Tue-Sat
Dinner not served Sun
18 seats ✱ Sunday Lunch £8.75 Dinner £13 Last dinner 9pm 7
P nc8yrs ⊁

## DOWN THOMAS Devon Map 02 SX55

### ★★58% Langdon Court

PL9 0DY ☎(0752)862358 FAX (0752) 863428
*Modernised Elizabethan mansion on an unclassified road between
Wembury and Down Thomas.*
15⇌(3fb) CTV in all bedrooms ® T ✳ sB&B⇌£28-£44
dB&B⇌£52-£64 ☒
100P ✿ pool room nc5yrs
♀ French V ♥ ♨ Sunday Lunch £8.75 Dinner £14.50-
£15.25&alc Last dinner 9.30pm
Credit Cards 1 2 3 5

## DRAYCOTT Derbyshire Map 08 SK43

### ★★★56% Tudor Court

Gypsy Ln DE7 3PB ☎(03317)4581 FAX (03317) 3133
*Standing in 8 acres of grounds, this modern hotel, built in
traditional style, offers good conference facilities. There is also a
popular night club within the complex.*
30⇌♠(8fb) CTV in all bedrooms ® T sB&B⇌♠£21.55-
£58.25 dB&B⇌♠£43-£73.50 ☒
( 300P ✿ CFA
♀ English & French V ♥ ♨ ⊁ Lunch £5.50-£6.95 High tea
£2.50-£6.50 Dinner £12.95-£14.95&alc Last dinner 10pm
Credit Cards 1 2 3 5 ④

## DRIFFIELD, GREAT Humberside Map 08 TA05

### ★★★67% Bell

46 Market Place YO25 7AP (Best Western)
☎Driffield(0377)46661 Telex no 52341 FAX (0377) 43228
*A good, modern leisure complex has been added to this interesting
coaching inn, which has been carefully modernised to provide good
facilities in comfortable bedrooms, yet still retain its character and
atmosphere.*
14⇌2₤ CTV in all bedrooms ® T ✘ (ex guide dogs)
sB&B⇌£59.50-£65.50 dB&B⇌£82.50-£91 ☒
( 50P ✿ CFA ⌷ (heated) squash snooker sauna solarium
gymnasium steam room whirlpool masseur nc12yrs *xmas*
V ♥ ♨ ⊁ Sunday Lunch £8-£9alc High tea £4-£6 Dinner £12-
£16alc Last dinner 9.30pm
Credit Cards 1 2 3 5

### ★★♨57% Wold House Country

Nafferton YO25 0LD (3m E A166) ☎Driffield(0377)44242
Closed 24-27 Dec
*Friendly, informal, family service is provided at this distinctive
country hotel which is set in spacious grounds, and enjoys
panoramic views over open countryside. Guests have use of the
swimming pool within the neatly maintained gardens.*
10rm(7⇌3♠)Annexe1♠(4fb) CTV in all bedrooms ®
sB&B£27 sB&B⇌♠£35-£38 dB&B£48-£55 dB&B⇌♠£55-£58
CTV 40P ✿ ⊃ (heated) snooker putting table tennis

V ♥ Sunday Lunch £7-£8 Dinner £12.50-£15 Last dinner 8.30pm
Credit Cards 1 3 £

---

★★★★ 70% **Château Impney**
WR9 0BN ☎(0905)774411 Telex no 336673 FAX (0905) 772371
Closed Xmas
*In the style of a French château, this beautiful and elegant hotel was built as a private house in the mid-19th century and stands in extensive landscaped parkland. Popular with a wide variety of guests, it offers good attentive service, well equipped bedrooms and many other attributes. It also offers arguably the best conference, function and exhibition facilities in the country, certainly in the Midlands.*
67⇨♠(1fb)1₩ CTV in all bedrooms T ✻ sB⇨♠£39.95-£89.95 dB⇨♠£49.95-£99.95 (room only)
Lift ℂ CTV 600P ✿ ♫ (hard)
♀ English & French V ♥ ⚏ ✻ Lunch £9.99-£10.99&alc Dinner £10.99-£15.99&alc Last dinner 9.30pm
Credit Cards 1 2 3 5

★★★★ 56% **Raven**
Saint Andrews St WR9 8DU ☎(0905)772224 Telex no 336673 FAX (0905) 772371
Closed Xmas
*At the time of inspection, this former coaching inn, located in the centre of the town, was being upgraded to provide more comfortable and modern accommodation. During the week it caters primarily for business people. The beamed restaurant, with its intimate alcoves, offers simple à la carte and table d'hôte menus.*
50⇨♠(2fb) CTV in all bedrooms T ✻ sB⇨♠£39.95-£89.95 dB⇨♠£49.95-£99.95 (room only)
Lift ℂ CTV 250P ✿
♀ English & French V ♥ ⚏ ✻ Lunch £9.99-£10.99&alc Dinner £12.99-£15.99&alc Last dinner 9.30pm
Credit Cards 1 2 3 5

⌂**Forte Travelodge**
Rashwood Hill WR9 8DA (2m N, on A38) (Forte)
☎Wychbold(052786)545 Central Res (0800) 850950
*Value for money accommodation and a convenient position on the A38, close to junction 5 of the M5, ensure that this standard Travelodge is always busy. All its well equipped rooms are identical, though one has been adapted to meet the needs of disabled guests, and an adjacent Little Chef restaurant is open all day for meals and snacks.*
32⇨♠(32fb) CTV in all bedrooms ® sB⇨♠£29.95 dB⇨♠£29.95 (room only)
ℂ 32P ♿
Credit Cards 1 2 3

---

★★ 60% **Chantry**
Church St S18 6QB ☎(0246)413014
*Set in attractive, well tended gardens, the Chantry Hotel provides hospitable and caring service. Bedrooms are very well cleaned and maintained and have good soft furnishings and modern bathrooms, but some rooms are compact.*
7⇨♠ CTV in all bedrooms S10% sB&B⇨♠£40-£45 dB&B⇨♠£50-£55
28P ♿ ✿
✻ Sunday Lunch £7-£7.50 Dinner £12-£14 Last dinner 8pm

★★ 53% **Manor**
10 High St S18 6PY ☎(0246)413971
RS Sun evenings
*A small, proprietor-run hotel, situated in Old Dronfield, and dating from the 16th and 18th centuries. The hotel reflects a period atmosphere with a beamed lounge bar and stylish restaurant, the latter offering good à la carte and daily menus.*

10⇨♠(1fb) CTV in all bedrooms ® ✻ sB&B⇨♠£38-£49 dB&B⇨♠£47-£65 ♨
17P
♀ English & French V ♥ ⚏ ✻ Lunch £4.30-£8.70&alc Dinner £12.95&alc Last dinner 10pm
Credit Cards 1 2 3 5

---

❀✕✕**The Old Monastery**
AB56 2JB (1m E off Deskford Rd) ☎Buckie(0542)32660
*This popular country restaurant – once, as the name suggests, a monastery – enjoys lovely views to Spey Bay and the Murray coast from its setting on a hill. Game and seafood are prominent on an interesting menu which offers a tempting range of dishes competently prepared by chef/patron Douglas Gray who makes excellent use of the best fresh produce available locally, and a friendly staff provides attentive service.*
Closed Sun, Mon, 2 wks Nov, 3 days Xmas/New Year, 3 wks Jan
♀ Scottish & French 40 seats Last lunch 1.45pm Last dinner 9.30pm 20 P nc8yrs ✂
Credit Cards 1 2 3

---

★★★ 65% **Buchanan Highland**
G63 0BQ (Scottish Highland)(Consort) ☎(0360)60588
Telex no 778215 FAX (0360)60943
*This long-established hotel stands in the village where one turns off for the east side of Loch Lomond. After upgrading, the hotel now has several new bedrooms, a leisure complex and banqueting facilities.*
51⇨♠(3fb)1₩ CTV in all bedrooms ® T sB&B⇨♠£64-£73 dB&B⇨♠£94-£105 ♨

→

★ ★
**CASTLE INN**

8-10 FRANCIS ST. DORNIE,
KYLE OF LOCHALSH
ROSS-SHIRE IV50 8TD
TEL 059985 205

Beautifully situated in the village of Dornie and only 2 minutes walk from Eilan Donan Castle with views over the Cullins of Skye this family run hotel is ideal for touring, walking & sea fishing.

The Hotel has been completely renovated to a high standard with 13 bedrooms — 8 en suite.

Delightful imaginative cooking

Children welcome

20 foot sea going launch for hire for trips & sea fishing

Only 10 minutes from ferry to Skye

Please write or telephone

《 100P ✿ ▭ (heated) squash sauna solarium gymnasium bowling green *xmas*

♀ Scottish & French **V** ✿ *꒰* Lunch £11.50-£13.50&alc High tea £10.50-£13 Dinner £18.25-£24&alc Last dinner 9.30pm

Credit Cards 1 2 3 4 5 £

---

### DUDLEY West Midlands Map **07** SO99

See also Himley

**★★★61%** *Ward Arms*

Birmingham Rd DY1 4RN (Crown & Raven) ☎(0384)458070 Telex no 335464

*Well equipped modern accommodation in recently refurbished rooms is provided by an hotel conveniently situated for access to the M5 and close to Birmingham. The popular Mrs Simpson's Carvery offers a choice of three daily joints in addition to its simple à la carte menu.*

48₌⇪♪ CTV in all bedrooms ⓡ **T**

《 150P

♀ English & French **V** ✿ *꒰* ✕ Last dinner 9.30pm

Credit Cards 1 2 3

**★★60%** *Station*

Birmingham Rd DY1 4RA (Crown & Raven) ☎(0384)253418 Telex no 335464 FAX (0384) 457503

*Situated in the heart of the Black Country, opposite Dudley Zoo and within walking distance of the town centre, this predominantly commercial hotel combines modern and well equipped accommodation with recently refurbished public areas which include the new Trindles Restaurant, serving popular meals in steak-house style.*

38₌⇪♪(7fb) CTV in all bedrooms ⓡ **T**

Lift 《 75P

♀ English & French **V** ✿ *꒰*

Credit Cards 1 2 3

**⛫Forte Travelodge**

Dudley Rd(3m W, on A461) (Forte)

☎(0384)481579 Central Res (0800) 850950

32₌⇪♪(32fb) CTV in all bedrooms ⓡ sB₌⇪♪£29.95 dB₌⇪♪£29.95 (room only)

《 32P 🚗

Credit Cards 1 2 3

---

### DULNAIN BRIDGE Highland *Morayshire* Map **14** NH92

**★★⚑67%** *Muckrach Lodge*

PH26 3LY ☎(047985)257 FAX (047985) 325

Closed 1-21 Nov

*This privately owned and run small hotel, situated in an elevated position and surrounded by ten acres of well maintained grounds close to the Dulnain River, was once a hunting lodge. Today it offers comfortable, thoughtfully appointed bedrooms with smart modern bathrooms, a quiet, relaxing lounge and a cosy bar where interesting sandwiches are a lunchtime speciality. Its position makes it a good base for exploring the many activities available in the Spey Valley.*

10₌⇪Annexe2₌⇪(3fb) CTV in all bedrooms ⓡ **T**

🦮 (ex guide dogs) sB&B₌⇪£32-£36 dB&B₌⇪£64-£72 🚲

50P 3🚗 🚲 ✿ ♪ ⚘

♀ British & French **V** Lunch £8.50-£15alc Dinner £17-£18.50&alc Last dinner 9pm

Credit Cards 1 2 3 5 £

---

### DULVERTON Somerset Map **03** SS92

**★★★⚑72%** *Carnarvon Arms*

TA22 9AE (2m S on B3222) ☎(0398)23302 FAX (0398) 24022

Closed 8-29 Feb

*This hotel, once a busy village station during the Victorian era, retains much of its character, and standing as it does at one of the entrances to the Exmoor National Park, is ideally sited for people*

---

*who like country pursuits. Its ample public rooms offer traditional standards of comfort, and the bedrooms are well equipped with modern facilities. The owner Mrs Toni Jones and her friendly staff create a welcoming atmosphere.*

25rm(22₌⇪1♪)(2fb) CTV in all bedrooms **T** sB&Bfr£35 sB&B₌⇪♪£38-£48 dB&B£70-£90 dB&B₌⇪♪£76-£96 🚲

120P 🚗 ✿ CFA ▭ (heated) ♪ (hard) ♪ snooker clay pigeon shooting *xmas*

**V** ✿ *꒰* ✕ Lunch £7.50-£9.50 Dinner fr£17.90 Last dinner 8.30pm

Credit Cards 1 3 £

---

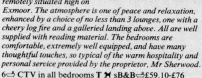

**★★🏵⚑ ASHWICK HOUSE**

TA22 9QD (3m NW off B3223) ☎(0398)23868

*This delightful Edwardian house, set in 6 acres of lawned and wooded grounds, is remotely situated high on Exmoor. The atmosphere is one of peace and relaxation, enhanced by a choice of no less than 3 lounges, one with a cheery log fire and a galleried landing above. All are well supplied with reading material. The bedrooms are comfortable, extremely well equipped, and have many thoughtful touches, so typical of the warm hospitality and personal service provided by the proprietor, Mr Sherwood.*

6₌⇪ CTV in all bedrooms **T** 🦮 sB&B₌⇪£59.10-£76 dB&B₌⇪£98.20-£136 (incl dinner) 🚲

25P 2🚘 (£2) 🚲 ✿ solarium nc8yrs *xmas*

♀ International ✿ *꒰* ✕ Sunday Lunch £14 Dinner £19.75 Last dinner 8.30pm

£

---

**★★64%** *Lion*

Bank Square TA22 9BW ☎(0398)23444

*Set on the edge of Exmoor, the Lion Hotel is believed to be at least 500 years old. It provides a good base for touring this lovely area, and major renovations have resulted in 12 well equipped en suite bedrooms. Guests can choose to relax in the cosy residents' lounge, the lounge bar or the popular tap bar.*

12₌⇪♪(1fb)1🛏 CTV in all bedrooms ⓡ **T**

CTV 6P ▭ (heated) ♪ (hard) ♪ ♻ snooker clay pigeon shooting ♫

**V** ✿ *꒰* Last dinner 9pm

Credit Cards 1 3

---

### DUMBARTON Strathclyde *Dunbartonshire* Map **10** NS37

**★★65%** *Dumbuck*

Glasgow Rd G82 1EG ☎(0389)34336 FAX (0389) 34336

*On the A814 on the eastern outskirts of the town, this popular business and function hotel in a converted 18th-century house has well equipped bedrooms and public areas with some character.*

22₌⇪♪(2fb) CTV in all bedrooms ⓡ **T** ✳ sB&B₌⇪♪£42.50 dB&B₌⇪♪£56

《 200P ✿ CFA pool table

**V** ✿ *꒰* ✳ Lunch £8.50 Dinner £10.95 Last dinner 9.30pm

Credit Cards 1 2 3 4 5

---

**⛫Forte Travelodge**

Milton G82 2TY (1m E, on A82 westbound) (Forte)

☎(0389)65202 Central Res (0800) 850950

*Situated on the north side of the River Clyde, 6 miles from Loch Lomond and 12 miles from Glasgow, this lodge offers practical*

*modern accommodation in double bedrooms, each with an
additional single divan. Meals are available in the adjacent Little
Chef, open from 7 am to 10 pm.*
32⇄♠(32fb) CTV in all bedrooms ® sB⇄♠£29.95
dB⇄♠£29.95 (room only)
《 32P 🚲
Credit Cards ①②③

---

**DUMFRIES** Dumfries & Galloway *Dumfriesshire*
Map **11** NX97 ☺

See also *Carrutherstown*
**★★★68% Station**
49 Lovers Walk DG1 1LT (Consort) ☎(0387)54316
FAX (0387) 50388
*A comfortable traditional hotel offering friendly service, inviting
bedrooms and an interesting range of good value menus.*
32⇄♠(1fb) CTV in all bedrooms ® **T** sB&B⇄♠£59-£73
dB&B⇄♠£73-£80 🄟
Lift 《 40P CFA ♫ ఉ *xmas*
♀ British, Italian & Spanish **V** ♥ ⚏ High tea £5.45 Dinner
£16&alc Last dinner 10pm
Credit Cards ①②③⑤ⓔ
**See advertisement on page 267**

**★★★66% Cairndale**
English St DG1 2DF (Inter-Hotels) ☎(0387)54111
Telex no 777530 FAX (0387) 50555
*A traditional hotel with comfortable bedrooms, interesting good
value menus and friendly service. Conveniently located very close
to the town centre.*
76⇄♠(4fb) CTV in all bedrooms ® **T** ✳ sB&B⇄♠£45-£75
dB&B⇄♠£75-£85 🄟
Lift 《 CTV 70P CFA *xmas*
♀ British, French & Italian **V** ♥ ⚏ ✂ ✳ Lunch fr£6.50 High
tea fr£5 Dinner fr£15 Last dinner 9.30pm
Credit Cards ①②③④⑤ⓔ
**See advertisement on page 267**

**★64% Skyline**
123 Irish St DG1 2NS ☎(0387)62416
Closed 25 Dec & 1-2 Jan
*Right in the centre of town, but set in a quiet side street and
conveniently provided with its own spacious car park, a friendly
little hotel under the personal supervision of its proprietors offers
modest but well decorated and efficiently maintained
accommodation.*
6rm(2♠)(2fb) CTV in all bedrooms ® ✗
CTV 20P
**V**

---

**DUNBAR** Lothian *East Lothian* Map **12** NT67

**★★66% Redheugh**
Bayswell Park EH42 1AE ☎(0368)62793
*Comfortable, well appointed bedrooms, home-cooked meals and
particularly friendly service are provided by an hotel quietly
located in a residential area.*
10⇄♠(2fb) CTV in all bedrooms ® **T** sB&B⇄♠£29.50-
£36.50 dB&B⇄♠£50-£65 🄟
CTV ✗ nc8yrs
**V** Dinner £11-£12.50&alc Last dinner 8.45pm
Credit Cards ①②③

**★★64% Bayswell**
Bayswell Park EH42 1AE (Exec Hotel) ☎(0368)62225
*On a clifftop overlooking Bass Rock, this friendly family-run hotel
has a snug bar, cosy lounge and smart restaurant. The redecorated
bedrooms are well equipped and comfortable.*
13⇄♠(4fb) CTV in all bedrooms ® **T** ✳ sB&B⇄♠£36-£38
dB&B⇄♠£54-£56 🄟
CTV 20P putting green *xmas*

$\rightarrow$

**D**

♀ British & Italian V ✿ ⚓ ✳ Bar Lunch £3.95-£9.50&alc High tea frf4.95 Dinner £5.50-£15.50alc Last dinner 9pm Credit Cards [1][2][3]

★⊕66% **The Courtyard Hotel & Restaurant**
Wood Bush Brae EH42 1HB ☎(0368)64169
RS first 3wks in Jan
6rm(1♠) CTV in all bedrooms ® ✳ sB&B£18 dB&B£34 dB&B♠£46
CTV 6P ⇄
♀ International ✳ Lunch £4.95&alc Dinner £10.50&alc Last dinner 9.30pm
Credit Cards [1][3]

---

**DUNBLANE** Central *Perthshire* Map **11** NN70

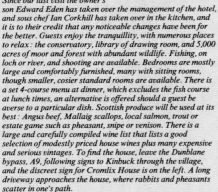

★★★

★★★⊕⊕ ♨
**CROMLIX HOUSE**

Kinbuck FK15 9JT (3 m NE B8033) (Pride of Britain)
☎(0786)822125
Telex no 779959
FAX (0786) 825450
RS Jan-Feb

*Since our last visit the owner's son Edward Eden has taken over the management of the hotel, and sous chef Ian Corkhill has taken over in the kitchen, and it is to their credit that any noticeable changes have been for the better. Guests enjoy the tranquillity, with numerous places to relax: the conservatory, library of drawing room, and 5,000 acres of moor and forest with abundant wildlife. Fishing, on loch or river, and shooting are available. Bedrooms are mostly large and comfortably furnished, many with sitting rooms, though smaller, cosier standard rooms are available. There is a set 4-course menu at dinner, which excludes the fish course at lunch times, an alternative is offered should a guest be averse to a particular dish. Scottish produce will be used at its best: Angus beef, Mallaig scallops, local salmon, trout or estate game such as pheasant, snipe or venison. There is a large and carefully compiled wine list that lists a good selection of modestly priced house wines plus many expensive and serious vintages. To find the house, leave the Dunblane bypass, A9, following signs to Kinbuck through the village, and the discreet sign for Cromlix House is on the left. A long driveway approaches the house, where rabbits and pheasants scatter in one's path.*

14⇔♠ CTV in all bedrooms ⊟
50P 1⛳ ⇄ ✿ CFA ♪ (hard) ♪ clay pigeon shooting croquet *xmas*
V ✿ ⚓
Credit Cards [1][2][3][5] ⓔ

---

**DUNDEE** Tayside *Angus* Map **11** NO43

★★★65% **Swallow**
Kingsway West, Invergowrie DD2 5JT (3.5m W off A972 Dundee Ring Road) (Swallow) ☎(0382)641122 Telex no 76694 FAX (0382) 568340
*Conveniently situated on the ring road, this former baronial hall has been extended to create a comfortable business and pleasure hotel with good conference and leisure facilities. Modern bedrooms are well equipped and the inviting public areas include an attractive conservatory restaurant.*
110⇔♠2⇄ ✂ in all bedrooms ® T ✳ sB&B⇔♠£80 dB&B⇔♠£95 ⊟
《80P ✿ CFA ▣ (heated) sauna solarium gymnasium *xmas*

♀ Scottish & French V ✿ ⚓ ✂ ✳ Lunch £9.50 Dinner £17&alc Last dinner 9.45pm
Credit Cards [1][2][3][5]

★★★62% **Angus Thistle**
10 Marketgait DD1 1QU (Mount Charlotte (TS)) ☎(0382)26874 Telex no 76456 FAX (0382) 22564
*This modern, purpose-built tourist and business hotel in the city centre is also a popular venue for local conferences and functions, featuring an attractive split level restaurant and comfortable cocktail bar, though lounge facilities are somewhat limited. Well equipped bedrooms have tasteful modern appointments and suites are available.*
58⇔♠(4fb)2⇄ ✂ in 11 bedrooms CTV in all bedrooms ® T (room only) ⊟
Lift 《 20P games room whirlpool
♀ International ✿ ⚓ ✂
Credit Cards [1][2][3][4][5]

---

**DUNDONNELL** Highland *Ross & Cromarty* Map **14** NH08

★★★70% **Dundonnell**
IV23 2QS (Inter-Hotels) ☎(085483)234 FAX (085483) 366
*Situated at the head of Little Loch Broom, this family-run Highland hotel is an ideal base for the touring holidaymaker. Public areas have an air of peaceful relaxation while the bedrooms are comfortably furnished in the modern style and well equipped.*
24⇔♠(2fb) CTV in all bedrooms ® T sB&B⇔♠£34.50-£42.50 dB&B⇔♠£59-£70 ⊟
60P CFA *xmas*
V ✿ ⚓ Dinner £17.50-£18.75&alc Last dinner 8.30pm
Credit Cards [1][3]

## AA ★★★ Country House

David and Mary Allen, your resident owners and hosts, welcome you to their country house hotel. Situated in 45 acres of trees and grassland, set back from the A75. The 28 individually appointed bedrooms, all have direct dial telephone, radio/alarm, colour TV and tea & coffee making facilities, all have en suite facilities and pleasant views of the surrounding countryside. Ground floor bedroom available. Copper Beech Restaurant, where you can enjoy excellent cuisine in the informal and relaxing surroundings of period setting. Conference facilities available. Many places of interest can be visited from this ideal location.

# Hetland Hall Hotel

CARRUTHERSTOWN,
DUMFRIES DG1 4JX.
TELEPHONE: 0387 84201
TELEX: 776819
FACSIMILE: 0387-84211

---

★ ★ ★

# Cairndale Hotel
### English Street
### Dumfries

## — FOR BUSINESS OR PLEASURE —

* Privately owned/managed
* 60 comfortable rooms with private facilities
* Executive rooms and suites
* Conference/Syndicate Meeting rooms
* Dinner Dance every Saturday night
* Traditional Scottish Ceilidh every Sunday Night during summer months
* Golfing Breaks from £50.00 per person includes: Golf on choice of 6 local courses

**Tel: (0387) 54111. Fax: (0387) 50555. Telex: 777530**

D

---

# Doesn't this sound like a good hotel?

Free parking; friendly staff; excellent food in a stylish restaurant or continental Cafe Bar; two bars; a pleasant bedroom with tea and coffee facilities, colour TV and bath or shower en suite; an ample supply of hot water, soap, shampoo, fluffy towels; all this and a warm comfy bed.

Doesn't that sound good to you?

## STATION HOTEL ★★★

Lovers Walk, Dumfries, Scotland DG1 1LT
Tel: (0387) 54316. Fax: (0387) 50388.

---

**DUNFERMLINE** Fife Map **11** NT08

### ★★★67% King Malcolm Thistle

Queensferry Rd, Wester Pitcorthie KY11 5DS (Mount Charlotte (TS)) ☎(0383)722611 Telex no 727721 FAX (0383) 730865

*Located on the southern outskirts of town and convenient for the Forth Road Bridge, this purpose-built hotel offers friendly service and well equipped bedrooms.*

48⇌🛏⁄in 12 bedrooms CTV in all bedrooms ® **T** (room only) 🍴

《 60P

♀ International ❖ ⚓ ⅄

Credit Cards ①②③④⑤

### ★★★⊛66% Keavil House

Crossford KY12 8QW (2m W A994) (Best Western) ☎(0383)736258 Telex no 728227 FAX (0383) 621600

*Set in its own ground with most of the bedrooms and the main restaurant looking out onto secluded lawns, this hotel continues to improve, attracting both business people and tourists, and at the same time expanding its banqueting reputation. There is an attractive conservatory restaurant serving innovative food under new chef Michael Scotford, and there is also a steakhouse style restaurant. A new leisure complex opened here in June 1991*

32⇌🛏(1fb)1🚻 CTV in all bedrooms ® **T** sB&B⇌🛏£50-£70 dB&B⇌🛏£60-£90 🍴

《 CTV 150P ❖ CFA ☒ (heated) sauna solarium gymnasium jacuzzi aerobics studio steam room ⚱ *xmas*

♀ International V ❖ ⅄ Lunch £10-£15alc Dinner £17-£20&alc Last dinner 9.30pm

Credit Cards ①②③⑤ ⓔ

### ★★★65% Pitbauchlie House

Aberdour Rd KY11 4PB (Consort) ☎(0383)722282 Telex no 727756 FAX (0383) 620738

*Friendly service features highly at this well managed hotel. Accommodation is comfortable, the bedrooms offering many extras. The dinner menu boasts a range of interesting dishes, and is very good value.*

40⇌🛏(2fb)1🚻 CTV in all bedrooms ® **T** sB&B⇌🛏fr£47 dB&B⇌🛏fr£63 🍴

《 70P ❖ CFA solarium gymnasium

V ❖ ⚓ Lunch fr£8.25 Dinner fr£14 Last dinner 9pm

Credit Cards ①②③⑤ ⓔ

### ★★★59% Pitfirrane Arms

Main St, Crossford KY12 8NJ (0.5 W A994) ☎(0383)736132 Telex no 728255 FAX (0383) 621760

*Situated in the village of Crossfield 1.5 miles west of the town, this business hotel has evolved from an old coaching inn. The menus offer a good choice of dishes, with an Italian influence, and bedrooms are compact but well equipped.*

38⇌🛏(1fb) CTV in all bedrooms ® **T** ✖ (ex guide dogs)

《 72P sauna solarium ♫

♀ Scottish & Italian V ❖ Last dinner 10.15pm

Credit Cards ①②③

### ★★76% Elgin

Charlestown KY11 3EE ☎Limekilns(0383)872257

*Friendly service and comfortable, well equipped bedrooms are features of the Elgin. Peacefully situated in the small coastal hamlet of Charlestown, it enjoys fine views across the Firth of Forth. Access is via the A985, the hotel being 4 miles south of Dunfermline or 4 miles west of the M90/A90 junction 1.*

13⇌🛏(3fb) CTV in all bedrooms ® **T** ✖ (ex guide dogs) sB&B⇌🛏£45-£48 dB&B⇌🛏£65-£70 🍴

70P ❖ ⚱

V ❖ ✱ Bar Lunch £5.50-£13.50alc Dinner £13-£20alc Last dinner 9pm

Credit Cards ①③

### ★★61% City

18 Bridge St KY12 8DA ☎(0383)722538

RS 1 & 2 Jan

*Town centre commercial hotel with neat well-equipped bedrooms.*

17⇌🛏(1fb)1🚻 CTV in all bedrooms ® **T** ✱ S10% sB&B⇌🛏£32.50-£36.50 dB&B⇌🛏£52-£55 🍴

《 20P

♀ French V ❖ ⚓ ✱ Lunch £6.50 High tea £4&alc Dinner £8.50-£10.95&alc Last dinner 9pm

Credit Cards ①②③⑤ ⓔ

---

**DUNHOLME** Lincolnshire Map **08** TF07

### ★★59% Four Seasons

Scothern Ln LN2 3QP ☎Welton(0673)60108 FAX (0673) 62784

*Set beside the A46 on the outskirts of Lincoln and flanked by its own well maintained gardens and large car park, this friendly hotel offers purpose- built motel-style accommodation with a convivial bar and restaurant in the main block.*

24⇌🛏(1fb) CTV in all bedrooms ® **T** ✱ sB&B⇌🛏£37.50-£45 dB&B⇌🛏£39.50-£60 🍴

《 CTV 130P ❖ ♫ *xmas*

♀ English & French V ❖ ⚓ ⅄ ✱ Lunch £8.95-£15 Dinner £8.95-£15 Last dinner 10pm

Credit Cards ①②③ ⓔ

---

**DUNKELD** Tayside *Perthshire* Map **11** NO04

### ★★★★67% Stakis Dunkeld House

PH8 0HX (Stakis) ☎(03502)771 Telex no 76657 FAX (03502) 8924

*Built by the seventh Duke of Atholl on the banks of the River Tay, and surrounded by extensive wooded grounds, this hotel retains some country house characteristics despite considerable extension by its present owners. Professional staff provide friendly service, and the food produced by chef George McIvor shows great promise, though the menu is fairly short. A modern leisure complex is the attractive nucleus of the time share lodges being built in the grounds, and sporting facilities also include tennis, shooting and, of course, fishing in the river.*

92⇌🛏(13fb)⁄in 24 bedrooms CTV in all bedrooms ® **T** ✖ (ex guide dogs) ✱ sB&B⇌🛏£97.65-£122.85 dB&B⇌🛏£108.15-£133.35 (incl dinner) 🍴

Lift 《 CTV 70P ❖ CFA ☒ (heated) ♪ (hard) ⚓ sauna solarium gymnasium table tennis archery croquet putting *xmas*

♀ International V ❖ ⚓

Credit Cards ①②③⑤

### ★★★⊛⊛⚐81% Kinnaird House

Kinnaird Estate PH8 0LB ☎Pitlochry(079682)440 due to change to (0796) 482440 FAX (079682) 289 due to change to (0796) 482289

Closed Feb

*This year's 'Best Newcomer' award winner for Scotland is peacefully set in a 9,000-acre estate overlooking the River Tay. A former hunting lodge, it has been sympathetically renovated and converted to create a welcome addition to the Scottish country house hotel scene. There is a house party atmosphere and a comfortable informality about the staff which puts guests immediately at ease. Modern fabrics have been used to good effect in the charming, well proportioned bedrooms, which are furnished with lovely antiques and throughtfully equipped with useful extras. Bathrooms are praiseworthy; day rooms are lavishly furnished, and fresh flowers abound. The cedar drawing room is especially inviting with its open fire and deep-cushioned easy chairs. There is a cosy study, a fine panelled billiard room and basement gun room. A highlight of any visit to Kinnaird is the originality and flair of Chef/Manager John Webber's cooking, presented in the stylish dining room with magnificent views over the Tay valley. A typical dinner might be 'titan' of smoked salmon and leeks with vegetable butter sauce, followed by a duo of boned quail set on tartlets of creamed endive served with rich red wine sauce together with a selection of fresh market vegetables. For pudding, perhaps chocolate pithiviers on a light cream sauce spiked with rum. The wine list is carefully selected and extensive, and to finish, coffee and petits fours are served in the drawing room. (See colour feature p38.)*

9⇄📺 CTV in all bedrooms T ✈ ✱ S% sB&B⇄📷£85-£120 dB&B⇄📷£120-£165 🍴

Lift 20P 🚲 ❀ ♪ (hard) ♪ snooker nc12yrs *xmas*

✿ S% Sunday Lunch £17.50-£21 Dinner £34.50 Last dinner 9pm

Credit Cards ①②③ £

See advertisement on page 271

★★★63% **Birnam**

Birnam PH8 0BQ (Consort) ☎(03502)462 Telex no 57515 FAX (03502) 8979

*This comfortable, friendly hotel, family run on traditional lines and situated just off the A9 on its southern approach to the town, features a spacious lounge, first-floor dining rooms and bedrooms with en suite facilities; all floors are served by a lift.*

28⇄📷(1fb)1🍴 CTV in all bedrooms ® T sB&B⇄📷£45-£75 dB&B⇄📷£70-£95 🍴

Lift 50P ❀ CFA

♡ English & French V ✿ ✱ Lunch £8.50-£9.50 Dinner £17.95-£18.95 Last dinner 8.30pm

Credit Cards ①②③⑤ £

---

DUNMOW, GREAT Essex Map **05** TL62

★★55% **The Saracen's Head**

High St CM6 1AG (Forte Hotels) ☎(0371)873901 FAX (0371) 875743

*This black and white early 17th-century coaching inn in the town centre provides comfortable accommodation, with a beamed open-plan lounge, bar and reception area. Most bedrooms are away from the road in a modernised extension.*

→

24⇨(3fb)✠in 7 bedrooms CTV in all bedrooms ® **T** ✱ S%
sB⇨£65 dB⇨£85 (room only) 🖪
50P CFA *xmas*
V ✿ ⬭ ✱ S% Lunch £9.20&alc Dinner £13.30&alc Last
dinner 9.30pm
Credit Cards 1 2 3 4 5

### ✸✕✕ Starr
Market Place CM6 1AX ☎Great Dunmow(0371)874321
FAX (0371) 876337
*This friendly restaurant in a 14th-century timbered building has a
cheerful bar serving lunchtime snacks and 8 well equipped
bedrooms in a converted stable block. Daily changing blackboard
menus feature English dishes using quality fresh produce. Dishes
enjoyed by our inspectors have included a steak and kidney pie,
served with new potatoes, parsnip purée and broccoli, and roast
guinea fowl with a red wine, lemon, black olive and herb sauce.
Desserts include hot puddings, fruit tarts, mousses and roulades.
The extensive wine list is reasonably priced even though there are
few bottles for under £10.*
Closed 1st wk Jan Lunch not served Sat
Dinner not served Sun
🍴 English & French V 60 seats ✱ Lunch fr£19 Dinner £19-£31
Last lunch 1.30pm Last dinner 9.30pm 16 P ✠
Credit Cards 1 2 3

---

**DUNNET** Highland *Caithness* Map **15** ND27

### ★★ 62% Northern Sands
KW14 8DX ☎Barrock(084785)270
*Near a lovely sandy beach, this small, family-run hotel is a popular
base for touring. Refurbishment has considerably enhanced the
public areas, which include a choice of well stocked bars and an
attractive restaurant. The à la carte menu offers a range of pasta
specialities and grills.*
9⇨📶(3fb) CTV in all bedrooms ® ✈ (ex guide dogs) ✱
sB&B⇨📶fr£29.50 dB&B⇨📶fr£46 🖪
CTV 50P
🍴 French & Italian V ✿ ⬭ ✱ Lunch £4.95-£10.95 Dinner £4-
£10&alc Last dinner 8.30pm
Credit Cards 1 3

---

**DUNOON** Strathclyde *Argyllshire* Map **10** NS17

### ★★ 76% Enmore
Marine Pde, Kirn PA23 8HH ☎(0369)2230 FAX (0369) 2148
Closed 2-12 Jan RS Nov-Feb
*Guests are assured of a warm welcome at this attractive family-run
hotel about a mile north of Dunoon, surrounded by pleasant
gardens and offering fine views over the Firth of Clyde. Angela and
David Wilson continue to run their hotel with enthusiasm, caring
for guests in a relaxed and informal manner. Individually
decorated bedrooms, several of which feature 4-poster beds, are
comfortably furnished and equipped with many thoughtful extras.*
11⇨📶(2fb)3🛏 CTV in all bedrooms ® **T** sB&B⇨📶£35-£55
dB&B⇨📶£70-£130 🖪
20P 🚗 ✿ squash games room 🎱 *xmas*
🍴 Scottish & French V ✿ ⬭ ✠ Lunch £10-£18alc High tea £6-
£10alc Dinner £19 Last dinner 8.30pm
Credit Cards 1 3 £

### ★★ 65% Firpark
Ardnadam PA23 8QG (3m N A815) ☎(0369)6506
*This detached mansion house enjoys prominent views of the Holy
Loch and the US submarine base. Run by the resident owner, Mrs
Pat Lamont, it offers comfortable bedrooms, a wide range of bar
meals, and friendly, attentive service.*
6rm(2⇨📶) CTV in all bedrooms ®
CTV 30P 🚗 ✿
✿ Last dinner 9pm

---

### ★★ 56% Abbeyhill
Dhailing Rd PA23 8EA ☎(0369)2204
*A family-run hotel set in its own garden on a hillside overlooking
the Firth of Clyde. It has a friendly informal atmosphere and
offers practical well equipped accommodation.*
14⇨📶(3fb) CTV in all bedrooms ® **T** sB&B⇨📶£28
dB&B⇨📶£42 🖪
40P 🚗 ✿
✿ Dinner fr£9 Last dinner 8.30pm
Credit Cards 1 2 3 £

### ★★ Hunter's Quay
Marine Pde, Hunter's Quay PA23 8JH ☎(0369)4190
*This friendly, family-run hotel stands opposite the ferry terminal,
overlooking the Firth of Clyde. In its comfortable dining room the
menu reflects good, imaginative cooking with an emphasis on
Scottish game dishes.*
18rm(5⇨2📶)(5fb) CTV in all bedrooms ® **T** sB&B£20-£27
sB&B⇨📶£20-£27 dB&B£30-£37 dB&B⇨📶£30-£37 🖪
⬭ CTV 20P ✿ CFA solarium sailing 🎵 *xmas*
🍴 Scottish & French V ✿ ⬭ Lunch £6.50&alc High tea
£3.95&alc Dinner £15&alc Last dinner 10pm
Credit Cards 1 3 5 £

### ✸✕✕ Beverley's
Ardfillayne Hotel, West Bay PA23 7QJ ☎(0369)2267
FAX (0369) 2501
*This small, hospitable country house hotel, unashamedly Victorian
in style, invites you to experience the charm and peaceful
tranquillity of a bygone era. In an elegant restaurant built in the
style of Charles Rennie Mackintosh, wood-panelled walls hung
with paintings and draperies provide the background to candlelit,
lace-covered tables set with silver and crystal, you can enjoy a
selection of main dishes based on good, fresh raw materials –
Scottish beef, game and seafood all being represented – and a
range of sweets that is second to none.*
Lunch not served (ex by arrangement)
🍴 French V 40 seats Last lunch 2pm Last dinner 9.30pm 20 P
✠
Credit Cards 1 2 3 5

---

**DUNSTABLE** Bedfordshire Map **04** TL02 ⊖

### ★★★ 69% *Old Palace Lodge*
Church St LU5 4RT ☎(0582)662201 FAX (0582) 696422
*This is a charming old ivy-clad building with plenty of character.
The spacious bedrooms have been thoughtfully furnished and
equipped, and although lounge facilities are limited, the bar lounge
is very comfortable. The well appointed restaurant offers a varied
menu of English-style dishes, well prepared from good ingredients.
A very friendly and well managed hotel.*
49⇨(6fb)2🛏✠in 6 bedrooms CTV in all bedrooms ® **T**
Lift ⬭ 70P 🚗
🍴 Continental V ✿ ⬭ Last dinner 10pm
Credit Cards 1 2 3 4 5

### ★★ 62% Highwayman
London Rd LU6 3DX ☎Luton(0582)601122 FAX (0582) 603812
*A considerable programme of refurbishment recently completed at
this popular commercial hotel on the A5 has resulted in attractive,
well equipped bedrooms and smartly tiled modern bathrooms.
Guests are assured of a friendly welcome from the long-established
team of staff.*
53⇨📶(3fb) CTV in all bedrooms ® **T** ✱ sB&B⇨📶£37-£47
dB&B⇨📶£46-£56 🖪
⬭ 60P CFA
V ✿ ⬭ ✱ Bar Lunch £1.15-£8alc Dinner £10.55-£18.45alc Last
dinner 9pm
Credit Cards 1 2 3 5

DUNSTER Somerset Map **03** SS94

★★★62% **The Luttrell Arms**
High St TA24 6SG (Forte Hotels) ☎(0643)821555
FAX (0643) 821567
*In the centre of this attractive Exmoor town, the Luttrell Arms dates back to the 15th century. Refurbishment has been carefully carried out to retain many original features and preserve the wealth of character and interest. Some of the bedrooms are in adjacent cottages but all have access from the main building. The split-level restaurant offers à la carte as well as the simple table d'hôte menu. The hotel has been under the same management for 23 years and has a welcoming, family-run atmosphere.*
27⇌4⊟ ⚹in 2 bedrooms CTV in all bedrooms ® **T** ✱ S%
sB⇌£75 dB⇌£85 (room only) ⊟
3⌂ (£1 per night) ✽ *xmas*
**V** ♧ ⊡ ⚹ ✱ S% Lunch fr£16alc Dinner £15.50&alc Last dinner 9.30pm
Credit Cards [1] [2] [3] [5]

★★67% **Exmoor House**
12 West St TA24 6SN ☎Minehead(0643)821268
Closed Dec & Jan
*An attractive listed Georgian town house personally run by the owners is in process of upgrading and co-ordinating its variety of bedrooms; two lounges are available for guests' use, and there is a pleasant walled garden at the rear of the hotel. Good family cooking is soundly based on local produce – using local recipes whenever possible. Smoking is not permitted on the premises.*
7⇌♪ ⚹in all bedrooms CTV in all bedrooms ®
sB&B⇌♪£30.50-£33 dB&B⇌♪£45-£50 ⊟
CTV ⊭ ✽ nc12yrs
**V** ♧ ⊡ ⚹ Bar Lunch £5.50-£7.50 Dinner fr£14.50 Last dinner 7.30pm
Credit Cards [1] [2] [3] [5] £

DUNVEGAN

See Skye, Isle of

DURHAM Co Durham Map **12** NZ24 ⊛

See also Thornley

★★★★68% **Royal County**
Old Elvet DH1 3JN (Swallow) ☎091-386 6821 Telex no 538238
FAX 091-386 0704
*Recently extended and refurbished to a very high standard, this old established hotel comprises well appointed bedrooms, comfortable lounge areas, a variety of restaurants and excellent leisure facilities; its river bank setting commands views of the nearby castle and cathedral.*
150⇌♪(4fb)1⊟ ⚹in 49 bedrooms CTV in all bedrooms ® **T**
✱ sB&B⇌♪£80-£95 dB&B⇌♪£95-£105 ⊟
Lift ☾ 120P CFA ⊠ (heated) sauna solarium gymnasium steam room plunge pool impulse showers ♫ *xmas*
♡ International **V** ♧ ⊡ ✱ Lunch £12.50&alc High tea £8.75-£14.75 Dinner £18.25&alc Last dinner 10.30pm
Credit Cards [1] [2] [3] [4] [5]

★★★69% **Ramside Hall**
Carrville DH1 1TD (3m NE A690) (Consort) ☎091-386 5282
Telex no 537681 FAX 091-386 0399
*An hotel set in parkland just off the A690, close to its junction with the A1(M), features a luxurious new accommodation wing which also contains the reception area and an elegant lounge; some of these bedrooms contain four poster beds and whirlpool baths, and there are 2 sumptuous Presidential Suites. Three eating options, versatile banqueting/conference facilities and recently landscaped gardens all add to the appeal of the establishment.*
82⇌♪(10fb)6⊟ ⚹in 36 bedrooms CTV in all bedrooms ® **T**
⊭ (ex guide dogs) ✱ sB&B⇌♪£63-£70 dB&B⇌♪£79.20-£88 ⊟
Lift ☾ ⊞ 700P ✽ CFA ♫ ⌂ *xmas*

→

V ⏸ ⚏ ✳ Lunch £8.50-£12.50&alc High tea £5.50-£8 Dinner £10.50-£15 Last dinner 10pm
Credit Cards [1] [2] [3] [5] ⓔ

### ★★★66% Three Tuns

New Elvet DH1 3AQ (Swallow) ☎091-386 4326 Telex no 583238 FAX 091-386 1406

*A short walk from the city centre, this old coaching inn retains some of its original features, whilst providing modern facilities for the business traveller.*

47⇨🛏(1fb)🗲in 16 bedrooms CTV in all bedrooms ® T ✳ S%
⟪ 60P CFA

🍴 English & French V ⏸ ⚏ ✳ Lunch £5.50-£8.95 Dinner £12.75&alc Last dinner 9.30pm
Credit Cards [1] [2] [3] [5]

### ★★★64% Hallgarth Manor

Pittington DH6 1AB (3m E between A690 & B2183) (Best Western) ☎091-372 1188 Telex no 537023 FAX 091-372 1249

*An hotel which was once a family house and which stands close to the village of Pittington, only 3.5 miles from the city, features a large new function room and comfortable public areas which include the well known Elemore Restaurant; equally popular is the Village Tavern adjacent to the main building. Bedrooms, though compact, are individually styled – many exposed beams and antique furnishings.*

23⇨🛏 CTV in all bedrooms ® T sB&B⇨🛏fr£65 dB&B⇨🛏fr£75 🏳
⟪ 101P ✻ CFA

🍴 International V ⏸ ⚏ ✳ Sunday Lunch fr£9.50 High tea fr£6.50 Dinner fr£16&alc Last dinner 9.15pm
Credit Cards [1] [2] [3] [5] ⓔ

### ★★★59% Bowburn Hall

Bowburn DH6 5NT (3m SE junc A177/A1(M)) ☎091-377 0311 Telex no 537681 FAX 091-377 3459

*Bowburn Hall is situated in 5 acres of grounds, 3 miles southeast of Durham and close to the A177 junction of the A1 (M). Recent upgrading has improved this friendly and informal hotel.*

19⇨ CTV in all bedrooms ® T ✖ ✳ sB&B⇨£48-£50 dB&B⇨fr£62 🏳
CTV 100P ✻ CFA

V ⏸ ⚏ ✳ Lunch fr£11.95&alc Dinner fr£11.95&alc Last dinner 10pm
Credit Cards [1] [2] [3] [5]

### ★★63% *Newton Grange*

Finchale Rd, Brasside, Newton Hall DH1 5SA ☎091-386 0872
*Very well equipped bedrooms and friendly service are features of this hotel converted from a 16th-century house and outbuildings, situated about 2.5 miles north of the city centre.*

13⇨🛏(3fb)1🛏 CTV in all bedrooms ® T ✖ (ex guide dogs)
⟪ 90P ⊞ ✻ ✱ ∪ ⊕

🍴 English & French V ⏸ ⚏ ✱ Last dinner 9.45pm
Credit Cards [1] [3] [5]

### ★★62% *Bridge Toby*

Croxdale DH1 3SP (2.25m S off A167) (Toby) ☎091-378 0524 Telex no 538156 FAX 091-378 9981

*On the A617 2.5 miles south of the city, a former inn houses the reception, lounges, bars and restaurant, while behind is a purpose-built block of motel-type bedrooms with parking immediately outside. Service is friendly and helpful.*

46⇨🛏(2fb)🗲in 16 bedrooms ®
⟪ 150P ✻

🍴 Mainly grills V ⏸ ⚏ ✱ Last dinner 9.45pm
Credit Cards [1] [2] [3] [5]

For key to symbols in English see the bookmark.

### ★67% Redhills

Redhills Ln, Crossgate Moor DH1 4AN ☎091-386 4331 Telex no 537681

*Attractive bedrooms and substantial meals are features of this friendly hotel situated just off the A167 on the outskirts of the city.*

6rm CTV in all bedrooms ® ✖ ✳ sB&Bfr£30 dB&Bfr£36 🏳 100P

V ⏸ ⚏ ✳ Lunch fr£7.25 Dinner fr£10.45 Last dinner 10pm
Credit Cards [1] [2] [3] [5]

---

**DUROR** Highland *Argyllshire* Map **14** NM95

### ★★❀❀77% Stewart

PA38 4BW (Best Western) ☎(063174)268 Telex no 94014994 FAX (063174) 328
Closed Nov-Etr

*Originally built in the style of a shooting lodge, this country house hotel lies in 5 acres of terraced gardens on a sheltered plateau with superb views southwards toward Loch Linnhe. The gardens are renowned for their azaleas and rhododendrons with their magnificent colours in May/June. The splendour of the gardens is matched by the cooking. The 4-course dinner menu offers minimal choice, but the emphasis is on fresh produce and good raw materials. The dining room is tastefully appointed and there is a comfortable first-floor lounge. All bedrooms are contained in an adjoining purpose-built extension, although functional they are well equipped and generally spacious.*

20⇨🛏(2fb) CTV in all bedrooms ® T sB&B⇨🛏£39.80 dB&B⇨🛏£79.80 🏳

30P ⊞ ✻ clay pigeon shooting sailing
⏸ ⚏ 🗲 Bar Lunch £2-£12 Dinner £25 Last dinner 9pm
Credit Cards [1] [2] [3] [5] ⓔ

---

**DUXFORD** Cambridgeshire Map **05** TL44

### ★★★64% Duxford Lodge

Ickleton Rd CB2 4RU ☎Cambridge(0223)836444 FAX (0223) 832271
RS Sat

*Set in its own beautifully maintained grounds and centrally located in the village, offering easy access to A11, A505 and the nearby Duxford War Museum, this hotel is run in the style of a country house. Well furnished, individually decorated rooms are complemented by comfortable, cosy public areas, the restaurant offering an above average menu of imaginative and skilfully prepared dishes.*

11⇨🛏Annexe5⇨ CTV in all bedrooms ® T S%
sB&B⇨🛏£46-£70 dB&B⇨🛏£66.50-£95 🏳

34P ⊞ ✻
🍴 English & French V S% Lunch £14.50-£16.50&alc Dinner £17.50-£21&alc Last dinner 9.30pm
Credit Cards [1] [2] [3] [5]

---

**DYSERTH** Clwyd Map **06** SJ07

### ★★★65% Graig Park Hotel & Country Club

LL18 6DX ☎Rhyl(0745)571022 FAX (0745) 571024

12⇨🛏(12fb) CTV in all bedrooms ® T ✖ (ex guide dogs) ✳ sB&B⇨🛏fr£36 dB&B⇨🛏fr£51

Lift ⟪ 80P ⊞ ✻ ▣ (heated) squash sauna solarium gymnasium steamroom ♫ *xmas*
🍴 International V ⏸ ⚏ 🗲 ✳ Lunch £14-£21.55alc Dinner £14-£21.55alc Last dinner 10pm
Credit Cards [1] [3]

The AA's star rating scheme is the market leader in hotel classification.

EARL SHILTON Leicestershire Map **04** SP49

★★63% **Fernleigh**

32 Wood St LE9 7ND ☎(0455)847011

*Completion of a new extension of thirteen good quality bedrooms, and a new lounge bar, together with improvements to existing public areas have made this a pleasant, sound hotel popular with business people.*

28⇨🛏(4fb)2🗗 CTV in all bedrooms ® T sB&B⇨🛏£25-£47.50 dB&B⇨🛏£35-£55 🏃

CTV 100P 10🐾 CFA solarium

♀ English, French & Italian V ♥ ⅅ ✱ Lunch £3.50-£8.25 Dinner fr£8.75&alc Last dinner 9.30pm

Credit Cards 1 3 ①

---

EARL STONHAM Suffolk Map **05** TM15

❀❀❀ ✕ ✕ *Mr Underhills*

Norwich Rd IP14 5DW ☎Stowmarket(0449)711206

*This is a small restaurant but it is homely and comfortable with attractive furnishings. There is a set menu and the cooking is of a very high standard. The wine list presents the customer with a good selection and service is friendly.*

Closed Sun, Mon & BH's Lunch not served Tue-Sat (ex by arrangement)

♀ English & French 24 seats Last dinner 8.30pm 10 P ✂

Credit Cards 1 3

---

EASINGTON Cleveland Map **08** NZ71

★★★❀♨69% *Grinkle Park*

TS13 4UB (2m S off unclass rd linking A174/A171)

☎Guisborough(0287) 640515 FAX (0287) 641278

*A Victorian manor house approached by a long, rhododendron-flanked drive, set in 32 acres of secluded grounds and gardens*

*whose lawns run down to the lake, offers accommodation in 20 individually designed bedrooms named after local places, birds and flora. Very comfortable lounges and bars are warmed by blazing open fires during the colder months, and a traditional dining room serves excellent and well presented meals which make good use of local produce in season. Menus feature such starters as terrine of fish, marinated salmon and roast quail, while main courses include fresh lobster, Barbary duck and Mediterranean beef; a choice of British farmhouse cheeses provides an alternative to the trolley selection of home-made sweets, and the well chosen wine list includes several examples from the New World.*

20⇨🛏🗗 CTV in all bedrooms ®

130P 2🐾 (£2 per night) ✱ ♪ (hard) ✦ snooker croquet

♀ English & French V ♥ ⅅ Last dinner 9.30pm

Credit Cards 1 2 3 5

---

EASINGWOLD North Yorkshire Map **08** SE56

★★★62% **The Garth**

York Rd YO6 3PG ☎(0347)22988

*Guests will find service friendly and informal at this small hotel managed by its resident proprietors, Gill and John Clayton; cosy modern bedroom accommodation is unaffected by traffic noise, while lounge areas, though compact, are both attractive and comfortable.*

10⇨🛏(1fb)✂in 5 bedrooms CTV in all bedrooms ® T ✖

sB&B⇨🛏£50 dB&B⇨🛏£75 🏃

40P 🚗 ✱ *xmas*

♀ European V ♥ ⅅ ✂ ✱ Lunch £11.25-£18.95alc High tea £1.50-£10alc Dinner £18.45-£25.45alc Last dinner 9.30pm

Credit Cards 1 3

---

A rosette means exceptional standards of cuisine.

## East Ayton - Eastbourne

★★★64% **East Ayton Lodge**
Moor Ln, Forge Valley YO13 9EW ☎Scarborough(0723)864227
FAX (0723) 862680
Closed Jan-12 Feb

*A pleasant country residence, built in the early 19th century and standing in its own well tended grounds on the edge of the road leading to the Forge Valley, has been converted to create a small but comfortable hotel. Bedrooms are equipped with good facilities and a wide range of food is served in an attractive restaurant and in the bar.*

11⇨↑Annexe6⇨↑(1fb)2⌘ CTV in all bedrooms ® T
sB&B⇨↑£35 dB&B⇨↑£45-£80 ⋒
CTV 50P ❖ CFA ⚘ *xmas*
♀ English & French V ❖ ✱ Lunch £9.50&alc Dinner £15&alc
Last dinner 9pm
Credit Cards ①②③⑤£

EASTBOURNE East Sussex Map **05** TV69
See **Town Plan Section**

★★★★★❀❀65% *Grand*
King Edwards Pde BN21 4EQ (De Vere) ☎(0323)412345
Telex no 87332 FAX (0323) 412233

*This popular seafront hotel has been host to many famous guests over the years and retains much of its Victorian grandeur. The pillared foyer is impressive with an attractive display of flowers, and lounges are spacious though simply furnished and would benefit from more comfortable seating. The larger of the two restaurants is for residents, it has a set price menu of traditional English food. The Mirabelle is more serious, with a set price and à la carte menu offering some interesting dishes. Chef Keith Mitchell's cooking is uncomplicated and honest, demonstrating good skills. Bedrooms vary in size and while some are quite compact they offer good facilities. Some sea-facing rooms have balconies, and the décor and furnishings are contemporary. There are good leisure facilities including a beauty salon and hairdressing.*

161⇨↑(10fb)1⌘ CTV in all bedrooms T
Lift ( 60P ⇎ ❖ ▢ (heated) ⌣ (heated) snooker sauna
solarium gymnasium spa bath hairdressing beauty & massage
♫ ⚘
♀ English & French V ❖ ⚎ Last dinner 10.30pm
Credit Cards ①②③④⑤

★★★★62% **Cavendish**
Grand Pde BN21 4DH (De Vere) ☎(0323)410222
Telex no 87579 FAX (0323) 410941

*An elegant hotel in a fine seafront position retains its charm and traditional feeling. The large and rather elaborate restaurant is complemented by a cocktail bar and popular sun lounge, whilst bedrooms are variable – those at the front offering some magnificent views.*

114⇨↑ CTV in all bedrooms ® T ✱ sB&B⇨↑£75.50-£81
dB&B⇨↑£124-£155 ⋒
Lift ( 50P CFA snooker games room *xmas*
♀ English & French V ❖ ⚎ ✱ Lunch £5-£10.50 Dinner £17
Last dinner 9.30pm
Credit Cards ①②③④⑤£

★★★71% **Lansdowne**
King Edward's Pde BN21 4EE (Best Western) ☎(0323)25174
Telex no 878624 FAX (0323) 39721
Closed 28 Dec-11 Jan

*This family-owned seafront hotel is particularly well managed and continues to provide traditional standards of service, staff throughout being willing, helpful and professional. Bedrooms all offer good levels of comfort, though they vary in style, and a choice of lounges includes one where smoking is prohibited.*

130⇨↑(6fb) CTV in all bedrooms ® T S10% sB&B⇨↑£48-
£62 dB&B⇨↑£74-£96 ⋒

Lift ( CTV 22☎ (£3.10 per night) CFA snooker games room
*xmas*
V ❖ ⚎ ✔ S10% Lunch £3.25-£10alc High tea fr£6.75 Dinner
fr£14.50 Last dinner 8.30pm
Credit Cards ①②③⑤£

★★★63% *The Wish Tower*
King Edward's Pde BN21 4EB ☎(0323)22676 FAX (0323) 21474

*Set in an ideal seafront location opposite the Wishtower and gardens, this hotel offers bedrooms ranging from the sumptuous to the modest – though plans to refurbish the latter category are now in hand, and new conference facilities are also to be added later this year. A comfortable lounge and basement restaurant are complemented by friendly, attentive and particularly well managed service throughout.*

67rm(59⇨↑)✔in 6 bedrooms CTV in all bedrooms ® T
Lift ( ☎ (£3 per day) ⇎
♀ English & French V ❖ ⚎ ✔ Last dinner 8.45pm
Credit Cards ①②③④⑤

★★★56% **Cumberland**
Grand Pde BN21 3YT ☎(0323)30342 FAX (0323) 646314

*A traditional seafront hotel opposite the bandstand offers a range of adequately comfortable bedrooms, all of which have identical facilities although the standards of décor vary ; upgrading of public areas is now complete.*

70⇨↑(5fb) CTV in all bedrooms ® T (incl dinner) ⋒
Lift ( CTV ✗ CFA *xmas*
♀ English & French V ❖ ⚎ ✱ Lunch £8.20 Dinner £11.20
Last dinner 8.30pm
Credit Cards ①②③£

★★★56% **Queens**
Marine Pde BN21 3DY (De Vere) ☎(0323)22822
Telex no 877736 FAX (0323) 31056

*Situated opposite the pier, this busy hotel has long been popular with small conference groups and weekend visitors. It offers well equipped bedrooms of good size, some facing the sea. There is also a large restaurant, feature bars and service which is both extensive and helpful.*

108⇨↑(5fb) CTV in all bedrooms ® T ✱ sB&B⇨↑£73-£78
dB&B⇨↑£115-£125 ⋒
Lift ( 90P CFA snooker *xmas*
♀ English & French V ❖ ⚎ ✱ Lunch fr£11.25 Dinner
fr£15.50 Last dinner 9pm
Credit Cards ①②③⑤

★★★55% **Chatsworth**
Grand Pde BN21 3YR ☎(0323)411016 FAX (0323) 643270
Closed Jan-mid Mar

*The personally-involved management of this fine, old-fashioned hotel with well furnished public rooms reflects traditional English style in its hospitality ; a prime seafront position means that many of the bedrooms have sea views, and service is extensive.*

45⇨↑(2fb) CTV in all bedrooms sB&B⇨↑£27.50-£40
dB&B⇨↑£55-£80 ⋒
Lift ( CTV ✗ CFA
❖ ⚎ ✱ Sunday Lunch fr£11.75 Dinner fr£12.74 Last dinner
8.30pm
Credit Cards ①③£

★★69% **Langham**
Royal Pde BN22 7AH ☎(0323)31451 FAX (0323) 646623
Closed 16 Nov-15 Mar

*This family-run hotel enjoys a prime position overlooking the sea. The bedrooms are constantly being upgraded and are now all en suite. Special interest weekends and in-house entertainment are regular features.*

87⇨↑(5fb) CTV in all bedrooms ® T ✱ sB&B⇨↑£29-£33
dB&B⇨↑£50-£58
Lift ( CTV 3☎ (£4 per night) ♫

🍴 European **V** ✆ ⚃ Lunch £6.50 Dinner £9.50 Last dinner 7.30pm
Credit Cards 1 3

★★67% **West Rocks**
Grand Pde BN21 4DL ☎(0323)25217
Closed mid Nov-20 Mar
*This well established seafront hotel attracts a regular and loyal clientèle. A cocktail bar has recently been added and there is a sun lounge as well as 2 comfortable lounges. Bedrooms are gradually being updated, but all are comfortable and well equipped. Service throughout is traditional, helpful and friendly.*
52rm(8⇨32♠)(4fb) CTV in all bedrooms ® **T** ✟ S10%
sB&B£22-£28 sB&B⇨♠£34-£41 dB&B£36-£44
dB&B⇨♠£44-£80 🖭
Lift ( CTV ♪ ⇔ CFA nc3yrs
🍴 English & French **V** ✆ ⚃ S10% Dinner £9 Last dinner 7.55pm
Credit Cards 1 2 3 5 ①

★★65% **Farrar's**
3-5 Wilmington Gardens BN21 4JN ☎(0323)23737
FAX (0323) 32902
*Conveniently situated in a peaceful location close to theatres and Water Gardens, this hotel offers car parking facilities and a lift for guests' convenience. Though some of the bedrooms might be considered dated, all are equipped with modern facilities, while public areas include a cocktail bar as well as a choice of lounges. The willing services of a friendly team of staff will help to make your stay enjoyable.*
45⇨♠(3fb) CTV in all bedrooms ® **T** sB&B⇨♠fr£30
dB&B⇨♠fr£60 🖭
Lift ( CTV 26P CFA *xmas*
**V** ✆ ⚃ S% Bar Lunch £2-£10 Dinner £14 Last dinner 8.30pm
Credit Cards 1 2 3 ①

**See advertisement on page 277**

**★★63% New Wilmington**

25 Compton St BN21 4DU ☎(0323)21219

Closed Jan & Feb

*This friendly family-run hotel is situated close to the theatres and seafront. The well maintained bedrooms are simply furnished and offer a good standard of comfort and all modern facilities. There is a pleasant lounge bar, a TV lounge and an attractive dining room.*

41⇌🛏(4fb) CTV in all bedrooms ® T sB&B⇌🛏£30-£35 dB&B⇌🛏£50-£62 (incl dinner) 🖥

Lift ℂ CTV 2🚗 (£3 per day) CFA ♫ xmas

♀ English, French & Italian ♦ ⚘ ✄ Bar Lunch £3.50-£6.50 Dinner £11.50 Last dinner 8pm

Credit Cards ①②③ ⓔ

**★❀69% Downland**

37 Lewes Rd BN21 2BU (Minotels) ☎(0323)32689

Closed Jan

(Rosette awarded for dinner only)

*A warm welcome awaits guests to this small hotel, personally run by its owners Stephanie and Patrick Faulkner and set just off the A22 in a residential area within easy reach of both town centre and seafront ; bedrooms are simple but freshly decorated, and all have modern conveniences. Chef/proprietor Patrick Faulkner is an enthusiastic exponent of the mix-and-match modern style, attempting some bravura combinations of flavours and textures. The short seasonal à la carte menu is supplemented by a few daily dishes, and there is a separate vegetarian menu. An inspection meal began with oysters, prawns and mussels, some still in the shell, in a well-flavoured sauce of garlic, herbs, cognac and cream. This was followed by quail, topped with a rather strong thyme and spring onion stuffing and wrapped in bacon, and served with two noisettes of venison fillet on a thick port-enriched sauce with wild mushrooms. Dessert was home-made coffee ice cream, sponge underneath and browned meringue on top, served on a very strong hot mocha sauce. Attentive and professional service is headed by Stephanie Faulkner.*

15⇌🛏(4fb)1🚃 CTV in all bedrooms ® T ✖ (ex guide dogs) sB&B⇌🛏£27.50-£37.50 dB&B⇌🛏£55-£75 🖥

CTV 10P 🚲 🐕 xmas

V ♦ ✳ Lunch £10.95-£15&alc Dinner fr£15&alc Last dinner 9pm

Credit Cards ①②③⑤ ⓔ

**★61% Oban**

King Edward's Pde BN21 4DS ☎(0323)31581

Closed Dec-Etr RS Nov

*Ideally situated in a sea-facing position which is also close to shops and theatres, this small, family-run hotel comprises bright, well equipped bedrooms with en suite facilities, a good lounge, small bar and verandah and basement restaurant ; service is prompt and cheerful throughout.*

31⇌🛏(3fb) CTV in all bedrooms ® T sB&B⇌🛏£24-£35 dB&B⇌🛏£48-£70 🖥

Lift ℂ CTV ♪ ♫

V ♦ ⚘ Bar Lunch £2.50-£5 High tea £2.50-£5.50 Dinner £9.50 Last dinner 7.30pm

ⓔ

**★58% Lathom**

4-6 Howard Square, Grand Pde BN21 4BG ☎(0323)641986

Closed Nov-Feb (ex Xmas & New Year)

*A friendly personally run hotel, offering attractive bedrooms with modern facilities, a small dining room and a lounge with live entertainment on some evenings.*

45rm(2⇌41🛏)(5fb) CTV in all bedrooms ® ✖

Lift ℂ 6P (£2 per day) 2🚗 (£2) xmas

V ♦

Credit Cards ①③

For key to symbols in English see the bookmark.

**❀❀ ✖ Byrons**

6 Crown St, Old Town BN21 1NX ☎(0323)20171

*This small restaurant in the old part of town has attracted a faithful clientèle for the past 21 years. Simon Scrutton's short menu is supplemented by daily specials, favouring free-range and organic produce wherever possible. Classic dishes are balanced by a selection of more imaginative creations. The inspection meal began with a hot spinach mousse, beautifully light in texture, served with a fresh parmesan sauce. Next came a fillet of brill with a delicate saffron and ginger sauce, accompanied by courgettes pan-fried in a successful mixture of olive oil, sugar, cinammon and balsamic vinegar. Hot orange Bakewell tart is served with slivers of nutty praline and Tia Maria parfait. The wine list is well chosen and sensibly priced and includes some Sussex wines.*

Closed Sun, 1 wk Xmas & BH Lunch not served Sat (bookings only Mon-Fri)

♀ French V 22 seats ✳ Lunch £14.95-£20alc Dinner £14.95-£20alc Last lunch 1.30pm Last dinner 10.30pm ✐ nc8yrs

Credit Cards ②③⑤

---

**EAST DEREHAM** Norfolk Map **09** TF91

**★★64% King's Head**

Norwich St NR19 1AD ☎Dereham(0362)693842 & 693283 FAX (0362) 693776

*A friendly 16th-century inn a few minutes walk from the town centre, with ample car parking and a walled garden with a bowling green. Bedrooms have all modern facilities, both in the annexe and in the original building, which retains its historic atmosphere.*

10rm(4⇌2🛏)Annexe5⇌🛏(1fb) CTV in all bedrooms ® T sB&Bfr£34 sB&B⇌🛏fr£37 dB&Bfr£46 dB&B⇌🛏fr£50 🖥

CTV 30P 3🚗 CFA ♪ (grass) bowling

♀ English, French & Italian V ♦ ✳ Lunch £7.50-£12.50&alc Dinner £9-£13&alc Last dinner 9pm

Credit Cards ①②③⑤ ⓔ

**★71% George**

Swaffham Rd NR19 2AZ ☎(0362)696801

*Privately owned and managed, with the assistance of a friendly team of local staff, this town-centre inn offers bedrooms well above the overall classification of the establishment, their cottage-style décor and country pine furniture being complemented by modern facilities.*

8⇌🛏(2fb) CTV in all bedrooms ® T ✳ sB&B⇌🛏£35.50-£38 dB&B⇌🛏£42-£44.50 🖥

40P

V ♦ ⚘ ✳ Lunch fr£7.50&alc

Credit Cards ①②③⑤

---

**EAST GRINSTEAD** West Sussex Map **05** TQ33 ◉

★★★

**★★★❀❀🕍**

**GRAVETYE MANOR**

RH19 4LJ (3m SW off unclass rd joining B2110 & B2028) (Relais et Châteaux) ☎Sharpthorne (0342)810567 Telex no 957239 FAX (0342) 810080

RS 25 Dec

*The epitome of the English country house, this fine Elizabethan manor steeped in history stands in the most famous natural garden in Britain. Present owner Peter Herbert, who has striven to remedy the neglect these grounds suffered after the death of their former owner, also plans improvements to the hotel, which should have a new north*

*wing by the spring of 1992. Head Chef Steven Morey makes good use of home-grown produce in the dishes, both simple and elaborate, featured on his seasonal à la carte and daily-changing table d'hôte menus; artistically presented, light and modern in style, they include Fresh Spinach and Marscapone Gnocchi, parfait of Chicken Livers or Mousseline of Lobster followed by such main courses as Collops of Brill, Tartlet of Dover Sole and Dublin Bay Prawns or a traditional Rabbit Pie, and a truly superb wine list accompanies the meal. Accommodation is in individually styled bedrooms furnished with some fine old pieces and provided with books and magazines as well as the more usual modern features; bathrooms, too, are well equipped, though not all have good shower facilities at present. Public areas which reflect foibles of earlier owners have large fireplaces where slow-burning wood from the estate emits both heat and a lovely aroma during the cooler months. Fresh flowers and pot plants abound, friendly staff with a good eye for detail provide old fashioned services, and everything gleams with cleanliness.*

18⇨1🛏 CTV in all bedrooms T ✕ ✳ sB⇨£94.87-£108.79 dB⇨£129.25-£223.25 (room only)

25P ♨ ✿ ⌒ croquet nc7yrs

♥ ✕ S% Lunch £22.35&alc Dinner £25.85&alc Last dinner 9.30pm

---

★★★❀66% **Woodbury House**

Lewes Rd RH19 8UD ☎(0342)313657 FAX (0342) 314801
RS 26 Dec & 1 Jan

*Conveniently located on the A22 south of the town centre, the accommodation has been tastefully furnished throughout and new bedrooms provide good levels of comfort. The restaurant has earned a good reputation locally for its food, and the bistro offers an alternative. The relaxed, informal atmosphere owes much to the personal involvement and commitment of the proprietors, Jane and Michael Medforth, and Chef Nigel Davies has special recognition for his cooking.*

13⇨🛏Annexe1🛏1🛏 CTV in all bedrooms ® T ✳ sB&B⇨🛏£55-£60 dB&B⇨🛏£65-£75 🎵

30P ♨ ✿ CFA

V ♥ ⚟ ✕ Lunch fr£16.50&alc Dinner fr£17.50&alc Last dinner 9.30pm

Credit Cards ①②③④⑤ ⑥

---

**EAST HORNDON** Essex Map **05** TQ68

⭐Forte Travelodge

CM13 3LL (on A127, eastbound) (Forte)
☎Brentwood(0277)810819 Central Res (0800) 850950
*Modern, value-for-money accommodation situated adjacent to a Little Chef restaurant. The good-sized bedrooms on two floors are well equipped and comfortable.*

22⇨🛏(22fb) CTV in all bedrooms ® sB⇨🛏£29.95 dB⇨🛏£29.95 (room only)

《 22P

Credit Cards ①②③

---

**EAST HORSLEY** Surrey Map **04** TQ05

★★★59% **Thatchers Resort**

Epsom Rd KT24 6TB (Resort) ☎(04865)4291 FAX (04865) 4222
*An attractive property with outdoor pool complex, located on the edge of the village, is within 30 minutes' drive of both Gatwick and Heathrow airports. Its bedrooms (some of which are situated in annexe buildings) are equipped to suit either holidaymakers or business visitors, while open-plan public areas have a modern appeal and the beamed restaurant offers both à la carte and table d'hôte menus.*

36⇨🛏Annexe23⇨🛏(4fb)2🛏✕in 6 bedrooms CTV in all bedrooms ® T ✕ (ex guide dogs) sB⇨🛏£70-£80 dB⇨🛏£80-£90 (room only) 🎵

→

E

277

《 60P ✿ CFA ⌒ (heated)
♀ English & French **V** ✿ _⚲_ Lunch £14.50&alc High tea £7.50
Dinner £17.50&alc Last dinner 9.30pm
Credit Cards ①②③⑤ⓔ

---

**EAST KILBRIDE** Strathclyde _Lanarkshire_ Map **11** NS65

★★★62% **Bruce Swallow**
Cornwall St G74 1AF (Swallow) ☎(03552)29771
Telex no 778428 FAX (03552) 42216
_This purpose-built business hotel, located conveniently close to the
town centre complex, provides bedrooms which are all well
equipped though they vary in style and size. There is no lounge bar
as such, drinks being served in the spacious general-purpose central
lounge._
79⇌🍴📶in 10 bedrooms CTV in all bedrooms ® **T** ✱
sB&B⇌🍴£55-£65 dB&B⇌🍴£72-£82
Lift 《 15P 25🎯 ♫
♀ International ✿ _⚲_ ✱ S% Lunch fr£6.95 High tea fr£5.50
Dinner fr£12.95&alc Last dinner 9.45pm
Credit Cards ①②③⑤ⓔ

★★★60% **Stuart**
2 Cornwall Way G74 1JR ☎(03552)21161 Telex no 778504
FAX (03552) 64410
Closed 25 Dec & 1 Jan
_Bedrooms in two styles, both varying in size, are available at this
town centre business hotel._
39⇌🍴(1fb)1🛏 CTV in all bedrooms ® **T** ✱ sB&B⇌🍴£47-
£57 dB&B⇌🍴£59-£72 🍴
Lift 《 ⊞ CTV 🏃 CFA ♫ _xmas_
♀ European **V** ✿ _⚲_ ✱ Lunch fr£7.15&alc High tea £7.50-£10
Dinner £12.95-£16&alc Last dinner 9.30pm
Credit Cards ①②③⑤

★★68% **Crutherland Country House**
Strathaven Rd G75 0QZ ☎(03552)37633
Closed 1 & 2 Jan
_Set in 37 acres of grounds off the A725 Strathaven road 2 miles
from the town centre, this tastefully refurbished hotel has a
comfortable lounge and an attractive conservatory restaurant.
Most of the bedrooms are in the modern extension, but there are 4
in the original house which reflect the period style of the building._
19⇌🍴(1fb) CTV in all bedrooms ® **T**
《 200P ✿ ✿ ♪
✿ ✱ Lunch fr£5.50&alc Dinner £16.95&alc Last dinner
9.30pm
Credit Cards ①②③

---

**EASTLEIGH** Hampshire Map **04** SU41

★★★63% **Forte Crest Southampton**
Leigh Rd, Passfield Av SO5 5PG (Forte Hotels) ☎(0703)619700
Telex no 47606 FAX (0703) 643945
_A well designed modern hotel with ample parking facilities,
conveniently situated for the business user, features spacious public
rooms which include an attractive split-level piano bar with a small
games area. The Beatrix Restaurant includes a buffet/carvery
alternative to its extensive à la carte and table d'hôte menus, and a
carefully compiled wine list is available ; the variety of bedrooms
offer a choice of styles and standards, the compact Business Centre
can provide executives with secretarial assistance, and a New
Sensations Leisure Centre was opened in 1990._
120⇌🍴(10fb)📶in 64 bedrooms CTV in all bedrooms ® **T** ✱
S% sB⇌🍴£82 dB⇌🍴£95 (room only) 🍴
Lift 《 120P CFA ⌒ (heated) sauna solarium gymnasium pool
table leisure club ♨ _xmas_
♀ English & French **V** ✿ _⚲_ ✂ ✱ S% Lunch £12.95&alc
Dinner £15.95&alc Last dinner 9.45pm
Credit Cards ①②③④⑤

---

⏱**Forte Travelodge**
Twyford Rd(off A335) (Forte)
☎(0703)616813 Central Res (0800) 850950
_This recently constructed 2-storey brick and timber building
adjoins the Ham Farm Harvester and pub on the A335 three-
quarters of a mile north of the town. Excellent budget
accommodation is provided – the price being the same whether the
room has one or four occupants – and there are open country views
from the rear of the building ; the thatched pub's bar meals
supplement those mainly char-grilled dishes available in the
restaurant._
32⇌🍴(32fb) CTV in all bedrooms ® sB⇌🍴£29.95
dB⇌🍴£29.95 (room only)
《 32P 🚲
Credit Cards ①②③

---

**EAST LINTON** Lothian Map **12** NT57

★★62% **The Harvesters**
Station Rd EH40 3DP ☎(0620)860395
_Conveniently located south of Edinburgh, only yards from the A1,
the hotel offers cosy bedrooms, good-value menus and friendly
sevice._
5⇌🍴Annexe7rm(4⇌🍴)(2fb) CTV in all bedrooms ® **T** ✱
sB&Bfr£32 sB&B⇌🍴fr£47 dB&Bfr£63 dB&B⇌🍴fr£72 🍴
CTV 30P ✿ ♪
♀ International **V** ✿ _⚲_ ✱ Lunch fr£4.75&alc High tea
fr£4.95alc Dinner £7.50-£19alc Last dinner 9pm
Credit Cards ①②③⑤ⓔ

---

**EAST PORTLEMOUTH** Devon Map **03** SX73

★★66% _Gara Rock_
TQ8 8PH (Minotels) ☎Salcombe(054884)2342
FAX (054884) 3033
Closed Nov-Etr
_Originally a coastguard station facing due south surrounded by
National Trust land, this family-run hotel with its dramatic
backdrop overlooks beautiful scenery and an expanse of sea. It is
geared to family holidays with special features for children of all
ages, and accommodation ranging from family rooms to suites and
self-catering flats around the grounds. Bedrooms in the hotel are
spotless, and nicely furnished with colonial style cane units. Public
rooms are comfortable and in keeping with the character of the
building, and the stylish restaurant provides worthy food. Services,
including early morning tea, are conducted by a willing team with
a welcoming, hospitable attitude._
21rm(14⇌🍴5🍴)(15fb) CTV in all bedrooms ® **T**
60P 🚲 ✿ ⌒ (heated) 🎾 (hard) ♪ games room ♨
♀ English & French **V** ✿ _⚲_ ✂ Last dinner 8.30pm
Credit Cards ①③⑤

---

**EATHORPE** Warwickshire Map **04** SP36

★★56% **Eathorpe Park**
Fosse Way CV33 9DQ (Exec Hotel) ☎Marton(0926)632245 &
632632 FAX (0926) 632481
Closed 25 Dec evening & 26 Dec
_This imposing Victorian hotel is situated on the Fosse Way, close
to the village centre. Improvements to the spacious public areas are
now complete, with many original features retained. Bedrooms are,
at the time of going to press, receiving the same attention._
14⇌🍴(3fb) CTV in all bedrooms ® **T** 🐕 (ex guide dogs) ✱
sB&B⇌🍴fr£40.50 dB&B⇌🍴£55-£65 🍴
CTV 200P ✿ CFA solarium
♀ English & French **V** ✿ _⚲_ ✱ Lunch £7.95-£15.95&alc
Dinner £12.95-£15.95&alc Last dinner 9.45pm
Credit Cards ①②③⑤ⓔ

## EBCHESTER Co Durham Map **12** NZ15

**★★★64%  The Raven**
Broomhill DH8 6RY (Consort) ☎(0207)560082 & 560367
FAX (0207) 560262
28⇆🛏(8fb)1⊞ CTV in all bedrooms ® **T ✱** S5%
sB&B⇆🛏£36-£53 dB&B⇆🛏£46-£70 🅡
《 CTV 100P ❖ CFA *xmas*
♀ English & French **V** ⇦ _�_ S5% Lunch £12.95&alc Dinner
£12.95&alc Last dinner 10pm
Credit Cards ①③⑤

## ECCLESHALL Staffordshire Map **07** SJ82

**★★65%  St George**
Castle St ST21 6DF ☎(0785)850300 FAX (0785) 851452
*Popular with business people, this fully-renovated inn at the centre
of the village offers good quality accommodation, a friendly local
bar atmosphere and a restaurant in traditional style which serves
good wholesome meals.*
10⇆🛏1⊞ CTV in all bedrooms ® **T ✱** sB&B⇆🛏fr£40
dB&B⇆🛏fr£60 Continental breakfast 🅡
17P 🚗
♀ English & French **V** ⇦ _⌷_ ✂ ✳ Lunch fr£8.25 Dinner
fr£11.95 Last dinner 9.30pm
Credit Cards ①②③⑤

## EDBURTON West Sussex Map **04** TQ21

**★★❀70%  Tottington Manor**
BN5 9LJ ☎Steyning(0903)815757 FAX (0903) 879331
Closed 25-27 Dec
*This small country pub has been taken up and transformed by
proprietors David and Kate Miller, and now provides extensive
catering in fresh, appealing surroundings. There is a brisk trade in
bar food of greater quality and interest than most bar meals. But it
is in the restaurant that David Miller makes the greatest use of his
skill, and experience gained during 3 years as executive chef at the
Ritz and 12 at Sheraton Park Tower. An international menu offers
dishes from the Far East, France and England. Food is light and
in the modern style, using mostly fresh ingredients and with an
emphasis on strong flavours. There is an atmosphere of warm
hospitality in this freshly decorated, cosy restaurant, and the six
pretty bedrooms provide many extra comforts, two retaining their
16th-century features.*
6⇆🛏 CTV in all bedrooms ® **T ✱** (ex guide dogs) ✳
sB&B⇆🛏£40-£46.50 dB&B⇆🛏£60-£67.50
100P ❖
♀ International **V** ⇦ ✳ Lunch £16.90-£25.75alc Dinner £16.90-
£25.75alc Last dinner 9.15pm
Credit Cards ①②③⑤

## EDENBRIDGE Kent Map **05** TQ44

**❀❀ ✕ ✕ ✕ Honours Mill**
87 High St TN8 5AU ☎(0732)866757
*A charming, characterful converted mill at the centre of the village
retains the old mill wheel as a feature of its small bar area. The
timbered dining room offers a set-price luncheon menu,
supplemented by daily specials, of such predominantly French
dishes as Red Mullet and Potato Terrine with an Anisette Sauce
and Calves' Liver with Tarragon Sauce, followed by rich desserts
served in generous portions; an all-French wine list accompanies
the meal. Though fairly expensive – particularly for an
establishment outside London – this restaurant has a lot to
recommend it.*
Closed Mon, 2 wks Jan & 2 wks Jun Lunch not served Sat
Dinner not served Sun
♀ French 38 seats Lunch £20.95&alc Last lunch 2pm Last
dinner 10pm 🅟 nc10yrs
Credit Cards ①③

## EDENHALL Cumbria Map **12** NY53

**★★63%  *Edenhall***
CA11 8SX ☎Langwathby(076881)454
*Peacefully set in the picturesque village of Edenhall, this friendly
traditional hotel has a comfortable lounge bar with an open fire, a
bright dining room and well equipped bedrooms with en suite
facilities.*
29⇆Annexe8⇆(3fb) CTV in 29 bedrooms ✱
⊞ CTV 80P 2♠ ❖
♀ English, French & Italian **V** ⇦ _⌷_ Last dinner 9pm
Credit Cards ①③

## EDINBURGH Lothian *Midlothian* Map **11** NT27 ⓔ

**See Town Plan Section**

**★★★★★❀❀69%  Caledonian**
Princes St EH1 2AB (Queens Moat)(Pride of Britain)
☎031-225 2433 Telex no 72179 FAX 031-225 6632
*The 'Cally', as it is affectionately known, now under new
ownership, is undergoing major improvements which will bring it up
to present day standards without destroying its original character.
Though some bedrooms are still inferior, many have been very well
refurbished – as has the Gazebo Restaurant, now renamed
Carriages. La Pompadour continues to enjoy a high reputation for
its cuisine under the direction of new Head Chef Tony Binks.*
237⇆🛏(16fb)1⊞⚘in 43 bedrooms CTV in all bedrooms **T
✱** (ex guide dogs) ✳ sB⇆🛏£125-£145 dB⇆🛏£165-£225
(room only) 🅡
Lift 《 110P CFA *xmas*
♀ Scottish & French **V** ⇦ _⌷_ ✂ ✳ Lunch £14-£19.50&alc
Dinner £23.50&alc Last dinner 10.30pm
Credit Cards ①②③⑤

**★★★★68%  Carlton Highland**
North Bridge EH1 1SD (Scottish Highland) ☎031-556 7277
Telex no 727001 FAX 031-556 2691
*This comfortable modern hotel, close to Waverley station and the
city's main attractions, provides generally spacious bedrooms and
its many facilities include a relaxing first-floor lounge, two
restaurants, a coffee shop, a sports and leisure complex, conference
and banqueting facilities and a night-club. Service is friendly and
efficient.*
207⇆🛏(20fb) CTV in all bedrooms ® **T** sB&B⇆🛏£92-£102
dB&B⇆🛏£128-£140 🅡
Lift 《 ⊞ 🏊 CFA 🔲 (heated) squash snooker sauna solarium
gymnasium jacuzzi table tennis dance studio creche 🎵 ♁ *xmas*
♀ Scottish & French **V** ⇦ _⌷_ ✳ Lunch £8-£16&alc High tea
fr£9 Dinner £8-£16&alc Last dinner 10.30pm
Credit Cards ①②③④⑤⑥

**★★★★❀63%  *George Hotel Inter-Continental***
19-21 George St EH2 2PB ☎031-225 1251 Telex no 72570
FAX 031-226 5644
*This busy hotel is within walking distance of the shops and many of
the city's places of interest. Le Chambertin restaurant provides an
à la carte menu of mainly classical French dishes and a small
'Taste of Scotland' menu which will introduce visitors to delights
such as Cullen Skink and Haggis. The large Carvers Table offers a
range of roasts and buffet dishes.*
195⇆🛏(10fb)⚘in 32 bedrooms CTV in all bedrooms ® **T ✱**
sB⇆🛏£115-£125 dB⇆🛏£145-£160 (room only) 🅡
Lift 《 24P CFA *xmas*
♀ Scottish, English & French **V** ⇦ _⌷_ ✂ ✳ Lunch £14-£17&alc
Dinner £15-£19&alc Last dinner 10pm
Credit Cards ①②③⑤⑥

**★★★★60%  *Dalmahoy Hotel, Golf & Country Club***
Kirknewton EH27 8EB ☎031-333 1845 Telex no 72205
FAX 031-335 3203
*Already renowned for its golf courses, this fine Georgian mansion
has been restored and extended to produce a hotel geared to*

→

**E**

*corporate and leisure markets. The original building houses public and conference rooms as well as 7 period bedrooms. The remaining bedrooms are in the adjacent building, along with the leisure centre, restaurant and bar. There is a covered walkway between the sites. The Dalmahoy is situated in extensive parkland off the A71 2.5 miles west of the city by pass.*

116↪🛏(3fb)✠in 19 bedrooms CTV in all bedrooms ® T ✻ (ex guide dogs)
Lift ⊄ 200P CFA 🖳 (heated) ▶ 18 ♟ (hard) squash snooker sauna solarium gymnasium
♀ Scottish & French ♥ ♨ ✠ Last dinner 9.45pm
Credit Cards ⑴ ⑵ ⑶ ⑸ ⓔ

### ★★★86% The Howard
Great King St EH3 6QH (Select) ☎031-557 3500
Telex no 727887 FAX 031-557 6515
*Splendidly appointed hotel in the city's Georgian New Town area with club-style lounges and cocktail bars and individually-styled bedrooms.*
16↪🛏3🛏 CTV in all bedrooms T ✻ (ex guide dogs)
Lift ⊄ 12P 🚗
V ♥ ♨ Last dinner 10pm
Credit Cards ⑴ ⑵ ⑶ ⑸

### ★★★⊛70% King James Thistle
107 St James Centre EH1 3SW (Mount Charlotte (TS))
☎031-556 0111 Telex no 727200 FAX 031-557 5333
*This comfortable modern hotel in the city centre – conveniently located just off Princes Street – will appeal to both businessmen and leisure travellers, providing popular conference and leisure facilities. A range of tastefully appointed and thoughtfully equipped standard and executive bedrooms is augmented by a number of suites, while the informal American-themed bar/diner on the third floor provides an alternative to the more sophisticated atmosphere of an attractive cocktail bar which stands beside the Restaurant Saint Jacques – an authentic French brasserie. Imaginative dishes are, for the most part, based on carefully selected fresh ingredients (though it should be noted that not all sweets are freshly made); a typical dinner might perhaps include Beaujolais ham with orange and hazelnut salad, collops of calves' livers on a bed of vegetables and rosemary-scented lentils with a light Amontillado dressing, and an almond tulip basket with liqueured fruits and a fresh raspberry coulis. Service throughout is willing and efficient.*
147↪🛏(20fb)✠in 14 bedrooms CTV in all bedrooms ® T (room only) 🍴
Lift ⊄ 21P 8🚗
♀ International ♥ ♨ ✠
Credit Cards ⑴ ⑵ ⑶ ⑷ ⑸

### ★★★69% Roxburghe
Charlotte Square EH2 4HG (Best Western) ☎031-225 3921
Telex no 727054 FAX 031-220 2518
*This long-established hotel is affectionately old-fashioned with traditional service standards, and is the ideal retreat from the bustle of the city. A fine example of Adam architecture, it overlooks an equally fine garden square. It has an elegant restaurant as well as a popular buttery, and morning coffee or afternoon tea can also be taken in the lounge. Bedrooms are well equipped and vary in style.*
75↪🛏1🛏 CTV in all bedrooms ® T S% sB&B↪🛏£72-£95 dB&B↪🛏£87-£120 🍴
Lift ⊄ ♟ 🚗 CFA xmas
♀ French V ♥ ♨ ✻ Lunch £9-£10.50&alc High tea £4.50-£7 Dinner £16.90-£17.50&alc Last dinner 10pm
Credit Cards ⑴ ⑵ ⑶ ⑸ ⓔ

### ★★★68% Bruntsfield
69/74 Bruntsfield Place EH10 4HH (Best Western)
☎031-229 1393 Telex no 727897 FAX 031-229 5634
*A privately owned hotel which appeals to both tourists and business people provides well equipped bedrooms in a variety of shapes and sizes, a comfortable foyer lounge, a choice of bars and a lively*

*restaurant/brasserie which includes the appropriately named Potting Shed, housed in a conservatory. Staff have a good attitude, service being friendly and attentive.*
50↪🛏(1fb)1🛏 CTV in all bedrooms ® T sB&B↪🛏£66.50-£75 dB&B↪🛏£95-£120 Continental breakfast 🍴
Lift ⊄ 25P CFA xmas
♀ International V ♥ ✠ Lunch £8&alc Dinner £17-£20&alc Last dinner 10pm
Credit Cards ⑴ ⑵ ⑶ ⑸ ⓔ

### ★★★67% Barnton Thistle
Queensferry Rd, Barnton EH4 6AS (Mount Charlotte (TS))
☎031-339 1144 Telex no 727928 FAX 031-339 5521
*On the western outskirts of the city, this business hotel has an attractive restaurant and cocktail lounge, and well equipped bedrooms.*
50↪🛏(9fb)1🛏✠in 10 bedrooms CTV in all bedrooms ® T (room only) 🍴
Lift ⊄ 100P sauna hairdresser
♀ International ♥ ♨ ✠
Credit Cards ⑴ ⑵ ⑶ ⑷ ⑸

### ★★★67% Capital Moat House
Clermiston Rd EH12 6UG (Queens Moat) ☎031-334 3391
Telex no 728284 FAX 031-334 9712
*Located close to the city centre in a pleasant and quiet location, this hotel offers well appointed bedrooms, a spacious bar and lounges, and a comprehensive leisure complex.*
98↪🛏(10fb)1🛏 CTV in all bedrooms ® T ✻ S10% sB↪🛏fr£67 dB↪🛏fr£82 (room only) 🍴
Lift ⊄ 150P CFA 🖳 (heated) sauna solarium gymnasium beautician xmas
♀ Scottish & French V ♥ ♨ ✻ Sunday Lunch £6.95-£7.95 Dinner fr£13.50&alc Last dinner 9.45pm
Credit Cards ⑴ ⑵ ⑶ ⑷ ⑸ ⓔ

### ★★★65% Forte Posthouse
Corstorphine Rd EH12 6UA (Forte Hotels) ☎031-334 0390
Telex no 727103 FAX 031-334 9237
*On western city approach and backed by Edinburgh Zoo this comfortable and spacious hotel offers fine views over the city.*
200↪🛏✠in 104 bedrooms CTV in all bedrooms ® T ✻ S% sB↪🛏fr£49.50 dB↪🛏fr£49.50 (room only) 🍴
Lift ⊄ 158P CFA xmas
V ♥ ♨ ✠ ✻ S% Lunch £10.95&alc Dinner £13.95&alc Last dinner 10.30pm
Credit Cards ⑴ ⑵ ⑶ ⑷ ⑸

### ★★★65% *Norton House*
Ingliston EH28 8LX ☎031-333 1275 Telex no 727232
FAX 031-333 5303
*Set in extensive parkland 6 miles from Edinburgh and close to the airport, this substantial Victorian mansion has been considerably extended and upgraded to provide every modern comfort for the business and leisure traveller. Public areas include an attractive conservatory restaurant, popular panelled cocktail bar and comfortable lounge. Bedrooms are well equipped and there is a range of conference and function facilities.*
19↪🛏(3fb) CTV in all bedrooms ®
⊄ 100P ✿ putting green pool table
♀ French V ♥ ♨ Last dinner 9.30pm
Credit Cards ⑴ ⑵ ⑶ ⑸

### ★★★65% Royal Scot
111 Glasgow Rd EH12 8NF (Swallow) ☎031-334 9191
Telex no 727197 FAX 031-316 4507
*This large purpose-built hotel is situated on the A8 on the western edge of the city, conveniently placed for the bypass and the airport. The restaurant incorporates a carvery in addition to the à la carte menu. Bedrooms in the south wing have been upgraded.*
259↪🛏(30fb)✠in 102 bedrooms CTV in all bedrooms ® T ✻ S% sB&B↪🛏fr£92 dB&B↪🛏fr£117 🍴

Lift ⟪ 300P ❀ CFA ▣ (heated) sauna solarium gymnasium pitch & putt steam room ♫ *xmas*
♔ International V ✿ ⚏ ✱ Lunch £17.75 High tea fr£5alc Dinner £17.75&alc Last dinner 10pm
Credit Cards ①②③⑤ⓔ

### ★★★64% Mount Royal

53 Princes St EH2 2DG (Jarvis) ☎031-225 7161 Telex no 727641 FAX 031-220 4671

*In a prime position overlooking Princes Street and the Castle, this popular tour-holiday hotel has bright well equipped modern bedrooms and a spacious lounge serving refreshments from 10 am to 9 pm. The adjoining restaurant offers à la carte and carvery meals.*

159⇨☖(14fb)⚸in 6 bedrooms CTV in all bedrooms Ⓡ T ✱
sB⇨☖£85-£99 dB⇨☖£107.50-£122.50 (room only) ▤
Lift ⟪ ⚲ CFA *xmas*
♔ Scottish & French V ✿ ⚏ ⚸ Lunch £7-£8.50 High tea fr£6 Dinner fr£15&alc Last dinner 9.30pm
Credit Cards ①②③④⑤

### ★★★63% Donmaree

21 Mayfield Gardens EH9 2BX ☎031-667 3641 FAX 031-667 9130

*With easy access from the city bypass, this friendly hotel offers a relaxing atmosphere, comfortable accommodation and interesting menus.*

17⇨☖ CTV in all bedrooms Ⓡ T ✱ sB&B⇨☖£35-£50
dB&B⇨☖£70-£80 ▤
⟪ 3P *xmas*
♔ French V ✿ ✱ Lunch £9&alc Dinner £9&alc Last dinner 10pm
Credit Cards ①②③⑤

**★★★62% Stakis Grosvenor**
Grosvenor St EH12 5EF (Stakis) ☎031-226 6001 Telex no 72445 FAX 031-220 2387
*This large hotel catering for conferences and coach tours has comfortable spacious lounge areas and both a carvery and a steakhouse restaurant.*
136⇨🎋(18fb)1🏠💺in 18 bedrooms CTV in all bedrooms ® T
✳ sB⇨🎋£86.10-£96.60 dB⇨🎋£110.25-£120.75 (room only) 🍴
Lift ℂ CTV 🅿 CFA *xmas*
♀ Scottish, French & Italian V ✿ 💯 💺
Credit Cards 1 2 3 5

**★★★57% Old Waverley**
Princes St EH2 2BY (Scottish Highland) ☎031-556 4648 Telex no 727050 FAX 031-557 6316
*This historic building on a corner site at the eastern end of Princes Street has recently refurbished bedrooms of varying size. The carvery restaurant, small bar and adjoining lounge serving teas and snacks are all popular during the day.*
66⇨🎋(6fb) CTV in all bedrooms ® T ✳ sB&B⇨🎋£71-£78 dB&B⇨🎋£107-£118 🍴
Lift ℂ 🅿 CFA *xmas*
V ✿ 💯 ✳ Lunch £4-£6 High tea fr£7 Dinner £10.25-£11.75&alc Last dinner 9.30pm
Credit Cards 1 2 3 5 £

**★★★56% Braid Hills**
134 Braid Rd, Braid Hills EH10 6JD (2.5m S A702)
☎031-447 8888 Telex no 72311 FAX 031-452 8477
*Conveniently situated on the A702 between the bypass and the city centre, this traditional hotel offers well appointed bedrooms, although some are rather compact.*
68⇨🎋2🏠💺in 8 bedrooms CTV in all bedrooms ® T ✳ S%
sB&B⇨🎋£60-£71.50 dB&B⇨🎋£70-£85.75 🍴
ℂ 38P ✿ CFA *xmas*
♀ Scottish & French V ✿ ✿ S% Lunch £6.50-£8.50&alc
Dinner £15.75&alc Last dinner 9pm
Credit Cards 1 2 3 5 £

**★★★54% Ellersly House**
4 Ellersly Rd EH12 6HZ (Jarvis) ☎031-337 6888
Telex no 727239 FAX 031-313 2543
*An extended period mansion set in its own grounds in a residential area close to the A8 on the western side of the city. The lounge, cocktail bar and restaurant offer modern comforts and the bedrooms, though rather dated, are well equipped.*
57⇨(3fb)1🏠💺in 10 bedrooms CTV in all bedrooms ® T ✳
S% sB⇨£70-£99 dB⇨£103.50-£124 (room only) 🍴
Lift ℂ 50P ✿ CFA croquet *xmas*
♀ International V ✿ 💯 ✳ Lunch fr£10 Dinner fr£18&alc Last dinner 9.30pm
Credit Cards 1 2 3 4 5 £

**★★67% Westbury**
92-98 St Johns Rd, Corstophine EH12 8AT ☎031-316 4466 FAX 031-316 4333
*Though the well appointed bedrooms of this new hotel are comfortable in traditional style, its open-plan theme bar features unusual bric à brac, modern music and friendly, informal service, whilst the menu offers a truly international cuisine.*
30⇨💺in 6 bedrooms CTV in all bedrooms ® T
ℂ 30P
♀ Continental V ✿ 💯 💺
Credit Cards 1 2 3

**★★63% Murrayfield**
18 Corstophine Rd EH12 6HN ☎031-337 1844
FAX 031-346 8159
*A pleasant old house, conveniently located on the outskirts of the city, and offering good access to the bypass, airport and road bridge. It has been modernised to provide comfortable, well appointed accommodation.*

23⇨🎋Annexe10🎋 CTV in all bedrooms ® T ✳
sB&B⇨🎋£57-£59.99 dB&B⇨🎋£68.75-£70 🍴
ℂ CTV 30P CFA
✿ 💯 ✳ Lunch £8.50 High tea £5.95 Dinner £12&alc Last dinner 9.30pm
Credit Cards 1 2 3 5 £

**★★61% Lady Nairne**
228 Willowbrae Rd EH8 7NG ☎031-661 3396
FAX 031-652 2789
*A welcoming village inn has been converted to provide comfortable accommodation comprising well appointed bedrooms and a cosily inviting lounge and bars. Service is warm and friendly throughout, and menus offer a good- value range of interesting dishes.*
33⇨🎋(1fb) CTV in all bedrooms ® T 🎋 (ex guide dogs)
Lift ℂ 100P
V ✿ 💯 💺 Last dinner 10pm
Credit Cards 1 2 3 5

**★★59% Harp Toby**
St John's Rd, Corstorphine EH12 (3.5m W on A8) (Toby)
☎031-334 4750
*Situated in Corstorphine village but on the A8 and convenient for the city bypass, this commercial hotel has a comfortable lounge bar and a carvery restaurant, both split level. Bedrooms are mostly compact but well equipped.*
27⇨🎋(2fb)💺in 9 bedrooms CTV in all bedrooms ®
ℂ 50P
✿ 💯 💺
Credit Cards 1 2 3 5

**★★59% Iona**
Strathearn Place EH9 2AL ☎031-447 6264 & 031-447 5050
FAX 031-452 8574
*A popular commercial hotel in a residential area 10 minutes' drive from the centre on the south side of the city has a busy bar with separate lounge as well as the residents' lounge upstairs. Bedrooms vary in size but are soundly furnished and well equipped, and the dining room serves lunches as well as evening meals.*
17rm(2⇨2🎋)Annexe4rm(2fb) CTV in all bedrooms ® T
sB&B£32.50-£48 dB&Bfr£58 dB&B⇨🎋fr£65.50
CTV 20P 🚲 CFA
V ✿ Lunch fr£7.50 Dinner fr£11.50alc Last dinner 9pm
Credit Cards 1 3

**★★58% Rothesay**
8 Rothesay Place EH3 7SL ☎031-225 4125 Telex no 727025
FAX 031-220 4350
*This terraced, family-run, commercial/tourist hotel provides keenly priced accommodation and public areas that include an attractive foyer lounge and small bar ; grills feature predominantly on the dinner menu.*
35rm(26⇨3🎋)(1fb) CTV in all bedrooms ® T sB&B£23-£29
sB&B⇨🎋£25-£46 dB&B£35-£45 dB&B⇨🎋£40-£70
Lift ℂ CTV 🅿
♀ Mainly grills ✿ 💯 Dinner £9.50-£18alc Last dinner 9pm
Credit Cards 1 2 3 4 5

**★★56% Suffolk Hall**
10 Craigmillar Park EH16 5NE ☎031-668 4333
FAX 031-668 4506
*Located in a residential area between the bypass and the city centre, this small hotel offers comfortable bedrooms and friendly, informal service.*
12rm(11⇨🎋)(4fb) CTV in all bedrooms ® T
🎋 (ex guide dogs) ✳ S% sB&B£35-£38 dB&B⇨🎋£50-£60 🍴
ℂ CTV 12P 🚲 ✿ CFA
V ✿ 💯
Credit Cards 1 2 3 £

### ★★55% **Clarendon**
Grosvenor St EH12 5EG (Scottish Highland) ☎031-337 7033
Telex no 72450 FAX 031-346 7606
*Recently refurbished, the quiet, friendly hotel is situated in the*
*attractive West End of the city.*
51⇅🌣(5fb) CTV in all bedrooms ® T sB&B⇅🌣£55-£65
dB&B⇅🌣£8-£92 🏠
Lift ℭ CTV 🅿 CFA *xmas*
V 🖑 🖾 Lunch fr£7.50&alc Dinner £10.25-£12&alc Last dinner
9.30pm
Credit Cards ①②③⑤ⓕ

### ★★51% *Cairn*
10-18 Windsor St EH7 5JR ☎031-557 0175 FAX 031-556 8221
*This informal hotel, conveniently situated to the east of the city*
*centre, has been completely refurbished to provide well equipped*
*bedrooms and bright public areas.*
52⇅🌣(12fb) CTV in all bedrooms ® T
ℭ CTV 🅿
🖾 Mainly grills V 🖑 🖾 Last dinner 9pm
Credit Cards ①②③⑤

### 🏠Forte Travelodge
Dreghorn Link(6m S, A720 Ring Rd South) (Forte)
☎031-441 4296 Central Res (0800) 850950
*Just off the city bypass between the junctions with the A70 and*
*A702 – come off at the junction signposted Colinton, Oxgangs –*
*this Travelodge has a southerly outlook towards the Pentland hills.*
*Meals are taken in the adjoining Little Chef, and there is a filling*
*station nearby.*
40⇅🌣(40fb) CTV in all bedrooms ® sB⇅🌣£29.95
dB⇅🌣£29.95 (room only)
ℭ 40P 🚐
Credit Cards ①②③

### ❀✕✕**L'Auberge**
56 St Mary's St EH1 1SX ☎031-556 5888
*You will find L'Auberge, one of the city's most popular restaurants,*
*just off the Royal Mile. Dishes are prepared from the best*
*available Scottish ingredients , but the innovative cooking, like the*
*atmosphere, is decidedly French. It offers a choice of menus and*
*the extensive wine list is worthy of note.*
Closed 26 Dec-2 Jan
🖾 French V 55 seats Lunch £9.50-£12.50&alc Dinner £19.50
Last lunch 2pm Last dinner 9.30pm 🅿
Credit Cards ①②③⑤

### ❀❀✕✕**Martins**
70 Rose St North Lane EH2 3DX ☎031-225 3106
*Tucked away in a small lane off the city's famous Rose Street, this*
*popular and now well established little restaurant continues to offer*
*reliable and imaginatively prepared food. The menu is constantly*
*changing, but may include dishes such as Mousseline of Salmon*
*with a delicate red pepper sauce, or pigeon breast in a sauce of*
*strawberry and port. Service is friendly and attentive.*
Closed Sun, Mon & 25 Dec-21 Jan Lunch not served Sat
28 seats Lunch £9.95-£14.95&alc Last lunch 2pm Last dinner
10pm 🅿 nc8yrs ✄
Credit Cards ①②③⑤

### ❀❀✕✕**The Vintners Room**
The Vaults, 87 Giles St, Leith EH6 6BZ ☎031-554 8423 &
031-554 6767
*Situated in the fashionable, historic port of Leith and revitalised by*
*Tim and Sue Cumming who previously owned the Hole in the Wall*
*at Bath, this restaurant and its wine bar occupy the ground floor of*
*a large stone building whose vaults date back to the twelfth century*
*and which is reputedly the oldest continuously-used commercial*
*premises in Scotland. Since it was initially used for the storage of*
*claret and then became the home of a wine and spirits merchants, it*
*is appropriate that its style of cuisine should perpetuate the 'auld*
*alliance' – Scottish seafood, meat and game being prepared in the*
*French provincial manner ; a small but carefully compiled main*
→

**E**

course selection varies according to availability, while starters and puddings offer a wide choice, but all dishes are notable for their honest, uncomplicated flavours. Food is also served in the bar.
Closed Sun ex during Edinburgh Festival & 2wks Xmas
♀ Scottish, French & Italian V 48 seats ✳ Lunch fr£12&alc Dinner fr£12&alc Last lunch 2.30pm Last dinner 10.30pm 3 P ⊱

Credit Cards ① ② ③

---

**EDZELL** Tayside *Angus* Map **15** NO56

★★★60% **Glenesk**
High St DD9 7TF ☎(03564)319 FAX (03564) 7333
*This family-run hotel beside the golf course is popular not only with golfers, but all types of guests. Public areas, including 2 attractive lounges offering traditional comforts, and bedrooms are comfortable and well equipped. In addition, there is a leisure complex and a full-size snooker table.*
25rm(23⇨🛇)(4fb) CTV in all bedrooms ® T ✳
sB&B⇨🛇fr£38 dB&B⇨🛇fr£68 🏠
150P 8🕭 ⇘ ✿ CFA ▱ (heated) ♪ snooker sauna solarium gymnasium *xmas*
V ✿ 🖵 ✳ Lunch fr£7.50 Dinner fr£11.50 Last dinner 8.45pm
Credit Cards ① ② ③ ⑤

★★56% **Panmure Arms**
52 High St DD9 7TA (Inter-Hotels) ☎(03564)420 & 427
*A relaxed atmosphere, good leisure facilities and well equipped bedrooms are provided by this extensively refurbished, family-run hotel at the edge of the village.*
16⇨🛇(2fb) CTV in all bedrooms ®
30P ▱ (heated) ♪ squash snooker sauna solarium
V ✿ ⊱ Last dinner 9pm
Credit Cards ① ② ③ ⑤

---

**EGHAM** Surrey Map **04** TQ07

★★★★64% **Runnymede**
Windsor Rd TW20 0AG ☎(0784)436171 Telex no 934900
FAX (0784) 436340
*A useful, purpose-built, modern hotel stands close to the M25 and Heathrow terminals yet retains an attractive riverside setting. Comfortable and pleasantly appointed public areas offer a choice of eating options, the well run River Room Restaurant being complemented by Charlie Bell's, a lively and more informal café bar. Bright, well equipped bedrooms have tidy bathrooms, good conference facilities are available, and staff combine seasoned professionalism with a cheery youthfulness.*
125⇨🛇(34fb) CTV in all bedrooms ® T ✳ sB⇨🛇£91.96-£107.29 dB⇨🛇£107.29-£132.83 (room only) 🏠
Lift ℂ 250P ✿ CFA putting green croquet ♪ *xmas*
♀ International V ✿ 🖵 ✳ Lunch £15.95-£17.45&alc Dinner £18.95-£20.95&alc Last dinner 9.45pm
Credit Cards ① ② ③ ⑤

**See advertisement under WINDSOR**

✿✿✿✕✕ **La Bonne Franquette**
5 High St TW20 9EA ☎(0784)439494 FAX (0784) 431473
*Cosy Anglo-French restaurant and bar featuring seasonal dishes with a good wine list and efficient service.*
Closed Sun, BHs & 25 & 26 Dec Lunch not served Sat
♀ French V 46 seats ✳ Lunch £17.50&alc Dinner £24.50&alc Last lunch 2pm Last dinner 9.30pm 16 P
Credit Cards ① ② ③ ⑤

---

**EGLWYSFACH** Dyfed Map **06** SN69

★★★✿✿♨♨72% **Ynyshir Hall**
SY20 8TA (Welsh Rarebits) ☎Glandyfi(0654)781209
FAX (0654) 781366
*This elegant Georgian house, once owned by Queen Victoria, stands in 12 acres of woodland and gardens off the A487 a few miles west of Machynlleth. Antiques, deep sofas and log fires*

abound, and the attractive bedrooms are all individually decorated and comfortable. Food features local fish, game and meat plus home-grown vegetables.
9⇨🛇1♨ CTV in all bedrooms T ✳ sB&B⇨🛇£45-£60 dB&B⇨🛇£75-£120 🏠
20P ⇘ ✿ CFA painting & drawing courses nc9yrs *xmas*
♀ Welsh, English & French V ✿ 🖵 ⊱ Lunch £19.50-£21 Dinner £19.50-£21 Last dinner 8.30pm
Credit Cards ① ③ £

---

**EGREMONT** Cumbria Map **11** NY01

★★★56% **Blackbeck Bridge Inn**
CA22 2NY (Blackbeck 2.75m A595) ☎Beckermet(094684)661
*This is mainly a commercial hotel, with an attractive little restaurant and a spacious lounge bar, situated on the A595, 3 miles south of Egremont. The bedrooms are well equipped, but those in the older part of the hotel are more compact.*
22⇨🛇(1fb)1♨ CTV in all bedrooms ®
60P ✿ ♫
♀ Mainly grills V ✿ 🖵 Last dinner 10pm
Credit Cards ① ② ③ ⑤

---

**ELCOT** Berkshire Map **04** SU36

★★★✿70% **Elcot Park Resort**
RG16 8NJ (1m N off A4) (Resort) ☎Kintbury(0488)58100
FAX (0488) 58288
*Dating back to 1678, this hotel is set in 16 acres of grounds amidst rolling countryside, with easy access to the M3 and M4. Bedrooms, both those in the main house and the terraced cottage annexe, are tastefully decorated and well equipped, and a further 42 are due for completion in May 1991 along with a new leisure and conference complex. A well balanced menu of traditional and modern English dishes is available in the elegant restaurant.*
57⇨🛇Annexe18⇨🛇(4fb)3♨⊱in 4 bedrooms CTV in all bedrooms ® T sB⇨🛇£77-£92 dB⇨🛇£87-£130 (room only) 🏠
ℂ 100P ✿ CFA ▱ (heated) ♟ (hard) sauna solarium gymnasium hot air ballooning clay pigeon shooting *xmas*
♀ English & Continental V ✿ 🖵 Lunch £15&alc Dinner £19.50&alc Last dinner 9.30pm
Credit Cards ① ② ③ ⑤

---

**ELGIN** Grampian *Morayshire* Map **15** NJ26

★★★71% **Mansion House**
The Haugh IV30 1AW ☎(0343)548811 FAX (0343) 547916
*Set amid mature trees and parkland this comfortably appointed hotel is an ideal base for businessmen and holidaymakers alike. It offers a good range of leisure facilities, imaginative food and bright cheery bedrooms. Staff are friendly and enthusiastic.*
24⇨🛇(4fb)16♨ CTV in all bedrooms ® T ✕ sB&B⇨🛇£59-£69 dB&B⇨🛇£90-£110 🏠
ℂ 30P ✿ CFA ▱ (heated) snooker sauna solarium gymnasium jacuzzi *xmas*
V ✿ 🖵 Lunch £10-£12.50 Dinner £18-£22.50alc Last dinner 9pm
Credit Cards ① ② ③

★★★57% **Eight Acres**
Sheriffmill IV30 3UN (Consort) ☎(0343)543077
FAX (0343) 540001
*Just west of the town beside the A96, this purpose-built hotel has a range of conference, function and leisure facilites very popular with business people and tour groups. Bars and lounges offer practical comforts and the bedrooms, which vary in size are mainly functional, are well equipped.*
57⇨🛇(5fb) CTV in all bedrooms ® T sB&B⇨🛇£46-£54 dB&B⇨🛇£63-£65 🏠
ℂ CTV 200P ✿ CFA ▱ (heated) squash snooker sauna solarium gymnasium ⚬ *xmas*

🍴 Scottish, French & Italian **V** ✿ ⬭ Lunch £5-£8 High tea £5-£8 Dinner frf14.50&alc Last dinner 9pm
Credit Cards 1️⃣ 2️⃣ 3️⃣ 5️⃣ £️

### ★★66% **Park House**
South St IV30 1JB ☎(0343)547695 & 543112 FAX (0343) 541594
*The basement restaurant of this impressive Georgian house on the western perimeter road enjoys a fine reputation, and the bedrooms are thoughtfully furnished and equipped (though rather compact in some cases).*
6⇆🛏 CTV in all bedrooms ® **T** ✳ sB&B⇆🛏£40 dB&B⇆🛏£60 🏠
《 30P
🍴 Scottish & French **V** ✿ ⬭
Credit Cards 1️⃣ 3️⃣ £️

### ★★60% *St Leonards*
Duff Av IV30 1QS ☎(0343)547350
*A pleasantly run family hotel situated in a quiet side road provides satisfactory accommodation and an extensive range of eating options.*
16rm(13⇆🛏)(2fb) CTV in all bedrooms ®
60P ✿
🍴 Scottish & French **V** ✿ ⬭ ✂ Last dinner 9pm
Credit Cards 1️⃣ 3️⃣

### ★★59% **Laichmoray**
Station Rd IV30 1QR ☎(0343)540045 FAX (0343) 540055
*Georgian-style, family run hotel with a friendly atmosphere. Modern, well equipped bedrooms are found in the new section of the hotel, while the others are more traditional. Choice of bars in this popular commercial hotel.*
34rm(33⇆🛏)(4fb) CTV in all bedrooms ® **T** ✳ sB&B£30.45-£45 sB&B⇆🛏£30.45-£45 dB&B⇆🛏£44-£70 🏠
CTV 60P ✿ CFA pool table darts *xmas*
**V** ✿ ⬭ Lunch £11.50-£13.50&alc High tea £7.50-£8.75 Dinner £11.50-£13&alc Last dinner 9.30pm
Credit Cards 1️⃣ 2️⃣ 3️⃣ 5️⃣

---

**ELIE** Fife Map **12** NO40

### ❀✕✕**Bouquet Garni**
51 High St KY9 1BZ ☎(O333)330374
*Andrew Kerecher comes of a family who run highly respected fish shops in Perth and St Andrews, and it is therefore no surprise to find that the small restaurant he owns with his wife Norah specialises in fresh seafood. The table d'hote dinner menu is augmented by daily specialities, depending on what is available, and may include game as well as fish. Dinner may start with a small wedge of smoked salmon, halibut and Arbroath smokie flan as an appetizer, before you embark on the choice of 5 or more starters, of which the wholemeal pastry case filled with mussels, cockles and prawns, topped with smoked bacon, creamed leeks and cheese with a crayfish sauce was found more than satisfying. The main course might be a trio of sea fillets – halibut, salmon and scallops – served with a well reduced fish fumet flavoured with tomato and fennel, in which the freshness of the fish is very evident. Puddings range from calorie rich mousses to healthier, fruit based concoctions. Particularly enjoyable was the chocolate mousse in a brandysnap basket, accompanied by prunes soaked in Tia Maria, served with a smooth sabayon sauce flavoured with Tia Maria and cinammon. Service is good, but our inspector commented unfavourably on the background music.*
Closed Sun, 1-8 Nov & 1st wk Jan-mid Feb
30 seats ✳ Lunch frf8.70alc Last lunch 1.30pm Last dinner 9.30pm ♪ ✂
Credit Cards 1️⃣ 3️⃣

*A rosette means exceptional standards of cuisine.*

---

**ELLESMERE PORT** Cheshire Map **07** SJ47

### ★★★66% *The Woodhey*
Welsh Rd, Little Sutton L66 4PS ☎051-339 5121
FAX 051-339 3214
*A recent complete refurbishment has given new life to this hotel, situated on the A550 just off junction 5 of the M53. There are now smart well equipped bedrooms, Woodies Grill Restaurant and a conference and banqueting suite accommodating up to 200 people.*
53⇆🛏 Annexe1⇆🛏(3fb) CTV in all bedrooms ® **T**
《 180P
**V** ✿ ⬭ Last dinner 10pm
Credit Cards 1️⃣ 2️⃣ 3️⃣ 5️⃣

### ★★62% *Berni Royal*
Childer Thornton L66 1QW ☎051-339 8101
*Situated on the A41, near junction 5 of the M53, this Georgian house with a modern bedroom wing offers comfortable accommodation, with a grill-style restaurant and a large well equipped function room.*
47⇆🛏(2fb)2⊞ CTV in all bedrooms ® **T** ✖ (ex guide dogs)
《 CTV 180P
🍴 Mainly grills **V** ✿ ⬭ ✂
Credit Cards 1️⃣ 2️⃣ 3️⃣ 5️⃣

---

**ELSTREE** Hertfordshire Map **04** TQ19

### ★★★63% **Edgwarebury**
Barnet Ln WD6 3RE (Lansbury) ☎081-953 8227
Telex no 918707 FAX 081-207 3668
*Originally a Tudor manor house and still set in the seclusion of 10-acre grounds – though within easy reach of the M1/M25/A1 and only 12 miles from London – this relaxing, friendly hotel offers public areas in the original building and well equipped bedrooms which are mostly contained in a modern extension.*
→

50⇨🛏🔔1🛏✂in 8 bedrooms CTV in all bedrooms ® T
✖ (ex guide dogs) sB&B⇨🔔fr£101 dB&B⇨🔔fr£114 🅿
( 120P 🚗 ❀ CFA ♪ (hard) *xmas*
♀ French V ♦ ⚏ ✂ Lunch fr£12&alc Dinner fr£12&alc
Credit Cards ①②③⑤

## ELTERWATER Cumbria Map **07** NY30

### ★★★❀66% **Langdale Hotel & Country Club**
LA22 9JD ☎Langdale(09667)302 FAX (09667) 694
(Rosette awarded for dinner only)
*This hotel combines stylish interiors and extensive leisure facilities within the 23 acres of landscaped woodlands and streams in which it stands. A commendable range of slate lodge and cottage bedrooms, which blend perfectly with the environment, have been tastefully decorated and furnished, some with spa baths. The pine-canopied Purdeys Restaurant offers interesting, imaginative cuisine, and service throughout is prompt and friendly.*
65⇨🔔(6fb)2🛏 CTV in all bedrooms ® T ✖ (ex guide dogs)
dB&B⇨🔔£100-£190 (incl dinner) 🅿
( 100P ❀ CFA 🏊 (heated) ♪ (hard) squash snooker sauna solarium gymnasium croquet ♫ 🎯 *xmas*
♀ International V ♦ ⚏ ✂ Sunday Lunch £10-£12.50alc
Dinner £19-£21&alc Last dinner 10pm
Credit Cards ①②③⑤ⓔ

### ★★🏵68% **Eltermere Country House**
LA22 9HY (On unclass rd between A593 & B5343)
☎Langdale(09667)207
Closed 25-26 Dec RS mid Nov-mid Feb
*A charming country house, overlooking Elterwater and the surrounding fells from its 2 acres of grounds and gardens, offers attractive bedrooms and two cosy lounges.*
18rm(15⇨🔔)(4fb) CTV in all bedrooms ® ✖ (ex guide dogs)
sB&B£26.50-£30.50 dB&B⇨🔔£53-£68 🅿
25P 🚗 ❀ putting
♀ English & Continental ♦ ✂ Dinner £17 Last dinner 7.30pm

## ELY Cambridgeshire Map **05** TL58

### ★★★60% **Fenlands Lodge**
Soham Rd, Stuntney CB7 5TR (2m SE A142) ☎(0353)667047
*Situated one mile south of the cathedral city on the A142, this small hotel complex, entirely run by proprietors Kevin and Vivien O'Brien, is surrounded by open countryside. The public areas, utilising the former farmhouse building, are very comfortably furnished. The rooms, arranged around a courtyard, are modestly furnished but reasonably comfortable.*
Annexe9⇨🔔 CTV in all bedrooms ® T ✳ sB&B⇨🔔£52
dB&B⇨🔔£64 🅿
( 25P CFA *xmas*
♀ English & French V ♦ ⚏ ✳ Lunch £10.95-£13&alc Dinner £13&alc Last dinner 9.30pm
Credit Cards ①②③⑤

### ★★55% **Lamb**
2 Lynn Rd CB7 4EJ (Queens Moat) ☎(0353)663574
FAX (0353) 666350
*This former coaching inn, situated close to the cathedral in the city centre, provides well equipped modern accommodation which is particularly popular with a business clientèle.*
32⇨🔔(6fb)2🛏 CTV in all bedrooms ® T ✳ sB&B⇨🔔£55-£60 dB&B⇨🔔£72-£75 🅿
( 14P 1🅿 CFA *xmas*
♀ English & French V ♦ ⚏ ✳ Lunch £9-£10.25&alc High tea fr£3.95 Dinner fr£13.50 Last dinner 9.45pm
Credit Cards ①②③⑤ⓔ

For key to symbols in English see the bookmark.

### ★58% **Nyton**
7 Barton Rd CB7 4HZ (Minotels) ☎(0353)662459
*A substantial period house in lovely grounds which has been converted to provide simple accommodation, all with en suite facilities, and elegant public areas. To find The Nyton: from the A10 into Ely the Barton road is on the right, signposted Barton/Newmarket.*
9⇨🔔Annexe5⇨🔔(2fb) CTV in all bedrooms ® ✖
sB&B⇨🔔£34-£39 dB&B⇨🔔£56-£60
25P ❀
V Lunch £15-£16 Dinner £15-£16 Last dinner 8.30pm
Credit Cards ①②③⑤ⓔ

### ○**Forte Travelodge**
(at roundabout A10/A142) (Forte)
☎Central Res (0800) 850950
Due to have opened Aug 1991
39⇨🔔

### ❀❀✖**Old Fire Engine House**
25 Saint Mary's St CB7 4ER ☎(0353)662582
*As its name suggests this delightful restaurant of character is sited in a former fire station, also home to an art gallery. A well compiled menu of good wholesome dishes includes tomato and onion soup, pigeon with bacon, rabbit and pork pie and a roast. Seconds are offered and are difficult to refuse but for the selection of puddings, home made ice creams and pies.*
Closed 2 wks fr 24 Dec & BH's
Dinner not served Sun
36 seats ✖ Lunch £14-£21alc Dinner £14-£21alc Last lunch 2pm Last dinner 9pm 8 P ✂
Credit Cards ①③

## EMBLETON Northumberland Map **12** NU22

### ★★*Dunstanburgh Castle*
NE66 3UN ☎(066576)203
*The family hotel stands in rural surroundings within easy reach of the sea.*
17rm(9⇨)(3fb) ®
CTV 20P 1🅿 🚗
♀ English & French ♦ ⚏
Credit Cards ①③

## EMPINGHAM Leicestershire Map **04** SK90

### ★★62% **The White Horse Inn**
Main St LE15 8PR ☎(078086)221 FAX (078086) 521
*Set in the small village of Empingham in the heart of Rutland's beautiful countryside, this 17th-century stone courthouse has been carefully modernised to provide attractive, characterful accommodation with good facilities, particularly in the stable block bedrooms, and a choice of bar meals or imaginative restaurant dishes.*
4⇨Annexe8⇨🔔(4fb)1🛏✂in 1 bedroom CTV in all bedrooms ® T ✳ sB&B⇨🔔£25-£35 dB&B⇨🔔£46-£60 🅿
60P CFA 🎯 *xmas*
♀ English & French V ♦ ⚏ ✂ ✳ Lunch £10.95&alc Dinner £10.95&alc Last dinner 9.45pm
Credit Cards ①②③⑤ⓔ

## EMSWORTH Hampshire Map **04** SU70

### ★★★65% **Brookfield**
Havant Rd PO10 7LF ☎(0243)373363 & 376383
FAX (0243) 376342
Closed 25 Dec-1 Jan
*A family-run hotel served by professional staff provides well equipped accommodation to which a further ten en suite rooms were added last year; the spacious Hermitage Restaurant offers value-for-money table d'hôte and à la carte menus, while parking facilities and pleasant gardens are added attractions.*

41⇩🌙1🛏 CTV in all bedrooms ® T 🐕 (ex guide dogs)
sB&B⇨🌙£55-£60 dB&B⇨🌙£68-£73 🏳
⟮ 130P 🚗 ✿ CFA
☺ English & French V ✹ ⏰ Lunch £11.95&alc Dinner
£11.95&alc Last dinner 9.30pm
Credit Cards ①②③⑤

### ✿✿ ✕✕ 36 On The Quay
47 South St PO10 7EG ☎Chichester(0243)375592 & 372257
*In this charming, elegantly furnished and comfortable restaurant a
table d'hôte menu offers excellent value for money. The menu
offers eight alternatives at each of the three courses. There is also a
separate imaginative sweet menu. Service is relaxed and
professional.*
Closed Sun Lunch not served Sat
☺ French V 40 seats ✻ Lunch £18.50&alc Last lunch 2pm Last
dinner 10pm 6 P nc9yrs ✂
Credit Cards ①②③④

---

### ENFIELD Greater London Map 04 TQ39

#### ★★★67% Enfield
52 Rowantree Rd EN2 8PW ☎081-366 3577 & 081-366 3511
Telex no 24571 FAX 081-366 2432
Closed 24 Dec-1 Jan
*A small hotel with much to commend it, offers accommodation in
spacious, comfortable, part-panelled rooms with quality beds,
leather-topped desks and en suite shower/WC facilities in most
cases. Mainly Italian staff are friendly and professional, the chef
providing an international menu of simple fresh food which
includes some classical dishes; Italian specialities are popular and
successful.*
33⇩🌙(1fb)1🛏 CTV in all bedrooms ® T 🐕 (ex guide dogs)
20P CFA sauna gymnasium ♨
☺ International V ✹ ⏰ Last dinner 10pm
Credit Cards ①③⑤£

See advertisement on page 289

#### ★★56% Holtwhites
92 Chase Side EN2 0QN ☎081-363 0124 FAX 081-366 9089
*An extended Victorian villa on a shopping thoroughfare just
outside Enfield's centre offers bedrooms of varying size and
comfort, mainly geared to the single commercial guest. Public
areas include a comfortable bar/TV lounge.*
30rm(28⇨🌙)(1fb) CTV in all bedrooms ® T
🐕 (ex guide dogs) sB&Bf£49 sB&B⇨🌙£45-£70
dB&B⇨🌙£50-£95 🏳
⟮ CTV 30P 4🚗 🚗 CFA nc5yrs
☺ International V ✹ ⏰ ✂ Bar Lunch £1.50-£8alc Dinner £6-
£19.50alc Last dinner 8.30pm
Credit Cards ①②③⑤£

---

### EPPING Essex Map 05 TL40

#### ★★★61% Forte Posthouse
High Rd, Bell Common CM16 4DG (Forte Hotels)
☎(0378)73137 Telex no 81617 FAX (0378) 560402
*Lying just south of Epping, this hotel is a purpose-built extension of
the old Bell Inn. Public areas in the original building are
comfortable and the bedrooms are in a separate annexe nearby. All
are spacious and well equipped.*
Annexe79⇨🌙(22fb)✂in 32 bedrooms CTV in all bedrooms
® T ✻ S% sB⇨🌙£39.50-£49.50 dB⇨🌙£39.50-£49.50 (room
only) 🏳
⟮ 95P CFA xmas
☺ English V ✹ ⏰ ✂ ✻ S% Lunch £7.50&alc Dinner
£13.95&alc Last dinner 10.30pm
Credit Cards ①②③④⑤

---

### EPSOM Surrey Map 04 TQ26

#### ★★62% Heathside
Brighton Rd KT20 6BW ☎Burgh Heath(0737)353355
FAX (0737) 370857
(For full entry see Burgh Heath)

---

### EPWORTH Humberside Map 08 SE70

#### ★★64% Red Lion
Market Place DN9 1EU ☎(0427)872208 FAX (0427) 874330
*This popular coaching inn has recently reopened after total
refurbishment. There is a choice of bars, with an all-day menu
available in the comfortable lounge bar and adjacent conservatory.
Bedrooms offer modern facilities, most having en suite bathrooms,
though a few rooms are quite compact. A small fitness centre is due
to open by 1992.*
14rm(5⇨8🌙)1🛏 CTV in all bedrooms ® T 🐕 (ex guide dogs)
✻ sB&B⇨🌙fr£29.50 dB&B⇨🌙fr£49.50 🏳
34P solarium gymnasium steam room *xmas*
V ✹ ⏰ ✻ Lunch £6.95&alc High tea fr£1.25alc Dinner
£6.95&alc Last dinner 10pm
Credit Cards ①②③⑤

---

### ERBISTOCK Clwyd Map 07 SJ34

#### ✿ ✕ Boat Inn
LL13 0DL ☎Bangor-on-Dee(0978)780143 FAX (0978) 780312
*Delightfully situated on the banks of the River Dee, this charming
500-year- old inn serves traditional British fare and substantial
desserts. Service is informal, friendly and attentive. In fine
weather, guests can enjoy aperitifs on the riverside.*
☺ English & French V 70 seats ✻ Lunch £10.95&alc Dinner
£13.95&alc Last lunch 2.15pm Last dinner 9.30pm 50 P
Credit Cards ①②③⑤

E

**ERISKA** Strathclyde *Argyllshire* Map **10** NM94

★★★

★★★⊛♨ **ISLE OF ERISKA**

PA37 1SD
☎Ledaig(063172)371
Telex no 777040
FAX (063172) 531
Closed Dec-mid Mar

*This unique baronial mansion stands on its own island of some 250 acres on the west coast of Scotland. The island, where guests are free to roam, has breathtakingly beautiful scenery and abundant wildlife. The Rev Buchanan Smith, a Church of Scotland Minister, and his family own and run this delightful hotel and care greatly for their guests comfort. There are lovely lounges where one can really unwind, and the library houses a small well stocked bar. Bedrooms, furnished in keeping with the building, offer comfort and good facilities. Dinner is a special occasion and a well produced 6-course menu is backed up by an admirable wine list. Very much a country house style of operation where one might be a personal guest in the family home, the Eriska is a worthy holder of our prestigious Red Star award; and the hotel is an ideal base from which to tour this lovely part of Scotland.*

16⇔(1fb) CTV in all bedrooms ® **T** sB&B⇔£122 dB&B⇔£139-£156 ⊟

《 36P ⇱ ✿ CFA ♫ (hard) ∪ croquet watersports putting
Lunch £6-£14 High tea £8-£9 Dinner £37 Last dinner 9pm
Credit Cards ①③

---

**ERMINGTON** Devon Map **02** SX65

★★⊛62% **Ermewood House**

Totnes Rd PL21 9NS (Exec Hotel) ☎Modbury(0548)830741
Closed 23 Dec-9 Jan

*This small hotel overlooking the River Erme and offering easy access to the A38 from its position in the South Hams, is run by its enthusiastic owners to provide a hospitable retreat and commendable meals. A daily-changing 5-course menu of traditional English dishes with some French influence, honestly based on quality produce, includes such noteworthy items as rich stock soups, a light salmon and mushroom timbale, and roasted medallions of beef in a tempting sauce; homemade puddings are equally delicious. Simple but well equipped bedrooms are in process of upgrading.*

12⇔ᛐ(1fb)1⚄ CTV in all bedrooms ® **T** sB&B⇔ᛐ£45 dB&B⇔ᛐ£60 ⊟
15P ⇱ ✿
♥ English & Continental ⋎ Dinner £17.50 Last dinner 8.30pm
Credit Cards ①③

**See advertisement under PLYMOUTH**

---

**ERPINGHAM** Norfolk Map **09** TG13

⊛⊛✕**Ark**

NR11 7QB ☎Cromer(0263)761535

*A much extended 18th-century flintstone cottage which was formerly a family home, located a mile from the A140 in Erpingham and reached by taking the second turning towards Cromer, 16 miles north of Norwich, features a small log-fired dining room and lounge with a simple, homely atmosphere. Sheila Kidd, a self-taught culinary enthusiast with a natural flair for combining ingredients to bring out their true flavours, produces such starters as fennel soup or mussels in juniper, these perhaps being followed by pheasant and guinea fowl pot-roasted with cider and apple, or salmon en croute with a light Muscadet sauce –*

*menus changing in line with seasonal availability. Bread is freshly baked, vegetables are home-grown, and service is professional though unpretentious.*

Closed Mon & 3 wks Oct Lunch not served Tue & Sat
Dinner not served Sun
♥ English & Continental **V** 30 seats ✳ Lunch £10-£15alc
Dinner £15-£19alc Last lunch 2pm Last dinner 9.30pm 20 P ⋎

---

**ERSKINE** Strathclyde *Renfrewshire* Map **11** NS47

★★★67% **Forte Posthouse Glasgow**

North Barr PA8 6AN (Forte Hotels) ☎041-812 0123
Telex no 777713 FAX 041-812 7642

*Lying on the south bank of the Clyde by the bridge, this large purpose built hotel caters very well for the business and conference market, with an extensive leisure complex among the facilities.*

166⇔ᛐ(16fb)⋎in 80 bedrooms CTV in all bedrooms ® **T** ✳
sB⇔ᛐ£39.50-£49.50 dB⇔ᛐ£39.50-£49.50 (room only) ⊟
Lift 《 ▥ 300P ❀ CFA ⊠ (heated) snooker sauna solarium gymnasium 9 hole pitch & putt ✍ *xmas*
♥ European **V** ♦ ⌞ ⋎ ✳ Lunch £10.75 Dinner £13.95&alc
Last dinner 10pm
Credit Cards ①②③⑤

---

**ESHER** Surrey

See **LONDON** plan 1*B1*(page 434)
★★62% **Haven**

Portsmouth Rd KT10 9AR (1 m NE on A307) (Inter-Hotels)
☎081-398 0023 FAX 081-398 9463

*A busy, 3-storey, family-run hotel, popular with a business clientele, offers good value for money in its particularly well equipped bedrooms and pleasant public areas. Simple meals are home-cooked, and friendly service is relaxed and cheerful.*

16⇔ᛐAnnexe4⇔ᛐ(4fb) CTV in all bedrooms ® **T**
sB&B⇔ᛐ£57-£65 dB&B⇔ᛐ£67.50-£75 ⊟
20P 1⧆ ⇱
♥ International **V** ♦ ⌞ Bar Lunch £4-£5 High tea £4-£6
Dinner £10-£12.50 Last dinner 8.30pm
Credit Cards ①②③④⑤£

⊛✕✕**Good Earth**

14-18 High St KT10 9RT ☎(0372)462489 & 466681
FAX 071-823 8769

*This attractive modern restaurant, while featuring all the old favourites, offers an interesting and extensive selection of regional Chinese dishes which makes it well worth a visit if you enjoy trying something different – Soft Shell Crabs in Peppercorn and Spiced Salt might be followed by an interesting Beef in Tangerine Peel and Hot Sauce, for example. There are several set menus (including an admirable vegetarian choice), or, if you have something to celebrate, the Imperial Banquet can be booked in advance. Service is professional and unfailingly attentive.*

Closed 24-27 Dec
♥ Cantonese, Pekinese & Szechuan **V** 100 seats ✳ Lunch £15-£30&alc Dinner £15-£30&alc Last lunch 2.30pm Last dinner 11pm ⋎
Credit Cards ①②③⑤

---

**ESKDALE GREEN** Cumbria Map **06** NY10

★★61% *Bower House Inn*

CA19 1TD ☎Eskdale(09403)244

*This country inn is popular with tourists and hillwalkers. Most of the bedrooms are contained in 2 annexe buildings.*

5⇔ᛐAnnexe17⇔ᛐ(3fb) CTV in all bedrooms ® **T** ✖
60P
♥ English & French **V** ♦
Credit Cards ①③

**ESKDALEMUIR** Dumfries & Galloway *Dumfriesshire*
Map **11** NY29

★★67% **Hart Manor**
DG13 0QQ ☎(03873)73217
Closed 25 Dec

*Set in beautiful countryside, this small hotel offers traditional accommodation and courteous, attentive service. Dinners are freshly prepared and are very good value.*

7rm(2⇨3♠)(2fb) CTV in all bedrooms ® ✳ sB&Bfr£23
sB&B⇨♠fr£26.50 dB&Bfr£47 dB&B⇨♠fr£52 🏲
CTV 30P 🚗 ❀ ♪
V ♥ ⅙ ✳ Sunday Lunch £4.50-£6.65alc Dinner £13.50-£16
Last dinner 8pm

---

**EVERCREECH** Somerset Map **03** ST63

★★57% **Pecking Mill Inn & Hotel**
BA4 6PG (On A371 1m W of village) ☎(0749)830336
*This well maintained 16th-century inn/hotel beside the A371 complements small but well equipped bedrooms by compact public areas which include a cosy restaurant offering a short, reasonably priced à la carte menu in which grills predominate.*

6♠ CTV in all bedrooms ® T ✳ sB&B♠£33 dB&B♠£44
23P 🚗
♗ Mainly grills ♥ ✳ Lunch £10-£15&alc Dinner £10-£15&alc
Last dinner 10pm
Credit Cards ①②③⑤

---

Restaurants and hotel restaurants
with rosettes have their names and addresses
tinted pink in the directory.

---

**EVERSHOT** Dorset Map **03** ST50

★★

★★❀❀ **SUMMER LODGE**
DT2 0JR ☎(0935)83424
FAX (0935) 83005
Closed 2-18 Jan

*A Georgian country house tucked behind the village centre in well kept gardens. Owners Nigel and Margaret Corbett personally supervise their charming and naturally hospitable staff. The dining room has been extended and refurbished, and Roger Jones with Tim Ford as his second in command continue to provide imaginative and well presented dishes. There is a daily set menu with a choice of main courses, supplemented by a short à la carte selection at dinner time. At breakfast an extensive range of fresh fruits, yoghurts and cereals is available on a self-service basis, followed by a cooked breakfast and homemade brioche, marmalade and jam. Bedrooms are extremely comfortable and attractively co-ordinated. Bathrooms in the main house have pretty hand-painted tiles; towels are generously sized, white and fluffy and there are no sachets of bath gel or shampoo to struggle with, but large bottles of Badedas and Jojoba shampoo. Behind the coach house bedrooms is a well screened pool and all-weather tennis court. Afternoon tea is set out in the drawing room, well replenished. At Summer Lodge, apart from bar drinks, wine and telephone, the price on the tariff is the price charged, there are no hidden extras.* →

11⇆Annexe6⇆(1fb) CTV in all bedrooms ® T ✱
sB&B⇆£90-£125 dB&B⇆£140-£250 (incl dinner) 🏳
CTV 40P ⚙ ❄ ⚌ (heated) ♪ (hard & grass )croquet
nc8yrs *xmas*
V ✆ ⚏ ✱ Lunch £17.50&alc Dinner fr£30&alc Last
dinner 8.30pm
Credit Cards ① ② ③

---

### ★69% The Acorn Inn
28 Fore St DT2 0JW ☎(0935)83228

*The Acorn, dating back to the 16th century, stands in the heart of a
peaceful village midway between Yeovil and Dorchester. Resident
proprietors Denise and Keith Morley have restored the property
over the years and offer cosy individualistic bedrooms, many with
original features. Lively public areas are nicely appointed and have
an olde worlde air. Candles Restaurant and the less formal
Candles Lounge Bar have an extensive menu of attractively
presented dishes served in hugely generous portions.*

8⇆🌂(2fb)2⚏ CTV in all bedrooms ® T ✱ sB&B⇆🌂£30-£50
dB&B⇆🌂£46-£80 🏳
《 CTV 40P pool tables skittles *xmas*
V ✆ ⚏ ⚿ ✱ Lunch £15-£20&alc Dinner £15-£20&alc Last
dinner 9.45pm
Credit Cards ① ③

---

### EVERSLEY Hampshire Map 04 SU76

### ❀✗✗✗New Mill
New Mill Rd RG27 0RA ☎(0734)732277 & 732105
FAX (0734) 328780

*A magnificent watermill with corn grinding equipment still in
working order, set amid delightful gardens in rural surroundings
beside the River Blackwater, which now houses a restaurant with
conservatory extension overlooking the water and a grill room. Its
short, seasonally-changing à la carte selection of dishes
(supplemented by a set-price menu at lunchtime) is accompanied
by a comprehensive wine list offering some fine wines and good
vintages, while well supervised service, though formal, has a
friendly touch.*

Closed Sun, Mon & 1st 2 wks Jan
V 80 seats ✱ Lunch fr£19.50&alc Dinner fr£25.50&alc Last
lunch 2pm Last dinner 10pm 70 P
Credit Cards ① ② ③ ⑤

---

### EVESHAM Hereford & Worcester Map 04 SP04

### ★★★66% The Evesham
Coopers Ln, off Waterside WR11 6DA ☎(0386)765566
FAX (0386) 765443
Closed 25 & 26 Dec

*An hotel dating from 1540 and ideally situated for both tourist and
business guest – standing 5 minutes' walk from the town and only
11 miles from the M5 – offers comfortable modern accomodation
which is well equipped and provided with such personal touches as
teddy bears and rubber ducks! A menu of interesting dishes is
complemented by a very extensive and unusual wine list, its vast
array representing almost all wine producing areas with the
exception of France and Germany.*

40⇆🌂(1fb) CTV in all bedrooms ® T S% sB&B⇆🌂£55-£61
dB&B⇆🌂£74-£88 🏳
50P ⚙ ❄ ▣ (heated) croquet putting
♀ International V ✆ ⚏ ✱ S% Lunch £10.40-£15.70alc Dinner
£15-£18.20alc Last dinner 9.30pm
Credit Cards ① ② ③ ⑤

---

A rosette means exceptional standards of cuisine.

---

### ★★★59% Northwick Arms
Waterside WR11 6BT (Resort) ☎(0386)40322 FAX (0386) 41070

*Set on the south bank of the River Avon a short walk from the town
centre, this small commercial and tourist hotel has a variety of
bedrooms, all of them well equipped, and pleasant public areas.
Flacons bar across the hotel courtyard is a popular local venue.*

25⇆🌂1⚏ CTV in all bedrooms ® T ✱ sB&B⇆🌂£46-£56
dB⇆🌂£61-£67 (room only) 🏳
《 90P CFA
♀ English & French V ✆ ⚏ ✱ Lunch fr£9.50 Dinner
fr£12.95&alc Last dinner 10pm
Credit Cards ① ② ③ ⑤

---

### ★★❀77% The Mill At Harvington
Anchor Ln, Harvington WR11 5NR (4.5m NE, off A439)
☎(0386)870688
Closed 24-27 Dec

*A 'Courtesy and Care' award winner 1991/1992 for the Midlands
and East Anglia region, this charming privately owned hotel,
created from a former malting mill and tucked away in its own 8
acres of wooded parkland off the A439, offers views of the River
Avon from all its rooms. Well equipped accommodation offers
good levels of comfort and such nice finishing touches as books,
magazines and playing cards, while a caring team of staff provides
outstanding hospitality and good old-fashioned standards of
service under the supervision of welcoming hosts. Meals are
prepared with skill, care and imagination, the menu featuring a
wide choice of interesting dishes based on the best of fresh produce.
(See colour feature on p18.)*

15⇆🌂 CTV in all bedrooms ® T ✖ (ex guide dogs)
sB&B⇆🌂fr£55 dB&B⇆🌂fr£85 🏳
50P ⚙ ❄ ⚌ (heated) ♪ croquet nc10yrs
♀ English & French Lunch £12.50-£14 Dinner £20-£24&alc
Last dinner 9.30pm
Credit Cards ① ③ ⑤

---

### ★★❀77% Riverside
The Parks, Offenham Rd WR11 5JP ☎(0386)446200
FAX (0386) 40021
RS Nov-Feb

*Follow the signs to Offenham from the town centre to find this
friendly cottage-style hotel, beautifully set by the River Avon. Both
the thoughtfully equipped bedrooms and lower floor public areas
are comfortable and attractively decorated, while the intimate
restaurant with adjacent bar offers an imaginative table d'hôte
menu that makes good use of fresh quality produce.*

7⇆🌂 CTV in all bedrooms ® T ✖ (ex guide dogs) ✱ S%
sB&B⇆🌂£51-£60 dB&B⇆🌂£71.50-£85 🏳
40P ❄ ♪ *xmas*
♀ English & French V ✆ ✱ Lunch £14.50-£17.95 Dinner
£17.95-£19.95 Last dinner 9pm
Credit Cards ① ③ ⑤

---

### ★★73% Waterside
56 Waterside WR11 6JZ ☎(0386)442420

*Proprietors Linda and David Young offer a warm welcome and
comfortable accommodation which is well equipped with an array
of modern facilities. The Waterside is ideal for both business
guests and tourists.*

8rm(2⇆4🌂)Annexe4⇆🌂(3fb) CTV in all bedrooms ® T
sB&B£24.50 sB&B⇆🌂£46.75 dB&B£39.90 dB&B⇆🌂£58.55
🏳
30P ⚙ ♪
V ✆ ⚏ ⚿
Credit Cards ① ② ③ ⑤

---

### ★56% Park View
Waterside WR11 6BS ☎(0386)442639
Closed 24 Dec-3 Jan

*A family-owned hotel just across the road from the river and with
easy access to the town centre. It offers a homely atmosphere and
good value for money, though accommodation is modest and rather
old fashioned.*

29rm(2fb) sB&B£17.75-£19.75 dB&B£34-£38
CTV 40P CFA
♻ ⚒ Bar Lunch £1.50-£4 Dinner £7.95-£9.25 Last dinner 7pm
Credit Cards ① ② ③

---

## EWLOE Clwyd Map 07 SJ36

★★★★ ✿70% St David's Park
Redrow House, St Davids Park CH5 3YB
☎Chester(0244)520800 FAX (0244) 520930
RS 24-31 Dec

*A completely new high quality hotel just north of the A55 off the
A494. Public rooms are semi-open plan with several comfortable
lounge areas. There is a smart bar, extensive conference/function
facilities and a very modern leisure centre. Staff are very attentive
and friendly and we hope that this will be maintained once the
newness wears off. Three types of menu are available in the
attractive restaurant, a good carvery, a good à la carte selection,
and an excellent chef's gourmet menu with up to 7 courses of
imaginative dishes using fresh produce and changed daily
accordingly.*

121⇨🛏(13fb)1🏠⚡in 30 bedrooms CTV in all bedrooms ® T
✳
Lift ℂ 240P ♣ 🖾 (heated) snooker sauna solarium gymnasium
turkish steam bath
V ♻ ⚒ ⚡ ✳ Lunch £9.95-£12.95&alc High tea £3-£8alc
Dinner £12.95-£15&alc Last dinner 10pm
Credit Cards ① ② ③ ⑤

**See advertisement under CHESTER**

---

## EXEBRIDGE Somerset Map 03 SS92

★★ 65% Anchor Inn
TA22 9AZ ☎Dulverton(0398)23433

*Set on the banks of the River Exe this delightful 16th-century inn
offers comfortable well appointed accommodation and a warm and
friendly atmosphere. Thoughtfully prepared dishes are served in
the restaurant.*

6⇨🛏(2fb)1🏠 CTV in all bedrooms ® T sB&B⇨🛏fr£37
dB&B⇨🛏£60-£64
CTV 100P ♣ ♪
V ♻ ⚒ ✳ Lunch fr£8.95 Dinner fr£14.50 Last dinner 9pm
Credit Cards ① ③

---

## EXETER Devon Map 03 SX99 ◎

See **Town Plan Section**
See also Stoke Canon & Topsham
★★★★ 68% Forte Crest
Southernhay East EX1 1QF (Forte Hotels) ☎(0392)412812
Telex no 42717 FAX (0392) 413549

*Centrally located near the cathedral, and offering its own good
parking facilities an hotel which is relatively new nevertheless has
an old world atmosphere. Bedrooms are well decorated, if slightly
small, and public areas are reminiscent of those of a country house,
with a dining room in formal style offering several menus of
English dishes. Leisure amenities include a sizeable indoor pool.*

110⇨🛏(6fb) in 55 bedrooms CTV in all bedrooms ® T ✳
sB⇨🛏fr£85 dB⇨🛏fr£95 (room only) 🍴
Lift ℂ 115P ♿ CFA 🖾 (heated) sauna solarium gymnasium
jacuzzi *xmas*
♀ International V ♻ ⚒ ⚡ ✳ S% Lunch £13&alc Dinner
£17&alc Last dinner 10pm
Credit Cards ① ② ③ ④ ⑤

★★★ 73% Royal Clarence
Cathedral Yard EX1 1HB (Queens Moat) ☎(0392)58464
Telex no 42551 FAX (0392) 439423

*After almost a year's closure and a top-to-toe refurbishment, this
character city-centre hotel now provides an exceptionally high
standard of accommodation. The upgrading has been
sympathetically carried out to retain many original features, and*

---

*the well equipped bedrooms are individually styled. All
departments are well managed, with willing and friendly staff. The
modern-style cuisine shows promise, but at the time of going to
press was very much in the formative stage.*

56⇨🛏(6fb)2🏠⚡in 8 bedrooms CTV in all bedrooms ® T
✠ (ex guide dogs) sB⇨🛏£55-£85 dB⇨🛏£75-£110 (room
only) 🍴
Lift ℂ 15P CFA *xmas*
♀ English & French V ♻ ⚒ Lunch £11-£15 Dinner £15-£20
Last dinner 9.45pm
Credit Cards ① ② ③ ④ ⑤ ⑥

★★★ 67% Rougemont
Queen St EX4 3SP (Mount Charlotte (TS)) ☎(0392)54982
Telex no 42455 FAX (0392) 420928

*Today's discerning traveller will appreciate the high standard of
modern comfort exhibited by this character hotel's bedrooms, now
all well furnished, pleasantly decorated and upgraded to offer an
extensive range of equipment ; similar improvements to public
areas are almost complete, and a good range of promptly executed
services is available. A position opposite Exeter Central station at
the heart of the city, the availability of conference facilities and a
choice of five function rooms make the establishment particularly
suitable for business clients.*

90⇨🛏(5fb)1🏠⚡in 13 bedrooms CTV in all bedrooms ® T
(room only) 🍴
Lift ℂ 40P *xmas*
♀ English & French V ♻ ⚒ ⚡
Credit Cards ① ② ③ ⑤

**See advertisement on page 293**

---

◐ Shell filling stations (7am–11pm) are
marked on the town plans.

---

★★★ ❀66% **St Olaves Court**

Mary Arches St EX4 3AZ ☎(0392)217736 FAX (0392) 413054

*A recent change of ownership has resulted in some positive moves, with a friendly style of operation and encouraging efforts to build on existing good food standards. This is a Georgian country house in secluded grounds right in the heart of the city. Some rooms are limited in space, public rooms in particular, but bedrooms are well equipped and there are a number of larger executive rooms which offer the luxury of en suite jacuzzis. David Mutter is the new executive chef working, we are pleased to note, in conjunction with Stephen Brown. Extra depth has been added to the cooking, with interesting and well balanced set menus, including dishes like baked John Dory with garden herbs and good cream sauce, rosettes of lamb with roasted sweetbreads, or collops of beef nicely set off with tagliatelli of leeks and Noilly Prat, which have been well received.*

11⇄Annexe4⇄(4fb) CTV in all bedrooms ® T ✕ (ex guide dogs) sB&B⇄£60-£65 dB&B⇄£72-£79 🍴 CTV 15P ❀ ❀ ♨

V ♦ ⚟ Lunch £19.50 Dinner £19.50-£22.50 Last dinner 9.30pm

Credit Cards 1 2 3 5

★★★ 64% *Buckerell Lodge Crest*

Topsham Rd EX2 4SQ ☎(0392)52451 Telex no 42410 FAX (0392) 412114

*A recent change to private ownership has brought changes to the style of this hotel, services now being run on more personal lines and a programme of refurbishment having been instigated. A modern establishment of some character, well sited for the city and M5 motorway, it offers accommodation in executive bedrooms equipped to meet all the needs of today's traveller; public areas include a brightly appointed restaurant serving well balanced menus which are supplemented by the good range of wholesome food available in the popular bar.*

54⇄🔌(2fb)⅄in 8 bedrooms CTV in all bedrooms ® T ⟨ 200P ⊞ ❀

♀ English & French V ♦ ⚟ ⅄ Last dinner 9.45pm

Credit Cards 1 2 3 4 5

★★★ 64% *White Hart*

65 South St EX1 1EE ☎(0392)79897 Telex no 42521 FAX (0392) 50159 Closed 25-26 Dec

*An ancient inn, centrally situated only a few yards from the site of the South Gate – through which Henry IV entered the city in 1452 – retains much of its original charm, particularly in the 15th-century wine room. Sympathetic restoration of the main building over the years has provided well equipped bedrooms in a range of sizes, their décor pleasantly softened with attractive fabrics, while a modern block contains slightly more functional accommodation. Public areas include several small lounges and reading rooms. The traditional Hotstlers Restaurant on the first floor and the popular Tap Room Bar with its Victorian Ale and Port House (complete with candlelit atmosphere, mahogany furniture and sawdust-covered floor), both offering an impressive selection of vintage ports, sherry and Madeira from the wood as well as fine wines. À la carte menus include a good range of informal but interesting old English dishes such as steak, kidney and oyster pie, while bar snacks include ham off the bone, and a small staff provides prompt, pleasant service on traditional lines.*

61rm(42⇄16🔌) CTV in all bedrooms T ✕ (ex guide dogs) Lift ⟨ CTV 80P ⊞

V ♦ ⚟ Last dinner 9.45pm

Credit Cards 1 2 3 5

★★★ 63% *Granada*

Moor Ln, Sandygate EX2 4AR (M5 jnct 30) (Granada) ☎(0392)74044 FAX (0392) 410406

*Conveniently positioned close to the M5, Exeter Airport and the city itself, this modern purpose-built hotel is geared to business and en-route travellers, with very well equipped comfortable bedrooms*

*and conference facilities. Public rooms are more restricted, with a small bar lounge and bright conservatory restaurant.*

76⇄🔌(22fb)⅄in 18 bedrooms CTV in all bedrooms ® T ✕ (ex guide dogs) S% sB⇄🔌fr£37 dB⇄🔌fr£41 (room only) 🍴

⟨ CTV 454P ❀

♀ English & French V ♦ ⚟ ⅄ ✳ Sunday Lunch fr£9.25 Dinner fr£12.50 Last dinner 9.30pm

Credit Cards 1 2 3 5

★★★ 61% **Countess Wear Lodge**

Topsham Rd, Exeter Bypass EX2 6HE (Queens Moat) ☎Topsham(0392)875441 Telex no 42551 FAX (0392) 876174

*Continued upgrading has now totally enclosed the previously open motel-style bedrooms of this lodge, providing improved standards of comfort for residents, and it is hoped that the next stage of this work will remedy the slightly restrictive dining room. Ideally situated off the M5 exit just outside the city, it offers accommodation ideally suited to the needs of the business traveller, compact but well decorated rooms featuring a good range of equipment and facilities. A new range of conference and function amenities is available, there is a cosy little reception lounge, and guests have a choice of eating options. The home-made fare and lighter snacks served in the relaxed surroundings of Reilly's Food and Wine Bar supplementing a more traditionally formal restaurant.*

44⇄🔌(1fb)⅄in 4 bedrooms CTV in all bedrooms ® T ✳ S% sB&B⇄🔌fr£54.50 dB&B⇄🔌fr£70 🍴

⟨ 120P ❀ CFA ♪ (hard) *xmas*

♀ English & French V ♦ ⚟ ✳ Lunch fr£14alc Dinner fr£10&alc Last dinner 9.45pm

Credit Cards 1 2 3 5 ④

★★★ 59% *Gipsy Hill*

Gipsy Hill Ln, Pinhoe EX1 3RN (3m E on B3181) (Consort) ☎(0392)65252 Telex no 57515 FAX (0392) 64302

*Commanding views over East Devon from its peaceful location, yet convenient for city, motorway and airport, an hotel popular with businessmen has recently upgraded bedrooms in its adjacent cottage annexe so that they now boast very good décor, furnishings and fabrics to complement their range of modern facilities; similar renovation is planned for the rooms in the small wing, which, though less spacious, are equally well equipped. Service is prompt and friendly throughout.*

20⇄🔌Annexe17⇄🔌(5fb)2⊞⅄in 3 bedrooms CTV in all bedrooms ® T sB&B⇄🔌£45-£57 dB&B⇄🔌£50-£75 🍴

⟨ 60P ❀ CFA ♪ *xmas*

♀ English & French V ♦ ⚟ ✳ Lunch £8.50-£10&alc Dinner £12.50-£15&alc Last dinner 9.30pm

Credit Cards 1 2 3 ④

See advertisement on page 295

★★★ 55% *Devon Motel*

Exeter Bypass, Matford EX2 8XU (Brend) ☎(0392)59268 Telex no 42551 FAX (0392) 413142

*This popular business hotel on the Exeter bypass has now refurbished two thirds of its compact but well equipped bedrooms to a high standard, with plans to update the more modest remainder. The restaurant and bars in the adjacent manor house provide a range of eating options including a lunchtime carvery.*

Annexe41⇄🔌(3fb) CTV in all bedrooms ® T sB&B⇄🔌£45-£55 dB&B⇄🔌£58-£66 🍴

⟨ 250P ❀ CFA ♪ ♨

♀ English & French V ♦ ⚟ Lunch £10&alc Dinner £12-£14&alc Last dinner 9pm

Credit Cards 1 2 3 5 ④

See advertisement on page 295

For key to symbols in English see the bookmark.

E

**E**

### ★★★ 50% *Exeter Arms Toby*
Rydon Ln, Middlemoor PH7 4BP (Toby) ☎(0392)435353
FAX (0392) 420826
*Modern purpose-built complex alongside primary road on outskirts of city.*
37⇨🛏(6fb)⚤in 10 bedrooms CTV in all bedrooms ®
🛏 (ex guide dogs)
( 380P
V ⁂ ⚓ ⚤ Last dinner 10pm
Credit Cards 1 2 3 5

### ★★ 67% St Andrews
28 Alphington Rd EX2 8HN (Exec Hotel) ☎(0392)76784
FAX (0392) 50249
Closed 24 Dec-1 Jan
*Very conveniently located and with the bonus of a car park, this long-established family-owned hotel is good value for money. The spotlessly clean bedrooms, while quite modest in size, are well furnished and particularly well equipped; bright public rooms include a cosy bar and separate lounge; and the dining room serves good home-cooked dishes. Friendly staff give prompt pleasant service.*
17⇨🛏(2fb) CTV in all bedrooms ® T 🛏 (ex guide dogs)
sB&B⇨🛏£39-£48.40 dB&B⇨🛏£59.50-£69.80 🍴
20P ⚤
⁂ ⚓ Dinner £10.50-£19alc Last dinner 8.15pm
Credit Cards 1 2 3

### ★★ 61% Fairwinds Hotel
EX6 7UD ☎(0392)832911
(For full entry see Kennford)

### ★★ 58% Red House
2 Whipton Village Rd EX4 8AR ☎(0392)56104
*A small family hotel with a busy bar and choice of catering, between carvery, à la carte and bar snacks. Bedrooms are compact, simply decorated and furnished, but well equipped with modern facilities to suit the more transient guest. Its location on the outskirts of the city with good access and parking make it popular with the business traveller.*
12⇨🛏(2fb) CTV in all bedrooms ® T 🍴
28P
♋ English & French V ⁂ ⚓
Credit Cards 1 3 £

---

### EXMOUTH Devon Map 03 SY08 ☺

### ★★★ 63% Royal Beacon
The Beacon EX8 2AF (Best Western) ☎(0395)264886
FAX (0395) 268890
*A former Georgian posting house, this family-owned and run hotel stands in an elevated position, overlooking the sea, the Exe estuary and the Torbay coastline. Recently modernised it offers bright, cosy rooms with an attractive restaurant nicely appointed and decorated. Bedrooms, some with commanding views, vary in size and quality, but are comfortable and well equipped. Since our last visit a pleasant new brigade of staff has been introduced, particularly the hospitable Continental team in the restaurant.*
35⇨🛏(3fb)2⚤⚤in 1 bedroom CTV in all bedrooms ® T
sB&B⇨🛏£42-£45.70 dB&B⇨🛏£72.60-£78.40 🍴
Lift CTV 15P 10🚗 (£2.50 per day) CFA ♟ (hard & grass)
snooker *xmas*
♋ English & French V ⁂ ⚓ ⚤ Lunch fr£8.45 High tea fr£4
Dinner fr£14.95&alc Last dinner 9.30pm
Credit Cards 1 2 3 4 5 £

### ★★★ 60% The Imperial
The Esplanade EX8 2SW (Forte Hotels) ☎(0395)274761
FAX (0395)265161
*This friendly company-owned hotel, set in its own grounds with extensive views over Lyme Bay, is now significantly upgrading its bedrooms – modern facilities being complemented by pleasing décor and fabrics. Bright public areas include an attractive, high-*
ceilinged restaurant, and a team of local staff offers pleasant service.
57⇨🛏(3fb)⚤in 10 bedrooms CTV in all bedrooms ® T ⁑
sB⇨🛏fr£65 dB⇨🛏fr£85 (room only) 🍴
Lift ( 58P ⁂ CFA ⚓ (heated) ♟ (hard) *xmas*
V ⁂ ⚓ ⁑ Sunday Lunch £8.95 Dinner £13.54 Last dinner 9pm
Credit Cards 1 2 3 4 5

### ★★ 65% Barn
Foxholes Hill, off Marine Dr EX8 2DF
☎(0395)274411 due to change to 224411
*This pretty Grade II listed building is an example of 'Arts and Crafts' architecture, by Edward Prior, a contemporary of William Morris. Set in its own small grounds and gardens with good car parking, in a quiet, elevated position with commanding sea and coastline views. Personally run by the owners and spotlessly clean throughout, the bedrooms are bright and well equipped with modern en suites; the public rooms include a comfortable lounge with good views, and a cosy little reception bar and dining room. A short table d'hôte menu offers plain traditional cooking.*
11⇨🛏(4fb) CTV in all bedrooms ® 🛏 sB&B⇨🛏£26-£35
dB&B⇨🛏£52-£60 🍴
30P 3🚗 (£1 per night) ⚤ ⁂ CFA ⚓ croquet putting green
V ⁂ ⚓ ⚤ Sunday Lunch fr7.50 Dinner fr£12 Last dinner
8pm
Credit Cards 1 3 £

### ★ 58% Aliston House
58 Salterton Rd EX8 3EW ☎(0395)274119
*A small informally run and conveniently positioned hotel with compact but comfortable public rooms. The bedrooms, while not spacious, are brightly appointed. Friendly service is provided by the owner and local staff, and there is a pretty, well kept garden and good car parking facilities.*
12rm(2⇨5🛏)Annexe2🛏(2fb) CTV in all bedrooms ® ⁑
sB&B£20-£22 sB&B⇨🛏£22-£24 dB&B£40-£42
dB&B⇨🛏£44-£46 🍴
CTV 16P CFA ⚓ *xmas*
V ⁂ ⚓ Lunch £6.50-£7.25 Dinner £7.25-£8.50&alc Last dinner
8.30pm
£

---

### FAIRFORD Gloucestershire Map 04 SP10

### ★★★ 60% Hyperion House
London St GL7 4AH (Consort) ☎Cirencester(0285)712349
FAX (0285) 713126
RS 1-7 Jan
*Situated in the heart of the village, this Cotswold stone house has been carefully refurbished and enlarged to provide well equipped bedrooms and bright, attractive open-plan public areas.*
29⇨🛏(3fb) CTV in all bedrooms ® T sB&B⇨🛏£60
dB&B⇨🛏£75 🍴
( 40P ⁂ CFA *xmas*
♋ English & Mediterranean V ⁂ ⚓ Sunday Lunch £12 Dinner
£13-£15&alc Last dinner 9.30pm
Credit Cards 1 2 3 5 £

---

### FAKENHAM Norfolk Map 09 TF92

### ★★ 59% *Crown*
Market Place NR21 9BP ☎(0328)851418
*Set in the centre of the town, its good-sized car park accessible via an archway from the main road, this charmingly old world hotel complements heavily beamed ceilings and fireplaces with a Victorian/cottage décor; well equipped bedrooms have every modern comfort, however, and a popular restaurant caters for healthy appetites.*
11⇨🛏 CTV in all bedrooms ® 🛏 (ex guide dogs)
25P
V ⁂ ⚓ ⚤ Last dinner 9.30pm
Credit Cards 1 2 3 5

## FALFIELD Avon Map 03 ST69

**★★64% Park Hotel & Restaurant**
GL12 8DR ☎(0454)260550
*Situated south of the village on the A38 and one mile from junction 14 of the M5, this small hotel occupies 4 acres of grounds, and parts of the original building are 400 years old. Bedrooms are comfortable, well furnished and equipped, and friendly and attentive services are provided by hosts Ken and Rouha Manley and their staff.*
10rm(4⇨3↑)(2fb) CTV in all bedrooms ® T
✠ (ex guide dogs)
CTV 120P ❀
♀ French V ♥ ⚑ ✂ Last dinner 10pm
Credit Cards 1 2 3

## FALKIRK Central *Stirlingshire* Map 11 NS88

**★★★62% Stakis Park**
Camelon Rd FK1 5RY (Stakis) ☎(0324)28331 Telex no 776502 FAX (0324) 611593
*This purpose-built business hotel on the west side of town provides well equipped bedrooms and a combined bar/foyer lounge.*
55⇨↑(3fb) CTV in all bedrooms ®
sB⇨↑£72.45 dB⇨↑£88.20 (room only) ➦
Lift ₵ 151P CFA
♀ English, French & Italian V ♥ ⚑ ✂
Credit Cards 1 2 3 5

🐚 Shell filling station, open 7am–11pm
(some 24 hours) throughout the year with leaded
and unleaded petrol, and diesel.

**F**

FALMOUTH Cornwall & Isles of Scilly Map **02** SW83

See **Town Plan Section**
See also Mawnan Smith

★★★⚘76% **Penmere Manor**

Mongleath Rd TR11 4PN (Best Western) ☎(0326)211411
Telex no 45608 FAX (0326) 317588
Closed 24-26 Dec

*This Georgian manor hotel, quietly situated in 5 acres of woodland and well tended gardens, has been in the ownership of the same dedicated family for well over 20 years. Garden bedrooms are superb, while the rest – though not as spacious – are steadily being renovated, refurbished and improved to offer excellent standards of comfort. Bolitho's Restaurant serves a choice of table d'hôte and à la carte menus accompanied by a good wine list, the Fountains Club provides smart leisure facilities, and personally managed service is friendly and helpful.*

39⇌🛏(15fb) CTV in all bedrooms ® T sB&B⇌🛏£52-£60 dB&B⇌🛏£77.50-£111.25 🍴
(50P ⛟ ❀ CFA 🏊 (heated) ⇌ (heated) sauna solarium gymnasium jacuzzi croquet table tennis ♫ *xmas*
V ৬ ⬭ ✂ Lunch £8.50-£10 Dinner £17.85-£20&alc Last dinner 9pm
Credit Cards 1 2 3 5

★★★69% **Greenbank**

Harbourside TR11 2SR ☎(0326)312440 Telex no 45240
FAX (0326) 211362
Closed 22-30 Dec & 1-6 Jan

*Tastefully upgraded, this long-established popular hotel combines the atmosphere of a byegone age with the comforts and amenities demanded by today's discerning guest. Bright, functional bedrooms – some with outstanding harbour views – feature large bathrooms, while the Nightingale Restaurant complements skilful cuisine with an outstanding wine list; service is very well managed and particularly helpful.*

61⇌🛏(8fb)✂in 2 bedrooms CTV in all bedrooms ® T ✳
sB&B⇌🛏£54.50-£60 dB&B⇌🛏£94-£150 🍴
Lift ( 50P 24🚗 CFA ♩ sauna solarium gymnasium hairdressing beauty salons ♫
♀ English & French ৬ ⬭ Lunch fr£9.75&alc Dinner fr£17.50&alc Last dinner 9.45pm
Credit Cards 1 2 3 5

★★★66% **Royal Duchy**

Cliff Rd TR11 4NX (Brend) ☎(0326)313042 Telex no 42551
FAX (0326) 319420

*In a delightful position overlooking the bay, this friendly commercial and holiday hotel offers good value. Bedrooms range from de luxe suites to compact family rooms, many recently refurbished. The restaurant serves generous portions of traditional dishes and there are attractive leisure facilities.*

50⇌🛏(9fb) CTV in all bedrooms ® T sB&B⇌🛏£49-£57 dB&B⇌🛏£86-£143 🍴
Lift ( CTV 50P ❀ 🏊 (heated) sauna solarium spa bath table tennis ⚘ *xmas*
♀ English & French V ৬ ⬭ Lunch £9&alc Dinner £15-£17&alc Last dinner 9pm
Credit Cards 1 2 3 5 £

★★★63% **Green Lawns**

Western Ter TR11 4QJ ☎(0326)312734 Telex no 45169
FAX (0326) 211427
Closed 24-30 Dec

*Spaciously comfortable lounges and bar now augment the recently extended and well appointed Sarah's Restaurant, where the skilfully-prepared dishes that make up the menu and traditional-style daily 'specials' are accompanied by a good wine list. Attentive service is well managed throughout, modern bedrooms are fully equipped and furnished in the 'open' style, guests have the use of a good leisure club, and there is excellent covered parking.*

40⇌🛏(8fb)2🛏 CTV in all bedrooms ® T sB&B⇌🛏£44-£65 dB&B⇌🛏£60-£92 🍴

( 60P 9🚗 ❀ CFA 🏊 (heated) ♪ (hard & grass )squash sauna solarium gymnasium jacuzzi ♫
♀ English & French V ৬ ⬭ ✂ Lunch £8-£35alc High tea £2-£10 Dinner £16.50-£17.50&alc Last dinner 10pm
Credit Cards 1 2 3 4 5 £

★★★63% **St Michaels**

Gyllyngvase Beach TR11 4NB (Consort) ☎(0326)312707 & 318084 Telex no 45540 FAX (0326) 319147

*A popular and busy resort hotel in its own grounds can boast spaciously stylish public areas, extensive leisure facilities and compact but well equipped bedrooms (though some annexe accommodation is less attractive). Many rooms enjoy views across the award-winning gardens to the nearby sea.*

57⇌🛏 Annexe18⇌🛏(22fb) CTV in all bedrooms ® T sB&B⇌🛏£49-£69 dB&B⇌🛏£88-£128 (incl dinner) 🍴
( 100P ❀ CFA 🏊 (heated) sauna solarium gymnasium jacuzzi windsurfing ⚘ *xmas*
♀ English & French V ৬ ⬭ ✂ ✳ Sunday Lunch £8&alc High tea £8.50 Dinner £14-£18&alc Last dinner 9.30pm
Credit Cards 1 2 3 5

★★★61% **Falmouth**

Castle Beach TR11 4NZ ☎(0326)312671 FAX (0326) 319533

*A fine Victorian hotel set in gardens facing the sea accommodates guests in generally spacious bedrooms – some with balconies and many offering sea views – which have recently been refurbished and upgraded. Guests can relax in a comfortable lounge or the popular Bermuda Bar, and meals are served in a formal restaurant. Conference and private dining rooms are also available, ample car parking is provided in the grounds, and an indoor leisure centre is planned for 1991.*

72⇌🛏(5fb)🛏 CTV in all bedrooms ® T sB&B⇌🛏£49.50-£61.60 dB&B⇌🛏£99-£173.80 (incl dinner) 🍴
Lift ( 150P ❀ CFA 🏊 (heated) ⇌ snooker sauna solarium croquet putting pool table *xmas*

→

**F**

♥ English, French & Italian **V** ♦ ⚗ ⅄ ✳ Lunch £6.90-£9.50
High tea £6.50 Dinner £17.50&alc Last dinner 9.30pm
Credit Cards ①②③⑤

---

**★★★ 60% Gyllyngdune Manor**
Melvill Rd TR11 4AR ☎(0326)312978 FAX (0326) 211881
Closed Jan

*This handsome Georgian manor house enjoys a superb hilltop
location, with rear views out to sea and front views out across the
estuary. Over the past months the bedrooms particularly have
undergone refurbishment, bringing the hotel into the 90s with
pretty co-ordinated bedrooms and good, modern facilities. Public
areas have also received some attention and are comfortably
appointed. The proprietors, Mrs Tarrant and her daughter
Deborah, are friendly and involved in the day-to-day running of
the hotel.*

30🛏🛉(3fb)3🛏 CTV in all bedrooms ® **T**
( 25P 2🛏 (charged) ✿ (heated) sauna solarium gymnasium
table tennis pool table ♫
♥ English & Continental **V** ♦ ⚗ Last dinner 9pm
Credit Cards ①②③⑤

---

**★★ 63% Broadmead**
66-68 Kimberley Park Rd TR11 2DD ☎(0326)315704 & 318036
Closed 23 Dec-5 Jan

*On a main road, close to the centre of town and opposite the
beautifully tended Kimberley Park, this small, family owned hotel
continues to be steadily upgraded and improved by the enthusiastic
young proprietors. Pretty bedrooms are individually styled and
each is well equipped with modern facilities. Public areas are
comfortably appointed and include a bright sun lounge, tiny bar
area and an open-plan foyer lounge.*

12rm(10🛏🛉) CTV in all bedrooms ® **T** ✳ sB&B£18
sB&B🛏🛉£21 dB&B🛏🛉£42-£48 🅿
CTV 8P 🚲
♦ ⚗ ⅄ ✳ Bar Lunch 95p-£2.95 Dinner £10.50 Last dinner
8pm
Credit Cards ①③

---

**★★ 61% Park Grove**
Kimberley Park Rd TR11 2DD ☎(0326)313276
FAX (0326) 211926
Closed Jan

*A personally run hotel, owned by the same family for the past 19
years, stands opposite Kimberley Park at the edge of the town
centre. Simple bedrooms and public areas are steadily being
equipped with modern facilities, and a regular clientele is attracted
by their homely, friendly and relaxed atmosphere. Specialist
golfing holidays are now available.*

17rm(15🛉)(4fb) CTV in all bedrooms ® **T** sB&B£22-£28
sB&B🛉£22-£28 dB&B🛉£44-£56
25P 3🛏
♦ ⚗ Lunch £4.50-£8.50
Credit Cards ①③⑤

---

**★★ 60% Carthion**
Cliff Rd TR11 4AP ☎(0326)313669
Closed Nov-Feb

*Set in a splendid, south-facing position on the seafront, this family-
owned hotel offers accommodation in comfortable, traditionally
furnished and decorated bedrooms with limited modern facilities.
Reasonably spacious public areas with bright, well appointed
lounges provide a pleasant, informal atmosphere, while involved
proprietors participate in the day-to-day running of the
establishment.*

18🛏🛉 CTV in all bedrooms ® sB&B🛏🛉£28.60-£31.70
dB&B🛏🛉£57.20-£63.40 🅿
18P 🚲 ✿ nc10yrs
♥ English & French **V** ♦ ⚗ ⅄ Dinner £12 Last dinner 8pm
Credit Cards ①②③⑤

---

**★★ 58% Lerryn Hotel**
De Pass Rd TR11 4BJ ☎(0326)312489
Closed 23-28 Dec

*Small hotel in a quiet position near seafront.*

20🛏🛉(2fb) CTV in all bedrooms ® sB&B🛏🛉£26-£31.50
dB&B🛏🛉£52-£63 (incl dinner)
12P 1🛏 (£1 per person)
♥ English & French **V** ♦ ⚗ ⅄ ✳ Lunch £6.95 High tea £5
Dinner £8.20&alc Last dinner 8pm
Credit Cards ①③ ⓔ

---

**FAREHAM** Hampshire Map **04** SU50 ⊘

See also **Titchfield**

**★★★★ ✿72% Solent**
Solent Business Park, Whiteley PO15 7AJ (5m NW, junc 9 off
M27) (Shire) ☎Locks Heath(0489)880000 FAX (0489) 880007
(Rosette awarded for dinner only)
88🛏🛉(9fb)5🛏⅄in 16 bedrooms CTV in all bedrooms ® **T** ✳
S% sB&B🛏🛉£87-£110 dB&B🛏🛉£101-£130 🅿
Lift ( 200P ✿ CFA ▦ (heated) squash snooker sauna solarium
gymnasium steam room spa pool *xmas*
♥ International **V** ♦ ⚗ ⅄ Lunch £10-£12&alc Dinner £14-
£19.50&alc Last dinner 9.45pm
Credit Cards ①②③⑤

---

**★★★ ✿67% Lysses House Hotel & Conference Centre**
51 High St PO16 7BQ ☎(0329)822622 FAX (0329) 822762

*Handsome and elegantly furnished, this Georgian-style hotel is
conveniently situated close to the M27 and major road links to
London. Primarily aimed at the executive market, catering
predominantly for business people and conferences, it offers bright
modern bedrooms practically equipped to meet the needs of the
short-stay guest – each even provided with a computer modem
point. Public areas, whilst not vast, are attractively furnished and
pleasing to the eye, and a good selection of meeting rooms doubles
as private dining rooms for functions. The restaurant offers varied
and interesting table d'hôte, à la carte and vegetarian menus of
honestly flavoured and generously served dishes, chef Clive Wright
describing his style of cuisine as modern French/English. A ham
and hazelnut terrine studded with pistachio nuts might be followed
by lightly steamed salmon in a mildly scented ginger cream sauce,
the main courses being accompanied by a tempting selection of
young, gently cooked vegetables, while simple desserts are
attractively presented with fresh fruit garnishes; a ginger-
flavoured moussecake with honey-flavoured crème anglaise is
particularly noteworthy. A short but well balanced wine list is
reasonably priced and contains some examples from the New
World and European countries other than France. Service is
efficient without being officiously attentive, and the atmosphere is
relaxed.*

21🛏🛉 CTV in all bedrooms ® **T** 🐕 (ex guide dogs) ✳
sB&B🛏🛉£36-£60 dB&B🛏🛉£46-£75
Lift ( 30P 🚲 ✿ nc12yrs
♥ English & French **V** ♦ ⚗ ✳ Lunch £10.95-£15&alc Dinner
£16.50-£18&alc Last dinner 9.45pm
Credit Cards ①②③⑤

---

**★★ 66% Red Lion**
East St PO16 0BP (Lansbury) ☎(0329)822640 Telex no 86204
FAX (0329) 823579

*This centrally located former coaching inn retains much of its
original character in the beams and exposed brickwork of its public
areas. Bedrooms are nicely coordinated and well equipped. Bar
meals are served as well as the à la carte selections in the
restaurant and the wine list includes popular items. Service is
friendly and relaxed.*

44🛏🛉(3fb)1🛏⅄in 6 bedrooms CTV in all bedrooms ®
🐕 (ex guide dogs) sB&B🛏🛉fr£76 dB&B🛏🛉fr£89 🅿
( CTV 136P 3🛏 🚲

→

F

♡ English & Continental **V** ✿ Lunch fr£12&alc Dinner
fr£12&alc Last dinner 10pm
Credit Cards ①②③⑤

★★ 63% **Maylings Manor**
11A Highlands Rd PO16 7XJ ☎(0329)286451
FAX (0329) 822584
*This extended Edwardian manor house is set in 2.5 acres on the
western edge of Fareham. Bedrooms, recently upgraded, are well
equipped, and the Cams Rose Restaurant offers a choice of menus
with light meals also served in the Raffles Bar. There are two
popular conference/function rooms.*
26rm(24⇔)(2fb)2∰ CTV in all bedrooms ® **T** ✱ S%
sB&B⇔↑£33-£48 dB&B⇔↑£43-£58 🅿
87P ❄ CFA ᴔ
♡ English & French **V** ✿ ♨ ✱ S% Lunch fr£10.50 Dinner
fr£10.50 Last dinner 9.30pm
Credit Cards ①②③⑤ⓔ

○**Forte Posthouse**
Cartwright Ln, Titchfield PO15 5RJ (Forte Hotels)
☎(0329)844866
Due to have opened Sep 1991
126⇔↑

---

**FARINGDON** Oxfordshire Map **04** SU29

★★★ 70% **Sudbury House Hotel & Conference Centre**
London St SN7 8AA ☎(0367)241272 FAX (0367) 242346
*A former family home on the edge of this market town has been
greatly extended to provide a conference-orientated hotel with 49
modern and extremely well equipped bedrooms. Public areas are
spacious and airy, meeting rooms being available both in the
original house and in a new wing; a tiered lecture theatre also
proves popular with large companies. The Folly Restaurant's table
d'hote and à la carte menus of interesting dishes, professionally
served by attentive staff, are supplemented by a carvery operation
at lunchtimes.*
49⇔↑✂in 10 bedrooms CTV in all bedrooms ® **T**
✖ (ex guide dogs) ✱ sB&B⇔↑£84.50 dB&B⇔↑£105 🅿
Lift ℂ 85P ❄ CFA croquet ♫ ᴔ *xmas*
**V** ✿ ♨ ✱ Lunch £12.50&alc High tea £1.50-£5.50 Dinner
£14.95&alc Last dinner 10pm
Credit Cards ①②③⑤

---

**FARNBOROUGH** Hampshire Map **04** SU85

★★★ 60% **Forte Crest**
Lynchford Rd GU14 6AZ (Forte Hotels) ☎(0252)545051
Telex no 859637 FAX (0252) 377210
*This imposing hotel of character has spacious public areas which
include a bar lounge, coffee shop and conservatory restaurant
offering a variety of menus, and Glades Leisure Club which is
currently being extended. Bedrooms are sited in a modern wing.
Staff throughout are friendly and efficient.*
110⇔↑✖2∰✂in 82 bedrooms CTV in all bedrooms ® **T** ✱
sB⇔↑fr£80 dB⇔↑£85-£110 (room only) 🅿
ℂ 170P CFA ▣ (heated) sauna solarium gymnasium health &
fitness centre ♫ *xmas*
♡ French **V** ✿ ♨ ✂ ✱ Lunch £13&alc Dinner £16&alc Last
dinner 10pm
Credit Cards ①②③④⑤

★★ 68% **Falcon**
Farnborough Rd GU14 6TH ☎(0252)545378 FAX (0252) 522539
Closed 24 Dec-2 Jan
*This commercial hotel opposite the Air Show ground offers
comfortable bedrooms which are well maintained and equipped;
public areas, though limited, are attractive, a restaurant with
conservatory extension serving an extensive table d'hôte menu.
Smartly uniformed staff provide friendly, relaxed service and there
is good on-site parking.*

30⇔↑(2fb)1∰✂in 8 bedrooms CTV in all bedrooms ® **T** ✖
sB&B⇔↑fr£65 dB&B⇔↑fr£75
30P ∰ CFA
♡ International **V** ✿ ♨ ✂ Lunch fr£12.50&alc Dinner
fr£12.50&alc Last dinner 9.30pm
Credit Cards ①②③

---

**FARNHAM** Surrey Map **04** SU84

★★★ 60% **Bush**
The Borough GU9 7NN (Forte Hotels) ☎(0252)715237
FAX (0252) 733530
*Conference organisers and businessmen are attracted by the quiet
meeting rooms and good car parking facilities available at this
extensively refurbished town centre coaching inn which dates from
the 17th century. Attractively decorated and well equipped
bedrooms all offer a good standard of comfort, and much of the
building's character is retained in the oak-panelled lounge, with its
coal fire, and the beamed Coachmans Bar. A pleasant coffee
lounge serves snacks which provide an alternative to the more
formal meals offered in an attractively appointed restaurant.*
68⇔↑(1fb)1∰✂in 20 bedrooms CTV in all bedrooms ® **T** ✱
sB⇔↑fr£70 dB⇔↑fr£85 (room only) 🅿
ℂ 80P ❄ CFA *xmas*
**V** ✿ ♨ ✂ ✱ Lunch £11.50&alc High tea £5.50 Dinner
£15.30&alc Last dinner 10pm
Credit Cards ①②③④⑤

★★★ 59% **Hog's Back**
Hog's Back GU10 1EX (Jarvis) ☎Runfold(02518)2345
Telex no 859352 FAX (02518) 3113
(For full entry see Seale)

★★ 57% **Trevena House**
Alton Rd GU10 5ER ☎(0252)716908 FAX (0252) 722583
Closed 24 Dec-4 Jan
*A delightful manor house in 5 acres of grounds stands beside the
A31 a mile from the town; built in the 1890's it retains much of its
Gothic Victorian character, the oak-panelled bar/lounge having
window seating and leaded windows. An attractive, homely
restaurant overlooks the gardens and outdoor swimming pool,
functional bedrooms in traditional style are equipped with modern
facilities, and service throughout is informal and unhurried under
the personal supervision of the proprietor.*
20⇔↑ CTV in all bedrooms ® ✖ (ex guide dogs) ✱
sB&B⇔↑fr£49 dB&B⇔↑fr£59 🅿
30P ∰ ❄ ⌒ (heated) ♪ (hard)
✿ ♨
Credit Cards ①②③

---

**FARRINGTON GURNEY** Avon Map **03** ST65

★★ 67% **Country Ways**
Marsh Ln BS18 5TT ☎Temple Cloud(0761)52449
FAX (0761) 53360
Closed 24-31 Dec
*The new proprietors, Janet and Gareth Richards, offer a warm
welcome to their guests at this small country hotel off the A37
south of the village. The 6 en suite bedrooms are full of character,
the attractive restaurant serves imaginative food and the staff are
friendly.*
6⇔↑ CTV in all bedrooms ® **T** ✖ ✱ sB&B⇔↑£50-£55
dB&B⇔↑£60-£65 🅿
12P ∰ ❄
✿ ♨ ✂ ✱ Lunch £15-£21alc Dinner £15-£21alc Last dinner
9pm
Credit Cards ①③⑤

**See advertisement under WELLS**

---

A rosette means exceptional standards of cuisine.

## FARTHING CORNER MOTORWAY SERVICE AREA
(M2) Kent Map **05** TQ86

⛛**Rank Motor Lodge**
Rainham ME8 8PQ (between juncts 4 & 5 M2) (Rank)
☎Medway(0634)377337 FAX (0634) 360848
58⇨🅿(12fb)⊁in 6 bedrooms CTV in all bedrooms ® ✳
sB&B⇨🅿£29.75 dB&B⇨🅿£37.75 Continental breakfast
55P
🍴 English & Continental V ✤ ⊋ ⊁ ✳ High tea £3-£6.05alc
Dinner £3-£6.05alc
Credit Cards ①②③⑤

## FAUGH Cumbria Map **12** NY55

★★★62% **String of Horses Inn**
CA4 9EG ☎Hayton(0228)70297 FAX (0228) 70675
RS 24-25 Dec
*A warm welcome awaits guests to this small hotel, personally run
by Mr & Mrs Tasker and set just off the A22 in a residential area
within easy reach of both town centre and seafront; bedrooms are
simple but freshly decorated, and all benefit from modern
conveniences. Chef Christopher Tasker offers a seasonal à la carte
menu of meat, fish, poultry and game which boasts some
innovative, imaginative dishes, the selection being extended by
daily 'specials'. Breast of quail and venison fillet with a rich Port
sauce and wild mushrooms has proved a popular choice, and both
hot puddings and delicious home-made ice creams are available for
dessert. The standard of cuisine is complemented by attentive and
professional service.*
14⇨🅿3🛏 CTV in all bedrooms ® T ✳ sB&B⇨🅿£58-£72
dB&B⇨🅿£65-£95 �
《50P ≜ (heated) sauna solarium whirlpool spa
🍴 English & French V ✤ ✳ Lunch £9-£10.50&alc Dinner
£16.95&alc Last dinner 10pm
Credit Cards ①②③⑤ⓔ

## FAVERSHAM Kent Map **05** TR06 ◎

★★★⊛72% *Throwley House*
Ashford Rd, Sheldwich ME13 0LT (2m S of M2 jnct 6 on A251 )
☎(0795)539168
*Attractively furnished bedrooms – thoughtfully provided with such
extras as fresh fruit, mineral water, bathrobes and a decanter of
sherry – together with an elegant drawing room complement a
restaurant where you can see two Throwley Bears as you enjoy the
high standard of cuisine which results from chefs Martin Barrett
and Stephen Cass applying considerable flair and professionalism
to the best of seasonal local produce; full flavoured sauces are
created by natural reduction, and even vegetables retain their own
flavours. Extensive services are available, and the hotel plans to
add more bedrooms and function facilities.*
12⇨🅿(1fb) CTV in all bedrooms ✖ (ex guide dogs)
《65P 🐎 ✿ ♡ putting green nc11yrs
🍴 French V ✤ ⊋ ⊁ Last dinner 10pm
Credit Cards ①②③⑤
**See advertisement under CANTERBURY**

⊛⊛⊛✕✕**Read's**
Painters Forstal ME13 0EE (2m S A251) ☎(0795)535344
*Set in the sleepy village of Painter's Forstal, and owned and run by
chef/patron David Pritchard and his wife for the past 14 years, this
restaurant achieves a consistently high quality, both the à la carte
and fair-priced luncheon table d'hôte menus promising imaginative,
tempting dishes prepared with considerable flair from fresh, good
quality produce. Once a supermarket, the restaurant still has a
rather dull exterior appearance, but the interior has been made
attractive by pastel décor and comfortable seating arrangements.
Professionally presented dishes, generously served and
accompanied by some pleasant sauces, include a smooth, full-
flavoured Chicken Liver Parfait and Pan-fried Lambs' Kidneys so
tender that they melt away; carefully prepared, fresh, seasonal
vegetables enhance the dishes on offer, and a wide-ranging wine list*

F

comprising some 200 bins includes some interesting vintages as
well as the old favourites.
Closed Sun, Mon, 26 Dec & last 2 wks Aug
♀ English & French **V** 44 seats Lunch £13.50&alc Dinner
£27.50&alc Last lunch 2pm Last dinner 10pm 40 P
Credit Cards [1][2][3][5]

---

FEARNAN Tayside *Perthshire* Map **11** NN74

★60% **Tigh-an-Loan**
PH15 2PF (Guestaccom) ☎Kenmore(08873)249 due to change
to (0887) 830249
Closed Oct-Etr
*This small family-run hotel set on the picturesque shore of Loch
Tay provides an ideal base for touring holidaymakers, offering
peaceful relaxation, traditional comforts and good home cooking.*
8rm(3⇨)(1fb) **R** sB&Bfr£22.50 sB&B⇨fr£25.50 dB&Bfr£45
dB&B⇨fr£51
CTV 25P ⚐ ❀ ♪
**V** ⚐ 및 Bar Lunch fr£5 Dinner fr£11.50 Last dinner 8pm
Credit Cards [1][3]

---

FEERING Essex Map **05** TL82

○**Forte Travelodge**
(A12 northbound) (Forte) ☎Central Res (0800) 850950
Due to have opened Winter 1991
40⇨**R**

---

FELIXSTOWE Suffolk Map **05** TM33

★★★69% **Orwell Moat House**
Hamilton Rd IP11 7DX (Queens Moat) ☎(0394)285511
Telex no 987676 FAX (0394) 670687
*Easily accessible from the A45 and conveniently close to the
railway station, this large hotel has greatly improved its public
areas, which now feature a choice of restaurant and bar facilities as
well as a comfortable and relaxing lounge. Well equipped
bedrooms are equally suitable for a variety of guests, including
delegates using the extensive conference/function facilities.*
58⇨**R**(10fb) CTV in all bedrooms **R T** sB⇨**R**fr£65
dB⇨**R**fr£85 (room only) **月**
Lift ( 150P 20🚗 ❀ CFA ♪
♀ English & French **V** ⚐ 및
Credit Cards [1][2][3][5][£]

★★★62% **Brook**
Orwell Rd IP11 7PF (Best Western) ☎(0394)278441
Telex no 987674
*A modern, well-furnished hotel situated in a residential area close
to the town centre and the sea.*
25⇨(1fb) CTV in all bedrooms **R** ✖
( 20P
⚐ 및
Credit Cards [1][2][3][5]

★★67% **Waverley**
2 Wolsey Gardens IP11 7DF (Minotels) ☎(0394)282811
Telex no 987568 FAX (0394) 670185
*A Victorian hotel perched on the cliff provides clean and well
equipped accommodation, many of its rooms enjoying good sea
views. Guests have a choice of eating options, the extensive bar
menu offering an alternative to the table d'hôte and à la carte
menus of the Wolsely Restaurant.*
19⇨**R**(4fb)1⊞ CTV in all bedrooms **R T** sB⇨**R**£44.50-
£49.50 dB⇨**R**£55.95-£61.25 (room only) **月**
30P CFA *xmas*
♀ English & Continental **V** ⚐ 및 Lunch £10.25&alc High tea
£4.50 Dinner £12.95&alc Last dinner 10.30pm
Credit Cards [1][2][3][5]

★★66%. **Marlborough**
Sea Front IP11 8BJ ☎(0394)285621 FAX (0394) 670724
*Situated on the seafront, the hotel offers comfortable well equipped
accommodation, a choice of menus and a popular 'joint of the day'
carvery. Conference and banqueting facilities are available.*
45⇨**R**(2fb)1⊞ CTV in all bedrooms **R T** ✳
sB&B⇨**R**£39.95-£46 dB&B⇨**R**£58.50-£61 **月**
Lift ( CTV 19P CFA windsurfing *xmas*
♀ English & French **V** ⚐ ✖ ✳ Lunch £7.25-£9.25&alc High
tea £2.05-£6.15 Dinner £10.95&alc Last dinner 9.45pm
Credit Cards [1][2][3][5]

---

FELLING Tyne & Wear Map **12** NZ26

⭐**Forte Travelodge**
Lean Ln NE10 8YB (on A194) (Forte)
☎091-438 3333 Central Res (0800) 850950
*Opened in 1989, this lodge is situated at the A1/A194 junction and
is very convenient for traffic using the Tyne Tunnel.*
41⇨**R**(41fb) CTV in all bedrooms **R** sB⇨**R**£29.95
dB⇨**R**£29.95 (room only)
( 41P ⚐
Credit Cards [1][2][3]

---

FELMINGHAM Norfolk Map **09** TG22

★★⚑72%. *Felmingham Hall Country House*
NR28 0LP ☎Swanton Abbott(069269)631 FAX (069269) 320
*This Elizabethan residence stands in 15 acres on the outskirts of
the village (hotel signed), located on the B1145 between
Clylesham and North Walsham. The small team of staff are both
hospitable and attentive, complementing the style and comfort of
the public rooms. The restaurant is equally attractive, though the
size of the menu varies in proportion to the rate of occupancy,
nonetheless there are some imaginative dishes using good quality
fresh produce. Upgrading of bedrooms continues, sizes vary, but all
have character and modern en suites.*
12⇨**R**Annexe6⇨**R**2⊞ CTV in all bedrooms **R T**
✖ (ex guide dogs)
P ⚐ ❀ ⚓ croquet nc12yrs
♀ English & French **V** ⚐ ✖ Last dinner 9.30pm
Credit Cards [1][2][3]

---

FENNY BRIDGES Devon Map **03** SY19

★66% *Fenny Bridges*
EX14 0BQ ☎Honiton(0404)850218 FAX (0404) 850920
*A Georgian house conveniently positioned beside the A30 now
serves as a popular hostelry combining friendly services and a
relaxing ambience with commendable standards of
accommodation which will appeal to either businessman or tourist.
Run by the same family for some 30 years, it has recently been
significantly upgraded to provide modern facilities in stylishly
appointed and individually decorated en suite bedrooms with co-
ordinated furnishings and fabrics, these rooms being complemented
by an attractive open-plan restaurant with bar and a busy public
bar.*
6⇨**R**(1fb)✖in 2 bedrooms CTV in all bedrooms **R T**
CTV 75P ❀ ♪
♀ English & French **V** ⚐ 및 ✖ Last dinner 10pm
Credit Cards [1][2][3][5]

★63% **Greyhound Inn**
EX14 0BJ (Chef & Brewer) ☎Honiton(0404)850380
*A small, thatched, roadside inn featuring a popular bar and bright
carvery restaurant with good hours of service is equally popular
with tourists and businessmen; bedrooms are comfortable and well
equipped, and a team of young staff provides friendly, informal
service.*
10⇨**R**1⊞ CTV in all bedrooms **R T** ✖ (ex guide dogs)
sB&B⇨**R**£38 dB&B⇨**R**£52 **月**

60P

♀ International **V** ✿ ⚏ ✔ Bar Lunch £2.95-£5.50alc
Credit Cards [1] [2] [3] [5]

---

**FENSTANTON** Cambridgeshire Map **04** TL36 ☺

⭧**Forte Travelodge**
A604, Huntingdon Rd(Forte)
☎(0954)30919 Central Res (0800) 850950
40⇨♠(40fb) CTV in all bedrooms ® sB⇨♠£29.95
dB⇨♠£29.95 (room only)
《 40P ⇴
Credit Cards [1] [2] [3]

---

**FERMAIN BAY**

See **Guernsey** under Channel Islands

---

**FERNDOWN** Dorset Map **04** SU00

★★★★ 65% **Dormy**
New Rd BH22 8ES (De Vere) ☎Bournemouth(0202)872121
Telex no 418301 FAX (0202) 895388
*This well established hotel still retains part of its original cottage
character, in spite of having been extended within its extensive
grounds. Accommodation is in various wings and cottages, some
connected to the main building. The conference market is catered
for at this hotel, and the leisure centre is one of the finest in this
part of the country. Staff are courteous and friendly, providing all
the expected levels of service. Ferndown is just north of
Bournemouth, and the hotel is off the A347, by the golf course.*
130⇨♠(8fb)2⌗ CTV in all bedrooms ® **T** ✱
sB&B⇨♠£62.50-£90 dB&B⇨♠£95-£130 ⊟
Lift 《 CTV 220P ✿ CFA ▣ (heated) ♪ (hard) squash snooker
sauna solarium gymnasium ♫ *xmas*
**V** ✿ ⚏ ✱ Lunch £12.95-£15 Dinner £18.50-£21 Last dinner
9.30pm
Credit Cards [1] [2] [3] [4] [5]
**See advertisement under BOURNEMOUTH**

★★ 58% **Coach House Inn**
Tricketts Cross BH22 9NW (junc A31/A348) (Consort)
☎(0202)861222 FAX (0202) 894130
*Motel-style accommodation is offered in four blocks situated
around the main building which houses an à la carte restaurant
and conference facilities.*
Annexe44⇨ CTV in all bedrooms ® **T** S% sB&B⇨£48-£53
dB&B⇨£68-£75 ⊟
100P 25🛏 CFA gymnasium
♀ English & Italian **V** ✿ ⚏ ✱ Lunch £7.25-£8.75&alc Dinner
£9.20-£10.50&alc Last dinner 9.30pm
Credit Cards [1] [2] [3] [5] ₤

---

**FERRYBRIDGE SERVICE AREA** West Yorkshire
Map **08** SE42

⭧**Granada Lodge**
WF11 0AF (A1/M62 jnct 33) (Granada)
☎Knottingley(0977)670488 FAX (0977) 672945
*Located at the junction of the M62 and A1, this modern purpose-
built lodge offers very good value accommodation, with well
equipped comfortable bedrooms. Meals can be obtained from the
adjacent service area restaurant.*
35⇨♠(6fb)✔in 5 bedrooms CTV in all bedrooms ®
✗ (ex guide dogs) S% sB⇨♠fr£31 dB⇨♠fr£34 (room only)
⊟
《 352P
**V** ✿ ⚏ ✔
Credit Cards [1] [2] [3] [5]

---

**FETTERCAIRN** Grampian *Kincardineshire* Map **15** NO67

★★ 64% **Ramsay Arms**
AB30 1XX (Exec Hotel) ☎(05614)334 FAX (05614) 500
*This family-run hotel in the village centre retains many period
features, including some fine woodwork. Bedrooms are furnished in
the traditional manner, and there is a comfortable lounge bar as
well as the relaxing residents' lounge on the first floor.*
12⇨♠(1fb)1⌗ CTV in all bedrooms ® **T** sB&B⇨♠£31
dB&B⇨♠£45 ⊟
12P ✿ sauna solarium gymnasium
**V** ✿ ⚏ ✱ Lunch £8.50-£20alc Dinner £8.50-£20alc Last dinner
9pm
Credit Cards [1] [3] ₤

---

**FILEY** North Yorkshire Map **08** TA18

★★ 69% **Wrangham House**
10 Stonegate, Hunmanby YO14 0NS (3m SW off A165)
☎Scarborough(0723)891333
*This one-time vicarage has lost nothing of its former charm. The
friendly atmosphere, the excellent home-cooking and the log fires
lit in the two very comfortable lounges on chillier days provide a
warm welcome. Bedrooms are all attractively decorated and
individually styled.*
9⇨♠Annexe4⇨♠✔in all bedrooms CTV in all bedrooms ®
✗ (ex guide dogs) S% sB&B⇨♠£30.75 dB&B⇨♠£61.50 ⊟
20P ⇴ ✿ CFA nc12yrs *xmas*
**V** ✿ ⚏ ✔ S% Lunch £7.55 High tea £4.95 Dinner £11.75&alc
Last dinner 8.30pm
Credit Cards [1] [2] [3] [5] ₤

---

**FINDON** West Sussex Map **04** TQ10

★★ 59% *Findon Manor*
High St BN14 0TA ☎(090671)2733
*Dating from the 16th century this old rectory has been thoughtfully
converted and provides bedrooms, which although not in pristine
condition, are comfortable and well equipped. Staff are helpful and
attentive.*
11⇨♠2⌗ CTV in all bedrooms ® **T**
30P
✿ ⚏
Credit Cards [1] [2] [3] [5]

---

**FIR TREE** Co Durham Map **12** NZ13

★★★ 70% **Helme Park Hall Country House**
DL13 4NW ☎Bishop Auckland(0388)730970
FAX (0388) 730970
*This much extended farmhouse, converted to hotel use in 1987,
stands in its own grounds just off the A68/A689 2 miles north of
Fir Tree; tastefully appointed and offering the services of friendly,
attentive staff, it commands superb views west over Wealdale and
the North Pennines from its elevated position.*
10⇨♠(3fb)1⌗ CTV in all bedrooms ® **T** ✗ (ex guide dogs)
sB&B⇨♠£48.95-£95.60 dB&B⇨♠£67-£95.60 ⊟
40P ✿ solarium *xmas*
♀ English & French **V** ✿ ⚏ Lunch £8.50-£15&alc Dinner
fr£15&alc Last dinner 9.30pm
Credit Cards [1] [2] [3] ₤

**See advertisement on page 305**

---

**FISHGUARD** Dyfed Map **02** SM93

★★ 61% **Cartref**
15-19 High St SA65 9AW ☎(0348)872430 FAX (0348) 874161
*This very friendly little hotel, situated at the middle of the market
town, is convenient both as a stopover for the Rosslare ferry and as
a base from which to tour the area. Bedrooms are bright and clean,
and guests can relax in a small bar or in one of the two comfortable
lounges.*

→

12rm(10⇔🟆🏠)(4fb)⊬in 4 bedrooms CTV in all bedrooms ✳ 🏳
《 CTV 20P 2🕿 🚲 CFA nc7yrs *xmas*
**V** 👁 ⚞ ⊬ ✳ Lunch fr£7.50&alc Dinner fr£7.50&alc Last
dinner 10pm
Credit Cards ①③£

★60% **Abergwaun**
The Market Square SA65 9HA 🕿(0348)872077
*This historic inn on the town square is a convenient touring base for
Pembrokeshire or stopover for the Irish ferry. Public rooms have
been completely refurbished and provide good facilities but,
although upgrading is taking place, bedrooms are still basically
appointed. Bumbles Bistro serves a good choice of snacks and
meals all day.*
11rm(3⇔🟆)(2fb) CTV in all bedrooms ® ✳ sB&B£19.50
dB&B£34 dB&B⇔🟆£45
CTV ⊁
🍴 English & French **V** 👁 ⚞ ✳ Sunday Lunch £3.50-£5.95
Dinner £9-£16alc Last dinner 9pm
Credit Cards ①②③

---

**FITTLEWORTH** West Sussex Map **04** TQ01

★★64% **Swan**
Lower St RH20 1EW 🕿(079882)429
*Bedrooms in this charming 14th-century village inn retain much of
the traditional character while offering all modern facilities. The
cosy beamed restaurant and the lounge bar with inglenook
fireplace are popular with the locals.*
10rm(6⇔2🟆)2🚲 CTV in all bedrooms ® 🏠 ✕ (ex guide dogs)
25P ✿ ∪
👁 ⚞ ⊬ Last dinner 9.30pm
Credit Cards ①②③⑤

---

**FIVE OAKS** West Sussex Map **04** TQ02

⏏ Forte Travelodge
RH14 9AE (on A29, northbound) (Forte)
🕿Billingshurst(0403)782711 Central Res (0800) 850950
*On the A29 north of Billingshurst, the lodge provides well
appointed ground floor accommodation, meals being taken at the
nearby Little Chef restaurant.*
26⇔🟆(26fb) CTV in all bedrooms ® sB⇔🟆£29.95
dB⇔🟆£29.95 (room only)
《 26P 🚲
Credit Cards ①②③

---

**FLADBURY** Hereford & Worcester Map **03** SO94

★★58% **The Chequers Inn**
Chequers Ln WR10 2PZ 🕿Evesham(0386)860276 & 860527
*Situated in the centre of a pretty Vale of Evesham village, this old
inn has been extensively renovated to provide modern, well
equipped bedrooms. The bars and carvery restaurant retain their
characterful beams and open fires, though limited lounge facilities
mean some comfort is lacking.*
8⇔🟆(1fb) CTV in all bedrooms ® **T** sB&B⇔🟆fr£38.50
dB&B⇔🟆fr£61.50 🏳
25P 🚲 🚶
**V** 👁 ✳ Lunch £7.50-£16alc Dinner £8.50-£16alc Last dinner
9.30pm
Credit Cards ①③£

---

**FLAMBOROUGH** Humberside Map **08** TA26

★68% **Flaneburg**
North Marine Rd YO15 1LF 🕿Bridlington(0262)850284
Closed Jan & Feb
*This friendly little hotel is personally run by resident proprietors
whose aim is to provide good, clean and comfortable
accommodation at a reasonable price; because of its size, mid-
week service can be limited out of season.*

13rm(8🟆)(2fb) CTV in all bedrooms ® 🏠
CTV 20P 🚲
**V** 👁

---

**FLEET** Hampshire Map **04** SU85

★★★56% *Lismoyne*
Church Rd GU13 8NA 🕿(0252)628555 FAX (0252) 811761
*Set in a quiet residential area and surrounded by over 2 acres of
pleasant gardens, a Victorian hotel offers a variety of bedrooms,
public rooms with old world charm, and the services of pleasant,
friendly staff.*
44⇔🟆(1fb)1🚲 CTV in all bedrooms ® **T**
《 80P ✿
🍴 English & French **V** 👁 ⚞ Last dinner 9.30pm
Credit Cards ①②③④⑤

---

**FLEET MOTORWAY SERVICE AREA (M3)** Hampshire
Map **04** SU75

◯ Forte Travelodge
RG27 8BN (between junc 4 & 5 westbound M3) (Forte)
🕿Central Res (0800) 850950
Due to have opened Sep 1991
40⇔🟆

---

**FLEETWOOD** Lancashire Map **07** SD34 ◎

★★★60% **North Euston**
The Esplanade FY7 6BN 🕿(0253)876525 FAX (0253) 777842
*In a prominent position overlooking the Wyre Estuary this hotel,
which dates back to 1841, has attractive bedrooms equipped with
modern facilities. The restaurant has recently undergone
refurbishment and the Chatterbox Bistro is being extended.*
56⇔🟆(2fb) CTV in all bedrooms ® **T** 🏠 ✕ (ex guide dogs)
sB&B⇔🟆fr£43 dB&B⇔🟆fr£59 🏳
Lift 《 60P CFA table tennis pool table *xmas*
👁 ⚞ Lunch fr£8.25&alc Dinner fr£13&alc Last dinner 9.30pm
Credit Cards ①②③⑤

---

**FLITWICK** Bedfordshire Map **04** TL03

★★★❀❀❀⚐72% **Flitwick Manor**
Church Rd MK45 1AE 🕿(0525)712242 Telex no 825562
Closed 24-28 Dec
*A warm, relaxing atmosphere pervades this solid 17th-century
country house, surrounded by rolling lawns and mature trees, and
with a distant view of the River Flit. The Music Room is a
charming lounge, where drinks are also served. The well appointed
restaurant overlooks the garden, and guests can enjoy the excellent
cooking of Duncan Poyser from the regularly changing menu,
mainly in the modern vein. Delicious flavours abounded in our
asparagus mousse with morels, chicken scented with lemon grass
and ginger, and a complex dessert of luscious walnut tart with
caramel ice cream. Bedrooms are spacious, comfortable, well
equipped and imaginatively decorated; many have good views,
some have 4-posters, spa baths, and one its own sauna. Three
downstairs rooms are air conditioned.*
15⇔🟆(2fb)5🚲 CTV in all bedrooms 🏠 (ex guide dogs) 🏳
50P 🚲 ✿ ♫ (hard) 🚶 croquet table tennis bicycles putting
*xmas*
**V** 👁 ⚞ ⊬ ✳ S10% Lunch £19.50-£23.50 High tea £6-£20
Dinner £12-£35&alc Last dinner 9.30pm
Credit Cards ①②③£

Red star hotels are each
highlighted by a pink
tinted panel.

## FLORE Northamptonshire Map **04** SP66

### ★★★64% **Heyford Manor**

The High St NN7 4LP (Lansbury) ☎Weedon(0327)349022
Telex no 312437 FAX (0327) 349017

*Close to junction 16 of the M1 and with easy access to
Northampton, this modern purpose-built hotel has an attractive
lounge and bar area, a restaurant with an imaginative menu and
comfortably furnished very well equipped bedrooms, with 2 rooms
adapted for the disabled.*

56⇨↰(7fb)⊬in 11 bedrooms CTV in all bedrooms ® **T**
✗ (ex guide dogs) sB&B⇨↰fr£77 dB&B⇨↰fr£90 ➡
《 CTV 100P CFA sauna gymnasium *xmas*
♀ English & Continental **V** ♡ ⚓ ⊬ Lunch fr£10.95&alc
Dinner fr£14.95&alc Last dinner 10pm
Credit Cards ①②③⑤

## FOCHABERS Grampian *Morayshire* Map **15** NJ35

### ★★58% **Gordon Arms**

High St IV32 7DH ☎(0343)820508 FAX (0343) 820300

*Situated on the main street close to the River Spey, this extended
former coaching inn is a popular base for anglers. Public areas
provide traditional comforts, while well equipped bedrooms have
practical modern facilities.*

13⇨↰(2fb)2⚓ CTV in all bedrooms ® **T** sB&B⇨↰£43
dB&B⇨↰£60 ➡
CTV 50P 2⚓ (£10 per day) ✿ CFA *xmas*
♀ Scottish, French & Italian **V** ♡ ⚓ ✳ Lunch £7.50&alc High
tea £5-£7.50 Dinner £8.50-£15&alc Last dinner 9.45pm
Credit Cards ①②③

## FOLKESTONE Kent Map **05** TR23

### ★★★59% **Clifton**

The Leas CT20 2EB (Consort) ☎(0303)851231 Telex no 57515

*New bedrooms are all furnished to an acceptable standard at this
popular hotel, while older accommodation is slowly being improved
to increase general comfort while retaining its original character.
Set in a fine position overlooking the sea, it attracts a loyal regular
clientele which appreciates its well appointed public rooms, the
personal involvement of its proprietors and the traditional service.*

80⇨↰(4fb) CTV in all bedrooms ® **T** sB&B⇨↰£49-£59.50
dB&B⇨↰£65-£74 ➡
Lift 《 ⚓ ✿ CFA solarium games room *xmas*
♀ English & French **V** ♡ ⚓ ✳ Lunch £9.50-£10.50&alc
Dinner £16-£17&alc Last dinner 9pm
Credit Cards ①②③⑤

### ★★61% **Wards**

39 Earls Ave CT20 2HB ☎(0303)45166 FAX (0303) 54480

*A small family-run hotel in a quiet residential area, but within
close proximity to the harbour and town centre. Bedrooms are
decorated in pastel shades with co-ordinating soft furnishings, and
equipped with all modern conveniences. Public areas are designed
with a 20s Gatsby theme. The hotel is soon to benefit from a private
car park to the rear, although there is adequate street parking.*

10⇨↰(3fb) CTV in all bedrooms ® **T** ✗ (ex guide dogs) ✳
sB&B⇨↰£42.50-£59.50 dB&B⇨↰£56-£86 ➡
20P ⚓ ♫ *xmas*
♀ English & French **V** ♡ ✳ Lunch £7.95-£9.95&alc
Credit Cards ①②③⑤

## FONTWELL West Sussex Map **04** SU90

### ⇧**Forte Travelodge**

BN18 0SB (on A27) (Forte)
☎Eastergate(0243)543973 Central Res (0800) 850950

*A block of modern, well-appointed family rooms stands to the rear
of the Little Chef restaurant at the A27/A29 roundabout, west of
the village.*

→

**F**

32⇆🌢(32fb) CTV in all bedrooms ® sB⇆🌢£29.95 dB⇆🌢£29.95 (room only)
《 40P 🚗
Credit Cards ①②③

---

**★★ 60%** *White Hart Inn*
SN14 8RP ☎Castle Combe(0249)782213

*Quietly situated by a trout stream, this friendly village inn with beams and open fires dates to 1533. Bar meals are available in the very popular bars or an à la carte menu in the dining room. Comfortable bedrooms with modern facilities are mostly located in annexes across the street.*

3🌢Annexe8⇆(1fb) CTV in all bedrooms ®
CTV 100P ❅ ⊇ (heated)
🍴 English & French **V** ✪ Last dinner 9.30pm
Credit Cards ①③

---

**★★ 66%** Ashburn Hotel & Restaurant
Damerham Rd SP6 1JP (Minotels) ☎(0425)652060

*A Victorian house with a large modern extension on the edge of the town in an elevated position. Bedrooms in the original building are attractive and have some period furniture, while rooms in the modern wing are more stereotyped. Front facing rooms have glorious views over neatly kept lawned gardens, swimming pool and the distant New Forest. The ground floor function room has been redecorated.*

23⇆🌢(3fb)1🛏 CTV in all bedrooms ® **T** S10%
sB&B⇆🌢£39.50 dB&B⇆🌢£70 🍴
CTV 60P ❅ CFA ⊇ (heated)
🍴 English & French **V** ✪ ⏛ ✗ Sunday Lunch £8.50 Dinner £12.95&alc Last dinner 9pm
Credit Cards ①③ ⑤

---

**❀❀✗The Three Lions**
Stuckton SP6 2HF ☎(0425)652489

*This cottage-style public house and restaurant – slightly off the beaten track, but discoverable by carefully following signs to Stuckton – has been run for many years now by hospitable hosts June and Karl Wadsack, the preponderance of German and Swedish dishes in its international range reflecting their countries of origin. Décor is a simple mix of pine furniture, lush plants and shining copper and brass, with certificates testifying to the establishment's many awards and achievements proudly displayed on the walls. Two blackboard menus listed a selection of such tempting dishes as Spinach and Edam Strudels, Summer Salad with Smoked Chicken, Sea-bream with Lemon and Lime Glaze and Beef Strogonoff, while an extensive and well compiled wine list offers some excellent vintages.*

Closed Mon, Sun, 22 Dec-8 Jan & 2 wks Jul/Aug
🍴 International 56 seats ✳ Lunch £11-£22.90alc Dinner £18.90-£29.65alc Last lunch 1.30pm Last dinner 9pm 40 P nc14yrs
Credit Cards ①③

---

**★★★ 65%** Roebuck
Wych Cross RH18 5JL (2m S junc A22/A275) (Jarvis)
☎(034282)3811 FAX (034282) 4790

*The well equipped bedrooms of this skilfully extended 16th-century house have recently undergone a complete refurbishment which has resulted in good standards of comfort and décor; staff throughout the hotel are friendly and welcoming.*

28⇆🌢 CTV in all bedrooms ® **T** ✳ sB⇆🌢£66.50 dB⇆🌢£76.50 (room only) 🍴
《 150P ❅ CFA pool table *xmas*

---

🍴 English & French **V** ✪ ⏛ ✳ Lunch £12.25-£14.95 Dinner fr£15.95&alc Last dinner 9.15pm
Credit Cards ①②③④⑤ ⓔ

---

**★★ 65%** Ramnee
Victoria Rd IV36 0BN (Inter-Hotels) ☎(0309)72410
FAX (0309) 73392

*Improvements continue at this well run business and holiday hotel, set in attractive gardens at the east end of town. The popular cocktail bar has been smartly refurbished, while bedrooms provide the expected comforts and facilities.*

20⇆🌢(3fb)1🛏 CTV in all bedrooms ® **T** S%
sB&B⇆🌢£39.50-£47.50 dB&B⇆🌢£58-£75 🍴
CTV 50P ❅ CFA shooting ♘
🍴 Scottish & French **V** ✪ ⏛ Lunch £8.50 Dinner £15&alc Last dinner 9pm
Credit Cards ①②③⑤

---

**★★ 56%** Royal
Tytler St IV36 0EL ☎(0309)72617

*A substantial Victorian building situated in the west end and convenient for the railway station. Public areas offer traditional comforts while the bedrooms provide practical commercial standards.*

20rm(1⇆5🌢)(4fb) CTV in all bedrooms ® **T** sB&B£24-£33 sB&B⇆🌢£33 dB&B£40-£44 dB&B⇆🌢£50 🍴
CTV 40P ❅ CFA pool room
🍴 European **V** ✪ ⏛ Lunch £3-£7 High tea £5-£11 Dinner £3.50-£11&alc Last dinner 8.30pm
Credit Cards ①②③ ⓔ

---

**★★ 65%** *The Brae*
PH32 4DG ☎(0320)6289
Closed Nov-mid Jan

*A small, comfortably appointed hotel, where owners Andrew and Mari Reive are constantly making improvements. There is a relaxing verandah lounge, a well stocked bar, and enjoyable home cooking is served in the candlelit dining rooms. Bedrooms are well equipped, though some are compact.*

8rm(2⇆3🌢)(1fb) CTV in all bedrooms ®
CTV 12P 🚗 ❅ nc7yrs
✗ Last dinner 8.15pm
Credit Cards ①③

---

**★★ 63%** *Caledonian*
PH32 4BQ ☎(0320)6256
Closed Oct-Mar

*A small, welcoming hotel on the main road close to the centre of the village. Improvements here are ongoing, and traditional services and comforts are offered together with good home cooking.*

12rm(2⇆2🌢)(2fb) ® **✈** (ex guide dogs)
CTV 20P ❅
🍴 Scottish & French **V** ✪ ⏛ ✗ Last dinner 9.30pm

---

**★★ 63%** Inchnacardoch Lodge
Loch Ness PH32 4BL (Minotels) ☎(0320)6258
Closed Dec-Mar

*North of the village just off the A82 overlooking Loch Ness, this former hunting lodge offers good value tourist accommodation. The hotel has a relaxing atmosphere, a bar and attractive restaurant. Traditionally appointed bedrooms are mostly spacious.*

16rm(15⇆🌢)(5fb) CTV in 8 bedrooms ® **T** sB&B⇆🌢£30-£55 dB&B£35-£45 dB&B⇆🌢£45-£70 🍴
CTV 40P 2🚗 ❅ CFA
🍴 International **V** ✪ ⏛ ✗ Bar Lunch £5-£12alc Dinner £17.50-£22.50 Last dinner 8.30pm
Credit Cards ①②③⑤ ⓔ

---

**★★61% Lovat Arms**

PH32 4DU ☎(0320)6206 FAX (0320) 6677

*Considerable improvements have taken place at this family-run hotel, situated in a commanding position overlooking the village and Loch Ness. Public rooms include relaxing lounges with open fires and a refurbished lively bar. Bedrooms of varying size and style are all well equipped and comfortable.*

21⇨🛏(4fb) CTV in all bedrooms ® T ✻ sB&B⇨🛏£23.50-£29.50 🍴

CTV 50P ✿ CFA putting *xmas*

V ♥ ⚌ ✻ Sunday Lunch fr£6.50 Dinner £12.50-£16.50 Last dinner 8.45pm

Credit Cards ①③④

---

FORTINGALL Tayside *Perthshire* Map **14** NN74

**★★61% Fortingall**

PH15 2NQ ☎Kenmore(08873)367

RS Nov-Feb

*This friendly family-run village hotel is a popular base for the visiting fisherman and touring holidaymaker alike. It has a relaxed atmosphere and provides traditional services and comforts. Good progress is being made with bedroom improvements.*

9rm(8⇨3🛏)(3fb) CTV in all bedrooms ® T sB&B⇨🛏£28-£35 dB&B£50-£56 dB&B⇨🛏£50-£56 🍴

CTV 15P 5🛏 ✿ ♪ sailing pony trekking

♀ French V ♥ ⚌ ✻ Lunch £4.50-£7 Dinner £15-£17 Last dinner 8.30pm

Credit Cards ①②③ⓔ

---

FORTON MOTORWAY SERVICE AREA (M6) Lancashire Map **07** SD45

**Rank Motor Lodge**

White Carr Ln, Bay Horse LA2 9DU (between juncts 32 & 33) (Rank) ☎Lancaster(0524)792227 FAX (0524) 792241

*Well equipped modern bedrooms and a 24-hour restaurant amid landscaped surroundings are provided at this service area lodge on the northbound carriageway of the M6 between junctions 32 and 33; also accessible to southbound traffic.*

41⇨🛏(21fb)⚟in 7 bedrooms ® ✻ sB&B⇨🛏£29.75 dB&B⇨🛏£37.75 Continental breakfast 60P

♀ English & Continental V ♥ ⚌ ⚟ ✻ High tea £3-£6.05alc Dinner £3-£6.05alc

Credit Cards ①②③⑤

---

FORT WILLIAM Highland *Inverness-shire* Map **14** NN17

★★★★

★★★★★✿✿ 🎖
**INVERLOCHY CASTLE**

PH33 6SN (3m NE A82)
☎(0397)702177
Telex no 776229
FAX (0397) 702953

Closed mid Nov-1 Mar

*Inverlochy Castle has built up a world-wide reputation, not only for its superb setting overlooking Ben Nevis, but for its elegance and hospitality. Few hotels can boast that they succeed in all areas, but this one can. The hotel exudes quality and comfort, apparent from the moment one steps into the elegant wood-panelled hall. The tastefully appointed drawing room and the attractive dining room with its polished tables are equally charming. New chef David Whiffen has brought his own style of cooking, although the cuisine remains basically British. Spacious bedrooms are*

*individually furnished with some fine pieces of furniture, attractive décor and co-ordinating soft furnishing. Mention must be made of the well appointed bathrooms, the majority of which have a separate, superbly high powered shower. The keen young staff are quite professional and well supervised and General Manager Michael Leonard ensures that a high standard is maintained.*

16⇨🛏 CTV in all bedrooms T ✻

《 16P 1🛏 🚗 ✿ ♪ (hard) ♪ snooker

♀ International V ⚌ ⚟

Credit Cards ①②③

---

**★★★✿69% Moorings**

Banavie PH33 7LY (3m N of Fort William off A830) (Exec Hotel) ☎Corpach(0397)772797 FAX (0397) 772441

Closed 24-27 Dec

*This popular family-run business and tourist hotel off the Mallaig road 3 miles from the town enjoys fine views of Ben Nevis from its position beside 'Neptune's Staircase' – a series of steeply graded locks on the Caledonian Canal. Public rooms are full of character, both the lounge and lounge bar being on 2 levels, attractively wood-panelled and decorated to a nautical theme. The restaurant serves food of a praiseworthy standard, its 4-course fixed-price menu featuring British produce, food is also available in the popular Mariner's wine bar, and service is friendly and attentive throughout.*

21⇨🛏Annexe3🛏(1fb)1🏠 CTV in all bedrooms ® T ✻ (ex guide dogs) sB&B⇨🛏£40-£76 dB&B⇨🛏£70-£90 🍴 60P ✿ CFA nc10yrs *xmas*

V ♥ ⚌ ⚟ Lunch £12-£18 Dinner £22&alc Last dinner 9.30pm

Credit Cards ①②③⑤

**See advertisement on page 309**

On the site of the original Hanoverian fort which gave this lovely village its name, close to Loch Ness, the Benedictine Monastery and the Caledonian Canal. The Lovat Arms offers 21 comfortable bedrooms with all modern facilities, a cocktail and public bar, spacious lounges and excellent food with daily changing menu. Half way between Inverness and Fort William and surrounded by some of Scotland's finest scenery it is ideally situated for exploration of the Great Glen with east and west coasts easily accessible.

A warm welcome is assured throughout the year. For further details please contact the resident proprietors:

**Hector and Mary MacLean
Lovat Arms Hotel
Fort Augustus
Inverness-shire PH32 4DU
Tel: 0320 6204/6206 Fax: 0320 6677**

## Fort William

**★★★ 58% Alexandra**
The Parade PH33 6AZ ☎(0397)702241 Telex no 777210
FAX (0397) 705554
*This popular coach tour hotel near the main shopping area is in traditional style with compact bedrooms equipped with modern facilities; those on the front give fine views across Loch Linnhe. The restaurant serves dinner, while the Great Food Shop is open for meals and snacks all day and evening.*
97⇨🌂(8fb) CTV in all bedrooms ® T sB⇨🌂£39-£69
dB⇨🌂£59-£94 (room only) 🅿
Lift ⓒ 50P CFA ♬ *xmas*
♡ Scottish & French V ✪ ⌧ ✕ ✳ Lunch £5-£10 High tea £5-£7 Dinner £6.50-£16 Last dinner 11pm
Credit Cards ①②③⑤

**★★ 62% Imperial**
Fraser's Square PH33 6DW ☎(0397)702040 & 703921
FAX (0397) 706277
Closed 3-31 Jan
*Situated in the town centre with views over Loch Linnhe, this friendly commercial and tour group hotel has undergone considerable refurbishment. Bedrooms provide the expected comforts and facilities and there is a choice of bars and lounges.*
34⇨🌂(3fb) CTV in all bedrooms ® ✳ sB&B⇨🌂£35-£42
dB&B⇨🌂£60-£66 🅿
CTV 20P CFA *xmas*
♡ Scottish & French ✕ ✳ Lunch £1.95-£12alc Dinner £12.50-£13.50&alc Last dinner 9pm
Credit Cards ①③ⓔ

**★★ 62% Nevis Bank**
Belford Rd PH33 6BY (Best Western) ☎(0397)705721
Telex no 94016892 FAX (0397) 706275
*A family-run hotel at the north end of the town with convenient access to Glen Nevis. The Nevis Bank is a popular base for business travellers as well as holidaymakers and climbing enthusiasts. There is a relaxed, informal atmosphere in the substantially refurbished public rooms, and bedrooms are well equipped, though limited in size and furnished in a rather practical style.*
35⇨🌂Annexe8⇨🌂(2fb) CTV in all bedrooms ® T
sB&B⇨🌂£41-£45 dB&B⇨🌂£60-£68 🅿
25P CFA sauna solarium gymnasium *xmas*
♡ Scottish & French V ✪ ⌧ ✳ Bar Lunch fr£7alc Dinner fr£15&alc Last dinner 9pm
Credit Cards ①②③⑤ⓔ

**★★ 60% Grand**
Gordon Square PH33 6DX ☎(0397)702928 FAX (0397) 705060
*A family-owned commercial hotel at the west end of the High Street, also popular with tour groups. Partial refurbishment has enhanced the public rooms, and while the bedrooms are well equipped they are rather practically furnished.*
33⇨🌂(4fb) CTV in all bedrooms ® sB&B⇨fr£26
dB&B⇨fr£48 🅿
ⓒ 20P CFA
V ✪ ⌧ Lunch £7.95-£8.50 Dinner fr£14.95 Last dinner 8.30pm
Credit Cards ①②③⑤ⓔ

**★★ 57% Milton**
North Rd PH33 6TG ☎(0397)702331 Telex no 777210
FAX (0397) 703695
RS Feb-mid Mar
*A popular base for visiting tour groups, this purpose-built holiday hotel is situated by the A82, north of the town centre overlooking Ben Nevis. The refurbished public rooms offer bright modern appointments, while the well equipped bedrooms have practical fitted units.*
56⇨🌂Annexe67⇨🌂(6fb) CTV in all bedrooms ® ✳
sB⇨🌂£34-£49 dB⇨🌂£56-£74 (room only) 🅿
ⓒ 150P

→

F

Scottish & French ✿ ⏴ ✻ High tea £4.50-£6 Dinner £10-£14 Last dinner 8.30pm
Credit Cards 1 2 3 4 5 £

★

★❀ **FACTOR'S HOUSE**

Torlundy PH33 6SN
☎(0397)705767
Telex no 776229
FAX (0397) 702953
Closed 16 Dec-15 Jan RS 16 Jan-14 Mar

*This lovely small hotel, nestling under Ben Nevis, has been expertly converted from what was the estate manager's house. Lovingly owned and run by Peter Hobbs and his caring staff, it offers excellent standards of service and great friendliness. Bedrooms are modern in style and are provided with good facilities. The lounge is a delightfully comfortable room displaying many family heirlooms. A good standard of cooking is offered. The blackboard menu offers a limited choice : 3 starters, 3 main courses, 2 desserts or cheese, and there is a small wine list available. Pancho, the owners' black labrador, a true 'tail-wagger', is everyone's friend and loves guests to take him for a walk – with Peter's permission of course.*

7⇨♠ CTV in all bedrooms T ✖ (ex guide dogs)
CTV 30P 🚗 ❀ ♬ (hard) ✔ sailing nc6yrs
Scottish & Continental Last dinner 9.30pm
Credit Cards 1 2 3 5

❀ ✕**Crannog**
☎(0397)705589 FAX (0397) 705026

*Crannog is a company based on the products of the sea, their operation includes a processing base and smokehouse, and now a speciality seafood restaurant in an ideal waterfront location. The building, converted from the ticket office of MacBrayne's shipping company, has subsequently been extended to provide a no-smoking verandah which takes full advantage of the view of Loch Linnhe. If they have a speciality, it must be the langoustines landed by their own boat. The friendliness here is the best our Inspector has experienced.*
Closed Nov
V 50 seats ✻ Lunch £8.65-£14.40alc Dinner £13.70-£18.40alc Last lunch 3pm Last dinner 10pm 12 P ✂
Credit Cards 1 3

**FOSSEBRIDGE** Gloucestershire Map **04** SP01

★★64% *Fossebridge Inn*
GL54 3JS ☎(0285)720721 FAX (0285) 720793
*Situated beside the river and bird sanctuary in the centre of the village, this historic inn has been tastefully modernised to provide comfortable en suite bedrooms, bars with character and a choice of buttery or more formal dining room. There is an extensive, well tended garden and a sun patio which are pleasant to use in the summer months.*
10⇨♠Annexe4⇨ CTV in all bedrooms ® T
CTV 50P ❀ ✔
English & French V ✿ ⏴ Last dinner 9.30pm
Credit Cards 1 2 3 5

The AA's star rating scheme is the market leader in hotel classification.

**FOUR MARKS** Hampshire Map **04** SU63

⌂**Forte Travelodge**
156 Winchester Rd GU34 5HZ (on A31, northbound) (Forte)
☎Alton(0420)62659 Central Res (0800) 850950
31⇨♠(31fb) CTV in all bedrooms ® sB⇨♠£29.95 dB⇨♠£29.95 (room only)
⏴ 31P 🚗
Credit Cards 1 2 3

**FOWEY** Cornwall & Isles of Scilly Map **02** SX15

★★75% **Marina**
Esplanade PL23 1HY ☎(0726)833315
Closed Nov-Feb
*Built in 1830 as a seaside villa for the Bishop of Truro, the Marina overlooks the Fowey estuary. This splendid view is enjoyed from several of the bedrooms, the neat walled gardens, the dining room and one of the comfortable little lounges. Bedrooms vary in size, they are well maintained and equipped and 4 have their own balconies. There is a high level of friendly service from owners David and Sheila Johns, their Chef Manager Stephen Vincent and the staff; not least their assistance in tackling Fowey's parking problems by providing courtesy transport on check-out.*
11⇨♠ CTV in all bedrooms ® T sB&B⇨♠£37.50-£55.50 dB&B⇨♠£50-£74 🛏
⏴ ✗ 🚗 ✔ windsurfing sailing
English & French V ✿ ✂ Lunch £5&alc High tea fr£3.50 Dinner fr£15.50&alc Last dinner 8.30pm
Credit Cards 1 2 3 5

❀❀ ✕✕*Food for Thought*
The Quay PL23 1AT ☎(0726)832221
*Fresh fish, transformed by the innovative skill of the chef/proprietor, is the speciality of this intimate restaurant set on the quayside of the picturesque Cornish village. Well-flavoured dishes are attractively presented and complemented by a wine list of medium length. Quenelles of Fowey River salmon, and the Rendezvous of freshly caught fish and shellfish with a lobster sauce are two popular choices.*
Closed early Jan-early Feb Lunch not served
French 40 seats Last dinner 9.30pm ✗ nc10yrs
Credit Cards 1 3

**FOWLMERE** Cambridgeshire Map **05** TL44

❀ ✕ ✕**The Chequers Inn**
SG8 7SR ☎(0763)208369
*A small characterful inn dating back to the 16th century, with ancient timbered walls and memorabilia of that era. The very small galleried restaurant offers an imaginative menu, where in addition to a daily roast, dishes such as chicken livers braised in a thick red wine sauce and salmon in a creamy fresh strawberry sauce are featured. Bar meals are also popular.*
Closed 25 Dec
English & French V 30 seats ✻ Lunch £14.25 Dinner £14-£24.30alc Last lunch 2pm Last dinner 10pm 50 P
Credit Cards 1 2 3 5

**FOWNHOPE** Hereford & Worcester Map **03** SO53

★★65% **Green Man Inn**
HR1 4PE ☎(0432)860243 FAX (0432) 860207
*This village inn, originally dating from 1485, has been considerably extended by the present owners. Bedrooms, both those in the main building and the pretty cottage annexe, have excellent modern amenities, and the beamed bars are cosy with open fires.*
10⇨♠Annexe5⇨♠(3fb)1🛏 CTV in all bedrooms ®
CTV 75P ❀ CFA ✔ xmas
✿ ⏴ ✻ Sunday Lunch £8.25 Dinner £4-£11.50 Last dinner 9pm
Credit Cards 1 2 3

FRAMLINGHAM Suffolk Map **05** TM26

**★★ 67% The Crown**

Market Hill IP13 9AN (Forte Hotels) ☎(0728)723521
FAX (0728) 724274

*A well managed hotel which looks on to the market place, with
timbered and beamed lounges. The accommodation is comfortable
and has all modern facilities. This hotel provides a good base for
the leisure user and all amenities for the commercial user.*
14⇦1🛏⊬in 4 bedrooms CTV in all bedrooms ® **T ✳**
sB⇦fr£65 dB⇦£85-£120 (room only) 🍴
30P *xmas*
**V** ۞ ⱬ ⊬ ✳ Lunch fr£9.50&alc Dinner £14.95&alc Last
dinner 9.30pm
Credit Cards 1 2 3 4 5

FRANKLEY MOTORWAY SERVICE AREA (M5) West
Midlands Map **07** SO98

**⬆Granada Lodge**

Illey Ln B32 4AR (3m SE at M5 Service Area) (Granada)
☎021-550 3261 FAX 021-501 2880

*Conveniently set between junctions 3 and 4 of the M5, on the
southbound carriageway, the popular lodge offers well equipped,
good value accommodation; it has its own meeting room, and
meals are available in the adjacent service area's Country Kitchen.*
61⇦🛏(13fb)⊬in 9 bedrooms CTV in all bedrooms ®
🅇 (ex guide dogs) S% sB⇦🛏fr£31 dB⇦🛏fr£34 (room only)
🍴
⊄ 152P

**See advertisement under BIRMINGHAM**

FRASERBURGH Grampian *Aberdeenshire* Map **15** NJ96

**★★ 60% Station**

Seaforth St AB4 5BB ☎(0346)23343 FAX (0346) 23171
*Conveniently situated in the town centre, a busy commercial hotel
which also caters for local functions provides a friendly atmosphere
and tastefully refurbished public areas; bedrooms, though well
equipped, remain plain and functional.*
20rm(3⇦2🛏)(3fb) CTV in all bedrooms ®
⊄ CTV 30P snooker solarium
**V** ۞ ⱬ
Credit Cards 1 2 3 5

FRESHWATER

See **Wight, Isle of**

FRESSINGFIELD Suffolk Map **05** TM27

**❀❀✕Fox & Goose**

IP21 5PB ☎(037986)247 FAX (037986) 8107
*Situated in this pretty village overlooking the church this timbered
inn which dates back to 1509 has recently been taken over by Ruth
and David Watson. The menu has influences from around the
world and many dishes are available as a starter portion or main
course. Our inspector enjoyed a fish soup containing assorted fish
and squid, accompanied by lightly spiced croutons followed by
rump of lamb, pink and served with a creamy broad bean and
rosemary sauce. Desserts included sticky toffee pudding, lemon
curd tart and a range of home-made ice creams and sorbets, but
our inspector found something a bit different too – roast
caramelised bananas with five-pepper ice cream so rich, sweet and
spicy.*
Closed Mon, Tue, 3 wks Sep & 2 wks Xmas
♈ English, French, Italian & Oriental **V** 50 seats Lunch £13-
£18alc Dinner £13-£18alc Last lunch 2pm Last dinner 9.30pm
20 P ⊬

FREUCHIE Fife Map **11** NO20

**★★ 62% Lomond Hills**

Parliament Square KY7 7EY (Exec Hotel)
☎Falkland(0337)57329 & 57498 FAX (0337) 58180
*Set in the centre of this small village, a former coaching inn offers
well equipped bedrooms which vary in size and style.*
25⇦🛏(3fb)1🛏⊬in 3 bedrooms CTV in all bedrooms ® **T**
sB&B⇦🛏£38-£44 dB&B⇦🛏£53-£60 🍴
30P CFA ▱ (heated) sauna solarium gymnasium skittle alley
👶
♈ Scottish & French **V** ۞ ⱬ ⊬ Lunch £10.50-£12.50 Dinner
£14-£16 Last dinner 9pm
Credit Cards 1 2 3 5 ⓔ

FRINTON-ON-SEA Essex Map **05** TM21

**★★ 65% Maplin**

Esplanade CO13 9EL ☎(0255)673832
Closed Jan
*This friendly owner-run Edwardian house on the Esplanade
provides comfortable accommodation, with oak-panelled lounges
and traditionally furnished bedrooms, many of them spacious and
with sea views. The dining room serves reliable, mainly English
dishes and good breakfasts.*
12rm(9⇦1🛏)(2fb) CTV in all bedrooms ® **T ✳** S10%
sB&B£35 sB&B⇦🛏£50 dB&B⇦🛏£80-£85
CTV 12P 🚲 ▱ (heated) nc10yrs *xmas*
**V** ۞ ⱬ ✳ S10% Lunch fr£15.85&alc Dinner fr£18.95&alc Last
dinner 9.30pm
Credit Cards 1 2 3 5

For key to symbols in English see the bookmark.

F

★69% **Rock**
The Esplanade, 1 Third Av CO13 9EQ ☎(0255)677194 & 675173
Closed Jan
*A personal welcome from Ben and Jan Benmore is given at this turn-of-the-century seafront hotel which has bright, clean and well equipped bedrooms and a convivial bar/lounge and wood-panelled dining room.*
6rm(5🌑)(3fb)1🛏 CTV in all bedrooms ® sB&B🌑£46.50-£48.50 dB&B🌑£58-£65
CTV 12P 🚗 solarium
V ✳ Lunch fr£9.95 Dinner fr£15&alc Last dinner 9pm
Credit Cards 1 2 3 5

---

## FROME Somerset Map 03 ST74

★★★62% **Mendip Lodge**
Bath Rd BA11 2HP (Best Western) ☎(0373)63223
Telex no 44832 FAX (0373) 63990
*The public areas of this hotel are in an Edwardian house surrounded by 3.5 acres of gardens and well surfaced car parking, while the bedrooms are in a motel-type block built in the 60s and 70s – smaller and more functional than the original style. Most rooms have superb views towards the Mendip Hills. Marmadukes Restaurant serves a selection of dishes featuring local produce, including imaginative vegetarian options. There are also conference and meeting rooms available.*
40🛏(12fb) CTV in all bedrooms ® T sB&B🛏£55-£61 dB&B🛏£70-£82 Continental breakfast 🍺
《 60P 12🏌 ✿ CFA
🍴 English & French V ♿ 🍷 Lunch £14.50-£17&alc Dinner £14.50-£17&alc Last dinner 9.30pm
Credit Cards 1 2 3 5

★★66% **George**
4 Market Place BA11 1AF ☎(0373)62584 FAX (0373) 51945
*A former coaching inn in the town centre with a friendly, informal atmosphere. Bedrooms have been upgraded to a high standard and the chef produces well prepared dishes on both menus.*
20🛏🌑(3fb)1🛏 CTV in all bedrooms ® T sB&B🛏🌑£43.50-£47 dB&B🛏🌑£55.50-£75 🍺
17🏌 CFA solarium
🍴 English & Continental V ♿ 🍷 ✂ Lunch £3.50-£12 Dinner £11.75&alc Last dinner 9.30pm
Credit Cards 1 2 3 5 £

---

## GAINSBOROUGH Lincolnshire Map 08 SK88

★★65% **Hickman-Hill**
Cox's Hill DN21 1HH ☎(0427)613639
*This privately owned detached Georgian house in the town centre, set in carefully maintained gardens with its own car park, offers modest but attractive accommodation which includes some larger and more comfortable bedrooms. Well cared for furnishings reflect the intimate involvement of the proprietors in the hotel's day-to-day running.*
8rm(3🛏3🌑)(1fb) CTV in all bedrooms ® S% sB&Bfr£38 sB&B🛏🌑fr£38 dB&Bfr£50 dB&B🛏🌑fr£50 🍺
CTV 25P 🚗 ✿ solarium *xmas*
V ♿ 🍷 ✳ Lunch fr£6.50 Dinner fr£10.50&alc Last dinner 9pm
Credit Cards 1 3

---

## GAIRLOCH Highland *Ross & Cromarty* Map 14 NG87

★★★65% **Creag Mor**
Charleston IV12 2AH ☎(0445)2068 FAX (0445) 2044
*Situated south of the village near the fishing harbour, this popular modern hotel has been considerably altered and improved to provide a comfortable base for the visiting holidaymaker and businessman alike. Staff are willing and friendly and there is a choice of bars and restaurants.*
17🛏🌑(1fb) CTV in all bedrooms ® T

《 29P ✿ CFA 🎿 🎵
V ♿ 🍷 ✳ Lunch fr£7 Dinner £16&alc Last dinner 9.30pm
Credit Cards 1 3

★★62% **The Old Inn**
Flowerdale IV21 2BD ☎(0445)2006 FAX (0445) 2445
*A welcoming atmosphere prevails at this former coaching inn overlooking the fishing harbour from a position just south of the village. Well equipped bedrooms provide practical modern appointments, while cosy bars serving real ale reflect much of the original character of the establishment. All-day food is now available in the Old Bridge Bistro, a new development which is proving very popular.*
14🛏🌑(4fb) CTV in all bedrooms ® T sB&B🛏🌑£22.50-£34.50 dB&B🛏🌑£45-£69 🍺
50P 🚗 CFA *xmas*
♿ 🍷 Lunch £6.50-£10.50alc Dinner £16.50&alc Last dinner 9pm
Credit Cards 1 2 3

---

## GALASHIELS Borders *Selkirkshire* Map 12 NT43

★★★67% *Kingsknowes*
Selkirk Rd TD1 3HY ☎(0896)58375
*This impressive Victorian sandstone mansion is situated just south of the town on the A7. The public areas are comfortably elegant, and the bedrooms, although modernised, have retained the original character and comfort.*
11rm(8🛏2🌑)(2fb) CTV in all bedrooms ®
50P 🚗 ✿ ♪ (hard)
V ♿ Last dinner 8.45pm
Credit Cards 1 2 3 4 5

★★★65% **Woodlands Country House Hotel & Restaurant**
Windyknowe Rd TD1 1RG ☎(0896)4722
*Set on a hillside overlooking the town centre, this impressive 19th-century house offers a tranquil atmosphere, comfortable spacious bedrooms and public areas, all well furnished, and interesting menus.*
9🛏🌑(3fb) CTV in all bedrooms ® T sB&B🛏🌑£40-£45 dB&B🛏🌑£65-£70 🍺
30P ✿ CFA
🍴 English & French V ♿ 🍷 Lunch £9.95&alc Dinner £12-£18alc Last dinner 9.30pm
Credit Cards 1 3 £

★★64% **Abbotsford Arms**
63 Stirling St TD1 1BY ☎(0896)2517
Closed 24-25, 31 Dec & 1 Jan
*Situated off the A7 on the fringe of the town centre, this friendly hotel offers comfortable accommodation and an extensive, good value menu available in both bar and restaurant.*
13rm(3🛏6🌑)(2fb) CTV in all bedrooms ® T
🐕 (ex guide dogs) sB&B£24-£26 sB&B🛏🌑£28-£30 dB&B£38-£40 dB&B🛏🌑£45-£50
《 CTV 15P 🚗 CFA
V ♿ 🍷
Credit Cards 1 3 £

---

## GARSTANG Lancashire Map 07 SD44

★★🏳72% **The Pickerings**
Garstang Rd, Catterall PR3 0HA (2m S B6430) ☎(0995)602133
FAX (0995) 602100
RS 26 & 27 Dec
*A small, personally run hotel surrounded by attractive and well maintained gardens. Bedrooms are particularly spacious and equipped to a high standard. The restaurant offers interesting menus which feature fresh local produce and the helpful young staff provide cheerful service.*
14🛏🌑(1fb)3🛏 CTV in all bedrooms ® T 🐕 (ex guide dogs)
sB&B🛏🌑£40-£55 dB&B🛏🌑£50-£95 🍺

50P ✿ *xmas*
♀ English & Continental **V** ✿ ✳ Lunch fr£10 Dinner £17.50-£27.50 Last dinner 10pm
Credit Cards ① ③ ⑤ ⓔ

### ★★68% **Crofters**
Cabus PR3 1PH (A6) (Consort) ☎(0995)604128
*A modern hotel offering well appointed bedrooms, attractive public areas and interesting menus. Service is courteous and friendly.*
19⇌↑(3fb) CTV in all bedrooms ® **T** ✳ sB&B⇌↑£40-£60 dB&B⇌↑£45-£70 ⊟
《 200P CFA ♫ *xmas*
♀ English & French **V** ✿ ✳ Lunch £8.12-£13&alc High tea £5.10-£5.90 Dinner £13&alc Last dinner 10pm
Credit Cards ① ② ③ ⑤ ⓔ

---

GARVE Highland *Ross & Cromarty* Map **14** NH36

### ★★❀64% **Inchbae Lodge**
Inchbae IV23 2PH ☎Aultguish(09975)269
(Rosette awarded for dinner only)
*This former hunting lodge is now a comfortable, family-run hotel providing modestly appointed bedrooms, spacious public areas including a cosy bar, and imaginative, well cooked food.*
6rm(3⇌)Annexe6↑(2fb) ® sB&B⇌↑£30.50-£32.50 dB&B£51-£55 dB&B⇌↑£51-£55 ⊟
30P ⊟ ✿ ✔ clay pigeon shooting *xmas*
♀ Scottish & French ✿ ⚐ Bar Lunch £3-£15alc High tea £3-£15alc Dinner £16.95 Last dinner 8.30pm
ⓔ

---

GATEHOUSE OF FLEET Dumfries & Galloway
*Kirkcudbrightshire* Map **11** NX55

### ★★★★66% **Cally Palace**
DG7 2DL ☎Gatehouse(0557)814341 Telex no 777088
FAX (0557) 814522
Closed 3 Jan-Feb
*Set in peaceful rural surroundings and with excellent views, this impressive country house has been sympathetically decorated and furnished to maintain some of its original splendour. There are a number of lounges with fine reproduction furniture, and the well appointed restaurant offers sound cooking from table d'hôte and à la carte menus. Attractive, refurbished bedrooms vary in size, but all are well equipped and comfortable. The hotel now has an indoor swimming pool.*
55⇌(7fb)1⊞ CTV in all bedrooms ® **T** sB&B⇌£44.50-£51.50 dB&B⇌£95-£113 ⊟
Lift 《 100P ⊟ ✿ CFA ⊡ (heated) ♪ (hard) ✔ sauna solarium croquet putting green ♫ *xmas*
♀ Scottish & French **V** ✿ ⚐ ✂ Lunch £8-£10.50 Dinner fr£18 Last dinner 9.30pm
Credit Cards ① ③

**See advertisement on page 315**

### ★★★65% **Murray Arms**
DG7 2HY ☎Gatehouse(0557)814207 FAX (0557) 814370
*A comfortable hotel with a relaxing atmosphere and friendly, courteous staff. In addition to the good value dinner menu there is an all day food operation offering a good range of hot and cold dishes.*
12⇌Annexe1⇌(3fb) CTV in all bedrooms ® **T** S10% sB&B⇌£40-£45 dB&B⇌£80-£90 ⊟
《 CTV 50P ✿ CFA croquet *xmas*
**V** ✿ ⚐ Bar Lunch £3-£10alc High tea £3.50-£9alc Dinner £16-£17.50 Last dinner 8.45pm
Credit Cards ① ② ③ ⑤ ⓔ

A rosette means exceptional standards of cuisine.

G

---

**GATESHEAD** Tyne & Wear Map **12** NZ26 ⊙

★★★ 66% **Swallow**
High West St NE8 1PE (Swallow) ☎091-477 1105
Telex no 53534 FAX 091-478 7214
*Situated just off the southern approach to Newcastle, this modern hotel offers spacious accommodation.*
103⇄↑(12fb)⊱in 19 bedrooms CTV in all bedrooms ® T ✳
sB&B⇄↑£72.50 dB&B⇄↑£85 🍴
Lift ⓒ 90P 100🚗 ⊡ (heated) sauna solarium gymnasium spa bath steam room ♫ *xmas*
♀ International V ♥ ⚏ ✳ Lunch £9.50-£11&alc Dinner £16.50-£18.50&alc Last dinner 10pm
Credit Cards ①②③④⑤ €

★★★ 63% **Springfield**
Durham Rd NE9 5BT (Jarvis) ☎091-477 4121 Telex no 538197
FAX 091-477 7213
*Well equipped accommodation – the bedrooms in the new wing being of a very high standard, though those in the original building are beginning to show their age – is provided by a friendly and popular hotel which stands beside the A6127 2 miles south of Newcastle city centre.*
60⇄↑(4fb)⊱in 7 bedrooms CTV in all bedrooms ® T S15%
sB⇄↑£65-£90 dB⇄↑£80-£100 (room only) 🍴
Lift ⓒ CTV 100P CFA *xmas*
♀ English & French V ♥ ⚏ ⊱ S% Lunch £5-£10.95 Dinner £13.95 Last dinner 9.30pm
Credit Cards ①②③④⑤ €

★★ ✿74% **Eslington Villa**
8 Station Rd, Low Fell NE9 6DR ☎091-487 6017
FAX 091-482 2359
Closed 25 Dec-2 Jan RS Sun evenings
*An Edwardian villa in a residential area of Gateshead houses this popular and attractive hotel whose owner, Mr Tulip has recently added a conservatory to increase the capacity of his restaurant. Both Mr Tulip and chef, Alan O'Nial previously worked at the Fisherman's Lodge in Newcastle, and fish frequently feature on the table d'hôte and à la carte menus in such dishes as steamed cabbage layered with fresh and smoked salmon; lightly curried monkfish; or prawns baked in filo pastry and served with fresh asparagus and cream sauce. The food is always enjoyable, but some dishes can be over-ambitious, with flavours competing not complementing each other. Main courses are accompanied by a large selection of vegetables, and this too can sometimes seem over-generous. Puddings are rich and delicious, who, for example, could resist the impressive panaché of dark, milk and white chocolate desserts and sauces. Staff are both pleasant and professional.*
12⇄↑(2fb)⊞ CTV in all bedrooms ® T sB&B⇄↑£35-£65 dB&B⇄↑£45-£75
ⓒ 15P 🚗 ✿
♀ English & French ⊱ Lunch £10.95-£12.50&alc Dinner £18.50-£21&alc Last dinner 10pm
Credit Cards ①②③⑤ €

---

**GATWICK AIRPORT (LONDON)** West Sussex
Map **04** TQ24

See **Town Plan Section** under **London Airports**
See also **Burgh Heath, Dorking, East Grinstead, Reigate and South Godstone**

★★★★ 67% **Copthorne**
Copthorne Rd RH10 3PG (on A264 2m E of A264/B2036 rbt)
☎Copthorne(0342)714971 Telex no 95500 FAX (0342) 717375
*Only minutes from the airport, this busy hotel is built around a 16th-century farmhouse in 100 acres of farm and woodland and offers excellent conference, leisure and function facilities. Public areas with beams, quarry floors and open fires include a bar lounge and pub and there is a choice of modern bedrooms, with the executive wing also housing a restaurant and self-service carvery.*
227⇄↑(10fb)4⊞⊱in 34 bedrooms CTV in all bedrooms ® T
sB⇄↑£98-£118 dB⇄↑£108-£118 (room only) 🍴
Lift ⓒ CTV 300P ✿ CFA squash sauna solarium gymnasium croquet putting petanque pit *xmas*
♀ English & Continental V ♥ ⚏ ✳ Lunch £15.10-£22&alc Dinner £16-£30&alc Last dinner 10.30pm
Credit Cards ①②③⑤ €

★★★★ 65% **Copthorne Effingham Park**
West Park Road, Copthorne RH10 3EU
☎Copthorne(0342)714994 Telex no 95649 FAX (0342) 716039
*An hotel set in 40 acres of lovely parkland and gardens provides spacious, well equipped accommodation, a few rooms having balconies and some being specially adapted to the needs of disabled guests. There are two restaurants – the relaxed McLaren Restaurant offering various light and carvery meals in a room adjoining the lounge bar, and the Wellingtonia, with its more formal service and dress requirements, standing in a delightful garden setting. Charlie's Bar Lounge forms part of the leisure club on the lower ground floor, and here, too, guests can enjoy a drink and light snack; this leisure and golf club is open to guests daily by appointment. Other amenities include a smart shop and a beauty and hairdressing salon.*
122⇄↑(6fb)⊱in 27 bedrooms CTV in all bedrooms ® T ✳
sB⇄↑£98-£118 dB⇄↑£108-£118 (room only) 🍴
Lift ⓒ 500P ✿ CFA ⊡ (heated) ▶ 9 sauna solarium gymnasium dance studio jacuzzi plunge pool ♫
♀ English & French V ♥ ⚏ ⊱ Lunch £16.95-£19.95&alc Dinner £8.50-£35alc Last dinner 10.30pm
Credit Cards ①②③⑤ €

★★★ 68% **Holiday Inn**
Langley Dr RH11 7SX (Holiday Inns Inc)
☎Crawley(0293)529991 Telex no 877311 FAX (0293) 515913
*Recently refurbished throughout, with major new features including the Crest Sensations Leisure Club and indoor pool, the prestigious Colonnade restaurant, La Brasserie, a cocktail lounge and a business centre. Function rooms are nearly complete, and the choice of compact bedrooms includes Lady Crest and Executive. Service is well-managed and helpful.*
223⇄↑(9fb)⊱in 45 bedrooms CTV in all bedrooms ® T
S10% sB⇄↑fr£65 dB⇄↑fr£65 (room only) 🍴
Lift ⓒ ▶ CFA ⊡ (heated) snooker sauna solarium gymnasium jacuzzi steam rooms games room pool *xmas*
V ♥ ⚏ ⊱ Lunch £12.50-£12.95 High tea £1.45-£5 Dinner £17.50&alc Last dinner 11pm
Credit Cards ①②③④⑤

★★★ 63% **Forte Crest**
Povey Cross Rd RH6 0BA (Forte Hotels) ☎Horley(0293)771621
Telex no 877351 FAX (0293) 771054
*This busy purpose-built hotel is geared to business and airport traffic, offering comfortable bedrooms equipped with up-to-date facilities, a restaurant with table d'hôte and à la carte menus, a coffee shop, lounge bar, room service and a courtesy airport bus service which operates at all hours.*
216⇄↑⊱in 165 bedrooms CTV in all bedrooms ® T ✳
sB⇄↑fr£75 dB⇄↑fr£85 (room only) 🍴
Lift ⓒ 300P ✿ CFA ⌂ (heated) *xmas*
♀ European V ♥ ⚏ ⊱ Lunch £10.50&alc High tea £8.50-£14.50 Dinner £14.50&alc Last dinner mdnt
Credit Cards ①②③④⑤

★★★ 63% *Goffs Park*
45 Goffs Park Road, Crawley RH11 8AX
☎Crawley(0293)535447 Telex no 87415 FAX (0293) 542050
*Situated in a residential area south of Crawley, this busy commercial hotel convenient for the airport has modernised well equipped bedrooms and a spacious restaurant with a modestly priced table d'hôte menu plus à la carte dishes. Pleasant staff offer attentive service.*
37⇄↑Annexe28⇄↑ CTV in all bedrooms ® T
ⓒ 92P
♀ English & French V ♥ ⚏ Last dinner 9.30pm
Credit Cards ①②③⑤

G

★★★62% **The George**
High St RH10 1BS (Forte Hotels) ☎Crawley(0293)524215
Telex no 87385 FAX (0293) 548565
*This traditional inn, with its rare gallows sign spanning the High*
*Street of Crawley's town centre, has a pleasant, recently*
*refurbished lounge/bar and a choice of well equipped bedrooms*
*between the modern extension and the original beamed building.*
*The Shires restaurant serves regional specialities.*
86⇨♠(3fb)2🛏✕in 43 bedrooms CTV in all bedrooms ® T ✱
sB⇨♠fr£70 dB⇨♠£90-£110 (room only) ☐
« 89P CFA *xmas*
V ✿ ⬚ ✕ ✻ Lunch fr£10.50&alc Dinner fr£14.25&alc Last
dinner 10pm
Credit Cards ①②③④⑤

★★★60% **Chequers Thistle**
Brighton Road, Horley RH6 8PH (Mount Charlotte (TS))
☎Horley(0293)786992 Telex no 877550 FAX (0293) 820625
*Though extended and modernised, this Tudor coaching inn retains*
*much of its original charm in the Halfway Halt Buttery and Bar,*
*and a welcoming fire still burns in the foyer lounge during the*
*winter months. All public areas have recently been refurbished, and*
*bedrooms are consistently comfortable and well equipped, even if*
*slightly compact. A courtesy bus service to the airport is available*
*for guests' convenience.*
78⇨♠(54fb)✕in 5 bedrooms CTV in all bedrooms ® T ✖
(room only) ☐
« 190P ⌂ (heated)
♥ International ✿ ⬚ ✕
Credit Cards ①②③④⑤

★★★59% **Gatwick Concorde**
Church Rd, Lowfield Heath, Crawley RH11 0PQ (Queens Moat)
☎Crawley(0293)533441 Telex no 87287 FAX (0293) 535369
*This purpose-built hotel has good access to the airport – some*
*rooms even overlook the runway. Bedrooms are well maintained*
*and equipped with modern facilities. The hotel offers a large and*
*popular bar restaurant, and a similar lounge area.*
121⇨♠(7fb) CTV in all bedrooms ® T S% sB⇨♠£49.50-£75
dB⇨♠£56-£90 (room only) ☐
Lift « ⊞ 137P (£2.70 per night) CFA
♥ English, French & Italian V ✿ ⬚ ✕ ✱ Lunch £8.50-
£10.95alc Dinner £12.95-£16.95alc Last dinner 9.30pm
Credit Cards ①②③⑤ⓔ

★★61% **Gatwick Manor**
London Rd, Lowfield Heath, Crawley RH10 2ST (Chef &
Brewer) ☎Crawley(0293)526301 & 535251 Telex no 87529
*A skilfully extended building, dating back to the 13th century and*
*set in its own grounds, provides adequate standards of comfort in*
*its well equipped, functional bedrooms ; public areas include two*
*Berni Restaurants where reliable menus are complemented by*
*good service, and a conference/banqueting suite. Car parking*
*facilities are extensive, and a courtesy coach service is available for*
*guests' use.*
30⇨♠(3fb) CTV in all bedrooms ® T ✖ (ex guide dogs)
sB&B⇨♠£73 dB&B⇨♠£81 ☐
« CTV 250P ❋
♥ International V ✿ ⬚ ✕ Bar Lunch £2.95-£5.50alc
Credit Cards ①②③⑤

If you have booked a
restaurant meal and cannot get there,
remember you have a contractual obligation
to cancel your booking.

G

★⊛ **LANGSHOTT MANOR**

Ladbroke Rd RH6 9LN
☎Crawley(0293)786680
FAX (0293) 783905

*Langshott Manor is a
beautiful Grade II listed
Elizabethan manor, lovingly
restored by Geoffrey and
Patrica Noble, who, with the enthusiastic help of their son
Christopher, have transformed it into an intimate and popular
retreat. The 5 bedrooms are delightfully individual, warm and
nicely styled with antiques, traditional furnishings and objets
d'art which blend well with the extensive modern comforts.
The en suite rooms are particularly spacious, bright and
efficient, yet full of Victorian charm and character. Each
bedroom boasts a library of reading material and a profusion
of fresh and dried flowers. The public rooms are equally
commendable; oak-panelled cosy lounges are warmed by open
fires, and are richly furnished by chesterfields and period
pieces. There are two dining rooms; one with an enormous
communal mahogany table – popular in such small hospitable
surroundings, and another giving more privacy. Hearty fresh
food is nicely prepared and there is a small, well chosen wine
list. The property itself is tucked away down a quiet country
lane amid small gardens, yet is very convenient for Gatwick
airport.*

5⇌ CTV in all bedrooms **T** ✗ (ex guide dogs) sB⇌£83
dB⇌£98 (room only) 🚭

CTV 18P 🚗 ✿ croquet

♡ English & French Lunch £15-£22 High tea £7.50 Dinner
£18.50-£25.50 Last dinner 9.30pm

Credit Cards ①②③⑤£

---

**GERRARDS CROSS** Buckinghamshire Map **04** TQ08

★★61% **Ethorpe**

Packhorse Rd SL9 8HY (Chef & Brewer) ☎(0753)882039
FAX (0753) 887012

*On the edge of the town stands a very busy steak house with a
bustling, popular bar and a relaxed atmosphere. Accommodation is
provided in tastefully decorated, comfortably furnished and well
equipped bedrooms.*

29⇌ℕ(4fb)🚽 CTV in all bedrooms ® **T** ✗ (ex guide dogs)
sB&B⇌ℕ£72-£81 dB&B⇌ℕ£88 🚭

℄ 80P ✿ CFA

♡ International **V** ♡ ☑ ✗ Bar Lunch £2.95-£5.50alc
Credit Cards ①②③⑤

---

**GIFFNOCK** Strathclyde *Renfrewshire* Map **11** NS55

★★★63% **Macdonald Thistle**

Eastwood Toll G46 6RA (Mount Charlotte (TS)) ☎041-638 2225
Telex no 779138 FAX 041-638 6231

*Thoughtfully equipped accommodation is provided at this modern
business hotel which stands beside the A77 on the southern
outskirts of the city; its friendly atmosphere and choice of 3 bars
also make it a popular venue for local functions.*

56⇌ℕ(1fb) CTV in all bedrooms ® **T** (room only) 🚭

℄ 200P sauna solarium gymnasium games room

♡ International ♡ ☑ ✗
Credit Cards ①②③④⑤

**See advertisement under GLASGOW**

---

**GIFFORD** Lothian *East Lothian* Map **12** NT56

★★71% *Tweeddale Arms*

EH41 4QU (Consort) ☎(062081)240

*This character village hotel offers good modern comforts combined
with old world charm and traditional hospitality. The smart
restaurant serves British and Continental cuisine. Bedrooms are
comfortable and well equipped and the relaxing lounge has an
inviting log fire when the weather demands it.*

15⇌ℕ(2fb) CTV in all bedrooms ®

🎱 snooker

**V** ♡ ☑ Last dinner 9pm

Credit Cards ①②③

---

**GILLAN** Cornwall & Isles of Scilly Map **02** SW72

★★62% *Tregildry*

TR12 6HG ☎Manaccan(032623)378

Closed 15 Oct-Etr

*Imaginative menus of well cooked dishes are offered at this family-
run hotel with elevated views over Falmouth Bay.*

10⇌ℕ(2fb) CTV in 6 bedrooms ®

CTV 20P 🚗 ✿

♡ International ♡ ☑ ✗ Last dinner 8.30pm

Credit Cards ①③

---

**GILLINGHAM Dorset** Map **03** ST82

★★

★★⊛⊛🛏
**STOCK HILL HOUSE**

Stock Hill SP8 5NR
☎(0747)823626
FAX (0747) 825628

Closed 1 wk in summer RS
Sun dinner, Mon

*Set in mature grounds at the
end of a beech-lined drive, this immaculate country hotel is a
perfect retreat. It is run with infinite loving care by Peter and
Nita Hauser, helped by delightful staff who all work together
to provide a uniquely happy atmosphere. Public rooms abound
with antiques, objects d'art, and fresh flowers, all richly
combined with extravagant ornamental décor. The
comfortable bedrooms are individually styled, cleverly
furnished, and abounding in swathes of attractive fabrics. The
Victorian garden provides much of the produce for Peter
Hauser's spotless kitchen – herbs and vegetables all year,
edible flowers and soft fruits during the summer. The robust
cuisine combines an Austrian background with French country
influences – the honest flavours speak for themselves. A dish
of spicy crab quenelles set on a bed of vegetables and served
with a rich creamy tomato sauce was very successful – almost
irreverant. It was an ideal prelude to a full-flavoured casserole
of Dorset hare, served with excellent home-made noodles. The
4-course dinner includes a soup, and might end with a choice
of tempting Austrian desserts, such as a Viennese Punsch
Torte drenched in rum. Wines are supplied mainly by the local
merchant, Robin Yapp, who specialises in wines from the Loire
and Rhône.*

8⇌ℕ1🛏 CTV in all bedrooms **T** ✗ ✳ sB&B⇌ℕ£80-£85
dB&B⇌ℕ£160-£170 (incl dinner)

25P 🚗 ✿ ♫ (hard) croquet nc7yrs *xmas*

♡ English, Austrian & French **V** ✗ ✳ Lunch £18.50
Dinner £26.50 Last dinner 8.45pm

Credit Cards ①③

**G**

## GILLINGHAM Kent Map **05** TQ76 ⊝

⇧**Rank Motor Lodge**
Rainham ME8 8PQ (Rank) 🕾Medway(0634)377337
FAX (0634) 360848
(For full entry see Farthing Corner Motorway Service Area (M2))

## GIRVAN Strathclyde *Ayrshire* Map **10** NX19

★★63% **King's Arms**
Dalrymple St KA26 9AE 🕾(0465)3322
*This family-run hotel places the emphasis on good food and friendly service, whilst golfing cocktails such as 'The Perfect Slice' are a feature of the Bunker bar. Recently upgraded, the bedrooms have en suite facilities.*
25⇆🛏🛇(4fb) CTV in all bedrooms ® **T** 🛏 (ex guide dogs)
sB&B⇆🛏£35 dB&B⇆🛏£50 🏴
《 100P 1🏊 (£2) CFA snooker *xmas*
🖤 Scottish & French **V** ⊗ ⊒
Credit Cards [1] [3] £

## GISBURN Lancashire Map **07** SD84

★★★❀65% **Stirk House**
BB7 4LJ (Consort) 🕾(0200)445581 Telex no 635238
FAX (0200) 445744
*This extended 16th-century manor house set in pleasant countryside just off the A59 has comfortable public rooms in the old building and modern bedrooms in the new wing. An elegant dining room offers good cuisine, and conference and banqueting facilities are available, plus indoor leisure activities.*
36⇆🛏Annexe12⇆(2fb)1🛏 CTV in all bedrooms ® **T**
🛏 (ex guide dogs) S10% sB&B⇆🛏£60.50-£71.50
dB&B⇆🛏£72.60-£82.50 🏴
《 100P ✿ CFA 🔲 (heated) squash sauna solarium gymnasium 🎵
🖤 English & French **V** ⊗ ⊒ ⊬ S10% Lunch £11.30-£13
Dinner £18.70&alc Last dinner 9.30pm
Credit Cards [1] [2] [3] [4] [5] £

## GITTISHAM Devon Map **03** SY19

★★★❀♨68% **Combe House**
EX14 0AD (Pride of Britain) 🕾Honiton(0404)42756 & 43560
FAX (0404) 46004
RS Jan-Feb
(Rosette awarded for dinner only)
*This large and impressive Elizabethan manor, managed by the same family for the past 30 years as a relaxed, friendly, country house hotel, features interesting individual touches throughout. The comfortable, comprehensively equipped bedrooms are generally spacious, though bathrooms vary in size, and a praiseworthy restaurant offers an imaginative and well presented range of such seasonal dishes as Autumn Terrine served with Crab Apple Jelly or Magret of Duck accompanied by a Sweet and Sour Sauce flavoured with Ginger. A long-serving staff – for whom nothing seems too much trouble – provide pleasant service.*
15⇆2🛏 CTV in all bedrooms **T** S12.5% sB&B⇆£62-£90
dB&B⇆£95-£120 🏴
50P 1🏊 (£2.50 per night) ⚅ ✿ ♪ croquet *xmas*
🖤 English & French **V** ⊗ S12.5% High tea fr£3.50 Dinner fr£21alc Last dinner 9.30pm
Credit Cards [1] [2] [3] [5]

## GLAMIS Tayside *Angus* Map **15** NO34

★★★♨71% *Castleton House*
DD8 1SJ 🕾(030784)340 FAX (030784) 506
Closed 1 Jan
*This welcoming and unpretentious country house hotel is set in 11 acres of gardens and woodland beside the A94 and is an ideal base*

*for holidaymaker and business traveller as well as the sporting enthusiast. Individually styled bedrooms have been thoughtfully equipped and feature luxury bathrooms. Public rooms with log fires invite relaxation and the attractive new conservatory restaurant has an interesting menu of well prepared dishes.*
6⇆🛏 CTV in all bedrooms ® **T** 🛏 (ex guide dogs)
15P ⚅ ✿ putting green
🖤 European **V** ⊗ ⊒ ⊬ Last dinner 9.30pm
Credit Cards [1] [2] [3]

## GLASGOW Strathclyde *Lanarkshire* Map **11** NS56 ⊝

See **Town Plan Section**
★★★★68% **Moat House International**
Congress Rd G3 8QT (Queens Moat) 🕾041-204 0733
Telex no 776244 FAX 041-221 2022
*This high-rise, mirrored glass hotel beside the Scottish Exhibition and Conference Centre – a prominent feature of the city redevelopment scheme – commands unrestricted river views from open-plan public areas which contain reception, lounges, bars, and the locally popular Mariner Restaurant (booking advisable at weekends). Amenities include a decent sized swimming pool, a small shop and abundant meeting/function rooms; friendly staff provide capable service throughout.*
284⇆🛏(45fb)⊬in 40 bedrooms CTV in all bedrooms ® **T** ✳
S% sB&B⇆🛏fr£56 dB&B⇆🛏fr£67 🏴
Lift 《 ⊞ CTV 300P ✿ 🔲 (heated) sauna solarium gymnasium
🎵 *xmas*
🖤 International **V** ⊗ ⊒ ⊬ ✳ Lunch £12.50-£14.50&alc Dinner
£12.50-£25&alc Last dinner 10.30pm
Credit Cards [1] [2] [3] [4]

For key to symbols in English see the bookmark.

G

# Glasgow

### ★★★★64% **Stakis Grosvenor**

1/10 Grosvenor Ter, Great Western Rd G12 0TA (Stakis)
☎041-339 8811 Telex no 776247 FAX 041-334 0710

*Helpful, attentive service and well equipped, spacious
accommodation with all up-to-date facilities are provided by a
modern commercial/conference hotel with helpful, attentive staff.
Public areas – though limited, and suffering from soft furnishings
and décor that look a little tired – are comfortable, including a
spacious lounge bar and an attractively appointed restaurant which
offers both table d'hôte and à la carte menus of adequately
prepared dishes.*

95⇌🌊(12fb)1🌊in 50 bedrooms CTV in all bedrooms ®
sB⇌🌊£93.45-£103.95 dB⇌🌊£109.20-£119.70 (room only) ▤
Lift ℂ 12P 70🛌 CFA
♀ French **V** ✿ ☑ ✂
Credit Cards ①②③④⑤

### ★★★★62% **Holiday Inn Glasgow**

Argyle St, Anderston G3 8RR (Holiday Inns) ☎041-226 5577
Telex no 776355 FAX 041-221 9202

*A popular commercial hotel which is undergoing complete
refurbishment throughout the public areas, which when complete
will provide modern, comfortable accommodation. Bedrooms are
spacious, comfortable and well equipped and staff are friendly and
efficient.*

298⇌🌊(80fb)✂in 38 bedrooms CTV in all bedrooms ® T
S10% sB⇌🌊fr£110 dB⇌🌊fr£130 (room only) ▤
Lift ℂ ⊞ 180P CFA ▱ (heated) squash sauna solarium
gymnasium heated whirlpool *xmas*
♀ European **V** ✿ ☑ ✂
Credit Cards ①②③④⑤

### ★★★★60% **Forte Crest**

Bothwell St G2 7EN (Forte Hotels) ☎041-248 2656
Telex no 77440 FAX 041-221 8986

*Situated in the city this busy conference and commercial hotel also
caters well for private guests. Bedrooms vary in size and there is a
choice of an à la carte restaurant and a carvery, the latter due for
complete refurbishment.*

251⇌🌊(32fb)✂in 54 bedrooms CTV in all bedrooms ® T ✳
sB⇌🌊fr£90 dB⇌🌊fr£100 (room only) ▤
Lift ℂ ⊞ 65P 600🛌 CFA ♬ *xmas*
♀ Scottish & French **V** ✿ ☑ ✂ ✳ Lunch £16.50&alc Dinner
£19.50&alc Last dinner 10pm
Credit Cards ①②③④⑤

### ★★★★59% **Hospitality Inn**

36 Cambridge St G2 3HN (Mount Charlotte (TS))
☎041-332 3311 Telex no 777334 FAX 041-332 4050

*This modern city-centre hotel, offering spacious bedrooms and
improving public areas which include both a restaurant and an
informal café, is much used by visitors – both famous and
otherwise – to the nearby television centre.*

307⇌🌊(3fb) CTV in all bedrooms ® (room only) ▤
Lift ℂ 250🛌 *xmas*
♀ Scottish, American & Danish **V** ✿ ☑
Credit Cards ①②③④⑤

---

★★★

★★★❀❀

ONE DEVONSHIRE GARDENS

1 Devonshire Gardens
G12 0UX ☎041-339 2001 &
041-334 9494
FAX 041-337 1663

*In the fashionable residential
west end, the original no 1 has
expanded to include no 2 and
no 3, and provides the most elegant and spacious*

---

*accommodation in the city, with bold décor, lovely French-
made cherrywood furniture, fine prints and multi-function
audio and video systems. Room service is a treat, charming
staff arrive with butler's trays and lay items out on available
tables. The 6-foot baths are luxurious, with marble surrounds
and large well lit mirrors. With the expansion, more lounge
space is available to residents and the public areas have a
regular local clientèle, particularly the restaurant, where chef
Andrew Fleming attracts customers with his modern classic
interpretations using excellent Scottish produce. Owner Ken
McCulloch believes that the customer is king and no request,
within reason, will go unattended, and we warmly
congratulate him for what he has achieved. At times, though,
we would like some of the staff to answer the doorbell more
quickly.*

18⇌🌊(2fb)6🌊 CTV in all bedrooms
ℂ 8P 🚲
♀ French ✿ ☑ Last dinner 10pm
Credit Cards ①②③④⑤

---

### ★★★❀73% **Town House**

West George St G2 1NG ☎041-332 3320 FAX 041-332 9756

*Although set right in the city centre, this small elegant hotel is
reminiscent of a superior country house; it has a quiet relaxed
atmosphere and retains many original architectural features.
Bedrooms match the style of the building, are very comfortable and
extremely well equipped.*

34⇌(2fb)2🌊✂in 10 bedrooms CTV in all bedrooms ® T
✖ (ex guide dogs) ✳ S10% sB⇌fr£80 dB⇌fr£91 (room only)
▤
Lift ℂ CFA *xmas*
**V** ✿ ☑ ✂ ✳ S10% Lunch fr£10.50&alc Dinner fr£19 Last
dinner 9.45pm
Credit Cards ①②③⑤ £

### ★★★71% **Copthorne Hotel**

George Square G2 1DS ☎041-332 6711 Telex no 778147
FAX 041-332 4264

*An hotel adjacent to Queen Street station, though completely
upgraded since its North British Hotel days, nevertheless retains
some fine traditional features from that era – notably the
spaciously lofty Connoisseur bedrooms and suites with their grand
period pieces. Well equipped bedrooms are modern in style and
more compact, while open-plan public areas include a restaurant
with popular café bar and a cosy conservatory area overlooking
George Square; morning coffee and afternoon tea are served in a
similar conservatory off Reception, and the cocktail lounge is
always open. A friendly staff provides attentive service throughout.*

141⇌🌊(1fb)1🌊✂in 14 bedrooms CTV in all bedrooms ® T
✖ (ex guide dogs) ✳ S% sB⇌🌊fr£82 dB⇌🌊fr£94 (room
only) ▤
Lift ℂ ♪ CFA *xmas*
♀ International **V** ✿ ☑ ✂ ✳ S% Lunch fr£13.95 Dinner
fr£14.95&alc Last dinner 10.30pm
Credit Cards ①②③⑤ £

### ★★★66% **Glasgow Crest**

377 Argyle St G2 8LL (Forte Hotels) ☎041-248 2355
Telex no 779652 FAX 041-221 1014

*This modern high-rise hotel, conveniently situated at the heart of
the city, provides a popular base for visiting businessmen.
Bedrooms are well equipped – though in some cases rather
compact – and the atmosphere is friendly.*

121⇌🌊✂in 79 bedrooms CTV in all bedrooms ® T
✖ (ex guide dogs) ✳ sB⇌🌊£79-£93 dB⇌🌊£91-£105 (room
only) ▤
Lift ℂ ♪ CFA *xmas*
♀ Continental **V** ✿ ☑ ✂ ✳ Lunch fr£9.25 Dinner £15.95 Last
dinner 9.45pm
Credit Cards ①②③④⑤

★★★ 66% **Tinto Firs Thistle**
470 Kilmarnock Rd G43 2BB (Mount Charlotte (TS))
☎041-637 2353 Telex no 778329 FAX 041-633 1340
*Purpose-built to provide well equipped bedrooms and a
comfortable cocktail lounge, this business and function hotel stands
beside the A77 on the south side of the city.*
28⇨♠(4fb)⊁in 2 bedrooms CTV in all bedrooms ® T (room
only) ⊟
《 46P ❀
♀ International ✿ ⚲ ⊬
Credit Cards ①②③④⑤

★★★ 63% **Kelvin Park Lorne**
923 Sauchiehall St G3 7TE (Queens Moat) ☎041-334 4891
Telex no 778935 FAX 041-337 1659
*A recently refurbished hotel situated in the west end within easy
reach of the Scottish Exhibition and Conference Centre appeals
particularly to the visiting businessman. Public areas offer modern
appointments and all bedrooms are well equipped although they
vary in size, the best being contained in the Aspley Wing.*
98⇨♠(7fb)2🛏⊁in 20 bedrooms CTV in all bedrooms ® T ✱
sB⇨♠£67.50-£140 dB⇨♠£78.50-£170 (room only) ⊟
Lift 《 40🏧 CFA ♫ *xmas*
♀ Scottish & French V ✿ ⚲ S% Lunch £7.50-£18&alc Dinner
£14.95-£25&alc Last dinner 10.30pm
Credit Cards ①②③④⑤ ④

★★★ 62% **Swallow**
517 Paisley Rd West G51 1RW (Swallow) ☎041-427 3146
Telex no 778795 FAX 041-427 4059
*Close to the M8, this purpose-built hotel has smart public areas, a
leisure centre and well equipped bedrooms of varying size and
style. The car park is security-patrolled.*
119⇨♠(1fb)⊁in 34 bedrooms CTV in all bedrooms ® T ✱
sB&B⇨♠fr£77 dB&B⇨♠fr£88 ⊟
Lift 《 150P ☒ (heated) sauna solarium gymnasium *xmas*
♀ English & French V ✿ ⚲
Credit Cards ①②③⑤

★★★ 61% **Sherbrooke**
11 Sherbrooke Av, Pollokshields G41 4PG ☎041-427 4227
FAX 041-427 5685
*In a residential area close to the M77, this popular family-run
commercial hotel, converted from a baronial mansion, gives good
views across the city and has been considerably refurbished in
recent years. Bedrooms vary, with some in a modern chalet-style
annexe and adjacent bungalow, but all are well equipped.*
10⇨♠Annexe11⇨♠(3fb)⊁in 2 bedrooms CTV in all
bedrooms ® T
《 CTV 50P ❀ CFA
♀ English & French V ✿ ⚲ ⊬ ✱ Lunch fr£8.50&alc High tea
fr£5.50&alc Dinner fr£16.50&alc Last dinner 10pm
Credit Cards ①②③⑤ ④
**See advertisement on page 321**

★★★ 60% **Jurys Pond**
Great Western Rd G12 0XP ☎041-334 8161 Telex no 776573
FAX 041-334 3846
*A purpose-built hotel and leisure centre, offering convenient access
to the northwest from its position just off the A82, provides
comfortable, well equipped bedrooms and seating throughout the
day in the two main bars though actual lounge facilities are
limited.*
134⇨♠(6fb)⊁in 55 bedrooms CTV in all bedrooms ® T ✱
sB⇨♠£42.45-£79 dB⇨♠£54.90-£89 (room only) ⊟
Lift 《 CTV 200P ❀ CFA ☒ (heated) sauna solarium
gymnasium *xmas*
♀ Scottish & European V ✿ ⚲ ⊬ ✱ Lunch £6.95&alc High
tea £6.25 Dinner £14.50&alc Last dinner 10pm
Credit Cards ①②③⑤ ④

## Glasgow - Glasgow Airport

### ★★★60% **Stakis Ingram**

Ingram St G1 1DQ (Stakis) ☎041-248 4401 Telex no 776470
FAX 041-226 5149

*A city centre hotel with accommodation geared mainly to the
business person. There is a restaurant and carvery.*

90⇔🏳(1fb)✗in 62 bedrooms CTV in all bedrooms ® T
sB⇔🏳£76.65-£87.15 dB⇔🏳£89.25-£99.75 (room only) 🖿

Lift ( ✗ CFA *xmas*

𝒱 Scottish, English & French **V** ✿ 🕮 ✗
Credit Cards ①②③⑤

### ★★★58% **Central**

99 Gordon St G1 3SF (Consort) ☎041-221 9680 Telex no 777771
FAX 041-226 3948

*This long established businessman's hotel is located in the heart of
the city, and is also a popular conference venue. It has been
substantially refurbished and offers a choice of lounges, a Carvery
restaurant and well equipped, modern bedrooms.*

221⇔🏳(10fb)✗in 60 bedrooms CTV in all bedrooms ® T
sB⇔🏳£55.75-£66 dB⇔🏳£70.50-£80.75 (room only) 🖿

Lift ( CFA 🖾 (heated) sauna solarium gymnasium hair &
beauty salon steamroom *xmas*

𝒱 European **V** ✿ 🕮 ✗ ✳ Lunch £9.75&alc Dinner £12&alc
Last dinner 9.30pm

Credit Cards ①②③⑤ ④

### ★★★64% **Ewington**

132 Queens Dr, Queens Park G42 8QW ☎041-423 1152
FAX 041-422 2030

*Substantially refurbished, and offering both well equipped
accommodation and a friendly atmosphere, this popular business
and tourist hotel is situated in a south side terrace overlooking
Queen's Park.*

45rm(36⇔🏳)(1fb)✗in 6 bedrooms CTV in all bedrooms ® T
✳ sB&B⇔🏳£49.50-£60 dB&B⇔🏳£76.50-£85 🖿

Lift ( 18P CFA snooker

𝒱 International **V** ✿ 🕮 ✳ Lunch £6.50-£10&alc High tea fr£6
Dinner fr£11.75&alc Last dinner 9pm

Credit Cards ①②③⑤ ④

### ❀ ✗✗**Buttery**

652 Argyle St G3 8UF ☎041-221 8188 FAX 041-204 4639

*This restaurant – its very civilised atmosphere and fine dining room
and lounge bar providing a Victorian oasis in a desert of inner city
development – remains very much a part of the city scene, as
popular as ever with both the business and 'personality' sectors.
Chef Stephen Johnson's cooking is unmistakably modern. The
dishes' descriptions promise some complicated, occasionally
bizarre combinations of ingredients and flavours; 'Fillet of beef on
a dark walnut and hazelnut sauce with a toasted sesame seed
yogurt' proved too nutty for the succulent beef, but simpler dishes
such as 'Wild mushroom raviolis in an English mustard and
tarragon sauce' proved successful. Desserts have included a
steamed pudding, a fruity crème brulée and a passion-fruit and
blackcurrant cheesecake on a vanilla pod cream. Service is
supervised by manager Jim Wilson who has a good rapport with
regulars.*

Closed Sun & BH's Lunch not served Sat

𝒱 Scottish & French **V** 50 seats Lunch fr£14.25&alc Dinner
£22.05-£33.45alc Last lunch 2.30pm Last dinner 10.30pm 30 P

Credit Cards ①②③⑤

### ❀❀ ✗✗*Killermont House Restaurant*

2022 Maryhill Rd, Maryhill Park G20 0AB ☎041-946 5412

*Set in its own grounds well back from the road, this tastefully
converted former manse now contains a restaurant (occupying two
rooms) and a small but comfortable lounge where aperitifs and
coffee are served, these surroundings combining with the attention
of fully involved hosts Mr and Mrs Abrami to create a country
house atmosphere. The à la carte selection of dishes reflects an
Italian/French influence, in contrast to the more traditional fixed-
price lunch and dinner menus, but the emphasis throughout is on*

*quality fresh ingredients, good honest flavours and attractive
presentation.*

Closed Mon & last wk Jul-1st wk Aug Lunch not served Sat
Dinner not served Sun

𝒱 French 60 seats Last lunch 2.15pm Last dinner 10pm 22 P

Credit Cards ①②③

### ❀❀ ✗✗*Rogano*

11 Exchange Place G1 3AN ☎041-248 4055 & 041-248 4913
FAX 041-248 2608

*A long established restaurant which still retains the aura of the
'30s has a good reputation for its seafood now, as it did then –
though its meat and game dishes are every bit as enjoyable. Chef
Jim Kerr brings a delicate touch to his cooking, allowing flavours
to 'breathe', a quality illustrated in his Steamed Scallops with
Spinach and Champagne Cream, the Sautée of Monkfish Tails
with Almonds and Oysters and a beautifully smooth Game Terrine
with Onion Marmalade which is rich in flavour yet still light in
texture. Desserts such as Baked Lemon Tart, Rich Caramel
Parfait or Bitter chocolate and Pistachio Cream make a refreshing
change from the predictable trolley range of sweets. Pre-dinner
drinks can be obtained from the bar – but this is a popular
rendezvous and a table may not always be available.*

Closed BH's Lunch not served Sun

**V** 50 seats ✳ Lunch £25-£35alc Dinner £25-£35alc Last lunch
2.30pm Last dinner 10.30pm ✗

Credit Cards ①②③⑤

### ❀ ✗*Mitchells*

North St, Charing Cross ☎041-204 4312

*Mitchells is one our our Best New Restaurants award winners this
year. Two split-level areas below a busy bistro and bar make up
this cosy little restaurant with its friendly, relaxing atmosphere
and service which strikes the right balance between formality and
informality. Chef/proprietor Robin Grey's market garden on the
Isle of Arran supplies the kitchen with its fresh produce, and he
brings an honest country influence to the modern style of cooking.
A good value table d'hôte menu augmented by a short à la carte
selection and a blackboard list of daily 'specials' feature Scottish
game, meats and seafood regularly in season, and lovers of good
soup will not be disappointed – the Crab Bisque being particularly
worthy of note. (See colour feature on p40.)*

P

---

**GLASGOW AIRPORT** Strathclyde *Renfrewshire*
Map **11** NS46

### ★★★★50% **Forte Crest**

Abbotsinch, Paisley PA3 2TR (Forte Hotels) ☎041-887 1212
Telex no 777733 FAX 041-887 3738

*A multi-storey hotel adjacent to the airport, with compact but well
sound-proofed bedrooms and a choice between a restaurant serving
à la carte meals and – better value – a carvery. Refurbishment is
overdue, but staff are helpful and friendly.*

297⇔🏳(9fb)✗in 158 bedrooms CTV in all bedrooms ® T ✳ S%
sB⇔🏳fr£75 dB⇔🏳£90-£116 (room only) 🖿

Lift ( 🖩 40P CFA solarium 🎵 *xmas*

**V** ✿ 🕮 ✗ ✳ S% Lunch £15.95&alc Dinner £15.95&alc Last
dinner 11pm

Credit Cards ①②③④⑤

### ★★★67% **Forte Posthouse Glasgow**

North Barr PA8 6AN (Forte Hotels) ☎041-812 0123
Telex no 777713 FAX 041-812 7642
(For full entry see Erskine)

### ★★★66% **Stakis Normandy**

Inchinnan Rd, Renfrew PA4 9EJ (2m NE A8) (Stakis)
☎041-886 4100 Telex no 778897 FAX 041-885 2366

*This large purpose-built hotel with a courtesy airport bus service
has extensive banqueting and function facilities. There are two
restaurants, the main one offering an impressive buffet/carvery at
both lunch and dinner. Bedrooms are compact and well equipped
and staff throughout are cheerful and attentive.*

141⇌♠(3fb)⊬in 16 bedrooms CTV in all bedrooms Ⓡ
sB⇌♠£76.65-£87.15 dB⇌♠£86.10-£96.60 (room only) 🖪
Lift ℂ 350P CFA golf driving range
♡ International ✿ ⏛
Credit Cards ①②③⑤

★★★ 62% **Glynhill Hotel & Leisure Club**
Paisley Rd PA4 8XB (2m E A741) ☎041-886 5555
Telex no 779536 FAX 041-885 2838
*Situated within easy reach of both airport and motorway, a
popular business, function and conference hotel which has
undergone major refurbishment offers tastefully appointed, well
equipped bedrooms, a choice of bars and restaurants, and extensive
leisure facilities.*
125⇌♠(40fb)2🛏⊬in 74 bedrooms CTV in all bedrooms Ⓡ T
sB&B⇌♠£60-£90 dB&B⇌♠£70-£100 🖪
ℂ 200P 30🚗 CFA ▣ (heated) snooker sauna solarium
gymnasium spa bath steam room ♫ *xmas*
♡ International V ✿ ⏛ ⊬ ✳ S10% Lunch £9-£10&alc Dinner
£12.95-£18&alc Last dinner 10.30pm
Credit Cards ①②③⑤ⓕ

★★★ 61% **Dean Park**
91 Glasgow Road, Renfrew PA4 8YB (3m NE A8) (Queens
Moat) ☎041-886 3771 Telex no 779032 FAX 041-885 0681
*A purpose-built commercial hotel lying between Renfrew and
junction 27 of the M8. All bedrooms are equally well equipped
though some have more modern furnishings and fittings than
others.*
120⇌♠(4fb) CTV in all bedrooms Ⓡ T sB&B⇌♠£66-£76
dB&B⇌♠£86-£96
ℂ 200P ✿ CFA solarium
♡ French V ✿ ⏛ ⊬ ✳ Lunch £8.25-£9.50 Dinner £12.95&alc
Last dinner 9.45pm
Credit Cards ①②③⑤

**★★**62% **Rockfield**

125 Renfrew Road, Paisley PA3 4EA (2m SE off A741)
☎041-889 6182 FAX 041-889 9526

*This informally friendly commercial hotel beside the A741 on the outskirts of Paisley, half a mile off the M8 at junction 27, offers modestly appointed but well equipped bedrooms and a good range of honest, home-cooked meals.*

20⇨↑(1fb)1⊞ CTV in all bedrooms ® T sB&B⇨↑fr£44 dB&B⇨↑fr£66

50P CFA

♀ European ✿ ⚹ Bar Lunch £2.25-£4.50 High tea £4.75-£7.85 Dinner fr£11.50&alc Last dinner 9.30pm

Credit Cards ①②③⑤ £

---

**★★**63% **George & Pilgrims Hotel & Restaurant**

1 High St BA6 9DP (Resort) ☎(0458)31146 FAX (0458) 32252
14⇨↑(1fb)3⊞ CTV in all bedrooms ® T ✽ sB&B⇨↑£45-£65 dB&B⇨↑£62-£82 ⊞

⊞ 5P CFA

V ✿ ⚹ ✽ Lunch fr£4.75 High tea fr£3.25 Dinner fr£6.50 Last dinner 10.30pm

Credit Cards ①②③⑤

---

❀❀✕✕ **Number Three Restaurant & Hotel**

3 Magdalene St BA6 9EW ☎(0458)32129

Closed Sun, Mon & 3 wks Jan Lunch not served all wk

♀ English & French V 28 seats Dinner £26 Last dinner 9pm 8 P ⚹

Credit Cards ①③

---

❀❀✕✕ *Barrett's*

31 Egremont St CO10 7SA ☎(0787)281573

*Behind the somewhat ordinary façade of this restaurant – originally a Victorian shop – lies a cosy, elegant interior where guests can enjoy a regularly changed, imaginative menu based on carefully selected local produce and flavoured with home-grown herbs. A well-balanced choice of fresh, light dishes includes Red Mullet with Warm Herbs, and Moist Sliced Breast of Pheasant on a Tangy Orange Sauce, with unusual between-course tempters. Hospitable proprietors personally supervise the attentive service offered by their staff.*

Closed Mon & 10 days Jan Lunch not served Tue-Sat
Dinner not served Sun

18 seats Last lunch 2pm Last dinner 9.30pm 10 P

Credit Cards ①③

---

**★★**61% **Glencoe**

PA39 4HW ☎Ballachulish(08552)245 & 673 FAX (08552) 492

*This long established Highland holiday hotel is situated beside the A82, at the west end of the village. Public areas offer comfortable modern appointments while the well equipped bedrooms are being considerably enhanced following recent refurbishment.*

15⇨↑(4fb) CTV in all bedrooms ® T ✽ sB&B⇨↑£39.50-£44 dB&B⇨↑£55-£64 ⊞

30P ✿ CFA games room ♪ xmas

V ✿ ⚹ ⚹ ✽ Bar Lunch £3.50-£5.50alc Dinner £17-£25 Last dinner 9.30pm

Credit Cards ①②③⑤ £

---

Restaurants and hotel restaurants
with rosettes have their names and addresses
tinted pink in the directory.

---

See Auchterarder

---

**★★**60% **Bein Inn**

PH2 9PY ☎(05773)216

*Set in picturesque Glenfarg, this former drovers' inn is a popular base for the businessman, tourist and sporting enthusiast. It offers an interesting blend of the old and new, and has a relaxed atmosphere. The best bedrooms are located in the annexe.*

9rm(7⇨)Annexe4⇨↑ CTV in all bedrooms ® T
✖ (ex guide dogs) sB&Bfr£33 sB&B⇨↑fr£36.50 dB&Bfr£45 dB&B⇨↑fr£50 ⊞

60P ⊞ ✿ xmas

♀ Scottish, English & French V ✿ ⚹ Lunch £5-£14&alc Dinner £12.50-£22alc Last dinner 9.30pm

Credit Cards ①③ £

**See advertisement under PERTH**

---

**★★**60% **Glenfarg**

Main St PH2 9NU ☎(05773)241

*This friendly family-run hotel in the village centre has been refurbished to provide good-value, comfortable accommodation and home-cooked meals largely using local produce.*

15⇨↑(2fb) CTV in all bedrooms ® ✽ sB&B⇨↑fr£23.50 dB&B⇨↑fr£47 ⊞

39P ✿ CFA xmas

V ✿ ⚹ ⚹ ✽ Bar Lunch £2.50-£7.25 High tea fr£5.45 Dinner fr£12.95 Last dinner 9pm

Credit Cards ①②③⑤ £

---

**★★**64% **Glenridding**

CA11 0PB (Best Western) ☎(07684)82228 FAX (07684) 82555
Closed 4-23 Jan

*A friendly family-run hotel in the village centre with fine views of Ullswater and the surrounding fells. Bedrooms are variable in shape and size but all have en suite facilities and are well equipped. The hotel is upgraded continually, the main lounge has recently been refurbished and by the time this guide goes to press other public areas will have been expanded and additional conference facilities provided.*

44⇨↑(6fb)2⊞ CTV in all bedrooms ® T sB&B⇨↑£41-£45 dB&B⇨↑£66-£72 ⊞

Lift 40P xmas

V ✿ ⚹ ⚹ Bar Lunch fr£5.25 Dinner £18.50-£19.50 Last dinner 9.30pm

Credit Cards ①②③⑤

---

**★★★**72% *Balgeddie House*

Balgeddie Way KY6 3ET ☎(0592)742511 FAX (0592) 621702
Closed 1 & 2 Jan

*A family-run and immaculately maintained mansion, popular with the business sector, enjoys a fine open outlook from its position northwest of the town; best access is via the A91 and B969 then up Formonthills Road through a housing estate. The spacious original accommodation is augmented by smaller conversions – all rooms being equally well equipped – and there is a separate pub serving bar food as well as the cocktail bar and lounge.*

18⇨↑(3fb) CTV in all bedrooms ® T ✖ (ex guide dogs)
CTV 100P ✿ ∪ pool table

♀ English & French V ✿ ⚹ Last dinner 9.30pm

Credit Cards ①②③

---

A rosette means exceptional standards of cuisine.

G

## ★★75% **Rescobie**

Valley Dr, Leslie KY6 3BQ ☎(0592)742143 FAX (0592) 620231

*Set in 2 acres of gardens in a quiet residential area, this period mansion is run as a small country house hotel. Popular with business people during the week for its good standard of cooking, friendly attentive service, cosy little bar and modern bedroom facilities.*

10⇨🛏 CTV in all bedrooms ® T ✣ (ex guide dogs)
sB&B⇨🛏 frf48 dB&B⇨🛏£60-£70 🖪
20P 🚗 ✿ ⚙

🍴 International V ✿ ⚗ ✳ Lunch £6.75-£8.85 Dinner £14&alc
Last dinner 9pm
Credit Cards ① ② ③ ⑤

## ★★53% *Greenside*

High St, Leslie KY6 3DA (2m W A911) ☎(0592)743453
FAX (0592) 756341
Closed 1 Jan

*Managed by the resident proprietors, this small hotel caters mainly for commercial visitors.*

12⇨🛏 CTV in all bedrooms ®
《 50P

🍴 English & French V ✿
Credit Cards ① ② ③

---

**GLENSHEE (SPITTAL OF)** Tayside *Perthshire*
Map **15** NO16

## ★★🏩64% **Dalmunzie House**

PH10 7QG ☎Glenshee(025085)224 FAX (025085) 225
Closed Nov-27 Dec

*An attractive, turreted house, situated in 6,000 acres of its own private glen with hills rising steeply to either side, offers a river in which guests may fish, as well as a 9-hole golf course. Very much the home of its proprietors, who welcome guests warmly, it is a great favourite with families – a splendid collection of bar games old and new compensating for the fact that the only television set is in the lounge – many bedrooms have lovely views, and all are refreshing in their décor and furnishing. Local staff help to create a friendly and informal atmosphere. Attractive ski packages are available in winter – the slopes of Glenshee being only 15 minutes away – but services and facilities are slightly curtailed during this season.*

17rm(15⇨🛏) sB&B£39-£44 sB&B⇨🛏£41-£46 dB&B£58-£74
dB&B⇨🛏£60-£76 🖪

Lift CTV 30P 2🚗 🚗 ✿ ▶ 9 ♫ (hard) ♪ clay pigeon shooting *xmas*

V ✿ ⚗ Bar Lunch £5-£7 Dinner £17 Last dinner 8.30pm
Credit Cards ① ③ ⓔ

## ★58% *Dalrulzion Highland*

PH10 7LJ ☎Blacklunans(025082)222

*A former hunting lodge, this small family-run roadside hotel caters for touring holidaymakers and winter ski enthusiasts. It offers a friendly atmosphere, simple practical bedrooms and public rooms that have benefited from partial refurbishment.*

12rm(5⇨🛏)(4fb) CTV in 7 bedrooms ® ✣ (ex guide dogs)
CTV 60P ✿ ♪ hang gliding pony trekking shooting ♬

🍴 Scottish & Continental V ✿ ⚗ Last dinner 9pm
Credit Cards ③

---

**GLENSHIEL (SHIEL BRIDGE)** Highland *Ross & Cromarty*
Map **14** NG91

## ★★64% **Kintail Lodge**

IV40 8HL ☎Glenshiel(059981)275 FAX (059981) 226
Closed 24 Dec-2 Jan RS Nov-Mar

*Improvements continue at this former shooting lodge, set on the shore of Loch Duich and surrounded by magnificent scenery. Bedrooms – many of which enjoy fine loch views – vary in shape and size but are generally comfortably if modestly furnished. Light*

→

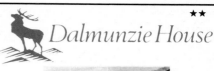

G

*lunches and teas are served in a conservatory which has now been added to the inviting public areas already existing.*

12rm(7⇨3🏠)(2fb) CTV in all bedrooms ® S% sB&B£40-£48 sB&B⇨🏠£42-£51 dB&B£80-£96 dB&B⇨🏠£84-£102 (incl dinner) 🛏

20P ⇖ ❋

♀ Scottish & French **V** ❖ ⚗ ✂ ✻ Lunch £10-£12alc Dinner £17-£20 Last dinner 8.30pm

Credit Cards ⬜1⬜ ⬜3⬜

---

**GLOSSOP** Derbyshire Map **07** SK09

**★★73% Wind in the Willows**

Derbyshire Level, off Sheffield Rd SK13 9PT (A57)
☎(0457)868001 FAX (0457) 853354

*Comfort, quality and a relaxed atmosphere are the hallmarks of this Victorian country house, pleasantly set in 5 acres of grounds adjacent to the local golf course. Traditional furnishings and open fires enhance the atmosphere of relaxed comfort.*

8⇨3🏠(1fb) CTV in all bedrooms ® **T** ✘ (ex guide dogs) ❋ sB&B⇨🏠£56-£76 dB&B⇨🏠£66-£98

CTV 12P ⇖ ❋ nc10yrs

❖ S% Dinner fr£18.95 Last dinner 7.30pm

Credit Cards ⬜1⬜ ⬜2⬜ ⬜3⬜

---

**GLOUCESTER** Gloucestershire Map **03** SO81 ⊙

**★★★❀❀76% Hatton Court**

Upton Hill, Upton St Leonards GL4 8DE (3m SE B4073)
☎(0452)617412 Telex no 437334 FAX (0452) 612945

*An ivy-clad 17th-century manor house has been carefully restored and extended to provide modern hotel facilities in beautiful surroundings. The comfortable bedrooms are situated in the main house and an adjacent wing and offer thoughtful extras such as fresh fruit and magazines. In the dining room chef Stuart Beard's imaginative food is complemented by a very extensive wine list.*

18⇨🏠 Annexe28⇨🏠2☷ CTV in all bedrooms ® **T** ✘ (ex guide dogs) sB&B⇨🏠£78-£88 dB&B⇨🏠£98-£118 🛏

《 75P ❋ CFA ⇔ (heated) croquet *xmas*

♀ English & French **V** ❖ ⚗ Lunch fr£15&alc Dinner £25-£35alc Last dinner 10pm

Credit Cards ⬜1⬜ ⬜2⬜ ⬜3⬜ ⬜5⬜ ⓔ

**★★★68% Gloucester Hotel & Country Club**

Robinswood Hill GL4 9EA (2.5m SE off B4073) (Jarvis)
☎(0452)525653 Telex no 43571 FAX (0452) 307212

*Set off the B4073, 3 miles south of the city centre, directly opposite Gloucester Ski Club, an hotel and leisure complex which has been completely refurbished over the past few years, now offers three types of very well equipped bedrooms, a choice of restaurants, good conference facilities and extensive indoor and outdoor leisure amenities.*

97⇨🏠Annexe10⇨🏠(11fb)✂in 15 bedrooms CTV in all bedrooms ® **T** S% sB⇨🏠£91.50-£102 dB⇨🏠£102-£112 (room only) 🛏

《 CTV 300P ❋ CFA ⊠ (heated) ▶ 18 ♟ (hard) squash snooker sauna solarium jacuzzi dry skiing skittle alley ♫ *xmas*

♀ English & French **V** ❖ ⚗ Lunch fr£13.50&alc Dinner £17.75&alc Last dinner 10pm

Credit Cards ⬜1⬜ ⬜2⬜ ⬜3⬜ ⬜5⬜ ⓔ

**★★★66% Forte Crest**

Crest Way, Barnwood GL4 7RX (Forte Hotels) ☎(0452)613311 Telex no 437273 FAX (0452) 371036

*Situated on the Barnwood bypass, 2 miles from the city centre, this modern hotel has recently been completely refurbished and now offers attractive open-plan public areas and comfortable well equipped bedrooms. There is a good indoor leisure centre and facilities for business meetings.*

123⇨🏠(30fb)✂in 80 bedrooms CTV in all bedrooms ® **T**

《 200P ❋ CFA ⊠ (heated) sauna solarium gymnasium spa pool steam room games area

♀ European **V** ❖ ⚗ ✂ ✻ Lunch fr£9.95&alc Dinner fr£17&alc Last dinner 10.15pm

Credit Cards ⬜1⬜ ⬜2⬜ ⬜3⬜ ⬜5⬜

**★★★61% Hatherley Manor**

Down Hatherley Ln GL2 9QA ☎(0452)730217 Telex no 437353 FAX (0452) 731032

*This 17th-century manor house, located beside the A38 close to junction 11 of the M5, offers accommodation with a good range of modern facilities – though rooms vary in size, some doubles being rather compact. Extensive function and conference facilities are available.*

56⇨🏠1☷ CTV in all bedrooms ® **T** ✘ (ex guide dogs)

《 350P ⇖ ❋ gymnasium

♀ English & French **V** ❖ ⚗ Last dinner 9.45pm

Credit Cards ⬜1⬜ ⬜2⬜ ⬜3⬜ ⬜4⬜ ⬜5⬜

**★★66% New County**

Southgate St GL1 2DU ☎(0452)307000 FAX (0452) 500487

*At the time of our inspection, this city-centre hotel was in the final stages of a complete refurbishment. Accommodation is well equipped with modern facilities designed with the business traveller in mind. Although there is no car park, there are public car parks within two minutes' walk.*

31⇨🏠(3fb) CTV in all bedrooms ® **T** ✘ (ex guide dogs)

《

**V** ❖ ⚗ Last dinner 9.30pm

Credit Cards ⬜1⬜ ⬜2⬜ ⬜3⬜ ⬜5⬜

**★★64% Twigworth Lodge**

Tewkesbury Rd, Twigworth GL2 9PG ☎(0452)730266 FAX (0452) 730099

*One mile north of the A40 roundabout on the A38 stands a Regency house which has been extended and converted to create a modern business hotel with well equipped bedrooms, a popular restaurant and an indoor swimming pool.*

30⇨🏠(3fb) CTV in all bedrooms ® **T** ❋ sB&B⇨🏠£45-£60 dB&B⇨🏠£62-£74 🛏

50P ❋ CFA ⊠ (heated)

♀ European **V** ❖ ⚗ ✻ Lunch £11.25-£21.75alc Dinner fr£10&alc Last dinner 10pm

Credit Cards ⬜1⬜ ⬜2⬜ ⬜3⬜ ⬜5⬜

**★64% Rotherfield House**

5 Horton Rd GL1 3PX ☎(0452)410500

*Situated off the A417 close to the city centre, this extended Victorian house offers comfortable public rooms and well equipped bedrooms, some with good en suite facilities. Friendly and attentive services are provided by the resident proprietors Alan and Juliet Eacott.*

13rm(8🏠)(2fb) CTV in all bedrooms ® sB&B£18.45-£27.75 sB&B🏠£27.75 dB&B🏠£37.55 🛏

CTV 9P ⇖

♀ English & Continental **V** ❖ ⚗ ✂ Lunch £7-£12alc Dinner £8.45&alc Last dinner 7.45pm

Credit Cards ⬜1⬜ ⬜2⬜ ⬜3⬜ ⬜5⬜ ⓔ

**○Bowden Hall Resort**

Bond End Ln, Upton St Leonards GL4 8ED (Resort)
☎(0452)614121

Open

72⇨🏠

---

**GLYN CEIRIOG** Clwyd Map **07** SJ23

**★★★62% Golden Pheasant**

LL20 7BB ☎(069172)281 FAX (069172) 281

*Parts of this hotel date back over 200 years, although extensive modern additions have been made in more recent times. Attractive public areas are complemented by well equipped bedrooms, all with en suite facilities.*

G

18⇨🚿(4fb)3⊞ CTV in all bedrooms ® **T** S10% sB&B⇨🚿£35.20-£59.50 dB&B⇨🚿£65.50-£108 ⊟
45P ❊ CFA ∪ game shooting during season ⌂ *xmas*
☋ English, French & Italian **V** ♧ ☕ Lunch £9.50 High tea £3.50-£5.50 Dinner £17.95-£19.95 Last dinner 9pm
Credit Cards [1] [2] [3] [5] £

**GOATHLAND** North Yorkshire Map **08** NZ80

**★★ ❀ 74% Mallyan Spout**
YO22 5AN ☎Whitby(0947)86206 & 86341
*Standing in its own grounds on the fringe of the unspoilt village, this attractive stone building celebrates its centenary in 1992. Prettily decorated bedrooms have modern facilities and caring service is provided by proprietors, Peter and Judith Heslop. Besides a wide range of bar meals, interesting good-value menus are offered in the intimate restaurant where freshly cooked dishes feature local produce.*
24rm(22⇨)(4fb)2⊞ CTV in all bedrooms **T** ✱ sB&B⇨£40-£50 dB&B⇨£60-£100 ⊟
50P ❊ CFA ⌂ *xmas*
☋ English & French **V** ♧ ☕ ⅟ ✱ Lunch fr£9.50 Dinner fr£17.50&alc Last dinner 8.30pm
Credit Cards [1] [2] [3] [5] £

**★★ 70% Inn On The Moor**
YO22 5LZ ☎Whitby(0947)86296 FAX (0947) 86484
*Situated in a moorland village, this traditionally styled hotel provides comfort in peaceful surroundings, with good lounges and well equipped bedrooms. Family-owned and run the inn offers good value and friendly service.*
24⇨🚿(2fb)4⊞ CTV in all bedrooms ® **T** sB&B⇨🚿£30-£50 dB&B⇨🚿£60-£80 ⊟
CTV 30P ❊ CFA croquet lawn hairdressing salon
**V** ♧ ☕ Lunch fr£7.50&alc High tea fr£2alc Dinner fr£12.50alc Last dinner 8.30pm
Credit Cards [1] [2] [3]

**★ 64% Whitfield House**
Darnholm YO22 5LA (Guestaccom) ☎Whitby(0947)86215
Closed 3 Nov-27 Feb
*Tucked away in a corner of the tiny village, this small friendly hotel offers neat if compact accommodation.*
9rm(2⇨6🚿)(1fb)⅟in all bedrooms ® sB&B⇨🚿£20 dB&B⇨🚿£40
CTV 10P ⊞ nc3yrs
♧ ☕ ⅟ Dinner £9.50-£13.50 Last dinner 6.30pm

**GODALMING** Surrey Map **04** SU94

**❀ ✕✕ Lakeview Restaurant**
Inn On The Lake, Ockford Rd GU7 1RH ☎(0483)415575 FAX (0483) 860445
*An elegant and attractively decorated restaurant, centred round an ornamental pond with fish and a fountain, overlooks the lake from an elevated position. The lounge and cocktail bars offer a comfortable setting in which to peruse a short à la carte selection and two fixed-price menus of dishes in modern British style, prepared with flair and representing excellent value for money. Popular choices include a terrine of lobster and scallops wrapped in spinach leaves, cutlets of lamb lightly crumbed with herbs on a Port sauce and escalope of salmon in a white wine and shallot sauce. An imaginative range of sweets contains delights like coffee parfait on a vanilla sabayon and tulip basket filled with a light chocolate soufflé on an orange sauce; filter, cappuccino or espresso coffee are available, a mainly European wine list of reasonable length accompanies the meal, and service is both friendly and attentive.*
☋ International **V** 80 seats ✱ Lunch £10.50-£15.50&alc Dinner £10.50-£15.50&alc Last lunch 2pm Last dinner 10pm 100 P
Credit Cards [1] [2] [3] [5]

Mallyan Spout Hotel

★★
Goathland, Whitby
N Yorkshire
YO22 5AN
Telephone:
(0947) 86206

1892-1992

A stone-built, ivy clad building situated on the green of a beautiful Yorkshire village overlooking the wide expanses of the famous moors. The hotel takes its name from a small picturesque waterfall flowing into a wooded valley, a short walk below the hotel. Three spacious lounges command a view of the garden, moors and the beautiful Esk Valley, and in the winter you are warmed by roaring fires. Mallyan Spout is an ideal location for outdoor pursuits or the peaceful pleasures of the fine food, good wines and friendly hospitality. 26 cottage style bedrooms with private bath including 4 new rooms with balconies and superb views.

★★★

HATHERLEY MANOR

Imagine you are on the edge of the Cotswolds in a 17th Century Manor House, set in nearly forty acres of pastoral beauty.

*SOUNDS IDYLLIC?*

Once completely moated, Hatherley Manor boasts many unique Jacobean features, and a beautiful walled garden. Yet tucked away behind all this splendour is a highly efficient Conference and Banqueting facility for anything from a small Company 'pow-wow' to a large AGM.

Perfectly situated for exploring the Cotswolds and within ten minutes of the Cathedral City of Gloucester and Regency Cheltenham.

Access to our little corner of Gloucester-shire could not be easier, we are just 4 miles from Junction 11 of the M5, on the A38 between Gloucester and Tewkesbury.

## GOLANT Cornwall & Isles of Scilly Map 02 SX15

### ★★64% Cormorant
PL23 1LL ☎Fowey(072683)3426
*Set above the picturesque fishing village and overlooking the Fowey Estuary, this small hotel offers friendly and attentive service and comfortable accommodation. There are magnificent views from all the bedrooms and the spacious lounge, and a wide choice of food is served in the intimate restaurant.*
11⇨⅄in 1 bedroom CTV in all bedrooms ® T
sB&B⇨£43.50-£53.50 dB&B⇨£62-£72 ⋒
24P ⇔ ❀ ⊠ (heated) nc10yrs *xmas*
♀ French V ❖ ⚏ ✻ Bar Lunch £2.50-£10alc High tea £5-£7.50alc Dinner £16.50-£19.50&alc Last dinner 9.30pm
Credit Cards ① ② ③

## GOLSPIE Highland *Sutherland* Map 14 NH89

### ★★65% Sutherland Arms
Old Bank Rd KW10 6RS ☎(0408)633234 & 633216
*A former coaching inn, sympathetically upgraded to meet modern expectations, but retaining much of its original charm. The Sutherland Arms is efficiently run under the personal supervision of resident owners Nancy and Colin Sutherland.*
16rm(9⇨2♠)(4fb)1⊞ CTV in all bedrooms ® T ✻ sB&Bfr£25 sB&B⇨♠fr£30 dB&Bfr£45 dB&B⇨♠fr£50 ⋒
CTV 25P ❀ CFA
V ❖ ⚏ ✻ Lunch £3.95-£9.50alc High tea £8-£12alc Dinner £15&alc Last dinner 9pm
Credit Cards ① ③

### ★★57% Golf Links
KW10 6TT ☎(04083)3408
*Set beside the golf-course and sandy beach, this small stone-built house includes a comfortable lounge and spacious dining room. It is a family-run hotel, popular with golfers and there is a small putting green within the grounds.*
9⇨♠ CTV in all bedrooms ® ✻ sB&B⇨♠£23-£26 dB&B⇨♠£46 ⋒
20P ⇔ ❀
♀ Scottish & French V ❖ ⚏ ✻ Bar Lunch £3-£8.95alc Dinner £13.50-£15.50alc Last dinner 8.30pm
Credit Cards ① ③

## GOMERSAL West Yorkshire Map 08 SE22

### ★★★66% *Gomersal Park*
Moor Ln BD19 4LT (Best Western) ☎Bradford(0274)869386 FAX (0274) 861042
*A converted country house built of attractive sandstone, standing in its own grounds in a rural location, yet close to the M62 motorway (junction 26). Bedrooms are attractively furnished and have good facilities. There is a comfortable foyer lounge, and an excellent leisure club is a recent addition. The hotel can be easily found by following signs to nearby Oakwood Hall.*
52⇨♠(5fb) CTV in all bedrooms ® T ✖ (ex guide dogs)
《 200P ❀ ⊠ (heated) sauna solarium gymnasium ♫
V ❖ ⚏ Last dinner 10pm
Credit Cards ① ② ③ ⑤

See advertisement under LEEDS

## GOODRICH Hereford & Worcester Map 03 SO51

### ★★57% Ye Hostelrie
HR9 6HX ☎Symonds Yat(0600)890241
*This privately owned inn in a quiet rural village close to the River Wye is popular with shooting and fishing parties. Accommodation is modest with old fashioned furnishings and few modern day facilities.*
8rm(2⇨5♠) CTV in all bedrooms ® sB&B⇨♠£30 dB&B⇨♠£44
CTV 25P ⇔ ❀

♀ English & Continental V ❖ Dinner £12&alc Last dinner 9pm

See advertisement under ROSS-ON-WYE

## GOODRINGTON
See Paignton

## GOODWOOD West Sussex Map 04 SU80

### ★★★65% Goodwood Park
PO18 0QB ☎Chichester(0243)775537 FAX (0243) 533802
*This once small hotel has been considerably but sympathetically developed, accommodation now being centred round extensive leisure facilites which include an 18-hole golf course, indoor swimming pool, squash and tennis courts, a fitness room and snooker tables. Some bedrooms are newer than others but all have been well equipped, while public areas include a choice of restaurants, and five bars; popular conference facilities are also available.*
89⇨(3fb)1⊞ CTV in all bedrooms ® T ✻ S% sB&B⇨£55-£100 dB&B⇨£80-£135 ⋒
《 CTV 300P ❀ CFA ⊠ (heated) ▶ 18 ♪ (hard) squash snooker sauna solarium gymnasium beauty salon ♨ *xmas*
♀ English & French V ❖ ⚏ ✻ Lunch £12.25-£14.25&alc Dinner £18.75-£22.95&alc Last dinner 9.30pm
Credit Cards ① ② ③ ⑤ ⓔ

## GOOLE Humberside Map 08 SE72

### ★★59% Clifton
1 Clifton Gardens, Boothferry Rd DN14 6AL ☎(0405)761336 FAX (0405) 762350
*The resident proprietor and his hard-working young team of staff create a friendly, informal atmosphere throughout this small, cosy hotel with its clean and modestly equipped bedrooms.*
10rm(5⇨3♠)1⊞ CTV in all bedrooms ® T ✻ sB&B£21-£27 sB&B⇨♠£35 dB&B⇨♠£35-£43 ⋒
CTV 8P
♀ English & Continental V ❖ ✻ Lunch fr£3.50 Dinner £5.30-£22.40alc Last dinner 9pm
Credit Cards ① ② ③ ⑤ ⓔ

## GORDANO MOTORWAY SERVICE AREA (M5) Avon Map 03 ST57 ⊖

### ⬆Forte Travelodge
BS20 9XG (Forte) ☎Pill(027581)3709 Central Res (0800) 850950
*Situated within the Gordano service centre on the A5 and thus very well placed for both Bristol city centre and Avonmouth, the lodge provides a good choice of eating options on site as well as the usual well equipped, good value bedroom accommodation.*
40⇨♠(40fb) CTV in all bedrooms ® sB⇨♠£29.95 dB⇨♠£29.95 (room only)
《 40P ⇔
Credit Cards ① ② ③

## GOREY
See Jersey under Channel Islands

## GORING Oxfordshire Map 04 SU68

### ❀✕The Leatherne Bottel
RG8 0HS ☎(0491)872667
*To a cosily attractive inn and a restaurant remotely situated beside the river chef Keith Read has brought an inventive style of modern cooking based on good local produce, while willing, attentive service is supervised by his partner, Annie Bonnet. The game and fish of the day offer an alternative to a smooth, rich Parfait of Wild Duck Livers, Shortcrust Pastry Tart filled with Fresh Snails, Maize-fed Guinea Fowl and Pan-fried Calves' Liver; British cheeses with home-made biscuits offer a fitting conclusion to the*

*meal, and the wine list contains examples both from France and the New World.*

**V** 50 seats Lunch £5-£30alc Dinner £5-£30alc Last lunch 2pm Last dinner 9.30pm P

Credit Cards ① ② ③

---

### GORLESTON-ON-SEA

See **Yarmouth, Great**

---

### GOSFORTH Cumbria Map **11** NY00

#### ★★ 65% **Westlakes**

CA20 1HP ☎(09467)25221

*A large house set in 40 acres of grounds at the A595/B5344 junction has recently been refurbished to offer good standards of accommodation and service. An extensive à la carte menu is available in its cosy restaurant.*

6⇌♠(1fb) CTV in all bedrooms ® **T** ✳ S% sB&B⇌♠£36.50 dB&B⇌♠£46.50

25P ✿

♀ English & French **V** ♥

Credit Cards ① ③

---

### GOSPORT Hampshire Map **04** SZ69

#### ★★ 57% **Anglesey**

Crescent Rd, Alverstoke PO12 2DH ☎(0705)582157 & 523932 FAX (0705) 502902

*A hotel set in a Regency terrace complements the à la carte menu of the elegant restaurant, featuring fish specialities, with an extensive value-for-money selection of bar meals. Well equipped bedrooms are undergoing refurbishment and the atmosphere is relaxed and friendly throughout.*

18⇌♠(1fb)1⊞ CTV in all bedrooms ® **T**

CTV 2🚗 (£1.50)

**V** ♥ Last dinner 9.30pm

Credit Cards ① ② ③

---

### GOUDHURST Kent Map **05** TQ73

#### ★★ 71% **Star & Eagle**

High St TN17 1AL ☎(0580)211512 & 211338

*Parts of this attractive and well-managed hotel date back to the early 14th century, and it has been tastfully modernised to retain such original features as low ceilings and oak beams. Bedrooms are particularly well furnished and equipped to a high standard, while both bar and restaurant offer attentive service.*

11rm(9⇌♠)2⊞ CTV in all bedrooms ® ✳ sB&B£40 sB&B⇌♠£50 dB&B£50 dB&B⇌♠£66-£80 🍴

24P CFA *xmas*

♀ European **V** ♥ ♨ ✳ Lunch £11.75&alc Dinner £15-£18alc Last dinner 9.30pm

Credit Cards ① ② ③ ⓔ

---

### GRANGE-OVER-SANDS Cumbria Map **07** SD47

#### ★★★ 65% **Grange**

Station Square LA11 6EJ (Consort) ☎(05395)33666 FAX (05395) 35064

*Accommodation which will appeal equally to tourist and commercial guest is housed in a substantial Victorian building which overlooks town and bay from its setting in well tended gardens.*

41⇌♠(6fb) CTV in all bedrooms ® **T** ✳ sB&B⇌♠£40-£44 dB&B⇌♠£64-£72 🍴

☾ CTV 100P ✿ CFA ♨ *xmas*

♀ English & French **V** ♥ ♨ ✳ Bar Lunch £6.50 High tea £7 Dinner £15.50&alc Last dinner 9.30pm

Credit Cards ① ② ③ ⑤

---

#### ★★ 69% **Netherwood**

Lindale Rd LA11 6ET ☎(05395)32552

*The hotel, an imposing building dating from the 19th century and retaining some fine interior wood panelling and carving, occupies a prime position in 11 acres of attractive gardens and woodland which overlook the Morecambe Bay estuary.*

32rm(29⇌♠)(5fb)⌁in 12 bedrooms CTV in all bedrooms ® **T** sB&B£37.75-£38.75 sB&B⇌♠£38.75-£44.75 dB&B£68.50-£75.50 dB&B⇌♠£75.50-£89.50 🍴

Lift ☾ CTV 160P ✿ CFA ▣ (heated) solarium gymnasium spa bath & steam room ♨

♀ English & French ♥ ♨ Lunch £9.25-£12&alc High tea £7.25-£10 Dinner £15.25-£20 Last dinner 8.30pm

---

#### ★★ ⚐ 66% **Graythwaite Manor**

Fernhill Rd LA11 7JE ☎(05395)32001 & 33755

*Large country house in beautiful grounds, with home grown produce used in restaurant. Situated high above the town, with superb views of the bay, the hotel offers tastefully refurbished, comfortable rooms where an old-fashioned charm prevails.*

21⇌♠(2fb) CTV in all bedrooms ® **T** ✕ (ex guide dogs) sB&B⇌♠£45.50-£60 dB&B⇌♠£80-£120 (incl dinner) 🍴

18P 14🚗 (£1) 🚳 ✿ CFA ♪ (hard) helicopter landing area putting

♀ English & French **V** ♥ ♨ ⌁ Lunch £9-£11.50 Dinner £17.50-£20 Last dinner 8.30pm

Credit Cards ① ③

---

#### ★ 68% **Clare House**

Park Rd LA11 7HQ ☎(05395)33026 & 34253

Closed Nov-Mar

*Situated beside the main road west of the town, overlooking Morecambe Bay from its gardens, this family-run establishment offers warm, comfortable accommodation some rooms having balconies and sea views. Particularly enjoyable meals are prepared by the proprietor's son, who makes good use of fresh local produce.* →

Set in eight acres of beautiful landscaped gardens and woodland on the hillside overlooking the Kent Estuary & Morecambe Bay, with the hills beyond, this lovely country house offers a haven of tranquillity in a busy world. 22 well-equipped bedrooms, all en suite, spacious lounges with log fires, excellent food & wines. Personally supervised by the proprietors.

*GRAYTHWAITE MANOR* ★★

H O T E L

**GRANGE-OVER-SANDS Cumbria, LA11 7JE. Tel: (05395) 32001**

---

17rm(16⇨🛏)(1fb) CTV in all bedrooms ® T
🏋 (ex guide dogs) sB&B⇨🛏£36-£39 dB&B⇨🛏£72-£78 (incl dinner) 🅿
CTV 18P 🌼 ❀ croquet putting nc5yrs
🕯 ⬚ ✠ ✳ Dinner £16-£18 Last dinner 7.15pm
£

★★★65% **Angel & Royal**
High St NG31 6PN (Forte Hotels) ☎(0476)65816
FAX (0476) 67149
*This character town centre coaching inn with easy access to the A1 is branded as a Heritage Hotel, it offers friendly and caring service, and well equipped, comfortable accommodation. In addition to the convivial bar, there are attractive lounges and the Kings Hall Restaurant, which provides the ideal setting for a medieval banquet.*
30⇨🛏✠in 10 bedrooms CTV in all bedrooms ® T ✳
sB⇨🛏fr£65 dB⇨🛏fr£85 (room only) 🅿
🕯 50P CFA *xmas*
🍽 English & French V 🕯 ⬚ ✠ ✳ Lunch £8.95&alc Dinner £13.95&alc Last dinner 9.45pm
Credit Cards ①②③④⑤

★★63% **Kings**
North Pde NG31 8AU (Minotels) ☎(0476)590800
*A Georgian house with a modern extension set in its own grounds, the hotel is privately owned and run. Recent extensive refurbishment has uplifted the quality and comfort of the bedrooms. There is a restaurant and all day orangery coffee shop and open lounge.*
22rm(21⇨🛏)(1fb)1🔔 CTV in all bedrooms ® T S% sB&B£28 sB&B⇨🛏£41 dB&B⇨🛏£56 🅿
🕯 36P ❀ CFA ♪ (hard) 🎵
🍽 French V 🕯 ⬚ ✠ Lunch £9.25-£14.25&alc Dinner £9.25-£14.25&alc Last dinner 9.30pm
Credit Cards ①②③⑤£

🏠**Forte Travelodge**
Grantham Service Area NG32 2AB (4m N on A1) (Forte)
☎(0476)77500 Central Res (0800) 850950
*Situated at the roundabout intersection of the B1174 and the A1 southbound, 3 miles north of Grantham, this is a standard Lodge with a Welcome Break service area open 24 hours.*
40⇨🛏(40fb) CTV in all bedrooms ® sB⇨🛏£29.95 dB⇨🛏£29.95 (room only)
🕯 40P 🚗
Credit Cards ①②③

❀❀✗**Harry's Place**
Great Gonerby NG31 8JS ☎(0476)61780
*An elegantly furnished dining room in a Georgian House where there is a dedicated and serious approach to food. This is Harry and Caroline's place. Harry committed to providing the finest quality raw materials irrespective of cost, and Caroline the charming and attentive hostess. The menu is small but very well balanced. Starters are biased towards fish, particularly Loch Fyne scallops, mussels and salmon. Loin of lamb roasted with vintage cider and rosemary was full of flavour, tender and pink with robust jus gravy, accompanied by fresh local asparagus and a medley of pasta and leek ribbons in a mint/cream dressing.*
Closed Sun & Mon (ex by prior arrangement) & Xmas wk
🍽 English & French 10 seats ✳ Lunch £26.50-£32alc Dinner £31-£38alc Last lunch 2pm Last dinner 9.30pm 4 P ✠
Credit Cards ①③

Hotels with red star ratings are
especially high quality.

★★★64% **Garth**
Castle Rd PH26 3HN (Inter-Hotels) ☎(0479)2836 & 2162
FAX (0479) 2116
*An extended 17th-century house in 4 acres of grounds has been extensively refurbished to provide every modern comfort and facility in its bright, cheerful bedrooms and relaxing public areas. Imaginative Taste of Scotland dishes are offered in the attractive split-level restaurant, and service is friendly.*
17⇨🛏 CTV in all bedrooms ® T 🏋 sB&B⇨🛏£33-£40 dB&B⇨🛏£66 🅿
22P 🚗 ❀
🍽 French V 🕯 ⬚ ✠ Sunday Lunch fr£5alc Dinner fr£19alc Last dinner 8.30pm
Credit Cards ①③④⑤

★★63% *Coppice*
Grant Rd PH26 3LD (Exec Hotel) ☎(0479)2688
*A family-run hotel set in its own wooded grounds in a quiet residential area provides a popular base for visiting tour groups, offering good-value accommodation, a comfortable lounge and well stocked bar, a friendly atmosphere prevailing throughout.*
26🛏(3fb) CTV in all bedrooms ®
CTV 50P ❀ shooting
V 🕯 ⬚
Credit Cards ①③

★★63% **Seafield Lodge**
Woodside Av PH26 3JN (Minotels) ☎(0479)2152
FAX (0479) 2340
Closed 4 Nov-9 Dec
*This small family-run hotel in a quiet residential area has a friendly atmosphere, popular with business people, tourists and sporting enthusiasts alike.*
14⇨🛏(2fb) CTV in all bedrooms ®
15P 🚗 ♪
V ✳ Bar Lunch £3-£6alc Dinner £15&alc Last dinner 9pm
Credit Cards ①③

★73% *Tyree House*
8 The Square PH26 3HF ☎(0479)2615
*A small friendly family-run hotel beside the town square has been tastefully refurbished throughout and offers good value accommodation, with compact but comfortable well equipped bedrooms.*
9🛏(1fb) CTV in all bedrooms ®
CTV 20P 🚗 ❀
V 🕯 Last dinner 9pm
Credit Cards ①③

★60% *Dunvegan*
Heathfield Rd PH26 3HX ☎(0479)2301
Closed 16-31 Oct & 23-27 Dec
*Quietly situated in a residential area close to the golf course, this small hotel is run in a friendly and informal manner by the resident proprietors. Neat bedrooms are modestly furnished and public areas are comfortable.*
8rm(2🛏)(5fb) ® ✳ sB&B£12.30-£13.30 dB&B£24.60-£26.60 dB&B🛏£31.80-£33.80 🅿
CTV 9P 1🚗 (£1) 🚗 *xmas*
🕯 ⬚ ✳ Bar Lunch fr£1.50 Dinner £10.75 Last dinner 7.30pm

★★★★64% **Wordsworth**
LA22 9SW ☎(09665)592 due to change to (05394) 35592
FAX (09665) 765 due to change to (05394) 35765
*Situated in the centre of the village, this comfortable well furnished hotel has bedrooms with good modern facilities. Attractive public areas include a comfortable lounge, cosy cocktail bar with adjacent conservatory overlooking the gardens and a restaurant that provides interesting à la carte dishes. There are good leisure*

*facilities, plus conference and banqueting rooms, and service is very friendly and efficient.*

37⇨🛏3🛁 CTV in all bedrooms **T** 🐾 (ex guide dogs)
sB&B⇨🛏£42-£54 dB&B⇨🛏£92-£132 🅿
Lift ₵ 60P 🚷 ❀ CFA ▣ (heated) sauna solarium gymnasium table tennis pool jacuzzi ♫ *xmas*
♅ English & French **V** ✆ ☞ Lunch £16-£18alc Dinner £27-£32alc Last dinner 9pm
Credit Cards [1][2][3][5] ⓔ

**See advertisement on page 331**

★★★ ❀ 🏨 **MICHAEL'S NOOK
COUNTRY HOUSE**

LA22 9RP (Pride of Britain)
☎(09665)496 due to change
to (05394) 35496
FAX (09665) 765 due to
change to (05394) 35765

*Peacefully situated in 3 acres
of attractively landscaped
gardens to the north of the village, this extended Victorian house of traditional Lakeland stone retains the feeling of a traditional country house where guests are warmly welcomed and made to feel immediately at home. There are impressive floral displays, blazing fires and a small menagerie of friendly animals, and the whole house is furnished with a wealth of fine furniture, paintings, rugs and porcelain, reflecting owner Reg Gifford's years as an antique dealer. Bedrooms, many of which enjoy lovely views of the surrounding countryside, vary in size but are all comfortably and tastefully furnished with quality fabrics and many thoughtful extras – but no door* →

## The Square, Grantown on Spey, Morayshire
## Telephone: (0479) 2615

Situated in the Square and sheltered by trees, ideal for family holidays. Only 10 minutes walk through the town for golf course, fishing, bowling green and tennis courts. Facilities for the sportsman with secure gun room and rod room. All nine bedrooms are tastefully decorated and have private facilities, TV and complimentary tea/coffee and biscuits. Comfortable residents lounge enjoys views across the square and is open at all times. Dinner can be provided in the à la carte restaurant open every evening. Ample parking. Full licence.

**Proprietors: Roy & Vyvian Nelson**

# Grasmere

*locks! Bathrooms range from original Victorian to sophisticated marble with double washbasins and separate shower cabinets. Dayrooms include an elegant drawing room with deep inviting sofas; while the richly decorated dining room, with its polished wood tables, gleaming silver and crystal, provides an intimate setting for the daily changing 5-course dinners of Chef Heinz Nagler. Charming and courteous service is provided throughout by a team of pleasant young staff.*

14⇨📺(2fb)1🏠 CTV in all bedrooms T ✕ sB&B⇨📺£105 dB&B⇨📺£155-£290 (incl dinner) 🍴

20P ⇔ ❖ CFA nc5yrs *xmas*

♀ English & French ⊁ Lunch £28 Dinner £38 Last dinner 8.30pm

Credit Cards 1 2 3 5

---

### ★★★❀70% The Swan

LA22 9RF (Forte Hotels) ☎(09665)551 due to change to (05394) 35551 FAX (09665) 741 due to change to (05394) 35741

*On the A591 just east of the village, this popular old hotel with comfortable very well equipped bedrooms, is full of traditional charm and hospitality. Public areas, with oak beams, open fires, fresh flowers and antiques, include a delightful restaurant specialising in local dishes.*

36⇨📺in 10 bedrooms CTV in all bedrooms ® T ✳ sB⇨📺£50-£70 dB⇨📺£80-£100 (room only) 🍴

40P ⇔ ❖ *xmas*

V ⊕ ⊡ ⊁ ✳ Lunch £10.50&alc Dinner £19.50&alc Last dinner 9pm

Credit Cards 1 2 3 4 5

---

### ★★★❀65% Gold Rill Country House

Red Bank Rd LA22 9PU ☎(09665)486 due to change to (05394) 35486

Closed Jan

(Rosette awarded for dinner only)

*Once a gentleman's residence, and still delightfully situated in 2 acres of lawns and gardens, this personally managed hotel with a warm, relaxed and friendly atmosphere prides itself on its high standard of cuisine, the à la carte menu of imaginative British dishes – which is changed daily – making good use of fresh local produce and seasonal specialities.*

18⇨📺(2fb) CTV in all bedrooms ® sB&B⇨📺£32-£44 dB&B⇨📺£64-£88 🍴

35P ⇔ ❖ ⌣ (heated) putting green croquet lawn *xmas*

⊕ ⊁ ✳ Bar Lunch fr£1.60 Dinner £17 Last dinner 8.30pm

Credit Cards 1 3 £

---

### ★★★62% Red Lion

Red Lion Square LA22 9SS (Consort) ☎(09665)456 due to change to (05394) 35456 FAX (09665) 34157

*A tourist hotel set at the heart of this popular village commands fine views over surrounding countryside.*

35⇨📺(3fb) CTV in all bedrooms ® T sB&B⇨📺£26-£37.50 dB&B⇨📺£52-£75 🍴

Lift 26P ❖ CFA *xmas*

V ⊕ ⊡ ⊁ Bar Lunch £2.50-£8 Dinner £14-£16&alc Last dinner 9pm

Credit Cards 1 2 3 5 £

---

### ★★71% Rothay Garden

Broadgate LA22 9RJ ☎(09665)334 due to change to (05394) 35334 FAX (09665) 723 due to change to (05394) 35723

*Situated at the edge of the village, this pleasant hotel provides caring service and has a comfortable lounge and bedrooms with good facilities. The attractive conservatory restaurant serves well prepared food.*

21⇨📺(2fb)5🏠 CTV in all bedrooms ® T ✳ sB&B⇨📺£43.50 dB&B⇨📺£77-£92 (incl dinner) 🍴

---

30P ⇔ ❖ CFA ♪ *xmas*

♀ English & Continental V ⊕ ⊡ ⊁

Credit Cards 1 3

### ★★67% Grasmere

Broadgate LA22 9TA ☎(09665)277 due to change to (05394) 35277

Closed Jan-8 Feb

*A friendly atmosphere prevails at this small, personally run hotel set in its own gardens with lawns leading down to the river. Dinner, served in the attractive dining room at 7.30pm, offers a good blend of quality and quantity. Bedrooms are thoughtfully equipped.*

12⇨📺1🏠 CTV in all bedrooms ® T sB&B⇨📺£35-£43 dB&B⇨📺£60-£82 🍴

14P ⇔ ❖ croquet nc7yrs *xmas*

♀ English & French ⊕ ⊁ Dinner £15.50-£17.50 Last dinner 8pm

Credit Cards 1 3

### ★★67% Oak Bank

Broadgate LA22 9TA (Guestaccom) ☎(09665)217 due to change to (05394) 35217

Closed Xmas-Jan

*This personally run hotel offers comfortable bedrooms and public areas which include an attractive conservatory dining room where guests can enjoy a 4-course dinner prepared from good raw ingredients and fresh local produce.*

14⇨📺(1fb)2🏠 CTV in all bedrooms ® T ✳ sB&B⇨📺£30-£38 dB&B⇨📺£60-£76 🍴

CTV 14P ⇔ ❖ ⚘

♀ English & Continental V ⊕ ⊡ ⊁ ✳ Bar Lunch £2.50-£6 High tea £5-£10 Dinner £15-£18 Last dinner 8pm

Credit Cards 1 3

---

★

★❀❀ WHITE MOSS HOUSE

Rydal Water LA22 9SE ☎(09665)295 due to change to (05394) 35295

Closed Dec-Feb

*A charming hotel in an ideal location overlooking Rydal Water. The atmosphere is warm and friendly and owners Susan and Peter Dixon ensure a comfortable stay. Bedrooms are individually decorated, well equipped and furnished to a high standard. Public rooms are limited, but comfortable and relaxing. Dinner is served at 8pm in the intimate dining room. Peter Dixon offers a set 5-course meal of carefully prepared, mainly British food. Interesting soups, such as broccoli and basil, start the meal, with a light fish course to follow – a bombe of brill with a centre of Brochester Brie, served with sorrel and watercress sauce. Perhaps crispy roast Lakeland mallard with sage and onion stuffing for main course, with damson, port and Pinot Noir sauce. There are mouthwatering puddings, including Kentish well pudding and chocolate orange velvet. An exceptionally fine wine list is available and wines are reasonably priced.*

5⇨Annexe2⇨📺1🏠 CTV in all bedrooms T ✕ S% dB&B⇨📺£70-£120

10P ⇔ ❖

⊁ S% Dinner £25-£28 Last dinner 8pm

Credit Cards 1 3

---

Hotels with red star ratings are especially high quality.

GRASSINGTON North Yorkshire Map **07** SE06

★60% *Black Horse*

Garrs Ln BD23 5AT ☎(0756)752770

*Quaint, prettily decorated bedrooms are an attractive feature of this family-run hotel, centrally located in a charming Dales village. Meals are wholesome and filling and the bar menu is especially popular.*

11⇨↑(1fb)2⇛ CTV in all bedrooms ®
CTV 2P
V ♥ Last dinner 9.30pm
Credit Cards ⑴ ⑶

---

GRAYSHOTT Hampshire Map **04** SU83

❀ ✕ **Woods Place**

Headley Rd GU26 6LB (1m SW B3002 off A3)
☎Hindhead(0428)605555

*This delightful little restaurant – once a butcher's shop – offers attractive surroundings with wood panelling and tiled walls, tasteful table settings and a friendly atmosphere; on a quiet evening you may well find chef Eric Norrgren enthusiastically serving the dishes that he has created. Both menu and wine list are compendious but nicely balanced, diners perhaps sampling light onion tartlet with aperitifs before choosing from a straightforward list of starters that might include a generous Mousseline of Leek and Asparagus followed by such skilfully prepared main courses as Fillet of Beef with a Wild Mushroom Sauce. Competent desserts complete a meal that is in general enjoyable, despite some minor disappointments over the past year.*

Closed Sun, Mon & 1 wk Xmas
♥ Continental **V** 35 seats Lunch £11.40-£17.20alc Dinner £11.40-£17.20alc Last lunch 3pm Last dinner 11pm ₱
Credit Cards ⑴ ⑵ ⑶ ⑸

G

**GREAT** Places incorporating the word 'Great' will be found under the actual place name – eg Great Yarmouth is listed under Yarmouth, Great.

---

**GREENLAW** Borders *Berwickshire* Map **12** NT74

### ★★👥63% Purves Hall
TD10 6UJ (4m SE off A697) ☎Leitholm(089084)558

*Enjoying an attractive rural setting, this charming, comfortable Edwardian country house hotel stands in 10 acres of secluded gardens and grounds off the A697, 4 miles south east of Greenlaw. Facilities include an outdoor heated swimming pool, a croquet lawn and a putting green; stables are also available.*

7⇌🏠(1fb) CTV in all bedrooms ® T ✱ sB&B⇌🏠£32-£40 dB&B⇌🏠£62-£68 🏠

20P 🚗 ❀ ⊃ (heated) ♪ (hard) croquet putting

🍴 International ❖ ♫ S% Lunch £10 Dinner £18 Last dinner 8.45pm

Credit Cards ①②③⑤£

---

**GRETA BRIDGE** Co Durham Map **12** NZ01

### ★★63% Morritt Arms
DL12 9SE ☎Teesdale(0833)27232 & 27392 FAX (0833) 27570

*Old coaching inn retaining Dickensian character.*

17⇌1🏠 CTV in all bedrooms ® T sB&B⇌£48 dB&B⇌£72 🏠

100P 3🚗 🚗 ❀ CFA ♫ *xmas*

🍴 English & French ❖ ♫ Sunday Lunch £12 Dinner £21 Last dinner 8.45pm

Credit Cards ①②③⑤£

---

**GRETNA (WITH GRETNA GREEN)** Dumfries & Galloway *Dumfriesshire* Map **11** NY36

### ★★68% Solway Lodge
Annan Rd CA6 5DN (Minotels) ☎Gretna(0461)38266 FAX (0461) 37791

Closed 25 & 26 Dec RS 10 Oct-Mar

*A comfortable hotel managed by friendly resident proprietors with a choice of cosy well appointed motel rooms or the very attractive main house rooms. Good value menus are offered.*

3⇌🏠Annexe7⇌🏠1🏠 CTV in all bedrooms ® T ✱ sB&B⇌🏠£32-£34.50 dB&B⇌🏠£45-£75

25P 🚗

V ❖ ♫ ✱ Bar Lunch £4-£12 Dinner £8-£15alc Last dinner 9pm

Credit Cards ①②③⑤

### ★★65% Gretna Chase
CA6 5JB (0.25m S on B721 in England) ☎Gretna(0461)37517

Closed Jan

*Situated on the English side of the River Sack, in award winning gardens, this comfortable hotel offers warm, friendly service and good value menus. A feature of the hotel is the interesting antique bric-à-brac, which abounds throughout.*

9rm(3⇌3🏠)1🏠 CTV in all bedrooms ® 🐾 (ex guide dogs) sB&Bfr£35 sB&B⇌🏠£45 dB&Bfr£48 dB&B⇌🏠£60-£80

40P ❀

🍴 English & French V ❖ Lunch £10.50-£15.50 Dinner £10.40-£17.65alc Last dinner 8.30pm

Credit Cards ①②③⑤£

### ⬆️Forte Travelodge
CA6 5HQ (on A74, northbound) (Forte) ☎Gretna(0461)37566 Central Res (0800) 850950

*This hotel offers modern accommodation, and is situated in a service area, adjoining the A74 just north of Gretna Green, with access from both north and southbound carriageways.*

---

41⇌🏠(41fb) CTV in all bedrooms ® sB⇌🏠£29.95 dB⇌🏠£29.95 (room only)

《41P 🚗

Credit Cards ①②③

---

**GRIMSBY** Humberside Map **08** TA20 ⊙

### ★★★64% Forte Crest
Littlecoates Rd DN34 4LX (Forte Hotels) ☎(0472)350295 Telex no 527776 FAX (0472) 241354

*Off the A1136 on the outskirts of town, this multi-storey modern hotel provides comfortable accommodation with a good range of facilities, though now a little dated in style. The restaurant has a good local reputation and there is a choice of bars.*

52⇌🏠(2fb)✂in 8 bedrooms CTV in all bedrooms ® T

Lift 《250P ❀ CFA

🍴 English & French V ❖ ♫ ✂

Credit Cards ①②③④⑤

### ★★★61% Grimsby Crest
St James' Square DN31 1EP (Forte Hotels) ☎(0472)359771 Telex no 527741 FAX (0472) 241427

Closed Xmas

*This purpose-built hotel is situated in the town centre adjacent to the main shopping area. Bedrooms are well equipped with modern facilities and meals and snacks are served throughout the day.*

125⇌🏠(6fb)✂in 20 bedrooms CTV in all bedrooms ® T ✱ S% sB⇌🏠£35-£61 dB⇌🏠£61-£73 (room only) 🏠

Lift 《100P CFA sauna gymnasium

🍴 English & French V ❖ ♫ ✂ ✱ S% Lunch £8.40 Dinner £13.95 Last dinner 10pm

Credit Cards ①②③④⑤

### ★★★59% Yarborough
Bethlehem St DN31 1LY (Consort) ☎(0472)242266

*Carefully restored to its original style, with attractive and elegant public areas, a Victorian hotel conveniently located beside the railway station offers well equipped and pleasantly decorated bedrooms, a comfortable lounge area and a choice of two bars.*

51⇌🏠(2fb)✂in 2 bedrooms CTV in all bedrooms ® T ✱ sB&B⇌🏠£35-£52.50 dB&B⇌🏠£45-£62.50

Lift 《10P CFA

🍴 English & French V ❖ ♫ ✱ Lunch £6.95 Dinner £10-£12&alc Last dinner 9.30pm

Credit Cards ①②③⑤

---

**GRIMSTON** Norfolk Map **09** TF72

### ★★★❀❀👥
**CONGHAM HALL COUNTRY HOUSE**

Lynn Rd PE32 1AH (Pride of Britain) ☎Hillington(0485)600250 Telex no 81508 FAX (0485) 601191

*Well manicured lawns and mature trees form the setting for this Georgian house standing in peaceful countryside a few miles from Sandringham. Owners Trevor and Christine Forecast extend a warm welcome to guests, investing in improvements every year, the latest being two excellent bedrooms and a splendid suite in the new wing of the original house. All the bedrooms, whether small or large, are furnished with every comfort and many little extra personal touches. Downstairs, drawing room and lounge bar are particularly appealing, and the meals served in the pleasant dining room are the creation of chef Clive*

*Jackson. There is both a set menu and an eight-course Menu
Gourmand. Presentation of dishes is a strong point, and
although some may find a few dishes over-complicated, he
cooks with imagination, and offers a wide choice, including a
selection of vegetarian dishes.*

14 ⇨ ♪ 2 ⌷ CTV in all bedrooms **T ✕** sB&B ⇨ ♪ £70-£120
dB&B ⇨ ♪ £105-£185 🄿

50P ⇛ ✿ ⌷ (heated) ♪ (hard) croquet jacuzzi cricket
nc12yrs *xmas*

**V** ⊕ ⅙ ✳ Lunch £15alc Dinner £30-£36alc Last dinner
9.30pm

Credit Cards ① ② ③ ⑤

**See advertisement under KING'S LYNN**

---

**GRINDLEFORD** Derbyshire Map **08** SK27

★★★64% **Maynard Arms**

Main Rd S30 1HN ☎Hope Valley(0433)30321
FAX (0433) 30445

*Situated in the Peak National Park with convenient access to
North Derbyshire and South Yorkshire, this popular hotel provides
polite efficient service and has pleasant public areas, particularly
the comfortable first-floor lounge.*

13rm(9 ⇨ 2 ♪)(1fb)2 ⌷ CTV in all bedrooms ® **T** sB&B£59-£65
sB&B ⇨ ♪ £59-£65 dB&B ⇨ ♪ £72-£76 🄿

CTV 90P 3 ⚫ ✿ CFA *xmas*

♀ English & French **V** ⊕ ⌷ Lunch £8.15-£9.55&alc Dinner
£14.50-£17.50&alc Last dinner 10.30pm

Credit Cards ① ② ③ ⑤ ⓔ

---

**GRIZEDALE** Cumbria Map **07** SD39

★★70% **Grizedale Lodge**

LA22 0QL ☎Hawkshead(09666)532 due to change to
Coniston(05394)36532
Closed Jan-mid Feb

*A peaceful, relaxing hotel in the idyllic surroundings of Grizedale
Forest, enthusiastically run by its friendly owners to provide
comfortable accommodation and skilfully prepared meals.*

7 ⇨ ♪ (1fb)1 ⌷ ⅙ in all bedrooms CTV ® ✕
sB&B ⇨ ♪ £45.50-£53 dB&B ⇨ ♪ £75-£90 (incl dinner) 🄿

20P ⇛ *xmas*

♀ English & French ⊕ ⌷ ⅙ Bar Lunch £1.50-£6.50alc Dinner
£16.95 Last dinner 8pm

Credit Cards ① ③

---

**GROBY** Leicestershire Map **04** SK50

★66% **Brant Inn**

Leicester Rd LE6 0DU ☎Leicester(0533)872703
FAX (0533) 875292

*To the northwest of the city of Leicester, on the A50, the Brant Inn
has been recently extended and the public areas refurbished
throughout. There is now a choice of 4 modern bar areas and a
large restaurant, all of which are popular with locals, creating a
lively atmosphere. By comparison the accommodation is modest.*

10rm CTV in all bedrooms ® **T ✳** sB&B£24.50-£29.50
dB&B£42.50-£49.50

200P ✿ CFA

♀ English & French **V ✳** Lunch fr£8.65&alc Dinner
fr£8.65&alc Last dinner 10pm

Credit Cards ① ③ ⑤

---

⊛ Shell filling station, open 7am–11pm
(some 24 hours) throughout the year with leaded
and unleaded petrol, and diesel.

---

**GUERNSEY**

See **Channel Islands**

---

**GUILDFORD** Surrey Map **04** SU94 ⊛

★★★★62% **Forte Crest**

Egerton Rd GU2 5XZ (Forte Hotels) ☎(0483)574444
Telex no 858572 FAX (0483) 302960

*This newly built modern hotel stands in landscaped grounds beside
the A3 Guildford bypass about 2 miles southwest of the city.
Accommodation comprises comfortable, well equipped bedrooms
(some of which are on the ground floor), two restaurants, a
spacious, well furnished lobby lounge and a club-style bar.
Extension conference/function facilities are available, together
with a Health Club and very good indoor leisure amenities.*

111 ⇨ ♪ CTV in all bedrooms ® **T ✳** sB ⇨ ♪ fr£85
dB ⇨ ♪ £95-£140 (room only) 🄿

⟨ 190P ✿ CFA ▱ (heated) sauna solarium gymnasium ♫
*xmas*

♀ European **V** ⊕ ⌷ ⅙ ✳ Lunch £13.50-£14.50alc Dinner £8-
£25alc Last dinner 11pm

Credit Cards ① ② ③ ⑤

★★★70% *The Manor at Newlands*

Newlands Corner GU4 8SE (3m E A25) ☎(0483)222624
FAX (0483) 211389
Closed 25(after lunch)-31 Dec

*This charming country manor house set in 9 acres of grounds has
tastefully decorated, comfortable bedrooms equipped to meet your
every need. Public areas include two bars and a newly refurbished
elegant restaurant with a choice of interesting à la carte or table
d'hôte menus that make good use of seasonal produce. Hospitable
staff provide courteous service.*

20 ⇨ ♪ (1fb) CTV in all bedrooms **T ✕** (ex guide dogs)

→

**G**

100P 5🛏 ✿
♥ English & French **V** ⚓ ⚱ Last dinner 9.30pm
Credit Cards ①②③④⑤

---

❀✕✕**Tollbridge**
Dereham Rd NR20 5NU ☎Foulsham(036284)359
*A riverside restaurant in the heart of the Norfolk countryside
which offers a simple modern English style of cuisine. The building,
next to the original bridge, has been cleverly extended. Although
the atmosphere is relaxed and informal, the idyllic location and
comfortable surroundings make it a perfect choice for a special
occasion. The menus represent good value; the quality of the
produce – particularly the lamb and vegetables – is excellent and
suits Patrick Murphy's style of cooking. The least amount of
seasoning the better. The confit of duck, crispened and served with
cranberry sauce is a great favourite here.*
Closed Mon & 1st 3 wks Jan Lunch not served Tue-Sat
Dinner not served Sun
♥ English & French 50 seats Sunday Lunch £9.50&alc Dinner
£23-£25.50 Last dinner 9pm 20 P ⚱
Credit Cards ①③

---

★★★

★★★❀🏊 **GREYWALLS**
Muirfield EH31 2EG (Pride of
Britain) ☎(0620)842144
FAX (0620) 842241
Closed Nov-Mar

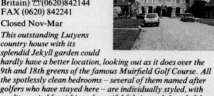

*This outstanding Lutyens
country house with its
splendid Jekyll garden could
hardly have a better location, looking out as it does over the
9th and 18th greens of the famous Muirfield Golf Course. All
the spotlessly clean bedrooms – several of them named after
golfers who have stayed here – are individually styled, with
quality period furnishings, beautiful fabrics and thoughtful
personal touches. Comfortable public areas enhanced by many
antiques, floral arrangements and open fires include a
beautiful wood-panelled library, two further lounges of
considerable charm and a pretty restaurant where guests can
enjoy a meal chosen from continually evolving set-price menus
accompanied by a well presented wine list. This family-run,
seasonally opening establishment achieves the near impossible
in maintaining the highest levels of comfort, a bright, willing
young staff contributing much to its reputation as one of
Scotland's leading hotels.*
17⇆♟Annexe5⇆1🛏 CTV in all bedrooms **T** ✱
sB&B⇆♟fr£77.65 dB&B⇆♟£122.61-£132.83 🛏
《 40P ❀✿ ♪ 𝒫 (hard) croquet shooting
⚓ ⚱ ✱ Lunch £13-£15 Dinner £30 Last dinner 9pm
Credit Cards ①②③④⑤

---

❀❀❀✕**La Potinière**
Main St EH31 2AA ☎(0620)843214
*Husband and wife team David and Hilary Brown have achieved
national acclaim with their simple formula – Hilary cooks, David
serves, and they open for 6 set meals each week. This does mean,
however, that booking is essential. The food is inspired by the best
of French cuisine and produced with great skill. Much the same
format is followed at every meal – soup, maybe a soufflé to follow,
with white meats mostly served at lunch and perhaps pigeon or
lamb at dinner. Brie is always served, but the desserts 'should*

---

*never be missed', said our inspector. The wine list is equally
noteworthy, and advice, if requested, is expertly given.*
Closed Wed, 1 wk Jun & Oct Lunch not served Sat & Fri
Dinner not served Sun-Thu
♥ French 32 seats ✱ Lunch £15.75 Dinner £24.50 Last lunch
1pm 10 P ⚱

---

❀❀❀✕✕✕**Horn of Plenty**
PL19 8JD ☎Tavistock(0822)832528
*New owners Elaine and Ian Gatehouse have settled well into their
stride at this long established restaurant in its peaceful setting
overlooking the Tamar Valley. Apéritifs are taken in the drawing
room or, weather permitting, on the vine-covered terrace. Table
d'hôte and a short à la carte menu are offered. Dishes, based on
fresh fish and local meat, appeal in aroma, presentation and taste,
and are carefully cooked. Sweets and the petits fours that round
off the meal are good, and service is attentive and friendly. The
restaurant also has seven comfortable bedrooms available.*
Closed 25 & 26 Dec Lunch not served Mon
♥ Continental **V** 48 seats Lunch £12.95-£16.80&alc Dinner
£22.50-£27.50&alc Last lunch 2pm Last dinner 9.30pm 30 P
nc13yrs
Credit Cards ①②③

---

★★65% **Unicorn**
Gunthorpe Bridge NG14 7FB (Inter-Hotels) ☎(0602)663612
FAX (0602) 664801
*A 17th-century coach house in an attractive location beside the
River Trent, the hotel has been recently refurbished throughout
and provides comfortable, modern accommodation and public
areas. Well equipped bedrooms are furnished in cheerful chintz.*
16⇆♟(3fb) CTV in all bedrooms ® **T** ✱ (ex guide dogs) ✱
sB&B⇆♟fr£47.50 dB&B⇆♟fr£57.50
140P ♪ water skiing boating
Credit Cards ①②③⑤

---

★★★55% *Cliff*
SA43 1PP ☎Cardigan(0239)613241 Telex no 48440
FAX (0239) 615391
*On the edge of Cardigan Bay with its own 9-hole golf course and
fine sea views, this family holiday hotel offers a good range of
leisure facilities. Public rooms are spacious and comfortable and a
programme is under way to upgrade the bedrooms.*
75⇆♟(4fb)2🛏 CTV in all bedrooms **T**
《 CTV 200P ❀ ⌷ (heated) ▶ 9 ♪ squash snooker sauna
solarium gymnasium sea fishing
♥ Welsh, English & French ⚓ ⚱ Last dinner 9pm
Credit Cards ①②③⑤

---

★63% *Sandsifter*
Godrevy Towans TR27 5ED ☎Hayle(0736)753314
*The restaurant of this small, family-run hotel near the National
Trust headland offers relaxed, friendly service and both à la carte
and table d'hôte menus (the choice at breakfast being particularly
good) ; its bar is popular with the locals and tourists alike, while
bedrooms are comfortable and well equipped, though compact.*
7⇆ CTV in all bedrooms ® ✈ (ex guide dogs)
80P ✿ nc12yrs
♥ English & French ⚓ ⚱ Last dinner 9pm
Credit Cards ①③

## HACKNESS North Yorkshire Map **08** SE99

**★★★ ♨68% Hackness Grange Country**
North Yorkshire National Park Y013 0JW (Best Western)
☎Scarborough(0723)882345 FAX (0723) 882391
*Set in 16 acres of grounds – complete with lake – at the heart of the North Yorkshire Moors National Park, this lovely hotel features an attractive restaurant serving food of a high standard, comfortable bedrooms with good facilities, and friendly, helpful service.*
11⇨Annexe15⇨♠(2fb)1⊞ CTV in all bedrooms ® T ⊁ ✱
sB&B⇨♠£49-£56 dB&B⇨♠£98-£112
( CTV 60P ⇞ ✿ ▣ (heated) ➤ 9 ♀ (hard) ♪ croquet *xmas*
V ♥ ⅍ ✱ Lunch £7.50-£8.50 Dinner £15.75-£16.25 Last dinner 9pm
Credit Cards ①②③⑤ⓔ
**See advertisement under SCARBOROUGH**

## HADLEY WOOD Greater London Map **04** TQ29

**★★★★60% West Lodge Park**
Cockfosters Rd EN4 0PY ☎081-440 8311 Telex no 24734
FAX 081-449 3698
*Set in 34 acres of parkland yet only 12 miles from central London, the original house, which dates from the 16th century, has been sympathetically extended over the years and the best bedrooms are in the new wing. The accommodation has been tastefully furnished, well equipped and individually decorated to retain a traditional elegance. There are bar billiards in the lounge and outdoor activities include putting, croquet and a fitness trail. Several meeting and function rooms are available.*
48⇨♠Annexe2⇨♠3⊞ CTV in all bedrooms ® T
⊁ (ex guide dogs) sB&B⇨♠£79.50-£89.50
dB&B⇨♠£107.50-£132.50 ⊟
Lift ( 200P ⇞ ✿ CFA putting croquet fitness trail
V ♥ ⬛ ✱ Lunch £16.50-£17.80&alc Dinner £17.80&alc Last dinner 9.45pm
Credit Cards ①②③

## HADLOW Kent Map **05** TQ65

**★★64% Leavers Manor**
Goose Green TN11 0JH ☎Tonbridge(0732)851442
FAX (0732) 851875
*An 18th-century Georgian manor house, skilfully extended, now operates as a good-value family-run hotel, the choice of individually furnished bedrooms in the main building now being supplemented by very spacious, comfortable and comprehensively equipped garden annexe accommodation. A restaurant with breakfast extension and the bar with its log fire are complemented by a superb function/banqueting suite and casually informal service is friendly and relaxed.*
10⇨♠Annexe20⇨♠(3fb) CTV in all bedrooms ® T
⊁ (ex guide dogs) ✱ sB&B⇨♠£35-£40 dB&B⇨♠£50-£60 ⊟
100P ⇞ ✿ CFA
♀ English & French ⬛ ✱ Lunch £8-£10 High tea fr£3 Dinner £9.50-£10.50 Last dinner 9.30pm
Credit Cards ①②③⑤

## HAILSHAM East Sussex Map **05** TQ50

**★★71% The Olde Forge**
Magham Down BN27 1PN ☎(0323)842893
Closed 25 Dec-2 Jan
*This charming 16th-century cottage hotel, conveniently located on the A271 1.5 miles east of Hailsham, offers cosy bedrooms, named after trees and all individually decorated and furnished to a high standard. Guests can enjoy a drink in the small bar/lounge with its welcoming log fire, and an intimate beamed restaurant with a local following features a choice of cooking being honest and reliable.*
8rm(1⇨5♠)1⊞ CTV in all bedrooms ® sB&B£32-£40
sB&B⇨♠£35-£40 dB&B⇨♠£40-£55 ⊟
→

12P ♨
♥ English & French **V** S10% Lunch £12.50-£15 Dinner £12.50-£15&alc Last dinner 9.15pm
Credit Cards 1 2 3 5 £

### ✿Forte Travelodge
Hellingly(on A22) (Forte)
☎(0323)844556 Central Res (0800) 850950
*On the A22 Eastbourne to London road at Boship Services, this lodge offers comfortable double rooms with sofabeds suitable for one adult, and a child's occasional bed. There is now one price per room which offers tremendous value. Meals and refreshments are available at the adjacent Happy Eater, open from 7am to 10pm.*
40⇌♠(40fb) CTV in all bedrooms ® sB⇌♠£29.95 dB⇌♠£29.95 (room only)
( 40P ♨
Credit Cards 1 2 3

### ✿Granada Lodge
Illey Ln B32 4AR (Granada) ☎021-550 3261 FAX 021-501 2880
(For full entry see Frankley Motorway Service Area (M5))

### ★★★ ❀❀73% Holdsworth House
Holmfield HX2 9TG (3m NW off A629 Keighley Road)
☎(0422)240024 Telex no 51574 FAX (0422) 245174
Closed 25 & 26 Dec
*This lovely stone-built 17th-century house with extensions stands in its own grounds just off the A629 Keighley road at Holmfield, about 3 miles from Halifax. All its beautifully furnished bedrooms have good facilities and some boast 4-poster beds and brass bedsteads, lounges are quite delightful, and a restaurant with lovely original oak-panelling provides an ideal atmosphere in which to enjoy the excellent meals produced by a capable French chef; service is very friendly and helpful throughout.*
40⇌♠(1fb)5⬚✂in 9 bedrooms CTV in all bedrooms **T** ✱
sB⇌♠£69-£86.50 dB&B⇌♠£86.50-£99.50 ♫
( 40P ✿ CFA
♥ English & French **V** ♿ ♨ ✂ ✱ Lunch £18.30-£26.65alc Dinner £18.30-£26.65alc Last dinner 9.30pm
Credit Cards 1 2 3 5

### ★★★67% The Imperial Crown
42/46 Horton St HX1 1BR ☎(0422)342342 FAX (0422) 349866
*This very well appointed hotel in the town centre, close to the railway station, features a new function/conference room housing a superb collection of old books, and very good bedrooms furnished to a high standard; a similarly high standard is maintained in the meals served in the Wallis Simpson restaurant with its fine collection of royal commemorative china.*
42⇌♠(3fb) CTV in all bedrooms ® **T** ✗
( CTV 16P ♨
♥ French **V** ♿ Last dinner 10pm
Credit Cards 1 2 3 5

### ★★★59% Wool Merchants
Mulcture Hall Rd HX1 1SP ☎(0422)368783 FAX (0422) 368783
*An hotel retaining the charming exterior of the wool warehouse from which it was converted offers very good value for money in its modern, well furnished accommodation.*
25⇌♠(2fb) CTV in all bedrooms ® **T** S% sB&B⇌♠£33-£52 dB&B⇌♠£48-£64
Lift CTV 200P CFA
♥ International **V** ♿ ♨ Lunch fr£6.95&alc Dinner £10.95&alc Last dinner 10pm
Credit Cards 1 2 3 £

### ★★60% Ulbster Arms
Bridge St KY12 6XY ☎(084783)206 & 641
*Traditional comforts and a friendly atmosphere are provided by this long established Highland hotel on the banks of the Thurso River, its position making it particularly popular with sporting enthusiasts.*
12rm(8⇌2♠) CTV in all bedrooms ® **T** ✱ sB&Bfr£32 sB&B⇌♠£34 dB&Bfr£64 dB&B⇌♠£68 ♫
CTV 30P 6☞ (£2 per day) ♨ ♪ shooting stalking
**V** ♿ ♨ Lunch fr£5alc High tea fr£6alc Dinner fr£17alc Last dinner 8.30pm
Credit Cards 1 3 £

### ✿Forte Travelodge
CH8 8RF (on A55, westbound) (Forte)
☎(0352)780952 Central Res (0800) 850950
*The well equipped modern accommodation available at this single-storey purpose-built lodge includes one bedroom designed to meet the needs of disabled guests. Situated on the westbound carriageway of the A55, the hotel overlooks the River Dee and Wirral Peninsula.*
31⇌♠(31fb) CTV in all bedrooms ® sB⇌♠£29.95 dB⇌♠£29.95 (room only)
( 32P ♨
Credit Cards 1 2 3

### ★★71% Crockstead Farm
BN8 6PT ☎(0825)880000 FAX (0825) 841252
*A recently converted Victorian barn set in peaceful rural surroundings beside an equestrian centre now offers accommodation in very attractive rooms – all reached from the verandah – which have limed oak furniture, Laura Ashley fabrics and all modern facilities; a restaurant and bar on two levels features genuine Victorian pictures, pine furniture on a tiled floor creating an appealing rustic atmosphere. An à la carte menu of nouvelle cuisine and English fare ranges from Fettuccine to Spotted Dick, and Director David Northolt takes an active part both in supervising meals and welcoming guests.*
12⇌♠ CTV in all bedrooms ® **T** ♫
( 100P ✿ ♪ (hard) ♫ ♫
♥ English & French **V** ♿ ♨ ✱ Lunch £6.95 High tea £3.50-£5 Dinner £17.50-£25alc Last dinner 10pm
Credit Cards 1 3

### ★★66% Halland Forge
BN8 6PW (Minotels) ☎(0825)840456 FAX (0825) 840773
*Conveniently situated on the A22, this family-run motel offers a range of dated, 70s-style, self-contained bedrooms. All provide adequate comfort and are particularly well equipped. The main hotel provides a lounge bar, attractive restaurant, and a coffee shop which is open for light snacks and meals throughout the day.*
Annexe20⇌♠2♨ CTV in all bedrooms ® **T** sB⇌♠£42.50-£46.75 dB⇌♠£53.50-£58.85 (room only) ♫
70P ✿ CFA nc5yrs
♥ English & French **V** ♿ ♨ ✱ Lunch £10.95-£12.95&alc Dinner £15.50-£17&alc Last dinner 9.30pm
Credit Cards 1 2 3 5 £

### ★★63% Owl
Main Rd YO8 9JH (4m W A63) ☎Selby(0757)228374 FAX (0757) 228125
*An 18th-century gentleman's residence has been converted and extended to provide a popular venue for functions and bar meals. Accommodation is neat and modestly furnished and the*

*atmosphere is friendly. Located on the A65, 5 miles from the A1 and 3 miles west of Selby.*

9⇌🟆(1fb)1🛏 CTV in all bedrooms ® T ✕ (ex guide dogs) 50P 🚗

V 🕉 ⚏ ✳ Lunch £1.20-£8alc High tea £1.20-£4alc Dinner £6-£15alc Last dinner 10pm

Credit Cards ① ② ③ £

## HAMILTON

See **Bothwell**

## HAMILTON MOTORWAY SERVICE AREA (M74)
Strathclyde Map **11** NS75

### ⌂Roadchef Lodge
M74 Northbound ML3 6JW ☎Hamilton(0698)891904 FAX (0698) 891682

Closed 25 & 26 Dec

36⇌(23fb) in 10 bedrooms CTV in all bedrooms ® T ✕ (ex guide dogs) ✳ sB⇌fr£36 dB⇌fr£42 (room only)

℄ 120P ✿ CFA

V ✂

Credit Cards ① ② ③ ⑤

## HAMPSON GREEN Lancashire Map **07** SD45

### ★★58% *Hampson House*
Hampson Ln LA2 0JB (off A6 at M6 junct 33) ☎Galgate(0524)751158

*Just off the A6 south of junction 33 of the M6, this conveniently located hotel offers modern accommodation suited to business and leisure travellers alike.*

13rm(6⇌5🟆)(3fb) CTV in all bedrooms ®

45P ✿ ℓ (grass)

🕉 ⚏

Credit Cards ① ③

## HANDFORTH Cheshire Map **07** SJ88

### ★★★★60% Belfry
Stanley Rd SK9 3LD ☎061-437 0511 Telex no 666358 FAX 061-499 0597

*A large, privately owned hotel situated on the A34, 3 miles east of Manchester International Airport and convenient for the city centre. It offers well equipped accommodation and is particularly popular with business people, including delegates using the conference facilities.*

81⇌ CTV in all bedrooms ® T ✳ sB⇌£73.50-£84.50 dB⇌£84.50-£94 (room only) 🛏

Lift ℄ 150P ✿ ♫

🍴 International V 🕉 ⚏ ✳ Lunch £12-£12.25&alc Dinner fr£15&alc Last dinner 10pm

Credit Cards ① ② ③ ⑤

See advertisement under MANCHESTER AIRPORT

## HAREWOOD West Yorkshire Map **08** SE34

### ★★★66% Harewood Arms
Harrogate Rd LS17 9LH ☎(0532)886566 FAX (0532) 886064

*Originally a coaching inn, and dating back to 1815, this hotel combines good, comfortable accommodation with friendly and efficient service.*

24⇌🟆(1fb) CTV in all bedrooms ® T ✳ sB&B⇌🟆£48-£70 dB&B⇌🟆£61.50-£80 🛏

℄ 100P ✿ xmas

🍴 English & French V 🕉 ⚏ ✳ Lunch £6.95-£9.50 Dinner £12.95-£15.95&alc Last dinner 10pm

Credit Cards ① ② ③ ④ ⑤

## HARLECH Gwynedd Map **06** SH53

See also **Talsarnau**

### ★★63% The Castle
Castle Square LL46 2YH ☎(0766)780529

*Personally run by the owners, and commanding fine sea views from its position next to the famous castle, the hotel has been refurbished throughout to provide warmth and comfort.*

10⇌🟆(2fb)1🛏 CTV in all bedrooms ® ✳ sB⇌🟆£28-£50 dB⇌🟆£38-£75 (room only)

CTV 30P (charged) 🚗 CFA ▶ 18 ℓ (hard) ∪ sauna

🍴 English & Continental V ✂ ✳ Lunch £7.50-£12 Dinner fr£12 Last dinner 9.30pm

Credit Cards ① ③

### ★59% Noddfa
Lower Rd LL46 2UB ☎(0766)780043

*This large stone-built gabled house, now a family-run hotel, is situated in an elevated position on the A496, close to the castle and overlooking St Davids Golf Course. It is fronted by a large terrace garden and car park, and provides simple but good quality accommodation.*

6rm(4⇌🟆)(1fb) CTV in all bedrooms ® ✕ (ex guide dogs) dB&B£28-£30 dB&B⇌🟆£32-£44 🛏

CTV 40P 🚗 ✿ archery nc3yrs xmas

🍴 International V ✳ Lunch £6-£13 High tea £2.50 Dinner £10.50-£13&alc Last dinner 8.30pm

Credit Cards ① ③ £

### ❀❀✕✕Cemlyn
High St LL46 2YA ☎(0766)780425

*This delightful restaurant occupies an unimposing Victorian building on the main street. The name does not mean 'frog', as supposed by at least one rival guide, but a bend or bow in a river; and it is named after the first lifeboat station in Wales. However, the place has been taken over by an army of frogs presented by* →

*satisfied customers to augment the collection begun by Chef/ Proprietor Ken Goody 10 years ago – he is a compulsive collector of objets d'art, bric-à-bac and pictures. He is an accomplished self-taught cook and his imaginative set price menu takes full advantage of seasonally fresh produce, and the atmosphere is that of a private dinner party.*

Closed mid Oct-Etr Lunch not served (ex by arrangement only)
♡ International V 62 seats Dinner £16.95-£20.95 Last dinner 9.30pm ♪ nc8yrs ⊬
Credit Cards [1] [3]

---

## HARLESTON Norfolk Map 05 TM28

### ★★ 54% *Swan*

The Thoroughfare IP20 9AG ☎(0379)852221

*A former coaching inn, dating back to 1551 and retaining many of its original features, offers simply furnished bedrooms equipped with most modern conveniences; the cosy, log-fired bar is popular with locals, and bar snacks provide an alternative to the restaurant's carvery menu.*

14⇨🛏(1fb) CTV in all bedrooms ® T
CTV 45P
♡ English & French V ♿ ⬛ ⊬ Last dinner 9.30pm
Credit Cards [1] [3]

---

## HARLOSH

See **Skye, Isle of**

---

## HARLOW Essex Map 05 TL41 ◉

### ★★★ 70% **Churchgate Manor**

Churchgate St, Old Harlow CM17 0JT (Best Western)
☎(0279)420246 Telex no 818289 FAX (0279) 437720

*An ancient manor retaining some of its original features and set in landscaped gardens now houses a restaurant and a 'quad' of well equipped, modern, executive style bedrooms; a number of suites and Super Executive rooms have recently been added. Ambitious levels of cooking, including flambé cuisine, are represented on à la carte and table d'hôte menus, while levels of service are good thoughout. Leisure and conference facilities are available, and the terrace and patio are pleasant places to relax on warmer days.*

85⇨(8fb) CTV in all bedrooms ® T ✳ sB&B⇨🛏£58-£89 dB&B⇨🛏£69-£109 ₧
《 120P ✿ CFA ⬛ (heated) sauna solarium gymnasium *xmas*
♡ English & French V ♿ ⬛ ✳ Lunch £15-£25alc Dinner £16.50-£17.50&alc Last dinner 9.45pm
Credit Cards [1] [2] [3] [5]

### ★★★ 65% **Harlow Moat House**

Southern Way CM18 7BA (Queens Moat) ☎(0279)422441
Telex no 81658 FAX (0279) 635094
Closed 24 Dec-3 Jan

*This efficiently run modern 2-storey hotel on the southern approach road to the town offers comfortable, well equipped bedrooms of good size, all similar in style though some are provided with additional comforts for the female traveller and some are designated no smoking. Restaurant staff give friendly service, and arriving guests receive a warm welcome at reception.*

120⇨🛏⊬in 20 bedrooms CTV in all bedrooms ® T
🐕 (ex guide dogs) ✳ sB&B⇨🛏£40-£75 dB&B⇨🛏£55-£90 ₧
《 180P CFA pool tables
♡ English & French V ♿ ⬛ ⊬ Lunch fr£15 Dinner fr£15&alc Last dinner 10pm
Credit Cards [1] [2] [3] [5] ④

### ★★★ 59% **Green Man**

Mulberry Green, Old Harlow CM17 0ET (Forte Hotels)
☎(0279)442521 Telex no 817972 FAX (0279) 626113

*This old coaching inn has a characterful public bar and timbered restaurant. A separate annexe houses function rooms with bedrooms on 3 levels above; all are of good size, with 16 of them*

---

*designated 'superior' while the rest are in various stages of refurbishment.*

Annexe55⇨🛏(1fb)⊬in 16 bedrooms CTV in all bedrooms ® T
✳ S17.5% sB⇨🛏£39.50-£65 dB⇨🛏£39.50-£70 (room only) ₧
《 75P CFA *xmas*
V ♿ ⬛ ⊬
Credit Cards [1] [2] [3] [5]

---

## HARLYN BAY Cornwall & Isles of Scilly Map 02 SW87

### ★ 66% **Polmark**

PL28 8SB (off B3276) ☎Padstow(0841)520206

*Set only a few minutes' walk from a sandy beach, this attractive stone house offers particularly comfortable public rooms, some well equipped, newly built bedrooms and some older-style simpler accommodation.*

13rm(8⇨3🛏)(2fb) ® ✳ sB&B£31-£32 sB&B⇨🛏£31-£32 dB&B£62-£64 dB&B⇨🛏£74-£76 (incl dinner)🛏
CTV 40P ✿ ⬠ (heated) *xmas*
V ♿ ⬛ Bar Lunch £2-£5 Dinner fr£12&alc Last dinner 7pm
Credit Cards [1] [3]

---

## HAROME

See **Helmsley**

---

## HARPENDEN Hertfordshire Map 04 TL11

### ★★★ 67% **Harpenden Moat House**

18 Southdown Rd AL5 1PE (Queens Moat) ☎(0582)764111
Telex no 826938 FAX (0582) 769858
Closed 26-31 Dec

*The former St Dominic's convent – much extended, but still retaining many Georgian features – offers comfortable accommodation in well furnished and equipped bedrooms which are generally spacious, though those in the main building tend to be more compact. Both the small open-plan lounge and the pleasant bar where you can enjoy a pre-dinner drink are newly refurbished, and an elegantly appointed restaurant with ornate ceiling paintings is particularly attractive. Staff are helpful and willing to please.*

18⇨🛏 Annexe35⇨🛏(3fb)2⬛⊬in 5 bedrooms CTV in all bedrooms ® T ✳ sB&B⇨🛏£84-£96 dB&B⇨🛏£109-£130 ₧
《 80P ✿ CFA boules croquet lawn
♡ French V ♿ ⬛ Lunch £13.75-£16&alc Dinner £17.75-£19.50&alc Last dinner 10pm
Credit Cards [1] [2] [3] [5] ④

### ★★★ 64% **Glen Eagle**

1 Luton Rd AL5 2PX ☎(0582)760271 FAX (0582) 460819

*A pleasant hotel, ideally situated for access to Luton Airport and the M1 motorway, has now been refurbished to offer functional, well equipped accommodation; public areas in country house style include a comfortable lounge bar and tastefully appointed restaurant. Caring, helpful staff provide traditional service.*

50⇨🛏(12fb)2⬛ CTV in all bedrooms ® T ✳ sB&B⇨🛏£78.50-£97 dB&B⇨🛏£97-£107 ₧
Lift 《 100P CFA *xmas*
♡ English & French V ♿ ⬛ ✳ Lunch £11-£14.80&alc Dinner £17.25&alc Last dinner 10pm
Credit Cards [1] [2] [3] [4] [5]

---

## HARRIS, ISLE OF Western Isles *Inverness-shire* Map 13

---

## TARBERT Map 13 NB10

### ★★ 61% *Harris*

PA85 3DL ☎Harris(0859)2154 FAX (0859) 2281

*Conveniently situated for the ferry terminal, this long-established family-run hotel offers traditional standards of hospitality and service with good home cooking. Bedrooms vary in size and are generally well maintained.*

25rm(13⇨4🛏)(2fb)

CTV 30P ✿ ⚙
V ✿ ⬚ ✗ Last dinner 8.30pm
Credit Cards ①③

---

## HARROGATE North Yorkshire Map 08 SE35

See also **Burnt Yates**

### ★★★★67% Moat House International
Kings Rd HG1 1XX (Queens Moat) ☎(0423)500000
Telex no 57575 FAX (0423) 524435

*This modern glass and redbrick high-rise hotel, linked to a Conference Centre, contrasts with the dignified spa town, but within are spacious and comfortable public rooms and bedrooms, some with fine views of the countryside. The Boulevard Restaurant has good fixed and à la carte menus, with discreet service.*

214➪↑✗in 56 bedrooms CTV in all bedrooms ® T ✱
sB&B➪↑£92-£98 dB&B➪↑£116.50-£125 ⊟
Lift ℂ ⊞ 130P *xmas*
♀ English & French V ✿ ⬚ ✱ Lunch £4.50-£25alc High tea £3.95-£8.50alc Dinner £14.95-£16.50&alc Last dinner 10pm
Credit Cards ①②③⑤ⓔ

### ★★★★64% Nidd Hall
Nidd HG3 3BN (Small Luxury Hotels) ☎(0423)771598
FAX (0423) 770931

*This fine country manor, within 23 acres of attractive grounds, complete with punt on the private lake, has only recently been converted to a spacious and elegant hotel. Bedrooms and bathrooms are mostly roomy, with their own individual style. The public rooms are peaceful and relaxing. The chef, Stuart Macleud, gives a touch of finesse to the cooking, in his own modern style, and for those seeking less formal arrangements, the hotel's leisure club in the basement has an Italian-themed 'Cellar' restaurant, which proves very popular. The hotel is best reached by taking the B6165, off the A61 at Ripley, and travelling a quarter of a mile towards Knaresborough. Nidd Hall is just 4 miles north of Harrogate.*

38➪↑Annexe20➪↑(1fb)4⊞✗in 12 bedrooms CTV in all bedrooms ® T ✖ (ex guide dogs) ✱ sB&B➪↑£83-£105 dB&B➪↑£125-£165 ⊟
Lift ℂ 90P ⇔ ✿ CFA ▱ (heated) ℘ (hard) ♪ squash snooker sauna solarium gymnasium beauty salon punting rowing ♫ *xmas*
♀ French V ✿ ⬚ ✱ Lunch fr£12.95 Dinner fr£26 Last dinner 9.30pm
Credit Cards ①②③⑤

### ★★★★63% The Majestic
Ripon Rd HG1 2HU (Forte Hotels) ☎(0423)568972
Telex no 57918 FAX (0423) 502283

*This impressive Victorian hotel, set in extensive grounds and well tended gardens close to the Conference Centre and town, has elegant public rooms with marbled pillars, chandeliers and many floral displays. The attractive traditional-style bedrooms have every modern facility, though a few rooms were still awaiting refurbishment at our last visit. The leisure club provides comprehensive facilities.*

156➪↑(10fb)✗in 46 bedrooms CTV in all bedrooms ® T ✱
S% sB➪↑£80 dB➪↑£90 (room only) ⊟
Lift ℂ 240P ✿ CFA ▱ (heated) ℘ (hard) squash snooker sauna gymnasium health & fitness centre beauty salon *xmas*
♀ International V ✿ ⬚ ✗ ✱ S% Sunday Lunch £11.50 Dinner £16.95&alc Last dinner 9.45pm
Credit Cards ①②③④⑤

### ★★★★58% The Crown
Crown Place HG1 2RZ (Forte Hotels) ☎(0423)567755
Telex no 57652 FAX (0423) 502284

*18th-century building near Valley Gardens and the Royal Baths.*

121➪↑(3fb)✗in 40 bedrooms CTV in all bedrooms ® T
Lift ℂ 50P CFA
V ✿ ⬚ ✗ Last dinner 9.30pm
Credit Cards ①②③④⑤

### ★★★🏵74% Boar's Head
Ripley HG3 3AY ☎(0423)771888 FAX (0423) 771509

*Recently refurbished by the proprietors Sir Thomas and Lady Ingilby, this delightful early 19th-century inn is part of the adjoining Ripley Castle complex and antiques and paintings from the castle help retain the traditional character. Lounges are comfortable and the elegant individually styled bedrooms include all modern facilities. Bar meals are available at lunch and dinner, while the intimate restaurant offers an imaginative and good value 4-course table d'hôte menu that changes regularly to make use of fresh seasonal produce. An enjoyable inspection meal included a spring vegetable soup and salmon and dover sole in a lemon and ginger cream sauce. There are home-made desserts and petits fours, and a well chosen wine list, all served with friendly professionalism.*

19➪↑Annexe6➪↑(2fb) CTV in all bedrooms ® T ✱
sB&B➪↑fr£75 dB&B➪↑£92-£110 ⊟
ℂ 60P 3🎠 ✿ ℘ (hard) *xmas*
♀ English & French V ✿ ⬚ ✱ Lunch £9.95-£12.95 Dinner fr£22 Last dinner 9.30pm
Credit Cards ①②③

### ★★★🏵71% White House
10 Park Pde HG1 5AH (Exec Hotel) ☎(0423)501388

*Jennie Forster, formerly a professional dancer and interior designer, has recently taken over this lovely Venetian style hotel, and taken with her David Lockwood, a renowned chef who has worked in many of Yorkshire's top eating places. He has rare skills with sauces and his home-made ravioli is something quite special. All fresh produce is used and presentation is exquisite – puddings are works of art. The daily changing menu is a set price for 5 courses, including British cheeses.*

13➪↑(1fb)1⊞ CTV in all bedrooms ®
CTV 10P ⇔ ✿
V ✿ ⬚ Last dinner 9pm
Credit Cards ①②③⑤

# HOB GREEN
## HOTEL AND RESTAURANT
### ★★★ 🍴

*For details see entry under MARKINGTON*

If you are looking to relax and unwind Hob Green will not disappoint you. Set in 870 acres midway between Harrogate and Ripon the hotel enjoys magnificent views of rolling countryside.

Whilst still retaining the atmosphere of a country house Hob Green incorporates all the facilities expected of a hotel of the 1990's with attention to detail and a desire for perfection being of paramount importance.

The restaurant has an excellent reputation with the menu being changed daily.

**MARKINGTON, HARROGATE HG3 3PJ.**
**Tel: Harrogate (0423) 770031 Fax: (0423) 771589**

★★★69% **Balmoral Hotel & Restaurant**

Franklin Mount HG1 5EJ ☎(0423)508208 FAX (0423) 530652

*Royalty is the motif throughout this elegant Victorian hotel, individually styled bedrooms, many with 4-posters, bearing such names as Highgrove, Elizabeth, Victoria, The Crown Room and The Windsor Suite. Public areas include an imaginative Oriental cocktail bar and a charming restaurant with chandeliers, magnificent displays of china and antique tables. A 6-course à la carte menu (the price of the main course determining that of the whole meal) continues the royal theme with Sole Clarence, Fillet of Beef Prince Albert and the roast lamb Guard of Honour.*

20⇔♠(2fb)8⊞ CTV in all bedrooms ® T S% sB⇔♠£60-£62 dB⇔♠£75-£80 (room only) 🍴

12P ❖ CFA solarium

V ♦ S% Dinner £16.50-£18.50&alc Last dinner 9pm

Credit Cards [1][2][3]ⓔ

★★★68% **Grants**

3-13 Swan Rd HG1 2SS ☎(0423)560666 FAX (0423) 502550

*Fronted by a flower-decked terrace, this well run, centrally located hotel is tastefully decorated throughout. Although some bedrooms are on the small side, they are comfortably furnished, attractive and well equipped. Service is provided by friendly, smartly dressed staff, and an interesting range of dishes is offered in the basement restaurant.*

41⇔♠(2fb)3⊞ CTV in all bedrooms ® T

Lift ℂ 26P CFA

♀ English & French V ♦ ◻ ✔ ✱ Lunch £9.75 High tea fr£5.50 Dinner fr£14.25 Last dinner 9.30pm

Credit Cards [1][2][3][5]ⓔ

★★★66% *Studley*

Swan Rd HG1 2SE ☎(0423)560425 Telex no 57506

*A busy and popular hotel conveniently situated in the centre of town. The French restaurant offers a wide range of dishes and efficient service.*

36⇔ CTV in all bedrooms ®

Lift ℂ CTV 14P nc8 yrs

♀ French ♦ Last dinner 10pm

Credit Cards [1][2][3][5]

★★★64% **Hospitality Inn**

Prospect Place, West Park HG1 1LB (Mount Charlotte (TS)) ☎(0423)564601 Telex no 57530 FAX (0423) 507508

*Overlooking 'The Stray', the hotel offers comfortable well equipped bedrooms and efficient service. The Oliver Twist Refectory and Copperfields Bar are full of character.*

71⇔♠(5fb) CTV in all bedrooms ® T 🍴

Lift ℂ 40P *xmas*

♀ English & French V ♦ ◻

Credit Cards [1][2][3][5]

★★★64% **Hotel St George**

1 Ripon Rd HG1 2SY (Swallow) ☎(0423)561431 Telex no 57995 FAX (0423) 530037

*An elegant Victorian building, centrally located opposite the town's conference and exhibition halls, now provides a good standard of accommodation, offering well equipped bedrooms, spacious public areas and a leisure centre.*

93⇔♠(14fb) CTV in all bedrooms ® T S% sB&B⇔♠fr£84 dB&B⇔♠fr£99 🍴

Lift ℂ 60P CFA ⬛ (heated) sauna solarium gymnasium boutique beautician masseuse whirlpool ∂ *xmas*

♀ English & French V ♦ ◻ S% Lunch £11.50&alc Dinner fr£16.25&alc Last dinner 9.30pm

Credit Cards [1][2][3][5]ⓔ

★★72% *Albany*

22-23 Harlow Moor Dr HG2 0JY ☎(0423)565890

*Close to the town centre in a quiet spot overlooking the Valley Gardens, this traditional hotel offers comfortable accommodation, good value home-cooked dinners and delightful, friendly service.*

14♠(3fb) CTV in all bedrooms ® ✗ (ex guide dogs) S% sB&B♠£22-£27 dB&B♠£40-£50 🍴

CTV

♀ English & Continental V ✔ ✱ Dinner £12 Last dinner 7.30pm

Credit Cards [1][3][5]ⓔ

★★72% **Russell**

Valley Dr HG2 0JN ☎(0423)509866 FAX (0423) 506185

Closed 27-30 Dec

*Just off the town centre in a peaceful location overlooking the Valley Gardens, this period hotel offers well equipped bedrooms, traditional service and a restaurant with a good value fixed price menu offering interesting freshly cooked dishes.*

34⇔♠(4fb) CTV in all bedrooms ® T ✱ (ex guide dogs) ✱ sB&B⇔♠£47.50-£49.50 dB&B⇔♠£62.95-£64.95 🍴

Lift ℂ ⅃ CFA

♀ French V ♦ ◻ ✔ ✱ Dinner £14.50-£15.75 Last dinner 10pm

Credit Cards [1][2][3][5]ⓔ

★★68% **Ascot House**

53 Kings Rd HG1 5HJ (Minotels) ☎(0423)531005 FAX (0423) 503523

Closed 28 Dec-5 Jan

*This privately owned Victorian house – beautifully converted to preserve many original features – stands in an attractive, mainly residential, area only a few minutes' walk from the town's conference centre. Bedrooms are all very well equipped, though they vary tremendously in size, and many have recently been refurbished; public areas are spaciously comfortable, and efficient service is provided by friendly staff.*

24rm(15⇔♠)(1fb) CTV in all bedrooms ® T ✱ sB&Bfr£39.50 sB&B⇔♠£42.50-£54.50 dB&B⇔♠£61.50-£83 🍴

14P *xmas*

♀ English & Continental V ♦ ◻ ✱ Bar Lunch £1.50-£6alc Dinner £12.95-£13.75&alc Last dinner 9pm

Credit Cards [1][2][3][5]ⓔ

★★68% *The Manor*

3 Clarence Dr HG1 2QE ☎(0423)503916

*Located in a quiet residential area close to the town centre, this friendly family-run hotel offers a good standard of accommodation, with well equipped comfortably furnished bedrooms, an attractive lounge and small restaurant, all spotlessly maintained.*

17⇔♠(1fb)✔in 1 bedroom CTV in all bedrooms ® T ✱ sB&B⇔♠£42-£52 dB&B⇔♠£62-£78 🍴

Lift 12P ⬛ *xmas*

♀ English & French V ♦ ◻ ✔ ✱ Lunch £12-£15 Dinner £16-£18&alc Last dinner 8.45pm

Credit Cards [1]ⓔ

★★67% **Abbey Lodge**

29-31 Ripon Rd HG1 2JL ☎(0423)569712

Closed 24-26 Dec

19rm(5⇔9♠)(2fb) CTV in all bedrooms ® ✱ sB&Bfr£21 sB&B⇔♠£24-£39.50 dB&Bfr£40 dB&B⇔♠£46 🍴

24P

V ♦ ✔ ✱ Dinner fr£9.50 Last dinner 9pm

Credit Cards [1][3]

★★67% **Green Park**

Valley Dr HG2 0JT (Consort) ☎(0423)504681 Telex no 57515 FAX (0423) 530811

*A traditional hotel, close to the town centre, overlooking the valley and park. The accommodation is comfortable and the service is friendly.*

43⇔♠(2fb)✔in 6 bedrooms CTV in all bedrooms ® T ✱ sB&B⇔♠£46 dB&B⇔♠£64.50 🍴

Lift ℂ 10P CFA *xmas*

→

H

# Harrogate

♀ International **V** ✿ ⟟ ✄ ✳ Bar Lunch £1.20-£5.75 Dinner £11&alc Last dinner 8.30pm
Credit Cards 1 2 3 5

## ★★64% Young's
15 York Rd, off Swan Rd HG1 2QL ☎(0423)567336 & 521231
FAX (0423) 500042
*Peacefully situated in the Duchy residential area yet within easy walking distance of the town centre, this small, privately owned hotel offers clean, comfortable and pleasantly appointed accommodation and a friendly, relaxed atmosphere.*
16⇨↑(2fb) CTV in all bedrooms ® **T** ✳ sB&B⇨↑£33-£42 dB&B⇨↑£50-£66 ⊟
18P ✿
♀ English & French ✳ Dinner £11.50-£13 Last dinner 7.30pm
Credit Cards 1 3

## ★★62% Fern
Swan Rd HG1 2SS (Inter-Hotels) ☎(0423)523866
Telex no 57583 FAX (0423) 501825
*Centrally located close to all of the town's amenities, the Fern Hotel is a privately owned establishment, which has been converted from a listed Victorian building. The Portico Restaurant provides an elegant setting for the extensive menu of freshly prepared food. There is a comfortable open plan lounge and bar. Bedrooms vary in size and standard, from the newly refurbished to the traditional and more modest rooms.*
27rm(26⇨)Annexe7⇨↑(4fb) CTV in all bedrooms ® **T** ✂ (ex guide dogs) ✳ sB⇨£35-£73.95 dB⇨£50-£95.50 (room only) ⊟
( ♪ CFA
♀ French **V** ✳ Bar Lunch fr£5 Dinner fr£13.95 Last dinner 9.30pm
Credit Cards 1 2 3 5

## ★★62% West Park
West Park HG1 1BL (Porterhouse) ☎(0423)524471
*This well-run friendly hotel in the town centre has functional but well equipped bedrooms and characterful Victorian-style public areas, which include a comfortable lounge bar, convivial public bar and attractive restaurant serving reasonably priced meals.*
17⇨↑ CTV in all bedrooms ® **T**
⊞ 20P
**V** ✿
Credit Cards 1 2 3 5

## ★73% Gables
2 West Grove Rd HG1 2AD ☎(0423)505625 FAX (0423) 561312
*A comfortable hotel in the heart of the town, near the exhibition centre, offers neat, well appointed bedrooms and the friendly services of resident proprietors.*
9rm(8⇨↑)(2fb) CTV in all bedrooms ® **T** sB&B⇨↑£23-£28.50 dB&B⇨↑£46-£57 ⊟
9P CFA
♀ Continental
Credit Cards 1 3 ⓔ

## ★72% Britannia Lodge
16 Swan Rd HG1 2SA ☎(0423)508482
*The epitome of a small residential hotel, and managed by residential proprietors, Britannia Lodge provides accommodation in individually and tastefully fitted bedrooms; public areas are warmly inviting, menus offer good value, and service is friendly.*
12⇨↑(4fb) CTV in all bedrooms ® **T** ✂ ✳ sB&B⇨↑£38-£45 dB&B⇨↑£49-£60 ⊟
⊞ CTV 6P 1☎ ⇏
♀ French **V** ✿ ⟟ ✄ Lunch £7 Dinner £12 Last dinner 7pm
Credit Cards 1 2 3 ⓔ

For key to symbols in English see the bookmark.

## ★70% Caesars
51 Valley Dr HG2 0JH ☎(0423)565818
Closed Xmas & New Year
*Competently prepared and attractively served meals are a feature of this comfortable, family-run hotel which stands close to the town centre, overlooking the Valley Gardens. Comfortably furnished bedrooms are well equipped and there is a pleasant lounge bar.*
9⇨↑(3fb) CTV in all bedrooms ® **T** ✂ (ex guide dogs) ✳ sB&B⇨↑£42.50-£50 dB&B⇨↑fr£60 ⊟
CTV ♪ ⇏
♀ English & French ✄ ✳ Dinner fr£14.50 Last dinner 8.30pm
Credit Cards 1 3 ⓔ

## ★70% Cavendish
3 Valley Dr HG2 0JJ ☎(0423)509637 FAX (0423) 504429
11⇨↑1⌘ CTV in all bedrooms ® **T** sB&B⇨↑£25-£30 dB&B⇨↑£55-£70
CTV ♪ ⇏
**V** ✄ Lunch £5-£6.50&alc High tea £5.50 Dinner £10-£15&alc Last dinner 10pm
Credit Cards 1 3 ⓔ

## ★69% Grafton
1-3 Franklin Mount HG1 5EJ ☎(0423)508491
FAX (0423) 523168
17rm(15⇨↑)(2fb) CTV in all bedrooms ® **T** ✳ sB&B£20-£21.50 sB&B⇨↑£23.50-£26 dB&B⇨↑£44-£50
CTV 2P
♀ International **V** ✿ ⟟ ✳ Lunch £1.50-£7.50 Dinner £9.50&alc Last dinner 9pm
Credit Cards 1 2 3 5 ⓔ

## ★67% Aston
7-9 Franklin Mount HG1 5EJ ☎(0432)564262 & 569534
Closed 3 Dec-1 Jan
*A small and cosy personally run hotel in a quiet area, offering well equipped bedrooms, a very comfortable lounge and attractive dining room with adjoining bar.*
15⇨↑ CTV in all bedrooms ® **T** S% sB&B⇨↑£25-£28 dB&B⇨↑£50-£65 ⊟
CTV 10P nc5yrs
✿ ⟟ ✄ S% Bar Lunch £5-£10alc High tea £1.50-£5alc Dinner £10.50-£12.50&alc Last dinner 7.30pm
Credit Cards 1 3 ⓔ

## ★65% Alvera Court
76 Kings Rd HG1 5JX ☎(0423)505735
*Comfortable, well appointed accommodation is provided by this small hotel situated opposite the conference centre, near the town centre; management by resident proprietors ensures that guests receive courteous service.*
12⇨↑(3fb) CTV in all bedrooms ® **T** ✂ (ex guide dogs) ✳ sB&B⇨↑£26.50-£32 dB&B⇨↑£53-£64 ⊟
CTV 4P ⇏ xmas
**V** ✳ Dinner fr£10.50&alc Last dinner 7pm
Credit Cards 1 3

## ★62% The Croft
42-46 Franklin Rd HG1 5EE ☎(0423)563326
*A small family-run hotel situated in the west end of the town, just a short walk from the centre's facilities, caters equally well for the business traveller or touring holidaymaker, its well equipped modern bedrooms and friendly atmosphere making a stay here good value for money.*
13⇨↑1⌘ CTV in all bedrooms ® **T** S% sB&B⇨↑£26-£29 dB&B⇨↑£46-£51.50 ⊟
10P
♀ English & French **V** ✿ ⟟ S% Lunch £9.50-£11.50&alc Dinner £9.50-£11.50&alc Last dinner 9.30pm
Credit Cards 1 3 ⓔ

## ✤✕Grundy's
21 Cheltenham Crescent HG1 1DH ☎(0423)502610

*A smart, attractive little restaurant situated near the Conference Centre offers an interesting and varied menu. Crab Terrine, for example, might be followed by roast duckling in a cream, white wine and green peppercorn sauce, the meal being concluded by a deliciously sticky toffee sponge.*

Closed Sun, BH's & 2 wks winter, 2 wks summer Lunch not served

♡ English & French **V** 40 seats ✱ Dinner £11.95-£12.75&alc
Last dinner 10pm ₽ nc10yrs
Credit Cards ⒈⒉⒊

## ✤✤✕Millers
1 Montpellier Mews HG1 2TG ☎(0423)530708

Closed Sun & 2 wks Xmas

Dinner not served Mon

♡ English & French 22 seats ✱ Lunch fr£12alc Dinner £35
Last lunch 2pm Last dinner 10pm ₽
Credit Cards ⒈⒊⒌

---

## HARROW Greater London

See **LONDON plan 1***B5*(page 434)

**★★ 66% Harrow**

Roxborough Bridge, 12-22 Pinner Rd HA1 4HZ ☎081-427 3435
Telex no 917898 FAX 081-861 1370
RS Xmas

*Deceptively large, this hotel offers accommodation on three floors of the main building and in two other buildings, one of which, Park House, is self contained. Though rooms vary in size they are all well designed to meet the needs of the business visitor, generously equipped with amenities, clean and well maintained; public areas are manned by a cheerful team of staff.*

76⇨👤(4fb)1🔔½in 3 bedrooms CTV in all bedrooms ® **T** ✱
sB&B⇨👤£48-£75 dB&B⇨👤£75-£90 🍴
《67P

♡ International **V** ❀ ⚆ ✱ Lunch £12.95 Dinner £14.95&alc
Last dinner 9.45pm
Credit Cards ⒈⒉⒊⒌£

## ★★ 65% *Lindal*
2 Hindes Rd HA1 1SJ ☎081-863 3164 FAX 081-427 5435

*Warm, friendly service is provided by the resident proprietors of this comfortable little hotel; bedrooms are well equipped and practical, while public areas include a panelled bar and romantic candlelit restaurant offering an à la carte menu of uncomplicated dishes.*

17rm(14⇨👤) CTV in all bedrooms ® **T**
《17P
**V** ❀ ⚆ ½ Last dinner 8.30pm
Credit Cards ⒈⒊

## ★★ 62% *Cumberland*
1 St Johns Rd HA1 2EF ☎081-863 4111 Telex no 917201
FAX 081-861 5668

*Privately owned commercial hotel with informal, friendly atmosphere.*

30⇨👤Annexe51⇨👤(3fb) CTV in all bedrooms ® **T**
✖ (ex guide dogs) sB&B⇨👤£38-£62 dB&B⇨👤£48-£75 🍴
《55P CFA

♡ English & French **V** ❀ ⚆ ½ ✱ S10% Lunch fr£6.95&alc
Dinner £11.95-£13.95&alc Last dinner 9.30pm
Credit Cards ⒈⒉⒊⒌

## ★★ 60% *Monksdene*
2-12 Northwick Park Rd HA1 2NT ☎081-427 2899
Telex no 919171 FAX 081-863 2314

Closed 25-31 Dec

*This mainly commercial hotel in a residential street, within easy reach of the centre and transport services, has well equipped, pleasantly decorated bedrooms of varying size in the main building and executive rooms in an adjacent annexe.*

→

H

66⇆🏠 Annexe24⇆(3fb) CTV in all bedrooms Ⓡ **T**
🏃 (ex guide dogs) ✱ sB&B⇆🏠£40-£62 dB&B⇆🏠£50-£77
《 CTV 65P CFA
♡ English & French **V** ✿ ⚆ ✱ Lunch £10.25-£14.95&alc
Dinner fr£14.95&alc Last dinner 9.45pm
Credit Cards ①②③⑤ⓔ

---

### HARTINGTON Derbyshire Map **07** SK16

★55% *Charles Cotton*
SK17 0AL ☎(029884)229
*This historic 15th-century hotel, named after the famous author/
angler, stands in the square of a sleepy village at the heart of the
Peak District. Bedrooms are simply furnished but clean, a good
range of food is available, and friendly staff provide helpful service.*
11rm(3fb) CTV in all bedrooms Ⓡ
CTV 50P ✿ ⚓
♡ English & French **V** ✿ ⚆ Last high tea 6pm
Credit Cards ①③

---

### HARTLEBURY Hereford & Worcester Map **07** SO87

○**Forte Travelodge**
Shorthill Nurseries DY11 6DR (A449 southbound) (Forte)
☎Central Res (0800) 850950
Due to have opened Sep 1991
32⇆🏠

---

### HARTLEPOOL Cleveland Map **08** NZ53

★★★55% **Marine**
5/7 The Front, Seaton Carew TS25 1BS ☎(0429)266244
FAX (0429) 864144
*Recently modernised and extended to a good standard, this hotel
stands in the Seaton Carew area of the town, overlooking the
sands. Bedrooms have all been thoughtfully equipped and
decorated. The large lounge bar is popular with all age groups, and
a pretty carvery restaurant offers good value.*
25⇆🏠(3fb)3🛏⚲in 3 bedrooms CTV in all bedrooms Ⓡ **T**
🏃 (ex guide dogs) ✱ sB&B⇆🏠£42 dB&B⇆🏠£52-£62 ♬
《 ⊞ 60P
**V** ✿ ⚆ ✹ ✱ Lunch £5-£8.25&alc Dinner £6.75-£8.25&alc Last
dinner 9.30pm
Credit Cards ①②③⑤

★★73% **Ryedale Moor**
3 Beaconsfield St, Headland TS24 0NX ☎(0429)231436
FAX (0429) 863787
*Managed by the friendly resident owners, this small hotel
overlooking the esplanade and within easy reach of the town
centre, has a relaxing atmosphere and provides comfortable well
equipped accommodation.*
13⇆🏠(2fb)⚲in 5 bedrooms CTV in all bedrooms Ⓡ **T** 🏃 ✱
sB&B⇆🏠£30-£39 dB&B⇆🏠£48-£54
《 ⊞ CTV 7P CFA nc12yrs
♡ French & Indian **V** ✿ ⚆ ✹ Lunch £3.50-£5.50&alc High
tea fr£3.50 Dinner £3.50-£5.50 Last dinner 9pm
Credit Cards ①②③⑤ⓔ

✿✕**Krimo's**
8 The Front, Seaton Carew TS25 1BS (2m S A178)
☎(0429)266120
*A modest yet delightful little restaurant on the seafront providing
extremely good value for money, particularly business lunches. The
emphasis is on good produce, with classic dishes prepared in the
light modern style. Service is friendly and informal.*
Closed Sun, Mon, 1st 2 wks Aug, 25-26 Dec & 1 Jan Lunch not
served Sat
♡ Algerian, French & Italian **V** 56 seats Lunch £4.50-
£8.80&alc Dinner £9.50-£18.85alc Last lunch 1.30pm Last
dinner 9.30pm 🌿
Credit Cards ①③

---

### HARVINGTON (NEAR EVESHAM) Hereford & Worcester
Map **04** SP04

See also Evesham
★★❀77% **The Mill At Harvington**
Anchor Ln, Harvington WR11 5NR ☎Evesham(0386)870688
(For full entry see Evesham)

---

### HARWICH Essex Map **05** TM23

★★❀❀67% **The Pier at Harwich**
The Quay CO12 3HH ☎(0255)241212 FAX (0206) 322752
*Situated on the quay, this small hotel has tastefully appointed and
well equipped bedrooms and a brasserie-style restaurant. It is,
however, renowned for its fish restaurant which serves superb
quality fish dishes along with a limited number of poultry and meat
dishes. The comprehensive wine list includes some fine vintage
wines.*
6⇆(2fb) CTV in all bedrooms Ⓡ **T** 🏃 (ex guide dogs) ✱
sB&B⇆£45-£60 dB&B⇆£62.50-£72.50 Continental breakfast
《 10P
♡ English & French **V** ✱ Lunch £10.50&alc Dinner £17.95-
£30.40alc Last dinner 9.30pm
Credit Cards ①③

★★59% **Tower**
Main Rd, Dovercourt CO12 3PJ ☎(0255)504952
FAX (0255) 504952
RS 25 & 26 Dec
*A late Victorian Italianate building, retaining many splendid
architectural features including a winged staircase and
eyecatching painted plasterwork on the bar and dining room
ceilings. Bedrooms on 2 floors are bright and modernised.*
15⇆🏠(2fb) CTV in all bedrooms Ⓡ **T** S% sB&B⇆🏠£37-£47
dB&B⇆🏠£52-£56 ♬
《 50P 1🏇 ⛟
**V** ✿ ⚆ ✱ Lunch fr£8.50 Dinner £10-£20alc Last dinner
9.30pm
Credit Cards ①②③⑤

★★55% **Cliff**
Marine Pde, Dovercourt CO12 3RE ☎(0255)503345 & 507373
FAX (0255) 240358
*Overlooking the bay, this white Victorian hotel has smart and
comfortable public areas with a choice of bars. The en suite
bedrooms are on 3 floors, many facing the sea and of reasonable
size, and about half have been redecorated.*
28⇆🏠 CTV in all bedrooms Ⓡ **T** ✱ sB&B⇆🏠£43
dB&B⇆🏠£53 ♬
《 60P CFA
**V** ✿ ⚆ ✱ Lunch £7.75&alc Dinner £9.75&alc Last dinner 9pm
Credit Cards ①②③④⑤

---

### HASLEMERE Surrey Map **04** SU93

★★★69% **Lythe Hill**
Petworth Rd GU27 3BQ (1.25m E B2131) ☎(0428)651251
FAX (0428) 644131
*Set in 14 acres of grounds, this original 14th-century farmhouse
has period rooms and a modern courtyard wing. The bedrooms are
individually decorated with considerable style and quality, and
guests have a choice of two restaurants along with 24-hour room
service.*
40⇆(8fb)1🛏 CTV in all bedrooms **T** ✱ sB⇆£74-£150
dB⇆£85-£150 (room only) ♬
《 200P ✿ CFA ♪ (hard) ⚓ boules croquet *xmas*
♡ English & French **V** ✿ ⚆ Lunch £16.50-£17.50&alc Dinner
£16.50&alc Last dinner 9.15pm
Credit Cards ①②③

❀❀❀ ✗ ✗ **Morels**

23/27 Lower St GU27 2NY ☎(0428)651462

*Chef-patron Jean-Yves Morel and his wife Mary-Anne have run this delightful restaurant for 11 years with a dedication and professionalism that has brought them increasing recognition from all quarters. The stylish blue and white dining room, with its interesting pictures and eye-catching flower displays, is a pleasant setting for the menus (both à la carte and prix fixe) which offer an appetising selection of traditional favourites, innovative ideas – for example the garlic and gruyère soufflé; the quails with cous-cous, ginger and spring onion, and French provincial dishes – their Boeuf Bourguignon is a very deep and refined version. Monsieur Morel welcomes the revival of interest in the more earthy rustic dishes. His cooking is full of flavour, from the crisp rolls to the vegetables, chosen individually for each main course, and the expresso coffee and excellent petits fours. The French wine list is reliable and the service attentive and unobtrusive.*

Closed Sun, Mon, 2 wks Feb, 2 wks Sep & BH's (ex Good Fri) Lunch not served Sat

♀ French V 48 seats ✱ Lunch fr£18&alc Dinner fr£21&alc Last lunch 1.45pm Last dinner 10pm *P*

Credit Cards ①②③

---

**HASTINGS & ST LEONARDS** East Sussex Map **05** TQ80

★★★69% **Beauport Park**

Battle Rd TN38 8EA (3m N off A2100) (Best Western) ☎Hastings(0424)851222 FAX (0424) 852465

*This elegant Georgian country house, set in 35 acres of grounds next to the golf course, serves afternoon tea, snacks and pre-dinner drinks in a peaceful lounge which is warmed by a log fire on cooler days; a traditionally appointed bar and restaurant overlook the splendid Italian sunken gardens. Outdoor leisure facilities include a swimming pool, tennis courts, putting green and croquet lawn. Attractive bedrooms are tastefully furnished and comprehensively equipped.*

23⇨♠(2fb)1⊞ CTV in all bedrooms ® ✱ sB&B⇨♠fr£62 dB&B⇨♠fr£80 ☒

60P 4🚗 (£1.50) ❖ CFA ⌂ (heated) ▶ 18 ♬ (hard) squash ∪ snooker putting croquet boules outdoor chess ♫ *xmas*

♀ French V ♥ ♨ ✱ Lunch £13.20-£14alc High tea fr£8alc Dinner £15.20-£16alc Last dinner 9.30pm

Credit Cards ①②③⑤

**See advertisement on page 347**

★★★69% **Cinque Ports**

Summerfields ☎Hastings(0424)439222 Telex no 957584 FAX (0424) 437277

*This newly built hotel offers accommodation made comfortable by quality furnishings and good beds. Elegantly attractive public rooms feature bare stone or wooden floors scattered with thick Chinese rugs and a dark blue Art Deco restaurant specialises in fresh fish. Many traditional services are retained, including early morning tea.*

40⇨♠(4fb) CTV in all bedrooms T ✖ (ex guide dogs) ✱ sB&B⇨♠£63-£70 dB&B⇨♠£81-£96 ☒

℃ 80P ❖ *xmas*

♥ ♨ ✱ S10% Lunch £12.50-£16&alc Dinner £17.50-£18.50&alc Last dinner 10pm

Credit Cards ①②③⑤

❀❀❀ ✗ **Roser's**

64 Eversfield Place TN37 6DB ☎Hastings(0424)712218

*Both the area and its seaside location make this an unlikely venue for a restaurant of the calibre of Roser's. Unassuming both inside and out, with dimpled windows and discreet boothed seating, it offers you a view of the busy kitchen through a glass door as you enter the dining room. A value-for-money set-price menu is available at both lunch and dinner, and the recently shortened à la carte selection is supplemented by a few 'specials' and fresh local fish as available. Chef/patron Gerald Rosers sharpens guests' appetites with hot and cold 'nibbles' or maybe a demi-tasse of frothy 'cappuchino' – a creamy carrot and courgette soup lightly*

H

*flavoured with curry – and fish/seafood features strongly among the starters, the Pike Soufflé with creamy smoked salmon and Beluga caviare sauce being a notable example. This might be followed by locally raised guinea fowl served with sweet roasted shallots and wild mushrooms set on a flavoursome red wine/meat glaze, while the short range of desserts features a chocolate mousse made with the finest Belgian chocolate and an unusual Apple Mille Feuilles – crisp apple layered with Calvados-flavoured crème patissière, a caramelised top and butterscotch sauce. Most of the wines on the impressive list are French, but there is also a good selection from Gemany. Service throughout is attentive, professional and genuinely caring.*
Closed Sun, Mon & 1st 2 wks Jan Lunch not served Sat
♀ French 40 seats Lunch £15.95&alc Dinner £20-£35alc Last lunch 2pm Last dinner 10.30pm ✗
Credit Cards ① ② ③ ⑤

---

## HATFIELD Hertfordshire Map **04** TL20

### ★★★ 61% **Hazel Grove**
Roehyde Way AL10 9AF (Best Western) ☎(0707)275701
Telex no 916580 FAX (0707) 266033
*Alongside the A1 just to the south of junction 3, this purpose-built hotel offers functional modern accommodation. All bedrooms are well equipped but the executive rooms offer a higher degree of comfort and quality, and are generally quieter. Public areas are fairly limited but include the split level Gallery Restaurant, a small bar and a gym.*
76⇆♠(14fb)⚲in 38 bedrooms CTV in all bedrooms ® T ✱
sB&B⇆♠£46-£87 dB&B⇆♠£56-£87 ☐
《120P CFA gymnasium *xmas*
♀ English & Continental V ✿ ⚖ ✱ Sunday Lunch £9.50-£12
Dinner £15.25-£17.25&alc Last dinner 9.30pm
Credit Cards ① ② ③ ⑤ ⓔ

---

## HATHERSAGE Derbyshire Map **08** SK28

### ★★★ 65% **George**
Main Rd S30 1BB (Lansbury) ☎Hope Valley(0433)50436
Telex no 547196 FAX (0433) 50099
*This small hotel converted from a 16th-century coaching inn has a warm and cosy atmosphere, with attractively decorated, well equipped bedrooms and comfortable public areas.*
18⇆♠(3fb)1⚄⚲in 5 bedrooms CTV in all bedrooms ® T
✖ (ex guide dogs) sB&B⇆♠fr£69 dB&B⇆♠fr£84 ☐
40P ✿ CFA *xmas*
♀ International V ✿ ⚲ Lunch fr£8.95&alc Dinner fr£15.45&alc Last dinner 10pm
Credit Cards ① ② ③ ⑤

### ★★ 57% **Hathersage Inn**
Main St S30 1BB ☎Hope Valley(0433)50259 FAX (0433) 51199
*A charming old inn, centrally located, popular with locals for its bar and food. Accommodation varies greatly from very good in the adjacent Morley House to very modest in some of the older rooms.*
11⇆♠Annexe4rm1⚄ CTV in all bedrooms ® T
sB&B⇆♠£55-£60 dB&B⇆♠£75-£80 ☐
20P *xmas*
V ✿ ⚖ ⚲ Sunday Lunch fr£9.95 Dinner fr£14.25 Last dinner 9.30pm
Credit Cards ① ② ③ ⑤ ⓔ

---

## HAVANT Hampshire Map **04** SU70 ◎

### ★★★ 60% **The Bear**
East St PO9 1AA (Lansbury) ☎(0705)486501 Telex no 869136
FAX (0705) 470551
*This 16th-century coaching inn – a Grade II listed building – at the heart of the town retains its original exterior but has been cleverly modernised inside, providing well equipped bedrooms (12 were added only 3 years ago), an attractive restaurant which offers both*

---

*à la carte and table d'hôte menus, and the recently refurbished Elizabethan bar.*
42⇆♠(3fb)1⚄⚲in 5 bedrooms CTV in all bedrooms ®
✖ (ex guide dogs) sB&B⇆♠£68-£79 dB&B⇆♠£81-£92 ☐
Lift 《90P CFA *xmas*
♀ European V ✿ ⚖ Lunch fr£12&alc Dinner fr£12&alc Last dinner 10.30pm
Credit Cards ① ② ③ ⑤

---

## HAVERFORDWEST Dyfed Map **02** SM91

### ★★ 61% **Hotel Mariners**
Mariners Square SA61 2DU ☎(0437)763353 FAX (0437) 764258
Closed 26-27 Dec & 1 Jan
*In operation since 1625, when the town was a thriving port and commercial centre, the hotel has now been carefully modernised to provide good accommodation. Public areas include a choice of bars, a small residents' lounge, a meeting room and a bar restaurant offering a wide range of dishes.*
32rm(31⇆♠)(5fb) CTV in all bedrooms ® T sB&Bfr£31.50
sB&B⇆♠£40-£55 dB&B⇆♠£66-£72 ☐
《40P CFA
♀ French V ✿ ⚖ Bar Lunch fr£6.50&alc Dinner fr£10&alc
Last dinner 9.30pm
Credit Cards ① ② ③ ⑤

### ★★ 57% **Pembroke House**
Spring Gardens SA61 2EJ ☎(0437)763652
*This creeper-clad Georgian house a few minutes walk from the town centre is now run by the friendly Davies family. Popular with business travellers, the hotel offers well equipped bedrooms, a spacious and comfortable lounge bar and a good choice of food.*
21rm(13⇆♠6♠)(4fb)1⚄ CTV in all bedrooms ® T ✱ sB&B£33
sB&B⇆♠£38 dB&B£55 dB&B⇆♠♠£60 ☐
CTV 18P
✿ ⚖ ✱ Dinner £9.90&alc Last dinner 9.30pm
Credit Cards ① ② ③ ⑤

---

## HAWES North Yorkshire Map **07** SD88

### ★★ 76% **Simonstone Hall**
Simonstone DL8 3LY ☎Wensleydale(0969)667255
FAX (0969) 667741
*A comfortable country house in a delightful setting with panoramic views on all sides. Bedrooms are individually designed with colour co-ordinated décor and fabrics. Lounges are inviting with many antiques and conversation pieces. Interesting menus cater for healthy eaters and include vegetarian dishes. Food is freshly prepared and attractively presented.*
10⇆♠1⚄ CTV in all bedrooms ® dB&B⇆♠£51-£67 ☐
24P ⚄ ✿ *xmas*
♀ English & French V ✿ ⚖ Lunch fr£12.50 Dinner fr£21.75&alc Last dinner 8.30pm
Credit Cards ① ③ ⓔ

### ★★ 74% **Rookhurst Georgian Country House**
Gayle DL8 3RT ☎Wensleydale(0969)667454
Closed 16 Dec-Jan
*The resident proprietors of this comfortable, impressive hotel in the tiny hamlet of Gayle, which stands in undulating countryside near Hawes, not only provide warm and spontaneous service but also personally prepare the home-cooked dishes served in the dining room.*
6rm(3⇆♠1♠)2⚄⚲in all bedrooms CTV in all bedrooms ®
✖ (ex guide dogs) sB&B£38-£42 dB&B⇆♠♠£90-£110 (incl dinner) ☐
10P ✿ nc12yrs
✿ ⚖ ⚲ Dinner £18-£25alc Last dinner 7.30pm
Credit Cards ① ③

---

**★★⚑69% Stone House**
Sedbusk DL8 3PT ☎Wensleydale(0969)667571
FAX (0969) 667720
Closed Jan RS mid Nov-Dec & Feb-mid Mar
*In a pleasant location just outside the town is this elegant, carefully modernised country house. Characterful lounges have open fires, and courteous, hospitable service is provided by the resident proprietors.*
15rm(14⇨🏱)(1fb)2🛏 CTV in all bedrooms ® T
sB&B⇨🏱£27 dB&Bfr£43 dB&B⇨🏱£54-£65 ⊟
15P ✿ CFA ♬ (grass) *xmas*
V ✇ ✠ Dinner £13.95 Last dinner 8pm
Credit Cards ①③

**★★62% Fountain**
Market Place DL8 3RD ☎(0969)667206
Closed 24-25 Dec
*Modernised town centre hotel, family owned and run.*
12⇨🏱(2fb)✠in 2 bedrooms CTV in all bedrooms ® T S%
sB&B⇨🏱£30 dB&B⇨🏱£52 ⊟
10P CFA
✇ S% Sunday Lunch £5.50 Dinner £11&alc Last dinner 9pm
Credit Cards ①③£

**★70% Herriots**
Main St DL8 3QU ☎(0969)667536
Closed Nov-Jan RS Feb-early Mar
*Relaxed, informal and friendly, this hotel is located in the centre of a quaint Dales town at the heart of Herriot country. Its six comfortable, clean and prettily decorated bedrooms are provided with en suite shower facilites, and the cosy, attractive restaurant features a short but interesting menu of freshly cooked dishes including home-made desserts.*
6🏱(1fb) CTV in all bedrooms ® sB&B🏱£30 dB&B🏱£46 ⊟
✠ ⚏ *xmas*
♀ International V Dinner £15-£20alc Last dinner 9.30pm
Credit Cards ①③

---

**HAWICK** Borders *Roxburghshire* Map **12** NT51

**★★71% Kirklands**
West Stewart Place TD9 8BH (Exec Hotel) ☎(0450)72263
FAX (0450) 370404
*A small traditional hotel offering spacious well-equipped bedrooms, inviting lounges and warm friendly service. The good-value dinner menu provides a varied choice.*
6rm(2⇨1🏱)Annexe7⇨🏱 CTV in all bedrooms ® T S%
sB&B£40-£43 sB&B⇨🏱£45-£48 dB&B£60-£65
dB&B⇨🏱£68-£70 ⊟
20P ✿ snooker games room ๗
♀ International V ✇ ✱ Lunch £4.25-£9.50alc Dinner £13.50-£16alc Last dinner 9.30pm
Credit Cards ①②③⑤£

---

**HAWKCHURCH** Devon Map **03** ST30

**★★★⚑71% Fairwater Head**
EX13 5TX ☎(02977)349
Closed 7 Dec-5 Mar
*An attractive small country house hotel in a rural setting with expansive views across open countryside and the sea beyond. Run on informal lines by the Austin and Lowe families this cosy retreat generates continued return business. Top marks for cleanliness with spotless bedrooms, all soundly finished and equipped with modern facilities. Some rooms in the adjacent garden complex have small patios. Public rooms include a comfortable lounge, small bar and simple, country-style dining room.*
14⇨🏱Annexe7⇨🏱 CTV in all bedrooms ® T ✱
sB&B⇨🏱£60-£71.50 dB&B⇨🏱£104-£125 (incl dinner) ⊟
30P ⚏ ✿ croquet ♬ ๗          →

H

❖ ⚸ ✂ ✳ Sunday Lunch £10.25 Dinner £17.75-£19.75 Last dinner 8.30pm
Credit Cards 1 2 3 5

**See advertisement under LYME REGIS**

---

## HAWKHURST Kent Map 05 TQ73

### ★★65% **Tudor Court**
Rye Rd TN18 5DA (Best Western) ☎(0580)752312
Telex no 957565 FAX (0580) 753966
*An attractive Georgian building with lovely rear gardens is situated on the A268 on the outskirts of the village. Service is friendly and the accommodation well equipped.*
18⇦🛌(1fb)2⏛ CTV in all bedrooms ® T S10%
sB&B⇦🛌fr£52 dB&B⇦🛌£82-£87 🍴
CTV 50P 2⏛ (£1.50) ❀ ♪ (hard) croquet clock golf childrens play area *xmas*
♥ International ❖ ⚸ ✂ S10% Lunch fr£11&alc Dinner fr£12.50 Last dinner 9.15pm
Credit Cards 1 2 3 5

---

## HAWKSHEAD (NEAR AMBLESIDE) Cumbria Map 07 SD39

### ★★❀⚏73% *Field Head House*
Outgate LA22 0PY ☎Hawkshead(09666)240
Closed 14 Jan-8 Feb RS Tue
*A delightful country house hotel situated in 6 acres of gardens and grounds, in a particularly peaceful area of the English lakes. The best local produce is used in cooking the 5-course set dinners (not available on Tuesdays) and there are also over 100 different wines to choose from. From Ambleside take the B5286 to Hawkshead, and turn right 0.5 miles past the Outgate Inn towards Firly Head.*
7⇦🛌(2fb)🛌in all bedrooms CTV in all bedrooms ®
15P ⇞ ❀ croquet
✂

### ★★⚏73% **Highfield House**
Hawkshead Hill LA22 0PN ☎Hawkshead(09666)344
Closed 24-26 Dec
*This is a friendly family run house standing on high ground in 2.5 acres of woodland gardens. Bedrooms are spacious, comfortable, very well maintained, and many have fine views of the surrounding countryside. Service is personal and attentive and the atmosphere is warm and hospitable.*
11rm(8⇦3🛌)(2fb) CTV in all bedrooms ® sB&B£24.20
sB&B⇦🛌£30.30 dB&B£45 dB&B⇦🛌£55.60-£62.50 🍴
12P ⇞ ❀
♥ English & Continental V ❖ ⚸ ✂ S% Dinner £14 Last dinner 8pm
Credit Cards 1 3

### ★★60% **Queen's Head**
Main St LA22 0NS ☎Hawkshead(09666)271
*This 17th-century inn at the centre of the village has modest bedrooms with attractive touches and an old world bar and dining room, popular for bar meals and evening à la carte dishes.*
10rm(1⇦5🛌)Annexe2⇦3(2fb)1⏛ CTV in 10 bedrooms ® T ✳ sB&B£28-£36 sB&B⇦3🛌£36 dB&B£42-£44 dB&B⇦3🛌£44-£51
CTV 10P nc8yrs *xmas*
♥ English & Continental V ❖ ✳ Lunch £3.75-£7.50 Dinner £11.75-£21alc Last dinner 9.30pm
Credit Cards 1 2 3 £

### ○**Tarn Hows**
Hawkshead Hill LA22 0PR ☎Hawkeshead(09666)696
FAX (09666) 294
Due to have opened Nov 1991
18⇦3🛌

---

## HAWNBY North Yorkshire Map 08 SE58

### ★★70% *Hawnby*
YO6 5QS ☎Bilsdale(04396)202
*This extremely comfortable little hotel is situated in the unspoilt and picturesque village of Hawnby, in the North Yorkshire Moors National Park. Bought by the family of the Earl of Mexborough, the hotel is personally supervised by Lady Mexborough, who has recently totally refurbished the hotel, using Laura Ashley fabrics and furniture. The 6 pretty bedrooms are all very well equipped, comfortable, individually decorated and all are fully en suite. The high standards are carried right through the hotel, and there is a cosy lounge, adjoining the dining room where traditional English food is freshly prepared and served. There is also a full range of bar snacks available in the character public bar. A warm welcome for guests is assured at this relaxing, comfortable and quality hotel.*
6⇦🛌 CTV in all bedrooms ® T ✳
25P ❀ ♪ (hard) ✔ nc8yrs
V ❖ ⚸ Last dinner 8.30pm
Credit Cards 1 3

---

## HAWORTH West Yorkshire Map 07 SE03

### ★★★58% **Five Flags**
Manywell Heights BD13 5EA (near junc A629/B6429)
☎Bradford(0274)834188 & 834594 FAX (0274) 833340
*A stone-built moorland hotel within reasonable distance of Halifax, Keighley and Bingley offers spaciously modern bedrooms with good facilities and 2 styles of dining.*
26⇦🛌(4fb) CTV in all bedrooms ® T ✳ ✳ sB&B⇦🛌£25-£48 dB&B⇦🛌£30-£59 🍴
⚸ CTV 100P ❀ CFA
♥ French, Greek & Italian V ❖ ✂ ✳ Lunch fr£6.95alc Dinner £13.95 Last dinner 11pm
Credit Cards 1 2 3 5 £

### ★★71% *The Rydings Country*
Bridgehouse Ln BD22 8QE ☎(0535)645206 & 646933
FAX (0535) 646997
*Close to Haworth's cobbled main street, Bill and Lesley Jackson's warm and comfortable small hotel offers attractively decorated, well furnished bedrooms with good facilities, a relaxing lounge and a country-style restaurant and conservatory bar, both serving a range of well-cooked dishes.*
10⇦🛌(2fb) CTV in all bedrooms ® T ✳ (ex guide dogs)
⚸ CTV 20P
♥ English, French & Italian V ❖ ⚸ Last dinner 10pm
Credit Cards 1 2 3 5

### ★★64% **Old White Lion**
6 West Ln BD22 8DU ☎(0535)642313 FAX (0535) 646222
*A small, cosy hotel at the top of the main cobbled street, conveniently situated for the Brontë Parsonage Museum. Public areas retain much of the hotel's historical character, and while some of the bedrooms are small, they are comfortably furnished with excellent beds, and several have lovely views.*
14⇦🛌(2fb) CTV in all bedrooms ® T ✳ (ex guide dogs) ✳ sB&B⇦🛌fr£30.50 dB&B⇦🛌fr£43.50 🍴
CTV 10P 2⏛ CFA *xmas*
♥ English & French V ❖ ✳ Lunch fr£5.25 Dinner fr£9 Last dinner 9.30pm
Credit Cards 1 2 3 5

**See advertisement under KEIGHLEY**

### ❀❀ ✕ ✕ **Weavers**
15 West Ln BD22 8DU ☎(0535)643822
*An attractive and comfortable little restaurant set in a row of former weavers' cottages. The menu features a good range of interesting home cooked meals such as sea food bake, beef pie and sticky pudding. Service is friendly.*
Closed Mon, 2 wks Xmas & 2 wks Jul Lunch not served Tue-Sat & Sun (Etr-Oct)

Dinner not served Sun
V 45 seats Sunday Lunch £12.50 Dinner £12.50&alc Last
dinner 9pm 🅿 ⊁
Credit Cards ①②③

---

**HAYDOCK** Merseyside Map **07** SJ59

★★★★61% **Haydock Thistle**
Penny Ln WA11 9SG (Mount Charlotte (TS))
☎Ashton-in-Makerfield(0942)272000 Telex no 67304
FAX (0942) 711092
*This striking modern hotel, with a Georgian-style façade and
formal courtyard gardens, is conveniently situated close to junction
23 of the M6. Spacious bedrooms are equipped to a high standard
and public areas comfortable and well planned, with extensive
leisure and conference facilities also available.*
139⇦(13fb)⊁in 30 bedrooms CTV in all bedrooms ® **T** (room
only) 🛏
《 180P ❄ 🖾 (heated) sauna solarium gymnasium pool table
steam room whirlpool *xmas*
♡ English & Continental **V** ✿ ⊡
Credit Cards ①②③④⑤

★★★67% **Forte Posthouse**
Lodge Ln, Newton-Le-Willows WA12 OJG (adj to M6 junct 23)
(Forte Hotels) ☎Wigan(0942)717878 Telex no 677672
FAX (0942) 718419
*Conveniently situated close to junction 23 of the M6, this purpose-
built comfortable hotel has a new wing of attractive bedrooms with
particularly smart bathrooms and has undergone total
refurbishment of other bedrooms and public areas. The carvery
restaurant remains popular, as does the well equipped leisure
centre.*
142⇦⊁in 21 bedrooms CTV in all bedrooms ® **T** ✳ S%
sB⇦£39.50-£49.50 dB⇦£39.50-£49.50 (room only)

→

H

Lift ( 197P ❖ CFA ▣ (heated) sauna solarium gymnasium *xmas*

♀ International **V** ⊕ ⚲ ✻ S% Lunch £10.95&alc Dinner £10.95&alc Last dinner 10.30pm

Credit Cards 1 2 3 5

### ⚘ Forte Travelodge

Piele Rd WA11 9TL (Forte)

☎(0942)272055 Central Res (0800) 850950

40⇔♠(40fb) CTV in all bedrooms ® sB⇔♠£29.95 dB⇔♠£29.95 (room only)

( 40P 🚗

Credit Cards 1 2 3

---

**HAYDON BRIDGE** Northumberland Map **12** NY86

### ★★61% Anchor

John Martin St NE47 6AB (Exec Hotel) ☎(0434)684227

*Overlooking the River Tyne from its position beside the bridge, this smart little hotel offers a pleasant atmosphere, attractively refurbished bedrooms and good value for money.*

12rm(10♠)(1fb) CTV in all bedrooms ® **T** sB&B£30-£32 sB&B♠£38-£40 dB&B£40-£43 dB&B♠£48-£51 🖳

25P ♪

♀ English & French **V** ⊕ ✻ Bar Lunch £3-£5alc Dinner fr£15alc Last dinner 8.30pm

Credit Cards 1 2 3 5 £

---

**HAYLE** Cornwall & Isles of Scilly Map **02** SW53 ⊖

### ★★57% *Hillside*

Angarrack TR27 5HZ (1m E of Hayle on unclass rd off A30) ☎(0736)752180

Closed 23-31 Dec & wknds Nov-3 Mar

*A cosy hotel in a small village just a short distance from Hayle, with simply appointed bedrooms and traditional public rooms. Parts of the house date back to the 16th century, and it is set around a walled garden. A limited choice of home cooking is available.*

10rm(1⇔4♠)(3fb) ✗ (ex guide dogs)

CTV 8P 🚗 ❖

**V** ⊕ ⚲ ✗ Last dinner 7.30pm

Credit Cards 1 3

---

**HAYLING ISLAND** Hampshire Map **04** SU70

### ★★★64% Forte Posthouse

Northney Rd PO11 0NQ (Forte Hotels) ☎(0705)465011

FAX (0705) 466468

*Overlooking the estuary from its setting on the northern shore of the island, this hotel offers 2 types of comfortable, well equipped bedroom – Executive Club and Standard – and excellent Health and Fitness Club amenities; refurbishment of the main restaurant is planned, and there is also a convenient coffee shop which operates from 10am until 10pm. Conference facilities are available, and friendly staff provide professional service throughout.*

96⇔(6fb)✗in 41 bedrooms CTV in all bedrooms ® **T** ✻ S% sB⇔£39.50-£49.50 dB⇔£39.50-£49.50 (room only) 🖳

( 150P ❖ CFA ▣ (heated) sauna solarium gymnasium

♀ English/French **V** ⊕ ⚲ ✻ Lunch £2.75-£10.95 Dinner £13.95 Last dinner 10pm

Credit Cards 1 2 3 4 5

---

**HAY-ON-WYE** Powys Map **03** SO24

### ★★★68% *The Swan*

Church St HR3 5DQ (Best Western) ☎(0497)821177 & 821188

FAX (0497) 821424

*Professionally run by the friendly Vaughan family, this Georgian hotel offers comfortable and relaxing public rooms, well equipped bedrooms and consistently good food. There is a good conference/ function facility and free fishing is available.*

15⇔♠Annexe4⇔♠(1fb)1🛏 CTV in all bedrooms ®

18P ♪

**V** ⊕ ⚲ ✗ Last dinner 9.30pm

Credit Cards 1 2 3 5

### ★★67% Old Black Lion

26 Lion St HR3 5AD ☎(0497)820841

*This characterful old inn with beamed ceilings and timbered walls, situated in the heart of the town, has individually furnished, comfortable bedrooms and a cosy lounge. The very popular bar and restaurant offer good quality food, with an extensive range of bar meals and an imaginative à la carte menu.*

6♠Annexe4rm(3⇔)(2fb) CTV in all bedrooms ® **T** sB&Bfr£16.95 sB&B⇔♠£25 dB&B⇔♠£42 🖳

CTV 20P 🚗 ♪ *xmas*

**V** ⊕ ✻ Lunch £6.95-£13alc Dinner £11-£15alc Last dinner 9pm

Credit Cards 1 3

### ★★64% *Kilvert Country*

The Bull Ring HR3 5AG ☎(0497)821042 Telex no 35315

FAX (0497) 821004

*A Jacobean house in the town centre has been converted to provide very comfortable bedrooms and a character bar, though lounge areas are restricted. Meals, which offer an imaginative choice, are particularly enjoyable, being both skilfully cooked and attractively presented.*

11⇔♠(1fb)✗in 3 bedrooms CTV in all bedrooms ®

( CTV 10P ❖ ♪

♀ International **V** ⊕ ⚲ ✗ Last dinner 10pm

Credit Cards 1 2 3

---

**HAYTOR** Devon Map **03** SX77

### ★★★✦75% Bel Alp House

TQ13 9XX ☎(0364)661217 FAX (0364) 661292

Closed Dec, Jan & Feb RS Nov & Mar

*Set in an elevated position on the south-eastern edge of Dartmoor, this elegant Edwardian country mansion commands breathtaking views across the moors to Torbay and the sea beyond. Nine spacious and individually decorated bedrooms offer every comfort for holidaymaker and business traveller alike, whilst the lounges provide relaxation. Décor is simple throughout the hotel, a carefully chosen blend of soft furnishings and antiques creating an atmosphere of warmth and quality. The set 5-course evening meal, prepared from first-class local produce, offers such alternatives as Persian chicken with a tomato, almond and sultana sauce, or roast rack of Devonshire lamb with a redcurrant and green pepper sauce, perhaps followed by hot brandied peach crunch. The food is complemented by a well balanced wine list.*

9⇔♠ CTV in all bedrooms ® **T** sB&B⇔♠£69-£84 dB&B⇔♠£126-£144

Lift 20P 🚗 ❖ snooker

♀ English & French ✗ Dinner fr£33 Last dinner 8.30pm

Credit Cards 1 3

### ★★69% Rock Inn

TQ13 9XP ☎(0364)661305 & 661465 FAX (0364) 661242

*Characterful family-run inn with cosy public rooms, a convivial bar serving real ale and a range of comfortable bedrooms with modern facilities. The restaurant and bar menus feature fresh local produce.*

9⇔♠(2fb)1🛏✗in 2 bedrooms CTV in all bedrooms ® **T** ✗ (ex guide dogs) 🖳

20P 🚗 ❖ *xmas*

♀ English & French **V** ⊕ ⚲ ✗

Credit Cards 1 2 3 £

---

Remember to book early for holiday and bank holiday times.

HEATHROW AIRPORT (LONDON) Greater London
Map **04** TQ07

See **Town Plan Section** under **London Airports**
See also **Hounslow and** Staines

★★★★ 65% **The Excelsior**
Bath Rd, West Drayton UB7 0DU (adj M4 spur at junc with A4)
(Forte Hotels) ☎081-759 6611 Telex no 24525
FAX 081-759 3421
*Extensive and stylish refurbishment has transformed an hotel
popular with airline travellers, culminating in the well designed,
air-conditioned and spaciously comfortable Crown Club bedrooms
together with new lounge and reception facilities. Existing rooms,
despite their physical restraints, have been upgraded, and themed
dining options include the original Carvery, the Café and the
elegant Manor Restaurant and Cocktail Bar. Other facilities
include an indoor swimming pool, keep fit club, shop, hairdresser,
British Airways desk and customer relations office. Efficient
concierge service, NCP car parking and coutesy coach transport to
and from the airport are provided.*
839➔🏳️🛏️ in 130 bedrooms CTV in all bedrooms ® T ✱ S%
sB➔🏳️£105-£130 dB➔🏳️£120-£145 (room only) 🍴
Lift ℂ ⊞ 477P (charged) CFA 🏊 (heated) sauna solarium
gymnasium health & fitness centre jacuzzi *xmas*
♿ English, French & Italian **V** ♦ ⚤ 🍴 ✱ S% Lunch £21.50
Dinner £14.95-£21.50&alc Last dinner midnt
Credit Cards ①②③④⑤

★★★★ 65% **Heathrow Sterling**
Terminal 4, Heathrow Airport TW6 3AF ☎081-759 7755
*The striking façade of this ultra-modern hotel will not appeal to all
tastes, but its direct covered link with terminal 4 makes it the ideal
stop-over for the travelling businessman. Behind its glass frontage
a vast atrium houses brasserie, café and the Windsor Restaurant,
where traditional English food is served. An extensive lounge and
bar area provides the opportunity for relaxation, and there is also a
small leisure complex. Bright, usefully equipped bedrooms are
entirely protected from airport noises, so those facing outwards are
preferable to the slightly gloomy ones overlooking the atrium.*
400➔🏳️ CTV in all bedrooms ® T ✱ sB➔🏳️£115-£130
dB➔🏳️£130-£145 (room only)
Lift ℂ ⊞ 250P (£3 per 24 hrs) CFA 🏊 (heated) sauna
gymnasium *xmas* Last dinner 11.30pm
Credit cards ①②③⑤

★★★★ 64% **Heathrow Penta**
Bath Rd TW6 2AQ ☎081-897 6363 Telex no 934660
FAX 081-897 1113
*Bedrooms are functional rather than luxurious at this airport hotel,
but they are all air-conditioned and double-glazed. Public areas
include an impressive marbled entrance hall, two theme bars – one
providing evening entertainment – and the London Chop House
Restaurant featuring good set meal and à la carte menus; the
popular leisure complex and swimming pool have recently reopened
after refurbishment. Room service and the coffee shop offer 24-
hour service and the hotel runs a courtesy coach to and from the
airport.*
636➔🏳️🛏️ in 15 bedrooms CTV in all bedrooms ® T
🐕 (ex guide dogs) S% sB➔🏳️fr£105 dB➔🏳️fr£119 (room
only) 🍴
Lift ℂ ⊞ 600P (£2.80) CFA 🏊 (heated) sauna solarium
gymnasium plunge pools fitness & aerobics classes *xmas*
♿ International **V** ♦ ⚤ 🍴 ✱ Lunch £11.75-£14.85 Dinner
fr£16 Last dinner 10.30pm
Credit Cards ①②③⑤ ⓔ

★★★★ 59% **Holiday Inn**
Stockley Rd, West Drayton UB7 9NA (2m N junc M4/A408)
(Holiday Inns Inc) ☎West Drayton(0895)445555
Telex no 934518 FAX (0895) 445122
*Close to junction 4 of the M4, this busy modern transit/conference
hotel has many very spacious comfortable bedrooms and luxury
suites. Rather confined public areas can become very congested.*

*The Farmhouse Kitchen is open all day for refreshments or you
can eat more formally in the Tudor Restaurant. There are good
leisure facilities, shops and a conference and business centre.*
380➔(220fb)🛏️ in 42 bedrooms CTV in all bedrooms ® T ✱
sB➔🏳️£94-£98 dB➔🏳️£108-£113 (room only) 🍴
Lift ℂ ⊞ 400P 🚌 ❄ CFA 🏊 (heated) ▶ 9 sauna solarium
gymnasium ⚽
♿ International **V** ♦ ⚤ 🍴 ✱ Lunch £15.70&alc Dinner
£15.70&alc Last dinner midnight
Credit Cards ①②③④⑤

★★★ 65% **Forte Crest**
Sipson Road, West Drayton UB7 0JU (2m N A408) (Forte
Hotels) ☎081-759 2323 Telex no 934280 FAX 081-897 8659
*A large, successful purpose-built hotel conveniently situated for
terminals 1, 2 and 3. Bedrooms are spacious and well equipped and
eating options include a commendable Chinese restaurant, popular
Italian bistro and a traditional carvery.*
569➔🏳️ (176fb)🛏️ in 300 bedrooms CTV in all bedrooms ® T
🐕 (ex guide dogs) ✱ S% sB➔🏳️£85-£100 dB➔🏳️£95-£110
(room only) 🍴
Lift ℂ ⊞ 400P CFA sauna solarium gymnasium *xmas*
♿ English, Chinese & Italian **V** ♦ ⚤ 🍴 ✱ S% Lunch
£14.95&alc Dinner £14.95&alc Last dinner 10.30pm
Credit Cards ①②③④⑤

★★★ 60% *Berkeley Arms*
Bath Road, Hounslow TW5 9QE (2.5m E on A4) (Jarvis)
☎081-897 2121 Telex no 935728 FAX 081-897 7014
*A small purpose-built, airport hotel, with pleasant open-plan public
areas, a carvery-style restaurant and spacious well equipped
bedrooms, all double glazed and many overlooking a courtyard
arbour. The few executive rooms are comfortable and attractively
decorated.*
56➔🏳️ CTV in all bedrooms ®
Lift ℂ 85P ❄ ♪
♿ International **V** ♦ ⚤ Last dinner 9.45pm
Credit Cards ①②③⑤

★★★ 60% **Master Robert**
Great West Rd TW5 0BD ☎081-570 6261 Telex no 9413782
FAX 081-569 4016
(For full entry see Hounslow)

★★★ 59% **The Ariel**
Bath Rd, UB3 5AJ (1.5m E junc A4/A437) (Forte Hotels)
☎081-759 2552 Telex no 21777 FAX 081-564 9265
*This modern building on the A4, has a colourful and comfortable
lobby/bar-lounge. There is also a carvery restaurant. Bedrooms
are comfortable and are being refurbished.*
180➔🏳️🛏️ in 36 bedrooms CTV in all bedrooms ® T
🐕 (ex guide dogs) ✱ S% sB➔🏳️£55-£65 dB➔🏳️£55-£65 (room
only) 🍴
Lift ℂ ⊞ 200P CFA *xmas*
**V** ♦ ⚤ 🍴 ✱ S% Lunch £12.50&alc Dinner £12.50&alc Last
dinner 10.30pm
Credit Cards ①②③④⑤

★★ 50% **Hotel Ibis Heathrow**
112/114 Bath Rd UB3 5AL ☎081-759 4888 Telex no 929014
FAX 081-564 7894
*The modern-style accommodation available at this hotel comprises
inexpensive rooms which, though functional, are reasonably
comfortable; service is limited, and open-plan public areas include
provision for guests to partake of light snacks as an alternative to
the more normal table d'hôte and à la carte menus.*
244➔🏳️ (4fb) CTV in all bedrooms T ✱ S% sB➔🏳️fr£55
dB➔🏳️fr£61 (room only) 🍴
Lift ⊞ 120P CFA *xmas*
♿ International **V** ♦ ⚤ ✱ S% Sunday Lunch £9.50 Dinner
£9.50 Last dinner 10.30pm
Credit Cards ①②③⑤

H

⌂**Granada Lodge**
M4 Service Area, North Hyde Ln TW5 9NA (Granada)
☎081-574 5875 FAX 081-574 1891
(For full entry see Heston)

---

**HEBDEN BRIDGE** West Yorkshire Map **07** SD92

★★★**70% Carlton**
Albert St HX7 8ES (Consort) ☎(0422)844400
FAX (0422) 843117
*Once the town's Co-operative store, this fully refurbished and*
*comfortable hotel now provides the dividend of a warm and*
*friendly atmosphere.*
18⇔🛏 CTV in all bedrooms ® T sB&B⇔🛏£55-£64
dB&B⇔🛏fr£74 🍴
Lift ⚓ CFA *xmas*
♀ English & French V ♥ ☲ Sunday Lunch £7.50-£9.95 Dinner
£10.95-£15.95 Last dinner 9.30pm
Credit Cards ①②③

★★**68% Hebden Lodge**
New Rd HX7 8AD (Exec Hotel) ☎(0422)845272
Closed 23-29 Dec
*A friendly and comfortable family-run hotel in the town centre,*
*opposite the canal marina. Bedrooms and public areas are well*
*furnished, interesting food is served in the charming restaurant and*
*guests are given a warm welcome.*
12⇔🛏(1fb) CTV in all bedrooms ® T ✳ S% sB&B⇔🛏£30-
£40 dB&B⇔🛏£60 🍴
⚓
♀ English & Continental V ♥ ☲ ✳ S% Lunch £7.60-£11.60alc
Dinner £14.75-£17.75 Last dinner 9pm
Credit Cards ①②③ⓔ

---

**HECKFIELD** Hampshire Map **04** SU76

★★**67% New Inn**
RG27 0LE ☎(0734)326374 FAX (0734) 326550
Closed 25-26 Dec
*An attractive and very popular pub includes a modern extension of*
*spaciously comfortable bedrooms furnished to a high standard and*
*equipped with modern facilities. The small restaurant serves simple*
*meals and a particularly popular range of bar food is available.*
16⇔🛏1🛁 CTV in all bedrooms ® T ✳ sB&B⇔🛏£47-£71
dB&B⇔🛏£57-£77 🍴
80P ⇔
V ♥ ☲
Credit Cards ①②③

---

**HEDGE END** Hampshire Map **04** SU41

★★★**63% Botleigh Grange**
SO3 2GA (Best Western) ☎Botley(0489)787700
FAX (0489) 788535
*This castellated period mansion with its attractive gardens and*
*ornamental lakes forms the focal point of a business complex.*
*Bedrooms in the modern wing, though mainly compact, are well*
*equipped and attractively co-ordinated, two four-poster rooms are*
*very popular, and refurbishment is planned for accommodation in*
*the original building. Food is available 24 hours a day, with a new*
*restaurant scheduled to open in August 1991.*
42⇔🛏(4fb)4🛁 CTV in all bedrooms ® T
⚓120P ✿ ⚑ putting
♀ English & French V ♥ ☲ Last dinner 10pm
Credit Cards ①②③⑤

**See advertisement under SOUTHAMPTON**

---

A rosette means exceptional standards of cuisine.

---

**HELENSBURGH** Strathclyde *Dunbartonshire* Map **10** NS28

★★★**58% *Commodore Toby***
112 West Clyde St G84 8ER (Toby) ☎(0436)76924
Telex no 778740
*This purpose-built seafront hotel on the north side of town offers*
*well equipped bedrooms, a coffee shop and a carvery restaurant.*
45⇔🛏 CTV in all bedrooms ®
Lift ⚓ 120P
V ♥ ☲ ✂ Last dinner 9.30pm
Credit Cards ①②③⑤

---

**HELFORD** Cornwall & Isles of Scilly Map **02** SW72

❀❀✕✕**Riverside**
TR12 6JU ☎Manaccan(032623)443
*A collection of cottages delightfully set beside a narrow creek off*
*the river estuary houses this charming and relaxing resaurant*
*owned by Susie Darrell. In summer, aperitifs are served outside,*
*otherwise at the tables. Chef David Rayner's menu changes daily*
*with the market; fish is, of course, its strong point, and is cooked*
*with skill and care.*
Closed Nov-Feb Lunch not served Mon-Thu, May-Jul
♀ English & French 30 seats Dinner £28-£30 Last dinner
9.30pm 10 P nc12yrs

---

**HELLIDON** Northamptonshire Map **04** SP55

★★★★❀❀**65% Hellidon Lakes Hotel & Country Club**
NN11 6LN ☎Daventry(0327)62550 FAX (0327) 63559
*Beautifully set in 210 acres of grounds five miles south of the town,*
*this small rather functional-looking hotel has been newly developed*
*as a luxury country club with a golf course. Tulipwood panelling*
*gives a warm feel to the comfortable public areas and attractively*
*furnished bedrooms, which are equipped with many thoughtful*
*extras. The club bar serves bar meals to 9.30pm while the*
*restaurant offers a very reasonably priced set menu of skilfully*
*cooked modern French dishes. Our inspector enjoyed a pigeon*
*terrine studded with green pistachios and delicately flavoured*
*chicken livers accompanied by baby vegetables of the highest*
*quality. Service is both efficient and hospitable.*
25⇔🛏1🛁 CTV in all bedrooms ® T ✕ (ex guide dogs) ✳
sB&B⇔🛏£70-£90 dB&B⇔🛏£85-£105 (room only) ®
⚓200P ⇔ ✿ ⚑ 18 ⚓ ∪ sauna solarium gymnasium nc14yrs
*xmas*
♀ French V ♥ ☲ ✂ ✳ Lunch £16.60 Dinner £23.50-£38.70alc
Last dinner 9.30pm
Credit Cards ①②③⑤

---

**HELMSLEY** North Yorkshire Map **08** SE68

★★★❀❀**78% Black Swan**
Market Place YO6 5BJ (Forte Hotels) ☎(0439)70466
Telex no 57538 FAX (0439) 70174
*Situated at the head of the market square, this delightful old inn*
*offers very comfortable accommodation and courteous spontaneous*
*service. The food is a strong feature, with imaginative daily*
*changing menus offering a choice of 2 or 3 courses at lunch and 4*
*or 6 courses at dinner.*
44⇔🛏(4fb)✂ in 9 bedrooms CTV in all bedrooms ® T ✳
sB⇔🛏£80 dB⇔🛏£110 (room only) ®
⚓ CTV 60P ✿ CFA croquet *xmas*
V ♥ ☲ ✂ ✳ Lunch fr£9.95 Dinner fr£28.50 Last dinner
9.30pm
Credit Cards ①②③⑤

★★★**68% Feversham Arms**
1 High St YO6 5AG (Best Western) ☎(0439)70766
Telex no 57966 FAX (0439) 70346
*This attractive well-furnished hotel in the centre of the village is set*
*in pleasant gardens with a tennis court and outdoor pool. The well*
*equipped bedrooms are warm and comfortable, service is friendly*

*and attentive and an extensive menu is available, many dishes having a Spanish influence, which is also reflected in the wine list.*
18⇨(4fb)5▣ CTV in all bedrooms ® T sB&B⇨£55-£65 dB&B⇨£76-£86 ⊟
30P ✲ CFA ⇌ (heated) ℘ (hard)
♁ English, French & Spanish V ♱ Lunch £14-£19&alc Dinner £20-£25&alc Last dinner 9.30pm
Credit Cards [1] [2] [3] [5]

**★★72% Pheasant**
Harome YO6 5JG (2.5m SE on unclass rd) ☎(0439)71241
Closed Jan-Feb
*Built around a rear courtyard and overlooking the village pond, this family-run hotel provides very comfortable bedrooms, courteous service and good value home-cooked dinners.*
12⇨Annexe2⇨ CTV in all bedrooms ® T sB&B⇨£42.90-£56.20 dB&B⇨£85.80-£112.40 (incl dinner) ⊟
20P ▦ ✲ nc12yrs
♱ ⚟ Bar Lunch £1.20-£8alc Dinner £17.50 Last dinner 8pm

**★★68% Crown**
Market Square YO6 5BJ ☎(0439)70297
*This renovated old coaching inn retains its historical character and charm while providing comfortable well equipped bedrooms. Wholesome fresh food is served almost all day and there is a choice of bars and lounges and a cosy little dining room with beams and an inglenook fireplace, popular for afternoon and high tea.*
14rm(12⇨♠)(1fb) CTV in all bedrooms ® T ✳ sB&B£26.60 sB&B⇨♠£28.60 dB&B⇨♠£57.20 ⊟
CTV 17P 3▲ ▦ ✲
V ♱ ⛾ ⚟ ✳ Lunch fr£7.65alc High tea fr£4.35alc Dinner fr£12.95alc Last dinner 8pm
Credit Cards [1] [3]

See advertisement on page 355

**★★65% Feathers**
Market Place YO6 5BH ☎(0439)70275
Closed 23 Dec-3 Jan
*Good service is provided by the resident proprietors of this local-stone hotel, parts of which date back to the 15th century. Bedrooms have good facilities, and the warm, friendly bar offers an excellent range of meals to supplement the interesting menus of the Stable restaurant.*
17rm(6⇌7♠)(4fb) CTV in all bedrooms ® ✱ sB&B£22-£26.50 sB&B⇌♠£26.50-£31.50 dB&B⇌♠£53 ⊟
CTV 12P 1⌂ ❖
♀ English & Continental V ✿ ✱ Sunday Lunch £8.25-£14.75 Dinner £14.50-£21.25 Last dinner 9pm
Credit Cards 1 2 3 5 £

**HELSTON** Cornwall & Isles of Scilly Map **02** SW62

**★★♣ 70% Nansloe Manor**
Meneage Rd TR13 0SB ☎(0326)574691
Closed 25-30 Dec
*Set within 4.5 acres of wooded grounds and enjoying rural views from all its windows, a Georgian/Victorian hotel features charming, individually furnished and decorated bedrooms and the Georgian restaurant serving an imaginative à la carte menu.*
7⇌♠1⊠ CTV in all bedrooms ® T sB&B⇌♠£30-£48 dB&B⇌♠£50-£84
40P ⇼ ❖ croquet nc10yrs
♀ English & Continental V ⚡ ✱ Lunch £10.75-£12.90alc Dinner £14.30-£20.50alc Last dinner 9.30pm
Credit Cards 1 2 3 £

**★★63% The Gwealdues**
Falmouth Rd TR13 8JX ☎(0326)572808 FAX (0326) 561388
*A small, friendly hotel, equally suitable for tourist or business guest and conveniently located beside the main Helston/Falmouth road, provides informal service in a relaxed atmosphere. Bright public rooms are popular for functions, and soundly furnished bedrooms have been well equipped with modern facilitities. An outdoor swimming pool is available for guests' use.*
12rm(4⇌5♠)(2fb) CTV in all bedrooms ® T sB&B£25 sB&B⇌♠£30 dB&B£30 dB&B⇌♠£40 ⊟
CTV 60P ⇼ CFA ⇸
V ✿ ⊈ S% Sunday Lunch £5 Dinner fr£9.95&alc Last dinner 9.30pm
Credit Cards 1 3 £

**HEMEL HEMPSTEAD** Hertfordshire Map **04** TL00 ⊛

**★★★58% Aubrey Park Hotel**
Hemel Hempstead Rd AL3 7AF ☎Redbourn(0582)792105
Telex no 82195 FAX (0582) 792001
(For full entry see Redbourn)

**★★★54% Forte Posthouse**
Breakspear Way HP2 4UA (Forte Hotels) ☎(0442)51122
Telex no 826902 FAX (0442) 211812
*Beside the A414 and convenient for junction 8 of the M1, this 60s hotel is beginning to show its age, and while bedrooms are well equipped they do vary in size and in the standard of décor and furnishings. Despite the surroundings staff are cheerful and friendly.*
Annexe103⇌(4fb)⚡in 35 bedrooms CTV in all bedrooms ® T ✱ sB⇌£39.50-£49.50 dB⇌£39.50-£49.50 (room only)
Lift ☾ 120P ❖ CFA *xmas*
♀ English & International V ✿ ⊈ ⚡ ✱ S% Lunch fr£8.95 Dinner fr£13.95&alc Last dinner 10pm
Credit Cards 1 2 3 5

⊛ Shell filling stations (7am–11pm) are marked on the town plans.

**HEMSWELL** Lincolnshire Map **08** SK99

**★★62% Hemswell Cliff**
Lancaster Green, Hemswell Cliff DN21 5TU ☎(042773)8181 & 8182 FAX (042773) 483
*Situated adjacent to the A631 Gainsborough to Grimsby road, this former RAF officers' mess is now a fine hotel with spacious public areas and well equipped, modestly furnished accommodation. Set in its own 10 acres, which include some well tended gardens.*
22⇌♠ CTV in all bedrooms ® T ✗ (ex guide dogs) sB&B⇌♠£40-£45 dB&B⇌♠£60-£65 ⊟
50P 22⌂ ❖ CFA squash *xmas*
♀ English & Continental V ✿ ⊈ Lunch £7.50-£8.50&alc Dinner £10.50-£14.50&alc Last dinner 9.30pm
Credit Cards 1 2 3 £

**HENLEY-IN-ARDEN** Warwickshire Map **07** SP16

**⊛✕✕Le Filbert Cottage**
64 High St B95 5BX ☎(05642)2700
*Invariably a haven of peace in the centre of an active village, the cottage is reminiscent of the English tea room it once was. Maurice Ricaud and his English wife have been here 10 years now, bringing the flavour of the mid-Pyrenées to Warwickshire. Monkfish and salmon appear frequently on the menu, and lemon and Dover sole are particular favourites. Maurice Ricaud's classical French training shows best in his sauces, beautifully made but virtually all in a cream style.*
Closed Sun, Mon, 26 Dec & BHs
♀ French 30 seats Lunch fr£15&alc Dinner £15-£30alc Last lunch 1.45pm Last dinner 9.45pm ⁄P nc6yrs
Credit Cards 1 2 3 4 5

**HENLEY-ON-THAMES** Oxfordshire Map **04** SU78

**★★★62% Red Lion**
Hart St RG9 2AR ☎(0491)572161 FAX (0491) 410039
*A family-owned hotel dating from the 16th century, beside the River Thames and Henley Bridge, with easy access to the town centre. Public areas have been upgraded to offer both comfort and character. Bedrooms are included in an ongoing major refurbishment programme which aims to provide 26 rooms with quality décor and furnishings, and modern facilities. A table d'hôte menu offers interesting dishes carefully prepared under the supervision of Chef Emil Forde. Canapes are served in the bar, followed by dishes such as thin layers of puff pastry and smoked salmon on a tomato and basil coulis, and breast of chicken filled with smoked bacon and mushroom, served with a reduction of its cooking juices; and there is a choice of rich puddings including hot fruit soufflés.*
26rm(23⇌♠)(1fb)1⊠ CTV in all bedrooms T ✗ sB£43-£46 sB⇌♠£70-£75 dB⇌♠£83-£95 (room only) ⊟
☾ 25P ⇼ CFA
♀ English & French V ✿ ⊈ S10% Lunch £19.50 Dinner £15-£25 Last dinner 10pm
Credit Cards 1 2 3

**HEREFORD** Hereford & Worcester Map **03** SO54

See also Much Birch
**★★★68% Hereford Moat House**
Belmont Rd HR2 7BP (Queens Moat) ☎(0432)354301
FAX (0432) 275114
*This good modern hotel, on the A465 to the south west of the city centre, provides comfortable and well equipped accommodation both in the main building and a motel-style block. A spacious foyer with comfortable seating leads through to an attractive restaurant which serves enjoyable meals.*
28⇌♠Annexe32⇌♠(2fb) CTV in all bedrooms ® T ✱ sB&B⇌♠£69.50 dB&B⇌♠£79.50 ⊟
☾ 150P ❖ CFA

♥ English & French V ❀ ⬛ ✂ ✳ Lunch £8-£9.50 Dinner £15
Last dinner 9.45pm
Credit Cards [1] [2] [3] [5]

★★★59% **The Green Dragon**
Broad St HR4 9BG (Forte Hotels) ☎(0432)272506
Telex no 35491 FAX (0432) 352139
*Improvements continue at this traditional hotel situated close to
the cathedral in the city centre and with its own car park. Newly
refurbished bedrooms are attractive and well equipped and public
rooms include an oak-panelled restaurant and a lounge serving
morning coffee and afternoon teas.*
88⬓4🛏✂in 9 bedrooms CTV in all bedrooms ® T ✳ S%
sB⬓£65 dB⬓£80 (room only) 🍴
Lift ℂ 80P 80🛆 CFA *xmas*
V ❀ ⬛ ✂ ✳ S% Lunch £9.95 Dinner £15.30&alc Last dinner
9.30pm
Credit Cards [1] [2] [3] [5]

★★69% **Merton Hotel & Governors Restaurant**
Commercial Rd HR1 2BD (Minotels) ☎(0432)265925
FAX (0432) 354983
RS Sun
*A friendly, privately-owned hotel near the city centre, popular with
tourists and business guests alike, offers quite well equipped
accommodation (though some single rooms are compact); cosy
public areas include the busy Governors Restaurant, which serves
an extensive range of dishes.*
15⬓🗲Annexe4⬓🗲(1fb) CTV in all bedrooms T ✳
sB&B⬓🗲£46.75-£52.25 dB&B⬓🗲£72-£78 🍴
CTV 6P CFA sauna solarium gymnasium steam room *xmas*
♥ International V ❀ ⬛ ✂ ✳ Lunch £11.25-£14&alc High tea
£9-£12 Dinner £17-£19&alc Last dinner 9.30pm
Credit Cards [1] [2] [3] [5] £

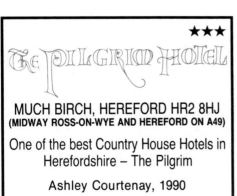

H

**★★65% Dormington Court Country House**
Dormington HR1 4DA (3.5m E off A438) ☎(0432)850370
*This old farm manor house – part Elizabethan, part Georgian, with a Grade II listing – enjoys a pleasant setting just off the A428 about 5 miles from the city. Now operating as a small, privately owned hotel, it provides accommodation in fresh, bright bedrooms which offer a good degree of comfort, while cosy, traditional public areas include a relaxing lounge overlooking the rear gardens and an intimate dining room. Hospitable proprietors create a friendly, welcoming atmosphere.*
7rm(6⇨)(1fb)1⊟ CTV in all bedrooms ® sB&Bfr£25 sB&B⇨£28-£32 dB&B£48-£50 dB&B⇨£56-£64 ⊨
16P ⌘ ✲ nc10yrs
♔ English & French V ♦ ☕ Lunch £12-£15alc Dinner £12-£18alc Last dinner 8.45pm
Credit Cards [1] [3]

**★★65% Munstone House Country**
Munstone HR1 3AH ☎(0432)267122
*Small and very friendly, the hotel provides spacious, well equipped bedrooms, comfortable lounges and a locally popular restaurant offering a good choice of food. Munstone is signposted off the A4103 Roman Road east off the A49.*
6rm(3⇨2↱)(1fb) CTV in all bedrooms ® ✱ sB&B⇨↱£26 dB&B⇨↱£43
CTV 25P ⌘ ✲ CFA *xmas*
V ♦ ☕ ✱ S% Lunch £3-£16&alc Dinner £3-£16&alc Last dinner 9.30pm
Credit Cards [1] [3] [5] £

**★★64% Netherwood Country House**
Tupsley HR1 1UT ☎(0432)272388
Closed 27-30 Dec
*A charming early Victorian country house in two acres of grounds and gardens, standing just off the A438 to the east of the city, which once belonged to the Baskerville family and is reputed to be the setting for Conan Doyle's famous novel. Today it offers accommodation in well-equipped bedrooms and friendly personal service by the proprietors.*
7rm(6⇨↱)(3fb)⚡in all bedrooms CTV in all bedrooms ® T ✗ (ex guide dogs) S% sB&B£42-£50 sB&B⇨↱£42-£50 dB&B£56-£65 dB&B⇨↱£56-£65 ⊨
CTV 36P ✲ CFA
V ♦ ☕ ✱ S% Lunch £11.50-£14.50&alc Dinner £14.50-£20&alc Last dinner 9pm
Credit Cards [1] [2] [3] £

**★★61% Somerville**
12 Bodenham Rd HR1 2TS ☎(0432)273991 FAX (0432) 266723
RS Xmas & New Year
*A large detached Edwardian house on the A438 Ledbury road half a mile northeast of the city centre has been converted to create a comfortable hotel with homely public rooms and well equipped accommodation.*
10rm(6⇨↱)(2fb)1⊟ CTV in all bedrooms ® T sB&B£24.50-£30 sB&B⇨↱£29.50-£33.50 dB&B£42 dB&B⇨↱£48 ⊨
CTV 12P ⌘ ✲ ⌂
♔ English & Continental V ♦ ☕ ⚡ Lunch £10.75 High tea £3.85-£5alc Dinner £10.75&alc Last dinner 8pm
Credit Cards [1] [2] [3]

**★★59% Castle Pool**
Castle St HR1 2NR (Exec Hotel) ☎(0432)356321
*A quietly located and privately owned hotel which was once a Bishop's Palace is set in a garden containing the remains of a moat, only minutes' walk from the cathedral and city centre. Room standards vary, most being modestly furnished but well equipped.*
26⇨↱(3fb)2⊟ CTV in all bedrooms ® T sB&B⇨↱fr£49 dB&B⇨↱£68-£80.50 ⊨
CTV 14P ✲ CFA *xmas*
♔ International V ♦ ☕ Lunch fr£9.25 Dinner fr£16.50 Last dinner 9.30pm
Credit Cards [1] [2] [3] [5]

### HERM

See Channel Islands

### HERSTMONCEUX East Sussex Map 05 TQ61

**★★★❀66% White Friars**
Boreham St BN27 4SE (Best Western) ☎(0323)832355 FAX (0323) 833882
*A pleasant 18th-century hotel with an elegant restaurant and cosy lounges offering a warm welcome and friendly service; bedrooms vary in style and size, some being housed in an adjacent cottage annexe, but all are well equipped.*
12⇨↱Annexe8⇨↱(2fb)2⊟ CTV in all bedrooms ® T sB&B⇨↱£40-£60 dB&B⇨↱£60-£90 ⊨
50P ✲ CFA putting croquet *xmas*
♔ English & French V ♦ ☕ ✱ Lunch £14.25-£28.50alc High tea £4-£10alc Dinner £14.25&alc Last dinner 10pm
Credit Cards [1] [2] [3] [5]

**★★60% Horse Shoe Inn**
Windmill Hill BN27 4RU (Resort) ☎Eastbourne(0323)833265 FAX (0323) 832001
*This inn has been designed in the Tudor style to fit in with the attractive village surroundings. Bedrooms, all doubles, have been identically furnished to a good standard with modern bathrooms, and are particularly well equipped. A cosy atmosphere is created by the wood-burning stove in the Squire Bar, and the Long Bar is popular with locals. The beamed and panelled Baron of Beef restaurant offers a traditional menu.*
15⇨↱ CTV in all bedrooms ® T ✱ sB&B⇨↱£41 dB&B⇨↱£51 ⊨
100P *xmas*
V ♦ ☕ ✱ Lunch £12.50&alc Dinner £12.50&alc Last dinner 10pm
Credit Cards [1] [2] [3] [5]

**❀ ✕✕Sundial**
BN27 4LA ☎(0323)832217
*This charming 17th-century cottage restaurant in attractive village setting features a garden terrace where you can take lunch or dinner during the summer months. Chef/patron Giuseppe Bertoli offers an extensive set and à la carte menu, supplemented by seasonal specialities, which displays French and Italian influences. Fresh Tortelloni in Parmesan Sauce can be recommended, as can the Bouillabaisse – each of them constituting a meal in itself; they can, however, be followed by grouse when in season, by the fish speciality, or by a classic Coq au Vin, all complemented by a superb wine list.*
Closed Mon, 5 Aug-3 Sep & 23 Dec-20 Jan
Dinner not served Sun
♔ French V 60 seats ✱ Lunch £11.50-£15.50&alc Dinner £24.50&alc Last lunch 2pm Last dinner 9.30pm 25 P ⚡
Credit Cards [1] [2] [3] [5]

### HERTFORD Hertfordshire Map 04 TL31

**★★★61% White Horse**
Hertingfordbury SG14 2LB (1m W on A414) (Forte Hotels) ☎(0992)586791 FAX (0992) 550809
*An hotel in pleasant village setting close to the town has undergone extensive refurbishment and now offers comfortable modern accommodation of a good standard; a welcoming atmosphere is provided by the attractive bar/lounge, with its two living flame fires.*
42⇨1⊟⚡in 12 bedrooms CTV in all bedrooms ® T ✱ sB⇨£70 dB⇨£90 (room only) ⊨
☾ 60P ✲ CFA ♫ *xmas*
V ♦ ☕ ⚡ Lunch £15.95 Dinner £16.95&alc Last dinner 10pm
Credit Cards [1] [2] [3] [4] [5]

## HESLEDEN Durham Map **08** NZ43

### ★★★67% **Hardwicke Hall Manor**

TS27 4PA (2.5m N of town on A1086)
☎Hartlepool(0429)836326 FAX (091) 5872334

*This historic mansion, now a flourishing hotel, was once the house of a colliery agent, and is said to have in the chimney one of the best preserved priest's holes in the country. Bedrooms are very attractive, comfortable and well equipped and the dining room offers a range of menus to suit all tastes. Situated on the B1281, it is east of Castle Eden and north-east of the village of Hesleden.*

11⇨♠(2fb)2⊞ CTV in all bedrooms ® T sB&B⇨♠£45-£55 dB&B⇨♠£55-£65 ▤

50P ❖ CFA

♡ English & French V ৬ ⊡

Credit Cards ①②③⑤ⓔ

## HESTON MOTORWAY SERVICE AREA (M4) Greater London

See **LONDON plan 1**A3(page 434)

### ⌂**Granada Lodge**

M4 Service Area, North Hyde Ln TW5 9NA (Granada)
☎081-574 5875 FAX 081-574 1891

*A lodge situated at the M4 motorway service area provides comfortable accommodation in spacious, well equipped bedrooms with smartly tiled bathrooms; meals can be taken at the nearby Country Kitchen Restaurant.*

46⇨♠(15fb)ⴥin 6 bedrooms CTV in all bedrooms ®
✻ (ex guide dogs) S% sB⇨♠fr£39 dB⇨♠fr£43 (room only)
℄ 135P

**See advertisement on page 353**

## HETHERSETT Norfolk Map **05** TG10

### ★★★70% **Park Farm**

NR9 3DL ☎Norwich(0603)810264 FAX (0603) 812104
Closed 25-29 Dec

*Set amid arable and pasture land, approached by a long tree-lined avenue, the hotel, a former farm and outbuildings, enjoys a quiet and secluded position only 6 miles south of Norwich, and just off the A11. The outbuildings have been tastefully converted in brick and pantile, in an informal courtyard arrangement, each providing well equipped and individually designed accommodation. An elegant restaurant offers a good selection of menus. All dishes use fresh ingredients, while the chef's monthly specialities have more skilfully prepared dishes with a light, delicate and imaginative style.*

6⇨♠Annexe32⇨♠(10fb)12⊞ⴥin 27 bedrooms CTV in all bedrooms ® T ✻ (ex guide dogs) ✻ sB&B⇨♠£55-£92 dB&B⇨♠£68-£109 ▤

100P 1❦ ⇔ ❖ CFA ⌦ (heated) ♪ (hard) sauna solarium gymnasium putting croquet jacuzzi games room ♫ *xmas*

♡ English & French V ৬ ⊡ ⴥ ✻ Lunch £9.70-£10.75 High tea fr£3.50 Dinner fr£11.75 Last dinner 9.30pm

Credit Cards ①②③④⑤ⓔ

**See advertisement under NORWICH**

## HETTON North Yorkshire

### ❀❀ ✕✕**Angel Inn**

☎(0756)73263 (0756) 73363

*One of our Best New Restaurant award winners this year, this lovely old Dales pub features a very attractively furnished restaurant with comfortable seating and quality appointments. Its two chef/owners combine to produce skilfully cooked and well presented dishes based on the best possible ingredients; fresh fish, Yorkshire meats and local farmhouse cheeses are always available, as are such temptations as sticky toffee pudding. Service is friendly yet professional and there is a well balanced 'whole world' wine list. (See colour feature on p40.)*

Lunch not served Mon-Sat
Dinner not served Sun
54 seats ✻ Sunday Lunch £14.80 Dinner £19.90 Last lunch 2.30pm Last dinner 9.30pm 20 P ⴥ
Credit Cards ①③

## HEVERSHAM Cumbria Map **07** SD48

### ★★★61% **Blue Bell**

Prince's Way LA7 7EE ☎Milnthorpe(05395)62018

*In rural surroundings a mile north of Milnthorpe on the A6, this hotel features attractive beamed bars, traditional lounges with open fires and a popular restaurant.*

21⇨♠ CTV in all bedrooms ® T ✻ (ex guide dogs)
sB&B⇨♠£46-£50 dB&B⇨♠£68-£75 ▤

CTV 100P CFA *xmas*

V ৬ ⊡ ⴥ Lunch £9.15-£9.45&alc Dinner £13.50-£14.50&alc Last dinner 9pm

Credit Cards ①②③ⓔ

## HEXHAM Northumberland Map **12** NY96

### ★★★70% **Beaumont**

Beaumont St NE46 3LT ☎(0434)602331
Closed 25-26 Dec & 1 Jan

*This town centre hotel has recently been extensively refurbished and is now a pleasant place to stay, with good lounges and bars offering all round comfort and friendly, attentive service.*

23⇨♠(1fb)1⊞ⴥin 15 bedrooms CTV in all bedrooms ® T ✻ ✻ sB&B⇨♠£47 dB&B⇨♠£75 ▤

Lift ℄ 6P CFA gymnasium fitness room

♡ International V ৬ ⊡ ⴥ ✻ Lunch £5.50-£12 Dinner £6.50-£18alc Last dinner 9.45pm

Credit Cards ①②③⑤

### ★★63% **Royal**

Priestpopple NE46 1PQ (Consort) ☎(0434)602270

*Pleasantly furnished and comfortable, this coaching inn at the centre of the town features both a traditional restaurant upstairs and a bistro at street level; bedrooms have good facilities and service is friendly throughout.*

24⇨♠(3fb) CTV in all bedrooms ® T S% sB&B⇨♠£38-£42 dB&B⇨♠£58-£62 ▤

CTV 24P CFA

♡ English, Scottish & French V ৬ ⴥ ✻ Lunch £7.50-£9 Dinner £12.50-£13.50&alc Last dinner 9.30pm

Credit Cards ①②③⑤ⓔ

### ★★62% **County**

Priestpopple NE46 1PS ☎(0434)602030

*This friendly, well-run hotel at the centre of the town provides good facilities in the bedrooms, public areas with a pleasing atmosphere, and a high standard of cuisine.*

9⇨♠ CTV in all bedrooms ® T ✻ sB&B⇨♠£42 dB&B⇨♠£55 ▤

℄ 2P

♡ International V ৬ ⊡ ✻ Lunch £5-£9.90alc High tea £2.75-£9alc Dinner £10.75-£20.50alc Last dinner 9.30pm

Credit Cards ①②③

## HIGHBRIDGE Somerset Map **03** ST34

### ★★59% **Sundowner**

74 Main Road, West Huntspill TA9 3QU (1m S on A38)
☎Burnham on Sea(0278)784766

*Comfortable accommodation, meals of a reasonable standard and a friendly, informal atmosphere are provided at this small, family-run commercial hotel.*

→

8⇨🅟(1fb) CTV in all bedrooms ℝ sB&B⇨🅟£30-£39 dB&B⇨🅟£38-£52 🅁
CTV 24P ✿ CFA
♀ English & French V ♦ ✱ Lunch £11.60-£23alc Dinner £11.60-£23alc Last dinner 10pm
Credit Cards ①②③

---

### HIGHCLIFFE Dorset Map 04 SZ29

⊛✗✗The Lord Bute
Lymington Rd BH23 4JS ☎Highcliffe-on-Sea(0425)278884
Closed Mon
Dinner not served Sun
♀ English & French V 60 seats ✱ Lunch £11.95 Dinner £18-£25alc Last lunch 2pm Last dinner 9.45pm 12 P nc10yrs
Credit Cards ①②③⑤

---

### HIGHER BURWARDSLEY Cheshire Map 07 SJ55

★★66% Pheasant Inn
CH3 9PQ ☎Tattenhall(0829)70434 FAX (0829) 71097
2⇨🅟Annexe6⇨🅟 CTV in all bedrooms ℝ T
✖ (ex guide dogs) ✱ sB&B⇨🅟£35-£45 dB&B⇨🅟£45-£55 🅁
60P ⟐ nc14yrs
V ♦ ✱ Sunday Lunch fr£9.50alc Dinner £10-£15alc Last dinner 9.30pm
Credit Cards ①②③⑤

---

### HIGH OFFLEY Staffordshire Map 07 SJ72

★★ ⊛78% Old Parsonage Coach House
ST20 0NE ☎Stafford(0785)284446 FAX (0785) 284527
*This delightful little hotel, overlooking a rural valley from its position beside the A519 in a tiny village between Eccleshall and Newport, boasts quality facilities that many larger hotels might well envy. Personally run by owners who offer a genuine welcome, it has already gained a good reputation for the innovative fixed-price menu presented by chef Richard Fletcher.*
4⇨🅟 CTV in all bedrooms ℝ T sB&B⇨🅟£35 dB&B⇨🅟£35 🅁
20P ⟐ ✿
♀ French V ♦ Lunch £11.50&alc Dinner £15&alc Last dinner 9.30pm
Credit Cards ①②③⑤£

---

### HIGH WYCOMBE Buckinghamshire Map 04 SU89 ◉

★★★65% Forte Posthouse
Handy Cross HP11 1TL (Forte Hotels) ☎(0494)442100
Telex no 83626 FAX (0494) 439071
*At the M40/A404 intersection between London and Oxford, this modern hotel caters mainly for business users, with excellent conference facilities, all air-conditioned. Public areas have been pleasingly refurbished and bedrooms are comfortable and well equipped.*
110⇨🅟(12fb)⊁in 40 bedrooms CTV in all bedrooms ℝ T
sB⇨🅟£39.50-£40.49 (room only) 🅁
⟮ 173P ✿ CFA pool table ⚬ xmas
♀ English & French V ♦ ⚖ ⊁ ✱ Lunch £7.85-£19alc Dinner £9-£19alc Last dinner 10.30pm
Credit Cards ①②③⑤

Red star hotels are each highlighted by a pink tinted panel.

---

### HILLINGDON Greater London

See LONDON plan 1A4(page 434)
★★★62% Master Brewer
Western Av UB10 9NX ☎Uxbridge(0895)51199
Telex no 946589 FAX (0895) 810330
*The main building on the A40 has an attractive foyer-lounge, a range of eating options and a popular mirrored lounge bar. The spacious well designed bedrooms are in a separate annexe, most overlooking a central garden.*
106⇨🅟 CTV in all bedrooms ℝ T ✱ sB⇨🅟£85-£87 dB⇨🅟£95-£97 (room only) 🅁
⟮ 200P ✿ CFA ⚬
♀ Continental V ♦ ⚖ ✱ Lunch £12-£21.50alc Dinner £12.50-£21.50alc Last dinner 11pm
Credit Cards ①②③⑤

---

### HILLINGTON Norfolk Map 09 TF72

★★61% Ffolkes Arms
Lynn Rd PE31 6BJ ☎(0485)600210 FAX (0485) 601196
*This character coaching inn, which was built over 300 years ago, has recently been completely modernised without losing its original character. A new accommodation annexe has been added which gives a good range of facilities, including ground floor bedrooms and a special room suitable for disabled guests. The hotel proves popular for its eating options, with a choice of bar snacks, carvery or à la carte.*
Annexe20⇨🅟(1fb)1⟐ CTV in all bedrooms ℝ T
✖ (ex guide dogs) ✱ sB&B⇨🅟£25 dB&B⇨🅟£35
Continental breakfast
200P ✿ CFA pool table xmas
♀ English & French V ♦ ⚖ ⊁ ✱ Lunch £6.50-£8.75&alc
High tea £2.95-£6.50 Dinner £8.75&alc Last dinner 9.45pm
Credit Cards ①②③

---

### HILTON PARK MOTORWAY SERVICE AREA (M6) West Midlands Map 07 SJ90

⟐Rank Motor Lodge
Hilton Park Services (M6), Essington WV11 2DR (on M6 between juncts 10a & 11) (Rank) ☎Cheslyn Hay(0922)414100 FAX (0922) 418762
*This lodge located on the southern carriageway of the M6, 7 miles from Wolverhampton, offers good value for money in exceptionally well equipped accommodation which has all modern facilities; meals are available in the adjacent Oasis service area.*
64⇨🅟(22fb)⊁in 6 bedrooms CTV in all bedrooms ℝ ✱
sB&B⇨🅟£29.75 dB&B⇨🅟£37.75 Continental breakfast
60P
♀ English & Continental V ♦ ⚖ ✱ Lunch £1.35-£5.35alc
High tea £3-£6.05alc Dinner £3-£6.05alc
Credit Cards ①②③⑤

---

### HIMLEY Staffordshire Map 07 SO89

★★★68% Himley Country Club & Hotel
School Rd DY3 4LG (Best Western)
☎Wombourne(0902)896716 FAX (0902) 896668
*A fully extended business hotel with well equipped rooms and friendly, attentive staff. It is situated just off the A449 signposted to Himley village, close to the business centres of the Black Country yet in a rural area.*
76⇨🅟 CTV in all bedrooms ℝ T ✖ (ex guide dogs)
sB⇨🅟£35-£50.50 dB⇨🅟£48-£65 (room only)
⟮ ⊞ 126P CFA
♀ Continental V ⚖ ✱ Lunch £8.25&alc Dinner £8.25-£8.95&alc Last dinner 10pm
Credit Cards ①②③⑤£

See advertisements under DUDLEY and WOLVERHAMPTON

★★68% **Himley House**
DY3 4LD (On A449 N of Stourbridge) (Chef & Brewer)
☎Wombourne(0902)892468 FAX (0902) 892604
*Grill-style meals served in the restaurant of this hotel on the A449*
*Stourbridge to Wolverhampton road represent good value for*
*money. The creeper-clad Regency-style house also offers a choice*
*of bars and a well maintained side garden.*
17⇨🛏Annexe7⇨🛏(2fb) CTV in all bedrooms ® T
🍴 (ex guide dogs) sB&B⇨🛏£52 dB&B⇨🛏£72 🅿
ℂ 120P ✻ CFA
♨ Interntional **V** ✿ ⚑ ✗ Bar Lunch £2.95-£5.50alc
Credit Cards [1][2][3][5]

**HINCKLEY** Leicestershire Map **04** SP49

★★★73% **Sketchley Grange**
Sketchley Ln, Burbage LE10 3HU (Best Western)
☎(0455)251133 FAX (0455) 631384
Closed 26-30 Dec
*Situated close to the A5/M69 Junction, this extensively developed*
*hotel with good conference and function facilities has modern well-*
*equipped bedrooms and an attractive à la carte restaurant plus a*
*carvery in the Victorian-style Grange Bar.*
33⇨🛏(9fb)2🛏 CTV in all bedrooms ® T sB&B⇨🛏£79-£83
dB&B⇨🛏£95-£99 🅿
ℂ 200P ✻ CFA 🏊
♨ English & French **V** ✿ ⚑ Lunch £9.50-£9.95&alc Dinner
£14.95&alc Last dinner 9.45pm
Credit Cards [1][2][3][5]

★★74% **Kings Hotel & Restaurant**
13/19 Mount Rd LE10 1AD ☎(0455)637193 FAX (0455) 636201
*A small privately owned hotel in a Victorian house set in a quiet*
*road close to the town centre. Bedrooms are individually styled,*
*with private bath or shower and good facilities, and the restaurant*
*serves a varied selection of dishes.*
7⇨🛏✗in 3 bedrooms CTV in all bedrooms ® T 🍴
sB&B⇨🛏£54.50-£59.50 dB&B⇨🛏£64.50-£69.50 🅿
12P 1🚗 (£5) ♫
♨ English, French & Hungarian **V** ✿ ✗ Lunch £12.50-
£17.50&alc Dinner £19.50-£25&alc Last dinner 9.30pm
Credit Cards [1][2][3][5] ⓔ

**HINDON** Wiltshire Map **03** ST93

★★70% **Lamb at Hindon**
SP3 6DP (Minotels) ☎(074789)573 FAX (074789) 605
*Full of character and charm, with parts of its original building*
*dating back to the 17th century, this inn at the heart of the sleepy*
*village is noted for a warm, friendly welcome and helpful service;*
*its proximity to the A303 makes it popular with a business clientele*
*and with locals. During recent years bedrooms have been upgraded*
*to combine an attractive décor with modern facilities, and inviting*
*public areas are warmed by log fires. The dining room offers an*
*interesting menu based on fresh, locally grown produce.*
15rm(12⇨1🛏) 1🛏 CTV in all bedrooms ® T
🍴 (ex guide dogs) sB&B⇨🛏£30-£38 dB&Bfr£50
dB&B⇨🛏£50-£65 🅿
CTV 26P ✻ ♪ shooting fishing *xmas*
✿ ⚑ ✗ Lunch £8.25-£17 Dinner £15.50-£18 Last dinner
9.30pm
Credit Cards [1][2][3]

*The AA's star rating scheme is the*
*market leader in hotel*
*classification.*

**HINTLESHAM** Suffolk Map **05** TM04

★★★✿✿✿🍴
**HINTLESHAM HALL**

IP8 3NS (Relais et Châteaux)
☎(047387)334 & 268
FAX (047387) 463
RS Sat
*This beautiful country house,*
*set in 23 acres of grounds,*
*dates back to the 16th century. Initially brought to the public*
*eye under the auspicies of Robert Carrier, and more recently*
*Ruth and David Watson, the hotel continues under the*
*excellent management of Tim O'Leary. Furnished throughout*
*with quality and comfort foremost, accommodation ranges in*
*scale from smaller bedrooms to comfortable suites, and public*
*areas are charming. The restaurant continues to thrive under*
*the management of Alan Ford, who spent 3 years as part of*
*Anton Mosimann's team at the Dorchester. Dishes form a now*
*well-established, seasonally changing repertoire, excelling in*
*the use of fresh, quality produce served with light sauces based*
*on fumets and reductions rather than creams. There are*
*conference and banqueting facilities, and a number of outdoor*
*persuits can be arranged, such as clay pigeon shooting and*
*fishing. An ideal location for both the leisure and business*
*user.*
33⇨🛏(1fb)2🛏✗in 12 bedrooms CTV in all bedrooms T
❋ sB&B⇨🛏£80-£140 dB&B⇨🛏£97.50-£300
Continental breakfast 🅿
ℂ 100P 🚗 ✻ CFA ⚑ 18 ♪ (hard) ♪ ∪ snooker croquet
clay & game shooting *xmas*
♨ English & French **V** ✗ ❋ Lunch £17.50 Dinner £29.50-
£37.50alc Last dinner 10pm
Credit Cards [1][2][3][5]

**HINTON** Hampshire Map **04** SZ29

★★67% **Old Vicarage**
Lyndhurst Rd BH23 7DY ☎Highcliffe(0425)277006
*A turn of the century red brick house in 4 acres. All newly*
*decorated and furnished to a high standard with modern*
*bedrooms, a comfortable dining room, bar/lounge and conservatory*
*tearoom.*
7⇨🛏 CTV in all bedrooms ® 🍴 (ex guide dogs)
sB&B⇨🛏fr£41.25 dB&B⇨🛏fr£57.20
20P 🚗 ✻ ≏ *xmas*
**V** ✿ ⚑ ✗ ❋ Lunch £3.95-£6.95 Dinner fr£12.50&alc Last
dinner 9pm
Credit Cards [1][3] ⓔ

**HINTON CHARTERHOUSE** Avon Map **03** ST75

★★★✿✿🍴77% **Homewood Park**
BA3 6BB (Between A36 & village) ☎Bath(0225)723731
FAX (0225) 723820
*This delightful house, dating mainly from the Georgian era, is set*
*in 10 acres of grounds in a village just 6 miles from Bath. Owned*
*by the Fentum family, the hotel is run in friendly style by their*
*daughter and son-in-law, Mrs and Mr Guening. The comfortable*
*lounge and cosy bar have an unpretentious 'lived-in' atmosphere,*
*enhanced by blazing fires in cold weather, and the bedrooms,*
*attractively furnished, are noteworthy for the exceptional comfort*
*of the beds and the high quality of the linen.*
15⇨🛏(2fb) CTV in all bedrooms T 🍴 S% sB&B⇨🛏£87.50-
£95 dB&B⇨🛏£100-£145 Continental breakfast 🅿

→

**H**

30P ⚘ ❀ ♫ (hard) croquet *xmas*
V ♤ ⬛ ⤬
Credit Cards 1️⃣ 2️⃣ 3️⃣ 4️⃣ 5️⃣

---

### HITCHIN Hertfordshire Map **04** TL12

★★★59% **Blakemore Thistle**
Little Wymondley SG4 7JJ (3m SE A602) (Mount Charlotte (TS)) ☎Stevenage(0438)355821 Telex no 825479
FAX (0438) 742114
*Situated on the A602 close to town this hotel offers refurbished bedrooms with excellent modern facilities. The public areas are, however, very dated and improvements are planned.*
83⇆🐾(6fb) CTV in all bedrooms ® T (room only) ♨
Lift ℂ 200P ❀ ⌇ (heated) sauna games room
♡ International ♤ ⬛
Credit Cards 1️⃣ 2️⃣ 3️⃣ 4️⃣ 5️⃣

---

### HOCKLEY HEATH West Midlands Map **07** SP17 ◎

★★★ ⬆⬆⬆✦ 77% **Nuthurst Grange Country House**
Nuthurst Grange Ln B94 5NL (off A34, 2m S junction 4 M42) ☎Lapworth(0564)783972 FAX (0564) 783919
*Nestling in the seclusion of 7.5 acres of grounds and woodland at the end of a long drive, yet within easy reach of the motorway network, this beautiful country house hotel offers spacious and luxuriously appointed guest rooms equipped with personal safes and thoughtfully provided with such extras as chocolates, fruit and mineral water. The well appointed restaurant, divided into 2 separate but adjoining dining areas, is at the heart of the hotel – chef/proprietor David Randolph's well deserved reputation for excellence having attracted an enthusiastic non-resident following; recommended dishes include stilton and Jerusalem artichoke soup, John Dory with saffron and chive sauce, hot chocolate soufflé and steamed walnut and orange pudding with toffee sauce. Public areas are limited for the amount of business that the establishment attracts, but the small lounge is very comfortable and guests are assured of attentive service from an eager young team of staff.*
15⇆🐾(2fb)1⊞ CTV in all bedrooms T ✱ (ex guide dogs)
sB&B⇆🐾frf85 dB&B⇆🐾£99-£135 Continental breakfast ♨
50P 6🚗 ⚘ ❀ croquet
♡ English & French V ♤ ⤬ ✳ Lunch £13.90-£17.90 Dinner £19.95-£35.50 Last dinner 9.30pm
Credit Cards 1️⃣ 2️⃣ 3️⃣ 5️⃣ £

---

### HOCKLIFFE Bedfordshire Map **04** SP92

⬆ Forte **Travelodge**
Watling St(3m N, on A5) (Forte)
☎(0525)211177 Central Res (0800) 850950
*A lodge on the A5 just south of Hockcliffe offers comfortable and reliable overnight accommodation, meals being available at the adjacent Little Chef.*
28⇆🐾(28fb) CTV in all bedrooms ® sB⇆🐾£29.95
dB⇆🐾£29.95 (room only)
ℂ 28P ⚘
Credit Cards 1️⃣ 2️⃣ 3️⃣

---

### HODNET Shropshire Map **07** SJ62

★★65% **Bear**
TF9 3NH ☎(063084)214 & 788 FAX (063084) 787
*This small hotel retains its character as a former village inn, with open fires and exposed beams in the overlapping restaurant and bar area, both popular for their food. Bedrooms are compact but well equipped.*
6⇆🐾2⊞ CTV in all bedrooms ® T ✱ (ex guide dogs)
sB&B⇆🐾£35-£37.50 dB&B⇆🐾£50-£55 ♨
100P ❀ CFA ♫
♡ International V ♤ ⬛ ⤬ ✳ Lunch £5-£8alc Dinner £8.50-£14alc Last dinner 10pm
Credit Cards 1️⃣ 3️⃣

---

### HOLDENBY Northamptonshire Map **04** SP66

⬆⬆⬆✕✕ **Lynton House Country Restaurant & Hotel**
The Croft NN6 8DJ ☎Northampton(0604)770777
*This delightful restaurant with rooms, formerly a rectory, enjoys a peaceful location close to Northampton on the Church Brampton to East Haddon road. The interesting choice of meals on offer is based on the best fresh produce, simple but excellently flavoured dishes being accompanied by particularly good vegetables. Service is generally efficient and attentive under the close supervision of the proprietors.*
Closed Sun, Xmas 3 days, 2 wks Aug Lunch not served Sat & Mon
♡ Italian V 55 seats Lunch £12.65-£15.86 Dinner fr£19.75 Last lunch 1.45pm Last dinner 9.45pm 25 P nc6yrs ⤬
Credit Cards 1️⃣ 3️⃣

---

### HOLFORD Somerset Map **03** ST14

★★⬆ 69% **Combe House**
TA5 1RZ ☎(027874)382
Closed Jan RS mid Nov-Dec & Feb-mid Mar
*A country house lying in a secluded valley of the Quantock Hills offers bedrooms with good facilities and cosy, comfortable public areas. Other attractions include beautiful gardens, a hard tennis court and a heated indoor swimming pool. Table d'hôte menus provide an extensive choice of good, home-cooked dishes, while staff are relaxed and friendly.*
20rm(13⇆2🐾)(2fb)⊞ CTV in all bedrooms ® T S%
sB&B£31-£33 sB&B⇆🐾£40-£42.50 dB&B£62-£66 dB&B⇆🐾£72-£87 ♨
15P ⚘ ❀ ▣ (heated) ♫ (hard) sauna solarium
♤ ⬛ ⤬ S% Bar Lunch £1.50-£7.75 Dinner £13.50-£18.50 Last dinner 8.30pm
Credit Cards 1️⃣ 2️⃣ 3️⃣

---

### HOLLINGBOURNE Kent Map **05** TQ85

★★★ 68% **Great Danes**
Ashford Rd ME17 1RE (Jarvis) ☎Maidstone(0622)30022
Telex no 96198 FAX (0622) 35290
*Considerably extended over the years this hotel offers a good choice of eating places, bars, comfortable sitting areas and modern bedrooms. Leisure facilities are particularly extensive and ideal for weekend breaks.*
126⇆🐾(10fb)⤬in 13 bedrooms CTV in all bedrooms ® T ✳
sB⇆🐾£81-£97 dB⇆🐾£97-£107.50 (room only) ♨
Lift ℂ 400P ❀ CFA ▣ (heated) ♫ (hard) ♦ snooker sauna solarium gymnasium pool table pitch & putt croquet jacuzzi *xmas*
♡ English & French V ♤ ⬛ ✳ S8% Lunch fr£14&alc Dinner fr£15.50&alc Last dinner 10pm
Credit Cards 1️⃣ 2️⃣ 3️⃣ 5️⃣

---

### HOLMES CHAPEL Cheshire Map **07** SJ76

★★★67% **Old Vicarage**
Knutsford Rd CW4 8EF ☎(0477)32041 FAX (0477) 35728
*Located on the A50 north of Holmes Chapel, this old house with a modern bedroom extension has a choice of restaurants, which provide imaginative cuisine, carefully prepared by the chef, Richard Birchall and his brigade.*
24⇆🐾 CTV in all bedrooms ® T ✱ (ex guide dogs) ✳
sB&B⇆🐾£60-£62 dB&B⇆🐾£70-£73 ♨
ℂ 70P CFA
♡ English & French V ♤ ⬛ ✳ Lunch £12.25&alc Dinner £16.25&alc Last dinner 10pm
Credit Cards 1️⃣ 2️⃣ 3️⃣

★★★61% **Holly Lodge Hotel & Restaurant**
68-70 London Rd CW4 7AS ☎(0477)37033 FAX (0477) 35823
RS 25 Dec-31 Jan & BH Mons
*A fully extended Victorian house on the A50/A54 crossroads, only*
*minutes from junction 18 of the M6 which provides well equipped*
*modern accommodation and a wide choice of dishes at both lunch*
*and dinner time in the Truffles Restaurant.*
34⇨🔊(2fb)1🏠½in 6 bedrooms CTV in all bedrooms ® T ✱
sB&B⇨🔊£29-£60 dB&B⇨🔊£46-£88 🏦
CFA *xmas*
♀ English & French V ♥ ✱ Lunch fr£7.50&alc Dinner
fr£11.95&alc Last dinner 9.45pm
Credit Cards ①②③④⑤

---

**HOLYHEAD**

See Trearddur Bay

---

**HOLYWELL** Clwyd Map **07** SJ17 ◉

See also Nannerch

★★★❀79% **Kinsale Hall Country House**
Llanerchymor CH8 9DT ☎(0745)560001 FAX (0745) 561298
*A fully modernised hotel in country house style, set in 100 acres of*
*parkland close to the A548 coastal road, provides comfortable*
*accommodation with every modern amenity and a large*
*conference/function suite that can accommodate up to 300 people*
*and cater for all business or social receptions. The Marlborough*
*restaurant offers quality cuisine, fixed price and à la carte menus*
*owing their inspiration to both French and Celtic influences, while*
*a less formal dining area serves more traditional carvery or grill*
*style meals.*
29⇨🔊½in 2 bedrooms CTV in all bedrooms ® T ✱
sB&B⇨🔊£40-£60 dB&B⇨🔊£55-£79.50 🏦
Lift ℂ 150P ❀ CFA ♾ snooker ♫ *xmas*
V ♥ ⚗ ½ ✱ Lunch £8.50-£12.95
Credit Cards ①②③⑤ⓔ

★★67% **Stamford Gate**
Halkyn Rd CH8 7SJ ☎(0352)712942 & 712968
FAX (0352) 713309
*Close to the A55 just south of the town centre, this privately owned*
*hotel has well equipped bedrooms and offers a choice of bars and a*
*large restaurant.*
12⇨🔊 CTV in all bedrooms ® T 🍴 ✱ sB&B⇨🔊£34-£36
dB&B⇨🔊£48-£52
100P CFA
♀ English & Italian V ♥ Lunch £8.50 Dinner £13.75&alc Last
dinner 10pm
Credit Cards ①③④

---

**HOLYWELL GREEN** West Yorkshire Map **07** SE01

★★68% **Rock Inn Hotel & Churchills Restaurant**
HX4 9BS ☎Halifax(0422)379721 FAX (0422) 379110
*This busy, well run hotel offers a good standard of accommodation,*
*an extensive choice of meals (served in the Churchill Restaurant or*
*bar) and friendly, helpful service.*
18⇨🔊 CTV in all bedrooms ® T ✱ sB&B⇨🔊£36-£51
dB&B⇨🔊£46-£62 🏦
100P 2🏠 ❀ CFA games room ♒ *xmas*
♀ English & French V ♥ ⚗ ✱ Lunch £8.50-£13 Dinner
fr£12.80 Last dinner 9.45pm
Credit Cards ①②③⑤ⓔ

---

**HONILEY** Warwickshire Map **04** SP27

★★★68% **Honiley Court**
Honiley CV8 1NP (3m W of Kenilworth on A4117) (Lansbury)
☎Kenilworth(0926)484234 FAX (0926) 484474
*Situated on the A4117 close to the village, this modern hotel is an*
*extension of the Honiley Boot Inn and combines up-to-date*
*facilities with some character. A night club, good conference rooms*

→

H

*and well-equipped bedrooms make it an ideal venue for both business and leisure guests.*

62⊸ CTV in all bedrooms ® T ✱ sB&B⊸fr£68 dB&B⊸fr£80 ⊟

Lift ( 250P ✿ CFA ⚗

🍴 English & French V ✌ ⊡ ✂ Sunday Lunch £7.95-£8.25&alc Dinner £13.75&alc Last dinner 10pm

Credit Cards ①②③⑤ⓔ

---

### HONITON Devon Map **03** ST10

#### ★★★ ⚑ 63% **Deer Park**

Weston EX14 0PG (2.5m W off A30) ☎(0404)41266
FAX (0404) 46598

*Dating back in parts to 1721 and set in 10 acres of parkland, a Georgian squire's mansion, conveniently positioned only 3 miles from the A30, is now a character hotel; many visitors are attracted by its situation beside the River Otter and its ownership of 5 miles of fishing rights. Comfortable, traditional public areas and spacious, well furnished accommodation are provided in the main house, though the adjacent cottage mews rooms now require upgrading to maintain standards.*

15⊸Annexe14⊸(2fb) CTV in all bedrooms T ✖ (ex guide dogs) S10% sB&B⊸£35-£80 dB&B⊸£55-£120 ⊟
( CTV 100P 4🚗 🚐 ✿ CFA ⊇ (heated) ♪ (hard) ✔ squash snooker sauna solarium croquet putting shooting ⚗ *xmas*
🍴 English & French V ✌ ⊡ ✱ Lunch £13-£15&alc High tea fr£5 Dinner £22.50-£25&alc Last dinner 10pm

Credit Cards ①②③⑤ⓔ

#### ★★ 66% **Home Farm**

Wilmington EX14 9JR (2m E) ☎Wilmington(040483)278
Closed Dec-Jan

*An attractive, thatched former farmhouse full of charm and character. The bedrooms are comfortable with co-ordinating colour schemes, some are approached from the garden and cobbled courtyard, and a good choice of dishes is served in the dining room.*

7rm(3⊸)Annexe6⊸ ℕ(3fb) CTV in all bedrooms ® T sB&B£24-£30 sB&B⊸ ℕ£30 dB&B£52 dB&B⊸ℕ£56 ⊟
CTV 25P ✿ golf practice nets
V ✌ ⊡ Sunday Lunch £3.75-£7.50alc Dinner £12-£16.50alc Last dinner 9pm

Credit Cards ①②③ⓔ

---

### HOOK Hampshire Map **04** SU75

#### ★★ 60% **Raven**

Station Rd RG27 9HS (0.75m N of M3 junc 5 on B3349) (Lansbury) ☎(0256)762541 Telex no 858901
FAX (0256) 768677

*Ideal for either business or leisure, and conveniently located near the station, this popular commercial hotel has been completely refurbished. Bedrooms are particularly well equipped. The spacious, lively bar lounge and the busy restaurant present a welcoming atmosphere.*

38⊸(3fb)1 🖛✂in 5 bedrooms CTV in all bedrooms ® ✖ (ex guide dogs) sB&B⊸fr£79 dB&B⊸fr£92 ⊟
( 100P sauna *xmas*
🍴 European V ✌ ⊡ ✂ Lunch fr£12&alc Dinner fr£12&alc Last dinner 10.30pm

Credit Cards ①②③④⑤

---

### HOOK Wiltshire Map **04** SU08

#### ★★ 70% **School House Hotel & Restaurant**

Hook St SN4 8EF ☎Swindon(0793)851198 Telex no 449703
FAX (0793) 851025

*The renovation of a former Victorian school house has created a spacious dining room and bar with lofty beamed and raftered ceilings, while a new extension provides comfortable bedrooms with antique furnishings and modern bathrooms. Lunch and dinner*

*menus feature a range of newer-style dishes prepared with fresh local ingredients.*

12⊸ ℕ CTV in all bedrooms ® T ✖ (ex guide dogs) ✱ S% sB&B⊸ℕ£67-£73.50 dB&B⊸ℕ£75-£82.50 ⊟
30P 🚐 ✿ ⚗ *xmas*
🍴 English & French V ✌ ⊡ ✂ ✱ S% Lunch £13.95-£15.50alc High tea £13.95-£15.50alc Dinner £16.50-£29.95alc Last dinner 10pm

Credit Cards ①②③⑤ⓔ

---

### HOOTON ROBERTS South Yorkshire Map **08** SK49

#### ★★ 70% **Earl of Strafford**

Doncaster Rd S65 4PF ☎Rotherham(0709)852737
FAX (0709) 851903

*Standing on the A630, ideally situated for access to the motorways, to Doncaster and to Rotherham, this friendly, family-run hotel provides comfortable, well appointed bedrooms, luxury bathrooms with whirlpool baths, and extensive leisure facilities.*

27⊸(3fb)🚾 CTV in 26 bedrooms ® T ✖ (ex guide dogs) S% sB&B⊸£57-£72 dB&B⊸£72-£87 ⊟
( 100P ✿ CFA ▣ (heated) snooker sauna solarium gymnasium 9hole putting green *xmas*
🍴 English & French V ✌ ⊡ S% Lunch £11.95-£14.95&alc Dinner £11.95-£14.95&alc Last dinner 10pm

Credit Cards ①②③⑤ⓔ

---

### HOPE COVE Devon Map **03** SX64

#### ★★ 67% **Cottage**

Inner Hope Cove TQ7 3HJ ☎Kingsbridge(0548)561555
Closed 2-30 Jan

*This cottage hotel is positioned overlooking the unspoilt harbour and coastline of Hope Cove. Comfortable public rooms are personally appointed and traditionally furnished. Eight of the bedrooms have been refurbished to de luxe standard and the others have excellent views and are quite well equipped.*

35rm(24⊸ℕ)(5fb) CTV in 29 bedrooms T S10% sB&B£29.85-£42.10 dB&B£59.70-£84.20 dB&B⊸ℕ£82-£117.20 (incl dinner) ⊟
CTV 50P 🚐 ✿ ⚗ *xmas*
🍴 English & French V ✌ ⊡ S10% Sunday Lunch £8.20 Dinner £15.85&alc Last dinner 8.45pm

#### ★★ 64% *Lantern Lodge*

TQ7 3HE ☎Kingsbridge(0548)561280
Closed Dec-Feb

*Perched on the headland, with unrestricted views out to sea, this cosy little hotel offers individually styled, well equipped and furnished accommodation. Recent upgrading of public rooms has substituted a new bar and bright restaurant for an unused lounge, but there is still a comfortable reading/quiet room and a sun lounge; the sheltered sun terrace beside the indoor swimming pool comes into its own on warmer days. A friendly atmosphere prevails, services being carried out in a fairly informal atmosphere.*

14⊸(1fb)3🚾 CTV in all bedrooms ® T ✖ (ex guide dogs)
15P 1🚘 🚐 ▣ (heated) sauna solarium putting green nc9yrs
🍴 English & French V ✌ ✂ Last dinner 8.30pm

Credit Cards ①③

#### ★★ 59% *Sun Bay*

Inner Hope Cove TQ7 3HH ☎Kingsbridge(0548)561371
Closed 19 Oct-27 Mar

*Overlooking the unspoilt harbour of Inner Hope Bay, on the edge of the village, this family-run hotel has a relaxed, informal atmosphere. Bedroom, whilst compact, are brightly decorated and have modern furnishings. Refreshments are served on the sun terrace in the summer.*

14rm(10⊸2ℕ)(7fb) CTV in all bedrooms ®
CTV 12P 🚐 ✿
V ✌ ⊡ Last dinner 8.30pm

HORLEY Hotels are listed under **Gatwick Airport**

---

**HORNBY** Lancashire Map **07** SD56

★★54% *Castle*

Main St LA28 8JT ☎(0468)21204

*Open fires and an olde worlde bar serving a wide range of home-made bar meals are features of this 17th-century former coaching inn in the village centre, which provides modest accommodation and a friendly atmosphere.*

13rm(4⇔4↑)(2fb) CTV in all bedrooms

50P 🚗

♡ English & Continental V ✿ ⚏

Credit Cards 1 2 3

---

**HORNING** Norfolk Map **09** TG31

★★★62% **Petersfield House**

Lower St NR12 8PF ☎(0692)630741 FAX (0692) 630745

*A family-run hotel in a superb position, tucked away in its own landscaped gardens close to the River Bure, providing friendly service and extending a warm welcome to guests. Comfortable, well-equipped rooms make it equally suitable for tourists and business people.*

18⇔↑(1fb) CTV in all bedrooms ® T ✱ sB&B⇔↑£53-£58 dB&B⇔↑£66-£76 🅱

70P 🚗 ✿ CFA ♪ ♫ *xmas*

♡ English & Continental V ✿ ⚏ ✱ Lunch fr£12&alc High tea fr£4.50 Dinner fr£14&alc Last dinner 9.30pm

Credit Cards 1 2 3 5

---

For key to symbols in English see the bookmark.

**★61% Swan**

Lower St NR12 8AA ☎(0692)630316

*Delightfully situated beside the River Bure in a charming Broadland village, this small hotel offers well furnished, attractively decorated bedrooms with good facilities and a bar that is very busy with passing boat trade.*

11⇄↑(2fb) CTV in all bedrooms ® ✗ (ex guide dogs)

150P ✿ ♪ billiards

V ✿ ⚏ Last dinner 9.30pm

Credit Cards ①②③⑤

---

**HORRABRIDGE** Devon Map **02** SX57

**★★66% Overcombe**

PL20 7RN ☎Yelverton(0822)853501

*In the village centre close to the main road, the hotel has comfortable, well modernised bedrooms and ample public areas where open fires burn in the colder months. Relaxed, friendly service and the provision of thoughtful extras combine to give a real 'home from home' feeling.*

11rm(10⇄↑)(2fb)1⊞ CTV in all bedrooms ® sB&B£19-£24.50 sB&B⇄↑£24-£24.50 dB&B£38-£43.50 dB&B⇄↑£43-£43.50 ⊟

CTV 10P ⇛ CFA croquet

V ⚞ Lunch £6-£8 High tea fr£4.50 Dinner fr£10.75 Last dinner 7.15pm

Credit Cards ①③ ⓔ

See advertisement under YELVERTON

---

**HORSFORTH** West Yorkshire Map **08** SE23

**❀✗Paris**

36a Town St LS18 4RJ ☎Leeds(0532)581885 & 580200

Lunch not served

♀ English & French V 86 seats ✳ Dinner fr£11.95&alc Last dinner 10.30pm 30 P

Credit Cards ①②③

---

**HORSHAM** West Sussex Map **04** TQ13 ⦿

**★★★★❀❀⚑70% South Lodge**

Brighton Rd RH13 6PS (Small Luxury Hotels)
☎Lower Beeding(0403)891711 Telex no 877765
FAX (0403) 891253

(For full entry see Lower Beeding)

**★★60% Ye Olde King's Head**

RH12 1EG ☎(0403)53126

*An historic coaching inn, set in the old part of town, which is popular with business guests and the locals who patronise the bar and coffee shop. Service is limited and the bedrooms vary in size and comfort, though all have the modern facilities expected nowadays.*

43rm(6⇄35↑)(2fb)1⊞ CTV in all bedrooms ® T
40P

V ✿ ⚏ Last dinner 9.45pm

Credit Cards ①②③⑤

---

**HORTON** Northamptonshire Map **04** SP85

**❀❀✗ ✗French Partridge**

NN7 2AP ☎Northampton(0604)870033

*Originally a coaching inn and farm, dating in part from 1622, this comfortable house in the village centre near the church once formed part of the estate of Lord Halifax, the first Chancellor of the Exchequer. Run as a restaurant by owners David and Mary Partridge for 28 years, it offers a standard so consistently high as to have attracted an enviable clientele of regular customers. It is essential both to book in advance and to adhere rigidly to the stated time – firstly because the tiny bar with its upholstered seating and waiting-room atmosphere seats only a third of the restaurant's capacity, and secondly, courses are freshly prepared in*

*small, manageable batches. The pace of the meal is quite slow, the emphasis being on relaxation and an excellence of quality that makes a visit here extremely good value for money.*

Closed Sun, Mon, 2 wks Xmas, 2 wks Etr & 3 wks Jul-Aug
Lunch not served

♀ French V 40 seats ✳ Dinner £20-£21 Last dinner 9pm 50 P ⚞

---

**HORTON-CUM-STUDLEY** Oxfordshire Map **04** SP51

**★★★❀❀⚑67% Studley Priory**

OX9 1AZ (Consort) ☎Stanton St John(086735)203 & 254
Telex no 262433 FAX (086735) 613

Closed 27 Dec-6 Jan

*A 12th-century former Benedictine nunnery set in 13 acres of grounds with superb views westwards to the Cotswolds. Bedrooms vary from the Elizabethan suite with its half tester (circa 1700) to the pretty rooms in the north wing. The Grand Hall and the drawing room are comfortable and inviting, and the cosy panelled bar is the ideal venue for a pre-dinner drink. The main restaurant was redecorated and relaunched in July 1990 to coincide with the arrival of Chef Geoff Welch. The table d'hôte menu offers value for money with a limited choice (2 at each course). Set menus featuring shellfish and vegetarian courses, and a short à la carte. Our inspector ate delicately flavoured lobster ravioli, tender Cotswold lamb with a rather syrupy jus, well balanced and not overpowered by rosemary; good vegetables (except the overcooked mange-tout), and chocolate torte with orange sauce. Presentation is in a modern style with no fussiness. There are lovely freshly baked rolls and creamy unsalted butter, and an extensive range of petits fours. The wine list features regional plus New and Old World wines.*

19⇄↑2⊞ CTV in all bedrooms ® T ✗ sB&B⇄↑£88-£110 dB&B⇄↑£98-£150 ⊟

100P 1⚘ ✿ CFA ⚶ (grass) croquet clay pigeon shooting *xmas*

♀ English & French V Lunch £22.50-£27.50&alc Dinner £22.50-£27.50&alc Last dinner 9.30pm

Credit Cards ①②③④⑤ⓔ

---

**HORWICH** Greater Manchester Map **07** SD61

**★★66% Swallowfield**

Chorley New Rd BL6 6HN ☎(0204)697914 FAX (0204) 68900

*Set back from the A673 on the east of the town and close to junction 6 of the M61, this friendly owner-run hotel has been considerably enlarged and public areas improved. Bedrooms are all comfortable and well equipped, with particularly smart modern bathrooms in the newer rooms.*

31⇄↑(6fb) CTV in all bedrooms ® T

35P ⇛ ✿

✿ ⚏ Last dinner 8.30pm

Credit Cards ①③

---

**HOUNSLOW** Greater London

See **LONDON plan 1***B3*(page 434)

**★★★60% Master Robert**

Great West Rd TW5 0BD (A4) ☎081-570 6261
Telex no 9413782 FAX 081-569 4016

*A commercial hotel beside the A4 includes the busy Robert Inn bar and a traditional steakhouse restaurant with separate lounge bar in its public areas. Accommodation is provided in 2 annexes and a series of chalets spaced out in a quiet setting to the rear of the main building; all bedrooms are of a good size and well equipped, those in the Hogarth Wing being the smartest – though the Airlie is currently undergoing refurbishment – and the chalets providing the best parking.*

100⇄↑(8fb) CTV in all bedrooms ® T ✗ (ex guide dogs) ✳ sB⇄↑£77-£80 dB⇄↑£87-£90 (room only) ⊟

⟨ 100P 35⚘ ✿ CFA

⚑ Mainly grills **V** ✿ 🖵 ⚒ ✳ Lunch £10.25-£14.50&alc Dinner £14.50-£15.50&alc Last dinner 11pm
Credit Cards ① ② ③ ⑤ ⓔ

## HOVE

See Brighton & Hove

### HOVINGHAM North Yorkshire Map **08** SE67

★★★65% *Worsley Hotel Arms*

YO6 4LA ☎(0653)628234 FAX (0653) 628130

*Situated within the peaceful and picturesque village of Hovingham, this hotel has recently undergone extensive refurbishment. There is a range of comfortable lounges for guests use, and the freshly prepared dishes can be enjoyed in the elegant restaurant. The bedrooms are individually decorated to a high standard, and all have en suite bathrooms. Some are situated in a cottage close by. The young staff provide a friendly service.*

14⇨1🛏 CTV in all bedrooms **T**
CTV 50P 3🏌 ✿ ⚙
**V** ✿ 🖵 Last dinner 9pm
Credit Cards ① ③

### HOW CAPLE Hereford & Worcester Map **03** SO63

★★62% **How Caple Grange**

HR1 4TF ☎(098986)208 FAX (098986) 301

*This impressive stone-built house, dating back to 1730 but considerably enlarged in Victorian times, stands in five acres of grounds and gardens on the B4224 between Hereford and Ross-on-Wye. Its spacious bedrooms are well equipped to suit tourist or business traveller, and leisure amenities include a solarium, sauna and jacuzzi, as well as an unheated swimming pool in the grounds.*

26rm(18⇨) CTV in all bedrooms ® **T** sB&B⇨£42.50 dB&B⇨£65 🏠
CTV 100P ✿ CFA 🏊 sauna solarium gymnasium putting *xmas*
✿ 🖵 Lunch £8-£9 Dinner fr£10 Last dinner 9pm

### HOWTOWN (NEAR POOLEY BRIDGE) Cumbria Map **12** NY41

★★★❀❀❀🛆
**SHARROW BAY COUNTRY HOUSE**

Sharrow Bay CA10 2LZ (at Pooley Bridge take unclass road S for 4m) (Relais et Châteaux) ☎Pooley Bridge(07684)86301 & 86483 FAX (07684) 86349

Closed end Nov-early Mar

*In a superb setting on Lake Ullswater, the hotel has been decorated and furnished with charm and imagination, and there is an impressive array of porcelain, pictures and antiques. None of the rooms in the house are large, but public rooms are comfortably appointed and offer a peaceful, relaxing asmosphere, and bedrooms are thoughtfully furnished with comfort in mind. The main house has 2 elegant dining rooms, one with lake views. Dinner is at 8pm and a set price menu is offered with a good selection of interesting dishes. Spanish Chef Juan Martin, a protegé of Francis Coulson, provides cooking of a high standard, making good use of fresh produce. Starting, perhaps, with fresh monkfish cooked in a reduction of wine and cream with tarragon and vegetables, or terrine of chicken with pistachio nuts, spiced oranges and Cumberland sauce. Main dishes include roast*

*saddle of hare with brandy and grape sauce. To finish, iced pineapple and lime mousse with strawberry sauce, or hot steamed lemon sponge with creamy egg custard. The well balanced wine list offers over 230 reasonably priced wines. Bank House, a mile away and also on the lakeside, offers equally comfortable accommodation, with good sized bedrooms, a superb lounge and a magnificent dining room. After 43 years, Brian Sack and Francis Coulson are beginning to hand responsibilities over to their staff. At times the pressure has told. We hope that such lapses are a temporary hiccup and that they will attain the high standards achieved by the owners, and for which the hotel is renowned.*

12rm(8⇨🛏)Annexe16⇨🛏 CTV in all bedrooms ® **T** ⚒
S15% sB&B⇨🛏£85 sB&B⇨🛏£85-£115 dB&B£150-£170 dB&B⇨🛏£220-£280 (incl dinner)
28P 2🏌 🚭 ✿ nc13yrs
⚑ English & French ✿ 🖵 ⚒ S15% Lunch £24-£30 Dinner £39.50 Last dinner 8.30pm

### HOWWOOD Strathclyde *Renfrewshire* Map **10** NS36

★★★62% **Bowfield Hotel & Country Club**

Lands of Bowfield PA9 1DB ☎Kilbarchan(05057)5225 FAX (05057) 5230

*First and foremost a leisure club, with bedrooms added in 1990, this complex occupies what was an old bleaching mill. Much of the character of the buildings has been retained, but bedrooms are modern and well equipped. Bowfield lies in an elevated rural location off the B776 a mile from Howwood.*

12⇨🛏(3fb) CTV in all bedrooms ® **T** ⚒ (ex guide dogs) ✳
sB&B⇨🛏£55-£65 dB&B⇨🛏£80-£90 🏠
CTV 100P 🚭 ✿ 🖵 (heated) squash snooker sauna solarium gymnasium jacuzzi spa & steam room
→

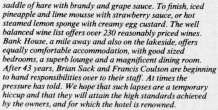

SOUTH LODGE HOTEL

Four star luxury in traditional country house set in 90 acres of beautiful Sussex parkland, with views over the South Downs.

Delicious cuisine by top chef Anthony Tobin, using local game and fish, with soft fruits and herbs from hotel's own walled garden.

Superbly appointed bedrooms and suites each individually decorated in true country house style.

Enjoy tennis, croquet, petanque, putting, fishing, horse riding or golf.

South Lodge is the perfect location for visiting the wealth of National Trust Gardens and Houses of Sussex.

**For full details, please contact:
South Lodge Hotel, Lower Beeding,
Near Horsham, West Sussex RH13 6PS.
Telephone: 0403 891711.**

♀ Scottish & French **V** ✿ ⚲ ⚼ ✱ Lunch £6-£12 Dinner £10-
£15&alc Last dinner 9.30pm
Credit Cards [1] [2] [3] [5]

---

See also Marsden

★★★65% *George*
St George's Square HD1 1JA ☎(0484)515444
FAX (0484) 435056

*Warm and friendly service is given at this popular town centre
hotel close to the railway station, where the inaugural meeting of
the Rugby League was held. The traditional-style restaurant
provides a good standard of cooking, including Yorkshire
specialities. An extensive refurbishment programme is currently
underway.*
59rm(47⇄)(2fb) CTV in all bedrooms ® **T**
Lift ( 24P
♀ International **V** ✿ ⚲ ⚼ Last dinner 9.45pm
Credit Cards [1] [2] [3] [5]

★★★62% *Briar Court*
Halifax Road, Birchencliffe HD3 3NT ☎(0484)519902
Telex no 518260 FAX (0484) 431812

*Conveniently situated close to the M62, this modern and
comfortable hotel offers good bedrooms. Friendly service and a
choice of dining styles are provided, including a very good Italian
restaurant.*
48⇄♠(3fb) CTV in all bedrooms ® **T** ✖ (ex guide dogs)
( 140P ✿
♀ English & Italian **V** ✿ ⚲ Last dinner 11.00pm
Credit Cards [1] [2] [3] [5]

★★68% *Huddersfield*
33-47 Kirkgate HD1 1QT ☎(0484)512111 Telex no 51575
FAX (0484) 435262

*A busy, family run hotel in the town centre, close to the ring road,
providing comfortable, well-equipped bedrooms, a bistro-style
restaurant, nightclub, wine bar and the popular Boy and Barrel
Inn.*
40⇄♠(4fb)2⊟ CTV in all bedrooms ® **T** sB&B⇄♠£30-£50
dB&B⇄♠£35-£70
Lift ( CTV 60P CFA sauna solarium jacuzzi pool table darts ♫
xmas
♀ English & French **V** ✿ Lunch £5-£10&alc Dinner £10-
£15&alc Last dinner 11.30pm
Credit Cards [1] [2] [3] [4] [5] ①

★★66% *The Cote Royde Country*
7 Halifax Rd, Edgerton HD3 3AN ☎(0484)547588
Telex no 518260 FAX (0484) 431812

*Set in its own grounds midway between junction 24 of the M62 and
the town centre, this former mill owner's mansion has been
refurbished to provide attractive accommodation. Bedrooms,
though not spacious, are well equipped with modern facilities and
the elegant public rooms include a panelled restaurant offering
good value set price menus.*
21⇄♠(1fb) CTV in all bedrooms ® **T** ✖
( CTV 20P ✿ sauna solarium gymnasium
♀ French **V** ✿ ⚲ Last dinner 9.30pm
Credit Cards [1] [2] [3] [5]

❀❀✕ *Weavers Shed*
Acre Mills, Knowl Rd, Golcar HD7 4AN (3m W off A62)
☎(0484)654284

*A converted weaver's shed retaining much of its original character,
situated a few miles from the town at Goldcar, enjoys local
following. Fresh market produce is used to create very British
dishes, menus changing to reflect seasonal availability; cooking is
sound and the food well presented. Home-made soup can be
followed by fish, meat or game and the sweets are noteworthy.
There is an adequate wine list, and service is particularly natural,
friendly and helpful.*

Closed Sun, Mon, 1st 2 wks Jan & last 2 wks Jul Lunch not
served Sat
40 seats Lunch £9.50&alc Dinner £22-£28alc Last lunch
1.45pm Last dinner 9pm 30 P
Credit Cards [1] [2] [3]

---

★★★★67% **Forte Crest**
Castle St HU1 2BX (Forte Hotels) ☎(0482)225221
Telex no 592777 FAX (0482) 213299

*Situated on a unique site within Hull's new marina, close to the city
centre, this Post House proves popular with visitors, as does the
Club House Restaurant that looks out over the moored yachts in
the marina.*
99⇄♠(12fb)⚼in 66 bedrooms CTV in all bedrooms ® **T** ✱
sB⇄♠fr£69 dB⇄♠fr£79 (room only) ⊟
Lift ( 130P ✿ CFA ⊟ (heated) sauna solarium gymnasium ◔
xmas
**V** ✿ ⚲ ⚼ ✱ S% Lunch £8.75-£9.50&alc Dinner £15.50&alc
Last dinner 10.30pm
Credit Cards [1] [2] [3] [5]

★★★73% **Grange Park**
Main St HU10 6EA (Best Western) ☎(0482)656488
Telex no 592773 FAX (0482) 655848
(For full entry see Willerby)

★★★70% **Willerby Manor**
Well Ln HU10 6ER ☎(0482)652616 Telex no 592629
FAX (0482) 653901
(For full entry see Willerby)

★★★67% **Forte Posthouse Hull**
Ferriby High Rd HU14 3LG (Forte Hotels) ☎(0482)645212
Telex no 592558 FAX (0482) 643332
(For full entry see North Ferriby)

★★★60% **Valiant House**
11 Anlaby Rd HU1 2PJ ☎(0482)23299 FAX (0482) 214730

*This commercial hotel next to the railway station in the town
centre has certainly improved under new ownership. Double
glazing has been added and the modern accommodation offers a
good range of facilities, with further refurbishment of public areas
and bedrooms continuing during 1991.*
59⇄♠ CTV in all bedrooms ® **T** ✖ (ex guide dogs)
sB&B⇄♠£35-£55 dB&B⇄♠£45-£65 ⊟
Lift ( 10P CFA
♀ English & French **V** ✿ ⚲ ✱ Bar Lunch £3-£10alc Dinner
£12.50-£13.50 Last dinner 9.30pm
Credit Cards [1] [2] [3] [5]

★★63% **Pearson Park**
Pearson Park HU5 2TQ ☎(0482)43043 FAX (0482) 447679
Closed 24 Dec-1 Jan

*This hotel enjoys a surprisingly different and delightful situation
within a well established and well kept public park, and yet is only
one mile from the city centre. Because of its location, it is both
handy for the city, yet offers a more peaceful environment,
enhanced by the personal attention of the proprietors and their
small team of staff.*
32⇄♠(4fb)1⊟ CTV in all bedrooms ® **T** sB&B⇄♠£30-£45
dB&B⇄♠£45-£60 ⊟
( 30P CFA
♀ English & French **V** ✿ ⚲ Lunch £7.15&alc Dinner
£9.50&alc Last dinner 9pm
Credit Cards [1] [2] [3] [5] ①

**See advertisement on page 369**

A rosette means exceptional standards of cuisine.

H

**★★62% Waterfront**
Dagger Ln HU1 2LS ☎(0482)227222
*This modern hotel, a converted dock warehouse dating from the Victorian era and tucked away in the 'old town', still retains much original character, the informal Sugar Dock Bistro being housed in its old arched brick cellars.*
30⇌↱2⊟ CTV in all bedrooms ® T sB⇌↱£39-£72 dB⇌↱£55-£88 (room only) ⊨
☾ 32P CFA
♀ English & French V ♧ ⊻ ✱ Sunday Lunch £7.50-£9.50 Dinner £10.50-£12.50&alc Last dinner 10pm
Credit Cards [1] [3] £

**⌂Campanile**
Beverley Rd, Freetown Way HU2 9AN (Campanile)
☎(0482)25530 Telex no 592840 FAX (0482) 587538
*A modern, purpose-built unit provides simple bedrooms as an annexe to the restaurant.*
Annexe50⇌↱ CTV in all bedrooms ® T S% sB⇌↱fr£36 dB⇌↱fr£36 (room only) ⊨
60P CFA *xmas*
♀ English & French Lunch £3.75-£8.90 Dinner £6.80-£8.90 Last dinner 10pm
Credit Cards [1] [3] £

**○Forte Travelodge**
Beacon Service Area, South Cave(A63 eastbound) (Forte)
☎Central Res (0800) 850950
Open
40⇌↱

**⊛✕✕Cerutti's**
10 Nelson St HU1 1XE ☎(0482)28501 FAX (0482) 587597
*This tiny restaurant – reached by following signs for Victoria Pier – stands in a pedestrianised area backed by a small car park and offering glimpses of shipping from its first-floor dining room. Here friendly, helpful proprietors Tony and Tina Cerutti offer an extensive menu which includes steak in 3 different guises for determined carnivores, but is otherwise devoted to seafood; scampi, scallops, monkfish, sea bream, halibut with various sauces and Dover sole in up to 7 styles are all featured, the dishes' attraction usually lying in the freshness of the fish and simplicity of preparation, though items like fish cakes and vegetable roulades have gained popularity.*
Closed Sun, 24 Dec-3 Jan & BHs Lunch not served Sat
♀ International 36 seats Lunch £14.50-£26alc Dinner £14.50-£26alc Last lunch 2.00pm Last dinner 9.30pm 10 P
Credit Cards [1] [3]

## HUMBIE Lothian *East Lothian* Map **12** NT46

**★★★♣66% Johnstounburn House**
EH36 5PL (1m S on A6137) (Mount Charlotte (TS))
☎(087533)696 FAX (087533) 626
*Set in forty acres of secluded grounds and gardens, this charming 17th-century house offers well-equipped, individually styled bedrooms and comfortable public rooms which make it easy to relax.*
11⇌↱Annexe9⇌↱(9fb) CTV in all bedrooms ® ⊨
20P ⇼ ✲ clay pigeon shooting *xmas*
V ♧
Credit Cards [1] [2] [3] [5]

## HUNGERFORD Berkshire Map **04** SU36

**★★★65% Bear**
Charnham St RG17 0EL (Resort) ☎(0488)682512
FAX (0488) 684357
*This famous inn dates from 1297, and much of its original character has been retained in a beamed restaurant and traditional bar with open fire, as well as in the exposed timbers of many bedrooms. Accommodation is comfortable and well equipped throughout, both in the main building and in two tastefully converted annexes set in a quiet position away from the road, and guests are welcomed by a cheerful team of staff.*
14⇌Annexe27⇌↱(2fb)1⊟ CTV in all bedrooms ® T ✱ sB⇌↱£70-£80 dB⇌↱£80-£95 (room only) ⊨
☾ 80P ⇼ CFA
V ♧ ⊻ Lunch £13.75&alc High tea fr£2 Dinner £17.95&alc Last dinner 9.30pm
Credit Cards [1] [2] [3] [5] £

**★★66% Three Swans**
117 High St RG17 0DL (Resort) ☎(0488)682721
FAX (0488) 681708
15⇌↱ CTV in all bedrooms ® T ✱ sB&B⇌↱fr£40 dB&B⇌↱fr£50 ⊨
40P CFA
V ♧ ⊻
Credit Cards [1] [2] [3] [5]

## HUNSTANTON Norfolk Map **09** TF64

**★★67% Caley Hall**
Old Hunstanton Rd PE36 6HH ☎(0485)533486
Closed Jan-Feb RS Sun evening
*The high volume of business – and particularly of guests returning here – is a good indication of the standards maintained at this privately owned and personally managed hotel standing amid well tended shrubberies beside the A49 in the attractive setting of Old Hunstanton. Conversion of former stables has provided well equipped accommodation to supplement those bedrooms contained in the 17th-century manor house.*
Annexe29rm(27⇌)(5fb) CTV in all bedrooms ® ✱ sB&B⇌£36-£39 dB&B⇌£52-£58 ⊨
50P ✲ CFA *xmas*

→

♡ International **V** ♨ Sunday Lunch £11.75 Dinner £11.75&alc
Last dinner 9pm
Credit Cards ① ③ ⓔ

★★61% **Lodge**
Old Hunstanton Rd PE36 6HX ☎(0485)532896
*A 17th-century former dower house a mile east of the town is now a friendly family-run hotel, offering comfortable modestly furnished bedrooms with modern amenities. The bar with an open fire is popular with locals and the restaurant has a small lounge area.*
16⇨♟(3fb) CTV in all bedrooms ® **T** ✳ sB&B⇨♟£30.60-£34 dB&B⇨♟£48.60-£54 ⊟
70P ✿ CFA snooker games room *xmas*
♡ English, French & Italian **V** ♨ ⚟ ✳ Lunch £11.25 Dinner £11.90-£29.55 Last dinner 9.30pm
Credit Cards ① ③ ⓔ

★57% *Wash & Tope*
Le Strange Ter PE36 5AJ ☎(0485)532250
*Close to the seafront, this traditional inn offers well-equipped comfortable accommodation, with reasonable-sized bedrooms decorated in pastel shades. The restaurant refurbishment should be completed by 1992.*
10rm(4⇨2♟)(1fb)1⊞ CTV in all bedrooms ®
12P 2🚗 pool
**V** ♨
Credit Cards ① ② ③

---

HUNSTRETE Avon Map **03** ST66

★★★

★★★❀❀⚑
**HUNSTRETE HOUSE**

BS18 4NS (CLIPPER)
☎Compton Dando
(0761)490490
FAX (0761) 490732
*This idyllically set country house hotel, with its lovely gardens and 92-acre deer park, provides a perfect base from which to explore the city of Bath. Thoughtfully and tastefully appointed throughout, it features comfortable lounge areas – warmed by log fires in winter – and two attractive restaurants, one of which is reserved for non-smokers; fine paintings and pleasing flower arrangements are to be found throughout the house. Individually decorated bedrooms contain some fine pieces of period furniture, while thoughtful extra touches are part of the warm welcome extended to guests. Chef Robert Elsmore produces uncomplicated menus of mainly British dishes, using vegetables and fruits from the extensive gardens whenever possible; the à la carte selection changes monthly, the set-price changes daily, and a sound wine list offers a range to suit most pockets. The warm, friendly atmosphere pervading the hotel stems largely from the caring attitude of a helpful staff and management.*
13⇨♟Annexe11⇨♟2⊞ CTV in all bedrooms **T**
✈ (ex guide dogs) sB&B⇨♟£95 dB&B⇨♟£150 ⊟
⟨ 40P 🚗 ✿ CFA ☂ (heated) ♫ (hard) croquet lawn nc9yrs *xmas*
♡ English & French **V** ♨ ⚟ ⅍ Lunch £16&alc Dinner fr£28.50&alc Last dinner 10pm
Credit Cards ① ③

**See advertisement under BATH**

---

For key to symbols in English see the bookmark.

---

HUNTINGDON Cambridgeshire Map **04** TL27 ☉

★★★❀71% **The Old Bridge**
PE18 6TQ ☎(0480)52681 Telex no 32706 FAX (0480) 411017
*Occupying an enviable riverside position in the town centre, this ivy-clad Georgian hotel has bedrooms which are individually designed and furnished in keeping with the style of the building. Meals are served throughout the day, the menu in the main restaurant offers imaginative and skilfully prepared dishes complemented by an extensive wine list.*
26⇨♟(3fb)1⊞ CTV in all bedrooms **T**
⟨ 50P CFA ⚓ private mooring for boats
**V** ♨ ⚟ Last dinner 10.15pm
Credit Cards ① ② ③ ⑤ ⓔ

★★★60% **The George**
George St PE18 6AB (Forte Hotels) ☎(0480)432444
FAX (0480) 453130
*Originally a posting house in Stuart times, this hotel has a galleried courtyard and offers well equipped accommodation suitable for business and leisure guests.*
24⇨♟(3fb)⅍in 7 bedrooms CTV in all bedrooms ® **T** ✳
sB⇨♟fr£75 dB⇨♟fr£95 (room only) ⊟
71P CFA *xmas*
**V** ♨ ⚟ ⅍ ✳ Lunch fr£6.08 Dinner fr£13 Last dinner 9.30pm
Credit Cards ① ② ③ ⑤

---

HUNTLY Grampian *Aberdeenshire* Map **15** NJ53

★★⚑56% **Castle**
AB54 4SH ☎(0466)792696 FAX (0466) 792641
*A popular retreat for anglers set in peaceful grounds on the edge of the town and close to the castle ruins. Spacious public areas offer homely comforts while modern day amenities are gradually being added to the simply appointed bedrooms.*
23rm(13⇨♟)(2fb)3⊞ CTV in 12 bedrooms ® ✳ sB&B£25-£30 sB&B⇨♟£32-£37 dB&B£39.50-£44.50 dB&B⇨♟£47.50-£52.50 ⊟
CTV 50P 3🚗 ✿ CFA ⚓ croquet putting green *xmas*
**V** ♨ ⚟ ⅍ ✳ Lunch fr£7.95&alc High tea £6.50-£7.50 Dinner fr£10&alc Last dinner 9pm
Credit Cards ① ② ③ ⓔ

---

HURLEY Berkshire Map **04** SU88

★★★❀64% **Ye Olde Bell**
SL6 5LX (Resort) ☎Littlewick Green(0628)825881
FAX (0628) 825939
*Built in 1135 and reputedly the oldest inn in England, this hotel set in an ornamental garden retains original beams and a cheery open fire in its small lounge and bar. All bedrooms enjoy 24-hour room service and are equipped to a high standard, while the oak-panelled restaurant offers an inviting menu of dishes in both traditional and modern vein.*
10⇨♟Annexe26⇨♟(3fb)3⊞⅍in 2 bedrooms CTV in all bedrooms ® **T** sB⇨♟£83-£95 dB⇨♟£97-£105 (room only) ⊟
⟨ 90P 🚗 ✿ CFA *xmas*
♡ English & French **V** ♨ ⚟ ⅍ ✳ Lunch £15.95&alc Dinner £18.95&alc Last dinner 9.30pm
Credit Cards ① ② ③ ⑤

---

HURSTBOURNE TARRANT Hampshire Map **04** SU35

★★❀⚑74% **Esseborne Manor**
SP41 0ER (Pride of Britain) ☎(0264)76444 FAX (0264) 76473
*This charming Georgian/Victorian building – originally a farm house – enjoys an almost park-like setting; its neat gardens contain a croquet lawn and hard tennis court. Individually furnished and decorated bedrooms (some contained in a coach house annexe at the rear of the main building) include such thoughtful extras as mints and bowls of fruit, the sitting room is*

*both comfortable and attractive, and a dining room with quality appointments offers a set main course menu with a choice of starters and puddings – alternative main courses being available at a small supplementary charge. The hotel is personally run by the Yeo family with the assistance of a small, hand-picked team of staff.*

6⇨🛏Annexe6⇨🛏1🛌 CTV in all bedrooms T
🏃 (ex guide dogs) sB&B⇨🛏£88 dB&B⇨🛏£99-£125 🍴
50P 🚗 ✿ ♪ (hard) croquet golf practice net nc12yrs
♀ English & French V ✿ ♨ Lunch £11.50-£15
Credit Cards 1 2 3 4 5 ④

---

**HURST GREEN** Lancashire Map **07** SD63

★★70% **Shireburn Arms**
BB6 9QJ ☎Stonyhurst(025486)518
Closed 1 Jan
*Well appointed bedrooms and cosy lounges are features of this charming country inn which enjoys views over the Ribble Valley from its position at the centre of the village. Oak beams and blazing log fires create a cosy atmosphere in the public areas, but pride of place goes to a new restaurant where both British and French cuisine can be enjoyed in a congenial and relaxed atmosphere.*
15⇨🛏(2fb)1🛌 CTV in all bedrooms ® T ✳ sB&B⇨🛏£52-£57.50 dB&B⇨🛏£92-£115 (incl dinner) 🍴
CTV 71P ✿ CFA putting green ♫ *xmas*
♀ English & French V ✿ ♨ ✳ Lunch £12.95
Credit Cards 1 2 3 ④

**See advertisement under PRESTON**

---

**HYTHE** Kent Map **05** TR13

★★★★65% **The Hythe Imperial**
Princes Pde CT21 6AE (Best Western) ☎(0303)267441
Telex no 965082 FAX (0303) 264610
*Most of the individually furnished bedrooms and suites of this well managed large hotel offer excellent inland or sea views as well as gracious standards of comfort and modern facilities; accommodation comes in a variety of sizes and shapes, however, and some bathrooms are rather compact. Conferences and banquets are well catered for, there are comprehensive indoor and outdoor leisure amenities, and friendly uniformed staff provide helpful service.*
100⇨🛏(5fb)4🛌 CTV in all bedrooms ® T 🏃 (ex guide dogs)
sB&B⇨🛏£76.50-£95 dB&B⇨🛏£112-£150 🍴
Lift ( 150P ✿ CFA ☒ (heated) ▶ 9 ♪ (hard & grass )squash snooker sauna solarium gymnasium croquet bowls putting beauty salon ♫ oộ *xmas*
♀ English & French V ✿ ♨ ✂ ✳ Lunch £16.50-£20&alc High tea £3.75-£7 Dinner £20-£25&alc Last dinner 9pm
Credit Cards 1 2 3 5

**See advertisement under PRELIMINARY SECTION**

★★★66% **Stade Court**
West Pde CT21 6DT (Best Western) ☎(0303)268263
Telex no 965082 FAX (0303) 261803
*In a prominent position overlooking the sea, this is a well managed hotel with a young team of helpful staff. Accommodation is comfortable, some rooms have small lounges facing the sea. Guests have use of the leisure facilities at the nearby Imperial Hotel.*
42⇨🛏(5fb) CTV in all bedrooms ® T ✳ sB&B⇨🛏£54-£62
dB&B⇨🛏£85-£95 🍴
Lift 12P 2🚗 (£3 per night) CFA ☒ (heated) ▶ 9 ♪ (hard & grass )squash snooker sauna solarium gymnasium *xmas*
♀ English & Continental V ✿ ♨ ✂ Lunch £8.50-£10 High tea £3.50-£5 Dinner £6-£17.50&alc Last dinner 9pm
Credit Cards 1 2 3 5

**See advertisement under PRELIMINARY SECTION**

---

**ILFORD** Greater London

See LONDON plan 1*F4*(page 435)
○**Forte Travelodge**
Beehive Ln ID4 5GR (Forte) ☎Central Res (0800) 850950
Due to have opened Winter 1991
32⇨🛏

---

**ILFRACOMBE** Devon Map **02** SS54

★★65% **Elmfield**
Torrs Park EX34 8AZ ☎(0271)863377
Closed Nov-Mar (ex Xmas)
*From an elevated position overlooking Ilfracombe and the surrounding countryside, this friendly hotel offers well-equipped bedrooms, comfortable public rooms and the use of a heated swimming pool.*
12rm(11🛏) CTV in all bedrooms ® T 🏃 sB&B🛏£33
dB&B🛏£66 (incl dinner) 🍴
14P 🚗 ✿ ☒ (heated) sauna solarium gymnasium pool table darts jacuzzi spa bath nc8yrs *xmas*
♀ English & Continental V ✂ ✳ Bar Lunch £6-£7.50&alc Dinner £10.50&alc Last dinner 7.30pm
Credit Cards 1 3

★★61% **Tracy House**
Belmont Rd EX34 8DR ☎(0271)863933 & 868979
Closed Nov-Feb RS Mar & Oct
*This informally-run hotel stands near the town centre yet within walking distance of beaches. All bedrooms offer good facilities and public areas are comfortably furnished, the bar promoting a pleasantly relaxed atmosphere and the dining room serving a simple table d'hôte menu.*
11rm(9⇨🛏)(2fb) CTV in all bedrooms ® T sB&B⇨🛏£22-£31 dB&B⇨🛏£44-£62 🍴
11P 1🚗 (£2) 🚗 ✿ putting

H

♀ English & Continental ♥ ⚗ ✱ Bar Lunch fr£3.50 Dinner fr£10 Last dinner 8pm
Credit Cards [1] [2] [3] ④

### ★★ 57% Ilfracombe Carlton
Runnacleave Rd EX34 8AR (Consort) ☎(0271)862446
FAX (0271) 865379

*A popular holiday hotel offering easy access to both town centre and beaches, and featuring daily entertainment during the season, provides accommodation in simply-appointed bedrooms. Spacious public areas include a dining room where the table d'hôte menu is changed nightly.*
48rm(20⇱20↑)(6fb) CTV in all bedrooms ® T
✖ (ex guide dogs) S% sB&B£25-£27.50 sB&B⇱↑£25-£27.50 dB&B£40-£45 dB&B⇱↑£45-£50 ᵮ
Lift ₵ 25P CFA ♫ *xmas*
♥ ⚗ ⅔ ✱ Lunch £4-£6.50 High tea £3-£5 Dinner £10.50 Last dinner 8.30pm
Credit Cards [1] [2] [3] ④

### ★★ 56% Arlington
Sommers Crescent EX34 9DP ☎(0271)862002 862252
FAX (0271) 862015
Closed midweek Nov-Feb

*Set in an elevated position with some sea views, this resort hotel caters in particular for the needs of family groups; the restaurant offers a four-course table d'hôte menu, entertainment is laid on during the season, and there is an outdoor swimming pool.*
29⇱↑(6fb) CTV in all bedrooms ® T sB&B⇱↑£24-£38 dB&B⇱↑£48-£76 (incl dinner) ᵮ
Lift CTV 30P CFA ⊇ (heated) sauna solarium *xmas*
♥ ⚗ ✱ Bar Lunch £2-£3 High tea £2-£3 Dinner £12.50 Last dinner 8pm
Credit Cards [1] [2] [3] ④

### ★★ 55% St Helier
Hillsborough Rd EX34 9QQ ☎Barnstaple(0271)864906
Closed Oct-Apr

*The family-run hotel occupies a commanding position with sea views, yet is within comfortable walking distance of shops, amusements, sports facilities and beaches.*
23rm(16⇱1↑)(8fb) CTV in all bedrooms ® sB&B£22-£23 sB&B⇱↑£24-£25 dB&B£40-£44 dB&B⇱↑£44-£48 ᵮ
CTV 20P 9🏌 ⊞ ✱ pool table
♀ English & Continental ♥ ⚗ Dinner £7-£7.50 Last dinner 7.30pm
Credit Cards [1] [3]

### ★ 57% Torrs
Torrs Park EX34 8AY ☎(0271)862334
Closed Nov-8 Mar

*A friendly, family-run resort hotel in an elevated position enjoying views over the sea, town and countryside. Bedrooms, whilst compact, are simply furnished and well equipped.*
14⇱↑(5fb) CTV in all bedrooms ® sB&B⇱↑£26-£28.50 dB&B⇱↑£52-£57 (incl dinner) ᵮ
16P ⊞ solarium nc5yrs
V ♥ ⚗ ⅔ ✱ Lunch £6.50-£9alc High tea fr£2.50alc Dinner fr£8.75&alc Last dinner 7.30pm
Credit Cards [1] [2] [3] [4] [5] ④

---

### ILKLEY West Yorkshire Map 07 SE14

### ★★★ 52% Cow & Calf
Moor Top LS29 8BT ☎(0943)607335 FAX (0943) 816022
Closed Xmas

*Family owned and informally run, an hotel which commands magnificent views down the Wharfe Valley from its position on the edge of the moor above the town offers prettily decorated bedrooms and public areas which include a choice of eating options.*
20⇱↑(1fb)1 ⊞⅔in 3 bedrooms CTV in all bedrooms ® T
sB&B⇱↑£55-£70 dB&B⇱↑£65-£80 ᵮ

100P ⊞ ✿ CFA
♀ English & French V ♥ Lunch £9.50-£10.50&alc Dinner £13.75-£14.75&alc Last dinner 9pm
Credit Cards [1] [2] [3] [4] [5]

### ★★ ✿76% Rombalds
11 West View, Wells Rd LS29 9JG ☎(0943)603201
FAX (0943) 816586
Closed 28-30 Dec

*The proprietors' personal supervision of this comfortable, tastefully furnished hotel ensures courteous, friendly service, and its restaurant features an imaginative range of freshly-prepared dishes complemented by a well-balanced wine list; on Sundays visitors can enjoy the 'Edwardian Breakfast' – a brunch which is served from breakfast time and through the lunch period.*
15⇱↑(5fb) CTV in all bedrooms ® T sB&B⇱↑£58-£80 dB&B⇱↑£84-£100 ᵮ
₵ 28P ⊞ CFA ♨ *xmas*
♀ English & Continental V ♥ ⚗ Lunch £9.70&alc High tea £5-£9alc Dinner £19-£30alc Last dinner 10pm
Credit Cards [1] [2] [3] [5] ④

### ★★ 60% Greystones
1 Ben Rhydding Rd LS29 8RJ ☎(0943)607408
Closed 25 Dec & 1 Jan

*An attractive detached stone house standing in its own grounds close to the town centre. Family-owned and run, it offers a sound standard of accommodation, service and food.*
10⇱↑(1fb) ® ✱ sB&B⇱↑£41 dB&B⇱↑£56
CTV 17P ✱
♥ ✱ S% Dinner £12.95 Last dinner 8.45pm
Credit Cards [1] [2] [3] [5]

### ★ 64% Grove
66 The Grove LS29 9PA ☎(0943)600298
Closed 24-31 Dec

*A delightful little hotel near the town centre, offering friendly service from the resident owners, very well-furnished and equipped bedrooms, a comfortable lounge and good home cooking in the small dining room.*
6⇱↑(2fb) CTV in all bedrooms ® sB&B⇱↑£36-£39 dB&B⇱↑£48-£50 ᵮ
CTV 5P ⊞ nc3yrs
Lunch £6-£10alc High tea £6-£8alc Dinner £8-£12alc Last dinner 7.30pm
Credit Cards [1] [3]

### ✿✿✿✿ ✖ ✖ ✖ Box Tree
Church St LS29 9DR ☎(0943)608484 FAX (0943) 816793

*Rich colour schemes, objets d'art and a profusion of oil paintings, prints and china give this long-established restaurant an atmosphere all of its own. In the evenings, a classical guitarist helps to set a relaxed tone, making this an ideal place for an intimate dinner. Guests have the option of eating from the Carte du Jour, with several items at each course, or the cheaper 3-course fixed price menu. Whatever is chosen, diners can be sure of a memorable evening. Chef Edward Denny combines sound technique with a flair for flavour that results in some well-constructed sauces – for example a wonderfully pungent smoked cheese sauce accompanying the Swiss Cheese Soufflé or the subtle Sauce Caramel compounding the richness of a liqueur-soaked chocolate marquise. Other highlights of the inspection meal were the perfectly cooked vegetables, and the ravioli filled with mushroom and tarragon that exploded with flavour in a fine sauce of consommé and wine, redolent of garlic and basil, and surrounding a noisette of lamb perched on a bed of spinach.*
Closed Mon, 25-26 Dec & 1 Jan Lunch not served Sat
Dinner not served Sun
♀ French V 50 seats ✱ Lunch fr£10.95 Dinner fr£24.75 Last lunch 2pm Last dinner 10pm 🅿 ♫
Credit Cards [1] [2] [3] [5]

### ILMINSTER Somerset Map 03 ST31 ◉

#### ★★ 62% Shrubbery

TA19 9AR (Consort) ☎(0460)52108 Telex no 46379
FAX (0460) 53660

*The characterful public areas of this popular Hamstone hotel –
quieter since the building of the Ilminster bypass – remain a
popular meeting place for local groups and societies, and a good
choice of dishes is offered on the menus of its intimate restaurant
and busy lounge bar. Ongoing bedroom refurbishment is resulting
in a pleasing balance of traditional styles, tasteful soft furnishings
and modern facilities.*

12⇌♠(3fb) CTV in all bedrooms ® T sB&B⇌♠£40-£70
dB&B⇌♠£60-£100 ♬
CTV 100P ❊ CFA ⬱ (heated) ♫ (grass) deep-sea fishing
V ♦ ⚏ Lunch £10-£22.50 Dinner £12.50-£22.50 Last dinner
9.30pm
Credit Cards ①②③④⑤ ⓔ

#### ⋔Forte Travelodge

(on A303) (Forte) ☎(0460)53748 Central Res (0800) 850950
*Excellent budget accommodation situated at the westerly end of
Ilminster bypass (take care, it is not dual carriageway), along with
a Happy Eater and a petrol station. Bedrooms are at ground and
first floor levels, ideal for single business occupancy, or overnight
accommodation for the touring family.*

32⇌♠(32fb) CTV in all bedrooms ® sB⇌♠£29.95
dB⇌♠£29.95 (room only)
⟮ 32P ⊞
Credit Cards ①②③

### IMMINGHAM Humberside Map 08 TA11

#### ★★ 62% Old Chapel Hotel & Restaurant

50 Station Rd DN40 3AY ☎(0469)572377 FAX (0469) 577883
*This small commercial hotel on the outskirts of the village offers
easy access to both the South Bank Industries and Humberside
Airport. A good choice of reasonably priced meals is provided in
the dining room. Modestly appointed en suite bedrooms, though
sometimes compact, are clean and well maintained, and service is
both friendly and informal.*

14⇌♠ CTV in all bedrooms ® T ✗ (ex guide dogs)
sB&B⇌♠£40 dB&B⇌♠£50
20P ❊
V ♦ ⚏ Lunch £7-£9&alc Dinner £9&alc Last dinner 9.30pm
Credit Cards ①②③⑤ ⓔ

### INCHNADAMPH Highland *Sutherland* Map 14 NC22

#### ★★ 60% Inchnadamph

IV27 4HL ☎Assynt(05712)202
Closed Nov-14 Mar
*Set amid spectacular scenery, this long-established, family-run
Highland hotel is an angler's paradise as well as being a popular
base for the touring holidaymaker. It has a friendly atmosphere,
offers a choice of cosy lounges, and provides traditional services
and comforts.*

27rm(10⇌)(5fb) ✱ sB&B£28.60-£31.35 dB&B£57.20-£62.70
dB&B⇌£62.70-£68.20
CTV 30P ⊞ ✔
V ♦ ⚏ ✱ Lunch £8 Dinner £11.50 Last dinner 7.30pm
Credit Cards ①③⑤

### INGATESTONE Essex Map 05 TQ69

#### ★★★ 65% Heybridge Moat House

Roman Rd CM4 9AB (Queens Moat) ☎(0277)355355
Telex no 995186 FAX (0277) 353288
*Part of this original banqueting and conference hotel dates to 1494,
with the bar and timbered restaurant outside the main building and
the bedrooms in a modern extension reached by a walkway; all are
identical, very spacious, comfortable and well equipped. Ermis*

*Kyprianou with his willing team keep this hybrid hotel in
harmonious order.*

22⇌♠(3fb) CTV in all bedrooms ® T ✗
⟮ CTV 200P ❊ ♬
♀ International V ♦ ⚏ Lunch fr£12&alc Dinner fr£12&alc
Last dinner 10.30pm
Credit Cards ①②③④⑤

### INGLESHAM Wiltshire Map 04 SU29

#### ❊✗ ✗ *Inglesham Forge*

SN6 7QY ☎Faringdon(0367)52298
*A welcoming log fire burns in this charming cottage restaurant
during the winter months, and proprietor Joan Morris provides
natural hospitality, anticipating your needs without being intrusive.
Chef Keith Bidwell creates two interesting set menus based on
fresh ingredients combined with herbs and vegetables which he
grows himself in the surrounding garden. Bouillabaisse, venison
and breast of duck served with a blackberry purée feature among
the choices available, and seasonal specialities are well worth
trying. The option of a savoury finish to the meal makes a pleasant
change.*

Closed Sun, last 2 wks Aug & 24-31 Dec Lunch not served Sat
& Mon
V 30 seats Last lunch 2pm Last dinner 9.30pm 15 P
Credit Cards ①②③⑤

### INSTOW Devon Map 02 SS43

#### ★★★ 67% Commodore

Marine Pde EX39 4JN ☎(0271)860347 FAX (0271) 861233
*Commanding beautiful views across the river to Appledore, this
hospitable family-run modern hotel set in its own grounds has
tastefully decorated, well equipped bedrooms and comfortable,
recently refurbished public areas. The restaurant's table d'hôte and
à la carte menus offer a wide choice, with fish and game specialities
in season.*

20⇌♠(3fb) CTV in all bedrooms ® T ✗ sB&B⇌♠£50-£56
dB&B⇌♠£79-£90 ♬
150P ⊞ ❊ *xmas*
♀ English & Continental V ♦ ⚏ ✱ Lunch fr£9.75&alc Dinner
fr£18&alc Last dinner 9.15pm
Credit Cards ①②③

### INVERARAY Strathclyde *Argyllshire* Map 10 NN00

#### ★★ 58% The Great Inn

Argyll Estates, Cherry Park PA32 8XB ☎(0499)2466
FAX (0499) 2421
*A long-established Highland tourist hotel, originally a coaching
inn, has been both renovated and upgraded. Much of its
accommodation has been modernised, and food is available
throughout the day and evening (in season), in either the attractive
dining room or the lounge bar.*

25rm(19⇌♠)(6fb)⤫in 5 bedrooms CTV in all bedrooms ® T
20P ♬
V ♦ ⚏ Last dinner 9pm
Credit Cards ①③

#### ★ 68% Fernpoint

PA32 8UX ☎(0499)2170
Closed 3 Nov-17 Dec & 8 Jan-mid Mar
*A period house with extensions set in its own gardens, near the pier,
with views out across Loch Fyne. As well as reasonably priced
dinners, a wide range of bar meals is served throughout the day
and evening. The bar has natural stone walls and a lofted ceiling
and features a good range of malt whiskies.*

6rm(4⇌♠)(4fb) CTV in all bedrooms ® ✱ sB&B⇌♠£30-£40
dB&B⇌♠£45-£64 ♬
⟮ CTV 12P ❊ *boating* *xmas*

→

373

V ✿ ♨ ❋ Bar Lunch £2-£5.50 High tea £5.50-£6.25 Dinner
£14-£15 Last dinner 10pm
Credit Cards [1] [3] £

---

**INVERGARRY** Highland *Inverness-shire* Map **14** NH30

**★★♨63%  Glengarry Castle**
PH35 4HW ☎(08093)254 FAX (08093) 207
Closed 21 Oct-6 Apr
*This converted Victorian mansion house is set in 60 acres of
secluded grounds beside the picturesque shore of Loch Oich, and
close to the ruin of Invergarry Castle. It has a welcoming
atmosphere and provides a restful base for holidaymakers.*
26rm(25⇨🏠)(4fb)2🛏 CTV in all bedrooms ® T sB&B£28.50-
£30.50 sB&B⇨🏠£35.50-£37.50 dB&B£48-£52 dB&B⇨🏠£58-
£77
CTV 30P 2🚗 ❖ ♪ (hard) ♪
♡ Scottish, English & Continental V ✿ ♨ Sunday Lunch £8
Dinner £14.50 Last dinner 8.30pm
Credit Cards [1] [3]

---

**INVERKEILOR** Tayside *Angus* Map **15** NO64

**❀✕Gordon's**
Homewood House, Main St DD11 5RN ☎(02413)364
(Rosette awarded for dinner only)
*In the relaxed, friendly atmosphere of this unpretentious little
village restaurant guests can select dishes in the French style from
an à la carte menu which, though short, is imaginative without
being over-adventurous; much care and skill goes into the
preparation of meals here, and excellent use is made of fresh
produce.*
Closed Mon & last 2 wks Jan
♡ Scottish & French **V** 25 seats ❋ Bar Lunch £5.95-£12 Dinner
£12.95&alc Last lunch 2.30pm Last dinner 9.30pm 6 P nc8yrs
♨
Credit Cards [1] [3]

---

**INVERMORISTON** Highland *Inverness-shire* Map **14** NH41

**★★68%  Glenmoriston Arms**
IV3 6YA ☎Glenmoriston(0320)51206
*This 200-year-old coaching inn beside the A82 has been
sympathetically upgraded to provide the comforts and facilities
expected by the modern-day traveller. In addition to well equipped
accommodation it offers a welcoming atmosphere, good food and a
cosy bar.*
8⇨🏠1🛏 CTV in all bedrooms ® T sB&B⇨🏠£30-£40
dB&B⇨🏠£50-£64 🏠
28P 🚗 ❖ ♪ stalking shooting
♡ European V ✿ ♨ Sunday Lunch £6 Dinner £16-£20.50&alc
Last dinner 8.30pm
Credit Cards [1] [3] £

---

**INVERNESS** Highland *Inverness-shire* Map **14** NH64

**See Town Plan Section**
**★★★★66%  Kingsmills**
Culcabock Rd IV2 3LP (Swallow) ☎(0463)237166
Telex no 75566 FAX (0463) 225208
*South of the town centre beside the golf course, this hotel has just
completed an ambitious redevelopment programme. It includes a
new wing of bedrooms providing a high standard of spacious and
comfortable accommodation, an extended foyer lounge, and a
conservatory which is a popular venue for bar lunches. The leisure
club has a good sized pool opening onto the attractive, well tended
gardens. In some areas staff lack the professional polish usual for
the classification, but more than make up for it with natural
Highland charm and friendliness. A pleasant table d'hôte lunch is
served in the restaurant, and in the evening the chef also provides
an innovative speciality menu.*

---

73⇨🏠Annexe6⇨🏠(22fb)♨in 33 bedrooms CTV in all
bedrooms ® T ❋ sB&B⇨🏠£80-£120 dB&B⇨🏠£97.50-£180
🏠
Lift ℂ 100P ❖ CFA 🖵 (heated) sauna solarium gymnasium
putting green hair salon *xmas*
V ✿ ♨ ♨ ❋ Lunch £9.50-£11 High tea £5-£8.50 Dinner £18-
£19.50&alc Last dinner 9.45pm
Credit Cards [1] [2] [3] [5]

**★★★★58%  Culloden House**
Culloden IV1 2NZ (2m E off A96) (Small Luxury Hotels)
☎(0463)790461 Telex no 75402 FAX (0463) 792181
*This impressive Georgian house is personally run in an informal
manner by the resident proprietors assisted by a team of friendly
young staff. In comparison to the public areas many of the
bedrooms and bathrooms are disappointingly decorated and
furnished, but a major programme of refurbishment is in hand.*
20⇨🏠(1fb)5🛏♨in 3 bedrooms CTV in all bedrooms T ✖ ❋
sB&B⇨🏠£99-£135 dB&B⇨🏠£135-£175 🏠
ℂ 50P 2🚗 🚗 ❖ CFA ♪ (hard) snooker sauna solarium
nc10yrs *xmas*
♡ Scottish & French V ✿ ♨ ♨ Lunch fr£12alc Dinner £27
Last dinner 9pm
Credit Cards [1] [2] [3] [5]

**★★★❀ ♨78%  Bunchrew House**
Bunchrew IV3 6TA (3m W off A862) ☎(0463)234917
FAX (0463) 710620
*On the shoreline of the Beauly Firth with fine views to the Black
Isles and Ben Wyns beyond, the hotel is quietly located in 15 acres
of landscaped gardens. The hospitality of owners Alan and Patsy
Wilson, their manager James Whyte and the keen young staff,
really sets this hotel apart. An additional 5 bedrooms have recently
been added, tastefully finished, though not as large or as individual
as the original 6. There is a comfortable wood-panelled lounge and
bar with natural fires. The dining room, with views of the Firth, is a
lovely setting for chef Aleks Mazurek's cooking, based on a simple
approach, bringing out the best in local produce.*
11⇨🏠(2fb)2🛏♨in 2 bedrooms CTV in all bedrooms T
✖ (ex guide dogs) sB&B⇨🏠£65-£85 dB&B⇨🏠£85-£115 🏠
40P 2🚗 🚗 ❖ CFA ♪ clay pigeon shooting putting green ♿
*xmas*
♡ International V ✿ ♨ ♨ Lunch £10.50 Dinner £20.50 Last
dinner 9pm
Credit Cards [1] [2] [3] £

**★★★74%  Craigmonie**
9 Annfield Rd IV2 3HX (Best Western) ☎(0463)231649
Telex no 94013304 FAX (0463) 233720
*An efficiently run business and tourist hotel in a quiet residential
area not far from the town centre. Public areas are tastefully
decorated in the modern style and include a well equipped leisure
centre. Bedrooms, which vary in size and design, provide all the
expected comforts and facilities.*
35⇨🏠(3fb)3🛏♨in 10 bedrooms CTV in all bedrooms ® T
✖ (ex guide dogs) ❋ sB&B⇨🏠£57-£66 dB&B⇨🏠£85-£106
Lift ℂ 60P ❖ CFA 🖵 (heated) sauna solarium gymnasium
beauty therapy treatments *xmas*
♡ Scottish & French V ✿ ♨ ♨ ❋ Lunch £6.95-£8.95 Dinner
fr£16.75 Last dinner 9pm
Credit Cards [1] [2] [3] [5]

**★★★61%  Caledonian**
Church St IV1 1DX (Jarvis) ☎(0463)235181 Telex no 75232
FAX (0463) 711206
*Many of the rooms in this smart modern hotel in the town centre
have views over the River Ness. Bedrooms, though rather poorly
heated, are well equipped and comfortable, with compact
bathrooms. Staff are friendly and there is a choice of bars, a
pleasant restaurant and a leisure centre.*
100⇨🏠(12fb) CTV in all bedrooms ® T ❋ sB⇨🏠£71-£80
dB⇨🏠£94-£105 (room only) 🏠

Lift ( ⊞ 80P CFA ▭ (heated) snooker sauna solarium gymnasium whirlpool spa-bath *xmas*
♀ International **V** ✿ ♨ ✱ Bar Lunch £6.50-£8.50alc Dinner £16.50-£18&alc Last dinner 9.30pm
Credit Cards [1][2][3][5] ⓔ

### ★★★ 59% Mercury

Nairn Rd IV2 3TR (junc A9/A96) (Mount Charlotte (TS)) ☎(0463)239666 Telex no 75377 FAX (0463) 711145

*This popular, purpose-built hotel offers convenient access to the A9 from its position on the eastern fringe of the town. Recent refurbishment has considerably enhanced ground-floor public areas, which now feature comfortable modern appointments, while bedrooms exhibit a variety of styles and standards – the best being on the second and third floors, as those on the top floor remain simple and functional.*

118↰↱(11fb)⊬in 6 bedrooms CTV in all bedrooms ® **T** (room only) ⊟
Lift ( 150P ❄ *xmas*
**V** ✿ ♨
Credit Cards [1][2][3][5]

### ★★★ 59% Palace

Ness Walk IV3 5NE ☎(0463)223243 Telex no 777210 FAX (0463) 236865

*Situated next to the river near the town centre and overlooking the picturesque castle, this popular business and tour group hotel has a friendly atmosphere. Public areas have been attractively refurbished and the well equipped bedrooms are gradually being improved, though some remain rather practical.*

43↰Annexe41↰(12fb) CTV in all bedrooms ® **T** sB↰£39-£69 dB↰£59-£94 (room only) ⊟
Lift ( 40P CFA *xmas*
♀ Scottish & French **V** ✿ ♨ ⊬ Bar Lunch £1.95-£6.50alc Dinner £14-£16&alc Last dinner 9pm
Credit Cards [1][2][3][5] ⓔ

---

### ★★❀≜ DUNAIN PARK

IV3 6JN ☎(0463)230512
FAX (0463) 224532
RS 2wks Nov & Feb

*This charming little shooting lodge, situated in 6 acres of wooded grounds just off the A82 to the southwest of the town, has been much improved by its present owners since they took it over 6 years ago. Guests are assured of a warm welcome to its homely atmosphere, individually styled and very well equipped bedrooms include an extension with 6 special suites, and drinks are served in both the comfortable lounges though there is no bar. Pictures and silk cuts adorn the walls of the restaurant's 3 well decorated and intimate little dining rooms. Self-taught chef Ann Nicholl is gaining a good reputation for a range of homemade specialities based on top quality ingredients, including vegetables and herbs from the garden, accompanied by freshly baked bread. A fairly short à la carte selection is changed daily, according to availability, though the steak menu (using Highland beef) remains constant; well presented dishes are served by a team of young girls in attractive floral dresses. There is a sideboard display of puddings and a more than adequate wine list.*

12rm(10↰)(2fb)1⊞ CTV in all bedrooms **T**
dB&B↰£100-£120 ⊟
20P ⬤ ▭ (heated) sauna croquet badminton *xmas*
♀ Scottish & French **V** ✿ ♨ ⊬ ✱ Lunch £10-£15.50alc Dinner £14-£26alc Last dinner 9pm
Credit Cards [1][2][3][5] ⓔ

### ★★ 71% Glen Mhor

10 Ness Bank IV2 4SG ☎(0463)234308 FAX (0463) 713170
Closed 31 Dec-2 Jan

*An efficiently run business and holiday hotel, delightfully situated on the south bank of the River Ness, near to the town centre. There is a choice of bars; the Riverside Restaurant offers an excellent wine list and provides reliable, imaginative cooking, while Nico's Bistro offers a range of Scottish and Italian specialities in a relaxed, informal setting. Well equipped bedrooms vary in size and style.*

20↰↱Annexe10↰↱(1fb)1⊞ CTV in all bedrooms ® **T**
sB&B↰↱fr£54 dB&B↰↱£67-£85 ⊟
30P CFA pool table *xmas*
♀ International **V** ✿ ♨ Lunch fr£8.50&alc High tea fr£8.50alc Dinner fr£19.75&alc Last dinner 9.30pm
Credit Cards [1][2][3][5] ⓔ

See advertisement on page 377

### ★★ 65% Lochardil House

Stratherrick Rd IV2 4LF ☎(0463)235995 FAX (0463) 713394

*Set in 5 acres of grounds about one and a half miles from the town centre, this family-owned business hotel is also a popular venue for local functions. The refurbished cocktail bar is attractive and modern, while the restaurant with its fine tapestries reflects the original Victorian character. Bedrooms vary in size but are well equipped.*

11↰↱(2fb) CTV in all bedrooms ® **T** ✻ (ex guide dogs)
sB&B↰↱£45-£60 dB&B↰↱£70-£85 ⊟
120P 3⬤ ❄
♀ Scottish & French **V** ✿ ♨ Lunch £5-£10alc High tea £3-£8alc Dinner £9-£20alc Last dinner 9pm
Credit Cards [1][2][3][5] ⓔ

### ★★61% Loch Ness House
Glenurquhart Rd IV3 6JL (Consort) ☎(0463)231248
FAX (0463) 239327
*Popular and family run, this business and tourist hotel stands in its own grounds beside the A82 on the fringe of the town, next to the Caledonian Canal and golf course. Public areas include an attractive restaurant, a lively bar and a lounge offering traditional comforts, while bedrooms are gradually being improved though some remain compact and functional as yet.*
23⇨♠(1fb)2⊞ CTV in all bedrooms ® T ✱ sB&B⇨♠£35-£60 dB&B⇨♠£45-£100 ♩
60P ⇴ ✿ CFA ♫ *xmas*
♡ Scottish & French V ♥ ⏛ Lunch £6.50-£12.50&alc High tea £4.50-£10.50alc Dinner £14.50-£16.50&alc Last dinner 9pm
Credit Cards ① ② ③ £

### ★★57% Beaufort
11 Culduthel Rd IV2 4AG ☎(0463)222897 FAX (0463) 243204
*A friendly family-run commercial hotel in a residential area, the Beaufort has an informal atmosphere and offers good value, practical accommodation.*
36♠(6fb) CTV in all bedrooms ® T ✱ sB&B♠£40-£45 dB&B♠£56-£60 ♩
⊞ 50P CFA ⚗
V ♥ ⏛ Lunch £6.50-£8.50 High tea £9.50-£12.50 Dinner £12-£15 Last dinner 10pm
Credit Cards ① ② ③ ⑤

### ★★57% Cummings
Church St IV1 1EN ☎(0463)232531 FAX (0463) 236541
*Conveniently located in the town centre with its rear private car park this is an old fashioned commercial hotel with modern bedrooms. Good function and banqueting facilities are available and bar meals are served at lunchtime.*
32rm(23⇨♠)(5fb) CTV in all bedrooms ® T
✖ (ex guide dogs) sB&B£33-£35 sB&B⇨♠£39-£42 dB&B£48-£50 dB&B⇨♠£56-£62
Lift ( CTV 25P CFA
V ♥ Lunch £4.75-£5.50 High tea £6-£7alc Dinner £8-£10&alc Last dinner 8pm
£

### ★64% Redcliffe
1 Gorden Ter IV2 3HD ☎(0463)232767
*Small and friendly, this family-run business and tourist hotel in a residential area not far from the town centre offers bedrooms which, though limited in size, are tastefully appointed and well equipped. Recent refurbishment has done much to enhance public areas.*
9rm(6♠)(1fb) CTV in all bedrooms ® T S% sB&B£12-£14 sB&B♠£25.54-£27.50 dB&B£32.68-£35 dB&B♠£37.80-£40 ♩
12P ✿
V ♥ ⏛ ✱ Sunday Lunch £4.50-£7.50 High tea £5-£11 Dinner £8-£16 Last dinner 9pm
Credit Cards ① ② ③

---

### INVERURIE Grampian *Aberdeenshire* Map 15 NJ72

### ★★★66% Strathburn
Burghmuir Dr AB5 9GY ☎(0467)24422 FAX (0467) 25133
*Clean, comfortable and well cared for, this small family-run business hotel on the western edge of the town offers bright public rooms appointed in modern style, and neatly furnished bedrooms which are all well equipped though some are compact.*
21⇨♠(2fb) CTV in all bedrooms ® T ✖ (ex guide dogs) sB&B⇨♠£40-£50 dB&B⇨♠£56-£68 ♩
40P ⇴
V ♥ ⏛ ✱ Lunch £5.75-£14.75&alc Dinner £14.75-£17.75&alc Last dinner 9.30pm
Credit Cards ① ② ③ £

### ★★57% Gordon Arms
Market Place AB51 9SA ☎(0467)20314 FAX (0467) 21792
*A small personally run hotel on the main street. It has an informal atmosphere and offers traditional services and appointments with good value, practical accommodation.*
11rm(6♠) CTV in all bedrooms ® T ✱ S% sB&B£26.95 sB&B♠£29.95 dB&B£37.50 dB&B♠£39.50 ♩
CTV ⨍
♡ European V ♥ ✱ S% Lunch £6.50-£7.50 High tea £3.50-£7.50 Dinner £7.50-£9.50 Last dinner 8pm
Credit Cards ① ② ③ ⑤

---

### IPSWICH Suffolk Map 05 TM14 ⊙

### ★★★ ❀❀ ⚑ HINTLESHAM HALL
IP8 3NS (Relais et Châteaux) ☎Hintlesham(047387)334 & 268
FAX (047387) 463
(For full entry see Hintlesham)

### ★★★❀71% Marlborough
Henley Rd IP1 3SP (Best Western) ☎(0473)257677
FAX (0473) 226927
*A privately owned and excellently managed hotel set in a residential area close to the northerly ring road, achieves a successful balance between the services and facilities required by commercial clients and those appreciated by the leisure user. Accommodation varies in quality and comfort, but public areas are elegant and include a restaurant featuring both à la carte and table d'hôte menus of dishes imaginatively and skilfully prepared from good ingredients.*
22⇨♠(3fb)⤪in 6 bedrooms CTV in all bedrooms ® T S% sB⇨♠£40-£80 dB⇨♠£80-£100 (room only) ♩
( 60P ⇴ ✿ CFA *xmas*
♡ English & French V ♥ ⏛ ✂ S% Lunch £11.50-£14.50&alc Dinner £18.50-£22&alc Last dinner 9.30pm
Credit Cards ① ② ③ ⑤

### ★★★64% Ipswich Moat House
London Rd, Copdock IP8 3JD (just off A12 near Copdock village) (Queens Moat) ☎Copdock(047386)444
Telex no 987207 FAX (047386) 801
*Three miles south of Ipswich, off the A12, this modern hotel is set in landscaped gardens and attracts those in search of leisure as well as a flourishing conference trade. Accommodation is attractively furnished and staff are pleasant and helpful.*
45⇨♠Annexe29⇨♠(2fb)1⊞ CTV in all bedrooms ® T ✱ sB⇨♠£46-£76 dB⇨♠£77-£88 (room only) ♩
Lift ( 400P ✿ CFA ⬒ (heated) sauna solarium gymnasium *xmas*
♡ English & Continental V ♥ ⏛ ✂ Lunch £12-£20 High tea £2-£4 Dinner fr£14&alc Last dinner 9.50pm
Credit Cards ① ② ③ ④ ⑤ £

### ★★★62% Novotel Ipswich
Greyfriars Rd IP1 1UP ☎(0473)232400 Telex no 987684 FAX (0473) 232414
*Located on the periphery of the city centre this hotel has open plan style public areas and spacious, well-equipped rooms well suited for both the business traveller and families alike. The restaurant/grill is open from 6am-midnight.*
101⇨♠(6fb)⤪in 38 bedrooms CTV in all bedrooms ® T
Lift 50P
♡ International V ♥ ⏛ ✂ Last dinner 11.30pm
Credit Cards ① ② ③ ⑤

### ★★★58% Forte Posthouse
London Rd IP2 0UA (Forte Hotels) ☎(0473)690313
Telex no 987150 FAX (0473) 680412
*Easy access to both the town and A45 is provided by this purpose-built hotel at the junction of the A1214 and the B1071. Geared successfully to the commercial and conference market, it offers an appropriate range of facilities and well equipped bedrooms, though bars still await a much-needed refurbishment.*

112🛏🏃(35fb)✄in 66 bedrooms CTV in all bedrooms ® T ✻
S% sB🛏🏃£39.50-£49.50 dB🛏🏃£39.50-£49.50 (room only) 🍴
《 200P ✿ CFA ⌂ (heated) *xmas*
V ✎ ⚇ ✄ S% Lunch £9.95&alc Dinner £14-£25alc Last
dinner 10.30pm
Credit Cards 1️⃣ 2️⃣ 3️⃣ 4️⃣ 5️⃣

### ✿ ✕✕The A La Carte

Orwell House, 4A Orwell Place IP4 1BB ☎(0473)230254
*Situated in the heart of the city centre, this building is believed to
have been a malthouse at some time and more recently a copper
studio. The two-in-one Restaurant House is an interesting and
attractive venue. The à la carte restaurant is on the galleried
mezzanine floor, and is more formally furnished than the
downstairs bistro. Service is quite formal but friendly and
informative. The menu offers a good variety of dishes with
particular emphasis on sea food, such as Lobster Valcany with a
light sauce, delicately flavoured with red and green peppers. There
is also a very good, small range of imaginative vegetarian dishes.
Head chef, John Pyne, continues to maintain the standard.*
Closed Sun, Mon, 26 Dec, 1 Jan & BH Mons Lunch not served
Sat
♈ French V 28 seats ✻ Lunch £7.50-£9.50&alc Dinner £7.50-
£9.50&alc Last lunch 2pm Last dinner 10pm 10 P ✄
Credit Cards 1️⃣ 2️⃣ 3️⃣ 5️⃣

---

IRVINE Strathclyde *Ayrshire* Map **10** NS33

### ★★★★55% Hospitality Inn

Annick Rd, Annickwater KA11 4LD (Mount Charlotte (TS))
☎(0294)74272 Telex no 777097 FAX (0294) 77287
*A programme of upgrading is planned by this large commercial/
conference hotel to maintain the high standard of its
accommodation; it is hoped that the shortfall in services for an
establishment of its type may also be rectified. Bedrooms are
roomy, comfortable and fully equipped, while well furnished and
spacious public areas include a choice of two restaurants – the
more formal Mirage, and the tropical atmosphere of the Lagoon
with its exotic plants and swimming pool.*
128🛏🏃(44fb)✄in 16 bedrooms CTV in all bedrooms ® T
(room only) 🍴
《 250P ✿ 🏊 (heated) ✒ jacuzzi football pitch *xmas*
♈ French V ✎ ⚇
Credit Cards 1️⃣ 2️⃣ 3️⃣ 4️⃣ 5️⃣

---

ISLAY, ISLE OF Strathclyde *Argyllshire* Map **10**

---

BOWMORE Map **10** NR35

### ★★57% Lochside

19 Shore St PA43 7LB ☎(049681)244 & 265
*This small hotel is situated on the main street, but backs onto the
shore of the loch and there are lovely views from the bar, the dining
room and some of the bedrooms. The hotel boasts an extensive
range of malt whiskies.*
7rm(2🛏)CTV in all bedrooms ® ✻ sB&B£21-£27
dB&B🛏£46-£50 🍴
✄ *xmas*
♈ International V ✎ ✻ Lunch £5-£25alc Dinner £10&alc Last
dinner 9pm
Credit Cards 1️⃣ 3️⃣

---

BRIDGEND Map **10** NR36

### ★★65% Bridgend

PA44 7PQ ☎Bowmore(049681)212 FAX (049681) 673
*This long established fishing and tourist hotel is located close to the
island's main road junction. Public rooms retain the hotel's
Victorian character, whilst the bedrooms, which vary in size, are
more modern and well equipped.*
10rm(5🛏4🏃)(3fb) CTV in all bedrooms ® T ✻ sB&B£30.50-
£35 sB&B🛏🏃£30.50-£35

→

30P ✿ CFA ♪
♨ ⚑ ✳ Lunch £12.50-£14.50 Dinner £14.50-£15.50 Last dinner 8pm
ⓔ

---

PORT ASKAIG Map **10** NR46

★★59% **Port Askaig**
PA46 7RD ☎(049684)245 FAX (049684) 295
9rm(2⇦2🛏)(1fb) CTV in all bedrooms ® ✳ sB&B£32-£35
sB&B⇦🛏£35-£38 dB&B£46-£50 dB&B⇦🛏£50-£58 🏰
CTV 15P 6🚗 🚗 ✿ nc5yrs
V ♨ ⚑ ✳ Lunch £7-£13.50 Dinner £14-£16 Last dinner 9pm
ⓔ

---

ISLE OF Places incorporating the words 'Isle of' or 'Isle' will be found under the actual name, eg Isle of Wight is listed under Wight, Isle of.

---

ISLE ORNSAY

See Skye, Isle of

---

IXWORTH Suffolk Map **05** TL97

❀❀❀✕✕**Theobalds**
68 High St IP31 2HJ ☎(0359)31707
*This period cottage at the heart of the village has been converted to create a spacious restaurant with cosy bar. The dinner menu changes continually, as optimum use is made of fresh seasonal produce, and chef/patron Simon Theobald's imaginative flair is demonstrated in such dishes as a terrine of sweetbreads and fennel; a more restricted choice of dishes is available at lunchtime, and there is a separate Sunday lunch menu. Meals are accompanied by a particularly good wine list which includes some fifty half bottles.*
Closed Mon, 25-26 Dec & BH's Lunch not served Sat Dinner not served Sun
♀ English & French V 36 seats ✳ Lunch £14.95&alc Dinner £23.50-£25.50alc Last lunch 2pm Last dinner 9.30pm ⚘ nc8yrs
✍
Credit Cards ①③

---

JERSEY

See Channel Islands

---

JEVINGTON East Sussex Map **05** TQ50

❀❀❀✕✕**Hungry Monk**
BN26 5QF ☎Polegate(0323)482178
*This well established restaurant is popular with locals of all ages, so booking is essential. Pre-dinner drinks are served in one of the two comfortable lounges, and here you can study the value for money set-price blackboard menu – nominally three courses – including coffee, delicious home-made chocolates and a glass of tawny port. A starter such as spicy parsnip soup or feuillette of Brie with mustard sauce might be followed by rack of lamb with garlic and flageolet beans or marinated guinea fowl with a cumin and coriander sauce, while puddings include such old favourites as Crème Brûlée and bread and butter pudding. An inglenook fire burns in the intimate atmosphere of the candlelit restaurant, and classical music plays in the background; service is always pleasant, though it can on occasions be considered too businesslike.*
Closed 24-26 Dec & BH Mons Lunch not served Mon-Sat (ex by reservation only)
♀ English & French V 38 seats ✳ Sunday Lunch £18.50-£19.50 Dinner £18.50-£19.50 Last dinner 10.15pm 14 P nc3yrs ✍

---

JOHN O'GROATS

See Halkirk and Lybster

---

KEGWORTH Leicestershire Map **08** SK42

★★★61% **Yew Lodge**
33 Packington Hill DE7 2DF ☎(0509)672518
Telex no 341995 Ref 211 FAX (0509) 674730
*The hotel's location, just off the A6 and conveniently close to junction 24 of the M1, makes it a popular venue for meetings and conferences with its predominantly commercial clientèle. Bedrooms are well equipped, although styles and sizes vary considerably.*
54⇦🛏(3fb) CTV in all bedrooms ® T sB&B⇦🛏£54.50-£57.50 dB&B⇦🛏£65.50-£69.50 🏰
Lift ℂ 120P CFA *xmas*
♀ English & French V ♨ ⚑ Lunch £4-£16alc High tea £4.50-£10alc Dinner £4.50-£20alc Last dinner 10pm
Credit Cards ①②③⑤ⓔ

---

KEIGHLEY West Yorkshire Map **07** SE04 ☺

★★68% **Dalesgate**
406 Skipton Rd, Utley BD20 6HP (2m NW A629)
☎(0535)664930 FAX (0535) 611253
*Well furnished and comfortable this family-run hotel near the town centre features very attractive bedrooms with good facilities and a cosy basement restaurant serving meals of a good standard.*
21⇦🛏(1fb) CTV in all bedrooms ® T ✳ sB&B⇦🛏£25.50-£38.50 dB&B⇦🛏£40-£48 🏰
ℂ 30P
V ✳ Dinner £4.50-£9.95&alc Last dinner 9pm
Credit Cards ①②③⑤ⓔ

---

KELSO Borders *Roxburghshire* Map **12** NT73

★★★64% **Ednam House**
Bridge St TD5 7HT ☎(0573)24168 FAX (0573) 26319
Closed 25 Dec-10 Jan
*Comfortably old fashioned and providing attentive service, this privately owned hotel offers spacious accommodation. The rear gardens lead down to the banks of the River Tweed.*
32⇦🛏(2fb) CTV in all bedrooms ® T sB&B⇦🛏fr£40 dB&B⇦🛏£60-£81 🏰
CTV 100P 🚗 ✿
V ♨ ⚑ Sunday Lunch £10 Dinner £17 Last dinner 9pm
Credit Cards ①③

★★★63% **Cross Keys**
36-37 The Square TD5 7HL (Exec Hotel) ☎(0573)23303
FAX (0573) 25792
*A modernised old coaching inn set at the head of the town square provides neat, well maintained accommodation and good value meals.*
24⇦🛏(4fb) CTV in all bedrooms ® T ✳ sB&B⇦🛏£36.50-£39.90 dB&B⇦🛏£49.80-£57 🏰
Lift ℂ ▦ CTV CFA snooker sauna solarium gymnasium *xmas*
♀ Scottish & Continental V ✳ Lunch £6.90 Dinner £13.90&alc Last dinner 9.15pm
Credit Cards ①②③⑤

★★★ ❀❀⚐77% **Sunlaws House**
Heiton TD5 8JZ (2m SW A698) ☎Roxburgh(05735)331
FAX (05735) 611
*This splendid 18th-century country house is situated 3 miles west of the town, off the A698, tucked away in over 200 acres of woodlands and well tended gardens. Owned by the Duke of Roxburghe, it offers sporting and leisure facilities as well as attractively furnished accommodation, with inviting lounges and very comfortable well equipped bedrooms. Cooking is of a high standard, with daily changing lunch and dinner menus of carefully prepared dishes that make use of fresh local fish, meat and game, complemented by a comprehensive wine list.*
22⇦🛏(2fb)2🛏 CTV in all bedrooms ® T ✘ (ex guide dogs)
🏰

( 30P ✿ CFA ♪ (hard) ✔ shooting croquet *xmas*
V ♥ ⚏ ✳ Lunch £13.75 Dinner £25 Last dinner 9.30 pm
Credit Cards 1 2 3 5 £
See advertisement in colour section.

---

## KENDAL Cumbria Map **07** SD59

### ★★★70% Riverside

Stramongate Bridge LA9 4BZ ☎(0539)724707
FAX (0539) 740274
Closed 25-26 Dec & 1 Jan

*A 17th-century tannery, situated by the River Kent in the town centre, has been sympathetically converted to create this popular business and tourist hotel. Modern public areas include a restaurant and informal buttery, and the spacious bedrooms are comfortable and well equipped.*

47➪🛏(4fb)✂in 4 bedrooms CTV in all bedrooms ® T
✖ (ex guide dogs) sB&B➪🛏fr£56 dB&B➪🛏fr£75 ⊟
Lift ( 160P CFA
♀ International V ♥ ⚏ Lunch £9.90-£10.50&alc Dinner £14.90-£15.90&alc Last dinner 10pm
Credit Cards 1 2 3 5 £

### ★★★57% Woolpack

Stricklandgate LA9 4ND ☎(0539)723852 Telex no 728256
FAX (0539) 728608

*A former coaching inn, situated in the centre of town, with car parking facilities at the rear. Bedrooms are modern and well equipped and the beamed Crown Bar was once Kendal's wool auction room.*

54➪🛏(5fb)✂in 6 bedrooms CTV in all bedrooms T ✳
sB&B➪🛏£62 dB&B➪🛏£75-£85 ⊟
( 60P CFA *xmas*
♀ English & French V ♥ ⚏ ✳ Bar Lunch £2.50-£4.75 Dinner £14.95&alc Last dinner 9.30pm
Credit Cards 1 2 3 £

### ★★69% Garden House

Fowl-ing Ln LA9 6PH ☎(0539)731131 FAX (0539) 740064
Closed 25 Dec-12 Jan

*This delightful Regency house stands in its own grounds and gardens at the edge of the town, just off the A685 and reached by turning into Fowl-ing Lane at the Shell Service Station. Fully equipped, individually furnished and decorated en suite bedrooms are complemented by a comfortable lounge, cosy bar and well appointed dining room extending into a new conservatory overlooking the garden.*

10➪🛏(2fb)1♨✂in 8 bedrooms CTV in all bedrooms ® T ✳
S% sB&B➪🛏£44.50-£49.50 dB&B➪🛏£64-£70 ⊟
40P ⛽ ✿
♀ English & French V ♥ ✂ ✳ S% Lunch £9.75-£12.75 Dinner £16.25-£17.50&alc Last dinner 9pm
Credit Cards 1 2 3 5 £

---

## KENILWORTH Warwickshire Map **04** SP27 ⊙

### ★★★60% De Montfort

The Square CV8 1ED (De Vere) ☎(0926)55944
FAX (0926) 57830

*Situated close to the town centre, this hotel offers well equipped bedrooms, conference facilities, and attractive public areas, including a choice of restaurant and coffee shop.*

96➪🛏 CTV in all bedrooms ® T ✳ sB&B➪🛏£37.50-£86
dB&B➪🛏£75-£129 ⊟
Lift ( 85P CFA pool table ♫ *xmas*
V ♥ ⚏ ✂ ✳ Lunch fr£14.25&alc Dinner fr£15.75&alc Last dinner 9.45pm
Credit Cards 1 2 3 5 £

K

### ★★ 64% **Clarendon House**
Old High St CV8 1LZ ☎(0926)57668 Telex no 311240
FAX (0926) 50669

*Parts of this inn located in the oldest area of town date back to 1430 and public rooms retain some original features. Modernised bedrooms, while compact, are well equipped with good en suite facilities.*
31⇨🛏(1fb)4🛏 CTV in all bedrooms ® T sB&B⇨🛏fr£60 dB&B⇨🛏£80-£85 🅿
30P 🚿 CFA
♀ European V ♥ Sunday Lunch £8.50-£9.50 Dinner £13.50-£17.50alc Last dinner 9.30pm
Credit Cards ①③④

### ❀❀❀✕ **Restaurant Bosquet**
97A Warwick Rd CV8 1HP ☎(0926)52463

*Difficult to spot among the proliferation of guesthouse and restaurant signs, the restaurant is modest in appearance, but the cooking of Frenchman Bernard Lignier is full of strong, clean flavours, with some adventurous flavour combinations, and food is served in generous portions. Jane Lignier is charming and friendly, and with a good knowledge of her husband's cooking she is able to guide diners through the menu.*
Closed Sun, Mon, BH's, 10 days Xmas, 1 wk Jul & 2wks Aug
Lunch not served (ex by reservation only)
♀ French 26 seats Last dinner 9.30pm ⚲
Credit Cards ①②③

### KENNFORD Devon Map 03 SX98

### ★★ 61% **Fairwinds**
EX6 7UD ☎Exeter(0392)832911
Closed 7-31 Dec
*This small hotel just south of Exeter near the A38/M5 is run in friendly, informal style by resident owners William and Maria Price. Bedrooms are cosy and well equipped, suited to business travellers and holidaymakers alike, and public rooms though rather confined are bright and homely.*
8rm(6⇨🛏)(1fb)⊁in 2 bedrooms CTV in all bedrooms ® T ✖ sB&B£25-£29 sB&B⇨🛏£40-£45 dB&B⇨🛏£49-£55 🅿
8P 🚿
V ⊁ Dinner £8.95-£12&alc Last dinner 8pm
Credit Cards ①③④

### KENTALLEN Highland *Argyllshire* Map 14 NN05

### ★★ ❀♨ 73% **Ardsheal House**
PA38 4BX ☎Duror(063174)227 FAX (063174) 342
Closed Nov-Mar
*Americans Robert and Jane Taylor offer true Scottish hospitality at their fine period house, set in well tended gardens looking out over pastureland grazed by sheep and cattle, across Loch Linnhe to the peaks of Morven. The atmosphere and furnishings here epitomise the country house. Expect to find radios, hairdryers and electric blankets in the bedrooms, but not TVs, telephones or kettles. Meals are taken in an attractive conservatory. Dinner, which is served at 8.30pm and no earlier, offers a minimal choice of dishes with the emphasis on country cooking in the modern style using good fresh produce and raw materials. Lunches are also available.*
13⇨🛏(1fb) sB&B⇨🛏£83.50 dB&B⇨🛏£120-£165 (incl dinner)
CTV 20P 🚿 ❀ ♪ (hard) snooker ♨
♀ International ♥ ♫ ⊁ ✳ Lunch £12-£17.50 High tea £7-£12 Dinner £31.50 Last dinner 8.30pm
Credit Cards ①②③

### ★★ 68% **Holly Tree**
Kentallen Pier PA38 4BY ☎Duror(063174)292
FAX (063174) 345
Closed Nov-mid Feb RS Xmas-New Year

*Beautifully set on the shore of Loch Linnhe and overlooking the Morven Hills, this delightful holiday hotel has been created by careful conversion of the former railway station. Cosy public areas where much of the original character has been preserved invite easy relaxation, the smart restaurant serves interesting and imaginative meals which are produced by the chef/patron, and most of the attractive modern bedrooms enjoy spectacular loch views.*
12⇨🛏(3fb) CTV in all bedrooms ® T ✳ sB&B⇨🛏£65 dB&B⇨🛏£122 (incl dinner) 🅿
30P ❀ ♪
♀ International ♥ ♫ ⊁ ✳ Lunch £4.50-£25alc Dinner £26 Last dinner 9.30pm
Credit Cards ①②③④

### KESWICK Cumbria Map 11 NY22

**See Town Plan Section**
See map 11 for details of other hotels in the vicinity

### ★★★ ❀73% **Brundholme Country House**
Brundholme Rd CA12 4NL ☎(07687)74495
Closed 20 Dec-Jan
*Converted to a stylish country house hotel in 1988, this fine Georgian mansion commands superb views across the town to the surrounding hills. The emphasis is on quality throughout, from the cosy cocktail lounge and large comfortable drawing room to the well equipped and often spacious bedrooms. Chef proprietor Ian Charlton's cooking is excellent, and his wife Lynn and their staff offer friendly and personal attention to guests at all times.*
12⇨🛏2🛏 CTV in all bedrooms ® T sB&B⇨🛏£57-£67 dB&B⇨🛏£114-£134 (incl dinner) 🅿
20P 🚿 ❀ CFA croquet bowls nc11yrs
♀ English & French V ♥ ⊁ Lunch £8-£15 Dinner £21-£21 Last dinner 8.45pm
Credit Cards ①③④

### ★★★ 57% **Derwentwater**
Portinscale CA12 5RE (Consort) ☎(07687)72538
FAX (07687) 71002
*An hotel which enjoys spectacular views across its lawned gardens to the lake and mountains beyond offers soundly equipped bedrooms and cosy public areas which are full of character. Grounds extending over 16 acres and a pleasant village setting make this an ideally peaceful retreat.*
52⇨🛏(2fb)2🛏 CTV in all bedrooms ® T ✳ sB&B⇨🛏£52-£59 dB&B⇨🛏£82-£94 🅿
Lift ℄120P ❀ CFA ♪ putting ♫ *xmas*
♀ English & French V ♥ ♫ ⊁ Bar Lunch £2.25-£9.50alc Dinner £14.95-£16.95&alc Last dinner 9.30pm
Credit Cards ①②③⑤④

### ★★ ❀♨ 74% **Dale Head Hall**
CA12 4TN ☎(07687)72478
(Rosette awarded for dinner only)
*Located 5 miles south of Keswick and situated in 3 acres of secluded gardens overlooking Thirlmere, this delightful family-run country house has parts dating back to the 16th century and is the only house on the lake. Many of the bedrooms, all with en suite facilities, have beautiful views over the lake. Delicious 5-course meals are complemented by a well chosen wine list.*
9⇨🛏(1fb)2🛏⊁in all bedrooms ® T ✖ sB&B⇨🛏£47.50-£50.50 dB&B⇨🛏£65-£85 🅿
20P 🚿 ❀ ♪ (grass) ♪ *xmas*
♥ ♫ ⊁ Dinner £14.95 Last dinner 8.30pm
Credit Cards ①③④
**See advertisement under Colour Supplement**

### ★★ 70% **Grange Country House**
Manor Brow, Ambleside Rd CA12 4BA ☎(07687)72500
Closed 3 Nov-21 Mar
*Standing just off the A591 Grasmere road on the outskirts of town, this charming hotel has been comfortably furnished and thoughtfully equipped by welcoming proprietors who successfully*

→

K

*create a relaxed, informal atmosphere. High standards of housekeeping are evident throughout the hotel, and individually decorated bedrooms continue to be upgraded, while the pleasant dining room overlooking the garden serves enjoyable, carefully prepared, home-cooked meals that make good use of fresh produce.*

10⇌🛏️2🚗 CTV in all bedrooms ® T dB&B⇌🛏️£60-£68.50 🍴
12P 1🏌️ 🚲 ℃ nc5yrs
V ✿ ♨ ✔ Dinner £14-£15.75 Last dinner 8pm
Credit Cards ①③⑥

### ★★🏌️68% Lyzzick Hall Country House
Under Skiddaw CA12 4PY ☎(07687)72277
Closed Feb

*This lovely old house, overlooking beautiful mountain scenery from its hillside setting, complements well furnished bedrooms with comfortable lounges. Service is both friendly and helpful, and an extensive range of dishes is served in the delightful restaurant.*

19⇌🛏️Annexe1⇌🛏️(4fb) CTV in all bedrooms ® T ✖️
sB&B⇌🛏️£27-£35 dB&B⇌🛏️£54-£70 🍴
40P 🚲 ❄ ⌇ (heated) 🚲
☪ International V ✿ ✱ Lunch £9.50-£12 Dinner £10-£17.50&alc Last dinner 9.30pm
Credit Cards ①②③⑤

### ★★66% Chaucer House
Ambleside Rd CA12 4DR ☎(07687)72318 & 73223
Closed 30 Nov-Jan

*In the public areas of this friendly, comfortable hotel, several spacious lounges (including one warmed by a real fire) are complemented by a very attractively appointed dining room and lounge bar.*

32rm(21⇌🛏️)(6fb)✱in 6 bedrooms CTV in 35 bedrooms ®
sB&B£22.40 sB&B⇌🛏️£29 dB&B£38 dB&B⇌🛏️£52.50 🍴
Lift 25P
☪ English & French V ✿ ✔ Dinner £10.30-£11.50 Last dinner 7.30pm
Credit Cards ①②③④⑥

### ★★66% Crow Park
The Heads CA12 5ER ☎(07687)72208

*This Victorian house stands in an elevated position overlooking the beautiful Borrowdale Valley; rooms at the rear command attractive views of Skiddaw. All the very well equipped bedrooms have private facilities, while public areas include a comfortable lounge and a bar decorated with interesting old photographs of the town.*

26rm(13⇌🛏️12🛏️)(1fb)1🚗 CTV in all bedrooms ® T ✱
sB&B⇌🛏️£19-£29 dB&B⇌🛏️£38-£58 🍴
CTV 26P 🚲 xmas
☪ English & Continental V ✿ ✔ Dinner £13.50 Last dinner 8pm
Credit Cards ①③⑥

### ★★64% Skiddaw
Main St CA12 5BN (Minotels) ☎(07687)72071
FAX (07687) 74850
Closed Xmas

*Conveniently situated in the town centre, this good value holiday and business hotel has comfortable bedrooms all with en suite facilities, a very comfortable first-floor lounge and a wide choice of bar meals or evening à la carte dishes.*

40⇌🛏️(7fb)1🚗 CTV in all bedrooms ® T ✱ sB⇌🛏️£26.50-£30 dB⇌🛏️£46-£54 (room only) 🍴
Lift 12P CFA sauna solarium
☪ English & French V ✿ ♨ ✱ Lunch £5-£7.50alc Dinner £8.50-£15alc Last dinner 9pm
Credit Cards ①②③⑥

---

A rosette means exceptional standards of cuisine.

---

### ★★62% *Queen's*
Main St CA12 5JF (Exec Hotel) ☎(07687)73333
FAX (07687) 71144
Closed 24-26 Dec

*Built of local stone and standing in the centre of town, this early Victorian former posting house is well equipped and is one of the oldest buildings in Keswick.*

35⇌🛏️(16fb) CTV in all bedrooms ® T ✖️
Lift 12🚗 (charged)
☪ English & French V ✿ ♨ Last dinner 9pm
Credit Cards ①②③⑤

### ★★59% Lairbeck
Vicarage Hill CA12 5QB ☎(07687)73373

*Family hotel with clean accommodation and good home cooking.*

14⇌🛏️(2fb) CTV in all bedrooms ® T ✖️ (ex guide dogs) S%
sB&B⇌🛏️£21-£27 dB&B⇌🛏️£42-£54 🍴
25P 🚲 ❄ croquet lawn *xmas*
☪ English & French ✔ S% Dinner £11-£12 Last dinner 8pm
Credit Cards ①③

### ★★🏌️59% Red House
Underskiddaw CA12 4QA (on A591) ☎(07687)72211

*Set amidst 8 acres of woodland just north of Keswick, this Victorian country house commands superb views of northern Lakeland. Always a popular hotel with families – its games and recreation cellar proves a boon in wet weather.*

22⇌🛏️(7fb)1🚗 CTV in all bedrooms ® sB&B⇌🛏️£30-£35
dB&B⇌🛏️£54-£65 🍴
CTV 25P 🚲 ❄ CFA ⌇ putting green games room 🚲 *xmas*
☪ European ✿ ✔ Dinner £17.50&alc Last dinner 8.30pm
Credit Cards ①②③⑥

### ★★55% Walpole
Station Rd CA12 4NA ☎(07687)72072

*Though this friendly, family run hotel stands almost at the centre of the town, it both overlooks a park and offers good views of the surrounding countryside. Most of its bedrooms have en suite facilities.*

17rm(10⇌🛏️)(4fb) CTV in all bedrooms ® sB&B£23
sB&B⇌🛏️£24.50 dB&B£46 dB&B⇌🛏️£49 🍴
9P 🚲 *xmas*
☪ English & French V Dinner £13&alc Last dinner 8pm
Credit Cards ①③⑥

### ★🚲79% Swinside Lodge
Newlands CA12 5UE ☎(07687)72948
Closed Dec-mid Feb

*This delightful Victorian lakeland house, situated in a most peaceful and unspoilt area of the English lakes, is 3 miles from Keswick, on the Portinscale to Grange road. Bedrooms are beautifully furnished and decorated and each has a private bath or shower room, colour television, radio, hair dryer and many more thoughtful extras. There are two charming sitting rooms, and an intimate candle lit dining room in which delicious 5-course suppers are served each evening.*

9rm(6⇌🛏️2🛏️) CTV in all bedrooms ® ✖️ (ex guide dogs)
sB&B⇌🛏️£52-£60 dB&B⇌🛏️£93-£100 (incl dinner) 🍴
10P 🚲 ❄ nc12yrs
✔ Dinner £18-£20 Last dinner 7.30pm

### ★73% Priorholm
Borrowdale Rd CA12 5DD ☎(07687)72745
Closed 5-31 Jan

*A very pleasantly furnished and comfortable family owned and run hotel, in a quiet side road just a short way from the town centre. Bedrooms have good facilities, and the hotel offers value for money.*

8rm(6⇌🛏️)(1fb) CTV in 7 bedrooms ® ✖️ sB&Bfr£17
dB&Bfr£38 dB&B⇌🛏️fr£52

**K**

CTV 7P ⊞
✗ Dinner £16.50 Last dinner 7.30pm
Credit Cards ① ③ ⓔ

★72% **Highfield**
The Heads CA12 5ER ☎(07687)72508
Closed Nov-Mar
*An immaculate hotel under the personal supervision of its resident proprietors enjoys splendid views towards Borrowdale from its elevated position. The atmosphere is particularly warm and friendly, the owners, who have lived in the area for many years, willingly giving advice and information on places of interest around the English Lakes.*
19rm(15⇨💧)(3fb) CTV in 15 bedrooms Ⓡ sB&Bfr£16.65
sB&B⇨💧fr£24.90 dB&B⇨💧£40.80-£49.80
CTV 19P ⊞ nc5yrs
V ♥ ⚏ ✗ ✱ Dinner £10&alc Last dinner 6.30pm

★67% *Latrigg Lodge*
Lake Rd CA12 5DQ ☎(07687)73545
*There is a continental feel to what is essentially a restaurant with bedrooms, situated in a cul de sac at the centre of town. Bedrooms, though fairly compact, are well furnished and equipped, and there is a quiet, comfortable first-floor lounge. Most enjoyable, reasonably priced evening meals are provided by the popular restaurant – and late sleepers will appreciate the fact that breakfast is served until 10am.*
7⇨💧1⊞ CTV in all bedrooms Ⓡ T
7P ⊞
⚏
Credit Cards ① ③

★67% **Linnett Hill**
4 Penrith Rd CA12 4HF ☎(07687)73109
*This small, friendly, family-run holiday hotel standing on the fringe of the town centre, opposite Fitz Park, provides good-value ensuite accommodation; public areas with a relaxed atmosphere include a homely lounge and cosy snug bar.*
10⇨💧✗in all bedrooms CTV in all bedrooms Ⓡ
✗ (ex guide dogs) ✱ sB&B⇨💧£21.25 dB&B⇨💧£38.50 🏁
12P nc5yrs
♡ International V ♥ ⚏ ✗ Bar Lunch fr£2 Dinner fr£9.50&alc
Last dinner 7pm
Credit Cards ① ③ ⓔ

<u>KEXBY</u> North Yorkshire Map **12** SE75

★★★68% **Kexby Bridge**
Hull Rd YO4 5LD ☎Wilberfoss(07595)8223 & 8154
FAX (07595) 8822
*A comfortable hotel, situated 3 miles along the A1078 York-Hull road, offers attractive accommodation in bright, well equipped bedrooms, good-value meals and friendly service.*
32⇨💧✗in 8 bedrooms CTV in all bedrooms Ⓡ T ✱
sB&B⇨💧£50 dB&B⇨💧£75 🏁
CTV 60P ✿ ⅌ 9 ♩ ♫ xmas
♡ English & French V ♥ ⚏ ✱ Bar Lunch fr£3.75 Dinner
fr£12.50 Last dinner 9.30pm
Credit Cards ① ③

<u>KEYSTON</u> Cambridgeshire Map **04** TL07

⊛✕✕**Pheasant Inn**
PE18 0RE ☎Bythorn(08014)241
*This unspoilt thatched inn is situated on the village green just a short distance from the A604. The timbered bar offers an excellent choice of bar meals, whilst the small, characterful restaurant features dishes such as pigeon terrine with rich Cumberland sauce and seafood casserole with a hint of garlic.*
Dinner not served 25 & 26 Dec

→

K

♀ English & French **V** 55 seats ✳ Bar Lunch £10-£14alc Last lunch 2pm Last dinner 10pm 50 P
Credit Cards 1️⃣2️⃣3️⃣5️⃣

---

**KIDDERMINSTER** Hereford & Worcester Map **07** SO87

**★★★★55% Stone Manor**
Stone DY10 4PJ (2m SE on A448) ☎(0562)777555
FAX (0562) 777834
RS 25 Dec
*An attractive, mock Tudor hotel, standing in 25 acres of woodland and gardens, Stone Manor has extensive conference and function facilities. Most of its bedrooms are modern and bright, but a few of the older rooms were, at the time of our inspection visit, beginning to show their age.*
53⇌🅿4🛏 CTV in all bedrooms ® **T** ✳ sB⇌🅿£74-£81.75 dB⇌🅿£89-£97 (room only)
《 CTV 400P ✿ CFA ⌁ ♬ (hard) croquet putting green
♀ International **V** ♿ ⚴ ✳ Lunch £10.75-£12.50&alc Dinner £15&alc Last dinner 10pm
Credit Cards 1️⃣2️⃣3️⃣5️⃣£

**★★★61% Granary Hotel & Restaurant**
Heath Ln, Shenstone DY10 4BS
☎Chaddesley Corbett(0562)777535 FAX (0562) 777722
Closed 25-26 Dec
*An hotel situated in rural surroundings on the A450 approximately 3 miles east of Kidderminster consists of a modern annexe providing functional, well equipped accommodation and an amenity block containing rather limited public areas; the Carvery Restaurant, which offers a simple choice of dishes, is popular with residents and non-residents alike.*
Annexe18⇌🅿 CTV in all bedrooms ® **T** ✳ sB&B⇌🅿£32.50-£43.50 dB&B⇌🅿£35-£55 Continental breakfast
《 60P ✿ CFA ♬
**V** ♿ ⚴ ✳ Lunch £9.50-£12.75 Dinner £8.50-£15.95 Last dinner 9.30pm
Credit Cards 1️⃣2️⃣3️⃣5️⃣£

**★★70% Gainsborough House**
Bewdley Hill DY11 6BS (Consort) ☎(0562)820041
Telex no 333058 FAX (0562) 66179
*This hotel, situated on the outskirts of the town (towards Bewdley) offers comfortable, recently refurbished bedrooms with attractive furnishings and good facilities; similar standards are maintained in the public and conference areas, making the establishment ideal for both leisure and business users. Service is professional, caring and friendly throughout.*
42⇌🅿(4fb)1🛏➟in 8 bedrooms CTV in all bedrooms ® **T** ✳ sB&B⇌🅿£55.50-£65 dB&B⇌🅿£70-£85 🍴
《 130P CFA *xmas*
♀ English & Continental **V** ♿ ⚴ ✳ Lunch £6.50-£12.95 Dinner frf12.95&alc Last dinner 10pm
Credit Cards 1️⃣2️⃣3️⃣5️⃣£

---

**KILCHRENAN** Strathclyde *Argyllshire* Map **10** NN02

**★★★★ ⚖73% Ardanaiseig**
PA35 1HE (Pride of Britain) ☎(08663)333 FAX (08663) 222
Closed end Oct-mid Apr
*Chef Lindsay Little has returned to this lovely hotel on the shores of Loch Awe, which is now under new ownership. He continues to demonstrate his youthful enthusiasm in his modern approach to cooking, taking full advantage of bountiful supplies of seafood and superb local meat and game from the west coast. Delicious meals are taken in the elegant spacious restaurant, where service is pleasant and correct. A meal starts with freshly baked rolls, which might accompany queen scallops, served with succulent lobster on an interesting salad, perhaps followed by a soup or a salmon pastry. Main courses could include grilled fillet of Angus beef with home-made pasta, or roast duckling with wild rice. Puddings are beautifully presented, and can include items such as chocolate tortes or brandy-snap baskets with fresh strawberries. The master*

*bedrooms in the main house are traditional and very spacious; others are more compact, but all are comfortable and prettily decorated, with thoughtful extra touches.*
14⇌🅿 CTV in all bedrooms **T** ➟
20P ⊞ ✿ ♬ (hard) ♩ snooker croquet clay pigeon shooting boating nc12yrs
♿ ⚴ ✂ Last dinner 9pm
Credit Cards 1️⃣2️⃣3️⃣5️⃣

**★★★⚖64% *Taychreggan***
PA35 1HQ ☎(08663)211 FAX (08663) 244
Closed Jan-Feb RS Oct-Dec
*Originally a ferry inn (the ferry, alas, has long since vanished) Taychreggan enjoys a magnificent setting on the shore of Loch Awe. The owners have extended the original building to give accommodation around a courtyard, in a style more reminiscent of the Continent of Europe than of Scotland.*
16rm(15⇌)1🛏 **T**
CTV 30P ⊞ ✿ ♩ clay pigeon shooting
♀ International ♿ ⚴ Last dinner 9pm
Credit Cards 1️⃣2️⃣3️⃣

---

**KILDRUMMY** Grampian *Aberdeenshire* Map **15** NJ41

**★★★★⊛ ⚖78% Kildrummy Castle**
AB33 8RA (Best Western) ☎(09755)71288 FAX (09755) 71345
Closed 4-31 Jan
*Situated in peaceful Donside and overlooking the ruins and beautiful gardens of the 13th-century Kildrummy Castle, this most comfortable hotel manages to blend old and new to great effect. The public areas have all the features expected in a grand house, such as elaborate, impressive fireplaces and tapestry-covered walls, and the bedrooms are spacious and well equipped. Kildrummy Castle is one of our 'Courtesy and Care' award winners 1991/1992 for Scotland (see colour feature on p20).*
16⇌🅿(4fb)1🛏 CTV in all bedrooms ® **T** sB&B⇌🅿£60 dB&B⇌🅿£96-£110 🍴
30P ⊞ ✿ ♩ snooker shooting ⚶ *xmas*
♀ Scottish & French **V** ♿ ⚴ ✂ Lunch £13-£15&alc Dinner £23-£24&alc Last dinner 9pm
Credit Cards 1️⃣2️⃣3️⃣4️⃣

---

**KILFINAN** Strathclyde *Argyll* Map **10** NR97

**★★⊛76% Kilfinan**
PA21 2EP ☎(070082)201 FAX (070082) 205
*This former coaching inn, situated in the Clachan, is one of Scotland's best kept secrets. Not many people come to this lovely part of the west coast. Managers Tony and Gina Wignell have made their mark here, with good honest food served by friendly local staff. Accommodation is refreshingly clean, well equipped and, most of the time, blissfully quiet. Activity centres around the adjoining public and lounge bars, where residents will soon feel at home among the locals. A small seating area has been created this past winter, in the back garden overlooking the burn towards Loch Fyne beyond.*
11⇌(1fb) CTV in all bedrooms **T** ➟ sB⇌£37 dB⇌£52-£62 (room only)
50P ⊞ ✿ ♩ clay pigeon shooting deer stalking *xmas*
♀ Scottish & French **V** ♿ ⚴ Bar Lunch £3.50-£10.50&alc Dinner £21-£25&alc Last dinner 9pm
Credit Cards 1️⃣2️⃣3️⃣

---

**KILLIECRANKIE** Tayside *Perthshire* Map **14** NN96

**★★⊛68% Killiecrankie**
PH16 5LG ☎Pitlochry(0796)3220 FAX (0796) 2451
Closed 3 Jan-Feb
(Rosette awarded for dinner only)
*Caring owners Colin and Carole Anderson are making good progress with their improvement programme at this delightful little*

**K**

*holiday hotel, set in 4 acres of wooded grounds beside the historic Pass of Killiecrankie. Colour televisions and direct dial telephones have been added to the comfortable bedrooms which retain the local craftsmen-made pine furniture, and additional en suite facilities are being installed. The atmosphere is warm and friendly and the first-floor lounge offers traditional comforts and quiet relaxation; while the cosy bar, with its sun lounge extension, is ideal for an apéritif, coffee or informal bar meal. Chef Paul Booth's daily changing table d'hôte dinner menu offers a choice of well prepard Scottish dishes featuring, according to season, game, seafood, venison, Angus beef and prime Scottish lamb. His cooking is imaginative and dinner at Killiecrankie is an enjoyable experience.*

11⇨♠(2fb) CTV in all bedrooms ® T sB&B⇨♠£35-£44 dB&B⇨♠£70-£84 ⊟
30P ⇎ ✲ croquet putting ⌂ *xmas*
V ✿ ⊒ ⅍ ✱ Bar Lunch £1.50-£10 Dinner £22.50-£23.50 Last dinner 8.30pm
Credit Cards [1] [2] [3] (£)

**See advertisement on page 387**

**KILLIN** Central *Perthshire* Map **11** NN53

**★★ 65% Morenish Lodge**
Loch Tayside FK21 8TX ☎(05672)258
Closed mid Oct-Etr

*Magnificent panoramic views across Loch Tay can be enjoyed from this country hotel which stands alone 2.5 miles north east of the town – that from the dining room being one of the most striking. Another attractive feature is the warm hospitality offered by friendly owners who are fully involved in the running of the hotel.*

13rm(4⇨8♠)(1fb)2⊠ ® ✖ sB&B⇨♠£35-£48 dB&B⇨♠£70-£76 (incl dinner) ⊟

→

CTV 20P ⇔ ❀ nc4yrs
❋ Dinner £13.50-£17.50 Last dinner 8.15pm
Credit Cards 1 3

### ★ 63% Falls of Dochart
Main St FK21 8UW ☎(05672)237
*This homely family-run hotel in the village centre offers modest, reasonably priced accommodation and cheery service. The restaurant is popular with the locals.*
9rm(1⇔5♠)(2fb) CTV in all bedrooms ® ❋ sB&B£21.50-£24.50 sB&B⇔♠£21.50-£24.50 dB&B£33-£38 dB&B⇔♠£38 用
CTV 20P *xmas*
V ❋ High tea £5-£6 Dinner £12-£20alc Last dinner 9pm
Credit Cards 1 3

### KILMARNOCK Strathclyde *Ayrshire* Map **10** NS43

### ★★★ 57% Howard Park
Glasgow Rd KA3 1UT ☎(0563)31211 Telex no 53168
FAX (0563) 27795
*A purpose built business hotel situated in the northern suburbs of the town on the old Glasgow road. Bedrooms are functional, and in addition to the restaurant there is a comfortable lounge bar. Traditional high teas are served, as well as buffet lunches and dinners.*
46⇔(6fb)⊁in 14 bedrooms CTV in all bedrooms ® T
Lift ℂ 200P
♀ Scottish & French V ☼ ♨ Last dinner 9.30pm
Credit Cards 1 2 3 5

### ○ Forte Travelodge
(Forte) ☎Central Res (0800) 850950
Due to have opened Winter 1991
40⇔♠

### KILMARTIN Strathclyde *Argyllshire* Map **10** NR89

### ❀✕ Cairn
PA31 8RQ ☎(05465)254
Closed Nov-Mar Lunch not served Mon
♀ Scottish & Continental V 50 seats Last lunch 3pm Last dinner 10pm 25 P
Credit Cards 1 2 3 5

### Strathclyde *Argyllshire* Map **10** NM81

### ★★ 62% Cuilfail
PA34 4XA ☎(08522)274 FAX (08522) 264
*This traditional Highland roadside hotel has been sympathetically renovated and refurbished to provide bedrooms which, although simply furnished, are spacious, comfortable and attractively decorated, together with a comfortable and relaxing lounge. Good, reasonably priced home-cooking is served in the bistro and pub as well as the dining room. Home-cooked meals, including genuine vegetarian dishes, are served in the popular bistro and pub as well as the dining room.*
12rm(3⇔3♠)(2fb) ® ❋ sB&Bfr£22.50 sB&B⇔♠£27.50 dB&Bfr£55 dB&B⇔♠£65 用
CTV 20P ⇔ ❀ CFA
V ☼ ♨ ⊁ ❋ Bar Lunch £2.50-£8 Dinner £8-£15 Last dinner 9pm
Credit Cards 1 3 £

### KILMUN Strathclyde *Argyllshire* Map **10** NS18

### ❀✕ Fern Grove
PA23 8SB ☎(036984)334
(Rosette awarded for dinner only)
*In an unpretentious little restaurant overlooking Holy Loch, Estralita Murray goes to great pains to provide very enjoyable well flavoured meals based on local products; friendly, attentive service*

*is offered by her husband, Ian, who is happy for guests to sample as many of the puddings as they can manage. A short, resonably priced wine list complements the daily changing dinner menu.*
Lunch not served ex by arrangement
V 26 seats Lunch £10.50-£18&alc Dinner £16-£28alc Last lunch 2pm Last dinner 9pm 5 P ⊁
Credit Cards 1 2 3 5

### KILWINNING Strathclyde *Ayrshire* Map **10** NS34

### ★★★⊞ 69% Montgreenan Mansion House
Montgreenan Estate KA13 7QZ (4m N of Irvine off A736, 3m E B785) (Best Western) ☎(0294)57733 Telex no 778525 FAX (0294) 85397
*An imposing period mansion in extensive gardens and grounds is noted particularly for its friendly service and fine, comfortably appointed public areas. Accommodation varies from the spaciously impressive master rooms to the more compact and modern ones at ground level which were introduced in 1990.*
21⇔♠↕ CTV in all bedrooms ® T ⊁ (ex guide dogs) ❋ sB&B⇔♠£60-£70 dB&B⇔♠£84-£133 用
Lift ℂ 50P ⇔ ❀ CFA ▶ 5 ♫ (hard) snooker clay pigeon shooting croquet *xmas*
♀ Scottish & French V ☼ ♨ ❋ Lunch £12.50 Dinner £23&alc Last dinner 9.30pm
Credit Cards 1 2 3 5 £

### KINCLAVEN Tayside *Perthshire* Map **11** NO13

### ★★★⊞ 77% Ballathie House
PH1 4QN (Best Western) ☎Meikleour(025083)268
Telex no 76216 FAX (025083) 396
Closed 17 Feb-2 Mar RS Dec-Feb
*Ten miles north of Perth, this impressive baronial mansion is superbly set in its own estate overlooking the River Tay. Sympathetic refurbishment has restored its grandeur, and day rooms are elegantly styled in a manner befitting the house. The comfortable bedrooms are individually decorated with modern fabrics used to good effect. Premier rooms are well proportioned and elegant, while 'standard' rooms are cosy, with a cottagey feel. Outdoor leisure persuits include fishing, clay pigeon shooting, tennis and croquet.*
27⇔♠(2fb)1↕ CTV in all bedrooms ® T sB&B⇔♠£48-£75 dB&B⇔♠£86-£145 用
50P ⇔ ❀ CFA ♫ (hard) ♪ putting croquet clay pigeon shooting *xmas*
♀ Scottish & Continental ☼ ♨ Lunch £12.75-£15&alc Dinner £22.50-£25&alc Last dinner 8.30pm
Credit Cards 1 2 3 5

### KINGHAM Oxfordshire Map **04** SP22

### ★★★ ❀69% Mill House Hotel & Restaurant
OX7 6UH ☎(0608)658188 Telex no 849041 FAX (0608) 658492
*A former 17th-century flour mill, crafted from Cotswold stone, in an idyllic setting amid rolling fields bordered by the mill stream. The old mill has been skilfully renovated and extended over the years to create a small hotel of character. Original features, including 2 bread ovens and the flagstone floors, have been retained, but combined with modern comforts. Bedrooms are pleasantly decorated and well equipped; and the warmth of the lounge and bar, where a log fire blazes in winter, is enhanced by the careful use of soft furnishings and antique pieces. The intimate dining room is also popular with non-residents, and the interesting table d'hôte menu is changed nightly. Head chef Jason Clarke and his team take pride in the production of modern English fare – the hot raspberry soufflé served with a tart plum sauce was most enjoyable.*
21rm(20⇔)(1fb)1↕ CTV in all bedrooms ® T ⊁ ❋ sB&B£46-£57 sB&B⇔♠£46-£57 dB&B⇔♠£72-£96 用
60P ❀ CFA ♪ croquet nc5yrs *xmas*

K

♀ English & French **V** ✿ ⌺ ✳ Lunch £13.25&alc Dinner £18.50&alc Last dinner 9.30pm
Credit Cards ① ② ③ ④ ⑤

---

### KINGSBRIDGE Devon Map 03 SX74

#### ★★★⚜76% Buckland-Tout-Saints

Goveton TQ7 2DS (2.5m NE on unclass rd) (Small Luxury Hotels) ☎(0548)853055 FAX (0548) 856261
Closed 3 Jan-2 Feb

*From its garden setting, this charming Queen Anne house commands views of the South Devon countryside. The hotel forms part of an estate whose written history goes back for nine centuries and, with its panelled lounges and dining room, offers true country-house hospitality. Standards of comfort are high and the restaurant menu, in the French and modern English style, offers such dishes as salad of wood pigeon (smoked on the premises), noisettes of lamb served with celeriac and a madeira sauce, with pear frangipan for dessert.*

12⇨🛏1🛁 CTV in all bedrooms **T** ✂ ✳ S10% sB&B⇨🛏£85-£95 dB&B⇨🛏£105 🍴
14P ⇨🏍 ✿ croquet putting nc8yrs *xmas*
✿ ⌺ ✔ ✳ S10% Lunch £10-£17.50 Dinner £27.50-£32.50 Last dinner 9pm
Credit Cards ① ② ③ ④ ⑤

#### ★★64% *Kings Arms*

Fore St TQ7 1AB (Exec Hotel) ☎(0548)852071
FAX (0548) 852977

*Though a fairly recent change of ownership has seen a welcome upgrading of accommodation at this character inn, the hospitable atmosphere and friendly service remain unchanged. Popular with locals and tourists alike, its busy bar and restaurant offer flexible catering arrangments and a good range of imaginative home-cooked dishes; meeting rooms, ballroom and a small indoor swimming pool are also available, and traditionally furnished bedrooms reflect the style and architecture of the building, the majority having four poster or half tester beds. Positioned at the heart of this historic town, the hotel provides a good base from which to tour South Devon and the South Hams.*

11rm(8⇨1🛏)10🛁 ®
CTV 40P ⇨ 🏊 (heated) nc8yrs
♀ English & French **V** ✿ ✔ Last dinner 9.00pm
Credit Cards ① ③

#### ★★55% Rockwood

Embankment Rd TQ7 1JZ ☎(0548)852480
Closed 24-27 Dec

*A small hotel, positioned close to the river estuary and providing a convenient base from which to tour South Devon, offers an informal atmosphere and friendly service from resident proprietors. Bedrooms, though compact, are soundly equipped, while the modestly sized restaurant features a good range of dishes on both set and à la carte menus.*

6⇨🛏 CTV in all bedrooms ® ✳ sB&B⇨🛏£25-£27 dB&B⇨🛏£46-£49 🍴
CTV 9P 3🍴 ⇨
♀ English & Continental **V** ✿ ⌺ ✔ ✳ Sunday Lunch £5.50-£7.50 Dinner fr£10.25&alc Last dinner 9pm
Credit Cards ① ③ £

See advertisement on page 389

---

### KING'S LYNN Norfolk Map 09 TF62 ◉

#### ★★★70% *Knights Hill*

Knights Hill Village, South Wootton PE30 3HQ (junct A148/A149) (Best Western) ☎(0553)675566 Telex no 818118
FAX (0553) 675568

*Situated on the outskirts of the town, at the junction of the A148 and A149, this hotel has been converted over recent years from a former hunting lodge into a sound hotel with excellent facilities for both the commercial and the leisure user. Accommodation is in either the renovated pantiled courtyard complex or in the stylish*

→

**K**

*Rising Lodge. There is a choice of bars and eating venues; the Garden Restaurant offers freshly made à la carte dishes and the Farmer's Arms offers real ale and a comprehensive popular menu in rustic surroundings. Friendly and competent staff provide good services.*

40⇨🏃Annexe18⇨🏃1🛏✕in 13 bedrooms CTV in all bedrooms Ⓡ T

( 350P ❀ ⌷ (heated) ♫ (hard) snooker sauna solarium gymnasium jogging circuit croquet spa bath ♫

♀ International V ❖ ⌷ ✕ Last dinner 9.30pm

Credit Cards [1] [2] [3] [5]

### ★★★65% Butterfly

Beveridge Way, Hardwick Narrows PE30 4NB (junct A10/A47) (Consort) ☎(0553)771707 Telex no 818313 FAX (0553) 768027

*Next to the A40/A47 roundabout, this friendly purpose-built hotel provides comfortable accommodation with particularly well designed single rooms. Open-plan public areas in rustic style include a popular restaurant and bar.*

50⇨🏃(2fb) CTV in all bedrooms Ⓡ T ✕ (ex guide dogs) S% sB⇨🏃£56.50-£58.50 dB⇨🏃£56.50-£58.50 (room only) 🛏

( 70P

♀ European V ❖ ⌷ ✕ S% Lunch £9.50-£10.50&alc Dinner £10.50-£11.50&alc Last dinner 10pm

Credit Cards [1] [2] [3] [5]

### ★★★64% The Duke's Head

Tuesday Market Pl PE30 1JS (Forte Hotels) ☎(0553)774996 Telex no 817349 FAX (0553) 763556

*A Victorian hotel centrally located in the market place provides a convenient and comfortable meeting place, its elegant lounge being a particularly popular venue. Banqueting and conference facilities are complemented by a choice of bars, and the hotel's relaxing atmosphere makes it popular with both leisure guests and commercial users.*

71⇨(2fb)✕in 20 bedrooms CTV in all bedrooms Ⓡ T ✳ S% sB⇨£65 dB⇨£85 (room only) 🛏

Lift ( 41P CFA *xmas*

♀ English & French V ❖ ⌷ ✕ ✳ Lunch £6.75 Dinner £15.50 Last dinner 10pm

Credit Cards [1] [2] [3] [5]

### ★★72% Stuart House

35 Goodwins Rd PE30 5QX ☎(0553)772169 Telex no 817209 Closed Xmas & New Year

*Situated in a quiet residential area, this very well-maintained hotel is run with friendly informality by the Squires and offers traditional comforts with all modern facilities.*

19rm(12⇨3🏃)(6fb) CTV in all bedrooms Ⓡ T ✕ CTV 25P

♀ European V Last dinner 8.30pm

Credit Cards [1] [2] [3]

### ★★63% Grange

Willow Park, South Wootton Ln PE30 3BP ☎(0553)673777 & 671222

*Friendly, informal service is provided by the resident proprietors of this small, well maintained hotel on the outskirts of the town. Bedrooms are generally of a comfortable size and equipped with modern facilities, these features making them a popular choice with businessmen during the week.*

6rm(3⇨2🏃)Annexe4⇨ CTV in all bedrooms Ⓡ 15P 1🚗

❖ ⌷ Last dinner 8.30pm

Credit Cards [1] [2] [3]

### ★★62% Globe

Tuesday Market Pl PE30 1EZ (Chef & Brewer) ☎(0553)772617 FAX (0553) 761315

*On a corner site in the Market Place, this well managed hotel with friendly efficient staff continues to be a popular meeting place, with a choice of bars and restaurants and well equipped bedrooms which offer good value for money.*

39⇨🏃(2fb) CTV in all bedrooms Ⓡ T ✕ (ex guide dogs) sB&B⇨🏃£44-£53 dB&B⇨🏃£62 🛏

( 20P 8🚗 CFA

♀ International V ❖ ⌷ ✕ Bar Lunch £2.95-£5.50alc

Credit Cards [1] [2] [3] [5]

### ★★62% The Tudor Rose

St Nicholas St, off Tuesday Market Pl PE30 1LR ☎(0553)762824 Telex no 818752 FAX (0553) 764894

*Comfortable, modestly furnished rooms and good service from a small team of staff are provided by this 15th-century inn just off Tuesday Market Place in the town centre. Bars feature beamed ceilings, as does a restaurant serving French/English cuisine which specialises in freshly caught local sea food and uses only the best of ingredients.*

14rm(11⇨🏃)(1fb) CTV in all bedrooms Ⓡ T sB&B⇨🏃£30-£40 dB&B⇨🏃£50 🛏

♫

♀ English & French V ❖ ⌷ ✕ Bar Lunch £4-£7alc Dinner £9.50&alc Last dinner 9pm

Credit Cards [1] [2] [3] [5]

## KINGSTEIGNTON Devon Map 03 SX87

### ★★★71% Passage House

Hackney Ln TQ12 3QH ☎Newton Abbot(0626)55515 FAX (0626) 63336

*A popular modern hotel in commercial style, though conveniently located just off the A380 Exeter-Torquay road, is tucked away overlooking the Teign Estuary, the wildlife of which provides the material for regular nature/conservation activities. Very comfortable, well equipped bedrooms with bright, quality en suite facilities are ideally suited to today's traveller, conference facilities are available, and a commendable leisure complex includes an attractive indoor pool, jet stream, sauna, solarium and beauty salon. The adjacent Passage House Inn combines more informal dining arrangements with a pub atmosphere, and there is excellent car parking on site.*

39⇨🏃✕in 3 bedrooms CTV in all bedrooms Ⓡ T ✳ sB&B⇨🏃£59-£69 dB&B⇨🏃£85-£95 🛏

Lift ( 300P ❀ CFA ⌷ (heated) ♪ sauna solarium gymnasium *xmas*

V ❖ ⌷ ✳ Lunch £9.50 Dinner £14.75&alc Last dinner 9.30pm

Credit Cards [1] [2] [3] [5] [£]

## KINGSTON UPON THAMES Greater London

### See LONDON plan 1 B2(page 434)

### ★★★64% Kingston Lodge

Kingston Hill KT2 7NP (Forte Hotels) ☎081-541 4481 Telex no 936034 FAX 081-547 1013

*A friendly hotel close to the town centre and popular with both businessmen and tourists alike. Accommodation throughout is bright, well furnished and comfortable and bedrooms are equipped with a good range of facilities for today's traveller. Service is prompt and hospitable.*

62⇨🏃1🛏✕in 20 bedrooms CTV in all bedrooms Ⓡ T ✳ sB⇨🏃£85-£95 dB⇨🏃£100-£113 (room only) 🛏

( 74P CFA ♫ *xmas*

V ❖ ⌷ ✳ Lunch £14.50&alc Dinner £16.50&alc Last dinner 10pm

Credit Cards [1] [2] [3] [5]

## KINGSWINFORD West Midlands Map 07 SO88

### ★★★58% The Kingfisher Hotel & Country Club

Kidderminster Rd, Wall Heath DY6 0EN ☎(0384)273763 & 401145 FAX (0384) 277094

*A renowned cabaret nightspot on the A449 between Kidderminster and Wolverhampton has been extended to provide good modern accommodation equipped with every convenience and particularly suitable for the business traveller.*

→

389

23⇨🤚(2fb) CTV in all bedrooms ® T 🏹 (ex guide dogs) ✻
sB&B⇨🤚£25-£45 dB&B⇨🤚£35-£58
《 200P ❀ ⊇ (heated) *xmas*
V ᵫ ⚫

Credit Cards ①②③④

**See advertisement under WOLVERHAMPTON**

---

**★★66% Burton**

Mill St HR5 3BQ (Exec Hotel) ☎(0544)230323

*A combination of friendly service, bright public areas and well-equipped bedrooms make this old town centre inn popular with both tourists and business people alike. Situated close to the Welsh Border and Offa's Dyke.*

15⇨🤚(3fb)1🛏 CTV in all bedrooms ® T sB&B⇨🤚fr£40
dB&B⇨🤚fr£53 🍴
50P ❀ *xmas*
🍽 International V ᵫ ⚫ Lunch fr£14 Dinner fr£14 Last dinner 9.30pm
④

Credit Cards ①②③⑤

---

**★★67% Columba House**

Manse Rd PH21 1JF ☎(0540)661402
Closed Nov-25 Dec

*A 19th-century manse in its own elevated grounds on the northern fringe of the village has been sympathetically converted and substantially refurbished to create this small, popular, family-run holiday hotel. Comfortably appointed, well equipped bedrooms are complemented by good home-cooking, the atmosphere throughout being relaxed and friendly.*

7⇨🤚(2fb) CTV in all bedrooms ® T dB&B⇨🤚£40-£56 🍴
12P 🚗 ❀ croquet 9-hole putting
V ᵫ ⚫ ⅄ ✻ Lunch fr£8.95 Dinner £14-£16 Last dinner 8.30pm
④

**★64% Osprey**

Ruthven Rd PH21 1EN ☎(0540)661510

*A small and hospitable family-run hotel peacefully set in the Spey Valley. It has a friendly informal atmosphere, with a choice of cosy lounges, a dining room serving home-cooked food and comfortable modestly furnished bedrooms.*

8rm(4⇨🤚) ✻ sB&B£32-£41 dB&B£64-£74 dB&B⇨🤚£68-£98 (incl dinner)
CTV 🚗 *xmas*
ᵫ ⚫

Credit Cards ①③

**❀❀ ✕ The Cross**

High St PH21 1HX ☎(0540)661762 & 661166
FAX (0540) 661080

*This unpretentious little restaurant, which continues to receive praise both from regular clients and those discovering it for the first time, features the uncomplicated cooking of Ruth Hadley, her unfailing ability to blend complementary ingredients achieving dishes of superb flavour and texture. The carefully balanced, set-price, 4-course menu normally offers a choice of three dishes per course with an emphasis on Scottish game, meat and fish – a mousseline of local pike on a prawn sauce and a fillet of beef with a mustard and red wine sauce proving truly memorable. Tony Hadley is the perfect host, providing attentive service and sharing his enthusiastic knowledge of wines with any customer who needs his advice. At the time of going to press, the restaurant was due to change location to The Cross, Ardbroilach Road, which is nearby, the telephone number remaining the same.*

Closed Mon, Sun, 1-25 Dec & 3 wks May/Jun Lunch not served

---

20 seats Dinner £23.50-£29.50 Last dinner 9.30pm 🚫 nc12yrs
⅄

Credit Cards ①③

---

**★★★63% Kinlochbervie**

IV27 4RP ☎(097182)275 FAX (097182) 438
RS mid Nov-Feb

*A welcoming atmosphere prevails at this modern holiday hotel, set on a hill with commanding views over the harbour and surrounding hills. The comfortable bedrooms are well equipped, day rooms invite relaxation, and the bars stock an impressive array of malt whiskies. The attractive restaurant offers a daily changing 4-course menu featuring fresh local produce, while the bistro offers a less formal alternative.*

14⇨🤚(3fb) CTV in all bedrooms ® T sB&B⇨🤚£50-£60
sB&B⇨🤚£50-£60 dB&B⇨🤚£130-£150 🍴
《 CTV 30P 🚗 ⚘ snooker
🍽 French ᵫ ⚫ Bar Lunch £7-£12.50 Dinner £28 Last dinner 8.30pm

Credit Cards ①②③⑤④

---

**★★★68% Windlestrae**

The Muirs KY13 7AS (Consort) ☎(0577)63217
FAX (0577) 64733

*Continual improvements are being made at this friendly family-run hotel, set in its own garden, including new conference facilities and an extended restaurant. Bedrooms remain comfortable and well equipped, with those in the original house refurbished to a high standard.*

19⇨🤚(3fb)1🛏 CTV in all bedrooms ® T sB&B⇨🤚£50-£52.50 dB&B⇨🤚£75-£105 🍴
《⊞ 60P 🚗 ❀ CFA sauna *xmas*
🍽 International V ᵫ ⚫ ⅄ Lunch £11.50-£17&alc Dinner £14.50-£17&alc Last dinner 9.30pm

Credit Cards ①②③⑤④

**★★★62% Green**

2 The Muirs KY13 7AS (Best Western) ☎(0577)63467
Telex no 76684 FAX (0577) 63180

*The wide range of leisure and sporting facilities are available at this popular business, holiday and conference hotel includes a curling rink and two 18-hole golf courses. An extensive refurbishment programme at present under way includes both the provision of a new bedroom wing and the enlargement of existing rooms.*

40⇨🤚(4fb)2🛏 CTV in all bedrooms ® T sB&B⇨🤚£60-£68
dB&B⇨🤚£85-£110 🍴
《 60P ❀ CFA ▣ (heated) ▶ 36 ⚐ squash sauna solarium gymnasium curling croquet putting 🚗 *xmas*
🍽 French V ᵫ ⚫ Bar Lunch £6.50-£13alc High tea £6.50-£8 Dinner £17-£19.50&alc Last dinner 9.30pm

Credit Cards ①②③⑤④

**★★65% Bridgend**

High St KY13 7EN ☎(0577)63413 FAX (0577) 64769

*A small family-run hotel at the south end of the town provides a popular base for holidaymakers and visiting businessmen alike. Bedrooms, though compact, are tastefully furnished and well equipped, while public areas are comfortably appointed in the modern style, including a choice of bars and both à la carte and carvery restaurants. Friendly staff offer willing service throughout.*

15⇨🤚(1fb)1🛏 CTV in all bedrooms ® T ✻
sB&B⇨🤚£34.50-£38.50 dB&B⇨🤚£44-£48 🍴
《 CTV 40P *xmas*
V ᵫ ⚫ Lunch £5.95-£12&alc High tea £6.50 Dinner £7.95-£15&alc Last dinner 10pm

Credit Cards ①②③⑤

**K**

★★ 62% *Kirklands*

20 High St KY13 7AN ☎(0577)63313

*Conveniently situated in the High Street, this former coaching inn has been substantially refurbished to provide comfortable modern accommodation.*

9⇨↑ CTV in all bedrooms ® T ✖ (ex guide dogs)

30P ✿

V ✿ ⬚ Last dinner 9pm

Credit Cards ①③

⬧Granada Lodge

Kincardine Rd KY13 7NQ (on A977, off junct 6 of M90) (Granada) ☎(0577)64646 FAX (0577) 64108

*Twenty-four hour catering and good value modern accommodation are provided at a popular motorway lodge situated at junction 6 of the M90, on the outskirts of the town.*

35⇨↑(15fb)✄in 6 bedrooms CTV in all bedrooms ®
✖ (ex guide dogs) S% sB⇨fr£29.50 dB⇨fr£32 (room only) ☄
( 127P

V ✿ ⬚

---

KINTBURY Berkshire Map 04 SU36

❀✖✕Dundas Arms

RG15 0UT ☎(0488)58263 & 58559 FAX (0488) 58568

*An old village inn beside the canal offers a warm atmosphere and friendly service, the cosy little dining room serving a short set-price menu supplemented by more interesting choices in the evening; simple, thoughtfully prepared dishes based on quality fresh produce enhanced by honest, flavoursome sauces are accompanied by a fine wine list which includes examples from the New World as well as some good clarets and Burgundies.*

Closed Sun, Mon & Xmas-New Year

♈ English & French 36 seats Last lunch 1.30pm Last dinner 9.15pm 50 P ✄

Credit Cards ①②③

---

KIRBY MISPERTON North Yorkshire Map 08 SE77

★★ 61% Beansheaf Restaurant Motel

Malton Rd YO17 0UE ☎(065386)614 & 488 FAX (065386) 370
RS Mon

*The friendly owners of this establishment have worked hard to create an informal atmosphere, modern value-for-money accommodation and a noteworthy restaurant which is popular with guests and local residents alike.*

20⇨↑(2fb)1⊞ CTV in all bedrooms ® T sB&B⇨↑£28-£30
dB&B⇨↑£46-£50 ☄

CTV 60P ✿ CFA sauna solarium *xmas*

♈ English & Continental V ✿ ⬚ ✄ Lunch £6.50-£7.50 High tea £6-£6.50 Dinner £6.50-£9.50 Last dinner 10pm

Credit Cards ①③Ⓔ

---

KIRBY MUXLOE Leicestershire Map 04 SK50

★★ 65% Castle Hotel & Restaurant

Main St LE9 9AP ☎Leicester(0533)395337 FAX (0533) 387868

*This former farmhouse in a village setting on the outskirts of the city is constructed of bricks and timbers from William Hastings' Kirby Muxloe Castle of 1480, a fortified manor house. The extensively restored building, which has operated as a restaurant since 1974, has now been extended and altered to provide clean and well equipped accommodation, all bedrooms having good modern bathrooms though some are compact. The proprietor and his small team of staff create a friendly, informal atmosphere in both restaurant and bar.*

4⇨↑Annexe8⇨↑(1fb)✄in 5 bedrooms CTV in all bedrooms
® T ✖ (ex guide dogs) ✳ sB⇨↑£30-£48 dB⇨↑£40-£70
(room only)

70P ✿ CFA

→

K

♀ English & French **V** ♥ ✤ Lunch £8.50-£10.50&alc Dinner £8.50-£10.50&alc Last dinner 9.30pm
Credit Cards 1 2 3 £

---

## KIRKBY FLEETHAM North Yorkshire Map **08** SE29

### ★★★73% **Kirkby Fleetham Hall**
DL7 0SU (Pride of Britain) ☎Northallerton(0609)748711
FAX (0609) 748747

*An impressive Georgian house in 30 acres of parkland, the hotel boasts its own lake and offers the advantages of a really peaceful atmosphere, spacious, comfortable lounges and bedrooms, charming staff and good, interesting cooking.*

22⇨♠(2fb)3∰ CTV in all bedrooms **T** ✳ sB&B⇨♠£75 dB&B⇨♠£120-£170 ♬
40P ⇔ ✤ CFA ♪ croquet clay pigeon shooting archery *xmas*
♀ British & French **V** ♥ ♁ ✳ Sunday Lunch £14 Dinner £24.75 Last dinner 9pm
Credit Cards 1 2 3 4 5 £

---

## KIRKBY LONSDALE Cumbria Map **07** SD67

### ★★★55% **Royal**
Main St LA6 2AE (Minotels) ☎(05242)71217
FAX (05242) 72228

*Set in the town centre, this former private residence was converted into a coaching inn in the 18th century and is now well known for its wide ranging bar meals and afternoon teas.*

20rm(15⇨1♠)1∰ CTV in all bedrooms ® S10%
CTV 25P 8☞ snooker ♫
**V** ♥ ♁ Last dinner 10pm
Credit Cards 1 2 3 5

### ★★69% **Whoop Hall Inn**
LA6 2HP ☎Carnforth(05242)71284 FAX (05242) 72154

*Situated just off the A65, 1 mile south-east of Kirkby Lonsdale, this inn has most of its attractive and well equipped bedrooms in a tastefully converted and modernised barn. A popular place at which to dine, the three-tiered restaurant offers a varied menu, and there is also a good selection of bar meals available. Above the restaurant is a comfortable galleried lounge.*

5⇨♠Annexe11⇨♠(3fb)2∰✂in 4 bedrooms CTV in all bedrooms ® **T** ✖ (ex guide dogs) sB&B⇨♠£37.50 dB&B⇨♠£52-£65 ♬
《 120P ✤ CFA *xmas*
♀ English & Italian **V** ♥ ♁ ✂ ✳ Lunch £4.50-£12alc High tea £5-£8alc Dinner £10-£20alc Last dinner 10pm
Credit Cards 1 3

### ⊛✕Cobwebs Country House & Restaurant
Leck, Cowan Bridge LA6 2HZ ☎(05242)72141

*Peacefully situated in large well kept gardens just to the north of the A65, this Victorian country house has been carefully restored by its friendly young proprietors, Yvonne Thompson and Paul Kelly. Yvonne prepares exciting and inventive daily menus using the best of local produce such as roast fillet of beef with horseradish, creamed onion and ginger sauce. Desserts are of course home-made, and there is an interesting selection of local cheese. Paul is justifiably proud of his extensive wine list which includes over 300 wines, many from the New World. He also looks after the service in the intimate dining room. Booking is essential here.*

Closed Jan-mid Mar Lunch not served
Dinner not served Sun
18 seats ✳ Dinner fr£25 Last dinner 7.30pm 20 P nc12yrs ✂
Credit Cards 1 3

Hotels with red star ratings are
especially high quality.

---

## KIRKBYMOORSIDE North Yorkshire Map **08** SE68

### ★★68% *George & Dragon*
17 Market Place YO6 6AA ☎(0751)31637

*Welcoming 13th-century inn with modern bedrooms in converted stables.*

14⇨♠Annexe8⇨♠(3fb) CTV in all bedrooms ® **T**
22P ✤
**V** ♥ Last dinner 9.30pm
Credit Cards 1 3

---

## KIRKBY STEPHEN Cumbria Map **12** NY70

### ★★62% **King's Arms**
Market St CA17 4QN ☎(07683)71378
Closed 25 Dec

*Resident proprietors create a warm, friendly atmosphere at this comfortable hotel which was originally a coaching inn. Set at the centre of the historic market town, it lies between the Yorkshire Dales and Lake District and is a good base for exploring both areas. Enjoyable, home-cooked dishes, including local specialities, are served in the attractive, antique-furnished dining room.*

10rm(1⇨2♠)(1fb) ® **T** ✳ sB&B£24.50 sB&B⇨♠£30 dB&B£42.50 dB&B⇨♠£49.50 ♬
CTV 4P 5☞
**V** ♥
Credit Cards 1 3

---

## KIRKCALDY Fife Map **11** NT29

### ★★★62% **Dean Park**
Chapel Level KY2 6QW ☎(0592)261635 FAX (0592) 261371

*This popular business hotel is situated 2 miles north of the town off the A910, but is now conveniently reached from the new A92, coming off at 'Kircaldy West' signs. It has inviting bars and an attractive restaurant. In addition to the main bedrooms there are detached and semi-detached bungalow style chalets, which are well proportioned if rather functional.*

45⇨♠Annexe12♠(5fb)2∰✂in 3 bedrooms CTV in all bedrooms ® **T** ✖ (ex guide dogs) sB&B⇨♠fr£40 dB&B⇨♠fr£52.50
《 150P ⇔ ✤ CFA snooker sauna gymnasium jaccuzi
♀ Scottish, French & Italian **V** ♥ ♁ ✳
Credit Cards 1 2 3 5 £

### ★★67% **The Belvedere**
Coxstool, West Wemyss KY1 4SN ☎(0592)54167
FAX (0592) 55279

*Formerly a restaurant with rooms, this interesting hotel which, architecturally, has a European influence, nestles peacefully at the foot of a hill in a small coastal conservation village. Most of the bedrooms are housed in a series of renovated cottage buildings, most of which are interconnected. There are fine views out across the Firth of Forth to Edinburgh. Good value meals are available and the wine list offers some bargains.*

5⇨♠Annexe16⇨♠(1fb) CTV in all bedrooms ® **T** ✖ (ex guide dogs) sB&B⇨♠fr£45 dB&B⇨♠fr£60 40P
♀ Scottish & French **V** ♥ ♁ ✳ Lunch £10-£14&alc Dinner £15-£20 Last dinner 9pm
Credit Cards 1 3 £

---

## KIRKCUDBRIGHT Dumfries & Galloway *Kirkcudbrightshire* Map **11** NX65

### ★★65% **Selkirk Arms**
Old High St DG6 4JG ☎(0557)30402 FAX (0557) 31639

*An hotel situated in the old part of this attractive fishing town, dating back to 1770 and reputedly the place where Burns wrote The Selkirk Grace, has been completely refurbished to provide attractive and comfortable public areas and bedrooms of a comparable standard, being well appointed and thoughtfully*

K

*equipped though fairly compact. Efficient housekeeping ensures good levels of service throughout.*

14⇨📺Annexe1⇨(2fb) CTV in all bedrooms ® T
sB&B⇨📺fr£40 dB&B⇨📺fr£67.50 🏠
4P 16🍴 ❋ *xmas*

♀ Scottish & Continental V ♦ ⚏ ❋ Dinner fr£14&alc Last dinner 9.30pm
Credit Cards 1️⃣ 2️⃣ 3️⃣ 5️⃣

---

**KIRKHILL** Highland *Inverness-shire* Map **14** NH54

★★65% **Inchmore**

IV5 7PX (at junc A862/B9164 ) ☎Inverness(0463)83296

*A popular and friendly roadside inn/hotel offering good standards of accommodation and service. There is a good range of bar meals, also available in the restaurant.*

6⇨(1fb) CTV in all bedrooms ® T sB&B⇨£28-£32
dB&B⇨£45-£50 🏠
80P

♦ ⚏ ❋ Lunch £6.50-£10alc Dinner £7.50-£15alc Last dinner 8.30pm
Credit Cards 1️⃣ 3️⃣ £

---

**KIRK LANGLEY** Derbyshire Map **08** SK23

★★53% **Meynell Arms**

Ashbourne Rd DE6 4NF (Minotels) ☎(033124)515

*This Georgian manor house on the A52 close to Derby, now a busy hotel, is well-known in the area for its value-for-money bar snacks.*

10rm(5⇨2📺)(2fb)2⚏ CTV in all bedrooms ® T sB&B£26-£30 sB&B⇨📺£32-£38 dB&B£42-£48 dB&B⇨📺£48-£56 🏠
100P ❋

V ♦ Lunch £11-£18alc Dinner £11-£18alc Last dinner 9.30pm
Credit Cards 1️⃣ 3️⃣ £

---

**KIRKMICHAEL** Tayside *Perthshire* Map **15** NO06

★★ ❀60% **Log Cabin**

PH10 7NB (Exec Hotel) ☎Strathardle(025081)288
FAX (025081) 402
(Rosette awarded for dinner only)

*Built from Norwegian pine logs in the midst of high moorland, this small friendly hotel provides practical modern accommodation, with attractive public areas and somewhat compact bedrooms. The imaginative mainly Scottish dishes served in the Edelweiss Restaurant make excellent use of fresh local produce, with game and seafood strongly featured.*

13⇨📺 CTV in 6 bedrooms ® sB&B⇨📺£25.85-£32.95 dB&B⇨📺£41.70-£47.90 🏠
CTV 50P ❋ CFA ⚓ shooting ski-ing *xmas*
V ♦ ⚏ ✕ Dinner £16.95 Last dinner 8.45pm
Credit Cards 1️⃣ 2️⃣ 3️⃣ 5️⃣

★★58% **The Aldchlappie**

PH10 7NS ☎Strathardle(025081)224 FAX (025081) 373

*On the south side of the village overlooking the River Ardle, this small family-run hotel offers friendly, informal service and good-value meals. A wide range of malt whiskies is available in the cosy bar. The hotel is closed during the day on Mondays but residents are catered for.*

5⇨📺(3fb)✕ in all bedrooms CTV in all bedrooms ® ❋
sB&B⇨📺fr£20.50 dB&B⇨📺fr£37
CTV 10P 🚗 ⚓
V ♦ ❋ Bar Lunch £2-£7 Dinner £12 Last dinner 9pm
Credit Cards 1️⃣ 2️⃣ 3️⃣

★56% **Strathlene**

Main Rd PH10 7NT ☎Strathardle(025081)347

*This family-run village hotel has an informal atmosphere and provides good value practical accommodation for the touring holiday-maker and winter ski enthusiast.*

7rm(5⇨📺)(1fb) ® sB&B£15-£20 sB&B⇨📺£17-£20 dB&B£30 dB&B⇨📺£36 🏠
CTV 3P 🚲 mountain bike hire
V ♦ Lunch £5-£11 Dinner £10 Last dinner 8.30pm
Credit Cards 1️⃣ 3️⃣ £

---

**KIRKWALL**

See **Orkney**

---

**KIRKWHELPINGTON** Northumberland Map **12** NY98

★★61% **The Knowesgate**

NE19 2SH (Inter-Hotels) ☎Otterburn(0830)40261

*Conveniently situated on the main A696 just north of the village, the Knowesgate offers good value. Furnishings are modern, and a good range of bar and restaurant meals are available.*

16⇨📺 CTV in all bedrooms ® T
100P games room
V ♦ ⚏ ✕
Credit Cards 1️⃣ 2️⃣ 3️⃣ 5️⃣

---

**KNARESBOROUGH** North Yorkshire Map **08** SE35

★★★69% **Dower House**

Bond End HG5 9AL (Best Western) ☎Harrogate(0423)863302
Telex no 57202 FAX (0423) 867665
Closed 25 Dec RS 24 & 26 Dec

*A lovely Grade II listed building offering good comforts and old-world charm. Bedrooms are well furnished, and those in the new extension are very spacious. Interesting dishes are served in the attractive restaurant which overlooks the well kept gardens. Ample lounge and bar facilities are provided and there is now a very good leisure club available to guests.*

28⇨📺Annexe4⇨📺(2fb) CTV in all bedrooms ® T ✕
sB&B⇨📺£48-£65 dB&B⇨📺£66-£95 🏠
《 80P 🚗 ❋ CFA ⊠ (heated) sauna solarium gymnasium
♀ English & French V ♦ ✕ Lunch £7.50-£12alc Dinner fr£16&alc Last dinner 9.30pm
Credit Cards 1️⃣ 2️⃣ 3️⃣ 5️⃣

❀✕**Four Park Place**

4 Park Place HG5 0ER ☎Harrogate(0423)868002

*A delightful and intimate restaurant to be found just off the High Street. The menu features interesting dishes skilfully prepared. Salmon, scallops, scampi, pigeon and veal are all to be found cooked and served in many different ways. There is also a good selection of starters and desserts. Service is attentive and unobtrusive.*

Closed Sun, 1 wk Jan, 1 wk Aug & 25-26 Dec Lunch not served Sat

28 seats Last lunch 2.30pm Last dinner 9.30pm 5 P nc5yrs ✕
Credit Cards 1️⃣ 3️⃣

---

**KNIGHTON** Powys Map **07** SO27

★★★66% **The Knighton**

Broad St LD7 1BL ☎(0547)520530 FAX (0547) 520529

*This hotel, built in 1860, adjoins the town's old assembly rooms which have now been converted to a very attractive function suite. The hotel has been completely modernised and features a magnificent galleried central staircase. A good choice of food is available, with vegetarians well catered for.*

15⇨📺 CTV in all bedrooms ® T
Lift 10P snooker
♀ International V ♦ ⚏ Last dinner 9.30pm
Credit Cards 1️⃣ 2️⃣ 3️⃣ 5️⃣

Remember to book early for holiday
and bank holiday times.

K

## ★★ ֍72% Milebrook House

Milebrook LD7 1LT (Welsh Rarebits) ☎(0547)528632
FAX (0547) 520509

*Situated just 2 miles east of the town alongside the A4113, this small 18th-century hotel is personally run by the friendly Marsden family. The accommodation is comfortable and well furnished and the cooking is in the capable hands of Beryl Marsden who uses vegetables and herbs from the hotel's kitchen garden. Fishing and bird watching are available in the grounds.*

6⇨♠ CTV in all bedrooms ® ✠ ✱ sB&B⇨♠£40.50 dB&B⇨♠£55 🏳

20P ✿ ♪ croquet badminton nc8yrs

♀ English & French V ✿ ✲ Lunch £10.75-£15.25 Dinner £15.75-£17.95 Last dinner 8.30pm

Credit Cards ① ③ ⓔ

---

### ★60% Talbot

WR6 5PH ☎(0886)21235 FAX (0886) 21060

Closed 25 Dec evening

*This inn is situated on the banks of the River Teme, close to the A44 between Worcester and Leominster. Bedrooms are well equipped, with simple furnishings and décor. The service is informal and casual, and staff are friendly. Hearty meals are served in the bar or in the small dining room.*

10rm(5⇨2♠)(2fb) CTV in all bedrooms ® T ✱ S% sB&B£25 sB&B⇨♠£31.50 dB&B£42.50 dB&B⇨♠£57.50 🏳

CTV 50P ✿ ♪ squash sauna

V ✿ ✲ ✱ Lunch £12-£25alc Dinner £12.50-£25alc Last dinner 9.30pm

Credit Cards ① ③ ⓔ

---

### ★★★68% Cottons

Manchester Rd WA16 0SU (Shire) ☎(0565)650333
FAX (0565) 755351

*This stylish hotel in rural surroundings just off junction 19 of the M6, half a mile north west of Knutsford, has very well equipped bedrooms, plus good conference facilities and a leisure club. The New Orleans French style of parts of the interior is reflected in some dishes on the menu.*

86⇨♠(6fb)3✠✲in 18 bedrooms CTV in all bedrooms ® T ✱ S% sB&B⇨♠£95.50-£115.50 dB&B⇨♠£112.50-£130.50 🏳

Lift ℭ 180P ✿ CFA ⬚ (heated) ℘ (hard) sauna solarium gymnasium spa bath *xmas*

♀ English & French V ✿ ✲

Credit Cards ① ② ③ ⑤

### ★★ ֍76% The Longview Hotel & Restaurant

Manchester Rd WA16 0LX (Exec Hotel) ☎(0565)632119
FAX (0565) 652402

Closed Xmas & New Year

*On the edge of the village, opposite the common, this Victorian hotel offers bedrooms and services that will meet the expectations of today's traveller; resident owner/managers greet guests warmly on arrival, and the restaurant is fast gaining a reputation for enjoyable, well prepared meals that include a good vegetarian selection.*

13⇨♠Annexe10⇨♠(4fb) CTV in all bedrooms ® T ✱ sB&B⇨♠£32-£50 dB&B⇨♠£55-£65 🏳

16P ⇔

♀ English & Continental V ✿ ✲ ✱ Bar Lunch fr£5.25 Dinner £14.25-£17.25 Last dinner 9pm

### ★★58% Royal George

King St WA16 6EE (Chef & Brewer) ☎(0565)634151
FAX (0565) 634955

*Standing at the centre of the well-known Cheshire town – which owes its fame to authoress Mrs Gaskell – this elegant Georgian*

*hotel offers bedrooms which have been modernised to a high standard and provided with en suite facilities, three also having four-poster beds.*

25⇨♠Annexe6⇨(4fb)3✠ CTV in all bedrooms ® T ✠ (ex guide dogs) sB&B⇨♠£62-£67 dB&B⇨♠£76 🏳

Lift ℭ 50P 7✿ CFA

♀ International V ✿ ✲ ✲ Bar Lunch £2.95-£5.50alc

Credit Cards ① ② ③ ⑤

### ⇧Forte Travelodge

Chester Rd, Tabley WA16 0PP (on A556, northbound) (Forte) ☎(0565)652187 Central Res (0800) 850950

*Located on the A556 to Manchester and the airport, off junction 19 of the M6, this busy lodge stands beside a Little Chef restaurant and a petrol station.*

32⇨♠(32fb) CTV in all bedrooms ® sB⇨♠£29.95 dB⇨♠£29.95 (room only)

ℭ 32P ⇔

Credit Cards ① ② ③

### ֍✕✕La Belle Epoque

60 King St WA16 6DT ☎(0565)633060 & 632661
FAX (0565) 634150

*A re-creation of a turn-of-the-century Parisian restaurant, with subdued lighting which is evocative of gaslight, vibrantly rich fabrics and objets d'art, provides the ideal setting in which to celebrate a special occasion. Fresh produce – most of it local – provides a sound basis for a range of dishes with a distinct or even robust flavour, generous use being made of herbs and crushed peppercorn. Loin of rabbit with Madeira is particularly to be recommended as a main course, and Pear William is noteworthy among the desserts for its excellent balance of flavours. A wine list of about 100 items, though predominantly French, includes a full range of house wines and some examples from the New World. Charming hosts Keith and Nerys Mooney are assisted by a helpful, friendly, young team of staff, and overnight accommodation is available in five en suite bedrooms.*

Closed Sun, 1st wk Jan & BHs Lunch not served

♀ French 85 seats ✱ Dinner £23-£30alc Last dinner 10.30pm ♪ nc14yrs

Credit Cards ① ② ③ ④ ⑤

---

### ★★65% Kyle

Main St IV40 8AB ☎Kyle(0599)4204

*Managed by the resident proprietors, this comfortable hotel offers warm, friendly service, well appointed bedrooms and good-value menus. It is also popular with coach parties.*

32⇨♠ CTV in all bedrooms ® T ✱ sB&B⇨♠£25-£35 dB&B⇨♠£50-£64 🏳

CTV 80P CFA ▶ 9 *xmas*

V ✿ ✲ ✱ Sunday Lunch £4.95 Dinner £9&alc Last dinner 9.30pm

Credit Cards ① ③

---

### ★★★64% Oaklands

Barton St DN37 7LF ☎Grimsby(0472)72248 FAX (0472) 78143

*Set in 5 acres of parkland on the A18, this country house has been extended to provide modern hotel facilities which include banqueting rooms and a small range of leisure amenities.*

46⇨♠(1fb)✲in 10 bedrooms CTV in all bedrooms ® T ✱ sB&B⇨♠£56 dB&B⇨♠£70 🏳

ℭ 200P ✿ CFA ⬚ (heated) sauna solarium gymnasium ♫ *xmas*

♀ English & French V ✿ ✲ Sunday Lunch £6-£7.95 Dinner £8-£10&alc Last dinner 9.30pm

Credit Cards ① ② ③ ⑤ ⓔ

**See advertisement under GRIMSBY**

K

## LAGG

See Arran, Isle of

### LAGGAN BRIDGE Highland *Inverness-shire* Map **14** NN69

★★★63% *Gaskmore House*
PH20 1BS ☎Laggan(05284)250 FAX (05284) 207
*This tastefully modernised hotel with fine views of the valley is run in country-house style, with log fires in the foyer and combined lounge and bar. Well equipped bedrooms vary in size, with two located in an adjacent lodge cottage.*
9⇌⇪Annexe2⇪(3fb) CTV in all bedrooms ® T
40P ✿
V ✿ ⚓ ✕ Last dinner 9pm
Credit Cards 1 3

### LAIRG Highland *Sutherland* Map **14** NC50

★★★60% Sutherland Arms
IV27 4AT (Scottish Highland) ☎(0549)2291 Telex no 778215
FAX (0549) 2261
Closed Nov-Mar
*Situated in the village and overlooking Loch Shin, this long-established fishing and tourist hotel offers traditional standards of hospitality and comfort. Bedrooms vary in shape and size but all are furnished and equipped in contemporary style.*
27rm(20⇌22⇪)(3fb) CTV in all bedrooms ® T ✳ sB&Bfr£37
sB&B⇌⇪£49-£54 dB&B⇌⇪£79-£86 🖼
30P ✿ ♪
✿ ⚓ ✳ Sunday Lunch £5.95-£6.50 Dinner £16-£20 Last dinner
8.30pm
Credit Cards 1 2 3 5

### LAMLASH

See Arran, Isle of

### LAMORNA COVE Cornwall & Isles of Scilly Map **02** SW42

★★★⚑60% *Lamorna Cove*
TR19 6XH (Inter-Hotels) ☎Penzance(0736)731411
*This former Cornish miners' church, in a remote location, has been converted into a cosy little hotel with a good choice of comfortably furnished lounges. Bedrooms vary in size and style, some being more simply furnished. There are good views of Lamorna Cove, a secluded garden patio with a swimming pool, and wholesome home cooking is served in the bright dining room.*
18⇌⇪(3fb)1🖼 CTV in all bedrooms
Lift 30P ♨ ✿ ⌇ (heated) sauna diving ⚗
✿ ⚓ ✕
Credit Cards 1 2 3

### LAMPETER Dyfed Map **02** SN54

★★★⚑66% Falcondale Country House
SA48 7RX ☎(0570)422910 FAX (0570) 423559
*Set in 12 acres of park and woodland a mile from the town centre, this 18th- century mansion provides well-equipped comfortably furnished bedrooms, a relaxing lounge cocktail bar with a log fire and a restaurant with a good choice of food. Hospitable staff provide attentive service.*
19⇌⇪(8fb)2🖼 CTV in all bedrooms ® T ⋈ S%
sB&B⇌⇪£43-£55 dB&B⇌⇪£62-£75 🖼
Lift 80P ✿ CFA ♪ (hard) ✐ putting green *xmas*
♀ English & French V ✿ ⚓ S% Dinner £17 Last dinner
9.30pm
Credit Cards 1 3

See advertisement on page 397

For key to symbols in English see the bookmark.

L

## LAMPHEY Dyfed Map **02** SN00

★★★❀ ♨65%, **Court**

SA71 5NT (Best Western) ☎(0646)672273 Telex no 48587 FAX (0646) 672480

*An imposing country mansion amid lawns and woodlands a mile from Pembroke on the Tenby side. Public rooms are spacious and comfortable, there are good function facilities and the attractive restaurant offers table d'hôte and extensive à la carte menus. Bedrooms are mostly well equipped and modern, and there is a good leisure centre with a small local membership.*

22⇨🚻 Annexe8⇨🚻(15fb) CTV in all bedrooms ® T sB&B⇨🚻£49-£64 dB&B⇨🚻£87-£110 🄋
▦ CTV 50P ❀ CFA 🏊 (heated) sauna solarium gymnasium ♨ *xmas*

♀ English & French V ✿ ⚌ Lunch £13.95-£14.95&alc High tea £1.55-£5.95 Dinner £13.95-£14.95&alc Last dinner 9pm

Credit Cards 1️⃣ 2️⃣ 3️⃣ 5️⃣

**See advertisement under PEMBROKE**

★★69% **Bethwaite's Lamphey Hall**

SA71 5NR ☎(0646)672394 FAX (0646) 672369

*This small, friendly hotel, set in a pretty village just outside Pembroke, provides accommodation in well equipped bedrooms; the open-plan lounge and restaurant is comfortably furnished, and there is a separate bistro bar.*

10⇨🚻(2fb) CTV in all bedrooms ® T ✹ sB&B⇨🚻£32 dB&B⇨🚻£51 🄋

30P 🚗 ❀ ♨

♀ English & French V ✿ ⚌ ✹

Credit Cards 1️⃣ 2️⃣ 3️⃣

## LANARK

**See Biggar**

## LANCASTER Lancashire Map **07** SD46 ◉

★★★67%, **Royal Kings Arms**

Market St LA1 1HP ☎(0524)32451 Telex no 65481 FAX (0524) 841698

*A splendidly restored hotel in the city centre close to the castle, with spacious lounges, comfortable bedrooms with every modern facility and an elegant restaurant with a minstrels' gallery. Smartly dressed staff are friendly and helpful.*

55⇨🚻(2fb) CTV in all bedrooms ® T

Lift ( 20P

♀ English & French V ✿ ⚌ Last dinner 9.30pm

Credit Cards 1️⃣ 2️⃣ 3️⃣ 5️⃣

★★★62% **Forte Posthouse**

Waterside Park, Caton Rd LA1 4RA (close to junc 34 M6) (Forte Hotels) ☎(0524)65999 Telex no 65363 FAX (0524) 841265

*A busy, purpose-built, modern hotel situated close to junction 34 of the M6 offers spacious bedrooms, those at the rear of the building overlooking the River Lune. Open-plan public areas include a buffet-style restaurant and good leisure facilities.*

110⇨🚻1🚗✹in 55 bedrooms CTV in all bedrooms ® T ✹ sB⇨🚻£39.50-£49.50 (room only) 🄋

Lift ( 200P 🚗 ❀ CFA 🏊 (heated) ♪ sauna solarium gymnasium health & fitness centre ♨ *xmas*

V ✿ ⚌ ✹ ✹ Lunch £12-£25alc Dinner £12-£25alc Last dinner 10.30pm

Credit Cards 1️⃣ 2️⃣ 3️⃣ 5️⃣

★★56% *Slyne Lodge*

Slyne LA2 6AZ (2m N on A6) ☎Hest Bank(0524)823389

*Situated on the A6, two miles north of Lancaster, this is a Beefeater Steak House restaurant and hotel. Bedrooms set at the rear have full en suite facilities.*

10⇨(3fb) CTV in all bedrooms ®

100P ❀ ♨

♀ Mainly grills V ✿ ⚌ ✹ Last dinner 10.30pm

Credit Cards 1️⃣ 2️⃣ 3️⃣ 4️⃣ 5️⃣

## LANDCROSS Devon Map **02** SS42

★★50%, *Beaconside*

EX39 5JL (1m SW on A388) ☎Bideford(02372)77205

*Comfortable small, secluded hotel with good food and atmosphere.*

9rm(4⇨2🚻)(2fb) CTV in all bedrooms ✹

CTV 16P ❀ ⌣ (heated) ♪ (hard)

✿ ⚌ ✹

Credit Cards 1️⃣ 5️⃣

## LAND'S END

See Sennen

## LANGAR Nottinghamshire Map **08** SK73

★❀♨70%, **Langar Hall**

NG13 9HG ☎Harby(0949)60559 FAX (0949) 61045

*Hidden by the church in a secluded position surveying the Vale of Belvoir, this is a charming house with apricot washed stucco, the former family home of proprietor Imogen Skirving. It is a friendly, quirky hotel, and while the accommodation offers modern facilities nothing detracts from the period façade. The flagstone hallways lead to the delightful lounges furnished with antiques, and the elegant restaurant. The latter is most successful and booking is essential. Chef Frank Vallat uses his native French cuisine and combines it effectively with European pulses and grains. The set menu offers fresh carp fillets with sorrel, a confit leg of duck with butter beans in tomato sauce, or lamb with couscous in garlic sauce. Desserts are very good, a hazelnut and rum flower (which looked rather like a toadstool), for example, and very nice crème Anglaise. After dinner entertainment is sometimes provided, in the form of a 30-minute Victorian melodrama or farce, performed by the staff – also actors from the local Scoundrel company. Service too is enjoyably theatrical.*

10⇨🚻(3fb)1🚗 CTV in all bedrooms ® T ✹ sB&B⇨🚻£46-£60 dB&B⇨🚻£46-£95 🄋

CTV 20P 🚗 ❀ *xmas*

♀ English & French ✿ ✹ Lunch £11.50-£20 Dinner £15-£25 Last dinner 9pm

Credit Cards 1️⃣ 3️⃣

## LANGBANK Strathclyde *Renfrewshire* Map **10** NS37

★★★❀❀♨72%, **Gleddoch House**

PA14 6YE ☎(047554)711 FAX (047554) 201

Closed 27 Dec & 1-2 Jan

*The former family home of shipping magnate Sir James Lithgow has now been sympathetically extended and converted to provide a country house hotel with good leisure facilities. Set in its own sizeable grounds, with an outlook over the River Clyde towards the Lomond hills, and complementing tastefully appointed, well equipped bedrooms by day rooms with welcoming open fires and comfortable chesterfields, this establishment has much to offer visiting businessman and leisure guest alike.*

33⇨🚻(6fb)1🚗 CTV in all bedrooms ® T sB&B⇨🚻£90-£100 dB&B⇨🚻£130-£170 🄋

( 100P ❀ CFA ► 18 squash ∪ snooker sauna plunge pool *xmas*

♀ Scottish & French V ✿ ⚌ Lunch £17&alc Dinner £30&alc Last dinner 9pm

Credit Cards 1️⃣ 2️⃣ 3️⃣ 5️⃣ ￡

## LANGDALE, GREAT

See Elterwater

## LANGHO Lancashire Map 07 SD73

★★★64% **Mytton Fold Farm**
Whalley Rd BB6 8AB ☎Blackburn(0254)240662
FAX (0254) 248119
RS Xmas wk

*A friendly family-run hotel sympathetically extended from converted farm buildings and offering comfortable attractive accommodation. A large well designed function suite with adjoining landscaped gardens has recently been added.*

27⇨🛏2🛏 CTV in all bedrooms ® T ✹ (ex guide dogs) ✱
sB&B⇨🛏£32-£51 dB&B⇨🛏£61.50-£81 ☐
150P ✿ CFA nc6yrs
V ♡ ✔ ✱ Sunday Lunch £7.50-£8.20 High tea £7.50-£8.20
Dinner £8-£22alc Last dinner 9.30pm
Credit Cards ①③ ⓔ

❀❀ ✕ ✕ ✕ **Northcote Manor**
Northcote Rd BB6 8BE ☎Blackburn(0254)240555
FAX (0254) 246568

*This charming Victorian house set in rural surroundings just off the A59, close to its junction with the A666, is highly acclaimed for its creative, modern cooking. A team of young chefs led by head chef Nigel Haworth produces dishes to suit all tastes, ranging from breast of Lunesdale duckling served in peppercorns and red wine to chicken filled with mushroom pâté on a watercress and mustard sauce; starters include a delicious Bouillabaisse and a game terrine, equally delectable home-made sweets complete the meal and the wine list is outstanding. The restaurant itself is elegant and six luxurious bedrooms are available for guests wishing to stay the night.*

Closed 26 Dec & 1 Jan
V 55 seats Lunch £12.30-£15&alc Dinner £19-£28alc Last lunch 1.30pm Last dinner 9.30pm 40 P
Credit Cards ①②③⑤

## LANGHOLM Dumfries & Galloway *Dumfriesshire* Map 11 NY38

★★56% **Eskdale**
Market Place DG13 0JH (Minotels) ☎(03873)80357
FAX (03873) 80357

*This town centre hotel offers good value menus and friendly service.*

16rm(3⇨7🛏)(2fb)✔in 3 bedrooms CTV in all bedrooms ® T
sB&Bfr£24 sB&B⇨🛏fr£26 dB&Bfr£38 dB&B⇨🛏fr£42
⊄ 10P CFA
V ♡ ⚲ ✱ Sunday Lunch £5.95 Dinner £10&alc Last dinner 8.30pm
Credit Cards ①③ ⓔ

**See advertisement on page 400**

## LANGLAND BAY West Glamorgan Map 02 SS68

See also **Mumbles and** Swansea
★★★60% **Osborne**
Rotherslade Rd SA3 4QL (Jarvis) ☎Swansea(0792)366274
FAX (0792) 363100

*Set in an enviable position on the cliffs, overlooking the lovely Langland Bay, this hotel caters for both holidaymakers and business guests. Meals and service are of a high standard, public areas are spaciously comfortable, and many bedrooms have been upgraded to a good standard.*

36rm(32⇨🛏🛏)(4fb) CTV in all bedrooms ® T ✱
sB&B⇨🛏fr£68.80 dB&B⇨🛏fr£83 ☐
Lift ⊄ 40P CFA *xmas*
☼ Welsh, English & French V ♡ ⚲ ✱ Sunday Lunch fr£10.75
Dinner fr£14.95 Last dinner 9pm
Credit Cards ①②③④⑤

K

★★67% **Langland Court**
Langland Court Rd SA3 4TD (Best Western)
☎Swansea(0792)361545 FAX (0792) 362302
*Within walking distance of Langland Bay, this Tudor-style house provides good modern accommodation. There is an impressive panelled restaurant and a galleried staircase, and new menus recently introduced give the promise of good food. The bedrooms are all well equipped and comfortable.*
16⇨🛏🏠Annexe5⇨🏠(5fb)1🛏⅟₂in 2 bedrooms CTV in all
bedrooms ® T ✖ (ex guide dogs) sB&B⇨🏠£52-£55
dB&B⇨🏠£70-£72 🏋
45P 4🎱 (charged) ❄ CFA
♀ English & Continental V ☼ Lunch £9.75-£10.25&alc Dinner fr£15&alc Last dinner 9.30pm
Credit Cards ①②③⑤

**See advertisement under SWANSEA**

---

**LANGSTONE** Gwent Map **03** ST38

★★64% **New Inn**
NP6 2JN (Porterhouse) ☎Newport(0633)412426
FAX (0633) 413679
*Standing beside the A48 just east of junction 24 of the M4, this is a popular hotel, its pretty bedrooms well equipped with modern facilities. The restaurant is much frequented by the locals.*
34⇨🏠(1fb) CTV in all bedrooms ® T ✖ (ex guide dogs) ✳
sB&B⇨🏠£52.50 dB&B⇨🏠£66.50 🏋
CTV 150P CFA
V ☼ ✳ Lunch £6.99-£7.50alc Dinner fr£5.95alc Last dinner 10pm
Credit Cards ①②③⑤

---

**LANGTOFT** Humberside Map **08** TA06

★★75% **Old Mill Hotel & Restaurant**
Mill Ln YO25 0BQ ☎Driffield(0377)87284
*Situated to the north of the village, high on the hills, this peaceful and genuinely hospitable hotel enjoys panoramic views of rolling farmland. Originally a restaurant, it has now been extended and refurbished to provide good hotel facilities which include thoughtfully equipped and well furnished bedrooms with modern bathrooms – though it is as an eating place that it is still particularly popular.*
8⇨🏠 CTV in all bedrooms ® T ✖ (ex guide dogs) S%
sB&B⇨🏠£40-£60 dB&B⇨🏠£60-£80 🏋
CTV 30P 🚲 nc14yrs
♀ English, French & Italian V ☼ ⅟₂ S% Lunch £15-£30alc
Dinner £15-£30alc Last dinner 10pm
Credit Cards ①③ⓔ

---

**LANREATH** Cornwall & Isles of Scilly Map **02** SX15

★★58% **Punch Bowl Inn**
PL13 2NX ☎(0503)20218 due to change to 220218
*The popular restaurant of this early 17th-century coaching inn offers both table d'hôte and à la carte menus, whilst an extensive selection of dishes is also available in the cosy bars, which have log fires and polished brasses. Bedrooms, named after Punch characters, range from antique-furnished to modern in style.*
14rm(10⇨2🏠)(2fb)3🛏 CTV in all bedrooms ® ✳ sB&B£17-£20 sB&B⇨🏠£24-£27.50 dB&B£34-£40 dB&B⇨🏠£48-£55 🏋
CTV 50P
V ☼ ⅟₂ ✳ Sunday Lunch £5.95 Dinner £9.50&alc Last dinner 9pm
Credit Cards ①③

**See advertisement under LOOE**

---

🐚 Shell filling stations (7am–11pm) are marked on the town plans.

---

**LARGS** Strathclyde *Ayrshire* Map **10** NS25

★★65% **Elderslie**
John St, Broomfields KA30 8DR ☎(0475)686460
FAX (0475) 672251
Closed 25-26 Dec
*Situated on the seafront with fine views out across the Firth of Clyde, this well maintained hotel attracts a mixed clientèle, including residential conferences. Bedrooms vary in size, some being particularly comfortable and spacious. En suite bathrooms are nicely appointed.*
25rm(9⇨4🏠) CTV in all bedrooms ® T sB&B£27.50-£33.50
sB&B⇨🏠£33.50 dB&B£55-£67 dB&B⇨🏠£67
CTV 30P ❄ *xmas*
☼ ✳ Lunch £9.95-£12.95 Dinner £11.95-£13.95 Last dinner 8.30pm
Credit Cards ①②③⑤ⓔ

★★59% **Springfield**
Greenock Rd KA30 8QL ☎(0475)673119 & 687475
*Situated adjacent to the local swimming pool and putting green, and with views out to the Isle of Cumbrae, this hotel caters for family holidaymakers and coach parties. Bedrooms vary in size, but are all bright and airy. A wide choice is offered at dinner, and portions are generous. The bar boasts an interesting range of malt whiskies.*
59rm(53⇨🏠)(4fb) CTV in all bedrooms ® T sB&B£25
sB&B⇨🏠£38 dB&B£42 dB&B⇨🏠£52 🏋
Lift CTV 80P ❄ CFA putting ♫ *xmas*
♀ Scottish, French & Italian V ☼ ⅟₂ ⅟₂ Lunch £3.75-£8.50&alc High tea £3.75-£9&alc Dinner £12.50&alc Last dinner 8.30pm
Credit Cards ①②③⑤

---

**LARKFIELD** Kent Map **05** TQ65

★★★62% **Larkfield Priory**
London Rd ME20 6HJ (Forte Hotels)
☎West Malling(0732)846858 Telex no 957420
FAX (0732) 846786
*The original building of this hotel has been sympathetically extended to provide modern, well furnished and equipped accommodation which includes executive club and four poster rooms. A comfortable through lounge and bar leads into the very popular Orchard Restaurant which offers a seasonal menu of professionally prepared dishes. Good meeting, conference and car parking facilities are available, polite staff are particularly helpful, and room service can be provided.*
52⇨🛏1🛏⅟₂in 17 bedrooms CTV in all bedrooms ® T ✳ S%
sB⇨🏠fr£70 dB⇨🏠fr£85 (room only) 🏋
☾80P ❄ CFA ♫ *xmas*
♀ English & French V ☼ ⅟₂ ⅟₂ ✳ S% Lunch £9.95-£11.20&alc Dinner £14.90&alc Last dinner 10pm
Credit Cards ①②③④⑤

---

**LASTINGHAM** North Yorkshire Map **08** SE79

★★👪75% *Lastingham Grange*
YO6 6TH ☎(07515)345
Closed mid Dec-Feb
*A 17th-century country house, providing comfortable bedrooms with many thoughtful extras, a relaxing lounge and good value dinner menus. The resident owners give warm attentive service.*
12⇨🏠 CTV in all bedrooms ®
30P 2🚗 🚲 ❄ 🏌
V ☼ ⅟₂ ⅟₂
Credit Cards ②⑤

---

**LAUNCESTON**

See Lifton

---

## LAVENHAM Suffolk Map 05 TL94

### ★★★ 68% The Swan

High St CO10 9QA (Forte Hotels) ☎(0787)247477
Telex no 987198 FAX (0787) 248286

*Set in a very popular village and dating from the 14th-century, this lovely timbered building retains much of its original character. Individually styled bedrooms are both fully equipped and comfortable, while public areas with quality furnishings include inviting lounges and a well appointed restaurant. The garden offers a delightful setting in which to enjoy an apéritif before a skilfully prepared and attractively presented dinner based on good fresh produce, and efficient staff provide an above average range of services.*

47⇌🏳2🛏½in 13 bedrooms CTV in all bedrooms Ⓡ T ✹ S%
sB⇌🏳fr£75 dB⇌🏳£95-£130 (room only) 🏳
₡ 60P ✿ CFA ♫ xmas
♀ English & French V ♦ ♫ ✹ ✹ S% Lunch £13.95&alc
Dinner £17.95&alc Last dinner 9.30pm
Credit Cards ①②③④⑤

### ★ 73% Angel

Market Place CO10 9QZ ☎Sudbury(0787)247388

*This 14th-century inn, which overlooks the market place of the historic and characterful town, combines the qualities of a cheerfully busy 'local' with those of a popular restaurant. Informal service is both friendly and helpful, outdoor eating and barbecues in the quiet garden at the rear being an attractive option during the summer months. Well equipped bedrooms with modern en suite facilities, are furnished in keeping with the character of the building.*

7⇌🏳(1fb) CTV in all bedrooms Ⓡ T ✹ sB&B⇌🏳£25-£30
dB&B⇌🏳£40-£50 🏳
CTV 5P ✿ ♪ (hard) ∪ ☂
V ♦ ✹ Lunch £9-£15alc Dinner £10-£17alc Last dinner 9.30pm
Credit Cards ①③

### ✾✕✕The Great House

Market Place CO10 9QZ ☎(0787)247431

*An extended 16th-century house with Georgian façade, set at the heart of this historic town, provides a character restaurant offering a menu which combines the best of French and English cuisine. Good use is made of fresh produce enhanced by light sauces, and fish – a regular feature – is skilfully used in a flavoursome Mediterranean fish soup; Magret Duck is served pink and tender with crisped edges, a fine cheese board is available, and a well chosen wine list complements the menu. Service is keen and friendly, staff showing an obvious desire to please, and an attractive courtyard at the rear of the building is adorned with an abundance of hanging baskets.*

Closed Mon (in winter)
Dinner not served Sun (in winter)
♀ Continental V 40 seats Lunch £9.90-£12.50 Dinner fr£13.95&alc Last lunch 2.30pm Last dinner 9.30pm 6 P
Credit Cards ①③

## LAWSHALL Suffolk Map 05 TL85

### ★★ 65% Corders

Bury Rd IP29 4PJ ☎(0284)830314

*A family-owned hotel situated on the outskirts of the village some 6 miles south of Bury St Edmunds offers guests a warm welcome and genuine hospitality. Well equipped and comfortable en suite accommodation is complemented by pleasant public areas, many rooms enjoying views over open countryside.*

8⇌🏳(2fb)1🛏 CTV in all bedrooms Ⓡ T ✹ (ex guide dogs)
CTV 30P ⊞ ✿ sauna jacuzzi nc5yrs
♀ English & French V ½ Last dinner 9pm
Credit Cards ①②③⑤

## LEA MARSTON Warwickshire Map 07 SP29

### ★★★ 65% Lea Marston Hotel & Leisure Complex

Haunch Ln B76 0BY ☎Curdworth(0675)470468
FAX (0675) 470871

*Located one mile from M42 junction 9 off the A4907 Kingsbury Road, this modern hotel is sited in a complex which includes a golf driving range, par-3 course and tennis courts. The hotel has spacious bedrooms, a popular restaurant and well-equipped conference rooms.*

19⇌🏳 CTV in all bedrooms Ⓡ T ✹ (ex guide dogs)
sB&B⇌🏳£47-£92 dB&B⇌🏳£47-£100 🏳
₡ CTV 165P ✿ CFA ▶ 9 ♪ (hard) sauna solarium gymnasium crown green bowls indoor bowls xmas
♀ English & French V ♦ ♫ Lunch £9.55&alc Dinner £10.35&alc Last dinner 10pm
Credit Cards ①②③€

**See advertisement under BIRMINGHAM**

## LEAMINGTON SPA (ROYAL) Warwickshire Map 04 SP36 ⊙

★★★ ✾✾✾✾🍴

**MALLORY COURT**

Harbury Ln, Bishop's Tachbrook CV33 9QB (2m S off A452) (Relais et Châteaux)
☎Leamington Spa (0926)330214
FAX (0926) 451714

*Built in the early 1900s, but classically styled to be the quintessential English country house in its 10 acres of mature grounds and gardens, Mallory Court has been well established by the conscientious partnership of Jeremy Mort and Allan Holland. Public rooms are comfortably furnished with rich chesterfields, lovely fabrics and assorted objets d'art. Bedrooms are individually styled, furnished with both antique and reproduction pieces and first class bedding. Flowers, biscuits and an abundance of reading material complement the good range of creature comforts; and quality toiletries in the bright en suites add a touch of luxury. One inspector has commented that the delightful wood-panelled restaurant is one of the most comfortable ever dined in, but more importantly the food stands up very well. While Allan is still very much at the helm in the kitchen, the introduction of Duncan Basterfield, ex Le Manoir aux Quat' Saisons, Great Milton, has added another dimension. Rich terrines, timbales of wild mushrooms or pressed sweetbreads can be followed by a commendable sautéed Gressingham duck, or baked rack of lamb with a sorrel and mint sauce, concluding with one of the excellent soufflés. The 3-course set price dinner is a little expensive, but the quality is there, and promising signs of higher accolades to come.*

10⇌🏳(1fb)1🛏 CTV in all bedrooms T ✹
sB&B⇌🏳fr£105 dB&B⇌🏳£125-£205 Continental breakfast 🏳
50P 2🛏 (£6) ⊞ ✿ ⌂ ♪ (hard) squash croquet nc 9yrs xmas
♀ French V ♦ ♫ Lunch £24.50-£26.50 Dinner fr£43.50 Last dinner 9.45pm
Credit Cards ①③

★★

**The Eskdale Hotel**

## Langholm, Dumfriesshire DG13 0JH
## Telephone: Langholm (03873) 80357

The Eskdale Hotel is a former coaching inn in the centre of Langholm on the Scottish border. The hotel offers a high degree of comfort, facilities and good quality home cooking. There are tea/coffee making facilities, colour TV, radio and full central heating in all rooms, ⅔ of rooms have en suite facilities. Lively atmosphere with two bars, games room and à la carte restaurant. Ample parking is available in the hotel which is a good base for touring the Border region. Fishing, shooting and golf are all available in the area. Fishing permits available from Hotel.

**L**

---

### ★★★67% Regent
77 The Parade CV32 4AX (Best Western) ☎(0926)427231
Telex no 311715 FAX (0926) 450728
*A thoroughly old-fashioned hotel for those who value traditional qualities of kindness and hospitality amid period splendour, along with all the comforts and facilities provided by thorough modernisation. There is a good choice of restaurants and bars, and the hotel caters very well for both leisure and commercial users, particularly women.*
80⇌🛏(7fb)1🛏 CTV in all bedrooms ® T ✱
sB&B⇌🛏£61.50-£82 dB&B⇌🛏£84.50-£99.50 🍴
Lift ℂ CTV 70P 30🚗 CFA table tennis pool table *xmas*
♡ English, French & Italian V ✿ ♨ ✱ Lunch fr£10.75 Dinner fr£15.25 Last dinner 10.45pm
Credit Cards ①②③⑤

### ★★★61% Falstaff
16-20 Warwick New Rd CV32 5JQ ☎(0926)312044
FAX (0926) 450574
*Situated on the outskirts of town this hotel is undergoing complete refurbishment to provide comfortable, well-equipped modern bedrooms and public areas of quality.*
65⇌🛏(3fb)2🛏 CTV in all bedrooms ® T ✖ (ex guide dogs)
✱ sB&B⇌🛏£30-£58.50 dB&B⇌🛏£38-£68.50 🍴
Lift ℂ 80P CFA *xmas*
♡ English & French V ✿ ♨ ✱ Lunch £7.95-£14 Dinner £14-£20&alc Last dinner 9.15pm
Credit Cards ①②③④⑤ ⓔ

### ★★★58% Manor House
Avenue Rd CV31 3NJ (Forte Hotels) ☎(0926)423251
FAX (0926) 425933
*This large detached Victorian hotel is situated close to the town centre, and is undergoing refurbishment to enhance the many original features which include spacious open-plan public areas. Bedrooms vary in size, but all have good en suite facilities.*
53⇌🛏(2fb)⊬in 21 bedrooms CTV in all bedrooms ® T ✱ S%
sB⇌🛏£65 dB⇌🛏£85 (room only) 🍴

---

Lift ℂ 130P ❀ *xmas*
V ✿ ♨ ⊬ ✱ S% Lunch £9.95 Dinner fr£14.95&alc Last dinner 10pm
Credit Cards ①②③④⑤

### ★★71% Tuscany
Warwick Place CV32 5DE ☎(0926)332233 FAX (0926) 332232
*This small, privately run hotel, close to the town centre, offers personal service and traditional comfort, with well furnished, generally spacious accommodation. Dishes served in the attractive dining room use organic produce, though choice can be limited. A no-smoking policy operates throughout.*
10⇌🛏(4fb)1🛏⊬in all bedrooms CTV in all bedrooms ® T ✖ (ex guide dogs) ✱ sB&B⇌🛏£47-£110 dB&B⇌🛏£67-£130 Continental breakfast 🍴
8P 🚗 *xmas*
♡ Continental V ✿ ♨ ⊬ ✱ Dinner fr£11.95&alc Last dinner 9.30pm
Credit Cards ①②③⑤ ⓔ

### ★★69% Adams
22 Avenue Rd CV31 3PQ ☎(0926)450742 & 422758
FAX (0926) 313110
*Run in the style of a small private hotel, this impressive Georgian residence has been tastefully converted to provide good modern accommodation that is well maintained and clean. Public rooms have recently been rearranged and now offer more flexibility and comfort. Good home cooked meals offer a limited choice, with a restricted meal service on Sundays.*
14⇌🛏 CTV in all bedrooms T ✖ sB&B⇌🛏£38-£50
dB&B⇌🛏£59.50-£65
14P 🚗 ❀
V ✿ ♨ ✱ Lunch £16-£20 Dinner £14-£18&alc Last dinner 8pm
Credit Cards ①②③⑤

### ★★61% Beech Lodge
Warwick New Rd CV32 5JJ ☎Leamington Spa(0926)422227
RS 24 Dec-3 Jan
*Personal service from the proprietors ensures a comfortable stay at this privately owned and run hotel midway between Leamington Spa and Warwick. Simply furnished bedrooms, though compact, offer a good range of modern facilities, the cosy public areas are welcoming and an attractive restaurant serves generous portions of home-cooked food.*
12rm(9⇌🛏) CTV in all bedrooms ® T sB&B£20-£29
sB&B⇌🛏£30-£42 dB&B⇌🛏£48-£58 🍴
CTV 16P 🚗
♡ English & French V Sunday Lunch £7.50-£8.50 Dinner £9.75-£16.75alc Last dinner 8pm
Credit Cards ①②③ ⓔ

### ★★60% Abbacourt
40 Kenilworth Rd CV32 6JF ☎Leamington Spa(0926)451755
FAX (0926) 450330
*Resident proprietors, aided by a small, helpful team, provide friendly and attentive service at this hotel, a large converted house beside the A452 in the residential outskirts of the town.*
24⇌🛏(4fb) CTV in all bedrooms ® T ✱ sB&B⇌🛏£35-£50
dB&B⇌🛏£55-£70 🍴
30P
♡ Continental V ✿ ♨ ✱ Bar Lunch £2.50-£3.50alc High tea £3.50-£5.50alc Dinner £9.50-£15alc Last dinner 10pm
Credit Cards ①②③④⑤

---

All black star hotels are given a
percentage grading within their star bands.
See 'Using the Guide' at the front of the book
for full details.

★

★ **LANSDOWNE**

87 Clarendon St CV32 4PF
☏Leamington Spa (0926)450505
FAX (0926) 420604
RS 24 Dec-7 Jan

*This elegant Regency building, conveniently situated close to the town centre, has recently been extended by the acquisition of the adjoining property. Most of the bedrooms have en suite facilities, and all are comfortable and equipped with many extras. Lounge and bar are cosy and tastefully decorated with quality furnishings. A table d'hôte menu offers freshly cooked dishes such as interesting home-made soups, chicken breast accompanied by a creamy lemon sauce, and coffee and tasty fudge conclude an enjoyable meal. Resident proprietors make guests feel welcome at this intimate and comfortable hotel which is also their home.*

15rm(12⇌♠)(1fb) CTV in 12 bedrooms ® T ✗ sB&B£28.65 sB&B⇌♠£49.85 dB&B£39.90 dB&B⇌♠£59.90 ⊟
CTV 11P ⇎ nc5yrs
♀ English, French & Italian ♦ Dinner £15.95 Last dinner 8.30pm
Credit Cards 1 3 £

**LEDBURY** Hereford & Worcester Map **03** SO73

**★★★52% Feathers**
High St HR8 1DS ☏(0531)5266 FAX (0531) 2001
*This high-street hotel retains much of the character of its Elizabethan origins, with sloping floors and exposed beams. Room sizes vary, some being quite compact, but all are individually decorated and have good modern facilities. As well as the restaurant there is the more informal 'Fuggles', and the busy bar is popular with locals.*
11⇌♠(2fb)1⊞ CTV in all bedrooms ® ✱ sB&B⇌♠fr£55.50 dB&B⇌♠fr£78.50 ⊟
☾ 10P 6⌂ CFA squash *xmas*
♀ English & French V ♦ ⊻ Lunch fr£10.95 Dinner fr£15 Last dinner 9.30pm
Credit Cards 1 2 3 5

**★★❀❀❀ ♜72% Hope End Country House**
Hope End HR8 1JQ (2.5m NE unclass rd) ☏(0531)3613 FAX (0531) 5697
Closed mid Dec-mid Feb RS Mon & Tue
*Hope End lies at the end of a hidden valley, in 40 acres of parkland that also contains a large walled garden where most of the food used in the kitchen is grown organically; guests are invited to explore and enjoy its diversity – over a hundred varieties of herbs and vegetables and 40 sorts of apples, as well as chickens and bantams. A 5-course menu of plain and simple home-cooked dishes in English country style offers three choices at each course, including a vegetarian option, and the meal ends with a selection of rare English farmhouse cheeses; bread is baked on the premises, there is an outstanding wine list, and the exceptionally friendly young staff provide informal, unobtrusive service. Advance booking is essential for non-residents. Facilities are excellent throughout the hotel, smart, pine-funished bedrooms being complemented by superior lounges.*
7⇌Annexe2⇌ CTV in 1 bedroom ® T ✗ ✱ sB&B⇌£84-£129 dB&B⇌£94-£139 ⊟
10P ⇎ ✲ nc14yrs
V ⚟ ✱ Dinner £29.50 Last dinner 8.30pm
Credit Cards 1 3

**★★62% The Verzons Country House**
Trumpet HR8 2PZ (3m W A438) ☏Trumpet(0531)670381
Closed 25-26 Dec
*An hotel in country house style – personally run by proprietors whose concern is to ensure the comfort of all guests staying in their home – stands beside the A438 west of the town. Its restaurant caters for all tastes, providing vegetarian options.*
10rm(7⇌♠)(2fb)1⊞ CTV in all bedrooms ® ✱ sB&Bfr£32 sB&B⇌♠fr£43 dB&Bfr£43 dB&B⇌♠£55-£65 ⊟
50P ✲
V ♦ ✱ Lunch £9.50&alc Dinner £11&alc Last dinner 9.15pm
Credit Cards 1 2 3

**LEEDS** West Yorkshire Map **08** SE33 ⊕

**★★★★71% Holiday Inn**
Wellington St LS1 4DL (Holiday Inns Inc) ☏(0532)442200
Telex no 557879 FAX (0532) 440460
*One of our 'Courtesy and Care' award winners 1991/1992 for the North of England, this very comfortable modern hotel is on the edge of the city centre. Bedrooms are very well furnished and there are good lounges available. The elegant restaurant provides an international range of well prepared dishes, and service by a team of dedicated staff is professional and friendly. There is a well designed leisure centre and good parking facilities. (See colour feature on p19.)*
125⇌♠2⊞ ⚟in 25 bedrooms CTV in all bedrooms ® T S% sB⇌♠£48-£130 dB⇌♠£96-£146 (room only) ⊟
Lift ☾ ⊞ 25P 100⌂ CFA ⊡ (heated) snooker sauna solarium gymnasium whirlpool spa beauty studio steam room *xmas*
♀ English & French V ♦ ⊻ ⚟ ✱ S% Lunch £12.50-£13.95&alc Dinner £17.50&alc Last dinner 10.30pm
Credit Cards 1 2 3 4 5 £

**★★★★ 66% The Queen's**
City Square LS1 1PL (Forte Hotels) ☎(0532)431323
Telex no 55161 FAX (0532) 425154
*Near the railway station, in the heart of the city centre, stands an hotel retaining something of the grandeur and charm which characterised it when it opened over 50 years ago. Recently refurbished bedrooms offer good facilities, the carvery provides an alternative to the gracious splendour of the Club House restaurant with its high standard of cuisine, and service is both friendly and professional. The new Palm Court lounge is due to open in 1991.*
188⇨♪↑in 62 bedrooms CTV in all bedrooms ® T ✳ S%
sB⇨↑£85 dB⇨↑£95 (room only) ♬
Lift ( ♪ *xmas*
♀ International V ❖ ⚗ ⅄ ✳ S% Lunch £10.75-£12.05 Dinner fr£13.80 Last dinner 10pm
Credit Cards ①②③④⑤

**★★★ ✿✿75% Haley's Hotel & Restaurant**
Shire Oak Rd, Headingley LS6 2DE ☎(0532)784446
FAX (0532) 753342
*Stylish, elegant and very comfortable throughout, this small luxury hotel is set in a quiet residential area at Headingly, close to the cricket ground. Bedrooms are well equipped with the modern amenities of a top-class hotel and include many thoughtful extras. In Haley's restaurant, Andrew Foster, one of the country's foremost young chefs, offers a choice of menus, dishes are of high acclaim, modern in style and beautifully presented. Haley's Hotel is our Our 'Best Newcomer' award winner for the North of England 1991/1992 (see colour feature on p37).*
22⇨↑ CTV in all bedrooms ® T ✂ (ex guide dogs) ✳
sB&B⇨↑£85 dB&B⇨↑£98 ♬
( 18P ⇔ CFA *xmas*
V ❖ ⚗ ⅄ Lunch £13.75&alc Dinner £17.95-£22.95&alc Last dinner 9.45pm
Credit Cards ①②③④

**★★★ 66% Forte Posthouse Leeds/Selby**
LS25 5LF (Forte Hotels) ☎South Milford(0977)682711
Telex no 557074 FAX (0977) 685462
(For full entry see Lumby)

**★★★ 65% Parkway**
Otley Rd LS16 8AG (Jarvis) ☎(0532)672551 Telex no 556614
FAX (0532) 674410
*On the A660 a mile north of the ring road, this modern well furnished hotel has very comfortable bedrooms and a good leisure centre. There is a choice of restaurants offering well prepared dishes and staff are friendly.*
103⇨↑(8fb)⅄in 11 bedrooms CTV in all bedrooms ® T ✳
S% sB⇨↑£87-£97 dB⇨↑£101.50-£112.50 (room only) ♬
Lift ( 350P ⇔ ✿ CFA ▭ (heated) ♪ (hard) snooker sauna solarium gymnasium steam room running track *xmas*
♀ English & French V ❖ ⚗ ⅄ S%
Credit Cards ①②③④⑤④

**★★★ 64% Stakis Windmill**
Mill Green View, Seacroft LS14 5QP (Stakis) ☎(0532)732323
Telex no 55452 FAX (0532) 323018
*A modern and well furnished hotel built around an old windmill, situated on the ring road, at its junction with the A64 York road.*
100⇨↑⅄in 22 bedrooms CTV in all bedrooms ® T
sB⇨↑£79.80-£90.30 dB⇨↑£93.45-£103.50 (room only) ♬
Lift ( 200P CFA *xmas*
♀ English, French & Italian ❖ ⚗ ✳
Credit Cards ①②③④⑤

**★★★ 50% Merrion**
Merrion Centre LS2 8NH (Mount Charlotte (TS))
☎(0532)439191 Telex no 55459 FAX (0532) 423527
*A functional city centre hotel.*
120⇨↑♪⅄in 42 bedrooms CTV in all bedrooms ® T (room only) ♬

Lift ( *xmas*
♀ English & French V ❖ ⚗
Credit Cards ①②③⑤

**★★58% Jester At Leek**
81 Mill St ST13 8EU ☎(0538)383997
Closed 26-28 Dec
*A popular restaurant serving generous portions of freshly prepared food, and accommodation in compact but warm and well-equipped bedrooms are the attractions of a family-run hostelry which stands beside the busy Macclesfield road in the town centre.*
14rm(9⇨2↑)(4fb) CTV in all bedrooms ® T sB&Bfr£30.75
sB&B⇨↑£33.95 dB&Bfr£44.95 dB&B⇨↑£47 ♬
70P CFA snooker
♀ English & Continental V ❖ ⚗ ⅄ Lunch £7.94-£8.95&alc Dinner £8.50-£15.90alc Last dinner 10pm
Credit Cards ①②③④

**★★63% Motel Leeming**
Great North Rd DL8 1DT ☎Bedale(0677)423611
FAX (0677) 424507
(For full entry see Bedale)

**★★61% White Rose**
DL7 9AY ☎Bedale(0677)422707 & 424941 FAX (0677) 425123
*A roadside hotel near the A1 and Leeming Air Base providing comfortable accommodation in well-equipped en suite bedrooms. Public areas include a lounge and a range of bars.*
18⇨↑(2fb) CTV in all bedrooms ® T sB&B⇨↑£28
dB&B⇨↑£42 ♬
CTV 50P CFA *xmas*
V ❖ ⚗ Lunch £5.50&alc High tea £6.50 Dinner £10.50&alc
Last dinner 9pm
Credit Cards ①②③⑤④

**★★★64% Belle Vue**
39 Marine Pde East PO13 9BW ☎Portsmouth(0705)550258
FAX (0705) 552624
Closed 25 & 26 Dec
*This busy commercial hotel on the sea front has been completely refurbished to a high standard. Bedrooms are particularly comfortable and well equipped and though public areas are limited there is a spacious bar. The bright restaurant offers a short à la carte menu.*
24⇨↑Annexe3⇨↑(4fb) CTV in all bedrooms ® T
sB⇨↑£50-£75 dB⇨↑£65-£95 (room only) ♬
( 55P CFA ♫
V ❖ ⅄ ✳ Lunch £12-£20alc Dinner £12-£20alc Last dinner 9.45pm
Credit Cards ①③④

See advertisement under FAREHAM

**★★★★63% Country Court**
Braunstone LE3 2WQ (Stakis) ☎(0533)630066 Telex no 34429
FAX (0533) 630627
*Conveniently located close to junction 21 of the M1, the M69 and A46, this modern hotel with its excellent conference facilities and good leisure club is popular with business people and for weekend breaks. Bedrooms are spacious and very well equipped, and the open-plan public areas comfortable.*
141⇨↑(39fb)⅄in 73 bedrooms CTV in all bedrooms ® T
✂ (ex guide dogs) sB⇨↑£84 dB⇨↑£94.50 (room only) ♬

( ⊞ 160P ♨ CFA 🖺 (heated) sauna solarium gymnasium jacuzzi
♥ English & Continental **V** ✪ ⊒ ✗
Credit Cards ⎡1⎤⎡2⎤⎡3⎤⎡5⎤

---

### ★★★★60% Holiday Inn
St Nicholas Circle LE1 5LX (Holiday Inns Inc) ☎(0533)531161
Telex no 341281 FAX (0533) 513169
*Large, purpose-built hotel close to the city centre, adjacent to multi-storey car park.*
188⇄🛏(99fb)✗in 79 bedrooms CTV in all bedrooms ® **T** sB⇄🛏£82-£85 dB⇄🛏£92-£95 (room only) 🗏
Lift ( ⊞ ♪ CFA 🖺 (heated) sauna solarium gymnasium whirl-pool health bar steam room
♥ International **V** ✪ ⊒ ✗ Lunch £12&alc High tea £4.50-£20 Dinner fr£17.50&alc Last dinner 10.15pm
Credit Cards ⎡1⎤⎡2⎤⎡3⎤⎡4⎤⎡5⎤

---

### ★★★★58% Grand
Granby St LE1 6ES (Jarvis) ☎(0533)555599 FAX (0533) 544736
Closed 24-27 Dec & 1 Jan
*Impressive Victorian city-centre building standing on the main A6.*
92⇄🛏(1fb)1♨✗in 21 bedrooms CTV in all bedrooms ® **T** ✱ S% sB⇄🛏£33.70-£93 dB⇄🛏£67.40-£104 (room only) 🗏
Lift ( 120P 8🖾 CFA ♫
♥ English & French **V** ✪ ⊒ ✱ S% Lunch £9.95&alc High tea £3.25-£4 Dinner £13.95&alc Last dinner 10pm
Credit Cards ⎡1⎤⎡2⎤⎡3⎤⎡5⎤ⓒ

---

### ★★★69% Belmont House
De Montfort St LE1 7GR (Best Western) ☎(0533)544773
FAX (0533) 470804
Closed 25-28 Dec
*Standards of service and comfort continue to improve at this popular hotel conveniently close to both the city centre and railway station. Recent improvements include 10 new bedrooms, additional meeting and function rooms, and some refurbished public areas.*
46⇄🛏Annexe22⇄🛏(7fb)✗in 9 bedrooms CTV in all bedrooms ® **T** sB&B⇄🛏£68.50-£88 dB&B⇄🛏£80-£92 🗏
Lift ( 60P CFA
♥ English & French **V** ✪ ⊒ ✱ Lunch £9.95-£10.95&alc Dinner £15.50&alc Last dinner 10pm
Credit Cards ⎡1⎤⎡2⎤⎡3⎤⎡5⎤

---

### ★★★65% Leicestershire Moat House
Wigston Rd, Oadby LE2 5QE (3m SE A6) (Queens Moat) ☎(0533)719441 Telex no 34474 FAX (0533) 720559
*The hotel is located adjacent to the A6 at Oadby, about three miles from the city centre. New bedrooms have proved popular and existing rooms have been refurbished to a similar standard. The popular Czars restaurant has a carvery and à la carte menu.*
57⇄🛏(4fb)✗in 14 bedrooms CTV in all bedrooms ® **T** sB⇄🛏fr£63 dB⇄🛏fr£74 (room only) 🗏
Lift ( CTV 160P ✿ CFA ♫
♥ English & French **V** ✪ ⊒ ✗ ✱ Lunch £10&alc Dinner £12.10&alc Last dinner 9.45pm
Credit Cards ⎡1⎤⎡2⎤⎡3⎤⎡5⎤ⓒ

---

### ★★★64% Leicester Forest Moat House
Hinckley Rd, Leicester Forest East LE3 3GH (Queens Moat) ☎(0533)394661 FAX (0533) 394952
RS 25-26 Dec
*On the A47 about 3 miles from the city centre, this hotel is popular during the week with business people who appreciate its well equipped bedrooms, its à la carte restaurant, and newly refurbished bar offering hot and cold buffet.*
34⇄🛏 CTV in all bedrooms ® **T** sB⇄🛏fr£58 dB⇄🛏fr£68 (room only) 🗏
( 200P ✿ CFA putting
♥ English & French **V** ✪ ⊒ Lunch £8-£10&alc Dinner fr£13&alc Last dinner 9.45pm
Credit Cards ⎡1⎤⎡2⎤⎡3⎤⎡5⎤

---

### ★★★62% Stage
299 Leicester Rd, Wigston Fields LE8 1JW (on A50) (Consort) ☎(0533)886161 FAX (0533) 811874
*On the A50, 3 miles south of the city centre and 3 miles from the M1/M69, this pleasant, privately owned hotel has new well equipped bedrooms, and was being further extended in 1991 to enlarge the attractive open-plan public areas and add 2 more function suites.*
79⇄🛏(8fb)2♨✗in 2 bedrooms CTV in all bedrooms ® **T** ✈ (ex guide dogs) sB&B⇄🛏£52-£62 dB&B⇄🛏£62-£72 🗏
200P CFA 🖺 (heated) sauna solarium gymnasium spa bath steam room *xmas*
♥ International **V** ✪ ⊒ ✗ Lunch £6.95-£9.95&alc High tea £4.50-£7.50 Dinner £12.95-£15.95&alc Last dinner 10pm
Credit Cards ⎡1⎤⎡2⎤⎡3⎤⎡4⎤⎡5⎤ⓒ

---

### ★★★60% Park International
Humberstone Rd LE5 3AT ☎(0533)620471 Telex no 341460 FAX (0533) 514211
*This busy, large hotel, situated in the heart of the city near the bus and coach station, offers a choice of eating options, modern style bedrooms and extensive conference facilities.*
220⇄🛏(7fb)✗in 22 bedrooms CTV in all bedrooms ® **T** sB⇄🛏£26.60-£67 dB⇄🛏£36.80-£77 (room only) 🗏
Lift ( 25🖾 CFA pool table *xmas*
♥ International **V** ✪ ⊒ ✱ Lunch £8.65-£11.90 Dinner £10.65-£13&alc Last dinner 10.30pm
Credit Cards ⎡1⎤⎡2⎤⎡3⎤⎡5⎤ⓒ

---

### ★★★60% Hotel Saint James
Abbey St LE1 3TE ☎(0533)510666 Telex no 342434 FAX (0533) 515183
*An hotel set on the top of a high, multi-storey car park at the centre of the city offers interesting panoramic views from its restaurant, though food is uninspiring; open-plan public areas provide plenty of*

→

**L**

---

*comfortable seating, and modern bedrooms are quite well equipped.*

72⇄🏛(3fb) CTV in all bedrooms ® T
Lift ( ♬ sauna solarium gymnasium steam room jacuzzi
♀ English & French V ❖ ᒼ Last dinner 10pm
Credit Cards ① ② ③ ⑤

### ★★★56% Forte Posthouse
Braunstone Ln East LE3 2FW (Forte Hotels) ☎(0533)630500
FAX (0533) 823623

*Situated on the A46 approach road to the city centre within a mile of junction 21 of the M1/M69, this very popular and busy modern hotel continues to upgrade its bedrooms; refurbishment of public areas and a new leisure complex are planned for 1991.*

172⇄(9fb)🏛🥢in 51 bedrooms CTV in all bedrooms ® T ✳
S% sB⇄🏛£39.50-£49.50 (room only) 🍴
Lift ( 240P CFA 🏊 xmas
♀ International V ❖ ᒼ 🥢 ✳ S% Lunch £8.95-£9.50 Dinner £13.95 Last dinner 10pm
Credit Cards ① ② ③ ④ ⑤

### ★★69% Red Cow
Hinckley Rd, Leicester Forest East LE3 3PG ☎(0533)387878
FAX (0533) 387878

*This popular old inn, 4 miles from the city centre on the A47, provides comfortable, well equipped bedrooms in a modern annexe. Much of its original character is retained in the extensively altered busy bars and cottage-style restaurant.*

31⇄🏛(27fb) CTV in all bedrooms ® T ✳ (ex guide dogs) ✳
sB&B⇄🏛£29-£42 dB&B⇄🏛£34.50-£49.50
120P 🏊
♀ English & French V ❖ ᒼ 🥢 ✳ Lunch £7.95&alc Dinner £7.95&alc Last dinner 10.30pm
Credit Cards ① ② ③ ⑤

### ★★64% Old Tudor Rectory
Main St, Glenfield LE3 8DG ☎(0533)320220
FAX (0533) 876002
Closed Xmas wk

*A small, privately owned hotel standing in an acre of grounds on the outskirts of the city dates back to the reign of Henry Tudor and has Jacobean and Queen Anne additions – all still evident in today's building. Bedrooms, though modestly furnished have a good range of facilities, while the lounge bar and Jacobean lounge provide residents with comfortable areas for relaxation. The restaurant is popular with locals.*

14⇄🏛Annexe3⇄🏛(3fb)2🏛 CTV in all bedrooms ® T S%
sB&B⇄🏛fr£34.50 dB&B⇄🏛fr£52.50 🍴
37P ✿ CFA solarium gymnasium beauty salon
V ❖ ᒼ ✳ Lunch £6.95-£7.95 Dinner fr£9.50 Last dinner 9.30pm
Credit Cards ① ③ £

### ★★63% Regency
360 London Rd LE2 2PL ☎(0533)709634 FAX (0533) 701375
*Conveniently situated on the A6 just 1.5 miles south of the city centre, this hotel is well equipped and provides good value for money. It is popular with business people, but equally suitable for tourists and others visiting the area.*

37⇄🏛(2fb) CTV in all bedrooms ® T ✳ (ex guide dogs) ✳
sB&B⇄🏛£27-£38 dB&B⇄🏛£42-£48
( 40P CFA xmas
♀ English & Continental V ❖ ✳ Lunch £6.95&alc Dinner £9.50&alc Last dinner 11pm
Credit Cards ① ② ③ ⑤

### ★★59% *Alexandra*
342 London Rd, Stoneygate LE2 2PJ ☎(0533)703056
FAX (0533) 705464
Closed Xmas
*This is a small family-run and owned hotel, situated a short distance from the city centre. It is a private hotel and predominantly caters for the commercial market. Fresh home-*

*cooked food is provided on a self-service basis, and is both tasty and wholesome.*

13rm(3⇄9🏛)(3fb) CTV in all bedrooms ® T ✳
CTV 16P 🚗
V ❖ ᒼ 🥢 Last dinner 8.30pm
Credit Cards ① ③

---

### LEIGH DELAMERE MOTORWAY SERVICE AREA (M4)
Wiltshire Map 03 ST87

### ⇧Granada Lodge
M4 Service Area SN14 6LB (Granada)
☎Chippenham(0666)837097 FAX (0666) 837112
*Conveniently situated on the M4 service area between junctions 17 and 18, a modern purpose-built bedroom block offers good value accommodation. Clean well furnished rooms are all complete with en suite bathrooms. There are non-smoking rooms as well as those especially adapted for the disabled.*

34⇄🏛(6fb)🥢in 8 bedrooms CTV in all bedrooms ®
✳ (ex guide dogs) S% sB⇄🏛fr£31 dB⇄🏛fr£34 (room only) 🍴
( 348P
V ❖ ᒼ

**See advertisement under SWINDON**

---

### LEIGHTON BUZZARD Bedfordshire Map 04 SP92 ⊙

### ★★★72% Swan
High St LU7 7EA ☎(0525)372148 FAX (0525) 370444
RS 25 Dec & 1 Jan

*Set in the centre of town this charming hotel, formerly a coaching inn, has been tastefully furnished and modernised to provide comfortable accommodation. The food is imaginative and service caring and efficient.*

# *They're all Original*

… each Everards Original Inn is unique. Built around the individual character of a traditional English pub, each has something different to offer.

All our hotels offer excellent value accomodation and have colour TV, Tea and Coffee making facilities, Hair Dryer, Trouser Press and Direct Dial Telephone. A number of non-smoking rooms are available at each hotel.

Additional features include an a la Carte restaurant and a spacious Lounge Bar which serves bar meals plus a good selection of traditional ales.

Original Inns all offer excellent facilities for families with a family conservatory and safe well equipped gardens for children.

## THE MILL ON THE SOAR

Conventry Road, Sutton in the Elms, Leicestershire Tel: 0455 282419
* 20 Ensuite Bedrooms   * Working Mill Wheel   * Fishing Lake

## BARDON HALL

Beveridge Lane, Bardon Hill, Nr Coalville, Leicestershire Tel: 0530 813644
35 Ensuite Bedrooms   * Close to M1 Junction 22   * Country Situation

## THE RED COW

Hinckley Road, Leicester Forest East, Leicester Tel: 0533 387878
* 31 Ensuite Bedrooms * Close to M1 & Leicester City * Attractive historic pub

## ALL HOTELS AA ★★

For further details of Everards Original Inns, please write to Dept AA, Everards Brewery Ltd, Castle Acres, Narborough, Leicester, LE9 5BY Tel: 0533 630900

38⇨♪(1fb)1♯⅍in 13 bedrooms CTV in all bedrooms ® T
✕ (ex guide dogs) sB&B⇨♪£65-£70 dB&B⇨♪£80-£120 ♬
《10P ♨ CFA
V ♥ ⚏ ⅍ Lunch £13.50-£15 Dinner £15-£17.50&alc Last
dinner 9.30pm
Credit Cards 1 2 3 5 £

---

## LEISTON Suffolk Map **05** TM46

### ★67% White Horse

Station Rd IP16 4HD ☎(0728)830694 FAX (0728) 833105
*This comfortable hotel in the centre of the town now includes a
children's play area in its large garden. It offers warm hospitality,
a popular bar and accommodation in bedrooms which, though quite
modest, are well equipped, clean and tidy.*
10rm(1⇨7♪)Annexe3♪(1fb) CTV in all bedrooms ® T
sB&B£29.50-£35 sB&B⇨♪fr£35 dB&Bfr£46 dB&B⇨♪fr£55
♬
CTV 14P 3☎ ❀ ♨ *xmas*
♡ English & French V ♥ ⚏ ⅍ Lunch £6.95-£14alc Dinner £8-
£14alc Last dinner 9.30pm
Credit Cards 1 3 £

---

## LENHAM Kent Map **05** TQ85

### ★★63% Dog & Bear

The Square ME17 2PG ☎Maidstone(0622)858219
FAX (0622) 859415
*Facing the village square, this hospitable old coaching inn has very
well equipped bedrooms, some in the new courtyard annexe, and
characterful public areas including a beamed bar with open fire,
lounge and restaurant. A function room and extensive car parking
are also available.*
25⇨♪(3fb)1♯ CTV in all bedrooms ® T sB&B⇨♪fr£43.50
dB&B⇨♪fr£56.50 ♬
40P CFA *xmas*
V ♥ ⚏ Lunch £6-£12alc Dinner £4-£7&alc Last dinner 10pm
Credit Cards 1 2 3 5 £

---

## LEOMINSTER Hereford & Worcester Map **03** SO45

### ★★★54% Talbot

West St HR6 8EP (Best Western) ☎(0568)616347
FAX (0568) 614880
*Parts of this town-centre hotel date back to the 15th century, and
much of its original charm and character has been retained in the
large-scale improvements recently undertaken by the new owners
to provide comfortable, well equipped accommodation which will
appeal equally to tourists and business users.*
20⇨♪(3fb) CTV in all bedrooms ® T sB&B⇨♪£47-£54
dB&B⇨♪£78-£92 ♬
20P CFA *xmas*
♡ English & French V ♥ ⚏ Lunch £10-£12&alc Dinner £16-
£18&alc Last dinner 9.30pm
Credit Cards 1 2 3 5 £

### ★★60% Royal Oak

South St HR6 8JA (Minotels) ☎(0568)612610
FAX (0568) 612710
*Close to the town centre, this former Georgian coaching inn
provides simple but comfortable accommodation and informal
service. Equally suitable for tourists and business people, its
ground floor annexe bedroom with access from the car park makes
it accessible for disabled guests.*
17⇨♪Annexe1⇨♪(2fb)1♯ CTV in all bedrooms ® ✳
sB&B⇨♪£28.50 dB&B⇨♪£45 ♬
CTV 24P 1☎ CFA
V ♥ ⚏ ✳ Lunch £10.50-£20alc High tea £2.75-£4alc Dinner
£10.50-£20alc Last dinner 9pm
Credit Cards 1 2 3 5

---

★❀🏛 MARSH COUNTRY

Eyton HR6 0AG
☎(0568)613952

*The industrious and talented
husband and wife partnership
of Jacqueline and Martin
Gilleland welcomes guests
warmly at this charming 14th-century timbered house set
amid attractive gardens in peaceful rural surroundings. A
pretty dining room overlooks the gardens where guests can
enjoy the skilful cooking, which is in Jacqueline's hands. The
limited set-price menus at lunch and dinner offering such
carefully prepared dishes as wholesome soups, avocado
mousse, fillet of beef with cheese sauce and roast breast of
duckling; a vegetarian option is available on request. Herbs
come from the garden and there is a good selection of British
cheeses, some local. Dessert might be brandy snaps filled with
strawberry mousse. A reasonably priced wine list carefully
selected to complement the style of cuisine includes a few good
clarets and Burgundies.*
6⇨♪⅍in all bedrooms CTV in all bedrooms T
✕ (ex guide dogs) sB&B⇨♪£74-£80 dB&B⇨♪£100-
£110 ♬
15P ♨ ❀ *xmas*
♡ French ♥ ⚏ ⅍ Lunch £17.50-£18 Dinner £25.50-
£28.50 Last dinner 9.30pm
Credit Cards 1 3 £

---

## LERWICK

See **Shetland**

---

## L'ETACQ

See **Jersey under** Channel Islands

---

## LETHAM Tayside *Angus* Map **15** NO54

### ★★★🏛66% Idvies House

DD8 2QJ ☎(030781)787 FAX (030781) 8933
Closed 24 Dec-2 Jan
*This family-run hotel, originally a Victorian mansion and still set
in 12 acres of wooded grounds amid the peaceful Angus
countryside, provides an ideal base for sporting enthusiasts as well
as business travellers and holidaymakers. Individually styled
bedrooms are well equipped, while public areas include an
attractive drawing room and a cosy bar that is a haven for the
whisky connoisseur, offering over 150 single malts.*
10⇨♪(1fb)2♯ CTV in all bedrooms ® T ✳ sB&B⇨♪£35-
£45 dB&B⇨♪£50-£70 ♬
60P ❀ squash croquet
V ♥ ✳ Lunch fr£11.50 High tea £5.75-£8.40 Dinner £13.50-
£17&alc Last dinner 9.30pm
Credit Cards 1 2 3 5 £

---

## LETTERFINLAY Highland *Inverness-shire* Map **14** NN29

### ★★64% Letterfinlay Lodge

PH34 4DZ (off A82) ☎Spean Bridge(039781)622
Closed Nov-Feb
*This popular family-run holiday hotel is situated beside the A82, 7
miles north of Spean Bridge, and enjoys a spectacular outlook over
Loch Lochy. The public rooms include a well stocked snug bar, a
cosy television room and an attractive sun lounge. Bedrooms vary
in size and style, and are for the most part simply appointed.*
13rm(11⇨♪)(5fb) S10% sB&B£18.50-£35 sB&B⇨♪£18.50-
£35 dB&B£37-£70 dB&B⇨♪£37-£70

⊞ CTV 100P 🚗 ✿ ♪
V ♨ ⬜ ✳ Bar Lunch £4-£9.50 Dinner £15.50-£16.50 Last
dinner 8.30pm
Credit Cards [1] [2] [3] [4] [5]

---

## LEVEN Fife Map 11 NO30

### ★★★ 59% New Caledonian
81 High St KY8 4NG ☎(0333)24101 FAX (0333) 21241
*Modern business hotel replacing one which was damaged by fire
some years ago.*
17⇨🛉(1fb) CTV in all bedrooms ® T ✳ sB&B⇨🛉fr£45
dB&B⇨🛉fr£60 🍴
( ⊞ CTV 50P CFA
♡ English & French V ♨ ⬜ 🌡 ✳ Lunch fr£6.95 High tea
fr£4.95 Dinner fr£13.95 Last dinner 9.30pm
Credit Cards [1] [2] [3] [5] ⓒ

---

## LEWDOWN Devon Map 02 SX48

★★

**LEWTRENCHARD MANOR**

EX20 4PN (Pride of Britain)
☎(056683)256 & 222
FAX (056683) 332

Closed 2-3 wks Jan/Feb

*A short distance south of the
busy A30, Lewtrenchard
Manor is hidden in a tranquil wooded valley on the western
edge of Dartmoor. The original building dates from 1620 and
its most famous son, Sabine Baring Gould (composer of
'Onward Christian Soldiers' among other hymns), added the
splendidly ornate ceilings in all the main rooms, dark
panelling in the dining rooms and many other fascinating
carvings and embellishments. All this architectural splendour
might be intimidating but, apart from the gallery, all the
public rooms are a friendly size with a choice of comfortable
furnishings, antiques, fresh flowers and open fires. Owners
Susan and James Murray offer a most friendly and unaffected
welcome, indeed this relaxing atmosphere is the lasting
memory of a stay here. The bedrooms, named after hymn
tunes, are now all attractively refurbished, with period
furniture and thoughtful touches: a tin of biscuits, a posy of
flowers, bottled water, quality toiletries and bathrobes. Some
are larger than others, some have more elaborate beds and
some enjoy wider views. At the time of going to press we heard
that chef David Shepherd had left to run his own restaurant;
the new chef in charge of the kitchen is now James Brown.*
8rm(7⇨🛉)2🛏 CTV in all bedrooms T sB&B⇨🛉£75-£90
dB&B⇨🛉£95-£130 🍴
50P 🚗 ✿ ♪ croquet clay pigeon shooting nc8yrs *xmas*
♡ English & French V ♨ ⬜ 🌡 ✳ Bar Lunch fr£3 High
tea fr£5 Dinner £22.50-£26.50&alc Last dinner 9.30pm
Credit Cards [1] [2] [3] [5]

---

## LEWES East Sussex Map 05 TQ41

### ★★★ 54% Shelleys
High St BN7 1XS (Mount Charlotte (TS)) ☎(0273)472361
FAX (0273) 483152
*This former inn, dating from 1526, was converted into a manor
house and became the home of the Shelley family in 1663. Now
providing comfortable accommodation and modern facilities, the
hotel also has a pretty restaurant offering a choice of menus.*
21⇨🛉2🛏 CTV in all bedrooms T (room only) 🍴

---

( 25P 3🏮 ✿ *xmas*
V ♨ ⬜
Credit Cards [1] [2] [3] [5]

### ★★ 60% White Hart
55 High St BN7 1XE (Best Western) ☎(0273)474676 & 476694
Telex no 878468 FAX (0273) 476695
*This 16th-century coaching inn is currently being extended and
refurbished. Many of the original features are being exposed and
restored. Bedrooms in the main house vary in shape and size, while
the comfortable annexe rooms offer a more uniform standard. The
restaurant comprises an elegant oak panelled room and a
Victorian conservatory, and there is a choice of carvery or an à la
carte menu. In addition, there is a small coffee shop, bar, and a
cosy lounge where a log fire burns on winter days.*
19rm(14⇨🛉)Annexe21⇨🛉(4fb)2🛏 CTV in all bedrooms ®
T
( 50P
♡ English & French V ♨ ⬜ 🌡 Last dinner 10pm
Credit Cards [1] [2] [3] [5]

---

## LEWIS, ISLE OF Western Isles *Ross & Cromarty* Map 13

---

## STORNOWAY Map 13 NB43

### ★★★ 66% Caberfeidh
PA87 2EU (Best Western) ☎(0851)702604 FAX (0851) 705572
*This purpose built hotel, situated on the southern approach to the
town, offers comfortable and well appointed accommodation.
Bedrooms with smart, modern bathrooms are equipped to a good
standard, and the recently refurbished public areas are attractive
and inviting. Service throughout is attentive and friendly.*
46⇨🛉 CTV in all bedrooms ® T ✳ sB&B⇨🛉£59-£64
dB&B⇨🛉£79-£84 🍴
Lift ( ⊞ CTV 100P ✿ CFA
♡ French V ♨ ⬜ Lunch fr£7.50 High tea fr£7 Dinner
fr£14&alc Last dinner 9.30pm
Credit Cards [1] [2] [3] [4] [5] ⓒ

---

## LEYBURN North Yorkshire Map 07 SE19

### ★ 60% Golden Lion
Market Place DL8 5AS ☎Wensleydale(0969)22161
Closed 25 & 26 Dec
*Well appointed, modern bedrooms and interesting menus which
represent good value for money are provided by this hotel at the
centre of the town.*
14rm(10⇨3🛉)(5fb) CTV in all bedrooms ® T sB&B£20-£25
sB&B⇨🛉£23-£28 dB&B£40-£50 dB&B⇨🛉£46-£56 🍴
Lift 130P 🚗
♡ English & Continental V ♨ ✳ Lunch £3.50-£8alc Dinner £8-
£15alc Last dinner 9pm
Credit Cards [1] [3]

---

## LEYLAND Lancashire Map 07 SD52 ⊙

### ★★★ 67% Pines
Clayton-le-Woods PR6 7ED (1m S of M6 junc 29 on A6)
☎Preston(0772)38551 FAX (0772) 38551
Closed 25 & 26 Dec
*A Victorian house with modern extensions, set in 4 acres of formal
gardens, having easy access to both the M6 and M61 from its
position on the A6 at Clayton le Woods. Recent upgrading of
public areas and the creation of 14 superior bedrooms has greatly
enhanced an hotel which already had a good reputation for its high
standard of cuisine and helpful, friendly service.*
39⇨🛉🌡in 8 bedrooms CTV in all bedrooms ® T 🍴 ✳
sB&B⇨🛉£47-£57 dB&B⇨🛉£52.35-£83.35 🍴
( 100P 🚗 ✿ CFA
V ♨ ⬜ ✳ Lunch £10.25&alc Dinner £13.75&alc Last dinner
9.30pm
Credit Cards [1] [2] [3]

## ★★★56% Leyland Resort

Leyland Way PR5 2JX (Resort) ☎Preston(0772)422922
Telex no 677651 FAX (0772) 622282

*Conveniently situated just off junction 28 of the M4, this hotel offers a wide range of conference and meeting rooms as well as planned bedrooms and ample public areas.*

93⇨♠(9fb)⊬in 10 bedrooms CTV in all bedrooms ® T ✱
sB⇨♠£55 dB⇨♠£68 (room only) 🛏
₡ CTV 150P CFA *xmas*
♥ English & French V ♥ ♨ ✱ Lunch £8.50 Dinner £12.95&alc Last dinner 10pm
Credit Cards ①②③⑤

---

## ★★★61% Little Barrow

Beacon St WS13 7AR ☎(0543)414500 FAX (0543) 415734

*Just a short distance from the centre of town and close to the Cathedral is this popular hotel. Bedrooms are well designed, particularly for the businessman, and Carters Restaurant enjoys a good reputation.*

24⇨ CTV in all bedrooms ® T 🐾 (ex guide dogs) S10%
sB&B⇨£60 dB&B⇨£70 🛏
₡ 🏢 CTV 70P
♥ French V ♥ S10% Lunch £8.50 Dinner £11.50 Last dinner 9.30pm
Credit Cards ①②③⑤

## ★★★59% George

Bird St WS13 6PR (Jarvis) ☎(0543)414822 FAX (0543) 415817
RS Xmas

*Situated close to the town centre and the cathedral, this 18th-century hotel caters for both tourist and business clientèle alike. The open plan lounge and bar areas are cosy and comfortable, and a good range of food is available, including a popular carvery.*

38⇨♠(3fb)⊬in 5 bedrooms CTV in all bedrooms ® T ✱
sB⇨♠£66.50-£73.50 dB⇨♠£73.50-£81 (room only) 🛏
₡ 40P 3🍴 CFA *xmas*
♥ International V ♥ ♨ ✱ Lunch £8-£10.25 Dinner £11-£14.50&alc Last dinner 9.30pm
Credit Cards ①②③⑤

## ★★72% Angel Croft

Beacon St WS13 7AA ☎(0543)258737 FAX (0543) 415605
Closed 25 & 26 Dec RS Sun evenings

*This Georgian house with well-tended gardens at its rear, standing on the edge of the town centre, offers friendly, helpful service, accommodation in warm, spacious bedrooms and freshly prepared cuisine which includes a tempting sweet trolley.*

11rm(3⇨6♠)Annexe8⇨♠(2fb)1🚪 CTV in all bedrooms ® T 🐾 (ex guide dogs)
60P ✿
♥ ♨ Last dinner 9pm
Credit Cards ①③⑤

## ★★63% Fradley Arms

Rykneld St, Fradley WS13 8RD (on A38, 3m NE)
☎Burton-on-Trent(0283)790186 & 790977 FAX (0283) 791464

*This family-run hotel on the busy A38 Birmingham-Derby road features a comfortable small restaurant, beamed bar and landscaped gardens which include a safe children's play area. A new function suite is also proving to be very popular.*

6⇨♠(1fb) CTV in all bedrooms ® T sB&B⇨♠£40-£44 dB&B⇨♠£52-£55 🛏
CTV 200P ✿ CFA childrens play area
♥ English & French V ♥ ♨ ✱ Lunch fr£6 Dinner fr£12.35 Last dinner 9.30pm
Credit Cards ①②③⑤ Ⓔ

---

## ★★★❀❀71% Arundell Arms

PL16 0AA (Best Western) ☎(0566)84666 due to change to 784666 FAX (0566) 84494 due to change to 784494
Closed 4 days Xmas

*A premier fishing hotel with 20 miles of its own waters on the River Tamar, this sympathetically renovated and hospitable coaching inn is suited to business as well as leisure guests. Individually styled bedrooms are equipped with modern comforts; attractive public areas have log fires, and include a stylish restaurant serving French and English dishes of notable quality and flair.*

24⇨♠Annexe5⇨♠ CTV in all bedrooms ® T
sB&B⇨♠£51-£56 dB&B⇨♠£80-£88 🛏
80P 🅿 ✿ CFA ♩ skittle alley games room *xmas*
♥ English & French V ♥ ♨ ⊬ Lunch £13.50-£14.75 Dinner £22.25-£24.50&alc Last dinner 9pm
Credit Cards ①②③⑤ Ⓔ

## ★★60% Lifton Cottage

PL16 0DR ☎(0566)84439 due to change to 784439

*A cosy atmosphere permeates the intimate, character public rooms and bright, compact, well-equipped bedrooms of this small family-run hotel. Its position beside the A30 makes an ideal base for touring the area.*

12rm(10⇨3♠)(3fb) CTV in all bedrooms ® T sB&B£24-£30 sB&B⇨♠£30 dB&B£43 dB&B⇨♠£50 🛏
CTV 25P ✿ CFA
V ♥ ♨ ⊬
Credit Cards ①②③⑤ Ⓔ

---

## ★★★⚑69% Cliffe

Crowe Hill BA3 6HY (Best Western) ☎(0225)723226
FAX (0225) 723871
RS 22 Dec-14 Jan

*Situated on top of Crowe Hill with glorious views across the beautiful Avon valley, the hotel dates back 165 years and is built in sturdy Bath stone. Bedrooms are tastefully furnished and well equipped with modern facilities; they vary in size but each is comfortable and well presented. Public areas are cosy and nicely appointed. The Coterie restaurant offers a small table d'hôte and à la carte menu which includes well prepared, imaginative dishes using good quality, fresh local ingredients. The young Canadian proprietors are very involved in the day-to-day running of the hotel and offer professional service. Hospitality is good and there is a friendly and relaxed atmosphere about the place.*

11⇨♠(3fb)1🚪 CTV in all bedrooms ® T ✱
sB&B⇨♠£66.50-£68 dB&B⇨♠£80-£105 🛏
40P 🅿 ✿ ⌣ (heated)
♥ English & French V ♥ ♨ ⊬ ✱ Lunch £13.50-£15 High tea £4-£9 Dinner £19-£21.50&alc Last dinner 9.30pm
Credit Cards ①②③⑤

---

## ★★★★63% The White Hart

Bailgate LN1 3AR (Forte Hotels) ☎(0522)26222 Telex no 56304 FAX (0522) 531798

*Early Georgian house with a slate Victorian façade, standing in the shadow of Lincoln cathedral.*

50⇨♠(4fb)⊬in 18 bedrooms CTV in all bedrooms ® ✱
sB⇨♠fr£80 dB⇨♠fr£105 (room only) 🛏
Lift ₡ 60P 35🍴 CFA ♫ ♨ *xmas*
V ♥ ♨ ✱ S% Lunch £10.95&alc Dinner fr£17.50 Last dinner 10pm
Credit Cards ①②③⑤

---

L

### ★★★▲68% Washingborough Hall Country House

Church Hill, Washingborough LN4 1BE (3m E B1190)
(Minotels) ☎(0522)790340 FAX (0522) 792936

*Neither fashionable nor pretentious, the accent is firmly on
comfort, hospitality and good service at this attractive, mellow
stone country house with grounds, located just outside Lincoln on
the B11. Popular with business and leisure users, the combination
of expected facilities and genuine care is most valued and provides
for a relaxing stay.*

14⇨📺2🛏⊁in 2 bedrooms CTV in all bedrooms ® T
sB&B⇨📺£47-£60 dB&B⇨📺£65-£82 🏋

50P 🚗 ❄ ⌬

♀ International **V** ♦ ☑ ⊁ ❋ Sunday Lunch £7.50-£10.50
Dinner fr£13.50&alc Last dinner 9pm

Credit Cards ①②③⑤£

### ★★★62% Forte Crest

Eastgate LN2 1PN (Forte Hotels) ☎(0522)520341
Telex no 56316 FAX (0522) 510780

*Ample car parking is available at a popular hotel conveniently
sited within easy walking distance of the city centre (though the
climb back is steep!) and equally suited to the needs of business or
leisure users. Recently refurbished accommodation is attractive
and well equipped, service is relaxed but competent, and public
areas include conference facilities, a convivial cocktail bar and
Squires Restaurant, which overlooks the floodlit Cathedral
opposite.*

70⇨(1fb)⊁in 46 bedrooms CTV in all bedrooms ® T ❋ S%
sB⇨£65 dB⇨£75 (room only) 🏋

Lift ⌬ ▤ 110P ❄ *xmas*

♀ English & French **V** ♦ ☑ ⊁ ❋ S% Lunch £8.95-£9.95&alc
Dinner fr£12.95 Last dinner 10pm

Credit Cards ①②③④⑤

### ★★★54% *Moor Lodge*

LN4 1HU (Consort) ☎(0522)791366 FAX (0522) 794389
(For full entry see Branston)

### ★★70% Hillcrest

15 Lindum Ter LN2 5RT (Guestaccom) ☎(0522)510182
Closed 20 Dec-3 Jan

*Just off the inner ring road (cathedral side), with access off Upper
Lindum Terrace, the Hillcrest is quietly located in a tree-lined
road with terraced gardens to the rear. Owned and run by Jennifer
Bennett, it offers an above average level of comfort and care.*

17⇨📺(4fb) CTV in all bedrooms ® T sB&B⇨📺£39.75
dB&B⇨📺£55.50 🏋

8P CFA

♀ International **V** ♦ ☑ ⊁ Bar Lunch £4-£7 Dinner £10-£13alc
Last dinner 8.45pm

Credit Cards ①②③£

### ★★66% Loudor

37 Newark Rd, North Hykeham LN6 8RB (3m SW A1434)
☎(0522)680333 & 500474 FAX (0522) 680403

*Despite its location on the busy A46, three miles south-west of the
city, this is a quiet, informal and friendly hotel where guests receive
personal service from the proprietors. Small and comfortable, the
house has been completely remodelled to provide accommodation
which is clean and very well maintained, though compact in some
instances.*

9⇨📺Annexe1📺(1fb) CTV in all bedrooms ® T ✈
sB&B⇨📺£30-£36 dB&B⇨📺£42-£45

12P 🚗

♀ English & French ♦ ⊁ Dinner £10-£14alc Last dinner
8.15pm

Credit Cards ①②③⑤

**See advertisement on page 411**

A rosette means exceptional standards of cuisine.

**L**

### ★★ 59% *Duke William*
44 Bailgate LN1 3AP ☎(0522)533351
Closed 25 Dec
*A small, friendly and well managed hotel with a busy public bar and simple well equipped accommodation. It is within walking distance of both the castle and the cathedral and has car parking access via Chapel Lane.*
11♠(3fb) CTV in all bedrooms ® T ✕ (ex guide dogs)
( 12P ⇔
V ⊹ Last dinner 9.30pm
Credit Cards ① ② ③ ⑤

### ★★ 59% Four Seasons
Scothern Ln LN2 3QP ☎Welton(0673)60108 FAX (0673) 62784
(For full entry see Dunholme)

### ★★ 56% Castle
Westgate LN1 3AS ☎(0522)538801 FAX (0522) 510291
*A Victorian school close to the cathedral and castle has been attractively converted to provide simple accommodation with modern facilities, including a comfortable combined bar/lounge and dining room. Service is friendly and informal.*
15⇨Annexe6♠(2fb) CTV in all bedrooms ® T
sB&B⇨♠£45.50-£50 dB&B⇨♠£60-£65 ⋤
21P *xmas*
♀ Continental V ⊹ ⬚ Lunch £5.25-£6.75 Dinner £11.50-£14.50&alc Last dinner 9.15pm
Credit Cards ① ② ③ ⑤ ⓔ

### ★★ 55% *Barbican*
Saint Marys St LN5 7EQ ☎(0522)528374 & 543811
*An unusual feature of this hotel is the Barnum's Lager Bar. Decorated and furnished on the Barnum's Circus theme, it certainly provides a lively atmosphere. Good standards of décor prevail throughout the public areas and the modern bedrooms which are individually furnished and well equipped, though some are rather compact.*
20rm(13♠)(2fb) CTV in all bedrooms ® T
CTV ✗
♀ Mainly grills V ⊹ ⬚ ✕ Last dinner 9.30pm
Credit Cards ① ② ③ ⑤

### ❀✕Wig & Mitre
29 Steep Hill LN2 1LU ☎(0522)535190
*In the fashionable cobbled lane between the cathedral and the castle, this 14th-century former bishop's lodgings has been a brasserie style inn for 14 years, the restaurant area being upstairs. Its style and atmosphere invites eclectic custom, from people popping in to meet friends, to those celebrating a special occasion. The à la carte menu changes every 5/6 weeks, while the daily menu changes in the morning and at 4pm. Dishes are simple, but the high quality of their raw materials and the skill of their preparation is obvious. A regular feature of either menu is a baked Swiss cheese soufflé served in a wide bowl with a creamy cheese and ham sauce.*
Closed 25 Dec
V 40 seats ✳ Lunch frf9.50&alc Dinner frf9.50&alc Last dinner 11pm ✗
Credit Cards ① ② ③ ⑤

---

### LINLITHGOW Lothian *West Lothian* Map 11 NS97

### ❀❀❀✕ ✕ ✕ Champany
EH49 7LU (2m NE off A904) ☎Philipstoun(050683)4532 & 4388 FAX (050683) 4302
Closed Sun & 24 Dec-9 Jan Lunch not served Sat
♀ International 48 seats Last lunch 2pm Last dinner 10pm 100 P nc8yrs
Credit Cards ① ② ③ ⑤

For key to symbols in English see the bookmark.

---

### LISKEARD Cornwall & Isles of Scilly Map 02 SX26

★★ ❀❀❀❀⚑ WELL HOUSE
St Keyne PL14 4RN
☎(0579)42001

*It may be the scent of jasmine round the door, or the sunlight which constantly changes the colour of the secluded valley below the house that gives Nick Wainford's Victorian manor its uniquely welcoming air, but whatever the reason, or occasion, Well House is an ideal and exclusive retreat. Nick and his dedicated small brigade of staff meet every guest with a combination of genuine hospitality and attentive service that makes each one feel more like a house guest than a hotel resident. The bedrooms are furnished in styles ranging from Art Deco to traditional country-house and decorated with water- colours and abundant fresh flowers. Meals, created by chef David Woolfall, are notable for the innovative style of the cooking and superb combinations of flavours.*
7⇨♠(1fb) CTV in all bedrooms T ✳ sB&B⇨♠£60 dB&B⇨♠£82-£105 Continental breakfast ⋤
30P ⇔ ✿ ⌒ (heated) ♪ (hard) croquet
⊹ ⬚ ✳ Lunch frf21 Dinner £24.95-£29.70 Last dinner 9pm
Credit Cards ① ② ③

---

### ★★⚑ 60% Country Castle
Station Rd PL14 4EB ☎(0579)42694
Closed Nov RS Jan & Feb
*Quietly set in 2.5 acres of grounds, with magnificent views over the Looe Valley, this hotel provides individually decorated and attractively furnished bedrooms and an elegant lounge. The personal involvement of the proprietors maintains old-fashioned standards of hospitality, serving wholesome food and offering individual service.*
11rm(5⇨5♠)(1fb) CTV in all bedrooms ® T ✳ sB&B⇨♠frf36.50 dB&B⇨♠£51-£61 ⋤
50P ⌒ croquet boule
♀ English & French V ⊹ ⬚ ✳ Bar Lunch £2.50-£5.50 Dinner frf13.50&alc Last dinner 7.45pm
Credit Cards ① ③ ⓔ

### ★★ 56% Lord Eliot
Castle St PL14 3AQ ☎(0579)42717 FAX (0579) 47593
*Small hotel built around the character house of a one-time country landlord.*
15rm(4⇨10♠)(3fb)✗in 2 bedrooms CTV in all bedrooms ® T
S% sB&B⇨♠£30-£42.30 dB&B⇨♠£47-£61.10 ⋤
( CTV 60P *xmas*
♀ English & French V ⊹ ⬚ S% Lunch £6.95-£9.95&alc Dinner £7.50-£10.50&alc Last dinner 9.30pm
Credit Cards ① ③ ⓔ

---

### LITTLEBOURNE Kent Map 05 TR25

### ★★ 62% *The Bow Window Inn*
High St CT3 1ST ☎Canterbury(0227)721264
*A 300-year-old cottage hotel situated just 3 miles from Canterbury has been tastefully modernised to preserve much of its original beamed character. Comfortable bedrooms are reasonably well equipped, the candlelit restaurant is attractively appointed, and friendly, informal service is personally supervised by the*

*proprietors. Planned improvements include additional bedrooms and a new function room.*
8⇨🛁(2fb)2🛏 CTV in all bedrooms Ⓡ ✖ (ex guide dogs) 20P
♀ English & French V ♥ ⚿ Last dinner 9.30pm
Credit Cards ①②③⑤
**See advertisement under CANTERBURY**

---

## LITTLE HALLINGBURY

See **Bishop's Stortford**

---

## LITTLE LANGDALE Cumbria Map **07** NY30

**★★64% Three Shires Inn**
LA22 9NZ ☎Langdale(09667)215
Closed Xmas-Jan RS mid Nov-mid Feb
*A charming slate-built inn at the meeting point of the three old county shires of Cumberland, Westmorland and Lancashire. Small, friendly and family-run it offers comfortable accommodation and good food.*
11rm(7⇨5🛁)(1fb) Ⓡ ✖ sB&B£25-£32 dB&B£50-£64 dB&B⇨🛁£50-£64 🗗
CTV 20P 2🅿 🚗 *xmas*
♀ British & Continental ♥ ⚿ ✂ Bar Lunch fr£4.50 Dinner fr£16 Last dinner 8pm
**See advertisement under AMBLESIDE**

---

## LITTLE WEIGHTON Humberside Map **08** SE93

**★★★🏅63% Rowley Manor**
Rowley Rd HU20 3XR ☎Hull(0482)848248 FAX (0482) 849900
*Tranquilly set amid attractive gardens which include a croquet lawn, its courteous staff supervised by resident proprietors, the hotel offers friendly service and a range of interesting menus.*
16⇨🛁2🛏 CTV in all bedrooms T ✳ sB&B⇨🛁£50-£60 dB&B⇨🛁£65-£85 🗗
( 80P ✿ solarium croquet *xmas*
♀ International V ♥ ⚿ ✳ Lunch £8.95-£13.95&alc High tea £1.95-£5alc Dinner fr£13.95&alc Last dinner 9.30pm
Credit Cards ①②③⑤

---

## LIVERPOOL Merseyside Map **07** SJ39 ◉

See **Town Plan Section**
See also **Blundellsands**
**★★★★59% Liverpool Moat House**
Paradise St L1 8JD (Queens Moat) ☎051-709 0181
Telex no 627270 FAX 051-709 2706
*Refurbishment has improved many of the bedrooms at this purpose-built hotel; beds are large and facilities are modern. Further improvements are planned to enhance the public areas which currently offer a choice of eating and drinking venues together with a leisure complex. The multi-storey car park adjacent to the hotel should be used as street parking is not advised.*
251⇨🛁(202fb)✂in 40 bedrooms CTV in all bedrooms Ⓡ T sB&B⇨🛁£88-£90 dB&B⇨🛁£112-£114 🗗
Lift ( ▦ ♪ 🖵 (heated) sauna solarium gymnasium whirlpool *xmas*
♀ English & French V ♥ ⚿ ✳ Lunch £12-£15&alc High tea £7-£12 Dinner £16-£20&alc Last dinner 10.30pm
Credit Cards ①②③④⑤ⓔ

**★★★★56% Atlantic Tower**
Chapel St L3 9RE (Mount Charlotte (TS)) ☎051-227 4444
Telex no 627070 FAX 051-236 3973
*Triangular in shape, and resembling the bow of a ship when seen from the quayside, this modern hotel set almost on the waterfront offers predominantly compact bedrooms, though some of them are extremely pleasant.* →

L

226⇨ 🏋 (6fb)⊬in 24 bedrooms CTV in all bedrooms ® T (room only) 🏬
Lift ℂ ▦ 60P 45🛌 *xmas*
♀ European V ♘ ⚫
Credit Cards ①②③④⑤

### ★★★ 63% Forte Crest

Lord Nelson St L3 5QB (Forte Hotels) ☎051-709 7050
Telex no 627954 FAX 051-709 2193
*This purpose-built hotel beside Lime Street station provides functional accommodation in bedrooms which, although showing their age, are equipped with modern facilities; planned refurbishment is still awaited.*
150⇨ (2fb)⊬in 100 bedrooms CTV in all bedrooms ® T ✳ S%
sB⇨fr£68 dB⇨fr£80 (room only) 🏬
Lift ℂ 300P (charged)
♀ French V ♘ ⚫ ⊬ ✳ S% Lunch £5-£15 Dinner £12.50 Last dinner 11pm
Credit Cards ①②③④⑤

### ★★★ 53% St George's

St John's Precinct, Lime St L1 1NQ (Forte Hotels)
☎051-709 7090 Telex no 627630 FAX 051-709 0137
*Part of a shopping centre built opposite Lime Street station in the early seventies, this city centre hotel provides functional accommodation which is now showing signs of age.*
155⇨⊬in 80 bedrooms CTV in all bedrooms ® T ✳ S%
sB⇨£65 dB⇨£85 (room only) 🏬
Lift ℂ ▦ 🖊 *xmas*
V ♘ ⚫ ⊬ ✳ Bar Lunch £2-£5.70alc Dinner £10.95-£15alc Last dinner 9.45pm
Credit Cards ①②③④⑤

### ★★ 63% Grange

Holmfield Rd, Aigburth L19 3PQ ☎051-427 2950
FAX 051-427 9055
*A comfortable small Victorian hotel with neat rear gardens situated in a residential area 1.5 miles from the airport and 3.5 miles from the city centre. Bedrooms of varying size and style are currently being improved and cosy public areas include a traditional dining room where enjoyable meals are served by friendly, smartly dressed staff.*
25⇨🏋(1fb)4🛌 CTV in all bedrooms ® T ✖ (ex guide dogs)
S% sB&B⇨🏋£32-£34 dB&B⇨🏋£50.20-£66.80 🏬
CTV 50P ❋ CFA
♀ French V ♘ ⚫ ⊬ ✳ Sunday Lunch £7.95 Dinner £13.30-£19.30&alc Last dinner 9pm
Credit Cards ①②③⑤ £

### ★★ 55% Green Park

4/6 Greenbank Dr L17 1AN ☎051-733 3382
*On the northern fringes of Sefton Park 2 miles from the city centre, this privately owned commercial hotel in a Victorian building offers modest, comfortable accommodation and friendly service.*
23rm(16⇨🏋)(3fb) CTV in all bedrooms ® T sB&B£28-£30
sB&B⇨🏋£32-£34 dB&B£38-£40 dB&B⇨🏋£42-£44
ℂ ▦ CTV 25P ❋ CFA
V ♘ ⚫ Lunch £5.25-£8.50&alc High tea £4&alc Dinner £5.25-£8.50&alc Last dinner 9.30pm
Credit Cards ①②③⑤

### ❋ ✖ ✖ Jenny's Seafood

The Old Ropery, Fenwick St L2 7NT ☎051-236 0332
*This comfortable basement restaurant just off Fenwick Street, at the heart of the city's commercial district, is a popular venue for business lunches. Service combines friendliness and professionalism, while the reasonably-priced menu's wide range includes a number of seafood specialities, though meat-eaters are also adequately catered for. The reliable cooking is classically inclined, such dishes as Sole, and Scampi Thermidor always being available; Sea Bass comes baked from the oven in a crust of sea salt and Bream is grilled with fresh rosemary. By comparison, puddings from the trolley are rather more ordinary.*

Closed Sun, 18 Aug-2 Sep & 25 Dec-4 Jan Lunch not served Sat Dinner not served Mon
♀ English & French 45 seats ✳ Lunch £12.50&alc Dinner £12.50 Last lunch 2.15pm Last dinner 10pm 🖊
Credit Cards ①②③

### LIZARD, THE Cornwall & Isles of Scilly Map 02 SW71

### ★★ 66% Housel Bay

Housel Cove TR12 7PG ☎The Lizard(0326)290417
FAX (0326) 290359
Closed Jan-10 Feb
*This owner-managed hotel – advertised as the most southerly in England – is constantly being improved and now offers a range of comfortable and well-equipped bedrooms in a mixture of styles. Spacious public areas include an attractive verandah bar with fine sea views where guests can relax over an aperitif before enjoying a good meal with friendly service.*
23⇨🏋2🛋⊬in 2 bedrooms CTV in all bedrooms ® T ✳
sB&B⇨🏋£25-£29 dB&B⇨🏋£50-£90 🏬
Lift CTV 25P 4🛌 (£2 per night) ❋ CFA *xmas*
♀ International V ♘ ⚫ ⊬ Sunday Lunch £5.75-£7.75 Dinner £10-£15&alc Last dinner 9pm
Credit Cards ①③

### ★ ❋ 70% Kynance Bay House

Penmenner Rd TR12 7NR ☎The Lizard(0326)290498
Closed 3 Jan-mid Feb
*Simplicity is the key to the success of this small, personally run hotel and restaurant. Owned by Sonia Rugg and Susan Giles, Sonia is in charge of the kitchen. Menus are available, but Sonia is just as happy to chat with guests and cook for them accordingly. She has no professional training as a chef, but a passion for food and cooking which is well reflected in her honest, wholesome dishes. Refreshingly unpretentious, the restaurant is steadily building up a reputation locally. The dining area is tiny, so early reservations are strongly advised, especially for dinner. Of particular note are the delicious apple and stilton crêpes, and the Scotch salmon in hollandaise sauce, delicately flavoured with fresh dill. The small selection of vegetables was perfectly cooked and served crisp. In addition to the 37 more typical and reasonably priced wines, the wine list includes 3 Cornish wines. There is an ever changing 'Executive' list to which they are happy to add a diner's choice, and the red house wine is usually interesting as it is the bin end of the moment. Our inspector very much enjoyed the simple, well cooked and nicely presented food here and found both Sonia and Susan super hostesses.*
9rm(7🏋)⊬in all bedrooms TV available ®
CTV 9P ❋
♀ Continental V ♘ ⚫ ⊬ Last dinner 9pm
Credit Cards ①②③⑤

### LLANARMON DYFFRYN CEIRIOG Clwyd Map 07 SJ13

### ★★ 71% West Arms

LL20 7LD (Welsh Rarebits) ☎(069176)665 FAX (069176) 622
*Our 'Courtesy and Care' award winner 1991/1992 for Wales, this former farmhouse and inn, dating back to the middle of the 16th century, enjoys mountain views from its delightful setting in a remote, picturesque village in the Ceiriog Valley. West Arms now serves as a privately owned and personally run hotel where the emphasis is very much on warm, friendly hospitality and service. Despite extensive improvement, it has not lost its original charm and character, retaining such features as exposed beams and welcoming log fires. Comfortable, well furnished bedrooms with their own bathrooms include 2 spacious private suites. (See colour feature on p17.)*
14⇨ (1fb)⊬in 5 bedrooms CTV in 2 bedrooms sB&B⇨£49.50-£55 dB&B⇨£78-£88 🏬
CTV 30P 2🛌 ⤷ ❋ CFA ♪ *xmas*
♀ English & Continental V ♘ ⚫ Sunday Lunch fr£11.50
Dinner fr£19.50 Last dinner 9pm
Credit Cards ①②③⑤ £

LLANBEDR Gwynedd Map **06** SH52

★★62% *Ty Mawr*
LL45 2NH ☎(034123)440
*A large stone house with extensive gardens on the outskirts of the village is now a personally run hotel, providing friendly service and well furnished modern accommodation, equally suitable for commercial guests and holidaymakers.*
10⇨🛏(2fb) CTV in all bedrooms ®
CTV 30P 🚗 ✳ ♪
🍴 Continental V ✪ 🍽 Last dinner 8.45pm

★★♨60% **Cae Nest Hall**
LL45 2NL ☎(034123)349
Closed Jan (ex Xmas & New Year)
*This 15th-century manor house enjoys a peaceful location on the outskirts of the village, within 3 acres of grounds. Owners Anita and Robert Mann offer friendly and informal service, while striving hard to upgrade all the accommodation. In the evenings, Robert, a talented pianist and organist, regularly entertains guests in the lounge.*
10⇨🛏(2fb)1🛏 CTV in all bedrooms ® ✈ (ex guide dogs)
S10% sB&B⇨🛏£22.50 dB&B⇨🛏£47 🍴
12P 🚗 ✳ xmas
🍴 British & Continental V ✂ S% Dinner £10.50 Last dinner 7.30pm

 Shell filling stations (7am–11pm) are marked on the town plans.

L

## LLANBERIS Gwynedd Map **06** SH56

### ★61% Gallt-y-Glyn
Caernarfon Rd LL55 4EL ☎(0286)870370
Closed 25 Dec RS 26 Dec
*This small, friendly hotel stands beside the A4086, just west of the village; understandably popular with climbers and walkers, it is nevertheless equally suitable for travelling business people.*
8rm(2♠)(1fb)↙in 1 bedroom ✖ ✳ sB&B£20 sB&B♠£25
dB&B£33 dB&B♠£39
CTV 12P ⇔ ✿
V ↙ ✳
Credit Cards 1 3

### ✾ ✖ ✖ Y Bistro
Glandwr, 43-45 Stryd Fawr LL55 4EU ☎(0286)871278
*As the name suggests, this is a simple restaurant, both in the style of cuisine and the premises. It is a very friendly, husband and wife operation. Danny Roberts looks after the front of house, while Nerys Roberts does the cooking. She produces a fixed price menu from which diners can choose 2, 3 or 4 courses. Dishes are variations on traditional Welsh recipes, using local produce. Several fish dishes, her personal favourites, are included.*
Closed 3 wks Jan Lunch not served
♀ Welsh & French V 50 seats Dinner £17.50-£23 Last dinner 9.30pm ✗ ↙
Credit Cards 1 2 3

## LLANDDEWI SKYRRID Gwent Map **03** SO31

### ✾✾ ✖ Walnut Tree Inn
NP7 8AW (3m NE of Abergavenny)
☎Abergavenny(0873)2797 due to change t o 852797
*It is probably as well to advise diners immediately that no credit cards are acceptable here, this can be a problem as it is not exactly cheap, but it is good value given the quality of the food. It is 28 years since Franco and Ann Taruschio came to this little inn at the base of Skirrid Fawr, and they have done much to raise the standards of food in what was known as a culinary desert. The menu leans heavily towards Franco's native Italian cooking, though he has adapted dishes to local produce – cockles instead of clams with a spaghetti sauce. The tiny bar and bistro have mostly Brittania pub-type tables, though a comfortable dining room is available in the evening.*
Closed Sun & Mon 4 days Xmas & 2 wks Feb
♀ French & Italian V 45 seats Last lunch 2.30pm Last dinner 10.15pm 30 P

## LLANDEGAI Gwynedd Map **06** SH57

### ⇧Rank Motor Lodge
Bangor Services, Junc A5/A55 LL57 4BG (Rank)
☎Bangor(0248)370345 FAX (0248) 355959
*A modern purpose-built 2-storey hotel on the outskirts of Bangor (on the A5 at its junction with the A55 coastal expressway), convenient for the Irish ferry terminal at Holyhead. Bedrooms are all well equipped and have en suite bath, shower and WC. Double, twin and family rooms are available, and 2 rooms designed for the disabled. An adjoining Restbite provides catering facilities: it is licensed and also has table service.*
34⇨♠(6fb)↙in 6 bedrooms CTV in all bedrooms ® ✳
sB&B⇨♠£29.75 dB&B⇨♠£37.75 Continental breakfast
160P CFA
♀ English & Continental V ↺ ⬚ ↙ ✳ Lunch £6.05-£10.64alc
High tea £6.05-£10.64alc Dinner £6.05-£10.64alc Last dinner 10pm
Credit Cards 1 2 3 5

For key to symbols in English see the bookmark.

## LLANDEILO Dyfed Map **02** SN62

### ★★★52% *Cawdor Arms*
SA19 6EN ☎(0558)823500
*This historic hotel, set at the centre of the town, is very much the hub of local activity. An ongoing programme of improvements has created spacious and outstandingly comfortable public areas, while bedrooms are all individually decorated and furnished. Good function facilities are available, and the restaurant provides a fixed-price 4-course menu.*
17⇨♠2♠ CTV in all bedrooms
7P
♀ English & French ↺ ⬚
Credit Cards 1 2 3 5

## LLANDOVERY Dyfed Map **03** SN73

See also Crugybar
### ★★65% Castle
Kings Rd SA20 0AW (Minotels) ☎(0550)20343
*This family-run old coaching inn in the centre of the market town has several bars, all full of character, a range of eating options and well equipped bedrooms with modern facilities.*
25rm(21⇨♠)(4fb)2♠ CTV in all bedrooms ® T ✳ sB&B£25
sB&B⇨♠£35 dB&B£50 dB&B⇨♠£60-£75
CTV 40P ♪ (hard) ♪
V ↺ ⬚ ✳ Lunch £2.25-£4.50&alc High tea £4-£4.50 Dinner £9.60-£26alc Last dinner 9pm
Credit Cards 1 3 £

## LLANDRILLO Clwyd Map **06** SJ03

### ★★★⚑76% Tyddyn Llan Country House Hotel & Restaurant
LL21 0ST (Welsh Rarebits) ☎(049084)264 FAX (049084)264
*This stylish 18th-century country house with 3 acres of attractively laid out gardens is lovingly cared for by owners Peter and Bridget Kindred, and local staff, providing comfortable accommodation and a relaxing atmosphere. The lounge is spacious, and in the recently extended elegant restaurant there is an imaginative 3-course set-price menu. A meal might begin with a vegetarian Welsh goat's cheese, wrapped in filo pastry sprinkled with sesame seed and served crisp and hot on a bed of mixed salad leaves, followed by roast partridge with chicken mousse stuffing. A dessert of bread and butter pudding is delicately presented, and coffee comes with home-made petits fours. Just prior to the publication of the guide, we were advised of a change of chef here: the new chef, Paul Whitecross, has recently joined Tyddn Llan from Lower Slaughter Manor, Gloucestershire.*
10⇨♠(2fb) ® T sB&B⇨♠£47.50-£51.70 dB&B⇨♠£73.50-£81.90 ♠
CTV 30P ⇔ ✿ CFA ♪ croquet lawn *xmas*
V ↺ ⬚ Sunday Lunch £12.50-£15 Dinner £19.50-£22&alc Last dinner 9.30pm
Credit Cards 1 3 £

## LLANDRINDOD WELLS Powys Map **03** SO06

See also Penybont
### ★★★59% Hotel Metropole
Temple St LD1 5DY (Best Western) ☎(0597)823700
FAX (0597) 824828
*A large well run hotel which has been in the same family for over a century. There is a mixture of bedrooms ranging from those with good quality furniture to some with quite basic appointments. Public areas are spacious and there is a fine leisure complex and extensive conference facilities. A good range of bar meals is served in the Spencer bar and a fixed price dinner in the large restaurant.*
121⇨♠(2fb)↙in 10 bedrooms CTV in all bedrooms ® T
sB&B⇨♠£50-£54 dB&B⇨♠£69.50-£74 ♠
Lift ( 150P ✿ CFA ⬭ (heated) sauna solarium steamroom whirlpool beauty salon *xmas*

414

♲ English & Continental V ♤ ⚎ ✻ Lunch fr£9.75 Dinner fr£15.50 Last dinner 9pm
Credit Cards ①②③④⑤ ⓔ

### ★★68% The Bell Country Inn
Llanyre LD1 6DY (Minotels) ☎(0597)823959
FAX (0597) 825899
9⇨♠(2fb) CTV in all bedrooms ® T ✻ sB&B⇨♠fr£28.20 dB&B⇨♠fr£51.25 ㅌ
20P
♲ English & French V ♤ ⚎ ✂ ✻ Sunday Lunch fr£7.50 High tea fr£2.50 Dinner £14.50 Last dinner 10pm
Credit Cards ①②③⑤ ⓔ

### ★★59% Hotel Commodore
Spa Rd LD1 5ER ☎(0597)822288 FAX (0597) 824828
*In the heart of the spa town, this popular hotel has recently been completely renovated to provide comfortable public rooms and modern well equipped bedrooms, though annexe rooms are rather small. Facilities include a swimming pool and squash courts.*
32⇨Annexe22⇨(6fb) CTV in all bedrooms ® T ✻ sB&B⇨£45-£47.50 dB&B⇨£60-£63 ㅌ
Lift ℂ CTV 100P ❄ ▱ (heated) squash *xmas*
♲ English & Continental V ♤ ⚎ Lunch fr£5 Dinner fr£9 Last dinner 9.15pm
Credit Cards ①②③ ⓔ

---

## LLANDUDNO Gwynedd Map **06** SH78

**See Town Plan Section**

★★★

★★★❀♨
**BODYSGALLEN HALL**

LL30 1RS (on A470
Llandudno link road)
(Small Luxury Hotels)
☎Aberconwy(0492)584466
Telex no 837108
FAX (0492) 582519

*Set in well kept gardens just south of Llandudno with outstanding views of Snowdonia, the house has been sympathetically restored to become one of the most popular country house hotels. Antiques and original paintings create a relaxing atmosphere, and fine public rooms feature oak panelling, splendid fireplaces and stone mullioned windows. There are 2 dining rooms, both well appointed, and Head Chef Martin James prepares imaginative food such as, to start, salmon, sole and prawn terrine served on a watercress mayonnaise, or mousseline of chicken wrapped in bacon and served with a sorrel mayonnaise and to follow, poached fillet of salmon served with a champagne and caviar sauce, or medallions of Welsh lamb served on an onion marmalade and fresh herbs. Dessert may include a hot lime tart with thick Jersey cream. The wine list includes a Welsh wine amongst the French and German bottles listed. The 19 bedrooms are very comfortable and well equipped, and there are 9 cottages grouped around the courtyard providing comfortable self-contained accommodation including beautifully furnished sitting rooms.*
19⇨♠Annexe9⇨♠(3fb)1♨ CTV in all bedrooms ® T S10% sB⇨♠£85-£115 dB⇨♠£112-£164 (room only) ㅌ
ℂ 70P 1♘ ∰ ❄ CFA ♪ (hard) croquet nc8yrs *xmas*
V ♤ ⚎ S10% Lunch £13.50-£15.50 Dinner £32 Last dinner 9.45pm
Credit Cards ①②③⑤

---

### ★★★❀73% Empire
Church Walks LL30 2HE ☎(0492)860555 FAX (0492) 860791
Closed 22 Dec-2 Jan
*A warm, comfortable hotel, personally managed to a high standard by the resident owners and their families, offers an extensive range of facilities which includes indoor and outdoor pools, sauna and solarium; bedrooms contain antiques complemented by every modern amenity (including satellite TV), lounges are designed for comfort, and good food is served in the delightful restaurant.*
56⇨Annexe8⇨(7fb) CTV in all bedrooms ® T S% sB&B⇨£42.50-£60 dB&B⇨£50-£90 ㅌ
Lift 40P 5♘ (£5 per night) ∰ CFA ▱ (heated) ⇱ (heated) sauna solarium indoor/outdoor heated whirlpools ♫
V ♤ ⚎ S% Sunday Lunch fr£9.70 Dinner fr£16.95 Last dinner 9.30pm
Credit Cards ①②③④⑤
**See advertisement in colour section**

### ★★★64% Gogarth Abbey
West Shore LL30 2QY ☎(0492)876211 FAX (0492) 879881
*Standing on the west shore with magnificent views of the Conwy Estuary, Anglesey and Snowdonia, Gogarth Abbey was built in 1862 by the Rev H G Liddell, whose daughter Alice was the inspiration for Lewis Carroll's 'Alice in Wonderland'. Now a privately owned hotel, it provides spacious public areas and well equipped bedrooms, the total refurbishment of which should be completed by the end of 1991. The hotel has its own heated indoor swimming pool, and 2 self-catering apartments.*
40⇨♠(4fb) CTV in all bedrooms ® T ✂ (ex guide dogs) ✻ sB&B⇨♠£30-£50 dB&B⇨♠£60-£100 ㅌ
ℂ 40P ❄ CFA ▱ (heated) sauna solarium table tennis boules croquet putting ♧ *xmas*
♲ English & French V ♤ ⚎ ✂ ✻ Lunch £8 High tea £3 Dinner £17.50 Last dinner 8.45pm
Credit Cards ①②③⑤ ⓔ

L

# Llandudno

### ★★★64% Imperial

The Promenade LL30 1AP (Best Western) ☎(0492)877466
Telex no 61606 FAX (0492) 878043

*Conveniently situated on the promenade with its own small car park, this large, privately owned hotel is within easy reach of the town centre and other amenities. Recently refurbished public areas are spacious and comfortable, bedrooms are well equipped, and there is a health and fitness centre as well as extensive conference and function facilities.*

100⇘↰(10fb) CTV in all bedrooms ® T sB&B⇘↰£45-£65 dB&B⇘↰£75-£115 ᕗ

Lift ℂ 40P CFA ▣ (heated) snooker sauna solarium gymnasium steam room beauty therapist hairdressing ♪ *xmas*
V ⍤ ⍿ ✳ Lunch £9.50-£10.50 Dinner £17.50-£19.50 Last dinner 9pm
Credit Cards ①②③⑤ⓔ

### ★★★64% St George's

The Promenade LL30 2LG ☎(0492)877544 Telex no 61520 FAX (0492) 878477

*A large and impressive Victorian building on the promenade overlooking Llandudno Bay. Extensive refurbishment undertaken during 1990 and 1991 has considerably improved the accommodation. In addition to the pleasant restaurant, cocktail bar and lounge, there is a coffee shop, a ballroom/function room with a magnificent ceiling and a well equipped health and beauty centre. The hotel also has its own car park.*

87⇘↰(4fb)1ᕀ CTV in all bedrooms ® T ✳ sB&B⇘↰£39-£51 dB&B⇘↰£72-£82 ᕗ

Lift ℂ 36P sauna solarium gymnasium hairdressing health & beauty salon *xmas*
V ⍤ ⍿
Credit Cards ①②③⑤ⓔ

### ★★★62% *Chatsworth House*

Central Promenade LL30 2XS ☎(0492)860788
Closed 28 Dec-12 Jan

*A large and privately owned hotel contained within an elegant Victorian terrace on the Promenade offers fine sea views from many of its rooms. Well equipped modern bedrooms are complemented by spacious public areas which include a choice of lounges and a charming Victorian-style coffee shop. Guests have the use of an indoor heated swimming pool, two solariums, a sauna and a jacuzzi, and a small car park is available at the rear of the hotel.*

58⇘↰(13fb)1ᕀ CTV in all bedrooms ® T
Lift ℂ 9P ▣ (heated) sauna solarium jacuzzi ♪
V ⍤ ⍿ ✲ Last dinner 8.30pm
Credit Cards ①③

### ★★★61% Risboro

Clement Av LL30 2ED (Inter-Hotels) ☎(0492)876343
Telex no 617117 FAX (0492) 879881

*Conveniently situated for access to both seafront and town centre, this large hotel also offers on-site car parking. Its well equipped bedrooms are equally suitable for holidaymakers or business people – notably delegates using the conference facilities; other amenities include a heated indoor swimming pool, a roof garden and a snooker room with full size table.*

65⇘↰(7fb)1ᕀ CTV in all bedrooms ® T sB&B⇘↰£33-£38 dB&B⇘↰£66-£76 ᕗ

Lift ℂ 40P CFA ▣ (heated) squash ∪ snooker sauna solarium gymnasium ♪ *xmas*
🍴 English & French V ⍤ ⍿ ✳ Lunch £7-£11 High tea fr£3
Dinner fr£17 Last dinner 8.45pm
Credit Cards ①②③⑤ⓔ

### ★★

### ★★❀❀ ST TUDNO

Promenade LL30 2LP
☎(0492)874411
Telex no 61400
FAX (0492) 860407
Closed 28 Dec-10 Jan

*Situated on the seafront, this is without doubt one of the nicest resort hotels in the country. Quite apart from the excellent appointments and comfortable accommodation, perhaps the strongest feature is the hospitality provided by the charming owners Martin and Janette Bland. The bedrooms are all individually decorated and furnished with thought and care, and all are well equipped with modern facilities. The public rooms, although small, have been tastefully appointed, and the bright garden room restaurant has a relaxing atmosphere. Chef David Harding offers an uncomplicated menu of mainly British cuisine, and his cooking is sound and honest. Service is both friendly and attentive, from willing, helpful staff.*

21⇘↰(4fb)1ᕀ CTV in all bedrooms ® T
✈ (ex guide dogs)
Lift 4P 2🚗 (£4) 🚲 ▣ (heated)
V ⍤ ⍿ ✲ Last dinner 9.30pm
Credit Cards ①②③

A rosette means exceptional standards of cuisine.

L

# Llandudno

## ★★ 72% Dunoon

Gloddaeth St LL30 2DW ☎(0492)860787 FAX (0492) 860031
Closed Nov-mid Mar

*A combination of friendly, attentive service, well equipped bedrooms and attractive public areas account for the well deserved popularity of this privately owned hotel. Close to the town centre, with access to the seafront and other amenities.*

56⇨🏠Annexe14⇨(22fb) CTV in all bedrooms ® T
✠ (ex guide dogs) S% sB&B⇨🏠£27-£33 dB&B⇨🏠£42-£66
Lift CTV 24P solarium
V ✿ ⚲ ✱ Lunch £7.50-£8.50 Dinner £10.50-£13 Last dinner 8pm
Credit Cards ①③

## ★★ 68% Belle Vue

26 North Pde LL30 2LP ☎(0492)879547
RS Nov & Mar

*From its elevated position near the pier, this friendly, personally run hotel commands excellent views of the town, bay and beach. The accommodation is impeccably maintained and the car park is a definite advantage during the holiday season.*

17⇨🏠(2fb) CTV in all bedrooms ® T sB&B⇨🏠£24.50-£28.50 dB&B⇨🏠£49-£57
Lift 12P ♨ table tennis
♿ French & Italian ✿ Bar Lunch £4-£5 Dinner £9 Last dinner 8pm
Credit Cards ①②③⑤ ⓔ

## ★★ 67% Merrion

Promenade, South Pde LL30 2LN ☎(0492)860022
FAX (0492) 860378
Closed Feb

*A friendly, family-run hotel on the seafront, opposite the lifeboat slipway and close to the local shopping area, features bright, spacious public rooms which include both an air-conditioned dining room whose table d'hôte menu offers a short but interesting selection and a smart French restaurant where guests can, for a supplement, enjoy a 'special occasion' meal. Over half the bedrooms enjoy sea views, some having balconies and others bay windows.*

67⇨🏠(7fb) CTV in all bedrooms ® T 🔥
Lift ( CTV 16P 25♨ *xmas*
♿ English & French V ✿ ⚲ ✱ Lunch £7.50-£8.50 High tea fr£3 Dinner fr£13.50 Last dinner 8.30pm
Credit Cards ①②③

## ★★ 67% Sandringham

West Pde LL30 2BD ☎(0492)876513 & 876447
RS 23-27 Dec

*The conscientious proprietors of this pleasant family hotel continue to make improvements. Set on the town's West Shore, with splendid views across the Conwy estuary, it offers well equipped en suite bedrooms, a nicely appointed restaurant and a pleasant lounge bar where a good range of bar meals is available, and a games room.*

18⇨🏠(4fb) CTV in all bedrooms ® T ✠ 🔥
6P CFA
V ✿ ⚵ ✱ S% Sunday Lunch £8.50-£9.50 Dinner £12&alc Last dinner 8pm
Credit Cards ①③⑤ ⓔ

## ★★ 66% Plas Fron Deg

48 Church Walks LL30 2HL ☎(0492)877267 & 860226
Closed Nov-Jan

*Set in a quiet side road within easy reach of both seafront and shopping area, and fronted by a large terraced garden, this beautifully preserved and maintained Victorian house retains such original features as exquisitely carved fireplaces and some magnificent stained glass windows. Bedrooms are comfortable and well equipped, and friendly proprietors provide informal but attentive service.*

9⇨🏠(1fb) CTV in all bedrooms ® T (incl dinner) 🔥
7P ♨ nc11yrs
V ⚵
Credit Cards ①③⑤ ⓔ

## ★★ 66% Tan-Lan

Great Orme's Rd, West Shore LL30 2AR (Minotels)
☎(0492)860221
Closed Nov-14 Mar

*A large, modern and much-extended house with its own car park, set in a quiet road close to the West Shore, now serves as a privately owned and personally run hotel providing well maintained accommodation with en suite facilities.*

18⇨🏠(4fb) CTV in all bedrooms ® ✱ sB&B⇨🏠£22.50-£24 dB&B⇨🏠£45-£48 🔥
15P ♨
♿ English, French & Italian ✿ ⚲ ✱ Lunch £6.50-£7.50 Dinner £10-£11 Last dinner 8pm
Credit Cards ①③ ⓔ

## ★★ 65% Bedford

Promenade LL30 1BN ☎(0492)876647

*Overlooking the bay from a position on the Promenade, convenient for the town centre and other amenities, this privately owned hotel also has the advantage of its own car park. Well furnished and equipped bedrooms provide en suite facilities, and a choice of restaurants includes one in Italian Trattoria style.*

27⇨🏠(2fb) CTV in all bedrooms ® ✱ sB&B⇨🏠£20-£27 dB&B⇨🏠£36-£50 🔥
Lift ( CTV 20P *xmas*
♿ English, French & Italian V ✿ ⚲ ✱ Bar Lunch £4-£20alc Dinner £10-£12&alc Last dinner 10.30pm
Credit Cards ①③

## ★★ 65% Bryn-y-Bia Lodge

Craigside LL30 3AS ☎(0492)49644 & 40459
Closed 23 Dec-2 Jan

*A delightful detached house set in its own grounds on the coastal road, near the Little Orme, features well equipped modern bedrooms and elegantly furnished public areas. Good food, ably prepared by the resident owner and served in an attractive dining room, high standards of hospitality and quality accommodation combine to make this hotel something a little special.*

13⇨🏠(2fb)1🛏 CTV in all bedrooms ® T ✱
sB&B⇨🏠£26.50-£33 dB&B⇨🏠£50-£59 🔥
20P ♨ ✿
♿ English & Continental V ✿ ⚵ ✱ Sunday Lunch £6.75-£7.25 Dinner £16&alc Last dinner 8.30pm
Credit Cards ①②③ ⓔ

## ★★ 65% *Rose Tor*

124 Mostyn St LL30 2SW ☎(0492)870433

*This very pleasant personally run hotel, close to both the town centre and seafront, offers well-equipped modern bedrooms equally suitable for tourists and commercial guests. There is a cosy bar and a restaurant with a carvery option.*

17⇨🏠(2fb) CTV in all bedrooms ® T
✗
V ✿ ⚵ Last dinner 9.30pm
Credit Cards ①②③

## ★★ 65% *Sefton Court*

Church Walks LL30 2HL ☎(0492)875262

*This attractive Victorian house with a terraced garden and private car park is situated at the foot of the Great Orme, close to the town centre and seafront. It offers quite well-equipped accommodation and friendly personal service.*

14rm(10⇨1🏠)(6fb)✗in 1 bedroom CTV in all bedrooms ®
CTV 13P
♿ Welsh, English & French V ✿ ⚲ ⚵ Last dinner 8pm
Credit Cards ①③

418

★★64% **Bromwell Court**
Promenade LL30 1BG ☎(0492)878416 & 874142
*This small and friendly family-run hotel is situated on the Promenade to the east of the town centre. It is very well maintained throughout and the bedrooms are well equipped.*
11⇦↑(2fb) CTV in all bedrooms ® T ✖ (ex guide dogs) ✱
sB&B⇦↑£23.50 dB&B⇦↑£43 🖪
🎵 🍴
V 🍽 ✱ Lunch £5 Dinner £9.50 Last dinner 7.30pm
Credit Cards ①③ⓔ

★★64% **Tynedale**
Central Promenade LL30 2XS ☎(0492)877426
40rm(39⇦↑)Annexe15rm(3fb) CTV in all bedrooms ®
✖ (ex guide dogs) ✱ sB&B⇦↑£22.50-£24.50 dB&B⇦↑£39-
£43 🖪
Lift ( 30P CFA ♫ *xmas*
♀ English & French V ♦ ⚲ 🍽 ✱ Lunch £6.99 High tea
fr£2.90 Dinner £9.50 Last dinner 7.30pm
Credit Cards ①③ⓔ

★★63% **Headlands**
Hill Ter LL30 2LS (Exec Hotel) ☎(0492)877485
Closed Jan-Feb
*A lovely old house at the foot of the Great Orme, now a privately owned hotel, commands spectacular views of the bay, town, Snowdonia and even the Conwy estuary from its elevated position. Personally run, it provides accommodation in well equipped bedrooms, the majority of which have en suite facilities, and also has the advantage of a parking area at the front.*
17rm(12⇦3↑)(4fb)2🖷 CTV in all bedrooms ® sB&B£26
sB&B⇦↑£26 dB&B⇦↑£52 🖪
CTV 7P 🍴 *xmas*
♦ 🍽 Dinner £16 Last dinner 8pm
Credit Cards ①②③⑤ⓔ

# Llandudno

## ★★63% Sunnymede

West Pde LL30 2BD ☎(0492)877130

Closed mid Nov-Feb

*Situated on the West Shore with good views across the Conwy estuary, this personally run hotel provides well equipped and well maintained accommodation.*

18rm(14⇌3🛏)(3fb)2🛏 CTV in all bedrooms ® ✳
sB&B⇌🛏£27-£36 dB&B⇌🛏£54-£71 (incl dinner) 🍴
18P

V 🌣 🗷 ✳ Bar Lunch £3-£7alc Dinner £11 Last dinner 7pm

Credit Cards 1 3 £

## ★★61% Royal

Church Walks LL30 2HW ☎(0492)876476 FAX (0492) 870210

*A well maintained, privately owned hotel which is reputed to be the oldest in the town nevertheless provides modern accommodation, many of the bedrooms having en suite facilities. Located at the foot of the Great Orme, it offers convenient access to town centre, beach and other amenities.*

37rm(28⇌3🛏)(11fb) CTV in all bedrooms ® T
✈ (ex guide dogs) ✳ sB&Bfr£21.50 sB&B⇌🛏fr£24 dB&B£43
dB&B⇌🛏£48-£58 🍴

Lift 30P ✿ CFA putting green ♨ *xmas*

♀ European V 🌣 🗷 Bar Lunch fr£1 Dinner fr£13 Last dinner 8pm

Credit Cards 1 3 £

## ★★61% Southcliffe

Hill Ter LL30 2LS ☎(0492)876277

Closed Nov-15 Dec & 5 Jan-Mar

*From its elevated position on the side of the Great Orme, a privately owned hotel catering for coach tour parties and particularly popular with elderly holiday makers enjoys superb views of beach, promenade and town. There is no car park, but street parking is usually available.*

30rm(19⇌5🛏)(7fb) CTV in all bedrooms ® ✳ S% sB&B£27.50
dB&B⇌🛏£51-£59 (incl dinner) 🍴

🎵 CFA ♬ nc7yrs *xmas*

🌣 🗷 ✳ Lunch £4.50-£6.50 Dinner £8&alc Last dinner 8.30pm

## ★★60% Castle

Vaughan St LL30 1AG ☎(0492)877694 & 876868

Closed Jan

*Large and privately owned, this hotel at the centre of the town has the advantage of its own car park. Recently refurbished bedrooms are equipped with en suite facilities, and the establishment caters for a wide range of customers, including coach parties and delegates attending local conferences.*

56rm(51⇌3🛏)(19fb) CTV in all bedrooms ® sB&B⇌🛏£21-£23 dB&B⇌🛏£42-£46

Lift ( 30P 7🏊 (£10 per wk) games room *xmas*

V 🌣 🗷 ✂ ✳ Lunch £5.50 Dinner £6.50-£8.50 Last dinner 7.30pm

Credit Cards 1 3 £

## ★★60% Somerset

St Georges Crescent, Promenade LL30 2LF ☎(0492)876540

Closed Nov-Feb

*A large privately owned hotel centrally situated on the promenade with a car park to the rear. All the bedrooms have en suite facilities and those at the front overlook the sea.*

37⇌🛏(4fb) CTV in all bedrooms ® ✳ sB&B⇌🛏£30-£34
dB&B⇌🛏£60-£68 (incl dinner)

Lift 20P *xmas*

V 🌣 ✂

Credit Cards 1 3

## ★★60% Wavecrest

St Georges Crescent, Central Promenade LL30 2LF
☎(0492)876540

Closed Nov-Mar

*This popular hotel on the central promenade has recently been redecorated throughout and all bedrooms now have en suite facilities. There is a choice of comfortable lounges, with live entertainment several times a week.*

41⇌🛏 CTV in all bedrooms ® ✳ sB&B⇌🛏£22-£24
dB&B⇌🛏£44-£48

Lift 12P

V 🌣 ✂ ✳ Bar Lunch £1.30-£3.50 Dinner £9 Last dinner 7.30pm

## ★★59% *Esplanade*

Glan-y-Mor Pde, Promenade LL30 2LL ☎(0492)860300
Telex no 61155 FAX (0492) 860418

*The simple but well equipped modern accommodation provided by a privately owned hotel which overlooks the pier from its setting on the Promenade is equally suitable for holidaymakers or business people; limited car parking facilities are available at the rear.*

57⇌🛏(16fb) CTV in all bedrooms ® T

Lift ( CTV 30P games room

♀ English & French 🌣 🗷 Last dinner 8.30pm

Credit Cards 1 2 3 5

## ★★58% *Four Oaks*

Promenade LL30 1AY ☎(0492)876506

RS Nov-Feb

*This large, privately owned hotel is situated on the promenade, within easy reach of the town centre. Many of its bedrooms enjoy sea views, and it is particularly popular with coach tour parties.*

57rm(19⇌8🛏)(25fb) CTV in all bedrooms ®

Lift ( CTV ♪ ♬ ♨

V 🌣 🗷 Last dinner 7.30pm

## ★★57% Ormescliffe

Promenade LL30 1BE ☎(0492)877191 FAX (0492) 860311

*A large hotel on the Promenade, conveniently located for access to the town centre and other amenities, caters mainly for coach party holidaymakers – being particularly popular with senior citizens.*

60⇌🛏(11fb) CTV in all bedrooms ® ✈ (ex guide dogs) ✳
sB&B⇌🛏£23.50-£25.50 dB&B⇌🛏£47-£51

Lift ( CTV 12P CFA pool table tennis *xmas*

♀ International 🌣 🗷 ✳ Bar Lunch £2-£6 Dinner £10 Last dinner 8pm

Credit Cards 1 3

## ★★55% Lynwood

Clonmel St LL30 2LE ☎(0492)876613

*Just a stone's throw away from the main promenade and the town centre, this cosy and friendly family-run hotel has recently been improved, and now provides well equipped bedrooms. There is a small bar and a large basement restaurant.*

26rm(23⇌5🛏)(3fb)1🛏 CTV in all bedrooms ® T
✈ (ex guide dogs) ✳ sB&B£27-£29 sB&B⇌🛏£29-£31
dB&B£44-£48 dB&B⇌🛏£48-£52

CFA games room *xmas*

V 🌣 🗷 ✂ ✳ Dinner £9-£10 Last dinner 7.30pm

Credit Cards 1 2 3

## ★75% Epperstone

15 Abbey Rd LL30 2EE ☎(0492)878746

Closed Jan-Feb

*Quietly located within a short walk of the seafront, this delightful 18th-century house, with many original fireplaces, provides cheerful bedrooms equipped with all modern facilities and a choice of two comfortable lounges.*

8⇌🛏(4fb)✂in 1 bedroom CTV in all bedrooms ® T S%
sB&B⇌🛏£22.50-£27.50 dB&B⇌🛏£45-£55 (incl dinner) 🍴
→

For key to symbols in English see the bookmark.

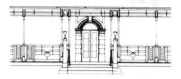

## PROMENADE, LLANDUDNO LL30 2LL
Tel: 0492-860300 (5 lines) Fax: 0492-860418

Premier sea front position. Ideally located for town and leisure facilities. Brochure and tariff on request from the resident manager.

60 comfortable rooms all with bathroom/shower and toilet en suite, colour TV, tea and coffee making facilities, radio/intercom, baby listening, shaver points, direct dial telephone, most have trouser press. Full central heating. Car park at rear. Fully licensed. Residents' lounges, lift, games room, small ballroom. Buttery open all year. Free membership of North Wales Golf Club for two. Open all year round — Xmas and New Year inclusive terms available — conferences — parties — Spring and Autumn breaks.

★ ★

**West Parade, Llandudno,
Gwynedd LL30 2BD
Tel: (0492) 877130**

Situated on the beautiful West Shore with magnificent views of the mountains and a short walk down a tree lined avenue to the busy town centre. The hotel has considerable charm, stylish furnished bedrooms. Most en suite including ground floor bedrooms. Satellite TV, radio and teamaking facilities in all rooms some bedrooms with four posters. Elegant lounges, one with a well stocked bar. Choice of menu, best local produce used. Large private car park.

★ ★

L

## Castle Hotel
### LLANDUDNO, N. WALES

Imposing detached Hotel enjoying its own adjoining spacious car park. All 56 bedrooms en-suite, colour TV and tea makers. Full central heating. Fully licensed. Quiet non smoking lounge. Residents bar lounge. Two restaurants and lunch time coffee lounge. Ballroom and games room.

**Castle Hotel, Vaughan Street, Llandudno.
Tel: (0492) 877694**

★ ★

★ ★

# HEADLANDS
# HOTEL

**Hill Terrace, Llandudno, Gwynedd LL30 2LS
Telephone 0492 877485**

Where comfort and cuisine are the most important ingredients for your holiday. Simply superb views over the Bay, Conwy Estuary and Snowdonia. Direct access to the country park and only 5 minutes to the shops. Bedrooms have en suite or private bath/shower, TV, radio, direct dial telephone, teas maid and central heating, some four poster beds. Why not spoil yourself – you deserve a holiday with a touch of luxury.

*Recommended by Les Routier and Ashley Courtenay.*

# Llandudno

⟨ 8P 🚗 ❀ *xmas*
♨ ♨ ✦ ✳ Dinner £9.50 Last dinner 7.30pm
Credit Cards ①③

### ★68% **Banham House**
2 St Davids Rd LL30 2UL ☎(0492)875680
*This small, bright hotel is run by the very friendly Sharpe family, and is situated in a quiet residential area, yet not too far away from the sea and shopping centre. There is a small, comfortable lounge, and modern bedrooms.*
8rm(2⇆4📰)(2fb) CTV in all bedrooms ® ✻ sB&B£17-£19 sB&B⇆📰£22-£24 dB&B£34-£38 dB&B⇆📰£38-£42
CTV 🅿 🚗 *xmas*
♨ ✦ Lunch £6 Dinner £6.50&alc Last dinner 7.30pm
£

### ★68% *Clontarf*
1 Great Ormes Rd, West Shore LL30 2AR ☎(0492)877621
Closed 30 Dec-Feb
*A small, select hotel, situated in the quieter part of the town and only a short distance from the West Shore, is managed by friendly proprietors who offer warm, clean and well-maintained accommodation.*
10rm(1⇆3📰)(2fb) ® ✻
CTV 10P 🚗 ❀ nc3yrs
V ♨ ♨ ✦ Last dinner 7.30pm

### ★67% **White Lodge**
9 Neville Crescent, Central Promenade LL30 1AT
☎(0492)877713
Closed Nov-Apr
12⇆📰(4fb) CTV in all bedrooms ® ✻ dB&B⇆📰fr£39 🍴
CTV 12P 🚗 nc5yrs
♨ ♨ ✦
Credit Cards ②

### ★66% **Gwesty Leamore**
40 Lloyd St LL30 2YG ☎(0492)875552
Closed Xmas
*A pleasant well maintained family-run hotel, conveniently situated for the town centre, beaches and theatres. Accommodation is modest but well equipped, and the proprietors are friendly and hospitable.*
12rm(1⇆6📰)(4fb) CTV in all bedrooms ® ✻ ✻ sB&B£20-£23 sB&B⇆📰£23-£25 dB&B£40-£46 dB&B⇆📰£42-£46 🍴
CTV 4P 🚗
V ✦ ✻ Bar Lunch £3-£5 Dinner £8-£10 Last dinner 7.30pm
£

### ★66% **Ravenhurst**
West Pde LL30 2BB ☎(0492)875525
Closed Dec-Jan
*A pleasant, privately owned and run hotel on the town's West Shore with well-kept accommodation with good facilities. The hotel has two traditional lounges and a games room.*
23⇆📰Annexe1⇆📰(4fb) CTV in all bedrooms ®
sB&B⇆📰£32.20-£34.90 dB&B⇆📰£64.40-£69.80 (incl dinner) 🍴
15P table tennis pool table 🎵
V ♨ ♨ Lunch £3.50-£5.50&alc Dinner £8.70-£9&alc Last dinner 7pm
Credit Cards ①②③⑤£

### ★63% *Crickleigh*
Lloyd St LL30 2YG ☎(0492)875926
*A pleasant, privately owned and personally run establishment which was once a pair of Victorian houses is undergoing steady improvement and modernisation. The dining room is decorated to a high standard, as are the bedrooms, many of which also have up-to-date shower and toilet facilities. The hotel benefits from having its own private car park and is conveniently located close to the town centre, within easy reach of promenade, pier and other amenities.*

15rm(7📰)(4fb) ® ✻ (ex guide dogs)
CTV 12P
🍴 International V ♨ ♨ Last dinner 7pm
Credit Cards ①③

### ★63% *Quinton*
36 Church Walks LL30 2HN ☎(0492)876879 & 875086
Closed Nov-Jan (ex Xmas)
*This is a comfortable, personally-run hotel situated northwest of the town centre between the two beaches. Popular with golfing parties.*
15rm(4⇆5📰)(8fb) CTV in all bedrooms ®
12P
♨ ♨
Credit Cards ①

### ★63% **Tan-y-Marian**
87 Abbey Rd, West Shore LL30 2AS ☎(0492)877727
Closed mid Oct-mid Mar
*This friendly small hotel enjoys good views from its position on the west shore. Bedrooms are very clean and well maintained, there is a small bar and comfortable residents' lounge, and good home cooking.*
8rm(3📰)(2fb) ® ✻ (ex guide dogs) ✻ S% sB&B£15-£18 dB&B£28-£34 dB&B📰£30-£36
CTV 5P 🚗 nc2yrs
V ✦ Bar Lunch £3-£5 Dinner fr£7 Last dinner 7pm

### ★62% *Branksome*
Lloyd St LL30 2YP ☎(0492)875989
Closed Jan-Mar
*A friendly atmosphere, caring owners who are continually improving facilities and a good position, just a few minutes level walk from both shops and Promenade, ensure that many guests return to this hotel.*
48rm(7⇆10📰)Annexe5rm(10fb)
CTV 12P sauna solarium gymnasium 🎵
🍴 English, French & Italian V ♨ ♨

### ★62% **Bryn-y-Mor**
North Pde LL30 2LP ☎(0492)876790 FAX (0492) 860825
*Situated on the promenade near the pier, the hotel is run by the very friendly and hospitable Ratcliffe family. Bedrooms are neat and pretty, there is a small bar for residents and a very comfortable lounge.*
18rm(7⇆9📰)(5fb) CTV in all bedrooms ® ✻ (ex guide dogs)
✻ sB&B£16.50-£21 sB&B⇆📰£28-£32 dB&B£30-£40 dB&B⇆📰£39-£50 🍴
CTV 1P
V ♨ ✻ Sunday Lunch £7.50-£8.50 Dinner £7.50-£9.50 Last dinner 7pm
Credit Cards ①②③⑤

### ★62% **Min-y-Don**
North Pde LL30 2LP ☎(0492)876511
Closed Nov-Jan
*A privately owned hotel situated at the northern end of the Promenade close to the pier and the amenities of the town centre.*
28rm(2⇆17📰)(12fb) CTV in all bedrooms ® ✻ sB&B£19-£19.50 sB&B⇆📰£21-£21.50 dB&B£38-£39 dB&B⇆📰£42-£43 🍴
⊞ CTV 5P *xmas*
V ♨ ♨ ✦ Bar Lunch £4-£4.50&alc Dinner £4.75-£6 Last dinner 7.30pm
Credit Cards ①③

### ★61% *Bron Orme*
54 Church Walks LL30 2HL ☎(0492)876735
Closed Nov-Feb
*A pleasant small family-run hotel offering excellent value and good home cooking. Set in its own grounds and sheltered by the Great Orme, it is located close to all the town's attractions.*

9rm(4♠)(2fb)® ✈ (ex guide dogs)
CTV ✗ ✿ nc5yrs
♡ English & French ♦ ⚓ ✂ Last dinner 7pm

★**61% Hilbre Court**
Great Ormes Rd, West Shore LL30 2AR ☎(0492)876632
Closed Nov-Feb (ex Xmas)
*Well maintained bedrooms, many with en suite facilities, are
provided by a family-run hotel near the West Shore, which also
offers convenient access to the town centre and other amenities.*
10rm(3⇨3♠)(1fb)✂in 2 bedrooms CTV in all bedrooms ®
sB&B£18-£20 sB&B⇨♠£19.50-£22.50 dB&B£38-£40
dB&B⇨♠£40-£45 ♬
CTV 6P ✿ *xmas*
V ♦ ⚓ ✂ ✱ Bar Lunch £2-£3alc Dinner £7.50 Last dinner
8pm
Credit Cards ①②③⑤

❀❀✕✕✕**La Mouette**
Merrion Hotel, Promenade LL30 2LN ☎(0492)860022
FAX (0492) 860378
*Situated at the pier end of the Promenade, this French restaurant
provides a high standard of cooking, prepared by chef Gareth
Bream, who pays fine attention to detail. The atmosphere is
intimate, with soft lighting and décor and good quality furnishings.
Service is provided by skilled and attentive French waiters.*
Closed Sun, Mon, Nov & 1 Jan-1 Mar Lunch not served (ex by
prior arrangement only)
♡ French V 32 seats ✱ Dinner £21-£28alc Last dinner 10pm 28
P nc10yrs ♬
Credit Cards ①②③

**LLANELLI** Dyfed Map **02** SN50

★★★**61% Diplomat**
Felinfoel SA15 3PJ (Best Western) ☎(0554)756156
FAX (0554) 751649
*A very popular hotel in an elevated position and boasting extensive,
much-used conference/function suites and an excellent leisure club.
Well equipped bedrooms with modern facilities are complemented
by comfortable open-plan lounge and bar areas.*
23⇨♠Annexe8⇨♠(2fb) CTV in all bedrooms ® ✱
sB&B⇨♠£61 dB&B⇨♠£71 ♬
Lift 300P ✿ CFA ▣ (heated) sauna solarium gymnasium
turkish bath ♬
♡ English & French V ♦ ⚓ ✱ Lunch £8.95-£10.95&alc
Dinner £13.95&alc Last dinner 9.45pm
Credit Cards ①②③⑤⑥

★★★**55% Stradey Park**
Furnace SA15 4HA (Forte Hotels) ☎(0554)758171
Telex no 48521 FAX (0554) 777974
*Set in an elevated position above the town, with sweeping views of
the sea, this large commercial and leisure hotel has spacious public
rooms and neat, clean bedrooms which are currently due to be
updated.*
80⇨♠(3fb)✂in 20 bedrooms CTV in all bedrooms ® ✱ S%
sB⇨frf50 dB⇨frf60 (room only) ♬
Lift ☾ 120P CFA *xmas*
V ♦ ⚓ ✂ ✱ S% Lunch frf7.95&alc Dinner £12.95&alc Last
dinner 9.30pm
Credit Cards ①②③④⑤

**LLANFAIR PWLLGWYNGYLL** Gwynedd Map **06** SH57

★★★**63%** *Carreg Bran Country*
Church Ln LL61 5YH ☎Llanfairpwll(0248)714224
Telex no 61464 FAX (0248) 715983
*Conveniently situated at the Anglesey end of the Britannia Bridge,
beside the A5/A4080 junction, this privately owned hotel offers
well equipped modern bedrooms which are equally popular with
tourists and businessmen (including delegates using the conference
facilities).*

29⇨♠Annexe4⇨♠(4fb) CTV in all bedrooms ® T
☾150P ✿
♡ Welsh & French V ♦ ⚓ Last dinner 10pm
Credit Cards ①②③⑤

**LLANFYLLIN** Powys Map **06** SJ11

★★♨**72% Bodfach Hall**
SY22 5HS ☎(069184)272
Closed 15 Nov-1 Mar
*Set back from the main road just north of the town, this elegant
17th-century country house with ornate ceilings and wood-panelled
walls nestles amid trees and lawns. Bedrooms and public areas are
comfortable and well equipped, food is good, and the hotel is
personally run by its friendly owners.*
9⇨♠(2fb) CTV in all bedrooms ® sB&B⇨♠£30-£31.50
dB&B⇨♠£60-£63 ♬
20P ✿ ✿ ✦ putting green
V ♦ Dinner frf14 Last dinner 8.45pm
Credit Cards ①②③

**LLANGAMMARCH WELLS** Powys Map **03** SN94

★★★❀♨**76% Lake**
LD4 4BS (Welsh Rarebits) ☎(05912)202 & 474
FAX (05912) 457
(Rosette awarded for dinner only)
*A privately owned mock-Tudor Victorian hotel, peacefully
positioned in 50 acres of grounds. Spacious public areas are
comfortably furnished with large armchairs, antique pieces and
open fires. The attractive bedrooms are individually decorated and
well furnished with modern facilities and thoughtful extras, and
many have their own small lounge areas. At dinner a short, daily
changing 4-course menu features fresh local produce, while
excellent home-made cakes are the highlight of the afternoon teas.*
→

L

*A wide range of sporting activities is available, including fishing on the River Irfon or the hotel's own lake. We are pleased to say that one of our 'Courtesy and Care' awards for Wales goes to Lake Hotel (see colour feature on p17).*

19⌐(1fb)3☵⊬in 6 bedrooms CTV in all bedrooms T ✳ S%
sB&B⌐£65 dB&B⌐£85-£105 🏠

《 70P 2⚫ ⇔ ✿ CFA ♪ (hard) ♪ snooker clay pigeon shooting *xmas*

♀ English & French ♥ ♬ ⊬ ✳ S% Lunch £12.50 Dinner £22.50 Last dinner 8.45pm

Credit Cards ① ② ③ ⓔ

---

## LLANGEFNI Gwynedd Map 06 SH47

### ★★★ ✾♨81% Tre-Ysgawen Hall

Capel Coch LL77 7UR ☎(0248)750750 FAX (0248) 750035

*Since winning the AA Best Newcomer award for 1991, Tre-Ysgawen Hall has gone from strength to strength. The late Victorian mansion, set in spacious grounds and gardens some four miles north of the town, was lovingly restored by Ray and Pat Craighead to provide an elegant country house hotel of the highest quality. Beautifully furnished bedrooms are complemented by delightful spacious public rooms, including a restaurant with an increasing reputation for the culinary skills of chef Steven Morris. The atmosphere is relaxing and hospitable, with young staff providing attentive personal service that is both professional and unpretentious.*

19⌐♖(5fb)3☵ CTV in all bedrooms T sB&B⌐£79-£152.25 dB&B⌐£103-£175 (room only) 🏠

《 110P ✿ CFA ▱ clay pigeon & game shooting *xmas*

♀ French V ♥ ♬ Lunch £10-£14.50 Dinner £18.50&alc Last dinner 9.30pm

Credit Cards ① ② ③ ⓔ

### ★★ 62% *Nant-yr-Odyn*

Llanfawr LL77 7YE (S of junction A5/A5114) ☎(0248)723354

*Formerly a block of old stonebuilt farm buildings cleverly converted into a small hotel, with well equipped bedrooms. Family run, in an informal manner, it is quietly situated 1.5 miles south of Llangefni and within easy reach of the A5.*

14⌐♖ CTV in all bedrooms ⓡ T ✖

30P ⇔

♥ ♬

Credit Cards ① ③

---

## LLANGOLLEN Clwyd Map 07 SJ24

### ★★★♨64% Bryn Howel

LL20 7UW (2.75m E on A539) ☎(0978)860331
FAX (0978) 860119
Closed 25 Dec

*This lovely old country mansion, now a privately owned hotel, is set in delightful grounds in the beautiful Vale of Llangollen. The attractive public areas and well equipped bedrooms are popular with tourists and business people alike.*

38⌐♖(1fb) CTV in all bedrooms ⓡ T sB&B⌐♖fr£60 dB&B⌐♖fr£89 🏠

Lift CTV 200P ✿ CFA ♪ sauna solarium

V ♥ ♬ Lunch £10.50-£11.50 Dinner fr£17.50 Last dinner 9.30pm

Credit Cards ① ② ③ ⓔ

### ★★★ 56% The Royal

Bridge St LL20 8PG (Forte Hotels) ☎(0978)860202
FAX (0978) 861824

*The hotel is situated in the centre of this popular tourist town, on the edge of the River Dee, and caters for tourists and business people alike.*

33⌐(3fb)⊬in 8 bedrooms CTV in all bedrooms ⓡ ✳ sB⌐£50 dB⌐£65 (room only) 🏠

《 20P CFA ♪ *xmas*

---

V ♥ ♬ ⊁ ✳ S% Lunch £7.95 Dinner £12.95&alc Last dinner 9.30pm

Credit Cards ① ② ③ ⑤

---

## LLANGURIG Powys Map 06 SN98

### ★★69% *Glansevern Arms*

Pant Mawr SY18 6SY (4m W on Aberystwyth Rd) ☎(05515)240
Closed 10 Days at Xmas

*Guests are assured of a warm welcome at this very pleasant small hotel, situated by the A44 in the Upper Wye Valley. Bedrooms are well decorated and cosy, there is a comfortable lounge and bar with log fires and the 6-course fixed-price menu is good value.*

8⌐♖ CTV in all bedrooms ⓡ

40P ⇔

♥ Last dinner 8pm

---

## LLANGYBI Gwent Map 03 ST39

### ★★★★61% Cwrt Bleddyn Hotel & Country Club

NP5 1PG ☎Tredunnock(0633)49521 FAX (0633) 49220

*This country mansion with modern extensions, set in attractive parkland between Caerleon and Usk, boasts an excellent leisure centre; quite good function and conference facilities are also available. Accommodation ranging from that contained in the modern annexe to three period rooms includes several luxurious suites, while public areas are relaxing and comfortable.*

29⌐♖Annexe7⌐♖(5fb)3☵ CTV in all bedrooms ⓡ T ✖ (ex guide dogs) ✳ sB&B⌐♖fr£68.50 dB&B⌐♖£87.50-£125 🏠

《 ▦ 100P ✿ CFA ▱ (heated) ♪ (hard) squash snooker sauna solarium gymnasium croquet boules clay pigeon shooting ⚓ *xmas*

♀ Welsh & French V ♥ ♬ ✳ Lunch £12.25-£18.95&alc Dinner £18.95&alc Last dinner 10pm

Credit Cards ① ② ③ ⑤

**See advertisement under USK**

---

## LLANRWST Gwynedd Map 06 SH76

### ★★★♨64% Plas Maenan Country House

Maenan LL26 0YR (3m N) ☎Dolgarrog(049269)232

*This large, late Victorian country house stands in 12 acres of grounds in an elevated position on the A470 on the east side of the Conwy Valley, from where it commands excellent views. Now a privately owned hotel, it was bought in early 1990 by Graham and Marjorie Turner, who have carried out extensive improvements bringing about a noticeable increase in the hotel's popularity.*

15⌐♖(2fb)1☵ CTV in all bedrooms ⓡ T ✖ ✳ sB&B⌐♖£30-£36 dB&B⌐♖£50-£58 🏠

80P ✿ CFA ♫ *xmas*

♀ Welsh, English & French V ♥ ♬ ✳ Lunch fr£8.50 Dinner fr£14 Last dinner 9pm

Credit Cards ① ③ ⑤ ⓔ

### ★★★62% *Maenan Abbey*

Maenan LL26 0UL (Exec Hotel) ☎Dolgarrog(049269)247 & 230

*This impressive Victorian building on the A470, 1.5miles north of the town, stands within pleasant gardens which include a children's play area. The spacious well-equipped bedrooms are equally suitable for holidaymakers and business guests.*

12⌐♖(2fb) CTV in all bedrooms ⓡ

60P ✿ ♪ clay pigeon shooting ♫

♀ Welsh, English & French V ♥ ♬

Credit Cards ① ② ③ ⑤

### ★★ ✾67% *Meadowsweet*

Station Rd LL26 0DS (Welsh Rarebits) ☎(0492)640732

*A pleasant small hotel on the A470 in the northern outskirts of the town, convenient for many local attractions such as Snowdonia National Park, Bodnant Gardens, Conwy and Llandudno.*

*Proprietor John Evans is an accomplished chef and his imaginative cooking has a well established reputation.*
10♦(3fb) CTV in all bedrooms T sB&B♦£39 dB&B♦£46-£70 ⊟
10P ⇔ *xmas*
♥ French V ♥ ⅍ ✳ Lunch fr£8.95 Dinner £12-£25&alc Last dinner 9.30pm
Credit Cards ① ③ ⓔ

★★63% *Eagles*
LL26 0LG ☎(0492)640454
*A large, stone-built inn – now privately owned and personally run – is set at the centre of this historic market town on the edge of Snowdonia National Park and offers an ideal base for visitors to either mountains or coast. Its well equipped bedrooms are equally suited to the needs of travelling business people.*
12⇌♦(5fb) CTV in all bedrooms ®
CTV 50P ✎ sauna solarium gymnasium pool ♨
♥ Welsh, English & French V ♥ ⅍ Last dinner 9pm
Credit Cards ① ③ ⑤

**LLANSANFFRAID GLAN CONWY** Clwyd Map **06** SH87

★★※※79% **The Old Rectory**
Llanrwst Rd LL28 5LF (Welsh Rarebits)
☎Aberconwy(0492)580611 FAX (0492) 584555
Closed 8 Dec-Jan
*This Georgian-style house is set in attractive gardens and overlooks the Conwy Valley, Conwy Castle and Snowdonia. It is run entirely by Michael and Wendy Vaughan: Michael is the friendly host while Wendy is responsible for the exceptional cuisine. She offers a 5-course menu – no choice, but she is happy to cater for preferences and diet requirements – and you should be prepared to spend 3 hours or more on a memorable food experience. Dining is communal except by special arrangement.* →

**L**

*The 4 bedrooms are elegantly furnished with fine antique pieces, and this is strictly a no-smoking house.*

4⇆♪✿🗗✱in all bedrooms CTV in all bedrooms ® T ✱ ✱
sB&B⇆♪£85 dB&B⇆♪£119-£129 (incl dinner) 🏳
10P 🚗 ✿ ♫ nc8yrs
♀ English & French ✕ ✱ Dinner £24.50 Last dinner 8pm
Credit Cards 1 3

---

### LLANTWIT MAJOR South Glamorgan Map **03** SS96

**★★66%** **West House Country Hotel & Restaurant**
West St CF6 9SP ☎(0446)792406 & 793726 FAX (0446) 796147
*A former 18th-century farmhouse has been converted into a very popular, modern hotel with an excellent conservatory lounge and a cosy bar. Staff are friendly and welcoming.*
21rm(15⇆3♪)(1fb)⁂ CTV in all bedrooms ® T ✱
sB&B£35-£42.50 sB&B⇆♪£42.50-£45 dB&B£45-£52.50
dB&B⇆♪£52.50-£62.50 🏳
《 CTV 60P CFA *xmas*
♀ English & French V ✿ ⊿ ✕ ✱ Lunch £2.50-£8.95 Dinner £11.50&alc Last dinner 9.30pm
Credit Cards 1 2 3

### ✿ ✕ ✕ *Flanders*

Flanders Rd CF6 9RL ☎(0446)792022
(Rosette awarded for dinner only)
*Now under new ownership and sporting a new name, this pleasant wood-panelled restaurant in a quiet area of the small Vale of Glamorgan town offers most enjoyable food, attractively presented and based on local produce whenever possible. Friendly staff provide attentive service, and guests can enjoy a pre-dinner drink in the comfortable bar.*
Lunch not served Sat
Dinner not served Sun & Mon
♀ English & French 85 seats Last lunch 2pm Last dinner 10pm
30 P
Credit Cards 1 2 3

---

### LLANWDDYN Powys Map **06** SJ01

**★★★⚑71%** **Lake Vyrnwy**
SY10 0LY ☎(069173)692 FAX (069173) 259
*Set in 24,000 acres of woodland at the foot of the Berwyn Mountains and overlooking Lake Vyrnwy, this superb country house hotel offers a wide range of outdoor sports facilities. Bedrooms are all well equipped. The elegant public rooms with log fires include a very relaxing lounge and a restaurant serving well-prepared food. The separate Tavern Bar is popular locally.*
30⇆♪(4fb)2⁂ CTV in all bedrooms T ✱ sB&B⇆♪£45.50-£76.50 dB&B⇆♪£68.50-£105 🏳
70P ✿ CFA ♟ (hard) ♪ game shooting sailing *xmas*
♀ British & French V ✿ ⊿ ✕ ✱ Lunch fr£9.45 High tea £3-£6 Dinner fr£19.25 Last dinner 9.30pm
Credit Cards 1 2 3 4 5

---

### LLANWNDA Gwynedd Map **06** SH45

**★★65%** **Stables**
LL54 5SD (Minotels) ☎(0286)830711 & 830935
FAX (0286) 830413
*On the A499 south of Caernarfon, on the edge of the Lleyn Peninsula, this privately owned motel-style hotel has well equipped bedrooms with en suite facilities, equally suitable for tourists and business travellers.*
Annexe14⇆♪(2fb)⁂ CTV in all bedrooms ® T ✱
sB&B⇆♪fr£36 dB&B⇆♪fr£45 Continental breakfast
40P ✿ ⌕
♀ International V ✱ Lunch £6.25-£8.20 Dinner £8.20-£9.96
Last dinner 9.30pm
Credit Cards 1 2 3

---

### LLECHRYD Dyfed Map **02** SN24

**★★★52%** *Castell Malgwyn*
SA43 2QA (0.5m S unclass rd towards Boncath) ☎(023987)382
*An elegant 18th-century mansion set in 40 acres of gardens and woodland. Inside, the hotel's public areas are spacious and comfortable while outside guests can use the heated swimming pool. Salmon and trout fishing in the Teifi is also available.*
22⇆♪(3fb) CTV in all bedrooms ®
50P ✿ ⌕ (heated) ♪ putting croquet
V ✿ ⊿ Last dinner 9.30pm
Credit Cards 1 2 3 5

---

### LLYSWEN Powys Map **03** SO13

**★★★★✿⚑74%** **Llangoed Hall**
LD3 0YP (Small Luxury Hotels) ☎Brecon(0874)754525
FAX (0874) 754545
*Lying off the A470 just north of the village and overlooking the Upper Wye Valley, this delightful country house which in part dates back to 1632, including the panelled library. It was splendidly restored by architect Sir William Clough Ellis in 1919. Now converted into an equally splendid and very hospitable hotel, it features a baronial hall with a massive gothic chimneypiece and finely carved staircase, elegantly furnished lounges and very comfortable well-equipped bedrooms. Food is of a high standard, with fixed price menus plus a small à la carte making good use of fresh local produce.*
23⇆(5fb)9⁂ CTV in all bedrooms T ✱ (ex guide dogs) ✱
sB&B⇆£95-£165 dB&B⇆£115-£230 🏳
《 80P 5🚗 🚗 ✿ CFA ♟ (hard) croquet nc8yrs *xmas*
V ✿ ⊿ ✕ ✱ Lunch £10.50-£14.50alc Dinner £25.50-£35.50alc
Last dinner 9.30pm
Credit Cards 1 2 3 5

**★★64%** **Griffin Inn**
LD3 0UR ☎(0874)754241
*A delightful inn situated alongside the A470 in the upper Wye Valley, between Builth Wells and Brecon, offers very comfortable furnished public areas which include 2 first-floor residents' lounges and character bars with a fisherman's theme and roaring log fires; here, or in the à la carte restaurant, a wide range of food is available.*
8rm(5⇆2♪) ® T sB&B£30-£35 sB&B⇆♪£30-£35
dB&B⇆♪£50-£60 🏳
CTV 14P 🚗 ♪
V ✿ ✕ Sunday Lunch fr£12.50alc Dinner fr£17.25alc Last dinner 9pm
Credit Cards 1 2 3 5

---

### LOCHBOISDALE

See South Uist, Isle of

---

### LOCHCARRON Highland Map **14** NG83

**★★61%** **Lochcarron**
IV54 8YS ☎(05202)226
*This popular family-run hotel is situated on the edge of the village overlooking the loch. It offers a choice of two small lounges, and fresh local seafood is a regular feature on the dinner menu. Bedrooms are comfortable and well equipped.*
10rm(9⇆5♪)(1fb) CTV in all bedrooms ® sB&B⇆♪£29.50
dB&B⇆♪£54-£66
30P 🚗 boat
V ✿ ✕ Lunch £6-£12alc Dinner £14.50&alc Last dinner 8.30pm
Credit Cards 1 3

For key to symbols in English see the bookmark.

L

**LOCHEARNHEAD** Central *Perthshire* Map **11** NN52

★ 68% **Mansewood Country House**
FK19 8NS ☎(05673)213
*A cosy, family-run hotel set in its own gardens on the southern outskirts of the village. Spotlessly maintained throughout, it has bright, neat bedrooms, a comfortable lounge and a snug bar.*
8rm(5➪1♠) ® ✻ sB&B£19 sB&B➪♠£22 dB&B£38
dB&B➪♠£44
16P ⇔ ✿ surfing sailing canoeing water-skiing
♥ ✂ ✻ Dinner £12&alc Last dinner 8.30pm
Credit Cards ①③⑥

★ 58% **Lochearnhead**
Lochside FK19 8PU ☎(05673)229 FAX (05673) 364
Closed mid Nov-Feb
*Home comforts and a friendly atmosphere are among the attractions of this small, family-run hotel, pleasantly situated on the picturesque shore of Loch Earn.*
14rm(1➪3♠) CTV in all bedrooms ® ✻ sB&B£20.90-£27.37
sB&B➪♠£20.90-£27.37 dB&B£33.40-£42.54
dB&B➪♠£33.40-£42.54
CTV 80P ⇔ ✿ ♫ ✦ squash water skiing windsurfing sailing
♥ Scottish & French V ♥ ⚏ ✻ Bar Lunch £2.50-£15.50
Dinner £15.50&alc Last dinner 9pm
Credit Cards ①②③⑤⑥

**LOCHGILPHEAD** Strathclyde Map **10** NR88

★★ 67% **The Stag**
Argyll St PA31 8NE ☎(0546)2496
*This well run commercial and tourist hotel in the town centre features well equipped bedrooms and an attractive restaurant with a small and comfortable adjoining lounge.*
17➪♠ CTV in all bedrooms ® T sB&B➪♠fr£30
dB&B➪♠fr£55 ☐
✦ CFA sauna solarium ♫ xmas
V ♥ ⚏ Lunch £4-£11alc Dinner £14-£16 Last dinner 8.30pm
Credit Cards ①③

**LOCHINVER** Highland *Sutherland* Map **14** NC02

★★★ 77% **Inver Lodge**
IV27 4LU (Best Western) ☎(05714)496 Telex no 75206
FAX (05714) 395
Closed 28 Oct-28 Apr
*Set on a hill above the village overlooking the picturesque bay and harbour, this modern sporting and holiday hotel has been refurbished to a high standard throughout. Bedrooms, all with splendid views, are spacious, elegantly appointed and well equipped. The comfortably furnished day rooms are bright and airy, the first-floor lounge being particularly popular with residents. Dinner is an enjoyable experience, with smartly turned out young staff who are very friendly and willing to please.*
20➪(2fb) CTV in all bedrooms ® T sB&B➪£66-£81
dB&B➪£103-£120 ☐
30P ⇔ ✿ ♫ snooker sauna solarium
♥ Scottish & French ♥ ⚏ S% Sunday Lunch £16 Dinner £26
Last dinner 9pm
Credit Cards ①②③⑤

**LOCKERBIE** Dumfries & Galloway *Dumfriesshire*
Map **11** NY18

★★★★ 66% **Dryfesdale**
DG11 2SF ☎(05762)2427 FAX (05762) 4187
*Peacefully situated in its own grounds and yet conveniently close to the A74, this former manse offers comfortable accommodation and is personally managed by the resident proprietors. In the attractive restaurant guests can enjoy not only well-prepared meals but also fine views of the surrounding countryside.*

15➪♠(1fb) CTV in all bedrooms ® T sB&B➪♠£45-£47
dB&B➪♠£67-£69 ☐
50P ✿ CFA ♨ xmas
♥ English & French V ♥ ⚏ Lunch fr£9&alc Dinner fr£14&alc
Last dinner 9.30pm
Credit Cards ①②③

★★ 74% **Somerton House**
Carlisle Rd DG11 2DR ☎(05762)2583 FAX (05762) 2384
Closed 25 Dec
*Individually appointed bedrooms, comfortably and tastefully fitted, are a feature of this charming Victorian house which has unusual, ornate wood and plasterwork. Service is relaxed but courteous, and the restaurant's freshly prepared dishes represent good value.*
7➪♠(2fb) CTV in all bedrooms ® T sB&B➪♠£35-£41
dB&B➪♠£51.50-£62 ☐
100P ✿
♥ International V ♥ ✂ Lunch £8.50-£15alc Dinner £12-£18.50alc Last dinner 9.30pm
Credit Cards ①②③⑥

★ 64% **Ravenshill House**
12 Dumfries Rd DG11 2EF ☎(05762)2882
*Set within its own walled garden and managed by resident proprietors, this small country house provides comfortable accommodation, good-value menus and friendly, informal service.*
7rm(6➪♠)(1fb)1 ⊞ CTV in all bedrooms ® T sB&Bfr£25
sB&B➪♠fr£29 dB&Bfr£40 dB&B➪♠fr£45 ☐
35P ✿
♥ Scottish, French & Italian V Sunday Lunch £7.50-£11alc
Dinner £7-£16alc Last dinner 9pm
Credit Cards ①②③⑥

*The* **Dryfesdale** *Hotel* ★★★
## Lockerbie
## Telephone 05762 2427

Quietly situated very close the A74 overlooking Lockerbie with panoramic views of the surrounding countryside.

A beautifully appointed family run hotel where comfort and relaxation are the keywords. 15 bedrooms all en suite and 6 on the ground floor with full facilities for disabled persons.

The restaurant has a renowned reputation and a wide selection of bar meals is also available.

Open all the year round.

# Lolworth

**LOLWORTH** Cambridgeshire Map **05** TL36

⌂**Forte Travelodge**
Huntingdon Rd CB3 8DR (on A604) (Forte)
☎Crafts Hill(0954)781335 Central Res (0800) 850950
*Standing beside a Little Chef restaurant on the northbound carriageway of the A604, 5m north of Cambridge, this lodge offers clean, well equipped accommodation which represents good value for money.*
20⇨↑(20fb) CTV in all bedrooms ® sB⇨↑£29.95
dB⇨↑£29.95 (room only)
《 50P ⇔
Credit Cards ① ② ③

# London hotels and restaurants

# London Postal Districts and ways in and out of London

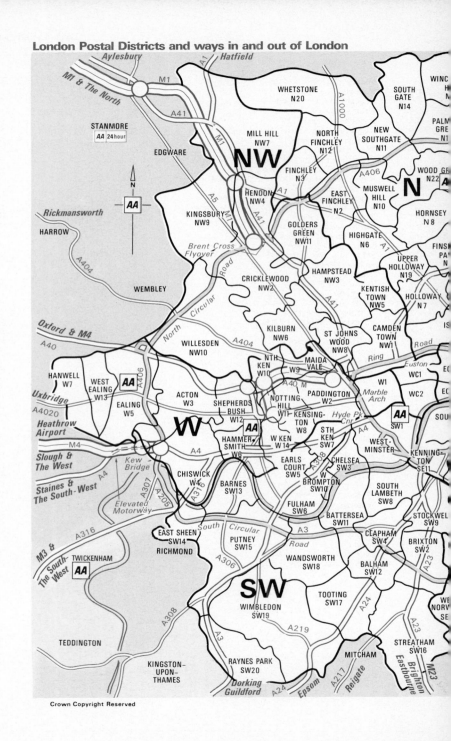

Crown Copyright Reserved

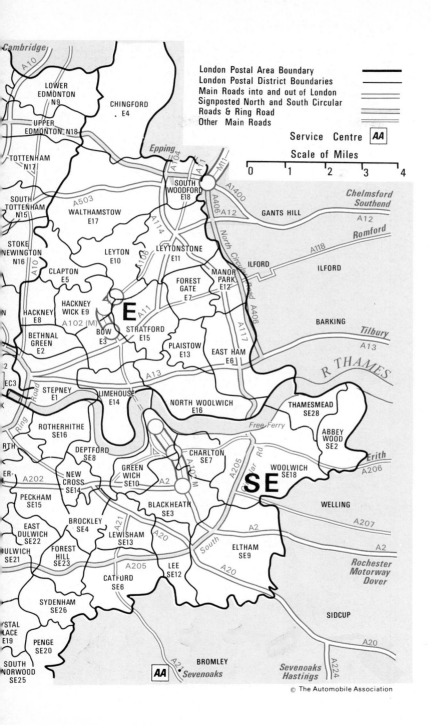

London Postal Area Boundary
London Postal District Boundaries
Main Roads into and out of London
Signposted North and South Circular
Roads & Ring Road
Other Main Roads

Service Centre **AA**

Scale of Miles

0   1   2   3   4

London

# London Plan 1

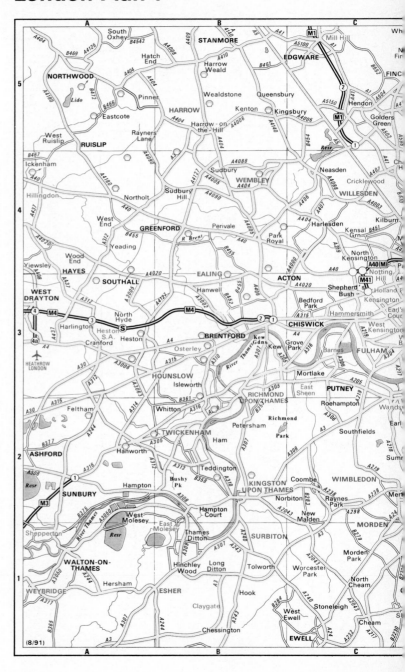

London

(8/91)

# London Plan 1

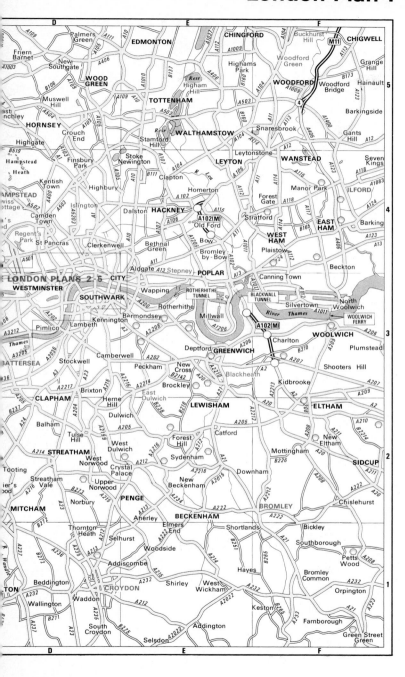

# London Plan 2

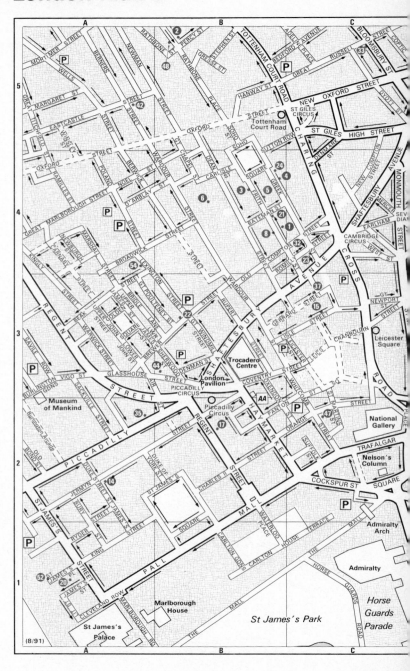

London

(8/91)

# London Plan 2

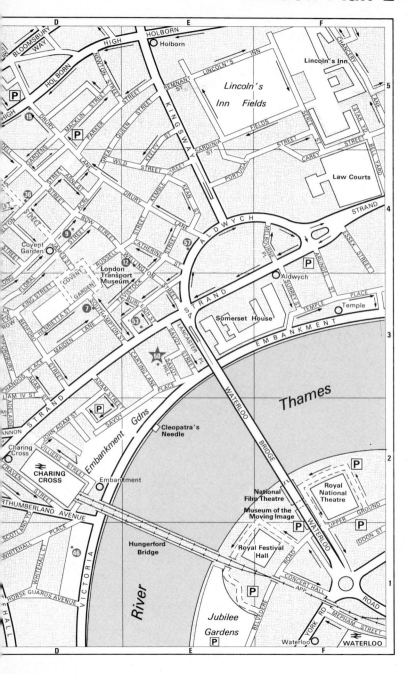

London

# London Plan 3

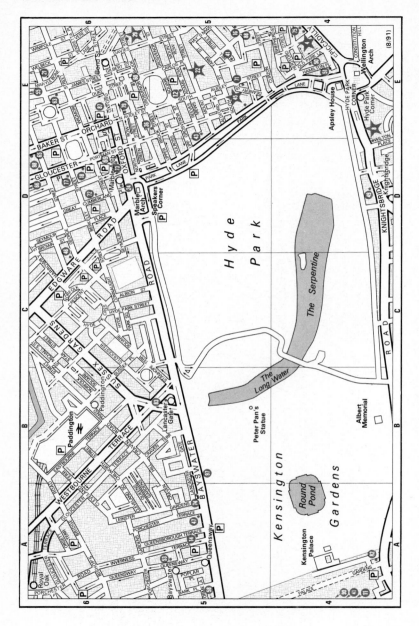

# London Plan 3

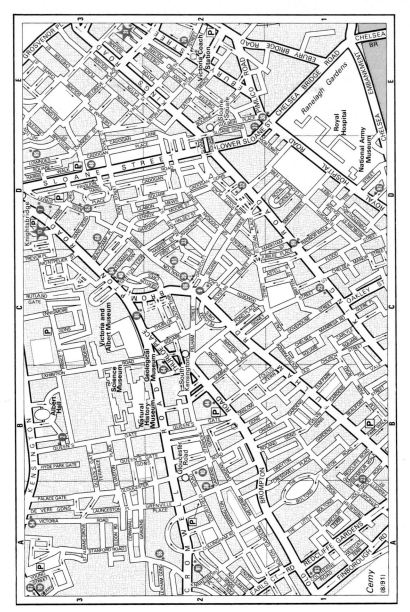

Cerny

(8/91)

# London Plan 4

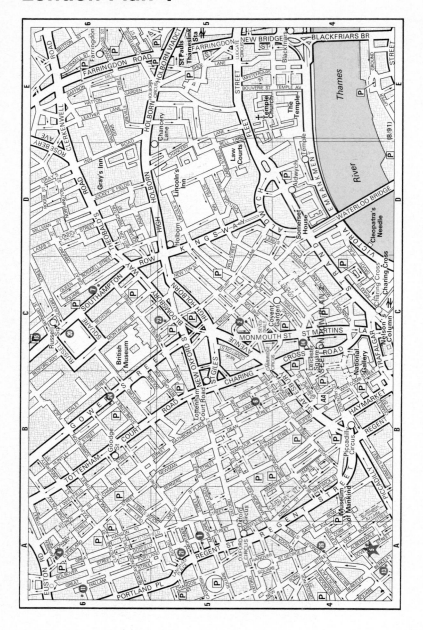

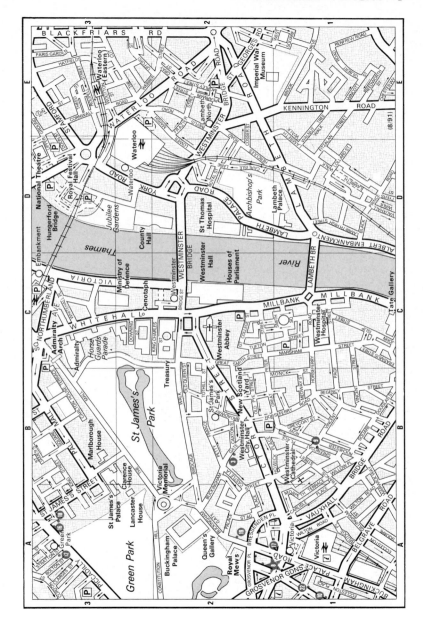

# London Plan 5

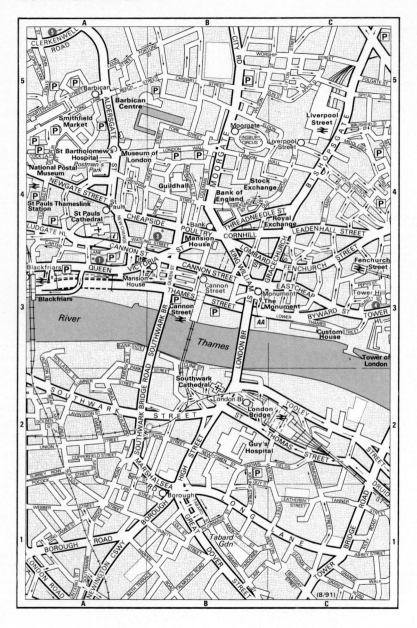

LONDON Greater London Plans 1-5, pages 434-442. (Small scale maps 4 & 5 at back of book.) A map of the London postal area appears on pages 432-433, listed below in postal district order, commencing East, then North, South and West, with a brief indication of the area covered. Detailed plans 2-5 show the locations of AA-appointed hotels and restaurants within the Central London postal districts which are indicated by a number, followed by a grid reference e.g. A5 to help you find the location. Plan 1 shows the districts covered within the outer area keyed by a grid reference e.g. A1. Other places within the county of London are listed under their respective place names and are also keyed to this plan or the main map section. If more detailed information is required the AA Motorists Map of London, on sale at AA offices, is in two parts: the 'West End and the City' shows one-way systems, car parks, stations, hotels, places of interest etc. 'Outer London' gives primary routes, car parks at suburban stations etc. A theatre map of the West End is included. For London Airports see town plan section at the back of this book.

## E1 STEPNEY AND EAST OF THE TOWER OF LONDON

### ★★★★60% Tower Thistle
St Katharine's Way E1 9LD (Mount Charlotte (TS))
☎071-481 2575 Telex no 885934 FAX 071-488 4106
*Overlooking Tower Bridge from its spectacular location on the banks of the Thames, this large modern hotel normally teems with activity. Smart public areas offer a range of eating options which include both the comfortable Princes Room and an informal café which doubles as a night club after dark. The rather functional bedrooms are shortly to be upgraded, and some of them offer splendid views, whilst service in most areas reflects a genuine desire to please.*
808⇄🛏(24fb) CTV in all bedrooms ® T � (room only) 🄿
Lift ( 🏢 136P (charged) 116🛥 (charged)
🍴 International ✤ ☕ ✦
Credit Cards ①②③④⑤

## EC1 CITY OF LONDON

### ⊛ ✕ Le Mesurier
113 Old St EC1V 9JR ☎071-251 8117
*This small French restaurant is very popular with the city's business community, so booking is advisable if you want to sample the French provincial dishes so expertly prepared by Gillian Enthoven. Recommended dishes include the herb brioche filled with chicken livers and bacon and the smoked salmon pâté, to be followed by sea bass with ratatouille and essence of red peppers or breast of pheasant with a whisky and grape sauce. To finish, hot soufflés, the restaurant's speciality, are much in demand and there is always one on the menu. White and dark chocolate terrine is also a favourite. The atmosphere is bustling and lively, with service at peak times somewhat stretched.*
Closed Sat, Sun, 24 Dec-2 Jan & 3 wks Aug
Dinner not served (ex by appointment only)
🍴 French 24 seats Lunch £25-£30alc Dinner £25-£30alc Last lunch 3pm Last dinner 8.30pm 🄿 nc5yrs
Credit Cards ①②③

### ⊛ ✕ Quality Chop House
94 Farringdon Rd EC1 ☎071-837 5093
*'Quality and civility' are the values prized by Charles Fontaine, formerly Head Chef at le Caprice, who owns and runs this attractive early 19th-century café with its convivial atmosphere. Tables, set in booths, are for 6 people and smaller parties are expected to share, which none of the patrons seem to mind. The menu changes daily, but many dishes are so popular – for example the salmon fishcakes, corned beef hash, and ribeye steak – that they are permanent features. The Chop House version of that English standby, sausage and mash, is well worth sampling, consisting of chargrilled Toulouse sausage served with beautifully made mashed potatoes and tasty onion gravy. Whether you choose a grill, a traditional British favourite, fish fresh from the market or*

*one of the more international dishes, the cooking is to be respected for its skill, honesty and lack of pretension. Customers are not expected to eat a 3-course meal unless they wish, but if you do, our inspector recommends the bread and butter pudding as 'memorable'. Booking is essential, and if you are in London on a Sunday, the Brunch is a very civilised way to start the day.*
Lunch not served Sat
🍴 British & French 42 seats ✳ Lunch £3.25-£25alc Dinner £3.25-£25alc Last lunch 3pm Last dinner midnight 🄿

## EC2 CITY OF LONDON

### ⊛⊛⊛ ✕ ✕ ✕ Le Poulbot
45 Cheapside EC2V 6AR ☎071-236 4379 FAX 071-622 5657
*Chef Nicholas Reade has taken charge of this well established City restaurant, one of the Roux brothers' highly successful enterprises. Standards remain high, but the emphasis has shifted a little, to a more straightforward style of modern French cuisine and a number of classical dishes such as Gratin Lyonnaise and Oeufs Florentines. The filet d'agneau rôti, jus de romarin, followed by a Tarte Tatin were our inspector's favourites. The set-price menu and short wine list continue to offer very good value for money.*
Closed Sat, Sun, Xmas & BH's
Dinner not served
🍴 French V 50 seats Last lunch 3pm 🄿 nc10yrs
Credit Cards ①②③⑤

## EC4 CITY OF LONDON

### ⊛⊛ ✕ ✕ City Miyama
17 Godliman St EC4V 5BD ☎071-489 1937
Closed Sat & Sun
🍴 Japanese V 85 seats ✳ Lunch £16-£45&alc Last lunch 2pm Last dinner 10pm 🄿
Credit Cards ①②③⑤

## N1 ISLINGTON

See LONDON plan 1*D4*

### ⊛ ✕ ✕ Frederick's
Camden Passage N1 8EG ☎071-359 2888 FAX 071-359 5173
*Dating back to the 18th century, and originally called 'The Gun', this very popular and well-appointed restaurant was renamed in honour of Prince Augustus Frederick who died in 1813. The enterprising menu is changed fortnightly but always includes some delectable puddings, and the formal service is very efficient.*
Closed Sun, 25-26 Dec, 1 Jan, Good Fri & BH Mons
🍴 International V 150 seats ✳ Lunch £16.95&alc Dinner £16.95 Last lunch 2.30pm Last dinner 11.30pm 🄿 ✦
Credit Cards ①②③④⑤

### ⊛⊛ ✕ Annas Place
90 Mildmay Park N1 4PR ☎071-249 9379
*A small very friendly Swedish café where simplicity and honesty combine to produce outstanding and authentic Swedish cooking. Anna's warm and sincere involvement is complemented by her loyal team of friendly staff. There is a good selection of wines on offer. This restaurant is marvellous value for money.*
Closed Sun, Mon, 2 wks Xmas, 2 wks Etr & 4 wks Aug
🍴 Swedish V 50 seats ✳ Lunch £15.50-£20.50alc Dinner £15.50-£20.50alc Last lunch 2.15pm Last dinner 10.30pm 🄿

## NW1 REGENT'S PARK

See LONDON plan 1*D4*

### ⊛⊛ ✕ ✕ Martin's
239 Baker St NW1 6XE ☎071-935 3130 & 071-935 0997
*Housed in no less a building than the reputed home of Sherlock Holmes, this smart eating establishment has culinary standards which would have met with the great sleuth's approval. Recently appointed chef Herbert Berger has a style of cooking that is*

→

London

*distinctly modern in approach, combining flavours in an assured and exciting manner. Our Inspector enjoyed a warm salad of rocket with scallops, sea bass and red mullet garnished with fresh parmesan and dressed with a warm olive oil and balsamic vinaigrette. Another example from the diverse à la carte menu is the lambs sweet breads braised in madeira with root vegetables and lentils. Service, however, requires a bit of polishing to match the skill in the kitchen.*

Closed Sat, Sun & BH's

♀ English & French 60 seats Lunch fr£23.50 Dinner £24.50-£39alc Last lunch 2pm Last dinner 10pm ✗ nc10yrs

Credit Cards ① ② ③ ⑤

### ※✕✕Sang Thai
12-14 Glentworth St NW1 4PG ☎071-935 4220

*The unusual but aesthetically pleasing appearance of this modern restaurant has been created by high ceilings, hanging lighting raft and silk panels adorning the walls. An extensive menu marks very spicy dishes as 'hot', and charming waitresses are only too happy to advise you in your choice. The Mut Cha Loy Noal (a hot and sour seafood soup) is further enhanced by a chilli paste, and the Kaeng Pa (beef Jungle curry with Thai aubergines, bamboo shoots and fresh basil) is particularly delicious; Pak Toom – lightly steamed vegetables with coconut milk – are fresh, crisp and worth trying. Owner Mrs Asefa Quayyum leads an all-female team who combine courteous service with memorable and healthy cuisine.*

Closed Xmas, New Year & BH's Lunch not served Sat & Sun

♀ Thai V 65 seats Lunch fr£12.95 Dinner fr£12.95 Last lunch 2.30pm Last dinner 11pm ✗

Credit Cards ① ② ③ ⑤

### ※✕Great Nepalese
48 Eversholt St NW1 ☎071-388 6737

*The simple, unassuming appearance of this restaurant belies the quality of its cuisine. Pleasant, helpful waiters are happy to explain the menu which, naturally, includes Nepalese starters and main dishes, as well as Tandoori meals and a variety of meat and fish curries. The vegetarian dishes were highly regarded by our inspector, who also recommended the Aloo Achar – a cold dish of potato, peas, chilli and powdered sesame.*

Closed 25 & 26 Dec

♀ Nepalese V 48 seats Last lunch 2.45pm Last dinner 11.30pm ✗

Credit Cards ① ② ③ ⑤

### NW2 CRICKLEWOOD, WILLESDEN

See LONDON plan 1*C4*

### ※✕Quincy's 84
675 Finchley Rd NW2 2JP ☎071-794 8499

*An attractive unpretentious restaurant run with relaxed charm by owner David Wardle and his friendly young staff. The short reasonably priced menu of imaginative dishes, including delicious lamb with apricot and thyme sauce, is supplemented by a choice of home-made soups and fresh fish. Good desserts and a modest French wine list.*

Closed Sun & Mon Lunch not served

♀ English & French V 30 seats ✳ Dinner fr£19.50 Last dinner 10.30pm ✗

Credit Cards ① ③

### NW3 HAMPSTEAD AND SWISS COTTAGE

See LONDON plan 1*D4*

### ★★★★ 65% Holiday Inn Swiss Cottage
128 King Henry's Rd, Swiss Cottage NW3 3ST (Holiday Inns) ☎071-722 7711 Telex no 267396 FAX 071-586 5822

*A modern multi-storey hotel with its own car park, conveniently situated for access to central London. Refurbished bedrooms are well equipped and quite spacious, and public areas very comfortable, with a pleasant airy restaurant and split-level lounge and cocktail bar serving a popular all-day menu. A gym has now*

*been added to the leisure club with its popular indoor swimming pool.*

303⇨♠(166fb)✗in 52 bedrooms CTV in all bedrooms ® T ✱ S% sB⇨♠£135-£155 dB⇨♠£157.50-£178 (room only) ♬ Lift ( ⊞ 50P 100🅰 CFA ⬛ (heated) sauna solarium gymnasium *xmas*

♀ International V ♿ ☑ ✗ ✱ S% Sunday Lunch fr£16alc Dinner fr£21alc Last dinner 10.30pm

Credit Cards ① ② ③ ④ ⑤ ⓔ

### ★★★ 64% Forte Posthouse
Haverstock Hill NW3 4RB (Forte Hotels) ☎071-794 8121 Telex no 262494 FAX 071-435 5586

*A refurbishment programme at this modern hotel has already improved the restaurant and bar and given an attractive new look to some of the bedrooms, and the new menu at Franklyn's Restaurant is proving popular. There is a good car park and access to the city is convenient from the nearby Belsize Park Station.*

138⇨♠(58fb)✗in 28 bedrooms CTV in all bedrooms ® T ✱ sB⇨♠£39.50-£49.50 dB⇨♠£39.50-£49.50 (room only) ♬ Lift ( 70P CFA *xmas*

V ♿ ☑ ✗ ✱ Lunch £12.65-£23alc High tea £3.20 Dinner £12.65-£23alc Last dinner 10pm

Credit Cards ① ② ③ ⑤

### ★★★ 59% Charles Bernard
5-7 Frognal, Hampstead NW3 6AL ☎071-794 0101 Telex no 23560 FAX 071-794 0100

*A well managed commercial hotel, ideal for weekend breaks, close to the Finchley Road with good access to the capital. Accommodation comprises well equipped bedrooms, quality compact bathrooms, a well designed lobby bar and lounge, and a small basement restaurant furnished in the bright modern style. The restaurant offers a popular choice of dishes and self-service breakfast buffet. An automatic lift serves all floors, and 24-hour room service is available.*

57⇨♠ CTV in all bedrooms ® T ✕ S% sB&B⇨♠£52.50-£73 dB&B⇨♠£63-£86 ♬ Lift ( CTV 15P

♀ English & French ♿ ☑ S% Lunch £9.75-£16alc High tea £3.50-£5.50alc Dinner £9.75-£16alc Last dinner 9.15pm

Credit Cards ① ② ③ ⑤ ⓔ

### ※※✕7 Pond Street
7 Pond St, Hampstead NW3 ☎071-435 1541

*Chef/proprietor Sandy Anderson opened this very popular all day Brasserie 18 months' ago. He offers excellent value for money with a blackboard lunch menu at £5.95 and also an à la carte and individually priced 'Today's Specials' menus. Our inspector enjoyed artichoke with fresh asparagus served with a delightful beurre blanc sauce followed by a fricassée of kidneys, sweetbreads, oyster mushrooms and Madeira, beautifully cooked with a jus lie and chanterelle mushrooms. Desserts include sticky toffee pudding. A short selection of French vintage wines are available by the glass and the house wine is good value at £7.50 a bottle. Industrious service is friendly and helpful contributing to an enjoyable experience. The 'downstairs' restaurant only opens for Saturday dinner and Sunday lunch.*

Closed Mon & 24-26 Dec

Dinner not served Sun

♀ International V 100 seats Lunch £5.95&alc Dinner fr£12alc Last dinner 10.30pm ✗ ✗

Credit Cards ① ③

### ※✕Zenw 3 Chinese
83 Hampstead High St NW3 1RE ☎071-794 7863 FAX 071-437 0641

*Interior and furnishings are in the 'Art Deco' style at this restaurant which provides the 'New Wave' style of cooking with salads, charcoal grills and iron plate food.*

Closed Xmas

♀ Chinese **V** 140 seats ✱ Lunch £15-£25alc Dinner £20-£35alc
Last dinner 11.30pm ⚞
Credit Cards ①②③④⑤

---

### NW7 MILL HILL

**See LONDON plan 1**C5

⊛✕✕**Good Earth**
143-145 Broadway, Mill Hill NW7 4RN ☎081-959 7011
FAX 071-823 8769
*Smart, cheerful and popular restaurant with appealing menu of
authentic Cantonese cooking.*
Closed 24-27 Dec
♀ Cantonese, Pekinese & Szechwan **V** 100 seats ✱ Lunch £15-
£30&alc Dinner £15-£30&alc Last lunch 2.30pm Last dinner
11.15pm 12 P
Credit Cards ①②③⑤

---

### NW8 ST JOHN'S WOOD

**See LONDON plan 1** D4

⊛✕**Greek Valley**
130 Boundary Rd NW8 ORH ☎071-624 3217
*Customers 'in the know' ask for the smoked, mixed meat sausage
(not listed on the menu) freshly made by Peta Bosnic who, with his
Effie, runs this unpretentious and increasingly popular Greek
restaurant. The majority of the dishes are home-made, of good
quality fresh ingredients. All the traditional specialities feature on
the menu and our inspector praised both the Moussaka, the
Loukanika (spicy, marinated, pork sausages) and the salads. The
house wine is a bargain at under £6, and there are some good
Greek and Cypriot wines to try, particularly the Galliga Ruby, a
red wine matured in oak barrels.*
Closed Sun Lunch not served Sat
♀ Greek **V** 62 seats ✱ Lunch £10.50-£12.50alc Dinner £10.50-
£12.50alc Last lunch 2.30pm Last dinner 11.30pm ⚞
Credit Cards ①③

---

### SE3 BLACKHEATH

**See LONDON plan 1** E3
★★ 64% **Bardon Lodge**
Stratheden Rd SE3 7TH ☎081-853 4051 FAX 081-858 7387
*Situated just off Blackheath, this elegant house has smart, well
furnished public rooms including a popular restaurant offering
fresh homemade food. Bedrooms vary in size, with some compact
singles, but all are well equipped and kept to a high standard.*
37rm(5⇨23🐾)(3fb)2🛏 CTV in all bedrooms ® **T**
✖ (ex guide dogs) sB&B£49 sB&B⇨🐾£59 dB&B£70
dB&B⇨🐾£82-£92 🈂
《 CTV 16P ❖ CFA
**V** ❖ ⚌ ✂ ✱ Dinner £12.60-£16.50 Last dinner 9.15pm
Credit Cards ①②③

⊛✕**Laicram Thai**
1 Blackheath Grove, Blackheath SE3 ☎081-852 4710
*This small restaurant is invitingly decorated with plants and Thai
ornaments. The individually priced dishes have descriptions, and
helpful staff are willing to explain further to novices of this Asian
cuisine. The mix of herbs and spices, curries and stir-fries makes
for a delicious variety. Laicram is the pretty blue and white
traditional porcelain on which the food is served.*
Closed 25-26 Dec & 1 Jan
**V** 45 seats ✱ Lunch £15alc Dinner £15alc Last lunch 2.30pm
Last dinner 11.30pm
P
Credit Cards ①②③

A rosette means exceptional standards of cuisine.

---

### SE22 EAST DULWICH

**See LONDON plan 1** E3

⊛✕**Thistells**
65 Lordship Ln SE22 ☎081-299 1921
Lunch not served Sat & Mon
Dinner not served Sun
♀ French **V** 30 seats Lunch £9.90-£25alc Dinner £9.90-£25alc
Last lunch 2.30pm Last dinner 10.30pm P
Credit Cards ①③

---

### SW1 WESTMINSTER

★★★★★⊛ **THE BERKELEY**

Wilton Place,
Knightsbridge SW1X 7RL
☎071-235 6000
Telex no 919252
FAX 071-235 4330
*With the completion of
extensive refurbishment this
busy hotel continues to offer
accommodation of a very high standard. Public rooms are not
spacious but are thoughtfully furnished and decorative. The
attractive restaurant remains popular offering a sound
standard of French cuisine and an interesting, well planned
wine list. The bedrooms, which vary in size, are comfortably
appointed and provided with modern facilities and thoughtful
extras. Good leisure facilities are available on the top floor: a* →

London

*heated swimming pool, sauna and gym. Service is professional yet with a friendly approach by helpful and willing staff.*

160➪ CTV in all bedrooms T 🌂 S15% sB➪frf£170 dB➪frf£215 (room only) 🆔

Lift (⊞ 50🚗 (£20 per 24hrs) ₩ CFA 🖥 (heated) sauna solarium gymnasium cinema 🎵 *xmas*

♀ International V ✿ ♨ Lunch fr£20.50&alc Dinner £30-£55alc Last dinner 10.45pm

Credit Cards ① ② ③ ⑤

★★★★★⊛⊛78% **The Hyde Park**

Knightsbridge SW1Y 7LA (Forte Hotels) ☎071-235 2000 Telex no 262057 FAX 071-235 4552

*The Grill Room, with its panelled walls and club-like atmosphere, is a popular eating place, excellently run by manager Mr Cacace. The menu changes according to season and at lunchtimes there are daily specials, which may include traditional English dishes like steak and kidney pie or roast beef with Yorkshire pudding. A meal from the à la carte menu might start with a warm salad of scallops and dill, or thinly sliced fillet of rabbit with walnuts, apple and pomegranate, to be followed by delicately pan-fried fillet of turbot with artichokes or pheasant on a bed of spinach, pine nuts and raisins, with a red-wine sauce.*

186➪2🛏⚲in 19 bedrooms CTV in all bedrooms T 🌂 ✱ sB➪frf£199 dB➪£225-£250 (room only) 🆔

Lift (⊞ ₽ ₩ CFA

♀ English French & Italian V ✿ ♨ ✱ Lunch fr£19.50&alc High tea frf£10.50 Dinner fr£21.50&alc Last dinner 9.30pm

Credit Cards ① ② ③ ④ ⑤

★★★★★⊛⊛73% **Hyatt Carlton Tower**

Cadogan Place SW1X 9PY ☎071-235 5411 Telex no 21944 FAX 071-235 9129

*A modern commercial hotel which has undergone further refurbishment to maintain the high standard always expected of this popular establishment. There is a relaxing lounge and a choice of 2 restaurants. The Rib Room offers a simple menu, and the attractive Chelsea Room, with its bright conservatory extension, has a comprehensive menu prepared with skill and imagination by Chef Bernard Gaume, including some interesting dishes. An extensive wine list, though still pricey, offers a very good selection of wines. Bedrooms are adequately appointed with modern facilities.*

224➪⚲in 23 bedrooms CTV in all bedrooms T 🌂 (ex guide dogs) ✱ S% dB➪frf£258.50 (room only) 🆔

Lift (⊞ 40🚗 (£2.50 per hour) ₩ ♪ (hard) sauna solarium gymnasium beauty treatment hair salon

♀ French and International V ✿ ♨ Lunch £23.50&alc High tea £15-£20alc Dinner £22-£35alc Last dinner 11.15pm

Credit Cards ① ② ③ ④ ⑤

★★★★⊛ **GORING**

Beeston Place, Grosvenor Gardens SW1W 0JW (Pride of Britain) ☎071-834 8211 Telex no 919166 FAX 071-834 4393

*This very popular and constantly improving family-run hotel continues to provide a hospitable atmosphere and thoughtful service in tasteful surroundings. Bedrooms vary in size, but all are comfortably appointed and well equipped with modern facilities, while public areas – though very limited, and always crowded because of The Goring's popularity – include an attractive and*

*elegant restaurant where new chef John Elliott offers reasonably priced table d'hôte and à la carte menus of imaginative dishes. A starter such as Langoustine Broth with Scallop Ravioli or Terrine of Guinea Fowl with cranberry chutney might be followed by Roulade of Salmon and Sole with spinach leaves and wild mushrooms, or Tournedos of Beef topped with herb crust and served with Stilton sauce, the meal ending with a selection of puddings that sometimes includes bread and butter pudding at lunchtime! The meal is accompanied by an extensive and well chosen list containing some 156 wines and catering for every taste and pocket. The Goring Hotel appears in our colour feature 'Hotel at Work' on page 27 of the guide.*

84➪ CTV in all bedrooms T 🌂 S10% sB➪£118-£128 dB➪£165-£175 (room only)

Lift (⊞ 10P (£10.00) 4🚗 (£10.00) ₩ CFA 🎵

♀ English & French V ✿ ♨ Lunch £20&alc Dinner £24&alc Last dinner 10pm

Credit Cards ① ② ③ ⑤

★★★★74% **Halkin**

5-6 Halkin St, Belgravia SW1X 7DJ (Small Luxury Hotels) ☎071-333 1000 Telex no 290308 FAX 071-333 1100

*The latest and most contemporary of the new wave style international London hotels, with a traditional dark brick and Belgravian townhouse exterior, and interior 'surprising' and airy interior. There is a mosaic marble-floored lobby, sitting area, and a glass fronted restaurant. Bedrooms include luxurious suites, studios and Halkin Rooms, all have been individually designed with distinctive modern furnishings, hi-tech equipment and full air conditioning. The relaxed Halkin Restaurant offers fine cuisine from a choice of innovative menus. Twenty-four hour room service is provided along with car parking, concierge, and full business facilities.*

41➪ CTV in all bedrooms T 🌂 (ex guide dogs) ✱ S% sB➪£211.50-£329 dB➪£211.50-£329 (room only) 🆔

Lift (⊞ CTV ₽ ₩

♀ International V ✿ ♨ ✱ S% Lunch £16.50-£20.50&alc Dinner £28.50&alc Last dinner 11pm

Credit Cards ① ② ③ ④ ⑤

★★★★⊛73% **Duke's**

35 St James's Place SW1A 1NY (Small Luxury Hotels) ☎071-491 4840 Telex no 28283 FAX 071-493 1264

*Delightfully situated in a flower-decked courtyard off St James's, this red-brick Edwardian hotel maintains a peaceful and exclusive atmosphere, fine paintings and quality furniture setting the tone of its cosy, intimate public areas. A reliable blend of English and French cuisine, soundly based on good ingredients, is enhanced by excellent sauces. Bedrooms and bathrooms, though well appointed, can be fairly compact, but more spacious accommodation is provided in a large number of elegant and particularly comfortable suites. Service throughout is smiling and attentive.*

64➪(2fb)1🆔 CTV in all bedrooms T 🌂 (ex guide dogs) sB&B➪frf£180 dB&B➪£215-£260 🆔

Lift (₩ CFA nc5yrs *xmas*

V ✿ ♨ ✱ Lunch £17.50-£19.95&alc Dinner £28.50&alc Last dinner 10pm

Credit Cards ① ② ③ ⑤

★★★★72% **Stafford**

16-18 St James's Place SW1A 1NJ (Small Luxury Hotels) ☎071-493 0111 Telex no 28602 FAX 071-493 7121

*In an unobtrusive setting in St James's Place just a short stroll from Piccadilly, this charming hotel offers a town house environment of quiet calm, with traditional courteous service, good food and fine wines. Bedrooms are individually furnished with quality soft fabrics and though some are rather compact, all are comfortable. A most deserving 'Courtesy and Care' award winner 1991/1992 for the London region (see colour feature on p16).*

74⇄🛏1🖵✂in 6 bedrooms CTV in all bedrooms T 🎯 ✳
sB⇄🕯£184 dB⇄🕯£200-£430 (room only) 🍽
Lift ( 🅿 🚲 CFA *xmas*
🍷 French V 🕯 ⚘ ✳ Lunch fr£25 Dinner fr£30&alc Last
dinner 10pm
Credit Cards ①②③④⑤

★★★★ 67% **Royal Westminster Thistle**
40 Buckingham Palace Rd SW1W 0QT (Mount Charlotte (TS))
☎071-834 1821 Telex no 916821 FAX 071-931 7542
*Bedrooms here are spacious and comfortable, with a good range of
modern facilities including air conditioning. The comfortable
lounge offers all-day refreshments and you can eat in the Parisian-
style café, open all day, or in the more formal Brasserie Saint
Germain, serving lunch and dinner. In the hotel's continuing
upgrading programme, half the rooms will be refurbished during
1991.*
134⇄🕯(69fb)✂in 67 bedrooms CTV in all bedrooms T 🎯
(room only) 🍽
Lift ( 🎹 🅿
🍷 English & French 🕯 ⚘ ✂
Credit Cards ①②③④⑤

★★★★ 63% **Forte Crest St James**
Jermyn St SW1Y 6JF (Forte Hotels) ☎071-930 2111
Telex no 263187 FAX 071-839 2125
*The proprietors of this modern hotel have been completely
refurbishing its bedrooms to provide greater comfort. Two rooms
have balconies with superb views over London and three floors are
for non-smokers. The restaurant offers an extensive à la carte
menu plus a buffet at lunchtime and there is a first-floor gallery
lounge serving refreshments all day, plus a bar. Service is
professional and attentive. A business centre is available from
11am to 7pm.*
256⇄🕯🖵 CTV in all bedrooms T sB⇄🕯fr£135
dB⇄🕯£145-£160 (room only) 🍽
Lift ( 80🚗 (£20 per 24hrs) CFA *xmas*
🍷 English & French V 🕯 ⚘ ✂ ✳ Lunch £12.50&alc
Credit Cards ①②③④⑤

★★★ 66% *Rubens*
Buckingham Palace Rd SW1W 0PS ☎071-834 6600
Telex no 916577 FAX 071-828 5401
*Opposite the Royal Mews, this well run hotel is ideally placed for
Victoria Station. Public rooms are air conditioned, and the Gallery
Lounge, cocktail bar and Masters Restaurant are comfortable and
modern. There is a full lounge service including afternoon tea, as
well as the self-service Masters Buffet Table, and 24-hour room
service. The best rooms, some rather compact, are on the 2nd floor.
Car parking is very difficult.*
191⇄🕯(3fb)✂in 44 bedrooms CTV in all bedrooms ® T
🎯 (ex guide dogs)
Lift ( 🅿
🍷 International V 🕯 ⚘ ✂ Last dinner 10pm
Credit Cards ①②③⑤

★★★ 65% **Royal Horseguards Thistle**
Whitehall Court SW1A 2EJ (Mount Charlotte (TS))
☎071-839 3400 Telex no 917096 FAX 071-925 2263
*This large imposing hotel has a splendid marbled entrance foyer.
Other public areas are equally grand and include a comfortable
lounge, coffee shop and club-like bar and restaurant. Bedrooms
range from the luxurious and spacious Executive rooms to the
rather gloomy Standard rooms, though there are plans for
improvements.*
376⇄🕯(98fb)✂in 95 bedrooms CTV in all bedrooms ® T 🎯
(room only) 🍽
Lift ( 🅿
🍷 International 🕯 ⚘ ✂
Credit Cards ①②③④⑤

London

★ **EBURY COURT**

28 Ebury St SW1 0LU
☎071-730 8147
FAX 071-823 5966

Closed 21 Dec-4 Jan

*This well known hotel, a
conversion of 5 adjoining
town houses, has now been
upgraded to provide more modern facilities while still
retaining its charm and character; a new management team
also maintains the warm, friendly atmosphere of previous
years. A number of more spacious bedrooms supplement the
original compact ones, all accommodation being attractively
decorated and equipped with colour TV, telephones and tea-
making facilities. Public areas include 2 small but comfortable
lounges, a well appointed cocktail bar and a new ground floor
restaurant, offering the same short menus of skilfully prepared
dishes and adequate wine list as the charming dining room in
the basement.*

46rm(22⇄🛏)(3fb)4🛏 CTV in all bedrooms ® T ✱
sB&B£60-£65 sB&B⇄🛏£95 dB&B£85 dB&B⇄🛏£110-
£125

Lift ( ✗ 🅿

V ✤ 🖵 ✱ Lunch £12-£20&alc High tea £15-£20&alc
Credit Cards 1 3 5

---

❀❀ ✗ ✗ ✗ **Auberge de Provence**
(St James Court Hotel), Buckingham Gate SW1E 6AF
☎071-821 1899 Telex no 938075 FAX 071-630 7587

*One of three restaurants at this hotel, the Auberge de Provence has
a distinctly Mediterranean décor, in keeping with the style of its
food which encompasses all the classic flavours of Provence (it is a
sister restaurant of the celebrated l'Ousteau de Beaumanière in
France). In addition to the carte, guests are also offered a menu
gastronomique and a menu dégustation. A meal might begin with
ravioli stuffed with flavoursome wild mushrooms and served with a
light, creamy truffle sauce. Sea bass to follow comes with a sauce
combining those classic Provençal flavours: fresh basil, olives, olive
oil and tomatoes. The selection of French cheeses is admirable, and
hot desserts are made to order. Their version of tarte tatin used
pears rather than apples, and was served with a tarragon ice
cream, to confuse the English palate. Prices are not cheap, but
neither are the ingredients.*

Closed Sun, BH's, 26 Dec-15 Jan Lunch not served Sat
♀ French V 88 seats Last lunch 2.30pm Last dinner 11pm
✗ ✤

Credit Cards 1 2 3 4 5

---

❀❀ ✗ ✗ **Le Caprice**
Arlington House, Arlington St SW1A 1RT ☎071-629 2239
FAX 071-493 9040

*Long a favourite in the theatrical world Le Caprice is the perfect
late night rendezvous (but book at least a week ahead) and the
sort of place where you can order a simple dish of scrambled eggs
as easily as a full 3-course meal. The Maître d'Hotel Mr Angelo
ensures that all will run smoothly and enjoyably, while the young
chef Mark Hix has been very successful in maintaining the
popularity of this brasserie and its reputation for good cooking.
Excellent teas and coffees are supplied by Fauchon of Paris. The
wine list has some good vintages and the house wine is particularly
good in length and flavour. There is an NCP car park close by.*

Closed 24 Dec pm-2 Jan am

♀ English, French, Italian & American V 70 seats ✱ Lunch
£18-£35alc Dinner £18-£35alc Last lunch 3pm Last dinner
mdnt ✗ nc5yrs
Credit Cards 1 2 3 5

---

❀❀ ✗ ✗ **Gavvers**
61-63 Lower Sloane St SW1W 8HP ☎071-730 5983 &
071-823 4772 FAX 071-622 5657

*A Roux Brothers enterprise, the restaurant offers a very popular,
value for money, fixed price menu, the charge covering not only
half a bottle of wine but also service and VAT.*

Closed Sun, Xmas-1 Jan & BH's Lunch not served Sat
♀ French V 58 seats ✱ Lunch £12.50-£14.75 Dinner £22.65-
£27.95 Last lunch 2.30pm Last dinner 11pm ✗
Credit Cards 1 2 3 5

---

❀❀ ✗ ✗ **Ristorante L'Incontro**
87 Pimlico Rd SW1W 8PH ☎071-730 3663 071-730 6327
FAX 071-730 5062

*Incorporating the best recipes from the Veneziana region, a well
balanced and interesting menu is offered here. Chef Biagiou di
Maria uses the best quality ingredients and market-fresh produce
with which to perform his traditional skills. Such dishes as Funghi
con Polenta, Pasta e Fagioli, Venetian Brown Soup, Seppioline
alla Briglia (grilled small cuttlefish) and Picceata al Mango (veal
escalopes with fresh mango sauce) are featured. Pasta is all home-
made and there is always a choice of delicious desserts. The wine
list includes a fine selection of Italian wines and a classic Bordeaux
section. Parking can be difficult and reservations are strongly
advised.*

Closed 25 Dec & Bank Holidays Lunch not served Sun
♀ Italian V 80 seats ✱ Lunch £16.50&alc Dinner £40-£50alc
Last lunch 2pm Last dinner 11.30pm P ♫
Credit Cards 1 2 3 4 5

---

❀ ✗ ✗ *Ken Lo's Memories of China*
67 Ebury St SW1W 0NZ ☎071-730 7734

*Ken Lo's restaurant, with its white décor, well-spaced screened
tables and formal yet friendly service, maintains its high standard
cuisine. The à la carte menu offers a wide choice of Chinese
favourites and specialities, such as Szechuan double-cooked pork,
and the interesting set menus vary from lobster feast to quick
executive luncheons. Dishes are freshly made with sauces
providing nicely balanced contrasts of flavour: Peking Kuo-Tieh
dumpling and crispy duck with pancakes were found particularly
enjoyable, and the wine list has a good choice of Bordeaux and
New World wines.*

Closed Sun & BH's

♀ Chinese V 80 seats Last dinner 10.45pm ✗
Credit Cards 1 2 3 5

---

❀❀ ✗ ✗ *Mijanou*
143 Ebury St SW1W 9QN ☎071-730 4099 FAX 071-823 6402

*Sonia and Neville Blech's established restaurant has just reopened
following a complete refurbishment. Regulars will be pleased that
the formula and style has changed little. However, the basement
dining room is now used as a bar and somewhere to smoke as
upstairs is now 'no smoking'. Sonia has devised 2 set price menus
with the option of eating 2 or 3 courses. Dishes tasted by our
inspector included the Gâteau de Pintadeau et de Foie Gras –
guinea fowl in a firm mousse set in a subtly flavoured orange
muscat and passion fruit jelly – followed by escalope of fresh tuna
served with lentils and a delicate ginger and soya sauce. There is
always a vegetarian option, with a dish such as ravioli stuffed with
pine kernels, herbs and mushrooms set on a tomato and watercress
coulis. Desserts include a special summer pudding with fruits
bound in a creamy yogurt mixture and a casing of sweet brown
bread made by Sonia. Coffee is served with good home-made petits
fours. Neville Blech supervises the front in a quiet, attentive
manner and he is also responsible for the excellent wine list.*

Closed Sat, Sun, 2 wks Xmas, 1 wk Etr, 3 wks Aug & BH's
♀ French V 30 seats Last lunch 2pm Last dinner 11pm ✗ ✤
Credit Cards 1 2 3 5

---

For key to symbols in English see the bookmark.

### ❀ ✕ ✕ Mitsukoshi
Dorland House, 14-16 Regent St SW1 4PH ☎071-930 0317
FAX 071-839 1167

☺ Japanese 100 seats ✹ Lunch £15 Dinner £30 Last lunch 2pm
Last dinner 10pm ✔

Credit Cards ① ② ③ ⑤

### ❀❀ ✕ ✕ *Salloos*
62-64 Kinnerton St SW1X 8ER ☎071-235 4444

*In a quiet street just off Knightsbridge, this unassuming first-floor
restaurant serves Pakistani cuisine of the finest standard, using no
artificial colourings: succulent tandoori dishes (all marinated for
24 hours), specialities such as Chicken Karahi and Hallem Akbari
(lamb in spiced lentils and wholewheat germ), fragrant freshly
cooked rice and newly fired naan bread. Waiters can be distant
and be prepared for hefty cover and service charges.*

Closed Sun & BH's

☺ Pakistani **V** 70 seats Last lunch 2.30pm Last dinner 11.15pm
✔

Credit Cards ① ② ③ ⑤

### ❀❀ ✕ ✕ Santini
29 Ebury St SW1W 0NZ ☎071-730 4094 & 071-730 8275
FAX 071-730 0544

*This stylish, modern Italian restaurant, frequented by the rich and
famous, offers an à la carte menu supplemented by monthly
changing specialities. Regional Venetian dishes are usually on the
menu, and though possibly the most interesting they are also the
most expensive; the set 2-course business lunch represents better
value for money, though it still incurs both cover and service
charges. A typical meal might include Tagliatelle Al Funghi
Dibosio (a delicious home-made pasta in a rich wild mushroom
sauce) followed perhaps by Branzino Santini (a whole sea bass
topped with a flavoursome balsamic vinegar, olive oil and fresh
herb dressing) and a dessert from the sweet trolley which, though
not particularly imaginative, features such Italian favourites as
Strawberries Romanoff and Tiramisu. The wine list, though
expensive and a little short on half bottles, features some of the
good wines of Italy (including some interesting dessert wines) with
no fewer than 10 Barolos. Speedy, attentive service can at times be
selective or impersonal.*

Closed Xmas, Etr & BH's Lunch not served Sat & Sun

☺ Italian **V** 60 seats ✹ Lunch £20&alc Dinner £38-£48alc Last
lunch 2.30pm Last dinner 11.30pm ✔

Credit Cards ① ② ③ ⑤

### ❀❀ ✕ Simply Nico
48a Rochester Row SW1P 1JU ☎071-630 8061

*This smart but bustling restaurant is the one Nico Ladenis did not
sell when he himself moved on to bigger and better premises. Chefs
have changed and the style has evolved beyond the 'very simple';
under the aegis of Andrew Jeffs, who trained with Nico and was
sous chef at Great Portland Street, so patrons can expect skilled
cooking, with light custards (exemplified in a most delicious starter
composed of a smoked haddock custard set on spinach), delicate
pastry and sound saucing. Steak and chips, on the other hand, are
normally available, so there is still a hint of simplicity. Much
enjoyed on a recent visit was the rustic duck comfit (good crisp
skin enclosing pungently flavoured duck within); for pudding there
was a choice of pear crumble or trifle. Though short, the wine list is
reliable and the other elements of the meal – olives, bread and
coffee – were all very good.*

Closed Sun & 4-27 Aug Lunch not served Sat

☺ French 48 seats ✹ Lunch fr£23 Dinner fr£23 Last lunch 2pm
Last dinner 11pm ✔ nc4yrs

Credit Cards ① ③ ⑤

Red star hotels are each
highlighted by a pink
tinted panel.

---

★★★★

★★★★❀❀❀❀ CAPITAL

Basil St, Knightsbridge
SW3 1AT (Relais et
Châteaux) ☎071-589 5171
Telex no 919042
FAX 071-225 0011

*Refurbishment of the
bedrooms has continued over
the last year to maintain the
high standards now expected of this busy town house hotel.
The rooms do vary in size, but have been tastefully decorated
and finished, and equipped with modern facilities and
thoughtful extras. Public rooms remain limited, but retain the
charm and the warm atmosphere which are so much a part of
this hotel. The attractive restaurant is as popular as ever,
largely because of Maitre Chef Philip Britten's cooking.
Menus have been thoughtfully prepared and include a set
priced fish menu which includes dishes like baked fillet of sea
bass with thyme and orange, and duck ballotine stuffed with
foie gras. Service throughout is highly professional and
friendly, another feature of this charming hotel.*

48⇦↑ CTV in all bedrooms T ✹ S15% sB⇦↑£150-£175
dB⇦↑£175-£265 (room only)

Lift ( ⊞ 12🚗 (£15) 🚗 CFA

☺ French **V** ♥ ☒ ✹ Lunch £20 Dinner fr£25&alc Last
dinner 11pm

Credit Cards ① ② ③ ④ ⑤

### ★★★71% *Basil Street*
Basil St, Knightsbridge SW3 1AH ☎071-581 3311
Telex no 28379 FAX 071-581 3693

*Just by Harrods in the centre of Knightsbridge, this independent
hotel with a long established standing management team has
retained its Edwardian comfort and elegance. Splendid stylishly
furnished public rooms offer a haven from London's bustle and the
hotel has many devotees.*

92rm(72⇦) CTV in all bedrooms

Lift ( ✔ 🚗

☺ International **V** ♥ ☒ Last dinner 9.45pm

Credit Cards ① ② ③ ④ ⑤

### ❀ ✕ ✕ ✕ Waltons
121 Walton St SW3 2HP ☎071-584 0204 FAX 071-581 2848

*Chef Tony Cameron has brought his own adventurous style of
cooking to this long-established and famous restaurant.
Surroundings are opulent, the wine list excellent, and diners may
choose between the prix fixe and the more expensive à la carte
menus. Service is very professional, but can be impersonal.*

Closed 25-26 Dec

☺ International **V** 65 seats ✹ Lunch £14.75&alc Dinner £30-
£45alc Last lunch 2.30pm Last dinner 11.30pm ✔

Credit Cards ① ② ③ ④ ⑤

### ❀❀❀ ✕ ✕ Bibendum
Michelin House, 81 Fulham Rd SW3 6RD ☎071-581 5817
FAX 071-823 7925

*Simon Hopkinson's restaurant, housed in the Old Michelin
building, maintains its popularity despite high prices. His cooking
is famous for robust flavours but, at least in the summer months, he
seems to have moved towards lighter saucing and flavours. Dishes
on the fixed price lunch menu tend to be less elaborate than in the
evenings, with dishes like hake and chips or fillets of brill, followed
by rhubarb fool or apricot and almond tart often featured. The
quality of the food here remains very high – try for example his
tomato and pesto tart – but popularity brings its own drawbacks*

→

*when it comes to the service which can sometimes seem rushed. The street level Oyster Bar, open all day, is also proving very popular.*

Closed 24-28 Dec

♕ Continental **V** 74 seats ✱ Lunch £31 Last lunch 2.30pm Last dinner 11.30pm ✔ nc5yrs

Credit Cards ①③

### ❀❀❀✕✕ *Dans*

119 Sydney St SW3 6NR ☎071-352 2718

*A well established and popular restaurant, especially in summer when guests eat in the attractive garden or conservatory. Lunch time dishes are individually priced, while in the evening a good value set price 2 or 3-course menu is offered, which also includes coffee. Chef Bernhard Engelhardt has a varied repertoire encompassing modern and traditional influences. By popular demand, some dishes are an almost permanent feature, such as the twice baked cheese and spinach soufflé, definitely not for calorie counters. German influences are apparent in the wholesome lentil and smoked pork soup. There are daily specials and vegetarian dishes, too. Our Inspector chose moist fillets of red mullet baked in sea salt with fresh tarragon, with a serve yourself selection of fresh vegetables. Indulgent desserts include Dan's truffle cake, rich and dense, served with a coffee bean sauce. The smart team of male waiting staff are pleasantly attentive.*

Closed BH's & Xmas-New Year

Dinner not served Sun

♕ English & French 50 seats Last lunch 2.30pm Last dinner 10.45pm ✔

Credit Cards ①②③⑤

### ❀❀✕✕ *Daphne's*

110-112 Draycott Av, Chelsea SW3 3AE ☎071-584 6883 & 071-589 4257

(Rosettes awarded for dinner only)

*Recently refurbished to reveal brick walls, two fireplaces and Yorkshire stone flooring, this fashionable and very popular restaurant provides attentive service from a particularly well supervised staff. In its candlelit atmosphere you can sample the delights of an à la carte menu with daily written specialities and recommendations. Game is featured in season, as is a varied selection of seafood – the Mousse de Poisson aux Crabe, with its tarragon flavoured crabmeat centre and fine shellfish sauce being well worth trying. Equally delectable are the whole roasted sweetbreads with caramelised shallots and a rich red wine sauce and the dessert soufflés (the latter of which must be ordered in advance). The French wine list offers a good choice.*

Closed Sun & BHs Lunch not served Sat

♕ English & French 95 seats Last lunch 2.30pm Last dinner mdnt ✔

Credit Cards ①②③⑤

### ❀✕✕ **English Garden**

10 Lincoln St SW3 2TS ☎071-584 7272 FAX 071-581 2848

*A small restaurant set in a typical Chelsea house just off the Kings Road, the English Garden has offered the same combination of an English menu and unobtrusive hospitality in elegant surroundings for 14 years now. The Marble Room features extravagant drapes and some large Ralph Hedley paintings of ornamental gardens, while the conservatory-roofed rear dining room contains some splendid dried flower displays. The menus – à la carte, with an additional short set menu at lunchtime – offer an exciting range of dishes including such perennial favourites as smoked salmon, roast rack of lamb with hazelnut crust and baked monkfish with warm peppercorn vinaigrette; desserts include light orange burnt cream, lemon flummery and the more challenging plum and almond duff with its strong plum sauce and clotted cream.*

Closed 25-26 Dec

**V** 65 seats ✱ Lunch fr£14.75&alc Dinner £22.50-£40&alc Last lunch 2.30pm Last dinner 11.30pm ✔

Credit Cards ①②③⑤

### ❀✕✕ **The English House**

3 Milner St SW3 2QA ☎071-584 3002 FAX 071-581 2848

*This elegant, well-appointed restaurant serves thoroughly researched traditional English dishes; supervision and service are excellent.*

Closed 25-26 Dec

**V** 40 seats Lunch £14.75&alc Dinner £25-£28alc Last lunch 2.30pm Last dinner 11.30pm ✔

Credit Cards ①②③⑤

### ❀✕✕ **Good Earth**

233 Brompton Rd SW3 2EP ☎071-584 3658 FAX 071-823 8769

*A loyal and appreciative clientèle ensure that this good, serious Chinese restaurant is always busy. Cantonese, Pekinese and Szechuan specialities offer a choice of styles ranging from fiery chilli dishes to the milder, delicate flavour of crispy lamb wrapped in lettuce and served with yellow plum sauce. Whole fish and fresh lobster are generally available at a market price.*

Closed 24-27 Dec

♕ Cantonese, Pekinese & Szechwan **V** 155 seats Lunch £17.50-£25.25&alc Dinner £17.50-£25.25&alc Last dinner 11.15pm ✔

Credit Cards ①②③⑤

### ❀✕✕ **Good Earth Restaurant**

91 Kings Rd, Chelsea SW3 ☎071-352 9231 071-352 4692 FAX 071-823 8769

*This branch of Good Earth, an established restaurant in the Kings Road, features attractive Chinese prints and screens in its street-level room; more tables are available downstairs. The menu offers a selection from the cuisine of Canton, Peking and Szechuan, including a good choice of vegetarian dishes. Fresh fish is cooked carefully with some exciting sauces, mussels being served with a delicious black soya bean and peppery chilli. Other reliable choices including Mu Shu Pork, its soft strips of pork and mushroom balanced with crisp vegetables, and the moist Kung Po Chicken, tastily flavoured with ginger – though perhaps not really spicy and hot.*

Closed 24-27 Dec

♕ Chinese **V** 65 seats ✱ Lunch £17-£22&alc Dinner £17-£22&alc Last lunch 2.30pm Last dinner 11.45pm ✔

Credit Cards ①②③⑤

### ❀✕✕ **St Quentin**

243 Brompton Rd SW3 2EP ☎071-589 8005 & 071-581 5131 FAX 071-584 6064

*This small, intimate brasserie offers a well chosen menu where the fish dishes are to be highly recommended. The wine list is comprehensive and offers a choice of reasonably priced bottles, the staff are friendly and efficient.*

♕ French 80 seats Last lunch 3pm Last dinner mdnt ✔ nc

Credit Cards ①②③⑤

### ❀✕✕ *Ménage à Trois*

15 Beauchamp Place SW3 1NQ ☎071-589 4252 & 071-589 0984 FAX 071-589 8860

*Situated just off the Brompton Road, this well established basement restaurant offers an informal atmosphere and an extensive menu designed to appeal to all tastes. The same might not apply, however, to the prints of nude females adorning every wall. Traditional English, American, European and Oriental influences are evident in the tasty dishes which are supported by a superb wine list. Interesting cocktails and live piano music are nice touches.*

Closed 25-26 Dec, Good Fri & Etr Sun Lunch not served Sat & Sun

♕ French **V** 70 seats Last lunch 3.15pm Last dinner 11.45pm ✔ ♫

Credit Cards ①②③⑤

A rosette means exceptional standards of cuisine.

❀❀❀❀ ✕ ✕ **TANTE CLAIRE**

68 Royal Hospital Rd SW3 4HP (Relais et Châteaux)
☎071-352 6045 & 071-351 0227 FAX 071-352 3257

*Close to the Chelsea Embankment, this little piece of France is far removed from its urban surroundings. Chef/Patron Pierre Koffmann comes from the south west of France, and that region is reflected in dishes such as Pied de Cochon which is very much associated with this restaurant. In no way luxurious, Tante Claire is certainly chic – art deco and a little Biedermeier. There is some seating in the reception foyer, but most guests are shown directly to the immaculately set tables where, along with the quickly served aperitif, an ameuse bouche is served. Manager Jean-Pierre Durantet is the very model of courtesy, carefully explaining the complex composition of the French menu to those who are unsure. As always, our inspectors are full of praise for the fine cooking, with such unusual dishes as coquilles St Jacques poëlléesa l'encre de seiche, providing not only a contrast of colours, but of flavours too. The lunch time menu is extremely popular, providing the opportunity to experience the food at more modest prices – booking is essential. Very much the master of his domain the chef seldom leaves his kitchen so consistency is assured.*
Closed Sat, Sun, BH's, 10 days Xmas
♡ French 38 seats ✱ Lunch £23.50&alc Dinner £50-£62alc
Last lunch 2pm Last dinner 11.15pm ✗
Credit Cards ① ② ③ ⑤

❀❀❀ ✕ ✕ *Turners*

87-89 Walton St SW3 2HP ☎071-584 6711

*In an area blessed with good restaurants, Turner's ranks among the best. Diners are welcomed by chef-patron Brian Turner who operates in kitchen and restaurant with equal ease. His sound cooking is basically French in style with some Mediterranean influences, resulting in good strong flavours. Dishes might include carpaccio of rabbit in olive oil, saffron mussel soup or crab sausage. A set menu changes at each meal, and an à la carte menu changes seasonally. The rather pricey wine list is exclusively French.*
Lunch not served Sat
♡ French 52 seats Last dinner 11pm ✗
Credit Cards ① ② ③ ⑤

❀ ✕ **Sud Ouest**

27-31 Basil St SW3 1BB ☎071-584 4484 FAX 071-581 2462

*Conviently placed for Harrods (at the back of the famous store) the theme of this restaurant is definitely rustic, with its dark blue and yellow walls, wooden floorboards and iron light fittings. If the décor is slightly self-conscious, the cooking, by David Shuttleworth, is sound and inventive, mainly based on regional French dishes of the type now called à la grand'mère! The terrine of aubergines, the feuilleté of snails, lamb with garlic and shallot confit, and the strongly flavoured duck and wild mushroom crêpinette with its punchy red-wine sauce are all good examples. That being said, a lighter hand was evident in the delicious paupiettes of salmon and oysters with butter sauce. Bread and vegetables are also good. Sweets might include prune and Armagnac mousse, or gratin of pink grapefruit. The waiters are both friendly and efficient. Next door to the restaurant is its lively sister café and downstairs there is a 'menu vitesse' at lunchtime.*
Closed Sun
♡ French **V** 120 seats Lunch £13.50-£15.50&alc Dinner fr£25alc Last lunch 3pm Last dinner 11pm ✗

### SW5 EARL'S COURT

★★★66% **Swallow International**

Cromwell Rd SW5 0TH (Swallow) ☎071-973 1000
Telex no 27260 FAX 071-244 8194

*Conveniently located beside a main road on the west side of the city, this deceptively large hotel is particularly attractive to tourists, offering a well equipped leisure centre and bedrooms in a wide range of sizes and styles. The Fountains Brasserie serves everything from snacks to main meals throughout the day, while the comfortable surroundings and international cuisine of Blayney's provide a pleasant venue for dinner.*

417⇨🇫(36fb)⊬in 39 bedrooms CTV in all bedrooms ® **T** ✱
S10% sB⇨🇫£95-£105 dB⇨🇫£110-£120 (room only) 🗲
Lift ℄ 45P (£12.50 per day) 30🍴 (£12.50 per day) CFA 🖂
(heated) sauna solarium gymnasium whirlpool spa turkish steamroom ♫ *xmas*
♡ International **V** ✧ ⬛ S10% Lunch £10-£14.50alc High tea £10-£14.50alc Dinner £10-£14.50alc Last dinner mdnt
Credit Cards ① ② ③ ⑤

❀ ✕ ✕ **Tiger Lee**

251 Old Brompton Rd SW5 9HP ☎071-370 2323 & 071-370 5970
Telex no 919660 FAX 071-244 6032

*A sophisticated and air-conditioned Chinese restaurant specialising in seafood and fish, features a menu offering a varied choice of skilfully cooked eel, squid, abalone, shark's fin and lobster – steamed fish in soy sauce being particularly enjoyable. Other dishes worthy of note are pan-fried scallops with black bean sauce, stuffed crab claw with prawn filling, and slices of beef stir-fried in an oyster sauce. A fine selection of French wine is available.*
Lunch not served
♡ Cantonese **V** 56 seats ✱ Dinner £24-£45alc Last dinner 11.15pm ✗ ⊬
Credit Cards ① ② ③ ⑤

### SW6 FULHAM

**See LONDON plan 1**C3

❀ ✕ ✕ **Hiders**

755 Fulham Rd SW6 ☎071-736 2331

*The ground floor area is deceptively small, but the downstairs is more spacious, and offers an informal, relaxing atmosphere. Chef Duvall offers a creative à la carte menu, changing every two weeks, and has a classical approach to good cooking, although our inspector did comment that desserts could improve. Sauces are the kitchen's strength, and the chicken supreme with mushroom sauce was highly praised. Service is attentive and observant under the supervision of the head waiter M. Ezio.*
Closed Sun, 1wk Xmas & BH's Lunch not served Sat
♡ French 60 seats Last lunch 2.30pm Last dinner 11.30pm ✗
Credit Cards ① ③

❀ ✕ **Tall Orders**

676 Fulham Rd SW6 ☎071-371 9673

*Unusual décor of bold, blue trunking snaking across the ceiling, a large mural and split-level seating adds to the charm of this cheerful modern restaurant. The system of serving food in Chinese steamers adds further to the fun of a meal here – everything you order comes at the same time, stacked in little bowls. A regularly changing menu with modern ideas and Mediterranean influences provides appetising combinations.*
**V** 120 seats ✱ Lunch £13.50-£15&alc Dinner £13.50-£15&alc Last dinner 11.30pm ✗ ⊬
Credit Cards ① ② ③

### SW7 SOUTH KENSINGTON

★★★★68% **Gloucester**

4-18 Harrington Gardens SW7 4LH (Rank) ☎071-373 6030
Telex no 917505 FAX 071-373 0409

*A modern purpose-built hotel with an open-plan foyer/lounge, a lobby bar with piano music at night and fully serviced lounge open 24 hours. The restaurant serves imaginative à la carte and table d'hôte menus, while the informal café is open all day for light meals; there is also a wine bar and real ale pub. Bedrooms are spacious and well equipped, with two floors of club rooms having their own private lounge on the sixth floor.*
550⇨🇫(2fb)⊬in 51 bedrooms CTV in all bedrooms ® **T** ✱
sB⇨🇫fr£138 dB⇨🇫fr£158 (room only) 🗲
Lift ℄ ⊞ 100🍴 (fr £6.50) CFA *xmas*

→

♀ English & Continental **V** ♻ ⏳ ✂ ✳ Lunch £15.50&alc
Dinner £21.90&alc Last dinner 10.30pm
Credit Cards 1 2 3 4 5

**★★★ 63% *Rembrandt***
Thurloe Place SW7 2RS ☎071-589 8100 Telex no 295828
FAX 071-225 3363

*Opposite the Victoria and Albert Museum and near Harrods, this smart hotel has attractive public rooms including a bar/lounge which is partly traditional and partly conservatory style. Bedrooms vary in shape and size and are generally well decorated and equipped. Guests can buy temporary membership of the luxurious health club next door.*

200 ⇌ (25fb) ⅓ ⧫ in 28 bedrooms CTV in all bedrooms ®
✈ (ex guide dogs)
Lift ( ⌁ ♪ ☒ (heated) sauna solarium gymnasium beauty parlour massage spa bath
**V** ♻ ⏳ Last dinner 9.30pm
Credit Cards 1 2 3 4 5

○ **Holiday Inn Kensington**
94-106 Cromwell Rd SW7 4ER (Holiday Inns Inc)
☎071-373 2222
Open
162 ⇌ ✈

❀❀ ✕ ✕ ✕ **190 Queen's Gate**
190 Queen's Gate SW7 5EU ☎071-581 5666 FAX 071-581 8172

*Occupying much of the Gore Hotel, the restaurant together with its adjacent bistro form part of a member's club 'for people in the restaurant, hotel, catering and supply industry'. Non-members are welcome but pay a little more. The Chef/Patron is Anthony Worrall-Thompson. The restaurant is in the basement where an attractive set price menu is presented by discreet young staff. Worrall-Thompson has combined new-wave Italian influences, the chargrill, and French provincial cuisine, with some skill and imagination. In the bistro the theme is the same, but the menu is longer and the dishes even more rustic. Both are popular and booking is a must.*

Closed Sun, Etr wknd, 23-30 Dec & 2 wks Aug Lunch not served Sat
♀ Mediterranean **V** 70 seats ✳ Lunch fr£14.50&alc Dinner £33.50-£38.50alc Last lunch 3pm Last dinner 11.30pm ♪
Credit Cards 1 2 3 5

❀❀ ✕ ✕ ✕ **Bombay Brasserie**
Courtfield Close, 140 Gloucester Rd SW7 4TH ☎071-370 4040 & 071-373 0971 FAX 071-835 1669

*The great days of the Raj are recalled in this huge, splendid restaurant and conservatory with elegant colonial atmosphere. Many regions of India are represented on the menu, ranging from Tandoori specialities from the nothwest frontier to milder Parsi and robust Goan dishes. There is a good proportion of vegetarian dishes too, and excellent sorbets round off the meal. A reasonably priced self-service buffet is provided at lunchtime, while the à la carte dinner menu is supplemented with a changing selection of less well known dishes. Popular with local residents and tourists alike, booking in advance is essential to secure a dinner table.*

♀ Indian **V** 175 seats Last lunch 2.45pm Last dinner mdnt ♪
Credit Cards 1 3

❀❀❀ ✕ ✕ **Hilaire**
68 Old Brompton Rd SW7 3JX ☎071-584 8993 & 071-584 7601
(Rosettes awarded for dinner only)

*This two-storey Kensington restaurant maintains a high standard of cooking. Here Bryan Webb uses his skill and flair to produce flavoursome dishes accompanied by well prepared fresh vegetables. The puddings will not disappoint and the wine list is well balanced and reasonably priced. A plainer menu is available at lunchtime.*

Closed Sun, 1 wk Xmas, Etr, last 2 wks Aug & BH's
♀ European **V** 40 seats Lunch £16.95-£20.90&alc Dinner £15.50-£19&alc Last lunch 2.30pm Last dinner 11.30pm ♪
Credit Cards 1 2 3 5

❀ ✕ **Tui**
19 Exhibition Rd SW7 2HE ☎071-584 8359

*This restaurant seems to reflect the discreet, contemplative side of the Thai character in its rather austere black and white décor and smiling but unobtrusive service. A short, appetising menu includes starters like fish cakes and dim sum dumplings, well known soups which include the lemony chicken Tom Kha Gai, traditional Thai specialities, curries (perhaps a tasty Gang Massaman Beef with peanut or coconut) and such noodle dishes as seafood with ginger-infused rice noodles. Singha beer and ginger tea are the beverages recommended to accompany this tasty and well balanced cuisine.*
Closed public hols
♀ Thai **V** 52 seats ✳ Lunch £8-£15alc Dinner £10-£22alc Last lunch 2.30pm Last dinner 11pm ♪
Credit Cards 1 2 3 5

---

**SW8 BATTERSEA**

See **LONDON plan** 1*D3*
See also **SW11**

❀❀❀❀ ✕ ✕ **L'ARLEQUIN**
123 Queenstown Rd SW8 3RM ☎071-622 0555

*Christian Delteil's discreet unassuming style is evident in the comfortable dining rooms, professional service and lack of elaboration on the French menu and in many of his dishes. Sound ingredients, especially fish, are allowed to stand for themselves; a delicious turbot mousse was well matched by a Sauternes butter sauce. More robust and varied ideas are often evident with game – slices of pigeon and pigs trotter with cabbage in a puff pastry basket had excellent textures and tastes. Desserts such as sorbets, creme caramel and tarte aux figues are skilful and without over complication. The mainly French wine list includes serious bottles but also plenty of more affordable wines.*

Closed Sat, Sun, 1 wk winter & 3 wks Aug
♀ French 45 seats Last dinner 10.30pm ♪ nc5yrs
Credit Cards 1 2 3 5

❀❀❀❀ ✕ ✕ **CAVALIERS'**
129 Queenstown Rd SW8 3RH ☎071-720 6960

*David Cavalier is one of the brave men who took over the site of Chez Nico and has in 4 years created his own solid reputation. This is in many ways a French restaurant: the ambience is elegant, staff are French, and the wine list predominantly so. Although it is written in English sub-editorialese titles, the menu is sound, an inviting mix of classic and modern styles. David Cavalier is a great enthusiast for food and cooking, and the results on the plate are superb, from the simplicity of quality fish and shellfish softly poached, to a dramatic pigeon dish, the bird jointed and assembled on a bed of cabbage-layered potato and topped with celeriac curls, garnished with a pungent jus and turned apples.*

Closed Sun, Mon, 2 wks Aug & 2 wks Xmas
♀ English & French 50 seats ✳ Lunch £18-£39 Dinner £39
Last lunch 2pm Last dinner 10.30pm ♪
Credit Cards 1 2 3 5

---

**SW10 WEST BROMPTON**

See **LONDON plan** 1*C3*

❀ ✕ ✕ *Chapter II*
47 Hollywood Rd SW10 9HX ☎071-351 1683 FAX 071-376 5083
*John Brinkley was fed up with serving traditional French fare and made the brave decision to transform his restaurant, Brinkley's, into the stylish Chapter 11 which serves Californian/Italian food. Now on just one floor with windows opening up at the front, and an attractive garden at the back where you can eat al fresco. The marinated olives, basil and chive mayonnaise and delicious ciabatte justifying the cover charge. An inspection meal commenced with salmon tartare minced with fresh dill and served with sour cream and well browned olive blinis. This was followed by a simple dish of grilled red mullet with basil, tomato and shallots, and a tangy olive oil dressing. Vegetables are extra – not surprising as all the main courses are under £8. The selection of*

*grilled vegetables was also dressed with olive oil. For dessert there is a range of tarts, a combination of chocolate mousse and some fruity mixtures. The chocolate and raspberry tart was pleasant enough. Service is casual, but friendly and attentive. John Brinkley also owns the wine bar and wine merchants (off license) next door, hence the interesting and varied selection of wines.*

Closed Sun, Xmas & Etr Lunch not served

♀ English & French **V** 60 seats Last dinner 11.30pm ⚑

Credit Cards ① ③

### ❀ ✕ ✕ Chutney Mary
525 Kings Rd, Chelsea sw10 ☎071-351 3113

*The name 'Chutney Mary' comes from a term used by conservative Indians to describe an Indian woman who was Anglicised in her dress and manner. Proclaiming itself the first Anglo/Indian restaurant, the cooking here follows this theme. Perhaps the pricing policy needs reappraisal, many will be outraged to find that the little dish of chickpeas offered with apéritifs in the Verandah Bar will appear on the final tab. This, with soggy papadums and undrinkable coffee on one inspection visit, detract from otherwise enjoyable cuisine. A good effort is made to match wines with curries, but it is best to stick to the good, though expensive beers such as Cobra.*

♀ English & Indian 110 seats ✱ Lunch £11.95-£14.50 Last lunch 2.30pm Last dinner 11.30pm ⚑

Credit Cards ① ② ③ ④ ⑤

### ❀ ✕ ✕ Ken Lo's Memories of China
Chelsea Harbour Yard, Chelsea Harbour sw10 ☎071-352 4953 FAX 071-351 2096

*Set in the heart of the latest and most fashionable of waterside developments, Ken Lo's second 'Memories of China' restaurant has a particularly popular and appealing contemporary atmosphere and offers an interesting à la carte traditional set meals and a Dim Sum bar. Our inspectors particularly recommend Peking Duck (one hour's notice required), Cantonese onion and ginger lobster, black bean sauced dishes and iron plate sizzled dishes, choosing the main ingredients. Service is particularly well supervised and an international wine list is augmented by a very good wine by the glass list. A take-away service is available.*

Closed 25-26 Dec & 1 Jan

Dinner not served Sun

♀ Chinese **V** 160 seats Last lunch 2.30pm Last dinner 10.45pm P

Credit Cards ① ② ③ ⑤

### ❀ ✕ ✕ Waterfront
Harbour Yard, Chelsea sw10 ☎071-352 4562 FAX 071-351 6576

*Housed in the fashionable Chelsea Harbour Development, the waterfront looks out on to the boat-filled harbour and offers restaurant, oyster bar and ordinary bar. Chef Diago Dellaporta has composed a very interesting and authentic à la carte menu, with all dishes freshly prepared and particularly well constructed sauces. His home-made fish cakes with a tomato and basil sauce were strongly recommended by our inspector. Desserts include the famous tiramisù and a delicious Bavarese alla fragola. There is also a daily set menu, excellent value at £16. Wines are predominantly Italian, as you might expect and the house wine, Settesoli 1989, was pleasant and fresh. After such praise for the food, it is a pity to have to say that we have found that the service can be indifferent and indisciplined at times.*

Closed 25-26 Dec & BH's

Dinner not served Sun

♀ Italian **V** 185 seats ✱ Lunch £16&alc Dinner £16&alc Last lunch 3pm Last dinner 11.30pm ⚑

Credit Cards ① ③

---

## SW11 BATTERSEA

See **LONDON** plan 1*D3*
See also **SW8**

### ❀❀ ✕ ✕ Le Chausson
Ransome's Dock, 35-37 Parkgate Rd sw11 ☎071-223 1611

*A new, modern restaurant which enjoys a unique location at Battersea's attractive Ransome's Dock has been elegantly designed to provide a comfortable 'bonne vivant' ambience in which to enjoy professionally prepared dishes from fixed-price and à la carte menus supplemented by such speciality recommendations as veal sweetbreads with a lobster sauce delicately flavoured with vanilla ; seafood starters include halibut with fresh ravioli and two sauces. Service is particularly attentive and helpful, and car parking facilities are available for dinner guests.*

Closed Sun

Lunch not served Sat 45 seats Last Lunch 3pm Last Dinner 11pm

### ❀ ✕ Osteria Antica Bologna
23 Northcote Rd sw11 ☎071-978 4771

*One of the flurry of regional Italian restaurants opening in the last few years, Osteria Antica has several features to commend it. The atmosphere is informal, bustling and friendly – no designer pretensions here – with simple closely-packed wooden tables topped with masonic symbol paper place mats, light wooden walls and wrought iron fittings and casually dressed willing young staff. Aurelio Spagnada has lived and worked in southern Italy and around Bologna; thus, his seasonally changing menu and daily blackboard list specialise in these two areas. There are salads, pastas, sauced dishes and pride of place – the lengthy choice of assaggi. These are small dishes to a make a starter, or a snack with several shared between friends. Marinata del Golfo was a plate of squid, prawns and white fish marinated in white wine vinegar and then crisply deep fried; Polpettine dei poveri were small cakes of pine nuts, parmesan and bread with a pungent tomato and onion garnish. Main courses include cuttlefish, goat, tuna, veal rolls – all with regional garnish. Cooking is straightforward, without fuss, and full of flavour. Partner Rochelle Porteous supervises front of house and arranges the all Italian wine list, which is well chosen and fairly priced ; there are a couple of house wines of each colour and the list changes balance depending on the season.*

Closed 2 wks Xmas & BH's

Dinner not served Sun

♀ Italian **V** 70 seats ✱ Lunch £6.50&alc Dinner fr£10alc Last dinner 11pm ⚑

Credit Cards ① ③

### ❀❀ ✕ Pollyanna's
2 Battersea Rise sw11 1ED ☎071-228 0316

*Richard Aldridge, a chef noted for his originality and inventiveness, produces attractive and well decorated dishes based on the finest ingredients and making use of an array of vegetables. The expensive but finely constructed duck liver foie gras terrine is to be recommended, as are the fillets of Dover sole with Champagne and chive sauce. Cheese soufflés are not always successful, but there are many tempting desserts to choose from and an excellent, varied and informative wine list is available. Service is particularly helpful, and a relaxing, congenial atmosphere is created by the personal involvement of the proprietor, Norman Price.*

Closed 4 days Xmas & 1 Jan Lunch not served Mon-Sat

Dinner not served Sun

♀ French **V** 40 seats Sunday Lunch fr£14.95 Dinner £19.95-£24.50 Last dinner mdnt ⚑

Credit Cards ① ② ③

---

Hotels with red star ratings are especially high quality.

For key to symbols in English see the bookmark.

## SW13 BARNES

### ✿ ✕ Riva

169 Church Rd, Barnes SW13 9HR ☎081-748 0434

*One of a clutch of recently opened Italian restaurants specialising in the so-called 'nuova cucina', Riva's menus are based on the cooking of Lombardy and Veneto, the region from which the owner, chef and wines originate. Tastes are robust and piquant and presentation of dishes is never artfully contrived. Favourites that you will often find on the menu include calf's liver with polenta, garlic and funghi; or cuttlefish risotto with ink sauce. There are good Italian bread and strongly flavoured vegetables to accompany the meal, and some rich desserts like tiramisù as well as fruits and ices. Riva is small, so booking is advisable, and the prices are currently good value.*

♡ Italian **V** 50 seats Lunch £17-£25alc Dinner £17-£25alc Last lunch 2.30pm Last dinner 11pm ✗

Credit Cards ① ③

## SW14 EAST SHEEN

**See LONDON plan 1***C3*

### ✿ ✕ Crowthers

481 Upper Richmond Rd West, East Sheen SW14 7PU ☎081-876 6372

(Rosette awarded for dinner only)

*Genial and extremely sociable, this small family-run restaurant has a loyal and regular local clientele which appreciates chef Philip Crowther's honest and uncomplicated approach to his cooking. From a range of carefully prepared and skilfully constructed dishes you might choose Mediterranean fish soup with rouille; supreme of free range chicken with fresh egg noodles and a wild mushroom sauce, finishing the meal with a very light lemon tart. The wine list contains examples from both France and the New World, helpful personal service is supervised by Shirley Crowther. It is possible to park in the street outside the hotel in the evening.*

Closed Sun (ex Mothers Day), 1 wk Xmas & 2 wks summer Lunch not served Sat & Mon

♡ French **V** 28 seats ✳ Lunch £14-£16.50 Dinner £22-£22&alc Last lunch 1.45pm Last dinner 10.45pm ✗

Credit Cards ① ② ③

## SW17 WANDSWORTH COMMON

**See LONDON plan 1***C2*

### ✿✿✿✿✿ ✕ ✕ HARVEY'S

2 Bellevue Rd, Wandsworth Rd SW17 7EQ ☎081-672 0114

*Marco Pierre White's chic little restaurant may be a little cramped, and service may from time to time be rather less than assured, but on the plate, where it counts, the customer can hardly fail to be impressed. The carte features many tried and tested dishes, some showing the influence of his mentors, and some that truly reflect his innovative genius. The set-price luncheon menu is often used as the breeding ground for new ideas which, if he is pleased with them, are later refined and added to the repertoire on a permanent basis. Some work better than others, but his consistency of touch is remarkable and a meal at Harvey's is invariably laced with memorable dishes. One such dish, a blanquette of scallops and langoustines, with delicately prepared cucumber and strips of ginger, was so good that it broke one's heart to come to the last mouthful. Other favourites, such as the delicious ravioli of sweetbreads, served with an intense truffle fumet, have been equally acclaimed. There is an excellent wine list of around 400 bins, but the seeker after bargains will have his work cut out to find any.*

Closed Sun, last 2 wks Aug & last wk Dec-1st wk Jan Lunch not served Sat

45 seats Last dinner 11pm ✗ nc5yrs

Credit Cards ① ② ③

## SW19 WIMBLEDON

**See LONDON plan 1***C2*

### ★★★★63% Cannizaro House

West Side, Wimbledon Common SW19 4UF (Mount Charlotte (TS)) ☎081-879 1464 Telex no 9413837 FAX 081-879 7338

*A fine location overlooking the park gives this Georgian manor house a relaxed country atmosphere. Well equipped accommodation ranges from standard rooms to four poster suites, some containing antique furnishings, while ornate public areas include a lobby lounge, cocktail lounge and intimate restaurant. Standards of service are generally acceptable, and chef Nigel Couzens presents table d'hôte and à la carte menus with some classical recommendations.*

48➪ ⚑4⊟ CTV in all bedrooms **T** (room only) ⚑

⦅60P ✿

♡ International ⌖ ⍁

Credit Cards ① ② ③ ④ ⑤

## W1 WEST END

★★★★★✿ CLARIDGE'S

Brook St W1A 2JQ
☎071-629 8860
Telex no 21872
FAX 071-499 2210

*The impressive entrance hall, with its marble floors, sparkling chandeliers and noble staircase reminds one that Claridges has, for about 100 years, been used as a pied à terre by some of Europe's oldest families. After a recent programme of refurbishment, particularly of most of the bedrooms, standards of comfort are now very high in all except a few singles. The foyer lounge remains one of the most fashionable meeting places in London, and the Hungarian quartet which provides soothing music at lunch and dinner times strikes just the right chord of nostalgia. A new terrace and mirrored mural by Christopher Ironside enhance the attractive restaurant and in the kitchen Chef de Cuisine Marjan Lesnik continues to ensure that the standards remain high; the menu is classical French but includes such English favourites as a simple roast 'with gravy' and traditional desserts such as an exquisite bread and butter pudding. Service throughout the hotel reflects the personality and dedication of the hotel's managing director, Ronald Jones.*

189➪⚑ CTV in all bedrooms **T** ✠ (ex guide dogs) S15% sB➪⚑fr£185 dB➪⚑fr£240 (room only) ⚑

Lift ⦅ ✗ ⇔ CFA ♫ xmas

♡ International **V** ⌖ ⍁ ✳ S15% Lunch £29-£45alc Dinner £29-£45alc Last dinner 11.15pm

Credit Cards ① ② ③ ⑤

★★★★★✿✿✿ CONNAUGHT

Carlos Place W1Y 6AL
☎071-499 7070

*Maître Cuisinier de France chef Michel Bourdin continues to promote the classical cuisine which is*

*establishing the Grill Room as one of the most reputable traditional restaurants in the country. Though there have, in the past, been occasional fluctuations in standard, his dishes continue to excite – noteworthy examples including the Pâté de Turbot Froid au Homard Sauce Pudeur, delicately cooked and presented to enhance the subtlety of the individual flavours, and Noisettes d'Agneau Edward VII – which are classic in both concept and execution, the first-class demi glacé sauce being richly enhanced with foie gras and truffles; vegetables are well cooked, and a trolley of predominantly British puddings followed by coffee (expresso, if preferred) brings the meal to an end. A popular lunchtime menu includes such choices as Boiled Silverside or Steak, Kidney and Mushroom Pie.*

90⇄⅜↾ CTV in all bedrooms ✻

Lift ⚓ ⅌ ⊞

♡ English & French ⬚

Credit Cards ①

★★★★★ ❀❀❀
**DORCHESTER**

53 Park Ln W1A 2HJ
☎071-629 8888
Telex no 887704
FAX 071-409 0114

*Reopened in the autumn of 1990 after almost 2 years of refurbishment, redecoration and refitting, this hotel now boasts beautifully restored public areas retaining all their original features and elegant charm. The traditional Grill Room and Terrace Restaurant are now augmented by a new Oriental Restaurant, set at the end of the gracious Promenade and providing sumptuous surroundings in which to enjoy excellent Cantonese cuisine. First-rate cocktails are served in the striking Dorchester Bar, and the hotel's amenities include a small arcade of shops, a little health spa in Art Deco style and a private club. Improvements are most obvious in the bedrooms, the smallest having been dispensed with and the remainder completely and individually overhauled, the majority being presented in country house style.*

252⇄⅜↾ 31⊞ CTV in all bedrooms T

Lift ⚓⊞ P ⊞ health club ♫

♡ English & French V ♥ ⬚

Credit Cards ①②③⑤

★★★★★ ❀❀❀ 78% **Inn on the Park**

Hamilton Place, Park Ln W1A 1AZ ☎071-499 0888
Telex no 22771 FAX 071-493 1895 & 6629

*One of the best 5-star hotels, overlooking Hyde Park from the southern end of Park Lane, offers a warm and relaxing atmosphere that is evident as soon as you step into the lofty, marble-floored and wood-panelled entrance lobby with its attractive floral displays. A lounge which is comfortable, though not large, serves all-day drinks/snacks and traditional afternoon tea, while spacious bedrooms furnished to the same high standard are all well equipped – some boasting FAX machines. The exclusive Four Seasons Restaurant features such dishes as Terrine de Legumes à la Provençale et Mozzarella (vegetarian terrine with Mozzarella), Blanc de Turbot Braise à la Moutarde Galloise (fillet of turbot braised in a delicate mustard seed sauce) and Pyramide de Chocolat Praline, Crème Vanille (layered chocolate with vanilla cream sauce). A list of 300 wines supplies a variety of prices to suit all pockets.*

228⇄⅜↾⅍in 48 bedrooms CTV in all bedrooms T ✻ ✳ S%
sB⇄⅜↾£223.25-£246.75 dB⇄⅜↾£276.12 (room only) 🅱
Lift ⚓⊞ 65🛏 (fr £3.60 2hrs) ⊞ CFA ♫ xmas
♡ International V ♥ ⬚ ⅍ Lunch £23.25-£27&alc High tea
£14&alc Dinner £25-£40&alc Last dinner mdnt
Credit Cards ①②③④⑤

★★★★★ ❀❀❀ 73% *Inter-Continental*

1 Hamilton Pl, Hyde Park Corner W1V 0QY ☎071-409 3131
Telex no 25853 FAX 071-493 3476

*A contemporary hotel at the foot of Park Lane, deceptively spacious, with the wide range of facilities demanded by today's international traveller – the small, well equipped fitness centre and plunge pool being just one example. Bedrooms are varied in size but work is underway to eliminate the smaller ones; and bathrooms, some now quite dated, are being improved to a high standard. There are several eating options, notably Le Soufflé which is quite atmospheric and has excellent staff. Most exciting is the cooking, supervised by Peter Kromberg. Soufflés are a feature of the menu, of course, but do not dominate it until the dessert stage. An appenzell cheese soufflé baked in crispy filo pastry, or smoked haddock with a perfectly poached egg at its centre are delightful starters, while for dessert the chocolate and candied kumquats are a highlight, or a soufflé flavoured with your favourite liqueur. Seafood, game and poultry figure strongly, with a good variety of vegetables. The 6-courses of Le Choix du Chef excite many regulars – portions are modest. Hamiltons is the lesser known dinner rendezvous, with dancing and views over the Royal Park. Fast food is served at the Coffee House, but inspectors found, yet again, that breakfasts fail to meet the high standards otherwise met in the rest of the hotel.*

467⇄⅜↾⅍in 58 bedrooms CTV in all bedrooms T
✻ (ex guide dogs)
Lift ⚓⊞ 100🛏 (£21.50 24 hrs) ⊞ sauna gymnasium health
centre ♫ →

★★★★ AA

**Ⅱ CANNIZARO HOUSE Ⅱ**

*West Side, Wimbledon Common,*
*London SW19 4UF*
*Telephone: 081 879 1464 Telex: 9413837*
*Facsimile: 081 879 7338*

This tranquil Georgian country house hotel overlooks delightful gardens and parkland. The 48 de luxe bedrooms are individually furnished and offer every modern comfort. Several four poster beds are also available. Superb cuisine with attentive service is offered in the Restaurant while the Grand Salon and Cocktail Bar are ideal for relaxing. Several meeting rooms are also available.

*For Reservations at over 90 Mount Charlotte Thistle Hotels telephone London: 071 937 8033 or Leeds: 0532 444866.*

A MOUNT CHARLOTTE THISTLE HOTEL

**London**

♀ English, French, Italian & Oriental **V** ♡ ♨ ⅍ Last dinner 11.30pm
Credit Cards ①②③④⑤

---

### ★★★★★🏶73% Ritz

Piccadilly W1V 9DG (Small Luxury Hotels) ☎071-493 8181 Telex no 267200 FAX 071-493 2687

*Probably the most popular London hotel for non-residents, the place to go for afternoon tea or a celebratory dinner, the Ritz restaurant is considered to be the loveliest and most elegant in the country, and there is live music to enhance the ambience. The hotel has many other strong features, none more so than the excellent hospitality and service provided by friendly, helful staff, with management much in evidence. Lounge facilities are somewhat limited and are on occasions taken over by non-residents. Bedrooms are quite spacious and superbly appointed with tasteful décor and furnishings. All are well equipped with guests' comfort much in mind. Chef Keith Stanley continues to improve his standard of cooking. His menus offer an interesting choice, and dishes are well prepared and elegantly presented. An excellent wine list is available to complement the cooking, with wines from many areas and a wide price range.*

129⇨🛏 CTV in all bedrooms **T** ⚔ S15% sB⇨🛏£190-£220 dB⇨🛏£220-£270 (room only) 🍴
Lift ( 🅿 🚢 CFA ♫ xmas
♀ International **V** ♡ ♨ S15% Lunch £27.50-£28.50 Dinner fr£39.50 Last dinner 10.45pm
Credit Cards ①②③④⑤

---

### ★★★★★70% Grosvenor House

Park Ln W1A 3AA (Forte Hotels) ☎071-499 6363 Telex no 24871 FAX 071-493 3341

*The complete refurbishment at present under way to improve the general standards of this hotel and provide more facilities will eventually include improvement of the main entrance. Bedrooms in a variety of sizes offer mixed degrees of comfort, but all are well equipped and there are some very good bathrooms. The spacious lounge is a popular venue for afternoon tea, and eating options allow for a choice of more or less formality in surroundings and style of cuisine. Willing staff provide professional service, and facilities include a number of shops, an excellent leisure centre and a good business area.*

454⇨🛏🐾in 70 bedrooms **T** ⚔ (ex guide dogs) ⚔ sB⇨🛏fr£195 dB⇨🛏£225-£690 (room only) 🍴
Lift ( 20P 100🚗 (charged) CFA 🏊 (heated) sauna solarium gymnasium health & fitness centre xmas
♀ English, French & Italian **V** ♡ ♨ ⅍ ⚔ Lunch fr£19.95&alc Dinner fr£22.50&alc Last dinner 10.30pm
Credit Cards ①②③④⑤

---

### ★★★★★🏶🏶🏶68% Le Meridien London

21 Piccadilly W1V 0BH ☎071-734 8000 Telex no 25795 FAX 071-437 3574

*Fast improving to be among the leading London hotels, the bedrooms here have been refurbished to a high standard, providing comfort and good modern equipment. Public areas are limited but tastefully appointed, and afternoon tea in the lounge is very popular. The hotel is probably best known for the elegant Oak Room restaurant, and the cooking of Executive Chef David Chambers and his skilful team which goes from strength to strength. Mention must also be made of Maître d' Tony Gear whose friendly charm completes an enjoyable experience. Leisure facilities are a strong feature of the hotel, and service throughout is efficient and professional, with friendly, helpful staff.*

260⇨🛏🚻 CTV in all bedrooms **T** ⚔ (ex guide dogs) ⚔ sB⇨🛏£205.65-£229.15 dB⇨🛏£229.15-£252.65 (room only) 🍴
Lift ( 🚢 🏊 (heated) squash snooker sauna solarium gymnasium health & leisure club ♫
♀ International **V** ♡ ⚔ Lunch fr£17&alc High tea £18-£26alc Dinner £18-£39alc Last dinner 11.30pm
Credit Cards ①②③④⑤

---

### ★★★★★62% The Churchill

30 Portman Square W1A 4ZX ☎071-486 5800 Telex no 264831 FAX 071-486 1255

*This pleasantly located modern hotel, overlooking Portman Square Gardens, is undergoing extensive refurbishment to extend and further improve its already elegant public areas. Bedrooms, though compact, are scheduled for similar upgrading, housekeeping standards are very good, and service is generally helpful and professional.*

452⇨🛏⅍in 66 bedrooms CTV in all bedrooms **T** ⚔ S15% sB⇨🛏£199.75-£217.38 dB⇨🛏£217.38-£240.66 (room only) 🍴
Lift ( 🎱 (charged) 🅿 🚢 ✿ CFA ♪ (hard) free membership tp David Lloyd club ♫ xmas
♀ International **V** ♡ ♨ ⅍ ⚔ Lunch £15-£25alc Dinner £15-£30alc Last dinner 11pm
Credit Cards ①②③④⑤

---

### ★★★★★58% May Fair Inter-Continental

Stratton St W1A 2AN ☎071-629 7777 Telex no 262526 FAX 071-629 1459

*This long-established hotel is now under new management. Facilities include an elegant restaurant, a popular coffee house and the new Starlight leisure club. A multi-million pound programme to redevelop most public areas is under review.*

293⇨🛏(14fb)⅍in 26 bedrooms CTV in all bedrooms **T** ⚔ (ex guide dogs) ⚔ sB⇨🛏£145-£210 dB⇨🛏£185-£210 (room only)
Lift ( 🚢 🅿 🚢 CFA 🏊 (heated) sauna solarium gymnasium xmas
♀ English & French **V** ♡ ♨ ⚔ Lunch £20&alc High tea £10.50&alc Dinner £27.50-£32.50&alc Last dinner 10.30pm
Credit Cards ①②③④⑤

★★★★🏶🏶🏶 **ATHENAEUM**

Piccadilly W1V 0BJ (Rank)(Pride of Britain) ☎071-499 3464 Telex no 261589 FAX 071-493 1860

*Further improvements have been made to maintain the high standard always expected at this popular hotel. Upgrading of the front of the house is planned for the coming year. The lounge is elegant, with some fine coordinating soft furnishings, mixed with comfortable seating, and a peaceful atmosphere. There are many colourful floral displays around the hotel, and the restaurant is very attractive with a predominantly pink colour scheme. New Chef David Marshall has now settled in and produces interesting set price and à la carte menus. Dishes are skilfully prepared and service is helpful. Bedrooms are thoughtfully appointed and offer all the modern facilities. Staff continue to offer service of the highest standard, which has become the hallmark of this hotel.*

112⇨🛏⅍in 27 bedrooms CTV in all bedrooms **T** ⚔ (ex guide dogs) ⚔ sB⇨🛏£178-£193 dB⇨🛏£198-£213 (room only) 🍴
Lift ( 🚢 300🚗 (£20.50) 🚢 xmas
♀ International **V** ♡ ♨ ⚔ Lunch £21.50-£22.50&alc Dinner £18-£21.50&alc Last dinner 10.30pm
Credit Cards ①②③④⑤

---

A rosette means exceptional standards of cuisine.

★★★★⚜ **BROWN'S**

Albemarle St, Dover St
W1A 4SW (Forte Hotels)
☎071-493 6020
Telex no 28686
FAX 071-493 9381

*This splendid old hotel, with entrances in Dover Street and Albemarle Street, remains the jewel in the Forte crown. The traditionally styled rooms are a delight: original wood panelling, intricate cornices and beautiful fresh flowers. High tea has been revived in one of the restaurants but their renowned afternoon teas remain a much sought-after treat for which booking is advisable. The club-like bar is a good place for a pre-dinner cocktail. In the formal l'Apéritif Restaurant, guests can enjoy the cooking of chef Martin Davis, who has been at Brown's for many years. Our inspector found the dishes most successful when not over-complicated. The bedrooms are comfortable and we are pleased to report that major refurbishment is now in progress. Staff are generally willing and helpful, and for the most part a good balance of professionalism and hospitality is achieved.*

133⇨🐾(2fb)⅍in 66 bedrooms CTV in all bedrooms **T**
**✗** (ex guide dogs) ✳ sB⇨🐾fr£160 dB⇨🐾£198-£255 (room only) 🛏

Lift ℂ 🅿 🚲 CFA gents hairdresser *xmas*

🍴 English & French **V** ✪ ⚼ ⅍ ✳ Lunch £26.50&alc High tea £15.50 Dinner £24.95-£27.95&alc Last dinner 9.30pm

Credit Cards ①②③⑤

---

★★★★⚜⚜75% **Portman Inter-Continental**
22 Portman Square W1H 9FL ☎071-486 5844 Telex no 261526
FAX 071-935 0537

*One of reasons for The Portman Inter-Continental being nominated as one of this year's 'Courtesy and Care' award winners, is the friendly atmosphere that pervades this well managed and understandably popular hotel which is evident in such details as the greeting of a uniformed doorman, the charm of the chambermaids, and the provison of delicious chocolates in rooms. Bedrooms contained in two tower blocks vary in size but all benefit from comprehensive room and valet services. Public areas include the first-floor Truffles Restaurant where chef David Dorricott produces such innovative and imaginative dishes as Tempora de Loup de Mer sur Matignon de Germes de Blè et Fenouiland where service is professional yet particularly friendly; on Sundays it is also the venue for the very popular Jazz Brunch. The hotel also offers an all-day informal restaurant combined with a well appointed traditional pub, extensive banqueting facilities and an adjoining NCP car park. (See colour feature on p16.)*

272⇨🐾⅍in 14 bedrooms CTV in all bedrooms **T**
**✗** (ex guide dogs) ✳ sB⇨🐾£211.50 dB⇨🐾£211.50 (room only) 🛏

Lift ℂ ⊞ 400🚌 (£15 per day) CFA 🎣 (hard) 🎵 *xmas*

🍴 French **V** ✪ ⚼ ⅍ ✳ S% Lunch £19.50-£20.50&alc Dinner £29.50&alc Last dinner 11.30pm

Credit Cards ①②③④⑤ⓔ

---

★★★★73% **Britannia Inter-Continental**
Grosvenor Square W1A 3AN ☎071-629 9400 Telex no 23941
FAX 071-629 7736

*A well maintained hotel overlooking Grosvenor Square boasts public areas which include not only a choice of bars and restaurants in contrasting styles but also an attractive Georgian shopping arcade. Three grades of bedroom offer increasing degrees of comfort, all being pleasantly furnished and appointed though standard rooms are fairly compact. Comprehensive room and valet*

service is always available, and guests are able to view their bills through the television.

315⇨⅍in 5 bedrooms CTV in all bedrooms **T**
**✗** (ex guide dogs) S% sB&B⇨£109-£269 dB&B⇨£109-£269 🛏

Lift ℂ ⊞ 15P CFA 🎵 *xmas*

🍴 English, American & Japanese **V** ✪ ⚼ ⅍ ✳ S% Lunch £21.30-£29&alc Dinner £21.30-£29.50&alc Last dinner 10.30pm

Credit Cards ①②③④⑤

---

★★★★73% **Montcalm**
Great Cumberland Place W1A 2LF ☎071-402 4288
Telex no 28710 FAX 071-724 9180

*This Georgian property in a tree-lined crescent, near Marble Arch, has been tastefully extended to provide well equipped comfortable bedrooms, including duplex and penthouse suites and studio rooms. Public areas, while limited, are relaxing and elegant, Les Celebrités restaurant serves interesting well prepared dishes and the professional service is friendly and attentive.*

115⇨🐾(9fb)⅍in 3 bedrooms CTV in all bedrooms **T**
**✗** (ex guide dogs) S% sB⇨🐾fr£169 dB⇨🐾fr£215 (room only) 🛏

Lift ℂ ⊞ 🅿 🚲 CFA

🍴 French **V** ✪ ⚼ ⅍ ✳ Lunch £17.50-£19.50 Dinner £24.50&alc Last dinner 10pm

Credit Cards ①②③④⑤

---

★★★★72% **Park Lane**
Piccadilly W1Y 8BX ☎071-499 6321 Telex no 21533
FAX 071-499 1965

*The Park Lane has an old-fashioned atmosphere based on traditional services, conscientious management and the continuity of several long-serving members of staff. Recent refurbishment has resulted in some opulent public rooms, notably the art deco ballroom, complete with silver leaf hand-painted décor, and the comfortable Palm Court lounge. There is a choice of dining: in the classical style of Bracewells or the less formal brasserie. The many small suites and bedrooms are in the process of refurbishment but like the public rooms they capture the essence of the traditional grand British hotel.*

321⇨🐾(32fb)⅍in 44 bedrooms CTV in all bedrooms **T**
sB⇨🐾£179-£209 dB⇨🐾£209-£250 (room only) 🛏

Lift ℂ 180🚌 (charged) CFA solarium gymnasium 🎵

🍴 International **V** ✪ ⚼ S% Lunch fr£17&alc Dinner fr£23&alc Last dinner 10.30pm

Credit Cards ①②③⑤

---

★★★★70% *London Marriott*
Grosvenor Square W1A 4AW ☎071-493 1232 Telex no 268101
FAX 071-491 3201

*Overlooking Grosvenor Square, this modern hotel offers a high standard of comfort with a range of nicely furnished and well equipped bedrooms. Public rooms are comfortably furnished and there is both a formal and an informal dining room. There is now a business centre and private dining with additional extensive function facilities.*

223⇨🐾(26fb) CTV in all bedrooms **T ✗** (ex guide dogs)

Lift ℂ ⊞ 🅿 🚲 🎵

🍴 International **V** ✪ ⚼ ⅍ Last dinner 12.30am

Credit Cards ①②③④⑤

---

★★★★68% **Selfridge**
Orchard St W1H 0JS (Mount Charlotte (TS)) ☎071-408 2080
Telex no 22361 FAX 071-409 2295

*A modern hotel with fine public rooms including a panelled lounge and country pub-style cocktail bar. There are two restaurants – one formal and very comfortable and the other very informal. Bedrooms tend to be small but very well equipped.*

296⇨🐾(25fb)⅍in 110 bedrooms CTV in all bedrooms **T ✗** (room only) 🛏

→

London

Lift ( ⊞ ♪
♀ International ✿ ♨ ✄
Credit Cards ① ② ③ ④ ⑤

### ★★★★66% The Westbury

Bond St, Conduit St W1A 4UH (Forte Hotels) ☎071-629 7755
Telex no 24378 FAX 071-495 1163

*An attractive hotel, ideally set in Mayfair, greets winter guests*
*with a glowing fire in its marbled foyer. The compact Polo Bar,*
*with its murals, leads into the gracious, pine-panelled Polo Lounge*
*which serves refreshments 24 hours a day, while a cosy and*
*tastefully appointed restaurant offers a range of interesting menus.*
*Individually decorated bedrooms – some of which are designated*
*'non smoking' – are attractive and comfortable, though en suite*
*facilities can be on the small side, whilst the valet room service is*
*polite and efficient.*

243↪🛏↑✄in 80 bedrooms CTV in all bedrooms T ✹ S%
sB↪🛏↑fr£155 dB↪🛏↑fr£180 (room only) 🍴
Lift ( ⊞ 16P CFA ♫ xmas
V ✿ ♨ ✄ ✹ S% Lunch £16-£25alc Dinner £16-£25alc Last
dinner 11pm
Credit Cards ① ② ③ ④ ⑤

### ★★★★59% Holiday Inn – Marble Arch

134 George St W1H 6DN (Holiday Inns) ☎071-723 1277
Telex no 27983 FAX 071-402 0666

*This well managed and modern hotel offers modern and well*
*equipped accommodation. The introduction of a new European*
*restaurant complements the existing brasserie. Free parking for*
*residents is available.*

241↪🛏↑(135fb)✄in 32 bedrooms CTV in all bedrooms ® T ✹
sB↪🛏↑fr£160 dB↪🛏↑fr£182 (room only) 🍴
Lift ( ⊞ 5P 60🛏 CFA 🖵 (heated) sauna solarium gymnasium
xmas
♀ European V ✿ ♨ ✄ ✹ Lunch fr£17.50 Dinner £15-
£17.50&alc Last dinner 11pm
Credit Cards ① ② ③ ④ ⑤

### ★★★★57% Ramada

10 Berners St W1A 3BA ☎071-636 1629 Telex no 25759
FAX 071-580 3972

*A magnificent lounge and dining room are the key features of this*
*hotel conveniently located just off Oxford Street. The successful*
*carvery lunch operation is supplemented by an à la carte menu, and*
*afternoon teas are also extremely popular. Bedrooms satisfy*
*modern commercial needs and the refurbishment programme*
*should now be complete.*

235↪🛏↑(10fb)✄in 105 bedrooms CTV in all bedrooms T ✹ ✹
S17.5% sB↪🛏↑£100-£145 dB↪🛏↑£100-£150 (room only) 🍴
Lift ( ♪ CFA xmas
♀ English & French V ✿ ♨ ✄ ✹ Lunch £13.50&alc Dinner
£15.75&alc Last dinner 10.30pm
Credit Cards ① ② ③ ④ ⑤

### ★★★★55% The Cumberland

Marble Arch W1A 4RF (Forte Hotels) ☎071-262 1234
Telex no 22215 FAX 071-724 4621

*This popular commercial and tourist hotel is continuing to upgrade*
*its accommodation and most rooms are now both well equipped*
*and comfortable, as are the lounges and reception area. The choice*
*of restaurants includes a carvery and a coffee shop as well as the*
*main restaurant and, for those who like the exotic, one in Japanese*
*style.*

894↪🛏↑(38fb)✄in 238 bedrooms CTV in all bedrooms ® T
✹ (ex guide dogs) ✹ sB↪🛏↑fr£95 dB↪🛏↑£130-£145 (room
only) 🍴
Lift ( ♪ CFA xmas
♀ English & Japanese V ✿ ♨ ✄ ✹ Lunch £14.25&alc Dinner
£14.25&alc Last dinner 10pm
Credit Cards ① ② ③ ④ ⑤

### ★★★★52% St George's

Langham Place W1N 8QS (Forte Hotels) ☎071-580 0111
Telex no 27274 FAX 071-436 7997

*This popular hotel just north of Oxford Circus is located at ninth*
*floor level and above, BBC offices occupying the floors below.*
*Accommodation is functional but well equipped, while public*
*rooms – which are, in some cases, in need of refurbishment –*
*include a top floor area with panoramic views over central London*
*and a split-level restaurant serving reliable grills.*

86↪🛏↑(8fb)✄in 11 bedrooms CTV in all bedrooms ® T ✹ S%
sB↪🛏↑£95 dB↪🛏↑£120 (room only) 🍴
Lift ( 2P CFA ♫ xmas
V ✿ ♨ ✄ ✹ S% Lunch £15.50&alc Dinner £15.50&alc Last
dinner 10pm
Credit Cards ① ② ③ ④ ⑤

### ★★★70% Chesterfield

35 Charles St W1X 8LX ☎071-491 2622 Telex no 269394
FAX 071-491 4793

*This traditional hotel in the heart of Mayfair has a luxurious*
*atmosphere enhanced by flowers and antiques in the public rooms,*
*which include a wood-panelled library lounge and the Butlers Grill*
*restaurant where two fixed price menus are available. Bedrooms*
*vary in size and degree of comfort but all are very well equipped*
*and have many thoughtful extras. Good housekeeping standards*
*prevail throughout, and 24-hour room service is available.*

110↪🛏↑(4fb)⊞✄in 2 bedrooms CTV in all bedrooms T
✹ (ex guide dogs) ✹ sB↪🛏↑£90-£115 dB↪🛏↑£150-£170 (room
only) 🍴
Lift ( ♪ ♨ CFA ♫
V ✿ ♨ Lunch fr£18alc Dinner fr£25alc Last dinner 10.30pm
Credit Cards ① ② ③ ⑤ £

### ★★★70% Clifton-Ford

47 Welbeck St W1M 8DN ☎071-486 6600 Telex no 22569
FAX 071-486 7492

*The modern exterior of this West End hotel belies the traditional*
*comfort and elegant furnishings of the interior, which includes*
*spacious lounge areas with a split-livel bar, a stylish restaurant and*
*a new large function suite. Spacious executive bedrooms and*
*luxurious suites equipped with every modern facility have many*
*thoughtful extras, and 24-hour room service is also provided.*

200↪🛏↑(4fb)✄in 27 bedrooms CTV in all bedrooms ® T ✹
S% sB↪🛏↑£112.80-£152.75 dB↪🛏↑£126.90-£170.38 (room
only) 🍴
Lift ( 20🛏 (£16) CFA ♫
♀ International V ✿ ♨ Lunch £10-£21.30alc High tea fr£7alc
Dinner £19.50-£30alc Last dinner 10pm
Credit Cards ① ② ③ ⑤

### ★★★66% Mandeville

Mandeville Place W1M 6BE ☎071-935 5599 Telex no 269487
FAX 071-935 9588

*This long established hospitable hotel offers a good choice of*
*traditional-style bedrooms equipped with modern facilities. Public*
*rooms include 2 restaurants, a pub and small lounge bar. Business*
*services are available, with a car park nearby at Selfridge's.*

165↪🛏↑ CTV in all bedrooms T ✹ (ex guide dogs) ✹
sB&B↪🛏↑fr£98 dB&B↪🛏↑fr£120 Continental breakfast 🍴
Lift ( ♪
♀ International V ✿ ✹ Lunch £12-£16alc Dinner £12-£16alc
Last dinner 10.30pm
Credit Cards ① ② ③ ⑤

### ★★★63% Mostyn

Bryanston St W1H 0DE ☎071-935 2361 Telex no 27656
FAX 071-487 2759

*Conveniently situated for Oxford Street shopping, this large hotel*
*dating to the 18th century and retaining many original features,*
*has modernised well- equipped bedrooms of varying size and*
*degrees of comfort. Public areas include a traditional foyer, well-*
*furnished bar lounge and the Planters Cafe Restaurant which is*

London

*open all day. Staff are friendly and attentive, and 24- hour room service is available.*
122⇋🛏(24fb) CTV in all bedrooms ® **T 🗙** (ex guide dogs)
Lift ℂ
**V** ✿ ♨ ⅙ Last dinner 11.45pm
Credit Cards ①②③⑤

### ★★★57% Mount Royal
Bryanston St, Marble Arch W1A 4UR (Mount Charlotte (TS))
☎071-629 8040 Telex no 23355 FAX 071-499 7792
*A 30s-built, large, long established tourist hotel, ideally located for shopping in Oxford Street. Accommodation is very dated but is slowly being upgraded. The best rooms are on the 2nd and 4th floors, and while most have useful dressing areas, bathrooms are very compact. Reception facilities and all public areas are on the 1st floor, reached by escalator. The coffee house is open all day for meals and light refreshments, and Harry's Bar is a well appointed meeting place.*
701⇋🛏(31fb)⅙in 40 bedrooms CTV in all bedrooms ® 🗙
Continental breakfast
Lift ℂ 🅿 *xmas*
🍴 Mainly grills ✿ ♨ ⅙
Credit Cards ①②③④⑤

### ★★52% Regent Palace
Glasshouse St, Piccadilly W1A 4BZ (Forte Hotels)
☎071-734 7000 Telex no 23740 FAX 071-734 6435
*Good accommodation in this outstanding value-for-money hotel, which does not however have any bathrooms en suite at present. Adjacent to Piccadilly Circus.*
887rm(12fb)⅙in 336 bedrooms CTV in all bedrooms ® **T ✱**
sBfr£39 dB£55-£68 (room only) ❚
Lift ℂ 🅿 CFA
**V** ✿ ♨ ⅙ ✱ Lunch fr£10.95 High tea fr£10.95 Dinner fr£13.95 Last dinner 9pm
Credit Cards ①②③④⑤

### ⊛⊛ ✕✕✕✕✕ Ninety Park Lane
90 Park Ln W1Y ☎071-409 1290 Telex no 24871
FAX 071-493 3341
*This elegant restaurant, attached to one of Forte Hotels' London flagships, Grosvenor House, has its entrance via a canopied walkway on Park Lane. There is a comfortable bar and sitting area where drinks are taken before your meal in the restaurant, an opulent room, with many objets d'art. The menu is restricted to an abbreviated à la carte, with the 7-course set menu drawing dishes from it and a small menu of lighter choices. Our inspector enjoyed a very good, if rather large, portion of terrine de foie gras followed by tender lamb medallions in crépinette, flavoured with marjoram; desserts were served from a trolley. Bread and butter are good and coffee excellent, but prices are very high.*
Closed Sun & BH's Lunch not served Sat
🍴 French **V** 78 seats ✱ Lunch fr£25&alc Dinner fr£50&alc Wine £10.50 Last lunch 2.45pm Last dinner 10.45pm 10 P nc5yrs ⅙ ♫
Credit Cards ①②③④⑤

### ⊛⊛⊛⊛⊛ ✕✕✕✕ LE GAVROCHE
43 Upper Brook St W1Y 1PF ☎071-408 0881 & 071-499 1826
FAX 071-409 0939
*How does one begin to describe a restaurant that has become so universally known, not just among lovers of fine food and avid readers of foodie magazines and guides, but among a vast number of people who may never see London let alone one of its most expensive restaurants. I speak of those who have marvelled at the skill, humour and exuberance of the Roux brothers as seen on TV. Michel is at the Waterside Bray and Albert here at Le Gavroche. Anyone who wants to try the best, in quality of cooking, in presentation, in close attentive service, should visit this restaurant. Located midway between Park Lane and the American Embassy on Grosvenor Square, its discreet, understated entrance gives no indication of the activity within and below street level. Reading about famous places one gets the impression that they are large,*

*but in reality there is comfortable space, with corners and pillars lending privacy, and above all the constant movement of staff. Food is presented with colour plate precision. Flavour is all important, and starts the taste buds with a dish of canapés, today's included rillette of pork of such intensity it was disappointing not to find it among the first courses to obtain a larger helping. The careful balance of ingredients in Côtelette de Pigeonneauet Tourte de Foie Gras were bewildering in their number but gave a combination of flavours that was inspired. A pièce de résistance, though, was La Gourmandine aux Chocolats, a must for chocoholics, it included a favourite of Griotte – tiny liqueur-steeped morello cherries coated in the strongest of bitter chocolate. An explosion of flavours. Petits fours, when on your own are excellent value, usually enough for 2, here doubly so, a range of some 14 exquisite items.*
Closed Sat, Sun & 22 Dec-4 Jan
🍴 French **V** 65 seats Lunch fr£30&alc Dinner fr£55&alc Last lunch 2pm Last dinner 11pm 🅿 nc6yrs
Credit Cards ①②③⑤

### ⊛⊛⊛ ✕✕✕ The Greenhouse
27A Hay's Mews W1X 7RJ ☎071-499 3331 Telex no 919042
FAX 071-225 0011
*Plenty of windows overlooking a paved courtyard or trellised wall, pale paintwork and restrained greenery are all well in keeping with the name of this popular Mayfair restaurant. In these pleasant, comfortable surroundings the emphasis is on British food, but evidence of continental influences is apparent in dishes such as beef carpaccio with parmesan. Traditional fare includes herrings and mustard sauce, braised oxtail and hot puddings. Although the wine list is not extensive, there are some well chosen bottles available.*
Closed 1wk after Xmas & BH's Lunch not served Sat
Dinner not served Sun
**V** 85 seats ✱ Lunch £20-£30alc Dinner £28-£35alc Last lunch 2.30pm Last dinner 11pm 🅿 nc5yrs
Credit Cards ①③④

London

# W1 West End

### ❀✕✕✕ *Princess Garden of Mayfair*
8-10 North Audley St W1Y 1FA ☎071-493 3223

*Quietly decorated and smart this large Chinese restaurant with a separate bar has an extensive menu of Pekinese and regional dishes such as Squid Superb, Steamed Dumplings and Mongolian Lamb, accompanied by a quality wine list.*

Closed Xmas & Etr
♥ Pekinese V 150 seats Last dinner 11.20pm ₽ nc7yrs
Credit Cards ①②③⑤

### ❀❀❀✕✕✕ Rue St Jacques
5 Charlotte St W1P 1HD ☎071-637 0222 FAX 071-637 0224

*After a number of less favourable reports, Chef/patron Gunther Schlender and his brigade appear to be back on the right track. The attractive menus, biased towards game in season, are always thoughtfully constructed. Bordering on heavy-handedness on occasions, sauces are rich and powerful, but by contrast, meats and vegetables are treated with much more restraint. Try a light brioche stuffed with delicious pink veal kidneys and sweetbreads and a port and cream sauce to start, and amongst main courses tested by our Inspectors, a fillet of lamb was beautifully roasted and arranged on a bed of very fine ratatouille, with a 'sparkling' pimento sauce. The three chocolate mousses must be tried. A fine wine list is not surprisingly inclined towards French selections, and the well supervised service is courteous and polite.*

Closed Sun, Xmas, Etr & BH's Lunch not served Sat
♥ French V 70 seats ✳ Lunch £23-£35&alc Dinner fr£35&alc Last lunch 2.30pm Last dinner 11pm ₽
Credit Cards ①②③⑤

### ❀❀✕✕ Au Jardin Des Gourmets
5 Greek St W1V 6NA ☎071-437 1816 FAX 071-437 0043

*A long-established French restaurant at the heart of Soho offers elegant surroundings in which to enjoy competently prepared dishes such as well-flavoured Feuilletes of Lambs Tongue, or Monk Fish and Lobster in a fresh-tasting Chive Butter Sauce, the food being complemented by an impressive and carefully chosen wine list.*

Closed Sun, Xmas & Etr Lunch not served Sat
♥ French 85 seats ✳ Lunch £14.75-£17.50&alc Dinner £16.95&alc Last lunch 2.15pm Last dinner 11.30pm ₽ ⌣
Credit Cards ①②③⑤

### ❀✕✕ La Bastide
50 Greek St W1V 5LQ ☎071-734 3300

*This elegant Georgian style restaurant creates a pleasant and caring ambience. Regional French dishes are the speciality, executed with a high degree of competence and there are fixed price menus as well as the à la carte. The wine list is comprehensive, with a good general appeal.*

Closed Sun & BH's Lunch not served Sat
♥ French V 45 seats ✳ Lunch £20-£23&alc Dinner £20-£23&alc Last lunch 2.30pm Last dinner 11.30pm ₽ nc12yrs
Credit Cards ①②③

### ❀❀❀❀❀✕✕ CHEZ NICO
35 Great Portland St W1N 5DD ☎071-436 8846
FAX 071-436 0134

*Chez Nico is clearly established as one of the most outstanding restaurants in the country, and Nico Ladenis now feels that he has achieved his main goal – the development of an uncomplicated and yet very refined style of cuisine which emphasises delicate and individual flavours and which is consistently good: sauces and fish dishes are particularly successful. The shortened lunch menu offers only two set-price meals, but these contain a sound choice of such classical and seasonal dishes as Ravioli de Homard au Beurre de Truffles and Tournedos de Boeuf à la Moutarde followed by apple tart or a rich ice cream and accompanied by a well balanced but costly wine list that includes interesting examples from the New World as well as some fine clarets and Burgundies.*

Closed Sun, Sat, Xmas-New Year, 3 wks Aug-Sep & 4 days Etr

♥ French V 48 seats ✳ Lunch £27.75-£60 Dinner £49-£62 Last lunch 2pm Last dinner 11pm P nc10yrs
Credit Cards ①③⑤

### ❀✕✕ Gay Hussar
2 Greek St W1V 6NB ☎071-437 0973

*Soho would not be the same without this efficiently friendly restaurant, unchanged since it first opened its doors in 1952. Chef Lazlo Holecz continues to provide authentic Hungarian cuisine, his menus including several 'dishes of the day', all served in gargantuan portions. Wild Cherry Soup and Veal Goulash are particularly recommended, as are such Transylvanian specialities as Stuffed Cabbage and the Mixed Grill; home-made Liptoi cheese is available, and the Turo's Palacsinta, sweet cheese pancake, should not be missed. The wine list features some rare Tokajis vintages dating from 1889 as well as Bulls' Blood and regional wines. Early reservation is strongly recommended, and car parking is very difficult.*

Closed Sun, 25 Dec, 1 Jan & BHs
♥ Hungarian V 70 seats ✳ Lunch £15&alc Dinner £16.20-£24.60alc Last lunch 2.30pm Last dinner 11pm ₽
Credit Cards ②

### ❀✕✕ Gopal's
12 Bateman St W1V 5TD ☎071-434 1621

*Many loyal customers have followed 'Gopal' from its early days in Wembley to its present west-end home, and they have not been disappointed. Chef proprietor N P Pittal has retained his individual style and consolidated his reputation for good, inventive cooking. Among his specialities are Dum Ka Murg, chicken steamed in a sealed pot with Hydernbadi spices and herbs; Vegetarian Thali with pilao rice, naan or roti; Pasanda Nawabi, sliced lamb cooked with fresh cream, home-made yoghourt and mixed nuts, or the excellent Tarka Dal which combines at least 7 different types of lentils, herbs and spices. Exciting, pungent fresh flavours, good quality ingredients and Mr Pittal's fine cooking add up to a memorable experience. Service, supervised by the elegant Mrs Christine Mathias, is excellent.*

Closed 25-26 Dec
♥ Indian V 45 seats Lunch fr£10&alc Dinner fr£10&alc Last lunch 2.45pm Last dinner 11.30pm ₽ nc12yrs ⌣
Credit Cards ①②③④⑤

### ❀✕✕ Langan's Brasserie
Stratton St W1X 5FD ☎071-491 8822

*Booking is essential at this popular, fashionable and sometimes noisy restaurant which continues to offer a very extensive daily menu. Long-time favourites include green pea and ham soup, Langan's seafood salad, black pudding with kidneys and bacon and bangers and mash with onion sauce. More skilful dishes include veal and mushroom terrine with cucumber chutney or poached halibut with prawn sauce. Among the traditional and satisfying puddings we can recommend the treacle tart with custard. Do remember that parking in this area of London can be extremely difficult.*

Closed Sun, public hols, Etr & Xmas Lunch not served Sat
♥ English & French V 200 seats ✳ Lunch £21.05-£38.70alc Dinner £21.05-£38.70alc Last lunch 3pm Last dinner 11.45pm ₽ ♫
Credit Cards ①②③⑤

### ❀✕✕ Lindsay House
21 Romilly St W1V 5TG ☎071-439 0450 FAX 071-581 2848
(Rosette awarded for lunch only)

*With the success of the proprietors' Chelsea restaurants this stylish town house has been furnished with antiques to provide the West End with British cuisine and one of the prettiest private dining rooms in town. Chef Manuel Martin's menus offer an interesting choice of starters, good main courses and home-made ice creams and sorbets; breads are home-made too. Notable dishes include the Fish Mousse wrapped in Sole Fillets, Medallions of Southdown Lamb with a Red Wine Sauce, and Floating Islands. Dinner before or after the theatre is readily available; service is well supervised, if a little distant at times; no pipes or cigars are*

*allowed in the main dining room – and remember to ring the door bell when you arrive! Car parking can be difficult.*
Closed 25-26 Dec
V 30 seats ✳ Lunch fr£14.75&alc Last lunch 2.30pm Last dinner mdnt ✗ ♫
Credit Cards ①②③⑤

### ✳✗✗ Mr Kai of Mayfair
65 South Audley St W1Y 5FD ☎071-493 8988
*A sophisticated restaurant in the heart of Mayfair with comfortable half-alcove tables and polished professional service, offering mainly Peking cuisine with some Cantonese additions. Specialities include aromatic duck, Peking chicken and sharks fin, with extra fish dishes such as whole sea bass often available.*
Closed Xmas
♡ Pekinese & Cantonese 120 seats ✳ Dinner fr£20&alc Last lunch 2.30pm Last dinner 11.15pm ✗ nc6yrs
Credit Cards ①②③⑤

### ✳✳✗✗ Odin's
27 Devonshire St W1N 1RJ ☎071-935 7296
*Initially established by the late Peter Langan, Odin's reflects the style of its restaurant manager, Dieter Schulot, who brought here the dry sense of humour, courtesy and proficiency that had made him such a notable asset to the Capital Hotel over many years. Head chef Chris German specialises in British cuisine, offering a lengthy à la carte menu which has proved very popular with the clientele. It would be a welcome innovation to include more half-bottles on the all-French wine list.*
Closed Sun, public hols, Etr & Xmas Lunch not served Sat
♡ French 60 seats ✳ Lunch £28.05-£37.90alc Dinner £28.05-£37.90alc Last lunch 2.30pm Last dinner 11.30pm ✗
Credit Cards ①②③⑤

### ✳✳✗✗ Stephen Bull
5-7 Blandford St W1H 3AA ☎071-486 9696
*This smart modern restaurant with its striking black and white décor, attracts a cosmopolitan crowd in the evenings. Originality and flair distinguish the cooking, which is in the main very successful, as for example in the excellent terrine of salmon and monkfish with a saffron balsamic vinaigrette. A celeriac soup, on the other hand, was found to be so strongly spiced as to defeat the celeriac flavour. Comfort has not been a strong point, but we understand that moves are afoot to refurbish over the next 12 months.*
Closed Sun & 23 Dec-2 Jan Lunch not served Sat
V 60 seats Lunch £20-£25alc Dinner £20-£25alc Last lunch 2.15pm Last dinner 11pm ✗
Credit Cards ①③

### ✳✳✳✗✗ Sutherlands
45 Lexington St W1R 3LG ☎071-434 3401 FAX 071-287 2997
*It is easy to miss this smart modern restaurant as you walk down Lexington Street, though the dark frontage and frosted windows attract local advertising and media people by the tableful. The interior décor is stylish and there is some interesting artwork. Garry Hollihead produces a splendid set price menu of sensible proportions, and a particularly good value lunch time alternative. There are moments of brilliance – breads are very good and desserts have been highly praised. Other courses receive mixed reports, but for all that, success outweighs disappointment and this is serious cuisine of increasing stature.*
Closed Sun & BH's Lunch not served Sat
♡ British & French V 45 seats Lunch fr£24&alc Dinner fr£39.50&alc Last lunch 2.15pm Last dinner 11.15pm ✗
Credit Cards ①②③

### ✳✳✗✗ Zen Central
20-22 Queen St W1X 7PJ ☎071-629 8103 & 071-629 8089 FAX 071-439 0681
*The third of the Zen restaurants, tucked away in residential Mayfair, favours a sleek, white and rather austere décor, a spiky ikebana-like flower adorning both table and menu cover. A*

*friendly, attentive welcome soon dispels any unease, however, and the operation's professionalism, smoothness and style are well suited to its location. An extensive range of appetising dishes includes splendid 'specials' (fluffy supreme shark's fin and roasted Peking duck, for example), seafood (notably a soft shell crab cooked in a piquant peppercorn sauce), dumplings, soups, vegetarian dishes and such refreshing desserts as ginger sorbet with ripe exotic fruits. Carefully prepared prawns and scallops in a delicious version of the traditional Szechuan 'sea-spice' sauce, tender marinated slices of duck with ginger, pineapple and fried pastry and Bok Choy cabbage poached with garlic proved particularly enjoyable. The reasonably chosen wine list is not cheap, however, and service and cover charges are still made.*
Closed 24-27 Dec
♡ Chinese V 110 seats ✳ Lunch £25-£40&alc Dinner £25-£40&alc Last lunch 2.30pm Last dinner 11.30pm P
Credit Cards ①②③④⑤

### ✳✳✳✗ Alastair Little
49 Frith St W1 ☎071-734 5183
*The high standards of cooking ensure that this small, fashionable restaurant maintains its popularity, so much so that advance booking is always advisable. The menu, changed at every meal, is short but imaginative; the wine list, on the other hand, is comprehensive and reasonably priced.*
Closed Sun, 1 wk Xmas & BH's Lunch not served Sat
♡ International V 36 seats ✳ Lunch £22-£43alc Wine £7.50 Last lunch 3pm Last dinner 11.30pm ✗

### ✳✗ Aunties
126 Cleveland St W1P 5DN ☎071-387 1548 & 071-387 3226
*English restaurant specialising in home-made pies.*
Closed Sun, 25-26 Dec, 1 Jan, PH's & 2 wks Aug Lunch not served Sat
30 seats Lunch £21.60 Dinner £21.60 Last lunch 2.30pm Last dinner 10.30pm ✗
Credit Cards ①②③⑤

### ✳✳✗ Bahn Thai
21a Frith St W1V 5TS ☎071-437 8504
*This well known restaurant has now become established in Soho, having moved there from Kensington some 5 years ago. Authentic Thai cuisine is served in two attractive rooms adorned with abundant jungle foliage and ethnic artefacts, the lengthy menu containing good short descriptions. Thai snacks such as Tord man Pla (spicy fish cakes with a sweet and sour peanut sauce) are used as starters, and main courses – including some delicious curries – make much use of seafood like crab claws, prawns and squid as well as meat and tofu. Pungent hot sauces (Nham Prik) accompany vegetable dishes, and soups are excellent, Tom Kha Gai (chicken seasoned with lemon grass and coconut) being the best known. Exotic fruits are used in the making of ices and the wine list includes Thai wine and beer; flavoured teas are also available. The restaurant is understandably popular, and booking is essential for an evening meal.*
Closed Xmas, 1 Jan & BH's
♡ Thai V 80 seats Last dinner 11.15pm P nc
Credit Cards ①②③

### ✳✳✗ Frith's
14 Frith St W1V 5TS ☎071-439 3370 & 071-734 7535
*An informal atmosphere, attentively efficient service and a varied, interesting menu all contribute to the popularity of this bright, modern hotel. The dishes offered in both the lunchtime table d'hôte and evening à la carte selections are expertly prepared from good fresh produce and accompanied by a short but comprehensive wine list.*
Closed Sun, 2 wks Xmas, Etr & BH's Lunch not served Sat
♡ British & Italian V 60 seats ✳ Lunch £20-£40alc Dinner £20-£40alc Last lunch 2.30pm Last dinner 11.15pm ✗
Credit Cards ①③

# W1 West End - W2 Bayswater, Paddington

### ❀✗ Jamdani
34 Charlotte St W1P 1HJ ☎071-636 1178 071-631 0417
FAX 071-323 0599
*Chef Naresh Matta maintains his reputation for skill in the production of authentic Indian meals, choosing the best from Southern India, Pakistan and the Punjab to create a short but varied list of freshly prepared tandoori, seafood, meat and vegetable dishes. Recommendations include the nan bread with sesame seeds, lamb pasanda with cream and almonds, and munsh kahari chicken cooked on an iron skillet with capiscums. Service is particularly efficient and well managed. Evening reservations are advisable, and guests should note that car parking can be very difficult.*
Closed Sun 23-30 Dec
♡ Indian **V** 75 seats Last lunch 2.45pm Last dinner 11.30pm ⊁
Credit Cards ①②③⑤

### ❀❀✗ L'Hippocampe
63 Frith St W1V 5TA ☎071-734 4545 FAX 071-287 1027
*Late of Fulham, Pierre Condou's stylish fish restaurant has moved to Soho and occupies premises decorated in attractive marine shades and patterns to complement Tim Hughes' inventive cooking. In addition to the adventurous à la carte menu there is a 3-course Menu du Jour which may or may not be available in the evening, depending on demand. Among the fine seafood dishes on offer, do not miss the West-Country oysters cultivated by Pierre's brother-in-law. The inspection meal began with rather garlicky shellfish ravioli served with a delicious olive-oil and coriander jus, followed by a generous portion of grilled fillets of red mullet on a bed of spinach with a delicate ginger and pepper sauce. Other dishes singled out for notice have included the Tarte Tatin of scallops with a Sauternes sauce and roast sea bass with langoustines and polenta. For dessert there was a warm lemon tart, accompanied by poached apple balls and sorbet described by the inspector as 'truly wonderful'.*
Closed Sun Lunch not served Sat
♡ French 60 seats ✳ Lunch £16-£18&alc Dinner £16-£18&alc Last lunch 2.30pm Last dinner 11.15pm ⊁
Credit Cards ①②③

### ❀❀✗ Ming
35-36 Greek St W1V 5LN ☎071-734 2721 & 071-437 0292
FAX 071-435 50812
*An attractive friendly little restaurant specialising in dishes which became part of the Chinese culinary tradition during the creative Ming Dynasty, 1368-1644. Recommendations include Yuunam Prawns fermented in Bean Curd, Gansu Duck simmered in herbs and Mr. Edward's Pork. Car parking can be very difficult.*
Closed Sun (ex Chinese New Year) & 25-26 Dec
♡ Chinese **V** 80 seats ✳ Lunch £12-£17.50&alc Dinner £12-£17.50&alc Last dinner 11.45pm ⊁⊱
Credit Cards ①②③④⑤

### ❀✗ New World
1 Gerrard Place W1V 7LL ☎071-734 0677 & 071-434 2508
*This large and popular Chinese restaurant offers a wide selection of dishes based on good-quality ingredients. Throughout the day heated trolleys circulate among the tables, enabling guests to choose from a tempting array of Dim Sum; service is generally courteous and friendly.*
Closed 25-26 Dec
♡ Chinese **V** 600 seats ✳ Lunch £6.60-£35&alc Last lunch 5.45pm Last dinner 11.30pm ⊁
Credit Cards ①②③⑤

### ❀✗ Tall Orders in Soho
2 St Anne's Court, Dean Street/Wardour St, Soho W1V 1DR
☎071-494 4941
Closed Sun Lunch not served Sat
**V** 135 seats ✳ Bar Lunch £1.95-£5.95alc Last dinner 11.30pm ⊁⊱
Credit Cards ①②③

### ❀✗ Woodlands
77 Marylebone Rd W1M 5GA ☎071-486 3862
FAX 081-908 0253
*This comfortable, simple restaurant has an inviting menu of freshly prepared southern Indian vegetarian dishes, many of them variations on the spicy vegetable filling in a crisp coating: rava dosa (semolina pancake), uthappam (pizza) or samosa might contain subtly spiced onion, potato, cream cheese and lentils. Enjoyable side dishes include puffy bhatura bread, spinach, coconut chutney and badam almond and saffron milkshake.*
Closed 25-26 Dec
♡ South Indian **V** 60 seats ⊁
Credit Cards ①②③⑤

### ❀✗ Yumi
110 George St W1H 6DJ ☎071-935-8320 FAX 071-486 1626
*The typical Japanese menu offers well prepared and interesting dishes. Guests are welcomed by traditionally dressed waitresses and at lunchtime there is a choice of reasonably priced set menus.*
Closed Sun, 2 wks Xmas, 1 wk Aug & Public Hols Lunch not served Sat
♡ Japanese 70 seats ✳ Lunch £18-£41&alc Dinner fr £41&alc Last dinner 10.30pm ⊁
Credit Cards ①②③⑤

## W2 BAYSWATER, PADDINGTON

### ★★★★ 72% White's
Lancaster Gate W2 3NR (Mount Charlotte (TS))
☎071-262 2711 Telex no 24771 FAX 071-262 2147
*This small hotel which overlooks Hyde Park offers high standards of service, cuisine and accommodation, and enjoys a club-like atmosphere. Helpful, correct and friendly service is provided by all staff.*
54⇔1 ∩⇔in 10 bedrooms CTV in all bedrooms **T** ✘ (ex guide dogs) (room only) ₽
Lift ⓒ 25P ⇔ ❄ xmas
♡ English & French **V** ✿ ⨎
Credit Cards ①②③④⑤

### ★★★★ ❀67% Royal Lancaster
Lancaster Ter W2 2TY (Rank) ☎071-262 6737 Telex no 24822 FAX 071-724 3191
*The bedrooms of this hotel include the better furnished Reserve Club and superior luxury suites which occupy the top 4 floors, commanding spendid views of Kensington Gardens, while tastefully appointed and well furnished public areas offer a choice of eating styles in La Rosette Restaurant and the Pavement Café; excellent conference and banqueting facilities are available, as are shops, a hairdressing salon and roof-top car parking. A well managed, professional staff offers both room and valet service.*
418⇔(4fb) CTV in all bedrooms **T** ✘ (ex guide dogs) ✳ sB⇔∩£148 dB⇔∩£168 (room only) ₽
Lift ⓒ 50P (£7.50-£10) 50 (£7.50-£10) ⇔ CFA ♫ xmas
♡ International **V** ✿ ⨎ ✳ Lunch £20.50&alc Dinner £23.50&alc Last dinner 10.45pm
Credit Cards ①②③④⑤

### ★★★ 65% London Embassy
150 Bayswater Rd W2 4RT (Jarvis) ☎071-229 1212
Telex no 27727 FAX 071-229 2623
*Opposite Kensington Gardens, this very popular commercially oriented hotel with a basement car park has a choice of modern well equipped comfortable bedrooms, a cocktail lounge, carvery restaurant and summer terrace, plus 2 conference rooms. 24-hour room service is available. An extensive bedroom upgrading programme is under way.*
193⇔∩✘in 10 bedrooms CTV in all bedrooms ® **T** ✘ (ex guide dogs) ✳ sB⇔∩£92-£117.50 dB⇔∩£107.50-£127.50 (room only) ₽
Lift ⓒ 20P 20 (£2) CFA

London

462

♀ International **V** ♥ ⌂ ✳ Lunch £13.95&alc Dinner
£13.95&alc Last dinner 10.15pm
Credit Cards [1] [2] [3] [5]

### ★★★62% Central Park
Queensborough Ter W2 3SS ☎071-229 2424 Telex no 27342
FAX 071-229 2904
*Just off the Bayswater Road and Hyde Park, this modern hotel is*
*conveniently situated. 24-hour room service is provided in the*
*modern bedrooms, which include all the expected facilities. The*
*ground floor lounge and bar area is bright and comfortable, and it*
*is popular for food and drink served throughout the day.*
251rm(210⇔31♠)(10fb) CTV in all bedrooms ® **T**
Lift ( 10P (£1.50) 20🚗 (£1.50) CFA sauna solarium
gymnasium *xmas*
♀ International **V** ♥ ⌂ ✳ Lunch fr£14.75 Dinner fr£14.75
Last dinner 10pm
Credit Cards [1] [2] [3] [5] (£)

### ★★★60% Park Court
75 Lancaster Gate, Hyde Park W2 3NN (Mount Charlotte (TS))
☎071-402 4272 Telex no 23922 FAX 071-706 4156
*This large and very popular tourist hotel has been partially*
*upgraded, bedrooms west of Reception now being particularly*
*comfortable and well furnished, though all accommodation is fully*
*equipped. A marble-tiled foyer contains the bar and sitting area,*
*there is a small shop, conference facilities are good, and the*
*Brrasserie is open throughout the day. Friendly, efficient staff offer*
*helpful service, and easy street car parking is generally available.*
398⇔♠(11fb)↙in 227 bedrooms CTV in all bedrooms ® **T**
(room only) 🛱
Lift ( ✗ ✿ *xmas*
**V** ♥ ⌂ ↙
Credit Cards [1] [2] [3] [4] [5]

### ★★★55% Hospitality Inn Bayswater
104/105 Bayswater Rd W2 3HL (Mount Charlotte (TS))
☎071-262 4461 Telex no 22667 FAX 071-706 4560
*A large but compact hotel whose first-floor public areas include a*
*restaurant and bar lounge offers views which vary in size and*
*quality of furnishings – the best being on the 8th and 9th floors –*
*although all are well equipped. Flexible conference facilities are*
*available, together with good car parking.*
175⇔♠ CTV in all bedrooms ® **T** (room only) 🛱
Lift ( ▦ 20P 40🚗 *xmas*
♀ International **V** ♥ ⌂
Credit Cards [1] [2] [3] [4] [5]

### ★★61% Delmere
130 Sussex Gardens, Hyde Park W2 1UB (Consort)
☎071-706 3344 Telex no 8953857 FAX 071-262 1863
*This small hotel, conveniently situated just off Hyde Park, offers*
*accommodation in compact bedrooms which have been well*
*furnished and equipped to meet the needs of short-stay guests; a*
*cosy lounge, small dispense bar and bright little restaurant are to*
*be found on the lower floors, a lift being available for guests' use.*
*Parking can be difficult (though restricted on-road parking is*
*permitted overnight), but there is a multi-storey car park within*
*walking distance.*
38⇔♠(2fb) CTV in all bedrooms ® **T** S% sB&B⇔♠£71.40
dB&B⇔♠£90.30 Continental breakfast 🛱
Lift ( 2P 🚗
♀ French & Italian **V** Dinner £9-£12.50 Last dinner 10.30pm
Credit Cards [1] [2] [3] [5] (£)

### ✸ ✗*Kalamara's*
76-78 Inverness Mews W2 3JQ ☎071-727 9122 & 071-727 2564
*There are two Kalamara's restaurants in Inverness Mews – a*
*smaller, unlicenced one and this, which provides an all-Greek wine*
*list to complement the authentic Greek cuisine.*
Closed Sun & BHs Lunch not served
♀ Greek **V** 86 seats Last dinner mdnt ✗
Credit Cards [1] [2] [3] [5]

### ✸ ✗*Veronica's*
3 Hereford Rd, Bayswater W2 4AB ☎071-229 5079 &
071-221 1452 FAX 071-229 1210
Closed public hols & BH Mon Lunch not served Sat
Dinner not served Sun
**V** 36 seats ✳ Lunch £10-£12&alc Dinner £10-£12&alc Last
lunch 2.30pm Last dinner 11.30pm ✗
Credit Cards [1] [2] [3] [5]

## W5 EALING

See LONDON plan 1*B4*
See also W13 Ealing (Northfields)
### ★★★70% Carnarvon
Ealing Common W5 3HN (Consort) ☎081-992 5399
Telex no 935114 FAX 081-992 7082
*Conveniently situated by Ealing Common close to the North*
*Circular Road and with extensive car parking facilities, this well*
*designed modern hotel has a choice of compact well equipped*
*bedrooms and attractive spacious public areas, with a large*
*function room, formal lobby, through-bar and restaurant with a*
*recommended carving trolley. Continuing good management and*
*smartly dressed staff provide helpful attentive service.*
145⇔♠↙in 30 bedrooms CTV in all bedrooms ® **T**
🐾 (ex guide dogs) ✳ sB⇔♠fr£79 dB⇔♠fr£99 (room only) 🛱
Lift ( 150P CFA
♀ European **V** ♥ ⌂ ↙ ✳ Lunch £14.50&alc Dinner
£14.50&alc Last dinner 9.30pm
Credit Cards [1] [2] [3] [5]

Remember to book early for holiday
and bank holiday times.

## W6 Hammersmith - W8 Kensington

### W6 HAMMERSMITH

**See LONDON plan 1***C3*

★★★56% *Novotel London*

1 Shortlands W6 8DR ☎081-741 1555 Telex no 934539
FAX 081-741 2120

*A large, modern and very functional hotel, conveniently located to give access to the A4 for Heathrow and Central London, provides accommodation in double-glazed rooms with a generally acceptable degree of comfort. Le Grill Restaurant is open for most of the day, while Le Pub offers an alternative in English style, and a room service continental breakfast is served as an alternative to the restaurant's self-service selection. Extensive function room and car parking facilities are available.*

640⇨⅒in 20 bedrooms CTV in all bedrooms
Lift ⊞ CTV 230🚗 (£6.50)
♥ English & French V ✿ ⬛ ⅒ Last dinner mdnt
Credit Cards ① ② ③ ⑤

★★58% **Premier West**

Glenthorne Rd W6 0LS ☎081-748 6181 FAX 081-748 2195

*A small, friendly and personally run commercial hotel, centrally located and with easy access to the West End and M4. The modern bedrooms, whilst compact, are well equipped and designed for the more transient guest, and public rooms offer a choice of bars, restaurant and patio terrace.*

26⇨🔦(7fb) CTV in all bedrooms ® T 🏥 (ex guide dogs) S%
sB&B⇨🔦£45-£65 dB&B⇨🔦£55-£75 🍴
《 CTV 6P ⛹ pool table
V ✿ ⬛ ⅒ S% Bar Lunch £2.50-£5.50 Dinner £8.95&alc Last dinner 10pm
Credit Cards ① ② ③ ⑤

❀❀ ✕ *River Cafe*

Thames Wharf Studio's, Rainville Rd, Hammersmith W6 9HA
☎071-381 8824

*A popular and fashionable restaurant in a converted Thames-side warehouse. The service, like the décor, is simple and uncomplicated and the Italian cuisine provides food which is fresh, simple and not over-refined.*

Closed 1 wk Xmas Lunch not served Mon
Dinner not served Sat & Sun
♥ Italian V 60 seats Last lunch 2.30pm Last dinner 9.15pm P
Credit Cards ① ③

### W8 KENSINGTON

**See LONDON plan 1***C3*

★★★★★❀❀63% **Royal Garden**

Kensington High St W8 4PT (Rank) ☎071-937 8000
Telex no 263151 FAX 071-938 4532

*A busy hotel with some bright, comfortably appointed public rooms and a choice of 2 restaurants: the less formal Garden Terrace, open throughout the day, and the Royal Roof Restaurant. Here, chef David Nicholls and his team offer an interesting menu and cooking that lives up to the high standard now expected of them. Bedrooms have been refurbished, and although some are quite compact they are well furnished and equipped. Hospitality is a strong feature of this hotel, with its helpful willing staff.*

398⇨🔦7🍴⅒in 10 bedrooms CTV in all bedrooms T
🏥 (ex guide dogs) ✱ sB⇨🔦£148-£228 dB⇨🔦£193-£228 (room only) 🍴
Lift 《 ⊞ 160🚗 (£16 per 24hrs) CFA ♫ xmas
♥ International V ✿ ⬛ ⅒ ✱ Lunch £14.50-£18.95&alc Dinner £53&alc Last dinner 11pm
Credit Cards ① ② ③ ④ ⑤

★★★★60% **Kensington Palace Thistle**

De Vere Gardens W8 5AF (Mount Charlotte (TS))
☎071-937 8121 Telex no 262422 FAX 071-937 2816
*The bedrooms at this popular hotel have recently been upgraded to provide modern facilities. The intimate restaurant provides an à la*

*carte menu and there is also a bright, informal café. Services are traditional although occasionally disappointing.*

298⇨🔦(27fb)⅒in 32 bedrooms CTV in all bedrooms ® T 🏥
Lift 《 ♪
♥ International ✿ ⬛
Credit Cards ① ② ③ ④ ⑤

★★★★57% **The Copthorne Tara London**

Scarsdale Place, off Wrights Ln W8 5SR ☎071-937 7211
Telex no 918834 FAX 071-937 7100

*Refurbishment of bedrooms continues at this busy, modern hotel situated in a quiet corner of Kensington; those awaiting work lack comfort and are rather dated. Guests have a choice of eating options in addition to an extensive room service menu. Tingles Promenade encompasses six different bar areas and has a lively atmosphere.*

828⇨🔦⅒in 96 bedrooms CTV in all bedrooms ® T
🏥 (ex guide dogs) S% sB⇨🔦fr£99 dB⇨🔦fr£114 (room only) 🍴
Lift 《 ⊞ 30P 80🚗 (£8 per 24hrs) CFA xmas
♥ French V ✿ ⬛ S% Lunch £12.40&alc High tea £8.80-£13.60alc Dinner £12.40&alc Last dinner 1am
Credit Cards ① ② ③ ④ ⑤

★★★65% **Kensington Close**

Wright's Ln W8 5SP (Forte Hotels) ☎071-937 8170
Telex no 23914 FAX 071-937 8289

*Recent extensive refurbishment and upgrading, now almost completed at this hotel, have provided a selection of de luxe non-smoking single bedrooms and a varied choice of more spacious rooms to suit all tastes on the 4th and 5th floors. The original good-value carvery offers an alternative to the Italian restaurant, and a leisure health club, conference centre, shop and car park are provided for guests' convenience, and the Terrace Bar and garden are very popular on warm summer evenings. Room service of continental breakfast is available.*

530⇨🔦⅒in 81 bedrooms CTV in all bedrooms ® T
🏥 (ex guide dogs) ✱ sB⇨🔦fr£85 dB⇨🔦fr£95 (room only) 🍴
Lift 《 150🚗 (£14 per 24hrs) ✿ CFA ⬛ (heated) squash sauna solarium gymnasium health & fitness centre xmas
♥ English & Italian V ✿ ⬛ ✱ Lunch £14.25&alc Dinner £14.25&alc Last dinner 11pm
Credit Cards ① ② ③ ⑤

★★55% **Hotel Lexham**

32-38 Lexham Gardens W8 5JU ☎071-373 6471
Telex no 268141 FAX 071-244 7827
Closed 23 Dec-2 Jan

*This traditional, privately run hotel in a quiet location offers good value for central London, with a choice of bedrooms, some recently refurbished with modern facilities and others currently being upgraded. It has two functional lounges and a dining room serving a simple daily changing table d'hôte menu (there is no bar and guests are invited to bring their own wines).*

66rm(48⇨🔦)(13fb) CTV in all bedrooms T 🏥 (ex guide dogs)
✱ sB&Bfr£34 sB&B⇨🔦fr£48.50 dB&Bfr£45
dB&B⇨🔦£62.50-£69.50 🍴
Lift 《 CTV ♪ ⛹ ✿
♥ English & Continental ✿ ⬛ ✱ Lunch fr£5alc Dinner fr£8.75 Last dinner 8pm
Credit Cards ① ③ ⓔ

❀❀ ✕✕ **Boyd's**

135 Kensington Church St W8 7LP ☎071-727 5452
FAX 071-221 0615

*In this fresh, modern, conservatory-style restaurant on two levels stylishly appointed green-stained tables are surrounded by profuse foliage. Now open 7 days a week, it offers a limited choice, but value-for-money 3-course lunch as well as the main à la carte, which provides a range of 6 to 7 options at each course. Lemon Tagliatelli, entwined with smoked salmon, is set on a tangy*

London

*dressing and garnished with shavings of fresh pumpkin, while the rather smooth Venison and Pistachio Terrine, though it lacks that distinctive gamey flavour, is very enjoyable, served with a sweet Cumberland sauce and delicious toasted brioche. Char-grilling is a speciality, and an oriental influence shows in the Ribeye of Scotch Beef marinated in orange, olive oil and garlic, garnished with watercress and wild mushrooms; desserts are less reliable, but ice creams made on the premises are worth trying. A predominantly French wine list opens with a good selection from the New World, and devotes a whole page to half bottles and includes a noteworthy range of whiskies (both Scotch and Irish), Cognacs and Armagnacs.*

Closed 1 wk Xmas
♀ French **V** 36 seats ✱ Lunch £14.50&alc Dinner £19.25-£29.50alc Last lunch 2.30pm Last dinner 10.30pm ✗
Credit Cards ①②③

### ❀❀❀ ✗✗ Clarke's
124 Kensington Church St W8 4BN ☎071-221 9225
FAX 071-229 4564

*This fresh, bright restaurant offers a short lunch menu and no choice at all in the evenings – but its quality is beyond question. Chef/patronne Sally Clarke's light, American and Eastern-influenced style is exemplified in dishes such as a deliciously spicy corn chowder, and char-grilled meat and fish with imaginative sauces and crisp vegetables. Breads and pastries are excellent, and the wine list includes a good North American range. The bakery and coffee shop next door also sells Californian wines and splendid home-made pickles.*

Closed Sat, Sun, Xmas, Etr & 3 wks Aug-Sep
♀ British, French & Italian **V** 90 seats Lunch fr£8 Last lunch 2pm Last dinner 11pm ✗
Credit Cards ①③

### ❀❀❀ ✗ Kensington Place
201/205 Kensington Church St W8 7LX ☎071-727 3184
FAX 071-229 2025

*Rowley Leigh presides over this lively, popular restaurant, situated at the Notting Hill end of Kensington Church Street, and open 12 hours a day. Cooking is excellent and dishes range from the homely (cod with parsley sauce or rabbit stew, for example), to the more imaginative, such as griddled foie gras with sweetcorn pancake, or the red and grey mullet with wild rice and ginger particularly enjoyed by our inspector. Service is relaxed and friendly but tables are very close together, so not ideal for private conversation. The set lunch is good value and there is a range of reasonably priced wines.*

Closed 25 Dec & Aug BH
♀ European **V** 90 seats ✱ Lunch £12.50&alc Dinner £15-£30alc Last lunch 3pm Last dinner 11.45pm ✗
Credit Cards ①③

---

### W11 HOLLAND PARK, NOTTING HILL
#### See LONDON plan 1*C3*

### ❀❀❀ ✗✗✗ Leith's
92 Kensington Park Rd W11 2PN ☎071-229 4481

*This sophisticated Kensington restaurant – its raw materials supplied as far as possible by fresh, organically grown produce from its owner's Gloucestershire farm – offers two seasonally changed, enterprising but uncomplicated menus, one of which is vegetarian. The hors d'oeuvres trolley presents such straightforward starters as smoked salmon parcels alongside more unusual items like lambs' tongue with raspberry vinegar dressing, main dishes include roast goose breast with juicy wild mushrooms and a shallot and port wine sauce, and the dessert trolley is augmented by a small but sensible selection of cheeses. A wine list worthy of note includes examples from the New World and Spain, and polite professional service is provided by an experienced, mostly Continental staff.*

Closed 25-26 Aug & 24-27 Dec Lunch not served

♀ International **V** 85 seats Dinner £29.50-£39.50 Last dinner 11.30pm ✗ nc7yrs
Credit Cards ①②③⑤

### ❀❀❀ ✗ Restaurant 192
192 Kensington Park Rd W11 2ES ☎071-229 0482

*192 began as a wine bar, but the food proved so successful that the basement is now used soley by diners. Upstairs is frequented by a particularly trendy set ; meals may be taken here without any obligation to eat more than one course. Diners may have to fit into a 'sitting', depending on how busy they are, but it is generally advisable to book. The décor is modern with ethnic touches, and the room is divided into 2 sections. The small kitchen is clearly visible through the hatches and the chefs peer through to size up the punters. Chef Maddalena Bonino changes the menu twice daily depending on what is available, the style encompasses a number of influences, and prices are reasonable. A marinated pigeon breast was served on a tangy tomato and onion salsa – a successful combination. This was followed by grilled swordfish served with ribbons of pickled cucumber and a flavoursome lobster and oil dressing. Our inspector particularly enjoyed the stir-fry of seafood with crisp vegetables, samphire, chilli, ginger and coriander. The young staff provides fairly snappy unobtrusive service, essential, given that some tables need to be turned. There is an interesting selection of wines, many available in a standard or large glass.*

Closed BH's Lunch not served Mon
♀ French **V** 80 seats ✱ Dinner £13.80-£20.80alc Last lunch 2.30pm Last dinner 11.30pm ✗
Credit Cards ①②③

---

The AA's star rating scheme is the market leader in hotel classification.

---

**London**

### W13 EALING (NORTHFIELDS)

**See LONDON plan 1***B4*
See also W5

#### ❋✕ **Maxim Chinese**

153-155 Northfield Av W13 9QT ☎081-567 1719 & 081-840 1086

*This very popular neighbourhood restaurant has built up both an excellent reputation and a loyal, regular clientèle. Authentic Peking dishes, freshly prepared and individually cooked, make good use of ginger, garlic and herbs, while sauces are particularly full of flavour. As well as the set fixed-price meal for two persons, an à la carte menu offers a challenging selection of such items as steamed scallops Peking style, shredded chicken in a black bean sauce, or fried pork with bean shoots and beef in oyster sauce. Service is both well managed and professional.*

Closed 25-28 Dec Lunch not served Sun

♀ Pekinese **V** 120 seats Lunch £7-£25&alc Dinner £7-£25&alc Last lunch 2.30pm Last dinner mdnt 🅿

Credit Cards 1 2 3 5

### W14 WEST KENSINGTON

#### ❋❋❋✕ *Chinon*

25 Richmond Way W14 0AS ☎071-602 5968 & 071-602 4082

*A popular, intimate, little restaurant with a warm atmosphere and friendly service offers set-price menus which vary according to season, chef Jonathan Hayes bringing an artistic touch to the range of skilfully prepared and presented dishes. Honestly made, flavoursome sauces are particularly noteworthy, as is the superbly cooked Breast of Duckling, and a limited selection of vegetables is attractively served; puddings are superb, though the choice is similarly restricted, and a short wine list features some interesting wines at reasonable prices.*

Closed Sun, Etr & Aug BH

**V** 28 seats Last lunch 2pm Last dinner 11pm 🅿 nc10yrs

Credit Cards 1 2 3

### WC1 BLOOMSBURY, HOLBORN

#### ★★★★ 56% **The Marlborough**

Bloomsbury St WC1B 3QD ☎071-636 5601 Telex no 298274 FAX 071-636 0532

*A large and busy commercial/tourist hotel – scheduled for complete refurbishment during 1991 provides some spacious, well equipped and comfortable bedrooms. The Brasserie Saint Martin offers both à la carte and set price menus, while the Duke's Head serves a good selection of informal meals and light snacks.*

169⇄🛏¥in 67 bedrooms CTV in all bedrooms ® **T** ✳ S%
sB⇄🛏fr£143 dB⇄🛏£167-£197 (room only)

Lift ( 🅿 CFA *xmas*

♀ French **V** ✿ ⌂ ⅙ Lunch £16.50&alc Dinner £16.50&alc Last dinner 11.30pm

Credit Cards 1 2 3 4 5

#### ★★★★ 50% **Hotel Russell**

Russell Square WC1B 5BE (Forte Hotels) ☎071-837 6470 Telex no 24615 FAX 071-837 2857

*This large Victorian hotel with marble pillars and staircases has an impressive historical elegance. Bedrooms vary: the best are at the front and some can be compact, but all are well equipped. The library/lounge serves traditional afternoon tea and there is a choice of 2 bars and 2 restaurants – a popular brasserie and a carvery.*

328⇄🛏(1fb)¥in 23 bedrooms CTV in all bedrooms **T** ✳
sB⇄🛏fr£95 dB⇄🛏£120-£216 (room only)

Lift ( 🅿 CFA *xmas*

**V** ✿ ⌂ ⅙ ✳ Lunch fr£15.50 High tea fr£5.75 Dinner fr£15.50 Last dinner 10pm

Credit Cards 1 2 3 4 5

#### ★★★ 69% **Forte Crest Bloomsbury**

Coram St WC1N 1HT (Forte Hotels) ☎071-837 1200 Telex no 22113 FAX 071-837 5374

*Situated between the West End and the City this hotel provides ideal facilities for both business and leisure visitors. Extensive refurbishment has transformed the hotel's exterior, the new stone façade is enhanced by a glass domed entrance. The first floor restaurant complex offers an extensive choice of meals, or try the informal Cafe Shaw. The hotel has a purpose built business centre.*

284⇄🛏(29fb)¥in 67 bedrooms CTV in all bedrooms ® **T**
✳ (ex guide dogs) ✳ sB⇄🛏fr£105 (room only)

Lift ( 100🅿 (charged) CFA steam room *xmas*

**V** ✿ ⌂ ⅙ ✳ Lunch fr£14.25 Dinner fr£14.25 Last dinner 11pm

Credit Cards 1 2 3 4 5

#### ★★★ 67% **Bonnington**

92 Southampton Row WC1B 4BH ☎071-242 2828 Telex no 261591 FAX 071-831 9170

*This centrally located, popular hotel has recently been upgraded and refurbished. Bedrooms are all well equipped with bright, modern en suite facilities, though some single bedrooms are a little compact. The open-plan foyer lounge and adjacent bar are well appointed.*

215⇄🛏(16fb)¥in 54 bedrooms CTV in all bedrooms ® **T** ✳
sB&B⇄🛏£55-£92 dB&B⇄🛏£90-£116

Lift ( CFA

♀ English & French **V** ✿ ⌂ ✳ Lunch £15-£18&alc Dinner £15-£18&alc Last dinner 11pm

Credit Cards 1 2 3 5 £

#### ★★★ 50% **London Ryan**

Gwynne Place, Kings Cross Rd WC1X 9QN (Mount Charlotte (TS)) ☎071-278 2480 Telex no 27728 FAX 071-837 3776

*Situated near Kings Cross, this hotel is popular with touring parties. Public areas have recently been attractively refurbished, and rooms on the top floor are recommended for their comfort and facilities.*

211⇄🛏(73fb)¥in 20 bedrooms CTV in all bedrooms ® **T**
✳ (ex guide dogs) Continental breakfast

Lift ( 28P 8🍴

♀ English & Continental **V** ✿ ⌂

Credit Cards 1 2 3 5

#### ★★ ❋ 68% **Academy**

17-21 Gower St WC1E 6HG ☎071-631 4115

*Originally 3 Georgian town houses, the Academy has been recently refurbished to a high standard. It benefits from a central location in the university quarter. Bedrooms vary in size, some being quite compact, but all have been attractively furnished. The basement GHQ Club Restaurant and Bar is, in contrast, stylishly modern. It is open throughout the day and Chef John O'Riordan offers a short set menu for lunch and dinner which is particularly good value, and an additional 'carte' in the evening when it is open only to residents, their guests and club members. Dishes may be simple in composition and presentation, but they are well executed. The Mediterranean fish soup was really a broth – light and flavoursome with some good chunks of seafood. A moist, whole roasted poussin was served with a rosemary jus. Gratin dauphinoise were memorable and vegetables al dente. A simple but creamy Grand Marnier parfait was served with a tart raspberry coulis. On summer days, drink or dine outside in the leafy patio garden.*

33rm(26⇄🛏)(2fb) CTV in all bedrooms ® **T**
✳ (ex guide dogs) ✳ sB£41.12 sB⇄🛏£76.38 dB£64.62 dB⇄🛏£92.83 (room only)

Lift 🅿 🍴 ♫ *xmas*

♀ English & French ✿ ⌂ Last dinner mdnt

Credit Cards 1 2 3 5

For key to symbols in English see the bookmark.

### ❀❀ ✕ Museum Street Cafe
47 Museum St WC1A 1LY ☎071-405 3211

*This small, basically furnished room is a hive of activity at mealtimes, and it is essential to book. Lunchtime menus include main courses served with salad; in the evening there is a 3-course menu with two choices at each stage. Home-baked breads are particularly popular, and many of the main courses are chargrilled – our inspector enjoyed chargrilled salmon with red peppers, baby capers and cumin, a light and successful combination. Home-made desserts are wonderful. The restaurant is unlicensed, but staff will happily open your bottles at no extra charge, making the menu even more affordable.*

Closed Sat, Sun 1wk Etr, 1wk Xmas & 2wks Summer
22 seats ✳ Lunch £6-£16alc Dinner £18.50 Last lunch 2.15pm
Last dinner 9.15pm ✗ ✼

### WC2 COVENT GARDEN

★★★★★

★★★★★ ❀❀❀ **THE SAVOY**

Strand WC2R 0EU
☎071-836 4343
Telex no 24234
FAX 071-240 6040

(Rosettes awarded for
Savoy Restaurant)

*Arguably the grandest of London's grand hotels, the Savoy's reputation for incomparable standards of traditional hotel keeping is jealously preserved by its director Herbert Striessnig. Elegant and gracious public rooms include the Thames Foyer, where that most English institution, afternoon tea, is enjoying a revival, also the famous and crowded American Bar, with its adjacent seafood bar, upstairs. The splendid, wood panelled Grill specialises in spectacular flambé dishes, and the fine French cuisine of Anton Edelmann can be savoured in the Savoy Restaurant with its riverside views; menus also include his 'Menu de Régime Naturel' of healthier and vegetarian dishes. Guests may also enjoy a dance as well as dining and they cannot fail to be impressed, as much by the staff as by their physical surroundings. From cloakroom attendant to porter, from barman to head waiter, from receptionist to lounge waitress, all combine professional courtesy and competence with warmth and good grace. Bedroom refurbishment continues and, as one might expect, great care is taken to preserve period features, particularly the wonderful Art-Deco fittings, while installing modern amenities and comforts.*

200⇨♠✼in 30 bedrooms CTV in all bedrooms **T**
✕ (ex guide dogs) S15% sB⇨♠frf175 dB⇨♠£200-£265 (room only) 🛏

Lift 🌙 58🛏 (£20 per 24hrs) 🚗 CFA ♫ *xmas*
♀ English & French V ✿ ⌨ Lunch £25.50-£28.50&alc
Dinner £32-£36&alc Last dinner 11.30pm
Credit Cards 1️⃣2️⃣3️⃣5️⃣

### ★★★★69% The Waldorf
Aldwych WC2B 4DD (Forte Hotels) ☎071-836 2400
Telex no 24574 FAX 071-836 7244

*Edwardian elegance is the keynote of this hotel, which originally opened in 1908, and this is now combined with modern amenities. Bedrooms vary considerably in size, but in compensation the hotel has many outstanding attractions – notably the Palm Court, the two bars and the Waldorf Restaurant.*

310⇨♠(11fb)2🚗✼in 44 bedrooms CTV in all bedrooms **T**
✕ (ex guide dogs) ✳ S% sB⇨♠£125 dB⇨♠£175 (room only) 🛏

Lift 🌙 ✗ CFA hairdressing salon ♫ *xmas*
♀ International V ✿ ⌨ ✼ ✳ S% Lunch £17.50&alc High tea £10.50-£16.75 Dinner £17.50-£25&alc Last dinner midnt
Credit Cards 1️⃣2️⃣3️⃣5️⃣

### ★★★67% Drury Lane Moat House
10 Drury Ln WC2B 5RE (Queens Moat) ☎071-836 6666
Telex no 8811395 FAX 071-831 1548

*Conveniently situated for central London and its theatres, this hotel offers very well equipped modern accommodation, the best being on the 9th and 10th floors. Public areas include a lobby lounge, Maudies Restaurant and a cocktail bar, all levels being accessible by lift. An efficiently friendly atmosphere prevails in most departments, extensive services generally being available 24 hours a day; limited under-cover car parking is provided, though it becomes full during the late afternoon, and uniformed porters will carry your baggage from the car park entrance.*

153⇨♠(15fb)✼in 20 bedrooms CTV in all bedrooms ®️ **T** ✳ S% sB⇨♠£122.50-£134.50 dB⇨♠£157.50-£173 (room only) 🛏
Lift 🌙 ⊞ 10🛏 (£10 per 24hrs) CFA
♀ French V ✿ ⌨ ✳ Lunch £14.85-£16&alc Dinner fr£14.85
Last dinner 10.30pm
Credit Cards 1️⃣2️⃣3️⃣4️⃣5️⃣£

### ★★★56% Strand Palace
Strand WC2R 0JJ (Forte Hotels) ☎071-836 8080 Telex no 24208
FAX 071-836 2077

*Conveniently located in theatreland, this long established well managed hotel has a large variety of bedrooms, now mostly upgraded in a thorough refurbishment programme, but all well equipped and with en suite facilities. There is a choice of bars and eating places, with a popular carvery, coffee house and Italian restaurant, plus conference and banqueting facilities.*

777⇨♠(24fb)✼in 224 bedrooms CTV in all bedrooms ®️ **T** ✳ S% sB⇨♠£75 dB⇨♠£95-£105 (room only) 🛏
Lift 🌙 ✗ CFA *xmas*
♀ International V ✿ ⌨ ✼ ✳ S% Lunch £14.25&alc Dinner £14.25&alc Last dinner 11.30pm
Credit Cards 1️⃣2️⃣3️⃣4️⃣5️⃣

### ★★★55% Royal Trafalgar Thistle
Whitcomb St WC2H 7HG (Mount Charlotte (TS))
☎071-930 4477 Telex no 298564 FAX 071-925 2149

*Conveniently situated alongside the National Gallery, accommodation here comprises a well appointed lobby lounge, a popular pub and the very informal Hamiltons Brasserie. Best bedrooms are on the 6th floor, while the 4th floor is reserved for non-smokers; all are well equipped but many are compact, particularly the small doubles.*

108⇨♠✼in 36 bedrooms CTV in all bedrooms ®️ **T** (room only) 🛏
Lift 🌙 ✗
♀ English & French ✿ ⌨ ✼
Credit Cards 1️⃣2️⃣3️⃣4️⃣5️⃣

### ❀❀ ✕✕✕✕Savoy Grill
Strand WC2R 0EU ☎071-836 4343 Telex no 24234
FAX 071-240 6040

*Maître chef David Sharland combines his talented creativity with the traditional dishes that are now synonymous with the Grill Room. Service is highly professional and very discreet in the fine Savoy tradition.*

Closed Sun & Aug Lunch not served Sat
♀ English & French V 80 seats ✳ Lunch £28-£60alc Dinner £32-£70alc Last lunch 2.30pm Last dinner 11.15pm ✗ nc12yrs
Credit Cards 1️⃣2️⃣3️⃣5️⃣

### ❀❀ ✕✕✕Boulestin
1A Covent Garden, Covent Garden WC2E 8PS
☎071-836 3819 & 071-836 7061 FAX 071-836 1283

*Although now owned by the Queens Moat hotel group, head chef David Thompson remains firmly and competently in control of the kitchen in this rather smart Covent Garden basement restaurant.*

→

*Dishes, based on produce drawn from all the main European markets, are interesting – if under-adventurous, and the 3-course set lunch represents particularly good value. Mr Andreas supervises good-humoured waiters with aplomb, and an added bonus is a particularly fine wine list.*

Closed Sun, 1 wk Xmas, BH's & last 2 wks Aug Lunch not served Sat

♀ French V 70 seats Lunch £18.75&alc Last lunch 2.30pm Last dinner 11.15pm 🅿 nc5yrs
Credit Cards ① ② ③ ④ ⑤

### ❀❀❀✕✕✕ Now and Zen
4a Upper St, St Martins Ln WC2H 9EA ☎071-497 0376
FAX 071-437 0641

*A visit to this recent addition to the burgeoning Zen group is much an experience for the eye as for the palate. The bold, two-floored glass frontage and glazed pavement lead into an interior whose central features, along with the now familiar use of white walls and mirrors to create space, is a waterfall running via opaque saucers down the oval linking the three balconied levels of the restaurant. The Pacific Rim-style menu also captures the imagination, and includes Sushi starters, prepared at the Sushi bar on the ground floor, and such celebrated Chinese specialities as shark's fin and Peking duck as well as dishes from other Asian countries. Desserts are, in the view of our inspector, less interesting, but the wine list offers a good showing of Californian wines.*

Closed 25-26 Dec

♀ Chinese V 200 seats Last lunch 3pm Last dinner mdnt 🅿
Credit Cards ① ② ③ ④ ⑤

### ❀❀✕✕ Neal Street
26 Neal St WC2 9PH ☎071-836 8368 FAX 071-497 1361
*The menu of this popular, fashionable, Italian restaurant features the authentic cuisine of its country of origin alongside such typically British seasonal game dishes as roast partridge; specialities prepared with Alba truffles are, as might be expected, pricey. A well chosen wine list includes vintages dating back to 1961. Service is friendly and the ambience of the basement bar lounge pleasant.*

Closed Sat, Sun & 1 wk Xmas

♀ Italian V 65 seats ✳ Lunch £29.90-£36.80alc Dinner £29.90-£36.80alc Last lunch 2.30pm Last dinner 11pm 🅿 nc5yrs
Credit Cards ① ② ③ ④ ⑤

### ❀✕ Fuing Shing
15 Lisle St WC2 ☎071-437 1539

Closed 25 & 26 Dec

♀ Cantonese V 85 seats Last dinner 11.30pm 🅿
Credit Cards ① ② ③ ⑤

### ❀✕ Orso
27 Wellington St WC2E 7DA ☎071-240 5269 Telex no 268735
FAX 071-497 2148

*This fashionable basement restaurant, a few doors down from the Royal Opera House, has been going for 5 years. It has white painted brick walls hung with black and white photographs, and a bustling atmosphere. Open all day, every day, Orso's menu changes slightly with every meal though the format stays very much the same – one side in Italian, the other in English translation. It offers small pizzas; pasta dishes as starters; appetisers in the antipasti mode, such as vitello tonnato, bruschetta, tasty marinated sardine fillets; main courses with Italian garnish, perhaps venison with polenta, pork with rosemary, tomato and grappa, or tasty pink char-grilled lamb with white and green beans. Cooking is straightforward and depends on the quality of the ingredients. Bread and coffee are good, but sweets have disappointed on several occasions. The wine list is all Italian, well chosen and fairly priced. Staff are pleasant but can be disorganised.*

Closed 24-25 Dec

♀ Italian V 100 seats ✳ Lunch £18-£25alc Dinner £18-£25alc Last dinner 11.45pm 🅿

### LONDON AIRPORTS
See under **Gatwick** & **Heathrow**

### LONG EATON Derbyshire Map **08** SK43
See also **Sandiacre**
#### ★★★61% *Novotel Nottingham Derby*
Bostock Ln NG10 4EP (S of M1 junc 25) ☎(0602)720106
Telex no 377585
*Conveniently located very near junction 25 of the M1 and consequently a popular rendezvous for meetings, this hotel is embarking on a major refurbishment of public areas which should allow guests to relax in a lighter and more comfortable environment; bedrooms, though reasonably spacious, are furnished in more modest style.*

110🔄📶(110fb) CTV in all bedrooms ®
Lift ▦ 180P ✿ 🔺 (heated) mini golf course putting green
♀ English & French V ⌂ ⚿ Last dinner mdnt
Credit Cards ① ② ③ ⑤

#### ★★60% Europa
20 Derby Rd NG10 1LW ☎(0602)728481
RS 23 Dec-2 Jan
*Actively involved proprietors create a friendly, informal atmosphere at this busy little commercial hotel which stands beside the A6005 at the centre of the town. Most of the clean, modestly appointed bedrooms have ensuite facilities, wholesome, freshly cooked meals are served in the dining room, and a range of refreshments is available during the day in a recently added conservatory.*

19rm(14🔄📶)(2fb) CTV in all bedrooms ® T
🐕 (ex guide dogs) ✳ sB£26-£33 sB🔄📶£33 dB£33 dB🔄📶£33 (room only)
◖ CTV 27P
V ⌂ ⚿ ✳ Lunch £6-£8 Dinner £7.50-£16alc Last dinner 8.30pm
Credit Cards ① ② ③ ⑤ ⓔ

### LONGHAM Dorset Map **04** SZ09
#### ★★★69% **Bridge House**
2 Ringwood Rd BH22 9AN ☎Bournemouth(0202)578828
Telex no 418484 FAX (0202) 572620
Closed 25 & 26 Dec
*Situated on the banks of the River Stour, this modern Mediterranean-style hotel offers comfortable accommodation, with prettily decorated well equipped bedrooms and bright public areas. A wide range of food is available in the riverside bar and carvery or more formal restaurant, served by friendly and helpful staff.*

37🔄📶3🎏 CTV in all bedrooms ® T 🐕 sB&B🔄📶£48-£52 dB&B🔄📶£55-£75 Continental breakfast 🍴
◖ 200P ✿ ✈
♀ English, French & Greek V ⌂ ⚿ ✂ ✳ Lunch £6.50-£12.50&alc High tea £3-£5&alc Dinner £10.50-£14.50&alc Last dinner 10pm
Credit Cards ① ② ③ ⓔ

### LONGHORSLEY Northumberland Map **12** NZ19
#### ★★★★ ❀75% **Linden Hall**
NE65 8XF ☎Morpeth(0670)516611 Telex no 538224
FAX (0670) 88544
*The 300 acres of woodland and parkland feature superb gardens as a setting for this delightful manor, whose history goes back to the 14th century. Rooms are comfortable, and furnished in keeping with the period of the house thus promoting a quiet, relaxing atmosphere. Keith Marshall is in charge of the kitchens and offers some interesting dishes and sound cooking for both the table d'hôte and à la carte menus. Home made ravioli or a leek and foie gras terrine to start with, followed by a main dish of layers of salmon, sole and smoked haddock or pan-fried collops of wild boar. Desserts are good, unless you prefer the fine farmhouse cheeses.*

45⇆🛏(4fb)4⌘ CTV in all bedrooms ℝ T S5%
sB&B⇆🛏£92.50-£112.50 dB&B⇆🛏£110-£195 🛏
Lift ℂ 260P ❋ CFA ♪ (hard) ♪ snooker sauna solarium
croquet putting clay pigeon shooting ♫ ♨ *xmas*
V ♥ ♨ Lunch £14.50-£19.50&alc High tea £5.50-£14.50alc
Dinner £19.50-£21.50&alc Last dinner 10pm
Credit Cards ① ② ③ ⑤ ④

**See advertisement under MORPETH**

---

**LONG MELFORD** Suffolk Map **05** TL84

★★★ 59% **The Bull**
Hall St CO10 9JG (Forte Hotels) ☎Sudbury(0787)78494
FAX (0787) 880307
*This former Posting House, close to the village green, offers every
modern convenience amidst the comfort and charm of open
fireplaces, wooden rafters and carvings. The Cordell Room
restaurant serves interesting, freshly-made dishes.*
25⇆🛏(3fb)⊬in 11 bedrooms CTV in all bedrooms ℝ T ✳ S%
sB⇆🛏fr£65 dB⇆🛏fr£80 (room only) 🛏
20P CFA *xmas*
V ♥ ♨ ✳ S% Lunch £10.95-£14.25&alc Dinner £15.95&alc
Last dinner 9.30pm
Credit Cards ① ② ③ ④ ⑤

---

❀ ✕ ✕ *Chimneys*
Hall St CO10 9JR ☎Sudbury(0787)79806 FAX (0787) 312294
*There has been a restaurant in this splendid timber framed house
for many years, and various owners and styles have come and gone,
but probably none better than Sam Chalmers. Once a chef himself,
he now hosts the dining room. leaving the kitchen in the capable
charge of Chef David Revill. Dishes are in the modern style, but
using classical influences and more interesting ideas from France.*
Closed Mon
Dinner not served Sun
♀ English & French V 50 seats Last lunch 2pm Last dinner
9.30pm 10 P
Credit Cards ① ③

---

❀ ✕ **Countrymen**
Black Lion Hotel, The Green CO10 9DN
☎Sudbury(0787)312356 FAX (0787) 74557
(Rosette awarded for dinner only)
*An established, privately owned and well furnished country
coaching inn, situated on the village green, provides a charming
lounge in which guests can browse over the choice of set menus
offered at both luncheon and dinner, each offering a variety of
freshly made dishes based on local produce, their flavours being
enhanced by fresh herbs. A good board of British cheeses
completes the meal, and speciality wines such as Elderberry are
included in a list which also offers plenty of half bottles.*
Closed Mon
Dinner not served Sun
V 52 seats ✳ Lunch £11.25-£16.25 Dinner £18.75-£26.25 Last
lunch 2pm Last dinner 9.30pm 6 P
Credit Cards ① ③

---

**LONGRIDGE** Lancashire Map **07** SD63

★★ 61% *Blackmoss Country House*
Chipping Rd, Thornley PR3 2TB (2m NE off Chipping rd)
☎(0772)783148
Closed 25 Dec
*Set in 3 acres of well tended lawns and gardens, this privately-
owned country-house hotel, located two miles north east of
Longridge, provides bright, well furnished accommodation.*
10⇆🛏(1fb)⊬in 2 bedrooms CTV in all bedrooms ℝ ✖
65P ❋ CFA ⊇ (heated) ♪ sauna pool table
⊬ Last dinner 9pm
Credit Cards ① ③ ⑤

---

❀ ✕ ✕ **Heathcotes**
Higher Rd PR3 3SY ☎(0772)784969 & 785713
*Paul Heathcote opened this charming restaurant with his partner
Deborah Jones in the summer of 1990. Situated in a rural area,
away from the main tourist routes, customers from all over the
surrounding area are drawn here by the exemplary cooking. Mr
Heathcote learned his skills at Sharrow Bay, the Connaught and
Le Manoir aux Quat' Saisons. His menu offers 6 or 7 choices for
each course, and among his specialities are Ravioli of Lobster with
mussel, tarragon and lobster juices, Braised Pig's Trotter filled
with onion and wild mushrooms, smooth parfait of quail served on
an artichoke heart; these to be followed, perhaps, by crisply
roasted breast of duckling with potato and apple rösti, braised
oxtail, lightly smoked, or pan-fried fillet of Angus beef with a rich
Burgundy sauce. Among an array of delicious sweets, the hot
peach soufflé is a must.*
Lunch not served Mon-Thu & Sat
V 40 seats ✳ Lunch £12.75-£15.50 Dinner £18-£29alc Last
lunch 2pm Last dinner 9.30pm 10 P
Credit Cards ① ③

---

**LONG SUTTON** Lincolnshire Map **09** TF42

⇧ **Forte Travelodge**
(on A17) (Forte) ☎(0406)362230 Central Res (0800) 850950
*Next to a Little Chef (open 7am-10pm), 12 miles west from King's
Lynn on the A17/B1359, half a mile from the village.*
40⇆🛏(40fb) CTV in all bedrooms ℝ sB⇆🛏£29.95
dB⇆🛏£29.95 (room only)
ℂ 40P ⇥
Credit Cards ① ② ③

---

A rosette means exceptional standards of cuisine.

★ ★ ★

*The Bull Hotel*
*Long Melford*

The Bull Hotel is set in the heart of medieval Long Melford,
fourteen miles from historic Bury St Edmunds and central
to Constable Country, Lavenham and many other picturesque
villages.
This fourteenth century timber framed building with
wooden rafters, carvings and open fire places offers
accommodation with full en-suite facilities, colour TV,
telephone and tea and coffee making facilities.
The Bull Hotel offers excellent cuisine in the Cordell
Restaurant and lunch time snacks are available in the bar.
Leisure Break Weekends commence at £45.00 per person
per night which is inclusive of full English breakfast, dinner
from the table d'hôte menu, accommodation, service and
value added tax. Special offers are available for children.

**For further information telephone (0787) 78494, or write
to: The Bull Hotel, Hall Street, Long Melford, Suffolk CO10
9JG. Fax: (0787) 880307.**

Trusthouse Forte Hotels

## LOOE Cornwall & Isles of Scilly Map **02** SX25

#### ★★★61% **Hannafore Point**
Marine Dr, Hannafore PL13 2DG (Best Western) ☎(05036)3273
Telex no 45604 FAX (05036) 3272
*In a spectacular position overlooking the bay, this hotel has
recently opened a leisure complex with a heated indoor pool,
squash court, gym and steam room. The majority of bedrooms
have been upgraded and there are plans to improve the public
areas. The restaurant offers a choice of menus with a Tiffin menu
available throughout the day.*
37⇔🟆(10fb) CTV in all bedrooms ® T sB&B⇔🟆£50.50-£73
dB&B⇔🟆£80-£110 🗒
Lift 🛗 35P CFA 🖃 (heated) squash sauna solarium gymnasium
*xmas*
🍴 English, French & Italian V ☼ ♨ ⅌ ✳ Sunday Lunch
fr£7.95 High tea fr£6 Dinner fr£16.75&alc Last dinner 9.30pm
Credit Cards ① ② ③ ⑤

#### ★★71% **Commonwood Manor**
St Martin's Rd PL13 1LP ☎(05036)2929
Closed Nov-Feb
*The well-appointed, personally-run hotel enjoys rural
surroundings, nestled into the hillside overlooking the harbour.
Comfortable lounges, well-appointed bedrooms and a warm,
friendly atmosphere combine to make your stay a pleasant one.*
10⇔🟆(2fb) CTV in all bedrooms ® T sB&B⇔🟆£31-£38
dB&B⇔🟆£38-£66
CTV 20P 🎦 ✿ ⌣ (heated) nc8yrs
🍴 English & Continental V ☼ ♨ Bar Lunch £2.50-£5.50
Dinner £9-£13 Last dinner 8pm
Credit Cards ① ② ③

#### ★★66% **Fieldhead**
Portuan Rd PL13 2DR (Minotels) ☎(05036)2689 due to change
to (0503) 262689 FAX (0503) 264114
Closed Dec-Jan
*Beautifully situated in an elevated position which commands views
over the bay and managed by proprietors who are totally involved
in the care of their guests, the hotel provides attractively co-
ordinated bedrooms and well presented public areas enhanced by a
backdrop of coastal scenery. The fixed-price dinner menu offers a
good choice supplemented by additional dishes, friendly staff give
attentive service, and the terraced rear garden has an outdoor pool
which is heated during the season.*
14rm(12⇔🟆)(2fb)1🛏 CTV in all bedrooms ® T
✖ (ex guide dogs) sB&B⇔🟆£32-£37 dB&B⇔🟆£54-£64 🗒
9P 5🐾 ✿ ⌣ (heated) nc5yrs
V ☼ ♨ ✳ Bar Lunch £1.50-£3.50 Dinner £12 Last dinner
8.30pm
Credit Cards ① ② ③

## LOSTWITHIEL Cornwall & Isles of Scilly Map **02** SX15

#### ★★★67% **Restormel Lodge**
Hillside Gardens PL22 0DD (Consort) ☎Bodmin(0208)872223
FAX (0208) 873568
*Conveniently situated in the town centre, with its own car park and
reception entrance, this well run popular hotel comprises modern,
well equipped accommodation, partly around and overlooking the
swimming pool, a central candlelit restaurant, and friendly and
informal service. Overall, this hotel offers good value for money,
and high levels of comfort in the bedrooms.*
21⇔🟆Annexe12⇔🟆(3fb) CTV in all bedrooms ® T
sB⇔🟆£36-£38 dB⇔🟆£46-£48 (room only) 🗒
40P ✿ CFA ⌣ (heated) *xmas*
V ☼ ♨ Bar Lunch £1-£10alc Dinner £14-£16&alc Last dinner
9.30pm
Credit Cards ① ② ③ ⑤ ⓔ

## LOUGHBOROUGH Leicestershire Map **08** SK51

#### ★★★62% **King's Head**
High St LE11 2QL (Jarvis) ☎(0509)233222 FAX (0509) 262911
RS Xmas
*Situated in the town centre and only 3 miles from the M1, this
hotel has well equipped bedrooms and good conference and
function facilities, making it particularly popular with business
people and also for weekend breaks.*
78⇔🟆(2fb)⅌in 24 bedrooms CTV in all bedrooms ® T ✳ S%
sB⇔🟆£69-£79 dB⇔🟆£79-£89 (room only) 🗒
Lift 🛗 80P CFA *xmas*
🍴 English & French V ☼ ♨ ✳ S% Lunch £9.50-£11.50 High
tea £2.50-£5.50 Dinner £13.50-£15.50&alc Last dinner 9.30pm
Credit Cards ① ② ③ ④ ⑤

#### ★★★57% **Cedars**
Cedar Rd LE11 2AB ☎(0509)214459 & 217834
FAX (0509) 233573
Closed 26-28 Dec RS Sun
*A well established hotel, popular with local businessmen and
diners, is situated off the A6 to the south of the town centre.
Modest bedrooms, up-to-date public areas and such extras as a
heated swimming pool in quiet gardens combine to make a stay
here a pleasurable experience.*
37⇔🟆(4fb) CTV in all bedrooms ® T ✳ sB&B⇔🟆£43-£45
dB&B⇔🟆£53 🗒
🛗 50P ✿ CFA ⌣ (heated) sauna solarium
V ☼ ✳ Lunch £7.65&alc Dinner £12.15-£19.10alc Last dinner
9.30pm
Credit Cards ① ② ③ ⑤

#### ★★54% *Great Central*
Great Central Rd LE11 1RW (Minotels) ☎(0509)263405
FAX (0509) 264130
RS 24-31 Dec
*A small commercial hotel standing close to the Old Great Central
Railway line. The modest accommodation has a relaxed, informal
atmosphere and the public bars are popular with the locals.*
18⇔🟆(1fb)1🛏 CTV in all bedrooms ® T
40P ♨
🍴 English & French V ☼ Last dinner 9pm
Credit Cards ① ② ③ ⑤

#### ❀❀❀ ✕✕ **Restaurant Roger Burdell**
The Manor House, Sparrow Hill LE11 1BT ☎(0509)231813
*A manor house which stands near the town centre, facing the
church, reflects the character of the timbered building by the décor
and furnishings of its 3 separate dining rooms. The imaginative,
interesting à la carte menu and chef's recommendations comprise
well prepared dishes based on fresh, usually local produce and
reflect seasonal patterns in such items as braised pheasant cooked
in cider with apple and juniper berries.*
Closed Sun & BH's (ex 25 Dec & Good Fri) Lunch not served
Mon
🍴 English, French & Italian V 45 seats Last lunch 2pm Last
dinner 9.15pm 6 P
Credit Cards ① ② ③

## LOUTH Lincolnshire Map **08** TF38

#### ★★65% *Priory*
Eastgate LN11 9AJ ☎(0507)602930
Closed 24 Dec-2 Jan
*There are fine views from both the lounge and bar of this town
centre hotel, for it stands in some 2 acres of lovely, well tended
gardens. Attractive accommodation is enhanced by a notably high
standard of housekeeping by the small team of staff.*
12rm(6⇔3🟆)(2fb) CTV in all bedrooms ® ✖ (ex guide dogs)
CTV 24P 🎦 ✿
V ☼ Last dinner 8.30pm
Credit Cards ① ③

**LOWER BEEDING** West Sussex Map **04** TQ22

★★★★❀❀♨70% **South Lodge**
Brighton Rd RH13 6PS (Small Luxury Hotels) ☎(0403)891711
Telex no 877765 FAX (0403) 891253

*The famous rhododendron collection and 90 acres of magnificent
grounds provide an outstanding setting for this charming early
Victorian house. There are spacious, individually designed
bedrooms, a panelled lounge furnished with antiques, and a library
bar. A 24-hour room service is available, and there are well
proportioned rooms for private functions and business use. The
Candlelit Restaurant overlooks the gardens, and service under the
watchful eye of General Manager David French, is individual,
caring and attentive, making every visit a special occasion. Chef
Anthony Tobin has put together a fine, understated à la carte
menu, which reflects his professional background developing his
craft with Nico Ladenis of Chez Nico. Dishes such as a soup of
local fish and shellfish served with garlic mayonnaise and croutons,
followed by medallions of veal topped with parsley and with a rich
rosemary sauce; warm mousse of foie gras with peeled grapes and
truffle sauce, and breast of English duckling with red wine sauce
and baby turnips, have all impressed our inspector. The wine list
includes a strong collection of New World wines and some fine
clarets; and there is a good-value house selection.*

39⇌2🛏 CTV in all bedrooms T ✹ (ex guide dogs) sB⇌£100-
£255 dB⇌£115-£255 (room only) 🍴
《 80P 🚗 ❖ CFA ♪ (hard) ✍ golf-driving net croquet shooting
♫ *xmas*
♡ English & French V ✿ ⚓ ✂ ✳ Lunch fr£15.50 Dinner £25-
£32&alc Last dinner 10.30pm
Credit Cards 1 2 3 4 5 ⓔ
**See advertisement under HORSHAM**

**L**

**LOWESTOFT** Suffolk Map **05** TM59 ⊖

**★★★63% Broadlands**
Bridge Rd, Oulton Broad NR32 3LN (Consort) ☎(0502)516031
Telex no 975621
*Part of a small shopping precinct in Oulton Broad this is a modern
purpose built hotel with friendly services and a lively convivial
atmosphere. It has a popular carvery and the Chequers disco.*
52⇌(2fb)1♿⊁in 6 bedrooms CTV in all bedrooms ® T
( CTV 120P ▣ (heated) snooker sauna solarium gymnasium
♨ English & Italian ♥ ⌶
Credit Cards ①②③⑤

**★★★57% Victoria**
Kirkley Cliff Rd NR33 0BZ ☎(0502)574433 FAX (0502) 501529
*This family hotel, with comfortable traditional style
accommodation, is situated on the southern side of Lowestoft in an
elevated position on the sea front. The restaurant offers a good
selection of mainly English dishes. Popular with both commercial
and leisure guests.*
36⇌🍳(6fb)1♿⊁in 25 bedrooms CTV in all bedrooms ® T
Lift ( CTV 50P ✿ ⌂ (heated) ♫
♨ English, French & Italian **V** ♥ ⌶ ⊁ Last dinner 10pm
Credit Cards ①②③⑤

**★61% Denes**
Corton Rd NR32 4PL (Toby) ☎(0502)564616 & 500679
*Situated in a pleasant residential area, north of the town on the
Lowestoft/Corton Road, this hotel provides attractive, clean and
very well equipped accommodation. The restaurant offers a
carvery selection of roasts and fresh vegetables and a small menu
of popular dishes.*
12🍳 CTV in all bedrooms ® T
15P
♨ Mainly grills **V** ♥ ⌶ ⊁ Last dinner 10pm
Credit Cards ①②③⑤

---

**LOWESWATER** Cumbria Map **11** NY12

**★66% Grange Country House**
CA13 0SU ☎Lamplugh(0946)861211 & 861570
Closed 20-30 Dec RS 1-19 Dec & 5 Jan-Feb
*A comfortable traditional hotel at the head of the lake, owned and
run by a friendly family.*
7rm(6⇌)Annexe5rm(4⇌)(1fb)2♿ CTV in all bedrooms ®
sB&B£26-£28 sB&B⇌£28-£30 dB&B£52-£56 dB&B⇌£56-£60
CTV 20P 2🚗 (charged) 🐾 ✿
**V** ♥ ⌶ ✻ Lunch £7.50-£9.50 High tea £6.50-£8.50 Dinner £12-
£14.50 Last dinner 8pm

---

**LUDLOW** Shropshire Map **07** SO57

**★★★❀69% Dinham Hall**
SY8 1EJ (Pride of Britain) ☎(0584)876464 & 873699
*A country house style of hotel in the heart of the historic town,
opposite the castle. Secluded gardens are overlooked by the
restaurant where enjoyable meals are prepared by Chef Michael
Aikman, demonstrating his international experience and flair.*
12⇌🍳(1fb)2♿ CTV in all bedrooms ® T 🐕 (ex guide dogs)
17P 🐾 ✿ sauna gymnasium nc6yrs
**V**
Credit Cards ①②③

**★★★❀69% Overton Grange**
SY8 4AD ☎(0584)873500 FAX (0584) 873524
*Major refurbishment of this Edwardian mansion standing in 2.5
acres of grounds on the edge of town has provided delightful
lounges and comfortable bedrooms. The atmosphere is relaxed and
friendly, and the intimate restaurant features the well prepared
dishes of chef Martin Williams, with a good choice from 2 daily
changing set menus and an à la carte menu; leave room for one of
his updated traditional English puddings.*

16rm(10⇌3🍳)(2fb) CTV in all bedrooms ® T
🐕 (ex guide dogs) sB&B£31-£35 sB&B⇌🍳£52-£55 dB&B£54-
£57 dB&B⇌🍳£72-£95 ⋔
80P ✿ croquet *xmas*
♨ English, French & Italian **V** ♥ ⌶ Lunch £11.50-£12.50
Dinner £14.95-£19.50 Last dinner 9.30pm
Credit Cards ①②③⑤£

**★★★68% The Feathers at Ludlow**
Bull Ring SY8 1AA ☎(0584)875261 FAX (0584) 876030
*The distinctive feature of this hotel – one of England's most famous
historical inns – is its very decorative timbered façade. Interior
décor reflects the building's age and character, while traditional
service and hospitality are continually maintained by a proprietor
and general manager who have worked together for many years.*
40⇌🍳(3fb)8♿⊁in 5 bedrooms CTV in all bedrooms ® T 🐕
(ex guide dogs) ✻ sB&B⇌🍳£62-£80 dB&B⇌🍳£88-£106 ⋔
Lift ( 37P CFA snooker *xmas*
**V** ♥ ⌶ ⊁ Lunch £8-£12&alc Dinner £6-£20alc Last dinner
9pm
Credit Cards ①②③④£

**★★65% Dinham Weir**
Dinham Bridge SY8 1EH ☎(0584)874431
*Modern bedrooms are well equipped, and some restaurant tables
overlook the river at this personally run small hotel in its pleasant
setting beside the weir.*
7⇌🍳1♿ CTV in all bedrooms ® T 🐕 sB&B⇌🍳£40-£55
dB&B⇌🍳£55-£60 ⋔
10P 🐾 nc5yrs *xmas*
**V** ♥ Lunch £8.50-£12.50&alc Dinner £10.50-£12.50&alc Last
dinner 9pm
Credit Cards ①②③⑤£

**★★63% Cliffe**
Dinham SY8 2JE ☎(0584)872063
*This small hotel, set at the foot of the town near the River Teme,
offers views of the ancient castle from its delightful grounds.
Modern bedrooms and a friendly atmosphere make it an ideal base
from which to tour the area.*
10rm(3⇌4🍳)(1fb) CTV in all bedrooms ® sB&Bfr£18
sB&B⇌🍳fr£25 dB&Bfr£35 dB&B⇌🍳fr£42 ⋔
50P 🐾 ✿ *xmas*
**V** ♥ ⌶ ✻ Lunch fr£6.50&alc Dinner fr£7&alc Last dinner
8.45pm
Credit Cards ①②③

---

**LUDWELL** Wiltshire Map **03** ST92

**★★67% Grove House**
SP7 9ND (2m E A30) ☎Donhead(0747)828365
Closed Dec-Jan
*This small personally run hotel, on the A30 2 miles east of
Ludwell, has comfortably furnished well decorated bedrooms, most
of which overlook the attractive rear gardens – where resident
badgers come to be fed. There is a cosy bar, a no-smoking lounge
and a dining room serving good home-cooked meals.*
11rm(4⇌6🍳)(1fb) CTV in all bedrooms ® sB&B⇌🍳£24-£26
dB&B⇌🍳£48-£52 ⋔
12P 🐾 nc5yrs
♨ English & Continental **V** ♥ ⊁ ✻ Bar Lunch £3-£7alc
Dinner £14-£16 Last dinner 7.30pm
Credit Cards ①③

---

**LUMBY** North Yorkshire Map **08** SE43

**★★★66% Forte Posthouse Leeds/Selby**
LS25 5LF (southern junc A1/A63) (Forte Hotels)
☎South Milford(0977)682711 Telex no 557074
FAX (0977) 685462

---

*A modern, purpose-built hotel situated at the junction of the A1/ A63 and close to the M62. Recently refurbished, this hotel offers greatly improved bedrooms, a leisure centre, two bars and the Traders' Restaurant.*

105⇨🛏(3fb)⚲in 43 bedrooms CTV in all bedrooms ® T ✱ sB⇨🛏£39.50-£49.50 dB⇨🛏£39.50-£49.50 (room only) 🛒
《 ⊞ 300P ❀ ▱ (heated) ♫ (hard) sauna 9 hole pitch & putt *xmas*
V ⊕ ⏁ ⚲ ✱ S% Lunch £12-£20alc Dinner £16-£25alc Last dinner 10pm
Credit Cards ①②③④⑤

---

LUNDIN LINKS Fife Map 12 NO40

★★★65% **Old Manor**
Leven Rd KY8 6AJ ☎(0333)320368 Telex no 727606
FAX (0333) 320911
*This extended mansion is popular with both business and golfing fraternities, looking across the golf course to the Firth of Forth from its setting on the edge of the village. A wing of modern bedrooms supplements the main building accommodation, and friendly staff provide helpful service throughout.*
19rm(15⇨)(2fb) CTV in all bedrooms ® T ✱ S10% sB&B£32-£50 sB&B⇨🛏£32-£58.50 dB&B£52-£68.50 dB&B⇨🛏£52-£78 🛒
《 80P ❀ CFA ⚙ *xmas*
⛾ Continental V ⊕ ⏁ ✱ Lunch £10.25&alc Dinner £18.75&alc Last dinner 9.30pm
Credit Cards ①②③ⓔ

---

Restaurants and hotel restaurants
with rosettes have their names and addresses
tinted pink in the directory.

# The Old Manor Hotel

*Leven Road, Lundin Links, Fife KY8 6AJ.*
*Telephone: 0333-320368*
*Fax: 0333-320911 Telex: 727606*

Situated on a hill overlooking Lundin Links golf course, an Open qualifying course with views over the Forth to the Lothians, the Old Manor Hotel has 20 rooms all with private facilities and radio, television etc.

The restaurant is renowned for the imaginative use of fresh local seafood and produce. The cocktail bar stocks over 100 malt whiskies, Bunter's Bar in the grounds offers pub grub in informal surroundings.

---

👑👑👑  ★★

# The Cliffe Hotel

**Dinham, Ludlow, Shropshire, SY8 2JE.**
**Tel: (0584) 872063.**

Nestling within its own delightful grounds, beside the River Teme, The Cliffe Hotel is the perfect base for touring the Heart of England.

All 10 bedrooms have colour TV, tea making equipment with full central heating, 7 are en-suite.

The Hotel has an excellent à la carte menu and extensive wine list.

Residents Lounge

Ample parking

Please write or telephone for further information.

L

---

## LUSS Strathclyde *Dunbartonshire* Map **10** NS39

### ★★54% **Inverbeg Inn**
Inverbeg G83 8PD (3m N on A82) ☎(043686)678
FAX (043686) 645
Closed 25 Dec
*An attractive inn with modern, comfortable facilities, the Inverbeg stands close to the banks of Loch Lomond.*
14rm(7⇨)(1fb)⊱in 3 bedrooms CTV in all bedrooms ® T
sB&B£25-£45 sB&B⇨£25-£45 dB&B£50-£65 dB&B⇨£50-£65
🅿
80P ✿ ✔ water skiing windsurfing *xmas*
♡ British & French V ⊹ ⏝ ⊱ Lunch £12-£15 Dinner £13.50-£25 Last dinner 9.30pm
Credit Cards ① ② ③ ⑥

## LUTON Bedfordshire Map **04** TL02 ◉

### ★★★67% **Forte Crest**
Waller Av, Dunstable Rd LU4 9RU (Forte Hotels)
☎(0582)575911 Telex no 825048 FAX (0582) 581589
*A modern commercial hotel usefully situated for the M1 has now almost completed a substantial upgrading which will result in very smartly decorated and well equipped accommodation including executive, study and Lady Crest rooms, Breakfast and dinner menus offer a good choice of dishes – many designed for the health-conscious eater – and friendly staff provide helpful service.*
93⇨🅝⊱in 17 bedrooms CTV in all bedrooms ® T
Lift ⊄ 150P
♡ English & French V ⊹ ⏝ ⊱
Credit Cards ① ② ③ ④ ⑤

### ★★★67% **Strathmore Thistle**
Arndale Centre LU1 2TR (Mount Charlotte (TS)) ☎(0582)34199
Telex no 825763 FAX (0582) 402528
*Situated within the Arndale shopping complex in the town centre, this well run hotel has a good range of public areas including two restaurants and bars; bedrooms are equally well equipped and furnished. Staff are friendly and efficient. Some free parking is available in the adjacent multi-storey upon checking in.*
150⇨🅝(7fb)⊱in 33 bedrooms CTV in all bedrooms ® T ✖ (room only) 🅿
Lift ⊄ 44P
♡ International ⊹ ⏝ ⊱
Credit Cards ① ② ③ ④ ⑤

### ★★★59% **Forte Posthouse**
Dunstable Rd LU4 8RQ (Forte Hotels) ☎(0582)575955
Telex no 826283 FAX (0582) 490065
*This good, well-equipped conference/commercial hotel offers an attractive restaurant and helpful service from friendly staff. Currently being upgraded.*
117⇨⊱in 62 bedrooms CTV in all bedrooms ® ✳ S%
sB⇨£39.50-£49.50 dB⇨£39.50-£49.50 (room only) 🅿
Lift ⊄ 180P ♪ snooker pool table *xmas*
♡ International V ⊹ ⏝ ⊱ ✳ S% Lunch £10-£30alc Dinner £10-£30alc Last dinner 10pm
Credit Cards ① ② ③ ④ ⑤

### ★★66% **Red Lion**
Castle St LU1 3AA (Lansbury) ☎(0582)413881 Telex no 826856
FAX (0582) 23864
*Check for directions around the one-way system to reach this extended Victorian inn near the town centre. Busy public areas include the popular Market Tavern, a spacious lounge bar, a cheerful restaurant and a coffee shop. Bedrooms vary in shape, but are attractively decorated and well equipped. There are good parking facilities.*
24⇨🅝 Annexe15⇨🅝(4fb)1 ⊱in 6 bedrooms CTV in all
bedrooms ® T ✖ (ex guide dogs) sB&B⇨🅝fr£75
dB&B⇨🅝fr£88
⊄ 50P CFA

♡ English & Continental V ⊹ ⏝ ⊱ Lunch fr£7.75 Dinner fr£12.35 Last dinner 10.30pm
Credit Cards ① ② ③ ⑤

## LUTTERWORTH Leicestershire Map **04** SP58

### ★★★69% **Denbigh Arms**
High St LE17 4AD (Resort) ☎(0455)553537 FAX (0455) 556627
*This modernised 18th-century coaching inn in the town centre continues to provide comfortable accommodation and friendly attentive service. Bedrooms, all with en suite bathrooms, are generally spacious and the very popular restaurant now provides a wide choice of meals.*
34⇨🅝(1fb)⊱in 3 bedrooms CTV in all bedrooms ® T ✳
sB&B⇨🅝fr£35 dB&B⇨🅝fr£45 🅿
⊄ 30P *xmas*
♡ English & French V ⊹ ⏝ ✳ Lunch £7.75-£9.50 Dinner £12.50&alc Last dinner 9.30pm
Credit Cards ① ② ③ ⑤

## LYBSTER Highland *Caithness* Map **15** ND23

### ★★60% *Portland Arms*
KW3 6BS ☎(05932)208
*This popular tourist, fishing and business hotel has been considerably modernised to provide modern comforts and facilities, yet retains much of its original staging post character.*
19⇨🅝(3fb)2🚼 CTV in all bedrooms ® T
⊄ CTV 50P ➤ 9 ✔
♡ Scottish & French V ⊹ ⏝ Last dinner 9.30pm
Credit Cards ① ③

## LYDDINGTON Leicestershire Map **04** SP89

### ★★★54% **Marquess of Exeter**
Main Rd LE15 9LT ☎Uppingham(0572)822477
FAX (0572) 821343
*This 16th-century coaching inn, set in the historical village of Lyddington, is surrounded by beautiful countryside. The bedroom accommodation is in an adjacent annexe at the rear of the inn, offering a range of facilities, and en suite bathrooms.*
Annexe17⇨🅝 CTV in all bedrooms ® T ✖ sB&B⇨🅝fr£55
dB&B⇨🅝fr£70 🅿
70P 🚗 ✿
♡ English & French V ⊹ ⏝ Lunch £15.35-£20&alc Dinner fr£15.35&alc Last dinner 9.45pm
Credit Cards ① ② ③ ⑤ ⑥

## LYDFORD Devon Map **02** SX58

### ★★⬩⬩67% **Lydford House**
EX20 4AU (Minotels) ☎(082282)347 FAX (082282) 442
*This delightful, granite-built country house was formerly the home of the Victorian artist William Widgery, whose scenes of Dartmoor still hang in the cosy residents' lounge. The Boulter family have gradually been upgrading the accommodation over a number of years. Service is personal and attentive, and the home cooking very enjoyable. Eight acres of gardens and pasture surround the property, and there is a riding school run by the owners' daughter.*
13rm(11⇨🅝)(2fb)1🚼⊱in 1 bedroom CTV in all bedrooms ®
T sB&B⇨🅝£28.50 dB&B⇨🅝£57 🅿
30P 🚗 ✿ CFA ⊍ nc5yrs
⊹ ⏝ ⊱ Sunday Lunch £7-£8 Dinner fr£12 Last dinner 8pm
Credit Cards ① ② ③

---

◉ Shell filling station, open 7am–11pm
(some 24 hours) throughout the year with leaded
and unleaded petrol, and diesel.

**LYDNEY** Gloucestershire Map **03** SO60

★★59% *Feathers*

High St GL15 5DN ☎Dean(0594)842815 & 842826

*There is a friendly atmosphere in this popular town-centre hotel, which offers a choice of à la carte dining room or carvery, and there are also good bar menus available.*

14⇨📶(3fb)1🛏✎in 2 bedrooms CTV in all bedrooms ® T 50P

V 🐾 ⚏ ✎ Last dinner 9pm

Credit Cards ⬜1 ⬜2 ⬜3

---

**LYME REGIS** Dorset Map **03** SY39

See also **Rousdon**

★★★69% **Alexandra**

Pound St DT7 3HZ ☎(0297)442010 & 443229

Closed 23 Dec-6 Feb

*This hotel, built in 1735, enjoys beautiful views across its garden to Lyme Bay from a prime position. Most bedrooms have been refurbished to a high standard, their décor enhanced by the use of attractive, colourful, coordinating fabrics; older public areas retain the charm and character of their origins. The dining room offers both table d'hôte and à la carte dinner menus of sound but not over-elaborate dishes, a modern sun lounge serves lunches, snacks and cream teas, and friendly staff provide efficient service throughout.*

24⇨📶(6fb) CTV in all bedrooms ® T sB&B⇨📶£50-£55 dB&B⇨📶£100-£130 (incl dinner) 🅱

24P 🚗 ✿ ⚬

♀ English & French V 🐾 ⚏ Lunch £10 Dinner £16.50&alc

Last dinner 8.30pm

Credit Cards ⬜1 ⬜3

**See advertisement on page 477**

**L**

**★★68% Buena Vista**

Pound St DT7 3HZ ☎(0297)442494

Closed Dec

*An hotel which was originally two Regency cottages stands in a pleasant garden, enjoying good views from its position high above the Cobb. The simple British fare served in the dining room includes remarkably good puddings. Guests can take their ease in a series of small lounges, and most of the clean, cosy bedrooms are decorated and furnished in cottage style. Friendly, caring staff create an informal holiday atmosphere.*

17⇔↟(1fb) CTV in all bedrooms ® T sB&B⇔↟£34-£38 dB&B⇔↟£60-£88 ◻

20P ⇔ ✿

V ♦ ⚌ ✔ Bar Lunch £2-£3.50 Dinner £9-£14&alc Last dinner 8.30pm

Credit Cards ①②③⑤

**★★66% St Michael's**

Pound St DT7 3HZ ☎(0297)442503

*This warm, friendly, family-run hotel offers views of the sea from its position high above the Cobb. Its fresh, clean accommodation provides some modern facilities, the dining room is spacious, and there is a comfortable lounge and sun lounge.*

13rm(5⇔7↟)(1fb)1◻ CTV in all bedrooms ® ✳ sB&B⇔↟£28-£36 dB&B⇔↟£56-£72

12P 1⇔ ✿ solarium hairdressing salon nc2yrs

♦ ⚌ ✔ ✳

Credit Cards ①③

**★★65% Dorset**

Silver St DT7 3HX ☎(0297)442482

Closed Nov-Mar

*Georgian in style but with later additions, this hotel is set high above the town with views over Golden Cap. Its clean and well-kept accommodation is ideal for holidaymakers, offering simply furnished bedrooms, good home cooking and a warm, friendly atmosphere.*

14rm(12⇔)(2fb) CTV in all bedrooms ® T sB&B⇔↟£33.75-£38.50 dB&B⇔↟£67.50-£77 (incl dinner) ◻

13P

V ♦ ⚌ ✳ S% Bar Lunch fr£4.50 Dinner fr£12 Last dinner 8pm

Credit Cards ①③

**★★65% Kersbrook**

Pound Rd DT7 3HX ☎(0297)442596

Closed 2 Dec-Jan

*A cosy, thatched cottage, dating back to the 18th century and offering spectacular views from its setting in beautiful terraced gardens high above Lyme Regis, provides easy access to both town and sea. Recent upgrading and refurbishment have added a new residents' lounge and extended the attractively appointed, intimate restaurant where both table d'hôte and à la carte menus of wholesome dishes are based on local produce. Individually decorated bedrooms, though not very spacious, are equipped to satisfy the discerning traveller, and a friendly, hospitable atmosphere pervades the hotel.*

10⇔↟✔in all bedrooms CTV in all bedrooms T sB&B⇔↟£45-£65 dB&B⇔↟£65-£75 ◻

14P ⇔ ✿

⚘ English, French & Italian V ♦ ✔ Sunday Lunch fr£9.95 Dinner fr£16.50&alc Last dinner 9pm

Credit Cards ①②③£

**★★64% Royal Lion**

Broad St DT7 3QF ☎(0297)445622 FAX (0297) 445859

*A busy town centre hotel of some character whose extensive public areas include 2 bars, a large first-floor restaurant. The modern leisure club, with its swimming pool and small gym, is an added attraction. Bedrooms vary considerably, while those in the original part of the building are more interesting, the modern wing provides generally more spacious accommodation and some sea views.*

30⇔↟(4fb)1◻ CTV in all bedrooms ® T sB&B⇔↟£30-£35 dB&B⇔↟£56-£70 ◻

36P ⇔ ◻ (heated) snooker gymnasium games room steam room

♦ ⚌ ✔ ✳ Sunday Lunch £7.50-£8.50 Dinner £12.95-£14.95 Last dinner 9pm

Credit Cards ①②③⑤

**★★62% Bay**

Marine Pde DT7 3JQ ☎(0297)442059

Closed Dec-Feb

*This family-owned and run hotel, with an informal atmosphere, has the distinction of being the only hotel on the front. It has an attractive bar and dining room, together with a sun terrace, and whilst bedrooms are not large, they are well kept.*

21rm(12⇔↟)(3fb) CTV in 20 bedrooms ® ✳ sB&B£26.50-£31.50 sB&B⇔↟£27.50-£32.50 dB&B£53-£63 dB&B⇔↟£57-£67 ◻

20⇔ ⇔ snooker sauna solarium gymnasium

⚘ English & French ♦ ⚌ ✳ Lunch £5-£14 High tea fr£6 Dinner fr£14.50&alc Last dinner 8.30pm

Credit Cards ①③

**★56% Tudor House**

Church St DT7 3BU ☎(0297)442472

Closed Nov-mid Mar

*Right in the centre of town, this historic hotel has two cosy lounges and a basement bar with its own spring. It offers warm, genuine hospitality.*

17rm(4⇔)(10fb) ® S10% sB&B£15.50-£19.50 dB&B£31-£39 dB&B⇔£34-£42

CTV 12P

♦ ⚌ S10% Bar Lunch £3 High tea £6

Credit Cards ①③

---

**LYMINGTON** Hampshire Map **04** SZ39

**★★★ ❀74% Stanwell House**

High St SO41 9AA (Clipper) ☎(0590)677123 FAX (0590) 677756 (Rosette awarded for dinner only)

*An attractive and deceptively spacious town house hotel with pleasant gardens at its rear individually decorated bedrooms and comfortable, well equipped public areas. The Railings Restaurant features à la carte and good-value fixed-price menus of such carefully created, imaginative dishes as chicken liver parfait with Cumberland sauce and medallions of pan-fried pork fillet served with apricots and ginger; fresh vegetables are served al dente, and though the choice of sweets on the set menu is very limited, their standard is good. Professional yet friendly management, together with the approachability of staff, well supervised in its provision of formal service, attracts a clientele ranging from businessmen to the yachting fraternity.*

35⇔1◻ CTV in all bedrooms ® T ✖ (ex guide dogs) sB&B⇔fr£72.50 dB&B⇔fr£98 ◻

℄ ✗ ⇔ ✿ ⚓ xmas

⚘ English & French V ♦ ⚌ Lunch fr£12&alc Dinner fr£20&alc Last dinner 9.30pm

Credit Cards ①③

**See advertisement on page 479**

**★★★⚑73% Passford House**

Mount Pleasant Ln SO41 8LS (2m NW on Sway rd) ☎(0590)682398 FAX (0590) 683494

*Quietly situated in well tended gardens and grounds, overlooking the New Forest from a position midway between Lymington and Sway, this hotel offers spacious lounges – one of which, like the bar, has an open fire – and a selection of conference and syndicate rooms; bedrooms vary in size and style though all are well equipped, and some have been upgraded to a superior standard. Service is both efficient and professional throughout. The Dolphin Leisure Centre incorporates an attractive indoor pool, sauna and* →

L

*spa pool, while oudoor facilities include a pool, croquet lawn, putting green and hard tennis court.*
54⇨↱Annexe2⇨↱(2fb)1▭ CTV in all bedrooms ® T ✱
sB&B⇨↱fr£75 dB&B⇨↱£107-£134 ⊟
☾ CTV 100P 4⌂ (£4) ⚘ ✲ CFA ▣ (heated) ⌓ (heated) ℘ (hard) sauna solarium gymnasium croquet putting table tennis pool table ⌂ *xmas*
☋ English & French V ✆ ⊻ ✱ Lunch fr£9.95&alc Dinner fr£18.50&alc Last dinner 9pm
Credit Cards 1 2 3

## LYMM Cheshire Map 07 SJ68

**★★★59% Lymm**
Whitbarrow Rd WA13 9AQ (De Vere) ☏(092575)2233
FAX (092575) 6035
RS New Year
*Located in a quiet residential area, this busy commercial hotel holds many conferences and functions, but at the weekends there is a competitive room rate. The hotel can be difficult to find unless you know the area, but they provide information sheets with clear directions.*
22⇨↱Annexe47⇨↱(1fb) CTV in all bedrooms ® T ✱
sB&B⇨↱£65-£77 dB&B⇨↱£80-£96 ⊟
☾ 120P CFA
☋ English & French V ✆ ⊻ ✱ S% Lunch £11.50&alc Dinner fr£14.50&alc Last dinner 10pm
Credit Cards 1 2 3 5

## LYMPSHAM Avon Map 03 ST35

**★★⚑64% Batch Farm Country**
BS24 0EX ☏Weston-super-Mare(0934)750371
Closed Xmas
*This small hotel, part of a working farm, is set in a tranquil rural location only a short drive from Weston-super-Mare. Soundly appointed accommodation offers some modern facilities, lounge areas are comfortable and there is a car park.*
8⇨(4fb)⚡in 2 bedrooms CTV in all bedrooms ® ⌘
sB&B⇨£31-£34 dB&B⇨£52-£56 ⊟
CTV 50P ⚘ ✲ ♩ snooker croquet
V ✆ ⊻ ⚡ ✱ Bar Lunch £5-£7alc Dinner £10-£12&alc Last dinner 8pm
Credit Cards 1 2 3 5 £

**See advertisement under WESTON-SUPER-MARE**

## LYMPSTONE Devon Map 03 SX98

**❀❀✕✕River House**
The Strand EX8 5EY ☏Exmouth(0395)265147
*This delightful restaurant is superbly situated beside the River Exe, and there are wonderful views over the estuary from both the lounge and the first-floor restaurant. Service is provided with a nice balance of professionalism and humour. Interesting dishes are prepared making good use of fruit and vegetables from the restaurant's own garden, as well as supplies of fresh local fish. The dessert list is particularly tempting, with home-made ice creams, and coffee and home-made fudge conclude particularly pleasing meals here.*
Closed Mon
Dinner not served Sun
☋ English & French V 34 seats Lunch £32.50 Dinner £32.50 Last lunch 1.30pm Last dinner 9.30pm ⁒ nc6yrs
Credit Cards 1 2 3

Red star hotels are each highlighted by a pink tinted panel.

## LYNDHURST Hampshire Map 04 SU30

**★★★❀⚑70% Parkhill**
Beaulieu Rd SO43 7FZ ☏(0703)282944 FAX (0703) 283268
*Set in park-like surroundings, this elegant Georgian hotel offers modern British cuisine prepared by chef Richard Turner and his team of staff. The food is imaginative and well cooked, using local produce wherever possible, with some unusual cheeses featured on the cheeseboard. Bedrooms are individually furnished and about to undergo refurbishment.*
15⇨↱Annexe5⇨↱(2fb)2▭ CTV in all bedrooms ® T ✱
sB&B⇨↱£44.50-£52 dB&B⇨↱£69-£84 ⊟
75P ⚘ ✲ CFA ⌓ (heated) ♩ croquet outdoor chess *xmas*
☋ English & French V ✆ ⊻ ⚡ ✱ Lunch £13.50-£15&alc High tea £2.75-£6.25alc Dinner £21.50&alc Last dinner 9.30pm
Credit Cards 1 2 3 4 5 £

**★★★68% Crown**
High St SO43 7NF (Best Western) ☏(0703)282922
Telex no 9312110733 FAX (0703) 282751
*An attractive period hotel, situated at the centre of this New Forest town with its one-way system, is pervaded by a comfortable feeling of wellbeing. Public areas feature a restaurant where straightforward cuisine – including a tempting range of home-made puddings – is complemented by a two-part wine list, the second section offering lesser known wines which represent good value for money; the main menu is supplemented by an extensive choice of bar meals and blackboard list of daily 'specials'. Most bedrooms have been refurbished to a good standard, and involved proprietors are assisted by a happy team of friendly staff in the day-to-day running of the hotel.*
40⇨↱(6fb)1▭ CTV in all bedrooms ® T sB&B⇨↱£52-£68 dB&B⇨↱£81-£108 ⊟
Lift ☾ CTV 60P CFA *xmas*
☋ European V ✆ ⊻ ✱ Lunch fr£13.80&alc Dinner fr£13.80&alc Last dinner 9.30pm
Credit Cards 1 2 3 5

**See advertisement also under SOUTHAMPTON**

**★★★62% Forest Lodge**
Pikes Hill, Romsey Rd SO43 7AS ☏(0703)283677
FAX (0703) 283719
*A Georgian hotel, set well back from the Romsey road and only minutes' walk from both the New Forest and town centre, has recently been extended to provide a new restaurant and refurbished throughout. The Red Admiral cellar wine bar features quality leather furniture, the à la carte menu has some sparks of inspiration, and there is an indoor swimming pool. Both management and staff are helpful and charming.*
23⇨↱(1fb)1▭⚡in 5 bedrooms CTV in all bedrooms ® T
sB&B⇨↱£44-£66 dB&B⇨↱£73-£95 ⊟
CTV 50P ✲ ⌓ (heated) pitch & putt ⌂ *xmas*
☋ European V ✆ ⊻ ⚡ Sunday Lunch £11 High tea fr£5.50 Dinner fr£11&alc Last dinner 8.45pm
Credit Cards 1 2 3 5 £

**★★★62% Lyndhurst Park**
High St SO43 7NL (Forestdale) ☏(0703)283923
FAX (0703) 283019
*This Georgian hotel at the heart of the New Forest benefits from extensive mature gardens, with an indoor swimming pool and tennis courts to the rear. Bedrooms vary in size and style but are all comfortable and well equipped – 3 having four-poster beds; an elegant restaurant which has recently been extended caters for conferences and functions as well as holidaymakers, while the Pizza Park provides the opportunity to enjoy a less formal meal.*
59⇨↱(3fb)3▭⚡in 3 bedrooms CTV in all bedrooms ® T ✱
sB&B⇨↱£40-£62.50 dB&B⇨↱£55-£77.50 ⊟
Lift ☾ 100P ✲ CFA ⌓ (heated) ℘ (hard) snooker sauna table tennis ♫ *xmas*
☋ English & Continental V ✆ ⊻ ⚡ ✱ Lunch £7-£8.75&alc High tea £5.50 Dinner £13.50-£16.95&alc Last dinner 10pm
Credit Cards 1 2 3 4 5

L

See also Lynton

★★★61% **Tors**

EX35 6NA ☎Lynton(0598)53236

Closed 4 Jan-Feb

*Comfortable hotel in 5 acres of grounds, set on a hill above Lynmouth. There are fine views over the bay.*

34rm(32⇌🛏)(5fb) CTV in all bedrooms ® T S%
sB&B⇌🛏£38-£83 dB&B⇌🛏£65-£100 🅿

Lift CTV 40P ✿ CFA ⌂ (heated) *xmas*

♀ English & French V ♥ ♨ Lunch £10-£15&alc Dinner £17&alc Last dinner 8.45pm

Credit Cards ①②③⑤ ⓔ

★★69% **Rising Sun**

Harbourside EX35 6EQ ☎Lynton(0598)53223
FAX (0598) 53480

*This character hotel, 14th-century smugglers' inn with magnificient views over the small harbour and East Lyn river, features an oak panelled and beamed restaurant and bar, the former of which has recently been refurbished to a high standard; though bedrooms are somewhat compact this is more than compensated for by the quality of their funishings and facilities. Shelley's Cottage (so named because the famous poet spent his honeymoon there in 1812), with its 4-poster bed and separate sitting room, has become a popular choice for newly-weds. Seafood and Exmoor game feature prominently on a menu of dishes prepared from fresh ingredients, and guests are assured of both a warm welcome and unfailingly attentive service.*

11⇌🛏Annexe5⇌🛏(2fb)🛏✂in 6 bedrooms CTV in all bedrooms ® T ✳ sB&B⇌🛏£35-£49.50 dB&B⇌🛏£70-£99 🅿

CTV ♪ 🚅 ✿ ♪ nc5yrs *xmas*

♀ English & French V ♥ ♨ ✳ S10% Lunch £15.95&alc Dinner £17.95&alc Last dinner 9pm

Credit Cards ①②③⑤ ⓔ

★★63% **Bath**

Sea Front EX35 6EL (Exec Hotel) ☎Lynton(0598)52238
Closed Nov-Feb RS Mar

*In a central location alongside the attractive village harbour, the Bath is a traditional hotel with a warm character, and a good range of hospitable services provided by local staff under enthusiastic management. Following recent significant upgrading, the hotel now offers bright, comfortable and well equipped bedrooms, well suited to the business traveller or holidaymaker. Many have commanding views out to sea.*

24⇌🛏(9fb) CTV in all bedrooms ® T S10% sB&B⇌🛏£30-£40 dB&B⇌🛏£52-£74 🅿

11P 4🚗 (£1.75 per night)

♀ English & French V ♥ ♨ S10% Lunch £5-£10&alc Dinner £14-£21 Last dinner 8.30pm

Credit Cards ①②③⑤ ⓔ

★69% **Rock House**

EX35 6EN ☎Lynton(0598)53508 FAX (0598) 52432

*A busy tea garden is one of the attractions of this delightful little Georgian hotel. Overlooking the harbour, it occupies a unique position beside the River Lyn, the foreshore and the Manor Gardens.*

6rm(1⇌3🛏)(2fb)1🛏 CTV in all bedrooms ® sB&B£23 sB&B⇌🛏£30 dB&B£46 dB&B⇌🛏£60 🅿

CTV 7P 🚅

♀ English & French V ♥ ♨ Lunch £9.65-£22.35alc Dinner £13&alc Last dinner 9pm

Credit Cards ①②③⑤

See also Lynmouth

★★★69% **Lynton Cottage**

North Walk EX35 6ED ☎(0598)52342 FAX (0598) 52597
Closed Jan

*Commanding beautiful views of the surrounding countryside and Bristol Channel, this relaxing country-house-style hotel continues to be personally and hospitably run by John and Maisie Jones and their daughter Judy. many bedrooms have been upgraded to provide a high standard of comfort and facilities, while the food remains a strong point, with a well balanced imaginative menu that makes good use of fresh quality produce.*

17⇌🛏1🛏 CTV in all bedrooms ® ✳ sB&B⇌🛏£55-£68.75 dB&B⇌🛏£110-£140 (incl dinner) 🅿

26P 🚅 ♨ nc10yrs

♀ French ♥ ♨ ✳ Lunch £15-£20 Dinner £18.50-£24 Last dinner 8.45pm

Credit Cards ①②③⑤ ⓔ

★★🔴65% *Hewitts*

North Walk EX35 6HJ ☎(0598)52293
RS mid Nov-mid Mar

*A friendly, relaxing atmosphere prevails at Robert and Susan Mahon's secluded cliff-top Victorian mansion now a stylish country house in 27 acres of woodland. Public rooms include a galleried lounge and intimate restaurant which features imaginative menus based on English cuisine with some French influence.*

12rm(9⇌🛏)(1fb)1🛏✂in 2 bedrooms CTV in all bedrooms

10P 🚅 ✿ clay pigeon shooting jaccuzi

V ♥ ♨ ✳ Last dinner 9.30pm

Credit Cards ①②③⑤

★★62% **Neubia House**

Lydiate Ln EX35 6AH (Guestaccom) ☎(0598)52309 & 53644
Closed 2 Dec-28 Feb

*This small, secluded character house features spotlessly clean en suite bedrooms that are brightly decorated, pleasantly furnished and well equipped, though not over spacious; a cheerful dining room with small dispense bar serves good home-cooked meals with particularly delectable puddings, and residents can relax in the quiet atmosphere of a first-floor lounge. With useful car parking on site, the hotel provides a good base from which to tour North Devon and the Exmoor National Park.*

12⇌🛏(3fb) CTV in all bedrooms ® T sB&B⇌🛏£28-£30 dB&B⇌🛏£56-£60 🅿

14P 🚅

V ✂ ♨ Dinner £12-£12.50 Last dinner 7.30pm

Credit Cards ①③ ⓔ

★★61% **Castle Hill House**

Castle Hill EX35 6JA ☎(0598)52291
Closed Nov-Feb

*This tall Victorian house in the town centre is personally run by welcoming new owners who create a pleasant, relaxing atmosphere. Bedrooms, now in process of being upgraded, are simply appointed but well equipped, and cosy public areas offer similarly pleasant surroundings. A short but good à la carte menu supplemented by daily blackboard 'specials' offers a good range of imaginative and wholesome home cooking.*

9⇌🛏(2fb) CTV in all bedrooms ® 🐾 (ex guide dogs) ✳ sB&B⇌🛏£20 dB&B⇌🛏£40 🅿

♪ 🚅

♀ English & Continental V ♥ ♨ ✂ ✳ Lunch £4.50-£6alc Dinner £8.50-£13.50alc Last dinner 9.30pm

Credit Cards ①③ ⓔ

Hotels with red star ratings are especially high quality.

🐚 Shell filling stations (7am–11pm) are marked on the town plans.

★★⁵⁹% **Crown**
Sinai Hill EX35 6AG (Inter-Hotels) ☎(0598)52253
Closed Jan

*The interior of this first-floor restaurant at the top of the High Street is more inspiring than its exterior would suggest, oak beams, an attractive décor and plenty of plants creating a pleasant setting in which to enjoy a meal. An established clientèle appreciates its interesting, good-value table d'hôte and à la carte menus of dishes based on good fresh produce, simply presented and without over-rich sauces. A typical meal might contain Venison Terrine with smoked bacon, freshly made fruity preserve and new baked garlic bread, followed by Beef Fillet, thinly sliced with fresh button mushrooms in a light Port and Stilton Sauce and served in a buttery puff pastry case. The proprietor is always ready to explain dishes to customers, and it is possible to taste the wine before buying it.*

16⊸🛏(6fb)5⌨ CTV in all bedrooms ® T ✳
sB&B⊸🛏£35.50-£41 dB&B⊸🛏£61-£65 🍽
20P 🚗 CFA *xmas*
♀ English & French V ❀ ✳ Bar Lunch £1.50-£3.95 Dinner £14&alc Last dinner 8.30pm
Credit Cards 1️⃣ 2️⃣ 3️⃣ 5️⃣ £

★★⁵⁹% **Sandrock**
Longmead EX35 6DH ☎(0598)53307
Closed Dec-Jan

*Compact, soundly appointed, spotlessly clean bedrooms and compact, cosy public rooms are provided by a friendly little touring and holiday hotel which has been owned by the same family for many years. Located conveniently close to the town centre, it also offers easy access to the expanses of Exmoor National Park and headland.*

9rm(5⊸2🛏)(3fb) CTV in all bedrooms ® T ✳ sB&B£18.50-£21 dB&B⊸🛏£39-£50 🍽
9P 🚗

🌀 🍷 ✳ Bar Lunch £3.50-£5 Dinner £10.50-£12 Last dinner 7.45pm
Credit Cards 1️⃣ 2️⃣ 3️⃣ £

See advertisement on page 483

★⚘⁶⁶% **Combe Park**
Hillsford Bridge EX35 6LE ☎(0598)52356
Closed mid Nov-mid Mar (ex Xmas)

*Former hunting lodge set in six acres of woodland.*

9rm(6⊸2🛏) ® sB&B⊸🛏£60 dB&B⊸🛏£84 (incl dinner)
CTV 11P 🚗 ❀ bird watching nc12yrs *xmas*
🍷 ✂ Dinner £17 Last dinner 7.30pm

★⁶⁶% **Seawood**
North Walk EX35 6HT ☎(0598)52272
Closed Dec-Feb

*A friendly family-run hotel of some charm and character, built in 1848 as a retreat for wealthy Victorian families. From its elevated position it offers magnificent views right across Lynmouth Bay and the grand headland of Countisbury where Exmoor meets the sea. Several bedrooms have recently been upgraded, all are spotlessly clean, with modern facilities and a good range of modern equipment. Public rooms are equally comfortable with a choice of lounges and a pretty little dining room where wholesome home cooking is served.*

12⊸🛏(1fb)4⌨ CTV in all bedrooms ® ✳ sB&B⊸🛏£27-£30 dB&B⊸🛏£56 🍽
10P 🚗 ❀
♀ English & Continental V ✳ Dinner fr£12.50 Last dinner 7.30pm
£

For key to symbols in English see the bookmark.

L

AA ★★★  **The Lynton Cottage Hotel**  Egon Ronay

Once the marine residence of a Knight of the Realm, this romantic Listed Building stands in its own grounds in Lynton's most private and beautiful spot. The "Cottage" has seventeen bedrooms and suites, each individually decorated with taste and care.

Exquisite food and a delightful friendly ambience are the hallmarks of this renowned hotel. Sitting on the Cottage terrace or in the elegant restaurant overlooking Lynmouth Bay, the hustle and bustle of the world seems a million miles away.

**Reservations & Info Tel: 0598 52342   Fax: 0598 52597. Lynton Devon EX35 6ED.**

## ★65% Rockvale

off Lee Rd EX35 6HW ☎(0598)52279 & 53343
Closed 15 Nov-15 Feb

*This small, personally-run hotel, which enjoys pleasant hill views across the village to Exmoor and Countisbury from grounds incorporating a very useful car park, stands only a few minutes' walk from the Victorian Cliff Railway that gives access to Lynmouth's picturesque harbour. Spotlessly clean throughout, it offers cosily warm bedrooms with modern facilities and homely, comfortably furnished public areas equipped with plenty of books; a neat little dining room provides home-cooked meals which are both wholesome and generously served. The establishment's peaceful location and friendly atmosphere make for a relaxing break.*

8rm(5⇨1♠)(2fb)1✿ CTV in all bedrooms TV in 1 bedroom
® T sB&B£27-£31 sB&B⇨♠£27-£31 dB&B⇨♠£43-£52 ♬
9P ✿ ✿ nc4yrs
✿ ⚊ Bar Lunch £3-£8 Dinner £10-£12 Last dinner 7.30pm
Credit Cards 1 3

## ★64% Chough's Nest

North Walk EX35 6HJ ☎(0598)53315
Closed mid Oct-Etr

*Set in an elevated position, as its name implies, this friendly little holiday hotel enjoys panoramic views over Lynmouth Bay to Countisbury Head; well suited to the needs of walkers, it stands in 2 acres of terraced woodland which give access to a a variety of coastal walks. Personally run by well established owners, it offers pleasant surroundings, wholesome home cooking and an informal style of service, retaining much of the character and charm that one would expect in a house that was once the seaside residence of a Dutch millionaire. Attractively decorated en suite bedrooms equipped with modern facilites complement a cosy residents' lounge and bright dining room, while the terrace is a popular place to relax on summer evenings.*

11⇨♠(2fb)2✿ CTV in all bedrooms ® ✈ sB&B⇨♠£23.50
dB&B⇨♠£47
10P ✿ ✿ nc2yrs
V ✿ ⚊ ✗ Dinner fr£10 Last dinner 7.30pm

## ★62% North Cliff

North Walk EX35 6HJ ☎(0598)52357
Closed 10 Nov-15 Feb

*Perched high up with glorious sea views, this small family-run holiday hotel offers a comfortable environment with bright public rooms and well equipped cosy bedrooms. Top marks for spotless housekeeping. Traditional wholesome food is offered from a set menu, with friendly service from hospitable owners and local staff.*

15rm(11⇨2♠)(2fb) CTV in 10 bedrooms ® sB&B£29-£30
sB&B⇨♠£32-£33 dB&B£58-£60 dB&B⇨♠£64-£66 (incl dinner)
CTV 15P ✿ table tennis pool table
✿ ✿
£

## ★60% Fairholme

North Walk EX35 6ED ☎(0598)52263
Closed Oct-Apr

*This small hotel stands in a breathtaking position overlooking the Bristol Channel.*

12rm(7⇨)(2fb) CTV in 4 bedrooms ✈ ✿ dB&B⇨£35
CTV 12P ✿ ✿ ⊠ (heated) sauna nc10yrs
✿ ⚊ ✗

---

## LYTHAM ST ANNES Lancashire Map 07 SD32 ☺

## ★★★★50% *Clifton Arms*

West Beach, Lytham FY8 5QJ (Lansbury) ☎(0253)739898
Telex no 677463 FAX (0253) 730657

*This extended traditional hotel on the seafront with a busy function and business trade offers very comfortable accommodation and friendly service. Some bedrooms at the front have views of the Ribble estuary and are quite spacious.*

41⇨♠1✿♬✗in 6 bedrooms CTV in all bedrooms ® T
Lift ℂ 50P sauna solarium jacuzzi
♡ English & French V ✿ ⚊ ✗ Last dinner 10pm
Credit Cards 1 2 3 5

## ★★★68% Bedford

307-311 Clifton Dr South FY8 1HN (Exec Hotel)
☎(0253)724636 FAX (0253) 729244

*A very friendly hotel, managed by the resident proprietors, providing comfortable accommodation throughout. There is a choice of eating options – the main restaurant, a coffee shop and a quaint lower-ground-floor bistro.*

36⇨♠(6fb)1✿ CTV in all bedrooms ® T sB&B⇨♠£32-£35
dB&B⇨♠£59-£74 ♬
Lift ℂ CTV 20P CFA sauna solarium gymnasium jacuzzi steam
room ♫ xmas
♡ English & Continental V ✿ ⚊ Sunday Lunch £6.50-£7.50
High tea fr£5.95alc Dinner £13.50-£14&alc Last dinner 8.30pm
Credit Cards 1 2 3 5

## ★★★68% Chadwick

South Promenade FY8 1NP ☎(0253)720061 FAX (0253) 714455

*A popular and continually improving hotel on the seafront, family owned and run for many years now, offers well equipped bedrooms of a good standard, comfortable sun lounge and a fine leisure centre.*

72⇨♠(24fb)2✿ CTV in all bedrooms ® T ✈ (ex guide dogs)
sB&B⇨♠£30.50-£35 dB&B⇨♠£42-£46 ♬
Lift ℂ 40P ✿ CFA ⊠ (heated) sauna solarium turkish bath
jacuzzi games room ♫ ⚙ xmas
♡ English & French V ✿ ⚊ ✗ Lunch £6.80-£7.40 Dinner
£11.50-£12.50&alc Last dinner 8.30pm
Credit Cards 1 2 3 5

## ★★66% St Ives

7-9 South Promenade FY8 1LS ☎(0253)720011
FAX (0253) 724447
Closed 24-26 Dec

*Spacious lounge areas, well appointed bedrooms and leisure facilities are features of this comfortable, well managed hotel.*

71rm(61⇨3♠)(44fb) CTV in all bedrooms ® T ✈ ✳ sB&B£25
sB&B⇨♠£36-£42 dB&B£50 dB&B⇨♠£57-£69 (incl dinner)
♬
ℂ ⊞ CTV 100P CFA ⊠ (heated) snooker sauna solarium ♫
xmas
♡ English & French V ✿ ⚊ ✳ Bar Lunch £1.40-£3.50 Dinner
£10.60 Last dinner 8.30pm
Credit Cards 1 2 3 5

## ★★62% *New Glendower*

North Promenade FY8 2 (Consort) ☎(0253)723241

*A large seafront hotel, refurbished to provide pleasant, comfortable public areas, offering accommodation in bedrooms which are all well equipped and maintained to a good standard. Those overlooking the sea are the more spacious and attractive.*

60⇨(17fb) CTV in all bedrooms ® T
ℂ CTV 45P ⊠ (heated) sauna solarium games room badminton
♫
V ✿ Last dinner 8pm
Credit Cards 1 2 3 5

## ★★58% Langdales

320-326 Clifton Dr North FY8 2PB ☎(0253)728657
FAX (0253) 729517

*Situated close to the town centre and to the sea, this adequately furnished, family-run hotel offers good value for money, and friendly, helpful service from the staff.*

40rm(22⇨14♠)(8fb)1✿ CTV in all bedrooms ® T
CTV 24P CFA ♫ xmas
✿ ⚊
Credit Cards 1 3

★ 61% **Lindum**
63-67 South Promenade FY8 1LZ ☎(0253)721534 & 722516
FAX (0253) 721364
*Dinner represents good value at this seafront hotel which provides friendly, unobtrusive service under the supervision of its resident owners.*
80⇨🛈(25fb) CTV in all bedrooms ® T ✳ sB&B⇨🛈£26-£30 dB&B⇨🛈£39-£45 🅿
Lift ℂ CTV 20P CFA sauna solarium jacuzzi *xmas*
V ♉ ⚏ ✳ Sunday Lunch £7 Dinner £10 Last dinner 7pm
Credit Cards ① ② ③ ⓔ

★ 60% *Ennes Court*
107 South Prom FY8 1NP ☎(0253)723731
*A small, friendly, sea-front hotel, personally supervised by the resident proprietors and offering well equipped bedrooms.*
10⇨🛈(2fb) CTV in all bedrooms ® ✖ (ex guide dogs)
CTV 9P ⇛ nc3yrs

★ 57% **Carlton**
61 South Promenade FY8 1LZ ☎(0253)721036
Closed Jan & Feb
*Pleasant, family-run hotel overlooking the promenade gardens.*
20rm(6⇨6🛈)(7fb) CTV in all bedrooms ® ✳ sB&B£17-£18 sB&B⇨🛈£19-£21 dB&B£34-£40 dB&B⇨🛈£38-£42
CTV 10P *xmas*
V ♉ ⚏ ✂ ✳ Lunch £5-£7 Dinner £5.50-£8 Last dinner 7pm
Credit Cards ① ③

MACCLESFIELD Cheshire Map 07 SJ97

See also Bollington & Pott Shrigley
★★ 65% **Park Villa**
Park Ln SK11 8AE ☎(0625)511428 & 614173
FAX (0625) 614637
*A detached house with delightful rear gardens, located on the edge of the town, numbers attentive personal service from the proprietors and the Bridge sessions held on a regular basis throughout the year among its attractions.*
7⇨🛈(2fb)✂in 2 bedrooms CTV in all bedrooms ® T sB&B⇨🛈£35-£45 dB&B⇨🛈£54-£66 🅿
Lift ℂ CTV 14P ⇛ CFA bridge courses *xmas*
V ♉ ⚏ ✂ Lunch £6.25-£10 High tea £5-£6.25 Dinner £8.50-£11 Last dinner 8.45pm
Credit Cards ① ② ③ ⑤ ⓔ

MACDUFF Grampian *Banffshire* Map 15 NJ76

★★ 60% **The Highland Haven**
Shore St AB44 1UB ☎(0261)32408 FAX (0261) 33652
*Situated on the waterfront overlooking the harbour, this small family-run hotel, popular with both commercial and holiday guests, has compact but comfortable well equipped bedrooms and public areas offering practical facilities.*
20⇨🛈(2fb) CTV in all bedrooms ® T sB&B⇨🛈£19.95-£34.95 dB&B⇨🛈£39-£49.50 🅿
ℂ CTV 6P CFA snooker sauna solarium gymnasium turkish steamroom whirlpool spa *xmas*
V ♉ ⚏ ✳ Lunch £1.95-£10alc High tea £3.25-£7.55alc Dinner £13.65&alc Last dinner 9pm
Credit Cards ① ③ ④ ⓔ

MACHYNLLETH Powys Map 06 SH70

★★ 62% **Dolguog Hall**
SY20 8UJ ☎(0654)702244 FAX (0654) 702530
*A 17th-century gentleman's residence with superb views over the Dyfi Valley from its position near the Dulas River is now the centre of a small holiday complex of log cabins, providing particularly comfortable public areas and offering a good choice of food.*
9⇨🛈(1fb) CTV in all bedrooms ® T ✖

→

L

20P ❀ ✎
♡ Continental **V** ☼ ☞ ✂ Last dinner 9pm
Credit Cards ①③⑤

### ★★ 61% Wynnstay Arms
Maengwyn St SY20 8AE ☎(0654)702941 FAX (0654) 703884
*An 18th-century coaching inn right in the centre of the Welsh
market town provides comfortable lounges and bars, and well
equipped bedrooms with bathrooms that are presently being
modernised.*
20⇨🛏(3fb)✂in 7 bedrooms CTV in all bedrooms ® **T** ✱
sB&B⇨🛏fr£36 dB&B⇨🛏fr£51 🖁
CTV 30P CFA ♫ *xmas*
**V** ☼ ☞ ✂ ✱ Sunday Lunch fr£8.75 Dinner fr£11.25 Last
dinner 9pm
Credit Cards ①②③⑤⑥

---

### MADELEY Staffordshire Map 07 SJ74

### ★★ 67% *Crewe Arms*
Wharf St, Madeley Heath CW3 9LP
☎Stoke-on-Trent(0782)750392
*This recently modernised and extended country inn now provides
good quality and well equipped bedrooms and relaxing bars and
lounges. There is a good choice of food, with bar meals and an à la
carte restaurant.*
10⇨🛏(2fb) CTV in all bedrooms ® **T** ✖ (ex guide dogs)
CTV 50P pool table
**V** ☼ ☞
Credit Cards ①③

---

### MAGOR Gwent Map 03 ST48

### ○Granada Lodge
(junc 23 M1) (Granada) ☎Central Res (0800) 555300
Due to open Spring 1992
41⇨🛏

**See advertisement under NEWPORT**

---

### MAIDENCOMBE
See Torquay

---

### MAIDENHEAD Berkshire Map 04 SU88

### ★★★★ ❀❀73% Fredrick's
Shoppenhangers Rd SL6 2PZ ☎(0628)35934 Telex no 849966
FAX (0628) 771054
Closed 24-30 Dec
*A fine hotel with manicured grounds hidden in the leafy residential
outskirts of the town. A turn of the century red brick house, its
discreet exterior obscures the splendid vision within, no ersatz
country house décor here: the reception lobby has bold, shining
chandeliers, mirrors and a waterfall. Further public areas include
the winter garden overlooking the terrace and garden, a stylish
cocktail bar and a comfortable, well run restaurant: home of some
very good cuisine, much on traditional lines. The bedrooms in the
original part of the house have recently been entirely refurbished
but all the rooms are spacious and comfortable, many with garden
views. Standards of service are very high, a happy blend of
formality and willing hospitality.*
37⇨🛏 CTV in all bedrooms **T** ✖ ✱ sB&B⇨🛏£87.50-£120
dB&B⇨🛏£145-£155
《 90P 🚗 ❀ CFA
♡ English & French **V** ☼ ✱ Lunch £19.50&alc Dinner
£28.50&alc Last dinner 9.45pm
Credit Cards ①②③⑤

*Hotels with red star ratings are
especially high quality.*

### ★★★ 67% Thames Riviera
At the Bridge SL6 8DW ☎(0628)74057 Telex no 846687
FAX (0628) 776586
*A new management team and expenditure on the part of the
owners have made considerable improvements to this hotel, a
substantial Victorian building overlooking bridge and river.
Bedrooms, whether in the main building (where they occupy 3
floors) or in the attractively designed Waterside Lodge on the
other side of the lawn and terrace, have been smartly refurbished
and well equipped; some also boast balconies over the Thames.
There is a comfortable bar where a pianist sometimes plays in the
evenings, also a daytime coffee shop and a well appointed
restaurant serving freshly prepared food. Standards of service are
high, and guests are assured of a warm welcome.*
34⇨🛏Annexe18⇨🛏(1fb)1🛏 CTV in all bedrooms ® **T**
✖ (ex guide dogs)
《 50P 10🚗 CFA ✎ ♫
♡ English & French **V** ☼ ☞ ✱
Credit Cards ①②③④⑤⑥

### ❀✖✖✖Shoppenhangers Manor
Manor Ln SL6 2RA (Holiday Inns Inc) ☎(0628)23444
Telex no 847502 FAX (0628) 770035
*This tastefully decorated and furnished manor house in
Elizabethan style, set in 18-acre grounds providing a relaxed
atmosphere, offers facilities for meetings, conferences and banquets
as well as a high-class restaurant featuring a fairly short but
balanced menu of interesting dishes freshly prepared from top-
quality produce by chef Robert Webster and his team. Starters
including a gâteau of vegetables with olive oil/parmesan dressing
and a terrine of duck with pistachio nuts can be followed by roast
fillet of veal with morel mushrooms or boiled Dover sole in a sauce
of preserved leeks and butter. Sweets range from hot peach soufflé
with an exotic fruit sauce, to crisp wafers with fresh raspberries
and a rhubarb sauce, and an excellent meal can be pleasantly
concluded with a choice of coffees and home-made petits fours. A
fine wine list complements the menu, and attentive, professional
service is given by a friendly staff.*
Closed Sun & BH's ex Xmas Day Lunch not served Sat
♡ International 40 seats ✱ Lunch £18.50 Dinner £29.95 Last
lunch 2pm Last dinner 10.30pm 80 P nc12yrs
Credit Cards ①②③⑤

---

### MAIDSTONE Kent Map 05 TQ75 ⊙

### ★★★★ 67% Maidstone Country Court
Bearsted Rd, Weavering ME14 5AA (Stakis) ☎(0622)34322
Telex no 965689 FAX (0622) 34600
*Opened in the spring of 1991 and conveniently situated for junction
7 of the M20, this mainly commercial hotel offers excellent
conference and business facilities. The excellent accommodation
available includes 8 ladies' rooms and 3 suites as well as 4 very
good rooms for disabled guests. A comfortably spacious foyer
lounge features a large white statue of Mercury, the Seasons
Restaurant serves meals in a variety of styles, and staff are both
professional and friendly. The superb leisure facilities provided by
Club Tropics are superintended by qualified professional staff.*
144⇨🛏(46fb)✂in 72 bedrooms CTV in all bedrooms ® **T**
sB⇨🛏£77 dB⇨🛏£91 (room only) 🖁
《 ⊞ 240P 🏊 (heated) sauna solarium gymnasium
♡ English & French **V** ☼ ☞ ✂ Lunch £11.50&alc Dinner
£15.75&alc Last dinner 10pm
Credit Cards ①②③⑤⑥

### ★★★ 67% Tudor Park
Ashford Rd, Bearstead ME14 4NQ ☎(0622)34334
Telex no 966655 FAX (0622) 35360
*Located two miles east of Maidstone, this modern hotel combines
extensive and exciting golf and country club facilities with
spacious, well equipped bedrooms and 24-hour room service. Public
areas include a cocktail lounge, piano bar, the Garden Restaurant
and the Waterside Grill. Extensive conference facilities are also
available.*

120⇌🏠(4fb)⅟in 29 bedrooms CTV in all bedrooms ® T ✻
sB&B⇌🏠£108 dB&B⇌🏠£125 🛏
《 CTV 200P ✿ CFA ⊠ (heated) ▶ 18 ℘ (hard) squash
snooker sauna solarium gymnasium table tennis health &
beauty salon ♫ ๏ xmas
V ✆ ⚏ ⅟ ✻ Lunch £12.50 High tea £2.50-£5 Dinner
£18.50&alc Last dinner 10pm
Credit Cards ① ② ③ ⑤ ⓔ

### ★★★ 62% Larkfield Priory
London Rd ME20 6HJ (Forte Hotels)
☎West Malling(0732)846858 Telex no 957420
FAX (0732) 846786
(For full entry see Larkfield)

### ★★ 61% Grange Moor
St Michael's Rd ME16 8BS (off A26) ☎(0622)677623
FAX (0622) 678246
*A friendly family-run hotel and free house situated off the A26
Tonbridge road, with well-equipped modern bedrooms, a Tudor-
style restaurant and attractive bars serving snacks and bar meals.
The Function Suite is very popular, and there are good car parking
facilities.*
36rm(1⇌31🏠)(3fb)3🛏 CTV in all bedrooms ® T ✻
sB&B£20-£35 sB&B⇌🏠£30-£45 dB&B£38-£46
dB&B⇌🏠£47-£52 🛏
60P
♀ English & French V ✆ ⚏ ✻ Lunch £12&alc Dinner
£12&alc Last dinner 10pm
Credit Cards ① ③

### ★★ 57% Boxley House
Boxley Rd, Boxley ME14 3DZ (3m N between A249 & A229)
(Exec Hotel) ☎(0622)692269 FAX (0622) 683536
*Set in 20 acres of parkland, this 17th century manor house retains
much of its original character, though accommodation has been
modernised and a choice of bedrooms similarly furnished in
traditional style is also available in an adjoining annex. A
combined function and dining room is augmented by a front bar
lounge, while various rooms at the back of the building are popular
for dinner dances, private dinners and wedding receptions;
breakfast is served in the first-floor dining room. Resident
proprietors personally supervise very informal service.*
11⇌🏠Annexe7⇌🏠(1fb)2🛏 CTV in all bedrooms ® T ✻
sB&B⇌🏠£49 dB&B⇌🏠£75-£85
150P 🚗 ✿ CFA ⊇ (heated)
♀ English & French V ✆ ⚏ ✻ Lunch £11.30-£15.95 Dinner
£15.95-£18.95 Last dinner 9.15pm
Credit Cards ① ② ③ ⑤

### ⊛⊛✕ ✕Sueffle
The Green, Bearsted ME14 4DW (2m E A20) ☎(0622)37065
*Chef Andy Blythe's dedicated and serious approach to cooking is
demonstrated in the light and individual style of the dishes on a
constantly changing blackboard selection offering a choice of two
fixed-price menus supplemented by recommendations which
include Cheese Soufflé, Fillets of Sole with a Butter Sauce, Fillet
of Beef with a Madeira Sauce, and Mignons of Pork with a
Roquefort Sauce. Home-made pasta, patisserie and breads
complement a good cheese board, and the wine list includes some
interesting bin ends and New World wines. Service is attentively
supervised by the proprietor's attractive wife Carole.*
Closed Sun, Mon, & 25-31 Dec Lunch not served Sat
♀ French V 40 seats ✻ Lunch £12.50-£28.90 Dinner £12.50-
£28.90 Last lunch 1.45pm Last dinner 9.45pm 14 P
Credit Cards ① ② ③ ⑤

The AA's star rating scheme is the
market leader in hotel
classification.

**M**

---

### MALDON Essex Map 05 TL80

**★★61%** *The Blue Boar*
Silver St CM9 7QE (Forte Hotels) ☎(0621)852681
FAX (0621) 856202

*Quietly set back from the main High Street – though centrally located – a coaching inn dating back to the 14th-century retains an attractive black and white façade outside and exposed timbers in the public areas. Bedrooms vary in shape, and a few are reached from the courtyard, but most have undergone refurbishment.*
20⇌🛏Annexe8⇌🛏(1fb)⚭in 12 bedrooms CTV in all bedrooms ® T
43P CFA
V ॐ ⌁ ⚭ Last dinner 9.30pm
Credit Cards ①②③④⑤

---

### MALLAIG Highland *Inverness-shire* Map 13 NM69

**★★61%** **Marine**
PH41 4PY ☎(0687)2217
Closed Xmas & New Year RS mid Nov-Mar
*Situated beside the railway station and close to the fishing harbour and ferry terminal, this family-run commercial and holiday hotel has been considerably upgraded to provide improved comforts and facilities.*
21rm(16⇌🛏)(2fb) CTV in all bedrooms ® sB&B£25-£32 sB&B⇌🛏£28-£32 dB&B£40-£44 dB&B⇌🛏£48-£56 ⏪
CTV 6P
ॐ ⌁ ✷ Bar Lunch fr£4.50alc Dinner £11.50-£13.50 Last dinner 8.30pm
Credit Cards ①②③

---

**★★55%** **West Highland**
PH41 4QZ ☎(0687)2210 FAX (0687) 2130
Closed 11 Oct-20 Apr
*This family-run Highland hotel enjoys a fine outlook over the Inner Minch towards Skye, Rhum and Eigg from its setting high on a hill above the town, and serves as a popular base for visiting tour groups. It offers traditional services and comforts together with good value practical accommodation.*
26⇌🛏(6fb) ® ✷ sB&B⇌🛏£26-£32 dB&B⇌🛏£52-£64 ⏪
CTV 30P ✷ CFA
V ॐ ⌁ ✷ Lunch £6-£7 Dinner £14-£15 Last dinner 8.30pm
Credit Cards ①③ⓔ

---

### MALLWYD Gwynedd Map 06 SH81

**★59%** *Brigand's Inn*
SY20 9HJ ☎Dinas Mawddwy(06504)208
Closed Feb
*This former 15th-century coaching inn, with later additions, is situated at the junction of the A458 and A470. It provides modest accommodation and is popular with fishermen.*
14rm(4⇌🛏1🛏)(2fb) ®
CTV 40P 🚬 ⚓
V ॐ ⌁
Credit Cards ①③

---

### MALMESBURY Wiltshire Map 03 ST98

**★★★🏆76%** **Whatley Manor**
Easton Grey SN16 0RB ☎(0666)822888 FAX (0666) 826120
*The manor stands in well kept gardens at the edge of the village, on the banks of the River Avon and close to Malmesbury. Accommodation is contained in three separate buildings – the Manor, the Courthouse and the Tudor Wing; each offers comfortable, well furnished and decorated bedrooms, the majority being individual in style, although those in the Courthouse are slightly more compact and standard in design. Impressive public areas with wood panelling, fresh flower arrangements and comfortable sofas are warmed by roaring log fires during the*

*winter months, and the attractive restaurant offers an interesting set-price menu and attentive service from helpful young staff.*
18⇌🛏Annexe11⇌(2fb)1⏪ CTV in all bedrooms ® T ✷
sB&B⇌£73.50-£84 dB&B⇌£101-£119.50 ⏪
(60P 🚬 ✷ CFA ⌁ (heated) ℘ (hard) ⚓ sauna solarium croquet putting table tennis jaccuzzi *xmas*
♥ English & Continental V ॐ ✷ Lunch £14.50-£15.50 Dinner fr£26.50 Last dinner 9pm
Credit Cards ①②③⑤

---

**★★★63%** **Old Bell**
Abbey Row SN16 0BW (CLIPPER) ☎(0666)822344
FAX (0666) 825145
*This historic hotel beside the Abbey retains many original features, including a 13th-century stone fireplace. Comfortable public areas include an elegant lounge, large bar and separate cocktail bar, and there is an attractive restaurant offering an interesting choice from the set or à la carte menus. Some bedrooms are new and compact, while others are more spacious and traditionally furnished, but all are well equipped.*
37⇌🛏Annexe1⇌🛏1⏪ CTV in all bedrooms ® T
✖ (ex guide dogs) sB&B⇌🛏£72.50 dB&B⇌🛏£98 ⏪
(30P ✷ CFA *xmas*
♥ English & French V ॐ ⌁ ✷ Lunch £12&alc Dinner £20&alc Last dinner 9.30pm
Credit Cards ①③

---

### MALTON North Yorkshire Map 08 SE77

**★★★🏆70%** **Burythorpe House**
Burythorpe YO17 9LB (4m S) ☎Burythorpe(065385)200
Closed 25-26 Dec
*This hotel enjoys a delightful rural situation, being set in seven acres of gardens and woodland about three miles from Malton; a tennis court is available for guests' use, comprehensive leisure facilities are contained in the Old Coach House, and there is a full-size snooker room in the main building. Bedrooms are both spacious and attractive, the lounge is inviting, dinner can be recommended and service is most courteous.*
10⇌🛏(2fb)2⏪ CTV in all bedrooms ® T ✖ (ex guide dogs)
✷ sB&B⇌🛏fr£45 dB&B⇌🛏£50-£100 ⏪
50P 🚬 ✷ ⌁ (heated) ℘ (hard) snooker sauna solarium gymnasium
♥ International V ॐ ✷ Lunch fr£9.25alc Dinner £12-£25alc Last dinner 9.30pm
Credit Cards ①③

---

**★★67%** **Talbot**
Yorkersgate YO13 0PB ☎(0653)694031 FAX (0653) 693355
*An attractive 18th-century house on the outskirts of town and overlooking the River Derwent. Traditional Yorkshire fayre is served in the elegant dining room, and the bedrooms, which vary in style from modern to traditional, are all well equipped.*
29⇌🛏(3fb)1⏪ CTV in all bedrooms ® T ✷ sB&B⇌🛏£39-£49 dB&B⇌🛏£66-£84 ⏪
(30P 6🚗 (£3 per night) ✷ CFA *xmas*
V ॐ ⌁ ✷ Lunch £8.50-£13.50 Dinner £14.50-£19.50 Last dinner 9pm
Credit Cards ①②③⑤ⓔ

---

**★60%** **Wentworth Arms**
Town St, Old Malton YO17 0HD ☎(0653)692618
Closed 25 Dec
*Bedrooms are modestly furnished and clean in this sound little coaching inn which dates back to the early 1700's and preserves some of its original beams and exposed stone walls in the cosy dining room.*
5rm(4🛏) CTV in all bedrooms ® ✖ sB&B🛏£20-£21 dB&B🛏£40-£42
30P 🚬 nc6yrs
ॐ ⌁ ✷ Lunch £4.50-£9.50alc
Credit Cards ①③

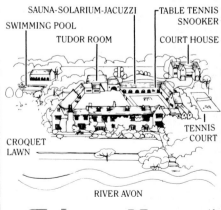

# Malvern

**★★★🏕65% Cottage in the Wood**
Holywell Rd, Malvern Wells WR14 4LG (3m S A449) (Consort)
☎(0684)573487 FAX (0684) 560662
*A privately owned hotel, high in the Malvern Hills with
breathtaking views across the Severn Valley. The hotel comprises 3
white-painted buildings almost hidden in 7 acres of thickly wooded
grounds. The Georgian Dower House is the main building housing
the reception, bar and dining room. Bedrooms, in the Coach House
and Beech House, are generally compact, but recently refurbished
with pretty décor and fabrics, and thoughtfully equipped.*
8⇔🅰Annexe12⇔🅰3🛏 CTV in all bedrooms ® T ✱
sB&B⇔🅰£62 dB&B⇔🅰£85-£120 🅁
50P 🚗 ✿ *xmas*
V 🕁 ⚏ ⅍ ✱ Lunch £7.50-£20&alc Dinner fr£20&alc Last
dinner 9pm
Credit Cards [1] [2] [3]

**★★★64% Colwall Park**
Colwall WR13 6QG (3m SW B4218) ☎(0684)40206
FAX (0684) 40847
*A pleasant, privately owned hotel on the A4218 on the southern
side of the town. Accommodation is well equipped and rooms at the
top of the building are fitted in pine.*
20⇔🅰(2fb) CTV in all bedrooms ® T sB&B⇔🅰£53.50-
£56.50 dB&B⇔🅰£76.50-£85 🅁
50P ✿ CFA croquet *xmas*
V 🕁 ⚏ Lunch £4.75-£10 High tea £3.75-£5 Dinner £16.50-£19
Last dinner 9pm
Credit Cards [1] [2] [3]

**★★★63% *Abbey***
Abbey Rd WR14 3ET (De Vere) ☎(0684)892332
Telex no 335008 FAX (0684) 892662
*This traditional, ivy-clad hotel is situated at the heart of the town,
next to the Benedictine Priory; a popular conference venue, it
offers comfortable, recently refurbished accommodation with good
modern facilities.*
105⇔🅰(4fb)1🛏 CTV in all bedrooms ® T
Lift ⟨ 120P ✿
V 🕁 ⚏ Last dinner 8.30pm
Credit Cards [1] [2] [3] [5]

**★★★58% Foley Arms**
Worcester Rd WR14 4QS (Best Western) ☎(0684)573397
FAX (0684) 569665
*The oldest hotel in the town, dating from 1810, offers good
hospitality in traditional style and efficient service;
accommodation standards vary, but all rooms have been equipped
with modern facilities and some have superb views across the
Severn Valley.*
26⇔🅰Annexe2⇔🅰(1fb)2🛏⅍in 1 bedroom CTV in all
bedrooms ® T sB&B⇔🅰£58-£68 dB&B⇔🅰£72-£110 🅁
⟨ 45P 4🚗 ✿ CFA *xmas*
V 🕁 ⚏ ⅍ Sunday Lunch £10.75-£12.75 High tea £5-£7.50
Dinner £14.50-£18.50&alc Last dinner 9.30pm
Credit Cards [1] [2] [3] [5] [£]

**★★🏕72% Holdfast Cottage**
Welland, Malvern Wells WR13 6NA (4m SE)
☎Hanley Swan(0684)310288
*This delightful small hotel, within its own grounds, is situated just
outside Malvern. The accommodation is attractive, and the
cottage-style décor and furnishings are enhanced by some
thoughtful extras – even a teddy bear and bath ducks. The public
areas are compact, but cosy and of good quality – the pleasant
dining room overlooks the garden. The menu is short and
interesting, making good use of fresh local produce. Service is
provided by the resident proprietors, Diana and Dennis
Beetlestone.*
8⇔🅰⅍in all bedrooms CTV in all bedrooms ® T
sB&B⇔🅰£34-£38 dB&B⇔🅰£66-£72 🅁

16P 🚗 ✿ croquet *xmas*
V 🕁 ⚏ ⅍ High tea £3.50-£7 Dinner fr£15&alc Last dinner
9pm
Credit Cards [1] [3] [£]

**★★★66% Royal Malvern**
Graham Rd WR14 2HN (Minotels) ☎(0684)563411
FAX (0684) 560514
Closed 25 Dec
*Equally suitable for business people and tourists, this 18th-century
town centre hotel has been tastefully converted to provide
comfortable and well equipped accommodation.*
14rm(12⇔🅰) CTV in all bedrooms ® T ✱ sB&Bfr£32
sB&B⇔🅰£45-£55 dB&Bfr£45 dB&B⇔🅰£55-£70 🅁
Lift 10P
V 🕁 ⚏ ⅍ ✱ Bar Lunch £6-£15alc Dinner £12-£25alc Last
dinner 9pm
Credit Cards [1] [2] [3] [5]

**★★64% Malvern Hills**
Wynds Point WR14 6DW (4m S A449) ☎Colwall(0684)40237 &
40690 FAX (0684) 40327
*Situated on the A449 between Malvern and Ledbury, close to the
Herefordshire Beacon. Most rooms have now been attractively
decorated and the comfortable accommodation is popular for
holiday and business purposes. There is an 'olde worlde' bar and a
small lounge for residents.*
16⇔🅰(1fb)1🛏 CTV in all bedrooms ® T sB&B⇔🅰£45
dB&B⇔🅰£68 🅁
CTV 35P 🚗 ✿ CFA solarium *xmas*
♉ English & French V 🕁 Sunday Lunch £10.50 High tea £4
Dinner £13&alc Last dinner 9.45pm
Credit Cards [1] [3]

**★★63% Cotford**
51 Graham Rd WR14 2JW ☎(0684)572427
Closed 25 Dec-11 Jan
*Built in 1851 for the Bishop of Worcester, this hotel is within
walking distance of the town centre. Rooms are simply furnished,
have good modern facilities and are suitable for business guests
and holidaymakers alike. A friendly, homely atmosphere prevails
throughout.*
16rm(7⇔5🅰)(3fb) CTV in all bedrooms ® T sB&B£30-£35
sB&B⇔🅰£30-£35 dB&B⇔🅰£55-£58
15P 🚗 ✿
V ⅍ Dinner £15 Last dinner 8pm
Credit Cards [1] [3]

**★★63% Essington**
Holywell Rd, Malvern Wells WR14 4LQ (3m S A449)
☎(0684)561177
*An early 19th-century house in two acres of terraced gardens
stands just off the A449 south of the town, offering excellent views
of the Severn Valley from its setting on the slopes of the Malvern
Hills. The reasonably well equipped accommodation that it
provides is equally suitable for tourists or business people.*
9⇔🅰(1fb)1🛏 CTV in all bedrooms ® sB&B⇔🅰£31-£35
dB&B⇔🅰£58-£62 🅁
30P 🚗 ✿ *xmas*
🕁 ⅍ Dinner £13-£15 Last dinner 8.15pm
Credit Cards [1] [3]

**★★63% Mount Pleasant**
Belle Vue Ter WR14 4PZ (Inter-Hotels) ☎(0684)561837
FAX (0684) 569968
Closed 25 & 26 Dec
*Set in attractive gardens, this large Georgian house, close to the
town centre, stands opposite the priory church. It is run in a
friendly and informal manner by the proprietors, who provide
comfortable and well-equipped accommodation for both tourists
and travelling business people. There are also facilities for
functions and conferences. The small intimate restaurant offers a
mainly Spanish theme menu and there is an adjoining coffee shop.*

M

15rm(11⇨3♠) CTV in all bedrooms ⓡ T ✖ (ex guide dogs)
sB&B£32-£36 sB&B⇨♠£40-£52 dB&B⇨♠£57.50-£69 ⋥
20P ✿ CFA nc7yrs
♀ English & Spanish V ⌂ � ✱ Lunch £9.50-£10.50 Dinner
£10.95-£12.95&alc Last dinner 9.30pm
Credit Cards ①②③⑤ⓔ

★★58% **Montrose**
23 Graham Rd WR14 2HU ☎(0684)572335
Closed 1 wk Xmas RS 12 Dec-2 Feb
*Reputedly the first purpose-built hotel in this famous spa resort,
this large old house is conveniently close to the town centre and
provides simple but comfortable accommodation with friendly
service.*
14rm(5⇨6♠)(3fb) CTV in all bedrooms ⓡ ✱ sB&B£30-£48
sB&B⇨♠£33-£48 dB&B⇨♠£50 ⋥
CTV 18P ✿
V � ✱ Lunch £10-£20 Dinner £12 Last dinner 7pm
Credit Cards ①②③

★69% *Oriel*
46 Worcester Rd WR14 4AA ☎(0684)892832
FAX (0684) 892169
*Attractive and well equipped accommodation is provided by a
pleasant, privately-run hotel whose bar and restaurant enjoy good
views across the Severn Valley. Public areas are somewhat limited
in size, but friendly staff offer a warm welcome and very attentive
service ; menus include some English dishes for guests not
adventurous enough to sample the mainly Arab cuisine.*
11rm(10⇨♠)(2fb) CTV in all bedrooms ⓡ T ✖
CTV P ✿ ⚙
♀ International V ⌂ ⊘ Last dinner 9.30pm
Credit Cards ①②③⑤

---

MAN, ISLE OF Map **06**

---

CASTLETOWN Map **06** SC26

★★★66% *Castletown Golf Links*
Fort Island(Best Western) ☎(0624)822201 Telex no 627636
FAX (0624) 824633
*An hotel at the sea's edge and adjoining the renowned 18-hole
championship golf links has, during recent years, undergone
considerable improvement – its wide range of facilities now
including a leisure complex with swimming pool, sauna, solarium
and an excellent billiard room. Several eating options are provided,
but pride of place must go to L'Orangerie with its varied and
interesting menu of French dishes, all prepared to a high standard.*
58rm(44⇨12♠)(1fb)1 ⊞ CTV in all bedrooms ⓡ T
⟮ CTV 100P ✿ ⊡ (heated) ▶ 18 snooker sauna solarium
shooting
♀ French V ⌂ ⊘ ✂ Last dinner 10pm
Credit Cards ①②③⑤

---

DOUGLAS Map **06** SC37

★★★68% **Empress**
Central Promenade ☎(0624)661155 Telex no 627772
FAX (0624) 673554
*This seafront hotel has been completely transformed by total
refurbishment and now offers particularly well appointed
accommodation. Attractively furnished bedrooms vary in size, but
all are well equipped and have stylish modern bathrooms.
Mirrored pillars and marble are used to good effect in the spacious
foyer lounge. Other public areas include a French-style brasserie
and a small basement leisure centre.*
102⇨♠(20fb) CTV in all bedrooms ⓡ T ✖ (ex guide dogs) ⋥
Lift ⟮ ⊞ ♪ 🚲 CFA ⊡ (heated) sauna solarium gymnasium
steam room
♀ International V ⌂ ⊘ ✂
Credit Cards ①③④ⓔ

M

## ★★★64% Palace Hotel & Casino

Central Promenade(Consort) ☎(0624)662662 Telex no 627742 FAX (0624) 625535

*This purpose-built hotel on the seafront offers a large range of facilities including a nightclub, casino, choice of cinemas and a particularly attractive and well equipped leisure and health club. Bedrooms, though not over spacious, are very well equipped, half of them giving views over the bay.*

135⇨ℝ CTV in all bedrooms ® T * sB&B⇨ℝ£72.50-£85 dB&B⇨ℝ£102.50-£115 ℞

Lift ℂ 80P CFA ⊠ (heated) snooker sauna solarium gymnasium beauty therapy cinema ♫ *xmas*

♡ English & European V ♥ ⊻ * Lunch £10.50&alc Dinner £16.95&alc Last dinner 10pm

Credit Cards ①②③⑤

## ★★★64% Sefton

Harris Promenade ☎(0624)626011 FAX (0624) 676004

*This long established and well run Victorian seafront hotel offers lively, modern and spacious public areas which include an attractive leisure complex and a variety of eating and drinking options. In contrast the bedrooms, though well equipped, are plain in style.*

80⇨ℝ(5fb) CTV in all bedrooms ® T ✕ (ex guide dogs) * sB&B⇨ℝ£31.50-£48 dB&B⇨ℝ£50-£67 ℞

Lift ℂ 52P ♿ CFA ⊠ (heated) sauna solarium gymnasium steam rooms beauty therapy service

V ♥ ⊻ ✕ Lunch £6-£11 High tea £3-£5 Dinner £12-£13 Last dinner 9.30pm

Credit Cards ①②③⑤

---

### RAMSEY Map **06** SC49

## ★★★★56% Grand Island

Bride Rd ☎(0624)812455 Telex no 629849 FAX (0624) 815291

*A privately owned hotel with grounds overlooking Ramsey Bay, to the north of the town. There is a good range of leisure facilities including a number of well maintained croquet lawns. While many bedrooms have lovely views, standard rooms are modestly furnished and several are very compact. Public areas are being enhanced by the liberal use of fabrics.*

54⇨ℝ(4fb)1♨ in 2 bedrooms CTV in all bedrooms ® T ✕ (ex guide dogs) S% sB&B⇨ℝ£54-£148 dB&B⇨ℝ£60-£148 ℞

Lift ℂ 150P ♿ ❀ CFA ⊠ (heated) ♠ (hard) ⊍ snooker sauna solarium gymnasium shooting steam room croquet putting *xmas*

♡ International V ♥ ⊻ * Lunch £11.75&alc Dinner £18.95&alc Last dinner 10pm

Credit Cards ①②③⑤④

---

### MANCHESTER Greater Manchester Map **07** SJ89

See **Town Plan Section**

See also Salford

## ★★★★65% Ramada Renaissance

Blackfriars St M3 2EQ ☎061-835 2555 Telex no 669699 FAX 061-835 3077

*A modern hotel in the city centre offers particularly spacious accommodation, the friendly attentions of cheerful staff and a good car parking service. In the evenings a pianist plays in the attractive, open-plan foyer bar and restaurant where guests enjoy a range of tasty dishes.*

205⇨ℝ(5fb) in 48 bedrooms CTV in all bedrooms ® T sB⇨ℝ£52-£70 dB⇨ℝ£52-£80 (room only) ℞

Lift ℂ 80♿ CFA *xmas*

V ♥ ⊻ * Lunch £13.50-£14.50&alc Dinner £14.50&alc Last dinner 10.30pm

Credit Cards ①②③④⑤

## ★★★★64% Holiday Inn Crowne Plaza

Peter St M60 2DS (Holiday Inns Inc) ☎061-236 3333 Telex no 667550 FAX 061-228 2241

*Centrally situated and adjacent to the G-Mex exhibition centre, this grand Edwardian hotel has been modernised but retains many original features. Spacious and lofty public areas include three restaurants, two bars, a basement leisure centre and extensive conference and banqueting facilities. Bedrooms vary in size and comfort but all have smart modern bathrooms. Efficient service is provided by plentiful, smartly dressed and friendly staff.*

303⇨ℝ(23fb)1♨ in 54 bedrooms CTV in all bedrooms T ✕ (ex guide dogs) sB⇨ℝ£118-£122 dB⇨ℝ£134-£138 (room only) ℞

Lift ℂ 40♿ CFA ⊠ (heated) squash sauna solarium gymnasium jacuzzi *xmas*

♡ English & French V ♥ ⊻ * Lunch £16.95 Dinner £16.95&alc Last dinner 10.30pm

Credit Cards ①②③⑤

## ★★★★61% Hotel Piccadilly

Piccadilly M60 1QR (Jarvis) ☎061-236 8414 Telex no 668765 FAX 061-228 1568

*Situated in the city centre, this hotel has been totally refurbished over recent years to provide comprehensive facilities. Bedrooms, though not large, are well equipped, public rooms are spacious and comfortable and a high standard of cuisine has been achieved in the elegant Pavilion and Verandah Restaurants.*

271⇨ℝ3♨ in 35 bedrooms CTV in all bedrooms ® T * sB⇨ℝ£100-£127.50 dB⇨ℝ£127.50-£148 (room only) ℞

Lift ℂ 80P CFA ⊠ (heated) sauna solarium gymnasium *xmas*

♡ English & French V ♥ ⊻ * Lunch £12.80&alc Dinner £13.80&alc Last dinner 10.30pm

Credit Cards ①②③④⑤ⓔ

## ★★★★60% Charterhouse

Oxford St M60 7HA ☎061-236 9999 FAX 061-236 0674

*This large and elegant Victorian building at the heart of the city – for most of its life the headquarters of a well known assurance company – has now been transformed into a luxurious hotel; individually designed bedrooms are spacious, comfortable and very well equipped, while the extensive downstairs lounge provides an ideal meeting place for both business and social purposes.*

58⇨ℝ(13fb) in 17 bedrooms CTV in all bedrooms ® T * S10% sB⇨ℝ£50-£90 dB⇨ℝ£65-£105 (room only) ℞

Lift ℂ 5P 20♿ ♫

V ♥ ⊻ * S10% Lunch £12.50-£15.50 Dinner £17.50&alc Last dinner 10.15pm

Credit Cards ①②③⑤

## ★★★★53% Portland Thistle

3/5 Portland St, Piccadilly Gdns M1 6DP (Mount Charlotte (TS)) ☎061-228 3400 Telex no 669157 FAX 061-228 6347

*Situated in the city centre, overlooking Piccadilly Gardens, this hotel features pleasant public areas which include a choice of bars and eating options; there is also a small leisure complex. Bedrooms and bathrooms tend to be compact, and although all are well equipped those on the upper floors are beginning to show their age.*

205⇨ℝ(6fb)2♨ in 51 bedrooms CTV in all bedrooms ® T (room only) ℞

Lift ℂ ⊞ ♪ ⊠ (heated) sauna solarium gymnasium whirlpool hairdresser

♡ International ♥ ⊻ ✕

Credit Cards ①②③④⑤

See advertisement on page 493

## ★★★62% Forte Posthouse

Palatine Rd, Northenden M22 4FH (Forte Hotels) ☎061-998 7090 Telex no 669248 FAX 061-946 0139

*Conveniently situated on the B5167 close to the M63 and M56, this very busy purpose-built hotel has extensively refurbished its bedrooms and public areas and now provides a good standard of modern accommodation.*

→

M

196⇦🏠🏠⊁in 98 bedrooms CTV in all bedrooms ® T ✱ S%
sB⇦🏠£39.50-£49.50 dB⇦🏠£39.50-£49.50 (room only) 🏧
Lift ( 250P 120🚗 xmas
V ♥ ⚤ ⊁ ✱ S% Lunch £8.75-£20 Dinner £13.95-£20 Last
dinner 10.30pm
Credit Cards ①②③④⑤

### ★★★58% **Willow Bank**
340-342 Wilmslow Rd, Fallowfield M14 6AF ☎061-224 0461
Telex no 668222 FAX 061-257 2561
*Conveniently situated beside the B5117, 3 miles from the city
centre, a converted Victorian house with modern extensions offers
functional accommodation and 24-hour room service.*
116⇦🏠(2fb) CTV in all bedrooms ® T ✖ (ex guide dogs) S%
sB⇦🏠£48-£52 dB⇦🏠£62-£69 (room only) 🏧
( CTV 70P 30🚗 CFA ♫
♈ English & Continental V ♥ ⚤ ⊁ S% Lunch fr£6.50&alc
Dinner fr£9.50&alc Last dinner 10.15pm
Credit Cards ①②③⑤①

### ★★★57% **Novotel Manchester West**
Worsley Brow M28 4YA ☎061-799 3535 Telex no 669586
FAX 061-703 8207
(For full entry see Worsley)

### ★★★52% **Parkers**
109-111 Corporation St M4 4DX ☎061-953 9550
FAX 061-835 3805
*Close to Victoria Station, in an area of the city undergoing re-
development, this Edwardian hotel offers sizeable bedrooms, a
spacious foyer and a large restaurant in period style. A variety of
conference and banqueting facilities are available, and for those in
need of exercise, there is a gym and sauna.*
112⇦🏠(8fb)1🛏 CTV in all bedrooms ® T ✱ sB⇦🏠£27-£57
dB⇦🏠£42.50-£78 (room only)
Lift ( 85P CFA sauna solarium gymnasium
♈ French V ♥ ⚤ ✱ Lunch £7.50-£8 Dinner £13&alc Last
dinner 10.15pm
Credit Cards ①②③⑤

### ★★66% **Crescent Gate**
Park Crescent, Victoria Park M14 5RE ☎061-224 0672
FAX 061-257 2822
Closed Xmas
*Relaxed and homely in atmosphere, this friendly, family-run hotel
stands in a peaceful and pleasant residential area just off the
B5117, within easy reach of the city centre and university.
Bedrooms, though not over-spacious, are well equipped, while a
pleasant lounge invites relaxation; service combines informality
with efficiency, and the neat dining room offers enjoyable home-
cooked meals.*
15rm(2⇦5🏠)Annexe11⇦🏠(1fb) CTV in all bedrooms ® T
sB&B£28 sB&B⇦🏠£35 dB&B⇦🏠£48
CTV 18P 🚲
V ♥ ⚤ ⊁ Bar Lunch £2.50-£4.50 Dinner £8.50 Last dinner
8pm
Credit Cards ①②③⑤①

### ★★62% **Mitre**
Cathedral Gates M3 1SW ☎061-834 4128 Telex no 669581
FAX 061-839 1646
*A long-established privately owned hotel in the oldest part of the
city, with a friendly atmosphere and comfortable well-equipped
bedrooms, the quietest overlooking the cathedral. The public bar
offers a range of meals during the day, while the small first-floor
bar and restaurant are open in the evening.*
28rm(20⇦🏠) CTV in all bedrooms ® T ✖ (ex guide dogs) S%
sB&B£50-£52 sB&B⇦🏠£55-£59 dB&B£60-£65
dB&B⇦🏠£65-£70 🏧
( CTV 🅿 CFA
♈ English & French V ♥ ⚤ ✱ Lunch £9-£10&alc Dinner £9-
£10&alc Last dinner 9.45pm
Credit Cards ①②③⑤①

### ⊛✖✖ **Woodlands**
33 Shepley Rd, Audenshaw M34 5DJ ☎061-336 4241
*A Victorian house situated just off the A6107 in a residential area
of Audenshaw provides a comfortable setting for a stylish yet
unpretentious little restaurant where service is both friendly and
correct. Cooking is commendably reliable and, although most
items are accompanied by rich sauces, chef William Mark Jackson
exhibits a lightness of touch which produces such delightful dishes
as a delicate warm scallop and spinach terrine with shallot butter
sauce. Fresh fish features strongly on both table d'hôte and à la
carte menus, though options like calves liver with apples and
Calvados are also available, and a reasonably priced list of
predominantly French wines should satisfy most tastes.*
Closed Mon, Sun (ex party bookings) 1 wk after Xmas, 1 wk
Etr & 2 wks Aug Lunch not served Sat (ex party bookings)
♈ French V 40 seats ✱ Lunch fr£3.65&alc Dinner
fr£15.65&alc Last lunch 2pm Last dinner 9.30pm 10 P
Credit Cards ①③

### ⊛⊛✖✖ **Yang Sing**
34 Princess St M1 4JY ☎061-236 2200 FAX 061-236 5934
*This bustling basement restaurant is well patronised by the local
Chinese community. The extensive menu contains several dishes
which should prove popular with the more adventurous diner, and a
good selection of Dim Sum is available during the day. Service is
decidedly easy going and informal.*
Closed 25 Dec
♈ Cantonese V 140 seats Last dinner 11pm 🅿
Credit Cards ①②③

### ⊛✖ **Little Yang Sing**
17 George St M1 4HE ☎061-228 7722
*This younger brother has taken over the premises (a semi basement
in Manchester's Chinatown, close to the Imperial Archway)
originally occupied by the Yang Sing, which has since moved to
larger premises. Warren Yeung, its owner, has made it into a
friendly, intimate restaurant, where helpful staff are happy to try to
explain the dishes. There is plenty of choice, and, in addition to the
usual Cantonese items, there are excellent dim sum, and some
casserole dishes, for example, braised brisket with spices. Flavours
were found by our inspector to be well judged in dishes such as
turbot with ginger sauce and sliced duck with pineapple and
ginger. Vegetarians should welcome the extensive Vegan menu
which offers dishes such as fresh asparagus with garlic sauce or
stuffed beancurd casserole.*
♈ Cantonese V 90 seats ✱ Lunch £6-£8&alc Dinner £6-£8&alc
Last lunch 3.30pm Last dinner 11.15pm 🅿
Credit Cards ①②③

### ⊛✖ **Market**
Edge St, 104 High St M4 1HQ ☎061-834 3743
*Founded in 1980 in premises along the street from its current
corner site, this small bohemian restaurant is run with great charm
by Anne O'Grady. There is a 40's style to décor, furnishings and
music, and while service is informal it is efficient and obliging. The
unpretentious surroundings are matched by honest good cooking,
with dishes drawn from all over the world, which might include
Thai fishcakes with chilli relish, dosa, baked samosas or caponata,
though British cooking is not neglected. Puddings are a feature, in
fact the Manchester Pudding Club meets here every other month,
with a similar 'club' based on starters on alternate months
(booking essential). Vegetarians are also very well catered for.*
Closed Sun, Mon, Aug, 1 wk Xmas & 1 wk Spring Lunch not
served
40 seats Dinner £14-£22alc Last dinner 9.30pm 🅿
Credit Cards ①②③⑤

**See advertisement on page 495**

---

A rosette means exceptional standards of cuisine.

493

**MANCHESTER AIRPORT** Greater Manchester
Map **07** SJ88

★★★59% **Wilmslow Moat House**

Altrincham Rd SK9 4LR (Queens Moat)
☎Wilmslow(0625)529201 Telex no 666401
FAX (0625) 531876

*Behind its distinctive Swiss Chalet exterior, this hotel offers every modern amenity, including excellent leisure facilities. Some of the bedrooms are compact, but the newer ones are sizeable. The public rooms in the older part of the hotel are due to be refurbished. Food is enjoyable and the staff are helpful.*
125⇌2🛏✍in 4 bedrooms CTV in all bedrooms ® T S17.5%
sB⇌£74-£78 dB⇌£84-£88 (room only) 🅿
Lift 《 400P ✿ CFA 🖵 (heated) squash snooker sauna solarium gymnasium jacuzzi steam room beauty therapy
♡ International V ✿ ⚖ Lunch £11-£11.50&alc Dinner £13.50-£14.50&alc Last dinner 10.30pm
Credit Cards ① ② ③ ⑤ ⑤

※※ ✕ ✕ **Moss Nook**
Ringway Rd, Moss Nook M22 5NA ☎061-437 4778
FAX 061-498 8089

*Despite its proximity to Manchester Airport, the sound of jet roar does not penetrate the effectively double-glazed bow windows of this long established restaurant. Inside has a Victorian feel with deep red walls, lace tablecloths, several decorative (chiming) clocks and formally dressed staff who remove silver cloches with a flourish. This is a popular place for business entertaining and consequently some of the prices are rather high, although the daily changing special dishes give more flexibility, and the 7-course Menu Surprise is good value. Fruit figures strongly in many of the dishes, apple and mango with black pudding, or passion fruit sauce with fish, for example, and sometimes these accompaniments are more successful than others. Overall, however, the cooking is consistently reliable.*
Closed Sun, Mon & 25 Dec-8 Jan Lunch not served Sat
♡ French 50 seats ✳ Lunch £16.50&alc Dinner £25&alc Last lunch 1.30pm Last dinner 9.30pm 50 P nc12yrs
Credit Cards ① ② ③

**MANORBIER** Dyfed Map **02** SS09

★★62% **Castle Mead**

SA70 7TA ☎(0834)871358
Closed Nov-Etr

*There are beautiful views of the sea, castle and church from the rear windows of this small family-run hotel, which stands at the head of a small wooded valley. Bedrooms are modestly furnished, but comfortable, and the food is consistantly good.*
5⇌Annexe3⇌(2fb)✍in 2 bedrooms CTV in all bedrooms ®
sB&B⇌fr£26 dB&B⇌fr£52 🅿
20P 🚗 ✿
V ✿ ⚖ Bar Lunch fr£2 Dinner fr£10 Last dinner 8pm
Credit Cards ① ② ③

**MANSFIELD** Nottinghamshire Map **08** SK56 ◉

★★64% **Pine Lodge**

281-283 Nottingham Rd NG18 4SE ☎(0623)22308
FAX (0623) 656819

*A family-run hotel on the edge of town set back from the A617, the main road to Nottingham. The bedrooms have most of the amenities required by the traveller, and there is a small, well maintained garden to the rear.*
21rm(19⇌🌑)(2fb) CTV in all bedrooms ® T ✖ ✳ sB&B£35-£36 sB&B⇌🌑£35-£43.50 dB&B⇌🌑£56-£60 🅿
40P 🚗 CFA sauna solarium
♡ English & Italian V ✿ ⚖ ✳ Dinner £11.75&alc Last dinner 9.30pm
Credit Cards ① ② ③ ⑤

**MARAZION** Cornwall & Isles of Scilly Map **02** SW53

★★66% **Mount Haven**

Turnpike Rd TR17 0DQ (Minotels) ☎Penzance(0736)710249
Closed 24-27 Dec RS Nov-Mar

*Set in its own grounds on the edge of the village, with panoramic views over Mount's Bay and St Michael's Mount, this personally-run hotel features some double rooms with small balconies; its split-level restaurant, decorated to a nautical theme, enjoys a good reputation locally.*
17⇌(5fb)1🛏 CTV in all bedrooms ® T sB&B⇌£22.50-£42 dB&B⇌£45-£62 🅿
40P 🚗
♡ English & French V ✿ ⚖ ✍ ✳ Sunday Lunch fr£8.50alc Dinner £13.25-£14&alc Last dinner 9pm
Credit Cards ① ② ③

**See advertisement under PENZANCE**

**MARCH** Cambridgeshire Map **05** TL49

★65% **Olde Griffin**

High St PE15 9EJ ☎(0354)52517 FAX (0354) 50086

*The proprietors, Dee and David Reeve have created a warm and friendly atmosphere at this former coaching inn located in the town centre. Public areas are undergoing sympathetic refurbishment and are due to re-open in the summer. Good rear car park.*
20rm(16⇌3🌑)(2fb) CTV in all bedrooms ® T ✖ ✳
sB&B⇌🌑£29.50-£39.50 dB&B⇌🌑£37.50-£55
50P CFA
♡ English & Continental V ✿ ✳ Lunch £4.75-£12.95 Dinner £10.75&alc Last dinner 9.30pm
Credit Cards ① ③ ⑤

**MARCHWIEL** Clwyd Map **07** SJ34

★★61% *Cross Lanes Hotel & Restaurant*

Cross Lanes LL13 0TF ☎Bangor-on-Dee(0978)780555
FAX (0978) 780568
RS 25-26 Dec

*A country house dating from the Victorian era, set in 7 acres of grounds on the A525, 3 miles southeast of Wrexham, is particularly popular with businessmen, including the delegates using its conference and function amenities. Bedrooms vary in size and style, but all are well equipped, while leisure facilities include an indoor swimming pool, a sauna and a croquet lawn.*
18⇌🌑(1fb)1🛏 CTV in all bedrooms ® T
80P ✿ 🖵 (heated) sauna
♡ International V ✿ ⚖ ✍ Last dinner 9pm
Credit Cards ① ② ③ ⑤

**MARFORD** Clwyd Map **07** SJ35

★64% **Trevor Arms**

Springfield Ln LL12 8TA ☎Chester(0244)570436 & 571550
*Small, pleasant and attractive, this village inn, conveniently situated within easy reach of the A483 Wrexham bypass, is popular with both tourists and travelling business people, its well equipped modern accommodation representing good value for money.*
10🌑Annexe5rm(3⇌)(1fb)1🛏 CTV in all bedrooms ® T
✖ (ex guide dogs) ✳ S% sB&B⇌🌑£26-£29.50
dB&B⇌🌑£32.50-£43 Continental breakfast 🅿
70P ✿ CFA 🚗
♡ European V ✿ ⚖ ✍ ✳ Sunday Lunch £6.50 Dinner £3.25-£5.95&alc Last dinner 10pm
Credit Cards ① ③ ⑤

Remember to book early for holiday
and bank holiday times.

M

## MARKET DRAYTON Shropshire Map 07 SJ63 ☺

### ★★★★ ⊛ ♨71% Goldstone Hall
Goldstone TF9 2NA (Exec Hotel) ☎Cheswardine(063086)202 & 487 FAX (063086) 585
*This personally run country house with very attractive gardens is situated in the hamlet of Goldstone, 2 miles off the A529 south of the town. It offers caring service, a relaxing atmosphere and comfortable lounges and bedrooms. The restaurant has a growing local reputation for its carefully cooked dishes that make use of good quality ingredients.*
8⇨♠1⊞ CTV in all bedrooms ® T ✖ (ex guide dogs) S%
sB&B⇨♠fr£51 dB&B⇨♠£64.50-£74.50 ⊟
60P ❀ ☐ ♪ snooker
V ✆ ⚗ Lunch £13.50&alc High tea fr£4.50 Dinner £19.90-£24.95alc Last dinner 10.30pm

### ★★70% Corbet Arms
High St TF9 1PY ☎(0630)652037 FAX (0630)652961
*Complete refurbishment has given a new lease of life to a centrally located hotel run in friendly, relaxed style by an enthusiastic team and providing tastefully furnished and quite spacious accommodation.*
11⇨♠ CTV in all bedrooms ® T ✳ sB&B⇨♠£36-£44
dB&B⇨♠£44-£56 ⊟
60P CFA crown green bowling *xmas*
V ✆ ⚗ ✱ Lunch £3.25-£7.50alc Dinner £3.25-£9.50alc Last dinner 10pm
Credit Cards ①②③⑤

### ★★63% Rosehill Manor
Rosehill TF9 2JF ☎Tern Hill(0630)638532
*This pleasant old house, now a small, privately owned and personally run hotel, stands in spacious grounds beside the A41, 2 miles southeast of its junction with the A53. Bedrooms – most of which have en suite facilites – are equally suitable for tourists or business people.*
6rm(4⇨♠)(1fb)1⊞ CTV in all bedrooms ® ✖ (ex guide dogs)
sB&B£26-£46 sB&B⇨♠£31-£46 dB&B£37-£60
dB&B⇨♠£48-£60 ⊟
20P ⇩ ❀
V Lunch £10.95-£14 Dinner £14.50-£15.50&alc Last dinner 8.30pm
Credit Cards ①②③ⓔ

## MARKET HARBOROUGH Leicestershire Map 04 SP78

### ★★★61% Three Swans
21 High St LE16 7NJ (Best Western) ☎(0858)466644
Telex no 342375 FAX (0858) 433101
*Improvements over recent years have continued with the addition of a modern bedroom annexe. The attractive first floor restaurant is popular and the bars are well frequented by locals.*
21⇨♠Annexe16⇨♠2⊞✱in 4 bedrooms CTV in all bedrooms ® T ✖ (ex guide dogs) sB&B⇨♠£69-£73
dB&B⇨♠£79-£83 ⊟
《 40P 8🚘 CFA
☿ International V ✆ ⚗ ✱ Lunch fr£10.95&alc High tea fr£2.35 Dinner fr£16.95&alc Last dinner 9.45pm
Credit Cards ①②③④⑤

## MARKET WEIGHTON Humberside Map 08 SE84

### ★★★73% Londesborough Arms
44 High St YO4 3AH ☎(0430)872214 FAX (0430) 872219
*This Georgian coaching inn in the town centre, now a privately owned and personally run hotel, has been extensively refurbished and restored to its former glory; no expense has been spared in the work, only the best period-style furnishings and fittings being used. Public areas with an abundance of wood panelling and leaded stained glass include a delightful, elegant restaurant, a coffee shop and a choice of two bars, while spaciously comfortable, well*

equipped bedrooms boast en suite bathrooms of a very high standard. A very good function/ballroom is available, and small business meetings can also be accommodated.
15⇨♠(2fb)1⊞ CTV in all bedrooms ® T ✖ (ex guide dogs)
✳ sB⇨♠£50 dB⇨♠£80 (room only)
《 CTV 30P *xmas*
☿ French V ✆ ⚗ ✱ ✱ Lunch £10 High tea £6 Dinner £20
Last dinner 10.30pm
Credit Cards ①②③

## MARKFIELD Leicestershire Map 08 SK41

### ★★★71% Field Head
Markfield Ln LE6 0PS (Lansbury) ☎(0530)245454
Telex no 342296 FAX (0530) 243740
*A farmhouse dating back to 1672 has been sympathetically extended and restored to create a modern hotel which offers comfortable, well-appointed public areas and good sized, fully equipped, attractively decorated bedrooms. The entrance is off the B5327 from its roundabout junction with the A50, and one mile from junction 22 of the M1. The entrance is not obvious, and if the turning off the A50 is missed a long detour cannot be avoided, as it is very dangerous to make a U-turn on this road.*
28⇨♠(2fb)1⊞✱in 6 bedrooms CTV in all bedrooms ® T
✖ (ex guide dogs) sB&B⇨♠fr£75 dB&B⇨♠fr£88 ⊟
《 70P CFA *xmas*
☿ English & French V ✆ ✱ Lunch fr£6.50&alc Dinner fr£15&alc Last dinner 10pm
Credit Cards ①②③⑤

### ⛪Granada Lodge
Little Shaw Ln LE6 0PP (Granada) ☎(0530)244237
FAX (0530) 244580
39⇨♠in 5 bedrooms CTV in all bedrooms ®
✖ (ex guide dogs) S% sB⇨♠fr£31 dB⇨♠fr£34 (room only) ⊟
148P
V ✆ ⚗ ✱
Credit Cards ①②③⑤

## MARKHAM MOOR Nottinghamshire Map 08 SK77 ☺

### ⛪Forte Travelodge
DN22 0QU (on A1 northbound) (Forte)
☎Retford(0777)838091 Central Res (0800) 850950
*This purpose-built modern unit adjacent to a Little Chef Restaurant stands on the northbound carriageway of the A1, but can easily be reached from either direction via the busy A1/A57 intersection roundabout.*
40⇨♠(40fb) CTV in all bedrooms ® sB⇨♠£29.95
dB⇨♠£29.95 (room only)
《 40P ⇩
Credit Cards ①②③

## MARKINCH Fife Map 11 NO20

### ★★★★ ♨73% *Balbirnie House*
Balbirnie Park KY7 6NE ☎Glenrothes(0592)610066
FAX (0592) 610529
*This splendid 18th-century mansion sits in extensive parkland – including a golf course – close to the new town of Glenrothes. Carefully restored, it combines comfort and elegance with the modern facilities expected by today's guest; bedrooms range from the sumptuous to the more modest, each having its individual style of furnishing and décor. While the informal Gamekeepers Room offers a simpler alternative to the restaurant's ambitious dishes, a good choice of meeting and function rooms have been provided to attract the business and seminar markets, and obliging staff render friendly service throughout.*
30⇨♠(9fb)1⊞ CTV in all bedrooms ® T
《 120P ❀ gymnasium
☿ International V ✆ ⚗ Last dinner 9.30pm
Credit Cards ①②③⑤

**See advertisement under ST ANDREWS**

**MARKINGTON** North Yorkshire Map **08** SE26

★★★❀♨76% **Hob Green**
HG3 3PJ (Best Western) ☎Harrogate(0423)770031
Telex no 57780 FAX (0423) 771589
*An hotel magnificently set in 870 acres of rolling Yorkshire
countryside, yet within easy reach of Harrogate and the A1,
provides a high standard of comfort in a peaceful, relaxed
atmosphere. Its two comfortable lounges are attractively
decorated, and the elegant dining room offers an ideal setting for
the enjoyment of freshly cooked meals. Individually decorated
bedrooms are equipped to an extremely high standard, and a
friendly young staff provides service which is discreet yet friendly.*
12⇄↟1🖪 CTV in all bedrooms ® T sB&B⇄↟£59-£65
dB&B⇄↟£75-£83 🏳
40P 🚗 ❀ croquet
♀ English & French V ♨ ⟐ Sunday Lunch £10.95-£12.95alc
Dinner £17.50-£25alc Last dinner 9.30pm
Credit Cards ①②③⑤

**See advertisement under HARROGATE**

**MARLBOROUGH** Wiltshire Map **04** SU16

★★★72% **Ivy House Hotel & Garden Restaurant**
High St SN8 1HJ ☎(0672)515333 Telex no 449703
FAX (0672) 515338
Closed 24 Dec-2 Jan
*This listed Georgian hotel overlooking the High Street has
individually styled bedrooms, located in the main building, in the
Beeches wing and in the Vines across the street; all are
comfortable and well equipped. The elegant Garden Restaurant
offers varied menus and an extensive wine list, while a small bistro
provides more informal meals. Service is very friendly and
attentive.*
12⇄↟Annexe16⇄↟(2fb) CTV in all bedrooms ® T ✱
sB&B⇄↟£50-£69.50 dB&B⇄↟£70-£89 🏳
30P 🚗
♀ English & French V ✱ Lunch £12.95 Dinner £18.50 Last
dinner 9.30pm
Credit Cards ①②③ⓔ

★★★59% **The Castle & Ball**
High St SN8 1LZ (Forte Hotels) ☎(0672)515201
FAX (0672) 515895
*This attractive 17th-century inn at the centre of the picturesque
market town has been modernised inside but retains its charm, with
a traditional cosy lounge and restaurant. Bedrooms are of differing
standards but all are well equipped. The young staff provide
friendly service.*
36⇄🍴in 11 bedrooms CTV in all bedrooms ® T ✱ S%
sB⇄fr£75 dB⇄fr£85 (room only) 🏳
48P *xmas*
V ♨ ⟐ 🍴 S% Lunch £9.95-£22.50 Dinner £15.50-£22.50&alc
Last dinner 9.30pm
Credit Cards ①②③④⑤

**MARLEY HILL** Tyne & Wear Map **12** NZ25

★★★66% **Beamish Park**
Beamish Burn Rd NE16 5EU ☎Stanley(0207)230666
FAX (0207) 281260
47⇄↟(7fb) CTV in all bedrooms ® T sB&B⇄↟fr£39
dB&B⇄↟fr£70 🏳
( CTV 100P ❀ CFA *xmas*
♀ English & French V ♨ ⟐ ✱ Bar Lunch £3.75-£7.50 Dinner
fr£15.35&alc Last dinner 9.30pm
Credit Cards ①②③⑤ⓔ

**MARLOW** Buckinghamshire Map **04** SU88

★★★★❀69%, *The Compleat Angler*
Marlow Bridge SL7 1RG (Forte Hotels) ☎(06284)4444 due to
change to (0628) 484444 Telex no 848644 FAX (06284) 6388
(Rosette awarded for dinner only)
*Ideally situated on the Thames, this relaxing hotel offers
individually styled well equipped bedrooms, with 18 new rooms
being added in 1991. The oak-beamed restaurant has a
magnificent view and imaginative dishes by chef Ferdinand Testka
are available on the gourmet set menu or à la carte. Professional
staff provide prompt and friendly service.*
46⇄2🖪🍴in 10 bedrooms CTV in all bedrooms T
( 100P 🚗 ❀ ♪ (hard) ♪ ♫
V ♨ ⟐ 🍴 Last dinner 10pm
Credit Cards ①②③④⑤

○●**Danesfield House**
Medmenham SL7 3ES (Small Luxury Hotels)
☎Maidenhead(0628)891010
Open
92⇄↟

**MARPLE** Greater Manchester Map **07** SJ98

★69%, **Springfield**
Station Rd SK6 6PA ☎061-449 0721
*A delightful small hotel situated beside the A626 in a residential
area to the northeast of Marple provides excellent standards of
housekeeping and friendly service under the personal management
of its resident owners. Comfortable, tastefully appointed public
areas are complemented by well equipped bedrooms with attractive
décor and furnishings.*
6⇄↟ CTV in all bedrooms ® T ✱ sB&B⇄↟£30-£40
dB&B⇄↟£40-£50 🏳

**M** →

## THE IVY HOUSE HOTEL

### and Garden Restaurant ★ ★ ★

**High Street, Marlborough, Wiltshire SN8 1HJ**
**Telephone: (0672) 515333**

This Grade II Georgian Residence, overlooking
the famous high street, has been completely
transformed by resident owners David Ball and
Josephine Scott into a 3 star luxury hotel which
offers the best in comfort, facilities and service.
Their aim is to provide first class hospitality and
service in a friendly country house hotel atmosphere. They offer quality accommodation, excellent food and wine and relaxing lounges and
bars. A team of dedicated and professional staff
ensure that guests to the Ivy House enjoy efficient and courteous service.

CTV 10P ⊞ ❀
♦ ⏉ ✳ Dinner fr£12.50 Last dinner 8.30pm
Credit Cards ①②③⑤

## MARSDEN West Yorkshire Map 07 SE01

★★★63% **Hey Green**
Waters Rd HD7 6NG ☎Huddersfield(0484)844235
FAX (0484) 847605
*At the end of a quiet country lane just off the A62 and set in 7 acres of woodland with a trout lake, this comfortable small hotel has well equipped bedrooms with quality modern furniture and serves well prepared meals.*
10⇄🅵(2fb)1⊞ CTV in all bedrooms Ⓡ T sB&B⇄🅵£55-£60
dB&B⇄🅵£70-£78 🅿
70P ❀ ♪ orienteering course
V ♦ ⏉ Lunch £7.95-£18 Dinner £16.50-£18 Last dinner 9pm
Credit Cards ①②③⑤ⓔ

## MARSTON MORETAINE Bedfordshire Map 04 SP94

⏠Forte Travelodge
Beancroft Rd Junction MK43 0PZ (on A421, northbound)
(Forte)☎Bedford(0234)766755 Central Res (0800) 850950
*A modern 2-storey building offering good quality, value-for-money accommodation with full en suite facilities; one room is suitable for the disabled. The adjacent Little Chef, open from 7am-10pm, provides popular snacks and grills.*
32⇄🅵(32fb) CTV in all bedrooms Ⓡ sB⇄🅵£29.95
dB⇄🅵£29.95 (room only)
⟮ 32P ⊞
Credit Cards ①②③

## MARTINHOE Devon Map 03 SS64

★❀⚌70% *Old Rectory*
EX31 4QT ☎Parracombe(05983)368
Closed Dec-Feb
*A one-time rectory built in the 1800s for the incumbent of the 11th-century church next door, it has been converted into a cosy, personally run retreat, surrounded by National Trust land and the Exmoor National Park. Sympathetic restoration provides individually styled bedrooms, on country lines yet with modern facilities, and character lounges, one non-smoking. There is also a sun lounge overlooking the sheltered garden.*
9⇄🅵 CTV in 5 bedrooms
14P ⊞ ❀ putting nc12yrs
V ♦ ⥅ Last dinner 7.45pm

## MARTOCK Somerset Map 03 ST41

★★★64% **The Hollies**
Bower Hinton TA12 6LG ☎(0935)822232
*This 17th-century Hamstone property peacefully located in the hamlet of Bower Hinton, just off the A303, houses a beamed bar and restaurant serving mainly grills with fresh vegetables and an imaginative choice of home-made puddings. Service is friendly, and each of the well equipped rooms in a modern, single-storey accommodation block in the grounds has patio doors opening onto a paved and grassy area.*
Annexe15⇄🅵(2fb)⥅in 4 bedrooms CTV in all bedrooms Ⓡ T
✳ sB&B⇄🅵£39.50 dB&B⇄🅵£55 🅿
CTV 50P ❀ CFA
V ✳ Lunch £7.95&alc Dinner £6-£9&alc Last dinner 9pm
Credit Cards ①③

**See advertisement under YEOVIL**

⊛ Shell filling stations (7am–11pm) are
marked on the town plans.

## MARWELL Hampshire Map 04 SU52

★★★63% **Marwell Resort**
Colden Common SO21 1JY (Resort) ☎Owslebury(0962)777681
FAX (0962) 777625
*Guests at this relaxed hotel in a tranquil woodland setting may well be awakened by the roaring of a tiger, for it stands near the edge of Marwell Zoo. Newly built of pine, in colonial style, it provides spacious, well equipped bedrooms in 3 pavilions among the trees; the formal restaurant is augmented by a useful coffee shop, and attractive leisure facilities will appeal both to family parties and to conference delegates.*
60⇄🅵(9fb)⥅in 6 bedrooms CTV in all bedrooms Ⓡ T ✳
sB⇄🅵£66-£71 dB⇄🅵£76-£81 (room only) 🅿
⟮ 150P CFA ⌸ (heated) sauna solarium gymnasium *xmas*
♡ English & Continental V ♦ ⏉ ✳ Lunch £10-£12.50&alc
Dinner £13-£16&alc Last dinner 9.30pm
Credit Cards ①②③⑤ⓔ

## MARYCULTER Grampian *Aberdeenshire* Map 15 NO89

★★★68% **Maryculter House**
AB1 6BB (Minotels) ☎Aberdeen(0224)732124
FAX (0224) 733510
*A splendid mansion set in 5 acres of grounds by the banks of the River Dee, 8 miles west of Aberdeen off the South Deeside road, proves a popular base for both travelling businessman and sporting enthusiast; small conference groups are also catered for. The house dates back to the 13th-century, and much of its original character is reflected in the public areas – particularly so in the baronial cocktail bar with its welcoming log fire and impressive vaulted ceiling. Well equipped and individually decorated bedrooms are fresh and airy, with pine furnishings and attractive, co-ordinated floral fabrics.*
12⇄🅵(2fb) CTV in all bedrooms Ⓡ T ✖ (ex guide dogs)
⟮ 100P ❀ CFA ▶ 18 ♪ clay pigeon shooting ♧
♡ European V ♦ ⏉ ⥅ Last dinner 9.45pm
Credit Cards ①②③⑤

## MARYPORT Cumbria Map 11 NY03

★★★64% *Ellenbank*
Birkby CA15 6RE (2m NE A596) ☎(0900)815233
*This impressive Victorian residence standing in its own grounds on a hill 2 miles from the town centre, has comfortably furnished public areas and bedrooms with good facilities, some of them situated in a new extension.*
26⇄🅵(3fb) CTV in all bedrooms Ⓡ T
CTV 40P ❀
♡ English & Continental V ♦ ⏉ Last dinner 9.30pm
Credit Cards ①③

★58% *Waverley*
Curzon St CA15 6LW ☎(0900)812115
*A town-centre hotel catering mainly for commercial clients provides accommodation of an adequate standard at value-for-money prices; an extensive range of food is available, and staff are both friendly and helpful.*
20rm(2⇄2🅵)(2fb) CTV in all bedrooms Ⓡ sB&Bfr£19
sB&B⇄🅵fr£28 dB&Bfr£34 dB&B⇄🅵fr£43 🅿
CTV ✗ CFA pool table
♡ English & Continental V ♦ ⏉ Lunch fr£6 High tea fr£4
Dinner fr£9 Last dinner 9.30pm
Credit Cards ①③ⓔ

## MARY TAVY Devon Map 02 SX57

★★⚌62% *Moorland Hall*
Brentor Rd PL19 9PY ☎(0822)810466
*Run on very relaxed and informal lines by the hospitable owners Gillian amd Andrew Farr, this cosy hotel was converted from a farmhouse and stands, with its Victorian additions, in 4 acres of*

M

*secluded gardens amid rural surroundings. Character public rooms overlook the garden, and home cooking by Gillian Farr is served in the comfortable dining room. Bedrooms are bright, combining modern facilities with the period character of the building. Moorland Hall is convenient for Plymouth and well positioned for touring.*
8⇔↱(1fb)2⊟ CTV in all bedrooms ® sB&B⇔↱£32-£32 dB&B⇔↱£50-£55.50
20P ⛶ ✲ croquet lawn *xmas*
☋ English & French **V** ⚟ Dinner £14.50 Last dinner 8pm
Credit Cards 1 3

MASHAM North Yorkshire Map **08** SE28

**★★♣74% Jervaulx Hall**
HG4 4PH ☎Bedale(0677)60235 FAX (0969) 23206
Closed mid Nov-mid Mar
*An elegant country house standing in its own grounds close to the Abbey provides comfort and tranquillity throughout. Individually fitted bedrooms are tastefully decorated in keeping with the style of the building, while lounges are well furnished and inviting.*
10⇔↱(1fb) ® dB&B⇔↱£91-£122 (incl dinner) ⊨
CTV 15P ⛶ ✲ croquet
✻ Dinner £16 Last dinner 8pm
£

MATLOCK Derbyshire Map **08** SK36

**★★★❀♣73% Riber Hall**
DE4 5JU (Pride of Britain) ☎(0629)582795 FAX (0629) 580475
*This Elizabethan country house hotel, which sits high above Matlock next to Riber Castle, has unspoilt views over open countryside. Thoughtfully restored, the house retains its period character with exposed woodwork and antique furniture throughout the public rooms and annexe bedrooms. Guests appreciate the imaginative skills of chef Jeremy Brazelle whose interesting menus are complemented by an extensive wine list.*
Annexe11⇔9⊟ CTV in all bedrooms ® **T** ✖ (ex guide dogs) ✻ sB&B⇔£76-£90 dB&B⇔£90-£134 Continental breakfast ⊨
50P ⛶ ✲ ℘ (hard) nc10yrs
☋ English & French **V** ♆ ⚲ ✻ Lunch fr£14 High tea £7-£10alc Dinner £25-£35alc Last dinner 9.30pm
Credit Cards 1 2 3 4 5 £

**★★★58% The New Bath**
New Bath Rd DE4 3PX (2m S A6) (Forte Hotels)
☎(0629)583275 FAX (0629) 580268
*Five acres of grounds overlooking the River Derwent surround this rambling hotel which is popular for leisure breaks as well as for conferences. Recent refurbishment has made the public rooms attractive and many of the bedrooms have beautiful views.*
55⇔⚟in 11 bedrooms CTV in all bedrooms ® ✻ S%
sB⇔fr£70 dB⇔fr£90 (room only) ⊨
☾ 200P ✲ ⛱ (heated) ℘ (hard) sauna solarium thermal plunge pool *xmas*
**V** ♆ ⚲ ⚟ ✻ S% Lunch £8.95 Dinner £13.90 Last dinner 9.30pm
Credit Cards 1 2 3 4 5

**★★67% Temple**
Temple Walk, Matlock Bath DE4 3PG ☎(0629)583911
FAX (0629) 580851
*Set high on a steep wooded hillside the hotel enjoys panoramic views of the 'Little Switzerland' scenery of picturesque Matlock Bath. Chef/patron Siegfried Essl has a good local reputation for his buffet-style and à la carte menus featuring seasonal specials, particularly game, when available.*
14⇔(1fb) CTV in all bedrooms ® **T** ✖ ✻ S10% sB&B⇔£36-£43 dB&B⇔£56-£59 ⊨
☾ CTV 40P ✲ *xmas*
☋ English, French & Austrian **V** ♆ ⚲ ⚟ Lunch £8-£18alc Dinner £12-£18alc Last dinner 9.45pm
Credit Cards 1 2 3 5

**★★♣65% Red House**
Old Rd, Darley Dale DE4 2ER (2.5m N A6) ☎(0629)734854
*Though situated within easy reach of all Derbyshire's attractions, the small, family owned and personally run hotel provides a rural retreat, each room having panoramic views of the countryside and the large rear garden inviting relaxation.*
7⇔↱Annexe2⇔↱3⊟ CTV in all bedrooms ® **T** sB&B⇔↱£45-£50 dB&B⇔↱£70-£75 ⊨
16P ⛶ ✲
☋ English & French **V** Sunday Lunch £10.95-£11.95 Dinner £16.50-£17.50 Last dinner 9pm
Credit Cards 1 2 3 5 £

**★★64% Gullivers Woodland Lodge**
Temple Walk, Matlock Bath DE4 3PG ☎(0629)580540
FAX (0629) 57710
*Part of the Gullivers Kingdom Theme Park and formerly called Woodlands Lodge, this attractive hotel is still owned and run by the same family in a friendly and informal style. Comfortable lodge-style bedroom accommodation is provided in the grounds, and the 'theme' restaurant features an animated Tiki bird show, popular with young children.*
Annexe14⇔(6fb) CTV in all bedrooms ® **T** ✖ (ex guide dogs) ✻ sB&B⇔£39.50-£49.50 dB&B⇔£49.50-£59.50 ⊨
30P ⛶ CFA *xmas*
☋ English & French **V** ♆ ⚲
Credit Cards 1 3

MAWDESLEY Lancashire Map **07** SD41

**★★75% Mawdesley Eating House and Hotel**
Hall Ln L40 2QZ ☎Rufford(0704)822552 & 821874
FAX (0704) 822096
*This small, neat complex includes a most attractive bedroom block which was recently added to an already well established restaurant; accommodation is extremely inviting and very well appointed, the restaurant's intimate atmosphere provides a pleasant setting in which to enjoy an interesting and good-value range of dishes, and service throughout is most courteous. Leisure facilities, including an indoor swimming pool, were almost completed at the time of inspection.*
25⇔↱(5fb)1⊟ CTV in all bedrooms ® **T** ✖ (ex guide dogs) ✻ sB&B⇔↱£30-£45 dB&B⇔↱£40-£55
100P ⊡ (heated) sauna solarium gymnasium
**V** ♆ ✻ Lunch fr£7.50
Credit Cards 1 2 3

MAWGAN PORTH Cornwall & Isles of Scilly Map **02** SW86

**★★64% Tredragon**
TR8 4DQ (Inter-Hotels) ☎St Mawgan(0637)860213
FAX (0637) 860269
*This hotel extends an hospitable welcome to guests that merits the description; commanding splendid sea views from its elevated position, it offers bedrooms with good facilities, an informal dining room where the table d'hôte menu is supplemented by a salad buffet, and the use of an indoor heated swimming pool, sauna and solarium.*
27⇔↱(12fb) CTV in all bedrooms ® **T** ✻ sB&B⇔↱£28.60-£41 dB&B⇔↱£49.50-£67 ⊨
CTV 30P ✲ CFA ⊡ (heated) sauna solarium ♧ *xmas*
☋ English & French **V** ♆ ⚲ ✻ Sunday Lunch £10.50-£11.50 Dinner £10.50-£12.50 Last dinner 8pm
Credit Cards 1 3 £

**See advertisement on page 501**

**MAWNAN SMITH** Cornwall & Isles of Scilly Map **02** SW72

★★★⚑♨73% **Meudon**
TR11 5HT ☎Falmouth(0326)250541 FAX (0326) 250543
Closed Dec-Feb

*An erstwhile private mansion, parts of which date back some 300
years, was converted to hotel use in 1966 and has been in the hands
of the same family ever since. Richly furnished public areas
warmed by log fires promote a pleasantly traditional atmosphere,
and sound meals are served in the glass terraced restaurant. A new
wing of local stone has been grafted onto the old building, and
many of the comfortable, well equipped bedrooms contained in it
enjoy views over the glorious 8-acre grounds with their sub-tropical
displays; these gardens, laid out originally by Capability Brown,
provide a sheltered valley that runs down to a private beach
surrounded by National Trust land – this area between the Fal and
Helford rivers being one of the most beautiful sections of the
Cornish coast.*

32⇨🛏(1fb) CTV in all bedrooms ® T ✳ 🖪
☾50P 2🐾 (£5 per night) ⇗ ✿ ⌨ Ừ nc5yrs *xmas*
♀ English & French V ⊕ ⬛
Credit Cards ①③⑤

**See advertisement under FALMOUTH**

★★★70% **Budock Vean**
TR11 5LG ☎Falmouth(0326)250288 FAX (0326) 250892
Closed Jan & Feb

*A professionally run golf hotel in country house style, set in
beautiful countryside and surrounded by 65 acres of mature
grounds and gardens which run down to the Helford River, has
recently been significantly upgraded. Character bedrooms, their
lines softened with pleasing pastel colours and complementary soft
fabrics, are well equipped and boast bright, modern en suite
facilities while spacious public rooms include a number of
comfortable lounges, a stylish restaurant and a convivial cocktail
bar. More energetic guests can choose between a challenging
parkland golf course, all-weather tennis courts and indoor
swimming pool complex (complete with its own log fire in winter).
Prompt and friendly service on traditional lines is provided by a
smartly dressed, well established staff.*

59⇨🛏(6fb)1🖿 CTV in all bedrooms T sB&B⇨🛏£55-£82
dB&B⇨🛏£110-£164 (incl dinner)
Lift ☾100P ⇗ ✿ ⬛(heated) ▶ 9 ℛ (hard) ♪ snooker *xmas*
♀ English & French V ⊕ ⬛ ✳ Bar Lunch £2.50-£10alc Dinner
£20.50&alc Last dinner 9pm
Credit Cards ①②③⑤

★★★62% **Trelawne**
TR11 5LG ☎Falmouth(0326)250226 250417 FAX (0326) 250909
Closed 30 Dec-14 Mar

*There is a country house atmosphere about this bright, spotlessly
clean hotel in its 2.5 acre grounds. Set in rural surroundings within
easy reach of the sea, it provides friendly service by local staff and
the attentive concern of involved owners; public areas, though
restricted in size, are attractively styled to create an intimate
atmosphere while bedrooms are well equipped and homely, if
compact in some cases. Imaginative cuisine makes good use of
quality produce and ingredients.*

15rm(13⇨🛏)(2fb) CTV in all bedrooms ® T sB&B⇨🛏£44-
£48 dB&B⇨🛏£77-£86 🖪
20P ⇗ ✿ ⬛(heated) *xmas*
⊕ ⬛ ✂ Bar Lunch £2-£6 Dinner £17.50&alc Last dinner
8.30pm
Credit Cards ①②③⑤

★★62% **Penmorvah Manor**
Penjerrick, Budock TR11 5ED (Minotels)
☎Falmouth(0326)250277

*This Victorian manor house, standing in 6 acres of grounds only 2
miles from the town, features a large function room opening onto
lawns – ideal for wedding receptions – and a restaurant serving
both fixed price and à la carte menus. Comfortable, well
coordinated and purpose-built bedrooms (opened early in 1991 and*

*reserved for non-smoking guests) supplement the large rooms with
modern furniture contained within the main building.*

27⇨🛏🛏(1fb) ✂ in 20 bedrooms CTV in all bedrooms ® T ✂
(ex guide dogs) sB&B⇨🛏£24.50-£35.75 dB&B£49-£71.50 🖪
150P CFA
V ⊕ ⬛ Dinner £13.50 Last dinner 8.30pm
Credit Cards ①②③

**See advertisement under FALMOUTH**

---

**MAYBOLE** Strathclyde *Ayrshire* Map **10** NS20

★★❀♨ **LADYBURN**
KA19 7SG
☎Crosshill(06554)585
FAX (06554) 580
(Rosette awarded for dinner
only)

*'Welcome to our home' is how
David and Jane Hepburn will
welcome you to their delightful house set in a beautifully quiet
valley in Ayrshire, yet still within easy distance of commercial
and tourist centres on the Clyde coast. Opened in June 1990,
this former Dower House has been restored to provide all the
modern comforts and is furnished and decorated with a
personal attention that makes one feel very much at home.
Guests can meet up before or after dinner in the comfortable
drawing room where a log fire burns, or there is a library
available with an excellent collection of books. Pretty
bedrooms with thoughtful extras like fresh fruit, books and
fresh milk with the tea making facilities have, with the
exception of one room, en suite facilities.
Hospitality at Ladyburn is second to none: nothing seems too
much trouble and this example from Jane and David seems to
rub off on the their polite and smartly dressed staff. Meals are
cooked in the light modern style making full use of excellent
local suppliers of fish, meat and vegetables, and fresh herbs
are already growing in the garden.*

8rm(4⇨3🛏)✂in all bedrooms CTV in all bedrooms ® T
✂ (ex guide dogs) sB&B⇨🛏£70 dB&B⇨🛏£130-£155
Continental breakfast (incl dinner) 🖪
12P ⇗ ✿ CFA croquet nc12yrs *xmas*
♀ Scottish & French V ⊕ ⬛ ✂ Lunch £10-£14.50 Dinner
£19.50&alc Last dinner 8.45pm
Credit Cards ①②③

---

**MAYPOOL (NEAR CHURSTON)** Devon Map **03** SX85

★★★62% **Lost & Found**
TQ5 0ET ☎Churston(0803)842442 FAX (0803) 845221

*Neatly tucked away in enviable rural surroundings, commanding
valley views over Dartmouth to the river estuary in the distance,
this small, family-managed hotel offers personal service in a
relaxed informal atmosphere. Public rooms, though a little
restrictive, are comfortably furnished and a good range of freshly
prepared food is served in the bright, well appointed surroundings
of its popular restaurant. Bedrooms vary in size, those at the front
of the building tending to be larger, but even the more compact
rooms are fully equipped, and plans for refurbishment are in hand.*

16⇨🛏(1fb)1🖿 CTV in all bedrooms ® T sB&B⇨🛏£64-£79
dB&B⇨🛏£118-£149 (incl dinner) 🖪
24P ⇗ ✿ *xmas*
♀ French V ⊕ ⬛ Sunday Lunch £8-£12&alc Dinner £17-
£25&alc Last dinner 9.30pm
Credit Cards ①②③

M

**MEALSGATE** Cumbria Map **11** NY24

★★66% **Pink House**
CA5 1JP ☎Low Ireby(09657)229

*A small and friendly family-run hotel with attractively decorated well equipped bedrooms, 2 comfortable lounges and a bar and small dining room both serving enjoyable food.*

6⇨🏠(2fb) CTV in all bedrooms ® **T** ✖ (ex guide dogs)
sB&B⇨🏠£36.50 dB&B⇨🏠£50 🅿
CTV 40P ✿ ⟡
𝄞 English & French **V** ✿ ⟐ Lunch £6-£11alc Dinner £7-£14alc Last dinner 9pm
Credit Cards ①③⑤

---

**MELBOURN** Cambridgeshire Map **05** TL34

✸✸ ✖✖ *The Pink Geranium*
Station Rd SG8 6DX ☎Royston(0763)260215
FAX (0763) 261936

*Unfortunately, due to a recent fire, this restaurant is at present closed.*

Closed Mon & 26 Dec
Dinner not served Sun
**V** 70 seats Last lunch 2.30pm Last dinner 10pm 25 P ✄
Credit Cards ①③

Remember to book early for holiday
and bank holiday times.

---

# LUXURY CORNISH COUNTRY HOUSE HOTEL

Idyllically situated in 65 acres, on the banks of the Helford River with private Golf Course, spectacular indoor pool and championship tennis courts – all free to guests.

Comfortable and stylish accommodation, superb cuisine with an excellent selection of wines.

Enjoy the unique atmosphere of this fine hotel.

Associated hotel Treglos Hotel, Padstow.

# BUDOCK VEAN
GOLF AND COUNTRY HOUSE HOTEL ★★★

FALMOUTH·CORNWALL·TR11 5LG TELEPHONE: (0326) 250288

**M**

---

---

| | |
|---|---|
| **MELKSHAM** Wiltshire Map **03** ST96 | **MELLING** Lancashire Map **07** SD57 |

★★★❀♨74% **Beechfield House**

Beanacre SN12 7PU (1m N A350) ☎(0225)703700
FAX (0225) 790118

*Despite its location in attractive countryside, a Victorian manor house built of yellow Bath stone and surrounded by carefully tended gardens offers convenient access to major routes and cities. Reasonably spacious bedrooms, recently redecorated in individual style and tastefully furnished, are very well equipped, while a small restaurant with a calm, restful atmosphere and views over the fountain serves a range of enjoyable dishes based on fine fresh ingredients – some from the hotel's own gardens. Other public areas include an attractive dining room and a warm, cosy lounge where pre-dinner drinks and liqueurs are served.*

24⇨1🛏⅟in 8 bedrooms CTV in all bedrooms **T**
✖ (ex guide dogs) ✳ S10% sB⇨fr£90 dB⇨fr£99 (room only) 🄿

40P 🚗 ✿ CFA ⌒ (heated) ♪ (grass) croquet *xmas*
V ♥ ᗱ ⅟ ✳ S10% Lunch £14.50-£17.50&alc
Credit Cards ①②③⑤ ⓔ

**See advertisement under BATH**

★★64% *Shaw Country*

Bath Rd, Shaw SN12 8EF (2m NW A365) ☎(0225)702836 & 790321 FAX (0225) 790275

*On the A635 in the village of Shaw, 2 miles northwest of the town, this attractive old building with its own grounds has been converted into a comfortable small hotel by its hospitable resident owners, providing well equipped bedrooms with simple, pretty décor and attractively furnished public areas.*

10⇨🅕(1fb)1🛏 CTV in all bedrooms ® **T** ✖
25P ✿ ⌒ (heated) ♨
♈ English & French **V** ♥ ᗱ Last dinner 9pm
Credit Cards ①②③

★★63% **Conigre Farm**

Semington Rd SN12 6BX ☎(0225)702229

*This 17th-century Cotswold stone farmhouse on the busy main road into the town centre has comfortable, simply decorated and well equipped bedrooms, some of them in a converted stable block a few yards from the main hotel. Public areas include a spacious conservatory lounge and a restaurant serving traditional English dishes.*

4rm(1⇨)Annexe5⇨🅕1🛏 CTV in all bedrooms ® **T** ✖
sB&B£29-£33 sB&B⇨🅕£36-£44 dB&B£48-£52
dB&B⇨🅕£54-£60 🄿

《 12P 2🚘 🚗 ✿
V ♥ ᗱ Lunch £3.95-£11.95&alc Dinner £8.95-£11.95&alc Last dinner 10pm
Credit Cards ①③

★★58% **Kings Arms**

Market Place SN12 6EX ☎(0225)707272 FAX (0225) 702085

*Built in attractive Bath stone and retaining its old world charm, this coaching inn at one end of the High Street provides ample car parking space at its rear. Bedrooms vary in size and standard, ranging from fairly spacious en suite rooms to smaller ones with shared facilities, but all are well equipped, while public areas include a spacious dining room, busy bar and attractive lounge area.*

14rm(10⇨🅕) CTV in all bedrooms ® **T** sB&B£32
sB&B⇨🅕£45 dB&B⇨🅕£55 🄿
40P CFA
V ♥ ᗱ Lunch fr£10 High tea fr£5.50 Dinner fr£11.50 Last dinner 9pm
Credit Cards ①②③⑤ ⓔ

For key to symbols in English see the bookmark.

★★61% **Melling Hall**

LA6 2RA (Exec Hotel) ☎Hornby(05242)21298

*A converted 17th-century manor house situated on the A683 at the northern edge of the village, with views over the Lune Valley. The sizeable bedrooms have been attractively redecorated and there are cosy bars, a traditional dining room and versatile function room. Friendly local staff provide willing service.*

14rm(7⇨3🅕)(1fb) CTV in all bedrooms ® **T** ✳ sB&B£26-£38
sB&B⇨🅕£35-£40 dB&B£40 dB&B⇨🅕£50-£52 🄿
40P ✿ *xmas*
♈ English & French ♥ ✳ Sunday Lunch fr£7.50 Dinner £7-£10&alc Last dinner 9.30pm
Credit Cards ①②③⑤ ⓔ

**MELROSE** Borders *Roxburghshire* Map **12** NT53

★★67% **Burt's**

The Square TD6 9PN ☎(089682)2285 FAX (089682) 2870

*Overlooking the market square, this early 18th-century converted town centre house under owner management now offers comfortable modern accommodation. Bedrooms vary in size but all are well equipped and public areas include a pleasant restaurant and popular lounge bar.*

21⇨🅕 CTV in all bedrooms ® **T** sB&B⇨🅕£39-£41
dB&B⇨🅕£64-£68 🄿
40P 🚗 ✿ snooker shooting game
♈ English & French **V** ♥ ✳ Lunch £14-£16 Dinner £18.50-£22&alc Last dinner 9.30pm
Credit Cards ①②③⑤

★★55% **George & Abbotsford**

TD6 9PD (Consort) ☎(089682)2308 FAX (089682) 3363

*A neat town-centre hotel with comfortable, traditionally styled bedrooms; interesting good value menus and friendly service.*

31⇨🅕(3fb)1🛏 CTV in all bedrooms ® **T** sB&B⇨🅕£39.50-£45 dB&B⇨🅕£64-£84 🄿
CTV 150P 1🚘 ✿ CFA *xmas*
♈ British & French **V** ♥ ✳ Lunch £2.50-£7 High tea £5.50 Dinner £13.50-£16&alc Last dinner 9.30pm
Credit Cards ①②③⑤ ⓔ

**MELTON MOWBRAY** Leicestershire Map **08** SK71

★★★

★★★❀♨
**STAPLEFORD PARK**

Stapleford LE14 2EF (Small
Luxury Hotels)
☎Wymondham
(057284)522
FAX (057284) 651

*This magnificent house dating back to the early 16th century, set in 500 acres of parkland and gardens laid out by Capability Brown, contains superb examples of several classical styles of architecture – not least the fine Edwardian stables. Genial host Bob Payton, a larger-than-life American, and his wife have lavished not only money but also devotion on the transformation of Stapleford Park into a luxury hotel; many of the well equipped quality bedrooms were individually styled by the world's best interior designers, whilst the tasteful décor and furnishings of spacious, relaxing public areas warmed by log fires are wholly sympathetic to the character of the building. Genuinely warm, caring service is attentive without being intrusive, and chef Rick Tramouto makes good use of the best fresh local produce in unusual and imaginative menus which combine American and European cuisine. Guests can enjoy a range of traditional country sports which include horse riding (with tuition if required), shooting and fishing; also available are croquet, tennis and miniature golf – and even ballooning can be arranged for the more adventurous.*

35⇌⇥1🛏 CTV in all bedrooms T dB&B⇌🌂£130-£290 Continental breakfast 🍽

Lift ℂ 120P 🚲 ✿ CFA ♪ (hard) ♪ ∪ mini golf croquet basketball shooting nc10yrs *xmas*

♀ American V ⚏ ⅔ ✳ Lunch £4.25-£16.50alc High tea fr£4.25alc Dinner £19.91&alc Last dinner 10.30pm

Credit Cards ①②③④⑤£

---

**★★★55% *Harboro'***

Burton St LE13 1AF (Forte Hotels) ☎(0664)60121

*Commercial hotel, which was formerly a coaching inn, situated on the A606.*

26⇌🌂(3fb)⅔in 5 bedrooms CTV in all bedrooms ®
✖ (ex guide dogs)
ℂ 40P
V ♁ ⚏ ⅔
Credit Cards ①②③

**★★62% *Sysonby Knoll***

Asfordby Rd LE13 0HP ☎(0664)63563 FAX (0664) 410364
Closed Xmas

*A much-extended house standing beside the A6006 about a mile from the town centre provides well equipped accommodation which is popular with tourists and business travellers alike; 6 bedrooms on the ground floor are particularly suitable for disabled guests. Pleasant gardens and grounds, which include a pitch and putt course and a swimming pool, stretch down to the River Eye.*

24rm(19⇌3🌂)Annexe1⇌(2fb)2🛏 CTV in all bedrooms ® T sB&Bfr£28.50 sB&B⇌🌂£33-£39.50 dB&B⇌🌂£42-£49 🍽 CTV 30P ✿ CFA ⌂

♀ English & French V ♁ Sunday Lunch fr£8alc Dinner £8.75-£9.50alc Last dinner 9pm

Credit Cards ①③

**See advertisement on page 505**

---

MELVICH Highland *Caithness* Map **14** NC86

**★★63% Melvich**

KW14 7YJ ☎(06413)206
RS 25 Dec & 1-2 Jan

*A relaxed, family-run hotel with a spectacular outlook over the estuary of the River Halladale to the Orkneys across the Pentland Firth. Public rooms are comfortable and traditionally appointed, and compact bedrooms provide the expected comforts and facilities.*

14🌂 CTV in all bedrooms ® ✳ sB&B🌂£28.50-£33 dB&B🌂£52-£58 🍽

10P 🚲 ✿ CFA ♪ snooker deer stalking bird watching ⌖
♀ Scottish, English, French & Italian V ♁ ⚏ ⅔ ✳ Bar Lunch £2-£10alc High tea £4.75-£8alc Dinner £14.50-£19alc Last dinner 8pm

Credit Cards ①②③£

**See advertisement under THURSO**

---

MENAI BRIDGE Gwynedd Map **06** SH57

**★★65% *Anglesey Arms***

LL59 5EA ☎(0248)712305

*Although company owned, this hotel is personally run in a friendly and informal manner by the resident managers. It is situated at the Anglesey end of the Telford Suspension Bridge and has attractive gardens to the rear. Following recent extensive refurbishment, all bedrooms and public areas have been redecorated to a high*

→

M

*standard, and a small conference or function room has been provided.*
17rm(10➪6♠) CTV in all bedrooms ®
CTV 25P ✿
V ♡ ⚖ Last dinner 10pm
Credit Cards ① ③

### ★★64% **Gazelle**
Glyn Garth LL59 5PD (2m NE A545) (Frederic Robinson)
☎(0248)713364 FAX (0248) 713167
*Pleasant and well furnished, commanding views of the Snowdonia mountains across the estuary, the hotel serves well cooked meals of a good standard in its restaurant and bars.*
9rm(4➪1♠) CTV in all bedrooms ® T ✗ (ex guide dogs) ✱
sB&B£28.50-£33 sB&B➪♠£33 dB&B£46.50 dB&B➪♠£62
40P ✿ sailing sea fishing watersports
♡ ⚖ ✱ Lunch £7.95-£8.95&alc
Credit Cards ① ③

---

**MERE** Wiltshire Map **03** ST83

### ★★59% **Old Ship**
Castle St BA12 6JE ☎(0747)860258 FAX (0747) 860501
*Dating from 1645, this attractive building of architectural interest has cosy public areas with wood panelling, high ceilings and open fires. Bedrooms, some in a modern annexe, are comfortable, simply furnished and well equipped and the first-floor restaurant with beams and a sloping roof serves some interesting dishes.*
14rm(6➪)Annexe10➪♠(3fb)2🛏 CTV in all bedrooms ® ✱
S% sB&B£35 sB&B➪♠£39 dB&B£47 dB&B➪♠£52 🍽
50P CFA
♈ English & French V ✱ Lunch £15-£21alc Dinner £15-£21alc
Last dinner 9.30pm
Credit Cards ① ③ ④

---

**MERIDEN** West Midlands Map **04** SP28

### ★★★70% **Forest of Arden Hotel, Golf & Country Club**
Maxstoke Ln CV7 7HR ☎(0676)22335 Telex no 312604
FAX (0676) 23711
*An impressive hotel and leisure development situated off the A45 and convenient for the Midlands motorway network. Rooms are comfortable and well equipped and most have superb views. There is an excellent range of both indoor and outdoor leisure facilities, including a championship golf course, swimming pool, squash courts and health and fitness studios. For eating, choose between the formal restaurant or the all-day poolside grill.*
152➪♠(4fb)⚥in 29 bedrooms CTV in all bedrooms ® T
✗ (ex guide dogs) ✱ S% sB&B➪♠£105-£115
dB&B➪♠£120-£135 🍽
Lift ⚓ 400P CFA 🏊 (heated) ▶ 18 ♣ (hard) ♪ squash snooker
sauna solarium gymnasium dance studio steam room beauty
salon *xmas*
V ♡ ⚖ ✱ Lunch fr£17&alc Dinner fr£17&alc Last dinner
9.45pm
Credit Cards ① ② ③ ⑤ ⑥

### ★★★68% **Manor**
CV7 7NH (De Vere) ☎(0676)22735 FAX (0676) 22186
*This very comfortable main road hotel close to the A45 and motorway network features generally spacious bedrooms which have been refurbished to a good standard, equipped with comfortable seating and a range of modern facilities. Attractive public areas include the Regency Restaurant, popular with both residents and non-residents, and the Triumph Bar which is open all day for light refreshments. A friendly management and staff provide hospitable, caring service throughout.*
74➪♠⚥in 11 bedrooms CTV in all bedrooms ® T
sB&B➪♠£85 dB&B➪♠£102 🍽
⚓ 250P ✿ CFA

♈ English & French V ♡ ⚖ ✱ Lunch £11.65-£15.25&alc
Dinner £15.25&alc Last dinner 10pm
Credit Cards ① ② ③ ⑤

---

**MERTHYR TYDFIL** Mid Glamorgan Map **03** SO00

See also **Nant-Ddu**

### ★★★64% **Baverstock**
The Heads Of Valley Rd CF44 0LX
☎(0685)6221 due to change t o 386221 FAX (0685) 723670
*A busy commercial hotel on the A465 Head of the Valleys road north of the town features well equipped bedrooms, spaciously comfortable public areas and extensive meeting/function facilities; a wide choice of food is available, and guests have the use of a small snooker room.*
53➪♠(3fb) CTV in all bedrooms ® T ✗ (ex guide dogs)
sB&B➪♠£49.50-£62 dB&B➪♠£61.50-£75 🍽
⚓ 300P ✿ CFA pool table *xmas*
♈ European V ♡ ⚖ Lunch fr£7.50&alc High tea fr£2.25
Dinner fr£13.50&alc Last dinner 10pm
Credit Cards ① ② ③ ⑤

### ★★67% **Tregenna**
Park Ter CF47 8RF ☎(0685)723627 & 82055
FAX (0685) 721951
*Friendly staff offer a warm welcome to this popular hotel which stands only a short walk from the town centre. Bedrooms are modern and comfortable, and there is an attractive à la carte restaurant – though a wide range of food is also served in the relaxing lounge and bar.*
14➪♠Annexe7➪♠(6fb)1🛏 CTV in all bedrooms ® T
sB&B➪♠£36-£39 dB&B➪♠£46-£50 🍽
⚓ CTV 26P CFA *xmas*
♈ English, Indian, Italian & Philippino V ♡ ⚖ Lunch
£7.50&alc High tea £5 Dinner £7.50&alc Last dinner 10pm
Credit Cards ① ② ③ ⑥

---

**MEVAGISSEY** Cornwall & Isles of Scilly Map **02** SX04

### ★★58% **Spa**
Polkirt PL26 6UY ☎(0726)842244
*Bedrooms are furnished in modern style, some having their own patio, at this family-run, terraced hotel which occupies a secluded hilltop position. Public areas include a popular bar complete with pool table, a small, cosy lounge and a dining room where wholesome home-cooked meals (including cream teas) are served. Guests' needs receive personal attention from the resident partner-proprietors.*
12rm(11➪♠)(4fb) CTV in all bedrooms ® ✱
sB&B➪♠£21.50-£25.50 dB&B➪♠£43-£51
CTV 14P ⚬ ✿ putting green pool table *xmas*
♈ English & French V ♡ ⚖ ✱ Bar Lunch £1.10-£3.90 Dinner
£11-£12 Last dinner 8pm
Credit Cards ① ② ③

### ★69% **Sharksfin**
The Quay PL26 6QU ☎(0726)843241
Closed Nov-Mar
*Housed in a dockside building originally connected with the fishing trade, this friendly and welcoming hotel offers harbour views from the characterful bar with its packing case counter, as well as from a popular candelit restaurant, the comfortable first-floor lounge and some bedrooms. Almost all rooms are modernised and well equipped, though several are compact. Parking can be difficult, so it is advisable to ask the hotel for advice.*
11rm(4♠)(2fb) CTV in all bedrooms ® T ✗ sB&B£17-£36
dB&B£31-£51 dB&B♠£42-£51
✗ ⚬
V ♡ ⚖ Lunch £3.60-£15.50alc Dinner £4.80-£25alc Last
dinner 9.50pm
Credit Cards ① ② ③ ⑤ ⑥

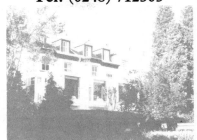

M

505

---

## MICKLEOVER Derbyshire Map **08** SK33

○**Mickleover Court**
Etwall Rd CE3 5XX ☎Derby(0332)521234
Due to have opened Oct 1991
80⇌🏠♠

---

## MICKLETON Gloucestershire Map **04** SP14

★★★60% **Three Ways**
GL55 6SB ☎(0386)438429 Telex no 337242 FAX (0386) 438118
*A traditional hotel, at the heart of a charming village, Three Ways is run by the Turner family, who are attentive and friendly hosts. Rooms have character as well as comfort, and the intimate dining room offers a good range of dishes. The selection of traditional English puddings is highly acclaimed.*
40⇌♠(5fb) CTV in all bedrooms ® ✳ sB&B⇌♠£40-£50
dB&B⇌♠£63-£73 🅿
《 37P ✿ CFA ♫ *xmas*
♀ English & Continental V ♥ ⚗ ✳ Sunday Lunch £10-£11.75
Dinner £15.50-£16.50 Last dinner 9pm
Credit Cards ①②③⑤€

---

## MIDDLEHAM North Yorkshire Map **07** SE18

★★✿72% **Millers House**
Market Place DL8 4NR ☎Wensleydale(0969)22630
Closed Jan
*A nicely proportioned Georgian house at the head of the market place. Bedrooms and public areas are attractively decorated and fitted with comfort in mind. Service is equally comfortable, under the supervision of resident proprietors Judith and Crossley Sunderland. While Crossley takes care of the wine list and stocks, Judith creates the imaginative dinners. Local produce is used wherever possible, including home-grown herbs and vegetables. The daily changing table d'hôte dinner menu is recommended for quality and value.*
7rm(6⇌3)1🛁 CTV in all bedrooms ® T ✗ (ex guide dogs)
sB&B£32.50 dB&B⇌£65-£75 🅿
8P ♨ nc10yrs *xmas*
♀ English & French V ♥ ⚖ Dinner fr£18.50 Last dinner 8.30pm
Credit Cards ①③

---

## MIDDLESBROUGH Cleveland Map **08** NZ42 ◉

★★★50% *Marton Way Toby*
Marton Rd TS4 3BS (Toby) ☎(0642)817651 Telex no 587783
Closed 25 Dec
*Situated in a residential area off the A172 south of the town, this modern hotel has well equipped utilitarian bedrooms set on two levels around a car park courtyard. Light and airy public areas in a separate block include a carvery restaurant, popular locally though it could be improved.*
53⇌(4fb)⚡in 18 bedrooms CTV in all bedrooms ®
《 500P
♀ British & Continental V ♥ ⚖
Credit Cards ①②③⑤

★★62% **Highfield**
358 Marton Rd TS4 2PA (Chef & Brewer) ☎(0642)817638
FAX (0642) 821219
*Set in its own grounds on the A1721, in a quiet residential area south of the town centre, the hotel offers comfortable, well equipped bedrooms and a large, popular restaurant.*
23⇌♠2🛁 CTV in all bedrooms ® T ✗ (ex guide dogs)
sB&B⇌♠£43-£49 dB&B⇌♠£56 🅿
《 CTV 100P 4🚗 CFA
♀ International V ♥ ⚖ ⚡ Bar Lunch £2.95-£5.50alc
Credit Cards ①②③⑤

★63% **The Grey House**
79 Cambridge Rd, Linthorpe TS5 5NL
☎Middlesborough(0642)817485
*Set within its own rose gardens, this handsome Victorian house offers comfortable traditional bedrooms and a most inviting spacious lounge. Service from the resident proprietors is friendly and informal.*
9⇌♠(1fb) CTV in all bedrooms ® ✳ sB&B⇌♠£30-£35
dB&B⇌♠fr£44
10P ♨ nc

---

## MIDDLETON-IN-TEESDALE Co Durham Map **12** NY92

★★63% **Teesdale**
Market Place DL12 0QG ☎Teesdale(0833)40264
*A family-run hotel in the centre of town, with attractively decorated bedrooms and a cosy upstairs residents' lounge. Ideally positioned for touring the area.*
13rm(7⇌3♠)(1fb)1🛁 CTV in all bedrooms T sB&B⇌♠fr£36
dB&B⇌♠fr£60 🅿
CTV 14P ♨ *xmas*
♀ English, French, German & Italian ♥ ⚖ ✳ Sunday Lunch fr£9.95 Dinner fr£15.95 Last dinner 8.30pm
Credit Cards ①③€

---

## MIDDLETON STONEY Oxfordshire Map **04** SP52

★★65% **Jersey Arms**
OX6 8SE ☎(086989)234 & 505 FAX (086989) 565
*A charming Cotswold inn with a warm, friendly atmosphere, privately owned and managed, providing spacious, comfortable and well equipped accommodation. The character rooms in the main building are supplemented by some in more modern style looking out onto the courtyard. Public areas are cosy, and the smart restaurant offers a carefully balanced menu of dishes skilfully prepared from fresh ingredients, accompanied by a short but reasonably priced list containing some quality wines.*
6⇌Annexe10⇌(3fb)1🛁 CTV in all bedrooms T
✗ (ex guide dogs) sB&B⇌£49.50-£70 dB&B⇌£59.50-£90 🅿
55P ♨ ✿
♀ English & French V ♥ ⚖ Lunch £15-£24alc Dinner £17.50-£27.50alc Last dinner 9.30pm
Credit Cards ①②③⑤

---

## MIDDLE WALLOP Hampshire Map **04** SU23

★★✿68% **Fifehead Manor**
SO20 8EG ☎Andover(0264)781565 FAX (0264) 781400
Closed 2wks Xmas
(Rosette awarded for dinner only)
*This small friendly manor house on the fringe of the village has spacious elegant bedrooms in the original building with single rooms in an annexe. The candlelit restaurant serves skilfully prepared dishes featuring fresh produce and game in season, complemented by a well balanced wine list.*
10⇌ CTV in all bedrooms T ✳ sB&B⇌£50 dB&B⇌£80-£100
🅿
50P ♨ ✿ CFA croquet
♀ English & French V ♥ ⚖ ✳ Lunch £18-£20&alc Dinner £24-£26&alc Last dinner 9.30pm
Credit Cards ①②③⑤

---

## MIDHURST West Sussex Map **04** SU82

See also Trotton
★★★66% **Spread Eagle**
South St GU29 9NH (Best Western) ☎(0730)816911
Telex no 86853 FAX (0730) 815668
*This hotel began life as a tavern back in 1430 and has been well documented as a famous coaching inn ever since. Individually decorated bedrooms vary in shape and size, log fires burn in the*

*cosy lounge bar during winter months, and individual Christmas puddings hang from the beams of the charming candlelit restaurant! Bar lunches can be enjoyed in the basement Coal Hole Bar, and professional service is provided throughout by staff who are genuinely eager to please.*

37⇩Annexe4♠5🛏✍in 4 bedrooms CTV in all bedrooms **T** S10% sB&B⇩♠£70-£95 dB&B⇩♠£80-£185 ▤

( 80P ✿ CFA *xmas*

♀ English & French ✿ ⬭ S10% Lunch £13.50-£26.50 Dinner £26.50-£32 Last dinner 9.30pm

Credit Cards 1 2 3 5 £

---

MIDSOMER NORTON Somerset Map **03** ST65

★★★ 68% **Centurion**

Charlton Ln BA3 4BD ☎(0761)417711 FAX (0761) 418357

*A recently extended hotel, run by a very pleasant family, stands adjacent to the Fosseway Country Club with its golf course, bowling green and other leisure amenities. It now provides well equipped bedrooms of a high quality, a very spacious and comfortable lounge overlooking the golf centre, and good conference facilities.*

44⇩♠(2fb) CTV in all bedrooms ® **T** ✖ (ex guide dogs) ✳ sB&B⇩♠£45-£57 dB&B⇩♠£55-£77 ▤

( 100P ✿ CFA ⬛ (heated) ▶ 9 squash snooker sauna bowling green sports field

♀ English & Continental **V** ✿ ⬭ ✳ Lunch £7.90-£8.90 Dinner fr£15.50&alc Last dinner 10pm

Credit Cards 1 2 3 5

---

MILDENHALL Suffolk Map **05** TL77

★★★ ⊛64% **Riverside**

Mill St IP28 7DP (Best Western) ☎(0638)717274 FAX (0638) 715997

*Set in grounds that run down to the River Lark at the rear, this town-centre hotel on the A1101 features pleasant bars with a friendly and relaxed atmosphere that have attracted a well established local trade. A small lounge in drawing room style offers quiet and comfort in which to relax, while a restaurant overlooking the river provides an interesting à la carte menu of dishes – skilfully prepared to traditional methods – supplemented by the chef's speciality list, which is also available in the bar. Bedrooms vary in size and shape but are generally well furnished and equipped.*

21rm(12⇩5♠)(4fb)1🛏 CTV in all bedrooms ® **T** sB&B⇩♠£45-£49 dB&B⇩♠£66-£72 ▤

Lift 45P ✿ CFA ⬥ private boats croquet *xmas*

♀ International **V** ✿ ⬭ ✳ Lunch £10-£14&alc High tea £6 Dinner £10-£14&alc Last dinner 9pm

Credit Cards 1 2 3 5

★★★ 64% **Smoke House Inn**

Beck Row IP28 8DH ☎(0638)713223 FAX (0638) 712202

*Located on the A1101 in the village of Beck Row, 3 miles from the centre of the town and 4 miles from the Barton Mills roundabout on the A11, this single-storey brick and pantile complex is based on a main building dating back to the 16th-century; its proximity to RAF Mildenhall makes it popular with American visitors, and services are tailored to their needs as well as those of the ordinary commercial user. The simply furnished but well maintained accommodation, reached along its somewhat lengthy corridor offers good facilities, and friendly staff are directed by a professional management team.*

105⇩Annexe10⇩(20fb) CTV in all bedrooms ® **T** ✖ (ex guide dogs) S10% sB&B⇩♠£66-£70 dB&B⇩♠£77-£85 ▤

( CTV 200P ✿ CFA ♪ (hard) snooker ♫ *xmas*

**V** ✿ ⬭ Lunch £9-£12 Dinner £12.50-£20&alc Last dinner 10pm

Credit Cards 1 2 3 5 £

---

★★ 62% **Bell**

High St IP28 7EA ☎(0638)717272 FAX (0638) 717057

*A soundly managed, ivy-clad inn located on the High Street with a car park to its rear (accessed via the Shopping Centre one-way system) attracts both commercial and leisure users with its comfortable, well equipped bedrooms and the friendly atmosphere of the bar and restaurant.*

17rm(14⇩2♠)(2fb) CTV in all bedrooms ® **T** ✳ sB&Bfr£27.50 sB&B⇩♠fr£40 dB&B⇩♠fr£55

24P CFA ♫ *xmas*

♀ English & Continental **V** ✿ ✳ Lunch £9.25 Dinner £9.25&alc Last dinner 9pm

Credit Cards 1 2 3 5 £

---

MILFORD HAVEN Dyfed Map **02** SM90

★★ 60% **Lord Nelson**

Hamilton Ter SA73 3AL ☎(0646)695341 FAX (0646) 694026

*This friendly commercial hotel overlooking the harbour provides well equipped bedrooms, a large comfortable bar with local character and a good choice of food.*

32⇩♠(1fb)1🛏✍in 2 bedrooms CTV in all bedrooms ® **T** ✖ (ex guide dogs) sB&B⇩♠fr£45 dB&B⇩♠fr£70 ▤

( CTV 26P ✿ CFA

♀ English, French & Italian **V** ✿ ✳ Lunch £8.50-£16 Dinner £11.60-£23 Last dinner 9.30pm

Credit Cards 1 2 3 5 £

**See advertisement on page 509**

---

Restaurants and hotel restaurants with rosettes have their names and addresses tinted pink in the directory.

**M**

## MILFORD ON SEA Hampshire Map **04** SZ29

**★★★72% South Lawn**

Lymington Rd SO41 0RF ☎Lymington(0590)643911
FAX (0590) 644820
Closed 20 Dec-12 Jan

*This attractive former dower house has been run as an hotel for the past 20 years by owners who believe personal service to be of paramount importance. Well maintained bedrooms in a variety of styles are complemented by public areas which include a comfortable lounge opening onto a gravelled terrace and a dining room offering value-for-money menus with a particularly noteworthy sweet trolley and a well chosen wine list specialising in German wines.*

24⇌↱(2fb) CTV in all bedrooms **T** ✱ sB&B⇌↱fr£49 dB&B⇌↱fr£86 ⊟
50P ✿ nc7yrs
International **V** Sunday Lunch fr£10 Dinner fr£14.50 Last dinner 8.30pm
Credit Cards [1] [3]

**See advertisement under LYMINGTON**

**★★★61% *Westover Hall***

Park Ln SO41 0PT ☎Lymington(0590)643044
FAX (0590) 644490

*Overlooking the foreshore and dating from 1897, this Victorian country house features an impressive panelled foyer with gallery; bedrooms are individually furnished and decorated, and the restaurant augments a short fixed-price menu by an imaginative à la carte selection. The hotel is personally run by its Swiss owners with a team of young, mainly French, staff.*

13⇌ CTV in all bedrooms ® **T**
50P ✿
English & French **V**
Credit Cards [1] [2] [3] [5]

**✿✿ ✕✕ Rocher's**

69/71 High St SO41 0QG ☎Lymington(0590)642340

*A small restaurant in cottage style offers a short but frequently changed à la carte menu in the warm and friendly atmosphere of its attractive pink dining room; chef Alain Rocher (formerly of the Chewton Glen Hotel, New Milton) favours the modern French style of cooking, though with some innovative touches. Dishes are carefully and honestly prepared, using only good fresh produce, and sauces are well made. There is a shortage of half bottles on the mainly French wine list, but staff are particularly pleasant and helpful.*

Closed Tue & 4 wks annually Lunch not served Mon-Sat
French 30 seats ✱ Sunday Lunch fr£11.50 Dinner £15-£20alc Last dinner 9.45pm nc10/14yrs
Credit Cards [2] [4]

## MILNGAVIE Strathclyde *Dunbartonshire* Map **11** NS57

**★★★65% Black Bull Thistle**

Main St G62 6BH (Mount Charlotte (TS)) ☎041-956 2291
Telex no 778323 FAX 041-956 1896

*This old village inn has been extended to create a business and function hotel that retains its period character with beamed public rooms hung with tapestries while offering bedrooms with all modern facilities. Service is friendly and attentive.*

27⇌↱(2fb) CTV in all bedrooms ® **T** (room only) ⊟
( 120P
International
Credit Cards [1] [2] [3] [4] [5]

Shell filling station, open 7am–11pm (some 24 hours) throughout the year with leaded and unleaded petrol, and diesel.

## MILTON Dyfed Map **02** SN00

**★★63% Milton Manor**

SA70 8PG (Exec Hotel) ☎Carew(0646)651398
FAX (0646) 651897

*This early 15th-century manor house stands in 6 acres of woodland just off the A477 Carmarthen-Pembroke road. Bedrooms are all modern and well equipped, while public areas include a restaurant offering a good choice of dishes on table d'hôte menus with additional à la carte options.*

19⇌↱(1fb) CTV in all bedrooms ® **T** sB&B⇌↱fr£36 dB&B⇌↱fr£48 ⊟
40P 3 ✿ CFA putting *xmas*
International **V** S% Lunch fr£12.50 Dinner fr£12.50&alc Last dinner 9.30pm
Credit Cards [1] [3]

## MILTON COMMON Oxfordshire Map **04** SP60

**★★★67% Belfry**

Brimpton Grange OX9 2JW (Inter-Hotels)
☎Great Milton(0844)279381 FAX (0844) 279624
Closed 25-30 Dec

*Peacefully set in extensive grounds and within easy access of the M40, this half-timbered extended Victorian country house offers spacious well equipped bedrooms, smart and comfortable public areas and extensive conference and leisure facilities. The restaurant serves enjoyable dishes and staff are efficient and friendly throughout.*

77⇌↱ CTV in all bedrooms ® **T** sB&B⇌↱£70-£87.50 dB&B⇌↱£85-£105 ⊟
( 200P ✿ CFA (heated) sauna solarium gymnasium
English & Continental **V** Lunch fr£14.50&alc Dinner £17.50-£19.50&alc Last dinner 9.30pm
Credit Cards [1] [2] [3] [5]

**See advertisement under OXFORD**

## MILTON, GREAT Oxfordshire Map **04** SP60

**★★★**

★★★✿✿✿✿✿

**LE MANOIR AUX QUAT' SAISONS**

OX9 7PD (Relais et Châteaux) ☎Great Milton (0844)278881
Telex no 837552
FAX (0844) 278847
Closed 23 Dec-16 Jan

*Raymond Blanc's 15th-century manor house is the perfect setting for the luxurious hotel it has now become, ably managed by Nicholas Dickinson who has gathered round him an excellent team to welcome guests and attend to their comfort. The bedrooms, individually and imaginatively decorated, offer every comfort for the guests who are, inevitably, drawn here by the reputation of the restaurant, one of the very best that this country can offer. Head Chef Clive Fretwell and his brigade produce consistently well created dishes, cooked with the utmost attention to detail. At lunchtimes there is a very popular Menu du Jour, and in the evenings the carte and the Menu Gourmand offer them a fine showcase for their talents. A much copied speciality is the crab soufflé encased in a fillet of sole and served with a delicate ginger and coriander sauce, perfectly cooked on the occasion of our visit. Raymond Blanc, as a keen lover of gardening as of cooking, has not neglected his kitchen garden, which now boasts 9 varieties of lettuce, 50 different vegetables and over 60 herbs. Despite some criticism of the timing of meals, Le*

*Manoir makes dining out an experience that, if not absolute
perfection, comes very near to it.*
19➪↾4⊞ CTV in all bedrooms T ✖ S% dB➪↾£165-
£275 (room only) ⊟
《 60P ❊ ≏ (heated) ♪ (hard) croquet
♀ French V ✖ ✱ S% Lunch £26.50-£29.50&alc High tea
fr£12.50 Dinner fr£59.50&alc Last dinner 10.30pm
Credit Cards ①②③④⑤

---

MILTON KEYNES Buckinghamshire Map **04** SP83 ◉

See also Newport Pagnell & Woburn
★★★★62% **Forte Crest**
500 Saxon Gate West MK9 2HQ (Forte Hotels) ☎(0908)667722
Telex no 826842 FAX (0908) 674714
*A modern hotel within the Business Exchange in central Milton
Keynes. The Atrium Restaurant forms the focal point with glass
fronted lifts to all 4 floors of bedrooms. The Club Room
Restaurant offers a choice of table d'hôte, à la carte, or Chef
Ronald Clarke's seasonal speciality menus. The Milton Bar and
Lounge provides a comfortable area, and the health and fitness
club in the basement has a good sized pool. Bedrooms are well
equipped, though twin rooms appear compact.*
163➪(4fb)✂in 50 bedrooms CTV in all bedrooms ℞ T
Lift 《 ⊞ 80P ⊠ (heated) sauna solarium gymnasium health &
fitness centre
V ✆ ⚏ ✂ Last dinner 10.30pm
Credit Cards ①②③⑤

★★★63% **Friendly**
Monks Way, Two Mile Ash MK8 8LY (junct A5/A422)
(Consort) ☎(0908)561666 Telex no 826152 FAX (0908) 568303
*A modern lodge-style operation close to major road network offers
well appointed accommodation; public areas, though limited,
include a carvery restaurant with some à la carte choices.*
88➪(20fb)2⊞✂in 20 bedrooms CTV in all bedrooms ℞ T
sB➪£53.25-£63.50 dB➪£70.50-£80.75 (room only) ⊟
《 CTV 76P ❊ CFA ⊠ (heated) sauna solarium gymnasium
♀ English & French V ✆ ⚏ ✂ Lunch fr£8.50 Dinner fr£12.75
Last dinner 10pm
Credit Cards ①②③⑤ ⓔ

○**Milton Keynes Hotel & Conference Centre**
Timbold Dr, Kents Hill MK7 6HL ☎(0908)694433
Open
147➪↾

---

MINEHEAD Somerset Map **03** SS94

★★★70% **Benares**
Northfield Rd TA24 5PT (Consort) ☎(0643)704911
Closed 6 Nov-21 Mar (ex Xmas)
*Quietly located in well tended gardens away from the bustle of the
town, the Benares is personally supervised by owners Peter
Maskrey and Ray Thomas and is particularly popular with visitors
to Exmoor. The hotel is comfortable, with recently refurbished
public areas and simply furnished bedrooms. An ample choice is
offered at dinner which comprises 5 courses and includes an
impressive array of delectable sweets. Breakfast is on a self-service
basis.*
19➪↾(3fb) CTV in all bedrooms ℞ T sB&B➪↾£35-£41
dB&B➪↾£65-£77.50 ⊟
20P 2ᘒ (£1.75) ⊞ ❊ ⚬ xmas
♀ English, French & Italian V ✆ ⚏ ✂ Bar Lunch £5-£15alc
Dinner £15.75 Last dinner 8.30pm
Credit Cards ①②③⑤

**See advertisement on page 511**

---

**★★★ 67% Northfield**
Northfield Rd TA24 5PU (Best Western) ☎(0643)705155
Telex no 42513 FAX (0643) 707715
*The Northfield is set in 2 acres of beautifully manicured gardens in a residential area a short walk from the seafront. Spacious public rooms are traditionally furnished. The dining room is in 2 sections, the Oak Room for non-smokers, and offers a typical table d'hôte menu with vegetarian choices. A lift is available to the 2 floors of simply furnished and comfortable bedrooms, many with sea views. The Dolphin Leisure Club includes a heated pool and mini gym.*
24⇌🚿(7fb) CTV in all bedrooms ® T sB&B⇌🚿fr£42 dB&B⇌🚿£74-£84 ₿
Lift 44P ⛟ ✲ (heated) gymnasium putting green steam room spa bath *xmas*
V ✲ ✲ ✲ ✲ Lunch fr£5 Dinner fr£12.95 Last dinner 8.30pm
Credit Cards 1 2 3 5 £

**★★ ✲ 72% Periton Park**
Middlecombe TA24 8SW ☎(0643)706885 FAX (0643) 702698
Closed Feb
*This Victorian country house with panoramic views over parkland and countryside to the distant coastline was taken over in 1990 by Richard and Angela Hunt who provide personal service. Bedrooms are spacious and attractive with particularly well equipped bathrooms, and the lounge roomy and comfortable with an open log fire. Food is a strong feature, with a seasonally changing menu using quality produce.*
8⇌🚿(1fb)✲in 1 bedroom CTV in all bedrooms ® T ✲ S% sB&B⇌🚿fr£57 dB&B⇌🚿fr£80 ₿
12P ⛟ ✲ U croquet nc12yrs *xmas*
✲ English & French V ✲ Dinner £15-£25alc Last dinner 9.30pm
Credit Cards 1 2 3

**★★ 61% Beaconwood**
Church Rd, North Hill TA24 5SB ☎(0643)702032
Closed Nov-Feb
*Peaceful, family-run hotel outside the town centre.*
16rm(13⇌🚿)(3fb) CTV in all bedrooms ® T sB&B£29.50-£35 sB&B⇌🚿£35-£40 dB&B£44-£55 dB&B⇌🚿£55-£60 ₿
( 25P ✲ ✲ (heated) ✲ (grass) ✲
V ✲ ✲ ✲ Bar Lunch £2.50-£5alc Dinner fr£12.50 Last dinner 8pm
Credit Cards 1 3 £

**★ 70% *Kingsway***
Ponsford Rd TA24 5DY ☎(0643)702313
Closed 7 Nov-21 Mar
*Resident proprietors Mr and Mrs Bodman provide a warm welcome and individual service at their small hotel, a level stroll from the seafront and High Street. There is an attractive lounge and light, airy bedrooms with comfortable beds and co-ordinated soft furnishings. Each has en suite facilities, colour TV and individually controlled heating. A limited choice menu is prepared from fresh local produce, and the cosy bar is well stocked.*
8⇌🚿(2fb) CTV in all bedrooms ®
CTV 8P ⛟ nc10yrs
✲ ✲ ✲

MINSTER LOVELL Oxfordshire Map **04** SP31

**★★★ ✲✲ 78% The Old Swan & Mill**
OX8 5RN ☎Witney(0993)774441 FAX (0993) 702002
*This 600-year-old inn has recently been completely refurbished to a very smart standard. The dining room, with its beams, wooden flooring, exposed stonework and open fires has much character and a cosy, friendly atmosphere. The young, enthusiastic Chef, Clive Dixon, has recently joined the professional and charming team of staff and his menus are proving very popular. His style is predominantly French and country styled. Dishes are imaginative yet simple, honest in flavour and unfussy in presentation. In addition to the à la carte menu, there are Cotswold luncheons, a 4-course table d'hôte and a 5-course Sunday lunch menu. Enjoyable dishes include a rich, smooth chicken liver parfait served with a small salad of mixed leaves and French beans, followed by a fillet of grey mullet with a soy and ginger dressing. Desserts are simple and very tasty. The good, varied wine list offers value for money.*
60⇌🚿(4fb)3✲ CTV in all bedrooms T ✲ sB&B⇌🚿£75-£115 dB&B⇌🚿£135-£165 ₿
( 60P ⛟ ✲ CFA ✲ (hard) ✲ croquet putting shooting table tennis *xmas*
V ✲ ✲ ✲ Lunch £7.50-£16.50&alc High tea £7.50 Dinner £25&alc Last dinner 10pm
Credit Cards 1 2 3 5 £

MISKIN Mid Glamorgan Map **03** ST08

**★★★ 69% Miskin Manor**
CF7 8ND ☎Pontyclun(0443)224204 FAX (0443) 237606
Closed 24-31 Dec
*An 18th-century manor set in 20 acres of attractive parkland, signposted from junction 34 of the M4, features bedrooms and public areas which are both particularly spacious and comfortable; the grounds contain timeshare apartments and a modern leisure centre.*
35⇌🚿2✲✲in 12 bedrooms CTV in all bedrooms T ✲ (ex guide dogs) ✲ sB⇌🚿fr£79 dB⇌🚿£99.50-£125 (room only) ₿
( 150P ⛟ ✲ CFA ✲ (heated) squash snooker sauna solarium gymnasium steam room badminton clay pigeon shoot
V ✲ ✲ ✲ ✲ S10% Lunch fr£17.50&alc Dinner fr£17.50&alc Last dinner 9.45pm
Credit Cards 1 2 3 5 £

**See advertisement under CARDIFF**

MOFFAT Dumfries & Galloway *Dumfriesshire* Map **11** NT00

See also Beattock

**★★★ 62% Moffat House**
High St DG10 9HL (Exec Hotel) ☎(0683)20039
FAX (0683) 21288
*A traditional family-run hotel featuring cosy bedrooms, inviting lounges and interesting menus both in the bar and restaurant.*
16⇌🚿Annexe4⇌🚿(3fb) CTV in all bedrooms ® T sB&B⇌🚿£37-£42 dB&B⇌🚿£60-£68 ₿
40P 2✲ ✲ CFA
✲ Scottish & French V ✲ ✲ Bar Lunch £2-£8alc
Credit Cards 1 2 3 5 £

**★★ ✲ 71% Beechwood Country House**
Harthope Place DG10 9RS ☎(0683)20210 FAX (0683) 20889
Closed Jan
*Surrounded by woodland, in an elevated position overlooking the town, this is a well run family hotel offering good standards of comfort and service. Interesting freshly cooked dishes are served in the pleasant restaurant. Bedrooms have attractive touches, and lounges are comfortable with welcoming log fires in winter.*
7⇌🚿(1fb) CTV in all bedrooms ® T sB&B⇌🚿£53.95-£60.40 dB&B⇌🚿£88.16-£98.50 (incl dinner) ₿
15P ⛟ ✲ *xmas*
✲ English & French V ✲ ✲ ✲ Sunday Lunch £11&alc Dinner £17.50 Last dinner 9pm
Credit Cards 1 2 3

**★★ 70% The Star**
44 High St DG10 9EF ☎(0683)20156
*Managed by the friendly owners, Timothy and Allison Leighfield, this comfortable hotel offers very good value menus throughout the day and evening. Lounge accommodation is somewhat limited, possibly due to its reputation as the narrowest hotel in Great Britain.*
8⇌🚿(1fb) CTV in all bedrooms ® T ✲ sB&B⇌🚿£32-£36 dB&B⇌🚿£42-£48 ₿
✲

V ♥ ♨ ⅍ ✳ Lunch £3.50-£8&alc High tea £5.50 Dinner £3.50-£8.50 Last dinner 9pm
Credit Cards ①③

★❀77% **Well View**
Ballplay Rd DG10 9JU ☎(0683)20184
*An attractive house standing within its own grounds overlooking the town, and offering comfortable bedrooms, inviting lounges and friendly, courteous service. The excellent 5-course dinners are the highlight of a stay here, the interesting home cooked dishes including some tempting puddings.*
7rm(5⇨🛏)(1fb)1⌻⅍in 2 bedrooms CTV in all bedrooms ®
sB&B⇨🛏£28-£38 dB&B⇨🛏£44-£74 🍴
8P ⌻ ❄ *xmas*
♥ Scottish & French ♥ ♨ ⅍ ✳ Lunch £7-£8 Dinner £13-£16
Last dinner 8.15pm
Credit Cards ①③£

---

MOLD Clwyd Map **07** SJ26

See also **Northop Hall**
★★63% **Bryn Awel**
Denbigh Rd CH7 1BL ☎(0352)758622 FAX (0352) 758625
*A privately owned hotel which has recently been refurbished, provides well equipped modern accommodation. Situated on the A541 on the NW edge of town.*
7⇨🛏Annexe10⇨🛏1⌻⅍in 5 bedrooms CTV in all bedrooms
® T sB&B⇨🛏£32 dB&B⇨🛏£45-£50 🍴
40P 4⌻ ❄ CFA ♨
♥ English & Continental V ♥ ♨ Lunch £9.95&alc Dinner £9.95&alc Last dinner 9.30pm
Credit Cards ①②③£

**M**

MONIAIVE Dumfries & Galloway *Dumfriesshire* Map **11** NX79

★★64% **Woodlea**
DG3 4EN ☎(08482)209
Closed Nov-mid Feb
*A complete family holiday is offered at this hotel, with a multitude of outdoor and indoor activities, which are organised by the friendly proprietor and his young staff.*
12rm(10⇨)(7fb) CTV in all bedrooms ® T ✱ sB&B⇨fr£33.57 dB&B⇨fr£67.14 (incl dinner) 🏟
CTV 20P ❄ ▢ (heated) ♪ (hard) sauna solarium pony riding croquet putting games room ♨
V ✧ ⚌ ✱ Bar Lunch fr50palc Dinner fr£13 Last dinner 8.30pm

MONK FRYSTON North Yorkshire Map **08** SE52

★★★⚑68% **Monk Fryston Hall**
LS25 5DU ☎South Milford(0977)682369 Telex no 556634 FAX (0977) 683544
*This historic manor house is situated in attractive and extensive grounds off the A63, close to the A1. There is a great wealth of charm and character in the oak panelled lounge and bar, where open fires burn in the cooler months. Bedrooms are located in a modern wing and in the original house. All are well equipped and comfortable, and although sizes may vary, on the whole most are attractive and comfortable. The young staff are friendly and efficient.*
29⇨🕭(2fb)1🛏 CTV in all bedrooms ® T sB&B⇨🕭£60-£80 dB&B⇨🕭£89-£100 🏟
⟨ 60P ♨ ❄ *xmas*
✧ ✔ Lunch £12.50-£14.50&alc Dinner £18-£21&alc Last dinner 9.30pm
Credit Cards ⑴ ⑵ ⑶

MONMOUTH Gwent Map **03** SO51

★★★61% **Kings Head**
Agincourt Square NP5 3DY ☎(0600)712177 FAX (0600) 713545
*This 17th-century coaching inn at the centre of the historic town offers accommodation in bedrooms which are well equipped with modern facilities although a little dated in style. Public areas include a range of function/conference amenities as well as a cosy bar with log fire and a cocktail bar, staff are friendly and helpful, and a large choice of food is available.*
29rm(27⇨🕭)(2fb)1🛏 CTV in all bedrooms ® T ✱ sB£37 sB⇨🕭£48-£57 dB⇨🕭£69 (room only) 🏟
⟨ 35P CFA *xmas*
V ✧ ✱ Lunch £12.50-£14 Dinner £18.50&alc Last dinner 9pm
Credit Cards ⑴ ⑵ ⑶ ⑸ ⓔ

★★❋70% **Riverside**
Cinderhill St NP5 3EY (Minotels) ☎(0600)715577 & 713236
*Young and enthusiastic proprietors Rodney and Judith Dodd have recently completed an extensive programme of improvements which have totally transformed all areas of this hotel. Not least the bedrooms, which are all en suite and well equipped. Situated close to the River Monnow at the western end of the town, the hotel is within easy reach of the A40.*
17⇨🕭(2fb) CTV in all bedrooms ® T sB&B⇨🕭£47 dB&B⇨🕭£69 🏟
30P CFA *xmas*
♀ European V ✧ ⚌ Dinner £8.25-£24alc Last dinner 9.30pm
Credit Cards ⑴ ⑶

MONTACUTE Somerset Map **03** ST41

★★64% **Kings Arms Inn**
TA15 6UU ☎Martock(0935)822513
Closed 25-26 Dec
*A charming well run village inn with a relaxing and informal atmosphere. The bedrooms have been comfortably and thoughtfully upgraded, whilst the restaurant offers food of a good standard.*
11⇨🕭1🛏 CTV in all bedrooms ® T 🍴 (ex guide dogs) ✱ sB&B⇨🕭£46-£59 dB&B⇨🕭£64-£79 🏟
15P ♨ ❄
♀ English & French V ✧ ⚌ ✔ ✱ Lunch fr£6.95 Dinner £14-£17.12alc Last dinner 9pm
Credit Cards ⑴ ⑵ ⑶ ⑸

See advertisement under YEOVIL

MONTROSE Tayside *Angus* Map **15** NO75

★★★59% **Park**
61 John St DD10 8RJ ☎(0674)73415 Telex no 76367 FAX (0674) 77091
*Situated midway between the town centre and beach, this family-run business and holiday hotel is also a popular venue for local functions. The original Victorian house has been extended and modernised to provide a choice of superior or standard bedrooms, all of them comfortable and well equipped.*
59rm(48⇨55🕭)(4fb) CTV in all bedrooms ® T sB&B£33 sB&B⇨🕭£35-£70 dB&B⇨🕭£55-£85 🏟
⟨ CTV 50P ❄ CFA ♨ *xmas*
V ✧ ⚌ ✱ Lunch £5.95-£7&alc Dinner £14&alc Last dinner 9.30pm
Credit Cards ⑴ ⑵ ⑶ ⑸ ⓔ

MORAR Highland *Inverness-shire* Map **13** NM69

★★58% **Morar**
PH40 4PA ☎Mallaig(0687)2346 FAX (0687) 2130
Closed 22 Oct-Mar
*On the edge of the village overlooking the silver sands this family-run hotel caters largely for tour groups. It offers traditional services and comforts together with en suite bedrooms which are practically furnished.*
27⇨🕭(3fb) CTV in 10 bedrooms ® sB&B⇨🕭£26-£32 dB&B⇨🕭£52-£64
CTV 50P CFA ⚓
V ✧ ⚌ Bar Lunch £1.50-£5 Dinner £14-£15 Last dinner 8.30pm

MORCOTT Leicestershire Map **04** SK90 ⊖

⌂**Forte Travelodge**
Uppingham(on A47, eastbound) (Forte)
☎(0572)87719 Central Res (0800) 850950
*In a pleasant location on the A47, in open countryside just half a mile west of the A6121 junction, next to a Little Chef restaurant and a Shell petrol station.*
40⇨🕭(40fb) CTV in all bedrooms ® sB⇨🕭£29.95 dB⇨🕭£29.95 (room only)
⟨ 40P
Credit Cards ⑴ ⑵ ⑶

MORDEN Greater London

See LONDON plan 1*C1*(page 434)
⌂**Forte Travelodge**
Epsom Rd(on A24) (Forte)
☎081-640 8227 Central Res (0800) 850950
*Comfortable, well arranged accommodation with 24-hour reception is provided by a lodge set well back from the A24. Drinks and meals are taken at the nearby Harvesters Restaurant.*

Red star hotels are each
highlighted by a pink
tinted panel.

32⇌🛏(32fb) CTV in all bedrooms ® sB⇌🛏£29.95
dB⇌🛏£29.95 (room only)
《 32P 🐕
Credit Cards ① ② ③

---

### MORECAMBE Lancashire Map 07 SD46 ◎

**★★★71% Headway**
Marine Rd East LA4 5AW ☎(0524)412525 FAX (0524) 832630
Closed 18 Dec-4 Jan RS Nov-Apr
*Modern, comfortable and providing courteously attentive service,
the hotel offers views across the bay to the Cumbrian fells.*
53⇌🛏(4fb) CTV in all bedrooms ® T 🐾 (ex guide dogs) ✳
sB&B⇌🛏£37 dB&B⇌🛏£60
Lift 《 20P CFA *xmas*
V 👌 ⚷ ✳ Bar Lunch fr£2.50 Dinner fr£10.50&alc Last dinner
8pm
Credit Cards ① ② ③ ⑤

**★★★66% Strathmore**
East Promenade LA4 5AP (Best Western) ☎(0524)421234
Telex no 65452 FAX (0524) 414242
*An hotel which caters well for both business and leisure users
enjoys a pleasant sea front position overlooking Morecambe Bay.
Bedrooms, though compact, are well equipped, public areas are
light and airy and car parking is available at the rear of the
building.*
51⇌🛏(6fb) CTV in all bedrooms ® T 🐾 (ex guide dogs)
S10% sB&B⇌🛏£47.50-£63 dB&B⇌🛏£62-£80 🍴
Lift 《 30P 12🚗 CFA *xmas*
🍷 French V 👌 ⚷ S10% Lunch £8.75-£10.75&alc High tea
£4.50-£5.50&alc Dinner £14.25-£16.25&alc Last dinner 10pm
Credit Cards ① ② ③ ⑤ ⓔ

**★★★52% Elms**
Bare LA4 6DD (Consort) ☎(0524)411501 Telex no 57515
FAX (0524) 831979
*Pleasant, comfortable hotel serving home grown English food.*
40⇌🛏(3fb)2🛏 CTV in all bedrooms ® T 🍴
Lift 《 CTV 70P ❋ CFA *xmas*
🍷 English & French V 👌 ⚷ S% Lunch fr£7.95 High tea £5-
£6.50 Dinner fr£11.95&alc Last dinner 9.30pm
Credit Cards ① ② ③ ⑤ ⓔ

**See advertisement on page 515**

**★★60% Clarendon**
Promenade, West End LA4 4EP ☎(0524)410180
Closed Xmas wk
*A traditional seaside hotel on the Promenade with modern
facilities in the well furnished bedrooms and a popular bar and
dining room.*
33rm(20⇌🛏7🛏)(4fb) CTV in all bedrooms ® T ✳
sB&B⇌🛏£29 dB&B⇌🛏£45 🍴
Lift 《 CTV 🎾 CFA games room
✳ Lunch £6.25 Dinner £9.25&alc Last dinner 9pm
Credit Cards ① ② ③ ④ ⑤ ⓔ

**★56% Channings**
455 Marine Rd East LA23 3HL ☎(0524)417925
Closed 28 Dec-3 Jan
18⇌🛏(4fb) CTV in all bedrooms ® ✳ sB&B⇌🛏£23.50
dB&B⇌🛏£37
👌 ⚷ ✳ Dinner £7.50 Last dinner 7pm
Credit Cards ① ③

---

### MORETONHAMPSTEAD Devon Map 03 SX78

**★★68% The White Hart**
The Square TQ13 8NF (Minotels) ☎(0647)40406
FAX (0647) 40565
*Built in 1637 and retaining much of the original character, this
small country hotel is an ideal base for touring the National Park*

*and is popular with walkers. The bustling bars contrast with the
peace of the traditionally furnished bedrooms; spotlessly clean
with a good range of modern equipment. Afternoon teas are served
in the comfortable lounge and a congenial restaurant offers
wholesome cooking in addition to a worthy range of bar food.
Enthusiastically run by proprietor Peter Morgan and a small team
of pleasant staff.*
20⇌🛏(3fb) CTV in all bedrooms ® T ✳ sB&B⇌🛏£37.50-
£47.50 dB&B⇌🛏£57.50-£61 🍴
12P CFA nc10yrs *xmas*
🍷 English & French V 👌 ⚷ ✂ Sunday Lunch £6 Dinner £10-
£15.50&alc Last dinner 8.30pm
Credit Cards ① ② ③ ⑤ ⓔ

**★★⚐64% *Glebe House***
North Bovey TQ13 (1.5m SW) ☎(0647)40544
Closed 20 Dec-Feb
*A charming hotel which was once the local vicarage stands in the
midst of the Dartmoor National Park. Proprietors Lorenzo and
Heather Manzi pride themselves on personal service, making you
feel very much like house guests, and Lorenzo creates an
interesting menu of good, honest home cooking which is influenced
by his previous position as head chef with ocean liners. Bedrooms
are spacious, if a little dated, while public areas are elegant and
relaxing in country house style.*
9⇌🛏(1fb) T
CTV 40P 🐕 ❋
🍷 International 👌 ⚷
Credit Cards ① ③

---

**★★★69% Manor House**
High St GL56 0LJ ☎(0608)50501 Telex no 837151
FAX (0608) 51481
*Set in the heart of the village, this friendly 16th-century manor
house of mellow Cotswold stone has comfortable, traditionally
furnished public areas with beams, mullioned windows and log
fires. Well-equipped bedrooms of varying style are currently being
totally refurbished, with the upgrading programme due for
completion by mid-1992.*
37⇌🛏4🛏 CTV in all bedrooms ® T 🐾 ✳ sB&B⇌🛏£63.50-
£77 dB&B⇌🛏£80-£98 🍴
Lift 《 25P 🐕 ❋ CFA ▨ (heated) ♪ (hard) sauna spa bath
*xmas*
🍷 English & French V 👌 ⚷ ✳ Lunch £10.75-£12.95 Dinner
£22.50&alc Last dinner 9.30pm
Credit Cards ① ② ③ ⑤

**★★61% The White Hart Royal**
High St GL56 0BA (Forte Hotels) ☎(0608)50731
FAX (0608) 50880
*A former coaching inn in the town centre, nestling among 18th and
19th-century houses beside the broad, tree-lined Fosse Way,
provides good standards of comfort whilst retaining such character
features as the cobbled entrance hall leading to a picturesque
courtyard and the huge fireplace which radiates warmth in the bar.
Efficient and friendly staff create a fittingly congenial atmosphere.*
18rm(9⇌🛏)1🛏✂in 5 bedrooms CTV in all bedrooms ® T ✳
S% sB£60 sB⇌🛏£65 dB£65 dB⇌🛏£70 (room only) 🍴
CTV 5P ❋ CFA *xmas*
V 👌 ⚷ ✂ ✳ S% Sunday Lunch £7.95 Dinner fr£12.95&alc
Last dinner 9.30pm
Credit Cards ① ② ③ ④ ⑤

**❀❀ ✕✕ Marsh Goose**
High St GL55 0AX ☎(0608)52111
*Gordon Campbell-Grey has moved on from The Feathers,
Woodstock to the Cotswold village of Moreton-in-Marsh to direct
operations in this lively restaurant. The Marsh Goose will surely be
another magnet to the visitor touring the area. Cotswold grey
stone, prints and photographs, log fires and antiques make a
comfortable background for people sitting down to enjoy Sonya*

→

**M**

*Kidney's outstanding cooking. From the 'real bread' flavour and texture of the tiny mixed rolls to the selection of coffees, the meal will be filled with surprises; thin slices of succulent, creamy textured smoked haddock sandwiched between two straw potato cakes, bright green, shredded young leeks, served with a thin, light butter sauce, and a main course of neatly trimmed lamb cutlets with a tiny amount of strong tasting duxelles of wild mushrooms are some of the dishes you can enjoy here. The menus, whether lunch or dinner, are considered excellent value for money and we welcome The Marsh Goose to our guide with our Best New Restaurant award for the Midland region, 1991/1992 (see colour feature on p39).*

Closed Mon
Dinner not served Sun
V 60 seats ✳ Lunch £12-£15alc Dinner £18.90-£24 Last lunch 2.30pm Last dinner 9.45pm ♪
Credit Cards [1] [3]

---

MORPETH Northumberland Map 12 NZ28 ◎

★★★★ ❀75% **Linden Hall**
NE65 8XF ☎(0670)516611 Telex no 538224 FAX (0670) 88544
(For full entry see Longhorsley)

---

MORTEHOE

See Woolacombe

---

MOTTRAM ST ANDREW Cheshire Map 07 SJ87

★★★70% *Mottram Hall*
Prestbury SK10 4QT (De Vere) ☎Prestbury(0625)828135
Telex no 668181 FAX (0625) 829284
*Georgian mansion built in 1721, standing in formal gardens surrounded by 120 acres of parkland.*
95⇄3🛏(10fb)8🛏⁄in 12 bedrooms CTV in all bedrooms ® T
《 250P 🚗 ❀ ▭ (heated) ♪ (hard & grass) ✦ squash snooker sauna solarium gymnasium croquet putting ♫
♀ English & French V ♿ ♫ Last dinner 9.45pm
Credit Cards [1] [2] [3] [5]

---

MOULSFORD-ON-THAMES Oxfordshire Map 04 SU58

★★❀❀71% *Beetle & Wedge*
Ferry Ln OX10 9JF ☎Cholsey(0491)651381
*A popular small hotel delightfully situated by the river offers a choice of eating options, the formal service and varied, imaginative menus of the restaurant being augmented by the Boat House's more relaxed style and longer menu – high standards of culinary skill being maintained in both cases; the comfortable lounge is of high quality and bedrooms are all well equipped although they vary in size. A restored Oxford barge can be hired for private parties, and seats and tables are available for al fresco meals by the river. Young staff provide friendly service.*
10⇄Annexe2🛏(1fb)1🛏 CTV in all bedrooms ®
54P ❀ ✦
V ♿ Last dinner 9.45pm
Credit Cards [1] [2] [3] [5]

---

MOULTON North Yorkshire Map 08 NZ20

❀✕✕ **Black Bull Inn**
DL10 6QJ ☎Darlington(0325)377289 FAX (0325) 377422
*The Pagendams have been running this village pub with its various eating rooms for over 28 years and it continues to attract a loyal local clientèle. For the first-time visitor the range of eating options may appear bewildering: at lunch times the bar is open for drinks and hot and cold snacks, while a small à la carte and 3-course table d'hôte menu are offered in the restaurant. In the evening a mahogany panelled restaurant opens to serve fresh seafood only, but advance bookings are not accepted. Reservations are necessary to secure a table in the elegant Brighton Belle, one of the original pullman carriages of 1932 which seats just 20, or the bright*

*Conservatory with its grapevine, plants and railway plaques. In both these areas meat and poultry supplement the wide selection of fish on the à la carte menu which changes seasonally. Cooking by Chef Stuart Birkett is assured, and he handles his quality ingredients with care.*
Closed Sun & 23-31 Dec Lunch not served Sat
100 seats ✳ Lunch £10.74-£15 Last lunch 2pm Last dinner 10.15pm 80 P nc7yrs
Credit Cards [1] [2] [3]

---

MOUNT HAWKE Cornwall & Isles of Scilly Map 02 SW74

★75% *Tregarthen Country Cottage*
Banns Rd TR4 8BW ☎Porthtowan(0209)890399
*A charming, cottage-style hotel, on the edge of the village and only two miles from beautiful sandy surfing beaches. The six bedrooms are tastefully decorated and the lounges and bar have a homely atmosphere. The menu, with a limited choice, is based on traditional home cooking.*
6⇄3🛏✕in all bedrooms ✈ (ex guide dogs)
CTV 12P 🚗 ❀
Last dinner 8pm

---

MOUSEHOLE Cornwall & Isles of Scilly Map 02 SW42

★★66% *Lobster Pot*
South Cliff TR19 6QX ☎Penzance(0736)731251
FAX (0736) 731140
Closed last 3 wks Jan RS Feb-mid Mar
*Recent significant upgrading has improved this delightful harbourside hotel and restaurant, and the extent of services available is normally associated with hotels of a higher classification. Literally hanging over the harbour, the cottagey bedrooms lack space because of architectural constraints, but are now pleasantly furnished and decorated. All bedrooms, in the main house or in former fishermen's cottages, are well equipped. The →*

★★★★ ❀

# LINDEN HALL HOTEL

WELCOME TO LINDEN HALL, THE FINEST COUNTRY HOUSE HOTEL IN NORTHUMBERLAND. Linden Hall is a magnificent Georgian House, set in 300 acres of splendid park and woodland. With an aura of grandeur both elegant yet informal, you'll appreciate all the comfort and attention you would expect from one of Britain's finest country house hotels.

**For a detailed brochure, write to:**
**Linden Hall Hotel, Longhorsley, Morpeth, Northumberland NE65 8XF**
**Tel No: (0670) 516611**

M

# Mitchell Inns & Hotels

Morecambe

## THE ELMS HOTEL
**3 Star**
**Bare Lane · Morecambe**
40 en-suite rooms. Telephones, TV, Radios, etc.
Large Car Park. Restaurant. Adjacent to sea.
**Telephone: 0524 411501. Fax: 0524 831979**

Morecambe

## THE CLARENDON HOTEL
**2 Star**
**Marine Road West · Morecambe**
33 en-suite rooms. Telephones, TV, Radio.
Restaurant. 2 bars.
**Telephone: 0524 410180**

Carnforth

## THE ROYAL STATION HOTEL
**2 Star**
12 en-suite rooms. Telephones, TV, Radios.
Restaurant. 2 bars.
1 mile from Junction 35 M6
**Telephone 0524 732033**

M

*lounge, cocktail bar and restaurant all enjoy harbour views, and the restaurant serves a good range of fresh dishes with fish predominating.*
13⇨♠♦Annexe12rm(7⇨2♠)(5fb) CTV in all bedrooms ® T ⚡

♡ English & French V ✿ ⚘ ⥼ Last dinner 9.45pm
Credit Cards ① ② ③

#### ★★59% **Carn Du**
Raginnis Hill TR19 6SS ☎Penzance(0736)731233
Closed Feb
*A friendly hotel, modestly appointed, serving worthy home-cooked food with the emphasis on fish. The elevated position offers unrestricted views over the south-west peninsula and out to sea. Bedrooms are a little small but soundly furnished.*
7⇨♠ CTV in all bedrooms ® ⼻ sB&B⇨♠£23-£28
dB&B⇨♠£46-£56 🅿
12P ⛟ ✿
♡ English & German V ✿ ⥼ Bar Lunch frf3.50 Dinner fr£13.75 Last dinner 8pm
Credit Cards ① ② ③

---

#### MUCH BIRCH Hereford & Worcester Map 03 SO53
#### ★★★59% **Pilgrim**
HR2 8HJ ☎Golden Valley(0981)540742 Telex no 35332
FAX (0981) 540620
*This privately owned hotel derives its name from the fact that the A49 on which it stands was the ancient route along which pilgrims travelled to the shrine of St Ethelbert at Hereford. Well equipped functional accommodation is scheduled for refurbishment, and traditional public areas include a cosy lounge as well as the beamed bar and restaurant.*
20⇨♠(1fb)2⛉ CTV in all bedrooms ® T sB&B⇨♠£52-£65
dB&B⇨♠£61.60-£77 🅿
40P ⛟ ✿ croquet putting pitch & putt badminton *xmas*
♡ English & French V ✿ ⚘ ⥼ Lunch £8.95 Dinner £18.50&alc Last dinner 9.45pm
Credit Cards ① ② ③ ⑤ ⓔ
**See advertisement under HEREFORD**

---

#### MUCH WENLOCK Shropshire Map 07 SO69
#### ★★72% **Wheatland Fox**
TF13 6AD ☎(0952)727292
Closed mid Dec-mid Jan
*This small and friendly family-run hotel on the edge of the town has a country house atmosphere and provides comfortable accommodation. Meals are all freshly prepared by Anne Nicholls.*
4⇨♠Annexe2⇨♠ CTV in all bedrooms ® T ⼻ ✱
sB&B⇨♠£45-£55 dB&B⇨♠£60-£70 🅿
12P ⛟ nc7yrs
♡ English & French V ✿ ✱ Dinner £16 Last dinner 9pm
Credit Cards ① ② ③ ⓔ

#### ★★57% **Gaskell Arms**
Bourton Rd TF13 6AQ ☎(0952)727212
*An attractive creeper-clad coaching inn run on traditional lines, with character bars and restaurant, which is popular both with locals and with visitors to the town.*
11rm(6⇨♠)(2fb) CTV in all bedrooms ® T ⼻ ✱ sB&B£26-£28 sB&B⇨♠£36-£38 dB&B£42-£44 dB&B⇨♠£52-£56
30P 1🚗 ✿ CFA
V ✿ ✱ Lunch £11.95&alc Dinner £10-£16alc Last dinner 9.30pm
Credit Cards ① ② ③ ⓔ

---

#### MUDEFORD
See Christchurch

---

#### MULL, ISLE OF Strathclyde *Argyllshire* Map 10

---

#### CRAIGNURE Map 10 NM73
#### ★★★58% **Isle Of Mull**
PA65 6BB (Scottish Highland) ☎(06802)351 Telex no 778215
FAX (06802) 462
Closed 2 Nov-24 Mar
*This purpose-built hotel, popular with coach tours, sits on the western shore of Craignure Bay, only half a mile from the ferry pier. There are fine views across the bay to the mainland.*
60⇨♠(8fb) CTV in all bedrooms ® T sB&B⇨♠£50-£52
dB&B⇨♠£80-£84 🅿
⟮ 50P ✿ pool table ♫
♡ British & French V ✿ ⚘ ✱ Bar Lunch £2.50-£7.65alc
Credit Cards ① ② ③ ⑤ ⓔ

---

#### PENNYGHAEL Map 10 NM52
#### ★★63% *Pennyghael*
PA70 6HB ☎(06814)205 & 288
Closed mid Jan-mid Mar
*This former byre has been through various stages of development and is now a charming little holiday hotel, by the shore of Loch Scridain on the road to the Iona ferry. Cottage-style bedrooms are well equipped and the atmosphere is informal and relaxed.*
6⇨ CTV in all bedrooms ® T
30P ✿
V ✿ ⚘ Last dinner 8.30pm
Credit Cards ① ③

---

#### TOBERMORY Map 13 NM55
#### ★63% **Ulva House**
PA75 6PR ☎(0688)2044
Closed Nov-Feb
*This family-run Victorian house sits high above the town, with splendid views of the bay. David Woodhouse, a talented artist and authority on the island's wildlife, organises wildlife expeditions, with the possibility of spotting otters, badgers and many other kinds of animals and birds. Joy Woodhouse's hearty cordon bleu dinners provide the perfect conclusion to the day.*
6rm(1♠)(3fb) ✱ sB&B£19.95-£29.95 dB&B£39.90
dB&B♠£51.10
CTV 8P ⛟ ✿ ⚘
♡ International V ✿ ✱ Lunch £13.20&alc Dinner £13.20&alc
Last dinner 8pm

#### ★56% **Mishnish**
Main St PA75 6NU ☎(0688)2009 FAX (0688) 2462
*This busy, harbour-front hotel has an attractive first floor restaurant, with views of the bay, and modestly decorated and furnished bedrooms. There are no lounge facilities. Entertainment is provided most evenings in the popular lounge bar.*
12rm(7⇨2♠)(2fb) CTV in all bedrooms ® ✱ sB&B£25-£30
sB&B⇨♠£25-£30 dB&B£50-£60 dB&B⇨♠£50-£60
⚡ ♪ ♫
V ✿ ⚘ ✱ Lunch £2.50-£12&alc Dinner £14&alc Last dinner 9pm

---

#### MULLION Cornwall & Isles of Scilly Map 02 SW61
#### ★★★73% **Polurrian**
TR12 7EN ☎(0326)240421 FAX (0326) 240083
Closed Nov-Mar
*In a magnificent clifftop location, 300 feet above its own secluded surfing beach, this fine hotel is set in 12 acres of terraced grounds. Recently refurbished, the accommodation offers a choice of tastefully furnished and well appointed, spacious bedrooms. There are extensive leisure facilities suitable for all the family. The candlelit restaurant and well appointed lounge bar are augmented*

*by the small non-smoking lounge. Extensive 24 hour service is available, and the atmosphere is very friendly.*
40rm(38⇨♠)(22fb)5⊞ CTV in all bedrooms **T** ✸
sB&B⇨♠£49-£84 dB&B⇨♠£98-£168 ⊟
《 80P ✿ CFA ☒ (heated) ⇲ (heated) ♪ (hard) squash snooker sauna solarium gymnasium cricket net whirlpool putting croquet ⚘
♀ English & French **V** ❂ ⏱ Lunch £10.50 High tea £7 Dinner £18&alc Last dinner 8.45pm
Credit Cards ①②③⑤

---

### MUMBLES (NEAR SWANSEA) West Glamorgan Map **02** SS68

See also Langland Bay **and** Swansea
★61% **St Anne's**
Western Ln SA3 4EY ☎Swansea(0792)369147 Telex no 498450
FAX (0222) 374671
*Many rooms in this popular holiday and commercial hotel overlooking Swansea Bay have fine views. Bedrooms are currently being improved and there is a comfortable residents' lounge and a new snooker facility.*
24rm(15⇨♠)Annexe4rm(2♠)(1fb) CTV in all bedrooms ® **T**
⋊ sB&B£26 sB&B⇨♠£30 dB&B£43 dB&B⇨♠£49.50 ⊟
CTV 50P ✿ snooker ⚘
**V** ❂ ⏱ ✸ Lunch £6-£8 High tea £3 Dinner £8.50-£9.50 Last dinner 8.30pm
Credit Cards ①③ ⓔ

---

### MUNGRISDALE Cumbria Map **11** NY33

★✸73% **The Mill**
CA11 0XR (Guestaccom) ☎Threlkeld(07687)79659
Closed Dec & Jan
*This year's Cumbrian winner of our 'Courtesy and Care' award lies 2 miles north of the A66, midway between Keswick and Penrith, a delightful country hotel tucked into the foot of the mountains with a trout stream at the front. Managed by resident proprietors, Eleanor and Richard Quinlan, service is courteous and attentive. There are comfortable lounges and inviting bedrooms, but the highlight of the day is the imaginative 5-course dinner prepared by Eleanor Quinlan. Home-made soups, bread and a mouthwatering range of puddings are featured alongside main courses which include vegetarian dishes as well as game, beef and lamb. (See colour feature on p18.)*
8rm(5⇨)(1fb) CTV in all bedrooms ® sB&B£25-£30
sB&B⇨£30-£36 dB&B£50-£56 dB&B⇨♠£62-£68
CTV 15P ⊞ ✿ ♩ games room ⚘
♀ English & French **V** ❂ ⏱ ✼ Dinner £17 Last dinner 8pm

---

### MUSSELBURGH Lothian *Midlothian* Map **11** NT37

⏏**Granada Lodge**
A1 Old Craighall EH21 8RE (Granada) ☎031-653 2427
FAX 031-653 6106
*This establishment is conveniently situated on the B6415, only a few yards from the junction of the A1 and the A720 Edinburgh bypass.*
44⇨♠(10fb) CTV in all bedrooms ® ⋊ (ex guide dogs) (room only) ⊟
《 90P
**V** ❂ ⏱ ✼
Credit Cards ①②③⑤
**See advertisement under EDINBURGH**

---

The AA's star rating scheme is the market leader in hotel classification.

---

### NAILSEA Avon Map **03** ST47

✸ ✕*Howard's Bistro*
2 King's Hill BS19 2AU ☎(0275)858348
Closed Mon (ex parties) Lunch not served Tue-Sat (ex parties)
Dinner not served Sun
♀ French **V** 36 seats Last dinner 10pm 4 P ✼
Credit Cards ①③

---

### NAILSWORTH Gloucestershire Map **03** ST89

✸✸ ✕✕*Flynn's*
3 Fountain St GL6 0BL ☎(0453)835567
*An intimate town-centre restaurant, tastefully furnished and decorated, features imaginative food individually prepared by its Australian-born chef – the goats' cheese and orange and Grand Marnier soufflés being particularly worthy of mention. The carefully selected wine list represents good value for money, and guests are assured of attentive, friendly service.*
Closed Sun Lunch not served Mon
♀ English, Australian & French **V** 40 seats ✸ Lunch £14.50
Last lunch 2pm Last dinner 9pm 5 P ✼
Credit Cards ①③

---

### NAIRN Highland *Nairnshire* Map **14** NH85

★★★★56% **Golf View**
Seabank Rd IV12 4HG (Rank) ☎(0667)52301 Telex no 75134
FAX (0667) 55267
*Set on the shore of the Moray Firth, with a beach at the bottom of its garden, this hotel in traditional style offers modernised accommodation that is ideal for golfers, business people or holidaying families. Facilities include an outdoor swimming pool, a putting green, a games room and a gymnasium.*

→

**M**

48⇨↑(3fb)1🛏 CTV in all bedrooms T ✳ sB&B⇨↑£56.50-£61.50 dB&B⇨↑£97-£115 🍴

Lift (( 40P ❋ CFA ➲ (heated) ♪ (hard) sauna putting green games room ♫ ♨ *xmas*

♀ Scottish & Continental ⇖ ♨ ✳ Lunch £5.95-£8.55&alc Dinner £20.50&alc Last dinner 9.15pm

Credit Cards 1 2 3 5

### ★★62% **Carnach House**

Delnies IV12 5NT (2m W A96) ☎(0667)52094

*This attractive Edwardian house stands in 8 acres of wooded grounds 2 miles west of the town, close to the A96 and within easy reach of Inverness airport. Bedrooms are generally spacious, traditional and well-appointed – several offering views of the Moray Firth – and there is a relaxing lounge and attractive cocktail bar; personal supervision by resident proprietors ensures that a stay here represents good value for money.*

14rm(12⇨↑)(1fb)1🛏 CTV in all bedrooms ℝ T sB&B⇨↑£35-£43 dB&B⇨↑£70-£80 🍴

15P ♨ ♨ ∪ *xmas*

♀ European V ⇖ ♨ ✂ Sunday Lunch fr£8.50 High tea 60p-£1.80 Dinner fr£16&alc Last dinner 9pm

Credit Cards 1 2 3

### ★★59% **Alton Burn**

Alton Burn Rd IV12 5ND ☎(0667)52051
RS Oct-Mar

*A family-run golfing and holiday hotel which enjoys pleasing views across the golf course to the Moray Firth from its setting on the western fringe of the town combines traditional services and practical comforts with a range of leisure facilities.*

19rm(14⇨3↑)Annexe7⇨↑(6fb) CTV in 25 bedrooms ℝ sB&Bfr£25 sB&B⇨↑fr£27.50 dB&Bfr£44 dB&B⇨↑fr£48 🍴 CTV 30P ❋ CFA ➲ (heated) ♪ (hard) ∪ putting green games room ♋

♀ International V ⇖ ✂ Sunday Lunch fr£7.50&alc Dinner fr£15.25&alc Last dinner 9pm

Credit Cards 1 3 £

---

NANNERCH Clwyd Map **07** SJ16

### ★72% **The Old Mill Guestlodge**

Melin-Y-Wern, Denbigh Rd CH7 5RH ☎Mold(0352)741542
Closed 7-26 Feb

7⇨↑(3fb)✂in all bedrooms CTV in all bedrooms ℝ T sB&B⇨↑£27.50-£32.50 dB&B⇨↑£42.50-£45 🍴

18P ❋ *xmas*

V ✂ Dinner £11-£16.50 Last dinner 8.30pm

Credit Cards 1 2 3 5

---

NANT-DDU (NEAR MERTHYR TYDFIL) Powys
Map **03** SO01

### ★★61% *Nant Ddu Lodge*

Cwm Taf CF48 2HY (5m N of Merthyr Tydfil on A470 near Brecon) (Minotels) ☎Merthyr Tydfil(0685)79111
FAX (0685) 77088

*Once the shooting lodge of Lord Tredegar, this modern hotel beside the A470 stands in very pleasant grounds 5 miles north of Merthyr Tydfil, near the Brecon Beacons. Well equipped bedrooms provide modern comforts and a good choice of food is available.*

15⇨↑(1fb)1🛏 CTV in all bedrooms ℝ T

30P ❋

V ⇖ ♨ Last dinner 9.30pm

Credit Cards 1 2 3 5

---

🐚 Shell filling stations (7am–11pm) are marked on the town plans.

---

NANTWICH Cheshire Map **07** SJ65

### ★★★🏩78% **Rookery Hall**

Worleston CW5 6DQ (2m N B5074) (Select) ☎(0270)610016
FAX (0270) 626027

*Situated outside Nantwich, this Georgian hotel continues to set high standards and has exciting prospects for the future. Conversion of an adjacent stable block into modern bedrooms and high quality meeting rooms was a new feature in 1991. Staff, under the personal direction of general manager David Tearle, are particularly courteous and attentive, and chef Chris Phillips' cooking has a robust style and wide range of flavours, and the menus contain some interesting vegetarian dishes. The restaurant is a good rendezvous for a special occasion; its dark mahogany, cut glass and candlelight give it a particularly romantic atmosphere.*

30⇨↑Annexe15⇨↑1🛏✂in 4 bedrooms CTV in all bedrooms T ✗ (ex guide dogs) ✳ sB&B⇨↑£87-£245 dB&B⇨↑£112-£245 🍴

Lift (( CTV 150P 1🏇♨ ❋ CFA ♪ (hard) ⚑ clay pigeon shooting putting croquet *xmas*

♀ English & French V ⇖ ♨ ✂ Lunch fr£16&alc Dinner fr£30&alc Last dinner 9.30pm

Credit Cards 1 2 3 5

### ★★66% **Alvaston Hall**

Middlewich Rd CW5 6PD (Rank) ☎(0270)624341
Telex no 36311 FAX (0270) 623395

*Set in rural surroundings off the A530, about two miles north of the town, this half-timbered Victorian hotel provides accommodation in well equipped bedrooms situated in the main building and elsewhere in the extensive grounds, and offers comprehensive leisure and conference facilities.*

50⇨↑Annexe43⇨↑(3fb) CTV in 88 bedrooms ℝ T ✳ sB&B⇨↑£49-£76 dB&B⇨↑£67-£91 🍴

(( 250P ♨ ▣ (heated) ♪ (hard) squash sauna solarium gymnasium whirlpool bath beauty therapist ♫ *xmas*

V ⇖ ♨ ✂ ✳ Lunch £14.95-£24.55alc Dinner £14.95-£24.55alc Last dinner 9.30pm

Credit Cards 1 2 3 4 5

### ★★63% **Crown**

High St CW5 5AS (Best Western) ☎(0270)625283
FAX (0270) 628047

*An attractive 16th-century timbered hotel facing into the pedestrianised area, but with a private car park to the rear reached by the inner ring road. There are 3 food operations: bar snacks, Just a Bite (a bistro style café), and the more formal Cavalier Restaurant. Bedrooms are smart and many still have original features such as beams and sloping floors.*

18⇨(2fb) CTV in all bedrooms ℝ T sB&B⇨£50-£55 dB&B⇨£55-£69 🍴

(( 60P CFA

♀ English & Continental V ⇖ ♨

Credit Cards 1 2 3 5

### ★★57% **Cedars Hotel & Restaurant**

136 Crewe Rd CW5 6NB ☎(0270)626455 FAX (0270) 626336

*This family-run hotel, located on the edge of the town, offers friendly service and generous meals. It is popular with business people during the week, and has a large function room which has its own bar.*

24rm(21⇨↑)Annexe3⇨↑(4fb) CTV in all bedrooms ℝ T ✳ sB&B£33 sB&B⇨↑£38 dB&B£42 dB&B⇨↑£49 🍴

(( 60P ❋ CFA *xmas*

♀ English & French V ⇖ ♨ ✂ ✳ Lunch £6.95-£12.50 Dinner £12.50&alc Last dinner 9.30pm

Credit Cards 1 3

### ○Forte Travelodge

Nantwich Rd, Calveley(3m N on A51) (Forte)
☎Central Res (0800) 850950
Due to have opened winter 1991

40⇨↑

---

## NARBERTH Dyfed Map **02** SN11

### ★★61% *Plas-Hyfryd*

Moorfield Rd SA67 7AB (Guestaccom) ☎(0834)860653

*Run by the Grimwood family, this very friendly small hotel, converted from an 18th-century rectory, has neat, bright bedrooms equipped with modern facilities, a comfortable lounge bar and small games room, and provides enjoyable food.*

12⇨🅵(1fb) CTV in all bedrooms ® T

CTV 30P ❀ ⌓ (heated)

♀ British, French & Spanish V ♥ ⚓ Last dinner 9.30pm

Credit Cards ①③

## NARBOROUGH Leicestershire Map **04** SP59

### ★★63% *Charnwood*

48 Leicester Rd LE9 5DF (off A46 2m S of M1, junc 21)
☎Leicester(0533)862218 FAX (0533) 750119
Closed 1 wk from 25 Dec RS Sun

*In a residential area of the village, just off the A46 and convenient for Leicester and both the M1 and M69, this hotel with a large garden has well equipped bedrooms and is popular with business clients.*

20⇨🅵 CTV in all bedrooms ® T

50P 🚗 ❀

♀ English & French V ♥ ⚓ Last dinner 9.30pm

Credit Cards ①②③

## NEATH West Glamorgan Map **03** SS79

### ★★64% *Castle Hotel*

The Parade SA11 1RB (Lansbury) ☎(0639)641119 & 643581
Telex no 48119 FAX (0639) 641624

*An old coaching inn reputedly frequented by Lord Nelson – and also the place where the Welsh Rugby Union was founded – has been completely modernised to provide comfortable bedrooms and bars and an attractive restaurant where good-value meals are available.*

28⇨🅵(8fb)1🛏✂in 4 bedrooms CTV in all bedrooms ® T
sB&B⇨🅵£20-£54 dB&B⇨🅵£40-£64 🅿

《 20P 6🚗 CFA sauna solarium

♀ English & Continental V ♥ ⚓ ✂ ✳ Lunch £7&alc Dinner £13&alc Last dinner 10pm

Credit Cards ①②③⑤ ⑤

### ★★61% *Cimla Court*

77 Cimla Rd SA11 3TT ☎(0639)645656

*This Victorian house, once a family residence, enjoys a prominent position overlooking the town; its once extensive grounds are now partially occupied by purpose-built motel bedrooms and the popular Abbey function suite.*

Annexe24⇨🅵(1fb) CTV in all bedrooms ® T sB&B⇨🅵£41-£43 dB&B⇨🅵£58-£65

100P 🚗 CFA ♫

V ♥ ⚓ ✳ Lunch £11.25&alc Dinner £11.25&alc Last dinner 9.30pm

Credit Cards ①②③⑤

## NEEDHAM MARKET Suffolk Map **05** TM05

### ★★64% *Limes*

IP6 8DQ (Select) ☎(0449)720305 FAX (0449) 722233
Closed Xmas

*Situated in the centre of the historic market town, this convivial little hotel dates back to the 15th century and public areas have and old-world character, though they look a little worn in places. Accommodation is comfortable and very well equipped.*

11⇨🅵(4fb) CTV in all bedrooms ® T

60P

♀ English & French V ♥ ⚓ Last dinner 9.30pm

Credit Cards ①②③⑤

### ○**Forte Travelodge**

Beacon Hill IP6 8NY (junc A45/A140) (Forte)
☎Central Res (0800) 850950
Due to have opened Winter 1991

40⇨🅵

## NEFYN Gwynedd Map **06** SH34

### ★60% *Caeau Capel*

Rhodfar Mor LL53 6EB ☎(0758)720240
Closed Nov-Etr

*A delightful house, standing in its own grounds close to the sea and an 18-hole golf course, offers good value for money in its pleasantly furnished, comfortable accommodation.*

15rm(9🅵)Annexe4⇨🅵(6fb) sB&B£21.22-£24 sB&B⇨🅵£25-£28.60 dB&B£42.44-£48 dB&B⇨🅵£50-£57.20 🅿

CTV 20P ❀ ♪ (grass) putting pool

V ♥ ⚓ Dinner £12.42-£13 Last dinner 7.30pm

Credit Cards ①③

## NETHER WASDALE Cumbria Map **11** NY10

### ★★61% *Low Wood Hall*

CA20 1ET ☎Wasdale(09467)26289
Closed Xmas & New Year

*Overlooking the village and the fells beyond, this Victorian country residence stands in its own grounds complete with a 4-acre wood. Some bedrooms are in a nearby cottage but all are well equipped and with private facilities. Attentive service is provided by the family owners.*

13⇨🅵 CTV in all bedrooms ® T ✂ ✳ sB&B⇨🅵fr£30 dB&B⇨🅵fr£48

CTV 24P 🚗 ❀ pool table

V ✂ ✳ Dinner fr £8 Last dinner 8.45pm ⑤

## NEVERN Dyfed Map **02** SN03

### ★★66% *Trewern Arms*

SA42 0NB ☎Newport(0239)820395

*Just off the A487 coast road, this charming extended 18th-century inn is set in a secluded valley. Bedrooms are spacious and modern and there are quite extensive comfortable public rooms.*

8⇨🅵(1fb) CTV in all bedrooms ®

CTV 100P ❀ ♪ ◡ solarium gymnasium pool table

V ♥ Last dinner 9.30pm

Credit Cards ①

## NEWARK-ON-TRENT Nottinghamshire Map **08** SK75

### ★★66% *Grange*

73 London Rd NG24 1RZ ☎Newark(0636)703399
FAX (0636) 702328
Closed 24 Dec-2 Jan

*A cheerful, well run hotel offering English-style cooking with daily specials featured in the lounge bar. Situated on the outskirts of town on the A1.*

10⇨🅵 Annexe5⇨🅵(2fb)1🛏 CTV in all bedrooms ® T ✂
sB&B⇨🅵£39.50-£45 dB&B⇨🅵£52.50-£59.50 🅿

19P 🚗 CFA

V ✳ Lunch £12.50-£15alc Dinner £9-£16alc Last dinner 9pm

Credit Cards ①③

### ★★60% *South Parade*

117-119 Baldertongate NG24 1RY (Minotels)
☎Newark(0636)703008 FAX (0522) 510182
Closed 21 Dec-2 Jan

*This three-storeyed Georgian house with a rear car park, situated on the Balderton road at the edge of town, provides simple, clean accommodation, with a basement restaurant and adjacent bar.*

16rm(10⇨🅵)(2fb) CTV in all bedrooms ® T sB&Bfr£34
sB&B⇨🅵fr£39.50 dB&Bfr£49 dB&B⇨🅵fr£54 🅿

《 10P CFA

**N**

♀ English & French **V** ♥ ♨ Sunday Lunch £6-£8 Dinner £12&alc Last dinner 8.30pm
Credit Cards ⓵ ⓶ ⓷ ⓔ

**★★55% _Midland_**
Muskham Rd NG24 1BL ☎(0636)73788
*This family-run budget style hotel lies adjacent to the cattle market near a railway line on the edge of town.*
10rm(2⇨)(2fb) CTV in all bedrooms ® ✖
CTV 20P
**V** ♥ Last dinner 8.30pm
Credit Cards ⓵ ⓶ ⓹

**⌂Forte Travelodge**
North Muskham NG23 6HT (3m N, on A1 southbound) (Forte)
☎Newark(0636)703635 Central Res (0800) 850950
*A modern, purpose-built establishment offering warm, well maintained bedrooms is situated adjacent to a Little Chef Restaurant on the southbound carriageway of the A1.*
30⇨♪(30fb) CTV in all bedrooms ® sB⇨♪£29.95
dB⇨♪£29.95 (room only)
《 30P ⇘
Credit Cards ⓵ ⓶ ⓷

**NEWBRIDGE** Cornwall & Isles of Scilly Map **02** SW43

**❀ ✕ ✕ _Enzo of Newbridge_**
TR20 8QH ☎Penzance(0736)63777
*Italian food is served with care and informality in this family-run restaurant. Anne Blows cooks under a copper canopy in full view of diners, while her son works in the kitchen and husband and daughter serve. After ordering in the cosy bar area, a trolley of cold anti-pasti is brought to the table for guests to make their choice. Main courses feature fresh pasta with tasty cream sauces and there are usually plenty of dishes based on locally caught fish. As the Blows are Scots, the tempting dessert trolley includes some typical Scottish dishes, such as the 'Crowdie', a delicious concoction of toasted oats, whipped cream, raspberries, honey and whiskey. Italian, French and New World wines are available at reasonable prices.*
Closed Thu (Dec-Apr) & 1-21 Nov Lunch not served
♀ Italian **V** 70 seats Last dinner 9.30pm 25 P ✂
Credit Cards ⓵ ⓶ ⓷ ⓹

**NEWBURY** Berkshire Map **04** SU46

See also Elcot **and** Thatcham
**★★★★63% Regency Park**
Bowling Green Rd RG13 3RP ☎Thatcham(0635)71555 due to change to 871555 Telex no 847844 FAX (0635) 71571 due to change to 871571
(For full entry see Thatcham)

**★★★★61% Foley Lodge**
Stockcross RG16 8JU ☎(0635)528770 FAX (0635) 528398
*Formerly a Victorian hunting lodge, this hotel is set in its own grounds about a mile from the centre of the town and offers both leisure and conference facilities. Tastefully decorated and well equipped bedrooms have views of the surrounding countryside; public areas have been carefully refurbished to preserve their original elegance, a conservatory extension houses the cocktail bar; there is a choice of eating options, an informal brasserie and a more intimate restaurant.*
69⇨♪(3fb)1⊞✂in 16 bedrooms CTV in all bedrooms ® T ✖ (ex guide dogs) sB&B⇨♪£54-£130 dB&B⇨♪£63-£170 ⊟
Lift 《 140P ❀ CFA ⌧ (heated) snooker croquet
♀ English & French **V** ♥ ♨ ✂ ✳ Lunch £19.50-£22.50&alc Dinner £19.50-£22.50&alc Last dinner 10pm
Credit Cards ⓵ ⓶ ⓷ ⓹

**★★★72% Millwaters**
London Rd RG13 2BY ☎(0635)528838 Telex no 83343 FAX (0635) 523406
*A graceful Georgian house in an attractive riverside setting has been made into a very comfortable and genuinely hospitable hotel of individual style. Well-furnished bedrooms with quality beds have numerous modern facilities and a converted barn houses a smart cocktail bar and restaurant serving a wide range of dishes.*
32⇨♪ (2fb) 3⊞ CTV in all bedrooms ® T ✳
sB&B⇨♪£81.75 dB&B⇨♪£104 Continental breakfast ⊟
50P ❀ ✔ croquet boules
♀ English & French ♥ ♨ ✳ Lunch £15&alc Last dinner 9pm
Credit cards ⓵ ⓶ ⓷ ⓹

**★★★56% The Chequers**
Oxford St RG13 1JB (Forte Hotels) ☎(0635)38000 FAX (0635) 37170
*A busy, recently upgraded hotel in the town centre, provides comfortable, fully equipped bedrooms which are equally suited to the needs of business or leisure user. Elegant, spacious and well appointed public areas include an attractive restaurant offering a choice of an à la carte and two set-price menus; cooking is sound, dishes freshly prepared, and service both friendly and helpful.*
56⇨(3fb)✂in 19 bedrooms CTV in all bedrooms ® ✳ S%
sB⇨fr£75 dB⇨fr£90 (room only) ⊟
《 ⊞ 60P ❀ *xmas*
**V** ♥ ♨ ✂ ✳ Lunch £6.65-£8.65 Dinner fr£14.85 Last dinner 9.30pm
Credit Cards ⓵ ⓶ ⓷ ⓹

**NEWBY BRIDGE** Cumbria Map **07** SD38

**★★★69% Whitewater**
The Lakeland Village LA12 8PX ☎(05395)31133 FAX (05395) 31881
*Imaginatively transformed from an old mill and occupying an imposing position beside the fast-flowing River Leven, this is a particularly well furnished and very comfortable hotel.*
35⇨♪(10fb)⊞ CTV in all bedrooms ® T ✖ (ex guide dogs) ✳ sB&B⇨♪£66.50 dB&B⇨♪£97 ⊟
Lift 《 50P ⇘ CFA ⌧ (heated) ♪ (hard) squash sauna solarium gymnasium putting ♫ *xmas*
**V** ♥ ♨ ✳ Sunday Lunch £8.95 High tea £3.50-£5 Dinner £16.50&alc Last dinner 9pm
Credit Cards ⓵ ⓶ ⓷ ⓹

**See advertisement on page 523**

**★★★68% Lakeside**
LA12 8AT (Consort) ☎(05395)31207 Telex no 65149 FAX (05395) 31699
*Beautifully located on the southern shore of Lake Windermere, next to the steam railway terminus and boat pier, this long established hotel has undergone extensive refurbishment and improvements. The new conservatory and many of the attractive comfortable bedrooms have fine lake views and service is helpful and friendly.*
74⇨♪(4fb)2⊞ CTV in all bedrooms ® T sB&B⇨♪fr£65 dB&B⇨♪fr£130 ⊟
Lift 《 CTV 100P ❀ CFA launching for boats private jetty *xmas*
**V** ♥ ♨ ✂ Sunday Lunch £9.50 Dinner £20 Last dinner 9.30pm
Credit Cards ⓵ ⓶ ⓷ ⓹

**See advertisement on page 523**

**★★★64% The Swan**
LA12 8NB (Exec Hotel) ☎(05395)31681 Telex no 65108 FAX (05395) 31917
Closed 2-14 Jan
*A very attractive coaching inn standing on the banks of the River Lune, providing spacious bedrooms, friendly service and a choice of dining styles.*

→

# Regency Park Hotel

## *SOMEWHERE SPECIAL IN ROYAL BERKSHIRE*

*If you are searching for a relaxing venue, look no further
than the Regency Park Hotel. Nestling peacefully in the idyllic Berkshire
countryside, it will soothe away your cares and provide you with
the facilities and service you would expect from a 4–Star Hotel.*

* **COMFORT AND RELAXATION**

*In the peace and quiet of our 50 triple–glazed luxury bedrooms with a host of facilities, including direct–line telephones and satellite TV. The hotel is an ideal centre for exploring the many places of interest in Royal Berkshire. Our many services include baby–sitting, limousine service and laundry/dry cleaning.*

* **ELEGANCE AND STYLE**

*Relax in the luxurious Fountains Bar, then enjoy excellent food in the sophisticated surroundings of the Terraces Restaurant. For private functions, dine in our spacious Parkside Room, complete with its own dance floor.*

* **SERVICES AND FACILITIES**

*We cater for individuals and a wide range of organisations. In purpose–designed suites our special business centre provides full conference facilities, fully equipped with audio–visual equipment. Fax/telex, typing and photocopying services are also available, together with a complete range of business services.*

* **LOCATION**

*At the Regency Park Hotel, our staff treat you as SOMEONE SPECIAL. We are just a short distance from the M4 Junction 13, but a world away from the hustle and bustle of everyday life.*

## *THE REGENCY PARK HOTEL*

*because you deserve something special
Call now for reservations or a copy of our brochure.*

**Bowling Green Road, Thatcham, Newbury, Berkshire, RG13 3RP**
**TELEPHONE: (0635) 871555**
**FAX: (0635) 871571   TELEX: 847844**

36⇨🚿(6fb) CTV in all bedrooms ® T ✈ (ex guide dogs) sB&B⇨🚿£50-£70 dB&B⇨🚿£84-£125 ⊟
CTV 100P 4🚗 ⊞ ✲ CFA ♩ croquet table tennis ♫ ⌂ *xmas*
☋ English & French V ♔ ☐ Sunday Lunch £9.25-£12 Dinner £15.75-£18&alc Last dinner 9.30pm
Credit Cards [1] [2] [3] [5]

**★★61% The Newby Bridge**
LA12 8NA ☎(05395)31222 FAX (0900) 823705
*This popular hotel on the main road near the river bridge at the southern end of Lake Windermere provides well equipped bedrooms, friendly service and an extensive range of food, available in the bar or in the pleasant restaurant.*
17⇨🚿(3fb)1⊞ CTV in all bedrooms ® T ⊟
100P ⊞ ✲ CFA ♩ *xmas*
☋ European V ♔ ☐ ⚔ ✱ Sunday Lunch £4.50 Dinner £14 Last dinner 9pm
Credit Cards [1] [2] [3] [5] £

## NEWCASTLE-UNDER-LYME Staffordshire Map 07 SJ84 ⊙

**★★★62% Clayton Lodge**
Clayton Rd ST5 4AF (A519) (Jarvis) ☎(0782)613093 FAX (0782) 711896
*A modern hotel on the A519 about a mile from junction 15 of the M6. Bedrooms are well equipped and extensive conference and banqueting facilities can cater for up to 300 delegates. The Cretan Garden restaurant offers a choice of meals from a dual priced fixed menu which changes daily.*
50⇨🚿(8fb)⚔in 8 bedrooms CTV in all bedrooms ® T (room only) ⊟
☾ 300P 6🚗 ✲ CFA
☋ English & French V ♔ ☐
Credit Cards [1] [2] [3] [4] [5]

**★★★61% Forte Posthouse**
Clayton Rd ST5 4DL (Forte Hotels) ☎(0782)717171 Telex no 36531 FAX (0782) 717138
*This popular modern hotel by junction 15 of the M6 has a good blend of facilities for both the tourist and business person, with well-equipped bedrooms, a choice of restaurants and a leisure complex.*
122⇨🚿(46fb)⚔in 54 bedrooms CTV in all bedrooms ® T ✱ S% sB⇨🚿£39.50-£49.50 dB⇨🚿£39.50-£49.50 (room only) ⊟
☾ 128P ✲ ⊡ (heated) sauna solarium gymnasium ⌂ *xmas*
V ♔ ☐ ⚔ ✱ Lunch £9.50-£10.50&alc Dinner £13.95&alc Last dinner 10.30pm
Credit Cards [1] [2] [3] [5]

**★★61% Borough Arms**
King St ST5 1HX ☎(0782)629421 Telex no 5715 FAX (0782) 712388
*The Borough Arms stands by the A53 just off the town centre. In its time it has been both a pottery and a brewery, before being converted into an hotel that is popular with business travellers and local people. Bedrooms in the main building have recently been refurbished to a good standard, and a similar programme of renovation is under way in the annexe.*
30⇨🚿Annexe15⇨ CTV in all bedrooms ® T ✈ (ex guide dogs) ✱ sB&B⇨🚿£35.75-£46 dB&B⇨🚿£50.60-£60.25
☾ 40P CFA
☋ International V ♔ ☐ ✱ Lunch £7.60-£8.97 Dinner £10.50-£11.50&alc Last dinner 10pm
Credit Cards [1] [2] [3] [5] £

**★56% The Deansfield**
98 Lancaster Rd ST5 1DS ☎(0782)619040
*Bedrooms with good facilities are available at this small, family owned and run hotel situated in a quiet side road near to the town centre.*
6🚿Annexe5🚿(2fb) CTV in all bedrooms ® T ✱ sB&B🚿£33 dB&B🚿£35 ⊟
☾ CTV 35P 1🚗 ⊞ ✲ ⌂ *xmas*
☋ English & French V ♔ ☐ ⚔ ✱ Lunch fr£3alc High tea fr£5alc Dinner fr£10alc Last dinner 9pm
Credit Cards [1] [2] [3] [5]

## NEWCASTLE UPON TYNE Tyne & Wear Map 12 NZ26 ⊙

See **Town Plan Section**
See also **Marley Hill, Seaton Burn & Whickham**

**★★★★65% Swallow Gosforth Park**
High Gosforth Park, Gosforth NE3 5HN (Swallow) ☎091-236 4111 Telex no 53655 FAX 091-236 8192
*Set 6 miles north of the city off the A1(M) and an equal distance from the airport, this well established modern hotel features a particularly good range of leisure facilities, both indoors and out. Two restaurants offer cuisine of a high standard, and most of the tastefully decorated, well appointed bedrooms enjoy a pleasant outlook over the surrounding parkland.*
178⇨🚿(14fb)3⊞⚔in 24 bedrooms CTV in all bedrooms ® T ✱ sB&B⇨🚿£98-£103 dB&B⇨🚿£120-£125 ⊟
Lift ☾ CTV 200P ✲ CFA ⊡ (heated) 𝒫 (hard) squash sauna solarium gymnasium spa pool steam room beauty therapy ⌂ *xmas*
☋ English & French V ♔ ☐ ✱ Lunch £15.45&alc Dinner £19.50&alc Last dinner 10.30pm
Credit Cards [1] [2] [3] [5] £

**★★★★64% The Copthorne Newcastle**
The Close, Quayside NE1 3RT ☎091-222 0333 Telex no 53340 FAX 091-230 1111
*The light sandstone façade of this hotel was designed to blend in with its environment, and a notable feature is its location on the banks of the Tyne, close to the city centre, with all bedrooms facing the river. The hotel offers many facilities, including 2 restaurants, a leisure centre, conference and banqueting rooms, a business centre and an extensive car park.*
156⇨🚿(16fb)⚔in 45 bedrooms CTV in all bedrooms ® T ✱ sB⇨🚿£36.25-£85 dB⇨🚿£72.50-£95 (room only) ⊟
Lift ☾ ⊞ CTV 180P 🚗 (charged) ⊡ (heated) sauna solarium gymnasium whirlpool ♫ *xmas*
☋ International V ♔ ☐ ⚔ ✱ Lunch £14.50-£20.50&alc Dinner £14.50-£20.50&alc Last dinner 10.15pm
Credit Cards [1] [2] [3] [5]

**★★★★54% Holiday Inn**
Great North Rd NE13 6BP (Holiday Inns) ☎091-236 5432 Telex no 53271 FAX 091-236 8091
(For full entry see Seaton Burn)

**★★★68% Washington Moat House**
Stone Cellar Rd, District 12, High Usworth NE37 1PH (Queens Moat) ☎091-417 2626 Telex no 537143 FAX 091-415 1166
(For full entry see Washington)

**★★★67% County Thistle**
Neville St NE99 1AH (Mount Charlotte (TS)) ☎091-232 2471 Telex no 537873 FAX 091-232 1285
*Conveniently situated directly opposite the railway station, this well run city centre hotel features tastefully appointed public areas which include the elegant, wood-panelled Cafe Mozart Restaurant and comfortable cocktail bar; guests preferring a livelier atmosphere can eat in the American themed Boston Bean Company Bar and Diner. Attractively furnished bedrooms are all equipped to good modern standards, and service throughout is provided by friendly, smartly uniformed staff.*
115⇨🚿(4fb)⚔in 10 bedrooms CTV in all bedrooms ® T (room only) ⊟
Lift ☾ 25P
☋ International ♔ ☐ ⚔
Credit Cards [1] [2] [3] [4] [5]

★★★66% **Swallow Hotel-Gateshead**
High West St NE8 1PE (Swallow) ☎091-477 1105
Telex no 53534 FAX 091-478 7214
(For full entry see Gateshead)

★★★65% **New Kent Hotel**
Osborne Rd NE2 2TB (Best Western) ☎091-281 1083
FAX 091-281 3369
*A friendly, family-operated hotel of modest size, set in a quiet
residential area within easy reach of the city centre, provides a
warm and welcoming atmosphere, good standards of
accommodation, and good sized modern public rooms.*
32⇔ ♠(4fb) CTV in all bedrooms ® T ✖ (ex guide dogs) ✱
sB&B⇔♠£35-£65 dB&B⇔♠£56-£76 ▤
《16P 🚗
♀ International V ✱ Dinner £12.90&alc Last dinner 10pm
Credit Cards ① ② ③ ④ ⑤ ⓔ

★★★64% *Novotel Newcastle*
Ponteland Rd, Kenton NE3 3HZ ☎091-214 0303
Telex no 53675 FAX 091-214 0633
*Large bedrooms, a spacious comfortable foyer, specially designed
and very well equipped conference and meeting rooms and a small
indoor heated swimming pool, with a mini gym and sauna, are
features of this hotel. It is the latest in the Novotel chain, and is
situated close to Newcastle Airport, adjacent to the new western
bypass.*
126⇔♠(126fb)⊁in 17 bedrooms CTV in all bedrooms ® T
Lift 260P ▣ (heated) sauna
♀ English & French V ♥ ♨ ⊁ Last dinner mdnt
Credit Cards ① ② ③ ⑤

A rosette means exceptional standards of cuisine.

# LAKESIDE HOTEL

*Newby Bridge, Cumbria LA12 8AT*
*Telephone (05395) 31207*
*Telex 65149 Fax (05395) 31699*
★★★
Unique tranquil setting: superb lake
frontage with private jetties and gardens
to lake shore. Both the bedrooms and
restaurant enjoy lake views.

Completely refurbished with a new
conservatory also overlooking lake,
while maintaining the character of a
traditional Lakeland hotel.
All rooms en-suite.

15 minutes from M6 exit 36.

AT
## NEWBY BRIDGE
Newby Bridge, Cumbria LA12 8NB.
Tel: Newby Bridge (05395) 31681
Telex: 65108 Fax: (05395) 31917

Situated at the Southern End of Lake
Windermere, The Swan provides an ideal base
either to confer or to explore the most beautiful
corner of England. 36 spacious bedrooms are
well appointed and include four de-luxe
bedrooms and a Suite each complete with their
own balcony. The Mailcoach Wine Bar and Tithe
Barn Restaurant provide a choice of dining
facilities to resident and non-resident guests. The
Swan Bar is open all day for drinks and/or coffee. Easy access from the M6 (Junction 36) and
ample on-premises Car
Park plus helipad. For
further details, contact
Reception. AA ★★★

# Whitewater Hotel
—— and ——
# Cascades
HEALTH & LEISURE CLUB

**Newby Bridge, Ulverston
Cumbria LA12 8PX
Telephone: 05395 31133
Fax: 05395 31881**
★★★
Originally a mill, this centuries old building
with its stone and slate construction and
impressive five storeys boasts all that is
best in modern hotel design and decor. All
35 bedrooms are en suite with an emphasis
on comfort reflected in furnishings of the
highest standard.

The hotel restaurant overlooks the terrace
where you can enjoy a delicious meal
complimented by the varied wine list.

The Health and Leisure Club offers a
variety of exercise and sporting activities
with expert advisers together with a health
spa staffed by fully trained beauty therapists.

N

# Newcastle upon Tyne

### ★★★63% Forte Crest
New Bridge St NE1 8BS (Forte Hotels) ☎091-232 6191
Telex no 53467 FAX 091-261 8529
*Functional accommodation and a choice of restaurants are offered by this modern city centre hotel.*
166⇆🛏✠in 58 bedrooms CTV in all bedrooms ® T ✳ S%
sB⇆🛏fr£78 dB⇆🛏fr£90 (room only) 🅿
Lift ( *xmas*
V ♥ ☑ ✠ ✳ S% Lunch £12&alc Dinner £15.50&alc Last dinner 10pm
Credit Cards 1 2 3 5

### ★★★63% Springfield
Durham Rd NE9 5BT (Jarvis) ☎091-477 4121 Telex no 538197
FAX 091-477 7213
(For full entry see Gateshead)

### ★★★63% Swallow
Newgate Arcade NE1 5SX ☎091-232 5025 Telex no 538230
FAX 091- 232 8428
*A modern city centre hotel with the benefit of its own car park, and featuring a fashionable restaurant on the 6th floor providing panoramic views of the city as well as a good standard of food.*
93⇆🛏✠in all bedrooms ® T ✳ S%
sB&B⇆🛏£59-£70 dB&B⇆🛏£69-£82 🅿
Lift ( CTV 120P CFA ♫ *xmas*
♡ English & French V ♥ ☑ ✳ Lunch £10.25&alc Dinner £16&alc Last dinner 10pm
Credit Cards 1 2 3 5

### ★★★61% Forte Posthouse
Emerson District 5 NE37 1LB (Forte Hotels) ☎091-416 2264
Telex no 537574 FAX 091-415 3371
(For full entry see Washington)

### ★★★58% Hospitality Inn
64 Osborne Rd, Jesmond NE2 2AT (Mount Charlotte (TS))
☎091-281 7881 Telex no 53636 FAX 091-281 6241
*The well equipped bedrooms of this hotel include four delightful suites, but eating facilities are limited to a coffee shop and small table d'hôte restaurant, unless guests care to make use of the Garden Restaurant at The Northumberland, a sister hotel which stands opposite.*
89⇆(6fb)1🛏✠in 10 bedrooms CTV in all bedrooms ® T
✠ (ex guide dogs) 🅿
Lift ( 90P 10🎱 (£3) sauna *xmas*
♡ English & French V ♥ ☑ ✠
Credit Cards 1 2 3 5

### ★★★57% Imperial
Jesmond Rd NE2 1PR (Swallow) ☎091-281 5511
Telex no 537972 FAX 091-281 8472
*A busy commercial hotel situated at Jesmond, a mile from the city centre, offers modern public areas – with a choice of restaurants – and a range of bedrooms, the best being designated non-smoking.*
129⇆(6fb)✠in 38 bedrooms CTV in all bedrooms ® T ✳
sB&B⇆£35-£70 dB&B⇆£70-£82 🅿
Lift ( 150🎱 CFA ▭ (heated) sauna solarium gymnasium steam room spa bath *xmas*
V ♥ ☑ ✳ Lunch £7.75&alc Dinner £14.25&alc Last dinner 9.45pm
Credit Cards 1 2 3 5 £

### ★★★57% Newcastle Moat House
Coast Rd NE28 9HP (Queens Moat) ☎091-262 8989 &
091-262 7044 Telex no 53583 FAX 091-263 4172
(For full entry see Wallsend)

### ★★60% Cairn
97/103 Osborne Road, Jesmond NE2 2TJ ☎091-281 1358
FAX 091-281 9031
*Recent upgrading has enhanced both the public rooms and the well-equipped bedrooms at this mainly commercial hotel. Situated close to the city centre within easy reach of the major road links.*

51⇆🛏(6fb)2🛏 CTV in all bedrooms ® T sB&B⇆🛏£52.50-£56.90 dB&B⇆🛏£62.50-£67.50 🅿
( 20P *xmas*
V ♥ ☑ ✳ Lunch £5.75-£9.50 High tea £5.50-£7.50 Dinner £9-£13&alc Last dinner 9.15pm
Credit Cards 1 2 3 5 £

### ★★59% Whites
38-40 Osborne Road, Jesmond NE2 2AL ☎091-281 5126
*A privately owned and family-run hotel, part of a Victorian terrace, in a popular area convenient for the city centre. There is an attractive restaurant and other cosy public rooms, including a cocktail bar. Bedrooms are well equipped, and there are useful car parking facilities at the rear.*
25rm(15⇆7🛏)(1fb) CTV in all bedrooms ® ✠
( CTV 30P
V ♥ ☑ Last dinner 9.30pm
Credit Cards 1 2 3 5

### ★64% Osborne
Osborne Road, Jesmond NE2 2AE ☎091-281 3385
*Although generally fairly compact and modestly furnished, bedrooms at this friendly hotel are comfortable and well equipped. Sound home cooking is served in the traditional dining room.*
25rm(1⇆9🛏) CTV in all bedrooms ® T sB&Bfr£32
sB&B⇆🛏fr£40 dB&Bfr£52 dB&B⇆🛏fr£60 🅿
CTV 6P 1🎱 (£2) ⌘
V ♥ ☑ Lunch fr£6 Dinner £7-£8.50 Last dinner 8.30pm
Credit Cards 1 3

### ⊛⊛ ✗✗✗21 Queen Street
Quayside NE1 3UG ☎091-222 0755 FAX 091-230 5875
*Firmly established under the shadow of the Tyne Bridge as the city's foremost eating place, this elegant restaurant oozes style ; in the décor (pale lilac walls hung with modern prints, flower arrangements, soft lighting and immaculate table appointments); in the service by well drilled, smartly groomed and attentive waiters; and finally in the accomplished cooking of chef/patron Terry Laybourne. The carte gives our inspector a choice with Provençale vegetables and basil, or medallions of Kielder venison with sour cherries, grapes, walnuts and pistachios to boned oxtail with veal stuffing or pig's trotter with veal sweetbreads and foie gras. Daily specials from the fish market provide dishes like chargrilled red mullet with garlic cream, tomato butter and basil, or poached salmon, fresh asparagus and Jersey Royals. Panaché of seafood with a well judged saffron sauce was a dish particularly appreciated by our inspector, who also recommends the good value of the set 3-course lunch.*
Closed Sun Lunch not served Sat
♡ French 50 seats ✳ Lunch £14.20&alc Dinner £23.80-£36.80alc Last lunch 2pm Last dinner 10.45pm ₽
Credit Cards 1 2 3 5

### ⊛ ✗✗✗Fishermans Lodge
Jesmond Dene, Jesmond NE7 7BQ ☎091-281 3281 &
091-281 3724 FAX 091-281 6410
*As you would expect from the name, fish is the speciality of this restaurant, owned by Franco and Pamela Cetoloni, set in Jesmond Dene Park, easily accessible from the city centre. Chef Steven Jobson shows a lightness of touch and modern influences in some of his dishes – for example the lemon sole and crab soufflé with a crab and ginger sauce – but also offers more traditional combinations, such as pan-fried lemon sole with meunière butter, surf and turf, half a dozen oysters, and classical sauces of langoustine, scallop, red wine or madeira.*
Closed Sun, BH's & 25-28 Dec Lunch not served Sat
♡ French V 65 seats Lunch £14.50-£16&alc Dinner £25-£40alc Last lunch 2pm Last dinner 11pm 45 P nc9yrs ✠
Credit Cards 1 2 3 5

**NEWCASTLE UPON TYNE AIRPORT** Tyne & Wear
Map **12** NZ17

**★★★64% Airport Moat House**
Woolsington NE13 8DJ (Queens Moat) ☎Ponteland(0661)24911
Telex no 537121 FAX (0661) 860157
*Only 250 yards from the airport and close to the western by-pass,
this modern hotel has bright comfortable public areas and
functional but well equipped bedrooms with 24-hour service.*
100⇌♪♥in 12 bedrooms CTV in all bedrooms ® T ✱
sB&B⇌♪♥£45-£66 dB&B⇌♪♥£55-£77 ⋒
Lift ℂ 200P CFA *xmas*
♀ English & French V ✿ ⚏ ✄ ✱ Lunch £10.50&alc Dinner
£13.50&alc Last dinner 9.45pm
Credit Cards ①②③⑤

---

**NEWMARKET** Suffolk Map **05** TL66

**★★★⊛65% Newmarket Moat House**
Moulton Rd CB8 8DY (Queens Moat) ☎(0638)667171
FAX (0638) 666533
*This small, friendly but professionally run hotel is located at the
edge of the town centre and the Heath. Good conference facilities
are complemented by comfortable, well equipped bedrooms, while
the restaurant's table d'hôte and à la carte menus appeal to all
tastes with a range of dishes that includes grill and vegetarian
choices, all based on fresh produce and enhanced by good service.*
49⇌♥(2fb) CTV in all bedrooms ® T sB&B⇌♥£70-£75
dB&B⇌♥£80-£95 ⋒
Lift ℂ CTV 60P 10⊛ CFA
♀ English & French V ✿ ⚏ Lunch fr£15&alc Dinner
fr£15&alc Last dinner 9.45pm
Credit Cards ①②③⑤

**★★71% Bedford Lodge**
Bury Rd CB8 7BX (Best Western) ☎(0638)663175
FAX (0638) 667391
*This Georgian former hunting lodge stands adjacent to riding
stables in 3 acres of pleasant secluded gardens close to the town
centre. Bedrooms are beautifully decorated and comfortably
furnished, with modern amenities, and the new extension will add
some 50 rooms to the existing accommodation. Public areas of an
equally high standard include conference/banqueting facilities, a
convivial bar, and the Godolphin Restaurant where a varied and
imaginative range of competently prepared dishes is served. A
warm welcome is offered by Manageress Mrs Drummond and her
small team.*
57⇌♥Annexe6⇌♥ CTV in all bedrooms ® T
sB&B⇌♥£60-£70 dB&B⇌♥£75-£85 ⋒
Lift ℂ CTV 90P ✿ CFA *xmas*
V ✿ ⚏ ✄ S10% Lunch fr£13.25&alc Dinner fr£13.25&alc Last
dinner 9.30pm
Credit Cards ①②③⑤ⓔ
See advertisement on page 527

**★★70% *Rosery Country House***
15 Church St, Exning CB8 7EH (2m NW B1103)
☎Exning(0638) 577312
*Situated just off the A45 this hotel offers genuine hospitality,
modest accommodation and comfortable, attractive public areas.*
11rm(7⇌1♥)1⊞ CTV in all bedrooms ® T ✖ (ex guide dogs)
20P ⊞ ✿ croquet ♒
♀ English & French V ✿ ⚏ Last dinner 9.30pm
Credit Cards ①②③⑤
See advertisement on page 527

**★★58% *White Hart***
High St CB8 8JP (Consort) ☎(0638)663051 FAX (0638) 667284
*Set on the town's main street, directly opposite the National Horse
Racing Museum, this former coaching inn, dating from the 16th
century, provides comfortable, well equipped accommodation
which is attractively furnished and decorated. The convivial*
→

*atmosphere of the public areas makes them popular with locals, while the restaurant offers some interesting dishes based on fresh produce.*
23⇨🛏1🛁 CTV in all rooms Ⓡ **T**
⊄ 30P
🍴 English & French **V** ✆ ⚓ Last dinner 9.30pm
Credit Cards 1 2 3 5

---

### NEW MILTON Hampshire Map 04 SZ29

★★★★⊛⊛⊛🏴

**CHEWTON GLEN**

Christchurch Rd BH25 6QS
(Relais et Châteaux)
☎Highcliffe(0425)275341
Telex no 41456
FAX (0425) 272310

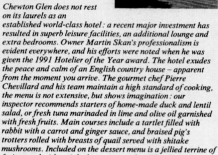

*Chewton Glen does not rest on its laurels as an*
*established world-class hotel : a recent major investment has resulted in superb leisure facilities, an additional lounge and extra bedrooms. Owner Martin Skan's professionalism is evident everywhere, and his efforts were noted when he was given the 1991 Hotelier of the Year award. The hotel exudes the peace and calm of an English country house – apparent from the moment you arrive. The gourmet chef Pierre Chevillard and his team maintain a high standard of cooking, the menu is not extensive, but shows imagination : our inspector recommends starters of home-made duck and lentil salad, or fresh tuna marinaded in lime and olive oil garnished with fresh fruits. Main courses include a tartlet filled with rabbit with a carrot and ginger sauce, and braised pig's trotters rolled with breasts of quail served with shitake mushrooms. Included on the dessert menu is a jellied terrine of fruit served with a pink champagne sorbet. The sommelier Gérard Basset is one of the best in the country, and the exciting wine list contains some 400 wines.*
58⇨🛏1🛁 CTV in all bedrooms **T** 🐕 (ex guide dogs) S10% dB⇨🛏£175-£400 (room only) 🍴
⊄ 100P ❊ CFA ▣ (heated) ⌣ (heated) ▶ 9 🎿 (hard) snooker sauna solarium gymnasium steam room treatment rooms hairdresser ♫ nc7yrs *xmas*
🍴 French **V** ✆ ⚓ ❊ S10% Lunch £22-£25 Dinner fr£40&alc Last dinner 9.30pm
Credit Cards 1 2 3 4 5

---

### NEWPORT Gwent Map 03 ST38

★★★★65% **Country Court**
Chepstow Rd, Langstone NP6 2LX (Stakis) ☎(0633)413737
Telex no 497147 FAX (0633) 413713
*This modern complex just off the M4 (on the Langstone side of junction 24) offers good all-round leisure and bar facilities, extensive public areas which are very comfortable, and well furnished bedrooms equipped with up-to-date facilities.*
141⇨🛏🏴(39fb)✄in 73 bedrooms CTV in all bedrooms Ⓡ **T**
🐕 (ex guide dogs) ❊ sB⇨🛏🏴£79.80 dB⇨🛏🏴£90.30 (room only)
🍴
⊄ ⊞ 160P CFA ▣ (heated) sauna solarium gymnasium jacuzzi
🍴 English & Continental **V** ✆ ⚓ ✄
Credit Cards 1 2 3 5

For key to symbols in English see the bookmark.

---

★★★★63% **Celtic Manor**
Coldra Woods NP6 2YA ☎(0633)413000 FAX (0633) 412910
*The 19th-century manor, once used as a maternity home, is situated close to the motorway. It offers well-appointed bedrooms, elegant public rooms, two good restaurants and a cellar bar.*
73⇨🛏🏴(1fb)2🛁 CTV in all bedrooms **T** 🐕 (ex guide dogs) ❊
S% sB⇨🛏🏴£84-£99 dB⇨🛏🏴£99-£150 (room only) 🍴
Lift ⊄ ⊞ 150P 1🚗 ❊ CFA ▣ (heated) sauna solarium gymnasium *xmas*
🍴 French **V** ✆ ⚓ ✄ ❊ Lunch £13.95-£15.95&alc Dinner £16-£20&alc Last dinner 10.30pm
Credit Cards 1 2 3 5

---

★★★67% **Kings**
High St NP9 1QU ☎(0633)842020 Telex no 497330
FAX (0633) 244667
Closed 25-30 Dec
*Good all-round facilities are provided by this popular and well run hotel which stands near the city centre, convenient for junction 26 of the M4. Bedrooms are well appointed, spaciously comfortable public areas include a popular carvery restaurant featuring an à la carte menu, and functions are very efficiently catered for.*
47⇨🛏🏴(10fb)✄in 2 bedrooms CTV in all bedrooms Ⓡ **T**
🐕 (ex guide dogs) ❊ S% sB&B⇨🛏🏴£54 dB&B⇨🛏🏴£64 🍴
Lift ⊄ 20P 10🚗 CFA
🍴 International **V** ✆ ⚓ ✄ ❊ S% Lunch £5.95-£7.50 Dinner £7.50-£13.95&alc Last dinner 9.30pm
Credit Cards 1 2 3 5 £

---

★★★60% *Westgate*
Commercial St NP1 1TT ☎(0633)244444 Telex no 498173
FAX (0633) 246616
*On the edge of the pedestrian area at the foot of Stow Hill, this historic hotel was famous in the 19th century as a centre of the Chartist movement. With modernised bedrooms, a cosy residents' lounge bar and locally popular Scrum Bar, a coffee shop and extensive conference and function facilities.*
69⇨🛏🏴(11fb) CTV in all bedrooms Ⓡ **T**
Lift ⊄ CTV
🍴 French & Italian **V** ✆ ⚓ ✄ Last dinner 10pm
Credit Cards 1 2 3 5

---

★★64% **New Inn Motel**
NP6 2JN (Porterhouse) ☎(0633)412426 FAX (0633) 413679
(For full entry see Langstone)

---

★★58% *Priory*
High St, Caerleon NP6 1XD (3m NE B4236) ☎(0633)421241
*A 16th-century building set in very attractive lawns and woodland in the centre of the historic town. Public rooms and function facilities are spacious and many bedrooms are modern. Stable bedrooms are more basic and all bathrooms are in need of modernisation.*
16⇨🛏🏴Annexe5⇨🛏🏴(1fb) CTV in all bedrooms Ⓡ 🐕
70P ❊ ▶ 9
🍴 English & French ✆ ⚓ Last dinner 9.45pm
Credit Cards 1 2 3

See advertisement on page 529

---

### NEWPORT Shropshire Map 07 SJ71

★★64% *Royal Victoria*
St Mary's Street TF10 7AB (Crown & Raven) ☎(0952)820331
Telex no 335464 FAX (0952) 820209
*A well run friendly hotel in the town centre offering comfortable well equipped bedrooms for both tourist and business person. The restaurant serves generous meals from a set or à la carte menu.*
24rm(16⇨🛏7🏴)(1fb) CTV in all bedrooms Ⓡ **T**
⊄ 100P
🍴 English & French **V** ✆ ⚓ Last dinner 10pm
Credit Cards 1 2 3

---

N

---

**NEWPORT PAGNELL** Buckinghamshire Map **04** SP84 ⊙

★★★66% **Coach House**

London Rd, Moulsoe MK16 0JA (Lansbury) ☎(0908)613688
Telex no 825341 FAX (0908) 617335
*Situated just south of the town close to the M1, this attractive
Georgian building has been sympathetically extended to form a
pleasant quadrangle. Thoughtfully decorated and furnished, it
offers comfortable, well equipped bedrooms and in the elegant
restaurant, with its central raised platform, both table d'hôte and à
la carte menus are available.*
49⇄♪♠(2fb)1♨✂in 15 bedrooms CTV in all bedrooms ® T
✖ (ex guide dogs) sB&B⇄♠fr£86 dB&B⇄♠fr£100 ◲
◖ 162P sauna solarium gymnasium
♡ English & Continental V ♦ ✄ Lunch fr£10.50 Dinner
fr£15.75 Last dinner 10pm
Credit Cards ①②③⑤

★★61% **Swan Revived**

High St MK16 8AR ☎(0908)610565 Telex no 826801
FAX (0908) 210995
*This family-run commercial hotel, recently upgraded to provide
comfortable accommodation in adequately furnished, well-
equipped rooms, offers a friendly, informal atmosphere and helpful
service; limited public areas include a well appointed restaurant
featuring an à la carte menu.*
42rm(40⇄♠)(2fb)1♨ CTV in 40 bedrooms ® T ✱
sB&B⇄♠£30-£60 dB&B⇄♠£42-£66 ◲
Lift ◖ 15P 3♠ CFA
♡ English & Continental V ♦ ✄ ✱ Lunch £10-£18alc Dinner
£10-£18alc Last dinner 10pm
Credit Cards ①②③④ ⓔ

---

**NEWQUAY** Cornwall & Isles of Scilly Map **02** SW86 ⊙

See **Town Plan Section**
★★★62% **Hotel Bristol**

Narrowcliff TR7 2PQ ☎(0637)875181 FAX (0637) 879347
*This extensive hotel has been in the same family for 3 generations,
providing traditional, friendly services. Bedrooms, many with sea
views, vary in size and are currently being upgraded. There are
generous lounge facilities, with a spacious restaurant, comfortable
bar lounge, function rooms and popular, if rather dated, indoor
leisure facilities. A private car park is available to the rear.*
76⇄♠(23fb) CTV in all bedrooms T sB&B⇄♠£42-£48
dB&B⇄♠£66-£88 ◲
Lift ◖ CTV 100P 5♠ (£4 per day) CFA ⊠ (heated) snooker
sauna solarium ♫ *xmas*
V ♦ ✄ S% Lunch fr£10.50 Dinner fr£16 Last dinner 8.30pm
Credit Cards ①②③⑤ ⓔ

★★★60% **Euro**

Esplanade Rd, Pentire TR7 1PS ☎(0637)873333
FAX (0637) 878717
*This modern resort hotel is in an elevated position above Fistral
Beach. The bedrooms are clean and comfortable, with en suite
facilites, direct dial telephones and remote control colour
televisions. The public areas have recently been completely
refurbished, and an excellent range of leisure facilities, including
indoor and outdoor pools, disco and crèche, is available. A simple
table d'hôte menu is offered in the spacious dining room.*
78rm(66⇄10♠)(39fb) CTV in all bedrooms ® T
sB&B⇄♠£29-£52 dB&B⇄♠£50-£96 (incl dinner) ◲
Lift ◖ 34P CFA ⊠ (heated) ⇔ sauna solarium games room
creche ♫ ⚅ *xmas*
V ♦ ✄ Bar Lunch £3.60-£9.50&alc Dinner fr£16&alc Last
dinner 8.30pm
Credit Cards ①②③④

A rosette means exceptional standards of cuisine.

★★★60% **Trebarwith**

Island Estate TR7 1BZ ☎(0637)872288
Closed Jan-14 Apr & 2 Nov-Dec
*Overlooking the bay from a particularly fine position, this
traditional hotel offers accommodation in a mixture of bedrooms;
there are wide open-plan lounge areas and a good indoor swimming
pool.*
41⇄♠(8fb)4♨ CTV in all bedrooms ® T ✖ (ex guide dogs)
sB&B⇄♠£30-£45 dB&B⇄♠£60-£90 (incl dinner)
◖ CTV 40P ❄ ⊠ (heated) ♪ snooker sauna solarium spa bath
video theatre games room ⚅
V ♦ ✄ Bar Lunch £1-£3 Dinner £12.50&alc Last dinner
8.30pm
Credit Cards ①③

★★★57% **Kilbirnie**

Narrowcliff TR7 2RS ☎(0637)875155 FAX (0637) 850769
*A stay at this busy family hotel, with its views across the
Barrowfields to the rugged coastline beyond, represents good value
for money, guests' comfort being ensured by proprietors who are
actively involved in its day-to-day running and long-term
improvements. Spaciously comfortable public areas complement
simply appointed bedrooms which are currently undergoing
refurbishment; leisure facilities are good and unpretentious meals
offer a limited choice.*
74⇄♠(17fb) CTV in all bedrooms ® T
Lift ◖ ⊞ CTV 60P 8♠ CFA ⊠ (heated) ⇔ (heated) snooker
sauna solarium table tennis ♫ ⚅
♦ ✄ Last dinner 8.30pm
Credit Cards ①③

**See advertisement on page 531**

★★★57% **Hotel Mordros**

4 Pentire Av TR7 1PA ☎(0637)876700
*This purpose-built hotel is in an elevated position overlooking
Fistral Beach. The bedrooms are spacious and simply furnished,
and the staff provide a friendly and relaxed service.*
30⇄♠(10fb) CTV in all bedrooms ® ✖
Lift CTV P ⇔ (heated) sauna solarium gymnasium ♫
♡ English & Continental ♦ ✄

★★★55% **Barrowfield**

Hilgrove Rd TR7 2QY ☎(0637)878878 FAX (0637) 879490
*Popular with coach parties, this large hotel comprises a variety of
modern, variable bedrooms, some with 4-posters and balconies.
Well used leisure facilities include a good snooker room and indoor
and outdoor swimming pools. Service is efficient and friendly, and
light lounge bar meals and snacks are available throughout the
day. There are plans to upgrade the bedrooms and build new
leisure facilities.*
81⇄♠(18fb)11♨ CTV in all bedrooms ® T sB&B⇄♠£38
dB&B⇄♠£76 ◲
Lift ◖ CTV 54P 16♠ ⊠ (heated) ⇔ (heated) snooker sauna
solarium gymnasium games room ♫ *xmas*
♡ French V ♦ ✄ Lunch £7.50-£12 Dinner £11.25-£11.50&alc
Last dinner 8.30pm
Credit Cards ①③

★★69% **Whipsiderry**

Trevelgue Road, Porth TR7 3LY ☎(0637)874777
Closed Nov-Etr
*A commanding position overlooking Porth Beach and bay gives
breathtaking views from many of the bedrooms and the bar lounge.
Proprietors Ann and Dick Drackford provide personal supervision
and extensive friendly services are available throughout the day. A
choice of bedrooms includes some located on the ground floor, and
all are furnished in the modern style. Live entertainment is
provided and badger watching has become a special feature after
sunset.*
24rm(5⇄14♠)(5fb) CTV in all bedrooms ® sB&B£16.50-
£26.50 sB&B⇄♠£19.50-£30 dB&B⇄♠£39-£60 ◲
CTV 30P ❄ ⇔ (heated) sauna putting green pool table ♫
*xmas*

→

♀ English & Continental **V** ✆ ⚌ Bar Lunch £1.50-£5alc High tea £7.50-£11.50alc Last dinner 8pm

---

★★64%, **Philema**
1 Esplanade Rd, Pentire TR7 1PY ☎(0637)872571
FAX (0637) 873188
Closed Nov-Feb
*An hotel offering panoramic views of Fisher Bay provides centrally heated, comfortably furnished accommodation equipped with modern amenities; public areas have been completely refurbished to create quality surroundings, and guests enjoying a table d'hôte meal in the dining room can now gaze into the indoor swimming pool through its feature windows.*
37rm(32⇌🇳)(24fb)1🛏 CTV in all bedrooms ® T ✳
sB&B£21-£27 sB&B⇌🇳£22-£28 dB&B£42-£58
dB&B⇌🇳£44-£60 (incl dinner) 🏳
34P 🚗 ⌷ (heated) sauna solarium table tennis pool table jacuzzi
♀ English & Continental **V** ✆ ⚌ ✳ Bar Lunch £1.10-£3 High tea £1.50-£4 Dinner £5-£8.50 Last dinner 7.30pm
Credit Cards ①③

★★63% **Corisande Manor**
Riverside Av, Pentire TR7 1PL (Exec Hotel) ☎(0637)872042
Closed 11 Oct-8 May
*A beautifully situated property – built in 1900 by an Austrian Count – features a first-floor dining room where guests can enjoy their table d'hôte meal beneath a ceiling made from the keel beams of a Spanish schooner wrecked in the bay 300 years ago, and other public areas are similarly steeped in history. Bedrooms are comfortable, though simply decorated, and most of them offer views over the Gannel estuary. The hotel has been in the hands of the Painter family for many years, and the proprietors extend a warm welcome to all who stay there.*
19rm(4⇌11🇳)(3fb) CTV in all bedrooms ® sB&B£20-£24
sB&B⇌🇳£22.50-£26 dB&B£40-£48 dB&B⇌🇳£44-£52 🏳
19P 🚗 ⌷ solarium croquet putting green outdoor chess nc3yrs
♀ English, French & Italian ✆ ⚌ Bar Lunch £4.20-£7.85
Dinner £12 Last dinner 8pm
Credit Cards ①③

★★59%, *Beachcroft*
Cliff Rd TR7 1SW ☎(0637)873022
Closed mid Oct-early Apr
*Large family hotel in its own gardens, close to the town centre and beach.*
69rm(29⇌25🇳)(12fb) CTV in 59 bedrooms ® T
Lift ₵ CTV 80P ⌷ ⌷ (heated) ⌷ (hard) sauna solarium games room putting ⚌
**V** ✆ ⚌
Credit Cards ①③

★★59% *Porth Veor Manor House*
Porthway TR7 3LW ☎(0637)873274
Closed Nov
*The John family have created a relaxed holiday atmosphere at this quietly situated hotel overlooking Porth Beach. Accommodation is simply furnished and decorated and meals are freshly prepared.*
16⇌🇳(3fb) CTV in all bedrooms ®
48P 🚗 ⌷ ♪ (grass) putting
♀ International **V** ✆ ⚌ ⌷ Last dinner 9pm
Credit Cards ①③

★★58% **Tremont**
Pentire Av TR7 1PB ☎(0637)872984
Closed Jan RS late Nov-Dec (ex Xmas & New Year) & Feb
*Overlooking Fistral Beach from its elevated position, a large, busy coaching hotel with cheerfully obliging staff provides well equipped basic bedrooms and simple, wholesome meals; leisure facilities are good and there is a children's play room.*
55rm(50⇌🇳)(25fb) CTV in all bedrooms ® T

Lift 60P ⌷ CFA ⌷ (heated) ♪ (hard) squash snooker sauna solarium gymnasium putting table tennis ♫ ⚌
✆ ⚌ Last dinner 5pm
Credit Cards ①③ ⓔ

★★57%, *Cedars*
Mount Wise TR7 2BA ☎(0637)874225
Closed Dec-Mar (ex Xmas)
*This family-run hotel commands some sea views from its elevated position in the centre of the town. Bedrooms are simple, but well equipped and public areas include a restaurant offering both table d'hôte and à la carte menus.*
36rm(15⇌16🇳)(8fb) CTV in all bedrooms ® T
CTV 40P 2🚗 ⌷ ⌷ (heated) sauna solarium gymnasium
✆ ⚌ ⌷

★★64% *Trevone*
Mount Wise TR7 2BP ☎(0637)873039
Closed 10 Oct-24 Apr
*Established in 1934, and still run by the founders' daughter, this hotel boasts a charming half-acre rear garden which may be viewed on request. Bedrooms are compact and simply co-ordinated, while comfortable public areas include a bar lounge featuring regular entertainment, a lounge with colour television and a dining room where guests enjoy generous portions of home-cooked dishes.*
32rm(27⇌5🇳)(3fb) ® ✈ (ex guide dogs) ✳ sB&B£15.35-£20.50
sB&B⇌🇳£16.35-£21.50 dB&B£30.70-£41 dB&B⇌🇳£32.70-£43 🏳
CTV 20P ⌷ games room
♀ English, French, Indian & Italian ✆ ⌿ ✳ Dinner £7.50-£10.50 Last dinner 7.30pm

★★58% *Lowenva*
103 Mount Wise TR7 2BT ☎(0637)873569
Closed Nov-Feb
*The open-plan lounge, bar and entertainment area of this centrally situated family-run holiday hotel is bright and airy, a limited choice of meals is offered in the dining room, and bedrooms are well equipped though simply furnished; the heated outdoor swimming-pool provides a sheltered sun-trap.*
18rm(12🇳)(8fb) CTV in all bedrooms ® sB&B£20-£31.50
sB&B🇳£20-£31.50 dB&B£38-£59 dB&B🇳£40-£63 (incl dinner)
CTV 15P ⌷ (heated) solarium pool table *xmas*
**V** ✆ ⚌ ⌿ ✳ Bar Lunch £2-£3.50 Dinner £5 Last dinner 7pm
Credit Cards ①③

---

NEW QUAY Dyfed Map **02** SN35

★★60%, **Black Lion**
SA45 9PT ☎(0545)560209
*Dating back to the early 19th century, and enjoying fine views over the harbour, this friendly inn has a character bar offering a choice of food. Bedrooms have been improved and equipped with modern amenities and there is a comfortable lounge.*
7rm(4⇌2🇳)(3fb) CTV in all bedrooms ® sB&B⇌🇳£24-£34
dB&B🇳£45-£55
CTV 40P ⌷
♀ British & Continental **V** ✆ Bar Lunch £2.50-£8.50alc Dinner £9.25-£14.25 Last dinner 9.30pm
Credit Cards ①②③⑤ⓔ

**See advertisement on page 533**

---

NEWTON ABBOT Devon Map **03** SX87

★★62%, **Queens**
Queen St TQ12 2EZ (Consort) ☎(0626)63133 & 54106
FAX (0626) 55179
*Owners Tony and Fay Jelly continue to improve this friendly traditional-style hotel by the station, with some older en suite bathrooms now being modernised to match the upgraded*

→

*bedrooms. The pleasant comfortable restaurant serves wholesome food, with more informal meals available in the popular bars.*
24rm(20⇗🛏)(1fb) CTV in all bedrooms ℝ **T** ✱ sB&Bfr£33 sB&B⇗🛏fr£43 dB&B⇗🛏fr£58 ♬
8P CFA *xmas*
♥ English & French **V** ♥ ⚏ ✱ Lunch £12.25&alc Dinner £12.25&alc Last dinner 9pm
Credit Cards ⬛1⬛3⬛ ⓔ

### ★64% Hazelwood
33A Torquay Rd TQ12 2LW ☎(0626)66130 & 65021
*A recent change of ownership has brought renewed enthusiasm and personal involvement to the management of this cosy little hotel with its stylish restaurant featuring ecclesiastical panelling. Popular with businessman and tourist alike, being conveniently positioned close to station and town centre, it provides accommodation in bedrooms which, though compact, are brightly appointed and well equipped with modern facilities.*
7rm(5⇗🛏) CTV in all bedrooms ℝ **T** sB&B£29.50 sB&B⇗🛏£35 dB&B£41 dB&B⇗🛏£49 ♬
10P 🚗
**V** ♥ ⚏ Lunch £6.50-£8.50 Dinner fr£10.50&alc Last dinner 8.30pm
Credit Cards ⬛1⬛3⬛ ⓔ

### NEWTON-LE-WILLOWS Merseyside Map 07 SJ59 ☺

### ★★60% Kirkfield
2/4 Church St WA12 9SU ☎(0925)228196 & 220489
*On the A49 opposite the church, this privately owned commercial hotel offers unpretentious accommodation at reasonable prices. Public areas include a comfortable lounge, pleasant bar and restaurant.*
16⇗🛏(1fb)1🛏 CTV in all bedrooms ℝ 🐾 (ex guide dogs)
CTV 50P
♥ ⚏
Credit Cards ⬛1⬛

### ★★57% The Pied Bull
58 High St WA12 9SH ☎Warrington(0925)224549
FAX (0442) 843745
*This public house in the town centre has functional modern bedrooms, some of them in a neighbouring cottage, and a spacious lounge bar and separate restaurant.*
11rm(2⇗5🛏)Annexe7⇗🛏 CTV in all bedrooms ℝ **T** 🐾 (ex guide dogs) sB&Bfr£31 sB&B⇗🛏fr£39.50 dB&Bfr£44 dB&B⇗🛏fr£51 ♬
CTV 45P 2🏠 CFA
**V** ♥ ⚏ ✂
Credit Cards ⬛1⬛3⬛ ⓔ

### NEWTONMORE Highland *Inverness-shire*

### ★★★63% Gaskmore House
PH20 1BS ☎Laggan(05284)250 FAX (05284) 207
(For full entry see Laggan Bridge)

### NEWTON POPPLEFORD Devon Map 03 SY08

### ★★64% Coach House Hotel
Southerton EX11 1SE ☎Colaton Raleigh(0395)68577
FAX (0395) 68946
Closed 2-31 Jan
*Set in 2.5 acres of landscaped gardens in a rural area, Graham and Barbie Carson's small hotel and restaurant is converted from the coach house of a former country estate. The operation is different from the usual hotel, the owners create a relaxed and informal country house-style environment. Bedrooms are individually decorated, well equipped and comfortable with some nice personal touches. Public rooms are quite compact, but in keeping with the style of the building. Graham's cooking offers good standards and an interesting and varied choice.*

6⇗🛏2🛏 CTV in all bedrooms ℝ **T** 🐾 (ex guide dogs) ✱ sB&B⇗🛏🛏£36-£47 dB&B⇗🛏🛏£62-£86 (incl dinner) ♬
CTV 16P 🚗 ✿ nc14yrs *xmas*
♥ International **V** ✂ ✱ Dinner £13.50&alc Last dinner 9pm
Credit Cards ⬛1⬛3⬛

### NEWTON SOLNEY Derbyshire Map 08 SK22

### ★★★56% The Newton Park
DE15 0SS (Jarvis) ☎Burton-on-Trent(0283)703568
FAX (0283) 703214
*Set on the edge of a quiet village, this hotel is a popular venue for business meetings and conferences. Bedrooms which have recently been refurbished offer a good range of modern facilities but some old rooms do not meet these standards and represent poor value.*
51⇗🛏🛏(2fb)✱in 5 bedrooms CTV in all bedrooms ℝ **T** ✱ sB⇗🛏🛏fr£89 dB⇗🛏🛏fr£95 (room only) ♬
Lift ℂ 120P ✿ CFA *xmas*
**V** ♥ ⚏ ✱ Lunch £8.95 Dinner fr£15.95&alc Last dinner 9.30pm
Credit Cards ⬛1⬛2⬛3⬛4⬛5⬛ ⓔ

### NEWTON STEWART Dumfries & Galloway *Wigtownshire* Map 10 NX46

### ★★★⚐64% Kirroughtree
Minnigaff DG8 8AN ☎(0671)2141 FAX (0671) 2425
Closed 4 Jan-3 Feb
*This hotel, located in a most tranquil setting within its own attractive grounds, is conveniently situated just off the A75. The bedrooms vary in size, and the dinner menu, although limited in range, offers dishes which are imaginative and very skilfully cooked and presented.*
20⇗🛏Annexe2⇗🛏🛏(2fb) CTV in all bedrooms **T**
ℂ 40P 🚗 ✿ bowls croquet pitch and putt nc10yrs
♥ French ♥ ⚏ ✂ Last dinner 9.30pm
Credit Cards ⬛1⬛2⬛3⬛5⬛

### ★★★57% Bruce
88 Queen St DG8 6JL ☎(0671)2294
Closed Dec & Jan
*An informal, family-run hotel with friendly personal service from the proprietors and their young staff, offering guests enjoyable, freshly prepared meals. There is an attractive and comfortable lounge bar and some bedrooms have recently been redecorated.*
18⇗🛏(2fb)1🛏 CTV in all bedrooms ℝ **T** S% sB&B⇗🛏🛏£35-£39 dB&B⇗🛏🛏£55-£61 ♬
20P 🚗 solarium gymnasium ⚙
♥ English & French **V** ♥ S% Lunch £6-£14alc Dinner £15.40-£17 Last dinner 8.30pm
Credit Cards ⬛1⬛2⬛3⬛5⬛ ⓔ

### ★★65% Creebridge House
DG8 6NP (Consort) ☎(0671)2121
*Close to the town centre, yet pleasantly located in attractive gardens, this hotel has established a good reputation for the food served in both its dining room and bar ; lounges are attractively furnished and decorated, while bedrooms, though simply appointed, are well-equipped.*
18⇗🛏🛏(2fb) CTV in all bedrooms ℝ **T** ✱ sB&B⇗🛏🛏£28-£36 dB&B⇗🛏🛏£56-£88 ♬
CTV 50P ✿ CFA ✒ *xmas*
♥ Scottish & French **V** ♥ ⚏ ✱ Bar Lunch £3.50-£12 High tea £6 Dinner £14.95-£15.75&alc Last dinner 8.30pm
Credit Cards ⬛1⬛3⬛ ⓔ

### ★★57% Crown
101 Queen St DG8 6JW ☎(0671)2727
*Neat and clean, if fairly modest, accommodation is provided in a listed building which stands beside the market on the eastern approach to the town, its pleasant bars well patronised by locals and visitors alike.*

10rm(5⇆1♠)(1fb) CTV in all bedrooms ® **T**
✗ (ex guide dogs) sB&B£20 sB&B⇆♠£26 dB&B£40
dB&B⇆♠£46
CTV 20P ♪
**V** ۵ ⅙ ✱
Credit Cards ⓵ ⓷ ⓔ

---

NEWTOWN Powys Map **06** SO19

★★63% **Elephant & Castle**
Broad St SY16 2BQ ☎(0686)626271 FAX (0686) 622123
RS 24-26 Dec
*A busy hotel located beside the River Severn in the town centre*
*offers a variety of bedrooms, those in the new annexe being*
*particularly well equipped ; a small but comfortable residents'*
*lounge augments its good range of bars, extensive function*
*facilities are provided, and a wide choice of food is available.*
25⇆♠ Annexe11⇆♠(3fb) CTV in all bedrooms ® **T** S%
sB&B⇆♠fr£42.35 dB&B⇆♠fr£60.50
《 ⊞ CTV 60P CFA ♪
**V** ۵ ▱ ✱ S% Lunch fr£7.70
Credit Cards ⓵ ⓶ ⓷ ⓹

---

NEWTOWN LINFORD Leicestershire Map **04** SK50

★★61% *Johnscliffe Hotel & Restaurant*
73 Main St LE6 OAF ☎Markfield(0530)242228 & 243281
Closed 24 Dec-4 Jan
*Friendly proprietors and staff create a relaxing and informal*
*atmosphere at this village hotel which is convenient for the*
*motorway. New bedrooms all offer modern en suite facilities.*
8rm(2⇆4♠)(1fb)3⊞ CTV in all bedrooms ® **T**
CTV 30P ✿
♡ English & French **V** ۵ ▱ Last dinner 9.45pm
Credit Cards ⓵ ⓶ ⓷ ⓹

**N**

---

## NOLTON HAVEN Dyfed Map **02** SM81

### ★★ 55% *Mariners Inn*

SA62 3NH ☎Camrose(0437)710469

*This village inn, situated in a beautiful cove within the Pembrokeshire National Park, has a comfortable bar popular with the locals and an attractive à la carte restaurant serving a good range of food. The cosy bedrooms are quite compact and are beginning to look rather dated.*

14⇨↟1⇱ CTV in all bedrooms ® T

70P ♉ snooker ஃ

♥ Welsh, English & French V ♥ ✂ Last dinner 9.30pm

Credit Cards ①③

---

## NORMAN CROSS Cambridgeshire Map **04** TL19

### ★★★ 63% Forte Posthouse Peterborough

Great North Rd PE7 3TB (Forte Hotels)
☎Peterborough(0733)240209 Telex no 32576
FAX (0733) 244455

*This modern, purpose-built hotel stands beside the southbound carriageway of the A1 at its junction with the A15 southwest of Peterborough. Executive, study and Lady Crest rooms are available as alternatives to standard accommodation, and although public areas are limited – and generally crowded – conference/banqueting facilities and a leisure centre are provided. Services run efficiently.*

94⇨↟⇱in 24 bedrooms CTV in all bedrooms ® T

⟨ 200P CFA ⊠ (heated) sauna solarium gymnasium games room leisure centre steam room ஃ

♥ International V ♥ ✍ ✂

Credit Cards ①②③④⑤

---

## NORMANTON Leicestershire Map **08** SK84

### ★★★ 72% Normanton Park

LE15 8RP (1m E unclass road) ☎Stamford(0780)720315
FAX (0780) 721086

*The hotel is situated on the south side of Rutland Water, 5 miles from Stamford and 6 miles from Oakham. Using the A606 follow signs for South Shore or Edith Weston then signs for Normanton Park. Converted from a magnificent coach house the hotel has modern accommodation with well equipped bedrooms and a popular restaurant.*

8⇨↟Annexe8⇨(5fb) CTV in all bedrooms ® T

sB&B⇨↟fr£46 dB&B⇨↟fr£66 ₧

⟨ CTV 60P ✿ CFA sailing canoeing windsurfing cycle hire ♫ *xmas*

♥ English & French V ♥ ✍ ✂ Lunch fr£12.95alc High tea fr£4.95alc Dinner fr£15alc Last dinner 9.50pm

Credit Cards ①②③④

**See advertisement under OAKHAM**

---

## NORTHALLERTON North Yorkshire Map **08** SE39

### ★★★ 72% Solberge Hall

Newby Wiske DL7 9ER (3.25m S off A167) (Best Western)
☎(0609)779191 Telex no 61686 FAX (0609) 780472

*A charming and relaxing country house hotel set in 10 acres of parkland, offering attractively furnished bedrooms with good facilities, comfortable and peaceful lounge areas and a good standard of cooking in the elegant restaurant. Service is friendly and attentive.*

30⇨(2fb)2⇱ CTV in all bedrooms ® T ✱ sB&B⇨£60-£68 dB&B⇨£72-£90 ₧

100P ✿ CFA snooker croquet clay pigeon shooting *xmas*

♥ English & French V ♥ ✍ ✱ Lunch fr£9.85alc Dinner £17.50-£21&alc Last dinner 9.30pm

Credit Cards ①②③⑤

---

### ★★★ 67% Sundial

Darlington Rd DL6 2XF ☎(0609)780525 FAX (0609) 780491

*Comfortable bedrooms equipped with every modern facility can be found at this hotel on the A167 just one mile north of the town. Traditional dishes are served in the restaurant by efficient staff.*

28⇨↟(8fb)✂in 22 bedrooms CTV in all bedrooms ® T ✱ sB⇨↟£39-£59 dB⇨↟£39-£69 (room only) ₧

⟨ 60P ✿ CFA ஃ

♥ English & French V ♥ ✍ ✱ Sunday Lunch £8.95 High tea £5.75 Dinner £13.50-£16alc Last dinner 9.30pm

Credit Cards ①②③⑤ £

---

### ★★ 69% The Golden Lion

Market Place DL7 8PP (Forte Hotels) ☎(0609)777411
FAX (0609) 773250

*A Georgian coaching inn in the market place now offers pleasant accommodation in comfortable, attractively refurbished bedrooms with excellent modern facilities; standards of housekeeping are very good and smartly dressed staff provide friendly service.*

26rm(21⇨↟)✂in 12 bedrooms CTV in all bedrooms ® T ✱ S% sBfr£65 dB⇨↟fr£85 (room only) ₧

CTV 100P *xmas*

V ♥ ✍ ✂ ✱ S% Lunch £7.95-£9.95&alc Dinner £13.50&alc Last dinner 9.30pm

Credit Cards ①②③⑤

---

## NORTHAMPTON Northamptonshire Map **04** SP76 ⊙

### ★★★★ 65% Northampton Country Court

100 Watering Ln, Collingtree NN4 0XW (Stakis)
☎(0604)700666 Telex no 312523 FAX (0604) 702850

*This recent addition to the town's hotels, ideally situated near junction 15 of the M1, features striking public areas which include the Court Lounge and Seasons Restaurant, impressive leisure facilities and modern, comfortable, well equipped accommodation.*

144⇨↟(46fb)✂in 79 bedrooms CTV in all bedrooms ® T ✱ sB⇨↟£40-£81 dB⇨↟£40-£91 (room only) ₧

⟨ 219P ✿ ⊠ (heated) sauna solarium gymnasium steam room spa bath *xmas*

♥ European V ♥ ✍ ✱ Lunch £11.50&alc Dinner £15.75&alc Last dinner 10pm

Credit Cards ①②③④⑤

---

### ★★★★ 59% Swallow

Eagle Dr NN4 0HW (off A5, between A428 & A508) (Swallow)
☎(0604)768700 Telex no 31562 FAX (0604) 769011

*A very modern purpose-built complex on the outskirts of town just off the southern ring road. Popular with business travellers, its leisure and conference facilities are extensive. Accommodation is well equipped and functional, and the hotel has 2 restaurants.*

122⇨↟✂in 38 bedrooms CTV in all bedrooms ® T S% sB&B⇨↟£35-£85 dB&B⇨↟£50-£115 ₧

⟨ 166P CFA ⊠ (heated) sauna solarium gymnasium jacuzzi steam room ♫ *xmas*

♥ French V ♥ ✍ S% Lunch £12.95-£17&alc Dinner £12.95-£17 Last dinner 10.30pm

Credit Cards ①②③⑤ £

---

### ★★★ 66% Northampton Moat House

Silver Street, Town Centre NN1 2TA (Queens Moat)
☎(0604)22441 Telex no 311142 FAX (0604) 230614
Closed 24-26 Dec

*Centrally situated in the town, the hotel offers comfortable, well equipped, modern accommodation and the use of Reflections Leisure Centre with jacuzzi, sauna, sunbed and hairdressing/ beauty salon; Le Jardin Restaurant (open all day) provides a choice of 3 menus each evening.*

142⇨↟(4fb)✂in 21 bedrooms CTV in all bedrooms ® T ✱ sB&B⇨↟£71 dB&B⇨↟£87 ₧

Lift ⟨ 200P CFA sauna solarium jacuzzi hairdresser

♥ English & French **V** ✿ ⬛ ✳ Lunch fr£12.25 High tea fr£6
Dinner fr£13.50 Last dinner 10.30pm
Credit Cards ①②③④⑤ⓔ

★★★63% **Westone Moat House**
Ashley Way, Weston Favell NN3 3EA (3m E off A45) (Queens
Moat) ☎(0604)406262 Telex no 312587 FAX (0604) 415023
Closed Xmas-1 Jan
*This hotel enjoys a secluded setting in a convenient position just off
the A45. The main part of the house dates from 1914, but rooms
have now been refurbished to provide a good range of modern
facilities, and the building has been substantially extended to
create annexe accommodation.*
30⇩Annexe36⇩(3fb)⚲in 15 bedrooms CTV in all bedrooms
® **T** sB&B⇩£27-£66 dB&B⇩£54-£76 🏳
Lift ℂ CTV 100P 2🏊 (£5) ✿ sauna solarium gymnasium
croquet putting
♥ International **V** ✿ ⬛ ✳ Lunch £12.50&alc Dinner
£13.50&alc Last dinner 9.45pm
Credit Cards ①②③⑤ⓔ
**See advertisement on page 537**

★★69% **Lime Trees**
8 Langham Place, Barrack Rd NN2 6AA (from city centre follow
sign A508 Leicester) (Inter-Hotels) ☎(0604)32188
FAX (0604) 233012
RS 27 Dec-New Year
*Improvements are constantly being made at this privately owned
hotel on the A508 just a mile from the town centre. The resident
proprietors and their friendly, willing staff provide a warm
welcome and efficient service. Rooms are well equipped and
comfortable, although the décor and furnishings are fairly modest.
1990 saw the opening of an attractive air-conditioned restaurant.*
21rm(19⇩🐾)(2fb)1🛏 CTV in all bedrooms ® **T** ✖ sB&B£25-
£30 sB&B⇩🐾£34-£48 dB&B⇩🐾£46-£62 🏳
CTV 20P 1🏊 🚲 CFA

→

N

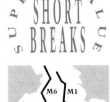

V ↻ ⅏ ✳ Bar Lunch £5-£7 Dinner £10-£13&alc Last dinner 9pm
Credit Cards 1 2 3 5 £

### ★★ 63% *Thorplands Toby*
Talavera Way, Round Spinney NN3 4RN (Toby)
☎(0604)494241
Closed 25, 26 Dec & 1 Jan
*An hotel with easy access to both the town and the M1 motorway features a modern block of well appointed bedrooms which are equally suited to the needs of business or leisure users; an amenity block across the car park contains the Toby Grill Restaurant and bars.*
30⇨(2fb)⊬in 8 bedrooms CTV in all bedrooms ® ✈
( 100P ✿ pool table
V ↻ ⅏ ⊬ Last dinner 10.30pm
Credit Cards 1 2 3 5

### ★★ 60% Grand
Gold St NN1 1RE ☎(0604)250511 Telex no 311198
FAX (0604) 234534
62⇨♠(2fb) CTV in all bedrooms ® T ✳ sB&B⇨♠fr£49.50 dB&B⇨♠fr£60 ▤
Lift ( 70P 20🚗 CFA
V ↻ ⅏ ✳ Lunch fr£6.50 Dinner fr£10&alc Last dinner 9.30pm
Credit Cards 1 2 3 5 £

### ⌂Forte Travelodge
Upton Way NN5 6EG (A45, towards M1 junct 16) (Forte)
☎(0604)758395 Central Res (0800) 850950
*A lodge which is particularly popular with business visitors to the town, being situated on the A45 towards junction 16 of the M1, provides value for money modern accommodation. Meals are available in the adjacent Little Chef restaurant.*
40⇨♠(40fb) CTV in all bedrooms ® sB⇨♠£29.95 dB⇨♠£29.95 (room only)
( 40P 🚬
Credit Cards 1 2 3

### NORTH BALLACHULISH Highland *Inverness-shire* Map 14 NN06

### ★★ 60% Loch Leven
Onich PH33 6SA ☎Onich(08553)236 & 459
*On the picturesque northern shore of Loch Leven, this family-run 17th-century coaching inn offers refurbished, well equipped bedrooms, a friendly atmosphere and a choice of well stocked bars.*
10⇨♠(1fb) CTV in all bedrooms ® T sB&B⇨♠£28-£32 dB&B⇨♠£56-£64
CTV 60P 🚬 ✿
♥ Scottish & Continental V ↻ ⅏ ⊬ Bar Lunch £3-£9alc Dinner £15-£18 Last dinner 8.30pm
Credit Cards 1 3

### NORTH BERWICK Lothian *East Lothian* Map 12 NT58

### ★★★ 64% The Marine
Cromwell Rd EH39 4LZ (Forte Hotels) ☎(0620)2406
Telex no 72550 FAX (0620) 4480
*A large, imposing conference and golfing hotel in the grand style overlooks the west golf course from a quiet setting in a residential area of the town. Most of its bedrooms are lofty and spacious, and some suites are available.*
83⇨♠⊬in 20 bedrooms CTV in all bedrooms ® T ✳ S%
sB⇨♠£60 dB⇨♠£80 (room only) ▤
Lift ( 200P 20🚗 ✿ CFA ⌁ (heated) ♪ (hard) squash snooker sauna solarium croquet ⚬⚬ *xmas*
♥ International V ↻ ⅏ ⊬ ✳ S% Lunch £8.50 Dinner £16.50&alc Last dinner 9.30pm
Credit Cards 1 2 3 4 5

### ★★ 61% Nether Abbey
20 Dirleton Av EH39 4BQ ☎(0620)2802 FAX (0620) 5298
*A family-run hotel which is quietly located on the outskirts of the town, with views over the Firth of Forth. At the time of our inspection, a programme of refurbishment was under way, the completed areas being very elegant and inviting.*
16rm(4⇨6♠)(5fb) CTV in all bedrooms ® T ✳ sB&Bfr£24 sB&B⇨♠fr£30 dB&B⇨♠fr£50 ▤
40P ✿ *xmas*
V ↻ Bar Lunch £2-£5alc High tea fr£5.75alc Dinner fr£11.50alc Last dinner 8.30pm
Credit Cards 1 3

### ★★ 56% Point Garry
West Bay Rd EH39 4AW ☎(0620)2380 FAX (0620) 2848
Closed Nov-Mar
*Popular with golfers, this family-run hotel overlooks the West Course and sea front. Some of the public areas have recently been refurbished and the modest bedrooms are gradually being improved.*
16rm(12⇨♠)(6fb) CTV in all bedrooms ® T ✳ sB&B£27 sB&B⇨♠£42 dB&B£56-£66 dB&B⇨♠£68-£84 ▤
14P 🚬 snooker
♥ International V ↻ ⅏ ✳ Dinner £11.95&alc Last dinner 9pm

### NORTH FERRIBY Humberside Map 08 SE92 ⊘

### ★★★ 67% Forte Posthouse Hull
Ferriby High Rd HU14 3LG (Forte Hotels) ☎Hull(0482)645212
Telex no 592558 FAX (0482) 643332
RS Xmas & New Year
*Overlooking the impressive Humber Bridge at the junction of the A63 and A15, this popular hotel offers comfortable, well equipped bedrooms and flexible eating options, with a good menu choice in the 4626 Restaurant, or light meals available all day in the Continental Café.*
97⇨♠⊬in 49 bedrooms CTV in all bedrooms ® T ✳ S%
sB⇨♠£39.50-£49.50 dB⇨♠£39.50-£49.50 (room only) ▤
( 140P ✿ CFA *xmas*
V ↻ ⅏ ⊬ ✳ S% Lunch £9.95&alc Dinner £13.95&alc Last dinner 10pm
Credit Cards 1 2 3 4 5

### NORTH HUISH Devon Map 03 SX75

## ★★

★★⊛⊛⊛⚖
**BROOKDALE HOUSE**

TQ10 9NR ☎Gara Bridge (054882)402 & 415

Closed 3-24 Jan

(Rosettes awarded for dinner only)

*The well-worn exterior of this former rectory built in the Tudor Gothic style, its lovely setting in secluded woodland, and the stream running through the grounds suggests the relaxed, comfortable atmosphere that pervades the interior, and appearances do not lie. Although not furnished in the 'grande luxe' style, bedrooms are attractive, equipped with all the personal touches that make guests feel at home, and the same thinking characterises the lounge, cosy bar and Regency-style dining room. The food provided by chef Terry Rich is one of the highlights of a stay here. The set menu is changed frequently but the standard of cooking is consistently high, with organically produced vegetables and free-range produce providing the basics of skilfully cooked dishes with sauces that complement the natural ingredients rather than over-powering them (special mention has been made of delicious guinea fowl with a light Madeira sauce and the dietician's nightmare – a wonderful sticky toffee pudding). 'A rare delight to come across such uncomplicated fare', was our inspector's comment. The owners are Charles and Carol Trevor-Roper, and Charles is particularly interested in wine, his knowledge showing in the well chosen, sensibly priced wine list. The other main virtue of Brookdale House is the welcome you receive from the staff and the quality of service they provide, a combination of professionalism and friendliness that has the knack of setting guests at their ease.*

6⇨Annexe2⇨ CTV in all bedrooms ® T ✕
20P ⊞ ✿ nc10yrs
✂ Last dinner 9pm
Credit Cards ① ③

---

**NORTHIAM** East Sussex Map **05** TQ82

★★ 68% **Hayes Arms**
Main St, Village Green TN31 6NN ☎(0797)253142
*A farmhouse dating back to the 15th century and extended in Georgian times now functions as a very attractive, comfortable hotel, furnished mainly with antiques and retaining such original features as exposed beams and log-burning inglenook fireplaces. A high standard of cooking makes good use of fresh quality ingredients and there is very cordial bar service personally provided by members of the proprietor's family.*
7⇨🛏 1🛁 CTV in all bedrooms ® T ✕ (ex guide dogs) ✳
sB&B⇨🛏£40-£42 dB&B⇨🛏£62-£66 🅿
40P ✿ CFA nc11yrs *xmas*
V ✆ ✆ ✳ Bar Lunch £2-£8alc Dinner £12-£18alc Last dinner 9pm
Credit Cards ① ③

---

**NORTHLEACH** Gloucestershire Map **04** SP11

★★ 64% **Wheatsheaf**
GL54 3EZ ☎Cotswold(0451)60244
*This old, creeper-clad inn with large gardens at its rear, stands at the heart of the Cotswold village. Personally run and friendly, it has recently been refurbished to offer improved standards in the bedrooms and main public areas.*
8⇨🛏 CTV in all bedrooms ® T ✳ sB&B⇨🛏fr£35
dB&B⇨🛏£50-£65 🅿
15P 3🚗 ⊞ ✿
V ✆ ✳ Lunch fr£15 Dinner fr£15 Last dinner 9.30pm
Credit Cards ① ③

---

**NORTHOP** Clwyd Map **07** SJ26 ☺

★★★ ❀🎀 79% *Soughton Hall*
CH7 6AB ☎(035286)811 Telex no 61267 FAX (035286) 382
Closed 1st 2 wks Jan
*Soughton Hall, built as a bishop's palace in 1714, is within 15 minute's drive of Chester, and is surrounded by 150 acres of parklands and informal gardens. Proprietors John and Rosemary Rodenhurst and family have extensively restored the house using only the best quality period furnishings and décor. Very much involved in its running they ensure a consistently high standard of attentive service. Young Chef Mark David Fletcher offers 3 set price menus, and uses only the best seasonally available fresh produce.*
12⇨🛏 1🛁 CTV in all bedrooms ® ✕
( CTV 40P ✿ ♬ (hard) croquet nc12yrs
V ✆ ✆ ✂ Last dinner 9.30pm
Credit Cards ① ② ③

---

**NORTHOP HALL** Clwyd Map **07** SJ26

★★★ 64% *The Chequers Country House Hotel*
Chester Rd CH7 6HJ (Inter-Hotels) ☎Deeside(0244)816181
FAX (0244) 814661
*Work to transform an hotel set in 40 acres of woodland – yet only minutes away from the A55 – to its former status is now well advanced. The dedication of the chef and the willing service provided by helpful staff make a visit here a pleasant experience.*
27⇨🛏(2fb)1🛁✂in 2 bedrooms CTV in all bedrooms ® T
100P 2🚗 ✿ CFA
♕ International V ✆ ✆ ✂ Last dinner 9.30pm
Credit Cards ① ② ③ ⓔ

See advertisement under MOLD

★★ 67% **Autolodge**
Gateway Services, Westbound A55 CH7 6HB
☎Chester(0244)550011 FAX (0244) 550763
*Located on the A55 Chester to Conwy road, this good business hotel provides lodge style accommodation – though with more extensive facilities – together with a conference room and an in-house restaurant offering an à la carte menu of home-cooked meals.*
38⇨🛏(38fb) CTV in all bedrooms ® T ✕ (ex guide dogs) ✳
S% sB⇨🛏£29.50 dB⇨🛏£29.50-£34 (room only) 🅿
( 45P ✿ CFA ⚓
V ✆ ✆ ✂ Dinner £5.50-£9.50&alc Last dinner 9.30pm
Credit Cards ① ② ③

⬘**Forte Travelodge**
(on A55, eastbound) (Forte)
☎(0244)816473 Central Res (0800) 850950
*A modern, purpose-built, 2-storey Lodge, providing comfortable accommodation including one room designed for the disabled. It is situated on the east bound carriageway of the A55 about 10 miles west of Chester, next to a Happy Eater restaurant.*

**N**

★ ★ ★

# 𝔚estone 𝔐oat 𝔥ouse

## ASHLEY WAY, WESTON FAVELL, NORTHAMPTON NN3 3EA
### Telephone: (0604) 406262

The Westone is a fine country house set in its own grounds, 10 minutes from the centre of Northampton and Junction 15 of the M1. There are 66 luxury bedrooms with private bathroom, direct dial telephone, colour television with video channel, tea and coffee making facilities, hair dryer and trouser press.
The hotel has a localy renowned restaurant which offers an extensive à la carte menu. There is a comfortable lounge bar with a log fire overlooking the terrace and croquet lawn. For extra relaxation there is a sauna, solarium and mini-gymnasium. Parking is available for 100 cars.

40⇨🚻🛏(40fb) CTV in all bedrooms ® sB⇨🛏£29.95
dB⇨🛏£29.95 (room only)
⟨ 40P 🚗
Credit Cards ① ② ③

---

### NORTH QUEENSFERRY Fife Map 11 NT18

★★★70% **Queensferry Lodge**
St Margaret's Head KY11 1HP ☎Inverkeithing(0383)410000
FAX (0383) 419708

*This modern purpose-built hotel enjoys a spectacular position on
the north side of the Firth of Forth with views of both the road and
rail bridges. Bedrooms are spacious and well equipped and there is
a choice of restaurants, plus a craft shop, heritage centre and
tourist information office.*

32⇨🛏 CTV in all bedrooms ® T ✳ sB&B⇨🛏£49
dB&B⇨🛏£50-£64 🈂

Lift ⟨ 130P ❀ CFA *xmas*

♔ Scottish & French V ♥ ⚏ ✔ ✳ Lunch £13-£20alc Dinner
£13-£20alc Last dinner 10pm
Credit Cards ① ② ③

---

### NORTH STOKE Oxfordshire Map 04 SU68

★★★❀74% *Springs*
Wallingford Rd 0X9 6BE ☎Wallingford(0491)36687
Telex no 849794 FAX (0491) 36877

*A superb 19th-century country house, one of the first to be built in
mock Tudor style during that era, stands in the heart of the
Thames Valley, its restaurant and many of the bedrooms
overlooking a shallow lake (floodlit during the evening) where hot
springs create an eerie mist. Spacious, well furnished and
attractively co-ordinated bedrooms are both smart and very
comfortable, many boasting excellent luxury bathrooms, while
handsome, wood-panelled public areas adorned with fresh flowers
include the Fourways Restaurant with its choice of table d'hôte or
à la carte menus and short but well balanced wine list. Dishes
skilfully prepared with special attention to texture and flavour are
effectively presented, staff are both charming and helpful, and the
warm, welcoming atmosphere also has an air of formality that is in
keeping with the grandeur of the setting.*

37⇨(4fb)2🏰 CTV in all bedrooms T ✘

⟨ 130P ❀ ⇨ (heated) ♪ (hard) sauna croquet putting nc14yrs

♔ English & French V ♥ ⚏ Last dinner 10.15pm
Credit Cards ① ② ③ ④ ⑤

---

### NORTH WALTHAM Hampshire Map 04 SU54

★★★63% **Wheatsheaf**
RG25 2BB (on A30) (Lansbury) ☎Dummer(0256)398282
Telex no 859775 FAX (0256) 398253

*Most of the spacious, well equipped bedrooms of this old coaching
inn are contained in a modern extension; the largely open-plan
ground floor public areas include both a Henekey Restaurant and
a bar (open all day) which serves an extensive menu of informal
snacks.*

28⇨🛏(1fb)1🏰 CTV in all bedrooms ® T sB&B⇨🛏fr£75
dB&B⇨🛏fr£88 🈂

⟨ 70P ❀ *xmas*

♔ Continental ♥ ⚏ ✳ Lunch fr£12&alc Dinner fr£12&alc
Last dinner 10.30pm
Credit Cards ① ② ③ ④ ⑤

---

### NORTHWICH Cheshire Map 07 SJ67 ◉

★★★65% *Hartford Hall*
School Ln, Hartford CW8 1PW (2m SW off bypass A556)
(Consort) ☎Hartford(0606)75711

*A 16th-century country mansion standing in its own extensive
grounds with a small lake, just off the A556 Northwich by-pass.
Bedrooms are well appointed and the public rooms are in character
with the historical style of the house.*

21⇨(1fb) CTV in all bedrooms ®
⟨ CTV 50P ❀ ♨
V ♥
Credit Cards ① ② ③ ⑤

---

### NORTH WOOTTON Somerset Map 03 ST54

★★64% *Crossways Inn Restaurant & Hotel*
BA4 4EU ☎Pilton(074989)237 & 476

*Located in a peaceful wine-producing village with beautiful rural
views, this friendly inn has a popular bar and restaurant serving
bar meals and an à la carte menu featuring grills and roasts.
Bedrooms vary in size and are well equipped.*

17⇨🛏(3fb) CTV in all bedrooms ® T ✘ (ex guide dogs)
CTV 150P 🚗 ❀
V ♥ ✔
Credit Cards ① ③

**See advertisement under WELLS**

---

### NORTON Shropshire Map 07 SJ70

★★76% **Hundred House**
Bridgnorth Rd TF11 9EE (on A442 6m N of Bridgnorth) (Exec
Hotel) ☎(095271)353 FAX (095271) 355

*Only a few miles from Telford town centre, this very popular
village inn has lots of character, with log fires, friendly hosts, good
home-cooked food and above all excellent accommodation in
individually styled, quite luxurious bedrooms. Reservations are
recommended.*

9⇨(5fb)3🏰 CTV in all bedrooms ® T sB&B⇨£59-£69
dB&B⇨£69-£79 🈂

40P ❀

♔ English & French V ♥ ⚏ Lunch £17.50-£19alc Dinner
£17.50-£19alc Last dinner 10pm
Credit Cards ① ② ③ ④

**See advertisement under TELFORD**

---

### NORWICH Norfolk Map 05 TG20 ◉

★★★★❀68% *Sprowston Manor*
Wroxham Road, Sprowston NR7 8RP (2m NE A1151) (Best
Western) ☎(0603)410871 Telex no 975356 FAX (0603) 423911

*On the A1151 Wroxham road just north of Norwich, this fine old
manor house has been considerably extended and improved and is
popular with both businessmen and tourists alike. Further
bedrooms and a leisure centre are under construction.*

103⇨🛏8🏰 CTV in all bedrooms ® T ✘ (ex guide dogs)
sB&B⇨🛏£81-£85 dB&B⇨🛏£91-£95 🈂

Lift ⟨ 120P ❀ CFA ▣ (heated) ▶ 18 sauna solarium
gymnasium croquet *xmas*

♔ English & French V ♥ ⚏ ✳ Lunch £10.95-£20&alc High
tea £10.95-£20 Dinner £14.95-£20 Last dinner 10pm
Credit Cards ① ② ③ ⑤ ④

★★★73% *Norwich Airport Ambassador*
Cromer Rd NR6 6JA ☎(0603)410544 FAX (0603) 789935

*Prominently situated on the A140 at the airport on the outskirts of
town, this hotel was built in 1990 and offers the latest facilities.
Bedrooms are spacious and thoughtfully equipped. Public areas
comprise a choice of eating places, a convivial public bar, extensive
conference facilities and a good leisure club with a decent sized
gym and swimming pool. All areas are double glazed and the
restaurant is air conditioned. Overall the current pricing policy
represents very good value for money.*

108⇨🛏3🏰✔in 12 bedrooms CTV in all bedrooms ® T
Lift ⟨ 320P ▣ (heated) sauna solarium gymnasium
♔ English & French V ♥ ⚏ ✔ Last dinner 10.30pm
Credit Cards ① ② ③ ④ ⑤

**★★★ 67% Maids Head**
Tombland NR3 1LB (Queens Moat) ☎(0603)761111
Telex no 975080 FAX (0603) 613688
*A successfully managed city centre hotel styled to attract both the leisure and commercial user. Recent refurbishment in public areas has brightened the lounges, bars and courtyard restaurant considerably. All the bedrooms are similarly equipped, though the larger ones are more comfortable.*
81⇌↱(2fb)1⊞ CTV in all bedrooms ® **T** ✱ sB&B⇌↱£79.50 dB&B⇌↱£97.50-£150 ⊟
Lift ☾ 80P 20⌂ CFA *xmas*
☋ English & French V ♈ ☕ ⅟ ✱ Lunch £9.75-£14alc Dinner £14.50&alc Last dinner 9.45pm
Credit Cards [1] [2] [3] [5] (£)

**★★★ 65% Forte Posthouse**
Ipswich Rd NR4 6EP (Forte Hotels) ☎(0603)56431
Telex no 975106 FAX (0603) 506400
*On the A140 south of the city centre, this purpose-built hotel is well managed. Recently refurbished throughout, it has a good range of leisure and business facilities.*
116⇌⅟in 44 bedrooms CTV in all bedrooms ® **T** ✱ S%
sB⇌£39.50-£49.50 dB⇌£39.50-£49.50 (room only) ⊟
☾ 200P ⊞ ✲ ⊡ (heated) sauna solarium gymnasium health & fitness centre *xmas*
☋ English & French V ♈ ☕ ⅟ ✱ Lunch fr£8.95 Dinner £13.95 Last dinner 10pm
Credit Cards [1] [2] [3] [5]

**★★★ 65% Hotel Nelson**
Prince of Wales Rd NR1 1DX ☎(0603)760260 Telex no 975203 FAX (0603) 620008
*Well situated alongside the river, across the road from the railway station and within walking distance of the city centre, this purpose built hotel offers a choice of bar and restaurants, all aptly named in nautical terms. The Trafalgar Restaurant offers a fine view over the river, and has a varied menu – meats and fish, smoked on the premises, a speciality. Accommodation is very well equipped and thoughtfully designed, appealing to both business people and holidaymakers.*
121⇌↱3⊞ CTV in all bedrooms ® **T** ⋈ (ex guide dogs) ✱
sB&B⇌↱fr£71 dB&B⇌↱fr£82.50 ⊟
Lift ☾ 119P 30⌂ ✲ CFA *xmas*
V ♈ ☕
Credit Cards [1] [2] [3] [5]

**★★★ 65% Hotel Norwich**
121-131 Boundary Rd NR3 2BA (Best Western) ☎(0603)787260
Telex no 975337 FAX (0603) 400466
*Situated north of the city on the A47 ring road, this hotel maintains high standards and is well managed. Accommodation is well equipped and comfortable. A new leisure complex is planned for the end of 1991.*
108⇌↱(15fb)⅟in 30 bedrooms CTV in all bedrooms ® **T** ⋈ (ex guide dogs) ✱ sB&B⇌↱fr£60.75 dB&B⇌↱fr£71 ⊟
☾ 225P CFA ⊡ (heated) solarium gymnasium *xmas*
☋ International V ♈ ☕ ⅟ ✱ Lunch £5-£20 Dinner fr£12.25 Last dinner 10pm
Credit Cards [1] [2] [3] [5] (£)

**★★★ 63% *Norwich Sport Village***
Drayton High Rd, Hellesdon NR6 5DU ☎(0603)788898
FAX (0603) 406845
*Just off the ring road north of the city, this purpose-built hotel cum sports centre provides simple, well equipped accommodation and extensive sports facilities, with a new three-pool leisure complex due to have opened in 1991. Service is friendly and informal.*
56⇌↱(2fb) CTV in all bedrooms ® **T**
Lift ☾ P ✲ ⊡ (heated) ℘ (hard) squash snooker sauna solarium gymnasium jacuzzi ⌂
V ♈ ☕
Credit Cards [1] [2] [3] [5]

**See advertisement on page 541**

**★★★ 60% Friendly**
2 Barnard Rd, Bowthorpe NR5 9JB (Consort) ☎(0603)741161
Telex no 975557 FAX (0603) 741500
*West of the city centre, on the A47, this modern purpose-built hotel has open-plan public areas leading to a carvery/buffet style restaurant offering a variety of freshly prepared dishes. The bedrooms are simply furnished in light woods and pastels, with 'Premier Plus' rooms particularly well equipped with the business guest in mind.*
80⇌↱(14fb)2⊞⅟in 11 bedrooms CTV in all bedrooms ® **T**
sB⇌↱£53.25-£63.50 dB⇌↱£70.50-£80.75 (room only) ⊟
☾ 100P CFA ⊡ (heated) sauna solarium gymnasium jacuzzi *xmas*
☋ English & French V ♈ ☕ ⅟ Lunch fr£8.50 Dinner fr£12.75 Last dinner 9.45pm
Credit Cards [1] [2] [3] [5] (£)

**See advertisement on page 541**

**★★ 65% Annesley**
6 Newmarket Rd NR2 2LA ☎(0603)624553 FAX (0603) 624553
Closed Xmas & New Year
*A Victorian house, situated on the Norwich/Thetford road close to the city centre, has been tastefully and sympathetically decorated to enhance its period features. Accommodation in bright, well-equipped rooms is complemented by caring personal service from the proprietors. The lovely garden at the rear of the hotel is overlooked by a vine-covered sun lounge.*
17⇌↱(1fb) CTV in all bedrooms ® **T** ⋈ (ex guide dogs) ✱
sB&B⇌↱fr£50 dB&B⇌↱fr£60 ⊟
30P ✲

→

N

♀ English & French **V** ♨ ⚲ ✻ Bar Lunch fr£5 Dinner fr£14
Last dinner 9pm
Credit Cards ①②③⑤

**★★65% Oaklands**
89 Yarmouth Rd, Thorpe St Andrew NR7 0HH ☎(0603)34471
FAX (0603) 700318

*This hotel, quietly located in its own grounds beside the Great Yarmouth road on the outskirts of the city, offers well equipped accommodation – many rooms being furnished to a standard above its classification – and comfortable, attractively furnished bars overlooking the gardens.*

39rm(38⇨♪♠)(4fb) CTV in all bedrooms ® **T** ♠
《 CTV 90P ❀ CFA *xmas*
**V** ♨ ⚲ Lunch £9.50&alc Dinner £13.50&alc Last dinner 9.30pm
Credit Cards ①②③⑤ ⓔ

**★★61% Arlington**
10 Arlington Ln, Newmarket Rd NR2 2DA ☎(0603)617841
FAX (0603) 663708

*An hotel situated just off the A11 in a quiet area south of the city provides well equipped accommodation, some recently refurbished rooms being particularly attractive and comfortable; public areas are limited but adequate to the needs of a mainly commercial clientèle. The dining room offers a choice of à la carte or carvery menus, and a competent team of pleasantly mannered mainly female staff.*

44⇨♠(3fb)1⚏ CTV in all bedrooms ® sB&B⇨♠£51-£60 dB&B⇨♠£60-£70 ♠
《 60P CFA ♬ *xmas*
♀ English & French **V** ♨ ⚲ ✻ Lunch £6.95-£15 Dinner fr£10.95 Last dinner 10pm
Credit Cards ①②③⑤ ⓔ

**See advertisement on page 543**

○**Forte Travelodge**
Southern Relief Rd, (Norwich by pass), Cringleford(on A47) (Forte) ☎Central Res (0800) 850950
Due to have opened Winter 1991
40⇨♠

❀❀❀ ✕ ✕ **Adlard's**
79 Upper St Giles Street NR2 1AB ☎(0603)633522

*David Adlard and his small team prepare dishes of the finest quality, delicately enhanced by well constructed sauces. Our inspector was especially complimentary about a ragôut of seafood with a coulis of red peppers, and a loin of venison with oyster mushrooms on a wild mushroom sauce. Service is friendly and it is pleasing to note that Adlard's is now serving lunch as well as dinner.*

Closed Sun & Mon Lunch not served Sat
♀ French 35 seats Lunch £15-£17 Dinner £25.50-£27 Last lunch 1.45pm Last dinner 9pm 🏌
Credit Cards ①③

❀❀ ✕ ✕ **Brasted's**
8-10 St Andrews Hill NR2 1AD ☎(0603)625949
FAX (0603) 766445

*Set in a quiet cobbled street near the city centre, behind cathedral and castle and next to Bridewell Prison (now a museum), this warm and intimate restaurant comprises Dining Room and Morning Room, both fashionably furnished with Laura Ashley fabrics and with Persian rugs on their polished floors. The charming, humorous host is John Brasted, whilst chef Paul Chipperfield reveals his love of simple, true flavours in a seasonally revised menu which takes advantage of excellent local produce to create such European and classic English dishes as ragôut of mussels and leeks with a mousseline, a ramekin of wild mushrooms topped with cheese, Beef Stroganoff or fresh salmon in a dill and oyster sauce. A small selection of unusual wines is included in the reasonably extensive and very well priced list.*

Closed Sun & last 2 wks Aug Lunch not served Sat

**V** 22 seats ✻ Lunch £9.50-£15&alc Dinner £19.25-£28alc Last lunch 2pm Last dinner 10pm 🏌
Credit Cards ①②③⑤

❀ ✕ ✕**Marco's**
17 Pottergate NR2 1DS ☎(0603)624044

*This bar and restaurant in the city centre, just off the market place, has been very carefully refurbished to provide a comfortable, intimate setting in which to enjoy a meal in classical Italian style. Lighter fish dishes provide an alternative to such traditional favourites as Spaghetti Carbonara and Pollo Alla Cacciatora, and an extensive range of Marco's own ice creams and sorbets is available. A full and reasonably priced wine list represents all regions of Italy.*

Closed Sun, Mon & 20 Aug-20 Sep
♀ Italian **V** 20 seats ✻ Lunch fr£16&alc Dinner £26-£32alc
Last lunch 2pm Last dinner 9.30pm 🏌 nc12yrs
Credit Cards ①②③④⑤

❀ ✕ **By Appointment**
27 St George's Street NR3 1AB ☎(0603)630730

*A truly charming, characterful and intimate little restaurant featuring antiques and collectors' bric à brac stands in the city centre, only a few yards from the river. Entered through a back yard, resplendent with greenery, and the small kitchen and scullery, it displays on a gilt-framed blackboard a menu consisting of 5 daily changing choices. Imaginative dishes combining quality fresh produce with herbs, fruit and wine include parcels of spiced lamb on a light mayonnaise, hot goose breast in Champagne and orange, and duck breast wrapped in vine leaves, while for dessert you might care to sample the bread and butter pudding. An excellent but reasonably priced wine list complements the menu, and service is informally attentive.*

Closed 1st 2 wks Sep
Dinner served by appointment only
**V** 30 seats ✻ Dinner £20-£30alc Last lunch 2pm Last dinner 9.30pm P nc12yrs
Credit Cards ①③

❀ ✕ *Greens Seafood*
82 Upper St Giles Street NR1 1AQ ☎(0603)623733

*A listed 18th-century building just off the city centre which offers a short list of seafood. Chef/Patron Dennis Compton is mainly self-taught and has a good feel for sauces. To supplement the à la carte menu, there is an imaginative daily blackboard menu. The rich décor lends itself particularly to candlelit dinners, and service is very attentive.*

Closed Sun, Mon, 10 days Xmas, 2 wks mid Aug & BH's Lunch not served Sat
**V** 48 seats Last lunch 2pm Last dinner 10.30pm 6 P nc8yrs ♬
Credit Cards ①③

NOTTINGHAM Nottinghamshire Map **08** SK54 ⊝

See **Town Plan Section**

**★★★★63% Royal Moat House International**
Wollaton St NG1 5RH (Queens Moat) ☎(0602)414444
Telex no 37101 FAX (0602) 475667
Closed 25-26 Dec

*This is a busy and most popular modern hotel with extensive public rooms, offering a choice of four restaurants and a similar number of bars. A unique and pleasant feature of the hotel is an arcade of tropical trees and plants giving access to the first floor bars and restaurants. Car parking is in the adjacent multi-storey car park.*

201⇨♠(20fb)⚭in 44 bedrooms CTV in all bedrooms ® **T** ✖ (ex guide dogs) S15% sB⇨♠£78 dB⇨♠£97 (room only) ♠
Lift 《 ⚏ 600P CFA squash solarium gymnasium *xmas*
♀ English, French & American **V** ♨ ⚲ ✂ ✻ Lunch £4.50-£11.50&alc Dinner £6.95-£14.50&alc Last dinner 11pm
Credit Cards ①②③⑤

★★★★59% **Forte Crest**
Saint James's St NG1 6BN (Forte Hotels) ☎(0602)470131
Telex no 37211 FAX (0602) 484366
*Just off the central ring road, with good views of city and castle from many rooms.*
139⇌↙in 90 bedrooms CTV in all bedrooms ® ✳ S%
sB⇌fr£70 dB⇌fr£80 (room only) 只
Lift ( ⊞ CTV ⚡ *xmas*
♡ English & French V ⧖ ⊡ ↙ ✳ S% Lunch £12.80&alc
Dinner fr£12.80&alc Last dinner 11pm
Credit Cards ①②③⑤

★★★69% **Swans Hotel & Restaurant**
84-90 Radcliffe Rd, West Bridgford NG2 5HH ☎(0602)814042
FAX (0602) 455745
*Situated on the A6011 very near to Trent Bridge cricket ground, this completely refurbished hotel has public areas full of floral displays, smart and well equipped bedrooms, and a restaurant offering skilfully prepared meals chosen from either a set menu which is changed daily or the à la carte selection.*
31⇌𝄫(2fb)↙in 2 bedrooms CTV in all bedrooms ® T
✖ (ex guide dogs) ✳ sB&B⇌𝄫£51-£57.50 dB&B⇌𝄫£64-£75
只
Lift ( 33P CFA ♫ *xmas*
♡ English & French V ⧖ ⊡ ✳ Lunch fr£7.95&alc Dinner
£9.95-£11.95&alc Last dinner 10pm
Credit Cards ①②③⑤

★★★66% **Nottingham Moat House**
Mansfield Rd NG5 2BT (Queens Moat) ☎(0602)602621
Telex no 377429 FAX (0602) 691506
*A modern hotel, barely a mile north of the city centre, which attracts a good deal of local trade as well as considerable conference and function business; much of this popularity stems from its extensive range of restaurants offering value-for-money meals served by cheerful staff.*

→

172⌕⁐♠✂in 66 bedrooms CTV in all bedrooms ® T
✖ (ex guide dogs) ✳ sB⌕⁐♠fr£47.50 dB⌕⁐♠fr£63.95 (room
only) 🛏
Lift ℂ 250P 90🚗 CFA
♡ International V ✿ � ✂ ✳ Lunch fr£7.66&alc Dinner
fr£11.09&alc Last dinner 11pm
Credit Cards ① ② ③ ⑤

**★★★ 61% Strathdon Thistle**
Derby Rd NG1 5FT (Mount Charlotte (TS)) ☎(0602)418501
Telex no 377185 FAX (0602) 483725
*A city-centre hotel popular with businessmen. The first floor
cocktail bar serves as a meeting area before dining in Bobbins
restaurant or the American-style diner. Parking is limited.*
69⌕⁐♠(8fb)✂in 8 bedrooms CTV in all bedrooms ® T (room
only) 🛏
Lift ℂ 10P 5🚗
♡ International ✿ � ✂
Credit Cards ① ② ③ ④ ⑤

**★★★ 59% Stakis Victoria**
Milton St NG1 3PZ (Stakis) ☎(0602)419561 Telex no 37401
FAX (0602) 484736
*A busy centrally located hotel with limited parking facilities, which
offers a comprehensive conference service for up to 200 delegates.
There is a choice of 2 bars, Squires having a continental
atmosphere.*
166⌕⁐♠(15fb)1✖✂in 23 bedrooms CTV in all bedrooms ® T
sB⌕⁐♠£71.40-£82.95 dB⌕⁐♠£87.15-£97.65 (room only) 🛏
Lift ℂ 25P CFA *xmas*
V ✿ ⊙ ✂ ✳
Credit Cards ① ② ③ ⑤

**★★ 67% Hotel Windsor Lodge**
116 Radcliffe Rd, West Bridgford NG2 5HG ☎(0602)813773
FAX (0602) 819405
Closed 25-26 Dec
*This family-run hotel offers good quality accommodation and a
simple, but enjoyable English menu in the restaurant, freshly
prepared to order. There is a small conference suite, which also
contains a snooker table and trim gym unit.*
49⌕⁐♠(15fb) CTV in all bedrooms ® T ✳ sB&B⌕⁐♠£35-£42
dB&B⌕⁐♠£40-£52
CTV 50P 🐾 CFA sauna gymnasium
Bar Lunch £2.50-£6 Dinner £10.75 Last dinner 8.30pm
Credit Cards ① ② ③ ⑤

**★★ 65% Rufford**
53 Melton Road, West Bridgford NG2 7NE ☎(0602)814202
FAX (0602) 455801
Closed Xmas
*This well run busy hotel close to Trent Bridge on the Melton road
has comfortable business-style bedrooms and a conservatory bar
where orders are taken for well cooked meals from a daily
changing fixed-price menu.*
35♠ CTV in all bedrooms ® T ✖ (ex guide dogs) ✳
sB&B♠£30.55-£39.95 dB&B♠£47-£54.05
ℂ CTV 35P
✿ ⊙ ✳ Dinner £11.75-£14.10 Last dinner 8pm
Credit Cards ① ② ③ ⑤

**★★ 65% Westminster Hotel**
310-318 Mansfield Rd, Carrington NG5 2EF (on A60 1.5m N of
town centre) ☎(0602)623023 FAX (0602) 691156
Closed 25 Dec-1 Jan
*This professionally-run hotel, situated on the edge of town, has
fully modernised, well equipped bedrooms. There is an intimate
restaurant that offers an extensive choice on the fixed-price menu.*
59⌕♠ CTV in all bedrooms ® T ✖ ✳ sB&B⌕♠£40-£44
dB&B⌕♠£50-£54 🛏
Lift ℂ 38P
→

♀ English & Continental ♦ ♨ ✳ Dinner £12.95-£14.95 Last dinner 9.15pm
Credit Cards ① ③

### ★★ 63% *Priory*
Derby Rd, Wollaton Vale NG8 2NR (Toby) ☎(0602)221691
*A well furnished busy hotel on the A52, 3 miles west of the city, offering modern well equipped bedrooms, all at the rear of the building, and a restaurant serving a varied choice of grills, with a lounge bar open all day.*
31⇄(4fb)⊬in 7 bedrooms CTV in all bedrooms ® T
✖ (ex guide dogs)
⊆ 200P
♀ Mainly grills V ♦ ♨ ⊬ Last dinner 10.15pm
Credit Cards ① ② ③ ⑤

### ★★ 62% **Balmoral**
55-57 Loughborough Rd, West Bridgford NG2 7LA
☎(0602)455020 & 818588 FAX (0602) 455683
*A popular family-run commercial hotel situated on the outskirts of the city beside the A60 Loughborough Road, provides good standards of cleanliness and maintenance throughout. Some of the bedrooms are compact, particularly 8 modestly appointed rooms on the top floor which are awaiting planned alterations and refurbishment. Predominantly good value grill menus are served in a friendly and informal manner, but at weekends the food operation and choice are more restricted.*
31⇄♠ CTV in all bedrooms ® T ✖ (ex guide dogs) ✳
sB&B⇄♠£26.50-£35.25 dB&B⇄♠£40-£49
⊆ CTV 33P
V ♦ ♨ ✳ Lunch £7-£9alc Dinner £8.50-£12.50alc Last dinner 8pm
Credit Cards ① ③

### ✿ ✖ ✖ **Les Artistes Gourmands**
61 Wollaton Rd, Beeston NG9 2NG ☎(0602)228288
*Eddy Keon has been instrumental in introducing his homeland to many local people, not only with his range of true French dishes and drinks described in various menus and leaflets, but with his advice on vineyards, routes, hotels, restaurants – even property. The double shop front certainly looks like a French café. A small modern extension houses the restaurant, the older part, the bistro. Children are welcome, and they are charged at £1.30 per foot height in the bistro. Food is boisterous, with lots of strong flavour, enhanced with herbs and alcohol in many sauces. The restaurant is more expensive and a little more formal. Smoking is discouraged.*
Closed Sun & 1 wk Jan Lunch not served Sat
♀ French V 70 seats ✳ Lunch £8.60-£19.90&alc Last lunch 1.45pm Last dinner 9.30pm 1 P ⊬
Credit Cards ① ② ③ ⑤

### ★★ 61% **Chase**
Higham Ln CV11 6AG (Porterhouse) ☎(0203)383406
FAX (0203) 344696
*A 19th-century manor house, set off the main Hinkley road east of the town centre, has become a busy modern hotel which attracts both businessmen and tourists; it has a popular bar and restaurant trade, steaks being the mainstay of the menu.*
28⇄♠ CTV in all bedrooms ® T ✳ sB&B⇄♠£44
dB&B⇄♠£55 ⋒
300P ✿ CFA childrens play area
V ♦ ♨ ⊬ ✳ Lunch £6.99-£7.50alc Dinner fr£5.95alc Last dinner 10pm
Credit Cards ① ② ③ ⑤

### ⌂Forte Travelodge
Bedworth CV12 0BN (2m S, on A444) (Forte)
☎(0203)382541 Central Res (0800) 850950
*On the south bound side of the A444 close to Nuneaton, this lodge offers well equipped value-for-money accommodation. Meals are*

available at the Little Chef on the opposite side of the dual carriageway.
40⇄♠(40fb) CTV in all bedrooms ® sB⇄♠£29.95
dB⇄♠£29.95 (room only)
⊆ 40P ♨
Credit Cards ① ② ③

### ⌂Griff House Travel Inn
Coventry Rd CV10 7PJ ☎(0203)343584 FAX (0203) 327156
Closed 25 & 26 Dec
*Situated south of the town near the A444/B413 junction and within easy access of the M6 and M69, this well kept lodge offers compact well equipped bedrooms, with a separate restaurant and bar operation and a good children's play area in the grounds.*
38⇄ CTV in all bedrooms ✖
120P ♨
♀ Mainly grills Last dinner 10.30pm
Credit Cards ① ② ③ ⑤

### ⌂*Longshoot Toby*
Watling St CV11 6JH (Toby) ☎(0203)329711 Telex no 311100
Closed 24 Dec-4 Jan
*Situated at the busy A5/A47 junction, a Toby restaurant operation with bars and a separate motel block of well equipped though now dated bedrooms.*
Annexe47⇄♠ CTV in all bedrooms ® ✖
⊆ 120P
V ♦ ⊬ Last dinner 10pm
Credit Cards ① ② ③ ⑤

### ✿ ✖ ✖ **Ryedale Lodge**
YO6 5XB ☎(04395)246
*Elegant small restaurant, delightfully converted from a Victorian railway station on the edge of the Vale of Pickering. The 4-course table d'hôte offers mainly English dishes such as pigeon pie, roast duck, breast of smoked goose and duck, and local Ryedale red deer, with a stimulating wine list and delicious desserts. Seven bedrooms provide commendable accommodation and more are planned.*
Closed Jan Lunch not served
♀ European V 30 seats ✳ Dinner £26.50 Last dinner 9.30pm
30 P ⊬
Credit Cards ① ③

### ★★★ ✿ 70% **Nutfield Priory**
RH1 4EN ☎Redhill(0737)822066 FAX (0737) 823321
*A magnificent building dating back to 1872, sympathetically restored to operate as a quality hotel, has now added to its spacious, comfortable and comprehensively equipped accommodation 12 new bedrooms which are individually furnished and decorated to a high standard. The intimate, elegantly appointed Cloisters Restaurant serves a short, seasonal à la carte menu including a vegetarian option as well as game, meat and fish, herbs from the garden being imaginatively used in flavouring. Rich, flavoursome Mussel Chowder – almost a meal in itself – is enhanced with tomato and tarragon, the tender, pink Duo of Partridge is served on a bed of red cabbage with a light, truffle-scented game jus, while desserts include a traditional bread and butter pudding or an Amaretto Bavarois with stewed fruit and maple syrup as alternatives to the more usual chocolate mousse. Coffee can be taken in the charming oak-panelled library or in an impressive lounge with the original stained glass windows and organ. Leisure facilities and meeting rooms are available, conferences are particularly well catered for, and service throughout is professional.*
52⇄♠ 2⊞⊬in 12 bedrooms CTV in all bedrooms T ✳ S10%
sB&B⇄♠£74-£80 dB&B⇄♠£95-£103 Continental breakfast
⋒

Lift ℂ 130P ⇔ ❋ CFA ⊟ (heated) squash snooker sauna solarium gymnasium badminton steam room beauty treatment *xmas*

V ✿ ☑ ⅙ ✳ S10% Lunch fr£16.50&alc Dinner fr£16.50&alc Last dinner 9.45pm

Credit Cards ① ② ③ ⑤ ⓔ

**See advertisement under REDHILL**

---

**OAKHAM** Leicestershire Map **04** SK80

★★★

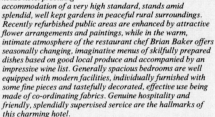

★★★❀❀❀❀⚑
**HAMBLETON HALL**

Hambleton LE15 8TH (3m E off A606) (Relais et Châteaux) ☎(0572)756991 FAX (0572) 724721

*A fine Victorian residence, now converted into a country house hotel providing accommodation of a very high standard, stands amid splendid, well kept gardens in peaceful rural surroundings. Recently refurbished public areas are enhanced by attractive flower arrangements and paintings, while in the warm, intimate atmosphere of the restaurant chef Brian Baker offers seasonally changing, imaginative menus of skilfully prepared dishes based on good local produce and accompanied by an impressive wine list. Generally spacious bedrooms are well equipped with modern facilities, individually furnished with some fine pieces and tastefully decorated, effective use being made of co-ordinating fabrics. Genuine hospitality and friendly, splendidly supervised service are the hallmarks of this charming hotel.*

15⇨↟1⊟ CTV in all bedrooms **T** ✳ sB&B⇨↟fr£105 dB&B⇨↟£105-£225 Continental breakfast ▤

Lift 40P ⇔ ❋ ⌣ (heated) ♪ (hard) *xmas*

V ✿ ✳ Lunch fr£17.50 Dinner fr£36.50 Last dinner 9.30pm

Credit Cards ① ③

---

★★★72% **Normanton Park**

LE15 8RP ☎Stamford(0780)720315 FAX (0780) 721086 (For full entry see Normanton)

★★★70% **Barnsdale Lodge**

The Avenue, Exton LE15 8AH (3m E on A606) ☎(0572)724678 FAX (0572) 724961

*Barnsdale Lodge is a country farmhouse hotel which is situated approximately 3 miles east of Oakham on the A606. This newly created hotel provides interesting, traditional English cuisine in the Edwardian-style restaurant, and a series of 3 individually-styled rooms. The Edwardian theme continues through all public rooms and the modern, comfortable bedrooms.*

17⇨↟(2fb)1⊟ CTV in all bedrooms ⓡ **T** ✳ sB&B⇨↟£46 dB&B⇨↟£66-£75 ▤

ℂ 150P ❋ CFA ⚘ *xmas*

V ✿ ☑ ⅙ ✳ Lunch £12.95&alc High tea £4.95 Dinner £16-£18alc Last dinner 9.30pm

Credit Cards ① ② ③ ⑤ ⓔ

---

A rosette means exceptional standards of cuisine.

---

★★★70% *Whipper-in Hotel*

Market Place LE15 6DT ☎(0572)756971 FAX (0572) 757759

*This popular hotel, furnished throughout with antiques, successfully preserves the atmosphere and character of its 17th-century building. Each of the comfortable and well equipped bedrooms is decorated in individual style, and meals are both interesting and of good quality – a feature appreciated both by a business clientele and the local community.*

21⇨↟Annexe3⇨↟2⊟ CTV in all bedrooms ⓡ **T** ℂ

V ✿ ☑ Last dinner 9.30pm

Credit Cards ① ② ③ ⑤

★★★65% **Crown**

Crown Walk, High St LE15 6AP ☎(0572)723631 FAX (0572) 724635 Closed 26-29 Dec

*Set above an attractive development of shops in the town centre, the hotel occupies the first floor of a recently refurbished 17th-century inn, offering en suite facilities throughout its well established, modestly appointed accommodation. Friendly, attentive service is provided both in the locally popular restaurant and comfortable lounge areas.*

16⇨↟ CTV in all bedrooms ⓡ **T** ✳ sB&B⇨↟£49.50 dB&B⇨↟↟£58.50 ▤

20P

❡ English & French V ✿ ☑ ✳ Lunch £11-£22alc Dinner £11-£22alc Last dinner 9.30pm

Credit Cards ① ② ③

**See advertisement on page 547**

---

Hotels with red star ratings are especially high quality.

## ★★63% The Boultons Country House

4 Catmose St LE15 6HW ☎(0572)722844 FAX (0572) 724473

*This hotel has recently undergone a major refurbishment and alteration programme resulting in a large function room and a new wing of modern bedrooms, which are decorated with Laura Ashley fabrics.*

25⇨🛏(2fb) CTV in all bedrooms ® T sB&B⇨🛏£37.50-£50 dB&B⇨🛏£55-£70 🅿

15P CFA *xmas*

♀ French V ♿ 𝒟 Lunch £8-£10&alc Dinner £14-£15&alc Last dinner 9.30pm

Credit Cards 1 2 3 5 £

---

OAKHILL Somerset Map 03 ST64

### ❀❀×× Oakhill House

Bath Rd BA3 5AQ ☎(0749)840180

*In the relaxed, informal atmosphere of this delightful 17th-century country house with its elegant bar and spacious dining room, the proprietors present a short, mainly English, menu of imaginative dishes based on local produce and making effective use of fruit sauces; poultry is raised on the premises and herbs are gathered from the garden.*

Closed Mon Lunch not served

Dinner not served Sun

V 45 seats Dinner £17.50 Last dinner 9.30pm 40 P ⚲

Credit Cards 1 3

---

OBAN Strathclyde *Argyllshire* Map 10 NM83

### ★★★60% Alexandra

Corran Esplanade PA34 5AA (Scottish Highland) ☎(0631)62381 Telex no 778215 FAX (0631) 64497

Closed Nov-Mar

*This popular coach-tour hotel on the waterfront enjoys fine views over the bay. A programme of gradual refurbishment is taking place, and standards of accommodation range from modest to good.*

55⇨🛏(1fb) CTV in all bedrooms ® T sB&B⇨🛏£51 dB&B⇨🛏£82 🅿

Lift ( 80P pool table ♫

♀ International V ♿ 𝒟 ✳ Bar Lunch £5 Dinner £13.75 Last dinner 9pm

Credit Cards 1 2 3 5 £

### ★★★56% Caledonian

Station Square PA34 5RT ☎(0631)63133 Telex no 777210 FAX (0631) 62998

*Situated in the centre of town close to the ferry terminal and railway station, this hotel is popular with tour groups. There is a fast food restaurant in addition to the main dining room.*

70⇨🛏(10fb) CTV in all bedrooms ® T ✳ sB⇨🛏£39-£69 dB⇨🛏£59-£89 (room only) 🅿

Lift ( 6P ⇔ *xmas*

♀ Scottish & French V ♿ 𝒟 ⚲

Credit Cards 1 2 3 5 £

### ★★❀76% Manor House

Gallanach Rd PA34 4LS ☎(0631)62087 FAX (0631) 63053

Closed 25 Dec-31 Jan

*This Georgian dower house, now a small elegant hotel, retains much of its original charm and character and has the quiet relaxed atmosphere of a country house. Bedrooms vary in size but are thoughtfully equipped, and the original kitchen range is a feature of the dining room; here seafood figures prominently on the dinner menu and the emphasis is on good, serious cooking using fresh produce.*

11⇨🛏 CTV in all bedrooms ® T dB&B⇨🛏£74-£150 (incl dinner) 🅿

20P ⇔ ❀ nc10yrs

♀ Scottish, French & German V ♿ ⚲

Credit Cards 1 3

## ★★61% Argyll

Corran Esplanade PA34 5PZ ☎(0631)62353 FAX (0631) 65472

*Compact, friendly and family-run, this hotel overlooking the pier and west bay was completely refurbished in 1991 to provide bright, attractive surroundings.*

27⇨🛏(5fb)2🖼 CTV in all bedrooms ® T ✳ sB&B⇨🛏£32-£40 dB&B⇨🛏£57-£77 🅿

( CTV 6P CFA ♫ *xmas*

♀ European V ♿ 𝒟 ✳ Lunch £2.90-£8.95&alc High tea £5.75 Dinner £12.50-£15.50&alc Last dinner 9pm

Credit Cards 1 2 3 5 £

### ★★59% Rowan Tree

George St PA34 5NX ☎(0631)62954

*A small, modern hotel which stands near the Esplanade, beside the cinema, provides friendly service and a short à la carte menu of enjoyable food; the combined foyer bar and lounge area offers an interesting outlook onto the main street in which it is situated.*

24⇨🛏 CTV in all bedrooms ® sB&B⇨🛏£28-£36 dB&B⇨🛏£46-£62

( 12P

♿ 𝒟 ✳

Credit Cards 1 2 3 5

### ★★58% Lancaster

Corran Esplanade PA34 5AD ☎(0631)62587

*A number of indoor leisure facilities are available in this extended Mock Tudor house which is pleasantly situated on the sea front with fine views of the bay and offshore islands. Bedrooms are all well equipped, though they tend to be compact and modestly furnished.*

27rm(3⇨21🛏)(3fb) CTV in all bedrooms ® ✳ sB&Bfr£23.50 sB&B⇨🛏fr£28.75 dB&B⇨🛏fr£50

20P ⇔ ▣ (heated) sauna solarium jacuzzi

V ♿ 𝒟 Lunch fr£5.75&alc Dinner £9.25-£11.50&alc Last dinner 8pm

Credit Cards 1 3

### ★🏩67% Foxholes

Cologin, Lerags PA34 4SE ☎(0631)64982

Closed Nov-Etr

7⇨🛏 CTV in all bedrooms ® ✖ ✳ sB&B⇨🛏£45 dB&B⇨🛏£72 (incl dinner) ✖

8P ⇔ nc7yrs

---

OCKLEY Surrey Map 04 TQ13

### ★★67% *Gatton Manor*

RH5 5PQ ☎Oakwood Hill(030679)555 FAX (030679) 713

*This small country house provides modern, comfortable bedrooms and has a very busy bar and restaurant. It is set in 200 acres of splendid grounds which includes an 18-hole golf course and, not surprisingly, is popular with golfers.*

10⇨🛏 CTV in all bedrooms ® T ✖ (ex guide dogs)

150P ⇔ ❀ ▶ 18 ♟ (grass) ⚓ bowling green

♀ English & French ♿ 𝒟 Last dinner 9.45pm

Credit Cards 1 3

---

ODIHAM Hampshire Map 04 SU75

### ★★67% George

High St RG25 1LP ☎(0256)702081 FAX (0256) 704213

*Easy access to the M3 is provided by this hotel, parts of which date back to the 15th-century. The individually furnished and decorated rooms within the main building retain much of their original character, while spacious annexe rooms maintain equally high standards of comfort. A sound choice of bar meals supplements the panelled restaurant's à la carte menu, and staff are friendly and relaxed.*

9⇨🛏 Annexe9⇨🛏(1fb)2🖼⚲in 3 bedrooms CTV in all bedrooms ® T ✳ sB&B⇨🛏£40-£58 dB&B⇨🛏£58-£68 🅿

20P ⇔ ❀

♋ English & French **V** ✿ ◻ ✳ Sunday Lunch fr£12.25 Dinner £18.75-£25.25alc Last dinner 10pm
Credit Cards 1 2 3 5

---

**OKEHAMPTON** Devon Map **02** SX59 ☉

⬆**Forte Travelodge**
Sourton Cross EX20 4LY (4m W, on A30) (Forte)
☎(0837)52124 Central Res (0800) 850950
*This clean, well maintained lodge provides easy access to Dartmoor and Cornwall from its position beside the A30; meals can be taken at the Little Chef Restaurant across the car park.*
32✑🐾(32fb) CTV in all bedrooms ® sB✑🐾£29.95
dB✑🐾£29.95 (room only)
⟨ 32P ⊟
Credit Cards 1 2 3

---

**OLD BURGHCLERE** Hampshire Map **04** SU45

❀✕✕**The Dew Pond**
RG15 9LH ☎Burghclere(063527)408
*This pretty extended farmhouse lies in a rural setting between Beacon Hill and the famous Watership Down: it is especially nice here on a fine day at lunchtime when you can enjoy the view. There is a small bar and a well kept restaurant, and is family run with a friendly and sedate atmosphere. Keith Marshall is in the kitchen and his menus are classically based though with some modern ideas such as crab gâteau with fromage frais, orange and gazpacho, or duck with honey, sesame and green peppercorns. The wine list offers a good variety, and service is by pleasant, neatly dressed waitresses.*
Closed Sun, Mon, 2 wks from 3rd Jan & 2 wks mid Aug Lunch not served Sat
→

O

547

♀ English & French **V** 40 seats ✳ Lunch £16-£18 Dinner £21-£25 Last lunch 2pm Last dinner 10pm 20 P nc3yrs
Credit Cards 1 3

---

## OLDBURY West Midlands Map **07** SO98

### ★★★74% *Jonathans'*
16-24 Wolverhampton Rd B68 0LH ☎021-429 3757
FAX 021-434 3107
*An hotel created from several shops and terraced properties, provides quite a landmark at the A4123/A456 junction with its exterior of chestnut coloured brick and tiles. Jonathan Baker and Jonathan Bedford, the owners, share a love of Victoriana which is in evidence throughout the very individual public areas and bedrooms, the latter combining Victorian furniture with the latest comforts, most having separate sitting rooms. Cuisine of a high standard is served against a background of panelled walls and polished antique tables – or you can enjoy a bistro atmosphere and less ambitious food in Littlejohns; the latest addition to the hotel is Baker Street, a Victorian area of cobbled alleys and tiny shops.*
10⇸2⇔¼⃗in 2 bedrooms CTV in all bedrooms ® **T**
✠ (ex guide dogs)
《 12P ⇱
**V** ♦ ⏛ Last dinner 10.30pm
Credit Cards 1 2 3

### ⇧Forte Travelodge
Wolverhampton Rd B69 2BH (on A4123, northbound) (Forte)
☎021-552 2967 Central Res (0800) 850550
*The well equipped modern accommodation provided by this popular lodge represents excellent value for money, meals being taken in the adjacent Little Chef restaurant; set beside the A4123, close to junction 2 of the M5, it offers convenient access to many nearby business centres.*
33⇸🏠(33fb) CTV in all bedrooms ® sB⇸🏠£29.95
dB⇸🏠£29.95 (room only)
《 33P ⇱
Credit Cards 1 2 3

---

## OLDHAM Greater Manchester Map **07** SD90

### ★★★70% **Hotel Smokies Park**
Ashton Rd, Bardsley OL8 3HX (Consort) ☎061-624 3405
Telex no 667490 FAX 061-627 5262
*A popular modern hotel, set beside the A627 midway between Oldham and Ashton-under-Lyne, combining comfortable, well appointed accommodation, excellent standards of housekeeping and friendly service from a smartly dressed young staff. There is a small but comprehensively equipped trimnasium for the exclusive use of guests, and a nightclub operates at weekends.*
47⇸🏠 CTV in all bedrooms ® **T** ✠ (ex guide dogs) ✳
sB&B⇸🏠£25-£75 dB&B⇸🏠£85-£85 ⊟
《 120P CFA sauna solarium gymnasium steam room
♀ English & French **V** ♦ ⏛ ✳ Lunch £8.50&alc Dinner £11.50&alc Last dinner 10.30pm
Credit Cards 1 2 3 5 £

### ★★★65% **Avant**
Windsor Rd, Manchester St OL8 4AS (Best Western)
☎061-627 5500 Telex no 668264 FAX 061-627 5896
*Standing next to the A62 to the southwest of the town centre, easily reached from either central Manchester or junction 20 of the M62, this modern, purpose-built hotel provides well equipped bedrooms with 24-hour room service; extensive function/conference facilities are available.*
103⇸🏠(2fb)¼⃗in 12 bedrooms CTV in all bedrooms ® **T** ✳
sB&B⇸🏠fr£63 dB&B⇸🏠fr£70 ⊟
Lift 《 120P CFA *xmas*
♀ English & French **V** ♦ ⏛ ⅟ ✳ Lunch £8.50-£13.95&alc Dinner fr£13.95&alc Last dinner 10pm
Credit Cards 1 2 3 5 £

---

### ★★★62% **The Bower**
Hollinwood Av, Chadderton OL9 8DE (2.25m SW A6104) (De Vere) ☎061-682 7254 FAX 061-683 4605
RS 25-31 Dec
*A former private residence set in its own grounds beside the A6104 at Chadderton has been extended and refurbished to provide well equipped bedrooms and attractive public areas as well as a range of conference and function facilities.*
66⇸🏠(1fb)1⃗⊞ CTV in all bedrooms ® **T** ⊟
《 140P ⇱
♀ Continental **V** ♦ ⏛ ✳ Lunch fr£11&alc Dinner fr£12&alc Last dinner 9.30pm
Credit Cards 1 2 3 5

### ★★70% **High Point**
Napier St OL1 1TR ☎061-624 4130 FAX 061-627 2757
*A friendly, family-run hotel with exceptionally well-appointed bedrooms. Situated in an elevated position looking towards the town centre. Recent expansion has enhanced the public areas.*
19rm(8⇸7🏠)(4fb)1⃗⊞ CTV in all bedrooms ® **T** ✳ sB&B£20-£35 sB&B⇸🏠£30-£40 dB&B£30-£45 dB&B⇸🏠£40-£55 ⊟
《 42P 2⮜ CFA ♫
♀ English & French **V** ♦ ⏛ ✳ Lunch £6.95 High tea £3.50 Dinner £9.95&alc Last dinner 9.45pm
Credit Cards 1 2 3 5

---

## OLD MELDRUM Grampian *Aberdeenshire* Map **15** NJ82

### ★66% **Meldrum Arms**
The Square AB51 0DS ☎(06512)2238 & 2505
*A friendly atmosphere pervades this small family-run hotel at the centre of the village, its well equipped and practical – though sometimes compact – en suite bedrooms and pleasantly appointed bar and restaurant appealing both to commercial guests and touring holidaymakers.*
7🏠 CTV in all bedrooms ® **T** ✠ ✳ sB&B🏠£30 dB&B🏠£42.50
25P
**V** ♦ ⏛ ✳ Bar Lunch £3.80-£5.95alc High tea £4.20-£8.20alc Dinner £7.70-£14.80alc Last dinner 9.30pm
Credit Cards 1 2 3

---

## OLD RAYNE Grampian *Aberdeenshire* Map **15** NJ62

### ★63% **Lodge**
AB2 6RY ☎(04645)205
*This homely small hotel in a hamlet just off the A96 has spacious bedrooms located in a chalet in the grounds. Within the main building are a comfortable lounge bar and attractive little dining room.*
1rmAnnexe5rm(4⇸🏠)(1fb) CTV in all bedrooms ® ✳ sB&B£30-£35 sB&B⇸🏠£35-£40 dB&B£40-£50 dB&B⇸🏠£45-£55
20P
♦ ⏛ ✳ Lunch £6.50 High tea £5.75 Dinner £12.50-£21 Last dinner 8.30pm
Credit Cards 1 3

---

## OLD SODBURY Avon Map **03** ST78

### ★★67% **Cross Hands**
BS17 6RJ ☎Chipping Sodbury(0454)313000 FAX (0454) 324409
RS Xmas Night
*This former posting house, situated on the A46/B4040 crossroads 2 miles north of the M4, has now been refurbished to meet the needs of the modern traveller. Bedrooms are both comfortable and very well equipped while public areas offer a blend of character and charm. A formal restaurant operates for both lunch and dinner.*
24rm(3⇸17🏠)1⃗⊞ CTV in all bedrooms ® **T** ✳ sB&B£31.50-£38.50 sB&B⇸🏠£44.50-£52.50 dB&B£52.50
dB&B⇸🏠£67.50-£77.50 Continental breakfast ⊟
《 200P ✿ CFA

♥ International **V** ✿ ✌ ✳ Lunch £10.95-£20.50&alc Dinner £12.50-£22alc Last dinner 10.30pm
Credit Cards ① ② ③ ⑤

---

ONICH Highland *Inverness-shire* Map **14** NN06

★★★65% **Lodge on the Loch**
Creag Dhu PH33 6RY ☎(08553)237 & 238 Telex no 94013696
FAX (08553) 463
Closed Nov-Jan (ex Xmas-New Year)
*Relaxing, family-run hotel with magnificent views of Loch Linnhe and surrounding mountains from most bedrooms. A ground floor bedroom has been specially designed for disabled guests.*
20rm(18⇗🅜)(2fb) CTV in all bedrooms ® T sB&B⇗🅜£33-£49 dB&B£36-£68 dB&B⇗🅜£66-£98 🍴
25P ♨ ✿ CFA *xmas*
♥ International **V** ✿ ⚓ ✌ Lunch £6-£8.50alc Dinner £18.50-£20&alc Last dinner 10pm
Credit Cards ① ③ ⓔ
**See advertisement under FORT WILLIAM**

★★69% **Allt-Nan-Ros**
PH33 6RY ☎(08553)210 & 250 FAX (08553) 462
Closed Nov-Mar
*A popular holiday hotel, overlooking Loch Linnhe and the surrounding mountains from a delightful setting in its own garden beside the A82, offers accommodation in comfortably furnished and well equipped bedrooms where attractive modern fabrics have been put to good use. A relaxed and friendly atmosphere pervades the bright, airy day rooms, and a fixed-price dinner menu features local game, salmon and seafood, the cuisine showing modern and French influences.*
21⇗🅜(2fb)1⚓ CTV in all bedrooms ® T sB&B⇗🅜£53.50-£66.50 dB&B⇗🅜£107-£133 🍴
50P ♨ ✿

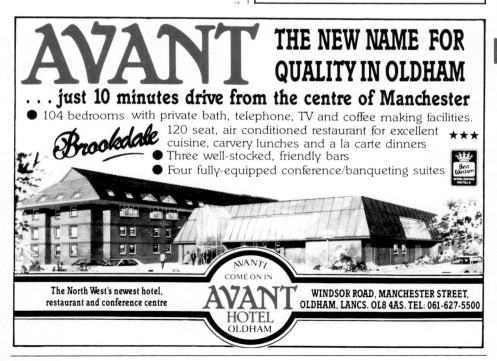

♀ Scottish & French ♨ ☕ ✂ Lunch £10-£15 Dinner £17.50-£21.50 Last dinner 8.30pm
Credit Cards ① ② ③ ⑤ ⓔ

### ★★65% **Onich**
PH33 6RY (Consort) ☎(08553)214 & 266 FAX (08553) 484
RS Nov-Mar

*Lovely views over Loch Linnhe to the Glencoe and Morven hills are enjoyed from this comfortable holiday hotel, which stands beside the A82 and has a garden extending to the lochside. The atmosphere is friendly, public rooms are tastefully furnished and bedrooms are comfortable and amply equipped, some having balconies.*

27⇔🅜(6fb) CTV in all bedrooms ® T ✳ sB&B⇔🅜£25-£40 dB&B⇔🅜£40-£80 🍴
50P 🚗 ❀ solarium gymnasium jacuzzi games room ௸
♀ International V ♨ ☕
Credit Cards ① ② ③ ⑤ ⓔ
**See advertisement under FORT WILLIAM**

### ★★56% **Creag Mhor**
PH33 6RY ☎(08553)379
Closed Nov-Mar

*Small and family run, this holiday hotel beside the A82 looks across Loch Linnhe to the mountains of Appin and the peaks around Glencoe. Public areas offer traditional comforts in a friendly atmosphere, and front-facing bedrooms have been partly upgraded though those to the rear of the house remain more simply appointed.*

14rm(9⇔🅜)(3fb) CTV in all bedrooms ® ✳ sB&B£17.50-£22.50 sB&B⇔🅜£22.50-£29.50 dB&B£35-£45 dB&B⇔🅜£45-£59 🍴
20P ❀ CFA ♪ xmas
V ♨ ✂ ✳ Bar Lunch £7-£10 Dinner £12.50-£16.50alc Last dinner 8.30pm
Credit Cards ① ③ ⓔ

---

### ONNELEY Staffordshire Map **07** SJ74

### ★★69% **Wheatsheaf Inn at Onneley**
Barhill Rd CW3 9QF ☎Stoke-On-Trent(0782)751581
FAX (0782) 751499

*A traditional English country inn, personally run by attentive hosts. A beamed restaurant is among the vast choice of eating options, covering everything from bar snacks to à la carte cuisine. Prettily furnished, individually designed bedrooms contain many extras designed to add to guests' comfort.*

5🅜 CTV in all bedrooms ® T sB&B🅜£37-£42 dB&B🅜£42-£52 🍴
150P ▶ 9 ♫
♀ English & French V ♨ ☕ Lunch fr£5.95&alc Dinner fr£14.95&alc Last dinner 9.30pm
Credit Cards ① ② ③ ⓔ

---

### ORFORD (NEAR WOODBRIDGE) Suffolk Map **05** TM44

### ★★64% **The Crown & Castle**
IP12 2LJ ☎Orford(0394)450205 FAX (0394) 450176

*Situated in the unspoilt village centre with views over Orford Ness and the nearby bird sanctuary, this 18th-century posting house is now benefiting from private ownership and offers well equipped accommodation with a cosy lounge and bar.*

10rm(1⇔)Annexe10⇔🅜(17fb)2🛏 CTV in all bedrooms ® T sB&Bfr£32.50 dB&B£55-£60 dB&B⇔🅜£60-£65 🍴
20P xmas
V ♨ ☕ ✂ ✳ Sunday Lunch fr£9 Dinner fr£12.50 Last dinner 8.45pm
Credit Cards ① ② ③ ⑤

---

### ORKNEY Map **16**

---

### KIRKWALL Map **16** HY41

### ★★61% *Ayre*
Ayre Rd KW15 1QX ☎(0856)3001
Closed 1-2 Jan

*This basic commercial hotel with two standards of accommodation offers some bedrooms which have been comfortably refurbished and others that, though rather dated, are nevertheless comfortable and spacious; all are well equipped and have colour television and telephones. Public areas offer, too, there is an attractive dining room with views of the harbour where guests can choose from quite simple but well prepared dishes, and a warmly hospitable atmosphere is created by caring management and helpful, friendly staff.*

32rm(4⇔6🅜)(2fb) CTV in all bedrooms ®
25P sauna trout & sea fishing
♀ International V ♨ ☕ Last dinner 9pm
Credit Cards ① ③

---

### ST MARGARET'S HOPE Map **16** ND48

### ❀ ✕ **Creel**
Front Rd KW17 2SL ☎(0856)83311

*A friendly restaurant standing on the seafront of this small village has earned a reputation as the best eating place on the island. Fresh local produce is the mainstay of the chef/patron's menu which, as one might expect, features many fish-based dishes. Partan Bree served with bannocks and terrine of salmon with a water vinaigrette are popular starters, to be followed by baked salmon in puff pastry with ginger and currants served with a mild tarragon sauce, or pork escalopes flamed in apple liqueur served with apple sauce. An Orkney speciality, Clootie Dumplings with vanilla sauce is only one of several interesting puddings.*
Closed Mon, Tue & Jan Lunch not served
V 40 seats ✳ Dinner £12-£18alc Last dinner 9.45pm 15 P
Credit Cards ① ③

---

### ORMSKIRK Lancashire Map **07** SD40

### ★★★67% **Beaufort**
High Ln, Burscough L40 7SN ☎Burscough(0704)892655
FAX (0704) 895135

*On the A59 a mile north of Ormskirk, this attractive modern hotel has spacious very well equipped bedrooms and a stylish restaurant offering a wide choice of dishes on its table d'hôte and à la carte menus.*

21⇔🅜 CTV in all bedrooms ® T ✳ sB&B⇔🅜£27-£54 dB&B⇔🅜£54-£67 🍴
《 126P 🚗
♀ International V ♨ ☕ Lunch £4-£16 Dinner £15.95 Last dinner 10pm
Credit Cards ① ② ③ ⓔ

---

### OSBOURNBY Lincolnshire Map **08** TF03

### ★59% **Whichcote Arms**
London Rd NG34 0DG ☎Culverthorpe(05295)239 & 500
*Located south of Sleaford in a quiet village on the A15, the bar at the Whichcote Arms is cheerful, popular with locals and warmed by a log fire in cooler weather. Accommodation is all en suite and modestly furnished; there is a small restaurant and banqueting room to the rear.*

7🅜(1fb) CTV in all bedrooms ® ✈ (ex guide dogs) ✳ sB&B🅜£25 dB&B🅜£34 🍴
40P ❀ CFA
♀ English & French V ♨ ☕ ✂ ✳ Lunch £6.95&alc
Credit Cards ① ③ ⓔ

## OSTERLEY Greater London

See **LONDON plan 1** *B3* (page 434)

★★**56%** **Osterley**

764 Great West Rd TW7 5NA (Consort) ☎081-568 9981
Telex no 915059 FAX 081-569 7819

*Once a Tudor-style pub, this hotel on the A4 has extended its
public areas by the addition of a conservatory. Functional but well
equipped bedrooms include some contained in a purpose-built
annexe.*

57⇨↿Annexe5rm(9fb) CTV in all bedrooms ® T ✳ S%
sB&B⇨↿£50-£70 dB&B£56-£77 dB&B⇨↿£56-£77
Continental breakfast ⊟
《 140P 3🏖
V ♥ ⚗ ✂ ✳ S% Lunch fr£9 High tea £3.50 Dinner
fr£10.50&alc Last dinner 10pm
Credit Cards ①②③⑤

## OSWESTRY Shropshire Map 07 SJ22 ☉

See also **Whittington**

★★★**67%** **Wynnstay**

Church St SY11 2SZ ☎(0691)655261 FAX (0691) 670606
*Completely transformed, this hotel now offers very comfortable
bedrooms and a ground floor area which consists of an elegant
library lounge bar, the Camellia restaurant, a conservatory and a
function/banqueting suite.*

27⇨↿(4fb)2🛏✂in 12 bedrooms CTV in all bedrooms ® T ✳
sB&B⇨↿£43-£55 dB&B⇨↿£50-£90 Continental breakfast
⊟
70P ✤ CFA crown green bowling *xmas*
♫ French V ♥ ⚗ ✂ ✳ Lunch £7.50-£10.50 High tea £2.50-
£6.95 Dinner £12.50&alc Last dinner 10pm
Credit Cards ①②③④⑤ ⑤

★★⚑**55%** **Sweeney Hall**

Morda SY10 9EU (1m S on A483) ☎(0691)652450
*This tranquil manor house with spacious grounds and grounds lies off
the A483 Oswestry by-pass and is reached via a long drive through
meadowland.*

9rm(6⇨↿) ® ✳ sB&B£26 sB&B⇨↿£30-£40 dB&B£43
dB&B⇨↿£49-£54
CTV 50P ⇚ ✤ putting green
♫ English, French & Italian V ♥ ✳ Lunch fr£11.50 Dinner
fr£11.50 Last dinner 9.30pm
Credit Cards ①③

⛬**Forte Travelodge**

Mile End Service Area SY11 4JA (junct A5/A483) (Forte)
☎(0691)658178 Central Res (0800) 850950
*A busy lodge on the junction of the A5 and A483 on the outskirts of
Oswestry. There is a Little Chef restaurant and a petrol station
within the same complex.*

40⇨↿(40fb) CTV in all bedrooms ® sB⇨↿£29.95
dB⇨↿£29.95 (room only)
《 40P ⇚
Credit Cards ①②③

## OTLEY West Yorkshire Map 08 SE24

★★★**66%** **Chevin Lodge Country Park**

Yorkgate LS21 3NU ☎(0943)467818 Telex no 51538
FAX (0943) 850335
*This hotel, built of Finnish logs, is located in 50 acres of birchwood
and there are some small lakes within the grounds. Bedrooms are
well furnished with some having patio doors giving access to the
grounds. A good standard of cooking is provided in the cosy
restaurant.*

18⇨↿Annexe34⇨↿(5fb) CTV in all bedrooms ® T
🐾 (ex guide dogs) ✳ sB&B⇨↿£55-£86.50 dB&B⇨↿£74.50-
£95 ⊟

《 ⊞ 100P ✤ CFA ♟ (hard) ♪ sauna solarium cycling games
room *xmas*
♫ English & French V ♥ ⚗ ✳ Lunch £10.50&alc Dinner
£15.50&alc Last dinner 9.30pm
Credit Cards ①②③

## OTTERBURN Northumberland Map 12 NY89

★★**61%** **Otterburn Tower**

NE19 1NP ☎(0830)20620
RS 25 Dec
*This historic building, standing in its own grounds, dates back to
1706 and offers bedrooms which are, for the most part, spacious
and attractively decorated, though lounge accommodation is, at
present, limited. Friendliness is the keynote of the establishment,
and the proprietors have created a genuine country house
atmosphere.*

11rm(5⇨3↿)(5fb)2🛏 CTV in 8 bedrooms TV in 1 bedroom
® T sB&B£30-£35 sB&B⇨↿£35-£40 dB&B£52.50
dB&B⇨↿£57.50-£65 ⊟
CTV 50P ✤ CFA ♪ *xmas*
V ♥ ⚗ Lunch £10-£12&alc Dinner £14.50-£15.50&alc Last
dinner 9.30pm
Credit Cards ①②③⑤ ⑤

## OTTERY ST MARY Devon Map 03 SY19

★★**68%** **Tumbling Weir Hotel & Restaurant**

EX11 1AO (Minotels) ☎(0404)812752
*A short riverside walk from the car park will bring guests to this
attractive thatched property with its modern extension; bedrooms
are well equipped, while the busy restaurant offers an extensive à la
carte menu, and guests are assured of both a warm welcome and
personal service.*

13⇨↿ CTV in all bedrooms ® T sB&B⇨↿fr£34
dB&B⇨↿fr£53 ⊟

→

**O**

CTV 3P ✿ CFA ♪ *xmas*
♀ French & Italian **V** ✟ ♨ ✗ ✳ Sunday Lunch £4.25-£8.75
Dinner £15.95 Last dinner 9.45pm
Credit Cards ① ② ③

---

## OUNDLE Northamptonshire Map **04** TL08

### ★★★66% **The Talbot**

New St PE8 4EA (Forte Hotels) ☎(0832)273621
FAX (0832) 274545

*This inn, dating back to 1626 and retaining many good*
*architectural features – notably transomed windows and a*
*beautiful Jacobean staircase – has considerably upgraded and*
*refurbished its public areas over recent years. Major improvements*
*will ensure that all bedrooms are of a high standard, comfortable*
*and well equipped by the end of 1991.*

40⇔(1fb) CTV in all bedrooms ® **T** S% sB⇔£65 dB⇔£85
(room only) ⊟
( 60P CFA ♨ *xmas*
**V** ✟ ✿ ✗ ✳ Lunch £8.95 Dinner £14.95&alc Last dinner
10pm
Credit Cards ① ② ③ ⑤

---

## OUTLANE West Yorkshire Map **07** SE01

### ★★★64% **Old Golf House Hotel**

New Hey Rd HD3 3YP (Lansbury) ☎Elland(0422)379311
Telex no 51324 FAX (0422) 372694

*A comfortable well furnished hotel set in open countryside close to*
*the M62. Newly refurbished bedrooms have good facilities and the*
*bar and attractive restaurant offer good value food served by*
*friendly staff.*

50⇔♠(3fb)2⊞✗in 4 bedrooms CTV in all bedrooms ® **T**
✈ (ex guide dogs) sB&B⇔♠£68-£77 dB&B⇔♠£81-£90 ⊟
( 70P ✿ CFA sauna solarium gymnasium *xmas*
♀ English & Continental **V** ✟ ✗ Lunch fr£8.50&alc Dinner
fr£13.50&alc Last dinner 10pm
Credit Cards ① ② ③ ⑤

---

## OVINGTON Northumberland Map **12** NZ06

### ★★58% **Highlander Inn**

NE42 6DH ☎Prudhoe(0661)32016

*A stone-built country inn, circa 1640, in the centre of the village 12*
*miles west of Newcastle-Upon-Tyne. Bedrooms are well equipped*
*and there is an attractive dining room renowned for its good food.*
*Terraced gardens at the rear look over meadowland towards the*
*valley.*

5rm(2⇔1♠)(2fb) CTV in all bedrooms ® **T** ✳ sB&B⇔£23-£26
sB&B⇔♠£30-£33 dB&B£35-£38 dB&B⇔♠£39-£43 ⊟
20P ✿ games room
♀ English & French **V** ✟ ✿ ✳ Lunch £7.25-£12.95&alc High
tea £1.25-£2.50 Dinner £12.95&alc Last dinner 9.30pm
Credit Cards ① ② ③

---

## OXFORD Oxfordshire Map **04** SP50 ◉

See **Town Plan Section**
See also **Milton Common**

### ★★★★54% **The Randolph**

Beaumont St OX1 2LN (Forte Hotels) ☎(0865)247481
Telex no 83446 FAX (0865) 791678

*An old city centre hotel of enormous character. The refurbishment*
*programme has now commenced in the bedrooms, and is completed*
*in the public areas which have been restored to their former*
*elegance and comfort.*

109⇔♠in 50 bedrooms CTV in all bedrooms ® **T** ✳ S%
sB⇔♠£95 dB⇔♠£115 (room only) ⊟
Lift ( 50🚗 CFA ♫ *xmas*
♀ International **V** ✟ ♨ ✗ ✳ Lunch £15 High tea £9.50
Dinner £22.50 Last dinner 10pm
Credit Cards ① ② ③ ④ ⑤

---

### ★★★❀❀❀❀❀♨♠ LE MANOIR AUX QUAT' SAISON

OX9 7PD (Relais et Châteaux) ☎Great Milton(0844)278881
Telex no 837552 FAX (0844) 278847
(For full entry see Milton, Great)

### ★★★❀❀♠67% **Studley Priory**

OX9 1AZ (Consort) ☎Stanton St John(086735)203 & 254
Telex no 262433 FAX (086735) 613
(For full entry see Horton-cum-Studley)

### ★★★64% *Cotswold Lodge*

66A Banbury Rd OX2 6JP ☎(0865)512121 Telex no 837127
Closed 25-30 Dec
52⇔(2fb) CTV in all bedrooms **T**
( 60P
♀ English & French **V** ✟ ♨ Last dinner 10.30pm
Credit Cards ① ② ③ ⑤

### ★★★64% **Oxford Moat House**

Godstow Rd, Wolvercote Rbt OX2 8AL (Queens Moat)
☎(0865)59933 Telex no 837926 FAX (0865) 310259

*Only 2 miles from the city centre and located conveniently close to*
*many major routes, this comfortable and smartly decorated*
*modern hotel, much used by commercial clients, provides friendly,*
*helpful service. The Beaumonts' Leisure Club includes a popular*
*brasserie-style restaurant where residents may dine more*
*informally than in the smart Oxford Blue Restaurant with its menu*
*of regional French dishes.*

155⇔(17fb)✗in 20 bedrooms CTV in all bedrooms ® **T**
sB&B⇔fr£87 dB&B⇔fr£105 ⊟
( 250P CFA ⊠ (heated) squash snooker sauna solarium
gymnasium whirlpool pitch & putt
♀ English & French **V** ✟ ♨ Lunch fr£10.50 Dinner fr£15.50
Last dinner 9.45pm
Credit Cards ① ② ③ ⑤

### ★★★59% **Linton Lodge**

Linton Rd OX2 6UJ ☎(0865)53461 Telex no 837093
FAX (0865) 310365

*In a quiet road just north of the city centre, this mainly commercial*
*hotel has been converted from 3 houses, making for nooks and*
*crannies and winding corridors. Bedrooms vary in size but are well*
*equipped with modern facilities. Public areas provide traditional*
*comfort and the young staff are mostly pleasant and helpful.*

71⇔♠(1fb)♨✗in 6 bedrooms CTV in all bedrooms ® **T**
sB⇔♠£85-£95 dB⇔♠£110-£120 (room only) ⊟
Lift ( 40P ✿ CFA pool table
♀ English & French **V** ✟ ♨ ✗ Lunch £11.50-£13.50 High tea
£5-£8 Dinner £16.50-£18.50&alc Last dinner 9.30pm
Credit Cards ① ② ③ ⑤ ⑥

### ★★★58% **Eastgate**

The High, Merton St OX1 4BE (Forte Hotels) ☎(0865)248244
Telex no 83302 FAX (0865) 791681

*Situated among imposing college buildings just off the High Street,*
*this hotel has been undergoing extensive improvement. Completed*
*bedrooms – all of which are comfortable and well equipped, even if*
*some are a little cramped – are attractively decorated. Public*
*areas have also been refurbished in traditional style, and a friendly*
*staff provides helpful service throughout.*

43⇔1♠✗in 7 bedrooms CTV in all bedrooms ® **T** ✳ S%
sB⇔£80 dB⇔£100 (room only) ⊟
Lift ( 43P CFA *xmas*
**V** ✟ ♨ ✗ ✳ Lunch £12.95 High tea fr£4.65 Dinner £14.95
Last dinner 10pm
Credit Cards ① ③ ④ ⑤

### ★★67% *The Tree Hotel*

Church Way, Iffley OX4 4EY (3m SE off A4158)
☎(0865)775974 & 778190 FAX (0865) 747554

*This Victorian public house in the quiet village of Iffley is*
*personally run by Ann and Dave Bowman as a small, friendly and*
*comfortable hotel. Bedrooms are attractively furnished and have*

*sparklingly clean en suite facilities, while downstairs is a convivial bar and small dining room that features home-cooked dishes.*
7⊸🛏(1fb)1🖵 CTV in all bedrooms ® T ✂ (ex guide dogs)
20P 3🚗 (£1 per night)
V ⊕ ⯑ ✗
Credit Cards [1] [2] [3]

★★60% **Welcome Lodge**
Peartree Roundabout OX2 8JZ (junc A34/A43) (Forte Hotels)
☎(0865)54301 Telex no 83202 FAX (0865) 513474
*Situated in a road services area 3 miles north of Oxford and close to major road lines, this motel offers comfortable well equipped bedrooms and has a small bar and bright carvery restaurant, with additional facilities available in the nearby Little Chef.*
100⊸(41fb)✗in 10 bedrooms CTV in all bedrooms ® 🖃
120P ✿ ≏ (heated)
♡ Mainly grills V ⊕ ⯑ ✗
Credit Cards [1] [2] [3] [4] [5]

★★57% **Victoria**
180 Abingdon Rd OX1 4RA ☎(0865)724536 Telex no 837031
FAX (0865) 794909
Closed 20 Dec-20 Jan
*This small and friendly family-run hotel just south of the city centre is popular with commercial users. Bedrooms, while quite compact, are comfortable and well equipped, with extra facilities currently being added. A small restaurant offers simple home-cooked dishes.*
23rm(13⊸1🛏)(2fb)1🖵 CTV in all bedrooms ® T ✳
sB&B£35.50-£37.50 sB&B⊸🛏£48.50-£52.50 dB&B£48.50-£52.50 dB&B⊸🛏£55.50-£65.50 🖃
CTV 17P CFA
♡ Italian & Yugoslav V ⊕ ⯑ ✗ ✳ Lunch fr£8.95&alc High tea fr£3.85 Dinner fr£12.75&alc Last dinner 9pm
Credit Cards [1] [3]

★60% **River**
17 Botley Rd OX2 0AA ☎(0865)243475 FAX (0865) 724306
Closed 21 Dec-2 Jan RS wknds
*Set by the Thames, this small family-run hotel has attractive public areas with pretty river views from the restaurant. Bedrooms of varied size, a few in an annexe across the road, are comfortable, freshly decorated and well equipped.*
16rm(5⊸7🛏)Annexe8rm(3⊸3🛏)(2fb) CTV in all bedrooms ® T ✂ (ex guide dogs) sB&B£35 sB&B⊸🛏£45-£50 dB&B⊸🛏£56-£62
CTV 25P ⛟ ✿ ♪
⊕ ⯑ Bar Lunch fr£3 Dinner £6.50-£10 Last dinner 7.30pm
Credit Cards [1] [3]

⊛ ✗✗**Bath Place**
4 & 5 Bath Place, Holywell St OX1 3SU ☎(0865)791812
FAX (0865) 791834
*Hidden away in a cobbled courtyard wedged between college buildings, the restaurant dates back to the 18th century and retains both character and charm. Dishes range from the relatively simple to more imaginative compositions, and all are well prepared, using good, fresh ingredients. A particularly enjoyable dish is the Supreme of free-range chicken in a grape and sauternes sauce, followed by a delicious home-made lemon tartlet, refreshingly tangy and full of zest. Service is well supervised, efficient and attentive.*
Closed Mon
Dinner not served Sun
♡ English & French V 36 seats ✳ Lunch £12.95&alc Dinner £21.95&alc Last lunch 2pm Last dinner 9.30pm 4 P
Credit Cards [1] [2] [3] [5]

For key to symbols in English see the bookmark.

# WANTAGE

*Excellent accommodation and traditional English Fayre.*

Close to the university city of Oxford and ideally situated for an overnight stay. The Bear Hotel offers the traveller superb standards of comfort and cuisine. This charming Georgian Coaching Inn is equally suitable for business accommodation or weekend breaks.

THE
**BEAR HOTEL**
WANTAGE
★★
**Market Place, Wantage**
**Tel: 02357 66366**

*Calotels*

# The Belfry Hotel

**Milton Common, Oxford OX9 2JW ★★★**
**Telephone: 0844 279381**
**Fax: 0844 279624**

80 bedrooms all with private facilities, colour TV, radio, telephone, tea/coffee facilities. LEISURE COMPLEX including indoor pool, sauna, solarium and mini gym. Parking 200 cars. Extensive conference facilities.
**40 minutes Heathrow. Situated on A40 near junction 7 of M40. Week-end Breaks.**

553

❀ ✗ ✗ **Paddyfield**
39-40 Hythe Bridge St OX1 2EP ☎(0865)248835
FAX (0235) 555912

*The lengthy menu provided by this streetside restaurant details both the different regions of Chinese cuisine and various culinary techniques; dishes may come from west (Szechuan hot fried scallops), north (chicken with cashews and yellow bean sauce) or south (pork Cantonese style) and can be sizzled, sautèed or stir-fried. Staff are well turned out and obliging, and a take-away service is available.*

Closed 25-27 Dec
♡ Cantonese, Pekinese & Szechuan **V** 150 seats ✻ Lunch fr£4.95&alc Last lunch 2.15pm Last dinner 11.45pm 20 P
Credit Cards ① ② ③

❀ ✗ **15 North Parade**
15 North Parade Av OX2 6LX ☎(0865)513773

*A popular, smart restaurant in a fashionable side street north of the city centre offers a cool décor and the comfort of cushioned bamboo chairs. Sensibly priced dishes in modern style avoid over-elaboration, the menu including chargrilled fillet steak, wild mushroom tartlet, chicken and coriander and vanilla bavarois; vegetarian options are available, and both bread and coffee are good. You can also take your own wine, for a corkage charge equivalent to the price of a bottle of the house wine (£8).*

Dinner not served Sun
♡ English & French **V** 60 seats ✻ Lunch £16-£27.75alc Dinner £16-£27.75alc Last lunch 2pm Last dinner 10pm 🅿 ✦
Credit Cards ① ③

---

**PADSTOW** Cornwall & Isles of Scilly Map **02** SW97

See also **Constantine Bay**

★★★58% **The Metropole**
Station Rd PL28 8DB (Forte Hotels) ☎(0841)532486
FAX (0841) 532867

*This large company owned hotel stands in an elevated position overlooking the harbour and river estuary. A choice of bedroom standards is available, the table d'hôte menus of the Harbour Restaurant – which is about to be refurbished – include a colourful sweet buffet, and friendly service is provided by mainly local staff.*

26⇄🛏(2fb)✦in 10 bedrooms CTV in all bedrooms ® **T** ✻ sB&B⇄🛏£49-£54 (incl dinner) ➡
▦50P ✿ ⌒ (heated) pitch & putt trampoline paddling pool *xmas*
**V** ✧ ⬚ ✦ ✻ Lunch £9.14-£11.20 Dinner £17.30 Last dinner 9.50pm
Credit Cards ① ② ③ ④ ⑤

★★59% *Old Custom House Inn*
South Quay PL28 8ED (St Austell Brewery) ☎(0841)532359
Closed Jan & Feb RS Nov, Dec & Etr

*An attractive period property overlooking the busy harbour, which has recently undergone extensive refurbishment. Cream teas are served in a new conservatory extension, and the bar, with its various areas and levels, is busy in season. The restaurant is well appointed and professionally run, extensive menus are available which make full use of local fish. Bedrooms are attractively co-ordinated and well equipped – the honeymoon suite has a four-poster bed and a double whirlpool bath. The hotel now has its own parking, a rarity in Padstow.*

24⇄(2fb) CTV in all bedrooms ®
CTV
♡ English & French **V** ✧ Last dinner 9.30pm
Credit Cards ① ② ③ ⑤

**See advertisement under ST AUSTELL**

★62% **St Petroc's House**
4 New St PL28 8EA ☎(0841)532700
Closed Jan-Feb
10rm(7⇄🛏)(3fb) CTV in all bedrooms ® **T** ✻ sB&B£25-£30 sB&B⇄🛏£30-£35 dB&B£40-£60 dB&B⇄🛏£50-£70 ➡

🅿 🚳
**V** ✦
Credit Cards ① ③

❀❀❀ ✗ ✗ **Seafood**
PL28 8BY ☎(0841)532485 FAX (0841) 533344
(Rosettes awarded for dinner only.)

*A rather classy restaurant with rooms virtually on the quayside in this, one of the prettiest of Cornwall's fishing villages. Most of the fish makes the short journey from the boat to Rick Stein's kitchen, where it is simply prepared. The good value set price menu and the attractive à la carte lists a token meat dish or two, but Stein's reputation has rested on his very accomplished fish cookery.*

Closed Sun, 15 Dec-1 Feb Lunch not served
♡ English & French 75 seats Dinner £25.50&alc Last dinner 9.30pm 10 P
Credit Cards ① ③

---

**PAIGNTON** Devon Map **03** SX86

★★★60% **Redcliffe**
Marine Dr TQ3 2NL ☎(0803)526397 FAX (0803) 528030

*Dating back to the turn of the century this extended building on the Esplanade offers a choice of bedrooms and public areas which have recently been upgraded. Function rooms are available during the winter.*

59⇄🛏(8fb) CTV in all bedrooms ® **T** 🐾 (ex guide dogs) sB&B⇄🛏£37-£45 dB&B⇄🛏£74-£90 ➡
Lift ℂ CTV 80P ✿ CFA ⌒ (heated) ♪ putting green table tennis ♫ *xmas*
♡ English & French **V** ✧ ⬚ Sunday Lunch fr£7.25 Dinner fr£12.50 Last dinner 8.30pm
Credit Cards ① ③

★★★58% **The Palace**
Esplanade Rd TQ4 6BJ (Forte Hotels) ☎(0803)555121
FAX (0803) 527974

*Set in its own well tended gardens near the seafront and providing both outdoor and indoor leisure facilities, this hotel offers accommodation in a range of warm, fully equipped bedrooms which are currently undergoing refurbishment. Bright, spacious public areas in modern style include a restaurant which serves a table d'hôte menu of simple dishes with some à la carte choices.*

52⇄🛏(1fb)✦in 14 bedrooms CTV in all bedrooms ® **T** ✻ sB&B⇄🛏£65-£70 dB&B⇄🛏£85-£100 (room only) ➡
Lift ℂ 60P ✿ CFA ⌒ 🅿 (hard) sauna solarium gymnasium games room ♫ ♨ *xmas*
**V** ✧ ⬚ ✦ ✻ Lunch £4 Dinner £15.32 Last dinner 9pm
Credit Cards ① ② ③ ⑤

★★68% **Sunhill**
Alta Vista Rd TQ4 6DA (Inter-Hotels) ☎(0803)557532
FAX (0803) 663850

*Overlooking the bay and with direct access to Goodrington Sands, this recently upgraded modern hotel offers a high standard of accommodation with well equipped bedrooms, some with balconies, and leisure and conference facilities. The informal restaurant serves freshly cooked dishes and staff are friendly and professional.*

29⇄🛏(3fb) CTV in all bedrooms ® **T** sB&B⇄🛏£27-£36 dB&B⇄🛏£54-£72 ➡
Lift 31P CFA snooker sauna solarium nc4yrs *xmas*
♡ English & French ✧ ⬚ ✦ Bar Lunch £1.50-£2.25 Dinner £11.50-£14 Last dinner 7.30pm
Credit Cards ① ② ③ ⓔ

★★60% *Dainton*
95 Dartmouth Rd, Three Beaches, Goodrington TQ4 6NA ☎(0803)550067 & 525901

*On a corner site with the side road leading to the beach, this busy small hotel in a Tudor-style modern building provides bright, compact bedrooms with modern facilities. Bar meals, table d'hôte and à la carte menus are available in the lively lounge bar and restaurant.*

11⇄🏠(3fb) CTV in all bedrooms ® T
《 CTV 20P 🚐 solarium ♫
🍴 English & Continental V ✧ ⚓ ✂ Last dinner 9.30pm
Credit Cards ① ③

### ★★58% Torbay Holiday Motel
Totnes Rd TQ4 7PP ☎(0803)558226 FAX (0803) 663375
Closed 24-31 Dec

*A modern motel complex on the Totnes road, about a mile from
Paignton and the local amenities. Spacious bedrooms in annexe
blocks offer good facilities and they are kept very warm in winter.
An extensive choice of dishes is available on table d'hôte, à la carte
and bar snack menus. On site amenities shared with self-catering
guests include indoor and outdoor pools.*

16⇄🏠 CTV in all bedrooms ® T sB&B⇄🏠£26-£30
dB&B⇄🏠£40-£48
150P 🚐 ✿ ▭ (heated) ⌇ (heated) sauna solarium gymnasium
crazy golf adventure playground
🍴 English & French V ✧ ✳ Bar Lunch £4.55-£10.55alc Dinner
£8.65&alc Last dinner 9pm
Credit Cards ① ③

### ★68% Oldway Links Hotel
21 Southfield Rd TQ3 2LZ ☎(0803)559332

*Set in its own grounds almost next to the police station, in an
elevated position with views across the town to the coastline
beyond, this completely refurbished hotel provides accommodation
in compact but well equipped bedrooms. Guests can relax in a cosy
bar with its flagged floor – the original kitchen of the house – and
the restaurant features a table d'hôte menu served in friendly
fashion by the wives of the partners. Car parking facilities are
available.*

13rm(4⇄6🏠)(2fb) CTV in all bedrooms ® sB&B£21.50-
£23.50 sB&B⇄🏠£21.50-£23.50 dB&B£43-£47 dB&B⇄🏠£43-
£47 🅿
40P 🚐 ✿ ♨

→

P

♡ English & French ♥ Dinner £10.50-£11.50&alc Last dinner
7.30pm
Credit Cards [1] [3] ①

★ 62% **Preston Sands**

10/12 Marine Pde TQ3 2NU ☎(0803)558718

*Bedrooms have fresh, modern décor and furnishings, while public
areas include a very attractive and comfortable lounge
complemented by a new bar and dining room. The hotel is well
managed and friendly, though both food and service tend to be
simple.*

26rm(4⇔3♠)(2fb) CTV in all bedrooms ® T ✱ sB&B£21-£24
sB&B⇔♠£22-£27 dB&B£40-£46 dB&B⇔♠£42-£54 ♬
CTV 24P nc10yrs
V ♥ ♨
Credit Cards [2] ①

★★★ 64% **Painswick**

Kemps Ln GL6 6YB ☎(0452)812160 Telex no 43605
FAX (0452) 814059

*Situated in the heart of this pretty Cotswold village, this former
Georgian rectory has been tastefully modernised, whilst retaining
many original features, including the fine panelled dining room and
the unique first-floor reception office which was once a private
chapel. Bedrooms are well equipped. Friendly service is provided
by resident owners Somerset and Helene Moore and their staff.*

19⇔♠(3fb)2☷ CTV in all bedrooms ® T ✱ sB&B⇔♠£55-
£105 dB&B⇔♠£75-£130 ♬
25P ⇔ ❋ CFA croquet *xmas*
V ♥ ♨ ⅍ ✱ Sunday Lunch £14.50&alc Dinner £21&alc Last
dinner 9.30pm
Credit Cards [1] [2] [3] ①

★★★ 67% **The Copper Inn**

Church Rd RG8 7AR (Resort) ☎Reading(0734)842244
Telex no 858699 FAX (0734) 845542

*A black and white, creeper-clad, 19th-century coaching inn with
eye-catching gables and awnings, providing accommodation in
comfortable, well equipped bedrooms, most of which overlook the
gardens (some being reached through the car park). Public areas
include an extensive lounge, a sitting room with sofas, pictures and
ornaments, and a restaurant which, despite recent changes of
ownership, offers a promising atmosphere of comfort and style.
Apéritifs and coffee are taken in the drawing room lounge, while
the meal itself is eaten in a French provincial style dining room.
Daily table d'hôte and more complex à la carte menus in modern
style contain such dishes as Scallop Gateau on a carrot and
kohlrabi rösti, and good Pot Roast Venison. It should be noted that
a meal here is not cheap – particularly if accompanied by wine.*

22⇔♠(1fb)1☷ CTV in all bedrooms ® T ✱ sB⇔♠£70-£80
dB⇔♠£80-£90 (room only) ♬
30P ⇔ ❋ CFA
♡ English & French V ♥ ♨ ✱ Lunch £13.50&alc Dinner
£16.95&alc Last dinner 9.30pm
Credit Cards [1] [2] [3] [5] ①

★★ 69% **Lindley**

Lancaster Ln WN8 7AB ☎(0257)462804
Closed 24, 25, 31 Dec & 1 Jan

*This attractive detached house stands in an elevated position on the
B5246 close to the village. Tastefully furnished and decorated
bedrooms in modern style are very well equipped and have en suite
facilities, while the fashionable restaurant enjoys fine views over
surrounding countryside.*

8⇔♠(1fb) CTV in all bedrooms ® T sB&B⇔♠£35-£45
dB&B⇔♠£50-£55
60P ⇔ ❋
♡ English & French V ♥ ♨ ⅍ Lunch £7.70-£8.30&alc Dinner
£11.80-£24.20alc Last dinner 9.30pm
Credit Cards [1] [2] [3]

★★★ 57% **The Ship**

The Parade L64 6SA (Forte Hotels) ☎051-336 3931
FAX 051-393 0051

*Relaxed, traditional small hotel with excellent views of the Dee
Estuary and its wild bird life.*

26⇔3☷2⇆ in 2 bedrooms CTV in all bedrooms ® ✱
sB⇔♠fr£50 dB⇔♠£60-£70 (room only)
☾ 100P ♬ *xmas*
♡ English & French V ♥ ♨ ⅍ ✱ Lunch fr£8.15 Dinner
fr£13.25&alc Last dinner 9.30pm
Credit Cards [1] [2] [3] [4] [5]

★★ 62% **Parkgate**

Boathouse Ln L64 6RD (Lansbury) ☎051-336 5001
Telex no 629469 FAX 051-336 8504

*A period house in landscaped grounds on the edge of the Dee
Marshes offers comfortable well equipped bedrooms and an
extended open-plan lounge bar and restaurant.*

27⇔♠(3fb)1☷⅍ in 5 bedrooms CTV in all bedrooms ® T
☾ 150P
♡ English & French V ♥ ♨ Last dinner 10pm
Credit Cards [1] [2] [3] [5]

★★★ 69% **Penhaven Country House**

EX39 5PL ☎Horns Cross(0237)451388 & 451711
FAX (0237) 451878

*Surrounded by 9 acres of mature gardens with a stream, this
former Victorian rectory, which stands just outside the village in
wooded countryside behind Bideford Bay, has been
sympathetically and lovingly restored to provide a pleasant little
hotel in country house style. Enthusiastic managers welcome
guests warmly into its hospitable atmosphere, and a dedicated
team of local staff renders reliable service. Comfortable, spotlessly
clean bedrooms are brightly furnished, pleasantly decorated and
well equipped, while 5 attractive cottage annexe suites include their
own fitted kitchens. Plans exist to extend the somewhat restricted
lounge and dining room facilities, but the limitations of space do
not detract from the quality of imaginative meals which are
expertly prepared from the best of local produce and attractively
presented accompanied by a reasonably priced wine list.*

12⇔♠1☷ CTV in all bedrooms ® T sB&B⇔♠£46-£80
dB&B⇔♠£95-£120 (incl dinner) ♬
50P ⇔ ❋ nature trail nc10yrs *xmas*
♡ English & French V ♥ ♨ ⅍ Lunch fr£8.95&alc Dinner
£13.75-£19&alc Last dinner 9pm
Credit Cards [1] [2] [3] [5] ①

❀ ✕ ✕ **Sportsman's Arms**

Wath-in-Nidderdale HG3 5PP (2m NW unclass rd)
☎Harrogate(0423)711306

*Nestling in the beautiful Nidderdale countryside, this restaurant is
housed in an attractive building dating from the 17th century.
Cuisine is basically British with game (in season), salmon, beef,
duck, pork and fish expertly cooked and served. The food is
complemented by an extensive wine list.*

Closed 25-26 Dec Lunch not served Mon-Sat
Dinner not served Sun

♀ English & Continental **V** 45 seats Sunday Lunch £12.50-£14.50 Dinner £17.50-£19.50&alc Last lunch 1.45pm Last dinner 9.30pm 30 P
Credit Cards 1 2 3 5

---

**PATHHEAD** Lothian *Midlothian* Map **11** NT36

★★★56% **Stair Arms**
EH37 5TX ☎Ford(0875)320277 FAX (0875) 320929
*Attractive bedrooms are a feature of this former coaching inn on the A68 north of the village. Good value meals are served in the Tudor style diner.*
12rm(11⇨3♠)(1fb)1⊞ CTV in all bedrooms ® **T**
✠ (ex guide dogs) ✱ S% sB&B⇨3♠£39-£48 dB&B⇨3♠£55 ⋒
⟨ 120P ✿ CFA childrens' play area *xmas*
**V** ♦ ⬛ Lunch fr£1.50
Credit Cards 1 2 3 £

---

**PATTERDALE** Cumbria Map **11** NY31

★★57% **Patterdale**
CA11 0NN ☎Glenridding(07684)82231 FAX (07684) 82440
Closed Jan-Feb
*This hotel has been owned by the same family for over 60 years and its recently upgraded bedrooms are of a good standard.*
57⇨3♠(4fb) CTV in all bedrooms ® **T** sB&B⇨3♠£28-£30
dB&B⇨3♠£56-£60
CTV 30P 1🐾 ✿ ♪ ♫ *xmas*
**V** ♦ S% Lunch fr£6.50 High tea fr£4.50 Dinner fr£13 Last dinner 8pm
Credit Cards 1 3 £

---

**PEASMARSH** East Sussex Map **05** TQ82

★★★68% **Flackley Ash**
TN31 6YH (Best Western) ☎(079721)651 Telex no 957210
FAX (079721) 510
*Set in open rural surroundings, this Georgian manor house has been thoughtfully extended. Bedrooms in the new wing provide a uniform standard of comfort, while executive rooms offer extra space and additional facilities. Rooms in the main house vary in size, but all are well furnished and equipped. There is a spacious bar lounge and restaurant and the attractive lounge has been recently refurbished. Leisure facilities include a swimming pool, mini gym and flotation tank.*
32⇨3♠(3fb)3⊞ CTV in all bedrooms ® **T** sB&B⇨♠£59-£63
dB&B⇨3♠£89 ⋒
70P ✿ CFA ⬛ (heated) sauna solarium gymnasium spa bath croquet beautician float tank *xmas*
♀ English & French **V** ♦ ⬛ ✠ Lunch £11.95-£12.95 High tea £4.50-£5.50 Dinner £15.50-£16.50&alc Last dinner 9.30pm
Credit Cards 1 2 3 5 £

*See advertisement under RYE*

---

**PEAT INN** Fife Map **12** NO40

❀❀❀ ✕✕**The Peat Inn**
KY15 5LH ☎(033484)206
*Chef/patron David Wilson's fine cooking draws guests from miles around to his cosy, friendly restaurant. He offers table d'hôte and à la carte menus in the evenings and a set luncheon menu which may start with an unusual but successful ragout of scallops, monkfish and pork, followed by breast of pigeon with wild mushrooms, with a caramelised apple pastry and custard sauce to round off the meal. The wine list is impressive.*
Closed Sun, Mon, 2 wks Jan & 2 wks Nov
♀ French 48 seats Lunch £17.50 Dinner fr£30&alc Last lunch 1pm Last dinner 9.30pm 24 P ✠
Credit Cards 1 2 3 5

---

**PEEBLES** Borders *Peeblesshire* Map **11** NT24

★★★64% **Peebles Hydro**
EH45 8LX (Consort) ☎(0721)20602 FAX (0721) 22999
*Set in its own well tended gardens and parkland, this popular hotel specialises in family holidays. Supervised children's activities are organised daily. They also have very good leisure facilities, signed walks through the grounds and spacious comfortable lounges.*
137⇨♠(25fb) CTV in all bedrooms ® **T** ✠ (ex guide dogs)
S% sB&B⇨3♠£58-£64 dB&B⇨3♠£79.50-£127.50 (incl dinner) ⋒
Lift ⟨ 200P ✿ CFA ⬛ (heated) ♈ (hard) squash ∪ snooker sauna solarium gymnasium pitch & putt badminton beautician ♫ 🐾 *xmas*
**V** ♦ ⬛ ✠ S% Lunch fr£10.75 Dinner fr£15.85 Last dinner 9pm
Credit Cards 1 2 3 5 £

★★★58% **Park**
Innerleithen Rd EH45 8BA ☎(0721)20451 FAX (0721) 22999
*This traditional town-centre hotel, set in an attractive garden, enjoys pleasant views over the surrounding countryside and offers accommodation in well equipped, comfortable bedrooms; after eating in the charming oak-panelled restaurant guests can relax in a comfortable lounge or make use (free of charge) of the sports and leisure facilities at the nearby Peebles Hotel Hydro, a sister hotel.*
24⇨3♠ Annexe1⇨1⊞ CTV in all bedrooms ® **T** ✱
sB&B⇨3♠£54.15-£60.95 dB&B⇨3♠£80.70-£126.75 (incl dinner) ⋒
⟨ 50P ✿ CFA *xmas*
**V** ♦ ⬛ ✱ Sunday Lunch £6-£10.25 Dinner £14.05-£15.05 Last dinner 9.30pm
Credit Cards 1 2 3 5 £

**P**

### ★★★50% The Tontine
High St EH45 8AJ (Forte Hotels) ☎(0721)20892
FAX (0721) 29732
*Traditional, friendly and well-equipped hotel in the centre of the picturesque town.*
37⇌🏃(3fb)1🛏✁in 18 bedrooms CTV in all bedrooms ® T 🖳
《21P 4🚗 CFA *xmas*
🍴 Scottish & French V ☺ ⚘ ✁
Credit Cards 1 2 3 5

### ★★🏋76% Cringletie House
EH45 8PL ☎Eddleston(07213)233 FAX (07213) 244
Closed 2 Jan-6 Mar
*A romantically splendid country house featuring crow-stepped gables and fairytale turrets. Owned and managed by the Maguire family, supported by a courteous and attentive staff, warm and spontaneous service is assured. Bedroom accommodation is cosy and inviting, as are the two spacious lounges. The home cooked dinners are very good value for money.*
13⇌🏃CTV in all bedrooms T sB&B⇌🏃£44-£55
dB&B⇌🏃£80 🖳
Lift 40P 🚗 ⚘ ♪ (hard) putting croquet
🍴 International V ☺ ⚘ ✁ Lunch fr£5alc Dinner £22.50 Last dinner 8.30pm
Credit Cards 1 3

### ★★67% Kingsmuir
Springhill Rd EH45 9EP ☎(0721)20151 FAX (0721) 21795
*Comfortable and friendly under the management of its resident proprietors, the hotel offers home-cooked meals in both bar and restaurant which represent particularly good value for money.*
10⇌🏃(2fb) CTV in all bedrooms ® T sB&B⇌🏃£33-£40
dB&B⇌🏃£58-£68 🖳
27P 🚗 ⚘ ♨
🍴 Scottish & French V ☺ ✁ 🖳 Lunch fr£8.50 Dinner £13.50&alc Last dinner 9pm
Credit Cards 1 2 3

### ★★🏋67% Venlaw Castle
Edinburgh Rd EH45 8QG ☎(0721)20384
Closed Nov-Mar
*Pleasantly secluded by trees, yet commanding beautiful views from its upper windows, this baronial-style house in the hills above the town has been owned by the same family for more than thirty years. Traditional standards of hospitality and service are maintained throughout, a particularly relaxing lounge and unique library bar being attractive features.*
12rm(5⇌5🏃)(4fb) CTV in all bedrooms ® T sB&B£22.50-£23.50 sB&B⇌🏃£35-£40 dB&B£41-£43 dB&B⇌🏃£53-£56 🖳
20P 🚗 ⚘
V ☺ ✁ Bar Lunch £5-£8 Dinner £9.50-£14.50 Last dinner 8pm
Credit Cards 1 2 3 4 5 ⓔ

---

## PELYNT Cornwall & Isles of Scilly Map 02 SX25

### ★★63% *Jubilee Inn*
PL13 2JZ ☎Lanreath(0503)20312
*An inn of charm and character has been tastefully modernised to provide comfortable accommodation; the atmosphere is relaxing and friendly, helpful service being rendered by charming staff.*
9⇌🏃(2fb)1🛏 CTV in all bedrooms
CTV 80P 6🚗 ⚘ ♨
🍴 English & Continental V ☺ ⚘ Last dinner 10pm
Credit Cards 1 3

---

## PEMBROKE Dyfed Map 02 SM90

See also Lamphey

---

*A rosette means exceptional standards of cuisine.*

---

### ★★60% Coach House Inn
116 Main St SA71 4HN ☎(0646)684602 FAX (0646) 687456
Closed 24-26 Dec
*A busy town centre hotel, this was once a coaching inn. The old courtyard is now a pleasant bar with a small gallery lounge above, and the bedrooms are all pine furnished. A good range of food is available in the bar and in the à la carte restaurant.*
14⇌🏃(3fb)✁in 4 bedrooms CTV in all bedrooms ® T ✳
sB&B⇌🏃£35 dB&B⇌🏃£49.50 🖳
10P ❀ solarium
🍴 English & French V ☺ ⚘ ✳ Dinner £15&alc Last dinner 9pm
Credit Cards 1 2 3 5 ⓔ

### ★★58% Old Kings Arms
Main St SA71 4JS ☎(0646)683611
Closed 25-26 Dec & 1 Jan
*Under the same family ownership for over 30 years, this old coaching inn in the town centre has compact bedrooms fitted with modern facilities and a large traditional-style residents' lounge. Food is available in the popular bars and attractive slab-floored restaurant with log fire.*
21⇌ CTV in all bedrooms ® T ✳ sB&B⇌£27-£34
dB&B⇌£44-£46
21P
V ☺ Lunch £7.50-£9.50alc Dinner £9.50-£12.50alc Last dinner 10pm
Credit Cards 1 2 3

---

## PEMBROKE DOCK Dyfed Map 02 SM90

### ★★★63% Cleddau Bridge
Essex Rd SA72 6UT (Consort) ☎Pembroke(0646)685961
FAX (0646) 685746
*A modern hotel with panoramic views of the Haven stands, as its name implies, beside the toll bridge on the southern shore line. Rooms are all at the same level, looking inwards to a central courtyard containing an outdoor pool.*
24⇌🏃 CTV in all bedrooms ® T ✳ sB&B⇌🏃fr£55
dB&B⇌🏃fr£70 🖳
《150P ❀ 🏊 (heated) ⚓ (heated) *xmas*
🍴 British & French V ☺ ✳ Lunch £9.25-£15&alc Dinner £13-£30alc Last dinner 9.30pm
Credit Cards 1 2 3 5

---

## PENARTH South Glamorgan Map 03 ST17

### ★65% Walton House
37 Victoria Rd CF6 2HY ☎(0222)707782 FAX (0222) 711012
RS Sun
*A small family-run hotel in a quiet residential part of town, which is both friendly and well managed. Very popular with business travellers, it has an attractive restaurant also much used by locals.*
13rm(10⇌🏃) CTV in all bedrooms ® T 🐾 (ex guide dogs) ✳
sB&B£22.50-£23.50 sB&B⇌🏃£27.50-£31 dB&B£40
dB&B⇌🏃£42.50
16P 🚗 ⚘
🍴 English, French, Italian & Spanish V ✳ Lunch £11.50&alc Dinner £11.50&alc Last dinner 9pm
Credit Cards 1 3

---

## PENCOED Mid Glamorgan Map 03 SS98

### ⌂Forte Travelodge
Old Mill, Felindre Rd CF3 5HU (on A473) (Forte)
☎(0656)864404 Central Res (0800) 850950
*This modern lodge located on the first road to the right off the A473 north from junction 35 of the M4, stands adjacent to a Harvester Restaurant where food is available between 11am and 11pm.*

---

40⇄🛏(40fb) CTV in all bedrooms ⓇsB⇄🛏£29.95
dB⇄🛏£29.95 (room only)
⓵40P ⇜
Credit Cards ① ② ③

○**St Marys**
St Marys Golf Club CF35 5EA ☎Bridgend(0656)860280
Due to have opened Aug 1991
24⇄🛏

---

**PENCRAIG** Hereford & Worcester Map **03** SO52

★★♨62% **Pencraig Court**
HR9 6HR (off A40) ☎Ross-on-Wye(0989)84306
Closed Nov-Feb
*Just off the A40, four miles south of Ross-on-Wye, this hotel is set in 3.5 acres of grounds, with some superb views of the surrounding countryside. The hotel is privately owned and has a relaxed, informal atmosphere.*
11⇄(2fb)1⊞ CTV in all bedrooms Ⓡ ✹ (ex guide dogs)
sB&B⇄£37-£44 dB&B⇄£52-£66 🍴
25P ✿ Ü
♀ English & French V ♥ ⏛ S% Bar Lunch fr£4 Dinner
fr£13.50 Last dinner 9pm
Credit Cards ① ② ③ ⑤

---

**PENMAEN** West Glamorgan Map **02** SS58

★★65% **Nicholaston House**
Nicholaston SA3 2HL ☎Swansea(0792)371317
*This 19th-century house with superb sea views, has been converted to provide modern, well equipped accommodation with attractive bedrooms and comfortable public rooms. Friendly service is provided by the proprietors Pat and Peter Lewis.*
11⇄(4fb)1⊞ CTV in all bedrooms Ⓡ ✹ (ex guide dogs) ✱
sB&B⇄£20.50-£42 dB&B⇄£37-£64 🍴

→

P

CTV 35P ✿ CFA snooker 9 hole putting green
V ✿ ✃ ✳ Sunday Lunch £8.50 Dinner £11.95&alc Last dinner 9pm
Credit Cards 1 3

---

PENNAL Gwynedd Map 06 SH60

★★60% **Llugwy Hall Country House**
SY20 9JX (1m E on A483) ☎(0654)791228 FAX (0654) 791231
Closed 24 Dec-2 Jan
*A 17th-century, stone-built house set in 40 acres of grounds on the banks of the River Dovey. Facilities include an outdoor pursuits centre with its own dormitory accommodation.*
15⇉🌑(4fb) CTV in all bedrooms ® T sB&B⇉🌑£44-£47
dB&B⇉🌑£78-£98 (incl dinner) 🞧
40P ✿ CFA croquet clay pigeon shooting
V ✿ 🗓 ✳ Sunday Lunch £6.50 Dinner £13.50 Last dinner 9pm
Credit Cards 1 2 3 5

★50% **Riverside**
SY20 9DW ☎(0654)791285
*A small village-centre pub offers modest accommodation and busy bars which do a brisk meal trade.*
7rm(1fb) ® ✳ sB&B£18.50-£20.50 dB&B£37-£42
CTV 60P 4🐾 ✿
V ✿ ✳ Lunch £3.95-£15&alc

---

PENNYGHAEL

See Mull, Isle of

---

PENRHYNDEUDRAETH Gwynedd Map 06 SH63

★★★76% **The Hotel Portmeirion**
Portmeirion LL48 6ET (2m W, Portmeirion village is S off A487)
☎Porthmadog(0766)770228 Telex no 61540
FAX (0766) 771331
Closed 13 Jan-7 Feb
*The Italianate village of Portmeirion remains a very popular tourist attraction, and the hotel, which reopened in 1988 after extensive rebuilding work, is an important part of it. The public areas, are each delightfully designed to a specific theme, and there are 14 beautifully decorated and furnished bedrooms. Further bedrooms are available in several cottages and buildings throughout the village. Each is individual in style and all enjoy magnificent views. The unique location, together with the friendly and attentive service by young and enthusiastic staff, ensures an enjoyable and memorable visit.*
14⇉🌑Annexe20⇉🌑(2fb)2🛏 CTV in all bedrooms ® T
✕ (ex guide dogs) ✳ sB⇉🌑£45-£105 dB⇉🌑£55-£115 (room only) 🞧
℄ 40P 🚗 ✿ CFA ⌲ (heated) *xmas*
🍴 French ✃ ✳ Sunday Lunch £16 Dinner £25 Last dinner 9.30pm
Credit Cards 1 2 3 5

---

PENRITH Cumbria Map 12 NY53 ⊙

See also Edenhall **and** Shap
★★★73% **North Lakes**
Ullswater Rd CA11 8QT (Shire) ☎(0768)68111
FAX (0768) 68291
*A well appointed hotel, close to the M6, with very good bedrooms and a leisure centre. Public areas are full of character with open beams and a stone fireplace. Service is friendly and helpful.*
85⇉🌑(6fb)4🛏✃in 12 bedrooms CTV in all bedrooms ® T ✳
S% sB&B⇉🌑£84-£104 dB&B⇉🌑£100-£120 🞧
Lift ℄ 150P CFA 🏊 (heated) squash snooker sauna solarium gymnasium spa pool *xmas*
🍴 English & French V ✿ 🗓
Credit Cards 1 2 3 4 5

★★64% **George**
Devonshire St CA1 7SU ☎(0768)62696 FAX (0768) 68223
Closed 25-26 Dec & 1 Jan
*This traditional coaching house hotel in the town centre provides its guests with good standards of comfort and service.*
31⇉🌑(1fb) CTV in all bedrooms ® T ✳ sB&B⇉🌑🌑fr£37
dB&B⇉🌑fr£51 🞧
℄ 30P
🍴 English & French ✿ 🗓 Lunch fr£7.30 Dinner fr£11.50 Last dinner 8.30pm
Credit Cards 1 3 ①

★★60% *Clifton Hill*
Clifton CA10 2EJ (2.75m S A6) ☎(0768)62717
*This large family-run hotel, set back from the A6 in its own gardens, 3 miles south of the town, has spacious public areas and recently upgraded bedrooms. It also offers organised tours of the Lake District.*
57⇉🌑(2fb) CTV in all bedrooms
CTV 200P 25🐾 ✿
V ✿ 🗓 ✃

★★58% **Roundthorn Country**
Beacon Edge CA11 8SJ ☎(0768)63952
Closed Nov-Feb RS Mar & Nov
*A detached, stone-built hotel which overlooks the town from a hillside setting offers accommodation in bedrooms with good facilities; friendly service is provided by the resident owners.*
7⇉🌑(2fb)2🛏 CTV in all bedrooms ® sB&B⇉🌑£27.50-£32.50 dB&B⇉🌑£45-£60 🞧
40P 2🐾 ✿ nc5yrs
✳ Dinner £15&alc Last dinner 5pm
Credit Cards 1 3 ①

★56% **Glen Cottage**
Corney Square CA11 7PX ☎(0768)62221
Closed 25-26 Dec & 1 Jan
*A popular and friendly small hotel situated in the centre of the town offers value for money accommodation of an adequate standard.*
7rm(4⇉🌑)(3fb) CTV in all bedrooms ® ✳ sB&B£23
sB&B⇉🌑£27 dB&B£33-£35 dB&B⇉🌑£37-£39
3🐾 (60p per night)
✿ ✳ Lunch £4.25-£5.75 Dinner £5.25-£6.75 Last dinner 9pm
Credit Cards 1 3

⬆Forte **Travelodge**
Redhills CA11 0DT (on A66) (Forte)
☎(0768)66958 Central Res (0800) 850950
*Set on the A66, just a short distance west of the M6 motorway, the lodge offers accommodation of a good standard; meals are available at an adjacent Little Chef restaurant.*
32⇉🌑(32fb) CTV in all bedrooms ® sB⇉🌑£29.95
dB⇉🌑£29.95 (room only)
℄ 32P 🚗
Credit Cards 1 2 3

---

PENYBONT Powys Map 03 SO16

★★63% **Severn Arms**
LD1 5UA ☎(059787)224 due to change to (0597) 851224
Closed Xmas wk
*A warm welcome awaits guests at this busy roadside inn, situated at the A44/A488 junction. Quaint bedrooms offer cosy accommodation, while the olde worlde bars and restaurant provide a good range of meals.*
10⇉🌑(6fb) CTV in all bedrooms ® T ✳ 🞧
CTV 20P ✿ CFA ✃
V ✿ Sunday Lunch fr£6.50 Dinner fr£11&alc Last dinner 9pm
Credit Cards 1 2 3

PENZANCE Cornwall & Isles of Scilly Map **02** SW43

### ★★★⚑⚑60% Higher Faugan

Newlyn TR18 5NS (off B3315) ☎(0736)62076 FAX (0736) 51648

*Built of Cornish stone in 1904 by the artist Stanhope Forbes RA, this small and informally run country house hotel commands fine views over the Southwest Peninsula from its setting in 10 acres of lawns and gardens. Bright, individually furnished bedrooms are well equipped with up-to-date facilities, cosy public areas include a snooker room, and there is an outdoor swimming pool. A short table d'hôte menu is available, and the informal service provided by owners and local staff is friendly though limited (particularly during the winter period).*

11⇨🖍(2fb)1🛏🖍in 3 bedrooms CTV in all bedrooms ® **T** ✱ sB&B⇨🖍£35-£45 dB&B⇨🖍£55-£68 🖪

《 20P 🚗 ❀ ⌇ (heated) ♪ (hard) snooker solarium gymnasium putting green *xmas*

♀ English, French & Italian **V** ✧ ⌒ 🖍 ✱ Bar Lunch £3.50-£6.50alc High tea £3.50-£4.50 Dinner £12.50-£15.50 Last dinner 8.30pm

Credit Cards ①②③⑤

### ★★★56% Queen's

The Promenade TR18 4HG ☎(0736)62371 FAX (0736) 50033

*A traditional hotel on the Promenade, currently undergoing refurbishment, offers bedrooms in a variety of styles, some more spacious and comfortable than others. A conscientious team of staff provides prompt service.*

71⇨🖍(9fb)3🛏 CTV in all bedrooms ® **T** sB&B⇨🖍£44-£48 dB&B⇨🖍£75-£90 🖪

Lift 《 CTV 50P CFA snooker sauna solarium gymnasium *xmas*
♀ English & French **V** ✧ ⌒ 🖍 Sunday Lunch fr£7.50&alc
Dinner £15-£18.50&alc Last dinner 8.45pm

Credit Cards ①②③⑤£

**★★★53% Mount Prospect**
Britons Hill TR18 3AE (Exec Hotel) ☎(0736)63117
FAX (0736) 50970
*Well appointed hotel in gardens overlooking Mounts Bay and*
*Penzance harbour.*
26⇨🟂(2fb)⚊in 6 bedrooms CTV in all bedrooms ® T
sB&B⇨🟂£34-£39 dB&B⇨🟂£60-£68 🅿
《 CTV 14P ❀ ⚊ (heated)
♉ English & Continental ✧ ⚏ Bar Lunch £3.50-£7.20 Dinner
fr£11.75&alc Last dinner 9pm
Credit Cards ① ② ③ ⑤ ⓔ

**★★62% Kenegie Manor**
Gulval TR20 8YN ☎(0736)69174 FAX (0736) 51219
*The hotel forms the focal point of a holiday village consisting of*
*around 100 units. It has good leisure facilities, including an indoor*
*pool and there is live entertainment in the Tudor Bar during the*
*season. Bedrooms are all pleasantly furnished to a similar*
*standard. The dining room offers a carvery-style operation at both*
*breakfast and dinner.*
21⇨🟂(9fb) CTV in all bedrooms ® T
⊞ CTV 80P ❀ CFA ⚊ (heated) ⚊ ♬ (hard) sauna solarium
⚗
V ✧ ⚏ ⚊ Last dinner 9.30pm
Credit Cards ① ③ ⓔ

**★★60% Sea & Horses**
6 Alexandra Ter TR18 4NX ☎(0736)61961
Closed mid Nov-mid Feb
*A homely atmosphere and good value for money are provided by a*
*small, personally-run hotel with views over St Mounts Bay. The*
*single-fronted, Victorian, mid-terrace premises offer simple,*
*comfortable bedrooms, honest, home-cooked meals and a good*
*standard of housekeeping throughout.*
11rm(2⇨6🟂)(4fb) CTV in all bedrooms ® T ✖ ✳ sB&B£18
sB&B⇨🟂£22 dB&B£36 dB&B⇨🟂£40-£44
8P 1🚗 (£1) 🚳
V ✧ ⚏ Bar Lunch £1-£4 Dinner £9.50 Last dinner 7.30pm
Credit Cards ① ③

**★73% Estoril**
46 Morrab Rd TR18 4EX ☎(0736)62468 & 67471
Closed Dec-Jan
*This comfortable private hotel, centrally situated a short walk from*
*both promenade and shops, provides accommodation in well*
*appointed, individually furnished bedrooms, wholesome home-*
*cooked meals, and a family atmosphere.*
10⇨🟂(2fb) CTV in all bedrooms ® T ✖ sB&B⇨🟂£22-£26
dB&B⇨🟂£44-£52 🅿
4P 🚳
V ⚊ Dinner £11 Last dinner 7.30pm
Credit Cards ① ③ ⓔ

**★70% Tarbert**
11-12 Clarence St TR18 2NU (Minotels) ☎(0736)63758
Closed 15 Dec-15 Jan
*Ideally situated for touring the Penwith Peninsula and West*
*Cornwall, this listed Georgian building within walking distance of*
*the town centre offers freshly decorated bedrooms (most with*
*Laura Ashley prints), well equipped and provided with en suite*
*facilities. Cosy lounges combine quality, character and charm,*
*whilst an informal dining room provides both table d'hôte and à la*
*carte menus, with personal service from the resident proprietors.*
12⇨🟂 CTV in all bedrooms ® T ✖ sB&B⇨🟂£27-£30
dB&B⇨🟂£48-£60 🅿
CTV 5P 🚳 nc12yrs
♉ English & French V ✧ ⚏ Bar Lunch £2-£3.50 Dinner
£12.25-£13&alc Last dinner 8.30pm
Credit Cards ① ② ③ ⑤

**PERELLE**
See Guernsey **under** Channel Islands

---

**★67% Beach Dunes**
Ramoth Way, Reen Sands TR6 0BY ☎Truro(0872)572263
FAX (0872) 573824
Closed Nov & Dec RS Jan & Feb
*Set in the sand dunes above the beach, at the end of its own private*
*road, a small, family-run hotel with a relaxed and friendly*
*atmosphere offers accommodation in well-equipped bedrooms.*
*Spacious lawns and patios provide ideal suntraps, and guests have*
*the use of the hotel's squash court and indoor swimming pool.*
7rm(3⇨🟂)Annexe3⇨🟂(2fb) CTV in all bedrooms ® T
✖ (ex guide dogs) sB&B£20.50-£25.50 dB&B£41-£51
dB&B⇨🟂£44-£51
15P 🚳 ❀ ⚊ (heated) squash nc3yrs
V ✧ ⚏ ⚊ S% Lunch £5-£8.50 Dinner £11.50 Last dinner
7.30pm
Credit Cards ① ③

---

**★60% Ednovean House**
Ednovean Ln TR20 9LZ (on A394 5m E of Penzance)
☎Penzance(0736)711071
*A personally-run hotel of character with fine views over the bay*
*and St Michael's Mount from its quiet rural setting. It has*
*comfortable public areas and bedrooms which, though compact, are*
*bright, well furnished and fully equipped. Good meals, which cater*
*for vegetarian and other diets, and a friendly, informal atmosphere*
*make this an ideal retreat. Guests can relax in the attractive,*
*mature gardens and the beach is only a short walk away.*
9rm(6🟂)(1fb) ® sB&B£18.50-£20 sB&B🟂£22-£24.50
dB&B£37-£40 dB&B🟂£44-£49 🅿
CTV 16P 🚳 ❀ putting green croquet *xmas*
V ✧ ⚏ ⚊
Credit Cards ① ② ③

---

See **Town Plan Section**

**★★★❀❀♨⚞78% Murrayshall Country House Hotel**
New Scone PH2 7PH ☎(0738)51171 Telex no 76197
FAX (0738) 52595
Closed 2-19 Jan
*A country-house hotel just north of Perth, Murrayshall has its own*
*golf course and separate club house so that golfing parties do not*
*intrude on the quiet atmosphere. The major attraction, however, is*
*the excellent cooking of master chef Bruce Sangster. The 4-course*
*table d'hôte menu provides a choice at each course and displays a*
*subtlety and skill rarely encountered outside London and the*
*Home Counties. A pianist and harpist provide entertainment in the*
*evenings, creating a relaxing atmosphere for diners.*
*Accommodation, especially in the main house, is spacious, though*
*rooms in the new wing are more compact.*
19⇨🟂(3fb) CTV in all bedrooms T sB&B⇨🟂£75-£90
dB&B⇨🟂£105-£135 🅿
《 50P 🚳 ❀ CFA ▶ 18 ♬ (hard) bowling green croquet
driving range ♬ *xmas*
♉ British & French V ✧ ⚏ ✳ Sunday Lunch £13.50-£15
Dinner £20-£24&alc Last dinner 9.30pm
Credit Cards ① ② ③ ⑤ ⓔ

**★★★67% Huntingtower**
Crieff Rd, Almondbank PH1 3JT (3m W off A85) ☎(0738)83771
FAX (0738) 83777
*A distinctive hotel with a mock Tudor frontage, set in landscaped*
*grounds just a short drive west of the city. Bedrooms are*
*comfortably appointed in the modern style and well equipped,*
*though some are limited in size. Several rooms offer en suite*
*jacuzzi baths. A programme of major refurbishment has*
*considerably enhanced the public areas, but work was still in*
*progress at the time of our visit.*

**P**

35⇱🛏(2fb)⊁in 5 bedrooms CTV in all bedrooms ® T
sB&B⇱🛏£55 dB&B⇱🛏£74 🚻
《 CTV 100P ✿ CFA sauna solarium gymnasium putting
turkish bath ஃ *xmas*
🍴 Scottish & Continental V ♥ ⠿ ⊁ ✳ Lunch £9.25-£10.85
Dinner fr£18.35&alc Last dinner 9.30pm
Credit Cards ①②③⑤ⓔ

See advertisement on page 565

**★★★63% Queens Hotel**
Leonard St PH2 8HB ☎(0738)25471 Telex no 76531
FAX (0738) 38496
*Opposite the railway station and close to the city centre, this
popular modern business and holiday hotel offers comfortable well
equipped accommodation and good leisure and conference
facilities.*
50rm(40⇱9🛏)(7fb)1🚪 CTV in all bedrooms ® T
🏋 (ex guide dogs) ✳ sB&B⇱🛏£59.50-£65 dB&B⇱🛏£77-£85
🚻
Lift 《 30P CFA ▭ (heated) sauna solarium gymnasium *xmas*
V ♥ ⠿ Lunch £7.75-£8.95 High tea £6.95-£7.75 Dinner
£12.95-£13.95&alc Last dinner 9.30pm
Credit Cards ①②③ⓔ

**★★★60% Newton House**
Glencarse PH2 7LX (Inter-Hotels) ☎Glencarse(073886)250
FAX (073886) 717
*The conversion of a former Dower House has created a
comfortable, family-run business and tourist hotel which provides
well equipped bedrooms – most of which have been refurbished –
good food and a friendly atmosphere.*
10⇱🛏(2fb) CTV in all bedrooms ® T sB&B⇱🛏£50-£56
dB&B⇱🛏£72 🚻
50P ✿ CFA ஃ *xmas*

→

♀ Scottish & French V ♺ ♨ ⚓ ⚔ Lunch £12.50&alc High tea £5.50-£12.50alc Dinner £16-£19.50&alc Last dinner 9pm
Credit Cards [1] [2] [3] [5] [£]

### ★★★59% Lovat

90 Glasgow Rd PH2 0LT ☎(0738)36555 Telex no 76531
FAX (0738) 43123

*Situated on the south side of town with convenient access to the bypass, this modern business and tourist hotel is also popular for conferences and functions. It offers a choice of bars and good-value practical accommodation in well equipped bedrooms of varying size.*

30⇨🛏(1fb) CTV in all bedrooms ® T ⚓ (ex guide dogs)
sB&B⇨🛏£46-£52 dB&B⇨🛏£64-£72 ☐
《 60P ♫ *xmas*
V ♺ ♨ ⚔ Lunch £6.50-£7.95 High tea £5.95-£7.25 Dinner £10.50-£11.95&alc Last dinner 9.30pm
Credit Cards [1] [2] [3]

### ★★★56% *Isle of Skye Toby*

Queen's Bridge, Dundee Rd PH2 7AB (Toby) ☎(0738)24471
Telex no 76185

*On the north side of the river, this popular business and tourist hotel also caters for local functions. It has comfortable well equipped bedrooms, the best of which are in the new wing, a carvery restaurant and choice of bars.*

56⇨🛏(2fb)⚔in 14 bedrooms CTV in all bedrooms ®
⚓ (ex guide dogs)
Lift 《 70P
♺ ♨ ⚔ Last dinner 9pm
Credit Cards [1] [2] [3] [5]

### ★★★56% Stakis City Mills

West Mill St PH1 5QP (Stakis) ☎(0738)28281 Telex no 778704
FAX (0738) 43423

*A former water mill has been converted and extended to create this popular city centre business hotel. It offers a choice of bars and restaurants, and compact well equipped bedrooms in 2 modern wings.*

78⇨🛏(2fb)2☐⚔in 50 bedrooms CTV in all bedrooms ® T
sB⇨🛏£66.15-£76.65 dB⇨🛏£78.75-£89.25 (room only) ☐
《 75P CFA *xmas*
♀ International V ♺ ♨ ⚔
Credit Cards [1] [2] [3] [5]

### ★★★52% The Royal George

Tay St PH1 5LD (Forte Hotels) ☎(0738)24455
FAX (0738) 30345

*A popular hotel standing beside the river and close to the town centre amenities. Refurbishment has considerably enhanced the public areas, but though bedroom improvements are underway, some rooms remain rather dated.*

42⇨🛏⚔in 14 bedrooms CTV in all bedrooms ® T ✳ sB⇨🛏fr£65
dB⇨🛏£85-£95 (room only) ☐
《 18P CFA *xmas*
♀ International V ♺ ♨ ⚔ ✳ Lunch fr£9.95 Dinner
fr£14.95&alc Last dinner 9.30pm
Credit Cards [1] [2] [3] [4] [5]

### ❀ ✕✕ *Number Thirty Three*

33 Saint George St PH1 5LA ☎(0738)33771

*Located in the heart of town this small sophisticated restaurant creates the modern concept of a 30's theme. Here the emphasis is on seafood though other tastes are catered for. Choice varies according to the season but a typical dinner might be Oak smoked Queenies with a piquant sauce, followed by baked monkfish with vegetable parcel accompanied by a delicate saffron sauce, and to finish sticky toffee pudding or perhaps a croque monsieur can be recommended.*

Closed Sun, Mon & 10 days Xmas-New Year
♀ Scottish & French V 48 seats Last lunch 2.30pm Last dinner 9.30pm ♪ nc5yrs
Credit Cards [1] [2] [3]

---

## PETERBOROUGH Cambridgeshire Map 04 TL19 ○

See also **Alwalton**

### ★★★★62% Swallow

Lynchwood PE2 0GB (Swallow) ☎(0733)371111 Telex no 32422
FAX (0733) 236725
(For full entry see Alwalton)

**See advertisement on page 567**

### ★★★68% Peterborough Moat House

Thorpe Wood PE3 6SG (Queens Moat) ☎(0733)260000
Telex no 32708 FAX (0733) 262737

*A modern, purpose-built hotel, set in its own grounds adjacent to Thorpe Wood Golf Course on the city's ring road, which continues to benefit from good management. Light, spacious public areas include a well appointed restaurant, library-style bar and extensive conference and function facilities, while well equipped bedrooms are identically furnished in light woods and co-ordinated pastel fabrics.*

125⇨🛏⚔in 45 bedrooms CTV in all bedrooms ® T ✳
sB⇨🛏£77.50 dB⇨🛏£77.50 (room only) ☐
Lift 《 230P ❀ CFA ☒ (heated) sauna solarium gymnasium jacuzzi spa pool ♫
♀ International V ♺ ♨ ⚔ ✳ Lunch £14.95&alc Dinner £14.95&alc Last dinner 9.45pm
Credit Cards [1] [2] [3] [5]

### ★★★65% Butterfly

Thorpe Meadows, Off Longthorpe Parkway PE3 6GA (Consort)
☎(0733)64240 Telex no 818360 FAX (0733) 65538

*Overlooking the rowing lake at Thorpe Meadows, the third and newest Butterfly hotel offers similar good-value accommodation and food, with cheerful open-plan public areas and comfortable bedrooms, including studio singles for business people.*

70⇨🛏(2fb) CTV in all bedrooms ® T ⚓ (ex guide dogs) S%
sB⇨🛏£59.50-£61.50 dB⇨🛏£59.50-£61.50 (room only) ☐
→

P

( 70P
♡ European V ☆ ⚫ ⚓ ✂ S% Lunch £9.50-£10.50&alc Dinner
£10.50-£11.50&alc Last dinner 10pm
Credit Cards 1 2 3 5

### ★★★63% Forte Posthouse Peterborough
Great North Rd PE7 3TB (Forte Hotels) ☎(0733)240209
Telex no 32576 FAX (0733) 244455
(For full entry see Norman Cross)

### ★★★60% Bull
Westgate PE1 1RB ☎(0733)61364 Telex no 329265
FAX (0733) 557304
*This characterful former coaching inn in the town centre provides
efficient friendly service and a good range of commerical facilities.
Bedrooms vary and have attractive soft furnishings.*
112⇌(3fb) CTV in all bedrooms ® T ✱ sB&B⇌fr£62.50
dB&B⇌fr£76 ⊟
( 100P CFA
♡ English & French V ☆ ⚫ ✱ Lunch fr£11.95 Dinner
fr£11.95&alc Last dinner 10.30pm
Credit Cards 1 2 3 5

### ⬆Forte Travelodge
Great North Rd PE7 3UR (Forte)
☎(0733)231109 Central Res (0800) 850950
(For full entry see Alwalton)

### PETERHEAD Grampian *Aberdeenshire* Map 15 NK14

### ★★★67% Waterside Inn
Fraserburgh Rd AB4 7BN (Consort) ☎(0779)71121
Telex no 739413 FAX (0779) 70670
*Popular with the business traveller, this purpose built low rise
modern hotel just north of the town centre offers well equipped
bedrooms with practical appointments, a choice of bars and
restaurants, and good conference, function and leisure facilities.*
70⇌𝄕 Annexe40⇌𝄕(40fb) CTV in all bedrooms ® T
( 250P ❀ ▦ (heated) snooker sauna solarium gymnasium
steam room spa bath ♫
♡ Scottish & French V ☆ ⚫
Credit Cards 1 2 3 5 £

### PETTY FRANCE Avon Map 03 ST78

### ★★★69% Petty France
GL9 1AF (on A46 S of junct with A433)
☎Didmarton(045423)361 FAX (045423) 768
*A former dower house in very attractive gardens, near to the A46.
The hotel is relaxing, with spacious, comfortable lounges, period
furniture and fresh flowers. The 8 large bedrooms are in the main
house, while the remainder in the converted stables are more
compact, and some are split-level. All are traditionally furnished
and well equipped.*
8⇌𝄕 Annexe12⇌𝄕(1fb)1 ▦ CTV in all bedrooms ® T ✱
sB&B⇌𝄕£59-£80 dB&B⇌𝄕£75-£95 Continental breakfast
⊟
50P ❀ ✿ CFA croquet *xmas*
♡ International V ☆ ⚫ ✂ ✱ Lunch £11-£15alc Dinner
fr£13.50&alc Last dinner 9.30pm
Credit Cards 1 2 3 5 £

### PETWORTH West Sussex Map 04 SU92

### ❀❀❀✕✕Soanes
Grove Ln GU28 0HY ☎(0798)43659
*Carol and Derek Godsmark have transformed their home into a
delightful restaurant in country house style, where beamed dining
rooms are complemented by a conservatory lounge bar and
reception area. Carol, who produces the beautifully cooked dishes
featured on the fixed-price menu with supplements, exhibits
individuality in such noteworthy dishes as chicken mousseline with
parsley stuffing served in a Sauterne, carrot and celery sauce, and*

*pot au feu of pigeon and foie gras with glazed shallots, carrots and
garlic on a brioche crouton with red wine sauce; the dessert menu
features puddings of comparable standard, and freshly made
cafetière coffee completes the meal. A selection of modest but well
chosen wines is available – some of them representing particularly
good value for money.*
Closed Mon, Tue, 1 wk Mar & 1 wk Nov Lunch not served
Wed-Sat
Dinner not served Sun
♡ French 28 seats ✱ Sunday Lunch fr£17.50 Last dinner 11pm
16 P
Credit Cards 1 3

### PEVENSEY East Sussex Map 05 TQ60

### ★★58% Priory Court
Castle Rd BN24 5LG ☎Eastbourne(0323)763150
*A busy free house which dates back to the 15th century and retains
a wealth of beams and original architectural features, standing in 2
acres of grounds opposite Pevensey Castle. It provides a choice of
bedrooms, lounge, restaurant and lounge bar which features a wide
range of bar snacks, friendly service being supervised throughout
by the resident proprietors.*
9rm(5⇌1𝄕)(1fb)2 ▦ CTV in 6 bedrooms ® ✱ sB&B£23-£32
sB&B⇌𝄕£32 dB&Bfr£38 dB&B⇌𝄕£48-£56
CTV 60P ✿ ❀
♡ Mainly grills V ☆ ⚫ ✱ Lunch £8.95&alc Dinner £9-£16alc
Last dinner 9.30pm
Credit Cards 1 3 £

### PICKERING North Yorkshire Map 08 SE78

### ★★68% Crossways Hotel
Eastgate YO18 7DW ☎(0751)72804
*A small and friendly owner-run hotel on the town's main
thoroughfare, offering attractive if compact bedrooms and good
value menus featuring Yorkshire fare.*
10rm(8⇌𝄕)(3fb) CTV in all bedrooms ® ✱ sB&B£25-£28
dB&B⇌𝄕£50-£56 ⊟
CTV 15P ✿ *xmas*
V ☆ ⚫ ✱ Sunday Lunch £8.50 Dinner £13.75 Last dinner 9pm
Credit Cards 1 3 £

### ★★67% Burgate House
17 Burgate YO18 7AU ☎(0751)73463
*This friendly family-run hotel in the town centre, partly dating
from the 16th century but mainly Victorian, provides comfortable
accommodation, with neat well equipped bedrooms.*
7rm(2⇌𝄕)(2fb) CTV in all bedrooms ® T ✖ (ex guide dogs) S%
sB&B£22-£32.50 sB&B⇌𝄕£32.50 dB&B£34-£50 dB&B⇌𝄕£55 ⊟
▦ CTV 8P ✿ *xmas*
♡ English & French V S% Lunch £6.95-£11 Dinner £11-£12.50
Last dinner 8.30pm
Credit Cards 1 3

### ★★65% Forest & Vale
Malton Rd YO18 7DL (Consort) ☎(0751)72722 Telex no 57515
*On the A170 with easy access to local facilities and the moors and
coast, this comfortable hotel with an attractive garden has spacious
public areas and neat well equipped bedrooms.*
16⇌𝄕 Annexe5⇌𝄕(3fb) CTV in all bedrooms ® T
sB&B⇌𝄕£42-£64 dB&B⇌𝄕£68-£88 ⊟
70P ✿ CFA
♡ English & French V ☆ ⚫ Lunch £7.50-£9.50&alc Dinner
£16.50&alc Last dinner 9.30pm
Credit Cards 1 2 3 5

Hotels with red star ratings are
especially high quality.

★★64% **White Swan**
Market Place YO18 7AA ☎(0751)72288
*Situated in the town centre, the stone-faced White Swan offers*
*well-equipped accommodation and a convivial atmosphere. The*
*restaurant St Emillion combines an interesting menu with an*
*extensive, quality wine list.*
13⇨🇳(1fb)⊁in 2 bedrooms CTV in all bedrooms ® **T**
sB&B⇨🇳£45-£58 dB&B⇨🇳£80-£120 (incl dinner) 🖪
35P ⇔ ❊ *xmas*
♀ English & French **V** ۞ Lunch £8.50-£10 Dinner £16.50-£18
Last dinner 9pm
Credit Cards ①③£

★61% **Cottage Leas Country**
Nova Ln, Middleton YO18 8PN (Consort) ☎(0751)72129
*Formerly a farmhouse, this small, family run hotel stands on the*
*edge of the North York Moors and is ideally placed for*
*holidaymakers. Food is all freshly prepared and served in an*
*attractive dining room overlooking the Vale of Pickering.*
12⇨🇳(2fb)2⊠ CTV in all bedrooms ® **T** sB&B⇨🇳£35-£38
dB&B⇨🇳£65-£67 🖪
60P ❊ ♬ (hard) croquet badminton *xmas*
♀ English & French **V** ۞ ⚏ ✳ Lunch £11.95-£12.95&alc High
tea £5-£6 Dinner £11.95-£12.95&alc Last dinner 9.30pm
Credit Cards ①③£

PIDDLETRENTHIDE Dorset Map **03** SY79

★★58% **Old Bakehouse**
DT2 7QR ☎(03004)305
Closed 25-26 Dec & Jan
*Resident proprietors offer a warm welcome to this charming little*
*hotel. What bedrooms lack in quality is made up for in character,*
*whilst the lounge and bar, though small, are comfortable.*
3⇨Annexe7⇨🇳3⊠ CTV in all bedrooms ®
sB&B⇨🇳£28.50 dB&B⇨🇳£50-£56 🖪
16P ⇔ ❊ ⚏ (heated) nc12yrs
♀ English & Continental **V** ✳ Dinner £15.50-£17.50 Last
dinner 9pm
Credit Cards ①③

PIERCEBRIDGE Co Durham Map **08** NZ21

★★64% **The George**
DL2 3SW ☎Darlington(0325)374576 FAX (0325) 374577
*A 16th-century coaching inn with a colourful history, situated on*
*the B6275 overlooking the River Tees. Characterful bars have*
*beams, open fires and lots of bric-à-brac. Comfortable well*
*equipped modern bedrooms are located in a converted stables and*
*mews annexe.*
22⇨🇳Annexe8⇨🇳1⊠ CTV in all bedrooms ® **T**
✷ (ex guide dogs) ✳ sB&B⇨🇳£42-£52 dB&B⇨🇳£52-£62 🖪
130P ❊ CFA ♪ *xmas*
**V** ۞ ⚏ ✳ Lunch £9-£14&alc High tea fr£9&alc Dinner £9-
£14&alc Last dinner 9.45pm
Credit Cards ①②③⑤

PITLOCHRY Tayside *Perthshire* Map **14** NN95

★★★♨69% **Pine Trees**
Strathview Ter PH16 5QR ☎(0796)2121 FAX (0796) 2460
Closed 4 Jan-1 Mar
*Set in beautiful grounds amidst mature pine trees, the MacLellan*
*family's welcoming Victorian country house hotel has a peaceful*
*relaxing atmosphere. Bedrooms are comfortable and well*
*equipped, and there is a choice of elegant lounges.*
18rm(17⇨🇳) CTV in all bedrooms ® **T** ✷ (ex guide dogs)
sB&B⇨🇳£38-£46 dB&B⇨🇳£72-£78 🖪
40P ⇔ ❊ putting *xmas*
♀ Scottish & French **V** ۞ ⚏ Lunch £12 Dinner £18 Last
dinner 8.30pm
Credit Cards ①③

P

# Pitlochry

## ★★★62% Green Park
Clunie Bridge Rd PH16 5JY ☎(0796)3248
Closed 2 Nov-26 Mar

*Set in its own grounds on the picturesque shores of Loch Faskally, this friendly, family-run hotel has a relaxed atmosphere and is an ideal base for the touring holidaymaker. It offers comfortable lounges and neatly decorated, well equipped bedrooms.*
37⇨🏶(10fb) CTV in all bedrooms ® T ✖ sB&B⇨🏶£31-£40 dB&B⇨🏶£62-£80 ⊟
50P 4🚗 (£1.50) ⚌ ✿ CFA ♪ putting table tennis bar billiards
♀ Scottish & French V ♥ ♨ ⅍ ✱ Dinner £16.50-£18.50 Last dinner 8.30pm
Credit Cards [1] [3]

## ★★★61% Pitlochry Hydro
Knockard Rd PH16 5JH (Scottish Highland) ☎(0796)2666
FAX (0796)2238
Closed Jan

*A good range of leisure facilities is available at this popular holiday and conference hotel which overlooks the town from the setting of its own grounds. Extensive refurbishment has done much to enhance its extensive public areas, and well equipped bedrooms offer every modern comfort.*
64⇨🏶(4fb) CTV in all bedrooms ® T ✖ (ex guide dogs)
sB&B⇨🏶£53-£59 dB&B⇨🏶£87-£96 ⊟
Lift ( CTV 100P ✿ CFA ☒ (heated) snooker sauna solarium gymnasium putting green croquet *xmas*
♀ Scottish, English & French V ♥ Bar Lunch £2-£8 Dinner £15&alc Last dinner 9pm
Credit Cards [1] [2] [3] [5] [£]

## ★★★56% Scotland's
40 Bonnethill Rd PH16 5BT (Best Western) ☎(0796)2292
Telex no 76392 FAX (0796) 3284

*Close to the town centre, this family-run conference and holiday hotel now has a leisure centre. Public areas are practically and traditionally furnished, while the bedrooms are gradually being improved and vary in size, style and quality of appointments.*
60⇨🏶(14fb) CTV in all bedrooms ® T sB&B⇨🏶£39-£57 dB&B⇨🏶£66-£94 ⊟
Lift ( CTV 80P ✿ CFA ☒ (heated) sauna solarium gymnasium pool table *xmas*
V ♥ ♨ ✱ Lunch fr£10.75 Dinner fr£15 Last dinner 9pm
Credit Cards [1] [2] [3] [5] [£]

## ★★★52% The Atholl Palace
Atholl Rd PH16 5LY (Forte Hotels) ☎(0796)2400
Telex no 76406 FAX (0796) 3036

*This popular business, holiday and conference hotel is set in its own extensive grounds on the south side of town and offers a good range of leisure facilities. The public areas offer traditional comforts but bedrooms remain somewhat practical and functional.*
84⇨🏶(6fb)1⚌⅍in 12 bedrooms CTV in all bedrooms ® T
Lift ( 150P ✿ CFA ⌂ (heated) ▶ 9 ♟ (hard) snooker sauna solarium pitch & putt ♨
V ♥ ♨ ⅍ Last dinner 9pm
Credit Cards [1] [2] [3] [4] [5]

## ★★69% Acarsaid
8 Atholl Rd PH16 5BX ☎(0796)2389
Closed 3 Jan-Feb

*This welcoming family-run hotel set in its own grounds at the east end of the town is a popular base for the touring holidaymaker. It has a choice of relaxing lounges and the comfortable bedrooms are well equipped.*
18⇨🏶(1fb) CTV in all bedrooms ® T ✖ sB&B⇨🏶£25-£35 dB&B⇨🏶£50-£70
20P ✿ putting *xmas*
♀ International ♥ ♨ ⅍ Lunch £5-£10alc Dinner £12.50-£16 Last dinner 8pm
Credit Cards [1] [3]

## ★★69% Birchwood
2 East Moulin Rd PH16 5DW (Inter-Hotels) ☎(0796)2477
Closed Nov-Feb

*A very well run and friendly hotel set in 4 acres of grounds and carefully tended gardens. The Birchwood is just a short distance from the town centre in an ideal touring location. Bedrooms are pleasantly furnished and good facilities are provided. There is a comfortable lounge, and extensive menus are available in the attractive dining room.*
12⇨🏶Annexe5🏶(4fb) CTV in all bedrooms ® T
sB&B⇨🏶£46-£51 dB&B⇨🏶£82-£92 (incl dinner) ⊟
25P ✿
♥ ♨ ⅍ Lunch £7-£10alc Dinner £17&alc Last dinner 8pm
Credit Cards [1] [3]

## ★★68% Dundarach
Perth Rd PH16 5DJ (Consort) ☎(0796)2862
RS 14 Nov-Feb

*A large house and grounds at the southern end of the village, this comfortable, good value hotel has recently been extensively refurbished. Bedrooms have good facilities and are well furnished. Family owned, the service is friendly and helpful.*
23rm(16⇨🏶)Annexe3⇨🏶(2fb) CTV in all bedrooms ® T
sB&B⇨🏶£30-£39 dB&B⇨🏶fr£60 ⊟
CTV 30P ✿ CFA
V ♥ ♨ ✱ Bar Lunch fr£2alc Dinner £14.50-£16.50 Last dinner 8pm
Credit Cards [1] [2] [3] [£]

## ★★✿67% *Westlands of Pitlochry*
160 Atholl Rd PH16 5AR (Guestaccom) ☎(0796)2266
Closed Jan

*A relaxed, family-run hotel set well back from the main road on the north side of town, fronted by lawns. Considerable improvements were made in 1991, encompassing a new wing of 6 tastefully appointed bedrooms, an attractive new restaurant, a new reception area, and a name change (formerly Airdanair). The quality of the food has improved too. George Ramage presents a set price 4-course dinner with choices. A prawn and asparagus mousse served on a fresh dill mustard sauce accompanied by cucumber salad, or poached egg tartlet coated with a light tarragon hollandaise garnished with smoked salmon strips, to tititlate the palate. For main course perhaps supreme of Scottish salmon on a bed of spinach, coated with coriander cream sauce; or noisettes of lamb cooked in a walnut and ginger jus with a hint of garlic. Sweets are all home-made and invariably include a hot pudding.*
9⇨🏶(1fb) CTV in all bedrooms ® T
18P ⚌ ✿ ♪
V ♥ ⅍ Last dinner 8.30pm
Credit Cards [1] [3]

## ★★65% Claymore
162 Atholl Rd PH16 5AR ☎(0796)2888
Closed 3 Jan-14 Feb

*Situated just west of the town centre, this small family-run hotel stands in its own well tended grounds and is a popular base for the touring holidaymaker. It is efficiently run by enthusiastic owners, Joyce and Harold Beaton, and offers neatly appointed public rooms, together with comfortable and well equipped bedrooms.*
7⇨🏶Annexe4rm(2🏶)(1fb) CTV in all bedrooms ® T
sB&B£20-£29 dB&B⇨🏶£40-£62 ⊟
25P ⚌ ✿ *xmas*
V ♥ ♨ ⅍ Bar Lunch £5.80-£13.50alc Dinner £12.50-£22.50alc Last dinner 9pm
Credit Cards [1] [3]

## ★★60% Craigvrack
West Moulin Rd PH16 5EQ (Minotels) ☎(0796)2399
FAX (0796) 3990
Closed Nov-Feb

*Rob and Janette Wallace's small, comfortable hotel is a popular base for holidaymakers. It has a friendly, informal atmosphere and the public rooms are peaceful and relaxing. The comfortable bedrooms are well equipped, though some are a little compact.*
19rm(8⇨6↑)(2fb) CTV in all bedrooms ® T sB&B£19-£34 sB&B⇨↑£24-£38 dB&B£38-£48 dB&B⇨↑£48-£56 ♭
22P ♫
V ✿ ✠ ✳ Bar Lunch £3.95&alc Dinner £14-£17&alc Last dinner 8.30pm
Credit Cards 1 2 3 £

★★55% **Craigower**
134/136 Atholl Rd PH16 5AB ☎(0796)2590
*Catering mainly for the tourist market, this small family-run hotel in the town centre offers a friendly atmosphere and good-value accommodation in bedrooms which are currently being refurbished.*
23⇨↑(5fb) CTV in all bedrooms ® sB&B⇨↑£20-£30 dB&B⇨↑£30-£50
CTV 15P *xmas*
V ✿ ⬛ ✠ Bar Lunch £3-£8 High tea £5.50-£8 Dinner £10 Last dinner 8.30pm
Credit Cards 1 3

★71% **Knockendarroch House**
Higher Oakfield PH16 5HT ☎(0796)3473
Closed 15 Nov-Mar
*A cheerfully furnished and comfortable house overlooking the town from its own grounds provides well furnished bedrooms, a superbly comfortable lounge and a pleasant restaurant serving a short but interesting dinner menu. Guests are assured of good hospitality and comforts at this family owned and run hotel.*
12⇨↑(1fb)2⊞ CTV in all bedrooms ® dB&B⇨↑£47.50-£64 ♭
→

( 12P ⇔ ❖ *xmas*
♀ Scottish & French **V**
Credit Cards 1 2 3 5

★**69%, Balrobin**
Higher Oakfield PH16 5HT ☎(0796)2901
Closed Nov-Feb
*A delightful, efficiently run small hotel, standing in its own grounds and commanding fine views over the surrounding hills, combines comfortable, well-equipped accommodation with the opportunity to enjoy good home cooking in its attractive dining room and to relax in an attractive lounge.*
15⇨❨(1fb) CTV in all bedrooms ® sB&B⇨❨£30.50-£34.50 dB&B⇨❨£61-£75 (incl dinner) ▤
15P ⇔ ❖ nc10yrs
✗ Dinner £12 Last dinner 7.30pm
£

★**60%, Craig Urrard**
10 Atholl Rd PH16 5BX ☎(0796)2346
*Situated at the east end of town, this small, friendly, family-run tourist hotel is well maintained and offers good value accommodation.*
10rm(6❨)Annexe2❨(3fb) CTV in all bedrooms ® ✗ ❋
sB&Bfr£18.50 dB&Bfr£37 dB&B❨fr£40
CTV 12P ⇔ ❖
✗ ❋ Bar Lunch £1.50-£5alc Dinner £9.25&alc Last dinner 8pm
Credit Cards 1 2 3

**PLOCKTON** Highland *Ross & Cromarty* Map **14** NG83
★★**76%, Haven**
IV52 8TW ☎(059984)223 & 334
Closed 21 Dec-9 Feb RS 10 Feb-1 Apr & Nov-20 Dec
*The unassuming frontage of this hotel belies the charm and comfort of its interior, and it is popular with both land and water based visitors to a village often considered the gem of West Highland coastal communities. Bedrooms are extremely well furnished and equipped to meet modern expectations, while two comfortable lounges – one reserved for non-smoking guests – provide a good choice of books, magazines and games; skilfully prepared meals are based on the best of local produce and served by a friendly staff under the supervision of the establishment's very approachable owners. The Haven Hotel is one of our 'Courtesy and Care' award winner 1991/1992 for Scotland (see colour feature on p19).*
13⇨❨ CTV in all bedrooms ® **T** sB&B⇨❨£30-£32 dB&B⇨❨£60-£64 ▤
7P nc7yrs
**V** ❣ ⊡ ✗ Lunch £4-£12alc Dinner £17-£20 Last dinner 8.30pm
Credit Cards 1 3

**PLYMOUTH** Devon Map **02** SX45 ⊙
See **Town Plan Section**
See also **Down Thomas**
★★★★**65%, Copthorne**
Armada Way PL1 1AR ☎(0752)224161 Telex no 45756
FAX (0752) 670688
*Many of this hotel's rooms overlook the part of the inner ring road system known as Western Approach, while others look out across one of the wide boulevards of the attractive city and its shops. Outwardly austere, it is bright and modern inside, served by friendly staff, offering a choice of eating positions in the formal à la carte Burlington Restaurant and brasserie-style Bentleys, and featuring a popular small leisure centre.*
135⇨❨(29fb)✗in 18 bedrooms CTV in all bedrooms ® **T** ❋
sB⇨❨£76-£80 dB⇨❨£87-£90 (room only) ▤
Lift ( 40🅿 CFA ▣ (heated) sauna solarium gymnasium pool table

♀ International **V** ❣ ⊡ ✗ ❋ Lunch £7.95&alc Dinner £11.50&alc Last dinner 10.30pm
Credit Cards 1 2 3 5 £

★★★★**53%, *Plymouth Moat House***
Armada Way PL1 2HJ (Queens Moat) ☎(0752)662866
Telex no 45637 FAX (0752) 673816
*Large, purpose built hotel located close to the city centre, Barbican and Hoe. The Penthouse carvery restaurant and bar on the 11th floor are popular for their magnificent views, but an à la carte restaurant beside reception serves a more imaginative menu. Bedrooms and public areas alike are about to undergo a major refurbishment programme which will provide décor and furnishings of a quality to attract both holidaymakers and commercial users.*
213⇨❨(106fb)✗in 14 bedrooms CTV in all bedrooms ® **T**
Lift ( ⊞ 30P 100🅿 ▣ (heated) sauna solarium gymnasium ♫
♀ Continental **V** ❣ ⊡ ✗ Last dinner 10pm
Credit Cards 1 2 3 5

★★★**65%, Forte Crest**
Cliff Rd, The Hoe PL1 3DL (Forte Hotels) ☎(0752)662828
Telex no 45442 FAX (0752) 660974
*Gloriously situated on Plymouth Hoe with panoramic views across the seafront from the public rooms and the front facing bedrooms. Spacious and well equipped, some of the bedrooms are to be upgraded and redecorated in 1992. The elegant Mayflower Restaurant offers a fairly extensive international menu, while the less formal Drakes Coffee Shop provides a full, but less complicated menu, which includes a children's choice.*
106⇨❨(86fb)✗in 32 bedrooms CTV in all bedrooms ® **T**
Lift ( 149P ❖ ➳ (heated)
♀ English & Continental **V** ❣ ⊡ ✗
Credit Cards 1 2 3 5

★★★**64%, Duke of Cornwall**
Millbay Rd PL1 3LG (Best Western) ☎(0752)266256
FAX (0752) 600062
70⇨❨(6fb)2⊞ CTV in all bedrooms ® **T** sB&B⇨❨£59.50-£67.50 dB&B⇨❨£74-£89.50 ▤
Lift ( 50P CFA *xmas*
♀ English & French **V** ❣ ⊡ Sunday Lunch £10-£10.75 Dinner £16-£22.50alc Last dinner 10pm
Credit Cards 1 2 3 5 £

★★★**64%, Elfordleigh**
Colebrook, Plympton PL7 5EB ☎(0752)336428
FAX (0752) 344581
*Within 65 acres of rolling grounds and countryside, the hotel has magnificent views over the Plym Valley, and is surrounded by its own golf course, gardens and woodland. The main house itself has been sympathetically restored, together with the sensitive addition of an attractive conservatory restaurant, and a bright, modern leisure complex. There is a choice of three bars, and of course, the golf club-house. Bedrooms are richly decorated in pleasing, coordinating colours and fabrics, with quality, fully-tiled en suites, and they are all well equipped. There is also a choice of dining, with a family country pantry for more informal eating, in conjunction with the conservatory à la carte restaurant. Services are conducted in a prompt and friendly manner. The hotel is located just outside the city, being convenient for the A38 and major link roads.*
18⇨❨(3fb)1⊞ CTV in all bedrooms ® ✗ S% sB&B⇨❨£50-£53.50 dB&B⇨❨£59-£89 ▤
CTV 250P ⇔ ❖ CFA ▣ (heated) ➳ (heated) ▶ 9 ♟ (hard)
♪ squash snooker sauna solarium gymnasium jacuzzi beauty therapy croquet *xmas*
♀ European **V** ❣ ⊡ ✗ ❋ Lunch £7.95 Dinner fr£16.25&alc Last dinner 9.30pm
Credit Cards 1 2 3 £

★★★ **63%** New Continental
Millbay Rd PL1 3LD ☎(0752)220782 Telex no 45193
FAX (0752) 227013
Closed 24 Dec-2 Jan
*Well-established city centre hotel close to the Hoe and the
Barbican. The comfortable bedrooms have good facilities and the
spacious restaurant offers a large selection of interesting dishes. A
large leisure complex includes an indoor heated pool and beauty
treatment room.*
100⇨🛏(14fb)2🚪 CTV in all bedrooms ® T S%
sB&B⇨🛏£55-£60 dB&B⇨🛏£66-£70 🍴
Lift ( 100P CFA ▣ (heated) sauna solarium gymnasium
♀ English, French & Greek V ♥ ✳ Lunch fr£8.50 Dinner
fr£12.75&alc Last dinner 10pm
Credit Cards 1 2 3 5 £

★★★ **61%** Strathmore
Elliot St, The Hoe PL1 2PP (Consort) ☎(0752)662101
Telex no 45193 FAX (0752) 223690
*This busy commercial hotel is part of a terrace, just a stone's throw
away from the celebrated Plymouth Hoe. All rooms have now been
refurbished, and are well appointed. A wide choice of dishes are on
offer in the charming restaurant, and service is provided by the
friendly team of staff.*
55⇨🛏(6fb)CTV in all bedrooms ® T S% sB&B⇨🛏£31-
£47.25 dB&B⇨🛏£42-£57.75 🍴
Lift ( ✗ CFA
♀ English & Continental V ♥ S% Lunch £8 Dinner £12&alc
Last dinner 10pm
Credit Cards 1 2 3 5 £

Remember to book early for holiday
and bank holiday times.

## THE DUKE OF CORNWALL HOTEL
★ ★ ★

MILLBAY ROAD, PLYMOUTH, DEVON PL1 3LG
Telephone: Plymouth 0752 266256 Fax: 0752 600062

Grade II listed Victorian Hotel recently refurbished to
a very high standard. Magnificent dining room lit by
crystal chandelier. All 70 bedrooms are ensuite and
unique in style and design. Private car park.
Conference facilities for up to 300. Close to the City
Centre, Plymouth Hoe and the Elizabethan
Barbican. Directly opposite Plymouth Pavilions
Conference and Leisure Centre.

# THE SOUTH WEST'S SHINING LIGHT OF QUALITY.

★★★★

P

## for business ....
## .... or pleasure

Ideally situated for those visiting the city,
beautiful coast and nearby Dartmoor, and
for the business person we offer both style
and comfort, in our well appointed
meeting rooms.
**Simply the brightest light in Plymouth.**

The

opthorne
Plymouth
Armada Way, Plymouth, Devon PL1 1AR
Tel (0752) 224161 Fax (0752) 670688

**★★★58% Novotel Plymouth**
Marsh Mills Roundabout, 270 Plymouth Rd PL6 8NH
☎(0752)221422 Telex no 45711
*This modern hotel, conveniently positioned beside the A38 just outside the city, provides accommodation best suited to the short stay guest, bedrooms being well equipped but rather functional. A range of conference/function rooms is available, though lounge facilities are restricted, and a small restaurant with a French theme offers attentive service.*
100⇨↖⁄in 19 bedrooms CTV in all bedrooms ® **T** ✱
sB⇨↖£51-£55 dB⇨↖£57-£60 (room only) 🛏
Lift ☾ 140P ✲ CFA ⛆
🍷 French **V** ♁ ☕ ⁄ ✱ Lunch £10.50-£11.80&alc Dinner £10.50-£11.80&alc Last dinner mdnt
Credit Cards 1 2 3 4 5

**★★65% Camelot**
5 Elliot St, The Hoe PL1 2PP (Minotels) ☎(0752)221255 & 669667 FAX (0752) 603660
*Near the Hoe and Barbican, and within walking distance of the city centre, this informal terraced hotel offers comfortable well equipped bedrooms, and compact public areas with a lively atmosphere; the latter include a cosy dining room serving an imaginative menu, and a bar where snacks are available.*
17⇨↖(4fb) CTV in all bedrooms ® **T** ✈ (ex guide dogs) ✱
sB&B⇨↖£40 dB&B⇨↖£55 🛏
CTV ⛟ CFA
🍷 English & French **V** ♁ ☕ Lunch £12.50&alc High tea £4 Dinner £12.50&alc Last dinner 9.30pm
Credit Cards 1 2 3 5 £

**★★65% Invicta**
11-12 Osborne Place, Lockyer Street, The Hoe PL1 2PU
☎(0752)664997 FAX (0752) 664994
Closed 25 Dec-5 Jan
*A family-owned hotel overlooking Drake's famous Bowling Green. Bedrooms are comfortable and well equipped, there is a choice of menus in the dining room and the public lounge bar offers a lively atmosphere.*
23rm(9⇨11↖)(4fb) CTV in all bedrooms ® **T**
✈ (ex guide dogs) sB&B£25-£26 sB&B⇨↖£38-£40
dB&B⇨↖£49-£52 🛏
CTV 10P
🍷 Mainly grills ♁ ☕ Dinner £8.50-£15&alc Last dinner 9pm
Credit Cards 1 3

P

**★★59% *Grosvenor***
9 Elliot Street, The Hoe PL1 2PP ☎(0752)260411
*This commercially orientated hotel, conveniently placed for Hoe, Barbican and city centre, has now been extended by the purchase of the property next door; some bedrooms have been refurbished, and lively public areas include an informal restaurant offering table d'hôte and à la carte menus.*
14rm(8⇨5↖) CTV in 13 bedrooms ® **T** ✈
CTV ⛟
♁ ☕
Credit Cards 1 2 3

**★68% *Victoria Court***
62/64 North Rd East PL4 6AL ☎(0752)668133
Closed 22 Dec-1 Jan
*A mid-terrace Victorian building just off the city centre, with restricted car parking at the rear, has been restored to its former glory over the past few years. Neatly presented and well equipped bedrooms make good use of limited space, the lounge connects with a lounge bar featuring real ale as well as a full range of apéritifs and spirits, and the lower ground floor dining room offers an ample choice at dinner.*
14rm(7↖)(4fb) CTV in all bedrooms ® **T** ✈
CTV 6P ⛟
**V** ♁ ☕ Last dinner 8pm
Credit Cards 1 3

**★61% Imperial**
Lockyer Street, The Hoe PL1 2QD ☎(0752)227311
FAX (0752) 674986
Closed 25-31 Dec
*Ideally situated between the famous Hoe and city centre, this value-for-money Victorian hotel offers well equipped bedrooms of various sizes. There is a recently refurbished bar, a comfortable lounge and a dining room where guests can enjoy their choice of simple dishes in a relaxed atmosphere; resident proprietors extend a warm welcome and ensure friendly service.*
22rm(4⇨12↖)(4fb) CTV in all bedrooms ® **T** ✈ S% sB&B£29
sB&B⇨↖£39-£39.50 dB&B£44 dB&B⇨↖£49-£49.50 🛏
CTV 16P CFA
**V** ♁ ☕ S% Bar Lunch £2-£5 Dinner £12.75-£12.95 Last dinner 8.15pm
Credit Cards 1 2 3 5 £

**★57% Drake**
1 & 2 Windsor Villas, Lockyer Street, The Hoe PL1 2QD
☎(0752)229730
Closed Xmas
*Situated between The Hoe and the city centre, this small hotel has some comfortable bedrooms with good facilities for the commercial and holiday traveller. The bar lounge has an adjacent pool room, and informal dishes are featured on the à la carte menu.*
36rm(27⇨↖)(3fb) CTV in all bedrooms ® **T**
✈ (ex guide dogs) ✱ sB&B£22.50-£24.50 sB&B⇨↖£32-£37
dB&B£36-£39 dB&B⇨↖£42-£47 🛏
25P ⛟
🍷 Mainly grills **V** ♁ ✱ Lunch £8.50&alc Dinner £8.50&alc Last dinner 9pm
Credit Cards 1 2 3 5

**⌂Campanile**
Marsh Mills, Longbridge Rd, Forder Valley PL6 8LD
(Campanile) ☎(0752)601087 Telex no 45544
FAX (0752) 223213
*Set beside the A38 about 1.5 miles from the city centre this Lodge has bedrooms with outside access from the car park. All are simply appointed with good facilities for the short-stay guest. Adjacent is a bistro-style restaurant with a French influence, and a bar.*
50⇨↖ CTV in all bedrooms ® **T** S% sB⇨↖fr£36
dB⇨↖fr£36 (room only) 🛏
56P ✲ *xmas*
🍷 English & French Lunch £3.75-£5 Dinner £6.80-£8.90 Last dinner 10pm
Credit Cards 1 3 £

**❀❀✕The Chez Nous**
13 Frankfort Gate PL1 1QA ☎(0752)266793
*This haven of good French cooking is a welcome discovery in the centre of Plymouth, and attracts a regular clientele who are greatly appreciative both of the atmosphere and the cuisine. Jacques and Suzanne Marchal present an excellent daily menu.*
Closed Sun, Mon, 3 wks Feb, 3 wks Sep & BH's
🍷 French 28 seats Lunch £26.50&alc Dinner £26.50&alc Last lunch 2pm Last dinner 10.30pm P̸
Credit Cards 1 2 3 5

## POCKLINGTON Humberside Map **08** SE84

**★★69% Barmby Moor Country**
Hull Rd, Barmby Moor YO4 5EZ ☎(0759)302700
10⇨↖(1fb) CTV in all bedrooms ® **T** ✈ (ex guide dogs) ✱
sB&B⇨↖£44 dB&B⇨↖£55 🛏
30P ⛟ ✲ ⛆ (heated)
**V** ♁ ⁄ S% Lunch £8 Dinner £13-£16alc Last dinner 8pm
Credit Cards 1 2 3

P

★★65% *Feathers*
Market Square YO4 2AH ☎(0759)303155
*This small market place inn proves a popular venue with local trade and hotel guests alike. The inn has well appointed bedrooms, in both the main house and the purpose-built annexe. A selection of good value menus is offered in the small restaurant.*
6⇅🐾Annexe6⇅(1fb)1🛏 CTV in all bedrooms ® T
✻ (ex guide dogs)
CTV 60P 6🍴
V ♥ Last dinner 9.30pm
Credit Cards ①②③⑤

---

PODIMORE Somerset Map **03** ST52

⛨**Forte Travelodge**
BA22 8JG (on A303, S of junct with A37) (Forte)
☎Yeovil(0935)840074 Central Res (0800) 850950
*Located at the roundabout junction of the A303 with the A37, this lodge offers excellent value family accommodation in new and well equipped bedrooms. Meals and light refreshments are available from 7am to 10pm in the Little Chef restaurant across the car park.*
31⇅🐾(31fb) CTV in all bedrooms ® sB⇅🐾£29.95
dB⇅🐾£29.95 (room only)
( 31P 🚗
Credit Cards ①②③

---

POLMONT Central *Stirlingshire* Map **11** NS97

★★★65% **Inchyra Grange**
Grange Rd FK2 0YB ☎(0324)711911 Telex no 777693
FAX (0324) 716134
*A family-owned business, conference and function hotel boasting an attractive leisure complex, which stands in its own grounds just north of junction 4 of the M9 motorway; bedrooms are well equipped and there are three suites available.*
33⇅🐾(5fb) CTV in all bedrooms ® T S% sB&B⇅🐾£65-£80
🛏
( 150P ✿ CFA ⊟ (heated) snooker sauna solarium
gymnasium jacuzzi steam room beauty therapy room
♀ Scottish & French V ♥ ⚓ ✻ Lunch £8.50-£12.50 High tea
£6-£10 Dinner £14.50-£16.50&alc Last dinner 9.30pm
Credit Cards ①②③⑤ⓔ

---

POLPERRO Cornwall & Isles of Scilly Map **02** SX25

★68% **Claremont**
Fore St PL13 2RG ☎(0503)72241
RS 16 Oct-23 Mar
*In a picturesque village setting, this family-run hotel is steadily being upgraded and improved. Bedrooms and public areas are small, but very comfortable and warmly furnished in an individual style. Parts of the building date back to the 17th-century, lending character and charm to the hotel. Proprietors Nelly Couturier and Gilles Peyrin create a warm and relaxed atmosphere. They are originally from France and the influence is unmistakable in the food. The simple, home-cooked fare is wholesome and enjoyable, and is offered from both à la carte and table d'hôte menus. The hotel car park is across the road.*
11rm(10⇅🐾)(3fb) CTV in all bedrooms ® T sB&B⇅🐾£18-£29 dB&B⇅🐾£37-£55 🛏
CTV 16P 🚗 xmas
♀ French ♥ ⚓ Bar Lunch £3.50-£6.50alc Dinner £11.50-£16.50&alc Last dinner 8.30pm
Credit Cards ①②③ⓔ

Red star hotels are each
highlighted by a pink
tinted panel.

---

POLZEATH Cornwall & Isles of Scilly Map **02** SW97

★★70% **Pentire Rocks**
PL27 6US ☎Trebetherick(0208)862213 FAX (0208) 862259
Closed 3 Jan-Feb
*A small relaxing holiday hotel, hospitably run by Clive and Christine Mason. There is a cosy bar and a stylish no-smoking restaurant where table d'hôte and à la carte menus offer generous traditional dishes well prepared by chef Graham Holder.*
16rm(1⇅14🐾)(2fb)1🛏 CTV in all bedrooms ® T
✻ (ex guide dogs)
CTV 20P 🚗 ✿ ⇘ (heated)
♀ English & French ♥ ⚓ Last dinner 9.30pm
Credit Cards ①③ⓔ

---

PONTERWYD Dyfed Map **06** SN78

★★58% **Dyffryn Castell**
SY23 3LB ☎(097085)237
*This former coaching inn, dating back over 400 years and set amid mountain scenery on the A44, 13 miles east of Aberystwyth, offers simple accommodation and all-round good value for money.*
9rm(3⇅3🐾)⚡in 2 bedrooms CTV in 4 bedrooms ® ✻
sB&B£17.50-£18.50 sB&B⇅🐾fr£18.50 dB&B£33-£35
dB&B⇅🐾fr£35 🛏
CTV 75P games room
V ♥ ✻ Sunday Lunch £7.50-£7.75 Dinner fr£7.50 Last dinner 6pm
Credit Cards ①③

---

POOLE Dorset Map **04** SZ09 ⊙

**For hotel locations see Town Plan Section under Bournemouth**
See also **Bournemouth**

★★★⊛76% **Salterns**
38 Salterns Way, Lilliput BH14 8JR (Best Western)
☎(0202)707321 FAX (0202) 707488
*This small, welcoming hotel has a fabulous location on Poole Harbour, with views across to Brownsea Island and the Purbeck Hills. The bedrooms and public rooms are spacious and very comfortable, and the hotel has its own yacht marina. Fine meals are featured in the dining room, where guests are offered either a table d'hôte menu or speciality menu – both offer very good value for money. Meals are prepared from quality fresh, often local, produce, and dishes are light and cooked in the modern style. Main courses might include roast fillet of lamb with spinach and rosemary sauce, or fresh tuna with a white wine, tomato and dill sauce. Service is friendly but professional, and there is a relaxed holiday atmosphere despite an established business clientele.*
16⇅ CTV in all bedrooms ® T ✻ sB⇅£60-£102 dB⇅£78.75-£120.75 (room only) 🛏
( 150P 🚗 ✿ CFA ⚓ squash snooker xmas
♀ English & French ♥ ⚓ ✻ Lunch £9.25-£20 Dinner £15-£25
Last dinner 10pm
Credit Cards ①②③⑤

★★★⊛73% **Mansion House**
Thames St BH15 1JN ☎(0202)685666 FAX (0202) 665709
*This discreet and extraordinarily comfortable hotel is famous for its food and well-patronised luncheon club, at which non-members are always welcome. Dishes tend towards British classics like silverside of beef with carrots and dumplings and treacle tart and custard. In the evenings, however, there is a wider range which always includes the roast of the day and a cold hors d'oeuvres table. The long wine list has a good selection of the better clarets and a reasonable choice of half bottles.*
28⇅🐾(2fb) CTV in all bedrooms T ✻ sB&B⇅🐾£75-£80
dB&B⇅🐾£110-£120 🛏
( 40P 🚗 CFA
♀ English & French V ♥ ⚓ Lunch £12-£17 High tea £7.50-£10.50 Dinner £15-£17.50&alc Last dinner 10pm
Credit Cards ①②③⑤ⓔ

★★★68% **Harbour Heights**

73 Haven Rd, Sandbanks BH13 7LW ☎(0202)707272
FAX (0202) 708594

*In a wonderful situation giving sweeping views of the bay, this well maintained family-run hotel has bedrooms of differing sizes, many of the larger front rooms having balconies, but all with modern fitments. The popular carvery provides counter service of inexpensive standard dishes, while the Harbour View restaurant offers à la carte and table d'hôte menus for which chef Carmine Santorello makes careful use of fresh produce, with local seafood a speciality. Simple appetisers might be followed by Poole Bay scallops in mornay sauce, or tournedos Rossini, and well made puddings such as fresh fruit roulade.*

49⇊🛏 CTV in all bedrooms ® T sB&B⇊🛏£47.50
dB&B⇊🛏£80 🍴
Lift ℂ 84P ✿ CFA ♫
♀ English French & Italian V ♥ ⌂ Sunday Lunch £12 High tea £5 Dinner £16&alc Last dinner 9.30pm
Credit Cards ①②③⑤

---

★★★68% **Haven**

Banks Rd, Sandbanks BH13 7QL ☎(0202)707333
FAX (0202) 708796

*An hotel which overlooks Poole harbour, Shell Bay and the Isle of Wight from its wonderful location on the top of the Sandbanks peninsula features comfortable and well furnished public areas with extensive conference facilities and leisure amenities which include both indoor and outdoor pools. Almost all the bedrooms are newly furnished, the larger rear rooms being particularly comfortable, and friendly staff provide helpful service.*

95⇊🛏(6fb) CTV in all bedrooms ® T 🦮 (ex guide dogs) ✳
sB&B⇊🛏£51-£64 dB&B⇊🛏£102-£123
Lift ℂ 150P 🚗 CFA 🏊 (heated) 🏊 (heated) ♬ (hard) squash sauna solarium gymnasium steam room spa pool ♫ *xmas*
♀ English & French V ♥ ⌂ ⅍ ✳ Lunch £10-£12.50&alc High tea £6-£7.50 Dinner £18-£20&alc Last dinner 10pm
Credit Cards ①②③⑤ £

See advertisement on page 577

---

★★★64% **Sandbanks**

Banks Rd, Sandbanks BH13 7PS ☎(0202)707377
FAX (0202) 708885

*In an outstanding location on Sandbanks beach and Poole Harbour, this hotel is ideally placed for family and water activity holidays. Many of the spacious bedrooms have been refurbished and those remaining, while a little spartan, are cheaper. Extensive public rooms include a ballroom with entertainment and indoor leisure facilities. An interesting table d'hôte menu offers something for everyone.*

105⇊🛏(27fb) CTV in all bedrooms ® T 🦮 (ex guide dogs)
sB&B⇊🛏£45-£55 dB&B⇊🛏£90-£110 🍴
Lift ℂ 200P ✿ CFA 🏊 (heated) sauna solarium gymnasium steam room ♨ *xmas*
♀ International V ♥ ⌂ Lunch £11 High tea £3-£5 Dinner £16 Last dinner 8.30pm
Credit Cards ①②③⑤ £

See advertisement on page 577

---

★★★60% *Dolphin*

High St BH15 1DU ☎(0202)673612 Telex no 417205
FAX (0202) 674197

*A purpose-built hotel in a central location where bedrooms, though on the small side, are generally furnished to a sound modern standard. Public areas offer an extensive range of food and services. There is a busy coffee shop with counter service and a large bar popular for its food and resident DJ. The small dining room has a carvery and an à la carte menu with more formal service.*

66⇊🛏1🛏 CTV in all bedrooms ®
Lift ℂ 50P
♀ French V ♥ ⌂ Last dinner 10.30pm
Credit Cards ①②③⑤

**★★63% Norfolk Lodge**
1 Flaghead Rd, Canford Cliffs BH14 7JL ☎(0202)708614 & 708661
*Well placed close to Sandbanks, this extended Victorian house with neat gardens is run with friendly informality as a family holiday hotel. Modern bedrooms are well equipped and public areas are bright and comfortable.*
19rm(17⇨↱)(4fb) CTV in all bedrooms ® T ✱ sB&B£25 sB&B⇨↱£34-£38 dB&B⇨↱£54 ⊟
16P ✿ ❖ *xmas*
✿ ☑ ⚔ ✱ Lunch £7-£9 Dinner £10 Last dinner 8pm
Credit Cards [1] [2] [3]

**★★59% Antelope**
High St BH15 1BP (Lansbury) ☎(0202)672029 Telex no 418387 FAX (0202) 678286
*A characterful old coaching inn not far from the quay provides renovated bedrooms with many modern facilities, while Henekey's restaurant offers an international menu served by cheerful young staff.*
21⇨↱(1fb)⚔in 3 bedrooms CTV in all bedrooms ®
✖ (ex guide dogs) sB&B⇨↱fr£65 dB&B⇨↱fr£78 ⊟
☾ 20P *xmas*
♡ European **V** ✿ ☑ Lunch fr£12&alc Dinner fr£12&alc Last dinner 10.30pm
Credit Cards [1] [2] [3] [4] [5]

**★★59% Sea Witch**
47 Haven Rd, Canford Cliffs BH13 7LH ☎(0202)707697
Closed 26 Dec-1 Jan
*A small proprietor-run hotel offering well equipped bedrooms and a choice of menus including local fresh fish.*
8⇨↱(2fb) CTV in all bedrooms ® **T** ✖ (ex guide dogs) sB&B⇨↱£42-£44 dB&B⇨↱£55-£60 ⊟
45P ✿ nc5yrs
♡ French Sunday Lunch £8.50 Dinner £11.50-£14&alc Last dinner 9.30pm
Credit Cards [1] [3]

**★65% Fairlight**
1 Golf Links Rd, Broadstone BH18 8BE (3m NW B3074) ☎(0202)694316 & 605349
*Bedrooms have deliberately been kept simple at this small, friendly hotel, but there is a comfortable television lounge which is warmed by an open fire in winter. Dinner is a set meal served at a fixed time, and a healthy wholefood alternative to the standard breakfast menu is available; all food is fresh and well prepared, and such traditional services as early morning tea are retained.*
10rm(7⇨↱)(1fb) ✱ sB&B£33-£36 sB&B⇨↱£35-£38 dB&B£54-£62 dB&B⇨↱£58-£64 (incl dinner) ⊟
CTV 10P ✿ ❖ CFA
**V** ✿ ⚔ Lunch £6 Dinner £10-£14 Last dinner 7.30pm
Credit Cards [1] [3]

**POOLEY BRIDGE** Cumbria Map **12** NY42

**★★63% Swiss Chalet Inn**
CA10 2NN ☎(07684)86215
Closed 3-18 Jan
*An attractive Swiss-style building close to the lake provides well furnished comfortable accommodation, a good range of food, and friendly, efficient service.*
9rm(8⇨↱)(1fb)1⊞ CTV in all bedrooms ® sB&B⇨↱£25-£30 dB&B⇨↱£40-£48 Continental breakfast
40P ❖ CFA
♡ English & Continental **V** ✿ ☑ ✱ Bar Lunch £3.85-£9.05alc Dinner £5.25-£15.65alc Last dinner 9.30pm
Credit Cards [1] [3] £

**See advertisement under ULLSWATER**

**POOL-IN-WHARFEDALE** West Yorkshire Map **08** SE24

**❀❀❀ ✕✕✕ Pool Court**
Pool Bank LS21 1EH ☎Leeds(0532)842288 FAX (0532) 843115
*Conveniently situated between Leeds, Bradford and Harrogate, this fine Georgian building provides diners with formal and elegant surroundings, yet the welcoming, helpful service ensures a comfortable atmosphere. The 4-course menu, priced according to the main course, does not change very often but always includes seasonal dishes and there are daily specials. Alternatively, the no-choice 3-course meal is available at a very reasonable price. Typical dishes might be roast Norfolk duckling, grilled fillet of beef with Bearnaise sauce or hot sole and lobster mousse with butter sauce. More innovative choices could include calves liver, roasted whole and served with a sherry vinegar sauce, or sweetbreads, scallops and vegetables accompanied by a carrot and cinnamon oil. Thoughtful pricing also applies to the wine list which has several good wines under the £10 mark.*
Closed Sun, Mon, 2 wks from 25 Dec & 2 wks mid-summer
Lunch not served (ex parties of over 10 by arrangement)
♡ British & French **V** 65 seats ✱ Dinner £10&alc Last dinner 9.30pm 65 P
Credit Cards [1] [2] [3] [5]

**PORLOCK** Somerset Map **03** SS84

**★★74% The Oaks**
Doverhay TA24 8ES ☎(0643)862265
*This Edwardian country hotel, surrounded by colourful gardens and set in an elevated position on the edge of the village, offers accommodation in well equipped bedrooms, attractively co-ordinated in pastel shades and furnished with hand-picked antiques. A pleasant dining room, extended and refurbished for 1991, serves unpretentious meals, based on fresh local produce providing a good choice at dinner and there is a reasonably priced wine list. Open fires in public areas and the caring attitude of welcoming hosts combine to create an atmosphere of wellbeing.*
11⇨↱(2fb) CTV in all bedrooms ® **T** S% sB&B⇨↱£37.50-£40 dB&B⇨↱£60-£65 ⊟
12P ✿ ❖ *xmas*
✿ ⚔ S% Dinner fr£16.50 Last dinner 8.30pm
£

**See advertisement on page 579**

**★★63% Anchor & Ship**
Porlock Harbour TA24 8PB ☎(0643)862636 FAX (0643) 862843
RS Jan
*Ten yards from the picturesque harbour stands this comfortable, informal establishment offering large, well-furnished bedrooms in the main hotel building and simpler, less expensive accommodation in the Ship Inn.*
22rm(18⇨↱)(2fb)1⊞ CTV in all bedrooms ® **T** S10% dB&B⇨↱£115.50 ⊟
25P ❖ CFA *xmas*
♡ English & French **V** ✿ ☑ S% Bar Lunch £1.65-£5alc Dinner £16&alc Last dinner 9pm
Credit Cards [1] [2] [3]

**See advertisement on page 579**

Red star hotels are each highlighted by a pink tinted panel.

# HOTEL GROUP

AA
★★★

# CHINE

The Chine is a magnificent hotel constructed in 1874, occupying one of Bournemouth's finest positions overlooking Poole Bay. The level of service is exceptional combining old world charm with a high standard of modern facilities. All 97 rooms are En-Suite with Baby Listening, Tea & Coffee making facilities, Satellite TV, In-House Video and Radio.

**BOSCOME SPA ROAD BOURNEMOUTH
BH5 1AX TEL: (0202) 396234**
FAX: (0202) 391737

# HAVEN

The Haven Hotel is ideally located at the sea's edge overlooking Poole Bay and Harbour.
The Hotel's superb position enjoys mild winters and sunny summers.
All 98 rooms are En-Suite with Baby Listening, Tea & Coffee making facilities, Satellite TV, In-House Video and Radio.

**SANDBANKS POOLE
BH13 7QL TEL: (0202) 707333**
FAX: (0202) 708796

# SANDBANKS

The ideal Family Hotel, is situated right on Sandbanks beach which holds the coveted EEC Blue Flag award for cleanliness.
Services include children's restaurant, nursery and activities, all 105 bedrooms are en-suite, many with balconies.
Rooms have Baby Listening, Tea & Coffee making facilities, Satellite TV, In-House Video and Radio.

**SANDBANKS POOLE
BH13 7PS TEL: (0202) 707377**
FAX: (0202) 708885

## PORT APPIN Strathclyde *Argyllshire* Map **14** NM94

★★★

★★★ ✿✿✿ **AIRDS**

PA38 4DF (Relais et
Châteaux)
☎Appin(063173)236 & 211
FAX (063173) 535

Closed 7 Jan-9 Mar

*The impression given by a
rather uninspiring entrance
and reception area here are rapidly dispelled by the courteous,
well trained, smart staff who take over from the moment you
arrive. They combine professionalism of the highest order with
an unintrusive warmth. Standards of housekeeping and
maintenance remain commendably high, and though a couple
of bedrooms are a little compact and those in the annexe more
modestly furnished, the overall quality of furnishings and
bathrooms is impressively high. Eric Allen, resplendent in a
kilt, is much in evidence, while his wife Betty and son Graham
are in charge of the kitchen. The fixed-price 4-course menu at
dinner offers British cuisine of a consistently high standard.
Fish features prominently, with dishes such as risotto of
lobster and scallops; the terrine of chicken livers, soups and
home-made desserts all receive critical acclaim. A meal in the
smart, well appointed dining room, with views across Loch
Linnhe to the hills beyond, is a rare delight, and it is not
surprising that so many guests return to stay at this most
tranquil and relaxing hotel.*

12⊸🛏Annexe2🛏 CTV in all bedrooms
🐾 (ex guide dogs) sB&B⊸🛏£115-£140 dB&B⊸🛏£180-
£203 (incl dinner)

30P ⇔ ❄ nc5yrs

♥ ⊑ ⫟ Bar Lunch £10-£15 Dinner £36 Last dinner
8.30pm

## PORT ASKAIG

See Islay, Isle of

## PORT GAVERNE Cornwall & Isles of Scilly Map **02** SX08

★★70% *Port Gaverne*

PL29 3SQ ☎Bodmin(0208)880244 FAX (0208) 880151
Closed 13 Jan-15 Feb

*Sheltering in a valley adjacent to the beach, this popular former inn
dating from the 16th century has been run by Fred and Midge
Ross for 22 years. Public areas are cosy and characterful, and the
split-level restaurant serves imaginative food featuring local fish.
Bedrooms vary from compact to spacious, all with modern
facilities. Self-catering units set around a courtyard garden are
also available.*

16⊸🛏Annexe3⊸🛏(5fb) CTV in 18 bedrooms ® T
CTV 30P ⇔

♥ International V ✿ ⊑ Last dinner 9.30pm
Credit Cards ① ② ③ ⑤

★★66% *Headlands*

PL29 3SH ☎Bodmin(0208)880260

*Beautifully situated to command panoramic coastal views across
the cove to Port Isaac, the hotel provides comfortable bedrooms
and public areas which take advantage of this breathtaking
outlook. Table d'hôte and à la carte menus on offer in the
attractive restaurant make good use of the best local produce, and
welcoming proprietors are on hand to render personal service.*

11⊸🛏(1fb) CTV in all bedrooms ® ✱ S10% sB&B⊸🛏£29-
£36 dB&B⊸🛏£58-£72 ⅌

35P ⇔ ❄ sauna *xmas*

♥ European V ✿ ⊑ ✱ S10% Bar Lunch £4-£9alc High tea
fr£2.95alc Dinner fr£12.50&alc Last dinner 9.30pm
Credit Cards ① ② ③ ⑤

## PORTHCAWL Mid Glamorgan Map **03** SS87

★★★58% *Seabank*

The Promenade CF36 3LU (Lansbury) ☎(0656)782261
Telex no 497797 FAX (0656) 785363

*Situated on the promenade, this well established hotel provides
modern bedrooms and extensive and comfortable public areas.
Conference facilities are of a good standard and are much in use
throughout the year.*

64⊸🛏(4fb)⫟in 6 bedrooms CTV in all bedrooms ® T
🐾 (ex guide dogs) ✱ sB&B⊸🛏£60-£65 dB&B⊸🛏£72-£77 ⅌
Lift ( 150P ❄ CFA sauna solarium gymnasium jacuzzi *xmas*
♥ English & French V ✿ ⊑ ⫟ ✱ Lunch £15-£25alc High tea
£3.20-£4.80 Dinner £14.25&alc Last dinner 9.45pm
Credit Cards ① ② ③ ⑤ ⓔ

★★64% *Glenaub*

50 Mary St CF36 3YA ☎(0656)788242

*A town-centre hotel, just a short walk from the seafront, provides a
good choice of food, modern well equipped bedrooms and a
comfortable lounge bar and conservatory.*

18⊸🛏 CTV in all bedrooms ® 🐾
CTV 12P ⇔
♥ International V ✿ ⊑ Last dinner 10pm
Credit Cards ① ② ③ ④ ⑤

★63% *Rose & Crown*

Heol-y-Capel, Nottage CF36 3ST (2m N B4283) (Chef & Brewer)
☎(0656)784850

*This small, friendly inn, a short drive from sea and town centre,
provides compact but comfortable and well-equipped bedrooms.
Though there is no residents' lounge, it offers a choice of 3 popular
bars, which the Country Carvery restaurant serves a range of
good-value meals which always includes a traditional roast.*

8⊸🛏(1fb) CTV in all bedrooms ® T 🐾 (ex guide dogs)
sB&B⊸🛏£43 dB&B⊸🛏£56 ⅌

12P

♥ International V ✿ ⊑ ⫟ ✱ Bar Lunch £2.95-£5.50alc
Credit Cards ① ② ③ ⑤

★60% *Brentwood*

37-41 Mary St CF36 3YN ☎(0656)782725 & 786815

*A busy hotel located just 100 yards from the sea front and the
shopping centre, convenient for both holidaymakers and
businessmen. Bedrooms are well-equipped with modern amenities
and the à la carte menu offers a good choice of dishes. The two
bars are popular with the locals.*

22rm(21⊸🛏)(5fb) CTV in all bedrooms ® T sB&B⊸🛏£24-
£28 dB&B⊸🛏£40-£50 ⅌
CTV 12P CFA games room
V Bar Lunch £3.95-£6.95&alc Dinner £8.95-£12.95&alc Last
dinner 10pm
Credit Cards ① ② ③ ⑤

## PORTHLEVEN Cornwall & Isles of Scilly Map **02** SW62

★★65% *Harbour*

Commercial Rd TR13 9JD (St Austell Brewery)
☎Helston(0326)573876
RS 25 Dec

*The brightly appointed, pine furnished and particularly
comfortable bedrooms of this delightful inn are equipped to meet
the expectations of today's more discerning traveller; some also
offer unrestricted views over the picturesque harbour beside which
it stands. The choice of bars includes a family room where children
of all ages are welcomed, and pleasant local staff provide prompt,
friendly service under the enthusiastic supervision of a resident
manager. An excellent touring base for the southwest peninsula of
Cornwall, the hotel is also very popular with businessmen.*

10rm(8⇨)(1fb) CTV in all bedrooms ® T ✖ (ex guide dogs) ✱
sB&B£20 sB&B⇨£29 dB&B£36 dB&B⇨£50
CTV 10P ♯♯ ♫
V ❦ ⚄ ✄ ✱ Lunch £4.95 Dinner £6-£12alc Last dinner 9.30pm
Credit Cards ① ② ③

**See advertisement under ST AUSTELL**

---

## PORT ISAAC Cornwall & Isles of Scilly Map **02** SW98

See also Port Gaverne

★★63% *Castle Rock*
4 New Rd PL29 3SB (Minotels) ☎Bodmin(0208)880300
Closed 5 Jan-Feb
*Set in an elevated position with spectacular views of the rugged
coastline this relaxed, friendly and mainly holiday hotel offers well
equipped comfortable accommodation. Dinners are freshly cooked
and wholesome, whilst bar meals are available at lunchtime.*
17rm(12⇨3ʛ)(3fb) CTV in 16 bedrooms ® T
CTV 20P ✿
V ❦ ⚄ ✄ Last dinner 8.30pm
Credit Cards ① ③

---

## PORTLAND Dorset Map **03** SY67

★★★57% **Portland Heights**
Yeates Corner DT5 2EN ☎(0305)821361 FAX (0305) 860081
*Set high above the village with fabulous views from the bar and
restaurant, along Chesil Beach to Lyme Regis on a clear day.
Bedrooms are modern in style, though some have older bathrooms.
The hotel offers extensive sports facilities, the restaurant has an
ambitious menu, and service is well intentioned.*
66⇨3ʛ(4fb)✄in 5 bedrooms CTV in all bedrooms ® T
sB&B⇨ʛ£59.50-£62 dB&B⇨ʛ£78-£82 ₽
《 160P CFA ➔ (heated) squash sauna solarium gymnasium
steam room *xmas*
♡ International V ❦ ⚄ ✄ ✱ S% Lunch £8-£9.50 Dinner £16-
£18&alc Last dinner 9.30pm
Credit Cards ① ② ③ ⑤ ⓔ

---

## PORT OF MENTEITH Central *Perthshire* Map **11** NN50

★★75% **Lake**
FK8 3RA ☎(08775)258 FAX (08775) 671
*Attractively situated on the shore of Lake Menteith, this former
manse has been carefully refurbished to a high standard, and
although bedrooms vary in size all are comfortably furnished and
have many thoughtful extras. The conservatory restaurant
overlooks the lake, with lighter meals available in the bar and
bistro.*
14⇨ʛ CTV in all bedrooms ® T dB&B⇨ʛ£74-£150 (incl
dinner) ₽
35P ♯♯ CFA nc9yrs *xmas*
♡ Scottish & French V ❦ ⚄ ✄
Credit Cards ① ③

---

## PORTPATRICK Dumfries & Galloway *Wigtownshire*
Map **10** NX05

★★★63% **Fernhill**
DG9 8TD ☎(077681)220 FAX (077681) 596
Closed Xmas
*Situated in an elevated position commanding fine panoramic views
over the village and out to sea, this enlarged Victorian house
provides comfortable accommodation. Bedrooms, although
compact and plainly decorated, are clean, fresh and well equipped.
Guests can relax in the elegant lounge and enjoyable meals are
served by friendly young staff in the bright, modern restaurant.*
15rm(14⇨ʛ)Annexe4⇨ʛ(1fb) CTV in all bedrooms ® T
sB&B⇨ʛ£50-£100 dB&B⇨ʛ£75-£120 ₽
50P ✿ ₰ *xmas*

♡ Scottish & French V ❦ ⚄ ✄ Sunday Lunch fr£8.50 Dinner
fr£17.50&alc Last dinner 10pm
Credit Cards ① ② ③ ⑤ ⓔ

★★★❀❀❀❀ ⚑
**KNOCKINAAM LODGE**
DG9 9AD (2m S on unclass
rd) (Pride of Britain)
☎(077681)471
FAX (077681) 435
Closed 5 Jan-14 Mar
*It would be difficult to find a
more secluded retreat: in idyllic surroundings overlooking the
sea and cliffs, with fine views, lovely gardens and a private
beach. The warm hospitality of the charming owners, Marcel
and Corinna Frichot, and their helpful staff is a strong feature
of the hotel. It is thoughtfully furnished and decorated
throughout, with comfortable sitting rooms, a small bar, and
the intimate dining room which plays an important part in the
operation. Young Chef Daniel Galmiche takes great pride in
his cooking and produces some interesting dishes. Bedrooms
are very comfortable, furnishings blending well with the
character of the house. Marcel has a passion for clocks and
many can be seen around the hotel.*
10⇨1⊞ CTV in all bedrooms T ✱ sB&B⇨fr£62.50
dB&B⇨£92-£125 ₽
25P ♯♯ ✿ croquet ₰
♡ French V ❦ ⚄ ✄ ✱ Lunch £18 High tea fr£10alc
Dinner £30 Last dinner 9pm
Credit Cards ① ② ③ ⑤

---

★★56% **Portpatrick**
DG9 8TQ (Mount Charlotte (TS)) ☎(077681)333
Closed last wk Nov-early Mar
*Large cliff-top resort hotel with good amenities for families with
children.*
57⇨ʛ(5fb) CTV in all bedrooms ® ₽
Lift 《 60P ✿ ➔ (heated) ▶ 9 ♫ (grass) snooker games room
*xmas*
♡ English & French V ❦ ⚄
Credit Cards ① ② ③ ⑤

---

★61% **Mount Stewart**
South Crescent DG9 8LE ☎(077681)291
*This traditional black-painted house by the harbour commands
striking sea views and offers modest but reasonably priced
accommodation and very friendly service. Freshly cooked meals
feature local seafood.*
6rm(3ʛ)(2fb) CTV in all bedrooms ® sB&B£17-£20
sB&Bʛ£25-£28 dB&B£34-£40 dB&Bʛ£38-£46
15P ♯♯
♡ International V Lunch £5-£10&alc High tea £5.95-£10.95
Dinner fr£10.50&alc Last dinner 10pm
Credit Cards ① ③

---

## PORTREE

See Skye, Isle of

---

## PORTSCATHO Cornwall & Isles of Scilly Map **02** SW83

★★★61% **Rosevine**
Porthcurnick Beach TR2 5EW ☎(0872)580206 & 580230
Closed Nov-Etr
*A privately owned Georgian manor house, set in 3.5 acres of
sheltered gardens and run along traditional lines. Bedrooms, some
with balconies, are gradually being upgraded whilst retaining*

many original features. The hotel has a good sun lounge and there is a large restaurant with dance floor.
14⇨🏃Annexe1⇨🏃(2fb) CTV in all bedrooms ® T
sB&B⇨🏃£40.75-£47 dB&B⇨🏃£75.50-£133 (incl dinner) 🅿
《 CTV 40P 🕸 ❄
♀ International V ✿ ⏛ ⅍ Bar Lunch £6.75-£8.50alc Dinner £19.50 Last dinner 8.30pm
Credit Cards ① ③

### ★★69% Gerrans Bay
Gerrans TR2 5ED ☎(0872)580338
Closed Nov-Mar (ex Xmas)
Personally supervised by proprietors, Ann and Brian Greaves, whose total commitment and attention to detail is reflected in this very well run hotel. Bedrooms are tastefully furnished and daily menus promote a good standard of cooking.
14rm(12⇨🏃)(2fb) ® sB&B⇨🏃£33-£39.50 dB&B⇨🏃£68-£82.50 (incl dinner)
CTV 16P 🕸 xmas
✿ ⏛ Sunday Lunch £8.50 Dinner £15-£17.25 Last dinner 8pm
Credit Cards ① ② ③

### ★★🏊61% Roseland House
Rosevine TR2 5EW ☎(0872)580644
Closed Dec-Feb
Situated on a clifftop and within 6 acres of National Trust and Heritage coastline, this privately owned hotel is efficiently run, and good home cooking is provided by the owner. Bedrooms are equipped to a good standard, and the public rooms are tastefully furnished. A wooded path leads down the cliff to a secluded beach. With its peaceful atmosphere, this is an ideal hotel in which to relax and unwind.
19⇨🏃(5fb)2🐾 🦮 (ex guide dogs)
CTV 25P 3🏐 🕸 ❄ 🚣 private beach nc5yrs
V ✿ ⏛ ⅍ Last dinner 8pm

---

**PORTSMOUTH & SOUTHSEA** Hampshire Map **04** SZ69 ◉

### ★★★68% Forte Crest
Pembroke Rd PO1 2TA (Forte Hotels)
☎Portsmouth(0705)827651 Telex no 86397
FAX (0705) 756715
A popular hotel for business users and for weekend leisure breaks. There is an extensive range of conference and seminar rooms complemented by the business centre, and, for relaxation, a professionally supervised leisure club. Bedrooms vary in standard and décor, Executive and Lady Executive rooms are available. The Promenade Restaurant has some self-service elements and an à la carte menu, and the Boulevard Café Bar stocks an impressive array of international bottled beers. Entertainment is offered on certain nights.
163⇨🏃(12fb)⅍in 36 bedrooms CTV in all bedrooms ® T ✳
sB⇨🏃fr£78 dB⇨🏃£91-£110 (room only) 🅿
Lift 《 80P 5🏐 CFA 🏊 (heated) sauna solarium gymnasium steam room ♨ xmas
V ✿ ⏛ ⅍ ✳ Lunch £5-£14&alc Dinner £16.75&alc Last dinner 10pm
Credit Cards ① ② ③ ④ ⑤

### ★★★67% Holiday Inn
North Harbour PO6 4SH (Holiday Inns)
☎Portsmouth(0705)383151 Telex no 86611
FAX (0705) 388701
Young staff provide pleasant service in this modern, purpose-built hotel which offers easy access to the motorway system from a position on the edge of the city. Its vast Holidrome interior has been divided to create attractive public areas which include a restaurant service with dishes inspired by the Roux Brothers, the addition of a snooker room has upgraded leisure facilities, and half the bedrooms have now been refurbished.
170⇨🏃(76fb)⅍in 23 bedrooms CTV in all bedrooms ® T ✳
S% sB⇨🏃£86-£112.50 dB⇨🏃£97-£112.50 (room only) 🅿

Lift 《 ▦ 200P ❄ CFA 🔲 (heated) squash snooker sauna solarium gymnasium adventure playground xmas
♀ English & French V ✿ ⏛ ⅍ ✳ Lunch £12.50-£12.95&alc Dinner fr£15.95&alc Last dinner 11pm
Credit Cards ① ② ③ ④ ⑤ ⓔ

### ★★★60% Hospitality Inn
St Helens Pde PO4 0RN (Mount Charlotte (TS))
☎Portsmouth(0705)731281 Telex no 86719
FAX (0705) 817572
This spacious seafront hotel offers 2 styles of attractively decorated well equipped bedrooms. Lounge facilities are limited but the spacious lounge bar is comfortable and the gracious restaurant with spectacular modern chandeliers features a good value table d'hôte menu and an à la carte. Service is efficient and friendly.
115⇨🏃(6fb)⅍in 13 bedrooms CTV in all bedrooms ® T (room only) 🅿
Lift 《 50P xmas
♀ English & French V ✿
Credit Cards ① ② ③ ⑤

### ★★64% Keppels Head
PO1 3DT (Forte Hotels) ☎Portsmouth(0705)833231
FAX (0705) 838688
A friendly, well established hotel with comfortable modernised bedrooms, the elegant front rooms having views across Portsmouth harbour. Raffles Restaurant offers à la carte and carvery-style menus and various meeting and function rooms are available.
27⇨🏃(6fb)⅍in 8 bedrooms CTV in all bedrooms ® T ✳ S%
sB⇨🏃fr£55 dB⇨🏃£70-£80 (room only) 🅿
Lift 《 ▦ 18P CFA xmas
V ✿ ⏛ ⅍ ✳ S% Lunch £9.95-£11.95&alc High tea fr£3.50 Dinner fr£13.95&alc Last dinner 9pm
Credit Cards ① ② ③ ④ ⑤

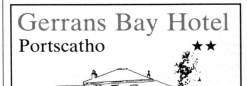

# Gerrans Bay Hotel
## Portscatho ★★

This small hotel, situated in the peaceful Roseland Peninsula, is an ideal centre for walking, birdwatching, fishing, sailing, windsurfing, and visiting the many beautiful Cornish Gardens. All rooms have private bathrooms.
Ann and Brian Greaves pride themselves on offering warm, personal friendly service and a varied menu using local produce.
Complimentary golf and bowls are available to Residents.
Restaurant is open daily for bar snacks and dinners.
Ample car parking.
**For Brochure – write or telephone.**
**GERRANS BAY HOTEL**
**Gerrans, Portscatho, Truro TR2 5ED**
**Telephone: PORTSCATHO (087258) 338**

★★63% **The Beaufort**
71 Festing Rd PO4 0NQ ☎Portsmouth(0705)823707
FAX (0705) 870270
*An hotel quietly situated just off the seafront, no more than a 5-minute walk from the Promenade, is very smart and comfortable following its recent extensive refurbishment programme. Practical but attractive bedrooms are furnished with style and flair, while public areas include a pleasant ground floor lounge complete with Chesterfield suites and a basement dining room and bar. The simple fare on offer is home-cooked by proprietors who remain closely involved with the day-to-day running of the establishment.*
19⇌🛏(3fb) CTV in all bedrooms ® T ✗ ✳ S%
sB&B⇌🛏£30-£38 dB&B⇌🛏£42-£48 🅿
10P
🐾 ⚗ ✳ S% High tea £2-£4 Dinner £9.50 Last dinner 8.30pm
Credit cards ①②③⑤

★★62% **Seacrest**
12 South Pde PO5 2JB (Minotels) ☎Portsmouth(0705)733192
FAX (0705) 832523
*This hotel, made up of two adjoining buildings, overlooks attractive public gardens from a prominent sea-facing position only yards from the Promenade. Recently refurbished in a smart and stylish manner, it offers bright, pretty bedrooms equipped with modern facilities and public areas which include a cosy bar, two lounges with handsome Chesterfield suites and a basement dining room and pleasant, cheery hospitality is provided by friendly proprietors who remain very involved in the day-to-day running of the hotel.*
26⇌🛏(2fb) CTV in all bedrooms ® T ✳ S% sB&B⇌🛏£30-£35 dB&B⇌🛏£40-£46 🅿
Lift 7P *xmas*
🐾 ⚗ ✂ ✳ Bar Lunch £2-£5 High tea fr£2 Dinner £9&alc Last dinner 7.30pm
Credit Cards ①②③

★★61% **Sandringham**
7 Osborne Rd, Clarence Pde PO5 3LR
☎Portsmouth(0705)822914 & 826969 FAX (0705) 822330
*On the seafront, set back a little from the Esplanade, this hotel has undergone a major refurbishment programme over the past 18 months. Bedrooms are now equipped in a modern style with good facilities. Public areas are spacious and are now complemented by a smart basement wine bar, where lunch and dinner are served as well as in the York Restaurant, with its simple table d'hôte menu.*
45⇌🛏(7fb)2🌙 CTV in all bedrooms ® T ✗ (ex guide dogs) ✳ sB&B⇌🛏£32 dB&B⇌🛏£46 🅿
Lift CTV ♫ *xmas*
♥ English & French V 🐾 ⚗ ✳ Lunch £6-£9 High tea £1-£4 Dinner £8.50-£9.50 Last dinner 9.30pm
Credit Cards ①②③⑤

★★60% **Westfield Hall**
65 Festing Rd PO4 0NQ ☎Portsmouth(0705)826971
FAX (0705) 870200
*A private hotel with its own large car park, quietly situated close to the seafront, provides recently refurbished accommodation which combines modern facilities with smart furnishings and an attractively coordinated décor. The traditional suite sitting room is complemented by a comfortably appointed sun lounge, and a basement dining room with a small dispense bar at one end offers a simple menu. Cheerful, friendly hosts are very much involved in the day-to-day running of the establishment.*
17rm(14⇌🛏)(4fb) CTV in all bedrooms ® T ✗ ✳ sB&B£21-£24 sB&B⇌🛏£32-£36 dB&B⇌🛏£42-£48 🅿
CTV 18P
✂ ✳ Dinner £9&alc Last dinner 7.30pm
Credit Cards ①②③

🐚 Shell filling stations (7am–11pm) are marked on the town plans.

⊛⊛ ✗ *Bistro Montparnasse*
103 Palmerston Rd PO5 3PS ☎Portsmouth(0705)816754
*A small bistro, brightly decorated, with a friendly informal atmosphere. Cooking is of a very good standard with a few specialities.*
Closed Sun, 1st 2 wks Jan & BH's Lunch not served
♥ French 42 seats Last dinner 10pm P nc5yrs
Credit Cards ①②③⑤

**PORT TALBOT** West Glamorgan Map **03** SS79 ⊖

★★★58% **Aberavan Beach**
Princess Margaret Way SA12 6QP (Consort) ☎(0639)884949
FAX (0639) 897885
*This friendly holiday hotel on the seafront was undergoing a modernisation programme during 1991 to provide spacious new public areas and improved bedrooms. A range of bar meals is available as well as the restaurant menus.*
66⇌(6fb) CTV in all bedrooms ® T sB&B⇌£40-£50 dB&B⇌£48-£54 🅿
Lift ⟨ 150P CFA 🖾 (heated) sauna ♫ *xmas*
♥ Welsh, English & French 🐾 ⚗ Sunday Lunch fr£7.50 Dinner fr£12.50&alc Last dinner 10.15pm
Credit Cards ①②③⑤⑥

**PORT WILLIAM** Dumfries & Galloway *Wigtownshire* Map **10** NX34

★★★♨63% **Corsemalzie House**
DG8 9RL (Inter-Hotels) ☎Mochrum(098886)254
Closed 21 Jan-5 Mar
*Peacefully set in 40 acres of woodland and gardens, this pleasant 19th-century country house offers friendly informal service. Attractively decorated bedrooms and public rooms are unpretentious and relaxing.*
14⇌🛏(1fb) CTV in all bedrooms ® T sB&B⇌🛏£39.50-£47.50 dB&B⇌🛏£59-£75 🅿
30P 🛉 ✿ ♪ croquet game shooting putting 🐾 *xmas*
♥ Scottish & French V 🐾 ⚗ Lunch £9.95-£12.95&alc Dinner £15.95-£18.95&alc Last dinner 9.15pm
Credit Cards ①③⑥

**POTT SHRIGLEY** Cheshire Map **07** SJ97

★★★★61% **Shrigley Hall Golf & Country Club**
Shrigley Park SK10 5SB ☎Bollington(0625)575757
FAX (0625) 573323
*This comfortable hotel offers a wide range of leisure activities including a championship golf course, squash and snooker with additional country pursuits available within the Estate. New conference and banqueting suites are nearing completion, and should prove popular with business guests.*
58⇌5🌙 CTV in all bedrooms ® T S% sB&B⇌£65-£85 dB&B⇌£85-£110 🅿
Lift ⟨ 600P 🛉 ✿ CFA 🖾 (heated) ▶ 18 ♗ (hard) ♪ squash snooker sauna solarium gymnasium jacuzzi beauty salon steam spa ♫ *xmas*
♥ English & International V 🐾 ⚗ ✂ ✳ S% Lunch fr£14.50 High tea fr£5.75 Dinner fr£19.50&alc Last dinner 9.45pm
Credit Cards ①②③④⑤

**POWBURN** Northumberland Map **12** NU01

★★⊛♨75% **Breamish House**
NE66 4LL ☎(066578)266 & 544 FAX (066578) 500
Closed Jan
*A charming house set in 5 acres of peaceful and well tended grounds. Bedrooms are well furnished and have lots of thoughtful extras provided. The lounges are comfortable and a good standard of home cooking is served in the delightful dining room.*

10rm(9⇨🏠)Annexe1⇨🏠 CTV in all bedrooms ® T ✱
sB&B⇨🏠£51-£62.50 dB&B£78-£95 dB&B⇨🏠£81.50-£126
(incl dinner) 🍴
30P 2🚗 🚗 ✿ nc12yrs *xmas*
♥ ⊡ ⚡ ✱ Sunday Lunch £12.50 Dinner £18.95 Last dinner
8pm

---

**POWFOOT** Dumfries & Galloway *Dumfriesshire*
Map **11** NY16

★★61% **Golf**
Links Av DG12 5PN ☎Cummertrees(04617)254
*On the Solway coast and next to an 18-hole golf course, this hotel
offers spacious public areas and a modern wing of superior
bedrooms. Friendly young staff offer polite, helpful service.*
19rm(9⇨🏠)(2fb) CTV in 15 bedrooms ® T ✖ (ex guide dogs)
sB&B£30 sB&B⇨🏠£40 dB&B£56 dB&B⇨🏠£68 🍴
⊞ CTV 100P 10🚗 CFA ▶ 18 ♪ pool table *xmas*
V ♥ ⊡ ✱ Lunch fr£5 High tea fr£5.50 Dinner fr£11.50 Last
dinner 8.15pm
Credit Cards 1 3 £

---

**PRESTBURY** Cheshire Map **07** SJ97

★★★62% **Bridge**
The Village SK10 4DQ ☎(0625)829326 FAX (0625) 827557
*A family-owned hotel dating back to the 18th century, stands on
the bank of the River Bollin at the centre of this delightful village,
Manchester Airport and the motorway network both being within
easy reach. The recent addition of a large, purpose-built wing has
provided well equipped modern accommodation, many of the
rooms having river views.*
23⇨🏠(4fb) CTV in all bedrooms ® T ✖ (ex guide dogs) ✱
sB&B⇨🏠£65-£87 dB&B⇨🏠£87-£97 🍴
P CTV 52P ✿ CFA ♫
V ✱ Lunch £8.20-£8.80 Dinner fr£9 Last dinner 9.45pm
Credit Cards 1 2 3 5

---

**PRESTEIGNE** Powys Map **03** SO36

★★64% **Radnorshire Arms**
High St LD8 2BE (Forte Hotels) ☎(0544)267406
FAX (0544) 260418
*This friendly 16th-century coaching inn with beams, oak panelling
and log fires has lots of character and provides comfortable
accommodation. Annexe bedrooms are modern, while bedrooms in
the main hotel retain their old world atmosphere.*
8⇨🏠Annexe8⇨🏠 ⚡in 8 bedrooms CTV in all bedrooms ® T
✱ sB&B⇨🏠fr£65 dB&B⇨🏠£80-£85 (room only) 🍴
50P 5🚗 ✿ CFA *xmas*
V ♥ ⊡ ⚡ ✱ Lunch fr£8alc High tea fr£3 Dinner fr£14 Last
dinner 9pm
Credit Cards 1 2 3 4 5

---

**PRESTON** Lancashire Map **07** SD52

See also **Barton**
★★★72% **Tickled Trout**
Preston New Rd, Samlesbury PR5 0UJ (Rank) ☎(0772)877671
Telex no 677625 FAX (0772) 877463
*This comfortable hotel combines modern bedroom accommodation
with a quaint old world restaurant and lounge. Situated just off
junction 31 of the M6.*
72⇨🏠(56fb)2🛏⚡in 10 bedrooms CTV in all bedrooms ® T
✱ sB&B⇨🏠£49-£74 dB&B⇨🏠£67-£89 🍴
⊄ 150P 6🚗 CFA ♪ sauna solarium gymnasium wave pool
steam room ♫ *xmas*
𝔾 International V ♥ ⊡ ✱ Lunch £9.25-£9.50&alc Dinner
£15.50-£16&alc Last dinner 9.45pm
Credit Cards 1 2 3 5

---

★★★68% **Broughton Park Hotel & Country Club**
Garstang Rd, Broughton PR3 5JB (3m N on A6)
☎(0772)864087 Telex no 67180
*A Victorian mansion, tastefully modernised and extended, in large
grounds on the A6 to Garstang, less than a mile from junction 1 of
the M55. Bedrooms are well equipped and there is a wide range of
leisure facilities including a swimming pool, fitness studios, squash
courts and snooker tables. There are also versatile conference
facilities.*
98⇨🏠(4fb)3🛏⚡in 11 bedrooms CTV in all bedrooms ® T
✖ (ex guide dogs) ✱ sB&B⇨🏠£85-£95 dB&B⇨🏠£95-£105
🍴
Lift ⊄ 220P ✿ CFA 🏊 (heated) squash snooker sauna solarium
gymnasium spa bath steam room beauty salon
𝔾 English & French V ♥ ⊡ ✱ Lunch £11.50-£13.50&alc
Dinner £16-£18.50&alc Last dinner 10pm
Credit Cards 1 2 3 5 £

---

★★★64% **Swallow Trafalgar**
Preston New Rd, Samlesbury PR5 0UL (Swallow)
☎(0772)877351 Telex no 677362 FAX (0772) 877424
*Situated at the A59/A677 junction a mile from junction 31 of the
M6, this former roadside public house is now a modern hotel with
comfortable bedrooms, bars, a restaurant, leisure facilities and
conference and function rooms.*
78⇨🏠in 16 bedrooms CTV in all bedrooms ® T ✱ S10%
sB&B⇨🏠fr£76 dB&B⇨🏠fr£87 🍴
Lift ⊄ 300P CFA 🏊 (heated) squash sauna solarium
gymnasium steam room spa pool *xmas*
𝔾 International V ♥ ⊡ ✱ S10% Lunch fr£8.95 Dinner
fr£13.55 Last dinner 9.30pm
Credit Cards 1 2 3 5

---

★★★60% **Forte Crest**
The Ringway PR1 3AU (Forte Hotels) ☎(0772)59411
Telex no 677147 FAX (0772) 201923
*The comfortable modern accommodation provided by this brick-
built town centre hotel is particularly popular with a business
clientele. Reception and an open-plan area containing the
restaurant and spacious lounge bar are housed on the first floor.
Car parking is limited, but guests may use an adjacent car park
free of charge.*
126⇨🏠(11fb)⚡in 79 bedrooms CTV in all bedrooms ® T ✱
sB⇨🏠fr£80 dB⇨🏠fr£84 (room only) 🍴
Lift ⊄ 30P CFA *xmas*
𝔾 International V ♥ ⊡ ⚡ ✱ Lunch £9.20&alc Dinner
£16.35&alc Last dinner 11pm
Credit Cards 1 2 3 4 5

---

★★★56% **Leyland Resort**
Leyland Way PR5 2JX (Resort) ☎(0772)422922
Telex no 677651 FAX (0772) 622282
(For full entry see Leyland)

---

★★★55% **Novotel Preston**
Reedfield Place, Walton Summit PR5 6AB ☎(0772)313331
Telex no 677164 FAX (0772) 627868
*Just east of junction 29 of the M6, this purpose-built hotel has
modern functional bedrooms, friendly staff and a restaurant that is
open all day.*
100⇨🏠(100fb)⚡in 5 bedrooms CTV in all bedrooms ® T ✱
sB⇨🏠fr£51.50 dB⇨🏠fr£51.50 (room only) 🍴
Lift ⊄ 120P ✿ CFA ⌂
𝔾 Continental V ♥ ⊡ Lunch £9.50-£10&alc Dinner £9.50-
£10.50&alc Last dinner 11.50pm
Credit Cards 1 2 3 5

---

★★69% **Claremont**
516 Blackpool Rd, Ashton-on-Ribble PR2 1HY ☎(0772)729738
FAX (0772) 726274
*A privately owned fully licensed hotel at the junction of Blackpool
Road and St Andrews Avenue, north-west of the town centre. This*

---

*is a relaxed and friendly establishment, set in its own well tended grounds and gardens with ample car parking space.*
14rm(12⇨🅵)(1fb) CTV in all bedrooms ® **T**
**✗** (ex guide dogs) ✳ sB&B£18-£30 sB&B⇨🅵£20-£36
dB&B⇨🅵£38-£49
25P ✿
**V** ♺ ⚌ ✳ Lunch £7.05 Dinner £8.50-£11.75alc Last dinner 8.30pm
Credit Cards 1 3

### ★★69% **Dean Court**
Brownedge Ln, Bamber Bridge PR5 6TB ☎(0772)35114
FAX (0772) 628703
*Close to junction 29 of the M6 and 3 miles south of the town centre, this comfortable family-run hotel offers true Lancashire hospitality. Bedrooms, which include 5 executive suites, are very well equipped and there is a choice of restaurants.*
9⇨🅵5🛏 CTV in all bedrooms ® **T** ✗ sB&B⇨🅵£25-£45
dB&B⇨🅵£37.50-£60
CTV 35P CFA nc10yrs
**V** ♺ ⚌ Sunday Lunch £6.95&alc Dinner £9.95&alc Last dinner 10pm
Credit Cards 1 3 £

### ★★69% **Vineyard**
Cinnamon Hill, Chorley Rd, Walton-Le-Dale PR5 4JN (2m S A49) ☎(0772)54646 (0772) 58967
Closed 25 Dec night & 1 Jan night
*In an elevated position to the south of the town, this attractive popular hotel has comfortable well equipped bedrooms and a restaurant and bar with a good local reputation. Conference and function facilities are also available.*
16⇨🅵(1fb) CTV in all bedrooms ® **T** ✳ sB&B⇨🅵£40-£55
dB&B⇨🅵£55-£72.50 🛏
🅒 200P CFA ♫
♱ French **V** ♺ ⚌ ✳ Lunch £5.70-£7.50&alc High tea £2-£3.50
Dinner £26&alc Last dinner 10pm
Credit Cards 1 2 3 5 £

### ★★★60% **Carlton Toby**
KA9 1TP (Toby) ☎(0292)76811 Telex no 778740
*Conveniently located on the Ayr/Prestwick road, this purpose-built hotel has a split-level carvery restaurant with a conservatory area and its own bar. Service throughout is by cheery obliging staff.*
39⇨🅵(2fb)⤬in 9 bedrooms CTV in all bedrooms ®
🅒 100P ✿ ♫
♱ European **V** ♺ ⚌ ⤬ Last dinner 10pm
Credit Cards 1 2 3 5

### ★★60% **Parkstone**
Esplanade KA9 1QN ☎(0292)77286
*This hotel, with its sensibly furnished bedrooms, lies on the seafront in a residential area close to the golf course.*
15⇨🅵(1fb) CTV in all bedrooms ® ✗ sB&B⇨🅵£36-£39
dB&B⇨🅵£54-£58 🛏
🅒 30P 4🚗 CFA
**V** ♺ Lunch £6.75-£7.25 High tea £5.25-£9.95 Dinner £12.95-£13.95 Last dinner 9pm
Credit Cards 1 2 3

### ★★60% **St Nicholas**
41 Ayr Rd KA9 1SY ☎(0292)79568
*Cosy, owner-run hotel which is continually being improved. Bedrooms are attractively decorated, and there are two bars. High teas are a speciality in the quieter residents' lounge.*
17rm(13⇨🅵)(7fb) CTV in all bedrooms ® **T**
✗ (ex guide dogs) ✳ S17.5% sB&Bfr£25 sB&B⇨🅵£32
dB&B£42 dB&B⇨🅵fr£54
CTV 50P CFA

**V** ♺ ✳ S17.5% Lunch £4.50-£5.50&alc High tea £6&alc Dinner £9.50&alc Last dinner 9.30pm
Credit Cards 1 2 3 5 £

### ❀ ✕ ✕ ✕ **Craxton Wood**
Parkgate Rd L66 9PB (on A540 junct A550) ☎051-339 4717
FAX 051-339 1740
*Part of a country house hotel surrounded by woodland, lawns and rose gardens, this restaurant is a popular venue for both lunch and dinner; food is well prepared by chef James Minnis, who personally checks on guests' enjoyment during the meal.*
Closed Sun, 2 wks end Aug & BH's
♱ French **V** 85 seats ✳ Lunch £21.65-£26.55alc Dinner £21.65-£26.55alc Last lunch 2pm Last dinner 10pm 60 P
Credit Cards 1 2 3 5

### ★★71% **Arun Cosmopolitan**
87 Lower St RH20 2BP ☎(0798)872162 FAX (0798) 872935
*A small, friendly hotel in the heart of the village, with an attractive garden overlooking the River Arun. Bedrooms are individually decorated with pretty soft furnishings, and equipped with all modern facilities and a few thoughtful extras! There is a cosy lounge, restaurant, and a bar which is popular with locals.*
6⇨🅵 CTV in all bedrooms ® **T** sB&B⇨🅵£38-£45
dB&B⇨🅵£60-£70 🛏
5P 10🚗
**V** ♺ ⚌ ✳ Sunday Lunch £6.25-£9.95 High tea £2.50-£4.50
Dinner £9.95-£12.95&alc Last dinner 9pm
Credit Cards 1 2 3 5 £

**★★68% Chequers**

Church Place RH20 1AD (Minotels) ☎(0798)872486
Telex no 67596 FAX (0798) 872715

*Very well managed by the same proprietors for many years, and continually being improved, this particularly friendly little cottage-style hotel near the Rectory offers a choice of modern or period-style bedrooms. Recent improvements include new facilities for meetings or small residential conferences and a conservatory.*

11➪ ↑(2fb)1🏥 CTV in all bedrooms ® T sB&B➪↑£40-£45
dB&B➪↑£60-£70 🅿

14P 🚗 ✿ xmas

V ❖ ㏒ S% Sunday Lunch fr£9.50 High tea fr£3.95 Dinner fr£15 Last dinner 8.30pm

Credit Cards ① ② ③ ⑤ ⓔ

**✿✿✕Stane Street Hollow**

Codmore Hill RH20 1BG ☎(0798)872819

*A charming little cottage restaurant specialising in both Swiss and French cuisine has been decorated in Swiss style, the effect being heightened by staff in traditional dress and suitable background music. Chef/owner René Kaiser uses fresh local produce, enhancing the flavour with lavish sauces; the varied menu of poultry, game and offal is supplemented by a Plat du Jour and a fish speciality, dishes of particular note being the fish knodels (a Swiss dish of lightly curried fish dumplings, breadcrumbed and fried, with a creamy yogurt sauce sprinkled with chives) and for dessert, a Mousse au Chocolat – one sweet and white chocolate, the other bitter and dark, served on a good crème anglaise. Smokers can adjourn to a small sitting room for coffee. German wines feature prominently on the good wine list, and service is both pleasant and attentive.*

Closed Sun, Mon, Tue, 2 wks May, 2 wks Oct & 24-28 Dec Lunch not served Sat

♀ French & Swiss V 35 seats Lunch £8&alc Dinner £18.50-£22.50alc Last lunch 1.15pm Last dinner 9pm 15 P ✂

---

**PURTON** Wiltshire Map **04** SU08

**★★★✿74% The Pear Tree at Purton**

Church End SN5 9ED ☎Swindon(0793)772100
FAX (0793) 772369

*An hotel built of local stone – formerly the vicarage of St Mary's church – stands 4 miles from Swindon on the edge of this village at the southern tip of the Cotswolds. The present proprietors purchased it 4 years ago as a restaurant, only recently adding the charmingly individual, fully equipped and comfortable en suite bedrooms. Public areas are attractive and well furnished, the smallest lounge being made particularly cosy by an open log fire. The restaurant – a conservatory overlooking Victorian gardens where tea is served during the summer months – offers a fixed-price menu of English-style dishes with a slight French bias, cuisine taking advantage of quality local produce and home-grown herbs in season. Enjoyable dishes include a light, smooth and full-flavoured smoked salmon mousse, fillet of scotch beef stuffed with smoked oysters and served with an armagnac gravy, and pears poached in sauterne with a chocolate and ginger sauce. An extensive wine list includes some lesser known examples from many corners of the globe, while friendly proprietors and staff are extremely helpful.*

18➪(2fb)3🏥 CTV in all bedrooms T sB&B➪£95
dB&B➪£95-£135 🅿

60P 🚗 ✿ CFA croquet 🏌

V ❖ ㏒ ✽ Lunch £16.50 Dinner £25 Last dinner 9.30pm

Credit Cards ① ② ③ ⑤ ⓔ

---

**PWLLHELI** Gwynedd Map **06** SH33

**★★✿✿✿⚓75% Plas Bodegroes Restaurant**

LL53 5TH (1.5m W on Nefyd rd) ☎(0758)612363
FAX (0758) 701247

Closed Nov-Feb & Mon ex BH's

*This delightful Grade II listed Georgian house seems to exist in a world of its own, surrounded by majestically mature trees with even the gravel parking bays hidden from its view. Public areas contain a comfortably upholstered sitting room and a small separate bar cleverly constructed from an old mahogany sideboard, mirroring exactly a lovely old door and its glazing; a dining room restfully decorated in greens and pinks is hung with the owner's accomplished landscape photographs as well as paintings which are either by local artists or depict local scenes. The proprietor's culinary flair is displayed in dishes which place great emphasis on freshness of taste, making good use of superb local produce which includes seafood and Welsh lamb and beef. Light and comfortable bedrooms are, above all, peaceful, and a young staff provides friendly service throughout.*

8➪↑2🏥 CTV in all bedrooms T S% sB&B➪↑£35-£65
dB&B➪↑£50-£100 🅿

25P 🚗 ✿ croquet

✂ S% Dinner £25-£27.50 Last dinner 9.30pm

Credit Cards ① ③

**★64% The Seahaven**

West End Pde LL53 5PN ☎(0758)612572

*Overlooking Cardigan Bay from a seafront position, this small hotel is equally popular with holiday-makers and commercial visitors, its warm and friendly proprietors going out of their way to ensure that all their guests feel at home.*

10rm(5↑)(2fb) CTV in all bedrooms ® ✽ sB&Bfr£18
sB&B↑fr£21 dB&Bfr£30 dB&B↑fr£36 🅿

CTV 🚗 nc3yrs

❖ ㏒ ✽ Lunch fr£6 Dinner fr£10 Last dinner 7.15pm
ⓔ

---

**QUORN** Leicestershire Map **08** SK51

**★★★★66% Quorn Country**

Charwood House, Leicester Rd LE12 8BB (on A6 in village centre) ☎(0509)415050 Telex no 347166 FAX (0509) 415557
RS 26 Dec & New Year

*At the centre of the village, on the A6 midway between Loughborough and Leicester, stands a hotel which, though not large, caters for all tastes in food, menus in the intimate Shires restaurant now being complemented by a lighter style of cuisine in the new conservatory Orangery. Entrance, car park and the majority of the spacious bedrooms are situated at the rear, well away from the traffic noise, but any rooms nearer the road have been triple-glazed (and a bypass planned for early 1992 will further diminish the problem). An ongoing programme of improvements and service from friendly staff make this a comfortable choice.*

19➪↑(1fb)1🏥 CTV in all bedrooms ® ✽ sB➪↑£49.50-£69.50 dB➪↑£64-£84 (room only) 🅿

㉇ 🎛 CTV 100P ✿ CFA ✎

♀ English & Continental V ❖ ㏒ ✽ Lunch £17.90-£35.65alc High tea £2.50-£5.95 Dinner £16.95-£17.95&alc Last dinner 10pm

Credit Cards ① ② ③ ⑤

See advertisement under LOUGHBOROUGH

---

**RAASAY, ISLE OF** Highland *Inverness-shire* Map **13** NG53

**★★62% Isle Of Raasay**

IV40 8PB ☎Isle of Raasay(047862)222 & 226
Closed Oct-Mar

*Peacefully situated and enjoying glorious views over the Sound of Raasay to the mountains of Skye, a Victorian house with practical modern extensions provides firm, neat accommodation with a most relaxing atmosphere. Popular with walkers, birdwatchers and nature-lovers in general. Car users should note that no petrol is available on the island.*

12➪↑ CTV in all bedrooms ® sB&B➪↑fr£30
dB&B➪↑fr£60

CTV 12P 🚗 ✿

P

♥ Scottish, French, Italian & Indian V ♦ ⚗ ✂ Bar Lunch fr£2.75 Dinner fr£17 Last dinner 7.30pm
ⓕ

## RAGLAN Gwent Map 03 SO40

### ★★63% Beaufort Arms
High St NP5 2DY ☎(0291)690412

*The public areas of this village-centre inn, parts of which date back to the 15th century, have considerable charm and character, while its well-equipped modern bedrooms are equally suitable for tourists or business clients.*

10↪♪Annexe5↪♪(2fb) CTV in all bedrooms ⓇT
✖ (ex guide dogs) ✱ sB&B↪♪£35 dB&B↪♪£45 ⊟
CTV 80P CFA *xmas*
♥ English, French & Italian V ♦ ⚗ ✱ Sunday Lunch £6.95
Dinner £6-£12&alc Last dinner 9.30pm
Credit Cards ①②③⑤ⓕ

## RAINHILL Merseyside Map 07 SJ49

### ★58% Rockland
View Rd L35 0LG ☎051-426 4603

*This family-run commercial hotel, set in its own grounds in a residential area close to the village centre and with easy access to the M62, offers generally spacious modestly furnished bedrooms, most with smart modern bathrooms.*

10rm(9↪)(2fb) CTV in all bedrooms Ⓡ sB&B£21-£29.50
sB&B↪£26-£34.50 dB&B£25-£42 dB&B↪£35-£52 ⊟
30P ✿
V ♦ ⚗ Lunch £5-£6&alc Dinner £9.45&alc Last dinner 8.15pm
Credit Cards ①③ⓕ

## RAMSBOTTOM Greater Manchester Map 07 SD71

### ★★★62% Old Mill
Springwood BL10 9DS ☎(0706)822991 FAX (0706) 822291

*This hotel has bedrooms located in the original building, and more spacious bedrooms are provided in the recently constructed modern wing above the leisure centre. The Garden Room Restaurant serves good value table d'hôte and extensive à la carte menus. On the ground floor, a small Trattoria Restaurant serves budget-priced Italian meals.*

36↪(3fb)1🛏 CTV in all bedrooms Ⓡ T ✖ ✱ sB&B↪£29.50-£43 dB&B↪£43.50-£60 ⊟
《 CTV 85P 🚗 CFA ⊠ (heated) sauna solarium gymnasium *xmas*
♥ French & Italian V ♦ ⚗ ✱ Lunch fr£7.75&alc Dinner fr£13.50&alc Last dinner 10.30pm
Credit Cards ①②③④⑤

### ✿ ✕The Village
16 Market Place BL0 9HT ☎(0706)825070

*An attractive little cottage-style restaurant, set in the market place of this old Lancashire town, serves a 6-course set meal at 8.30pm; the menu offers no choices (apart from a range of delicious sweets), and table reservations – well in advance for Saturdays – are strongly advised. Much local produce is used in the creation of a daily-changing selection of dishes which includes excellent home-made soups, guinea fowl cooked in a variety of ways, poached salmon and at least six vegetables. Unpasteurised British cheeses are favoured on the cheese board, and a very well chosen wine list accompanies the meal.*

Closed Sun & Mon Lunch not served
20 seats ✱ Dinner £24-£29.50 Last dinner 8pm P nc15yrs ✂
Credit Cards ①③

*For key to symbols in English see the bookmark.*

## RAMSEY Cambridgeshire Map 04 TL28

### ★★63% George
63-65 High St PE17 1AA (Minotels) ☎(0487)815264
FAX (0487) 710732

11↪♪(1fb)1🛏 CTV in all bedrooms Ⓡ T ✱ sB&B↪♪£40
dB&B↪♪£55 ⊟
40P *xmas*
♥ International V ♦ ⚗ ✱ Lunch £11.95&alc Dinner £11.95&alc Last dinner 9.30pm
Credit Cards ①②③⑤

## RAMSEY

See Man, Isle of

## RAMSGATE Kent Map 05 TR36

### ★★★59% Marina Resort
Harbour Pde CT11 8LJ (Resort) ☎(0843)588276
FAX (0843) 586866

*A recently built hotel overlooking the harbour provides very well equipped modern bedrooms, though those at the front of the building are compact. Public areas include Health club leisure facilities as well as a small lobby lounge, while the individualistic but professional cuisine reflected in the table d'hôte and à la carte menus of the Admiral's Restaurant are augmented by the extensive though less formal range of meals available in the Admiral's Bar. Service throughout is friendly, helpful and well managed.*

59↪♪(4fb)1🛏✂in 6 bedrooms CTV in all bedrooms Ⓡ T ✱
sB↪♪fr£58 dB↪♪fr£70 (room only) ⊟
Lift 《 ♪ CFA ⊠ (heated) sauna solarium exercise equipment jacuzzi *xmas*
♥ English & Continental V ♦ ⚗ ✱ Sunday Lunch fr£10.75
Dinner fr£14.60&alc Last dinner 10pm
Credit Cards ①②③⑤ⓕ

## RAMSGILL North Yorkshire Map 07 SE17

### ★★72% Yorke Arms
HG3 5RL ☎Harrogate(0423)755243 FAX (0943) 870122

*In a picturesque Dales village, the Yorke Arms has prettily decorated bedrooms and although some are rather small, they are all well equipped. Meals are available in the popular bar as well as in the restaurant and there is also a comfortable lounge for residents.*

13↪♪(2fb) CTV in all bedrooms Ⓡ T ✖ sB&B↪fr£52
dB&B↪♪£70-£85 ⊟
20P ✿ *xmas*
V ♦ ⚗ ✂ Lunch £11.50-£14.95 Dinner £14.95-£15.50&alc
Last dinner 9pm
Credit Cards ①③ⓕ

## RANGEWORTHY Avon Map 03 ST68

### ★★♨68% Rangeworthy Court
Church Ln, Wotton Rd BS17 5ND (Exec Hotel)
☎(0454)228347 & 228473 FAX (0454) 228945

*This imposing manor house, signposted off the B4058 and the home of Lord Chief Justice Sir Matthew Hale in the 17th-century, has been carefully improved to create an hotel which offers modern facilities whilst still retaining much of its original charm. Comfortable bedrooms are well equipped, and public areas are kept cosy by open log fires during the cooler months.*

16↪♪(2fb)2🛏 CTV in all bedrooms Ⓡ T S% sB&B↪♪£48-£53 dB&B↪♪£66-£75 ⊟
50P 🚗 ✿ (heated) *xmas*
V ♦ S% Lunch £9.50-£10.95 Dinner £15-£17.50&alc Last dinner 9pm
Credit Cards ①②③⑤ⓕ
**See advertisement under BRISTOL**

## RAVENGLASS Cumbria Map **06** SD09

### ★59% **Pennington Arms**
CA18 1SD ☎(0229)717222 & 717626

*Situated in the village on the estuary of the Rivers Esk, Mite and Irt, this friendly inn offers a good range of food and fairly simple accommodation at a value-for-money price.*

17rm(5⇔2↑)Annexe12rm(2⇔1↑)(6fb) ℝ ✱ sB&B£15-£22 sB&B⇔↑£21-£28 dB&B£28-£34 dB&B⇔↑£28-£34 ₽
CTV 50P 3🚗 CFA pool table
V ♡ ⚏ ✱ Lunch £7.60 High tea £7.60 Dinner £8.50-£11.55 Last dinner 10pm

## RAVENSCAR North Yorkshire Map **08** NZ90

### ★★★60% **Raven Hall**
Raven Hall Hotel YO13 OET ☎Scarborough(0723)870353
FAX (0723) 870072

*Once the retreat of George III, this pleasant hotel is set in 100 acres of grounds high above the sea and commands impressive views from its clifftop position. The comfortable accommodation offers all modern facilities and leisure amenities include a snooker room and outdoor pool.*

53⇔↑(14fb) CTV in all bedrooms ℝ ✱ sB&B⇔↑£62.50-£89.50 dB&B⇔↑£111.50-£153 (incl dinner) ₽
(200P 2🚗 (charged) ✿ CFA ⌿ ▶ 9 ♬ (hard) snooker crown green bowls croquet giant chess ♫ *xmas*
V ♡ ⚏ ✱ Lunch fr£13.75 Dinner fr£16.50&alc Last dinner 9pm
Credit Cards ①②③⑤€

**See advertisement under SCARBOROUGH**

## RAVENSTONEDALE Cumbria Map **07** NY70

### ★★ ֎70% **Black Swan**
CA17 4NG ☎Newbiggin-on-Lune(05396)23204

*Mr and Mrs Stuart are justly proud of this delightful stone-built hotel, standing in the centre of a sleepy Lakeland village, which offers guests every comfort, not the least of which are the pleasures of the table. Chef Graham Bamber offers a daily 5-course menu, with a choice of first and main courses, and a tempting selection of puddings. The cooking is skilful, presentation is attractive and, what is even better, the meals offer real value for money.*

14rm(8⇔3↑)Annexe4⇔↑(1fb) CTV in all bedrooms ℝ T ✱ sB&B£41 sB&B⇔↑£41 dB&B£57 dB&B⇔↑£57 ₽
CTV 30P 🚲 ✿ ♬ (hard) ♪ 👓 *xmas*
V ♡ ⚏ ⅙ ✱ Lunch £8.50&alc High tea £2-£3.50 Dinner £18&alc Last dinner 9pm
Credit Cards ①②③€

### ★★65% **The Fat Lamb**
Cross Bank CA17 4LL ☎Newbiggin-on-Lune(05396)23242

*A pleasant stone building erected in the 17th-century as a farmhouse has been converted to create this warm and comfortable hotel. Set in rolling hills and dales on the A683 between Kirkby Stephen and Sedbergh, it offers good public areas (notably a characterful bar) and well furnished accommodation which includes some ground floor rooms.*

12⇔(4fb) ℝ sB&B⇔£30-£33 dB&B⇔£47-£52 ₽
CTV 60P ✿ *xmas*
☢ International V ♡ ⚏ ⅙ Lunch £13-£16 Dinner £15.50-£17.50 Last dinner 9pm
€

If you have booked a
restaurant meal and cannot get there,
remember you have a contractual obligation
to cancel your booking.

## READING Berkshire Map **04** SU77 ☺

### ★★★★64% **Caversham**
Caversham Bridge, Richfield Av RG1 8BD (Queens Moat)
☎(0734)391818 Telex no 846933 FAX (0734) 391665

*This modern hotel with good leisure facilities is beautifully situated on the bank of the Thames and offers spacious open-plan public rooms, a bright conservatory-style restaurant with an interesting menu, and compact but well equipped bedrooms.*

114⇔↑(6fb) 🖾⅙in 15 bedrooms CTV in all bedrooms ℝ T ✱ sB⇔↑£98 dB⇔↑£98 (room only) ₽
Lift (200P CFA ⌷ (heated) sauna solarium gymnasium *xmas*
V ♡ ⚏ ⅙ ✱ Lunch frf14.50&alc High tea fr£4 Dinner frf18.75&alc Last dinner 10pm
Credit Cards ①②③⑤€

### ★★★★60% **Ramada**
Oxford Rd RG1 7RH ☎(0734)586222 Telex no 847785
FAX (0734) 597842

*A modern purpose-built hotel in a central location with bright well appointed public rooms and a choice of restaurants. Bedrooms are well equipped and air conditioned, and leisure facilities include an attractive swimming pool and gym. Free car parking for guests is available in the near by multi-storey.*

196⇔↑(100fb)⅙in 49 bedrooms CTV in all bedrooms ℝ T ✖ (ex guide dogs) S10% sB⇔↑£106-£109 dB⇔↑£109-£119 (room only) ₽
Lift (75🚗 CFA ⌷ (heated) sauna solarium gymnasium turkish bath jacuzzi beauty salon ♫
☢ International V ♡ ⚏ ⅙ ✱ Lunch £10.50-£35&alc High tea fr£1.20 Dinner £35&alc Last dinner 11.30pm
Credit Cards ①②③⑤€

### ★★★68% **Kirtons Farm Country Club**
Pingewood RG3 3UN ☎(0734)500885 FAX (0734) 391996

81⇔↑(10fb)⅙in 15 bedrooms CTV in all bedrooms ℝ T ✱ sB⇔↑£83-£93 dB⇔↑£93-£103 (room only) ₽
Lift (⊞ CTV 200P ✿ CFA ⌷ (heated) ♬ (hard) ♪ squash snooker sauna solarium gymnasium jetskiing waterskiing quad bikes ♫ 👓 *xmas*
☢ English & French V ♡ ⚏ ✱ Lunch £10.50-£13.50&alc High tea £4.50-£15 Dinner frf17.50&alc Last dinner 10.30pm
Credit Cards ①②③⑤

### ★★★65% **Forte Posthouse**
Basingstoke Rd RG2 0SL (Forte Hotels) ☎(0734)875485
Telex no 849160 FAX (0734) 311958

*The public areas of this low modern hotel on the southern side of the town include a popular open-plan bar and lobby lounge which is probably going to be redeveloped during 1991. Major refurbishment of bedrooms – now almost completed – is creating smart, well equipped and up-to-date accommodation which includes some particularly stylish and comfortable Executive rooms.*

138⇔↑⅙in 71 bedrooms CTV in all bedrooms ℝ T ✱ S% sB⇔↑£49.50 dB⇔↑£64.50 (room only) ₽
(240P ✿ CFA ⌷ (heated) sauna solarium gymnasium health & fitness centre 👓 *xmas*
☢ English & French V ♡ ⚏ ⅙ ✱ S% Lunch £9.75-£13.95&alc Dinner £13.95&alc Last dinner 10.30pm
Credit Cards ①②③④⑤

### ★★62% **George**
King St RG1 2HE (Chef & Brewer) ☎(0734)573445
FAX (0734) 508614

*An hotel whose black and white Tudor façade overlooks the bustling town centre offers many facilities to locals and visitors alike, its public areas including two popular bars and a typical Berni restaurant. Bedrooms vary in size and are located on three floors, but all are similarly well appointed and equipped.*

68⇔↑(2fb) CTV in all bedrooms ℝ T ✖ (ex guide dogs) sB&B⇔↑£62-£67 dB&B⇔↑£73 ₽

《 CFA
🍴 International **V** ♥ ⚌ ✔ Lunch fr£8&alc
Credit Cards ① ② ③ ⑤

---

**REDBOURN** Hertfordshire Map **04** TL11 ⊙

★★★58% **Aubrey Park**
Hemel Hempstead Rd AL3 7AF ☎(0582)792105 Telex no 82195
FAX (0582) 792001
*Set in 6 acres of grounds, this much extended hotel offers differing
standards of bedrooms: attractively decorated deluxe rooms with
all modern comforts including spa baths, and more basic rooms in
the older wing, due to be updated. There is a choice of restaurants,
a modern comfortable lounge bar, an outdoor pool and good car
parking.*
119🛏️🚿(2fb) CTV in all bedrooms ® **T ✖** (ex guide dogs)
sB🛏️🚿£45-£92 dB🛏️🚿£80-£102 (room only) 🈁
《 160P ✿ CFA ⌂ (heated)
🍴 English & French **V** ♥ ⚌ ✳ Lunch £12.35-£16.50&alc
Dinner £18.35-£19.50&alc Last dinner 10.pm
Credit Cards ① ② ③ ④ ⑤ ⑥

R

## REDBROOK Clwyd Map **07** SJ54

★★59% **Redbrook Hunting Lodge**
Wrexham Rd SY13 3ET (Inter-Hotels)
☎Redbrook Maelor(094873)204 & 533
(For full entry see Whitchurch (Shropshire))

## REDCAR Cleveland Map **08** NZ62 ☺

★★★67% **Park**
Granville Ter TS10 3AR ☎(0642)490888 FAX (0642) 486147
*Close to the town centre, this seafront hotel offers attractive,
comfortable accommodation and a very popular restaurant, with a
carvery as well as a small à la carte selection.*
26⇨🌂 CTV in all bedrooms ® T 🗶 (ex guide dogs) S%
sB&B⇨🌂£25-£62 dB&B⇨🌂£42-£72 🖪
⊄ 20P 🖰 CFA
𝒴 English & French **V** ♥ 🖤 S% Lunch £5-£8.25&alc Dinner
£6.75-£8.25&alc Last dinner 9.30pm
Credit Cards ① ② ③ ⑤

## REDDITCH Hereford & Worcester Map **07** SP06 ☺

★★★60% **Southcrest**
Pool Bank, Southcrest B97 4JG ☎(0527)541511 Telex no 338455
FAX (0527) 402600
Closed 24 Dec-2 Jan & BH's RS Sun evenings
*This privately owned hotel, though only a couple of minutes' drive
from the town centre and within easy reach of the NEC, enjoys the
seclusion provided by 6 acres of grounds and woodland. Most of its
bedrooms are functional in style, being contained in a modern
extension, but a certain amount of more attractive and better
quality accommodation is available in the main building.*
58⇨🌂(2fb)2🖨 CTV in all bedrooms ® T S% sB&B⇨🌂£70-
£77 dB&B⇨🌂£77-£87 🖪
⊄ 100P 🖰 CFA
𝒴 French **V** ♥ ✳ Lunch £11-£11.50&alc Dinner £13-
£13.50&alc Last dinner 9.15pm
Credit Cards ① ② ③ ⑤ ⓔ

⌂**Campanile**
Far Moor Ln, Winyates Green B98 0SD (Campanile)
☎(0527)510710 Telex no 339608 FAX (0527) 517269
*Value for money accommodation is offered at this Campanile
situated to the west of the town and with easy access to the M42.
The restaurant is popular with guests and non-residents alike and a
meeting room is available.*
Annexe50⇨🌂 CTV in all bedrooms ® T sB⇨🌂fr£36
dB⇨🌂fr£36 (room only) 🖪
CTV 60P 🖰 CFA
𝒴 English & French **V** ♥ 🖤 Lunch £3.75-£5 Dinner £6.80-
£8.90 Last dinner 10pm
Credit Cards ① ③ ⓔ

## REDHILL

**See**Nutfield

## REDLYNCH Wiltshire Map **04** SU22

❀ ✗✗**Langley Wood**
SP5 2PB ☎Romsey(0794)390348
*An attractive, creeper-clad house, set in its own pleasant grounds
among dense woodland at the edge of the village, which offers an
imaginative menu and a wine list that are both reasonably priced.
It is run by a husband and wife team – she cooking with flair and
he bringing humour and professionalism to the task of serving.*
Closed Mon, Tue & 2-3 wks Jan/Feb Lunch not served all
week (ex by reservation only)
Dinner not served Sun
𝒴 English & French **V** 30 seats Sunday Lunch £12 Dinner
£13.50-£21alc Last dinner 11pm 30 P
Credit Cards ① ② ③ ⑤

## REDRUTH Cornwall & Isles of Scilly Map **02** SW64

★★★62% **Penventon**
TR15 1TE ☎(0209)214141
*A character Georgian residence with long established family
management providing a good range of facilities. Public rooms
have been restored and upgraded recently and elegant lounges are
richly furnished and ornately decorated with Italian marble,
Venetian chandeliers, French tapestries, oil paintings and bronzes.
The Dining Galleries restaurant serves an extensive range of
international cuisine. Well equipped bedrooms come in a range of
sizes, and most are comfortably appointed. There are plans to
upgrade some of the smaller single rooms in conjunction with a
buiding project for additional bedrooms. Other amenities include a
bright indoor leisure complex with pool, sauna/solarium, beauty
salon and a stylish ballroom. The Twilight Zone nightclub in the
grounds is well insulated for sound.*
50⇨🌂(3fb)1🖨 CTV in all bedrooms ® T
⊄ 100P ✳ 🖃 (heated) snooker sauna solarium gymnasium
leisure spa jacuzzi masseuse
𝒴 English French & Italian **V** ♥ 🖤 Last dinner 9.30pm
Credit Cards ① ② ③

★★69% **Aviary Court**
Mary's Well, Illogan TR16 4QZ ☎Portreath(0209)842256
*The Studley family have continued to improve this charming 300-
year-old Cornish country house set in well-tended grounds on the
edge of Illogan Woods between Redruth and Portreath. The small
welcoming hotel now has more spacious bedrooms, individually
and attractively decorated, with extensive modern facilities and
many little extras. Cosy comfortable public rooms include a new
lounge and Mrs Studley makes good use of quality Cornish
produce in the generous meals served in the attractive restaurant.*
6⇨🌂(1fb) CTV in all bedrooms ® T 🗶 sB&B⇨🌂£35.75-
£41.25 dB&B⇨🌂£51.75-£57.25
25P 🖮 ✳ CFA nc3yrs →

★★★

# NUTFIELD PRIORY

Set amidst 40 acres of gardens and
parkland, this elegant country house
hotel offers, quite simply, the finest
Surrey has to offer.

**Whether dining or staying — a visit to
Nutfield Priory is always a memorable
experience.**

For further details please contact:
Nutfield Priory, Nutfield,
Redhill, Surrey RH1 4EN
**Telephone: (0737) 822072**

R

♀ English & French Sunday Lunch £8.75 Dinner £10.75&alc
Last dinner 8.45pm
Credit Cards ②⑤

**★★✿❀69% Inn for All Seasons**
Treleigh TR16 4AP ☎(0209)219511 FAX (0209) 219751
*Initial impressions can be misleading, for behind the façade of this
modern-looking roadside inn lies a small but very worthy hotel
whose convenient position beside the A30 has made it popular with
both tourists and business travellers. Recently taken over by new
owners, it has undergone quite a transformation, imaginative use of
rich colours and attractive stencil work enhancing individually
decorated cosy rooms, equipped with modern facilities and quality
en suite bathrooms. A pleasantly characterised ground floor with a
comfortably furnished open bar contains the Chart Room
Restaurant which features head Chef Gary Hunt's commendable
cooking, his well balanced and imaginative menus offering honest
flavours, rich sauces and carefully presented vegetables. Such
favourites as pigeon breast and pine kernel salad, chicken liver
pâté, supreme of chicken with a shellfish sauce, braised pheasant
with garlic and mushrooms and salmon with a provinçale sauce are
followed by an array of home-made puddings ranging from the
smooth chocolate marquis with honey dressing to 'old faithfuls' like
bread and butter pudding ; a tempting selection of bar food is also
available.*
12⤳♠ CTV in all bedrooms ® T ✹ sB&B⤳♠fr£35
dB&B⤳♠fr£50 ➡
100P CFA nc10yrs
♀ International V ♢ ✹ Sunday Lunch £8.50 Dinner £13.85-
£19.35alc Last dinner 9.30pm
Credit Cards ①③⑥

See advertisement under TRURO

**★★68% Crossroads**
Scorrier TR16 5BP (2m E off A30) ☎(0209)820551
FAX (0209) 820551
*An hotel almost adjacent to the A30, conveniently located for both
tourists and commercial users, offers good car parking on site and
a choice of accommodation standards – executive bedrooms being
larger, more comfortable and of a generally higher quality, though
all are well equipped with modern facilities. There is also a choice
of restaurant, and the à la carte menu features a wide selection of
interesting dishes. Popular bars provide friendly, informal
attention while the good range of room service available matches
that more normally associated with establishments of a higher
classification.*
35rm(33⤳)(2fb) CTV in all bedrooms ® T sB&B⤳£34-£39
dB&B⤳£45-£58 ➡
Lift 140P CFA
♀ English & French V ♢ ♫ Lunch £8-£10 Dinner £10-£12
Last dinner 9.30pm
Credit Cards ①②③⑤⑥

**RED WHARF BAY** Gwynedd Map **06** SH58

**★61% Min-y-Don**
LL75 8RJ ☎Tynygongl(0248)852596
RS Nov-Feb
*A privately owned hotel situated next to the beach and enjoying
views across the sands and bay. The bedrooms have modern
furnishings, some have ensuite facilities and television.*
15rm(3⤳3♠)(4fb) CTV in 6 bedrooms ®
CTV 60P ✿
♢ ♫
Credit Cards ①③

The AA's star rating scheme is the
market leader in hotel
classification.

**REDWORTH** Co Durham Map **08** NZ22

**★★★★66% Redworth Hall Hotel & Country Club**
DL5 6NL (Consort) ☎Bishop Auckland(0388)772442
FAX (0388) 775112
*An impressive 16th-century hall set in 25 acres of secluded grounds
and gardens stands just off the A6072 only a few minutes' drive
from the A1(M). Though a new bedroom wing and comprehensive
leisure centre have recently been added, the splendour of the
beautiful Jacobean mansion has been retained by ensuring that
little of the new building is visible from the front of the hotel.
Several of the main house's elegantly decorated and furnished
bedrooms contain four poster beds and antiques, and even in the
well equipped new rooms period-style furniture blends effectively
with its surroundings. Public areas include sumptuous lounges, two
restaurants, comprehensive conference/banqueting facilities and an
excellent health club with a special playroom for children, provision
for the disabled, a Roman-style swimming pool, saunas, squash
and tennis courts and snooker tables.*
100⤳♠❦3➡✹in 35 bedrooms CTV in all bedrooms ® T
sB&B⤳♠£79.50-£95.90 dB&B⤳♠£99.50-£114.50 ➡
Lift ( ▦ 200P ✿ CFA ⊠ (heated) ♪ (hard) squash snooker
sauna solarium gymnasium croquet spa pool ♫ xmas
♀ British & French V ♢ ♫ ✹ ✹ Lunch fr£12.95&alc Dinner
£16-£23&alc Last dinner 10pm
Credit Cards ①②③⑤⑥

**REIGATE** Surrey Map **04** TQ25 ◎

**★★★65% Reigate Manor Hotel**
Reigate Hill RH2 9PF (Best Western) ☎(0737)240125
Telex no 927845 FAX (0737) 223883
*On Reigate Hill, close to the M25, this is a popular venue for
conferences and for the business traveller. The original manor
house has been extended to provide a uniform standard of
comfortable and well equipped bedrooms. Rooms in the main house
vary in shape and size and are of a more dated style. Facilities
include a mini gym, sauna and solarium for residents only.*
51⤳♠(1fb)1➡ CTV in all bedrooms ® T ✖ (ex guide dogs)
sB⤳♠£66.50-£86 dB⤳♠£92-£98 (room only) ➡
( 130P CFA sauna solarium gymnasium
♀ English & French V ♢ ♫ Lunch £12.80-£14&alc Dinner
£17.65-£19.25&alc Last dinner 10pm
Credit Cards ①②③⑤⑥

**★★★61% Bridge House**
Reigate Hill RH2 9RP ☎(0737)246801 & 244821
Telex no 268810 FAX (0737) 223756
*Built in the '60s, and commanding attractive views of the valley
from its hillside setting, the hotel offers accommodation in rooms
which are, for the most part, spacious, functional and having
balconies. Lounge facilities are limited, but there is a large
restaurant where the resident band plays 4 evenings a week.*
40⤳♠(3fb) CTV in all bedrooms ® T ✖ ✹ sB&B⤳♠£40-
£68 dB&B⤳♠£50-£90 Continental breakfast ➡
( 110P ⇔ CFA ♫ xmas
♀ English & French V ♢ ✹ S12.5% Lunch £14 Dinner £18-£22
Last dinner 10pm
Credit Cards ①②③⑤

**RENFREW** For hotels see **Glasgow Airport**

**RENISHAW** Derbyshire Map **08** SK47

**★★★61% Sitwell Arms Osprey**
S31 9WE (Toby) ☎Eckington(0246)435226 Telex no 547303
Closed Xmas day evening
*Set in 6 acres of grounds by the golf club and only a mile from
junction 30 of the M1, this extended and converted 18th-century
inn provides well equipped modern bedrooms of spacious size
except for 5 small singles on the top floor. The recently upgraded
meeting rooms offer a wide range of facilities.*
30⤳♠✄in 10 bedrooms CTV in all bedrooms ®

℃ 150P ❊ ⬦
♬ English & French **V** ✿ ⚇ ✄ Last dinner 9.30pm
Credit Cards ①②③⑤

---

**RETFORD (EAST)** Nottinghamshire Map **08** SK78

★★★**65% West Retford**
24 North Rd DN22 7XG (Situated on A638) (Rank)
🏠East Retford(0777)706333 Telex no 56143
FAX (0777) 709951
*Located on the road to Barnby Moor, this well managed hotel on
the outskirts of town has recently had its rooms modernised to a
high and comfortable standard. All accommodation is in annexe
wings. There is an elegant restaurant offering an extensive range of
dishes.*
Annexe 57⊶🌢(36fb)✄in 9 bedrooms CTV in all bedrooms ®
**T** ✱ sB&B⊶🌢£41-£71 dB&B⊶🌢£62-£86 🎴
℃ 130P ❊ CFA ♬ *xmas*
♬ French **V** ✿ ⚇ ✱ Lunch £10.75&alc Dinner £17-£18&alc
Last dinner 10pm
Credit Cards ①②③⑤

---

**REYNOLDSTON** West Glamorgan Map **02** SS48

★★⚸**70% Fairyhill Country House**
SA3 1BS (Welsh Rarebits) 🏠Gower(0792)390139
FAX (0792) 391358
Closed Nov-Feb
*A carefully restored 18th-century mansion at the heart of the
Gower, set in 24 acres of woodland with its own trout stream,
provides a warmly hospitable atmsophere, smart, well equipped
bedrooms (which include two new stable rooms) and elegant
lounges with woodburning stoves.*
11⊶🌢Annexe2⊶🌢 CTV in all bedrooms ® **T** ✱
sB&B⊶🌢£65-£75 dB&B⊶🌢£75-£85
50P ⊞ ❊ ♪ sauna
♬ English & French **V** ✿ ✱ Sunday Lunch £11.95 Dinner £20-
£24alc Last dinner 9pm
Credit Cards ①③

---

**RHAYADER** Powys Map **06** SN96

★★**67% *Elan Hotel***
West St LD6 5AF 🏠(0597)810373
*This small very friendly hotel in the centre of the picturesque mid-
Wales town has bright and cosy bedrooms equipped with modern
facilities. There is a small residents' bar, comfortable spacious
lounge with an inglenook fireplace and a restaurant serving good
value meals.*
11rm(1⊶6🌢)(1fb) CTV in all bedrooms ® **T**
CTV 12P
**V** ✿ ⚇ Last dinner 8.30pm
Credit Cards ①③

★★**61% *Elan Valley Hotel***
LD6 5HN (2.5m W of Rhayader) 🏠(0597)810448
*Situated in beautiful rural surroundings near the village of Elan,
this relaxing hotel provides modern bedrooms, two bars and a
spacious lounge with a full size snooker table.*
12rm(2⊶5🌢)(1fb) TV available ®
CTV 50P 2🚗 (£2) ❊ ♪ snooker
**V** ✿ Last dinner 8pm
Credit Cards ①③

---

**RHU** Strathclyde *Dunbartonshire* Map **10** NS28

★★★**57% Rosslea Hall**
G84 8NF 🏠(0436)820684 Telex no 778695 FAX (0436) 820897
*A 19th-century mansion set in its own grounds by the shore of
Gareloch has been extended to form a business and function hotel
with a range of eating options.*
31⊶🌢(1fb) CTV in all bedrooms ® **T**

---

℃ ▦ 80P ❊ CFA
♬ Scottish & French **V** ✿ ⚇ Last dinner 9.30pm
Credit Cards ①②③⑤

---

**RICHMOND** North Yorkshire Map **07** NZ10 ◉

★★**67%, King's Head**
Market Place DL10 4HS (Consort) 🏠(0748)850220
FAX (0748) 850635
*Centrally situated in the Market Square, this hotel has an elegant
restaurant, coffee shop and a quaint bar. Bedrooms vary in size
and style, all are well equipped and have luxurious bathrooms.*
24⊶🌢Annexe4⊶🌢(1fb)3🎴✄in 11 bedrooms CTV in all
bedrooms ® **T** ✱ sB&B⊶🌢£53 dB&B⊶🌢£77-£90 🎴
℃ 25P CFA ♬ *xmas*
♬ International **V** ✿ ⚇ ✄ Sunday Lunch £9.50 Dinner
£16&alc Last dinner 9.15pm
Credit Cards ①②③④⑤

★★**59% Frenchgate**
59-61 Frenchgate DL10 7AE 🏠(0748)822087 & 823596
Closed Dec-Feb
*Originally a Georgian town house, the hotel is set in a quiet cobbled
street in one of the attractive original gates to the old walled town.
Bedrooms are simply furnished but well equipped, there are several
cosy lounge areas for guests' use and the proprietors offer friendly,
efficient service.*
13rm(3⊶4🌢) CTV in all bedrooms ® **T** sB&B£27
sB&B⊶🌢£36 dB&B£51 dB&B⊶🌢£58 🎴
6P ⊞ nc7yrs
Dinner £11.50&alc Last dinner 8.30pm
Credit Cards ①②③⑤

**R**

## RICHMOND UPON THAMES Greater London

See **LONDON plan 1** *B3*(page 434)

★★★64% **Richmond Hill**

146-150 Richmond Hill TW10 6RW (Best Western)
☎081-940 2247 & 081-940 5466 Telex no 21844
FAX 081-940 5424

*This attractive Georgian property near Richmond Park and overlooking the Thames Valley has a variety of comfortable bedrooms, including a dozen executive rooms, many of which are gradually being upgraded. A busy commercial and conference trade means that public areas, which include a cosy bar and elegant dining room, can become crowded*

123⇌♠(9fb)1⌷ CTV in all bedrooms ® ✱ sB&B⇌♠£80-£90 dB&B⇌♠£95-£105 ⊟

Lift ℂ 150P CFA squash *xmas*

♡ English & French **V** ♦ ⚏ ✱ Lunch £14-£15&alc Dinner £18-£20&alc Last dinner 9pm

Credit Cards ①②③⑤

---

## RIDGEWAY Derbyshire Map **08** SK48

⊛⊛⊛ ✕✕✕**Old Vicarage**

Ridgeway Moor S12 3XW ☎(0742)475814 FAX (0742) 477079

*Andrew and Tessa Bramley run this very popular restaurant which caters for clientele who make the pilgrimage from over a wide local area. Food, based mainly on English and European regional dishes, is consistently well cooked, and flavours are authentic. The atmosphere is perhaps a touch theatrical, with waitresses in Victorian dress, waiters in white gloves, but is well suited to the style of the conservatory dining room. Great attention is paid to the selection and cooking of vegetables to suit each individual main course, and there is also a separate vegetable course before the main course, which is a welcome innovation. Booking is advisable.*

Closed Sun, Mon & 26 Dec-6 Jan

♡ English, French, Italian & Eastern 50 seats Lunch £12-£30 Dinner £12-£30 25 P ✄

Credit Cards ①②③

---

## RINGWOOD Hampshire Map **04** SU10

★★★67% **Tyrrells Ford Country House**

Avon BH23 7BH (4m S on B3347) ☎Bransgore(0425)72646 FAX (0425) 72262

*Guests can watch rabbits and pheasants from the windows of this relaxed yet professional hotel, set as it is in 10 acres of lawns and woodland. Comprehensively equipped bedrooms vary in size but are all of a good standard, while the spacious galleried lounge is similarly well furnished. Public areas also include a popular bar, 2 conference/function suites and the Rufus on the first floor and the ground-floor Avon, which can accommodate up to 150 guests.*

16⇌♠ CTV in all bedrooms ® **T** ✖ (ex guide dogs) ✱ sB&B⇌♠£45-£55 dB&B⇌♠£65-£85 ⊟

100P ❖ CFA *xmas*

♡ English & French **V** ✱ Lunch £10.95-£12.95 Dinner fr£15.95&alc Last dinner 10pm

Credit Cards ①③

**See advertisement under CHRISTCHURCH**

★★70% **Struan Hotel & Restaurant**

Horton Rd, Ashley Heath BH24 2EG (2m W in Dorset)
☎(0425)473553 & 473029 FAX (0425) 480529

*A busy little hotel peacefully situated in a wooded residential area 2 miles from Ringwood, which is personally run by its totally involved owners. Bedrooms are of a superb standard, each individually and strikingly decorated to a Scottish theme, while an extensive range of bar meals supplements the à la carte menu and the traditional Sunday lunch where a choice of joints from the trolley represents excellent value for money.*

10⇌♠(1fb) CTV in all bedrooms ® **T** sB&B⇌♠£50-£55 dB&B⇌♠£66-£71 ⊟

CTV 75P ❖ solarium ♫

---

♡ English & French **V** ♦ ⚏ ✱ Lunch £12-£14&alc High tea £7.50 Dinner £15&alc Last dinner 9.30pm

Credit Cards ①②③⑤

★⊛77% **Moortown Lodge Hotel**

244, Christchurch Rd BH24 3AS ☎(0425)471404

Closed 24 Dec-14 Jan

*Jilly and Bob Burrows-Jones have successfully created an individual hotel with a friendly, relaxed atmosphere, and offering excellent value for money. A very good table d'hôte menu includes dishes such as steak and kidney, beef in beer pie, and lamb in a pastry case. Bedrooms are cosy and compact and there is a comfortable lounge.*

6rm(1⇌4♠)(1fb) CTV in all bedrooms ® **T** ✖ sB&B£29 sB&B⇌♠£38-£42 dB&B⇌♠£52-£60 ⊟

8P ⌁

♡ British & French **V** ✂ Dinner £11.95-£14.50&alc Last dinner 8.30pm

Credit Cards ①③

---

## RIPLEY Surrey Map **04** TQ05

⊛⊛ ✕✕**Michels**

13 High St GU23 6AQ ☎(0483)224777 & 222940

Closed Mon Xmas & New Year Lunch not served Sat Dinner not served Sun

**V** 50 seats ✱ Lunch £17.50-£23&alc Dinner £20&alc Last lunch 1.45pm Last dinner 9pm 3 P

Credit Cards ①③④

---

## RIPON North Yorkshire Map **08** SE37

★★★67% **Ripon Spa**

Park St HG4 2BU (Best Western) ☎(0765)602172
Telex no 57780 FAX (0765) 690770

*Set in 7 acres of gardens a short walk from the city centre, this traditional hotel has spacious and elegant public areas with an interesting menu available in either the restaurant or bar. Bedrooms are well furnished and equipped, some with four-poster beds, and friendly professional staff provide very good service.*

40⇌♠(5fb)2⌷ CTV in all bedrooms ® **T** ✱ sB&B⇌♠£49.20-£67.50 dB&B⇌♠£68.40-£91 ⊟

Lift ℂ CTV 80P ❖ CFA *xmas*

**V** ♦ ⚏ ✱ Lunch £9-£12&alc Dinner £13.95-£16.50&alc Last dinner 9pm

Credit Cards ①②③⑤ ⓔ

★★77% *Bridge*

16-18 Magdalen Rd HG4 1HX ☎(0765)603687

*Standing conveniently close to the town centre on the banks of the River Ure, this comfortable hotel complements tastefully fitted bedrooms with a range of inviting lounges. Guests are assured of friendly, courteous service from the owning family, and dinner can be especially recommended.*

15⇌♠(7fb)1⌷ ✂in 4 bedrooms CTV in all bedrooms ® ✖ (ex guide dogs)

15P ⌁

♡ English, French & Italian **V** ♦ ⚏ ✂ Last dinner 9.30pm

Credit Cards ①②③⑤

★★56% **Unicorn**

Market Place HG4 1BP (Consort) ☎(0765)602202
Telex no 57515 FAX (0765) 600321

RS 24-27 Dec

*This historic posting house with a black and white Georgian façade, centrally situated in the town's medieval market place, is now a family-run commercial hotel offering modestly appointed accommodation. Public areas include 2 lively bars and a quieter residents' lounge on the first floor.*

33⇌♠(4fb) CTV in all bedrooms ® **T** sB&B⇌♠£36-£40 dB&B⇌♠£45-£52 ⊟

ℂ 15P 4⊜ CFA

♀ English & French **V** ♥ ⬛ Lunch £6-£7.50 Dinner £12.50-£14 Last dinner 9pm
Credit Cards 1 2 3 5 ⓔ

---

## RIPPONDEN West Yorkshire Map **07** SE01

### ❋✕✕Over The Bridge
Millfold HX6 4DJ ☎Halifax(0422)823722
*This charming stone-built restaurant beside a babbling stream is, as its name suggests, just over the bridge in the centre of the village. Service is both friendly and attentive, and food is very well produced from the finest ingredients, the good range of interesting dishes featured on the set-price menu being complemented by a 'whole world' wine list.*
Closed Sun & BH's Lunch not served
♀ English & French 48 seats ❋ Dinner £20.50 Last dinner 9.30pm 50 P nc10yrs
Credit Cards 1 2 3

---

## ROADE Northamptonshire Map **04** SP75

### ❋❋✕Roadhouse
16 High St NN7 2NW ☎(0604)863372
*An attractive, popular restaurant in the High Street where our Inspector particularly enjoyed the homemade leek soup, chicken stuffed with spinach and oyster mushrooms, followed by a wonderful honey parfait with prunes. Just a short drive from junction 15 of the M1.*
Closed Sun, Mon & 3 wks summer Lunch not served Sat
♀ French 32 seats ❋ Lunch fr£14&alc Dinner £18-£23alc Last lunch 1.45pm Last dinner 10pm 15 P nc5yrs
Credit Cards 1 3

---

## ROBIN HOOD'S BAY North Yorkshire Map **08** NZ90

### ★ 64% Grosvenor
Station Rd YO22 4RA ☎Whitby(0947)880320
*A small family-run hotel, modestly furnished with good standards of cleanliness and good menus. Situated opposite a large car park and tennis courts in the upper part of the village.*
13rm(3⇨2🟦)(2fb) CTV in 6 bedrooms ® T 🗙 (ex guide dogs) CTV
♥ Last dinner 9pm
Credit Cards 1 3

---

## ROCHDALE Greater Manchester Map **07** SD81 ◎

### ★★★ 68% Norton Grange
Manchester Rd, Castleton OL11 2XZ (Rank) ☎(0706)30788
FAX (0706) 49313
*Convenient for the M62, its 9-acre grounds standing beside the A664 at Castletown, this Victorian mansion has been refurbished and extended to provide well appointed bedrooms, those in a new wing being particularly comfortable. The hotel is popular for conferences, for which it is comprehensively equipped, and a pleasant staff provides helpful service.*
50⇨🟦(28fb)1🟦 CTV in all bedrooms ® T ❋ sB&B⇨🟦£39-£70 dB&B⇨🟦£57-£85 🟥
Lift ⟪ 150P ❋ CFA *xmas*
♀ International **V** ♥ ⬛
Credit Cards 1 2 3 4 5

### ★★ 61% Midway
Manchester Rd, Castleton OL11 2XX ☎(0706)32881
Telex no 635220 FAX (0706) 53522
*Clean, warm accommodation in refurbished bedrooms which now offer both en suite baths and showers is provided by this friendly commercial hotel situated beside the A664 at Castleton.*
24⇨🟦1🟦 CTV in all bedrooms ® T 🗙 ❋ sB&B⇨🟦£40 dB&B⇨🟦£51-£61.50 🟥
⟪🟦 100P CFA *xmas*

---

♀ English & French **V** ⬛ ❋ Lunch £5.90-£13 Dinner £5.15-£15 Last dinner 10.30pm
Credit Cards 1 2 3

---

## ROCHESTER Kent Map **05** TQ76 ◎

### ★★★ 69% Bridgewood Manor Hotel
Bridgewood Roundabout, Maidstone Rd ME5 9AX (Best Western) ☎Medway(0634)201333 Telex no 965864
FAX (0634) 201330
*This modern, purpose-built hotel of unique Gothic design is located east of Rochester at the junction of the A2/A229, leaving the M2 at junction 3. The spacious lounge has modern and antique furnishings, whilst the restaurant offers an imaginative choice of menus, using good fresh produce.*
100⇨(12fb) CTV in all bedrooms ® T sB&B⇨£76.50-£95 dB&B⇨£112-£150 🟥
Lift ⟪ 178P ❋ CFA ⬛ (heated) ♪ (hard) snooker sauna solarium gymnasium spa bath ⏴ *xmas*
♀ English & French **V** ♥ ⬛ ❋ Lunch £16.50-£20&alc High tea £3.25-£7 Dinner £20-£25&alc Last dinner 10pm
Credit Cards 1 2 3 5
See advertisement under PRELIMINARY SECTION

### ★★★ 66% Forte Crest
Maidstone Rd ME5 9SF (on A229 1m N of M2 jnct 3) (Forte Hotels) ☎Medway(0634)687111 Telex no 965933
FAX (0634) 684512
*This busy commercial hotel, situated on the Maidstone road not far from Chatham, provides a popular local meeting place in its open-plan lounge/bar area; the recently added Business Centre and Health Club are also well utilised. Brightly decorated, well maintained bedrooms equipped with modern facilities will appeal to both businessman and weekend leisure user, and staff throughout are friendly and helpful – the standard of service in the restaurant being particularly noteworthy.*
→

R

105⇨🏳(7fb)🛏in 70 bedrooms CTV in all bedrooms ® T ✳
sB&B⇨🏳£40-£81 dB&B⇨🏳£40-£92 🏳
Lift ℂ 150P CFA ⌧ (heated) sauna solarium gymnasium spa
bath steam room ♫ ♨ *xmas*
🍴 English & French V ⅋ 🍷 🛏 ✳ Lunch fr£12.95&alc High
tea fr£4.50 Dinner fr£16.50&alc Last dinner 11pm
Credit Cards ①②③④⑤

### ★★64% Royal Victoria & Bull Hotel
16-18 High St ME1 1PX ☎(0634)846266 FAX (0634) 832312
28rm(21⇨🏳)(2fb)1🛏 CTV in all bedrooms ® T sB£38
sB⇨🏳£45 dB£45 dB⇨🏳£55 (room only)
ℂ CTV 25P CFA ♫
🍴 International V ⅋ 🍷 🛏 Lunch £8-£12alc Dinner £10-£15alc
Last dinner 11pm
Credit Cards ①②③⑤ⓔ

## ROCHFORD Essex Map 05 TQ89

### ★★★66% Hotel Renouf
Bradley Way SS4 1BU ☎Southend-on-Sea(0702)541334
Telex no 995158 FAX (0702) 549563
(Rosette awarded for dinner only)
*Situated in the town centre with access off Back Street, this is a*
*modern purpose-built hotel offering well equipped, attractive*
*accommodation and public areas which benefit from air-*
*conditioning. The skilfully prepared dishes served in the restaurant*
*are predominently French, and are complemented by a well chosen*
*wine list.*
24⇨🏳(1fb) CTV in all bedrooms ® T S% sB&B⇨🏳£47-
£57.50 dB&B⇨🏳£68-£78
ℂ 🏢 CTV 25P 🚗 ❄ *xmas*
🍴 French V S10% Lunch £19.50&alc Dinner £19.50&alc Last
dinner 10pm
Credit Cards ①②③⑤

## ROCK (NEAR ST MINVER) Cornwall & Isles of Scilly
Map 02 SW97

### ★★67% St Enodoc
PL27 6LA ☎Trebetherick(020886)3394 FAX (020886) 3394
*Enjoying splendid views over the Camel estuary, this friendly hotel*
*has a popular leisure club with squash courts, snooker tables, gym,*
*sauna and whirlpool bath. The varied bedrooms are continually*
*being upgraded and a short table d'hôte menu is offered in the*
*candlelit restaurant, with bar meals also available.*
13⇨🏳(2fb) CTV in all bedrooms S10%
33P 🚗 ❄ squash snooker sauna solarium gymnasium water-
skiing windsurfing pony-trekking
🍴 English & Continental V ⅋ 🍷 Last dinner 9.30pm
Credit Cards ①②③

## ROCKCLIFFE Dumfries & Galloway *Kirkcudbrightshire*
Map 11 NX85

### ★★★♨68% *Baron's Craig*
DG5 4QF ☎(055663)225
Closed mid Oct-Etr
*Handsome mansion, set peacefully in woodland with colourful*
*gardens and views of the Solway and Rough Firths. Both*
*traditional and modern bedrooms are offered, and there is a smart*
*cocktail bar.*
27rm(20⇨🏳)(2fb) CTV in all bedrooms T
50P 🚗 ❄ putting
🍴 International ⅋ 🍷 Last dinner 9pm
Credit Cards ①③

Hotels with red star ratings are
especially high quality.

## ROMALDKIRK Durham Map 12 NY92

### ★★❀70% Rose & Crown
DL12 9EB ☎Teesdale(0833)50213 FAX (0833) 50828
Closed 25 & 26 Dec
*Built in 1733, this former coaching inn in the centre of the village,*
*retains much of its original character despite its many modern*
*facilities. There is a cosy bar, with old photographs, brass and*
*copper setting off the stone walls, and an inviting open fire. Good*
*food can be enjoyed in the lovely oak-panelled dining room as well*
*as in the bar. Bedrooms, all en suite, are furnished in a style*
*appropriate to the building. This is a warm and friendly hotel*
*under the personal supervision of the owners, Christopher and*
*Alison Davy.*
6⇨🏳Annexe5⇨🏳(1fb)1🛏 CTV in all bedrooms ® T ✳
sB&B⇨🏳£45-£50.50 dB&B⇨🏳£63.50-£77 🏳
40P
🍴 English & French ⅋ 🍷 ✳ Sunday Lunch £9.75 Dinner £18-
£20 Last dinner 9.15pm
Credit Cards ①③ⓔ

## ROMSEY Hampshire Map 04 SU32

### ★★★64% Potters Heron Hotel
SO51 9ZF (Lansbury) ☎Southampton(0703)266611
Telex no 47459 FAX (0703) 251359
(For full entry see Ampfield)

### ★★★63% The White Horse
Market Place SO51 8ZJ (Forte Hotels) ☎(0794)512431
FAX (0794) 517485
*Behind its Georgian façade, the White Horse Hotel reveals many*
*interesting features, including several Tudor wall paintings and*
*traces of an Elizabethan Mummers' Gallery. The Lucella Dixon*
*Restaurant offers table d'hôte and à la carte menus, and an*
*extensive range of drinks and traditional ales is available in the*
*bar. In the summer months seating is available in the attractive*
*courtyard. Bedrooms vary in standard but are well equipped.*
33⇨🏳(7fb)🛏in 11 bedrooms CTV in all bedrooms ® T ✳
sB⇨🏳fr£70 dB⇨🏳fr£90 (room only) 🏳
ℂ 60P CFA
V ⅋ 🍷 🛏 ✳ Lunch £9.75&alc Dinner £14.95&alc Last dinner
9.30pm
Credit Cards ①②③④⑤

### ★★★60% New Forest Heathlands
Romsey Rd, Ower SO51 6ZJ (Consort)
☎Southampton(0703)814333 Telex no 8954665
FAX (0703) 812123
RS Sat
*Originally the Vine Inn, the New Forest Heathlands has been*
*modernised to provide facilities for business guests and*
*holidaymakers. Bedrooms have been upgraded, and executive*
*rooms have whirlpool baths. Staff are friendly and helpful. Table*
*d'hôte and à la carte menus are served in the spacious restaurant.*
52⇨🏳(2fb) CTV in all bedrooms ® T sB&B⇨🏳£63-£77
dB&B⇨🏳£77-£92 🏳
ℂ 150P ❄ CFA sauna solarium gymnasium mini-golf jacuzzis
croquet
🍴 International V ⅋ 🍷 Lunch £7.75-£8.75 High tea £3-£6
Dinner £14.75-£15.75&alc Last dinner 9.15pm
Credit Cards ①②③⑤
**See advertisement under SOUTHAMPTON**

### ❀❀❀ ✕✕Old Manor House
21 Palmerston St SO51 8GF ☎(0794)517353
*The beamed restaurant of this 16th-century manor house, with its*
*inglenook fireplace, features comfortably furnished tables decked*
*with posies of fresh flowers; a choice of fixed price menus is*
*available at lunch time, and just one at dinner, but dishes are*
*inviting and standards of cuisine consistently high. Langoustine*
*wrapped in fillet of duck with seafood sauce, an evenly pink fillet of*
*lamb and a mille feuilles aux trois chocolats are particularly*

**R**

*noteworthy, the bread trolley offers an immense variety, and a wine list of over 600 bins represents many countries. The service provided by a young French staff is prompt and very courteous, the entire operation of the hotel proceeding admirably smoothly.*

Closed Mon & 24-30 Dec

Dinner not served Sun

♀ French 46 seats ✳ Lunch £14.50-£21.50 Dinner fr£33 Last lunch 2pm Last dinner 9.30pm 12 P

Credit Cards 1 3

---

### ROSEBANK Strathclyde *Lanarkshire* Map **11** NS84

★★★61% **Popinjay**

Lanark Rd ML8 5OB (Consort) ☎Crossford(055586)441 FAX (055586) 204

*A mock-Tudor building in an attractive riverside setting – the focal point of this small Clyde Valley village – provides pleasantly appointed and very well equipped (though sometimes rather compact) bedroom accommodation; during the summer months an appealing range of eating options that includes restaurant meals, carvery lunches, bar snacks and barbecues makes it a popular venue.*

36⇔↑Annexe4⇔↑(1fb)2⊞ CTV in all bedrooms ® T ✳ sB&B⇔↑£46-£52 dB&B⇔↑£55-£66 ⊟

( 100P ✿ CFA ✔ ⚬

♀ International V ♥ ♨ ✳ Lunch fr£7.45&alc Dinner fr£12.50&alc Last dinner 10pm

Credit Cards 1 2 3 5

---

### ROSEDALE ABBEY North Yorkshire Map **08** SE79

★★★68% **Blacksmiths Arms**

Hartoft End YO18 8EN ☎Lastingham(07515)331

*This former 16th-century farmhouse carefully restored and extended, is now a cosy and attractive hotel with period furniture and open fires in winter. The building, however, still retains much of its old world charm and character. Bedrooms have been individually designed, and the dining room, in which delectable dishes are served from a 4-course menu, has been charmingly appointed, and the interesting bars with horse brasses and beams, provide an atmosphere in total character with the building.*

14⇔↑ CTV in all bedrooms ® T ✖ sB&B⇔↑£45-£50 dB&B⇔↑£78-£88 ⊟

80P ✿ CFA

♀ English & French V ♥ ♨ ✂ S% Lunch £12.95 Dinner £18.50 Last dinner 8.45pm

Credit Cards 1 3 5 £

★★70% **Milburn Arms**

YO18 8RA (Guestaccom) ☎Lastingham(07515)312

RS 24 & 25 Dec

*A delightful country inn converted to offer comfortable well equipped accommodation while retaining its original character.*

3⇔↑Annexe8⇔↑(2fb)1⊞ CTV in all bedrooms ® T ✳ sB&B⇔↑£42-£46 dB&B⇔↑£64-£75 ⊟

35P ✿ pool table *xmas*

♀ English & French V ♥ ✂ Sunday Lunch £8.50 Dinner £15-£17.50&alc Last dinner 9pm

Credit Cards 1 3 £

★★63% **White Horse Farm**

YO18 8SE (Minotels) ☎Lastingham(07515)239

Closed 25 Dec

*Set on the hillside above the village, this very friendly hotel has panoramic views over the valley and offers comfortable well equipped bedrooms and characterful public rooms with log fires and exposed beams.*

11⇔↑Annexe4⇔↑(2fb) CTV in all bedrooms ® sB&B⇔↑£30-£42 dB&B⇔↑£60-£69 ⊟

50P ✿ CFA *xmas*

---

♀ English & Continental V Sunday Lunch £7-£10 High tea £2.50-£5alc Dinner £15.50-£18 Last dinner 8.45pm

Credit Cards 1 2 3 5 £

---

### ROSEHALL Highland *Sutherland* Map **14** NC40

★★58% **Achness**

IV27 4BD ☎(054984)239 FAX (054984) 324

Closed Oct-Feb

*A popular anglers' retreat, this small highland hotel offers comfort and relaxation in its refurbished public areas and bedrooms which remain simple and practical. Satisfying home cooked dinners are provided at the self-service hot buffet.*

5rmAnnexe7⇔↑ TV in 6 bedrooms ® ✳ S10%

CTV 40P ✿ ✿ ✔ clay pigeon shooting

V ♥ ♨ ✳ Bar Lunch 85p-£7.95 Dinner £16.75 Last dinner 8pm

Credit Cards 1 3 £

**See advertisement on page 599**

---

### ROSSETT Clwyd Map **07** SJ35

★★★73% **Llyndir Hall**

LL12 0AY (Consort) ☎Chester(0244)571648 FAX (0244) 571258

*This large country house, set in 6 acres, has recently been considerably extended to provide good quality, well equipped accommodation, a leisure centre and conference facilities. It is located on the edge of the village, midway between Wrexham and Chester, and within easy reach of the A483.*

38⇔↑(4fb)✂in 3 bedrooms CTV in all bedrooms ® T ✖ (ex guide dogs) sB&B⇔↑£68-£78 dB&B⇔↑£98-£150 ⊟

( 120P ✿ CFA ▭ (heated) solarium gymnasium croquet spa bath steam room ⚬ *xmas*

♀ English & French V ♥ ♨ ✂ ✳ Lunch £12.50-£14.50 Dinner £14.50-£26 Last dinner 10pm

Credit Cards 1 2 3 5 £

**See advertisement under CHESTER**

**R**

### ★★★ 70% Rossett Hall

Chester Rd LL12 0DE (Best Western) ☎Chester(0244)571000
FAX (0244) 571505

*This lovely old Georgian hall, set in 3 acres of grounds and gardens midway between Chester and Wrexham, within easy reach of the A483, is now a privately owned and personally run hotel providing friendly, attentive service. The majority of the well equipped bedrooms are contained in a modern, purpose-built wing, two on the ground floor being designed to meet the needs of disabled guests.*

30⇆(2fb) CTV in all bedrooms ⓇT sB&B⇆£61-£68 dB&B⇆£80.70-£88 ➡

( 90P ✷ CFA ♫ ♨

♀ International V ⌖ ⌐ ✳ Lunch £10.25 Dinner £16.50&alc
Last dinner 10pm

Credit Cards 1 2 3 5 £

**See advertisement under CHESTER**

---

### ★★★ 64% Mount Pleasant

Great North Rd DN11 0HP (On A638 Great North Rd 1.5m E of village) (Consort) ☎Doncaster(0302)868696 & 868219
FAX (0302) 865130
Closed 25 Dec

*Situated on the A638 half-way between Bawtry and Doncaster, this much extended building was formerly the estate house to Rossington Hall and dates back to the 1700s. It now offers good accommodation in comfortable surroundings including a range of cosy quiet lounges.*

33⇆(2fb)4➡ CTV in all bedrooms ⓇT ✻ (ex guide dogs)
sB&B⇆£48-£56 dB&B⇆£58-£60 ➡

( 100P 2➡ (£1 per night) ✷ CFA

♀ English & French V ⌖ ⌐ ✳ Lunch £7.95-£10.95&alc High tea £7.95-£8.50 Dinner £11.50-£13.50&alc Last dinner 10pm

Credit Cards 1 2 3 5 £

**See advertisement under DONCASTER**

---

See also **Goodrich, Pencraig and Symonds Yat**

### ★★★ 66% Royal

Palace Pound HR9 5HZ (Forte Hotels) ☎(0989)65105
FAX (0989) 768058

*A traditional hotel, built in 1837 in a prime position above the horseshoe bend of the Rive Wye, offering courteous service and a good range of modern facilites. Some of the comfortable well equipped bedrooms have small balconies overlooking the gardens and there is a pleasant dining room and lounge, plus conference rooms.*

40⇆(4fb)⨯11 bedrooms CTV in all bedrooms ⓇT ✳
sB⇆fr£70 dB⇆£90-£100 (room only) ➡

70P ✷ CFA ♩ xmas

V ⌖ ⌐ ⨯ ✳ Lunch £8.95-£22.50 Dinner £14.95-£22.50 Last dinner 10pm

Credit Cards 1 2 3 4 5

### ★★★♨ 65% Pengethley Manor

HR9 6LL (4m N on A49 Hereford rd) (Best Western) ☎Harewood End(098987)211 FAX (098987) 238

*A manor dating back to the reign of Henry VIII, enjoys a beautiful location in 15-acre grounds set well back from the A49. Standards of accommodation vary, but refurbishment continues, and the hotel is a popular conference venue – delegates taking advantage of the outdoor swimming pool, trout lake and mini golf facilities. High levels of hospitality are maintained throughout.*

11⇆Annexe13⇆(3fb)4➡ CTV in all bedrooms ⓇT
sB&B⇆£67-£115 dB&B⇆£100-£154 ➡

70P ✷ CFA ⌑ (heated) ♩ snooker 9 hole mini golf croquet

♀ English & French V ⌖ ⌐ ✳ Lunch fr£14 Dinner fr£19&alc
Last dinner 9.30pm

Credit Cards 1 2 3 5 £

### ★★※※ WHARTON LODGE COUNTRY HOUSE

Weston-under-Penyard
HR9 7JX ☎(0989)81795
FAX (0989) 81700

*A striking Georgian house in 15 acres of parkland on the A40 Gloucester road just outside Ross-on-Wye.*
*Despite its proximity to a busy road, the impression is that of a peaceful country house. Each bedroom is individually styled with lavish use of fabrics, carefully chosen furniture and modern facilities. There are 2 sunny drawing rooms with french windows out onto the terrace, and an elegant dining room where well balanced dishes are offered from a 4-course table d'hôte or à la carte menu. The proprietors, the Gough family, firmly believe in good old fashioned service, which is both attentive and unobtrusive. Mrs Gough is a lively hostess, and the glorious fresh flowers are a credit to her.*

9⇆1➡ CTV in all bedrooms T ✻ (ex guide dogs) ✳
sB&B⇆fr£90 dB&B⇆£90-£120 ➡

30P ⇦ ✷ ∪ shooting nc8yrs xmas

V ⌖ ⌐ Lunch fr£16 Dinner fr£25&alc Last dinner 9.30pm

Credit Cards 1 2 3 5 £

---

### ★★♨ 75% Peterstow Country House

Peterstow HR9 6LB ☎(0989)62826 FAX (0989) 67264

*A beautiful Georgian rectory surrounded by its own 25 acres of woodland and pasture stands in the Lower Wye Valley, just off the A49, 3 miles from Ross-on-Wye. Lovingly restored by its owners, it provides a very comfortable small hotel offering a warm welcome and excellent standards of accommodation. Bedrooms vary from the spaciously grand to compact and 'cottagey', but all boast antique furnishings complemented by quality décor and fabrics, while public areas include an attractive drawing room and a restaurant whose interesting menu is soundly based on the best of local produce.*

9⇆(3fb) CTV in all bedrooms ⓇT ✻ (ex guide dogs)
sB&B⇆£38.50-£69 dB&B⇆£50-£90 ➡

60P ⇦ ✷ CFA ♩ clay pigeon shooting nc8yrs xmas

♀ English & French V ⌖ ⌐ ✳ Lunch £12.50&alc Dinner £19.50&alc Last dinner 9pm

Credit Cards 1 2 3 5 £

### ★★♨ 71% Glewstone Court

Glewstone HR9 6AW ☎Llangarron(098984)367
FAX (098984) 282
Closed 25-27 Dec

*A delightful country house hotel in 3 acres of grounds surrounded by orchards. Christine and William Reeve-Tucker have transformed the house from delapidation into a beautiful hotel providing spacious and comfortable accommodation with some very thoughtful, and amusing, touches. A range of paint finishes has been used in the décor with some lovely stencilling.*

7⇆ CTV in all bedrooms ⓇT sB&B⇆£49-£59 dB&B⇆£75-£88 ➡

20P ⇦ ✷ ♩ croquet lawn hot air ballooning

♀ English & French V ⌖ Lunch fr£15 Dinner fr£19 Last dinner 9.30pm

Credit Cards 1 3

R

**★★66% Hunsdon Manor**
Gloucester Rd, Weston-Under-Penyard HR9 7PE (2m E A40)
☎(0989)62748 & 63376 FAX (0989) 768348

*Built on the site of a 16th-century manor house that was a gift
from Elizabeth I to her cousin, Baron Hunsdon, this hotel stands
beside the A40, 2 miles to the southeast of Ross-on-Wye.
Accommodation is thoughtfully equipped, both in the main building
and the converted coach house, while friendly staff offer both a
warm welcome and helpful service.*

13⇨🝙Annexe12⇨🝙(3fb)2🏻 CTV in all bedrooms ® T ✱
sB&B⇨🝙£38-£45 dB&B⇨🝙£50-£60 🏳

55P 🚗 ✿ sauna solarium
♥ English & French V ♥ ⚏ ✱ Sunday Lunch £12.50 Dinner
£12.50&alc Last dinner 9.30pm
Credit Cards ① ② ③ ⑤ ⑤

See advertisement on page 601

**★★66% Orles Barn**
Wilton HR9 6AE ☎(0989)62155 FAX (0989) 768470
Closed Nov

*Standing less than a mile from the town centre, in one-and-a-half
acre grounds that include a swimming pool, this former farm offers
accommodation in rooms which are all well-maintained and
attractive, though some are quite compact; a restaurant
overlooking the garden provides guests with a good selection of
English and Continental dishes.*

9rm(8⇨🝙)(1fb) CTV in all bedrooms ® sB&B⇨🝙£35-£50
dB&B⇨🝙£50-£70 🏳

《20P ✿ ⇨ (heated) ♿
♥ English, French & Spanish V ♥ ⚏ ✱ Lunch fr£8.95&alc
High tea £2.50-£7 Dinner £9.75-£10.50&alc Last dinner 9pm
Credit Cards ① ② ③ ⑤ ⑤

R

### ★★65% **Bridge House**
Wilton HR9 6AA (adjacent A40/A49 junc) ☎(0989)62655
*Situated just west of the town, in the village of Wilton, this lovely old house with gardens stretching to the river provides comfortable, well equipped accommodation and friendly hospitality. Though popular with holidaymakers, many of whom return regularly, it is equally suitable for business travellers.*
7⇨🛏1🛁 CTV in all bedrooms Ⓡ **T ✖** sB&B⇨🛁£31.50-£33 dB&B⇨🛁£53-£56 🍴
CTV 14P 🚗 ❋ nc10yrs *xmas*
♥ English & French **V** Sunday Lunch £9.75-£10.75 Dinner £11.50-£12.25&alc Last dinner 9pm
Credit Cards 1 3

### ★★63% **King's Head**
8 High St HR9 5HL ☎(0989)763174
Closed 24-26 Dec
*A 14th-century town centre inn where the well equipped bedrooms and public areas retain their olde worlde charm. The lounge bar is popular with hotel guests and residents alike, and meals make the most of fresh local produce.*
16⇨Annexe10⇨(6fb) CTV in all bedrooms Ⓡ **T** sB&B⇨£38-£40 dB&B⇨£60-£65 🍴
20P 🚗
**V** ♥ 🍽 Sunday Lunch £5.50-£8.50 Dinner £10-£16alc Last dinner 9pm
Credit Cards 1 3 £

### ★★58% **Chasedale**
Walford Rd HR9 5PQ ☎(0989)62423
*Dating back to 1850, the house is surrounded by gardens, including a large kitchen garden. Bedrooms are modestly furnished and the owners are very involved in the running of the hotel.*
10rm(9⇨)(3fb)✄in 1 bedroom CTV in all bedrooms Ⓡ **T ✖** sB&B⇨fr£32 dB&Bfr£38.50 dB&B⇨fr£51 🍴
14P 🚗 ❋ *xmas*
♥ English & French **V** ♥ 🍽 ✄ ✖ Lunch fr£8.25 Dinner fr£10.75 Last dinner 9pm
Credit Cards 1 3 4 5 £

---

### ROSTHWAITE Cumbria Map **11** NY21
See also **Borrowdale**

### ★★★61% **Scafell**
CA12 5XB ☎Keswick(07687)77208 FAX (07687) 77280
Closed 2 Jan-9 Feb
*Family-owned and run, this hotel is set in the very heart of impressive Borrowdale. Well furnished bedrooms offer good facilities, lounges are warmed by open fires during the winter, a restaurant serves a range of interesting dishes, and a dedicated staff provides warm and friendly service.*
20⇨🛁(3fb) CTV in all bedrooms Ⓡ **T ✖** sB&B⇨🛁£37-£49 dB&B⇨🛁£74-£98 (incl dinner) 🍴
50P 🚗 ❋ *xmas*
♥ International **V** ♥ 🍽 Sunday Lunch fr£10 Dinner fr£16.95 Last dinner 9.15pm
Credit Cards 1 3

---

### ROSYTH Fife Map **11** NT18

### ★★59% **Gladyer Inn**
Heath Rd, off Ridley Dr KY11 2BT
☎Inverkeithing(0383)419977 FAX (0383) 411728
*On the eastern edge of the town, this family-run commercial inn was purpose built in 1987 and is a popular venue for local functions. It offers practical modern furnishings together with good value accommodation in bedrooms which, though compact, are well equipped.*

21⇨🛁(3fb) CTV in all bedrooms Ⓡ **T ✖** sB&B⇨🛁£25 dB&B⇨🛁£35
《 CTV 81P *xmas*
**V** ♥ 🍽 ✖
Credit Cards 1 2 3

---

### ROTHBURY Northumberland Map **12** NU00

### ★★64% **Coquet Vale**
Station Rd NE65 9QN ☎(0669)20305 FAX (0669) 20814
*Friendly service, a good-value range of interesting menus and accommodation in spacious, comfortable bedrooms are provided at this privately owned small hotel.*
14rm(4⇨8🛁)(6fb) CTV in all bedrooms Ⓡ **T**
✖ (ex guide dogs)
40P ❋ CFA
**V** ♥ Last dinner 9pm
Credit Cards 1 3

---

### ROTHERHAM South Yorkshire Map **08** SK49 ⊙
See also **Thurcroft**

### ★★★66% **Rotherham Moat House**
Moorgate Rd S60 2BG (Queens Moat) ☎(0709)364902
Telex no 547810 FAX (0709) 368960
*A purpose-built hotel on the A618 approaching the town centre from the south. Over the last few years a third floor of bedrooms has been added to the hotel. These are modern and well furnished in comparison to the remaining rooms which are rather dated – the compact bathrooms are currently being redecorated. The leisure club is also undergoing extensive refurbishment.*

→

R

R

83⇨🐾(6fb)1⇔⅄in 22 bedrooms CTV in all bedrooms Ⓡ T
S10% sB⇨🐾£31-£70 dB⇨🐾£40-£79 (room only) 🅿
Lift ℂ CTV 95P CFA sauna solarium gymnasium jacuzzi ♫
♡ English & French V ♥ �’ ⅄ ✳ Lunch £7&alc Dinner
£13.75&alc Last dinner 9.45pm
Credit Cards ① ② ③ ④ ⑤ ⓔ

★★69% **Brentwood**
Moorgate Rd S60 2TY ☎(0709)382772 FAX (0709) 820289
Closed 26 & 27 Dec RS BH's

*A mile from the town centre and near the General Hospital, this
very popular hotel provides a wide range of food in its attractive
restaurant. Bedrooms are mostly modern and comfortable, and
there is an attractive leafy garden.*

33⇨🐾Annexe10⇨🐾(4fb)2⇔ CTV in all bedrooms Ⓡ T ✳
sB&B⇨🐾£20-£54 dB&B⇨🐾£35-£65 🅿
ℂ 60P ✿ ♪ (grass) ৬
♡ English & Continental V ♥ ✳ Lunch £9.50&alc Dinner
£15.50&alc Last dinner 9.30pm
Credit Cards ① ② ③ ⑤ ⓔ

★68% **Elton**
Main St, Bramley S66 0SF (3m E A631) ☎(0709)545681
FAX (0709) 549100

*A popular small hotel in the village of Bramley on the A631, half a
mile from junction 1 of the M18. Helpful and friendly staff provide
a most hospitable atmosphere, while a good range of dishes are
available in the restaurant.*

13⇨🐾Annexe16⇨🐾(4fb) CTV in all bedrooms Ⓡ T
sB&B⇨🐾£32-£58 dB&B⇨🐾£56-£72 🅿
ℂ 44P
♡ English & French V ♥ �’ Lunch £9.95&alc Dinner
£15.50&alc Last dinner 9.30pm
Credit Cards ① ② ③ ⑤ ⓔ

○**Beeches Hotel & Leisure**
West Bawtry Rd S60 4NA ☎(0709)830630
Open
111⇨🐾

## ROTHERWICK Hampshire Map 04 SU75

★★★★⚑80% **Tylney Hall**
RG27 9AJ (Small Luxury Hotels) ☎(0256)764881
Telex no 859864 FAX (0256) 768141

*A tree-lined drive leads to this privately owned country house set in
66 acres of beautifully kept parkland and gardens. The Victorian
mansion was respectfully restored in 1985 and typifies the great
house of the period, yet offers every modern amenity. There are 91
spacious bedrooms and suites, individually decorated and lavishly
furnished. All have been carefully equipped with many thoughtful
extras: boxed soaps, mineral waters, bath robes, baskets of exotic
fruit and fresh flowers. There is a range of luxurious lounges where
log fires blaze in winter months, and ornate plasterwork sets off the
graceful ambience. A leisure complex has been provided in a
courtyard building and includes indoor and outdoor pools, snooker,
sauna and gym; while golf and tennis are available in the grounds.
There are 9 private rooms for parties, meetings and seminars.
Interesting dishes are a feature of the menus compiled by head chef
Stephen Hine, such as local venison pâté complemented by a tangy
Cumberland sauce, or breast of maize-fed chicken served with a
light mousseline of tomato and basil, which is a little overpowered
by the dry sherry sauce. A selection of puddings includes some
traditional favourites like steamed sultana sponge served with a
tart lemon sauce. A team of well trained and managed staff
welcome guests to Tylney Hall and assure them of special care and
attention.*

35⇨🐾Annexe56⇨🐾(1fb)3⇔ CTV in all bedrooms Ⓡ T
✖ (ex guide dogs) ✳ S10% sB&B⇨🐾£89-£225 dB&B⇨🐾£108-
£225 🅿
Lift ℂ 120P ⇔ ✿ CFA ▣ (heated) ⇨ (heated) ♪ (hard)
snooker sauna gymnasium croquet ♫ xmas

♡ English & French V ♥ ⚹ ⅄ ✳ S% Lunch £18.50&alc
Dinner £26.50&alc Last dinner 9.30pm
Credit Cards ① ② ③ ⑤

**See advertisement under BASINGSTOKE**

## ROTHES Grampian *Morayshire* Map 15 NJ24

★★★⚑64% **Rothes Glen**
AB38 7AH ☎(03403)254 & 255 FAX (03403) 566
Closed Jan

*Set in 40 acres of grounds at the head of the Glen of Rothes, this
impressive baronial mansion has an informal atmosphere. Public
rooms are comfortable and elegant, with antiques and fresh flowers
adding to the appeal. Bedrooms vary in size and style but all are
well equipped.*

16rm(13⇨🐾)(4fb) CTV in all bedrooms S10% sB&B£48.50
sB&B⇨🐾£71.60 dB&B£76.75 dB&B⇨🐾£107.45 🅿
CTV 40P ⇔ ✿ CFA
♥ ⚹ S10% Lunch £13.75 Dinner £26.15 Last dinner 9pm
Credit Cards ① ② ③ ⑤

## ROTHESAY

See **Bute, Isle of**

## ROTHLEY Leicestershire Map 08 SK51

★★★70% **Rothley Court**
Westfield Ln LE7 7LG (Forte Hotels) ☎Leicester(0533)374141
Telex no 342811 FAX (0533) 374483

*The Court has a long and fascinating history, beginning with a
mention in the Domesday Book of 1086. Now it is a comfortable
country hotel with a polite team of young staff who provide
attentive service throughout the hotel.*

15⇨🐾Annexe21⇨🐾(3fb)2⇔⅄in 8 bedrooms CTV in all
bedrooms Ⓡ T ✳ sB⇨🐾£70-£80 dB⇨🐾£80-£90 (room only)
🅿
ℂ 100P ✿ CFA croquet xmas
♡ French V ♥ ⚹ ⅄ ✳ Lunch £10.75-£12&alc
Credit Cards ① ② ③ ⑤

## ROTTINGDEAN East Sussex Map 05 TQ30

★★61% *White Horse*
Marine Dr BN2 7HB ☎Brighton(0273)300301

*In a prime seaside location with extensive views, this hotel offers
well-equipped modern accommodation decorated in Laura Ashley
designs. There is a contemporary restaurant, a smart cocktail bar
and a lively lounge bar where lunches are served.*

17⇨(2fb)2⇔ CTV in all bedrooms Ⓡ ✖ (ex guide dogs)
Lift ℂ 45P ▶
V ♥ ⚹ ⅄ Last dinner 10pm
Credit Cards ① ② ③ ⑤

## ROUSDON Devon Map 03 SY29

★★64% **Orchard Country**
DT7 3XW ☎Lyme Regis(0297)442972
Closed Nov-Mar

*A peaceful little hotel in immaculate gardens set back from the
A3052 between Lyme Regis and Seaton. There is a comfortable
lounge with dispense bar, and a well maintained dining room,
together with useful modern bedrooms providing essential
facilities. Housekeeping standards are good under the careful
direction of the resident owners. Daily changing menus offer a
straightforward choice.*

12⇨🐾 CTV in all bedrooms Ⓡ sB&B⇨🐾£30-£35
dB&B⇨🐾£54-£62 🅿
CTV 30P ✿ nc8yrs
♥ ⚹ ⅄ Bar Lunch £3 High tea £3 Dinner £12.50 Last dinner
8.15pm
Credit Cards ① ③ ⓔ

R

ROWARDENNAN Central *Stirlingshire* Map **10** NS39

### ★ 61% Rowardennan Hotel Loch Lomond
G63 0AR ☎Balmaha(036087)273 FAX (036087) 251
Closed Nov RS Oct-Mar
*A modest but homely hotel situated amidst rugged scenery at the end of the road on the east side of Loch Lomond. Popular with walkers travelling the West Highland Way, which passes the hotel. It offers a good range of bar meals and an interesting dinner menu in season.*
11rm(1⇨)(2fb) CTV in 6 bedrooms Ⓡ sB&B£20-£23 dB&B£38-£45 dB&B⇨fr£45
CTV 50P 🚑 water-skiing boating
V ✿ Bar Lunch £3-£8 Dinner £10-£15 Last dinner 8.45pm
£

ROWEN Gwynedd Map **06** SH77

### ★★⚑ 63% Tir-y-Coed Country House
LL32 8TP ☎Tynygroes(0492)650219
Closed Xmas RS Nov-Feb
*This large, well maintained house is set in spacious mature gardens and is situated on the edge of a small village in the picturesque Conwy Valley.*
7⇨🜂 Annexe1🜂(1fb) CTV in all bedrooms Ⓡ
sB&B⇨🜂£20.75-£24.50 dB&B⇨🜂£39-£44.50 🄿
8P 🚑 ✿
✿ ⬙ ✂ Bar Lunch £2.25-£5.50alc Dinner £9.95 Last dinner 7.30pm
£

ROWSLEY Derbyshire Map **08** SK26

### ★★★ 57% Peacock
DE4 2EB (Jarvis) ☎Matlock(0629)733518 FAX (0629) 732671
*Popular with visitors and locals, the restaurant here is particularly busy. Accommodation in the main house is of a good standard and there are simpler, lower-priced rooms available in the cottage annexe.*
14⇨🜂(3fb)1🖭 CTV in all bedrooms Ⓡ T sB&B⇨🜂£85.20-£95.20 dB&B⇨🜂£114.40-£124.70 🄿
《 45P 🚑 ✿ ✒ *xmas*
V ✿ ⬙ S% Lunch £8.25-£12.95 Dinner fr£23.50&alc Last dinner 9.15pm
Credit Cards ①②③⑤

### ★★⚑ 71% East Lodge Country House
DE4 2EF ☎Matlock(0629)734474 FAX (0629) 733949
*This country house hotel is set in 10 acres of attractive gardens and grounds, and the proprietors, with their small team of staff, provide a personal friendly service. The accommodation has recently been extended, and offers rooms that are well equipped and furnished.*
14⇨🜂(1fb) CTV in all bedrooms Ⓡ T 🗶 sB&B⇨🜂£42-£50 dB&B⇨🜂£64-£80
30P 🚑 ✿ croquet lawn *xmas*
✿ International ✿ ⬙ ✲ Lunch £8.50-£18.50&alc Dinner £16.50-£19.50 Last dinner 8.30pm
Credit Cards ①②③£

ROY BRIDGE Highland *Inverness-shire* Map **14** NN28

### ★★ 59% Glenspean Lodge
PH31 4AW ☎Spean Bridge(039781)223 FAX (039781) 660
*Improvements continue at this family-run holiday and sporting hotel, in well tended grounds 2 miles east of the village. Public rooms have been substantially refurbished over the past few years and offer comfortable appointments. Bedrooms are tastefully decorated and have smart modern bathrooms. Replacement furniture was being fitted at the time of our visit.*
12rm(9⇨🜂)(2fb) CTV in all bedrooms Ⓡ T sB&B£20-£22 sB&B⇨🜂£28-£30 dB&B£40-£44 dB&B⇨🜂£56-£60 🄿

CTV 30P 1🚗 (£5 per night) ✲ ✒ clay pigeon & rough shooting stalking *xmas*
✿ Scottish & French V ✿ ⬙ ✂ ✲ Bar Lunch £1.10-£6.85alc Dinner fr£14.50alc Last dinner 9.30pm
Credit Cards ①③

**See advertisement on page 605**

ROZEL BAY

See **Jersey** under **Channel Islands**

RUABON Clwyd Map **07** SJ34

### ★★ 59% Wynnstay Arms
High St LL14 6BL ☎(0978)822187
*In the centre of the village, which is not by-passed, is this mainly 19th-century coaching inn with modest but comfortable accommodation and friendly, hospitable staff. The fine old stable block was the headquarters of Watkin-Wynn's private army, which fought in the Crimean War.*
9rm(3⇨)(1fb) CTV in all bedrooms Ⓡ ✲ sB&B£27 sB&B⇨£33 dB&B£42 dB&B⇨£48
80P 2🚗 CFA
✿ English & French V ✿ ✲ Lunch fr£10alc Dinner £5-£8&alc Last dinner 9.45pm
Credit Cards ①②③④⑤£

RUAN HIGH LANES Cornwall & Isles of Scilly Map **02** SW93

### ★★ 71% Hundred House
TR2 5JR ☎Truro(0872)501336
Closed Nov-Feb
*An old Cornish house dating from 1790 which has been extensively refurbished by the owners Mike and Kitty Eccles. Bedrooms are individually furnished and public areas include a small library, a* →

R

*comfortable, spacious bar lounge and separate sitting room.
Service is friendly and informal.*

10⇨♠ CTV in all bedrooms ® ✱ sB&B⇨♠£34-£42
dB&B⇨♠£68-£84 (incl dinner) 🛲

15P ⇖ ❈ croquet nc6yrs

۞ ♨ ⅄ ✱ Bar Lunch fr£2.50alc Dinner fr£16.50&alc Last
dinner 6pm

Credit Cards ①③

★★★69% **Pendower**

Gerrans Bay TR2 5LW ☎Truro(0872)501257
FAX (0452) 410440
Etr-Oct

*A tranquil hotel in a lovely position down a leafy lane with
wonderful views out to sea. Bedrooms are bright and simply
furnished in a comfortable style. At present they lack modern
facilities, but there is a TV lounge in addition to 2 quiet lounges, a
bar and attractively appointed dining room. The peace of the hotel
is guarded by the proprietors who believe that this is the quality
most valued by their guests.*

14⇨♠(2fb) sB&B⇨♠£40-£52 dB&B⇨♠£80-£104 (incl
dinner)

CTV 16P 3🏎 (£2 per day) ⇖ ❈

V ۞ ♨ ⅄ ✱ Sunday Lunch £13.50 Dinner £17.50 Last dinner
9pm

Credit Cards ①②③

RUGBY Warwickshire Map **04** SP57 ◎

★★★66% **Forte Posthouse Northampton/Rugby**

NN6 7XR (Forte Hotels) ☎Crick(0788)822101
FAX (0788) 823955
(For full entry see Crick)

★★★60% **Grosvenor**

Clifton Rd CV21 3QQ ☎(0788)535686 FAX (0788) 541297
*This hotel, formerly three late Victorian houses, has been totally
refurbished during the past four years and now provides modern
well-equipped bedrooms and imaginative food standards. The hotel
also has a new indoor swimming pool and fitness complex.*

21⇨♠ CTV in all bedrooms ® T ✖ (ex guide dogs) ✱
sB&B⇨♠fr£67.50 dB&B⇨♠fr£77.50 🛲

《 210P ⇖ CFA 🖼 (heated) sauna solarium gymnasium jacuzzi
♫ *xmas*

V ۞ ♨ ✱ Lunch fr£12.25&alc Dinner fr£17.95&alc Last
dinner 10pm

Credit Cards ①②③⑤

★★★64% **Hillmorton Manor**

78 High St, Hillmorton CV21 4EE (2m SE off A428)
☎(0788)565533 & 572403
*This privately owned commercial hotel standing 2 miles southeast
of the town centre, close to the B4429 junction, features
comfortable, well equipped bedrooms and a locally popular à la
carte restaurant.*

11⇨♠(1fb) CTV in all bedrooms ® T ✖ (ex guide dogs) ✱
sB&B⇨♠£37-£48 dB&B⇨♠£48-£70

40P

۞ English & French V ۞ ✱ Lunch £9&alc Dinner £6.95-
£13.95alc Last dinner 10pm

Credit Cards ①②③④

RUGELEY Staffordshire Map **07** SK01 ◎

★★59% **Cedar Tree**

Main Road, Brereton WS15 1DY ☎(0889)584241
Closed 3 days Xmas RS Sun evenings

*A busy, modest business hotel on the A51 between Rugeley and
Lichfield. The restaurant and bar have a traditional style of décor
and offer a range of menus to suit all tastes.*

14rm(7⇨)Annexe14⇨♠(1fb) CTV in 25 bedrooms ® T ✖ ✱
sB&B£21-£23 sB&B⇨♠£27-£29 dB&B£40 dB&B⇨♠£44-£48
CTV 200P CFA squash solarium

۞ English & French V ۞ ✱ Lunch fr£6.75 Dinner fr£9&alc
Last dinner 9.30pm

Credit Cards ①②③⑤

⇧**Forte Travelodge**

Western Springs Rd WS11 2AS (on A51/B5013) (Forte)
☎(0889)570096 Central Res (0800) 850950
*Set at the A51/B5013 junction, this busy lodge stands close to the
town centre and opposite the local bus station ; refreshments can be
obtained from the Little Chef restaurant next door.*

32⇨♠(32fb) CTV in all bedrooms ® sB⇨♠£29.95
dB⇨♠£29.95 (room only)

《 32P ⇖

Credit Cards ①②③

RUNCORN Cheshire Map **07** SJ58

★★★★66% **Forte Crest**

Wood Ln, Beechwood WA7 3HA (Forte Hotels) ☎(0928)714000
Telex no 627426 FAX (0928) 714611
*A busy hotel popular with both business people and tourists. There
is a splendid leisure centre with two pools – one for children. The
Crest is in a residential area, to find it follow the signs to
Beechwood from junction 12 of the M56.*

134⇨♠(4fb)⅄in 86 bedrooms CTV in all bedrooms ® T ✱
sB⇨♠fr£80 dB⇨♠£92-£106 (room only) 🛲

Lift 《 210P ⇖ CFA 🖼 (heated) sauna solarium gymnasium
steam room spa bath pool tables ♫ ♨ *xmas*

۞ Continental V ۞ ♨ ⅄ ✱ Lunch fr£7.95&alc Dinner
fr£16.50&alc Last dinner 9.45pm

Credit Cards ①②③④⑤

RUSHDEN Northamptonshire Map **04** SP96

★★59% **The Rilton Hotel**

High St NN10 1BT ☎Wellingborough(0933)312189
FAX (0933) 58593
*A privately owned, predominantly commercial hotel on the A6 in
the town centre. Rooms are well equipped and generally spacious.
The restaurant has a newly introduced à la carte menu, and the bar
is busy with both residents and locals.*

23⇨♠1🛏 CTV in all bedrooms ® T ✱ sB&B⇨♠fr£32.50
dB&B⇨♠fr£42.50

CTV 50P CFA

V ۞ ♨

Credit Cards ①③ ⑤

⇧**Forte Travelodge**

Saunders Lodge(on A45) (Forte) ☎Central Res (0800) 850950
*A newly opened Travelodge offering functional value-for-money
accommodation is situated on the A45 near Rushden, 14 miles east
of Northampton. Meals are available in the adjacent Little Chef
restaurant.*

40⇨♠(40fb) CTV in all bedrooms ® sB⇨♠£29.95
dB⇨♠£29.95 (room only)

《 40P ⇖

Credit Cards ①②③

RUSHYFORD Co Durham Map **08** NZ22

★★★59% **Eden Arms Swallow Hotel**

DL17 0LL (Swallow) ☎Bishop Auckland(0388)720541
FAX (0388) 721871
*The modern accommodation available at this coaching inn –
considerably enlarged since it was a posting house for coaches
running between Darlington and Durham – is now enhanced by the
addition of a small leisure centre and a coffee shop serving light
meals.*

46⇨♠(4fb)1🛏⅄in 20 bedrooms CTV in all bedrooms ® T ✱
sB&B⇨♠£45-£65 dB&B⇨♠£70-£85 🛲

《 200P ❈ 🖼 (heated) sauna solarium gymnasium jacuzzi
steam room impulse shower *xmas*

♡ English & French **V** ♧ ⏨ ✳ Lunch £6-£8.95&alc High tea £5-£7.50 Dinner £12.95&alc Last dinner 9.30pm
Credit Cards ① ② ③ ⑤ ⓔ

---

**RUSPER** West Sussex Map **04** TQ23

★★★64% **Ghyll Manor**

RH12 4PX (Forte Hotels) ☎(0293)871571 Telex no 877557
FAX (0293) 871419

*This sympathetically furnished and historic manor house retains an atmosphere of traditional permanence, though the provision of accommodation has now extended into several annexes, cottages, courtyard bedrooms and stable mews – the latter being the most modern addition. A particularly attractive candlelit restaurant demonstrates the individuality and professional skill of the chef in enterprising à la carte selections and fixed-price menus – a typical meal including, perhaps, a Terrine of Salmon and Sole followed by Fillet of Venison and a choice of hot individual puddings. Guests can relax in a small, beamed lounge with dispense-style bar, and extensive services are normally available on request.*

28⇠🖙(2fb)5🖪⛌in 3 bedrooms CTV in all bedrooms ® **T** ✳
sB⇠🖙fr£80 dB⇠🖙£95-£130 (room only) 🝙
《150P ✿ CFA ⌂ (heated) ♗ (hard) sauna solarium ♫ *xmas*
**V** ♧ ⏨ ⛌ ✳ Lunch fr£16 Dinner fr£16.50&alc Last dinner 10pm
Credit Cards ① ② ③ ④ ⑤

---

**RUTHIN** Clwyd Map **06** SJ15

★★★63% **Ruthin Castle**

LL15 2NU (Best Western) ☎(08242)2664 Telex no 61169
FAX (08242) 5978

*Set in 30 acres of parkland within walking distance of the town centre, this converted castle with conference and function facilities includes the 13th-century ruins of Edward I's original building and features regular medieval banquets. Bars, sitting rooms and restaurant are spacious and comfortable, as are the well equipped bedrooms, though bathrooms are tending to look rather dated. Friendly staff provide attentive service.*

58⇠🖙(6fb)1🖪 CTV in all bedrooms ® **T** � (ex guide dogs)
sB&B⇠🖙£50-£65 dB&B⇠🖙£71-£99 🝙
Lift 《 CTV 200P ✿ CFA ♩ snooker *xmas*
♡ International **V** ♧ ⏨ Sunday Lunch £8.45-£9.25 Dinner £14.95-£15.95&alc Last dinner 9.30pm
Credit Cards ① ② ③ ⑤ ⓔ

**See advertisement on page 607**

---

**RYDE**

See **Wight, Isle of**

---

**RYE** East Sussex Map **05** TQ92

★★★64% **Mermaid Inn**

Mermaid St TN31 7EU ☎(0797)223065 Telex no 957141
FAX (0797) 226995

*An historic inn – rebuilt in 1420 and claiming to be one of the oldest in England – retains its original charm in traditionally furnished and beamed lounges where open fires blaze in winter. Bedrooms vary from the grand Elizabethan chamber with its four-poster bed to more compact modern rooms which are nevertheless not devoid of character. A good choice of fresh seasonal produce is served in the restaurant, and hospitable staff create a warm, welcoming atmosphere throughout.*

28rm(21⇠5🖙)3🖪 CTV in 14 bedrooms **T** ✶ (ex guide dogs)
S10% sB&B⇠🖙£64-£70 dB&B⇠🖙£92-£110 🝙
《 CTV 25P nc8yrs *xmas*
**V** ♧ S10% Lunch £14.50-£18.50&alc Dinner £18.50-£21&alc Last dinner 9.15pm
Credit Cards ① ② ③ ④ ⑤

**R**

## ★★ 68% The George

High St TN31 7JP (Forte Hotels) ☎(0797)222114
FAX (0797) 224065

*A coaching inn dating back to 1575 which retains some of its
original features, including the open log fire and oak beams, yet
still offers modern comforts. The bedrooms are well equipped and
many have been tastefully refurbished. The friendly young staff
complete the welcoming atmosphere.*

22⇄♪(2fb)⊬in 6 bedrooms CTV in all bedrooms ® T ✳
sB⇄♪fr£65 dB⇄♪£80-£100 (room only) ♬
9P 9🚗 CFA *xmas*
V ✇ ⊒ ⊬ ✳ Lunch £8.25-£9.25 Dinner fr£13&alc Last dinner
9.30pm
Credit Cards ⃞1 ⃞2 ⃞3 ⃞4 ⃞5

## ★★ 65% Broomhill Lodge

Rye Foreign TN31 7UN (1.5m N on A268) ☎Iden(07978)421
due to change to (0797) 280421

*This refurbished early 19th-century country house has a friendly
relaxing atmosphere. The attractive bedrooms are well equipped
and there is a comfortable lounge with a log fire, a restaurant
offering table d'hôte and à la carte menus of a good standard, plus
some leisure facilities.*

12⇄♪1🛏 CTV in all bedrooms ® T ✖ (ex guide dogs) ✳
sB&B⇄♪£38 dB&B⇄♪£59-£71 ♬
20P ✿ CFA snooker sauna nc5yrs *xmas*
♀ English & French V ✇ ⊒ ✳ Lunch £7.50 Dinner
£11.50&alc Last dinner 9.30pm
Credit Cards ⃞1 ⃞2 ⃞3

## ★ 60% Playden Oasts

Peasmarsh Rd, Playden TN31 7UL ☎(0797)223502

*Standing on the edge of the historic town of Rye, and mentioned in
the Domesday Book, the hotel was used in bygone years for drying
hops, grown in nearby fields, which were used to flavour local ales
and beers. Dating from 1800, it was still in use until 1965, and the
restaurant exhibits the original charm and architecture. The
bedrooms in this small, informal and friendly hotel, are simply
furnished and soundly equipped with modern facilities such as
direct dial telephones, colour televisions and compact en suite
bathrooms.*

5⇄♪Annexe3♪(2fb) CTV in all bedrooms ® T
✖ (ex guide dogs) sB&B⇄♪£20-£35 dB&B⇄♪£40-£60 ♬
20P ✿ CFA *xmas*
♀ English & French V ✇ ⊒ S% Lunch £6-£12alc High tea £4-
£6alc Dinner £8-£15alc Last dinner 9pm
Credit Cards ⃞1 ⃞2 ⃞3 ⃞4 ⃞5 ⃞£

## ✿✿✿✕ *Landgate Bistro*

5-6 Landgate TN31 7LH ☎(0797)222829

*Toni Ferguson-Lees and Nick Parkin have created an interesting
and varied menu changing with the seasons, at this well established
and informal bistro. Among the dishes regularly featured are the
'very fishy stew' served with aïoli and garlic bread, local squid with
white wine, tomatoes and garlic, and pigeon breasts in red wine
sauce. Vegetarians are welcome, there is usually a vegetarian flan,
soups made with a vegetable stock, and several starters that can
also be ordered as a main course. The wine list is well chosen and
reasonably priced, and the small list of after dinner drinks is well
worth considering.*

Closed Sun, Mon, Xmas, 1 wk Jun & 2 wks Oct Lunch not
served
♀ British & French V 34 seats Last dinner 9.30pm ⊁
Credit Cards ⃞1 ⃞2 ⃞3 ⃞5

## SAFFRON WALDEN Essex Map 05 TL53

## ★★ 65% *Saffron*

10-18 High St CB10 1AY ☎(0799)22676 Telex no 81653
FAX (0799) 513979

*A friendly 16th-century inn combining old world charm and
modern comforts, and currently being upgraded by the new owners.
Bedrooms are of varying shape and size, some with low beams. The*

---

*panelled bar is very popular with locals and good bar snacks and
imaginative restaurant menus are available.*

21rm(8⇄8♪)(2fb)1🛏 CTV in all bedrooms ® T
10P
♀ English & French V ✇ Last dinner 9.30pm
Credit Cards ⃞1 ⃞3

## ST AGNES Cornwall & Isles of Scilly Map 02 SW75

## ★★ 64% Rosemundy House

Rosemundy TR5 0UF ☎(087255)2101
Closed 4 Oct-15 Apr

*Delightful country-house style hotel, parts of which date back to
1780, set in 4 acres of wooded gardens close to the village centre.
This is a busy holiday hotel offering exceptional value for money.*

44rm(43⇄♪)(16fb) CTV in all bedrooms ® sB&B⇄♪£25-
£38 dB&B⇄♪£50-£76 (incl dinner)
CTV 50P ✿ ✿ CFA ⌇ (heated) badminton games room
croquet putting
✇ ⊒ ⊬ Bar Lunch £2.50-£4.50 Dinner £11 Last dinner 8pm

## ★★ ♨ 61% Rose in Vale Country House

Rose in Vale, Mithian TR5 0QD ☎(087255)2202
Closed Nov-Feb

*This attractive Georgian house with a modern extension is set in
pleasant grounds within a secluded valley. The bedrooms, though
not particularly spacious, are well equipped and have en-suite
facilities and there is a choice of comfortable lounges.*

17⇄♪(3fb)1🛏 CTV in all bedrooms ® T sB&B⇄♪£33-£41
dB&B⇄♪£60.50-£86 (incl dinner) ♬
CTV 20P ✿ ✿ ⌇ (heated) solarium croquet badminton table
tennis billiards
♀ English & Continental ✇ ⊒ ⊬ Bar Lunch £6.75-£8.50alc
Dinner £15.95&alc Last dinner 8pm
Credit Cards ⃞1 ⃞3

## ★★ 57% *Beach*

Porthtowan TR4 8AE ☎Porthtowan(0209)890228
Closed Jan & last 2 wks Nov

*An hotel in a unique position, overlooking the sandy beach from a
cliffside setting, does consequently involve many downward steps to
its lower public areas. Well equipped modern bedrooms – many
with excellent sea views – are complemented by two lounges, a bar
and a small restaurant offering daily table d'hôte menus of freshly
prepared dishes; personally supervised service is particularly
helpful and friendly. This is an ideal location for sunbathing and
surfing, the hotel steps leading directly onto the beach.*

13rm(7♪)(5fb) CTV in all bedrooms ® T
13P ✿ ✿
♀ English & French V Last dinner 8pm
Credit Cards ⃞1 ⃞2 ⃞3 ⃞5

See advertisement under TRURO

## ★ 67% Sunholme

Goonvrea Rd TR5 0NW ☎(087255)2318 & 2154
Closed Jan-16 Feb

*Panoramic views of the countryside and coastline are given from
this pleasing personally run small hotel. Public areas are
comfortable and well coordinated, bedrooms are neat and compact,
with en suite showers, and the dining room provides honest home
cooking.*

10♪(3fb) TV available ® T ✳ sB&B♪£25-£28 dB&B♪£50-
£56 ♬
CTV 10P ✿ ✿ *xmas*
✇ ⊒ ⊬
Credit Cards ⃞1 ⃞2 ⃞3

Remember to book early for holiday
and bank holiday times.

S

ST ALBANS Hertfordshire Map **04** TL10 ⊙

### ★★★ ❀75% Sopwell House Hotel & Country Club

Cottonmill Ln, Sopwell AL1 2HQ (Best Western)
☎(0727)864477 Telex no 927823 FAX (0727) 44741

*An extended 18th-century mansion set in peaceful grounds has been partly refurbished to provide comfortable public rooms and bedrooms equipped with many modern facilities. The attractive conservatory restaurant serves carefully prepared dishes using fresh produce. A leisure complex is under construction, adding to the good conference facilities.*

84⇨🛏(6fb)22🛏 CTV in all bedrooms ® T sB⇨🛏£64.75-£99.75 dB⇨🛏£74.75-£109.75 (room only) 🛏
Lift ( 175P ❖ CFA ⊠ (heated) snooker sauna solarium gymnasium health & beauty spa steam room whirlpool *xmas*
V ♥ ⌑ ⚄ ✱ Lunch £16.50-£18.50&alc Dinner fr£18.50&alc Last dinner 9.30pm
Credit Cards ① ② ③ ⑤ ⓔ

### ★★★ 71% Noke Thistle

Watford Rd AL2 3DS (2.75m S at junct A405/B4630) (Mount Charlotte (TS)) ☎(0727)54252 Telex no 893834 FAX (0727) 41906

*A popular, well managed hotel conveniently located 2.75 miles south of the town centre, at the A411/B4630 junction, has recently been extended to add a range of new, spacious and very comfortable bedrooms to existing accommodation which, though compact, is nevertheless equipped with every modern facility. The restaurant's new conservatory and cocktail bar overlook attractive gardens, excellent conference facilities are also available.*

111⇨🛏(4fb)⚄in 5 bedrooms CTV in all bedrooms ® T (room only) 🛏
( 150P ❖
♀ International ♥ ⌑ ⚄
Credit Cards ① ② ③ ④ ⑤

### ★★★ 60% St Michael's Manor

Fishpool St AL3 4RY ☎(0727)864444 Telex no 917647 FAX (0727) 48909
Closed 27-30 Dec

*A Grade II listed manor house dating back to 1586 and set in 5 acres of beautifully maintained grounds provides good, friendly, old-fashioned hospitality. Though bedrooms might be considered dated, they are equipped with all modern facilities and bathrooms are gradually being refurbished, while public areas include a charming oak-panelled lounge containing many antique pieces and a spacious bar/lounge looking out onto the gardens.*

22⇨🛏4🛏 CTV in all bedrooms T S10% sB&B⇨🛏£60-£90 dB&B⇨🛏£80-£110
( CTV 80P 🛏 ❖ nc12yrs
♀ English & French V ✱ Lunch £16.50-£17.50&alc Dinner £18.50-£19&alc Last dinner 9pm
Credit Cards ① ② ③ ⑤

---

ST ANDREWS Fife Map **12** NO51

★★★★❀ **ST ANDREWS OLD COURSE HOTEL**

Old Station Rd KY16 9SP (Small Luxury Hotels)
☎(0334)74371
Telex no 76280
FAX (0334) 77668

*This charming hotel overlooking the famous Old Course Links Golf Course has recently been extended and totally refurbished to provide every modern amenity while*

*retaining the warmest traditions of hospitality and comfort. Guests will find a sprig of white heather on the pillow when beds are turned down in the elegant balconied bedrooms, which have luxurious bathrooms with many extras. Public rooms are dignified and beautifully furnished, with a comfortable and intimate library lounge, sumptuous top-floor cocktail bar and delightful conservatory alongside the 17th hole, where afternoon teas consisting of delicious home-baked specialities are served by the ever willing and helpful staff. While the upstairs Grill Room serves a good range of dishes at both lunch and dinner, it is the downstairs restaurant which is this year awarded a rosette for its high standard of cuisine. Among many delectable dishes on the à la carte and table d'hôte menus are the salad of pan-seared foie gras with truffle vinaigrette, poached brill on strips of fennel with a saffron butter sauce and supreme of salmon with scallop mousseline. Sweets are also delicious and the wine list is comprehensive. The hotel also has a very good spa club and almost obligatory golf shop.*

125⇨🛏 CTV in all bedrooms T ✱ sB⇨🛏£92-£169 dB⇨🛏£123-£189 (room only) 🛏
Lift ( 150P ❖ CFA ⊠ (heated) sauna solarium gymnasium health spa jacuzzi
♀ Scottish & French V ♥ ⌑ ⚄ ✱ Lunch £10.50-£12.50&alc Dinner £25-£35&alc Last dinner 10pm
Credit Cards ① ② ③ ⑤ ⓔ

### ★★★★ 60% Rusacks

Pilmour Links KY16 9JQ (Forte Hotels) ☎(0334)74321 FAX (0334) 77896

*Rusacks Hotel occupies a position overlooking the 1st and 18th fairways of the famous Links Golf Course – towards the expanse of beach beyond, and yet is close to the town centre. This makes this well established resort hotel the ideal base for golfers and families. Public areas retain a sense of elegance and the principal lounge offers fine views. Bedrooms provide the expected levels of comfort, with tasteful décor.*

50⇨🛏⚄in 5 bedrooms CTV in all bedrooms ® T ✱ sB⇨🛏£85-£90 dB⇨🛏£120-£145 (room only) 🛏
Lift ( 35P 🛏 CFA sauna solarium *xmas*
V ♥ ⌑ ⚄ ✱ Lunch fr£14.50 High tea £3.75-£9.95 Dinner fr£24.95&alc Last dinner 10pm
Credit Cards ① ② ③ ④ ⑤

### ★★★ 71% St Andrews Golf

40 The Scores KY16 9AS ☎(0334)72611 Telex no 94013267 FAX (0334) 72188

*Within walking distance of the famous golf courses and with fine views out to sea, this family-run hotel and tourist hotel is attractively furbished, with period styling in the restaurant and lounge. The bedrooms, which vary in size, are all well appointed and thoughtfully equipped, front facing rooms are particularly popular. Service throughout is friendly and attentive.*

23⇨🛏(10fb)1🛏 CTV in all bedrooms ® T sB&B⇨🛏£58.50-£68 dB&B⇨🛏£92-£120 🛏
Lift ( 6P CFA sauna solarium *xmas*
♀ Scottish & French V ♥ ⌑ ⚄ Lunch £12 High tea £12 Dinner £20.50&alc Last dinner 9.30pm
Credit Cards ① ② ③ ④ ⑤ ⓔ

### ★★★ ❀68% Rufflets Country House

Strathkinness Low Rd KY16 9TX ☎(0334)72594 FAX (0334) 78703
(Rosette awarded for dinner only)

*A well managed, family-run hotel peacefully set in 10 acres of award winning grounds and gardens just 1.5 miles west of the town. Spacious public rooms are comfortably furnished and look out over the garden. Attractive fabrics have been used to good effect in the individually decorated bedrooms; all tastefully appointed and well equipped. The Garden Restaurant enjoys a*

S

*sound local reputation, and the emphasis is on Scottish dishes prepared from the best local produce. The table d'hôte menu is changed daily and reflects seasonal availability of the raw ingredients.*

17⇆♠Annexe3⇆♠(2fb)1⚅⊬in 5 bedrooms CTV in all bedrooms ⓡ **T** ✘ (ex guide dogs) S10% sB&B⇆♠£50-£65 dB&B⇆♠£100-£130 ❧

℄ 50P 2⚅ (£1 per night) ⇔ ❊ CFA putting ◑ *xmas*

**V** ♡ ⊬ S10% Lunch £11-£14 Dinner £19.50-£21&alc Last dinner 9.30pm

Credit Cards ①②③⑤

★★★62% **Scores**

76 The Scores KY16 9BB (Best Western) ☎(0334)72451
FAX (0334) 73947
Closed 24-27 Dec

*Close to the famous golf course and enjoying views over the beach, this hotel is popular with the golfing fraternity, tourists and business travellers. In addition to the restaurant there is a very popular coffee shop, both offer good value.*

30⇆♠(1fb) CTV in all bedrooms ⓡ **T** sB&B⇆♠£42-£68 dB&B⇆♠fr£70 ❧

Lift ℄ 10P ⇔ ❊ CFA

♥ English & French **V** ♡ ⊵ ✱ Lunch fr£7.50alc Dinner £16-£22&alc Last dinner 9.30pm

Credit Cards ①②③④⑤

★★★67% **Ardgowan**

2 Playfair Ter KY16 9HX (Consort) ☎(0334)72970
FAX (0334)78380
Closed 25 Dec-15 Jan RS Nov-24 Dec & 16 Jan-Apr

*A wide range of very reasonably priced dishes is available from 6.30pm in the attractive dining room of this family-run hotel, and bar meals are served in the downstairs bar.* ⓡ

13rm(11⇆♠)(2fb) CTV in all bedrooms ⓡ sB&Bfr£20 sB&B⇆♠£27.50-£42 dB&B⇆♠£45-£62

→

**S**

CTV
♀ Scottish & French **V** Bar Lunch £7.35-£10.50alc Dinner £7.85-£17.50alc Last dinner 9.30pm
Credit Cards ①③

★★❀66% **Parklands Hotel & Restaurant**
Kinburn Castle, Double Dykes Rd KY16 9DS ☎(0334)73620

*A period mansion located on the west side of the town, opposite Kinburn Park but only minutes' walk from the town centre, offers plainly decorated but well equipped bedrooms and a small cocktail bar. The main emphasis is on food, modern-style dishes being soundly based on the best of fresh Scottish produce. A typical 3-course dinner might include a starter of Fresh Sole and Scallops wrapped in Filo Pastry, oven-baked and served on a rich Lobster and Cream Sauce, followed by Beef Bordelaise accompanied by seasonal vegetables or a crisp salad, with a delicious Fresh Blueberry Vanilla Pot as dessert; additional courses can be taken, the price varying accordingly. Sunday dinners are limited to a cold buffet.*

15rm(8⇪1♠)(2fb)⊬in 3 bedrooms CTV in all bedrooms ® T ✘ (ex guide dogs) ✱ sB&Bfr£26 sB&B⇪♠fr£38.50 dB&Bfr£47.50 dB&B⇪♠fr£64 ⊟
15P
♀ French **V** ✿ ⊬ ✱ Lunch £1.50-£9 Dinner fr£15&alc Last dinner 8.30pm
Credit Cards ①③

★★64% **Russell Hotel**
26 The Scores KY16 9AS ☎(0334)73447 FAX (0334) 78851
Closed 25 Dec-mid Jan
*Small family-run hotel with views of the sea.*
9rm(1⇪6♠)(1fb) CTV in all bedrooms ® T ✘ (ex guide dogs) sB&B£25-£40 sB&B⇪♠£25-£50 dB&B£40-£55 dB&B⇪♠£55-£65 ⊟
CTV ⅌ ⊞
♀ Scottish & French **V** ✿ ⊬ ✱ Bar Lunch £1.75-£6.95alc Dinner £13.75-£16.75alc Last dinner 9.30pm
Credit Cards ①②③ ⓔ

❀✕**The Grange Inn**
Grange Rd KY16 8LJ ☎(0334)72670 FAX (0334) 78703
*An attractive country inn on the coast road just outside the town centre features a restaurant with natural stone walls, an intimate atmosphere and charming service. Chef Simon Lynch cooks in an unshowy, traditional style, with a particular fondness for fish. A choice of six starters, main courses and desserts is supplemented by a no-choice middle course and separate cheese course; coffee with home-made petits fours is included in the price. Particularly enjoyable dishes are a starter of pan-fried slices of huss served in a light, creamy, curried sauce with a garnish of grapes and a dessert of gratin of pear, nectarine apple and raspberries under a sabayon sauce topped with almonds. The wine list is extensive; a half bottle of house wine is £3.75.*
Closed Mon Lunch not served Tue-Fri
**V** 34 seats ✱ Lunch £10-£12 Dinner £18-£21 Last lunch 2pm Last dinner 9.30pm 20 P ⊬
Credit Cards ①②③⑤

ST ANNES
See **Lytham St Annes**

ST ASAPH Clwyd Map **06** SJ07

★★★68% **Talardy Park**
The Roe LL17 0HY ☎(0745)584957 FAX (0745) 584385
*A popular and busy hotel, conveniently situated at the A55/A525 junction on the outskirts of the town, features spaciously attractive public areas and comfortable well equipped bedrooms which are equally suitable for travelling business people or tourists.*
11⇪♠(1fb)1⊞ CTV in all bedrooms ® T ✘ (ex guide dogs) ✱ sB⇪♠£41.12 dB⇪♠£49.35 (room only)

《 CTV 120P ⊞ ✿ ☙
**V** ✿ ⊡ ⊬ ✱ Lunch £7.50 Dinner £12&alc Last dinner 10pm
Credit Cards ①②③⑤

★★★62% **Oriel House**
Upper Denbigh Rd LL17 0LW ☎(0745)582716
FAX (0745) 582716
*This former school set in its own grounds just south of the town has attractive public areas and modern well-equipped bedrooms equally suited to family holidaymakers and business people, plus extensive conference and function facilities.*
19⇪♠(1fb)1⊞ CTV in all bedrooms ® T ✱ sB&B⇪♠£40-£55 dB&B⇪♠£66-£77 ⊟
200P ✿ CFA ♪ snooker
♀ English & French **V** ✿ ⊡ ✱ Lunch fr£15&alc High tea £1.80-£13.85 Dinner £15.50-£24.60alc Last dinner 9.45pm
Credit Cards ①②③⑤ ⓔ

★★67% **Plas Elwy Hotel & Restaurant**
The Roe LL17 0LT (Exec Hotel) ☎(0745)582263 & 582089
FAX (0745) 583864
Closed 26-31 Dec
*Conveniently situated by the A55 on the edge of town, this small and pleasant privately owned hotel has a popular restaurant and well equipped bedrooms which include six good quality new rooms in a purpose-built annexe.*
7⇪♠Annexe6⇪♠(2fb)1⊞ CTV in all bedrooms ® T ✘ (ex guide dogs) sB&B⇪♠£38-£43 dB&B⇪♠£52-£59 ⊟
CTV 28P ⊞
**V** ✿ ⊬ Sunday Lunch £8.50 Dinner £12.50&alc Last dinner 10pm
Credit Cards ①②③⑤ ⓔ

ST AUBIN
See **Jersey** under **Channel Islands**

ST AUSTELL Cornwall & Isles of Scilly Map **02** SX05

★★★★61% **Carlyon Bay**
Sea Rd, Carlyon Bay PL25 3RD (Brend) ☎Par(072681)2304
Telex no 42551 FAX (072681) 4938
*Well established, and popular with businessmen, family parties and tourists alike, the hotel is set in 250 acres of mature grounds and gardens; recreational activities are extensive, an attractive indoor and outdoor leisure complex including the adjacent Carlyon Golf Club. Traditionally styled public areas offer a choice of lounges which, like the restaurant, command unspoiled sea views, and though bedrooms vary in size (those at the front being more spacious) they have recently been refurbished and equipped with a good range of modern facilities which includes satellite television. Hospitable staff offer willing help in all departments, and room service is available.*
73⇪♠(14fb) CTV in all bedrooms ® T ✘ (ex guide dogs) sB&B⇪♠£64-£79 dB&B⇪♠£120-£182 ⊟
Lift 《 CTV 100P 1🅿 (£8 per day) ⊞ ✿ ☒ (heated) ⌆ (heated) ⏹ 18 ♪ (hard) snooker sauna solarium spa bath table tennis putting ♫ ♨ *xmas*
♀ English & French **V** ✿ ⊡ Lunch £11&alc Dinner £18&alc Last dinner 9pm
Credit Cards ①②③⑤ ⓔ

★★★63% **Cliff Head**
Sea Rd, Carlyon Bay PL25 3RB (2m E off A390)
☎Par(072681)2345 FAX (072681) 5571
*Situated close to the beach this modernised hotel provides comfortable public areas and well-equipped bedrooms.*
48rm(30⇪4♠)(10fb) CTV in all bedrooms ® T ✱ sB&B⇪♠£32-£35.25 dB&B⇪♠£54-£62 ⊟
《 CTV 60P 8🅿 ✿ CFA ⌆ (heated) sauna solarium gymnasium pool table *xmas*

---

S

---

S

V ✿ ⚘ ⚲ Lunch £5.50-£12 High tea £1.50 Dinner £12&alc
Last dinner 9.30pm
Credit Cards ① ② ③ ⑤

★★★ 60% *Porth Avallen*
Sea Rd, Carlyon Bay PL25 3SG ☎Par(072681)2802 & 2183
FAX (072681) 7097
Closed Xmas & New Year

*Occupying a prominent position overlooking Carlyon Bay, and
privately run on traditional lines, this hotel offers a choice of
bedrooms furnished in different styles. Space is restricted in the
dining room, but lounges are comfortable and the bar and function
room are popular with local societies; a newly appointed chef
presents a 6-course table d'hôte menu.*
23rm(18⇔1⋔)(2fb)2⚘ CTV in all bedrooms ⓇT
✠ (ex guide dogs)
⟮ CTV 50P 2⚘ ✿
♡ English & French V ✿ ⚘ Last dinner 8.30pm
Credit Cards ① ② ③ ⑤

★★ ❀⚘ 75% **Boscundle Manor**
Tregrehan PL25 3RL (2m E off A390) ☎Par(072681)3557
FAX (072681) 4997
Closed mid Oct-Etr

*A 16th-century manor house, lovingly furnished with some
impressive antiques, has been skilfully extended to provide a varied
choice of well equipped bedrooms. An improved bar, fireside lounge
and tasteful dining room have been augmented by a conservatory
breakfast room overlooking the garden, and the Wheal Eliza
Woodland, now being developed, contains 2 golf practice greens.
Cordial hosts provide personal service and individual attention.*
7⇔⋔Annexe3⇔⋔ CTV in all bedrooms ⓇT S%
sB&B⇔⋔£65-£80 dB&B⇔⋔£110
15P ⚘ ✿ ⊡ (heated) ▶ gymnasium croquet practice golf
course
♡ International Dinner £20 Last dinner 9pm
Credit Cards ① ③

★★ 61% White Hart
Church St PL25 4AT (St Austell Brewery) ☎(0726)72100
Closed 25 & 26 Dec

*A traditional town centre hostelry dating from the early 18th
century. A relaxed, informal atmosphere pervades the spacious
lobby and 2 attractive bars. Bedrooms vary in size and are prettily
decorated and well equipped. Check about parking arrangements
when booking.*
18⇔⋔ CTV in all bedrooms ⓇT ✠ (ex guide dogs) ✷
sB&B⇔⋔£40-£45 dB&B⇔⋔£65-£75 ☐
CFA
V ✿ ⚘ ✷ Lunch £7-£8 Dinner £12-£13 Last dinner 8.30pm
Credit Cards ① ② ③ ⑤ ⓔ

★ 65% Selwood House
60 Alexandra Rd PL25 4QN ☎(0726)65707 FAX (0726) 68951
11⇔⋔(2fb) CTV in all bedrooms Ⓡ sB&B⇔⋔£31-£35
dB&B⇔⋔£59-£66
CTV 12P CFA
V ✿ ⚘ ✷
Credit Cards ① ② ③ ⑤

★★ 65% **Buccleuch Arms**
The Green TD6 0EW ☎(0835)22243 FAX (0835) 23965
*A red sandstone hotel on the A68 beside the village cricket ground
features well appointed bedrooms and a comfortable lounge; a new
function room enhances previous conference facilities, there is a
secluded garden, and arrangements can be made for guests who
want to hunt, shoot or fish.*
19rm(17⇔⋔)(1fb) CTV in all bedrooms ⓇT ✷ sB&B£28-£34
sB&B⇔⋔£34 dB&B£60 dB&B⇔⋔£62 ☐
50P 2⚘ ✿ CFA *xmas*

♡ International V ✿ ⚘ ✷ ✷ Lunch £6.70-£8.70&alc Dinner
£8.70-£13.70&alc Last dinner 10pm
Credit Cards ① ② ③ ⑤ ⓔ

See Jersey **under** Channel Islands

★★ 66% **Forge Restaurant & Motel**
SA33 4NA ☎(0994)230300 FAX (0994) 230300
Closed 25 & 26 Dec

*A popular hotel standing beside the A40 a mile east of the village
offers very well furnished and equipped accommodation in a
modern bedroom annexe which lies well back from the road; the
restaurant is open all day for snacks, teas and good value à la carte
meals, while an adjacent leisure area provides a swimming pool
and small gymnasium.*
Annexe18⇔⋔(4fb) CTV in all bedrooms ⓇT ✷
sB&B⇔⋔£33 dB&B⇔⋔£55
80P ⚘ ✿ ⊡ (heated) sauna gymnasium
♡ Mainly grills V ✿ ⚘ ✷ ✷ Lunch £5.50-£14alc
Credit Cards ① ③ ⓔ

★★ 63% *Tufted Duck*
AB4 5YS ☎Inverallochy(03465)2481 2482/3 FAX (03465)2475
*A friendly family-run hotel with commanding sea views. Public
rooms are comfortably appointed in the modern style, and the
extensive à la carte menu in the bright restaurant offers a varied
choice. Bedrooms have sturdy fitted units and are well equipped.*
18⇔⋔(4fb) CTV in all bedrooms ⓇT
⟮ 50P ✿ ✦
♡ Scottish, French & Italian V ✿ ⚘ ✷ Last dinner 9.30pm
Credit Cards ① ② ③ ⑤

S

## ST DAVID'S Dyfed Map **02** SM72

### ★★★❀ ♨64% **Warpool Court**
SA62 6BN ☎(0437)720300 FAX (0437) 720676

*This professionally run hotel was once the cathedral choir school. Set in attractive lawns and overlooking the sea, it features a unique collection of 3,000 wall tiles which are positioned throughout the house. Bedrooms and public rooms are comfortably appointed and food is consistently good, with local produce used wherever possible.*

25⇨♠(3fb) CTV in all bedrooms ® **T** sB&B⇨♠£45-£60 dB&B⇨♠£80-£134 ℝ

100P ❀ CFA ⬛ (heated) ♫ (hard) sauna gymnasium croquet pool table childrens play area *xmas*

♀ English & French **V** ✿ ⬚ ✴ Lunch £12.50-£23 High tea £5.50-£7.50 Dinner £23-£28&alc Last dinner 9.15pm
Credit Cards ①②③④⑤

### ★★64% **St Non's**
SA62 6 (Welsh Rarebits) ☎(0437)720239 FAX (0437) 721839

*Equally popular with holidaymakers and business travellers, this hotel provides spacious public areas, good, comfortable bedrooms and attentively friendly service.*

24⇨(5fb) CTV in all bedrooms ® **T**
60P ♫

♀ International **V** ✿ ⬚ Last dinner 9pm
Credit Cards ①②③

### ★★60% **Old Cross**
Cross Square SA62 6SP ☎(0437)720387
Closed Nov-Feb

*Set right in the centre of this lovely city, this creeper-clad inn is just a stone's throw from the cathedral. The bedrooms, although on the small side, are equipped with modern facilities and there is a choice of relaxing lounges.*

16⇨♠(5fb)✗in 3 bedrooms CTV in all bedrooms ® **T** ✈ (ex guide dogs) sB&B⇨♠£25-£30 dB&B⇨♠£50-£60 ℝ
18P ♨

♀ European & Oriental **V** ✿ Bar Lunch £1-£6.50alc Dinner £13&alc Last dinner 8.30pm
Credit Cards ①③ ⓔ

## ST FILLANS Tayside *Perthshire* Map **11** NN62

### ★★★❀65% **The Four Seasons Hotel**
PH6 2NF ☎(076485)333
Closed mid Nov-Feb
(Rosette awarded for dinner only)

*Genuine hospitality together with enjoyable food and superb views are all part of the appeal of this family-run holiday hotel on the fringe of the picturesque village. Bedrooms are mostly spacious and several of them overlook Loch Earn. There are a number of small lounges which invite relaxation, and a snug bar where one may enjoy a pre-dinner drink. Chef Andrew Scott makes full use of fresh produce, much of it local, to produce imaginative dishes reflecting Scottish flavours.*

12⇨♠(2fb) CTV in all bedrooms ® **T** dB&B⇨♠£56-£78
25P ♨ CFA

♀ International **V** ✿ ⬚ ✗ ✴ Lunch £11.50&alc Dinner £18-£22alc Last dinner 9.30pm
Credit Cards ①②③ ⓔ

## ST HELENS Merseyside Map **07** SJ59 ◐

### ★★★67% **Forte Posthouse**
Lodge Ln, Newton-Le-Willows WA12 0JG (Forte Hotels)
☎Wigan(0942)717878 Telex no 677672 FAX (0942) 718419
(For full entry see Haydock)

## ST HELIER
See Jersey **under** Channel Islands

## ST IVES **Cambridgeshire** Map **04** TL37

### ★★★64% **Slepe Hall**
Ramsey Rd PE17 4RB ☎(0480)63122 FAX (0480) 300706
Closed 25-26 Dec

*This small, comfortable hotel in an attractive ivy-clad building of 1854 set in its own grounds offers friendly professional services. The recently refurbished bedrooms are delightful and there is a choice of restaurant menus and bar meals.*

16rm(15⇨♠)(1fb)1▦ CTV in all bedrooms ® **T** sB&B⇨♠fr£56 dB&B⇨♠fr£68 ℝ
70P 1🐾 CFA

**V** ✿ ⬚ ✗ Lunch fr£12.95&alc Dinner fr£12.95&alc Last dinner 9.45pm
Credit Cards ①②③⑤

### ★★★58% **Dolphin**
Bridge Foot, London Rd PE17 4EP ☎(0480)66966
FAX (0480) 495597

*Close to the town centre, yet enjoying fine views over the surrounding countryside from its riverside location, this purpose-built modern hotel offers comfortable accommodation, a spacious restaurant and efficient service. Ample car parking facilities also make it popular with non-residents, particularly for the cold lunchtime buffet. Public areas can be limited but in fine weather the River Bar is extended by picnic benches outside which makes it popular with locals.*

31⇨♠Annexe16⇨♠ CTV in all bedrooms ® **T** ℝ
(80P ❀ CFA ♫

♀ English & French **V** ✿ ⬚ ✴ Lunch £15-£20&alc Dinner £15-£20&alc Last dinner 9.30pm
Credit Cards ①②③⑤

### ★★★64% **St Ives Motel**
London Rd PE17 4EX ☎(0480)63857 FAX (0480) 492027
RS 25 & 26 Dec

*Situated on the outskirts of town, yet with easy access to the centre and the A604, the motel-style accommodation offered here is fully en suite and pleasantly furnished in light woods and pastel shades. The bar areas are busy and the atmosphere friendly; stable management ensuring a smoothly running operation.*

16⇨♠(2fb) CTV in all bedrooms ® **T** sB&B⇨♠£33-£41.50 dB&B⇨♠£51.30-£60.50 ℝ
80P 🐾 ❀ CFA

♀ English & French **V** ✿ ⬚ ✴ Lunch £9-£12.50 Dinner fr£12.50&alc Last dinner 9.30pm
Credit Cards ①②③⑤ ⓔ

## ST IVES **Cornwall & Isles of Scilly** Map **02** SW54

### ★★★68% **Porthminster**
The Terrace TR26 2BN (Best Western) ☎Penzance(0736)795221
FAX (0736) 797043

*Set in a prominent position with commanding views of St Ives Bay and just a short step from the beach, this friendly holiday hotel has undergone significant refurbishment over recent times. Public rooms are spacious and elegant and there is a new indoor leisure complex.*

49⇨♠(11fb) CTV in all bedrooms ® **T** sB&B⇨♠£45-£53 dB&B⇨♠£90-£106 ℝ
Lift ( CTV 40P 3🐾 ❀ ⬛ (heated) ⬚ (heated) sauna solarium gymnasium ⬚ *xmas*

♀ English & French ✿ Lunch £18.25-£27alc Dinner £16.50&alc Last dinner 8.30pm
Credit Cards ①②③④⑤ ⓔ

A rosette means exceptional standards of cuisine.

### ★★★ ❀64% Garrack

Higher Ayr TR26 3AA ☎Penzance(0736)796199
FAX (0736) 798955

*An intimate country house style of hotel in 2 acres of grounds, with commanding views over Porthmeor beach and St Ives Bay. Most of the rooms in the house are in keeping with the style of the building, and while additional rooms in the wing are rather functional, they are large and have glorious sea views. Public rooms are restricted but cosy, and Olivers Restaurant, with Graham Jones in charge of the kitchen, promotes worthy food standards. Seafood, including fresh lobster available from the hotel's own storage, is featured daily, with dishes such as breast of pigeon and magret of duck with artichokes to placate the carnivores.*

16⇨🛏Annexe2rm(3fb) CTV in 19 bedrooms **T** ✳
sB&B⇨🛏£31-£35 dB&B⇨🛏£62-£92 🍴
CTV 30P 🚗 ❀ 🖃 (heated) sauna solarium *xmas*
♀ English & French ❀ ⚓ Sunday Lunch £7 High tea £5
Dinner £14.50&alc Last dinner 8.30pm
Credit Cards 1 2 3 4 5 £

### ★★★ 61% *Chy-an-Drea*

The Terrace TR26 2BP (Consort) ☎Penzance(0736)795076
Closed Dec-12 Mar

*In a prominent position close to the beach and with commanding views over St Ives bay, this family-run hotel provides good value for money in a friendly environment. Public rooms are bright and comfortable, and there is a small leisure complex for the use of residents. Bedrooms vary in size and singles at the front are compact, but have patio/balconies giving glorious views across the beach and sea. A set menu offers traditional cuisine.*

33⇨🛏(4fb) CTV in all bedrooms ® **T**
5P 20🚗 🚗 jacuzzi fitness equipment nc5yrs
♀ English & French ❀ Last dinner 8.30pm
Credit Cards 1 2 3 5

**S**

**★★★58% *Carbis Bay***
Carbis Bay TR26 2NP ☎Penzance(0736)795311
Closed Dec-Etr
*A large detached hotel in a prominent position overlooking its own private beach and the Bay. Recently upgraded bedrooms offer modern standards of comfort, with friendly service from local staff.*
32rm(30⇌♠)(9fb)1⊞ CTV in all bedrooms ® T
CTV 200P 6⊠ ❊ ⇌ (heated) ♩ snooker private beach ♫
☋ English & Continental ♈ ⊡ Last dinner 8.30pm
Credit Cards 1 2 3 5

**★★66% *Pedn-Olva***
The Warren TR26 2EA ☎Penzance(0736)796222
*Good work continues at this charming holiday hotel, perched right at the water's edge on a rocky promontory with unrestricted views over St Ives Bay and the harbour. Personally managed, and with a friendly atmosphere, the hotel offers comfortable public rooms, a bright dining room with good menus and hours of service normally associated with hotels of a higher classification. Facilities include an outdoor swimming pool, sun terraces and a terrace restaurant for outdoor dining. Bedrooms are compact but spotlessly clean and equipped to a modern standard.*
20⇌♠Annexe4rm(2fb) CTV in all bedrooms ®
☾ ⊭ ⇌ (heated) ♫
☋ English & French V ♈ ⊡
Credit Cards 1 3

**★★65% Boskerris**
Boskerris Rd, Carbis Bay TR26 2NQ ☎Penzance(0736)795295
FAX (0736) 798632
Closed Nov-Xmas & 29 Dec-Etr RS Xmas
*This well-appointed country house-style hotel enjoys glorious coastal views. Meals are carefully cooked and well balanced.*
13rm(11⇌♠)Annexe5⇌♠(4fb) CTV in all bedrooms ® T ✱
sB&B£33-£41.61 dB&B⇌♠£79.40-£96 (incl dinner) ⊟
CTV 20P ⊞ ❊ ⇌ (heated) putting games room *xmas*
☋ English & French V ♈ ⊡ ⊁ Bar Lunch £1.10-£2.50 Dinner £15 Last dinner 8.30pm
Credit Cards 1 3 5 £

**★★64% Skidden House**
Skidden Hill TR26 2DU ☎Penzance(0736)796899 & 798619
RS Jan-Feb
*This 16th-century building, tucked away in the narrow streets of the town and close to the beaches, has had a colourful history: a transit point for Royalists in the Civil War and after the Restoration a brothel. Now a cosy, personally run hotel and restaurant offering compact but spotlessly clean and well equipped bedrooms. The intimate restaurant serves a good range of home-cooked dishes. Breakfast is quite a treat, particularly the Continental beakfast with home-made brioche. Access is a little difficult but limited parking is available.*
7♠ CTV in all bedrooms ® T sB&B♠£32-£37.50 dB&B♠£60-£75 ⊟
CTV 7P ⊞ *xmas*
☋ English & French V ⊁ Bar Lunch £9-£15alc Dinner £17.50-£19&alc Last dinner 9.30pm
Credit Cards 1 2 3 5 £

**★★62% Cornwallis**
Headland Rd, Carbis Bay TR26 2NR ☎Penzance(0736)795294
*This friendly, family holiday hotel enjoys an elevated position commanding an unrestricted outlook across Carbis Bay to the sea and coastline beyond. Personally run by enthusiastic proprietors, it offers well appointed bedrooms in a variety of sizes, the majority having fine views, and a terraced garden containing an attractive swimming pool.*
12rm(7⇌3♠)(3fb) CTV in all bedrooms ® ✗ ✱ sB&B£21.15-£29.03 sB&B⇌♠£22.32-£30.21 dB&B£42.30-£58.06 dB&B⇌♠£44.64-£60.42 ⊟
12P ⊞ ❊ ⇌ (heated) pool table
V ♈ ⊡ ⊁ ✱ Bar Lunch 95p-£2.50 Dinner £7-£9 Last dinner 7.30pm
Credit Cards 1 3

**★★59% Chy-an-Dour**
Trelyon Av TR26 2AD ☎Penzance(0736)796436
FAX (0736) 795772
*Friendly, personally run holiday hotel in a peaceful setting with superb views of St Ives and the bay. Public rooms are comfortable and the bedrooms, though compact, are soundly equipped.*
23⇌♠(2fb) CTV in all bedrooms ® T ✗ (ex guide dogs)
sB&B⇌♠£28.50-£31.50 dB&B⇌♠£64-£80 (incl dinner) ⊟
Lift CTV 23P ❊ CFA *xmas*
☋ English & Continental V ♈ ⊁ ✱ Bar Lunch £1-£2.50 Dinner £9-£11.50 Last dinner 8pm
Credit Cards 1 3 £

**★★59% St Uny**
Carbis Bay TR26 2NQ ☎Penzance(0736)795011
Closed early Oct-mid Apr
*A castle-style family hotel set in 2 acres of grounds and gardens close to the beach with commanding views over Carbis Bay. Public rooms include a spacious open plan lounge, a cosy television lounge, a congenial bar and a pleasant dining room where wholesome cooking is served. Bedrooms tend to be a little functional although the views compensate to a degree.*
30rm(14⇌5♠)(4fb)1⊞ ✗ sB&B£27-£31 sB&B⇌♠£33-£40 dB&B£54-£62 dB&B⇌♠£66-£80 (incl dinner) ⊟
CTV 28P 4⊠ ❊ snooker table tennis 9 hole putting green nc5yrs
V ♈ ⊡ ⊁ Dinner £12 Last dinner 8pm
Credit Cards 1 3

**★★58% Chy-an-Albany**
Albany Ter TR26 2BS ☎Penzance(0736)796759
Closed Nov-Mar RS Xmas
*A friendly family holiday hotel with a pleasant informal atmosphere. Most bedrooms have been refurbished by the enthusiastic new owners, these are bright and comfortable, and several have splendid views over the town and St Ives Bay.*
40rm(8⇌18♠)(13fb) CTV in all bedrooms ®
✗ (ex guide dogs) sB&B£25-£37 sB&B⇌♠£28-£40 dB&B£50-£74 dB&B⇌♠£56-£80 (incl dinner) ⊟
35P *xmas*
V ♈ ⊡ ⊁ ✱ Bar Lunch £1.50-£4 Dinner £10 Last dinner 7.30pm
Credit Cards 1 2 3 £

**★55% Dunmar**
Pednolver Ter TR26 2EL ☎Penzance(0736)796117
*A small, family-run holiday hotel, close to the town centre and beaches, in an elevated position with views over St Ives bay. Compact bedrooms are modestly furnished but many have modern en suites. The atmosphere is informal and the cosy dining room offers traditional dishes from a set menu.*
17rm(4⇌7♠)(7fb) CTV in 15 bedrooms TV in 2 bedrooms ®
✱ sB&B£14.50-£22 sB&B⇌♠£16.50-£24 dB&B£29-£44 dB&B⇌♠£33-£48 ⊟
CTV 20P
♈ ⊡ ⊁
Credit Cards 1 3 £

**ST LAWRENCE**

See Jersey under Channel Islands

**ST LAWRENCE**

See Wight, Isle of

For key to symbols in English see the bookmark.

S

## ST LEONARDS Dorset Map **04** SU10

★★★67% **St Leonards Hotel**
BH24 2NP (Lansbury) ☎(0425)471220 Telex no 418215
FAX (0425) 480274

*Clever planning has made good use of restricted space in the pleasant interior of this modern, purpose-built hotel on the A31. Its well decorated, comfortable (and, for the most part, spacious) accommodation is well equipped, and no smoking rooms are available. The small lounge areas and bar are supplemented by a popular pub attached to the hotel – common ground for residents and locals. Service throughout is friendly and helpful, guests of every kind being warmly welcomed though trade is predominantly commercial.*

33🖇🏋(4fb)1📺🕿in 5 bedrooms CTV in all bedrooms ® T ✠
sB&B🖇🏋fr£75 dB&B🖇🏋fr£88 🏤
( 250P ✿ sauna gymnasium
🍴 European V 🕏 🕏 Lunch fr£12&alc Dinner fr£12&alc Last dinner 10pm
Credit Cards 1 2 3 5

## ST LEONARDS-ON-SEA

See Hastings & St Leonards

## ST MARGARET'S AT CLIFFE  Kent Map **05** TR34

❀ ✕✕ **Wallets Court**
West Cliffe CT15 6EW ☎Dover(0304)852424
FAX (0304) 853430

*Chris and Lea Oakley run this popular restaurant in a restored Jacobean farmhouse in a quiet location between Tunbridge Wells and Dover. During the week there is a set 3-course dinner, and on Saturdays (booking essential) they branch out into a 5-course gourmet dinner, which could be described as home cooking at its very best. Terrines are Chris's speciality and particularly recommended on the inspection visit was the Kentish venison*

*terrine served with Cumberland sauce. The loin of pork with onion sauce was also praised and the marmalade pudding with orange sauce was described as 'divine'.*
Closed Sun & Xmas
Dinner not served Sun & Mon
🍴 English & French 40 seats Dinner £18.50-£25 Last dinner 9pm 30 P 🕏
Credit Cards 1 3

## ST MARGARET'S HOPE

See Orkney

## ST MARTIN

See Guernsey **under** Channel Islands

## ST MARY CHURCH

See Torquay

## ST MARY'S

See Scilly, Isles of

## ST MAWES  Cornwall & Isles of Scilly Map **02** SW83

★★★61% **Idle Rocks**
Tredenham Rd TR2 5AN ☎(0326)270771 FAX (0326) 270062
*Superbly situated right on the water's edge, this hotel has excellent views over the sea. Hotel bedrooms have been extensively upgraded and individually furnished, and the service is particularly helpful and well managed. The standard of cuisine continues to improve, and the service is particularly helpful and well managed. Future plans include more bedroom improvements, upgrading and continued development.*
17🖇🏋Annexe6🖇🏋(6fb) CTV in all bedrooms ® T
sB&B🖇🏋£20-£48 dB&B🖇🏋£40-£96 🏤
🎿 🚲 xmas

★ ★ ★

# THE CARBIS BAY HOTEL

## CARBIS BAY, ST IVES, CORNWALL TR26 2NP
### Telephone 0736-795311

Ideally situated by our own beach. Beautiful views across St Ives Bay. 28 rooms, most with private bathroom, all with Colour Television, radio, intercom and baby listening service.
Holiday flats also available.
Excellent English and French cuisine.
Renowned for our superb selection of wines — definitely the hotel for lovers of fine wines. Heated swimming pool, sheltered sunbathing area.
Good centre for walking, riding, surfing and sight seeing.
One mile from West Cornwall Golf Club.

Open Easter to November.
Special terms for early and late season bookings.
Please write or phone for our colour brochure.
Resident Proprietor Mr M W Baker.

♔ English & Continental **V** ♦ ⚓ ✗ Sunday Lunch £9.95
Dinner £14-£23alc Last dinner 9.30pm
Credit Cards 1 2 3 5 £

**★★❀71%, *Rising Sun***
TR2 5DJ (St Austell Brewery) ☎(0326)270233
*This popular and well managed waterside inn offers well equipped
and attractive compact bedrooms and friendly service. The dining
room is elegant and there is a well furnished cocktail bar. The good
standards of cooking are complemented by an excellent wine list,
and freshly prepared lunch-time bar meals are served on the front
patio.*
12rm(9⇔)✗in all bedrooms CTV in all bedrooms ®
6P ⏍ nc10 yrs
♔ English, French & Italian ♦ ⚓ Last dinner 9pm
Credit Cards 1 2 3
**See advertisement under ST AUSTELL**

**★★57%, St Mawes**
The Seafront TR2 5DW ☎(0326)270266
Closed Dec & Jan
*Owned by Mr and Mrs Burrows for many years now, this seafront
hotel, with lovely views out across the harbour, offers simple
accommodation including 2 rooms with balconies. Public areas are
full of character, with a narrow, beamed bar and a partially
panelled dining room.*
7rm(5⇔) CTV in all bedrooms ® ✳ S10% sB&B⇔£40-£48
dB&B⇔£70-£88 (incl dinner) ⛟
✗ ⏍ nc5yrs
♔ English & French **V** ♦ ✳ Lunch £9.50-£14alc Dinner £15-
£23alc Last dinner 8.15pm
Credit Cards 1 3

---

ST MAWGAN Cornwall & Isles of Scilly Map **02** SW86

**★★71% Dalswinton**
TR8 4EZ ☎(0637)860385
*A fine Victorian house, overlooking this charming village from a
commanding position, has been carefully converted into an hotel of
character, with a variety of small public rooms and comfortable,
well equipped bedrooms. The hotel also boasts a spacious, well-
tended garden and a heated outdoor swimming pool which is
available for guests' use during the warmer months.*
9⇔♠(4fb) CTV in all bedrooms ® sB&B⇔♠£22.50-£30
dB&B⇔♠£45-£60 (incl dinner) ⛟
CTV 15P ⏍ ✳ ⌣ (heated) ♨ xmas
♔ English & Continental ♦ ⚓ ✗ ✳ Bar Lunch £1.45-£3.95
High tea fr£1.70 Dinner £8.50 Last dinner 9pm
Credit Cards 1 3

---

ST MELLION Cornwall & Isles of Scilly Map **02** SX36

**★★★68%, St Mellion**
St Mellion Golf & County Club PL12 6SD
☎Liskeard(0579)50101 FAX (0579) 50116
Closed Xmas
*With its very good leisure facilities, this fine Golf and Country
Club has steadily improved the quality of the accommodation.
Service is well managed and helpful. The establishment offers good
value for business guests and holidaymakers alike.*
Annexe24⇔♠✗in 12 bedrooms CTV in all bedrooms ® **T** ✗
✳ sB&B⇔♠£34-£54 dB&B⇔♠£51-£90 ⛟
ℂ CTV 500P ⏍ ✳ CFA ⌧ ▶ 18 ♿ (hard) squash
snooker sauna solarium gymnasium badminton table tennis
keep fit jacuzzi ♨
♔ English & Continental **V** ♦ ⚓ ✳ Sunday Lunch £8.75-£9.25
High tea £3.50-£15 Dinner £17.85-£22 Last dinner 9.30pm
Credit Cards 1 2 3 5

---

ST NEOTS Cambridgeshire Map **04** TL16

**★★64%, Abbotsley Golf**
Eynesbury Hardwicke PE19 4XN ☎Huntingdon(0480)74000
FAX (0480) 403280
15⇔♠✗in 4 bedrooms CTV in all bedrooms ® **T** ✳
sB&B⇔♠£45-£50 dB&B⇔♠£55-£60 ⛟
CTV 50P ⏍ ✳ CFA ▶ 18 squash snooker sauna solarium
**V** ✗ ✳ Lunch £10-£12 Dinner £15-£20&alc Last dinner
9.30pm
Credit Cards 1 3

---

ST PETER
See **Jersey under** Channel Islands

---

ST PETER PORT
See **Guernsey under** Channel Islands

---

ST SAVIOUR
See **Jersey under** Channel Islands

---

ST WENN Cornwall & Isles of Scilly Map **02** SW96

**★♨61%, *Wenn Manor***
☎St Austell(0726)890240
*This rambling old manor house is set in 4 acres of peaceful
countryside, way off the beaten track. There is a cosy bar, a
spacious dining room and bedrooms of a good size.*
8rm(6⇔1♠)(1fb) CTV in all bedrooms ®
20P 1🏠 ⏍ ✳ ⌣ (heated) putting croquet
♦ ⚓ Last dinner 7.30pm
Credit Cards 1 3

---

SALCOMBE Devon Map **03** SX73

Telephone numbers are liable to change during the currency of
this guide.

**★★★❀79%, Tides Reach**
South Sands TQ8 8LJ ☎(054884)3466 due to change to
(0548) 843466 FAX (054884) 3954 due to change to
(0548)843954
Closed Dec-Feb
*This elegant and up-to-date hotel in a beautiful tree-sheltered
setting above South Sands, just inside the entrance to the
Salcombe Estuary, is surrounded by gardens containing an
ornamental lake. Personally owned and run, it provides the
attentive services of professionally supervised staff. Décor
throughout is bright and modern, quality fabrics being carefully
chosen to create a tasteful atmosphere which is enhanced in the
public areas by colourful flower arrangements. Comfortable,
relaxing bedrooms are well equipped, a superbly maintained leisure
complex offers excellent facilities, and the Garden Restaurant's
table d'hote menu (supplemented by some à la carte choices and
accompanied by a carefully chosen wine list) includes home made
soups, fresh local fish and game, and an interesting selection of
English cheeses.*
39⇔♠(5fb) CTV in all bedrooms **T** S% sB&B⇔♠£58-£80
dB&B⇔♠£105-£175 (incl dinner) ⛟
Lift ℂ 100P ⏍ ✳ ⌧ (heated) squash snooker sauna solarium
gymnasium windsurfing nc8yrs
♔ English & Continental **V** ♦ ⚓ S% Bar Lunch £2.50-£8.95
Dinner fr£24.25&alc Last dinner 9.30pm
Credit Cards 1 2 3 5

**★★★❀72%, Soar Mill Cove**
Soar Mill Cove, Malborough TQ7 3DS (3m W of town off A381
at Malborough) ☎Kingsbridge(0548)561566
FAX (0548) 561223
Closed 29 Dec-11 Feb
*The cove – reached via the village of Malborough, and often
described as the most beautiful in England – offers secluded
bathing and accommodation in a family-run hotel which is*

**S**

*constantly improving its standards. Modern-styled bedrooms are well equipped and include private sun patios, while the mainly open-plan public areas are comfortably equipped with quality furniture and warmed by a log fire in cooler weather. Imaginative food is complemented by a well balanced wine list, while the proprietors and their efficient staff provide friendly, attentive service. Both indoor and outdoor swimming pools are available for guests' use.*

14⇔(2fb) CTV in all bedrooms ® T ✱ sB&B⇔£54-£70 dB&B⇔£108-£120 ♬

30P 🚗 ❄ ▱ (heated) ⌿ ♪ (grass) ⚷ *xmas*

♀ International ✿ ♨ Lunch £10-£25&alc High tea £7 Dinner £26-£35&alc Last dinner 9pm

Credit Cards 1 3

### ★★★70% **Bolt Head**

TQ8 8LL (Best Western) ☎(054884)3751 FAX (054884) 3060 Closed mid Nov-mid Mar

*An efficiently attentive management and staff provide a warm welcome to this privately owned hotel in Swiss chalet style which boasts a peaceful location adjacent to National Trust property, overlooking the sea and the beautiful Salcombe estuary from a prominent position 140ft above sea level. Public areas, which take maximum advantage of the breathtaking views, have all been tastefully decorated and comfortably furnished, while accommodation offers a uniform style of décor and good facilities; many of the bedrooms have sea-facing balconies, and those at the rear of the building give easy access to the outdoor heated pool and sun terrace. The restaurant's table d'hôte menu features interesting choices of fish, meat and vegetarian dishes, all carefully prepared from fresh produce.*

28⇔♠(6fb) CTV in all bedrooms ® T ✱ sB&B⇔♠£49-£70.50 dB&B⇔♠£98-£141 (incl dinner) ♬

30P 🚗 ❄ ⌿ (heated)

→

**S**

English & French **V** ✪ ⅃⅄ ✱ Lunch £6.50-£10 Dinner £19.95-£32.90 Last dinner 9pm
Credit Cards ① ② ③ ⑤

### ★★65% **Grafton Towers**

Moult Rd, South Sands TQ8 8LG ☎(054884)2882
Closed mid Oct-Mar

*A Victorian mansion, peacefully situated away from the town centre and overlooking the estuary, provides bright bedrooms, imaginative food, and a warm welcome.*

14rm(9⇨3♠) CTV in 12 bedrooms ® ✱ sB&B£29-£32
sB&B⇨♠£29-£32 dB&B⇨♠£60-£65 ⊟
12P ⊞ ✿

English and French **V** ✱ Dinner fr£13.50 Last dinner 8pm
Credit Cards ① ③

### ★69% **Woodgrange Hotel**

Devon Rd TQ8 8HJ (Minotels) ☎(054884)2439
FAX (054884) 2006
Closed Nov-Etr

*This small hotel faces due south overlooking the estuary, and resident proprietors Mary and Peter Fleig extend a warm welcome to guests. The atmosphere is cheerful and informal, bedrooms are comfortable and very well equipped, and the cosy lounge has a beautiful view. There is a well stocked bar and home-cooked fare is featured on the table d'hôte menu.*

9⇨♠(1fb) CTV in all bedrooms ® **T** ✱ sB&B⇨♠£24-£26
dB&B⇨♠£48-£52 ⊟
12P ⊞

✪ ⅃⅄ ✱ Bar Lunch £2-£5 Dinner £12.50-£15 Last dinner 7.30pm
Credit Cards ① ② ③ ⑤ ⓔ

### ★65% **Sunny Cliff**

Cliff Rd TQ8 8JU ☎(054884)2207
RS Nov-Mar

*This small and friendly hotel, whose terraced garden ends at the water's edge, commands particularly fine views across the estuary. Some of its bedrooms are compact, but all are brightly decorated and furnished and a number have en suite facilities. During the season an attractive dining room offers a wide menu which includes some interesting dishes, but only bed and breakfast accommodation is available from November to March. Guests have the use of an outdoor swimming pool.*

15rm(7⇨5♠)Annexe4⇨3♠(3fb) CTV in all bedrooms ®
sB&B£26-£31 sB&B⇨♠£30-£35 dB&B£52-£62
dB&B⇨♠£60-£70 ⊟
16P 2⊞ ✿ ⌒ (heated) ✎ moorings and landing stage
English & French ✪ ⅃⅄ Bar Lunch £1.50-£4.50 High tea £2.50-£5 Dinner £11.50 Last dinner 8pm
Credit Cards ① ③

### SALFORD Greater Manchester Map **07** SJ89 ⊖

See also **Manchester**

### ★64% *Inn of Good Hope*

226 Eccles Old Rd M6 8AG ☎061-707 6178

*A lively public house occupying a corner site on the A578 near Hope Hospital provides very well equipped en suite bedrooms of a higher standard than its classification would suggest. The restaurant has a limited menu of mostly grills, and service is cheerfully informal.*

8⇨♠ CTV in all bedrooms ® **T** ✖ (ex guide dogs)
50P ⊞
International **V** ✪ Last dinner 9.30pm
Credit Cards ① ② ③ ⑤

### ★62% *Beaucliffe*

254 Eccles Old Rd, Pendleton M6 8ES ☎061-789 5092
FAX 061-787 7739
Closed 25 Dec

---

*Set back from the A576, this popular residential hotel has attractive public areas and more modest bedrooms, well heated in winter. The restaurant provides friendly service, though only bar meals are available at weekends.*

21rm(2⇨15♠)(2fb) CTV in all bedrooms ® ✖
CTV 25P ⊞
European **V** ✪ ⅃⅄ Last dinner 8.45pm
Credit Cards ① ② ③ ⑤

---

### SALISBURY Wiltshire Map **04** SU12

### ★★★68% **The White Hart**

Saint John St SP1 2SD (Forte Hotels) ☎(0722)327476
FAX (0722) 412761

*A well managed hotel with young, friendly staff, in a central location close to the Cathedral. Cream teas are served in the comfortable foyer lounge, whilst the dining room offers a choice of menus.*

68⇨♠(3fb)⅄in 20 bedrooms CTV in all bedrooms ® **T** ✱
sB⇨♠fr£70 dB⇨♠£90-£110 (room only) ⊟
℄ 90P 12⊞ CFA *xmas*
**V** ✪ ⅃⅄ Lunch fr£8.95&alc High tea £1.10-£5.95 Dinner fr£14.95&alc Last dinner 9.30pm
Credit Cards ① ② ③ ④ ⑤

### ★★★65% **Red Lion**

Milford St SP1 2AN (Best Western) ☎(0722)323334
Telex no 477674 FAX (0722) 325756

*This creeper-clad former coaching inn in the town centre partly dates to the 13th century and has public areas of much historical interest and charm. Attractively decorated bedrooms vary from characterful older rooms to newer, more modern-style rooms. Family-run for over 75 years, the hotel is currently undergoing refurbishment to a high standard.*

56⇨♠(4fb)3⊞ CTV in all bedrooms ® **T** ✖ (ex guide dogs)
sB&B⇨♠£56-£70 dB&B⇨♠£86-£100 ⊟
Lift ℄ 8P 10⊞ CFA *xmas*
English & French **V** ✪ ⅃⅄ Lunch £11-£12&alc Dinner £14-£15&alc Last dinner 9pm
Credit Cards ① ② ③ ⑤

### ★★★60% **Rose & Crown**

Harnham Rd, Harnham SP2 8JQ (Queens Moat)
☎(0722)327908 Telex no 47224 FAX (0722) 339816

*Prettily set by the River Avon, this hospitable hotel partly dates from the 13th-century and has cosy bar areas and a modern conservatory-style restaurant with fine river views. Most bedrooms are quite spacious, with those in the oldest part recently refurbished to a high standard while retaining their oak-beamed charm. Many rooms in the new wing overlook the river, some leading out into the gardens.*

28⇨♠(6fb)1⊞ CTV in all bedrooms ® **T** ✱ sB&B⇨♠£75-£95 dB&B⇨♠£105-£150 ⊟
℄ 40P ✿ CFA *xmas*
English & French **V** ✪ ⅃⅄ ⅄ Lunch £9.50-£14.50&alc Dinner £13.50-£16.50&alc Last dinner 9.30pm
Credit Cards ① ② ③ ⑤

### ★★65% **Trafalgar**

33 Milford St SP1 2AP (Resort) ☎(0722)338686
FAX (0722) 414496

*This small hotel in the city centre partly dates back to the 15th century and offers attractive comfortably furnished public rooms and bedrooms – all of which are well equipped though a few singles are particularly compact. A planned refurbishment programme will enlarge the restaurant and add more bedrooms.*

18⇨♠1⊞ CTV in all bedrooms ® **T** ✱ sB&B⇨♠fr£46
dB&B⇨♠fr£61 ⊟
✎ ⊞ CFA
International **V** ✪ ⅃⅄ ✱ Bar Lunch £1.95-£4.95 Dinner £4.95-£11 Last dinner 9.30pm
Credit Cards ① ② ③ ⑤

★★ 60% **County**
Bridge St SP1 2ND (Chef & Brewer) ☎(0722)320229
FAX (0722) 414313
*In a prime position beside the River Avon and close to the town
centre, this convivial 19th-century hotel offers comfortable well-
equipped bedrooms of modern design. The bars and Berni
restaurant attract a busy local trade.*
31⇨ℜ(3fb) CTV in all bedrooms ℜ T ✻ (ex guide dogs)
sB&B⇨ℜ£55-£65 dB&B⇨ℜ£73 ⊟
⟨ 31P CFA
♀ International V ♥ ♨ ⅙ Lunch fr£8.50alc Dinner fr£8.50alc
Last dinner 10pm
Credit Cards ⒈ ⒉ ⒊ ⒌

★★ 50% **Cathedral**
Milford St SP1 2AJ ☎(0722)320144
*Situated close to the shops and Cathedral Close, this hotel dates
from the 1700s. It has a lively public bar, grill-type restaurant and
first floor lounge; bedrooms are simply furnished and have some
modern facilities.*
30rm(15⇨4ℜ)(3fb)1♯ CTV in all bedrooms ℜ
✻ (ex guide dogs)
Lift ⟨ ♪
♀ English & French V ♥ Last dinner 9pm
Credit Cards ⒈ ⒊

---

SALTASH Cornwall & Isles of Scilly Map **02** SX45 ☉

⬠**Granada Lodge**
Callington Rd, Carkeel PL12 6LF (Granada)
☎Plymouth(0752)848408 FAX (0752) 848346
*Situated on the A38 close to the Tamar Bridge and Plymouth, this
Lodge has pleasing, well equipped bedrooms. There is a well
designed and very clean self-service restaurant offering some
cooked-to-order dishes.*
32ℜ(14fb)⅙in 5 bedrooms CTV in all bedrooms ℜ
✻ (ex guide dogs) S% sBℜfr£29.50 dBℜfr£32 (room only) ⊟
⟨ 144P

**See advertisement on page 623**

---

SAMPFORD PEVERELL Devon Map **03** ST01

⬠**Forte Travelodge**
Sampford Peverell Service Area EX16 7HD (junc 27, M5) (Forte)
☎Tiverton(0884)821087 Central Res (0800) 850950
*A warm welcome awaits guests at any time of the day or night in
this lodge set beside the M5 at its junction with the North Devon
link road – a position giving easy access to the counties of
Devonshire and Somerset. Spotlessly clean rooms offer good
facilities, and there is a Little Chef restaurant 20 yards across the
car park.*
40⇨ℜ(40fb) CTV in all bedrooms ℜ sB⇨ℜ£29.95
dB⇨ℜ£29.95 (room only)
40P ♿
♀ Mainly grills
Credit Cards ⒈ ⒉ ⒊

---

SANDBACH Cheshire Map **07** SJ76

★★★ 65% **Chimney House**
Congleton Rd CW11 0ST (Lansbury) ☎Crewe(0270)764141
Telex no 367323 FAX (0270) 768916
*This Tudor-style hotel has had a modern extension in the style of
the original building. Set in 8 acres of wooded countryside, the
hotel is conveniently positioned half a mile from junction 17 of the
M6. Bedrooms are well decorated and equipped. The Patio
Restaurant offers a choice of à la carte or fixed-price menus.*
50⇨(2fb)⅙in 6 bedrooms CTV in all bedrooms ℜ T
✻ (ex guide dogs) ✽ sB&B⇨£70 dB&B⇨£82 ⊟
⟨ 110P ❁ CFA sauna solarium *xmas*

→

S

♥ English & French **V** ♦ ⚬ ✳ Lunch £11 Dinner £16 Last dinner 10pm
Credit Cards ① ② ③ ⑤

**★★★ ⊛62%, *Old Hall***
Newcastle Rd CW11 0AL ☎Crewe(0270)761221
FAX (0270) 762551
*A characterful hotel dating back to 1656, richly endowed with beams and original wood panelling, even boasts an underground passage to the parish church. A welcoming atmosphere prevails, and the restaurant is proving very popular – particularly at weekends.*
12⇗🏠Annexe3⇗🏠(2fb)4⌷ CTV in all bedrooms ® **T**
Lift ( 50P ⇜
♥ English & Continental **V** ♦ ⚬ ⅄ Last dinner 9pm
Credit Cards ① ② ③

**★★★ 62%, Saxon Cross**
Holmes Chapel Rd CW11 9SE (M6 Junc 17)
☎Crewe(0270)763281 FAX (0270) 768723
*A modern, motel-type establishment just off junction 17 of the M6 (follow signs towards Congleton on the A534, then first left onto the A5022) which attracts a busy function and conference trade. Bedrooms, which are all on the ground floor, are quite spacious and well equipped.*
52⇗🏠(13fb)⅄in 5 bedrooms CTV in all bedrooms ® **T** ✳
sB&B⇗🏠£33-£54 dB&B⇗🏠£45-£68 🍴
( 200P ❀ CFA
♥ English & French **V** ♦ ⚬ ✳ Lunch £8.20-£8.60 Dinner £14.50&alc Last dinner 9.30pm
Credit Cards ① ② ③ ⑤ ⓔ

## SANDBANKS
See Poole

## SANDIACRE Derbyshire Map 08 SK43
See also Long Eaton
**★★★ 58%, Forte Posthouse Nottingham/Derby**
Bostocks Ln NG10 5NJ (N of M1 junc 25) (Forte Hotels)
☎(0602)397800 Telex no 377378 FAX (0602) 490469
*Conveniently situated for the M1 motorway (junction 25), this hotel is popular with the business community during the week, and more increasingly with leisure users on competitively priced weekend breaks. One of the more dated Posthouses, it has recently seen a refurbishment of its oldest rooms to provide a more consistent standard of accommodation.*
97⇗🏠⅄in 50 bedrooms CTV in 107 bedrooms ® ✳
sB⇗🏠£39.50-£49.50 dB⇗🏠£39.50-£49.50 (room only) 🍴
( ▦180P ❀ *xmas*
**V** ♦ ⚬ ⅃
Credit Cards ① ② ③ ④ ⑤

## SANDIWAY Cheshire Map 07 SJ67 ☺
**★★★ ⊛⊛⚟ 79% Nunsmere Hall Country House**
Tarporley Rd CW8 2ES ☎Northwich(0606)889100
FAX (0606) 889055
*This quality hotel, reached by a winding wooded drive off the A49, is virtually surrounded by a lake and woodland. Its elegant, romantic aura is enhanced by the warm welcome and personal service offered by its involved owners and by the innovative French-style cuisine served in a recently refurbished restaurant whose menu changes each day; the additional accommodation soon to be provided will be in keeping with the luxuriously attractive rooms already available. Holiday guests and businessmen alike will appreciate the chance to relax and unwind afforded by this traditional country house.*
32⇗🏠 CTV in all bedrooms ® **T** ✗ (ex guide dogs) S%
sB&B⇗🏠£90-£175 dB&B⇗🏠£110-£200 🍴
Lift ( CTV 30P ⇜ ❀ nc12yrs *xmas*

**V** ♦ ⚬ ⅄ ⅃ Lunch £14-£19alc Dinner £35-£40alc Last dinner 9.30pm
Credit Cards ① ② ③

## SANDOWN
See Wight, Isle of

## SANQUHAR Dumfries & Galloway *Dumfriesshire* Map 11 NS70
**★★65%, *Blackaddie House***
Blackaddie Rd DG4 6JJ ☎(0659)50270
*Friendly, informal service is a feature of this small, spotlessly maintained country hotel. The focal point is the cosy bar, with a welcoming fire in season. Originally a farmhouse, it has characteristics of a country house, with gardens that back right onto the River Nith. Apart from the 2 family rooms, bedrooms are on the small side, but there is a comfortable lounge. The hotel is on the north east side of the village half a mile from the main road.*
9⇗🏠(2fb) CTV in all bedrooms ® ✗ (ex guide dogs)
20P ⇜ ❀ ▶ 9 ↲ ☉ game shooting ⚙
**V** ♦ Last dinner 9pm
Credit Cards ① ③

**★★64% Mennockfoot Lodge**
Mennock DG4 6HS ☎(0659)50382 & 50477
*In a lovely riverside location just off the A76, this friendly hotel is managed by resident proprietors and offers cosy chalet-style accommodation and interesting menus.*
1⇗Annexe8⇗🏠(1fb) CTV in all bedrooms ® **T**
sB&B⇗🏠£30-£35 dB&B⇗🏠£45-£50
CTV 25P ❀ ⚙
♥ British & Continental **V** ♦ ✳ Lunch £5-£8alc Dinner £13&alc Last dinner 8.30pm
Credit Cards ① ③ ⓔ

## SARN PARK MOTORWAY SERVICE AREA (M4) Mid Glamorgan Map 03 SS98
**⟐ForteTravelodge**
Sarn Park Motorway Services CF32 9RW (junction 36, M4) (Forte) ☎Bridgend(0656)659218 Central Res (0800) 850950
*Good facilities are provided by this modern Lodge at junction 36 of the M4, and food is available 24 hours a day at the adjacent service area.*
40⇗🏠(40fb) CTV in all bedrooms ® sB⇗🏠£29.95
dB⇗🏠£29.95 (room only)
( 40P ⇜
♥ Mainly grills
Credit Cards ① ② ③

## SARRE Kent Map 05 TR26
**★★63% Crown Inn**
Ramsgate Rd CT7 0LF ☎Thanet(0843)47808 FAX (0843) 47914
*Established in 1500 and steeped in local history, this attractive inn, which still produces its famous Huguenot Cherry Brandy, has been completely modernised to offer comfortable, fully equipped accommodation and friendly, well managed service. Bedrooms in the main building have original beams and exposed brick walls, while a split-level restaurant features the original flooring. Bar meals provide an alternative to this restaurant's interesting à la carte menu of professionally prepared dishes. A lounge/meeting room is available on the first floor, and car parking is very accessible.*
12⇗🏠(1fb)1⌷ CTV in all bedrooms ® **T** sB&B⇗🏠fr£43.50
dB&B⇗🏠fr£56.50 🍴
CTV 25P *xmas*
**V** ♦ ⚬ ⅃ Sunday Lunch £11.50-£12.50alc Dinner £15-£20alc Last dinner 9.30pm
Credit Cards ① ② ③ ⑤ ⓔ

**SAUNDERSFOOT** Dyfed Map **02** SN10

**★★★66% St Brides**
St Brides Hill SA69 9NH (Inter-Hotels) ☎(0834)812304
Telex no 48350 FAX (0834) 813303
Closed 1-19 Jan
*Excellent views are available from many of the rooms of this modern hotel overlooking the harbour and beach. Professionally run by the same family for almost 25 years, it offers well equipped accommodation which ranges in size from the ordinary to those with small lounge areas. Public rooms are spaciously comfortable, and friendly staff provide helpful service.*
45⇨↑(4fb)1 ⊟ ⅍in 4 bedrooms CTV in all bedrooms ® T
sB&B⇨↑£55-£76.50 dB&B⇨↑£89-£120 ⊟
( 70P ✲ CFA ⇌ (heated) sauna ♫ *xmas*
♉ English & French V ♈ ♍ Lunch £11.50-£13.50&alc Dinner £16.50-£18.50&alc Last dinner 9.15pm
Credit Cards 1 2 3 5

**★★64% *Rhodewood House***
St Brides Hill SA69 9NU ☎(0834)812200 FAX (0834) 811863
*This busy family-run resort hotel offers well-equipped bedrooms, regular entertainment in Taff's Bar and facilities for snooker.*
34⇨↑(6fb)⅍in 6 bedrooms CTV in all bedrooms ® T
70P ✲ snooker solarium ♫ ⌂
V ♈ ♍ ⅍ Last dinner 9.30pm
Credit Cards 1 2 3 5

**See advertisement under TENBY**

**★★63% Merlewood**
St Brides Hill SA69 9NP ☎(0834)812421 & 813295
Closed Nov-Etr
*A busy, family-run, seasonal hotel which commands panoramic views of the coastline from its situation just off St Bride's Hill offers modern accommodation, spacious grounds in which to relax and ample car parking facilities.*

→

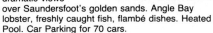

S

34rm(17⇨13👜)(8fb) CTV in all bedrooms ®
✖ (ex guide dogs) ✻ sB&Bfr£27 sB&B⇨👜fr£29.50
dB&B⇨👜fr£54 🅿
34P ✾ ⌂ (heated) ⁂ xmas
V ⚏ ✻ S% Lunch £8.50 Dinner £9 Last dinner 8pm
Credit Cards ⒈ ⒊

### ★★60% Glen Beach
Swallow Tree Woods SA69 9DE ☎(0834)813430
*This small family-run holiday hotel, also popular with business
people, is situated on the approach to the resort, and is set within
attractive woodland. Bedrooms, although a little dated, are well
equipped and a holiday disco bar has recently been extended.*
13⇨👜(3fb)1▦ CTV in all bedrooms ® T ✻ sB&B⇨👜£32
dB&B⇨👜£44-£59 🅿
CTV 35P ✾ CFA solarium mid-Sep-Mar xmas
♡ English & French V ♥ ✻ Sunday Lunch £5.95 Dinner
£12.50 Last dinner 8.45pm
Credit Cards ⒈ ⒉ ⒊ ⓔ

### SAUNDERTON Buckinghamshire Map 04 SP70

### ★★62% Rose & Crown
Wycombe Rd HP17 9NP (Exec Hotel)
☎Princes Risborough(08444)5299 & 2241 FAX (08444) 3140
Closed 25-31 Dec
*A 140-year-old, modernised roadside hotel and restaurant with a
bright, attractive public bar. The bedrooms are well equipped and
comfortable and the informal restaurant offers a range of dishes
from à la carte and blackboard menus.*
17rm(14⇨👜) CTV in all bedrooms ® T ✖ (ex guide dogs) ✻
sB&B£40.50 sB&B⇨👜£58.50-£67 dB&B⇨👜£71.25-£77 🅿
50P ✾
♡ English & French ♥ ⚏ ✻ Lunch £12.50-£14.50&alc High
tea £16.95-£24alc Dinner £14.50-£16.50 Last dinner 9.30pm
Credit Cards ⒈ ⒉ ⒊ ⒌ ⓔ

### SAUNTON Devon Map 02 SS43

### ★★★★59% Saunton Sands
EX33 1LQ (Brend) ☎Croyde(0271)890212 Telex no 42551
FAX (0271) 890145
*This beautifully situated hotel with direct access to the beach
commands sweeping sea views and offers a full range of services in
traditional, warmly hospitable style. Ideal for family holidays, it
has extensive leisure and recreational facilities, spacious and
comfortable public rooms, and a restaurant with a choice of menus.
Bedrooms vary in size, the larger front ones having glorious views;
some older en suite rooms were in the process of being refurbished.*
92⇨👜(39fb) CTV in all bedrooms ® T ✖ (ex guide dogs)
sB&B⇨👜£66-£80 dB&B⇨👜£121-£164 🅿
Lift ⓒ CTV 140P 2🚗 ⊞ ✾ ▢ (heated) ℘ (hard) squash
snooker sauna solarium putting table tennis spa bath ♫ ⁂
xmas
♡ English & French V ♥ ⚏ Lunch £12.50&alc Dinner
£17&alc Last dinner 9pm
Credit Cards ⒈ ⒉ ⒊ ⒌ ⓔ

### ★★64% Preston House
EX33 1LG ☎Croyde(0271)890472 FAX (0271) 890555
RS Dec-Feb
*Set in its own gardens overlooking the ten mile sweep of Barnstaple
Bay this Victorian hotel has direct access to the beach. Bedrooms
are individually decorated, well equipped and all have en-suite
bathrooms. Breakfast is served in the attractive conservatory
which faces the sea.*
15⇨👜2▦ CTV in all bedrooms ® T ✖ sB&B⇨👜£30-£52.50
dB&B⇨👜£60-£85 🅿
CTV 20P ⊞ ✾ CFA ℘ (hard) sauna solarium clay pigeon
shooting nc12yrs xmas

♡ English & Continental V ♥ ⚏ Sunday Lunch £8.50-£20alc
Dinner fr£13&alc Last dinner 8.30pm
Credit Cards ⒈ ⒊

### SAVERNAKE
See Burbage

### SCALASAIG
See Colonsay, Isle of

### SCARBOROUGH North Yorkshire Map 08 TA08 ⊘
See **Town Plan Section**
### ★★★64% Holbeck Hall
Seacliff Rd YO11 2XX ☎(0723)374374 FAX (0723) 351114
*In a delightful position overlooking the South Bay and harbour this
hotel has an impressive panelled hallway, a very comfortable
lounge with a conservatory and bedrooms with good facilities.
There are excellent sea views from the restaurant.*
30⇨👜(3fb) CTV in all bedrooms T ✖ ✻ sB&B⇨👜£43.55-
£53.65 dB&B⇨👜£87.10-£107.30 🅿
ⓒ CTV 50P ⊞ ✾ CFA xmas
♡ English & French ♥ ⚏ ✻ Lunch fr£9.95 Dinner
fr£17.50&alc Last dinner 9.30pm
Credit Cards ⒈ ⒉ ⒊ ⒌

### ★★★64% Hotel St Nicholas
St Nicholas Cliff YO11 2EU ☎(0723)364101 Telex no 52351
FAX (0723) 500538
*Occupying a central position on St Nicholas Cliff overlooking
South Bay, the St Nicholas Hotel caters ideally for business
people, providing mostly modern, recently refurbished
accommodation. Bedrooms are attractively decorated and well
equipped, though some are quite compact. Spacious, comfortable
public areas, including open-plan lounges, are attractively*
→

S

S

*furnished in the modern style; there is a leisure centre and also a coffee shop. The hotel has limited car parking facilities.*
141⇨ ╠(18fb)4⌘ CTV in all bedrooms ⓡ T
Lift ⦅ 15⩔ (£3) ⌼ (heated) sauna solarium children's games room
V ⌂ ⏛ Last dinner 9pm
Credit Cards ①②③⑤

### ★★★♨♨64%, Wrea Head Country
Scalby YO13 0PB (3m NW off A171) ☎(0723)378211
FAX (0723) 371780
*Peacefully situated in 14 acres of landscaped gardens, this converted Victorian house is run in a quiet, friendly manner; individually decorated bedrooms vary in shape and size, many enjoying fine views of the surrounding countryside, while pleasant wood-panelled public areas boast a fine collect of paintings and objets d'art.*
21⇨╠(2fb) CTV in all bedrooms T ⋈ sB&B⇨╠£45-£49.50
dB&B⇨╠£90-£150 ⌸
⦅ 50P 4⩔ (£3 per night) ⌗ ❈ CFA putting green croquet *xmas*
♀ English & French V ⌂ ⏛ Lunch £10.50-£17.50 Dinner
£17.50-£30 Last dinner 9.30pm
Credit Cards ①②③ⓔ

### ★★★63% *Esplanade*
Belmont Rd YO11 2AA ☎(0723)360382 FAX (0723) 376137
*Commanding fine views of South Bay and the harbour, this extensively refurbished hotel retains much of its Victorian elegance while offering every modern amenity. All bedrooms now have full en suite facilities and there is a range of relaxing public rooms.*
73⇨╠(9fb) CTV in all bedrooms ⓡ T
Lift ⦅ CTV 24P ❈ darts table tennis
♀ English & French V ⌂ ⏛ Last dinner 9pm
Credit Cards ①②③⑤

### ★★★62% Palm Court
Nicholas Cliff YO11 2ES ☎(0723)368161 Telex no 527579
FAX (0723) 371547
*An hotel managed by resident proprietors, ably assisted by willing and friendly young staff who provide spontaneous and cheerful service, combines comfortable and well appointed accommodation with very popular leisure facilities.*
51⇨╠(11fb) CTV in all bedrooms ⓡ T ⋈ (ex guide dogs) ✱
sB&B⇨╠£28-£34 dB&B⇨╠£56-£68 ⌸
Lift ⦅ CTV 6P 80⩔ ⌼ (heated) sauna ♫ *xmas*
♀ English & French V ⌂ ⏛ ✱ Sunday Lunch £8.25 Dinner
£10.75&alc Last dinner 9pm
Credit Cards ①②③⑤ⓔ

### ★★69% Gridley's Crescent
The Crescent YO11 2PP ☎(0723)360929 FAX (0723) 354126
*This attractive listed building has been carefully converted into a very comfortable hotel. All bedrooms are well equipped and nicely furnished and guests have a choice of restaurants. The Gridley's own and manage the hotel in a professional manner.*
20⇨╠1⌘ in 5 bedrooms CTV in all bedrooms ⓡ T
⋈ (ex guide dogs) sB&B⇨╠£37.50-£47.50 dB&B⇨╠£65-£75
⌸
Lift ⦅ ⨎ ⌗ CFA nc6yrs
V ⌂ ⏛ Sunday Lunch fr£8.25 Dinner fr£13.50&alc Last dinner 10pm
Credit Cards ①③

### ★★67% Red Lea
Prince of Wales Ter YO11 2AJ ☎(0723)362431
FAX (0723) 371230
*This friendly hotel overlooks parkland from an attractive setting just off the seafront. Bedrooms are spacious, lounges comfortable, and leisure facilities include an indoor swimming pool.*
67⇨╠(7fb) CTV in all bedrooms ⓡ T ⋈ ✱ sB&B⇨╠£26.50-
£27.50 dB&B⇨╠£53-£55

Lift ⦅ CTV ⨎ CFA ⌼ (heated) sauna solarium gymnasium
*xmas*
♀ International ⌂ ⏛ ⅋ ✱ Lunch fr£7 Dinner fr£10 Last
dinner 8.30pm
Credit Cards ①③

### ★★66%, Bradley Court
7-9 Filey Rd, South Cliff YO11 2SE ☎(0723)360476
FAX (0723) 376661
*This comfortable, well appointed hotel, recently extensively refurbished, stands near to South Cliff and only a short distance from the town centre; individually decorated bedrooms are fully equipped, public areas include an attractive lounge bar and the popular Sizzles Restaurant, and a young staff provides friendly service.*
40rm(22⇨17╠)(3fb) CTV in all bedrooms ⓡ T ⋈ ✱
sB&B⇨╠£33-£39 dB&B⇨╠£66-£78 ⌸
Lift ⦅ 40P CFA *xmas*
⌂ ⏛ ⅋
Credit Cards ①②③ⓔ

### ★★62% The Pickwick Inn
Huntriss Row YO11 2ED ☎(0723)375787 FAX (0723) 374284
*This comfortable town centre hotel has very well equipped bedrooms, one now with a 4-poster bed. The popular bars offer bar meals or you can eat in the first-floor restaurant. There are public car parking facilities (charged) opposite.*
11⇨╠ CTV in all bedrooms ⓡ T ⋈ (ex guide dogs) ✱
sB&B⇨╠fr£27 dB&B⇨╠£44-£55 ⌸
Lift ⦅ *xmas*
♀ English & French V ✱ Lunch £3-£15alc Dinner fr£9.50&alc
Last dinner 10pm
Credit Cards ①②③⑤ⓔ

### ★★61% Southlands
15 West St, South Cliff YO11 2QW (Consort) ☎(0723)361461
Telex no 57515 FAX (0723) 376035
Closed Jan-Feb
*A well furnished and comfortable traditional seaside hotel, personally owned and run, and offering good home comforts. Situated on South Cliff, near the Esplanade.*
58⇨╠(8fb) CTV in all bedrooms ⓡ T ✱ sB&B⇨╠£20-£36
dB&B⇨╠£40-£62 ⌸
Lift ⦅ CTV 45P CFA ♫
V ⌂ ⏛ ⅋ Lunch fr£7.95 Dinner fr£11 Last dinner 8.30pm
Credit Cards ①②③⑤ⓔ

### ★★57% Brooklands
Esplanade Gardens, South Cliff YO11 2AW ☎(0723)376576 &
361608
Closed Dec-last 2wks Mar
*Comfortable and friendly, this hotel is on the South Cliff, a short walk from the Esplanade. The bedrooms have good facilities, and the lounges are comfortable.*
61rm(48⇨4╠)(9fb) CTV in all bedrooms ⓡ T
⋈ (ex guide dogs) sB&B£23.50-£25 sB&B⇨╠£25.50-£27
dB&B£47-£50 dB&B⇨╠£51-£54
Lift 1⩔ (£1 per night) CFA pool table ♫
V ⌂ ⏛ ✱ Lunch £5 High tea £1.25-£4 Dinner £8 Last dinner
8pm
Credit Cards ①③ⓔ

**See advertisement on page 629**

### ★★51% Central
1-3 The Crescent YO11 2PW ☎(0723)365766
*A centrally located hotel offering basic bedroom accommodation and good, simple meals based on quality ingredients, many dishes being char-grilled; the restaurant – which features an open display kitchen – serves a table d'hôte dinner at 7:00 pm and an à la carte menu after 7.30.*
39rm(13⇨8╠)(3fb) CTV in all bedrooms ⓡ T sB&Bfr£28.75
sB&B⇨╠fr£33.25 dB&Bfr£50.50 dB&B⇨╠fr£59.50 ⌸

→

S

Lift 18P *xmas*
♀ English & Continental **V** ✿ ✱ Dinner fr£7.75&alc Last dinner 9.30pm
Credit Cards ①②③⑤ⓔ

### ❀✕✕ Lanterna Ristorante
33 Queen St YO11 1HQ ☎(0723)363616
*This charming bow-fronted restaurant, converted from an empty shop in a listed building not far from the centre of the town, was opened by Gianni Arecco and his English wife Janet over 18 years ago and quickly gained an excellent reputation for authentic Italian cuisine which it has maintained ever since. The proprietor originally hails from Piedmont, the gastronomic and wine-growing area of Northern Italy which has obviously influenced his tastes, but gained experience at both Claridge's and The White House before settling in Yorkshire. The à la carte menu which is constant in content, is supplemented by a special menu which changes to feature seasonal specialities. All dishes are cooked to order, meat, fish and poultry being of a high standard; pasta is home-made and the meringues and hot zabaglione are simply delicious. To find the restaurant, follow the main street from the railway station end and take the second road left, where it is about 300 yards along.*
Closed Sun & Mon Lunch not served
♀ Continental **V** 36 seats Dinner £14.82-£17.87alc Last dinner 9.30pm ✗ nc2yrs
Credit Cards ① ③

---

## SCILLY, ISLES OF No map

---

## ST MARY'S

### ★★68% *Tregarthens*
Hugh Town TR21 0PP (Best Western) ☎Scillonia(0720)22540
FAX (0720) 22089
Closed Nov-mid Mar
*Ideally situated just above the bay, overlooking St Mary's harbour and commanding views across the water to the islands of Fresco, Bryher and Samson, this popular hotel successfully combines modern comfort with quaintness and charm. The recent major refurbishment programme has provided bright, well equipped bedrooms and spacious, richly appointed public areas, food is imaginative, and local staff offer prompt, friendly service under enthusiastic management.*
32rm(24⇆)Annexe1rm(5fb) CTV in all bedrooms ® **T** ✖
♀ English & French **V** ✿ ☑ Last dinner 8pm
Credit Cards ①②③⑤

---

## TRESCO

### ★★★ ❀76% **The Island**
TR24 0PU ☎Scillonia(0720)22883 FAX (0720) 23008
Closed Nov-Feb
*Whether you touch down by helicopter at Abbey Gardens or arrive by boat at the quay, the hotel's own unique transport will take you across this very pretty island, past a private beach to the hotel itself, neatly tucked away in mature sub-tropical gardens. A range of superior, tastefully styled bedrooms, each with its own terrace patio, is richly appointed and – like many of the other rooms – offers dramatic panoramic views out to sea and across to the other islands. Public rooms have been delightfully refurbished, the restaurant being extended and a new cocktail bar lounge added, and these surroundings, together with good food standards and prompt, hospitable service create a delightfully relaxing retreat in a very attractive part of the world. For the more energetic, there are a swimming pool and newly provided tennis facilities.*
40⇆↑ CTV in all bedrooms ® **T** ✖ (ex guide dogs) ✱
sB&B⇆↑£74-£100 dB&B⇆↑£85-£120 (incl dinner)
CTV ✗ ⇛ ✿ CFA ⊇ (heated) ♫ (hard) ◢ croquet boating table tennis

---

♀ English & Continental **V** ✿ ☑ ✱ Lunch £2.50-£17alc Dinner £22.50-£27.50alc Last dinner 9pm
Credit Cards ①②③

### ★★ ❀64% **New Inn**
TR24 0QQ ☎Scillonia(0720)22844
*First impressions can be misleading, for this small, informally friendly, pub-style hotel in an attractive harbour setting offers a wealth of services and warm hospitality to residents and non-residents alike. Cosy, functional bars bustle with customers, while chef Graham Shone's imaginative cooking creates honest dishes which make good use of seasonal local and imported produce. Fresh, bright Tresco lobster simply served with butter sauce and rosemary might, for example, be followed by roasted pheasant in a leek and Port jus or baked cutlets of tender pink lamb with a nicely rounded crab and mushroom concasse, and tempting home-made puddings are complemented by a well balanced and reasonably priced wine list.*
12rm(10⇆) CTV in all bedrooms ® **T** ✖ (ex guide dogs)
sB&B£33-£55 dB&B⇆↑£66-£110 (incl dinner) ₱
✗ ⇛ ☑ (heated) sea fishing *xmas*
**V** ✿ Dinner £12.50-£16.50 Last dinner 8.30pm

---

## SCOLE Norfolk Map **05** TM17

### ★★55% **Scole Inn**
IP21 4DR (Best Western) ☎Diss(0379)740481
FAX (0379) 740762
*A 17th-century coaching inn of red brick, rich in history and displaying the Dutch influence common in East Anglia in its gabled façade, stands at the busy junction of the A140/143 east of the town. Two styles of accommodation are available, the purpose-fitted and compact rooms of the annexe complementing the more characterful ones in the main building. Most areas are looking tired and neglected, but service is cheerful.*
12⇆↑Annexe11⇆↑(2fb)3⇛✗in 3 bedrooms CTV in all bedrooms ® **T** ✱ sB&B⇆↑£46-£51 dB&B⇆↑£63.50-£71.75 ₱
CTV 60P *xmas*
♀ English & French **V** ✿ ☑ ✱ S10% Lunch fr£9.95 Dinner fr£12.95 Last dinner 10pm
Credit Cards ①②③⑤

**See advertisement on page 60**

---

## SCOTCH CORNER (NEAR RICHMOND) North Yorkshire Map **08** NZ20

### ★★★65% **Scotch Corner**
DL10 6NR (Best Western) ☎Richmond(0748)850900
Telex no 587447 FAX (0748) 825417
*An hotel conveniently located on the roundabout at the A1/A66 junction which offers friendly, helpful service and extensive dining arrangements; spacious public areas and bedrooms are all well designed and furnished.*
90⇆↑(4fb)1⇛ CTV in all bedrooms ® **T** ✱
sB&B⇆↑£29.50-£70 dB&B⇆↑£59-£90 ₱
Lift ℂ 250P CFA ♫ *xmas*
**V** ✿ ☑ ✱ ✱ Lunch fr£11.75&alc Dinner fr£13.95&alc Last dinner 10pm
Credit Cards ①②③⑤ⓔ

### ⬦Forte Travelodge
Skeeby DL10 5EQ (0.5m S on A1) (Forte)
☎Richmond(0748)3768 Central Res (0800) 850950
*A Lodge/Little Chef situated on the northbound carriageway of the A1, 3 miles south of Scotch Corner.*
40⇆↑(40fb) CTV in all bedrooms ® sB⇆↑£29.95 dB⇆↑£29.95 (room only)
ℂ 40P ⇛
Credit Cards ①②③

⬆**Rank Motor Lodge**
A1/A66, Middleton Tyas Ln DL10 6PQ (Rank)
☎Darlington(0325)377177 FAX (0325) 377890
*A modern, well-furnished lodge, situated east of the roundabout at the A1/A66 junction, representing very good value for money.*
50⇆(16fb)⚲in 7 bedrooms CTV in all bedrooms ® ✶
sB&B⇆£29.75 dB&B⇆£39.75 Continental breakfast
53P
♀ English & Continental **V** ✿ ⚇ ⚲ ✶ Lunch £6.05-£10.64alc
High tea £6.05-£10.64alc Dinner £6.05-£10.64alc Last dinner
10pm
Credit Cards ①②③⑤

---

SCOURIE Highland *Sutherland* Map **14** NC14

★★68% **Eddrachilles**
Badcall Bay IV27 4TH ☎(0971)2080 due to change to 502080
FAX (0971) 2477
Closed Nov-Feb
*Set in peaceful grounds looking over Badcall Bay, this efficiently run holiday hotel has been extended and refurbished to provide modern comforts and facilities. The stone-walled, flag stone-floored restaurant reflects the original character of the former manse, while the sun lounge invites relaxation. The well maintained bedrooms have modern appointments and are thoughtfully equipped.*
11⇆ℚ(1fb) CTV in all bedrooms ® **T ✖** (ex guide dogs)
sB&B⇆ℚ£34.20-£51.65 dB&B⇆ℚ£58.40-£67.80 ⁋
25P ⊞ ❀ ✔ boats for hire nc3yrs
**V** ✿ Bar Lunch fr£3.50 Dinner fr£10.10&alc Last dinner 8pm
Credit Cards ①③

★★64% **Scourie**
IV27 4SX (Exec Hotel) ☎(0971)2396 FAX (0971) 2423
Closed Nov-mid Mar RS mid Mar-mid May
*A comfortably appointed and friendly Highland hotel, an established favourite with the angling fraternity, also provides an ideal base for the touring holidaymaker.*
18rm(16⇆)Annexe2⇆(2fb) ® **T** sB&B£24-£26.90
sB&B⇆£29.90-£35.50 dB&B£42.95-£47.50 dB&B⇆£55.90-£62.50 ⁋
30P ⊞ ✔
♀ British & French ✿ Sunday Lunch fr£8 Dinner fr£12.50
Last dinner 8.30pm
Credit Cards ①②③⑤

---

SCUNTHORPE Humberside Map **08** SE81 ⊖

★★★64% **Wortley House**
Rowland Rd DN16 1SU ☎(0724)842223 Telex no 527837
FAX (0724) 280646
*This well maintained commercial hotel close to the railway station and town centre offers a sound standard of modernised accommodation, bedrooms being well equipped to meet the needs of the businessman; local staff provide friendly, informal service.*
38⇆ℚ(2fb)3⊞ CTV in all bedrooms ® **T** ✶ S10%
sB&B⇆ℚ£40-£60 dB&B⇆ℚ£45-£70 ⁋
⟨ 100P CFA *xmas*
♀ English & French **V** ✿ ⚇ ⚲ ✶ S10% Lunch £7.75-£9&alc
Dinner £9&alc Last dinner 9.30pm
Credit Cards ①②③④⑤

★★63% **Royal**
Doncaster Rd DN15 7DE (Forte Hotels) ☎(0724)282233
Telex no 527479 FAX (0724)281826
RS Public Hols
*Popular, comfortable villa-style hotel with a relaxing atmosphere.*
33⇆ℚ(1fb)⚲in 6 bedrooms CTV in all bedrooms ® ✶
sB⇆ℚfr£50 dB⇆ℚ£65-£75 (room only) ⁋
⟨ 33P CFA *xmas*

→

**S**

V ❦ ⚘ ✂ ✳ Sunday Lunch fr£7.10 Dinner fr£13.25&alc Last
dinner 8.45pm
Credit Cards 1 2 3 4 5

---

## SEAFORD East Sussex Map **05** TV49

### ❀✕✕Quincy's
42 High St ☎(0323)895490
*A cosy and instantly appealing High Street restaurant with
attractively appointed tables, classical music in the background
and an unpretentious list of apéritifs. It offers a good-value set-
price 2 or 3 course menu on which some dishes incur a small
supplement. Chef/proprietor Ian Dowding creates an interesting
menu which makes good use of local fish, game and meat but does
not forget the vegetarian. Seafood terrine is served with a
controversial raspberry cream, while the crispy Gressingham duck
is more successfully complemented by a tart lime, honey and
peppercorn sauce. Desserts are particularly good, the hot lemon
pudding with butterscotch sauce and a hot chocolate soufflé both
being memorable, and ice creams are home-made.*
Closed Mon Lunch not served ex Sun
♀ International **V** 32 seats ✳ Sunday Lunch £14.95-£18.95
Dinner £14.95-£18.95 Last dinner 10pm ⌡
Credit Cards 1 3

---

## SEAHOUSES Northumberland Map **12** NU23

### ★★74% Beach House
Sea Front NE68 7SR ☎(0665)720337 FAX (0665) 720921
Closed Nov-Mar
*This very comfortable seafront hotel has pretty bedrooms with
many little extras. The two lounges and the restaurant have
uninterrupted sea views, and the home-cooked dinners are very
good value.*
14⇨🛏(3fb) CTV in all bedrooms ® T sB&B⇨🛏£25.50-£36
dB&B⇨🛏£51-£65 🍴
CTV 16P 🚗 ✿ spa bath games table
**V** ❦ ✂ Dinner £16 Last dinner 8pm
Credit Cards 1 3 £

### ★★70% Olde Ship
NE68 7RD ☎(0665)720200
Closed Dec-Jan
*This charming harbour hotel, owned and managed by the same
family for more than 80 years, still retains its friendly atmosphere
and traditional standards of service whilst also offering the modern
facilities expected by today's traveller.*
12⇨🛏Annexe4⇨🛏(1fb)2🛏 CTV in all bedrooms ® T 🐾
sB&B⇨🛏£27-£32 dB&B⇨🛏£54-£64 🍴
CTV 14P 2🚗 🚗 putting green nc10yrs
**V** ❦ ⚘ Lunch fr£6 Dinner fr£12.50 Last dinner 8.30pm
Credit Cards 1 3

---

## SEALE Surrey Map **04** SU84

### ★★★59% Hog's Back
Hog's Back GU10 1EX (on A31) (Jarvis) ☎Runfold(02518)2345
Telex no 859352 FAX (02518) 3113
*Alongside the busy A31, this long-established hotel now offers
modern and attractive public areas, including a pleasant and well
equipped leisure centre. The majority of the bedrooms are
beginning to show their age, though the new Executive rooms
provide a very good standard of accommodation.*
75⇨🛏(6fb)✂in 10 bedrooms CTV in all bedrooms ® T ✳
sB⇨🛏£87.50-£99.50 dB⇨🛏£99.50-£112.50 (room only) 🍴
《130P ✿ 🖂 (heated) snooker sauna solarium gymnasium
*xmas*
♀ English & French **V** ❦ ✳ Lunch £12-£16.50&alc Dinner
£12-£16.50&alc Last dinner 9.30pm
Credit Cards 1 2 3 4 5 £

---

## SEATON BURN Tyne & Wear Map **12** NZ27

### ★★★★54% Holiday Inn
Great North Rd NE13 6BP (Holiday Inns) ☎091-236 5432
Telex no 53271 FAX 091-236 8091 ⊘
*Conveniently situated close to Newcastle Airport, this purpose-
built, low-rise hotel provides accommodation which is slowly being
upgraded, though some rooms remain functional. Car parking
facilities are good, with a courtesy bus service to the airport, there
are leisure amenities, and service is generally willing and friendly –
especially in the busy carvery-style restaurant.*
150⇨🛏(77fb)✂in 10 bedrooms CTV in all bedrooms ® T ✳
sB⇨🛏£84.50-£107.50 dB⇨🛏£94.50-£122.50 (room only) 🍴
《⊞ 200P ✿ CFA 🖂 (heated) sauna solarium gymnasium ♫
*xmas*
♀ International **V** ❦ ⚘ ✂ Lunch fr£15.95 Dinner
fr£17.50&alc Last dinner 10.30pm
Credit Cards 1 2 3 4 5 £

---

## SEAVIEW

See Wight, Isle of

---

## SEDBERGH Cumbria Map **07** SD69

### ★★66% *Oakdene Country House*
Garsdale Rd LA10 5JN ☎(05396)20280
Closed Jan & Feb
*A friendly Victorian house set in its own grounds on the A684 a
mile east of the town, giving fine views of the countryside.
Bedrooms are comfortable and well furnished and there is a
relaxing lounge with a log fire, a separate cosy bar and a choice of
menus available at dinner.*
6⇨🛏(1fb) CTV in all bedrooms ® 🐾
15P 🚗 ✿ nc8yrs
♀ English, French & Italian Last dinner 8.45pm
Credit Cards 1 3

---

## SEDGEFIELD Co Durham Map **08** NZ32

### ★★★65% Hardwick Hall
TS21 2EH ☎(0740)20253 Telex no 537681 FAX (0740) 22771
*This elegant 18th-century country-house hotel stands in well
tended grounds, which supply the flowers that enhance the
attractive public rooms. The bedrooms are very well equipped and
the restaurant has recently been totally refurbished.*
17⇨🛏(2fb) CTV in all bedrooms ® T 🐾 (ex guide dogs) ✳
sB&B⇨🛏£52-£60 dB&B⇨🛏£60-£75 🍴
200P ✿ ♨
♀ English & French **V** ❦ ⚘ ✳ Lunch fr£8.50&alc High tea
fr£4.50 Dinner fr£9.95&alc Last dinner 9.30pm
Credit Cards 1 2 3 5

### ★★66% Crosshill
1 The Square TS21 2AB ☎(0740)20153 & 21206
*A friendly hotel, in the centre of the village facing the church,
which offers well equipped bedrooms and an attractive dining
room. Hearty eaters will enjoy the substantial dinners served in the
comfortable restaurant, while the lounge/bar offers an alternative
range of bar meals and snacks.*
8⇨🛏(2fb) CTV in all bedrooms ® T ✳ sB&B⇨🛏£47-£50
dB&B⇨🛏£58-£62 🍴
《 CTV 9P *xmas*
♀ English & Continental **V** ❦ ⚘ Lunch fr£7.25 High tea
fr£4.50 Dinner fr£15.50 Last dinner 9.30pm
Credit Cards 1 2 3 £

Restaurants and hotel restaurants
with rosettes have their names and addresses
tinted pink in the directory.

S

## SEDGEMOOR MOTORWAY SERVICE AREA (M5)
Somerset Map **03** ST35

### ✦Forte Travelodge
BS24 0JL (junc 22 M5 northbound) (Forte)
☎Weston-Super-Mare(0934)750831
Central Res (0800) 850950

*Modern, purpose-built block of well-equipped rooms offering good value, family accommodation. Food is available in the nearby service area between 7am and 10pm.*

40⇨🛏(40fb) CTV in all bedrooms ® sB⇨🛏£29.95
dB⇨🛏£29.95 (room only)
( 40P 🚭

Credit Cards ①②③

---

## SEDLESCOMBE East Sussex Map **05** TQ71

### ★★69% *Brickwall*
The Green TN33 0QA ☎(0424)870253 FAX (08424) 870785
*A welcoming manor house with Tudor origins retains a good deal of character, though it now provides modern bedroom extensions supplying well equipped accommodation. A popular restaurant maintains good standards of food and service, and the hotel has a lively, hospitable atmosphere.*

23⇨🛏(2fb)4🛏 CTV in all bedrooms ® T sB&B⇨🛏£45-£47
dB&B⇨🛏£58-£60 🖪
25P 🚭 ❀ CFA ⌂ (heated) *xmas*
♀ English, French & Italian V ✆ ✳ Lunch £9-£12 Dinner £13-£17 Last dinner 9pm
Credit Cards ①②③⑤

---

## SELBY North Yorkshire Map **08** SE63

### ★★65% *Londesborough Arms*
Market Place YO8 0NS ☎(0757)707355
*Standing at the head of the market place, an impressive old coaching inn has been converted to provide comfortable modern facilities whilst retaining its original character and atmosphere.*

27rm(14⇨9🛏)(1fb)1🛏 CTV in all bedrooms ® T
🍴 (ex guide dogs)
( CTV 18P 6🚗 ♫
V ✆ ✍ Last dinner 9.30pm
Credit Cards ①②③⑤

### ★★63% Owl
Main Rd YO8 9JH ☎(0757)2282374 FAX (0757) 228125
(For full entry see Hambleton (4m W A63))

---

## SELKIRK Borders *Selkirkshire* Map **12** NT42

### ★62% Heatherlie House
Heatherlie Park TD7 5AL ☎(0750)21200
*Quietly situated within its own well-kept gardens this small hotel offers comfortable accommodation and interesting home-cooked dishes.*

7rm(6🛏)(2fb) CTV in all bedrooms ® 🍴 sB&Bfr£19
sB&B🛏£25 dB&B🛏£40 🖪
12P 🚭 ❀
♀ European V ✔ ✳ High tea £5.75-£9 Dinner £8.75&alc Last dinner 8pm
Credit Cards ①③

---

## SENNEN Cornwall & Isles of Scilly Map **02** SW32

### ★★★65% The State House
TR19 7AA ☎Penzance(0736)871844 FAX (0736) 871812
*This refurbished hotel, set on the cliff top at Lands End against a dramatic backdrop which takes in the Long Ships Lighthouse and sometimes even the Isles of Scilly beyond, promotes comfortable modern standards under the ownership of Peter de Savary. In the well appointed surroundings of the Observatory Restaurant – made, as its name implies, of glass – guests are offered a good choice of well prepared dishes from both set and à la carte menus,*

*while lighter meals are available in the adjoining bar. Brightly decorated bedrooms in modern style are equipped to meet the needs of today's traveller. Residents at the hotel are entitled to free entry into the adjacent imaginative theme park.*

34⇨(1fb)3🛏✍ in 5 bedrooms CTV in all bedrooms ® T
🍴 (ex guide dogs) S% sB&B⇨£25.50-£60 dB&B⇨£50-£110 🖪
( 50P CFA ♫ 🐕 *xmas*
♀ English & French V ✆ ✍ ✍ S% Lunch £7.95-£18.50&alc
High tea £3.50-£5.95 Dinner £14-£20&alc Last dinner 9.30pm
Credit Cards ①②③
**See advertisement under LANDS END**

### ★★64% *Old Success Inn*
Sennen Cove TR19 7DG ☎(0736)871232
*Set in an enviable beach-side position against the panoramic backdrop of Sennen Cove, this busy, fully licensed little holiday hotel, with its character bars, provides a popular venue for both tourists and the locals. Cosy bedrooms are spotlessly clean, well decorated and appointed, many of them offering good views across the cove, while the equally bright and comfortable public rooms include a restaurant serving skilfully cooked meals which make effective use of fresh ingredients. Personally managed, the hotel provides a pleasant retreat or an ideal base from which to explore the tip of Cornwall.*

11rm(9⇨)2🛏 CTV in all bedrooms ® 🍴
CTV 30P
✆ ✍
Credit Cards ③

---

## SETTLE North Yorkshire Map **07** SD86 ◎

### ★★★62% *Falcon Manor*
Skipton Rd BD24 9BD (Consort) ☎(0729)823814
FAX (0729) 822087
*This impressive manor house has been comfortably converted to provide individually fitted bedrooms and spacious public areas. Meals available throughout the day and evening offer a good selection of dishes.*

15⇨🛏Annexe5⇨🛏(3fb)2🛏 CTV in all bedrooms ® T
sB&B⇨🛏£49-£65 dB&B⇨🛏£68-£100 🖪
85P ❀ CFA bowling green *xmas*
♀ English & Continental V ✆ ✍ ✳ Lunch £8.50-£9 High tea £3-£8alc Dinner £16.75-£17.50&alc Last dinner 9.30pm
Credit Cards ①③⑤£

### ★★73% *Royal Oak*
Market Place BD24 9ED ☎(0729)822561
Closed Xmas day night
*Dating from 1684 this is a busy, friendly family run hotel. The en suite bedrooms are pretty and very well equipped and the elegant oak panelled restaurant provides a good standard of cuisine; bar meals are also popular.*

6⇨🛏 CTV in all bedrooms ® 🍴 (ex guide dogs) ✳
sB⇨🛏£34.50 dB⇨🛏£57.50 (room only)
20P 🚗
♀ English & French V ✆ ✍ Sunday Lunch £9-£9.70 High tea £4.75-£6.55 Dinner £14-£20alc Last dinner 10pm

---

## SEVENOAKS Kent Map **05** TQ55 ◎

### ★★★65% *Royal Oak*
Upper High St TN14 5PG ☎(0732)451109 FAX (0732) 740187
*Originally a coaching inn, this popular and well managed hotel has been completely refurbished and upgraded by the new owners. The Victorian themed bar leads into an elegant, comfortable restaurant and small conservatory lounge; standards of cuisine are high and service is helpful and attentive.*

23rm(19⇨2🛏)Annexe16⇨🛏 CTV in 21 bedrooms ® T
( 50P
♀ English & French V ✆ ✍ ✍ Last dinner 9.30pm
Credit Cards ①②③⑤

**S**

**★★59% Sevenoaks Park**
Seal Hollow Rd TN13 3SH ☎(0732)454245 Telex no 95571
FAX (0732) 457468
*The public areas of this friendly, efficient and family-run hotel
include a newly refurbished and extended restaurant and lounge.
There are also some well appointed annexe rooms peacefully
located in the grounds.*
16rm(3⇌3🛏)Annexe10⇌🛏(3fb) CTV in all bedrooms ® T
🗶 (ex guide dogs) ✷ sB&B£30 sB&B⇌🛏£40-£50 dB&B£40
dB&B⇌🛏£50-£65 🖳
CTV 33P 🚗 ✿ ⌁ (heated) ♫
♀ English & French V ♨ ♨ ✷ Sunday Lunch £5.50-£9.50&alc
High tea £1.50-£2.50alc Dinner £9.50-£12.50&alc Last dinner
9pm
Credit Cards ① ② ③ ⑤

---

**SHAFTESBURY** Dorset Map **03** ST82

**★★★65% Royal Chase**
Royal Chase Roundabout SP7 8DB (Best Western)
☎(0747)53355 Telex no 418414 FAX (0747) 51969
*Public areas have recently been refurbished at the Royal Chase
and there is now a smart restaurant, the Byzant, which serves a
fixed price menu of interesting fresh dishes. There is a pleasant bar
and a smaller, less formal and less expensive restaurant. Bedrooms
vary from small, budget priced and basic to freshly decorated and
purpose-built.*
35⇌🛏(15fb) CTV in all bedrooms ® T S% sB&B⇌🛏£47.50-
£67 dB&B⇌🛏£70.50-£109 🖳
CTV 100P ✿ CFA ⌁ (heated) solarium croquet putting
turkish steam bath ⚬ *xmas*
V ♨ ♨ ✷ Lunch £7.50-£19.50alc Dinner fr£19.50alc Last
dinner 9.45pm
Credit Cards ① ② ③ ⑤

**★★★58% The Grosvenor**
The Commons SP7 8JA (Forte Hotels) ☎(0747)52282
FAX (0747) 54755
*A former coaching inn, set at the centre of the small market town
and undergoing gradual improvement, offers public areas which
include a busy, popular bar and a first-floor lounge with the most
wonderful Chevy Chase antique carved sideboard; bedrooms vary
in size, and many have been redecorated.*
41⇌🛏(5fb)2🛏🛏 in 16 bedrooms CTV in all bedrooms ®
sB&B🛏fr£70 dB&B⇌🛏£80-£95 (room only) 🖳
🏌 CFA *xmas*
V ♨ ♨ ✷ ✷ Bar Lunch £3.50-£8 Dinner £12.95&alc Last
dinner 9.30pm
Credit Cards ① ② ③ ④ ⑤

---

**SHALDON**

See Teignmouth

**SHANKLIN**

See Wight, Isle of

**SHAP** Cumbria Map **12** NY51

**★★66% Shap Wells**
CA10 3QU (situated 3m SW of Shap Village off A6)
☎(09316)628 & 744 FAX (09316) 377
Closed 2 Jan-14 Feb
*A family-managed hotel peacefully situated in its own grounds
between the A6 and M6 (with access to both), offers friendly and
informal service. Bedroom improvements continue, as does the
upgrading of spacious public areas.*
90rm(88⇌🛏)(11fb) CTV in all bedrooms ® T ✷
sB&B⇌🛏£36-£50 dB&B⇌🛏£55-£75 🖳
CTV 200P ✿ CFA ♟ (hard) snooker
♀ English & French V ♨ ✷ Lunch £6.50-£7.50 Dinner £12.50-
£14.50&alc Last dinner 8.30pm
Credit Cards ① ② ③ ⑤

See advertisement under KENDAL

---

**SHARDLOW** Derbyshire Map **08** SK43

**★★63% The Lady In Grey**
Wilne Ln DE7 2HA ☎Derby(0332)792331
*This fully restored old house offers comfortable accommodation in
modern, well equipped bedrooms. The restaurant, which overlooks
attractive gardens, emphasises Spanish cuisine and offers a good,
reasonably priced wine list.*
9⇌🛏(2fb)2🛏 CTV in all bedrooms ® T 🗶 ✷ sB&B⇌🛏£35-
£60 dB&B⇌🛏£52-£70
30P 🚗 ✿
♀ International V ✷ ✷ Lunch £8&alc Dinner £11.25&alc Last
dinner 9.45pm
Credit Cards ① ② ③ ⑤

---

**SHEDFIELD** Hampshire Map **04** SU51

**★★★66% Meon Valley**
Sandy Ln SO3 2LZ ☎Wickham(0329)833455 Telex no 86272
FAX (0329) 834411
83⇌🛏(2fb)✷in 16 bedrooms CTV in all bedrooms ® T
🗶 (ex guide dogs) ✷ S10% sB&B⇌🛏£80-£88 dB&B⇌🛏£90-£98
🖳
《 CTV 1000P ✿ CFA ⌁ (heated) ▶ 18 ♟ (hard) squash
snooker sauna solarium gymnasium health & beauty salon
dance studio *xmas*
♀ English & French V ♨ ♨ ✷ Lunch fr£12.50 High tea
fr£1.20 Dinner fr£19 Last dinner 10pm
Credit Cards ① ② ③ ⑤ ⑤

---

**SHEFFIELD** South Yorkshire Map **08** SK38 ☉

**★★★★57% Grosvenor House**
Charter Square S1 3EH (Forte Hotels) ☎(0742)720041
Telex no 54312 FAX (0742) 757199
*Modern, 14-storey hotel in the town centre.*
103⇌🛏in 38 bedrooms CTV in all bedrooms ® T ✷
sB⇌fr£80 dB⇌fr£90 (room only) 🖳
Lift 《 80🛏 (charged) CFA *xmas*
♀ International V ♨ ♨ ✷ ✷ Lunch fr£12.50 Dinner
fr£17.50&alc Last dinner 10pm
Credit Cards ① ② ③ ④ ⑤

**★★★ ❀❀71% Charnwood**
10 Sharrow Ln S11 8AA ☎(0742)589411 FAX (0742) 555107
*Major alterations and extensions now completed, this hotel
provides two very different and exciting eating options – the
French-inspired Brasserie Leo for a casual meal, and Henfrey's
where chef Wayne Bosworth creates his own style of modern
British cuisine with a range of simple, but true-flavoured and
attractively presented dishes in which fish is prominently featured.
Accommodation remains comfortable and well equipped, and the
additional banqueting and meetings rooms are already proving
popular.*
22⇌🛏(1fb) CTV in all bedrooms ® T 🗶 (ex guide dogs) ✷
sB&B⇌🛏£75 dB&B⇌🛏£90
《 22P 🚗 CFA
V ♨ ♨ ✷ ✷ Lunch £10.95 Dinner £10.95&alc Last dinner
10pm
Credit Cards ① ② ③ ⑤ ⑤

**★★★71% Sheffield Moat House**
Chesterfield Rd South S8 8BW (Queens Moat) ☎(0742)375376
FAX (0742) 378140
Closed 25-26 Dec
*This new hotel has proved deservedly popular. Clean and well
maintained, it provides efficient friendly service, extensive*

*conference and banqueting facilities and a well equipped indoor leisure centre. Modern bedrooms are comfortable with good facilities.*

95⇔⌐(9fb)⊬in 20 bedrooms CTV in all bedrooms ® T ✱ sB⇔⌐£40-£71 dB⇔⌐£50-£84 (room only) ⊟

Lift ☾ 260P ❊ ⊡ (heated) sauna solarium gymnasium health & beauty treatment room

☋ English & French V ♔ ☕ ⊬ ✱ S% Lunch £8.50-£10.25&alc Dinner £13.50&alc Last dinner 10pm

Credit Cards [1] [2] [3] [5]

---

**★★★ 69% Harley**

334 Glossop Rd S10 2HW ☎(0742)752288 FAX (0742) 722383

RS Sun

*Situated west of the city centre on the inner ring road, close to its junction with the A57, this hotel has been extensively refurbished over recent years to offer elegant public areas of a very high standard and good quality, well equipped, modern bedrooms with en suite shower facilities. Meal service is restricted on Sunday evenings, but residents are provided with a light meal free of charge and more substantial dishes can be supplied with advance warning. There is no car park, but street parking can usually be found without too much difficulty, and the hotel both supplies burglar alarms for guests' vehicles and operates a video surveillance system for added security.*

22⇔⌐⊬in 11 bedrooms CTV in all bedrooms ® T ✗ (ex guide dogs) ✱ sB⇔⌐£50-£70 dB⇔⌐£75-£80 (room only)

☾ P ⊞ ♫ nc12yrs

☋ English & French V ♔ ☕ ⊬ ✱ Lunch fr£9.75 Dinner fr£17.50&alc Last dinner 9.45pm

Credit Cards [1] [2] [3] [5]

---

**★★★ 67% Dinnington Hall Hotel**

Falcon Way S31 3NY ☎Worksop(0909)569661

FAX (0909)563441

(For full entry see Dinnington)

---

**★★★ 65% Beauchief**

161 Abbeydale Rd S7 2QW (Lansbury) ☎(0742)620500

Telex no 54164 FAX (0742) 350197

*An original coaching inn, pleasantly set amongst trees, has been extended and modernised to provide a good standard of well appointed accommodation; its restaurant is complemented by the popular Michel's Cellar Bar, and pleasant staff create a lively, friendly atmosphere throughout.*

41⇔⌐(2fb)2⊠⊬in 11 bedrooms CTV in all bedrooms ® T ✗ (ex guide dogs) sB&B⇔⌐fr£79 dB&B⇔⌐fr£92 ⊟

☾ 200P ❊ CFA sauna solarium gymnasium

☋ English & Continental V ♔ ⊬

Credit Cards [1] [2] [3] [5]

---

**★★★ 65% Mosborough Hall**

High St, Mosborough S19 5AE (7m SE A616) ☎(0742)484353

FAX (0742) 477042

*On the city's outskirts 5 miles from junction 30 of the M1, this peaceful 16th-century manor house with a new wing of modern bedrooms is run in friendly country house style. Extensive refurbishment of the public areas to provide more comfort was due for completion in 1991.*

23⇔⌐(1fb)3⊠ CTV in all bedrooms ® T ✱ sB&B⇔⌐£57-£67 dB&B⇔⌐£67-£87 ⊟

☾ CTV 100P ❊ CFA

☋ English & French V ♔ ☕ ⊬ ✱ Lunch £3.50-£6.50 Dinner fr£14.95&alc Last dinner 9.30pm

Credit Cards [1] [2] [3] (£)

---

**★★★ 64% Forte Crest**

Manchester Rd, Broomhill S10 5DX (Forte Hotels)

☎(0742)670067 Telex no 547293 FAX (0742) 682620

*A modern, 12 storey hotel with impressive views over the city and the surrounding countryside. Guests have free access to the popular health and fitness club.*

135⇔⌐⊬in 36 bedrooms CTV in all bedrooms ® T ✱ S% sB⇔⌐fr£69 dB⇔⌐£79-£89 (room only) ⊟

Lift ☾ 120P CFA ⊡ (heated) sauna solarium gymnasium health & fitness centre *xmas*

V ♔ ☕ ⊬ ✱ S% Lunch fr£10.95&alc High tea fr£2.75 Dinner fr£14.95&alc Last dinner 11pm

Credit Cards [1] [2] [3] [4] [5]

---

**★★★ 63% Swallow**

Kenwood Rd S7 1NQ (Swallow) ☎(0742)583811

Telex no 547030 FAX (0742) 500138

*Modern hotel situated in own grounds and gardens, close to city centre. Recently updated public rooms offer comfort and relaxation in pleasant surroundings.*

141⇔⌐ CTV in all bedrooms ® T ✱ S% sB&B⇔⌐£78 dB&B⇔⌐£92 ⊟

Lift ☾ 200P ❊ CFA ⊡ (heated) ⚲ sauna solarium gymnasium spa bath mimi gym steam room *xmas*

☋ English & French V ♔ ☕ ✱ Lunch fr£11.50&alc Dinner fr£15&alc Last dinner 10pm

Credit Cards [1] [2] [3] [5]

---

**★★★ 62% Staindrop Lodge**

Ln End S30 4UH ☎(0742)846727 FAX (0742) 846783

(For full entry see Chapeltown)

---

**★★★ 60% Granada**

340 Prince of Wales Rd S2 1FF (Granada) ☎(0742)530935

FAX (0742) 642731

*Situated at the A6102/A57/A630 junction about 1.5 miles from the city centre, this modern, purpose-built hotel offers bedrooms identical to those of the Granada Lodges – all with en suite bathrooms and a good range of facilities; accommodation is available for diabled guests, and some rooms are reserved for non-smokers. The Platters Restaurant provides a flexible range of snacks throughout the day, lunch and dinner time menus being* →

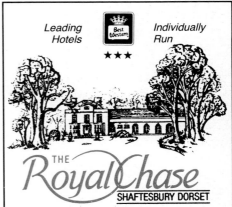

*composed mainly of grills and daily specials. A compact bar and small meeting room are also avaiable.*

61⇨🌂(10fb)⊁in 10 bedrooms CTV in all bedrooms ® T 🗶 (ex guide dogs) S% sB⇨🌂fr£40 dB⇨🌂fr£44 (room only) 🎜

《 93P

🍴 English & French V ৬ ♨ ⊁ ✳ Sunday Lunch fr£9.25 Dinner fr£12.50 Last dinner 9.30pm

Credit Cards ① ② ③ ⑤

## ★★69% Rutland

452 Glossop Rd, Broomhill S10 2PY ☎(0742)664411 Telex no 547500 FAX (0742) 670348

*Seven detached stone houses, interconnected by walkways, form a modern hotel which is popular with businessmen. Public rooms include a spacious reception lounge with separate public lounge, writing room and small, intimate restaurant with adjoining cocktail bar. An extremely good bedroom annexe stands close by.*

73rm(68⇨1🌂)Annexe17⇨🌂(9fb) CTV in all bedrooms ® T ✳ sB&B⇨🌂£40-£66 dB&B⇨🌂£60-£78 🎜

Lift 《 CTV 80P CFA *xmas*

V ৬ ♨ ✳ Lunch £4.20-£7.95 Dinner £9.95 Last dinner 9.30pm

Credit Cards ① ② ③ ⑤

## ★★68% Andrews Park

48 Kenwood Rd S7 1NQ ☎(0742)500111 & 501103 FAX (0742) 555423

*Friendly proprietors are actively involved in the running of a genuinely hospitable little hotel, ensuring high standards of cleanliness and maintenance. Accommodation is comfortable and reasonably well equipped, though some rooms are compact.*

11rm(2⇨5🌂)Annexe2⇨🌂(2fb) CTV in all bedrooms ® T S10% sB&B£35-£40 sB&B⇨🌂£35-£40 dB&B⇨🌂£47-£54

《 CTV 15P

V ৬ ♨ ✳ Lunch £6.50-£9.50 High tea £2.50-£7.50 Dinner £8.50-£11.95 Last dinner 8.45pm

Credit Cards ① ② ③ ⑥

## ★★65% Roslyn Court

178-180 Psalter Ln, Brincliffe S11 8US ☎(0742)666188 FAX (0742) 684279

*A popular hotel in a residential area on the city outskirts, offering modern, generally compact accommodation. A busy function trade restricts service at weekends.*

31⇨🌂(2fb) CTV in all bedrooms ® ✳ sB&B⇨🌂£29-£43 dB&B⇨🌂£43-£57.50

《 CTV 25P

🍴 English & French V ৬ ♨ ✳ Sunday Lunch fr£6.25 Dinner fr£8.50&alc Last dinner 8.45pm

Credit Cards ① ② ③ ⑤ ⑥

## ⏚Comfort Inn

George St S1 2PF ☎(0742)739939 FAX (0742) 768332 Closed 24 Dec-3 Jan

*In the very heart of the city, this Lodge provides bedrooms which, though compact, are modern and very well equipped. There is a pleasant bistro-style restaurant open from breakfast through to 5.30pm. For dinner you will need to seek out one of the numerous restaurants nearby.*

50⇨🌂(2fb)⊁in 7 bedrooms CTV in all bedrooms ® T

Lift 《 ⅌

V ৬ ♨ ⊁

Credit Cards ① ② ③ ⑤

## ○Holiday Inn Royal Victoria

Victoria Station Rd S4 7YE (Holiday Inns Inc) ☎(0742)768822 Telex no 547539 FAX (0742) 724519

Open

100⇨🌂

---

## SHEPPERTON Surrey

**See LONDON plan 1A1**(page 434)

### ★★★57% Shepperton Moat House

Felix Ln TW17 8NP (Queens Moat) ☎Walton-on-Thames(0932)241404 Telex no 928170 FAX (0932) 245231 Closed 26-30 Dec

*A busy hotel close to the Thames, built in the early 1970s, which is primarily geared to the needs of commercial guests and conferences. Leisure facilities include a mini gym and sauna. Bedrooms – though dated and functional – provide a good standard of comfort, and the restaurant's carvery operation is supplemented by room service snacks.*

156⇨🌂(5fb) CTV in all bedrooms ® T sB&B⇨🌂£78-£82.50 dB&B⇨🌂£98-£103 🎜

Lift 《 225P ✿ CFA snooker sauna solarium gymnasium putting 🎜

🍴 English & French V ৬ ♨ Lunch fr£15.75 Dinner fr£15.75 Last dinner 10pm

Credit Cards ① ② ③ ⑤

---

## SHEPTON MALLET Somerset Map 03 ST64

### ★★70% Thatched Cottage Inn

63-67 Charlton Rd BA4 5QF ☎(0749)342058 FAX (0749) 343265

*A 300-year-old thatched building on the eastern outskirts of the town has recently been refurbished to provide accommodation in individually decorated and furnished beamed bedrooms which are all named after birds. The Parlour à la carte restaurant has a relaxed atmosphere, and an extensive range of meals is also available in spacious bar areas which have been comfortably furnished in pine whilst retaining many original features.*

8⇨🌂 CTV in all bedrooms ® T 🗶 (ex guide dogs) ✳ sB&B⇨🌂£42.50-£49.50 dB&B⇨🌂£64.50-£69.50 🎜

《 40P nc5yrs

🍴 French V ৬ ♨ ⊁ ✳ Lunch £14.50-£25alc Dinner £12.50-£17&alc Last dinner 9.30pm

Credit Cards ① ③

### ⊛ ✗ ✗ Bowlish House

Wells Rd, Bowlish BA4 5JD (on the Wells road A371) ☎(0749)342022

Closed 24-27 Dec Lunch not served all week (ex by prior arrangement)

🍴 International V 26 seats Dinner £19.50 Last dinner 9.30pm 10 P ⊁

Credit Cards ① ③

### ⊛ ✗ Blostin's

29 Waterloo Rd BA4 5HH ☎(0749)343648

*An attractively decorated, shop fronted restaurant with a warm, friendly atmosphere. Husband and wife team Nick and Lynne Read offer uncomplicated and well prepared dishes. There is a blackboard, set price and short à la carte menu.*

Closed Sun, Mon, 3-19 Jan, 1-8 Jun & 1 wk Etr Lunch not served all week (ex prior arrangement Tue-Fri)

🍴 French 30 seats Lunch £10.50 Dinner £12.95-£13.95&alc Last lunch 1.45pm Last dinner 9.30pm ⅌

Credit Cards ① ③

---

## SHERBORNE Dorset Map 03 ST61

### ★★★70% Eastbury

Long St DT9 3BY (Clipper) ☎(0935)813131 Telex no 46644 FAX (0935) 817296

*This characterful, attractive and centrally situated Georgian town house offers a warm, relaxing atmosphere and well managed service. Bedrooms are of good size and comfortably equipped, while tastefully appointed public areas include pleasant lounges and a light, airy restaurant, where the well prepared dishes featured in table d'hôte and à la carte menus are accompanied by an excellent wine list.*

15⇨(1fb)1🍴 CTV in all bedrooms ® T 🐕 (ex guide dogs) sB&B⇨£72.50 dB&B⇨£98 🏳

24P 🚗 ♣ croquet ⛳ *xmas*

♥ English & French V ✿ 🍷 Lunch £12&alc Dinner fr£20&alc Last dinner 9.30pm

Credit Cards 1 3

★★★ 63% **Antelope**

Greenhill DT9 4EP ☎Yeovil(0935)812077 FAX (0935) 816473

*This 17th-century building on the edge of the town centre has been completely refurbished to provide comfortable well equipped bedrooms and a large lounge bar. The restaurant features traditional Italian cooking by the enthusiastic Italian chef. Helpful staff provide attentive service in an informal atmosphere.*

19⇨♠(1fb)2🍴 CTV in all bedrooms ® T ✳

sB&B⇨♠£29.95-£39.95 dB&B⇨♠£39.95-£49.95 🏳

€ 22P CFA

♥ English & Italian V ✿ 🍷 S% Lunch £7.50-£20alc Dinner £7.50-£20alc Last dinner 11.30pm

Credit Cards 1 2 3 5 £

★★★ 60% **Forte Posthouse**

Horsecastles Ln DT9 6BB (Forte Hotels) ☎(0935)813191 Telex no 46522 FAX (0935) 816493

*This modern hotel, set in its own grounds at the edge of the town, offers spacious, well equipped bedrooms by a small but comfortable open-plan bar and lounge area; a refurbishment programme is now under way, about half the rooms having been completed.*

60⇨♠(12fb)⤢in 30 bedrooms CTV in all bedrooms ® T ✳

S% sB⇨♠£39.50-£49.50 dB⇨♠£39.50-£49.50 (room only) 🏳

€ 🏓 100P ♣ CFA croquet putting ⛳ *xmas*

→

S

V ♿ ⚗ ✀ ✳ S% Lunch £10.95 High tea £1.95 Dinner
£13.95&alc Last dinner 10.30pm
Credit Cards [1][2][3][5]

### ★★60% *Half Moon Toby*
Half Moon St DT9 3LN (Toby) ☎(0935)812017
*A centrally located hotel, close to the abbey, which is popular for
its bar and carvery restaurant. Comfortable bedrooms provide
modern facilties, but lounge seating is limited.*
15⇨🛏(2fb)✀in 4 bedrooms CTV in all bedrooms ®
44P (charged) ⏶ pool table skittles
V ♿ ✀ Last dinner 10pm
Credit Cards [1][2][3]

### ✳ ✗ ✗Pheasants
24 Greenhill DT9 4EW ☎(0935)815252
*This attractive stone house at the top of the High Street,
refurbished to a high standard, features a cosy bar and
comfortable lounge in addition to its well appointed dining room; a
menu of modern English dishes based on local ingredients
(including game) provides clear, robust flavours, and service is
friendly yet discreet.*
Closed Mon & 2 wks Jan
Dinner not served Sun
🍽 English & French V 40 seats ✳ Lunch £9.75-£11.25&alc
Dinner £18.50&alc Last lunch 2pm Last dinner 10.30pm 10 P
Credit Cards [1][3]

---

## SHERFIELD ON LODDON Hampshire Map 04 SU65

### ★★65% *Wessex House*
Reading Rd RG27 0EX ☎Basingstoke(0256)882243
FAX (0256) 881131
Closed 25 Dec-1 Jan
*This friendly hotel, which stands in a small village 5 miles from
Basingstoke, offers easy access to both M4 and M3 motorways.
Bedrooms are modern and well equipped, the bar lounge (though
quite compact) is bright and comfortable, and a more spacious
restaurant offers an à la carte menu every evening except Sunday,
when a table d'hôte meal is available at lunch time.*
17⇨🛏 CTV in all bedrooms ® T ✘ (ex guide dogs)
dB&B⇨🛏£59
℄ 49P
V Sunday Lunch £8.95 Dinner £9.50-£13.95 Last dinner
9.30pm
Credit Cards [1][2][3][5]

**See advertisement on page 109**

---

## SHERINGHAM Norfolk Map 09 TG14

### ★★65% *Beaumaris*
South St NR26 8LL ☎(0263)822370
Closed 19 Dec-Jan
*A popular small hotel with delightful lounges attracts both local
trade and leisure users; friendly, caring service is still its hallmark,
though management has now been passed over to the proprietors'
daughter and her husband.*
24rm(17⇨5🛏)(5fb) CTV in all bedrooms ® T sB&Bfr£25.50
sB&B⇨🛏£29.50 dB&Bfr£53 dB&B⇨🛏£60 ⏵
CTV 25P
V ♿ ⚗ ✳ Lunch fr£8.95&alc High tea fr£4 Dinner
fr£13.25&alc Last dinner 8.30pm
Credit Cards [1][2][3]

### ★★62% *Southlands*
South St NR26 8LL ☎(0263)822679
Closed Oct-Etr
*This privately owned, seasonally operated family hotel with a
friendly, caring atmosphere features public areas dominated by a
large and very comfortably furnished lounge where guests can
relax peacefully. Bedrooms combine modern facilities with
traditional furnishings.*

18rm(13⇨1🛏)(1fb) CTV in all bedrooms ® ✳
15P CFA
✀ ✳

---

## SHETLAND Map 16

---

## BRAE Map 16 HU36

### ★★★⚑67% *Busta House*
ZE2 9QN ☎(080622)506 Telex no 9312100218
FAX (080622) 588
Closed 23 Dec-2 Jan
*An 18th-century mansion house, situated on the western shores of
Busta Voe, with a private road leading down to its own little
harbour. It offers compact but well-equipped bedrooms, two
comfortable lounges and a cosy country bar; the restaurant
features a short, carefully chosen dinner menu of good quality
which uses only local produce.*
20⇨🛏1⏧ CTV in all bedrooms ® T ✳ sB&B⇨🛏£51
dB&B⇨🛏£66.50-£72.50 ⏵
35P ⏶ sea fishing water sports
🍽 International V ♿ ⚗ ✀ Bar Lunch £7.65-£14.65 Dinner
£18.50-£19.90 Last dinner 9pm
Credit Cards [1][2][3][5]

---

## LERWICK Map 16 HU44

### ★★★66% *Shetland*
Holmsgarth Rd ZE1 0PW ☎(0595)5515 Telex no 75432
FAX (0595) 5828
*Standing opposite the car ferry terminal, this purpose-built,
modern hotel provides spacious bedrooms and the services of
friendly staff.*
66⇨🛏(4fb)✀in 5 bedrooms CTV in all bedrooms ® T
sB&B⇨🛏£58 dB&B⇨🛏£72 ⏵
Lift ℄ 150P ⏶ CFA ⊡ (heated) sauna solarium gymnasium
V ♿ ⚗ ✳ Lunch £6.95-£10 Dinner £13.75-£19&alc Last dinner
9.30pm
Credit Cards [1][2][3][4][5]

### ★★★58% *Lerwick*
South Rd ZE1 0RB ☎(0595)2166 Telex no 75128
FAX (0595) 4419
*There are fine views of the bay from this tourist/commercial hotel,
purpose-built in the seventies.*
31⇨🛏(1fb) CTV in all bedrooms ® T ✘ (ex guide dogs) ✳
sB&B⇨🛏£51.75 dB&B⇨🛏£65.50 ⏵
℄ 30P CFA
🍽 International V ♿ ⚗ ✳ Lunch £6.50-£7.95alc Dinner
£13.95&alc Last dinner 9pm
Credit Cards [1][2][3][£]

### ★★★56% *Kveldsro House*
ZE1 0AN ☎(0595)2195
*Standing in a quiet area of the town, this small business hotel offers
functional but thoughtfully equipped bedrooms, sound menus which
combine quality with quantity, and limited lounge facilities.*
14rm(9⇨) CTV in all bedrooms ® T ✘ (ex guide dogs)
28P ⏶
V ♿ ⚗

---

## SHIELDAIG Highland *Ross & Cromarty* Map 14 NG85

### ★★66% *Tigh an Eilean*
IV54 8XN ☎(05205)251
Closed Nov-Etr
*This small friendly hotel is set on Shieldaig's picturesque
waterfront. The compact bedrooms have been decorated to a high
standard and the three peaceful lounges are cosy, one containing a
bar. Fresh local seafood is a feature of the short dinner menu.*

S

13rm(4⇌1♠)(2fb) ®
CTV 15P ⇔ ♪
Credit Cards ①③

---

## SHIFNAL Shropshire Map 07 SJ70

★★★★※63% **Park House**
Silvermere Park, Park St TF11 9BA (Rank)
☎Telford(0952)460128 Telex no 35438 FAX (0952) 461658
*This extensive complex of leisure accommodation is located on the Wolverhampton side of the town. Formed by linking 2 country houses and their grounds, the hotel has built a well-deserved reputation for high standards of comfort and friendly caring staff. Recent conversion of a cottage-style annexe adds further accommodation.*
54⇌♠(2fb)⅍in 2 bedrooms CTV in all bedrooms ® T ✱
sB&B⇌♠£56-£82 dB&B⇌♠£82-£97 ⊟
Lift ℂ 160P ✿ ▭ (heated) sauna solarium jacuzzi *xmas*
♀ French V ♥ ⚻ ⅍ ✱ Lunch £11-£25alc Dinner £12.50-£25alc Last dinner 10.30pm
Credit Cards ①②③⑤

---

## SHINFIELD Berkshire Map 04 SU76

❀❀❀❀ ✕ ✕ ✕ **L'ORTOLAN**
Church Ln RG2 9BY ☎Reading(0734)883783
FAX (0734) 885391
*Chef John Burton-Race continues to justify our high praise for his imaginative and provocative standards of cooking. He must rank among the few British chefs who through his innovative and self indulgent style succeeds where so many have failed – though his creations get larger and more complex every year. The informative fixed price and à la carte menu is a joy to read, and includes dishes such as ballotine de pieds de cochon au ris de veau: a stuffed ballotine of pig's trotter filled with a chicken mousseline spiked with veal sweetbreads and set on a fine port wine sauce. For dessert, the Assiette Chocolatière couldn't fail with so many different styles of French chocolate. The restaurant's new conservatory lounge extension provides much needed extra space.*
Closed Mon, last 2 wks Feb & last 2 wks Aug
Dinner not served Sun
♀ French V 55 seats ✱ Lunch £29.50-£48 Dinner £29.50-£48
Last lunch 2.15pm Last dinner 10.15pm 30 P
Credit Cards ①②③⑤

---

## SHIPDHAM Norfolk Map 05 TF90

★66% **Pound Green**
Pound Green Ln IP25 7LS (4m SW East Dereham)
☎Dereham(0362)820165
*This friendly, family-run hotel off the A1075 offers caring service and comfortable, well equipped accommodation for both tourists and business travellers, including an à la carte restaurant and outdoor swimming pool.*
12rm(7♠)(2fb) CTV in all bedrooms ® ✱ sB&B£22.50-£29.50
sB&B♠fr£29.50 dB&Bfr£36 dB&B♠fr£48 ⊟
CTV 60P 2☎ ✿ CFA ⇌ (heated)
♀ English & Continental V ♥ ⚻ Lunch £8.50-£17.50alc
Dinner £10.50-£17.50alc Last dinner 9.30pm
Credit Cards ①③£

---

## SHIPHAM Somerset Map 03 ST45

★★★※♨67% **Daneswood House**
Cuck Hill BS25 1RD ☎Winscombe(093484)3145 & 3945
FAX (093484) 3824
RS 24 Dec-6 Jan
*Built in the Edwardian era as an homeopathic health hydro, this charming hotel offers spectacular views across the countryside; bedrooms range from the elegance of the honeymoon suite with its antique furniture and kingsize bed to garden suites with separate*

---

*lounges, gallery bedrooms and whirlpool spa baths – all accommodation being provided with every conceivable extra. Elegant Edwardian-style public areas include a restaurant serving traditional English and French cuisine with nouvelle influences.*
9⇌♠Annexe3⇌♠(3fb) CTV in all bedrooms ® T
✈ (ex guide dogs) ✱ sB&B⇌♠£57.50-£67.50 dB&B⇌♠£65-£112.50 ⊟
ℂ 25P 2☎ ⇔ ✿ CFA
♀ English & Continental V ♥ ⚻ ⅍ ✱ Lunch £12.95-£14.95
Credit Cards ①②③⑤ £

---

## SHIPTON-UNDER-WYCHWOOD Oxfordshire
Map 04 SP21

★★※63% **Shaven Crown**
OX7 6BA ☎(0993)830330
*An attractive family-run hotel, once a hospice to Bravern Abbey, reflects its 14th-century origins in a wealth of beams and exposed stone walls. Pride of place must go to an intimate candle-lit restaurant where very good value fixed price menus offer a wide choice of predominantly French dishes, though such traditional English specialities as Jugged Hare and Spotted Dick are included. The bar, which is reached through a courtyard from the main entrance, also offers an extensive range of meals and snacks. Bedrooms vary in shape and size, but all are comfortable, equipped with modern conveniences and well maintained.*
9rm(5⇌3♠)(1fb)⊠ CTV in all bedrooms ®
✈ (ex guide dogs) ✱ sB&B⇌♠£31 dB&B⇌♠£67-£69 ⊟
15P ✿ bowling green *xmas*
♀ Continental V ♥ ⚻ ✱ Sunday Lunch £14.50 Dinner £17.50
Last dinner 9.30pm
Credit Cards ①③

**S**

## ⊛✕ Lamb Inn
High St OX7 6DQ ☎(0993)830465

*This character Cotswold inn features a small restaurant with bright, cosy surroundings where service is friendly and informal. Although the menu is short, its limited range of dishes is prepared with a degree of imagination and flair, making good use of quality produce.*

Closed Mon 25 Dec-1 Jan

Dinner not served Sun

V 30 seats ✻ Sunday Lunch £12.50 Dinner £17.50 Last dinner 9.30pm 25 P nc14yrs ⅍

Credit Cards ①②③

---

**SHRAWLEY** Hereford & Worcester Map **07** SO86

### ★★★64% Lenchford
WR6 6TB ☎Worcester(0905)620229 FAX (0905) 621125
Closed 24, 25 & 26 Dec

*This family-run hotel enjoys an idyllic setting on the banks of the River Severn in a quiet rural location 6 miles north of Worcester.*

16rm(14⇨1♠)(1fb) CTV in all bedrooms ® T ✻ ✻ sB&B⇨♠£35-£47 dB&B⇨♠£45-£61.50 ⊟

50P ✿ CFA ⌷ (heated) ♪

♀ English & French V ♔ ✻ Lunch fr£10.95 Dinner £11.70-£18.85alc Last dinner 9.30pm

Credit Cards ①②③⑤ⓔ

**See advertisement under WORCESTER**

---

**SHREWSBURY** Shropshire Map **07** SJ41

### ★★★★58% Albrighton Hall
Albrighton SY4 3AG (2.5m N on A528) (Rank)
☎Bomere Heath(0939)291000 Telex no 35726
FAX (0939) 291123

*Beautifully preserved 17th-century house, set in 14 acres of gardens and grounds, providing high standards of accommodation and facilities for conferences and functions.*

29⇨♠Annexe10⇨♠(2fb)6⊞ CTV in all bedrooms ® T ✻ sB&B⇨♠£56-£87 dB&B⇨♠£76-£102 ⊟

⟮ 120P ✿ CFA ⌷ (heated) squash snooker sauna solarium gymnasium aerobics room beauty room *xmas*

♀ International V ♔ ♫ ✻ Lunch £10.25&alc Dinner £15&alc Last dinner 10.30pm

Credit Cards ①②③⑤

### ★★★⊛♨73% Albright Hussey
Ellesmere Rd SY4 3AF ☎Bomere Heath(0939)290571
FAX (0939) 291143

*The quality of services, accommodation and cuisine, combined with its unique façade and interior, make this small hotel dating back to 1292 one of the most popular in the area. Approached from the A528 Ellesmere-Shrewsbury road, it has a long driveway passing through farmland.*

5⇨Annexe1♠1⊞ CTV in all bedrooms ® T sB&B⇨♠£60-£88 dB&B⇨♠£77-£110 ⊟

⟮ 50P ✿ CFA nc3yrs *xmas*

♀ English & Italian V ♫ ⅍ Lunch £8-£10.50&alc Dinner £14.50-£26alc Last dinner 10pm

Credit Cards ①②③④ⓔ

### ★★★67% Prince Rupert
Butcher Row SY1 1UQ (Queens Moat) ☎(0743)236000
Telex no 35100 FAX (0743) 357306

*Refurbishment is now complete at the Prince Rupert, giving the hotel a new lease of life with modern rooms and facilities. There is a choice of restaurants, one in the main building and a trattoria across the road serving Italian delicacies. Traditional, personal service is still one of the hotel's greatest strengths.*

65⇨(4fb)2⊞ CTV in all bedrooms ® T ✻ sB&B⇨♠£64.50-£67 dB&B⇨♠£77-£81 ⊟

Lift ⟮ 60P CFA games room

---

♀ English, French & Italian V ♔ ♫ ✻ Lunch £10.75&alc Dinner fr£15.85&alc Last dinner 10.15pm

Credit Cards ①②③⑤

### ★★★62% The Lion
Wyle Cop SY1 1UY (Forte Hotels) ☎(0743)353107
FAX (0743) 352744

*An elegant Georgian building in the heart of the town, with its own covered parking area. Public rooms include comfortable lounges offering refreshments throughout the day, a restaurant and a ballroom which has recently been refurbished to its original grandeur.*

59⇨♠(1fb)1⊞⅍in 14 bedrooms CTV in all bedrooms ® T ✻ sB⇨♠£60 dB⇨♠£80 (room only) ⊟

Lift ⟮ 35P 35⊞ CFA *xmas*

V ♔ ♫ ⅍ ✻ S% Lunch £8.95&alc Dinner £14.95&alc Last dinner 10pm

Credit Cards ①②③④⑤

### ★★★61% Radbrook Hall
Radbrook Rd SY3 9BQ (Chef & Brewer) ☎(0743)236676
FAX (0743) 59194

*A busy commercial hotel on the outskirts of town, reached by following the signs to Bishops Castle (A488) off the ring road. Facilities include a grill-style restaurant and a health centre.*

28⇨♠(3fb)1⊞ CTV in all bedrooms ® T ✻ (ex guide dogs) sB&B⇨♠£51-£58 dB&B⇨♠£65-£65 ⊟

⟮ CTV 250P ✿ CFA squash sauna solarium gymnasium games room

♀ International V ♔ ♫ ⅍ Bar Lunch £2.95-£5.50alc

Credit Cards ①②③⑤

### ★★68% Shelton Hall
Shelton SY3 8BH (2m NW A5) ☎(0743)343982
Closed Xmas

*By the A5, a mile and a half from the town centre, this small family-run hotel with attractive gardens has a friendly country house atmosphere and offers warm, well equipped bedrooms and good food in its popular restaurant.*

10rm(9⇨♠)(2fb) CTV in all bedrooms ® T ✻ ✻ sB&B⇨♠£54 dB&B⇨♠£64

CTV 50P ⇗ ✿

♀ English & Continental V ♔ ✻ Sunday Lunch £12 Dinner £16.50 Last dinner 8.30pm

Credit Cards ①③

### ★★61% The Shrewsbury
Bridge Place, Mardol SY1 1TU ☎(0743)231246
FAX (0743) 247701

*Friendly service and smart, well equipped bedrooms are provided in this privately owned hotel close to the town centre and by the Welsh bridge.*

24⇨♠(6fb) CTV in all bedrooms ® T ✻ sB&B⇨♠£36-£45 dB&B⇨♠£56 ⊟

⟮ CTV 34P CFA

V ♔ ✻ Dinner fr£10.90 Last dinner 9pm

Credit Cards ①②③⑤ⓔ

### ★★60% Lion & Pheasant
49-50 Wyle Cop SY1 1XJ (Consort) ☎(0743)236288
FAX (0743) 343740

*On the edge of the town centre, this historic beamed inn provides comfortable accommodation. Staff are helpful and the bar and restaurant serve enjoyable meals.*

20rm(4⇨13♠)(1fb) CTV in all bedrooms ® T sB&B£25-£28.75 sB&B⇨♠£25.50-£44.50 dB&B£44-£48 dB&B⇨♠£47-£56.20 ⊟

CTV 20P CFA

♀ English & French V ♔ ♫ Lunch £6.95-£15 Dinner £10.95-£13.95&alc Last dinner 9.30pm

Credit Cards ①②③⑤ⓔ

## SIBSON Leicestershire Map 04 SK30

**★★65% Millers Hotel & Restaurant**

Main Rd CV13 6LB (6m N of Nuneaton on A444 road to Burton)
☎Tamworth(0827)880223 FAX (0827) 880223

*This one-time bakery and watermill, now a popular small hotel, retains many features of its past including the working waterwheel. Offering easy access to both the M42 and M6 from its position on the A444 between Nuneaton and Burton-on-Trent, it provides well equipped bedrooms with modern facilities and a bar and restaurant much frequented by locals.*

40⇔♪(1fb)2♨ CTV in all bedrooms ® T sB&B⇔♪£51 dB&B⇔♪£61 ♙

℄ CTV 100P 2🚗 (£3 per night) CFA games room ⚬ xmas
♀ English & ContinentaL V ⚙ ⚼ ✳
Credit Cards ①②③⑤

## SIDMOUTH Devon Map 03 SY18

**★★★★67% Belmont**

The Esplanade EX10 8RX (Brend) ☎(0395)512555
Telex no 42551 FAX (0395) 579154

*Built as a private residence in the 18th century, this hotel has been refurbished to retain much of the style and elegance of the Georgian period. Spaciously comfortable lounges and a compact restaurant are complemented by bedrooms equipped to uniformly modern standards, some also offering sea views. High levels of traditional hospitality and friendly, well managed service are maintained.*

54⇔♪(10fb) CTV in all bedrooms ® T ✖ (ex guide dogs)
sB&B⇔♪£67-£75 dB&B⇔♪£105-£150 ♙
Lift ℄ 45P 🚗 ✳ putting green ♫ ⚬ xmas
♀ English & French V ⚙ ⚼ Lunch £10.75&alc Dinner £16.50&alc Last dinner 9pm
Credit Cards ①②③⑤ £

**★★★★65% Victoria**

Esplanade EX10 8RY (Brend) ☎(0395)512651 Telex no 42551
FAX (0395) 579154

*The unique atmosphere of Victorian permanence here is coupled with friendly but efficiently professional standards of service – room service being particularly noteworthy. Bedrooms are bright and well furnished, there is extensive comfortable lounge accommodation and comprehensive indoor and outdoor leisure facilities which include the Hunting Lodge Poolside Bar and Buttery.*

61⇔♪(18fb) CTV in all bedrooms T ✖ (ex guide dogs)
sB&B⇔♪£69-£77 dB&B⇔♪£114-£174 ♙
Lift ℄ 100P 4🚗 (£4 per day) 🚗 ✳ ▣ (heated) ⊇ (heated) ♪ (hard) snooker sauna solarium spa bath putting green ⚬ xmas
♀ English & French V ⚙ ⚼ Lunch £11&alc Dinner £17.50-£19.50&alc Last dinner 9pm
Credit Cards ①②③⑤ £

*See advertisement on page 641*

**★★★78% Riviera**

The Esplanade EX10 8AY ☎(0395)515201 Telex no 42551
FAX (0395) 577775

*A fine Regency style property on the esplanade overlooking Lyme Bay. The emphasis here is on a warm welcome and old-fashioned, attentive service which, combined with present day comforts, make it a haven for holidaymakers in this beautiful part of East Devon. Well equipped bedrooms are pleasantly decorated, and there are thoughtful touches such as fresh flowers and fruit. Many bedrooms share the glorious sea view with the elegant lounge and busy dining room, where an extensive choice of home-cooked dishes are offered from table d'hôte and à la carte menus. Local seafood is a speciality and portions are generous. A pianist plays some evenings in the Regency Bar.*

34⇔♪(6fb) CTV in all bedrooms T sB&B⇔♪£48-£69
dB&B⇔♪£96-£138 (incl dinner) ♙
Lift ℄ 12P 9🚗 (£2.50) ✳ CFA xmas

→

**S**

# Sidmouth

♀ English & French **V** ↻ ⚅ Lunch £10.95&alc Dinner
£17.50&alc Last dinner 9pm
Credit Cards ① ② ③ ⑤

See advertisement on page 643

## ★★★70% **Westcliff**
Manor Rd EX10 8RU ☎(0395)513252 FAX (0395) 578203
Closed 21 Dec-1 Feb RS 3 Nov-22 Dec & 1 Feb-6 Apr
*Standing in 2 acres of award-winning gardens overlooking the sea,
this family-owned hotel offers high standards of traditional service
and warm hospitality. Bedrooms are well equipped and tastefully
decorated, some with sea-facing balconies, and there are
comfortable lounges, a cocktail bar and intimate restaurant, plus
modern leisure facilities.*
40⇨🏻(15fb) CTV in all bedrooms ® **T** ✖ sB&B⇨🏻£47.30-
£67.65 dB&B⇨🏻£86-£141.46 (incl dinner) 🏬
Lift CTV 40P 🚗 ❋ CFA ⌷ (heated) solarium gymnasium
croquet, putting, jacuzzi, pool table ♫
♀ English & Continental **V** ↻ ⚅ ✂ Sunday Lunch fr£9
Dinner £17.50&alc Last dinner 8.30pm
Credit Cards ① ③

## ★★★60% **Royal Glen**
Glen Rd EX10 8RW ☎(0395)513221 & 578124
*The residence of the former Duke and Duchess of Kent and their
daughter Princess Victoria, later to become Queen, stands in its
own grounds and offers a wealth of history and character. Some
bedrooms are compact but all are furnished in keeping with the
Victorian Style. A table d'hôte menu offers some choice of dishes.*
34rm(22⇨10🏻)(4fb) CTV in all bedrooms **T** sB&B£21-£30
sB&B⇨🏻£24-£35 dB&B⇨🏻£48-£93 🏬
CTV 16P 8🚗 (£1 per night) 🚗 ⌷ (heated) nc8yrs
♀ English & French ↻ ⚅ ✱ Lunch fr£6.95 Dinner fr£12 Last
dinner 8pm
Credit Cards ① ② ③

## ★★★59% **Salcombe Hill House**
Beatlands Rd EX10 8JQ ☎(0395)514697
Closed Nov-Feb
*A hotel situated about half a mile from the sea front achieves a
country house feeling under the management of proprietors of 35
years' standing; guests have the use of a well tended garden and
swimming pool.*
31⇨🏻(5fb) CTV in all bedrooms ® **T** sB&B⇨🏻£30-£52
dB&B⇨🏻£60-£104 (incl dinner) 🏬
Lift ℂ 35P 4🚗 (£2.75 daily) 🚗 ❋ ⌷ (heated) ♫ (grass) putting
games room nc3yrs
**V** ↻ ⚅ ✂ ✱ Lunch £8-£9&alc Dinner £12-£15 Last dinner
8.30pm
Credit Cards ① ③ ⑤

## ★★★57% **Fortfield**
Station Rd EX10 8NU ☎(0395)512403
*A family managed hotel in its own gardens and within easy
walking distance of the sea front. It offers simply decorated and
furnished bedrooms, a high standard of service and naturally
friendly staff.*
52⇨🏻Annexe3⇨🏻(7fb) CTV in all bedrooms ® **T** ✱
sB&B⇨🏻£34-£51 dB&B⇨🏻£68-£102 🏬
Lift ℂ CTV 60P ❋ 🖂 (heated) sauna solarium games room
putting green 🐾 *xmas*
**V** ↻ ⚅ ✂ ✱ Sunday Lunch £10 High tea £2-£5 Dinner £13
Last dinner 8.30pm
Credit Cards ① ② ③ ⑤

## ★★💺70% **Brownlands**
Sid Rd EX10 9AG ☎(0395)513053
Closed Nov & Jan RS Dec
*Beautifully situated on the slopes of Salcombe Hill with glorious
views over Sidmouth and Lyme Bay, this hotel has brightly
decorated bedrooms with good facilities and tastefully furnished
public rooms. The resident proprietors extend a warm welcome to
guests seeking a relaxing stay in their peaceful home.*

15⇨🏻(1fb) CTV in all bedrooms ® **T** sB&B⇨🏻£40-£43.50
dB&B⇨🏻£80-£104.50 (incl dinner) 🏬
CTV 25P 🚗 ❋ ♫ (hard) putting nc8yrs *xmas*
♀ International **V** ↻ ⚅ ✂ Sunday Lunch £8.75-£9.50 Dinner
£16.50 Last dinner 8pm

## ★★70% **Mount Pleasant**
Salcombe Rd EX12 8JA ☎(0395)514694
Closed Oct-Etr
*An attractive early Georgian residence with well kept gardens
which is convenient for the seafront and town centre. A high
standard of comfort is maintained throughout the bedrooms which
are all tastefully decorated. There is a bar lounge and a lounge for
non-smokers, and in the intimate dining room a limited choice of
traditional home-cooked fare is offered from a table d'hôte menu.*
16⇨🏻(1fb) CTV in all bedrooms ® sB&B⇨🏻£24-£28
dB&B⇨🏻£48-£56 🏬
CTV 22P 1🚗 🚗 ❋ ♛ 9 nc8yrs
**V** ↻ ⚅ ✂
£

## ★★68% **Abbeydale**
Manor Rd EX10 8RP ☎(0395)512060
Closed 3 Nov-27 Mar (ex 24-27 Dec)
*A friendly family-run hotel set in sheltered grounds and within
easy reach of the beach, town centre and Connaught Gardens.
Bedrooms are well equipped and the recently refurbished public
areas very comfortable. The informal dining room serves a nightly
changing table d'hôte menu.*
18⇨🏻(2fb) CTV in all bedrooms ® **T** ✖ sB&B⇨🏻£25-£35
dB&B⇨🏻£50-£70 🏬
Lift 24P 🚗 ❋ nc4yrs *xmas*
♀ English & French ↻ ⚅ ✂ ✱ Bar Lunch £4.50-£8alc Dinner
£15 Last dinner 8pm

## ★★66% **Kingswood**
Esplanade EX10 8AX ☎(0395)516367
Closed mid Nov-mid Mar
*This popular, friendly, family-run hotel enjoys glorious views from
its central position on the sea front. All its tastefully decorated and
well furnished en suite bedrooms are equipped to meet the needs of
either commercial visitors or holidaymakers, a spacious lounge
combines comfort with quality, and the informal dining room offers
a table d'hôte menu.*
26⇨🏻(7fb)1🖮 CTV in all bedrooms ® **T** sB&B⇨🏻£26-£28
dB&B⇨🏻£52-£56 🏬
Lift CTV 7P 2🚗 (£10pw)
↻ ⚅ Bar Lunch £1.50-£4alc Dinner £8.50-£10.50 Last dinner
7.30pm
£

See advertisement on page 643

## ★★65% **Littlecourt**
Seafield Rd EX10 8HF ☎(0395)515279
Closed 2 Nov-21 Dec & 29 Dec-10 Mar RS 22-28 Dec
*This attractive character property is within walking distance of the
sea front and town centre. Public areas, refurbished over the
winter, combine comfort and modern quality, and bedrooms are
tastefully decorated.*
21rm(12⇨6🏻)(3fb) CTV in all bedrooms ® ✱ sB&B£25.15-
£35.75 sB&B⇨🏻£25.50-£45.45 dB&B⇨🏻£51-£92 (incl
dinner) 🏬
CTV 17P ❋ CFA ⌷ (heated) *xmas*
♀ English & French **V** ↻ ⚅ ✂ ✱ Lunch fr£5.50 High tea
fr£2.35 Dinner fr£10.50 Last dinner 8pm
Credit Cards ① ② ③ £

## ★★63% **Royal York & Faulkner**
Esplanade EX10 8AZ ☎(0395)513043 & 513184
FAX (0395) 577472
Closed 3 Jan-3 Feb
*The Royal York, a fine example of Regency architecture, was
Sidmouth's first purpose-built hotel and dates from 1811. After*

→

641

*joining with the adjacent Faulkener Hotel in 1970, a spacious modern property was formed, with excellent views and good facilities. Bedrooms are clean and comfortable and there is a choice of lounges. A spa bath, solarium and sauna are available throughout the day. The hotel is now under the personal supervision of Mr and Mrs Peter Hook, whose family have owned the property for nearly 50 years.*

68⇨🛏(8fb) CTV in all bedrooms ® T sB&B⇨🛏£25-£48.50 dB&B⇨🛏£50-£97 (incl dinner) 🗎

Lift CTV 10P CFA sauna solarium gymnasium jacuzzi spa pool bowls *xmas*

♀ English & French **V** ✿ ⚘ Lunch fr£6.25&alc Dinner fr£13 Last dinner 8.30pm

Credit Cards ①③

### ★★ 54% *Woodlands*

Station Rd EX10 8HG ☎(0395)513120

*Set in its own attractive gardens, this family-owned hotel is only a short walk from the seafront. Some of the compact bedrooms have en suite bathrooms, while there is a choice of lounges, one with colour television.*

30rm(14⇨4🛏)(1fb) CTV in 4 bedrooms ®

CTV 22P ✿ ✿ putting nc3yrs

✿ ⚘ Last dinner 8pm

Credit Cards ①③

### ★★ 50% *Westbourne*

Manor Rd EX10 8RR ☎(0395)513774

Closed Nov-Feb

*This family-run hotel, quietly situated within easy reach of beaches and the town centre, offers some bedrooms with en suite facilities and serves a choice of meals from a single table d'hôte menu in the dining room.*

14rm(8⇨1🛏)(2fb) CTV in all bedrooms ®

16P ✿

**V** ✿ ⚘ ⌿ Last dinner 7.30pm

Credit Cards ①③

---

### SILCHESTER Hampshire Map **04** SU66

#### ★★★ 60% **Romans**

Little London Rd RG7 2PN (Best Western) ☎(0734)700421 Telex no 858122 FAX (0734) 700691

Closed Xmas & New Year

*An attractive Lutyens designed country house set back from the village road in well tended gardens. Bedrooms in the main house are more spacious than the study rooms in the purpose-built annexe, and have well co-ordinated soft furnishings and antique furniture. All are well maintained with good facilities. A short table d'hôte and an à la carte menu offer the diner a varied choice. There is an outdoor heated (April-September) pool and 2 hard tennis courts.*

11⇨Annexe13⇨🛏(1fb)1🛏 CTV in all bedrooms ® T ✱ sB&B⇨🛏£65-£75 dB&B⇨🛏£75-£80 🗎

《 40P ✿ ✿ CFA ⌣ (heated)

♀ European ✿ ✱ Lunch £11-£15&alc Dinner £15-£18&alc Last dinner 9pm

Credit Cards ①②③⑤£

---

### SILLOTH Cumbria Map **11** NY15

#### ★★★ 70% *The Skinburness Hotel*

CA5 4QY ☎(06973)32332

*Set on the Solway Firth, this hotel has been completely refurbished to a high standard. It offers very comfortable bedrooms, peaceful lounges and good cooking served in the attractive restaurant.*

25⇨🛏 CTV in all bedrooms ®

70P ✿ snooker sauna solarium gymnasium ♫

♀ English & French **V** ✿ ⚘ Last dinner 9pm

Credit Cards ①②③⑤

---

### ★★ 66% **Golf**

Criffel St CA5 4AB ☎(06973)31438 FAX (06973) 32582 Closed 25 Dec

*Bedrooms with good facilities and a restaurant serving a wide range of dishes are provided by this family owned and run licenced hotel which overlooks the Solway Firth on Cumbria's north coast.*

22⇨🛏(4fb)1🛏 CTV in all bedrooms ® ✱ sB&B⇨🛏fr£38.85 dB&B⇨🛏fr£55.20 🗎

♪

♀ English & Continental ✿ ⚘ ✱ Lunch fr£8.50 Dinner fr£13.80 Last dinner 9.15pm

Credit Cards ①②③⑤

---

### SILVERDALE Lancashire Map **07** SD47

#### ★ 59% *Silverdale*

Shore Rd LA5 0TP ☎(0524)701206

*Recent upgrading of some bedrooms has enhanced this hotel which is situated in an area of natural beauty, close to Morcambe Bay. Popular bar meals and real ale can be enjoyed in the traditional bars or a more formal meal can be taken in the attractive dining room with its stone fire place and view over the bay.*

10rm(1⇨1🛏)(2fb) CTV in all bedrooms ® T

30P

**V** ✿ ⚘

Credit Cards ①③

---

### SIMONSBATH Somerset Map **03** SS73

#### ★★⚑ 72% **Simonsbath House**

TA24 7SH ☎Exford(064383)259 Closed Dec-Jan

*An impressive 17th-century house in a sheltered valley overlooking the River Barle. Mr and Mrs Burns and their loyal staff provide a friendly, relaxed atmosphere with a high degree of comfort. Charming bedrooms are individually decorated and equipped with modern facilities. The restaurant is well appointed with sparkling cut glass and shining cutlery. Mrs Burns cooks imaginatively using fresh local ingredients. There are 3 self-catering cottages and a bistro-style restaurant in a separate building in the grounds.*

7⇨🛏3🛏 CTV in all bedrooms ® T ✱ sB&B⇨🛏£41.50-£57 dB&B⇨🛏£73-£84 🗎

40P ✿ ✿ nc10yrs

✿ ⚘ ⌿ Dinner £17.50-£19.50alc Last dinner 8.30pm

Credit Cards ①②③⑤£

---

### SIX MILE BOTTOM Cambridgeshire Map **05** TL55

#### ★★★ 72% **Swynford Paddocks**

CB8 0UE ☎(063870)234 FAX (063870) 283

Closed 3-5 days over Xmas & New Year RS Sat lunch-closed

*A former country mansion with gabled roof and attractive greenery stands in well maintained gardens on the A1304, 6 miles southwest of Newmarket and within easy reach of Cambridge, this position making it popular with tourists as well as commercial users and those with an interest in horse racing. The house retains many original features; panelled rooms are furnished in keeping with its period, and the balustrade and galleried hallway leads to a range of quality bedrooms with luxurious bathrooms, some offering higher levels of comfort than would be expected from its classification.*

15⇨🛏2🛏 CTV in all bedrooms ® T S% sB&B⇨🛏£66.50-£75 dB&B⇨🛏£102.50-£150 🗎

120P ✿ ✿ ♪ (hard) croquet putting outdoor chess ♫ *xmas*

♀ English & French **V** ✿ ⚘ S% Lunch £14.50-£16.50 Dinner £19.95-£22.50&alc Last dinner 9.30pm

Credit Cards ①②③⑤

---

◉ Shell filling stations (7am–11pm) are marked on the town plans.

S

## SKEABOST BRIDGE

See Skye, Isle of

## SKEGNESS Lincolnshire Map 09 TF56

★★★60% **Crown**
Drummond Rd, Seacroft PE25 3AB ☎(0754)610760
FAX (0754) 610847
*Situated 1.5 miles from the resort's town centre, this completely refurbished hotel offers modern, well equipped bedrooms. There are function suites available, and both business people and holidaymakers are catered for.*
27⇄✆(7fb) ✕ (ex guide dogs) ✳ sB&B⇄✆£42
dB&B⇄✆£62 ╕
Lift ⊞ CTV 90P CFA ▭ (heated) *xmas*
V ✪ ⚏ ✳ Lunch £8-£11.95
Credit Cards ① ③ £

## SKELMORLIE Strathclyde *Ayrshire* Map 10 NS16

★★★⚑60% **Manor Park**
PA17 5HE ☎Wemyss Bay(0475)520832
*This fine, personally run country mansion epitomises traditional style and values. Set in an elevated position amid delightful gardens and grounds, giving superb views across the Firth of Clyde, it has several commodious bedrooms, a relaxing spacious lounge and a cocktail bar with an impressive range of whiskies.*
10⇄✆Annexe13⇄✆ CTV in all bedrooms ® T ✕ ✳
sB&B⇄✆£40-£60 dB&B⇄✆£60-£100 ╕
150P ✿ CFA *xmas*
♀ Scottish & Continental V ✪ ⚏ ✳ Lunch fr£11.75&alc High tea fr£6.95 Dinner £17.50-£19.50&alc Last dinner 9.30pm
Credit Cards ① ② ③ ⑤ £

S

## SKIPTON North Yorkshire Map **07** SD95

**★★★❀67%, *Randell's***
Keighley Rd, Snaygill BD23 2TA ☎(0756)700100
FAX (0756) 700107
(Rosette awarded for dinner only)
*On the A629 a mile from the town centre, this large modern hotel built of natural stone has very well equipped bedrooms with quality furnishings and some suites with separate lounges. Facilities include a comprehensive health and leisure centre, a crèche, and excellent banqueting. The restaurant serves international cuisine of a high standard, with Potkins Pantry open all day for lighter meals.*
61⇄♠(8fb)1🛏 CTV in all bedrooms ® T
Lift 《 CTV 150P 🏊 (heated) squash snooker sauna solarium gymnasium whirlpool spa steam room ⚽
V ✿ ⌑ ⊁
Credit Cards 1 2 3 5

**★66% Herriots**
Broughton Rd BD23 1RT ☎(0756)792781
*Situated opposite the railway station and close to the town centre, this recently refurbished hotel is managed by the resident proprietor and offers friendly service, extensive, good value menus and comfortable accommodation.*
11⇄♠(1fb) CTV in all bedrooms ® ✳ sB&B⇄♠£34-£44 dB&B⇄♠£45-£52 🛏
25P *xmas*
♈ International V ⊁ ✳ Lunch £5.50-£8 Dinner £7-£14 Last dinner 9.45pm
Credit Cards 1 3

**⇧Forte Travelodge**
Gargrave Rd BD23 1UD (A65/A59 roundabout) (Forte)
☎(0756)798091 Central Res (0800) 850950
*Well maintained modern accommodation and a Little Chef restaurant which is open from 7am until 10pm are features of a lodge set beside the ring road to the west of the town.*
32⇄♠(32fb) CTV in all bedrooms ® sB⇄♠£29.95 dB⇄♠£29.95 (room only)
《 55P ⊞
Credit Cards 1 2 3

## SKYE, ISLE OF Highland *Inverness-shire* Map **13**

## ARDVASAR Map **13** NG60

**★★❀69% Ardvasar**
IV45 8RS ☎(04714)223
Closed 24-25 Dec & 1-3 Jan RS Nov-Mar
(Rosette awarded for dinner only)
*Justifiably popular, this whitewashed 18th-century coaching inn has superb views across the Sound of Sleat and is handily placed for users of the Armadale/Mallaig ferry. The owners provide high standards of housekeeping, hospitality and cuisine and owner-chef Bill Fowler makes good use of seafood and other local produce in his good-value set-price dinners. His cooking is straightforward and regionally based, with dishes such as smoked Tarskavaig venison fillet with rowanberry jelly, Cullen skink and cock-a-leekie soup, Skye lamb chops with honey and almonds or, at its simplest (and supplementary cost) lobster. Local cheeses may be more interesting than the creamy desserts and sympathetic service is by smartly dressed local staff. At the bar, there's a good selection of hot and cold food.*
10⇄♠(3fb) CTV in 7 bedrooms ® ✖ (ex guide dogs)
sB&B⇄♠£26-£32 dB&B⇄♠£55-£62
CTV 30P ⊞ CFA
♈ Scottish & French V ✿ ✳ Lunch £6-£10&alc Dinner £16.50-£20&alc Last dinner 8.30pm
Credit Cards 1 3

## BROADFORD Map **13** NG62

**★★54% Broadford**
IV49 9AB ☎(04712)204 FAX (04712) 414
RS Nov-Mar
*Dating from 1611, and originally an inn, this extended and modernised hotel beside the main road provides functional accommodation popular with tour groups.*
20⇄♠Annexe9⇄♠(3fb) CTV in all bedrooms ® T S%
sB&B⇄♠£28-£32.50 dB&B⇄♠£56-£65 🛏
100P ❀ CFA ✔ gymnasium
V ✿ ⌑
Credit Cards 1 3

## COLBOST Map **13** NG24

**❀✖Three Chimneys**
IV55 8ZT ☎Glendale(047081)258
*In a remote but beautiful corner of Skye, overlooking Loch Dunvegan, a sympathetically converted crofter's cottage features a beamed ceiling, exposed stone walls and candle-lit tables, these cosy, atmospheric surroundings provide a perfect background to the enjoyment of well-cooked food based on good local ingredients. Menus are à la carte, the simpler lunchtime range offering such dishes as Partan Pie or Stovies, whilst in the evening – when booking is essential – you may enjoy wild Skye salmon, scallops or steak; delicious home-made bread and puddings may accompany either meal.*
Closed Sun Nov-Mar
♈ Scottish V 35 seats Lunch £2.50-£20alc Dinner £15-£40alc Last lunch 2pm Last dinner 9pm 30 P ⊁
Credit Cards 1 3

## CULNACNOC Map **13** NG56

**★❀74% Glenview Inn**
IV51 9JH ☎Staffin(047062)248
RS end Oct-Etr
*The spectacular coastal scenery is just one of the attractions of this simple Highland inn that makes booking essential. Chef Linda Thomson loves experimenting with textures and flavours and her menu includes combinations such as venison served with quince sauce and potato and poppy seed pasta, or guinea fowl stuffed with courgettes and cream cheese and garnished with raspberries. Relaxed, friendly service adds to the enjoyment of a meal here.*
6rm(3♠) CTV in all bedrooms ® sB&B£25 dB&B£50 dB&B♠£55 🛏
15P ⊞ ❀
✿ ⌑ ✳ Bar Lunch £1.50-£5.75alc
Credit Cards 1 3

## DUNVEGAN Map **13** NG24

**★★64% Atholl House**
IV55 8WA ☎(047022)219 FAX (047022) 481
Closed Nov
*Situated near the loch overlooking Macleod's Tables, this small family-run hotel has a friendly atmosphere. The refurbished public areas are pleasantly relaxing and the bedrooms are equipped with modern comforts.*
9rm(7⇄♠)(2fb) CTV in all bedrooms ® T
12P ⊞
V ✿ ⌑ ⊁ Last dinner 9.30pm
Credit Cards 1 3

◉ Shell filling station, open 7am–11pm (some 24 hours) throughout the year with leaded and unleaded petrol, and diesel.

## HARLOSH Map 13 NG24

**★❀76% Harlosh House**
IV55 8ZG ☎Dunvegan(047022)367
Closed mid Oct-Etr
*Beautifully situated overlooking Loch Caroy, with spectacular views of the Cuillins, the islands of Bracadale and Macleod's Tables, this charming small hotel is an ideal base for a touring holiday. It offers genuine hospitality and the friendly proprietors, Peter and Lindsey Elford, have attractively refurbished the bedrooms. The highlight of a visit here must be the excellent dinners featuring superb local seafood which Peter prepares each evening with great care.*
6rm(5⇌ƒ)(3fb) TV available ® ✗ (ex guide dogs) sB&B£35-£56 sB&B⇌ƒ£40-£70 dB&B£56 dB&B⇌ƒ£70
10P ⛿ ❊
♕ Scottish & French ✗ Dinner £15-£30alc Last dinner 9pm
Credit Cards 1 3

## ISLE ORNSAY Map 13 NG61

**★★❀❀♛69% Kinloch Lodge**
IV43 8QY ☎(04713)214 & 333 FAX (04713) 277
Closed Dec-14 Mar
(Rosettes awarded for dinner only)
*Set at the head of Loch Na Dal amid spectacular, rugged mountain scenery, Lord and Lady Macdonald's small hotel is the ideal spot for a relaxing holiday. The atmosphere is that of a family home, and there are 2 elegant drawing rooms where one may sit in comfort by welcoming log fires. The pretty bedrooms are well kept and furnished with a mixture of modern and traditional pieces. Over the years, Lady Macdonald's innovative cooking has gained international acclaim. Only the best raw ingredients are used in the preparation of the imaginative dishes on the small choice dinner menu. Dining at Kinloch is a truly pleasurable experience.*
10rm(8⇌) ® sB&Bfr£30 sB&B⇌£85 dB&Bfr£60 dB&B⇌£170
CTV 18P ⛿ ❊ ♪ stalking
♨ ⊕ ✗ Dinner £35 Last dinner 8pm
Credit Cards 1 3

**★★66% Duisdale**
IV43 8QW ☎(04713)202 FAX (04713) 363
Closed 5 Jan-17 Apr
*Set in its own grounds, overlooking the picturesque Sound of Sleat, this converted hunting lodge is popular with holidaymakers and tour groups. It has a friendly atmosphere. Public rooms with welcoming log fires offer traditional comforts. The modestly furnished bedrooms provide good-value accommodation. Enjoyable home-cooked meals are prepared from fresh local produce.*
19rm(14⇌ƒ)(4fb)1⛿ ® sB&Bfr£22 sB&B⇌ƒ£37.50-£54 dB&Bfr£44 dB&B⇌ƒ£68-£79 ⛿
CTV 20P ❊ croquet putting *xmas*
V ♨ ⊕ S% Lunch £5-£8 Dinner fr£17.80 Last dinner 8.30pm
Credit Cards 1 3

**★61% Hotel Eilean Iarmain**
IV43 8QR ☎(04713)332 FAX (04713) 260
*A small Highland inn, peacefully situated beside a natural harbour, overlooking the Sound of Sleat and mainland mountains. It offers traditional services provided by gaelic speaking staff. Enjoyable homecooking, supported by an imaginative wine list, is served in the cosy dining room.*
6rm(4⇌ƒ)Annexe6⇌(2fb)1⛿ ® T ✱ S10% sB&B£36.50-£42.50 dB&B£53 dB&B⇌ƒ£65-£85 ⛿
TV 30P ❊ ♪
V ♨ ⊕ ✱ S10% Bar Lunch £4.25-£7.50 Dinner £19.25 Last dinner 8.30pm
Credit Cards 1 3

S

**PORTREE** Map **13** NG44

**★★★50% Cuillin Hills**
IV51 9LU ☎(0478)2003 FAX (0478) 3092
*Pleasantly situated just outside the town and enjoying fine views of the Cuillins, this extended one-time shooting lodge offers traditional and modest accommodation.*
17⇌↱Annexe9⇌↱(5fb) CTV in all bedrooms ® **T** S% sB&B⇌↱£30-£50 dB&B⇌↱£50-£80 ⊟
☾ 50P ❁ CFA snooker ⌂ *xmas*
**V** ♆ ⚲ ✱ S% Lunch £6.75-£16 High tea £7.50-£10 Dinner £16&alc Last dinner 9pm
Credit Cards 1 3

**★★69% Rosedale**
IV51 9DB ☎(0478)3131 FAX (0478) 2531
Closed Oct-mid May
*A privately owned waterfront hotel – dating from the early 19th century and originally 3 separate buildings – has gradually expanded and developed to provide well maintained, up-to-date accommodation. The majority of bedrooms are new, smartly decorated and comfortably furnished, though some are quite compact, while a maze of narrow corridors and stairways link public areas which include two traditional lounges and a small first-floor dining room overlooking Portree's harbour.*
20⇌↱Annexe3⇌↱(1fb) CTV in all bedrooms ® **T** sB&B⇌↱£32-£34 dB&B⇌↱£60-£68 ⊟
18P ⇎
✱ Dinner £16-£17 Last dinner 8.30pm
Credit Cards 1 3

**★★65% *Royal***
IV51 9BU (Consort) ☎(0478)2525 FAX (0478) 3198
*Located in the town centre and overlooking Portree Bay this well run traditional hotel offers functional accommodation, several bars and a popular all day bistro.*
25⇌↱(6fb) CTV in all bedrooms ®
4P ⇎
**V** ♆ ⚲ ⚞ Last dinner 9pm
Credit Cards 1 3

**★62% Isles**
Somerled Square IV51 9EH ☎(0478)2129
Closed Nov-Mar
*A small, privately owned hotel situated in the centre of Portree, with well equipped bedrooms. There is no bar as such, but hot drinks can be served to residents in the lounge.*
10rm(5↱) CTV in all bedrooms ® sB&B£21-£23 dB&B↱£50-£56
CTV Ᵽ ❁ clay pigeon shooting
S% Lunch £4-£10alc Dinner £6-£15alc Last dinner 8.30pm

**SKEABOST BRIDGE** Map **13** NG44

**★★★⚑66% Skeabost House**
IV51 9NR ☎(047032)202
Closed Nov-Mar
*Peacefully situated in attractive, well kept gardens which include a 9-hole golf course, and surrounded by 12 acres of woodland, this whitewashed former hunting lodge enjoys fine views over Loch Snizort. Most of the bedrooms are individually decorated and traditionally furnished and although several are fairly compact there are spacious and comfortable public areas in which to relax. Service is provided by the resident proprietors aided by a friendly young staff – and the availablity of 8 miles of fishing on the River Snizort makes it a popular choice with anglers.*
21⇌↱Annexe5⇌(3fb)1⊠ CTV in all bedrooms ® **T** sB&B⇌↱£37-£42 dB&B⇌↱£70-£94
☾ CTV 40P ❁ ▶ 9 ♩ snooker
☋ Scottish & French **V** ♆ ⚲ Bar Lunch £6.50-£8.50alc Dinner £20 Last dinner 8.30pm
Credit Cards 1 3

**STRUAN** Map **13** NG33

**★60% *Ullinish Lodge***
IV56 8FD ☎(047072)214
Closed mid Oct-Etr
*An 18th-century lodge overlooking Loch Hartport to the Cuillin Hills has been extended and converted into this family-run hotel with a relaxed atmosphere and traditional comforts.*
8rm(5↱)(2fb) ®
CTV 12P ❁ ♩ rough shooting
**V** ♆ ⚲ Last dinner 8pm

**TEANGUE** Map **13** NG60

**★★66% Toravaig House**
IV44 8RJ ☎Isle Ornsay(04713)231
Closed Nov-Etr
*A small family-owned hotel, set in 8 acres of attractive grounds beside the Broadford-Armadale road, offers well maintained, individually decorated and traditionally furnished bedrooms; public areas include a small bar and cosy residents' lounge.*
9⇌↱ CTV in all bedrooms ® ✱ sB&B⇌↱£37-£42 dB&B⇌↱£58-£64 ⊟
CTV 20P ⇎ ❁
♆ ⚲ ⚞ ✱ Lunch £10 High tea £8 Dinner £17 Last dinner 8pm
Credit Cards 1 3 £

**UIG** Map **13** NG36

**★★66% Uig**
IV51 9YE ☎(047042)205 FAX (047042) 308
Closed 8 Oct-mid Apr
*This family-run hotel, situated in an elevated position and enjoying fine views over the bay, offers comfortable, well maintained accommodation, light and airy bedrooms being equipped with modern facilities while public areas retain a homely charm.*
11⇌↱Annexe6⇌↱(1fb) CTV in all bedrooms ® **T** ✱ sB&B⇌↱fr£34 dB&B⇌↱fr£68 ⊟
20P ⇎ ❁ U nc12yrs
**V** ♆ ⚲ ⚞ Bar Lunch fr£3alc High tea fr£6alc Dinner fr£18alc Last dinner 8pm
Credit Cards 1 2 3 4 5

**★71% Ferry Inn**
IV51 9XP ☎(047042)242
Closed Xmas day & 1-2 Jan RS Nov-Etr
*This roadside Highland inn is, as its name suggests, conveniently situated for those using the ferries to the Outer Hebrides. Some bedrooms remain compact, but they have been smartly refurbished to a very good standard and are equipped with modern facilities; attractively appointed and spotlessly clean public areas include a choice of two small bars and a comfortable lounge and dining room*
6⇌↱(2fb) CTV in all bedrooms ® sB&B⇌↱£20-£30 dB&B⇌↱£46-£50
CTV 12P ⇎
**V** ♆ ⚲ ✱ Lunch £2-£5alc Dinner £4-£10alc Last dinner 9pm
Credit Cards 1 3

**SLEAFORD** Lincolnshire Map **08** TF04

**★★67% Mallards**
Eastgate NG34 7DJ (Consort) ☎(0529)303062
FAX (0529) 303459
*In the town centre (A153 Horncastle direction), this listed building with an attractive façade backs onto a large public car park where free spaces are allocated to the hotel. Since their appointment, Mr and Mrs Lewin have worked hard to provide services and facilities in response to their guests' requirements. These include full en suite facilities and a lounge bar.*
10⇌↱(1fb) CTV in all bedrooms ® **T** sB&B⇌↱£39 dB&B⇌↱£49 ⊟
8P ⇎

♀ English & French **V** ♥ ⚗ ✻ Lunch £7-£17alc Dinner £10-£17alc Last dinner 9pm
Credit Cards ① ② ③ ⓔ

### ⚓Forte Travelodge
Holdingham(1m N, at roundabout A17/A15) (Forte)
☎Central Res (0800) 850950
*Located on the edge of the town at the roundabout junction of the A17/A15, this Travelodge opened in April 1991. It offers a good standard of accommodation, and the adjacent Little Chef is open 7am-10pm. A service station is currently being built on the site.*
40⇨ 🐾(40fb) CTV in all bedrooms ® sB⇨🐾£29.95 dB⇨🐾£29.95 (room only)
《 40P 🚗
Credit Cards ① ② ③

---

### SLINFOLD West Sussex Map **04** TQ13

### ★★★68% Random Hall
Stane St RH13 7QX ☎Horsham(0403)790558 & 790852
FAX (0403) 791046
*This charming 16th-century Sussex farmhouse has been skilfully converted to provide a range of quality bedrooms which are tastefully decorated. The bar and lounge area are particularly welcoming and the young team of staff create a friendly atmosphere.*
16rm(15⇨🐾)(2fb)2🛏 CTV in all bedrooms ® T sB&B⇨🐾£60 dB&B⇨🐾£80 🅿
CTV 40P 🚗 *xmas*
**V** ♥ ⚗ ✻ Lunch £8.75-£13.25&alc High tea £4.95 Dinner fr£14.75&alc Last dinner 10pm
Credit Cards ① ② ③ ⓔ

---

### SLOUGH Berkshire Map **04** SU97 ⊙

### ★★★★64% Holiday Inn Slough/Windsor
Ditton Road, Langley SL3 8PT (Holiday Inns) ☎(0753)544244
Telex no 848646 FAX (0753) 540272
*An hotel conveniently situated beside junction 5 of the M4 should have completed 53 additional bedrooms by the end of 1991. Existing bedrooms are spacious and vary in style, a selection of conference, function and syndicate rooms is available, and well presented leisure facilities with a busy club membership include a jogging terrace and children's play area. La Galerie Restaurant provides a buffet breakfast and lunch, the raised section being used at dinner when an à la carte and popular table d'hôte/carvery menu is served. The foyer area is very well serviced, and there is live music in the evenings.*
352⇨🐾(102fb)⤢in 50 bedrooms CTV in all bedrooms ® T S10%⇨🐾£117.13-£135.15 dB⇨🐾£127.73-£146.28 (room only) 🅿
Lift 《 🎱 402P ❀ CFA ☒ (heated) ♪ (hard) sauna solarium gymnasium table tennis whirlpool jogging track ♫ *xmas*
♀ International **V** ♥ ⚗ ⤢ ✻ S10% Lunch £18.95 High tea £7.75 Dinner £18.95&alc Last dinner 11pm
Credit Cards ① ② ③ ⑤

---

### SMALLWAYS North Yorkshire Map **12** NZ11

### ★52% A66 Motel
DL11 7QW ☎Teesdale(0833)27334
*Situated on the A66 west of Scotch Corner, this small motel offers modest compact bedrooms, a spacious bar lounge and friendly service.*
6rm(1⇨) CTV in all bedrooms
30P ❀
**V** ♥ Last dinner 10.30pm
Credit Cards ① ③ ⑤

---

### SNAKE PASS Derbyshire Map **07** SK19

### ★★61% Snake Pass Inn
S30 2BJ (on A57 Sheffield to Glossop rd)
☎Hope Valley(0433)51480
*This small inn was built in 1821 for travellers on the then newly constructed turnpike between Manchester and Sheffield, now the A57. It is about halfway between these cities, in the remote and spectacular scenery of the High Peak. The area abounds with footpaths, including the Pennine Way, and the inn is therefore popular with ramblers and walkers.*
7⇨(1fb)1🛏 CTV in all bedrooms ® ✻ sB&B⇨🐾fr£25 dB&B⇨🐾fr£45 🅿
40P ❀ CFA *xmas*
**V** ♥ ⚗ ✻
Credit Cards ① ③ ⓔ

See advertisement under SHEFFIELD

---

### SOLIHULL West Midlands Map **07** SP17 ⊙

### ★★★★61% Brookes
61 Homer Rd B91 3QD (Queens Moat) ☎021-711 4700
Telex no 333355 FAX 021-711 2696
*This recently opened hotel, close to the town centre and offering convenient access to both the NEC and airport, features attractively decorated accommodation with an excellent range of modern facilities; suites, executive rooms and a room designed to meet the needs of disabled guests are all available. The wide choice of dishes and formal operation of Brookes Restaurant are complemented by the more relaxed style of Jaspers Brasserie, a popular venue for informal meals throughout the day, and a good range of room service meals is also provided. An impressive leisure centre boasts a good range of activities which include a swimming pool and gym.*
115⇨🐾(5fb)⤢in 42 bedrooms CTV in all bedrooms ® T S% sB⇨🐾£82-£92 dB⇨🐾£97-£107 (room only) 🅿
Lift 《 164P ❀ CFA ☒ (heated) sauna solarium gymnasium ♫
♀ International **V** ♥ ⚗ ✻ Lunch fr£10.75&alc Dinner fr£14.85&alc Last dinner 10.30pm
Credit Cards ① ② ③ ④ ⑤

See advertisement under BIRMINGHAM

### ★★★65% Regency
Stratford Rd, Shirley B90 4EB (Crown & Raven) ☎021-745 6119
Telex no 334400 FAX 021-733 3801
*A modern hotel situated on the A34, close to the town centre and junction 4 of the M42. Recent work has resulted in additional attractive and well equipped bedrooms and leisure amenities. Extensive conference and banqueting facilities are available.*
112⇨🐾(10fb)⤢in 59 bedrooms CTV in all bedrooms ® T
Lift 《 300P ☒ (heated) sauna solarium gymnasium
♀ French **V** ♥ ⚗ ⤢ Last dinner 10pm
Credit Cards ① ② ③

### ★★★64% St John's Swallow
651 Warwick Rd B91 1AT (Swallow) ☎021-711 3000
Telex no 339352 FAX 021-705 6629
*This hotel is sited on the outskirts of the town, close to the centre of the Midlands motorway network. Though some rooms are compact, accommodation is modern and well equipped, and the Swallow Leisure Club offers a wide range of facilities for guests' use.*
180⇨🐾(6fb) CTV in all bedrooms ® T ✻ sB&B⇨🐾fr£78 dB&B⇨🐾fr£95 🅿
Lift 《 CTV 380P ❀ CFA ☒ (heated) sauna solarium gymnasium ♫ *xmas*
♀ English & French **V** ♥ ⚗ ✻ Lunch fr£12.50&alc Dinner £17.50-£18&alc Last dinner 9.45pm
Credit Cards ① ② ③ ④ ⑤

**S**

★★★63% **George**

High St B91 3RF (Jarvis) ☎021-711 2121 Telex no 334134
FAX 021-711 3374

*A well managed modern hotel in the town centre, extended from a 16th-century coaching inn. All bedrooms are well equipped with facilities for business travellers, though the executive rooms are more spacious. The restaurant overlooks the country's second oldest bowling green and offers an à la carte menu plus a carvery option.*

74⇨🛏(5fb)1🖵🖵in 20 bedrooms CTV in all bedrooms ® T ✱
sB⇨🛏£75-£90 dB⇨🛏£100.50-£115 (room only) 🖻
Lift ℂ 120P CFA *xmas*

🍽 English & French V ♥ ⌑ ✶ S% Lunch £12-£16&alc Dinner £15.50-£18.50&alc Last dinner 9.45pm
Credit Cards ①②③④⑤

★★63% **Saracens Head**

Stratford Road, Shirley B90 3AG (Porterhouse) ☎021-733 3888
FAX 021-733 2762

*A busy hotel situated on the A34 close to Birmingham and junction 4 of the M42, the Saracens Head provides accommodation which is generally spacious, comfortable and well equipped. There is a popular Steak House restaurant, and quieter facilities have been set aside for residents preferring not to use the lively public bar.*

34⇨🛏 CTV in all bedrooms ® T 🛏 (ex guide dogs) ✶
sB&B⇨🛏£52 dB&B⇨🛏£67.50 🖻
ℂ 100P CFA

V ♥ ✶ Lunch £6.99-£7.50alc Dinner fr£5.95alc Last dinner 10pm
Credit Cards ①②③⑤

★★57% **Flemings**

141 Warwick Rd, Olton B92 7HW ☎021-706 0371
FAX 021- 706 4494
Closed 4 days Xmas

*This hotel is particularly popular with business travellers as it offers a home-from-home atmosphere. Rooms are a mixture of standards and sizes, and staff are friendly.*

84⇨🛏(4fb) CTV in all bedrooms ® T ✶ sB&B⇨🛏£32-£54
dB&B⇨🛏£43-£67.50 🖻
ℂ CTV 85P ❖ CFA snooker

🍽 Asian & European V ♥ ⌑ ✶ Lunch £8-£12.50&alc Dinner £11.30&alc Last dinner 9.30pm
Credit Cards ①②③⑤

❀ ✕✕**Liaison French Cuisine**

761 Old Lode Ln B92 8JE ☎021-743 3993

*A 6-course menu based on good fresh produce is provided by the new owners of this restaurant situated just off the A45, within easy reach of both the town centre and NEC. Starters might include poached scallops seasoned with truffles, or terrine of rabbit, followed perhaps by a main course of steamed brill in a Champagne sauce or medallions of beef with a crown of wild mushrooms.*

Closed Sun, Mon, 1 wk Xmas & 1 wk Aug Lunch not served all week (ex by prior arrangement)

🍽 French V 32 seats Lunch £18.50 Dinner £23.50&alc Wine £7.95 Last lunch 2.30pm 10 P
Credit Cards ①②③⑤

★★77% **Collaven Manor**

EX20 4HH ☎Bridestowe(083786)217 & 522 FAX (083786) 570
Closed 22 Dec-6 Jan

*This beautiful little stone-built manor house dating from the 15th century and partially covered in creeper stands amid 5 acres of well kept gardens and grounds on the northwest edge of Dartmoor. Nine en suite bedrooms have been tastefully decorated, well equipped and provided with such thoughtful extras as complimentary sherry, fruit baskets and dried flower arrangements. The emphasis in the public areas is on warmth and comfort, but the original gracious style of the building has been*

*retained in exposed beams, stone walls and very attractive inglenook fireplaces. The proprietors are on hand to welcome guests, and an interesting choice of dishes is available on the restaurant's table d'hôte lunch and dinner menus.*

9⇨🛏1🖵 CTV in all bedrooms ® T 🛏 ✶ sB&B⇨🛏£51.10
dB&B⇨🛏£78.70-£95 🖻
20P 🖵 ❖ croquet clay pigeon shooting putting
🍽 Mainly grills V ♥ ⌑ ✶ Lunch £9.95 Dinner fr£15.50
Last dinner 9pm
Credit Cards ①③£

See **Town Plan Section**
See also Shedfield

★★★62% **Southampton Moat House**

Highfield Ln, Portswood SO9 1YQ (Queens Moat)
☎(0703)559555 Telex no 47186 FAX (0703) 583910

*Situated just off the main street of Portswood, a suburb of the city, this hotel provides excellent parking facilities and accommodation in bedrooms refurbished to a comfortable standard and equipped with hairdriers, trouser presses and a video channel. A selection of conference and function rooms is available, the Hamilton Restaurant serves a value-for-money table d'hôte menu supplemented by an imaginative à la carte choice, and the Cityside Bar promotes a local pub atmosphere.*

66⇨🛏(6fb) CTV in all bedrooms ® T ✶ sB&B⇨🛏£61.50-
£66 dB&B⇨🛏£86.85-£92 🖻
ℂ 100P *xmas*

🍽 International V ♥ ⌑ ✶ Lunch £11.35-£14.50&alc Dinner £13-£14.50&alc Last dinner 10pm
Credit Cards ①②③④⑤

★★★62% **Southampton Park**

Cumberland Place SO9 4NY (Forestdale) ☎(0703)223467
FAX (0703) 332538
Closed 25 & 26 Dec nights

*In a central position, this hotel has a new leisure club with a well-equipped gymnasium and superb indoor pool. Guests can choose to eat in either the main restaurant or the bistro-style cellar restaurant which offers an imaginative menu.*

71⇨🛏 CTV in all bedrooms ® T sB&B⇨🛏£37-£74
dB&B⇨🛏£55-£94 🖻
Lift ℂ 🖵 CFA 🖵 (heated) sauna solarium gymnasium massage, jet stream, jacuzzi
🍽 English & French V ♥ ⌑ ✶ Lunch £9.50-£12.50&alc Dinner £12.50&alc Last dinner 11pm
Credit Cards ①②③⑤£

★★★60% **Novotel Southampton**

1 West Quay Rd SO1 0RA ☎(0703)330550 Telex no 477641
FAX (0703) 222158

*This purpose built, well sound-proofed hotel was opened in 1990. There are functional bedrooms, and food is available all day in Le Grill Restaurant. The establishment is a French-concept hotel, with French management, and there is a small leisure facility for the use of hotel guests only. The first floor bedrooms are all non-smoking.*

121⇨🛏in 21 bedrooms CTV in all bedrooms ® T ✶ S%
sB⇨🛏fr£59.50 dB⇨🛏fr£59.50 (room only) 🖻
Lift ℂ 🖵 300P CFA 🖵 (heated) sauna gymnasium
🍽 International V ♥ ⌑ ✶ ✶ S% Lunch £6.50-£17.70alc Dinner fr£10.75&alc Last dinner mdnt
Credit Cards ①②③⑤

★★★59% **Forte Posthouse**

Herbert Walker Av SO1 0HJ (Forte Hotels) ☎(0703)330777
FAX (0703) 332510

*This professionally managed hotel, with its smartly dressed staff and good on-site parking, features 9 floors of bedrooms with panoramic views over the Solent, city or shipyard and docks. The efficiently supervised health and fitness centre is well equipped, and*

→

*a major refurbishment of ground floor areas – together with such accommodation as has not already been upgraded – is imminent.*
128⇄↑(14fb)⊁in 50 bedrooms CTV in all bedrooms ® T ✱ S% sB⇄↑£39.50-£49.50 (room only) 🍴
Lift ( 250P ✿ CFA ⌷ (heated) sauna solarium gymnasium spa bath *xmas*
♡ English & Continental V ⊕ ⚹ ✘ ✱ Lunch fr£10.95&alc Dinner £13.95&alc Last dinner 10.30pm
Credit Cards ① ② ③ ④ ⑤

### ★★★56% The Dolphin
High St SO9 2DS (Forte Hotels) ☎(0703)339955
Telex no 477735 FAX (0703) 333650
*This city centre hotel in traditional style has an elegant first-floor restaurant serving 2 fixed-price menus and an attractive bar, plus function and conference rooms. Major refurbishment of the dated and varying bedrooms was being undertaken in 1991.*
73⇄↑(2fb)↑⊁in 14 bedrooms CTV in all bedrooms ® T ✱ sB⇄↑£65 dB⇄↑£80 (room only) 🍴
Lift ( ⊞ 90P CFA health & fitness facilities *xmas*
♡ English & Continental V ⊕ ⚹ ✘ ✱ Lunch £9.95&alc Dinner £14.95&alc Last dinner 9.45pm
Credit Cards ① ② ③ ④ ⑤

### ★★★52% The Polygon
Cumberland Place SO9 4GD (Forte Hotels) ☎(0703)330055
Telex no 47175 FAX (0703) 332435
*Public areas at this city centre commercial hotel are about to undergo major refurbishment. Bedrooms here range from the spacious and well co-ordinated to compact basic single rooms. A choice of menus is offered in the Club House restaurant.*
119⇄↑(1fb) CTV in all bedrooms ® T ✱ sB⇄↑fr£60 dB⇄↑£70-£110 (room only) 🍴
Lift ( 120P CFA *xmas*
♡ International V ⊕ ⚹ ✘ ✱ Lunch fr£10.75&alc Dinner fr£16.95&alc Last dinner 9.45pm
Credit Cards ① ② ③ ⑤

### ★★63% Elizabeth House
43-44 The Avenue SO1 2SX ☎(0703)224327
*A small, family owned and run hotel with a friendly atmosphere offers bedrooms that are furnished in a utilitarian manner but provided with modern facilities, a smart dining room and a cellar bar – the whole providing good commercial accommodation.*
24rm(9⇄11↑) CTV in all bedrooms ® T sB&Bfr£35 sB&B⇄↑£45 dB&B⇄↑£55 🍴
CTV 20P ⏍ CFA
V ⊕ Lunch £11.50-£17alc Dinner £11.50-£17alc Last dinner 9.15pm
Credit Cards ① ② ③ ⑤ ⓔ

### ★★57% Star
High St SO9 4ZA ☎(0703)339939 FAX (0703) 335291
Closed 24-26 Dec
*Centrally situated, with an attractive reception and small lounge area, this friendly hotel is continually being refurbished and upgraded. A good choice of meals is available.*
45rm(38⇄↑)⊁in 7 bedrooms CTV in all bedrooms ® T ✱ S% sB&B£20-£36 sB&B⇄↑£34-£54 dB&B⇄↑£46-£66 🍴
Lift ( 20P 10⏍ CFA
V ⊕ ✱ Lunch £5.75-£7.95&alc Dinner £11.95-£15.95alc Last dinner 9pm
Credit Cards ① ② ③ ⑤

### ✿ ✗ ✗ Browns Brasserie
Frobisher House, Nelson Gate, Commercial Rd SO1 0GX
☎(0703)332615
*Hidden behind a glass shop front on the ground floor of a modern office block, Brown's – really more a restaurant than a brasserie – has a cool, stylish and somewhat austere décor enlivened by patches of colour in panels and painted canvas screen on the ceiling. The menu is similarly modern and individualistic, offering such unusual combinations as veal and seafood, lamb and quail*

*with separate garnishes or beef with two mustard sauces. Dishes are presented in the latest style; sea bass fillet, for example, being served on a concasse of peppers, tomato, herbs and olive oil, but over-elaboration sometimes leads to inconsistency though food is generally enjoyable.*
Closed Sun, Xmas eve & New Years eve
♡ British & French V 44 seats ✱ Lunch £11.95-£12.50&alc Dinner £14.95-£19.50&alc Last lunch 2.30pm Last dinner 11pm P nc12yrs ♫
Credit Cards ① ② ③ ⑤

### ✿ ✗ Golden Palace
17A Above Bar St SO1 0DQ ☎(0703)226636
*This restaurant at the heart of the city centre, perched above a High Street shoe shop, is typically Chinese in its simple but richly coloured décor. Set meals are available, but the most interesting dishes are featured on a lengthy à la carte menu which includes a good choice of imaginatively cooked meat, fish and vegetables. The traditional crispy duck and the baked beef with special sauce (a rather sweet, fruity blend flavoured with cinnamon) are quite delicious, and Dim Sum – tasty parcels of pork, beef and prawn, home-made and freshly prepared – are served at main meals. Service is friendly, courteous and obliging.*
♡ English & Chinese V 87 seats Last dinner 11.45pm ⚑
Credit Cards ① ② ③ ⑤

---

## SOUTH BRENT Devon Map 03 SX66

### ★★✿⚑74% Glazebrook House Hotel & Restaurant
TQ10 9SE ☎(0364)73322 FAX (0364) 72350
*An elegant mid-Victorian country house in 4 acres of well kept gardens, Glazebrook is the home of Sue and Laurence Cowley and their young family. In 5 years of ownership they have completed a tasteful refurbishment of all the bedrooms, bar-lounge and dining room. The emphasis is on quality, modern comforts and extras much as mineral water, magazines and fresh flowers. Table d'hôte and à la carte menus offer interesting dishes including roast breast of pigeon with glazed fresh pear and a rich red wine sauce, or succulent boned loin of Devonshire lamb with a mousse of walnut and mild garlic, served on a peppercorn sauce. All prepared from best fresh produce by chef David Merriman. Seafood and vegetarian dishes are featured, and traditional desserts like fruit filled bread and butter pudding with a tangy apricot sauce.*
11⇄↑(3fb)⊁in 1 bedroom CTV in all bedrooms ® T ✖ 🍴
CTV 50P ⏍ ✿ *xmas*
♡ English & French V ⊕ ⚹ ✘
Credit Cards ① ② ③ ④ ⓔ

---

## SOUTHEND-ON-SEA Essex Map 05 TQ88

### ★★65% Camelia
178 Eastern Esplanade, Thorpe Bay SS1 3AA ☎(0702)587917 & 582099 FAX (0702) 585704
*This small smart and hospitable hotel has been completely rebuilt and provides well furnished bedrooms, popular with business people during the week. Bar and lounge space is rather limited but the sizeable dining room has a busy local trade, with dinner dances at weekends.*
16⇄↑(1fb)1⏍ CTV in all bedrooms ® T ✖ (ex guide dogs) ✱ sB&B⇄↑£40-£65 dB&B⇄↑£50-£80 🍴
100P ♫
♡ English & French V ✱ Lunch £9.50 Dinner £12.50&alc Last dinner 10.30pm
Credit Cards ① ③ ⓔ

### ★★64% Schulers Hotel & Restaurant
161 Eastern Esplanade SS1 2YB ☎Southend(0702)610172
Closed 24 Dec-2 Jan RS Sun pm & Mon lunch
*This small well-run hotel centres on its Swiss Chalet Restaurant where chef/patron Manfred Schuler offers a choice of well-cooked traditional dishes with seafood a speciality. There is a bar-function room and a comfortable lounge, and bedrooms are bright and modern, some with sea views.*

S

9rm(5⇌↑)(1fb) CTV in all bedrooms ® T ✕ (ex guide dogs)
✳ sB&Bfr£30.75 sB&B⇌↑fr£41 dB&Bfr£38.95
dB&B⇌↑£49.20-£61.50
14P
♡ International V ✳ S10% Lunch £8.25-£15.50 Dinner £11.50-£15 Last dinner 9.45pm
Credit Cards ①②③⑤ⓔ

### ★★ 61% Erlsmere
24/32 Pembury Rd, off Station Rd, Westcliff-on-Sea SS0 8DS
☎(0702)349025 FAX (0702) 337724
*Quietly located in a mainly residential area just off the seafront, this hotel offers well equipped accommodation, the majority of rooms being recently refurbished – some in romantic style. Shasha's Restaurant serves an adventurous à la carte menu, and guests can relax in the Wellington Bar at the rear of the building. Friendly service is provided by a young, uniformed staff.*
31⇌↑(2fb)4⊞⅍in 2 bedrooms CTV in all bedrooms ® T
✕ (ex guide dogs) ✳ sB&B⇌↑£43-£50 dB&B⇌↑£53-£60 ☐
⟅ CTV 13P ⌣ (heated) *xmas*
♡ English & French V ✿ ⚒ ⅍ ✳ S10% Lunch £8.50-£12&alc
High tea £3-£5 Dinner £8.50-£12&alc Last dinner 10.15pm
Credit Cards ①②③⑤

### ★ 69% Balmoral
34 Valkyrie Rd, Westcliffe-on-Sea SS0 8BU ☎(0702)342947
FAX (0702) 337828
*Set in a residential road a short walk from Westcliff seafront and station, this cheerful owner-run hotel is very well maintained, with a cosy lounge, a bar attached to the dining room and bright well-equipped bedrooms of varying size.*
22⇌↑(4fb) CTV in all bedrooms ® T ✳ sB&B⇌↑£37.50-£45 dB&B⇌↑£52-£59 ☐
CTV 19P ⊞ CFA
♡ English & French ✿ ⚒ ✳ Dinner £9&alc Last dinner
7.30pm
Credit Cards ①③

### SOUTH GODSTONE Surrey Map 05 TQ34 ⊙

### ⊛⊛✕✕✕La Bonne Auberge
Tilburstow Hill RH9 8JY ☎(0342)892318 FAX (0342) 893435
*An attractive Victorian house in quiet rural setting has an interior subtly redolent of France, with its parquet floor, brick fireplace, copperware and pictures. Menus in modern style focus on flavour and delicacy, a typical meal including, perhaps, warm asparagus mousse followed by salmon and sole with samphire and vermouth and a delicious almond and pear tart.*
Closed Mon & 26-30 Dec
Dinner not served Sun
♡ French V 75 seats Lunch £14-£23 Dinner £25-£35&alc Last
lunch 2pm Last dinner 10pm 50 P ♪
Credit Cards ①②③⑤

### SOUTH MIMMS Hertfordshire Map 04 TL20

### ★★★ 65% Forte Posthouse
Bignells Corner EN6 3NH (junc A1/A6) (Forte Hotels)
☎Potters Bar(0707)43311 Telex no 299162 FAX (0707) 46728
RS Xmas
*This busy, modern hotel has comfortable well equipped bedrooms and refurbished public areas. Sensations leisure club offers a wide range of facilities and the hotel has a business centre.*
120⇌↑⅍in 60 bedrooms CTV in all bedrooms ® T
✕ (ex guide dogs) ✳ sB⇌↑£39.50-£49.50 dB⇌↑£39.50-£49.50 (room only) ☐
⟅ 200P ⊞ CFA ☒ (heated) sauna solarium gymnasium
outdoor childrens play area pool tables ⚬
♡ International V ✿ ⚒ ⅍ ✳ Lunch £8-£25alc Dinner £8-£25alc Last dinner 10.30pm
Credit Cards ①②③④⑤

### ⌂Forte Travelodge
Bignells Corner EN6 3QQ (junc 23, M25) (Forte)
☎Central Res (0800) 850950
*Conveniently situated just off the A1(M) at South Mimms services, this recently opened Travelodge offers excellent value accommodation with just one price per room. Bedrooms are all identically furnished and equipped to a good standard, each with a double bed and sofabed. All have modern en suite facilities. Meals and refreshments are available at the adjacent Welcome break services.*
52⇌↑(52fb) CTV in all bedrooms ® sB⇌↑£29.95
dB⇌↑£29.95 (room only)
⟅ 52P ⊞
Credit Cards ①②③

### SOUTH MOLTON Devon Map 03 SS72

★★⊛⊛⊛⚔
**WHITECHAPEL MANOR**
EX36 3EG ☎(0769) 573377 &
2554 FAX (0769) 573797

*This rather beautiful Elizabethan building has been painstakingly restored by the present owners John and Patricia Shapland, after years of neglect as a private residence. Many of the original old features have been preserved – exposed beams, attractive panelling and paintings, and a magnificent carved oak screen at one end of the 'great hall'. The public areas have been comfortably and tastefully* →

S

*appointed in a sympathetic style. The overall effect is informal – and even more so in the bright dining room, where the charming Shaplands are assisted by polite and helpful staff, and treated to the fine cuisine of Thierry Lepretre-Granet. His sensibly sized set-price menus offer cooking of the highest order, using mostly local lamb, beef and fish from Cornwall and Scotland. A springtime main course might well be tender lamb served with a herb crust and a natural jus, and for pudding a hot chocolate torte with orange sauce. There is a carefully chosen wine list to complement the menus. The 10 bedrooms are very pretty with high quality soft furnishings, and thoughtful extras include mineral water and beautiful fresh flowers. This peaceful hotel is the ideal retreat, and guests will enjoy very high levels of comfort, cuisine, and hospitality.*

10⇨🌂🛏🎜 CTV in all bedrooms **T** ✖ ✱ sB&B⇨🌂£60-£75 dB&B⇨🌂£90-£170 🖪

40P 🚗 ✿ *xmas*

♀ French ۵ 𝒰 ⅙ ✱ Lunch £25.50 Dinner £35.50 Last dinner 8.45pm

Credit Cards 1 3

---

### ★★🏍73% Marsh Hall
EX36 3HQ (1.25m N towards North Molton) ☎(07695)2666 FAX (07695) 4230

*A country house and grounds in an elevated position close to the North Devon link road. Marsh Hall, part 17th century with a Victorian frontage, has been sympathetically modernised with 7 well equipped rooms providing en suite facilities. The public rooms are comfortably furnished and the emphasis is on peace and quiet. A table d'hôte menu is offered in the informal dining room and the friendly service is by the resident proprietors.*

7⇨🌂🌂 CTV in all bedrooms ® **T** ✱ sB&B⇨🌂£36-£49.50 dB&B⇨🌂£72-£99 🖪

15P 🚗 ✿ nc12yrs *xmas*

♀ English & Continental **V** ۵ ✱ Lunch fr£8.50 Dinner fr£17.50 Last dinner 8.30pm

Credit Cards 1 3

---

### SOUTH NORMANTON Derbyshire Map 08 SK45

### ★★★69% Swallow
Carter Ln East DE55 2EH (junct 28 of M1) (Swallow) ☎Ripley(0773)812000 Telex no 377264 FAX (0733) 580032

*The hotel was extended and refurbished in 1990 to give guests more comfortable lounge and bar areas and new banqueting/meeting rooms. The coffee shop and Pavilion restaurant offer a choice of snacks and à la carte menus and the comprehensive indoor leisure facilities are particularly popular with families at weekends.*

161⇨🌂(6fb)⅙in 61 bedrooms CTV in all bedrooms ® **T** S% sB&B⇨🌂£82 dB&B⇨🌂£100 🖪

《 200P ✿ 🏊 (heated) sauna solarium gymnasium jacuzzi steam room *xmas*

♀ International **V** ۵ 𝒰 ⅙ S% Lunch £12.50 Dinner £18.50 Last dinner 10.30pm

Credit Cards 1 2 3 4 5 ⓔ

---

### SOUTHPORT Merseyside Map 07 SD31

### ★★★62% Royal Clifton
Promenade PR8 1RB (Best Western) ☎(0704)533771 Telex no 677191 FAX (0704) 500657

*Popular for conferences and functions, this large hotel occupies a prominent position overlooking the Promenade. Bedrooms are gradually being refurbished to a good standard and there is a well equipped leisure club.*

107⇨🌂🌂(2fb)2🛏⅙in 2 bedrooms CTV in all bedrooms ® **T** sB&B⇨🌂£65-£71.50 dB&B⇨🌂£81.50-£86.50 🖪

Lift 《 40P CFA 🖸 (heated) sauna solarium gymnasium sunbed jacuzzi 🎜 *xmas*

♀ English & French ۵ 𝒰 ✱ Lunch £2-£18alc High tea £1-£8alc Dinner £6-£30alc Last dinner 9.45pm

Credit Cards 1 2 3 5 ⓔ

---

### ★★★61% Scarisbrick
Lord St PR8 1NZ ☎(0704)543000 FAX (0704) 533335

*This refurbished Victorian hotel in the town centre offers well equipped modern bedrooms, some of which overlook fashionable Lord Street. A disco is included among its popular and lively bars, but those seeking quieter surroundings will prefer the pleasant restaurant and cocktail bar on the first floor.*

66⇨🌂🌂(5fb)6🛏 CTV in all bedrooms ® **T** sB&B⇨🌂🌂£60-£80 dB&B⇨🌂🌂£75-£130 🖪

Lift 《 40P 12🚗 CFA pool tables games room 🎜 *xmas*

♀ English & French **V** ۵ 𝒰 ⅙ Lunch £5.60-£8.50&alc High tea £4.60-£7.50 Dinner £12-£15&alc Last dinner 9.30pm

Credit Cards 1 2 3 5 ⓔ

---

### ★★68% Balmoral Lodge
41 Queens Rd PR9 9EX ☎(0704)544298 FAX (0704) 501224

*This friendly family-run hotel in an Edwardian property within easy reach of the town centre has well-equipped bedrooms, particularly those in the garden wing, and a comfortable lounge and pleasant Tudor-style bar.*

15⇨🌂🌂(1fb)🛏 CTV in all bedrooms ® **T** ✖ sB&B⇨🌂🌂£28-£55 dB&B⇨🌂🌂£55-£66 🖪

CTV 10P 🚗 sauna

✱ Bar Lunch £3-£5 Dinner £9.50-£12&alc Last dinner 8.30pm

Credit Cards 1 2 3 5 ⓔ

---

### ★★67% Stutelea Hotel & Leisure Club
Alexandra Rd PR9 0NB ☎(0704)544220 FAX (0704) 500232

*Considerable refurbishment has taken place at this popular family-run hotel in a quiet residential area within easy reach of the town centre. Well equipped comfortably furnished bedrooms, some with balconies overlooking the attractive rear gardens, now have smart modern bathrooms and there is a well equipped leisure centre.*

20⇨🌂🌂(3fb)2🛏 CTV in all bedrooms ® **T** ✖ (ex guide dogs) sB&B⇨🌂🌂£40-£45 dB&B⇨🌂🌂£60-£65 🖪

Lift CTV 18P 🚗 ✿ 🖸 (heated) sauna solarium gymnasium games room jacuzzi keep fit classes

۵ 𝒰 Bar Lunch £2-£5 High tea £5-£7 Dinner £7-£14alc Last dinner 8.30pm

Credit Cards 1 2 3 5 ⓔ

---

### ★★65% Bold
Lord St PR9 0BE ☎(0704)532578 FAX (0704) 32528

*Lively and popular, an hotel at the northern end of fashionable Lord Street offers a choice of eating and drinking styles, the spaciously modern Raphael's Bar Café and all-day bistro being complemented by a more intimate à la carte restaurant which now has its own comfortable, quiet lounge. Refurbished bedrooms combine functional fittings with attractive coordinated fabrics, and a friendly young staff provides willing service.*

22rm(15⇨6🌂)(4fb) CTV in all bedrooms ® **T** ✖ (ex guide dogs)

《 8P 🎜

♀ English, French & Italian **V** ۵ 𝒰 Last dinner 9.45pm

Credit Cards 1 2 3 4 5

---

### ★★60% Lockerbie House
11 Trafalgar Rd, Birkdale PR8 2EA ☎(0704)565298

*Situated in a quiet residential area, convenient for Birkdale Station and not far from the famous golf course, this small hotel is run in a friendly and informal manner by the enthusiastic proprietors. Bedrooms continue to be improved, most are spacious and comfortable.*

14⇨🌂(3fb) CTV in all bedrooms ®

**S**

CTV 14P 2⇔ ✿ snooker ♪
V ✿ ⌂ Last dinner 8pm
Credit Cards ①②③⑤

★★59% **Shelbourne**
1 Lord St PR8 2BH ☎(0704)541252 & 530278
FAX (0704) 501293
18⇥♠(2fb)✂in 3 bedrooms CTV in all bedrooms ® T
sB&B⇥♠£30-£36 dB&B⇥♠£40-£48
18P ⇔ CFA Games room nc8yrs
V ✿ ✂ Lunch £6.95-£6.95 Dinner £8.95-£10.95&alc Last
dinner 9pm
Credit Cards ①②③ⓔ

★★55% **Metropole**
Portland St PR8 1LL ☎(0704)536836
*Improvements continue to be made at this family-run hotel at the
southern end of Bold Street. Though some bedrooms are compact
and modestly furnished, redecorated public areas are more
comfortable and inviting.*
25rm(9⇥9♠)(3fb) CTV in all bedrooms ® T sB&B22.50-
£24.50 sB&B⇥♠£30.50-£33.50 dB&B£38-£44.50
dB&B⇥♠£52.50-£59.50 ⌸
CTV 12P ⇔ snooker *xmas*
♀ English & French ✿ Lunch £4.50-£9.50 Dinner fr£10 Last
dinner 8.30pm
Credit Cards ①②③

All black star hotels are given a
percentage grading within their star bands.
See 'Using the Guide' at the front of the book
for full details.

**S**

## SOUTH QUEENSFERRY Lothian *West Lothian* Map **11** NT17

### ★★★ 61% *Forth Bridges Moat House*

Forth Bridge EH30 9SF (Queens Moat) ☎031-331 1199
Telex no 727430 FAX 031-319 1733

*Situated on the south side of the Forth Road Bridge, this purpose-built hotel offers fine views of the road and rail bridges: the latter is now illuminated at night. Bedrooms are well equipped, and the majority that look out on to the Firth of Forth are of good size.*

108➪🅟(30fb)⊬in 5 bedrooms CTV in all bedrooms ® T
Lift ℂ 200P ❀ 🖃 (heated) squash snooker sauna solarium gymnasium
🍴 English & French **V** ✆ ⏴⏵ ℒ Last dinner 9.45pm
Credit Cards ①②③⑤

---

## SOUTHSEA

See Portsmouth & Southsea

---

## SOUTH SHIELDS Tyne & Wear Map **12** NZ36

### ★★★ 58% *Sea*

Sea Rd NE33 2LD ☎091-427 0999 Telex no 53533
FAX 091-454 0500
Closed 25-27 Dec

*A mainly commercial hotel on the seafront and overlooking the harbour mouth, amusement park and other leisure facilities. At the time of the last inspection bedrooms were still being upgraded to a good modern standard. Service is friendly and helpful.*

33➪🅟(2fb)1🛏 CTV in all bedrooms ® T sB&B➪🅟£58-£60 dB&B➪🅟£65-£75 🍴
ℂ 40P CFA
🍴 English & French **V** ✆ ⏴⏵ ℒ Lunch £6.50-£7.50&alc High tea £2.95-£3.50 Dinner £8.95-£9.50&alc Last dinner 9.30pm
Credit Cards ①②③⑤

---

## SOUTH UIST, ISLE OF Western Isles *Inverness-shire* Map **13**

## LOCHBOISDALE Map **13** NF71

### ★★ 57% *Lochboisdale*

PA81 5TH ☎(08784)332 FAX (08784) 367

*This friendly fishing hotel, situated beside the harbour and ferry terminal, is slowly being improved. The walls of the public areas, which include a comfortable lounge, lounge bar and a refurbished dining room, are adorned with fishing prints and local paintings. Bedrooms are modestly furnished and equipped.*

20rm(11➪)(1fb)®
CTV 50P ❀ ♪ snooker birdwatching trips ♫ ஃ
🍴 French **V** ✆ ⏴⏵ ℒ
Credit Cards ①③

---

## SOUTHWAITE MOTORWAY SERVICE AREA (M6) Cumbria Map **12** NY44

### ⇧Granada Lodge

Broadfield Site CA4 0NT (on M6) (Granada)
☎Southwaite(06974)73131 FAX (06974) 73669

*This well furnished modern lodge, located between junctions 41 and 42 of the M6, can be reached from either side though it actually stands on the southbound carriageway. The well appointed bedrooms it provides represent very good value for money.*

39➪🅟(10fb)⊬in 6 bedrooms CTV in all bedrooms ®
🏹 (ex guide dogs) S% sB➪🅟fr£31 dB➪🅟fr£34 (room only) 🍴
ℂ 323P

**See advertisement under CARLISLE**

---

## SOUTH WALSHAM Norfolk Map **09** TG31

### ★★★ 59% South Walsham Hall

The Street NR13 6DQ ☎(060549)378 & 591 FAX (060549) 519
Closed 1-15 Jan

*This historic country house dates back to the 11th century and is mentioned in the Domesday book. Set in a peaceful location, amid the sloping lawns, great trees and beautiful lakes of its own magnificent grounds, it offers a selection of bedrooms ranging from the grand to the modest but all providing similar facilities.*

10➪🅟Annexe7➪(2fb) CTV in all bedrooms ® T ✱
sB&B➪🅟£40-£80 dB&B➪🅟£60-£120 🍴
50P 🚑 ❀ ❀ ⚊ (heated) ℘ (hard) ♪ squash ∪ sauna solarium gymnasium *xmas*
🍴 English & French **V** ✆ ⏴⏵ ℒ ✱ Lunch £12-£13.50&alc Dinner £13.50&alc Last dinner 9.45pm
Credit Cards ①②③⑤ ⓔ

---

## SOUTHWELL Nottinghamshire Map **08** SK75

### ★★★ 65% Saracen's Head

Market Place NG25 0HE (Forte Hotels) ☎(0636)812701
Telex no 377201 FAX (0636) 815408

*This attractive and traditionally half timbered hotel at the heart of the town features 4 character bedrooms, one with the original Jacobean wall designs on display; additional modern accommodation is provided in a rear wing. After long awaited refurbishment, the public areas are now also an asset to the establishment.*

27➪1🛏⊬in 12 bedrooms CTV in all bedrooms ® T ✱
sB➪🅟fr£65 dB➪🅟£85-£130 (room only) 🍴
ℂ 80P 2🚗 CFA *xmas*
**V** ✆ ⏴⏵ ⊬ ✱ Lunch fr£9.75&alc Dinner fr£14.95&alc Last dinner 9.45pm
Credit Cards ①②③④⑤

---

## SOUTH WITHAM Lincolnshire Map **08** SK91

### ⇧Forte Travelodge

New Fox LE15 8AU (on A1, northbound) (Forte)
☎Thistleton(057283)586 Central Res (0800) 850950

*Situated about 9 miles south of Grantham on the northbound side of the A1. For southbound traffic, take the turning signed South Witham and then rejoin the dual carriageway northbound. There is a Little Chef restaurant adjacent.*

32➪🅟(32fb) CTV in all bedrooms ® sB➪🅟£29.95 dB➪🅟£29.95 (room only)
ℂ 32P 🚳
Credit Cards ①②③

---

## SOUTHWOLD Suffolk Map **05** TM57

### ★★★ ❀69% Swan

Market Place IP18 6EG ☎(0502)722186 FAX (0502) 724800

*Located in the centre of the town, this well managed renovated 17th-century inn provides comfortable accommodation and attractive public areas. The restaurant offers a choice of set menus, all of which use fresh, carefully prepared produce, and a good reasonably priced wine list.*

27➪🅟Annexe18➪(2fb) CTV in all bedrooms T ✱
sB&B➪🅟£40-£62 dB&B➪🅟£76-£98 🍴
Lift ℂ 50P 🚳 CFA *xmas*
**V** ✆ ⏴⏵ ℒ ⊬ ✱ Lunch £9.75-£12.75alc High tea £3-£6alc Dinner £15.95-£24.95alc Last dinner 9.30pm
Credit Cards ①②③

### ★★ ❀67% Crown Southwold

90 High St IP18 6DP ☎(0502)722275 FAX (0502) 724805
Closed 1st & 2nd wk Jan

*This busy inn situated in the main street provides rather compact but characterful accommodation and is very popular both for its bars, which serve a wide choice of good wines from Adnams, and*

*restaurant, offering an imaginative daily-changing menu using fresh produce.*
12rm(8⇨1🛏)(1fb) CTV in all bedrooms 🕊 (ex guide dogs)
15P 8🚗🚗 CFA *xmas*
✋ 🎳 ⚡ ✻ Lunch £14.75 High tea £17.75
Credit Cards ①②③

---

### SOUTH ZEAL Devon Map 03 SX69

★★62% **Oxenham Arms**
EX20 2JT ☎Okehampton(0837)840244 & 840577
*This village inn, dating back to the 12th century, exhibits a wealth of character and interesting architectural detail in exposed beams, arched door surrounds and original granite pillars and open fireplaces. Simply decorated bedrooms (some of which have en suite bathrooms) are furnished with heavy antique pieces. Bars are popular locally, as are the table d'hôte and bar snack menus available in the intimate dining room.*
8rm(7⇨🛏) CTV in all bedrooms Ⓡ T sB&B£35-£45
sB&B⇨🛏£38 dB&B£45 dB&B⇨🛏£55-£60
CTV 8P 🚗 ❄ *xmas*
🍴 International V ✋ 🎳 Lunch £8.50-£11.50 Dinner £15.50-£17.50 Last dinner 9pm
Credit Cards ①②③⑤ Ⓔ

---

### SOWERBY BRIDGE West Yorkshire Map 07 SE02

★★72% **The Hobbit**
Hob Ln, Norlands HX6 3QL ☎Halifax(0422)832202
FAX (0422) 835381
*An attractive stone-built hotel with fine views over the valley below. There is a good range of food here, especially in the popular bar. Staff are very friendly and helpful, and the bedrooms well furnished and comfortable.*
17⇨🛏Annexe5⇨🛏(2fb)1🎹 CTV in all bedrooms Ⓡ T 🕊
sB&B⇨🛏£40-£55 dB&B⇨🛏£59-£69 🏳
100P CFA 🎵 *xmas*
🍴 English, French & Italian V 🎳 ✻ Lunch £7.50 Dinner £9.95-£12.95 Last dinner 10.30pm
Credit Cards ①②③

---

### SPALDING Lincolnshire Map 08 TF22

★★66% **Woodlands**
80 Pinchbeck Rd PE11 1QF ☎(0775)769933 FAX (0775) 711369
*Situated towards the outskirts of the town on the A16 Boston road, this detached Edwardian house is set in its own grounds. The recently refurbished restaurant opens out on to lovely gardens. There is a light, airy bar and a connecting lounge. Accommodation is well equipped and comfortable, and friendly service is provided by the small team of staff.*
18⇨🛏(1fb)✂in 2 bedrooms CTV in all bedrooms Ⓡ T ✻
sB&B⇨🛏£30-£51 dB&B⇨🛏£45-£60 🏳
CTV 60P ❄ CFA 🏊
🍴 English & French V ✋ 🎳 ✻ Lunch £4.50-£12.50&alc
Dinner £10.75-£12.50&alc Last dinner 10pm
Credit Cards ①②③⑤ Ⓔ

---

### SPEAN BRIDGE Highland *Inverness-shire* Map 14 NN28

See also **Letterfinlay and Roy Bridge**
★★58% *Spean Bridge*
PH34 4ES ☎(039781)250
*This traditional family-run tourist hotel on the main road in the village centre has an interconnecting purpose-built wing with 5 attractive new bedrooms. Chalets grouped at the rear provide ten more bedrooms with modern facilities.*
22⇨🛏Annexe10⇨🛏(4fb) CTV in 22 bedrooms Ⓡ
CTV 50P ▶ 9 ⌗ snooker games room
V ✋ 🎳 Last dinner 9pm
Credit Cards ①③⑤

---

### STADDLE BRIDGE North Yorkshire Map 08 SE49

❀❀ ✕✕*McCoys (Tontine Inn)*
DL6 3JB ☎East Harsley(060982)671
*This one-time pub, the Cleveland Tontine, has long been locally popular, as much for its extraordinary décor and atmosphere as for its good cooking. Run by three brothers, Eugene, Peter and Tom McCoy, the theme is early 20th-century nostalia, Kentia palms grace the lounge with its flower-cushioned, fraying sofas and chairs, blazing coal fire, bamboo tables and lacy net curtains, while the candle-lit dining room is dominated by huge Japanese parasols and muzak from the thirties and forties. The menu rarely changes and shows a predilection for truffles and foie gras in many dishes. Our inspector particularly commended the home-made ravioli filled with a delicate langoustine mousse enhanced by lemon and truffles accompanied by a pungent lobster sauce, but felt that some of the dishes (lamb brought to the table without its advertised accompaniment of artichoke heart, wild mushrooms and foie gras) suggested that the kitchens might be resting on their laurels. Service is friendly, but speed did not seem to be their forte. There is also a bistro, where the menu changes more frequently and prices are more competitive. Six bedrooms are now available.*
Closed Sun, 25-26 Dec & 1 Jan Lunch not served
🍴 International V 60 seats Last lunch 2pm Last dinner 11pm
80 P
Credit Cards ①②③⑤

---

### STAFFORD Staffordshire Map 07 SJ92 ⊙

★★★64% **Tillington Hall**
Eccleshall Rd ST16 1JJ (De Vere) ☎(0785)53531
FAX (0785) 59223
RS Xmas & New Year
*This friendly hotel in commercial style, located in a quiet residential area on the Eccleshall road out of the town, caters ably for conference delegates during the week. The leisure complex at its rear is well patronised, both by residents and club members.*
90⇨🛏(3fb)1🎹✂in 16 bedrooms CTV in all bedrooms Ⓡ T ✻
sB&B⇨🛏£54-£83 dB&B⇨🛏£86-£97 🏳
Lift ⟮ 150P CFA 🏊 (heated) ♪ (hard) snooker gymnasium
table tennis jacuzzi 🎵 *xmas*
🍴 English, French & German V ✋ 🎳 ✂ ✻ Lunch fr£9&alc
Dinner fr£12.50&alc Last dinner 9.45pm
Credit Cards ①②③⑤ Ⓔ

★★65% *Garth*
Wolverhampton Rd, Moss Pit ST17 9JR (Crown & Raven)
☎(0785)56124 Telex no 36479 FAX (0785) 55152
RS 25-26 Dec
*A good business hotel, conveniently sited close to junction 13 of the M6. There are plans to upgrade slightly dated public areas in line with its comfortable and well equipped bedrooms.*
60⇨🛏(2fb)✂in 20 bedrooms CTV in all bedrooms Ⓡ T
⟮ 175P ❄
🍴 English & French V ✋ 🎳 Last dinner 10pm
Credit Cards ①②③

★★60% *Swan*
Greengate St ST16 2JA (Chef & Brewer) ☎(0785)58142
FAX (0785) 223372
*This old coaching inn is situated in the centre of town with its own car park to the rear. It offers compact bedrooms with Laura Ashley décor on the upper floors, and a series of bars and the ever popular grill restaurant on the ground floor.*
32⇨🛏(5fb)🎹 CTV in all bedrooms Ⓡ T 🕊 (ex guide dogs)
sB&B⇨🛏£45-£49 dB&B⇨🛏£66 🏳
⟮ 50P
V ✋ ✂ Bar Lunch £2.95-£5.50alc
Credit Cards ①②③⑤

### ★★59% *Vine*

Salter St ST16 2JU (Crown & Raven) ☎(0785)51071 & 44112
Telex no 36479 FAX (0785) 46612

*This 17th-century creeper-clad inn just off the main shopping centre retains its historical character. The popular public areas were looking rather worn at the last inspection, but bedrooms were in good decorative order and have all modern amenities.*

27⇨🏠(1fb) CTV in all bedrooms ® T

30P

♡ English & French V ♥ ♨

Credit Cards ①②③

### ★★57% *Abbey*

65-68 Lichfield Rd ST17 4LW ☎(0785)58531
Closed 23 Dec-7 Jan

*This busy commercial hotel on the edge of town has a rear car park. At weekends the restaurant offers a restricted service, bar snacks only are available but these can be served in the dining room.*

21rm(1⇨6🏠)(1fb) CTV in all bedrooms ® ✗ sB&B£19-£21 sB&B⇨🏠£28.50-£31 dB&B£33-£36 dB&B⇨🏠£42-£60 🏠

CTV 21P 5🏠 (£3 per night) 🐾

♡ English & French V ♥ Bar Lunch £2.50-£5 Dinner £6.50-£7.50&alc Last dinner 8.30pm

Credit Cards ①③

### ★★52% *Albridge*

73 Wolverhampton Rd ST17 4AW ☎(0785)54100
Closed Xmas Day RS 26-31 Dec

*A budget conscious commercial hotel on the A449. The dining room offers a selection of grill type meals, and snacks are also available in the bar or the small games room.*

11rm(7⇨🏠)Annexe8rm(2🏠)(2fb) CTV in 12 bedrooms ® T S% sB&Bfr£22 sB&B⇨🏠fr£24.15 dB&Bfr£32.50 dB&B⇨🏠fr£39.50 🏠

CTV 20P pool table darts

V ♥ ♨ ✗ ✳ S% Bar Lunch £3.50&alc Dinner fr£6.95&alc Last dinner 9.45pm

Credit Cards ①②③⑤

---

### STAINES Surrey Map **04** TQ07

### ★★★59% *The Thames Lodge*

Thames St TW18 4SF (Forte Hotels) ☎(0784)464433
Telex no 8812552 FAX (0784) 454858

*Its superb roadside location and good car parking facilities make this hotel an ideal venue for business and social occasions. Both the popular Packhorse Bar and the restaurant, with its views of the river, have recently benefited from complete refurbishment, and the work necessary to bring a selection of the annexe bedrooms up to a comfortable, well equipped standard, will soon begin.*

44⇨🏠✗in 8 bedrooms CTV in all bedrooms ® T ✳ S% sB⇨🏠fr£75 dB⇨🏠fr£95 (room only) 🏠

《 60P CFA *xmas*

V ♥ ♨ ✗ ✳ Lunch £12&alc Dinner £15.50&alc Last dinner 10pm

Credit Cards ①②③④⑤

---

### STAMFORD Lincolnshire Map **04** TF00

### ★★★75% *George of Stamford*

St Martins PE9 2LB ☎(0780)55171 Telex no 32578
FAX (0780) 57070

*This popular and particularly well managed coaching inn at the heart of the town retains many original features. Extensive public areas are tastefully furnished to provide the utmost luxury, enhanced with beautiful plants and floral arrangements. A restaurant is included, offering an imaginative range of skilfully prepared dishes complemented by a very fine wine list, while individually designed bedrooms are well equipped and service is excellent throughout.*

47⇨🏠(2fb)4🏠 CTV in all bedrooms T ✳ sB&B⇨🏠£66-£91.50 dB&B⇨🏠£97.50-£154 🏠

《 120P ✿ CFA croquet *xmas*

♡ English, French & Italian V ♥ ♨ ✗ ✳ Lunch £16.70-£32.50alc Dinner £16.70-£32.50alc Last dinner 10.30pm

Credit Cards ①②③⑤

### ★★★69% Garden House

St Martin's PE9 2LP ☎(0780)63359 Telex no 329230
FAX (0780) 63339

*A charming small hotel owned and run by the Gorrie family who offer a refreshing and honest style of hospitality. Public areas are attractively furnished, and enhanced by a colourful conservatory overlooking the carefully tended walled garden. Bedrooms do vary, though all are thoughtfully furnished with an eye to detail and cleanliness.*

20⇨🏠(1fb)1🏠 CTV in all bedrooms ® T sB&B⇨🏠fr£58.50 dB&B⇨🏠fr£76.50 🏠

25P 5🏠 ✿ ♨

♡ English & French V ♥ ♨ Lunch fr£15alc Dinner fr£15alc Last dinner 9.30pm

Credit Cards ①②③ £

### ★★62% *Lady Anne's*

37-38 High Street, St Martins PE9 2LJ ☎(0780)53175
Telex no 32376 FAX (0780) 65422
Closed 27-30 Dec

*Personally supervised by the proprietors, and a popular venue for weddings and conferences, the hotel is set in its own pleasant grounds on the B1081 south of the town, easily accessible from the A1.*

28rm(17⇨9🏠)(6fb)2🏠 CTV in all bedrooms ® T ✳ sB&B£40-£46.20 sB&B⇨🏠£40-£46.20 dB&B£50-£63 dB&B⇨🏠£50-£63 🏠

CTV 150P ✿ 🏊 (heated) ♪ (hard) *xmas*

V ♥ ♨ ✳ Lunch £13.50 High tea £5 Dinner £13.50 Last dinner 9.30pm

Credit Cards ①②③④⑤

### ★★56% Crown

All Saints Place PE9 2AG ☎(0780)63136 FAX (0780) 56111
Closed 25 Dec

*A well furnished, small hotel situated in the town centre. Accommodation is generally comfortable with a good standard of cleanliness, and tasty dishes are served in the restaurants.*

18rm(5⇨10🏠)(2fb)1🏠 CTV in all bedrooms ® T ✳ sB&B£37.50 sB&B⇨🏠£42 dB&B£48 dB&B⇨🏠£55

40P CFA

♡ European V ♥ ♨ ✳ Lunch £7.75 Dinner £8.95&alc Last dinner 9.30pm

Credit Cards ①②③⑤

---

### STANDISH Greater Manchester Map **07** SD51

### ★★★69% *Kilhey Court Hotel*

Chorley Rd WN1 2XN (on A5106 1.5m N of A49/A5106 junct) (Best Western) ☎(0257)472100 Telex no 67460
FAX (0257) 422401

*Now considerably extended to provide a small leisure centre, café bar and more modern bedrooms, this well established comfortable hotel is set in 10 acres of grounds and gardens above the Worthington Lakes. The popular restaurant has fine views and there is a wide range of function and conference rooms as well as a nightclub at weekends.*

54⇨(4fb)1🏠✗in 10 bedrooms CTV in all bedrooms ® T

Lift 《 CTV 180P ✿ 🏊 🏊 ✎ sauna solarium gymnasium steam room spa bath ♨

V ♥ ♨ Last dinner 10pm

Credit Cards ①②③⑤

**★★★ 64% Almond Brook Moat House**
Almond Brook Rd WN6 0SR (Queens Moat) ☎(0257)425588
Telex no 677662 FAX (0257) 427327
Closed 25-30 Dec
126⇌✿🏠(33fb)⊁in 5 bedrooms CTV in all bedrooms ® T
sB&B⇌🏠frf85 dB&B⇌🏠frf95 ➡
Lift ℂ ⊞ 400P CFA ▣ (heated) sauna solarium gymnasium ♫
🎦 English & French V ⌖ ⯑ ⊁
Credit Cards ①②③④⑤

---

**STANLEY Co Durham** Map **12** NZ15

**★★ 64% South Causey Hotel & Equestrian Centre**
Beamish Burn Rd DH9 0LS ☎(0207)235555 FAX (0207) 230137
*This friendly family owned hotel is created from old farm buildings
and incorporates an equestrian centre. It is situated among fields
and paddocks off the A6076 north of Stanley and just down the
road from the renowned Beamish Open Air Museum.*
16⇌🏠 CTV in all bedrooms ® T ✱ S10% sB&B⇌🏠frf44
dB&B⇌🏠frf54 ➡
ℂ ⊞ CTV 100P ✿ ⌣ ♫ ✿ *xmas*
V ⌖ ⯑ ✱ S10% Lunch £3.50-£15alc High tea £2-£5alc Dinner
£5-£15alc Last dinner 9.30pm
Credit Cards ①②③

---

**STANLEY Tayside** Map **11** NO13

**★★ 57% The Tayside**
Mill St PH1 4NL (6m N of Perth) ☎(0738)828249
FAX (0738) 33449
*An Edwardian building has been converted and extended to
provide a quiet village hotel which is a popular base for fishing,
shooting and golfing enthusiasts, combining traditional comforts
with practical accommodation.*
17rm(2⇌11🏠)(2fb) CTV in all bedrooms ® ✱ sB&B£17.50-
£19.50 sB&B⇌🏠£29.50-£37.50 dB&B£29-£39 dB&B⇌🏠£49-
£55 ➡
50P 4🐾 CFA *xmas*
V ⌖ ⯑ ✱ Lunch £4.50-£12.50alc Dinner frf13.75&alc Last
dinner 8.30pm
Credit Cards ①③ ⓔ

---

**STANSTED AIRPORT Essex** Map **05** TL52

**★★★ 61% Stansted Harlequin**
Round Coppice Rd CM24 8SE ☎Bishop Stortford(0279)680800
Telex no 818840 FAX (0279) 680890
*This new, purpose-built hotel on the airport periphery aims to meet
the needs of travellers and to attract conference business.
Bedrooms are equipped with air conditioning and triple glazing,
their slightly functional style lifted by geometrically patterned
fabrics in jaunty colours. At present services are a little informal,
designed for the visitor on the move, but tariffs are set accordingly.*
249⇌🏠(5fb)⊁in 30 bedrooms CTV in all bedrooms ® T
🐕 (ex guide dogs) ✱ sB&B⇌🏠frf65 dB&B⇌🏠frf75
Continental breakfast
Lift ⊞ 250P CFA ▣ (heated) sauna solarium gymnasium
steam room whirlpool
🎦 Continental V ⌖ ⯑ ⊁ ✱ S% Lunch £10.50-£20 Dinner
frf12.50 Last dinner 11.15pm
Credit Cards ①②③⑤

---

**STAVERTON Devon** Map **03** SX76

**★ 69% *Sea Trout Inn***
TQ9 6PA ☎(080426)274
*A comfortable village inn in a peaceful situation offering attentive
service from the resident owners.*
10⇌🏠(2fb)1🛏 CTV in all bedrooms ® T
70P 🚲
🎦 English & French V ⌖ Last dinner 9.45pm
Credit Cards ①③

---

**STAVERTON Northamptonshire** Map **04** SP56

**★★★ 70% Staverton Park Hotel & Golfing Complex**
NN11 6JT ☎(0327)705911 FAX (0327) 300821
*Conveniently situated on the outskirts of Daventry, close to the M1
and M40 motorways, Staverton Park is an impressive hotel and
golfing complex with its own 18-hole course. Accommodation is
very well equipped and extensive public areas include the Garden
Room restaurant and indoor leisure facilities such as a sauna,
solarium and a trimnasium.*
50⇌🏠⊁in 4 bedrooms CTV in all bedrooms ® T
🐕 (ex guide dogs) ✱ sB&B⇌🏠£85-£105 dB&B⇌🏠£105-£115
➡
ℂ 250P CFA ▶ 18 snooker sauna solarium trimnasium ♫ *xmas*
🎦 International V ⌖ ⯑ ✱
Credit Cards ①②③⑤ⓔ
**See advertisement under NORTHAMPTON**

---

**STEEPLE ASTON Oxfordshire** Map **04** SP42

**★★★ 59% *Hopcrofts Holt***
OX5 3QQ (Mount Charlotte (TS)) ☎(0869)40259
FAX (0869) 40865
*An extended character inn between Oxford and Banbury offering
well equipped bedrooms and a range of conference and meeting
rooms. Table d'hôte and à la carte menus are available in the
informal restaurant, adjacent to the main function suite and a busy
public bar.*
88rm(71⇌15🏠)(2fb) CTV in all bedrooms ® T
ℂ CTV 200P ✿ games room
🎦 English & French V ⌖ ⯑ Last dinner 9.30pm
Credit Cards ①②③⑤

**S**

**STEPPS** Strathclyde *Lanarkshire* Map **11** NS66

★★★64% **Garfield House**
Cumbernauld Rd G33 6HW ☎041-779 2111
*This popular business hotel just off the A80 Stirling road has a relaxing foyer lounge and a restaurant with a good-value à la carte lunch menu. Most bedrooms are in the modern extension, with good facilities; the few in the original Victorian house are traditionally furnished.*
27➬🛏(2fb)⊁in 4 bedrooms CTV in all bedrooms ® T
sB&B➬🛏£52-£62 dB&B➬🛏£62-£72 🖪
《 80P CFA *xmas*
V ⊹ ⚌ ⊁ ✴ Lunch £4.50-£12.50alc High tea £4.50-£12.50alc
Dinner fr£16.50 Last dinner 9.30pm
Credit Cards ①②③⑤ⓔ

**STEVENAGE** Hertfordshire Map **04** TL22

★★★60% **Hertford Park**
Danestrete SG1 1EJ (Queens Moat) ☎(0438)350661
Telex no 825697 FAX (0438) 741880
*Set at the heart of the new town shopping centre, close to the railway station and only a mile from the A1(M), this predominantly commercial hotel offers functional rooms equipped with good modern facilities; a nearby car park is available for guests' use.*
100➬🛏in 24 bedrooms CTV in all bedrooms ® T
sB&B➬🛏£30-£72 dB&B➬🛏£42-£78 🖪
Lift 《 ⚑ CFA
⚐ International V ⊹ ⚌ Lunch £10.50-£12&alc Dinner £12-£12.50&alc Last dinner 9.45pm
Credit Cards ①②③④⑤ⓔ

★★★59% **Blakemore Thistle**
Little Wymondley SG4 7JJ (Mount Charlotte (TS))
☎(0438)355821 Telex no 825479 FAX (0438) 742114
(For full entry see Hitchin)

★★★57% *Novotel Stevenage*
Knebworth Park SG1 2AX ☎(0438)742299 Telex no 826132
FAX (0438) 723872
*An hotel well placed at the junction of the A1 and the A602 provides functional accommodation which is ideal for business travellers, though the rooms are somewhat lacking in quality and comfort. The grill restaurant is open throughout the day from 6am until midnight.*
101➬(101fb) CTV in all bedrooms ® T
Lift 《 120P ✿ ⚊ (heated)
⚐ International V ⊹ ⚌ ⊁ Last dinner mdnt
Credit Cards ①②③⑤

★★★56% **Stevenage Moat House**
High St, Old Town SG1 3AZ (Queens Moat) ☎(0438)359111
FAX (0438) 742169
*This popular and historic hotel in the old town is currently undergoing major refurbishment, starting with the bedrooms which vary in size and are dated and functional. There is a choice between an à la carte restaurant and a traditional carvery adjoining the cosy public bar.*
60➬🛏(4fb)⊁in 11 bedrooms CTV in all bedrooms ® T S%
sB&B➬🛏£45-£85 dB&B➬🛏£50-£95 🖪
《 100P ✿ CFA
⚐ English & French V ⊹ ⚌ ⊁ ✴ Lunch £9.95-£12.95&alc
Dinner £12.93-£13.75&alc Last dinner 9.45pm
Credit Cards ①②③④⑤

★★★54% **Forte Posthouse**
Old London Rd, Broadwater SG2 8DS (Forte Hotels)
☎(0438)365444 Telex no 825505 FAX (0438) 741308
*Charming 15th century inn with modern bedrooms.*
54➬🛏⊁in 27 bedrooms CTV in all bedrooms ® T ✴
sB➬🛏£39.50-£49.50 dB➬🛏£39.50-£49.50 (room only) 🖪
《 ⊞ 80P ✿ CFA *xmas*

⚐ English & French V ⊹ ⚌ ⊁ ✴ Lunch fr£9.50&alc Dinner
fr£13.95&alc Last dinner 10pm
Credit Cards ①②③④⑤

**STEWARTON** Strathclyde *Ayrshire* Map **10** NS44

★★★🏵 ♨75% **Chapeltoun House**
KA3 3ED ☎(0560)82696 FAX (0560) 85100
*This fine period mansion is set in 20 acres of wooded grounds and gardens, off the B796 2 miles southwest of the town. Colin and Graeme McKenzie cosset their guests in the best tradition of country house hospitality. Individually decorated bedrooms are extremely well equipped, with many thoughtful touches, and tastefully furnished public rooms are comfortable and relaxing. Imaginative menus feature fresh local produce, cooked in modern style, artistically presented and of unstinting portions.*
8➬🛏1🚻 CTV in all bedrooms T sB&B➬🛏£69-£84
dB&B➬🛏£99-£129 🖪
50P ⇛ ✿ ⚑ nc12yrs
⚐ French V ⊹ ⚌ ⊁ ✴ Lunch £16&alc Dinner £25 Last dinner
9pm
Credit Cards ①②③ⓔ

**STILTON** Cambridgeshire Map **04** TL18

★★★67% **Bell Inn**
Great North Rd PE7 3RA ☎Peterborough(0733)241066
FAX (0733) 245173
*Situated on the A1 with easy access to Peterborough, this is a good modernisation of a coaching inn, with original features highlighted in the various bars, lounges and restaurant. The de luxe bedrooms are more spacious and have whirlpools, and there are two four-poster rooms, but all offer clean, comfortable and attractive accommodation.*
19➬🛏(1fb)2🚻⊁in 4 bedrooms CTV in all bedrooms ® T
✈ (ex guide dogs) sB&B➬🛏£60-£70 dB&B➬🛏£75-£90 🖪
《 30P ⇛
⚐ English & French V ⊹ ⚌ ⊁ Lunch £8.50-£9.50&alc Dinner
£12.13.50&alc Last dinner 9.30pm
Credit Cards ①②③⑤ⓔ

**STIRLING** Central *Stirlingshire* Map **11** NS79

See also **Bridge of Allan**

★★★★🏵65% **Stirling Highland**
Spittal St FK8 1DU (Scottish Highland) ☎(0786)75444
Telex no 776857 FAX (0786) 62929
*This new hotel, which opened in March 1991, was created by converting and extending what used to be the old Stirling High School. A unique venture, retaining the character of the fine original building while providing the quality and amenities of a top class hotel. It is on the road up to the castle and commands superb views across the town and surrounding countryside. The bedrooms are in the new wing, which almost creates a quadrangle with the existing buildings. Also there are 2 restaurants, comfortable lounges, a cocktail bar and a leisure club. Scholars restaurant offers a modern interpretation of classical cooking using Scottish produce. Staff are well groomed and friendly, and have a good attitude.*
76➬🛏(21fb)4🚻⊁in 12 bedrooms CTV in all bedrooms ® T
✴ sB&B➬🛏£60-£80 dB&B➬🛏£80-£110 🖪
Lift 《 96P 🖃 (heated) squash snooker sauna solarium
gymnasium beautician spa bath steam room ♪ *xmas*
V ⊹ ⚌ ⊁ ✴ Lunch £9-£12&alc Dinner £15-£18&alc Last
dinner 10.30pm
Credit Cards ①②③⑤

Hotels with red star ratings are
especially high quality.

**★★ 59% Terraces**
4 Melville Ter FK8 2ND (Consort) ☎(0786)72268
FAX (0786) 50314
*This small Georgian house, situated in a tree-lined terrace convenient for the town centre, has been converted to provide compact, well equipped accommodation; bedrooms are being refurbished, and the atmosphere is friendly.*
18⇨🌂(4fb) CTV in all bedrooms ® T ✳ sB&B⇨🌂fr£49.50
dB&B⇨🌂fr£62.50 🏳
《 25P CFA *xmas*
♈ International V ⌂ ⅙ ✳ Lunch £12.50-£20alc Dinner £10.75-£12.50 Last dinner 9pm
Credit Cards ① ② ③ ⑤ ⓔ

**★★ 55% King Robert**
Glasgow Rd, Bannockburn FK7 0LT
☎Bannockburn(0786)811666 FAX (0786) 811507
*This purpose-built hotel, situated next to the Battle of Bannockburn Heritage Centre, combines practical commercial standards with functional but well equipped bedrooms.*
53⇨🌂(3fb)⅙in 3 bedrooms CTV in all bedrooms ® T
✖ (ex guide dogs) ✳ sB&B⇨🌂£39.95-£49.95 dB&B⇨🌂£59-£69 🏳
《 CTV 100P ❈ CFA *xmas*
V ⌂ ⅏ ✳ Bar Lunch £4.95-£7.95
Credit Cards ① ② ③ ⑤ ⓔ

**⌂Granada Lodge**
Pirnhall Roundabout, Snabhead FK7 8EU (junct M9/M80)
(Granada) ☎(0786)815033 FAX (0786) 815900
*Meals can be obtained from the adjacent Country Kitchen restaurant.*
37⇨(10fb)⅙in 5 bedrooms CTV in all bedrooms ®
✖ (ex guide dogs) S% sB⇨fr£29.50 dB⇨fr£32 (room only) 🏳
《 143P
V ⌂ ⅏ ⅙ Dinner fr£6

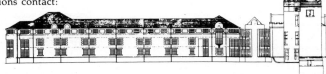
S

### ★★★56% **Grosvenor**

High St SO20 6EU (Lansbury) ☎Andover(0264)810606
Telex no 477677 FAX (0264) 810747

*This traditionally styled hotel with many classic Georgian features,
set in a sleepy village in the pretty Test Valley, offers
accommodation in attractively decorated bedrooms, all well
equipped with modern facilities and most of reasonable size. The
restaurant, though small, is impressively wood panelled with
pictures of horses which were famous when Stockbridge had a
racecourse. Popular with both commercial and leisure guests, the
establishment also has a good local following.*

25⇌1📞⊬in 5 bedrooms CTV in all bedrooms ® **T**
✖ (ex guide dogs) sB&B⇌fr£74 dB&B⇌fr£88 ⊟
( 60P ⇎ ✿ sauna
♡ Continental V ✧ ♨ Lunch fr£12&alc Dinner fr£12&alc
Last dinner 10.30pm
Credit Cards [1][2][3][5]

### ★★★67% **Bramhall Moat House**

Bramhall Ln South SK7 2EB (Queens Moat) ☎061-439 8116
Telex no 668464 FAX 061-440 8071
(For full entry see Bramhall)

### ★★★61% **Alma Lodge**

149 Buxton Rd SK2 6EL (Jarvis) ☎061-483 4431
Telex no 665026 FAX 061-483 1983
RS Xmas

*On the A6 to the south of the town centre and convenient for
junction 12 of the M63, this busy commercial hotel converted from
a Victorian residence has wood panelling and an ornate plaster
ceiling in the foyer lounge. Bedrooms both in the new wing and
original house are well equipped and service throughout is friendly
and professional.*

56rm(52⇌)(2fb)⊬in 4 bedrooms CTV in all bedrooms ® **T** ✱
sB£29.50 sB⇌£70-£79.50 dB⇌£79.50-£99.50 (room only) ⊟
( 200P CFA ♫
♡ English & French V ✧ ♨ ✱ Lunch £8.50-£12.25&alc
Dinner fr£12.25&alc Last dinner 9.30pm
Credit Cards [1][2][3][4][5]

### ★★70% **Red Lion Inn**

112 Buxton Rd, High Ln SK6 8ED ☎Disley(0663)765227
FAX (0663) 762170

*This well maintained inn beside the A6 at High Lane offers
accommodation in tastefully appointed bedrooms equipped with all
modern amenities and small, well lit bathrooms. Attractive ground
floor areas include limited lounge space and a popular all-day
brasserie cum café bar serving a good range of reasonably priced
meals.*

6⇌📞(1fb) CTV in all bedrooms ® **T** ✖ (ex guide dogs) ✱
sB&B⇌📞£25.50-£46.50 dB&B⇌📞£44-£58.50
100P ⇎
**V** ✧ ♨ ⊬ ✱ Lunch £5.95&alc Dinner £10.25 Last dinner
10pm
Credit Cards [1][2][3][5]

### ★★70% *Saxonholme*

230 Wellington Rd SK4 2QN ☎061-432 2335 FAX 061-431 8076
*On the A6 just north of the town centre, this recently extended and
refurbished hotel has bedrooms with good modern facilities and a
pleasant dining room serving interesting food. Friendly staff give
helpful service.*

30⇌📞(4fb)⊬in 12 bedrooms CTV in all bedrooms ® **T**
Lift ( 30P
♡ International V ✧ ♨ ⊬ Last dinner 9.15pm
Credit Cards [1][3]

### ★★62% *Wycliffe Villa*

74 Edgeley Rd, Edgeley SK3 9NQ ☎061-477 5395
RS Sun & BH's

*Close to the M63 and three miles from Stockport centre, this
friendly hotel has recently been extended and refurbished and
offers comfortable accommodation with well-equipped bedrooms.
The restaurant specialises in Italian food.*

12⇌📞 CTV in all bedrooms ® ✖
CTV 20P ⇎ nc5yrs
♡ English, French & Italian **V** Last dinner 9.30pm
Credit Cards [1][2][3][5]

### ★★60% **Rudyard Toby**

271 Wellington Rd North, Heaton Chapel SK4 5BP (1.5m N off
A6) (Toby) ☎061-432 2753 Telex no 668594

*This modernised Victorian red brick house set back from the A6 to
the north of the town centre has comfortable well equipped
bedrooms and pleasant public areas, including 2 bars and a carvery
restaurant where young staff provide friendly service.*

21⇌📞(2fb)⊬in 8 bedrooms CTV in all bedrooms ®
( 82P Golf
**V** ✧ ♨ ⊬ Last dinner 10pm
Credit Cards [1][2][3][4][5]

### ★60% **Acton Court**

Buxton Rd SK2 7AB ☎061-483 6172 FAX 061-483 0147
Closed Boxing Day, New Year & Bank Hols
*Improvements are gradually being made to this privately owned
commercial hotel which stands beside the A6 about 2 miles south of
the town centre. Cheerful staff serve enjoyable, reasonably priced
meals in a beamed restaurant, and the popular lounge bar boasts
an extensive collection of sporting photographs; the best bedrooms
are contained in a new wing.*

35rm(15⇌15📞) CTV in all bedrooms ® **T** ✱ sB&B£27-£35
sB&B⇌📞£34-£45 dB&B£37-£48 dB&B⇌📞£45-£58
( CTV 200P ✿ CFA
♡ French **V** Lunch £5.95 Dinner £8.50&alc Last dinner
10pm
Credit Cards [1][2][3][5]

### ★★★★55% **Swallow**

10 John Walker Square TS18 1AQ (Swallow) ☎(0642)679721
Telex no 587895 FAX (0642) 601714

*An attractive leisure centre is now available in the basement of this
modern town centre hotel which caters well for the business guest.
A convenient, undercover free public car park is situated behind the
hotel.*

124⇌📞⊬in 25 bedrooms CTV in all bedrooms ® **T** ✱
sB&B⇌📞fr£79 dB&B⇌📞fr£95 ⊟
Lift ( 400P ⊜ CFA ▨ (heated) sauna solarium gymnasium
jacuzzi steam room *xmas*
♡ English & French **V** ✧ ♨ ⊬
Credit Cards [1][2][3][4][5][£]

### ★★★68% **Parkmore**

636 Yarm Rd, Eaglescliffe TS16 0DH (3m S A19) (Best Western)
☎(0642)786815 Telex no 58298 FAX (0642) 790485
*On the A167 about 3 miles southeast of Stockton, within easy
access of the northwest's commercial centres, this comfortable
privately owned hotel with an attractive garden and good car
parking facilities has recently extended the original porticoed
Victorian house to provide well equipped bedrooms and an
excellent leisure centre. Service is friendly and efficient.*

55⇌📞(3fb)4⇎⊬in 4 bedrooms CTV in all bedrooms ® **T**
sB&B⇌📞£52-£59 dB&B⇌📞£64-£74 ⊟
( CTV 140P ✿ CFA ▨ (heated) snooker sauna solarium
gymnasium jacuzzi steam room beauty salon
♡ English & French **V** ✧ ♨ ⊬ Lunch £9-£11.50 Dinner
£14.50-£16&alc Last dinner 9.30pm
Credit Cards [1][2][3][5]

### ★★★60% Forte Posthouse Teeside
Low Ln, Thornaby-on-Tees TS17 9LW (Forte Hotels)
☎Middlesbrough(0642)591213 FAX (0642) 594989
*A purpose-built hotel, situated southeast of Stockton on the A144, offering a choice of restaurants, coffee shop and an extensive range of conference facilities. Bedrooms are undergoing refurbishment.*
135⇨♪♚in 62 bedrooms CTV in all bedrooms ® T ✱
sB⇨♪£39.50-£49.50 dB⇨♪£39.50-£49.50 (room only) ➡
《⊞ 250P ✿ CFA sauna solarium *xmas*
V ✿ ⚏ ✂ ✱ Lunch £8.75-£10.95 Dinner £13.95 Last dinner 10.30pm
Credit Cards ①②③⑤

### ★★★55% Billingham Arms
The Causeway, Billingham TS23 2HD (3m NE A19)
☎(0642)553661 & 360880 Telex no 587746 FAX (0642) 552104
*A town centre, commercial hotel with easy access to the A19. Several bedrooms have recently been refurbished. The Edwardian theme restaurant, Bertie's, displays large photographs of Edward VII and other celebrities of the era.*
69⇨♪(6fb)2🛏✂in 4 bedrooms CTV in all bedrooms ® T ✱
sB⇨♪£36-£48 dB⇨♪£55-£62 (room only) ➡
Lift 《▤ 150P 2🐾 CFA solarium pool table *xmas*
♀ International V ✿ ⚏ ✱ Lunch fr£7.50&alc Dinner fr£12.95&alc Last dinner 11pm
Credit Cards ①②③④⑤£
**See advertisement under BILLINGHAM**

### ★★62% *Claireville*
519 Yarm Rd, Eaglescliffe TS16 9BG (3m S A135)
☎(0642)780378 FAX (0642) 784109
RS Xmas & New Year
*Set in its own grounds and gardens on the A135, 3 miles south of the town, this friendly, family-run hotel has recently substantially improved its accommodation, most bedrooms now having full en suite facilities.*
19rm(16⇨♪)(2fb) CTV in all bedrooms ®
CTV 20P ✿
♀ English & French V ✿ ⚏ Last dinner 8.30pm
Credit Cards ①③⑤

### ★66% *Stonyroyd*
187 Oxbridge Ln TS18 4JB ☎(0642)607734
*In a quiet residential area about two miles from the centre of Stockton, this small hotel is owned and run by Elizabeth Povey, who not only gives her personal attention to her guests, but also cooks the evening meals. Bedrooms are, on the whole, compact, but well equipped.*
13rm(8♪)(1fb) CTV in all bedrooms ® ✖
CTV 6P 🚗 solarium
♀ International V Last dinner 8pm
Credit Cards ①③

---

### STOKE CANON Devon Map 03 SX99

### ★★★73% Barton Cross Hotel & Restaurant
Huxham EX5 4EJ ☎Exeter(0392)841245 & 841584
Telex no 42603 FAX (0392) 50402
*Dating back to the 17th century this hotel has attractive inglenook fireplaces, exposed beams and a thatched roof. Bedrooms have been carefully decorated and are exceptionally well equipped for both business clients and holidaymakers. Carefully prepared dishes are served in the interesting galleried restaurant and service throughout is warm and friendly.*
6⇨♪ CTV in all bedrooms ® T sB&B⇨♪£68-£75
dB&B⇨♪£85-£90 ➡
24P 🚗 ✿ windsurfing instruction *xmas*
V ✿ ⚏ ✱ Lunch £18.50-£23alc Dinner £18.50-£23alc Last dinner 9.30pm
Credit Cards ①②③④⑤
**See advertisement under EXETER**

---

### STOKE D'ABERNON Surrey Map 04 TQ15

### ★★★❀71% Woodlands Park
Woodlands Ln KT11 3QB (Select) ☎Oxshott(037284)3933
Telex no 919246
*A delightful mansion set in 10 acres of lawns has retained much of its Victorian splendour. Tastefully decorated bedrooms provide modern facilities and a few thoughtful extras, while public areas include the magnificent Grand Hall, with its log fire, stained glass, engraved ceiling and elaborate carved balcony. Here guests can enjoy a pre-dinner drink before proceeding to Bryant's, a restaurant named after a Victorian watchmaker. In the intimate atmosphere created by elegantly appointed, candlelit tables and a resident harpist, chef Nigel Beckett presents a reasonably priced 5-course set menu supplemented by a daily à la carte selection which also includes a daily market section and vegetarian options, and is accompanied by a lengthy but quite young wine list which features a good choice of half bottles and a few examples from outside France. Much frequented by businessmen, the hotel maintains a formal atmosphere, its young team of staff presenting a professional front though they sometimes lack finesse.*
59rm(58⇨♪)2🛏 CTV in 58 bedrooms ® T ✖ (ex guide dogs)
✱ sB⇨♪£95-£105 dB⇨♪£120-£140 (room only) ➡
Lift 《 150P ✿ ℘ (hard) croquet putting *xmas*
♀ English & French V ✿ ⚏ ✱ Lunch £13.50-£16.50 Dinner fr£23&alc Last dinner 10pm
Credit Cards ①②③⑤£

---

### STOKE GABRIEL Devon Map 03 SX85

### ★★★♨71% Gabriel Court
TQ9 6SF ☎(080428)206 & 267
Closed Feb
*Set in its own walled and beautifully kept Elizabethan terraced gardens, this former manor house of great character dates back to 1487. It is located on the edge of the peaceful village of Stoke Gabriel, which lies beside the River Dart. The grounds also house an outdoor heated swimming pool and croquet lawn. The bedrooms are comfortable, and although some of the bathrooms are a little compact, all rooms have good facilities. Log fires blaze in the lounges during the colder months, and in the summer, drinks from the bar can be enjoyed in the gardens or on the patios. The table d'hôte menu is made up of traditional English dishes. Warm hospitality and professional service is provided by the Beacom family and their friendly team of staff.*
20⇨♪ CTV in all bedrooms ® T sB&B⇨♪£51-£57
dB&B⇨♪£75-£80
CTV 13P 7🐾 🚗 ✿ CFA ⊒ (heated) croquet 🐾 *xmas*
✿ ⚏ ✱ Sunday Lunch £11-£15 Dinner £20-£25 Last dinner 8.30pm
Credit Cards ①②③⑤

---

### STOKE-ON-TRENT Staffordshire Map 07 SJ84 ◉
See also Newcastle-under-Lyme
### ★★★78% *Hanchurch Manor*
Hanchurch ST4 8SD ☎(0782)643030 FAX (0782) 643035
*This delightful Grade II listed building, now a privately owned and personally run hotel, stands within 9 acres of lovely grounds beside the A519, just south of junction 15 of the M6. Well appointed, tastefully furnished accommodation is of a very good standard, public areas are relaxing and attentive professional service is provided by a friendly staff under the personal direction of one of the owners. Close proximity to Stoke-on-Trent makes the establishment popular with business guests, but it is also ideal for tourists and provides a good venue for weekend breaks.*
7⇨Annexe5⇨♪2🛏 CTV in all bedrooms T ✖
《 25P 🚗 ✿ ♪ nc12yrs
V ✿ ⚏ ✂ Last dinner 9.30pm
Credit Cards ①②③⑤

**S**

### ★★★ 70% Stakis Grand
66 Trinity St, Hanley ST1 5NB (Stakis) ☎(0782)202361
Telex no 367264 FAX (0782) 286464

*This completely redeveloped hotel in Hanley town centre maintains traditional standards of service, provided by friendly professional staff. It offers modern bedrooms and a restaurant with a carvery and à la carte menu, plus a leisure centre and extensive function rooms.*

128⇌🛏(55fb)✁in 30 bedrooms CTV in all bedrooms ® T
✗ (ex guide dogs) sB⇌🛏£81.90-£92.40 dB⇌🛏£93.45-£103.95 (room only) 🅿

Lift ₵ 175P CFA 🏊 (heated) sauna solarium gymnasium whirlpool spa *xmas*

V ♦ ⚏ ✠ ✳

Credit Cards ①②③⑤

### ★★★ 67% Haydon House
1-13 Haydon St, Basford ST4 6JD ☎(0782)711311
FAX (0782) 717470

*A busy family-run hotel situated in a quiet residential area just off the A53 Newcastle to Hanley road, which reflects the Victorian era in its attractively decorated restaurant and lounge bars. Some superior annexe bedrooms also echo the theme.*

18⇌🛏Annexe14⇌🛏(4fb)🗗 CTV in all bedrooms ® T ✳
sB⇌🛏£52-£72 dB⇌🛏£60-£78 (room only) 🅿

52P CFA *xmas*

♀ English & French V ♦ ⚏ ✳ Lunch £14.50&alc High tea £4.50-£8.50 Dinner £15.95&alc Last dinner 9.45pm

Credit Cards ①②③⑤

### ★★★ 62% Clayton Lodge
Clayton Rd ST5 4AF (Jarvis)
☎Newcastle-under-Lyme(0782)613093 FAX (0782) 711896
(For full entry see Newcastle-under-Lyme)

### ★★ 55% Crown
Times Square, Longton ST3 1HD ☎(0782)599343
Telex no 57515 FAX (0782) 598062

*This modernised business hotel, which stands close to Longton town centre and a railway line, boasts a conference/banqueting suite that can accommodate 50-140 people.*

40⇌🛏 CTV in all bedrooms ® T ✗ (ex guide dogs) ✳
sB&B⇌🛏£31.90-£40.50 dB&B⇌🛏£46-£52.15

CTV 38P CFA

♀ International V ♦ ⚏ ✳ Lunch £7.10-£7.85 Dinner £10.45-£11.20&alc Last dinner 10pm

Credit Cards ①②③⑤ ⓔ

### ○Moat House
Etruria Hall, Festival Way, Etruria ST1 5BQ (Queens Moat)
☎Central Res (0800) 289330
Due to have opened Sep 1991
147⇌🛏

---

## STONE Staffordshire Map 07 SJ93

### ★★★ 63% Stone House
ST15 0BQ (Lansbury) ☎(0785)815531 FAX (0785) 814764

*There are tennis courts and a putting/croquet green in the well tended gardens of this fully modernised hotel. Other facilities include a leisure centre and function/conference rooms.*

50⇌🛏(2fb)2🗗✁in 5 bedrooms CTV in all bedrooms ® T
sB&B⇌🛏£78 dB&B⇌🛏£90 🅿

₵ CTV 100P ✿ CFA 🏊 (heated) ♪ (hard) sauna solarium gymnasium croquet putting green

♀ International V ♦ ⚏ ✳ Lunch £8.50-£9.50 Dinner £15-£16.50&alc Last dinner 10pm

Credit Cards ①②③⑤ ⓔ

---

*A rosette means exceptional standards of cuisine.*

---

## STON EASTON Somerset Map 03 ST65

★★★

★★★❀🍴♨
**STON EASTON PARK**

BA3 4DF (Relais et Châteaux)
☎Chewton Mendip (076121)631 due to change to (0761) 241631
FAX (076121) 377 due to change to (0761) 241377

*Magnificence is the hallmark of this imposing Palladian mansion set in grounds laid out by Humphry Repton, one of the foremost landscape gardeners of his day. Bought by Peter and Christine Smedley as a private residence in 1978, they opened it as a hotel ten years ago and have gradually expanded the accommodation ever since, having recently converted a cottage in the grounds, and restored the huge Victorian kitchen garden. Public rooms are superbly proportioned and ornately decorated. Staff, under the leadership of Manager Kevin Marchant, offer attentive and personal service.*

19⇌🛏Annexe2⇌🛏6🗗 CTV in all bedrooms ® T
✗ (ex guide dogs) ✳ sB&B⇌🛏£95-£325 dB&B⇌🛏£135-£325 Continental breakfast 🅿

CTV 100P 🗗 ✿ CFA ♪ (hard) snooker croquet hot air ballooning nc12yrs *xmas*

♀ English & French V ♦ ⚏ ✳ Lunch fr£24 Dinner fr£35 Last dinner 9.30pm

Credit Cards ①②③⑤

---

## STONEHAVEN Grampian *Kincardineshire* Map 15 NO88

### ★★ 54% County
Arduthie Rd AB3 2EH ☎(0569)64386

*Situated on the western edge of the town close to the railway station and with easy access to the by-pass, this busy commercial and function hotel offers a choice of bars as well as leisure facilities. Simple practical bedrooms are gradually being improved by the new owners.*

14⇌🛏(2fb) CTV in all bedrooms ® T ✗ (ex guide dogs) ✳
sB&B⇌🛏fr£40 dB&B⇌🛏fr£60 🅿

40P ✿ CFA squash sauna solarium gymnasium

♀ Scottish, English & Italian V ♦ ✳ Bar Lunch fr£6.50&alc Dinner fr£7.50alc Last dinner 9pm

Credit Cards ①③ ⓔ

---

## STONEHOUSE Gloucestershire Map 03 SO80 ●

### ★★★ 67% Stonehouse Court
Bristol Rd GL10 3RA (Clipper) ☎(0453)825155
FAX (0453) 824611

*Situated a mile east of M5 junction 13 on the A419, this imposing Grade II listed house has been tastefully refurbished and extended to provide public areas of character and quality. Most of the modern and well equipped bedrooms are in the garden wing, which enjoys uninterrupted views of the surrounding countryside. Five acres of attractive grounds and good modern conference facilities make this an ideal venue for the business and leisure customer.*

37⇌🛏1🗗 CTV in all bedrooms ® T ✗ (ex guide dogs)
sB&B⇌🛏fr£72.50 dB&B⇌🛏fr£98 🅿

₵ 150P ✿ croquet bowls ⊶ *xmas*

♀ English & French V ♦ ⚏ Lunch fr£12&alc Dinner fr£20&alc Last dinner 9.30pm

Credit Cards ①③

---

S

## STONOR Oxfordshire Map **04** SU78

**★★❀❀76% Stonor Arms**
RG9 6HE ☎Turville Heath(049163)345 FAX (049163) 8863
9⇥↟ CTV in all bedrooms ® T ✠ (ex guide dogs)
sB&B⇥↟£82.50-£127.50 dB&B⇥↟£92.50-£137.50
Continental breakfast ☒
36P ⇔ ❁
✱ Lunch £12.35-£21.75alc Dinner £27.50-£32&alc Last dinner
9.30pm
Credit Cards ① ③

## STORNOWAY

See **Lewis, Isle of**

## STORRINGTON West Sussex Map **04** TQ01

**❀❀❀ ✕ ✕ ✕Manleys**
Manleys Hill RH20 4BT ☎(0903)742331
*This attractive house and beautiful garden, quietly set in the heart
of West Sussex, make the ideal setting for a superb meal; the
restaurant is tastefully decorated in pastel shades, and a young
staff offers friendly but professional service. Chef Karl Löderer
creates an interesting menu with both classic and original
combinations. Starters such as authentic Mediterranean fish soup
or a mille feuilles of salmon in a langoustine sauce can be followed
by a carefully prepared fish dish like grilled sea bass on a bed of
oriental calmars (a vegetable), by a magret of duck or by one of
the Austrian specialities; desserts worthy of note are the stuffed,
poached peaches served with an orange cream, and the Grand
Marnier parfait with praline sauce. The meal is complemented by
an extensive wine list containing some fine wines and vintages.*
Closed Mon & 1st 2 wks Jan
Dinner not served Sun
♥ Austrian & French **V** 45 seats Lunch fr£18.60&alc Dinner
fr£33&alc Last lunch 2pm Last dinner 9.30pm 25 P
Credit Cards ① ② ③ ⑤

## STOURBRIDGE West Midlands Map **07** SO88

**★★65% Talbot**
High St DY8 1DW (Crown & Raven) ☎(0384)394350
Telex no 335464 FAX (0384) 371318
*A 16th-century coaching inn within the town centre retains such
original features as sloping floors and exposed beams; some older-
style single accommodation is compact, but most rooms have now
been attractively decorated and furnished in pine.*
25rm(13⇥7↟)(4fb)1⇔ CTV in all bedrooms ® T
《 25P
♥ English & French **V** ⊕ ⬚
Credit Cards ① ② ③

## STOURPORT-ON-SEVERN Hereford & Worcester
Map **07** SO87

**★★★63% Stourport Moat House**
35 Hartlebury Rd DY13 9LT (Queens Moat) ☎(0299)827733
FAX (02993) 78520
*All the bedrooms at this hotel have now been refurbished to a good
standard and are very well equipped. Facilities include a leisure
club, squash courts, an outdoor swimming pool and a nightclub
(open only at weekends).*
68⇥↟(8fb)⊁in 6 bedrooms CTV in all bedrooms ® T
sB&B⇥↟£65-£68 dB&B⇥↟£75-£78 ☒
《 400P ❁ CFA ⌿ ▸ ♪ (hard) squash snooker sauna
gymnasium clay pigeon shooting golf driving range ⚕
♥ English & French **V** ⊕ ⬚ ⊁ ✱ Lunch £10.75-£11.95&alc
Dinner £12.95-£14.50&alc Last dinner 9.45pm
Credit Cards ① ② ③ ⑤ ⓔ

S

★★62% **Swan**

High St DY13 8BX (Porterhouse) ☎(02993)71661
FAX (0299) 827650

*This 18th-century building in the town centre has been greatly extended to provide comfortable accommodation with modern facilities. Service is friendly and caring, and the restaurant serves the popular Porterhouse menu featuring a range of steaks and grills.*

33⇔↑(2fb) CTV in all bedrooms ® T ✱ sB&B⇔↑£47 dB&B⇔↑£61.50 ⊠
CTV 60P CFA
V ✧ ✱ Lunch £6.99-£7.50alc Dinner fr£5.95alc Last dinner 10pm
Credit Cards ①②③⑤

---

**STOW BEDON** Norfolk Map **05** TL99

★★65% **Earles**

Stow Bedon House NR17 1BX (1m E of A1075)
☎Caston(095383)284

*A former country house in the village of Stow Bedon, comfortably furnished throughout, features an attractive terrace and grounds with a good-sized swimming pool. The restaurant serves an à la carte selection of cooked-to-order dishes.*

4⇔↑Annexe1⇔3⊠ CTV in all bedrooms ® T
✗ (ex guide dogs) ✱ S10% sB&B⇔↑£40-£55 dB&B⇔↑£70-£100 ⊠
《 CTV 30P ♨ ✿ CFA ⊠ (heated) sauna solarium keep fit classes beauty salon *xmas*
♥ English & Continental V ✧ ✱ Lunch £12.95&alc Dinner £12.95&alc Last dinner 9.15pm
Credit Cards ①③ⓔ

---

**STOWMARKET** Suffolk Map **05** TM05

★★57% **Cedars**

Needham Rd IP14 2AJ (Minotels) ☎(0449)612668
FAX (0449) 674704
Closed Xmas-New Year

*This personally-run hotel stands on the outskirts of the town, close to the industrial estate. Bedrooms on the ground floor offer a uniformly functional 70s style, while those in the main building vary in size and retain some features of the original 16th-century farmhouse. Guests can choose to eat either in an attractive beamed dining room or in the relaxed atmosphere of a bar/lounge which is popular with locals.*

24⇔↑(2fb) CTV in all bedrooms ® T sB&B⇔↑£40-£42.50 dB&B⇔↑£50-£55 ⊠
75P ✿ CFA
♥ English & French ✧ ✷ Lunch £8-£15alc Dinner £8-£15alc Last dinner 9pm
Credit Cards ①②③⑤ⓔ

⇧**Forte Travelodge**

IP14 3PY (on A45) (Forte)
☎(0449)615347 Central Res (0800) 850950

*One of the more recently opened lodges, set back from the Little Chef restaurant and service area beside the westbound carriageway of the A45, 3 miles northwest of the town, offers good value for money in its clean and well maintained accommodation.*

40⇔↑(40fb) ® sB⇔↑£29.95 dB⇔↑£29.95 (room only)
《 40P ♨
Credit Cards ①②③

---

**STOW-ON-THE-WOLD** Gloucestershire Map **04** SP12

★★★✿✿77% **Wyck Hill House**

Burford Rd GL54 1HY ☎Cotswold(0451)31936 Telex no 43611
FAX (0451) 32243

*Well kept lawns and flower beds brighten the approach to this attractive country house hotel, on the A424 road out of Stow. Peter Robinson and his staff ensure a welcoming atmosphere, and chef*

*Ian Smith creates meals which have earned the hotel an excellent local reputation. Working mostly with good British produce, he devises an imaginative menu featuring dishes such as ballotine of rabbit filled with herb mousse and served on a salad of beans, leeks, tomato and walnuts; fillet of sea bass served with ravioli filled with crab on a coriander-flavoured lemon-butter sauce, or from the vegetarian menu, an enticing spinach and cheese strüdel with tomato and basil sauce, and an aubergine, tomato and courgette charlotte accompanied by a rosemary-flavoured sauce. Interesting combinations of hot and cold sweets include a lemon trio, with creamy mousse, a sharp sorbet and a piping hot soufflé arranged on a raspberry sauce and decorated with a border of piped chocolate.*

16⇔↑Annexe15⇔↑(3fb)3⊠ CTV in all bedrooms ® T sB&B⇔↑£75-£120 dB&B⇔↑£95-£175 ⊠
Lift 《 100P ✿ croquet clay pigeon shooting ⅍ *xmas*
♥ British & French V ✧ ✷ ✰ Lunch £14.95 High tea £7.50 Dinner £28-£38alc Last dinner 9.30pm
Credit Cards ①②③⑤ⓔ

---

★★★61% **The Unicorn**

Sheep St GL54 1HQ (Forte Hotels) ☎Cotswold(0451)30257
FAX (0451) 31090

*Situated on the main crossroads, this well known hostelry offers public areas of character and charm and a range of en suite bedrooms of varying degrees of style and comfort. Service is friendly and attentive.*

20⇔↑2⊠✷in 2 bedrooms CTV in all bedrooms ® T ✱ sB⇔↑fr£65 dB⇔↑£80-£95 (room only) ⊠
CTV 45P *xmas*
V ✧ ✷ ✰ ✱ Lunch fr£10.95 Dinner fr£14.95 Last dinner 9.30pm
Credit Cards ①②③④⑤

★★77% **Grapevine**

Sheep St GL54 1AU (Best Western) ☎Cotswold(0451)30344
Telex no 43423 FAX (0451) 32278
Closed 25 Dec-8 Jan

*A charming Cotswold hotel, privately owned and run by Sandra Elliot along with a friendly team of caring staff. Guest rooms are comfortable, well equipped and have some thoughtful finishing touches; and public areas have a truly welcoming atmosphere. The airy restaurant with its vine-clad ceiling provides an attractive setting for Chef Lesley Pridmore's enjoyable light dishes. The Grapevine, recipient of our 'Courtesy and Care' award last year, provides an exceptional level of service and hospitality.*

13⇔↑Annexe10⇔↑(3fb)1⊠✷in 4 bedrooms CTV in all bedrooms ® T ✗ sB&B⇔↑£66-£86 dB&B⇔↑£92-£132 ⊠
23P ♨ ♫
♥ English, French & Italian V ✧ ✷ ✰ ✱ Lunch £6.55-£7.85alc High tea fr£3.75alc Dinner fr£17.50 Last dinner 9.30pm
Credit Cards ①②③⑤ⓔ

★★70% **Fosse Manor**

GL54 1JX (Consort) ☎Cotswold(0451)30354 FAX (0451) 32486
Closed 24 Dec-5 Jan

*Built in the style of a Cotswold manor house and set back from the A429, this hotel provides comfortable accommodation in individually decorated rooms. Charming and attractive public areas include an elegant dining room, a delightful lounge and a convivial bar which offers very popular bar meals. Service – personally supervised by the proprietor – is both friendly and efficient.*

14⇔↑Annexe6rm(2⇔↑)(6fb)1⊠ CTV in all bedrooms ® T sB&Bfr£45 sB&B⇔↑£45-£65 dB&Bfr£90 dB&B⇔↑£90-£124 ⊠
CTV 40P ♨ ✿ CFA solarium croquet ⅍
♥ English & Continental V ✧ ✷ ✰ ✱ Lunch fr£13.95&alc Dinner fr£17.95&alc Last dinner 9.30pm
Credit Cards ①②③⑤

★★70% **Stow Lodge**

The Square GL54 1AB ☎Cotswold(0451)30485

Closed 20 Dec-mid Jan

*With driveway entrances off the town centre square and directly from the A429, which bypasses the centre, the hotel has an excellent location, further enhanced by gardens of mature trees, lawns and a church with churchyard to one side. Bedrooms are warm and comfortable, various sizes and shapes in the old house, and more modern in the coach house which includes some ground-floor rooms. Service is friendly, and typically British food is served piping hot in generous portions.*

12rm(10⇨➘)Annexe10⇨➘(2fb)1🛏✂in 1 bedroom CTV in all bedrooms Ⓡ ✖ ✳ sB&B⇨➘£32-£45 dB&B⇨➘£48-£71 🏳

⟆ 30P 🚗 ✿ nc5yrs

✿ ✂ ✳ Bar Lunch £8.75-£16alc Dinner £12-£13&alc Last dinner 9pm

Credit Cards ② ⑤

★★64% **Old Farmhouse**

Lower Swell GL54 1LF (1m W B4068) ☎Cotswold(0451)30232

*A 16th-century farmhouse situated in a peaceful hamlet a mile west of Stow, which has been converted into a small hotel, offering friendly service and simple comfortable accommodation with modern facilities.*

7rm(5⇨➘➘)Annexe7⇨➘(1fb)2🛏 CTV in all bedrooms Ⓡ T S% sB&B£21.20 sB&B⇨➘£44.50-£60 dB&B£42.40 dB&B⇨➘£66-£89 🏳

25P 🚗 ✿ *xmas*

♈ International V ✿ ⬛ ✂ S% Sunday Lunch £12.75 High tea £2.75 Dinner £13.50-£14 Last dinner 9pm

Credit Cards ① ③

**See advertisement on page 667**

★ ★

**FOSSE·MANOR** HOTEL

**Fosse Way**
**Stow on the Wold**
**Gloucestershire GL54 1JX**
**Tel: (0451) 30354   Fax: (0451) 32486**

Standing in sixteen acres of beautiful gardens 1 mile south of Stow-on-the-Wold on the A429. Ideally situated for Cotswolds, Stratford, Oxford, Cheltenham and Worcester. Tastefully decorated with a warm family welcome. Excellent food and efficient staff.

# Stow Lodge Hotel★★

The Square, Stow-on-the-Wold,
Cheltenham, Glos. GL54 1AB
Tel: (0451) 30485

Set back in its own grounds far enough from the Market Square to allow guests complete peace and relaxation. 20 bedrooms, all with private bath and toilet, television, radio, tea and coffee-making facilities. Full central heating. Open log fires in both the Bar and Lounge. The restaurant which is non smoking seats 30 persons and offers a varied table d'hôte menu and à la carte with traditional English fare at its very best. Fully licensed Bar offering a selection of light lunches daily to the traveller not wishing to linger. Private Car park for approx 30 cars.
*A perfect centre for touring the Cotswolds and Shakespeare country.*

# WYCK HILL HOUSE ❀❀ ★★★

*Country Hotel and Restaurant*
*Stow-on-the-Wold Gloucestershire GL54 1HY*

*T*his lovely 18th Century Manor House is set in almost 100 acres of grounds overlooking the Windrush Valley in the heart of the Cotswolds.

30 luxuriously appointed bedrooms and the elegant lounges and restaurant provide a delightful atmosphere in which to relax and enjoy Ian Smith's fine classical cuisine.

**Telephone: 0451 31936  Fax: 0451 32243**
*2 miles south of Stow, on the Burford Road (A424).*

S

### ★★63% Old Stocks
The Square GL54 1AF ☎Cotswold(0451)30666
FAX (0451) 870014
Closed 17-27 Dec

*Standing next to the green, this hotel comprises three 16th and
17th-century buildings which have been tastefully upgraded and
refurbished to retain their original character. Bedrooms are all en
suite and equipped with modern facilities, though the nature of the
building means that some are rather compact. Under the personal
supervision of the resident proprietors, service is friendly and
informal.*

16⇔↑(1fb) CTV in all bedrooms ® T sB&B⇔↑£33-£38
dB&B⇔↑£66-£76 ⊟
CTV 14P ✿ CFA ⅙ xmas
V ♥ ⚿ Sunday Lunch £8.95-£15.95 Dinner £8.95-£15.95 Last
dinner 9.30pm
Credit Cards ①②③ ⓔ

---

### STRACHUR Strathclyde *Argyllshire* Map **10** NN00

### ★★★62% Creggans Inn
PA27 8BX (Minotels) ☎(036986)279 FAX (036986) 637
*This long established roadside inn sits looking out across Loch
Fyne. Its dinner menu, with an international flavour, makes it a
popular place to eat, although the best of Scottish meats and
seafoods are still featured. The simply furnished bedrooms have a
pretty cottage style appearance.*

21rm(17⇔↑) CTV in all bedrooms T sB&Bfr£40
sB&B⇔↑fr£45 dB&Bfr£90 dB&B⇔↑fr£100 ⊟
CTV 80P ✿ CFA ✔ xmas
♀ French V ♥ ⚿ ⤬ ✳ Bar Lunch fr£10alc High tea fr£10alc
Dinner fr£24alc Last dinner 9pm
Credit Cards ①②③⑤ ⓔ

---

### STRANRAER Dumfries & Galloway *Wigtownshire*
Map **10** NX06

### ★★★74% North West Castle
DG9 8EH (Exec Hotel) ☎(0776)4413 FAX (0776) 2646
*Family owned and managed this spacious, elegant hotel has been
sympathetically modernised and extended to provide a wide range
of leisure and recreational facilities. Many of the comfortable, well
equipped bedrooms enjoy fine views of Loch Ryan.*

74⇔↑(12fb)1⊡ CTV in all bedrooms ® T ✠ (ex guide dogs)
sB&B⇔↑£52-£82 dB&B⇔↑£78-£116 ⊟
Lift ( 100P ⇛ CFA ◱ (heated) snooker sauna solarium
gymnasium curling (Oct-Apr) games room xmas
V ♥ ⚿ Bar Lunch £10-£16alc Dinner fr£20&alc Last dinner
9.30pm

---

### STRATFIELD TURGIS Hampshire Map **04** SU65

### ★★64% Wellington Arms
RG27 0AS ☎Basingstoke(0256)882214 Telex no 265871
FAX (0256) 882934
*This former coaching inn with Georgian façade, set in rural
surroundings north of Basingstoke, has now been completely
refurbished. Predominantly commercial, with an informal
atmosphere, it offers compact but fully equipped accommodation
which contains some interesting French antique furniture; an
additional 22 bedrooms will be provided by the extension at present
in progress. Public areas are limited, but there is a comfortable
lounge bar serving a good choice of meals to supplement those
featured on the à la carte and table d'hôte menus of the well
appointed restaurant.*

35⇔↑(2fb)1⊟↼in 3 bedrooms CTV in all bedrooms ® T ✳
sB&B⇔↑£45-£85 dB&B⇔↑£55-£95 ⊟
150P ✿ CFA xmas
V ♥ ⚿ ✳ Lunch £13.50-£18.50&alc Dinner £13.50-£18.50&alc
Last dinner 10pm
Credit Cards ①②③⑤ ⓔ

---

See **Town Plan Section**

### ★★★★64% Welcombe
Warwick Rd CV37 0NR ☎(0789)295252 Telex no 31347
FAX (0789) 414666
Closed 28 Dec-3 Jan

*Standing on the outskirts of Stratford in a parkland estate which
offers an 18-hole golf course and two all-weather floodlit tennis
courts, this Jacobean mansion features truly traditional service
rendered by a charming and efficient staff. Public rooms are
comfortable, and a major refurbishment programme is upgrading
most bedrooms to a luxurious standard – including many suites
and four poster rooms – though the older, garden wing
accommodation remains simple.*

76⇔↑(2fb)7⊡ CTV in all bedrooms T sB&B⇔↑£90-£110
dB&B⇔↑£125-£180 ⊟
( 200P 6⊜ ✿ CFA ▶ 18 ℒ (hard) snooker putting table tennis
xmas
♀ English & French V ♥ ⚿ Lunch fr£17.50&alc Dinner
fr£27.50&alc Last dinner 9.30pm
Credit Cards ①②③⑤

### ★★★★58% Moat House International
Bridgefoot CV37 6YR (Queens Moat) ☎(0789)414411
Telex no 311127 FAX (0789) 298589

*This low, purpose-built hotel by the river and a short walk from the
theatre offers good conference and function facilities and a new
indoor leisure complex. Bedrooms, all similar, are comfortable,
well equipped and air conditioned. There are 2 bars, a nightclub,
shops and a choice of carvery or à la carte restaurants offering
reliable cooking.*

247⇔↑(20fb)↼in 64 bedrooms CTV in all bedrooms ® T ✳
sB&B⇔↑£84.25 dB&B⇔↑£112.50 ⊟
Lift ( ⊞ CTV 350P ✿ CFA ◱ (heated) ✔ snooker sauna
solarium gymnasium steam room beautician ♫
♀ British & French V ♥ ⚿ ✳ Lunch fr£10.95 High tea fr£5.75
Dinner fr£13.25 Last dinner 11pm
Credit Cards ①②③⑤ ⓔ

### ★★★★52% The Shakespeare
Chapel St CV37 6ER (Forte Hotels) ☎(0789)294771
Telex no 311181 FAX (0789) 415411

*This magnificent building in the town centre with its gables and
timbered façade dates from around 1637. Current refurbishment
of most of the public areas emphasises comfort while retaining
historical character. Bedrooms vary greatly in size and quality but
all have en suite bathrooms and are equipped with similar modern
facilities.*

70⇔↑3⊟↼in 20 bedrooms CTV in all bedrooms ® T ✳
sB⇔↑fr£75 dB⇔↑£95-£120 (room only) ⊟
Lift ( 45P CFA ✔ xmas
♀ English & Continental V ♥ ⚿ ✠ ✳ Lunch £11.25-
£12.50&alc High tea fr£2.50 Dinner fr£16.50&alc Last dinner
10pm
Credit Cards ①②③④⑤

### ★★★✿✿✿⚑76% Billesley Manor Hotel
B49 6NF (Queens Moat)(Small Luxury Hotels) ☎(0789)400888
Telex no 312599 FAX (0789) 764145
(For full entry see Billesley)

### ★★★✿74% Salford Hall
WR11 5UT (Best Western) ☎Evesham(0386)871300
Telex no 336682 FAX (0386) 871301
(For full entry see Abbot's Salford)

**See advertisement on page 669**

### ★★★74% Windmill Park Hotel & Country Club
Warwick Rd CV37 0PY (Best Western) ☎(0789)731173
FAX (0789) 731131

*On the Warwick road about 2.5 miles out of town with easy access
to major road networks, this hotel, opened relatively recently,
offers modern accommodation which has proved very popular, as*

→

**S**

S

*have the conference facilities, and the young staff have grown in confidence, providing good service with a ready smile.*
100⇨(4fb)8⌘ CTV in all bedrooms ® T sB&B⇨£75-£80 dB&B⇨£90-£95 ➡
Lift ℭ 220P ❋ CFA ⊠ (heated) ♪ (hard) sauna solarium gymnasium steam room *xmas*
V ✿ ⏛ Lunch £11-£14&alc Dinner £13-£15&alc Last dinner 9.45pm
Credit Cards [1] [2] [3] [5]

★★★61% **Charlecote Pheasant Country**
CV35 9EW (Queens Moat) ☎(0789)470333 FAX (0789) 470222
(For full entry see Charlecote)

★★★60% *Dukes*
Payton St CV37 6UA ☎(0789)269300 Telex no 31430
FAX (0789) 414700
Closed 2 days Xmas
*Situated in the Georgian 'new town' area close to the centre, this fine building has been carefully restored to create a modern hotel whilst retaining many original features. There is a spacious lounge and intimate themed restaurant, and bedrooms, although mainly small, are well equipped.*
22⇨♣2⌘ CTV in all bedrooms ® T ✹
30P ⇱ ❋ nc12yrs
♥ European V ✿ Last dinner 9.45pm
Credit Cards [1] [2] [3] [5]

★★★59% **Alveston Manor**
Clopton Bridge CV37 7HP (Forte Hotels) ☎(0789)204581
Telex no 31324 FAX (0789) 414095
*An attractive hotel with well kept gardens just across the river from the theatre and town centre. Afternoon tea can be enjoyed in the cocktail bar which has 16th-century oak panelling.*
108⇨♣(6fb)1⇱❋in 30 bedrooms CTV in all bedrooms ® T
❋ sB⇨♣fr£75 dB⇨♣£95-£115 (room only) ➡
ℭ 200P ❋ CFA pitch & putt *xmas*
V ✿ ⏛ ❋ Lunch fr£12.95&alc Dinner fr£17.95&alc Last dinner 9.30pm
Credit Cards [1] [2] [3] [4] [5]

★★★54% **Falcon**
Chapel St CV37 6HA (Queens Moat) ☎(0789)205777
Telex no 312522 FAX (0789) 414260
*This historic town-centre inn has been serving the traveller since 1640. Over the years it has been extended and improved to provide modern facilities whilst retaining many original features including fine panelling, oak beams and open log fires.*
73⇨♣(13fb)1⇱❋in 27 bedrooms CTV in all bedrooms ® T
S% sB&B⇨♣£67-£77 dB&B⇨♣£88-£99 ➡
Lift ℭ 100P 24🚗 ❋ CFA *xmas*
♥ French V ✿ S% Lunch £12.50-£14.50 High tea £4.50-£10alc Dinner £14.50-£20 Last dinner 9pm
Credit Cards [1] [2] [3] [4] [5] ⓔ

★★★50% **Forte Posthouse**
Bridgefoot CV37 7LT (Forte Hotels) ☎(0789)266761
FAX (0789) 414547
*Standing beside the River Avon, the hotel is conveniently placed for both town and theatre. It offers guests comfortable bedrooms and a choice of menus.*
60⇨♣1⇱❋in 30 bedrooms CTV in all bedrooms ® T ❋
sB⇨♣£39.50-£49.50 dB⇨♣£39.50-£49.50 (room only) ➡
ℭ ▦ 100P ❋ CFA *xmas*
V ✿ ⏛ ❋ ❋ Lunch £9.75 Dinner £14.25 Last dinner 10.30pm
Credit Cards [1] [2] [3] [4] [5]

★★★50% **The White Swan**
Rother St CV37 6NH (Forte Hotels) ☎(0789)297022
FAX (0789) 268773

*A half-timbered building near Shakespeare's birthplace, opposite the American Fountain, retains many original features including fine carved panelling; bedrooms vary in both style and standard, but all are well equipped.*
37⇨♣(3fb)2⇱❋in 12 bedrooms CTV in all bedrooms ® T ❋
sB⇨♣fr£65 dB⇨♣£80-£97 (room only) ➡
ℭ 12P CFA ♫ *xmas*
V ✿ ⏛ ❋ ❋ Lunch £8.95-£9.50 Dinner £14.95 Last dinner 9pm
Credit Cards [1] [2] [3] [4] [5]

★★73% **Stratford House**
Sheep St CV37 6EF ☎(0789)268288 FAX (0789) 295580
Closed Xmas RS 3 days from Xmas day
*In the heart of Stratford's shopping area and close to the Royal Shakespeare Theatre, this lovely Georgian building is filled with flowers. Shepherds Restaurant is light and airy and it is here that chef Michael Young maintains a sound reputation for his excellent modern British cooking. Bedrooms are a little compact but comfortably furnished and staff are caring and friendly.*
11rm(7⇨3♣)(1fb) CTV in all bedrooms ® T ✹ ❋
sB&B⇨♣£51-£66 dB&B⇨♣£55-£82 ➡
ℭ ♪ ⇱ nc2yrs
♥ English & French V ❋ Lunch £10.50-£14alc Dinner £14-£20.50alc Last dinner 9.30pm
Credit Cards [1] [2] [3] [5] ⓔ

★★65% **The Coach House Hotel**
16-17 Warwick Rd CV37 6YW ☎(0789)204109 & 299468
FAX (0789) 415916
*This part-Georgian house with adjacent Victorian addition, set on the A439 Warwick road at the edge of the town centre, has been improved to provide comfortable, well equipped bedrooms and an intimate lower-level restaurant which offers a good choice of well cooked dishes at reasonable prices.*
10⇨♣Annexe13rm(8⇨♣)(3fb)1⇱❋in 3 bedrooms CTV in all bedrooms ® T ✹ (ex guide dogs) sB&Bfr£21
sB&B⇨♣£38-£45 dB&Bfr£39 dB&B⇨♣£54-£88 ➡
30P CFA *xmas*
♥ English & French V ✿ ⏛ ❋ Lunch £9.95&alc High tea fr£2.95 Dinner £6-£10.25&alc Last dinner 10.30pm
Credit Cards [1] [2] [3] ⓔ

See advertisement on page 671

★★60% *Swan House*
The Green CV37 9XJ ☎(0789)67030 due to change to 267030
FAX (0789) 204875
(For full entry see Wilmcote)

See advertisement on page 671

STRATHAVEN Strathclyde Map **11** NS74

★★56% **Strathaven**
Hamilton Rd ML10 6SZ (Consort) ☎(0357)21778
Telex no 776496 FAX (0357) 20789
*A business and function hotel created from a period mansion on the edge of the town, off the A723. Some bedrooms are compact but all are very well equipped.*
10⇨♣ CTV in all bedrooms ® T S10% sB&B⇨♣fr£55
dB&B⇨♣fr£70 ➡
ℭ 80P
♥ French V ✿ ❋ Lunch fr£7 High tea fr£5 Dinner fr£13 Last dinner 10pm
Credit Cards [1] [2] [3] [4] [5]

STRATHBLANE Central *Stirlingshire* Map **11** NS57

★★69% **Kirkhouse Inn**
G63 9AA (Minotels) ☎Blanefield(0360)70621 FAX (0360) 70896
*A popular business hotel in a commuter village standing amid attractive countryside, with the Campsie Hills as its backdrop. Bedrooms are well equipped, while both restaurant and bar offer food of a good standard at lunch or dinner.*

→

**S**

S

15⇔♠(2fb)1⬚ CTV in all bedrooms ® sB&B⇔♠£60-£65 dB&B⇔♠£85-£90 ₽
《 350P *xmas*
♡ Scottish & French **V** ♦ ℤ Lunch £10.50-£11.50 Dinner £11-£12&alc Last dinner 9.30pm
Credit Cards ①②③⑤£

---

**STRATHPEFFER** Highland *Ross & Cromarty* Map **14** NH45

**★★65% Brunstane Lodge**
Golf Rd IV14 9AT ☎(0997)21261
Closed 1 & 2 Jan RS mid Oct-Apr
*Substantially refurbished over the years by caring owners, this charming modern hotel stands in peaceful grounds on the edge of the village. Bedrooms, though compact, are comfortably appointed, and thoughtfully equipped public areas include a well stocked bar with inviting open fire and an attractive first-floor lounge overlooking the surrounding hills. Housekeeping is commendable, and a relaxing atmosphere prevails.*
6rm(2⇔3♠)(1fb) CTV in all bedrooms ® ✱ sB&B£20-£22 dB&B⇔♠£37-£42 ₽
CTV 20P ✿ CFA ♿
**V** ✂ Bar Lunch £3-£5 Dinner £12-£15 Last dinner 8.30pm
Credit Cards ①③

**★★64% Holly Lodge**
IV14 9AR ☎(0997)21254
*This attractive stone-built hotel stands in its own grounds overlooking the Victorian spa resort of Strathpeffer. It offers warm hospitality and good food influenced by a mind of the orient. The public rooms – in particular the charming residents' lounge area and the comfortable bedrooms also have an oriental feel about them.*
7rm(3⇔3♠) CTV in all bedrooms ®
CTV 15P 2🚗 🚲 ✿ shooting ♫
♡ Scottish & Oriental ♦ ℤ Last dinner 9pm

---

**STRATHYRE** Central *Perthshire* Map **11** NN51

**★58% The Inn**
Main St FK18 8NA ☎(08774)224
*Practical, value-for-money accommodation and a comfortable atmosphere are features of this small, family-run roadside inn which dates back to the early 18th century.*
6rm(4⇔) ®
CTV 30P
♡ Mainly grills ♦ ℤ Last dinner 8.30pm

---

**STREATLEY** Berkshire Map **04** SU58

**★★★◉73% Swan Diplomat**
High St RG8 9HR ☎Goring-on-Thames(0491)873737
Telex no 848259 FAX (0491) 872554
*This personally run and hospitable hotel stands against a backdrop of wooded countryside in delightful surroundings beside the river; once an inn, and now both sympathetically enlarged and significantly upgraded, it is a firm favourite with businessman and tourist alike. Spotlessly clean, well furnished and equipped bedrooms, many with pretty little terrace balconies over the water, are complemented by cosy, traditionally furnished lounges with a cottagey atmosphere, the Riverside Restaurant, conference/meeting rooms and a bright new leisure complex.*
46⇔♠1⬚✂in 2 bedrooms CTV in all bedrooms ® T ✱
sB&B⇔♠£82-£97 dB&B⇔♠£110-£125 (room only) ₽
《 CTV 146P ✿ CFA 🖃 (heated) sauna solarium gymnasium croquet row boat hire badminton *xmas*
♡ French **V** ♦ ℤ ✱ Lunch £18-£21.50&alc Dinner £21.50-£23.50&alc Last dinner 9.30pm
Credit Cards ①②③⑤£

---

**STREET** Somerset Map **03** ST43

**★★★66% Bear**
53 High St BA16 0EF ☎(0458)42021 FAX (0458) 840007
*An attractive stone-built house, near to its owners, Clarks', Shoe Museum, is managed by a subsidiary of the P & O group. Set in pleasant, well kept gardens with good car parking facilities, it offers quality accommodation, the traditional rooms in the main building being supplemented by those of more modern style in Rose Cottage; a large area of the Cobbler Bar is reserved for non-smokers. Service is provided by a well established staff, many of whom have long-service records.*
10⇔♠Annexe5⇔(3fb) CTV in all bedrooms ® T ✱
sB&B⇔♠£30-£60 dB&B⇔♠£50-£80 ₽
《 36P ✿ *xmas*
♡ English & French **V** ♦ ℤ ✂ Lunch £4.95-£6.50 Dinner £15-£25alc Last dinner 9.30pm
Credit Cards ①②③

---

**STREETLY** West Midlands Map **07** SP09

**★★61% Parson & Clerk Motel**
Chester Rd B73 6SP (junc A452/B4138) (Porterhouse)
☎021-353 1747 FAX 021-352 1340
Closed 24-26 Dec
*Conveniently located in the heart of the Midlands, close to major business centres and motorway routes, this motel comprises a block of very well equipped bedrooms with a breakfast room and small bar, while across the car park is a popular Porterhouse restaurant.*
30⇔♠ CTV in all bedrooms ® T ✱ (ex guide dogs) ✱
sB&B⇔♠£43.50 dB&B⇔♠£55 ₽
CTV 100P CFA
**V** ♦ ℤ ✱ Lunch £6.99-£7.50alc Dinner frf5.95alc Last dinner 10pm
Credit Cards ①②③⑤

---

**STRETTON Cheshire** Map **07** SJ68

**★★71% Old Vicarage**
Stretton Rd WA4 4NS ☎Warrington(0925)730706
FAX (0925) 730740
*This hotel just off junction 10 of the M56 exhibits many features more usually associated with an establishment of a higher classification, especially in the public areas and services. A good, varied choice of dishes (many with interesting sauces) and a comprehensive wine list are available in the restaurant.*
26⇔♠(2fb)1⬚ CTV in all bedrooms ® T ✱ sB&B⇔♠£51-£55 dB&B⇔♠£65-£75 ₽
Lift 《 150P ✿ CFA
**V** ♦ ℤ ✂ ✱ Lunch £8.90&alc Dinner £13.90&alc Last dinner 9.30pm
Credit Cards ①②③

---

**STRETTON Leicestershire** Map **08** SK91

**★★68% Ram Jam Inn**
Great North Rd LE15 7QX ☎Stamford(0780)410776
Telex no 342888 FAX (0572) 724721
Closed 25 Dec
*This unusual modern development of an old inn has proved popular with travellers on the A1, situated as it is on the northbound carriageway after the B668 turn-off; southbound traffic should take the B668 signposted Oakham and follow hotel signs. Eating options varying from high quality fast food to full meals are available from 7.00am until 11pm, and recently refurbished accommodation is both well equipped and comfortable.*
Annexe8⇔(2fb) CTV in all bedrooms ® T ✱ sB&B⇔£39 dB&B⇔£49 (room only)
100P ✿ CFA
♡ English & Continental **V** ♦ ℤ ✱ Lunch £9-£13 High tea frf3.50 Dinner £13-£16 Last dinner 10.30pm
Credit Cards ①②③

**STRONTIAN** Highland *Argyllshire* Map **14** NM86

★★69% **Kilcamb Lodge**
PH36 4HY ☎(0967)2257
Closed 21 Oct-Etr

*The dedicated owners of this charming small hotel by the picturesque shore of Loch Sunart, are constantly striving to develop and to improve standards. Guests are assured of a warm welcome, comfortable, tastefully decorated bedrooms and relaxing public areas which include a dining room serving a short but imaginative dinner menu of dishes prepared from fresh local produce.*

9rm(2⇌6↑)(1fb) ® ✹ sB&B⇌↑fr£56 dB&B⇌↑fr£112 (incl dinner) ➡
CTV 20P ⊞ ✿
♨ Scottish & French V ♥ ✔ Dinner £22.50 Last dinner 7pm

★★59% **Loch Sunart**
PH36 4HZ ☎(0967)2471
Closed Nov-Etr

*Situated on the edge of the village overlooking Loch Sunart this family-run Highland hotel is a popular base for the touring holiday-maker. It has a homely atmosphere with modest, traditional appointments and reliable home cooking served in the small dining room.*

11⇌↑(1fb) ® sB&B⇌↑£23.80 dB&B⇌↑£47.60 ➡
CTV 30P ⊞ ✿
♥ ⚏ ✔ Bar Lunch £1.10-£9 Dinner fr£17 Last dinner 7.30pm

★★59% **Strontian**
PH36 4HZ ☎(0967)2029

7rm(5⇌5↑)(1fb) CTV in all bedrooms ® T ✱ dB&B⇌↑£40-£70 ➡
30P ⊞ ✿ *xmas*
→

**S**

♨ ⬚ ✻ Lunch £5-£9.50&alc Dinner £5.50-£15alc Last dinner 9pm
Credit Cards [1] [3]

---

## STROUD Gloucestershire Map **03** SO80

See also **Amberley** and **Painswick**

### ★★★ ✿66% **Eastington Grange**
Stonehouse, Eastington GL10 3RT ☎(0453)791511
FAX (0453) 791513

*Half a mile from junction 13 of the M5, beside a service area on the A419, stands a former rectory dating from the late Georgian period. Now tastefully restored into a hotel of charm and character, it meets the needs of present day travellers with comfortable, well equipped bedrooms and public areas where décor enhances many of the building's original features; the conservatory-extended restaurant provides a delightful setting in which to enjoy the imaginative food produced by chef Mark Lawson-Smith.*

13⇨♪🐾1🖵 CTV in all bedrooms ® T ✻ sB&B⇨🐾£65-£75
dB&B⇨🐾£75 ⊟
100P 🐾 ✿
V ♨ ⬚ ✻ Lunch £15.95-£20&alc Dinner £15.95-£20&alc
Last dinner 9.30pm
Credit Cards [1] [2] [3] [5] ⓔ

### ★★★ ⚑ 65% **Burleigh Court**
Minchinhampton GL5 2PF (2.5m SE off A419)
☎Brimscombe(0453)883804 FAX (0453) 886870
Closed 25 Dec-4 Jan RS Sun

*Situated 3 miles from the town centre off the A419 this fine Georgian house is in a commanding position overlooking the surrounding countryside. It has well equipped bedrooms of differing standards, comfortable public areas and an attractive garden with a putting green. Good food and friendly services are provided by the Benson family and their staff.*

11⇨🐾(1fb) Annexe6⇨🐾(1fb) CTV in all bedrooms ® T
✠ (ex guide dogs) sB&B⇨🐾£59-£64 dB&B⇨🐾£76-£94 ⊟
40P 1🛏 🐾 ✿ ⬚ (heated) putting green ⚘
♨ English & French V ♨ ⬚ ✕ Lunch £11.40-£11.95 High tea
£3-£7alc Dinner £16-£25alc Last dinner 8.45pm
Credit Cards [1] [2] [3] [5]

### ★★★ 56% **The Bear of Rodborough**
Rodborough Common GL5 5DE (.5m SW) (Forte Hotels)
☎(0453)878522 FAX (0453) 872523

*Situated on the edge of the common with fine views over the surrounding countryside this historic inn offers character public areas with good food and service standards provided by friendly, attentive staff. Bedrooms vary in style and standard, some are in need of redecoration and we understand that there is a planned improvement programme.*

47⇨🐾(1fb) 🐾in 15 bedrooms CTV in all bedrooms ® T ✻
sB⇨🐾fr£65 dB⇨🐾£80-£100 (room only) ⊟
🄯 200P ✿ CFA croquet 🎵 xmas
V ♨ ⬚ ✕ ✻ Lunch £9.50&alc Dinner £14.95&alc Last dinner
9.30pm
Credit Cards [1] [2] [3] [4] [5]

### ★★ 68% **London**
30-31 London Rd GL5 2AJ ☎(0453)759992

*On the A419 east of the town centre, this hotel has undergone major improvements and offers good open plan public areas, and most of the modern well equipped bedrooms have en suite facilities. Friendly and attentive service is provided by hosts Ronald and Rosemarie Portal and their young staff.*

12rm(2⇨6🐾) CTV in all bedrooms ® T ✠ ✻ sB&B£26-£29
sB&B⇨🐾£35-£45 dB&B£39 dB&B⇨🐾£49-£59 ⊟
10P 🐾 nc2yrs
♨ Continental V ♨ ⬚ ✕ ✻ Lunch £5.25-£7&alc Dinner
fr£12.50&alc Last dinner 9.30pm
Credit Cards [1] [2] [3] [4] [5] ⓔ

### ★★65% **Imperial**
Station Rd GL5 3AP (Chef & Brewer) ☎(0453)764077
FAX (0453) 751314

*Very pretty, well equipped bedrooms and a popular restaurant specialising in good grills are offered by this ivy-clad hotel directly opposite the railway station.*

25⇨3🐾(2fb)2🖵 CTV in all bedrooms ® T ✠ (ex guide dogs)
sB&B⇨🐾£44-£48 dB&B⇨🐾£61-£61 ⊟
15P
♨ International V ♨ ⬚ ✕ Bar Lunch £2.95-£5.50alc
Credit Cards [1] [2] [3] [5]

### ★★63% *The Bell*
Wallbridge GL5 3JA ☎(0453)763556

*This small, privately owned and run hotel is situated in the town centre of Stroud, within a short distance of the railway and bus stations. The hotel is also convenient for the M5, being only 5 miles from junction 13. Rooms have been recently refurbished and offer good, modern facilities, equally suited to the business traveller or the tourist. There is a small bar, which is popular with locals, and an attractive dining room serving a good choice of dishes.*

12rm(4⇨5🐾)(1fb)1🖵 CTV in all bedrooms ® T
✠ (ex guide dogs)
CTV 20P
♨ Continental V ♨ ⬚ Last dinner 9.30pm
Credit Cards [1] [3]

### ⚑⚑⚑ ✕Oakes
169 Slad Rd GL5 1RG ☎(0453)759950

*This immaculately maintained stone house is on the B4070, signposted Slad from the town centre and stands high above the town. You will be met by Caroline Oakes, who is a most friendly and attentive hostess who quickly makes visitors feel at ease. A choice of 3 fixed-price menus is offered and it is quite possible to jump from one to another, but at lunch time, this top quality restaurant offers a superb value-for-money menu where a light meal, still of award winning style, is approximately half the price of the à la carte. However, it is still the place for that special occasion dinner, as the evening atmosphere is delightful. Dishes have such distinctive flavours – ragout of sea food, for example, will have each type of fish easily identifiable, and vegetables, described by one Inspector as 'good enough to turn a meat-eater into a vegetarian' were perfectly cooked and seasoned. Some dishes may be a little too innovative. 'Bread and butter pudding' needed a designer label – it was more simply a lovely baked custard with a thin lid of fruit bread, with a gorgeous flavour, and so light, but hardly the stuff of schoolboy dreams. However, it is Chris Oakes' immaculate cooking that is the entitlement, and not dish titles, and together with his wife, Caroline, they have continued to maintain exacting standards, and to widen their circle of satisfied and regular customers.*

Closed Mon & end Dec-end Jan & 2 wks Aug
Dinner not served Sun
♨ English & French V 30 seats ✻ Lunch £13-£36 Dinner £28-£36 Last lunch 1.45pm Last dinner 9.30pm 12 P
Credit Cards [1] [3]

---

## STRUAN

See **Skye, Isle of**

---

## STUDLAND Dorset Map **04** SZ08

### ★★★67% **Knoll House**
Ferry Rd BH19 3AH ☎(092944)251 FAX (092944) 423
Closed Nov-Mar

*Beautifully set in a National Trust reserve with views over the sea, this welcoming and very comfortable hotel caters for family holidays, with good leisure amenities and many special facilities for children. Well kept bedrooms, many with sea views, vary in size.*

57rm(42⇌🏠)Annexe22rm(15⇌🏠)(30fb) **T** S% sB&B£51-£65 sB&B⇌🏠£64-£77 dB&B£102-£130 dB&B⇌🏠£119-£154 (incl dinner)
《 CTV 100P 🚗 ❖ ⌐ (heated) ▶ 9 ♫ (hard) sauna solarium gymnasium jacuzzi leisure centre ♧
♡ ⚗ S% Lunch fr£14 Dinner fr£15 Last dinner 8.30pm

---

**★★🛁63% Manor House**
BH19 3AU ☎(092944)288
Closed 19 Dec-Jan
*Set in peaceful gardens overlooking the beach, this Gothic-style building has curiously shaped bedrooms, some with splendid wood carving, and a cosy lounge and panelled bar. The intimate dining room serves a short menu of well prepared English dishes.*
20⇌🏠(9fb)4🚻 CTV in all bedrooms ® **T** ✳ sB&B⇌🏠£40-£45 dB&B⇌🏠£55-£75 🍴
40P 🚗 ❖ ♫ (hard) nc5yrs
♀ English & French **V** ♡ ⚗ ✂ Bar Lunch £2.50-£5 High tea £3-£4 Dinner fr£18 Last dinner 8.30pm
Credit Cards ① ③ ⓔ

---

STURMINSTER NEWTON Dorset Map **03** ST71

**★★★ ❀❀64% Plumber Manor**
Hazelbury Bryan Rd DT10 2AF ☎(0258)72507
FAX (0258) 73370
Closed Feb
6rm(5⇌🏠)Annexe10⇌🏠 CTV in all bedrooms ® **T**
✖ (ex guide dogs) S% sB&B£55-£75 sB&B⇌🏠£55-£75 dB&B£80-£120 dB&B⇌🏠£80-£120 🍴
30P 🚗 ❖ ♫ (hard) nc12yrs
♀ English & French **V** S% Dinner £20-£25 Last dinner 9.30pm
Credit Cards ① ② ③ ⑤

---

SUDBURY **Derbyshire**

**★★★65% The Boars Head**
Lichfield Rd DE6 5GX ☎Burton-on-Trent(0283)820344
FAX (0283) 820075
*This one-time inn stands half a mile from the village of Sudbury, just one mile south of the A50 on the A515 Lichfield road. Originally part of the Vernon estate, it has now been expanded to provide comfortable, well equipped accommodation attractively furnished with Sanderson fabrics. Public rooms include comfortable lounges, a convivial bar with log fire and a choice of restaurant. Friendly staff display a genuine concern for guests' wellbeing.*
22⇌🏠 CTV in all bedrooms ® **T** ✖ (ex guide dogs) ✳
sB&B⇌🏠£30-£52.50 dB&B⇌🏠£40-£62.50
《 85P *xmas*
♀ International **V** ♡ ⚗ ✳ Lunch £8.95-£10.95&alc Dinner £10.95&alc Last dinner 9.30pm
Credit Cards ① ② ③ ⑤ ⓔ

---

SUDBURY **Suffolk** Map **05** TL84

**★★★61% Mill**
Walnut Tree Ln CO10 6BD (Consort) ☎(0787)75544
Telex no 987623 FAX (0787) 73027
*This converted mill, dating back almost 300 years and overlooking the mill pool from its peaceful setting, is soon to benefit from a major refurbishment. Two styles of accommodation are available, Mill House rooms being attractively decorated in pastel shades whereas those in the wing are more dated. The old mill wheel is still turning and divides the bar from the restaurant which used to be the millhouse.*
50⇌🏠(2fb)1🚻 CTV in all bedrooms ® **T** sB&B⇌🏠£50-£55 dB&B⇌🏠£78-£98 🍴
《 60P CFA ♪ *xmas*
→

**S**

✿ English & French **V** ✿ ⚿ Lunch £10.50&alc Dinner £17.50-£21&alc Last dinner 9.30pm
Credit Cards [1] [2] [3] [5] [£]

### ❀❀ ✕ **Mabey's Brasserie**

47 Gainsborough St CO10 7SS ☎(0787)74298

*A winning mix of owner-managed hospitality, comfortable informal atmosphere, very reasonable prices and above all the excellent cooking of Robert Mabey, who can be seen at work in the open kitchen area of his simple brasserie. The extensive blackboard menu of inviting traditional dishes uses top-quality ingredients, which are left intact, cooked with skill, then sauced or garnished. Regular dishes include Japanese prawn tempura, warm chicken and bacon salad and, among winter favourites, a splendid steak and kidney pudding and various game dishes. Salmon with a herb crust and champagne sauce and roast duck with a vivid sage and onion gravy were memorable. Desserts include delectable passion fruit parfait and blackcurrant sorbet, with hot puddings often on offer. The short reasonably priced wine list carefully chosen from several countries complements the wholesome, delicious cooking.*

Closed Sun, Mon, 10 days Xmas & BH's
✿ International **V** 38 seats ✳ Lunch £12-£20alc Dinner £12-£20alc Last lunch 2pm Last dinner 10pm ✈
Credit Cards [1] [3]

---

### SUNDERLAND Tyne & Wear Map **12** NZ35 ◎

#### ★★★72% **Swallow**

Queen's Pde, Seaburn SR6 8DB (Swallow) ☎091-529 2041
Telex no 53168 FAX 091-529 4227

*Recently refurbished, this seafront hotel offers extremely comfortable, well furnished bedrooms and public areas which include a fully equipped leisure complex as well as a most inviting bar lounge, separate lounge and elegant restaurant. Particularly courteous and attentive service is provided by young local staff.*
66⇌✿(3fb)✂ in 25 bedrooms CTV in all bedrooms ® **T** ✳
sB&B⇌✿£75-£90 dB&B⇌✿£90-£125 ⊟
Lift ℂ CTV 110P ▱ (heated) sauna solarium gymnasium *xmas*
✿ English & French **V** ✿ ⚿ ✳ Lunch £10.50-£12.50&alc
Dinner £17.50-£21&alc Last dinner 9.30pm
Credit Cards [1] [2] [3] [5]

#### ★★63% **Roker**

Roker Ter SR6 0PH (Chef & Brewer) ☎091-567 1786
FAX 091-510 0289

*Comfortable accommodation and friendly, informal service are offered at this seafront hotel.*
45⇌✿(8fb) CTV in all bedrooms ® **T** ✖ (ex guide dogs)
sB&B⇌✿£44-£51 dB&B⇌✿£56 ⊟
ℂ 200P CFA
✿ International **V** ✿ ⚿ ✂ Bar Lunch £2.95-£5.50alc
Credit Cards [1] [2] [3] [5]

#### ★★55% *Mowbray Park*

Toward Rd SR1 1PR ☎091-567 8221 Telex no 587746
*A commercial hotel in the centre of town adjacent to Mowbray Park. The bedrooms are modestly furnished and decorated but well equipped. A programme of refurbishment is planned.*
52rm(33⇌2✿)(5fb) CTV in all bedrooms ®
Lift ℂ CTV 400P (charged) 20🚗 (charged)
✿ French **V** ✿ ⚿ ✂
Credit Cards [1] [2] [3] [4] [5]

#### ★64% **Gelt House**

23 St Bede's Ter SR2 8HS (Exec Hotel) ☎091-567 2990
FAX 091-510 0724
Closed Xmas-New Year
*All bedrooms now have en suite facilities, direct dial telephones and colour television at this friendly, privately owned Victorian town-house hotel which stands in a conservation area near Mowbray Park. Public areas include a comfortable residents' lounge and cosy downstairs bar.*

---

13⇌✿Annexe8✿(1fb) CTV in all bedrooms ® **T** ✖ ✳
sB&B⇌✿fr£35 dB&B⇌✿fr£42
ℂ 14P ⊞
✂ ✳ Dinner fr£8 Last dinner 8.00pm
Credit Cards [1] [2] [3] [5]

---

### SURBITON Greater London

See **LONDON plan** 1*B1*(page 434)

#### ❀❀ ✕ **Chez Max**

85 Maple Rd KT6 4AW ☎081-399 2365

*In this cool, stylish restaurant with crisp tablecloths and mirrored walls, set in a residential shopping arcade, Max Markarian offers a short French menu (with English descriptions) featuring such simple dishes as a rich, dark onion soup and lamb with Madeira sauce as well as some newer classics like escalope of salmon with piquant creamy sorrel sauce or stuffed quails, and a range of sweets that includes a delicious coffee soufflé glacé. Reliable cuisine is accompanied by a quirkily French wine list – short on grower information – which is strong on clarets.*

Closed Sun, Mon, 25-26 Dec, 1-2 Jan & Good Fri Lunch not served Sat
✿ French **V** 40 seats ✳ Lunch £17.75 Dinner £15-£16.75&alc
Last lunch 2pm Last dinner 10pm ✈ nc7yrs
Credit Cards [1] [2] [3] [5]

---

### SUTTON Greater London

See **LONDON plan** 1*B1*(page 434)

#### ○**Holiday Inn**

Gibson Rd SM1 2RF (Holiday Inns Inc) ☎081-770 1311
Telex no 911319 FAX 081-770 1539
Open
116⇌✿

#### ❀❀ ✕ **Partners Brasserie**

23 Stonecot Hill SM3 9HB ☎081-644 7743

*'Partners' have moved their principal operation to Dorking and called their smartly redecorated cosy restaurant in Sutton a 'Brasserie'. The reasonably priced menu includes what owner Andrew Thomason calls, with tongue in cheek, 'dishes' – venison burgers, salmon fish cakes, rice pudding, as well as more modern favourites like duck breast salad and roast cod with olive oil, garlic and herbs. Chef Tim Franklin handles the range with assurance, producing dishes of good taste and texture. Cooking on our visit was really good: a smooth pungent mussel soup, rich meaty silverside and cheese dumplings, and a tangy rhubarb bavarois. The short wine list offers a well chosen, mainly French selection with a few New World bottles, at modest prices but with halves limited to the house wines.*

Closed Mon & 25 Dec-4 Jan Lunch not served Sat
Dinner not served Sun
✿ English & French **V** 30 seats ✳ Lunch £12-£18alc Dinner £12-£18alc Last lunch 2pm Last dinner 9.30pm ✈ nc10yrs
Credit Cards [1] [2] [3] [5]

---

### SUTTON BENGER Wiltshire Map **03** ST97

#### ★★★55% **Bell House**

SN15 4RH ☎Seagry(0249)720401
RS 25 Dec pm

*Set in a pretty village, yet only a few miles from the M4, this friendly hotel includes some areas which date back 500 years; bedrooms in a variety of sizes are individually decorated in traditional style, the Carriage Bar boasts a handsome mahogany bar, and the restaurant provides an Olde English speciality choice in addition to its more continental range of dishes.*
12⇌✿Annexe2⇌✿(2fb)1 ⊞ CTV in all bedrooms ® **T** ✳
sB&B⇌✿£44.50-£50.50 dB&B⇌✿£68-£80.50 Continental breakfast ⊟
40P ✿ CFA

**S**

♀ International **V** ✤ ✔ ✳ Lunch £9.50-£18.50alc Dinner £9.50-£18.50alc Last dinner 10.30pm
Credit Cards ① ② ③ ⑤

---

**SUTTON COLDFIELD** West Midlands Map **07** SP19

★★★★ ❀❀74% **New Hall**
Walmley Rd B76 8QX (Mount Charlotte (TS))(Small Luxury Hotels) ☎021-378 2442 Telex no 333580 FAX 021-378 4637
*Reputedly the oldest fully moated manor house in England, New Hall's history dates back to the 13th century. The hotel, although close to Birmingham, is surrounded by 26 acres of woodland and garden and is very comfortably appointed, a particular feature being the majestic Great Hall, now the dining room, where the menus, devised by the new chef, Glen Purcell, are already proving popular. The range of services offered is extensive and traditional, ably supervised by Caroline and Ian Parkes, who manage the hotel superbly.*
64⇌🏠2⊠ CTV in all bedrooms **T** (room only) 🛏
《 80P ❀ croquet archery
♀ International **V** ✤ ⬛ ✔
Credit Cards ① ② ③ ④ ⑤

★★★★55% **Penns Hall**
Penns Ln, Walmley B76 8LH (Jarvis) ☎021-351 3111
Telex no 335789 FAX 021-313 1297
*Just south of the town, the original house dates from the 17th century but is now considerably extended to include a very good leisure centre. The facilities are popular with the locals, and this is also a conference venue.*
114⇌🏠✔in 13 bedrooms CTV in all bedrooms ® **T** (room only) 🛏
Lift 《 500P ❀ CFA ⬛ (heated) ⤨ squash snooker sauna solarium gymnasium steam & beauty room childrens play area
♫ *xmas*
♀ French & Italian **V** ✤ ⬛ ✳ Lunch fr£18 High tea fr£5 Dinner fr£19 Last dinner 10pm
Credit Cards ① ② ③ ④ ⑤

★★★ 67% **Moor Hall**
Moor Hall Dr, Four Oaks B75 6LN (Best Western)
☎021-308 3751 Telex no 335127 FAX 021-308 8974
*A privately owned hotel in a pleasant residential area overlooking the adjacent golf course. The executive rooms are very spacious and comfortable and the majority of the standard rooms have now been refurbished. The health and fitness centre provides a wide range of facilities including a swimming pool, gymnasium and treatment rooms. For eating, Jakes Winer/Diner for an informal atmosphere, or the French restaurant where service is efficient and hospitable.*
75⇌🏠(3fb)3⊠✔in 5 bedrooms CTV in all bedrooms ® **T** ✳
sB&B⇌🏠£77-£90 dB&B⇌🏠£87-£105 🛏
Lift 《 180P ❀ CFA ⬛ (heated) sauna solarium gymnasium
*xmas*
♀ International **V** ✤ ⬛ ✳ Lunch £8-£10 Dinner £17.50-£19.50 Last dinner 10.30pm
Credit Cards ① ② ③ ④ ⑤

★★★ 60% **Sutton Court**
60-66 Lichfield Rd B74 2NA (Consort) ☎021-355 6071
Telex no 334175 FAX 021-355 0083
*This popular privately run hotel in an extended Victorian mansion, with easy access to motorway networks, local golf courses and Birmingham town centre, has very well equipped bedrooms throughout, although some are less spacious than others. The restaurant offers an imaginative choice of dishes and service is professional and helpful.*
56⇌🏠Annexe8⇌🏠(9fb)1⊠✔in 13 bedrooms CTV in all bedrooms ® **T** S% sB&B⇌🏠£41-£77 dB&B⇌🏠£53-£89 🛏
《 90P CFA *xmas*
♀ International **V** ✤ ⬛ ✔ S% Lunch fr£9.95&alc Dinner fr£15.50&alc Last dinner 10pm

Credit Cards ① ② ③ ④ ⑤ ⓔ

See advertisement also under **BIRMINGHAM (NATIONAL EXHIBITION CENTRE)**
See advertisement on page 677

★★ 63% **Berni Royal**
High St B72 1UD (Chef & Brewer) ☎021-355 8222
FAX 021-355 1837
*Dating from the 19th century this centrally situated hotel was once the home of photographer William Morris Grundy. The accommodation has been modernised with attractive floral décor, pine furnishings and excellent facilities.There are two bars and a popular Berni restaurant.*
22⇌🏠(3fb) CTV in all bedrooms ® **T** ✖ (ex guide dogs)
sB&B⇌🏠£50-£56 dB&B⇌🏠£67 🛏
《 80P CFA
♀ International **V** ✤ ⬛ ✔ Bar Lunch £2.95-£5.50alc
Credit Cards ① ② ③ ⑤

★★ 60% **The Lady Windsor**
17 Anchorage Rd B74 2PJ ☎021-354 5181 FAX 021-355 0095
*A commercial hotel on a busy residential road on the edge of town, with an attractive restaurant overlooking the rear gardens. Bedrooms vary considerably in style and size, from well furnished new rooms to quite compact and modest older rooms.*
26⇌🏠(2fb)2⊠ CTV in all bedrooms ® **T** ✖ S%
sB&B⇌🏠£38-£45 dB&B⇌🏠£55-£65 🛏
《 CTV 46P ❀ CFA *xmas*
♀ British & Continental **V** ✤ ⬛ S% Lunch fr£10.95 Dinner fr£10.95&alc Last dinner 9.30pm
Credit Cards ① ② ③

For key to symbols in English see the bookmark.

**S**

# Sutton Coldfield - Swallowfield

## ⌂Forte Travelodge
Boldmere Rd B73 5UP (2m S, on B4142) (Forte)
☎Central Res (0800) 850950

*Well equipped, value-for-money accommodation is provided at this Travelodge on the B4142, 2 miles from Sutton Coldfield. The M6 is only 4 miles away and Birmingham is a 6-mile drive. The adjacent Harvester Restaurant opens for breakfast, lunch and dinner.*

32⇔🛏(32fb) CTV in all bedrooms ® sB⇔🛏£29.95
dB⇔🛏£29.95 (room only)
《 32P 🚗
Credit Cards 1 2 3

## SUTTON IN THE ELMS Leicestershire Map 04 SP59

### ★★63% *Mill On The Soar*
Coventry Rd LE9 6QD ☎Hinckley(0455)282419
*A pleasant country inn with a purpose-built annexe housing well-equipped modern bedrooms. Its facilities include a children's playground and a rare breeds farm. It is within easy reach of the M1 and the M69.*

20⇔🛏(10fb) CTV in all bedrooms ® T
200P ❀ ♪
V ♥ ⌑ Last dinner 10pm
Credit Cards 1 2 3 5

## SUTTON ON SEA Lincolnshire Map 09 TF58

### ★★65% **Grange & Links**
Sea Ln, Sandilands LN12 2RA ☎(0507)441334
FAX (0507) 443033

*The Grange is situated within a few minutes' walk of the beach, or the hotel's own golf course. The range of public rooms is now quite varied, there is an attractive large restaurant, a bar, lounge areas with comfortable seating, and additional conference and meeting rooms. Open fires are lit in winter months. Accommodation is on 3 levels, new rooms are well equipped while old rooms are more traditionally furnished.*

23⇔🛏(9fb)1🛏 CTV in all bedrooms ® T ✳ sB&B⇔🛏fr£50
dB&B⇔🛏fr£65 🍴
《 CTV 60P ❀ CFA ▶ 18 ♪ (hard) snooker croquet bowls
putting *xmas*
♡ French V ♥ ✳ Sunday Lunch fr£11.50 Dinner fr£15alc Last
dinner 8.30pm
Credit Cards 1 2 3 5

## SUTTON SCOTNEY Hampshire Map 04 SU43 ◎

### ⌂Forte Travelodge (South)
A34 Trunk Rd Southside SO21 3JY (on A34 southside) (Forte)
☎Winchester(0962)760779 Central Res (0800) 850950

*Excellent value-for-money accommodation, including one room designed specifically for the disabled, is provided in a purpose-built, single-storey, T-shaped building which stands well back from the A34; guests can eat in the adjoining Little Chef restaurant and coffee shop.*

40⇔🛏(40fb) CTV in all bedrooms ® sB⇔🛏£29.95
dB⇔🛏£29.95 (room only)
《 40P 🚗
♡ Mainly grills
Credit Cards 1 2 3

### ⌂Forte Travelodge (North)
SO21 3JY (on A34 northside) (Forte)
☎Winchester(0962)761016 Central Res (0800) 850950

*Excellent value budget-price accommodation is provided in a purpose-built, single storey block which stands adjacent to the Welcome Break Granary Food operation.*

31⇔🛏(31fb) CTV in all bedrooms ® sB⇔🛏£29.95
dB⇔🛏£29.95 (room only)
《 31P 🚗
Credit Cards 1 2 3

## SUTTON UPON DERWENT Humberside Map 08 SE74

### ★★63% **Old Rectory**
YO4 5BX ☎York(0904)608548

*A former rectory in which guests can enjoy peace and quiet while being looked after by the friendly owners and their staff. Freshly prepared, straightforward cooking is much appreciated by the guests.*

6rm(2🛏)(2fb) CTV in all bedrooms ® sB&B£30-£40
dB&B£44-£48 dB&B🛏£48-£50 🍴
50P 🚗 ❀
♥ ✳
Credit Cards 1

## SWAFFHAM Norfolk Map 05 TF80

### ★★★❀61% **George**
Station Rd PE37 7LJ (Consort) ☎(0760)721238
FAX (0760) 725333

*Set adjacent to the Market Place, its Georgian façade giving way to a modern and comfortable hotel, the George is owned and managed by the Collins family who work very hard to provide a good level of service, cheerfully assisted by their small staff. The bedrooms are due for refurbishment, although they are well maintained. There is a choice of bar meals, table d'hôte and à la carte, and the mainly English dishes are competently prepared from good fresh produce. Imaginative use is made of herbs to brighten and to add depth, in carrot and coriander soup, for example, followed by pigeon breast served pink accompanied by a honey based sauce, with treacle tart and custard to finish.*

27rm(24⇔🛏)(1fb)1🛏 CTV in all bedrooms ® T
sB&B⇔🛏£45-£55 dB&B⇔🛏£59-£69 🍴
《 100P CFA *xmas*
♡ English & French V ♥ ⌑ Lunch £7.50-£14.50&alc High tea
£2-£7.50&alc Dinner £7.50-£14.50&alc Last dinner 9.30pm
Credit Cards 1 2 3 4 5 £

### ★★69% **Grady's Country House**
Norwich Rd PE37 7QS ☎(0760)23355

*An attractive Georgian country house, family owned and run to provide cheerful hospitality and efficient service, stands in its own grounds a few minutes' walk from the market place. Accommodation is provided in particularly clean and well maintained bedrooms with a good level of facilities, public areas within the hotel include limited lounge seating, and there is an impressive conference/banqueting annexe.*

12⇔🛏(1fb)1🛏 CTV in all bedrooms ® T sB&B⇔🛏£40
dB&B⇔🛏£50 🍴
《 70P CFA ♪ *xmas*
♡ English & French V ♥ ⌑ Lunch £15.95&alc Dinner
£15.95&alc Last dinner 9.30pm
Credit Cards 1 3

## SWALLOWFIELD Berkshire Map 04 SU76

### ★★63% *The Mill House*
RG7 1PY ☎Reading(0734)883124 Telex no 847423
*This pleasant Georgian building with a garden running beside the River Loddon has comfortable well equipped bedrooms of varying size. Downstairs is a high-ceilinged lounge bar, and the restaurant menu offers a wide choice.*

10⇔🛏(2fb)1🛏 CTV in all bedrooms ®
40P 🚗 ❀ ♪
♡ French V ♥ ⌑ Last dinner 10pm
Credit Cards 1 2 3 5

Red star hotels are each
highlighted by a pink
tinted panel.

676

SWANAGE Dorset Map **04** SZ07

★★★65% **Grand**

Burlington Rd BH19 1LU (Best Western) ☎(0929)423353
FAX (0929) 427068

*The Grand is in a lovely cliff-top location with steps down from the garden to a private beach. Newly decorated public rooms are smart and comfortable, and the dining room offers a wide choice of fresh food. Bedrooms are light and airy, with distinctive modern furniture, and most have recently been redecorated. There is a pleasantly relaxed holiday atmosphere and a live pianist plays some evenings.*

30⇄🏠(5fb)1🖳 CTV in all bedrooms ® T sB&B⇄🏠£41-£46 dB&B⇄🏠£82-£92 🅿

Lift ℂ15P ✿ 🖂 (heated) ♪ sauna solarium gymnasium spa bath table tennis pool table ♫ *xmas*

♡ English & French V ✿ 𝒟 ⅙ ✱ Lunch £9-£16alc Dinner £12.95-£13.95&alc Last dinner 9.30pm

Credit Cards ①②③⑤ⓕ

**See advertisement on page 679**

★★★60% **The Pines**

Burlington Rd BH19 1LT ☎(0929)425211 Telex no 418297 FAX (0929) 422075

*Set on a clifftop giving excellent views, this welcoming personally run holiday hotel provides modestly furnished but generally good sized bedrooms with modern facilities, including several family suites. The lounge and bar are comfortable and the dining room provides an interesting menu of home-cooked dishes.*

51rm(49⇄🏠)(26fb) CTV in all bedrooms ® T ✱ sB&B£37-£42 sB&B⇄🏠£37-£42 dB&B£74-£84 dB&B⇄🏠£74-£84 🅿

Lift ℂ60P 🚗 ✿ ♨ *xmas*

♡ Continental V ✿ 𝒟 ✱ Lunch fr£9.50 Dinner fr£16.85 Last dinner 9pm

Credit Cards ①③

SWANICK

See **Alfreton**

SWANSEA West Glamorgan Map **03** SS69 ◉

See also **Langland Bay** and **Mumbles**

★★★★59% **Forte Crest**

The Kingsway Circle SA1 5LS (Forte Hotels) ☎(0792)651074 Telex no 48309 FAX (0792) 456044

*Formerly the Dragon, this hotel has re-opened with a new name after nearly 2 years of refurbishment. The building is modern, with shops around its base, and is in the heart of the city centre. Some bedrooms are a little compact but all are well equipped and comfortable. The good size swimming pool and gym are attractive added features.*

99⇄🏠(12fb)⅙in 64 bedrooms CTV in all bedrooms ® T ✱ sB⇄🏠fr£59.50 dB⇄🏠£69.50-£79.50 (room only) 🅿

Lift ℂ40P CFA 🖂 (heated) sauna solarium gymnasium *xmas*

♡ International V ✿ 𝒟 ⅙ ✱ Lunch £10.50-£12.50&alc High tea fr£5.25 Dinner fr£16.50&alc Last dinner 10.30pm

Credit Cards ①②③⑤

★★★63% **Fforest**

Pontardulais Rd, Fforestfach SA5 4BA (on A483 1.5m S of M4 junc 47) (Lansbury) ☎(0792)588711 Telex no 48105 FAX (0792) 586219

*Conveniently situated about a mile on the Swansea side of the M4's junction 47, this popular commercial hotel offers a good modern accommodation block, comfortable bars and public rooms and extensive function facilities.*

34⇄🏠in 4 bedrooms CTV in all bedrooms ® T ✈ (ex guide dogs) sB&B⇄🏠£66 dB&B⇄🏠£78 🅿

ℂ CTV 100P CFA sauna solarium

♡ English & French V ✿ 𝒟 ⅙ ✱ Lunch £8.50-£8.75&alc Dinner £12.95&alc Last dinner 10.30pm

Credit Cards ①②③⑤

**S**

## Swansea

### ★★★ 58% Dolphin
Whitewalls SA1 3AB ☎(0792)650011 Telex no 48128
FAX (0792) 642871

*A busy commercial hotel in the centre of the city, with free parking in a local car park. There is a popular coffee lounge at street level, with bars and other public rooms on the first floor. Bedrooms are currently being upgraded and the extensive fuction suites are also to be improved. A good range of bar food is available and there is a choice of a fixed price menu or full à la carte in the attractive restaurant.*

65⇌🛏(5fb) CTV in all bedrooms ® T sB⇌🛏£49.50-£55 dB⇌🛏£59.50-£65 (room only) ⌸
Lift ( 🥢 CFA
♀ English & Continental V ♥ 🍷 ✱ Lunch fr£5.95 High tea fr£4.50 Dinner fr£12.50 Last dinner 9.30pm
Credit Cards ① ② ③ ⑤ ⓔ

### ★★ ⊛71% Beaumont
72 Walter Rd SA1 4QA ☎(0792)643956 FAX (0792) 643044

*Situated between the city centre and the uplands area this is a well-run commercial and family hotel. Public areas are comfortable and relaxing, the food is good and the staff very friendly. Bedrooms vary in size, all are well furnished and equipped.*

17⇌🛏1🚪⅍in 1 bedroom CTV in all bedrooms ® T ✱ sB&B⇌🛏£47.50-£58 dB&B⇌🛏£59.50-£80
10P 🚲
♀ Welsh, French & Italian V ♥ 🍷 ✱ Dinner £9.75-£26alc Last dinner 9.30pm
Credit Cards ① ② ③ ⑤

### ★★ 65% Nicholaston House
Nicholaston SA3 2HL ☎(0792)371317
(For full entry see Penmaen)

### ★★ 62% Oak Tree Parc
Birchgrove Rd SA7 9JR ☎Skewen(0792)817781
FAX (0792) 814542
(For full entry see Birchgrove)

### ★ 73% Windsor Lodge
Mount Pleasant SA1 6EG ☎(0792)642158 & 652744
FAX (0792) 648996
Closed 25-26 Dec

*An attractive Georgian house, close to the town centre and very popular with a business clientele, features attractive bedrooms which, though on the small side, are all well equipped with modern facilities. The cosy restaurant provides a good choice of food, there is a comfortable lounge, and friendly staff offer help throughout.*

19rm(11⇌4🛏) CTV in all bedrooms ® T sB&B£35-£45 sB&B⇌🛏£45 dB&B£45-£56 dB&B⇌🛏£56 ⌸
25P 1🚗 (£2) 🚲 sauna
♀ English & French V ♥ Lunch £10-£16.50 High tea £2.50-£6.50 Dinner £12-£18 Last dinner 9.30pm
Credit Cards ① ② ③ ⑤ ⓔ

### ★ 65% Parkway
253 Gower Rd, Sketty SA2 9JL ☎(0792)201632
FAX (0792) 201839
Closed 25 Dec-1 Jan

*Situated on Gower Road in a residential suburb, this extended house offers attractive open-plan public areas and modern well-equipped bedrooms. Mr and Mrs Wearing and their staff provide friendly service.*

15🛏 CTV in all bedrooms ® T ✱ sB&B🛏£35 dB&B🛏£45 ⌸
CTV 16P 🚲 ⌐ games room
✱ Dinner £7.50&alc Last dinner 8pm
Credit Cards ① ② ③ ⑤ ⓔ

### ⊛✕Keenans
82 St Helens Rd SA1 4BQ ☎(0792)644111

*A Best New Restaurant award winner in this year's guide, this small, attractive and comfortable restaurant, situated near City Hall and the St Helens Rugby and Cricket Ground, is run by Chris Keenan, who provides carefully produced dishes featuring*

→

# At the Gateway to the Gower.

15 bedrooms all with en-suite shower/wc, tea/coffee trays, TV, radio, telephone. Licensed bar, coffee lounge, TV room. Private car parking.

Proprietors Bruce & Heather Wearing.

## PARKWAY HOTEL
**253, Gower Road, Sketty, Swansea SA2 9JL**
Tel: Swansea (0792) 201632
Fax No: (0792) 201839
**OPEN ALL YEAR**

## LANGLAND COURT HOTEL
**LANGLAND COURT ROAD
LANGLAND, SWANSEA SA3 4TD
TELEPHONE: (0792) 361545
Fax: (0792) 362302**

A delightful Tudor-style country house in its own grounds overlooking Langland Bay. Oak-panelled entrance hall, restaurant, galleried staircase. Cosy lounges; characterful 'Polly's wine bar' with log fires. Superb beaches and scenery. International and local cuisine. Honeymoon suites. Award winning.

AA ★ ★

*Prices include full breakfast.*

**"THE COUNTRY HOUSE HOTEL BY THE SEA"**

S

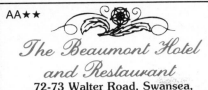

*interesting combinations of flavour, accompanied by a well chosen wine list. Presentation is most attractive and friendly staff offer attentive service. (See colour feature on p39.)*
Closed Sun, Mon & 24 Dec-2 Jan Lunch not served Sat
♀ Welsh & French **V** 26 seats Last lunch 2pm Last dinner 10pm ⨏
Credit Cards ①③

---

### SWANWICK Hampshire Map **04** SU50

❋ ✕ ✕ **Yew Tree Farm Restaurant**
152 Botley Rd SO3 7BU ☎Locks Heath(0489)577291
*A handsome Georgian house has been converted to provide an interesting restaurant with three separate dining areas. Priding itself on specialising in seasonal fish and game dishes, it features a lunchtime table d'hôte menu which, though not extensive, includes, for example, red mullet with a shrimp sauce and Dover sole with a cream, ginger and crab-flavoured sauce. The wine list is chosen to complement these specialities, and professional but friendly and relaxed service creates a pleasant atmosphere.*
Closed Mon & 1st 2 wks Jan Lunch not served Sat
Dinner not served Sun
♀ English & French **V** 40 seats ✻ Lunch £10.95-£13.50 Dinner £18.50-£21.50 Last lunch 2pm Last dinner 10pm 30 P ⨏
Credit Cards ①②③

---

### SWAVESEY Cambridgeshire Map **04** TL36

○**Forte Travelodge**
A604 Cambridge Rd(Forte) ☎Central Res (0800) 850950
Open
40⇨🈺

---

### SWAY Hampshire Map **04** SZ29

★★ ❋❋❋78% **Gordleton Mill**
Silver St SO41 6DJ ☎Lymington(0590)682219
FAX (0590) 683073
Closed 7-21 Jan
*An old mill house beautifully situated by the mill pond with landscaped gardens, pretty bridges and ducks. Recently renovated and redecorated, the hotel is one of our 'Best Newcomers' this year. There are 2 lounges (one no-smoking) with comfortable furniture and relaxing décor. The restaurant, Le Provence, is a great attraction. It is a fine room, Provence style, with a white wooden ceiling, paved and tiled floor and wrought iron light fittings, and a worthy setting for the superb cooking of Jean-Christophe Novelli. The menus, with French titles and good English descriptions, change regularly depending on daily purchasing. The dishes are prettily presented without irritating fuss, and they are sophisticated with various flavours and ideas working well together, pungent saucing and good technical skills (bread, pastry, petits fours). The French cuisine is a mix of classic (home smoked salmon, pan-fried fillet of beef); more modern (lamb with goats cheese soufflé, tartare of trout and cucumber); and regional (pigs trotter with ox tongue and wild mushrooms, duck confit). Excellent. The service at all times is most professional, willing and friendly. There is a very good hotel in the making here. (See colour feature on p34.)*
7⇨🈺⨏in 4 bedrooms CTV in all bedrooms **T** ✻ ✻
sB&B⇨🈺£57-£100 dB&B⇨🈺£85-£120
🎰40P ⇔ ✻ nc7yrs
♀ French **V** ⊗ ⚏ ⨏✻ Lunch £12-£17&alc
Credit Cards ①②③

★★54% **White Rose**
Station Rd SO41 6BA (Exec Hotel) ☎Lymington(0590)682754
*This substantial, red-brick house with neat, carefully maintained grounds stands in a village near the heart of the New Forest. Bedrooms are plain, functional and well equipped, while an attractive bar serving value for money snacks is popular with locals as well as hotel residents.*

---

11rm(9⇨🈺)(2fb) CTV in all bedrooms Ⓡ **T** S10% sB&B£37 sB&B⇨🈺£45 dB&B£58 dB&B⇨🈺£74 🅱
Lift 50P ⇔ ✻ ⊇ *xmas*
**V** ⊗ ⚏ S10% Lunch £7.50-£10&alc Dinner £8.50-£12.50&alc Last dinner 9pm
Credit Cards ①②③ⓔ

---

### SWINDON Wiltshire Map **04** SU18 ⊙

See also **Inglesham**

★★★★ ❋72% **Blunsdon House Hotel & Leisure Club**
Blunsdon SN2 4AD (3m N off A419) (Best Western)
☎(0793)721701 Telex no 444491 FAX (0793) 721056
*One of our 1991/1992 'Courtesy and Care' award winners, this four-star hotel whose many different facilities appeal to a variety of guests provides fine settings for an enjoyable meal in the smartly appointed Ridge Restaurant and comfortable, panelled Zan's lounge bar. Traditional luxuries like smoked salmon, Chateaubriand and Crêpes Suzette Flambées are balanced by such dishes in the lighter modern style as calves' liver salad with sherry vinegar dressing and turbot imaginatively garnished with a roulade of cabbage and seaweed and a fromage frais sauce; there is a trolley of cream-based desserts and British farmhouse wine list; service is extremely friendly, professional and attentive. (See colour feature on p15.)*
88⇨🈺(13fb)5🎰 CTV in all bedrooms Ⓡ **T** ✻ (ex guide dogs)
sB&B⇨🈺£90-£97.50 dB&B⇨🈺£100-£107.50 🅱
Lift ℂ 300P ✻ CFA 🏊 (heated) ♪ (hard) squash snooker sauna solarium gymnasium spa pool skittles beauty therapy *xmas*
♀ English & French **V** ⊗ ⚏ Lunch £12.50&alc Dinner £12.50&alc Last dinner 10pm
Credit Cards ①②③⑤ⓔ

★★★★61% **Holiday Inn**
Piper's Way SN3 1SH (Holiday Inns) ☎(0793)512121
Telex no 445789 FAX (0793) 513114
*This is a modern, purpose-built hotel, attractively designed, and occupying a convenient site on the edge of town. The public areas are spacious and very well maintained, with an impressive leisure complex, whilst the comfortable bedrooms are equipped to the highest standards. The young staff provide a friendly style of service that will prove popular with the business guest.*
158⇨🈺(48fb)⨏in 20 bedrooms CTV in all bedrooms Ⓡ **T** ✻
sB⇨🈺£60-£170 dB⇨🈺£60-£180 (room only) 🅱
Lift ℂ 190P ✻ CFA 🏊 (heated) ♪ (hard) squash sauna solarium gymnasium Turkish steam bath ♫ *xmas*
♀ English & Continental **V** ⊗ ⚏ ✻ ✻ Lunch £11.50-£14.25&alc Dinner fr£16.50&alc Last dinner 10.15pm
Credit Cards ①②③④⑤

★★★ ❋❋73% **Chiseldon House**
New Rd, Chiseldon SN4 0NE ☎(0793)741010
FAX (0793) 741059
20⇨🈺2🎰 CTV in all bedrooms Ⓡ **T** ✻ (ex guide dogs) ✻
sB&B⇨🈺£60-£75 dB&B⇨🈺£80-£120 🅱
ℂ 35P ⇔ ✻ ⊇ (heated) *xmas*
**V** ⊗ ⚏ ✻⨏ Lunch £14.50 Dinner £21.50&alc Last dinner 10pm
Credit Cards ①②③⑤

★★★64% **Forte Posthouse**
Marlborough Rd SN3 6AQ (Forte Hotels) ☎(0793)524601
Telex no 444464 FAX (0793) 512887
*Conveniently situated close to the town centre and motorway links, this modern purpose-built hotel with good leisure facilities has undergone recent upgrading. Comfortable bedrooms are equipped with modern facilities and improved public areas that include a restaurant serving table d'hôte and à la carte menus and a range of conference suites.*
100⇨🈺(24fb)⨏in 50 bedrooms CTV in all bedrooms Ⓡ **T** ✻
sB⇨🈺£39.50-£49.50 dB⇨🈺£39.50-£49.50 (room only) 🅱

℄ 200P ❖ CFA ▭ (heated) sauna solarium gymnasium jacuzzi
*xmas*
♀ English & Continental **V** ♥ ◻ ✂ ✳ Lunch fr£9.50&alc
Dinner fr£13.95&alc Last dinner 10.30pm
Credit Cards [1] [2] [3] [5]

### ★★★ 62%, Wiltshire

Fleming Way SN1 1TN (Mount Charlotte (TS)) ☎(0793)528282
Telex no 444250 FAX (0793) 541283
*A purpose-built hotel in the town centre with complimentary car
parking facilities in an adjacent multi-storey car park. Recent
refurbishment has resulted in comfortable bedrooms with a high
standard of furnishings, similar good work is planned for the public
areas. The hotel is popular with commercial guests.*
93⇌🛏 CTV in all bedrooms ® **T** (room only) 🛏
Lift ℄ 🎜 *xmas*
♀ English & French **V** ♥ ◻
Credit Cards [1] [2] [3] [5]

### ★★★ 60%, Forte Crest

Oxford Rd, Stratton St Margaret SN3 4TL (3m NE A420) (Forte
Hotels) ☎(0793)831333 Telex no 444456 FAX (0793) 831401
*Situated outside the town centre with easy access to the M4, this
hotel is geared to business needs, with extensive parking and
conference facilities, a wide range of well equipped bedrooms and
modern, open-plan public areas. The restaurant offers a choice of
menus including vegetarian and diabetic.*
94⇌🛏(13fb)✂in 23 bedrooms CTV in all bedrooms ® **T** ✳
sB⇌🛏£77-£92 dB⇌🛏£90-£105 (room only) 🛏
℄ 150P ❖ CFA pool table
♀ European **V** ♥ ◻ ✂ ✳ Lunch £13.50&alc Dinner
£16.95&alc Last dinner 10pm
Credit Cards [1] [2] [3] [4] [5]

### ★★★ 57%, *The South Marston Hotel & Country Club*

Sandy Ln, South Marston SN3 4SL ☎(0793)827777
Telex no 444634 FAX (0793) 827879
*In the quiet village of South Marston but convenient for motorway
links and only 4 miles from Swindon centre, this hotel has various
conference rooms and a large, locally popular leisure complex with
a bar/coffee lounge sometimes used for discos. Bright modern
bedrooms of reasonable size are situated in an adjacent block.*
40⇌🛏(4fb) CTV in all bedrooms ® **T**
℄ CTV 200P 1🐾 ❖ ▭ (heated) ⌁ (heated) squash snooker
sauna solarium gymnasium badminton spa bath table tennis ♧
♀ English & French **V** ✂ Last dinner 9.45pm
Credit Cards [1] [2] [3] [5]

### ★★★ 55%, Goddard Arms

High St, Old Town SN1 3EW (Forte Hotels) ☎(0793)692313
FAX (0793) 512984
*This pleasant hotel, set in 3 acres of grounds, comprises an ivy-clad
Cotswold stone building with two modern bedroom annexes.
Current refurbishment of the rather tired-looking bedrooms is
providing attractively decorated, fully modernised rooms. Public
areas have a hunting and fishing theme, including the Hunting
Lodge restaurant.*
18⇌🛏Annexe47⇌🛏✂in 9 bedrooms CTV in all bedrooms
® **T** ✳ sB⇌🛏fr£70 dB⇌🛏fr£85 (room only) 🛏
℄ 120P ❖ CFA *xmas*
**V** ♥ ◻ ✂ ✳ Sunday Lunch £9.15 Dinner £14.95 Last dinner
9.30pm
Credit Cards [1] [2] [3] [5]

### ○ De Vere

Shawridge Leisure Park, Whitehill Way(De Vere)
☎(0793)878785
Due to open Feb 1992
165⇌🛏

**S**

SYMONDS YAT (EAST) Hereford & Worcester
Map **03** SO51

★★65% **Royal**

HR9 6JL ☎Symonds Yat(0600)890238
Closed 28 Dec-30 Jan RS Nov-10 Jan & Feb

*This peaceful hotel in a superb location on the banks of the River Wye is ideally placed for touring the Wye Valley. The comfortable accommodation is equally suitable for tourists and business travellers alike.*

20⇨🔌4🛏 ® T 🛩 (ex guide dogs) ✳ sB&B⇨🔌£29.50
dB&B⇨🔌£59-£69 🍴

80P 🚲 ❋ CFA 🏊 sauna solarium abseiling canoeing clay pigeon shooting nc12yrs *xmas*

♀ British, French & Italian V ✿ 🗠 Sunday Lunch £9.25
Dinner fr£15.50&alc Last dinner 8.30pm

Credit Cards ①②③

---

SYMONDS YAT (WEST) Hereford & Worcester
Map **03** SO51

★★64% **Paddocks**

HR9 6BL ☎(0600)890246 FAX (0600) 890964

*This large hotel, set in one of the most popular and picturesque parts of the Wye Valley, but easily reached from the A40, offers well equipped accommodation which is equally suitable for tourists or business guests. Coach parties and users of the extensive function suite also increase its trade. Outdoor facilities include a tennis court and a pitch-and-putt course.*

26⇨🔌(2fb) CTV in all bedrooms ® T ✳ sB&B⇨🔌fr£33
dB&B⇨🔌fr£66 🍴

150P ❋ CFA 🎾 (hard) pitch & putt nc12yrs

♀ English & French V ✿ 🗠 Lunch £1.95-£17alc High tea £2.75-£9alc Last high tea 5pm

Credit Cards ①③⑤⑥

---

TAIN Highland *Ross & Cromarty* Map **14** NH78

★★★65% **Morangie House**

Morangie Rd IV19 1PY ☎(0862)892281 FAX (0862) 892872

*An imposing Victorian mansion standing in three acres of grounds to the north of Tain with uninterrupted views to Dornoch Firth. Bedrooms offer a high standard of comfort whatever their size, and décor is in keeping with the period. Public rooms retain their Victorian stained-glass windows.*

11⇨🔌(1fb)1🛏 CTV in all bedrooms ® T sB&B⇨🔌£35-£45
dB&B⇨🔌£60-£70 🍴

30P ❋ CFA

♀ Scottish & Continental V ✿ 🗠 ✳ Lunch £6.50-£15.50&alc High tea £5-£10&alc Dinner £5-£10&alc Last dinner 10pm

Credit Cards ①②③⑤

★★★56% *Royal*

High St IV19 1AB (Minotels) ☎(0862)892013
FAX (0862) 893450

*A family-run commercial hotel in the centre of town, also catering for tour groups. Public areas have been partially refurbished, though bedrooms remain somewhat functional.*

25rm(9⇨13🔌) CTV in all bedrooms ® T
10P 6🚗 (£2)

V ✿ 🗠 Last dinner 9pm

Credit Cards ①②③⑤

---

TALKE Staffordshire Map **07** SJ85

★★★64% **Granada**

North Links ST7 1UP (Granada) ☎(0782)777148
FAX (0782) 777162

*A brand new hotel situated where the A34 and A500 meet, convenient for junction 16 of the M6, complements particularly well equipped bedrooms by a small but very comfortable first-floor residents' lounge. Good function/meetings facilities are available,*

*and a wide choice of food is available in either the Silver Platter Restaurant or adjoining Corner Kitchen which is open all day for reasonably priced snacks and teas.*

62⇨🔌 CTV in all bedrooms ® 🛩 (ex guide dogs) S%
sB⇨🔌fr£40 dB⇨🔌fr£44 (room only) 🍴

🌙 50P ♿

✿ 🗠 Sunday Lunch fr£9.25 Dinner fr£12.50

**See advertisement under STOKE-ON-TRENT**

---

TALLAND BAY Cornwall & Isles of Scilly Map **02** SX25

★★★🏷72% **Talland Bay**

PL13 2JB (Inter-Hotels) ☎Polperro(0503)72667
FAX (0503) 72940
Closed 2 Jan-10 Feb

*Parts of this lovely old Cornish country house date back to the 16th century, and it is attractively set in mature gardens against a dramatic backdrop of sea and headland. Guests return year after year, however, not only for its location and comfortable surroundings, but also for the warmth of hospitality and prompt service. Individually styled bedrooms – many enjoying glorious sea views – combine traditional furnishings with modern facilities and comforts; spotlessly clean like the public areas, they are finished with such nice personal touches as flowers, complimentary sherry and quality toiletries. The cosy, south-facing sitting rooms open onto the terrace, providing an ideal venue for morning coffee or afternoon tea, while the restaurant's straightforward dinner menu features local seafood including Looe lobsters.*

20⇨🔌Annexe2⇨🔌(2fb)2🛏 CTV in all bedrooms ® T ✳
sB&B⇨🔌£51.50-£80 dB&B⇨🔌£102-£180 (incl dinner) 🍴

25P 🚲 ❋ CFA ⌛ (heated) sauna solarium croquet games room putting *xmas*

♀ English & French V ✿ 🗠 Sunday Lunch £7.75 High tea £6-£7 Dinner £18&alc Last dinner 9pm

Credit Cards ①②③⑤

★60% **Allhays Country House**

PL13 2JB ☎Polperro(0503)72434 FAX (0503) 72929
Closed 24 Dec-7 Jan

6rm(3⇨🔌)Annexe1⇨🔌(1fb)1🛏🚬in 1 bedroom CTV in all bedrooms ® T sB&B£26-£33 sB&B⇨🔌£33-£36 dB&B£52 dB&B⇨🔌£66-£72 🍴

12P 🚲 ❋ croquet putting nc10yrs

V ✿ 🗠 🚬 Bar Lunch £2-£8 Dinner £12.50&alc Last dinner 9pm

Credit Cards ①③

---

TALSARNAU Gwynedd Map **06** SH63

★★

★★🏵🏷 **MAES Y NEUADD**

LL47 6YA ( 2m SE on unclass rd off B4573) (Pride of Britain)
☎Harlech(0766)780200
FAX (0766) 780211
Closed 7-22 Dec

*It is now 10 years since the Slatter and Horsyall families combined their many talents into providing one of Wales' most treasured hotels. Older parts of the house date from around the 14th century, and can still be seen in the present bar, but additions from the 16th, 18th, and 20th centuries have been eclipsed by the recent work of joining the Coach House to the main building and creating a fine new reception and lounge. Bright yellow and fawn colours, fresh white paintwork and natural stone and wood are highlighted by fresh flowers and plants, complemented by paintings and prints. Bedrooms vary in size and shape, but all are comfortable. The more modest rooms in the main house have pine furnishings; the newer suites have very imaginative décor, with coordinated accessories and soft furnishings. Chef Andrew Taylor sets about his job with great diligence and considerable skill, and has recently turned his creative talents to ice creams, concocting unusual – and popular – flavours such as Madras curry and whole grain mustard. Set on its hillside overlooking Tremadoc Bay and Snowdonia, the two families and their charming staff have made this a relaxing and peaceful refuge.*

12⇌♪ Annexe4⇌♪ 1 ⊞ CTV in all bedrooms **T** sB&B⇌♪£43-£94 dB&B⇌♪£97-£136 ⊟

50P ⊕ ✲ croquet lawn nc7yrs *xmas*

**V** ♦ ☑ ✂ Lunch £12.50-£14.50 Dinner £24 Last dinner 9pm

Credit Cards [1] [2] [3] [5] Ⓔ

---

★★64% ***Tregwylan***

LL47 6YG ☎Penrhyndeudraeth(0766)770424

*This large Edwardian house commanding fine views over Cardigan Bay was acquired by the present owners some 20 years ago and converted into a small and welcoming family-run hotel. Comfortable bedrooms, most with en suite facilities, are equally suitable for holidaymakers and business people.*

10rm(8⇌♪)(3fb) CTV in all bedrooms ® ✗ (ex guide dogs)

CTV 20P ⊕ ✲

**V** ♦ ☑ Last dinner 8.30pm

Credit Cards [1] [3]

## TAL-Y-BONT (NEAR CONWY) Gwynedd Map **06** SH76

★★63% **Lodge**

LL32 8YX ☎Dolgarrog(049269)766 FAX (049269) 534

*This privately owned hotel is situated on the B5106, in the picturesque Conwy Valley, between Conwy and Betwys-y-Coed. The bedrooms are well equipped and are contained within a purpose-built annexe block.*

Annexe10⇌ CTV in all bedrooms ® ✱ sB&B⇌£30-£37.50 dB&B⇌£46-£50 ⊟

50P ✲ *xmas*

♀ British & French **V** ♦ ☑ ✂ ✱ Lunch fr£4.70&alc Dinner £13.50&alc Last dinner 9pm

Credit Cards [1] [3] Ⓔ

## TALYBONT-ON-USK Powys Map **03** SO12

★★67% ***Aberclydach House***

Aber LD3 7YS (2m SW) ☎(087487)361 FAX (087487) 436

*An elegant eighteenth-century house, set in a wooded valley within the Brecons National Park, has been carefully modernised to provide well equipped bedrooms and comfortable public areas; meals are of a high standard, and speciality activity holidays are available.*

11⇌♪ ✂in 4 bedrooms CTV in all bedrooms ® **T** ✗

CTV 14P ✲

**V** ♦ ☑ ✂ Last dinner 8.30pm

Credit Cards [1] [3]

## TAL-Y-LLYN Gwynedd Map **06** SH70

★★65% **Tyn-y-Cornel**

LL36 9AJ ☎Abergynolwyn(0654)782282 782223 FAX (0654) 782679

*Delightfully situated on the lake shore amid mountain scenery, this comfortable 19th-century hotel is popular with fishermen as well as business and holiday guests. It has well-equipped modern bedrooms and attractive public areas, plus some leisure facilities.*

6⇌♪ Annexe9⇌♪(2fb) CTV in all bedrooms ® **T**

60P 3⌂ ⊕ ✲ CFA ⌒(heated) ✓ sauna solarium mountain bikes & helmets for hire

♀ English & Continental **V** ♦ ☑ Last dinner 9.30pm

Credit Cards [1] [2] [3] [5]

---

★

★❀ **MINFFORDD**

Minffordd LL36 9AJ

☎Corris(0654)761665

Closed Jan-Feb RS Nov-Dec & Mar

*Once a 17th-century drover's inn, the Minffordd is in a delightful setting, nestled in the peaceful Dysynni Valley. This is a family-run hotel with Bernard Pickles, his wife and 2 sons, Jonathan and William, very much involved. Public areas are interestingly appointed and include a comfortable lounge, a small bar and a cosy, timbered dining room with a staircase at its centre. Bedrooms vary in size but are thoughtfully furnished and equipped, with many welcoming touches. Jonathan is responsible for the cooking which is straightforward and expertly prepared using as much fresh local produce as possible. His menu changes daily is is at a set price. Dishes might include fillet of smoked mackerel with horseradish sauce, various home-made soups such as Yorkshire mushroom soup and main dishes like wild rabbit casserole in white wine, or roast leg of Welsh lamb. The wine list is short, simple and reasonably priced.*

6⇌♪ ® **T** ✗ sB&B⇌♪£50-£59 dB&B⇌♪£80-£98 (incl dinner) ⊟

12P ⊕ ✲ nc3yrs *xmas*

→



T

♨ ⊬ Dinner £15.50-£16.50 Last dinner 8.30pm
Credit Cards 1 3 5

---

## TAMWORTH Staffordshire Map **07** SK20

⇧**Granada Lodge**
(A5/M42 junct 10) (Granada) ☎(0827)260123
FAX (0827) 260145
*A large lodge beside junction 10 of the M42 (the A5 intersection) offers well equipped bedrooms which can even boast limited room service.*
63⇄ৗ↑(10fb)⊬in 20 bedrooms CTV in all bedrooms ®
✖ (ex guide dogs) S% sB⇄৹↑fr£31 dB⇄৹↑fr£34 (room only)
🏥
⋘ 229P

---

## TANGUSDALE

See Barra, Isle of

---

## TAPLOW Buckinghamshire Map **04** SU98

★★★★★ ⊛⊛ 🏩 **CLIVEDEN**

SL6 0JF (Small Luxury
Hotels) ☎Maidenhead
(0628)668561
Telex no 846562
FAX (0628) 661837
*A magnificent stately home – once the family home of the Astors, and now owned by the National Trust who lease it to Blakeney Hotels – has been transformed to create some of the best accommodation in the country. Set amid almost 400 acres of woodland, parkland and formal gardens, with grounds running down to the Thames, it provides a wide range of leisure pursuits which includes a very fine indoor swimming pool and health centre. Individually styled and classically influenced bedrooms offer the highest levels of quality and comfort and are, for the most part, very spacious; gracious public areas are very opulent and comfortable, and the great hall and library together with smaller sitting rooms, are steeped in history. Fresh flowers are in every room. The simplicity of the main dining room and informal basement grill room is a refreshing contrast to the panelled Rococo breakfast room dating from the 18th century. Enjoyable meals are served in a formal atmosphere by very professional staff and are classical in style. Standards of service are excellent and unobtrusive to reflect the level of formality that the Management feel is appropriate. Ron Maxfield, the talented young chef, is now beginning to show skill and flair in his cooking producing exceptionally good soups and sauces. The menu changes seasonally and might include such dishes as lasagne of lobster with langoustine, tomato and truffle dressing; duck magret with Chinese spices or a dessert of hot mirabelle soufflé and liquorice ice cream; combinations which sound rather risky, but which our inspector found were handled with subtlety and skill and presented without fussiness. There is a splendid catalogue of wines with vintages, countries, growers, dessert wines and half bottles listed.*
25⇄৹↑Annexe6⇄ৗ↑2🛏⊬in 1 bedroom CTV in all
bedrooms **T** ✳ S% sB&B⇄ৗ↑fr£185 dB&B⇄ৗ↑fr£208
Continental breakfast 🏥
Lift ⋘ 30P 3�car 🚲 ✿ CFA 🏊 (heated) ⌿ (heated) ▶ 4 ◢
(hard) ♪ squash ∪ snooker sauna solarium gymnasium
indoor tennis turkish bath massage *xmas*

V ⊬ ✳ S% Lunch fr£27.50&alc Dinner fr£36alc Last
dinner 9.30pm
Credit Cards 1 2 3 4 5

---

## TARBERT

See Harris, Isle of

---

## TARBERT LOCH FYNE Strathclyde *Argyllshire*
Map **10** NR86

★★★61% **Stonefield Castle**
PA29 6YJ ☎Tarbert(0880)820836 FAX (0880) 820929
*This fine period mansion lies two miles north of Tarbert, in secluded wooded grounds on the shores of Loch Fynne. Views, particularly from the restaurant to the Isle of Arran are magnificent; and the gardens are renowned for their exotic trees and shrubs. Public rooms are spacious, some bedrooms are situated in a purpose-built wing.*
33rm(30⇄ৗ2↑)(4fb) CTV in all bedrooms ® **T** ✳
sB&B⇄ৗ↑fr£45.99 dB&B⇄ৗ↑fr£75.62 (incl dinner) 🏥
Lift ⋘ CTV 50P ✿ CFA ⌿ (heated) ♪ snooker sauna solarium
🐾 *xmas*
♨ ⊑ ⊬ Lunch £1.25-£10alc Dinner £22.50-£32.50 Last dinner
10pm
Credit Cards 1 2 3 5 £

★59% *West Loch*
PA29 6YF ☎Tarbert(08802)283
*This small, modest, roadside hotel is situated two miles south of Tarbert and is convenient for those crossing to or from Islay.*
7rm(2fb)
CTV 20P 🚲 ✿
🍴 International V ♨ ⊑ ⊬ Last dinner 8.30pm

---

## TARPORLEY Cheshire Map **07** SJ56

★★★69% **The Wild Boar**
Whitchurch Rd, Beeston CW6 9NW (2.5m S off A49) (Rank)
☎Bunbury(0829)260309 Telex no 61222 FAX (0829) 261081
*Located on the A49 about 3 miles south of Tarporley. A new building with good bedroom accommodation has been constructed looking out over the beautiful rolling countryside and blending perfectly with the striking mock-Tudor style of the elegant restaurant which adjoins. The restaurant itself is quickly earning favour for its high standard of cuisine.*
37⇄ৗ↑(19fb) CTV in all bedrooms ® **T** ✳ sB&B⇄ৗ↑£51-£74
dB&B⇄ৗ↑£72-£89 🏥
⋘ 70P ✿ CFA *xmas*
🍴 English & French V ♨ ⊑ ✳ Lunch £11.25-£12.50&alc
Dinner £16.50-£18.50&alc Last dinner 10pm
Credit Cards 1 2 3 5

★★ 🏩64% **The Willington Hall**
Willington CW6 0NB (3m NW off unclass rd linking A51 & A54)
☎Kelsall(0829)52321 FAX (0829) 52596
Closed 25 Dec
*An Elizabethan-style house in 17 acres of parkland and gardens surrounded by pastureland, views of which may be enjoyed from the dining room. Bar snacks are also available at lunch and at dinner.*
10⇄↑(1fb) CTV in all bedrooms ® **T** ✳ sB&B⇄ৗ↑£55
dB&B⇄ৗ↑£80
60P 🚗 🚲 ✿ ◢ (hard)
V Lunch £12-£13&alc Dinner £14.50-£25alc Last dinner
9.30pm
Credit Cards 1 3 5

---

A rosette means exceptional standards of cuisine.

TAUNTON Somerset Map **03** ST22 ⊙

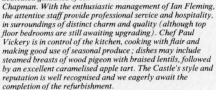

★★★❀❀ **CASTLE**

Castle Green TA1 1NF
(Small Luxury Hotels)
☎(0823)272671
FAX (0823) 336066

*It is very reassuring to
welcome back the Castle
Hotel, still under the
dedicated guidance of Kit
Chapman. With the enthusiastic management of Ian Fleming,
the attentive staff provide professional service and hospitality,
in surroundings of distinct charm and quality (although top
floor bedrooms are still awaiting upgrading). Chef Paul
Vickery is in control of the kitchen, cooking with flair and
making good use of seasonal produce; dishes may include
steamed breasts of wood pigeon with braised lentils, followed
by an excellent caramelised apple tart. The Castle's style and
reputation is well recognised and we eagerly await the
completion of the refurbishment.*

33⇆♠1🛏 CTV in all bedrooms T ✳ sB&B⇆♠£75-£145
dB&B⇆♠£99-£180 🄵

Lift ⦅ 30P 2🚗 (£5 per day) 🚭 ❅ CFA *xmas*

V ⊘ ♨ ✳ S% Lunch £13.90-£14.90&alc Dinner
£22.50&alc Last dinner 9pm

Credit Cards ① ② ③ ⑤ ⓔ

★★★64% **Forte Posthouse**
Deane Gate Av TA1 2UA (Forte Hotels) ☎(0823)332222
Telex no 46703 FAX (0823) 332266
*Situated by junction 25 of the M5, this hotel has comfortable well-
equipped modern bedrooms, arranged in wings around a small
lounge atrium. Vale Restaurant offers carvery and à la carte
menus, with a notable breakfast and starter buffet, served by
friendly waitresses. A mini-gym, function and conference rooms
are available.*
97⇆♠✂in 48 bedrooms CTV in all bedrooms ® T ✳
sB⇆♠£39.50-£49.50 dB⇆♠£39.50-£49.50 (room only) 🄵
Lift ⦅ 300P CFA sauna gymnasium *xmas*
🄰 English & Continental V ⊘ ♨ ✂ ✳ Lunch £10.95&alc
Dinner fr£13.95&alc Last dinner 10.30pm
Credit Cards ① ② ③ ⑤

★★★62% **Rumwell Manor**
Rumwell TA4 1EL ☎(0823)461902 FAX (0823) 254861
*This Georgian house, surrounded by its own grounds and enjoying
views across Somerset countryside towards the Blackdown Hills,
now offers 20 additional en suite bedrooms, all individually
decorated and furnished, in a recently added coach house annexe.
Lounge and bar are comfortable, the dining room serves both table
d'hôte and à la carte meals, and guests are warmly welcomed by
the resident proprietors and their friendly staff.*
10⇆♠(3fb)3🛏✂in 2 bedrooms CTV in all bedrooms ® T ✳
sB&B⇆♠£49.50-£54.50 dB&B⇆♠£65-£75 🄵
CTV 30P 🚭 ❅ ⌂
🄰 English & French V ⊘ ♨ ✂ ✳ Lunch fr£10.50 Dinner
fr£14.50&alc Last dinner 8.30pm
Credit Cards ① ② ③ ⑤ ⓔ

★★★56% **The County**
East St TA1 3LT (Forte Hotels) ☎(0823)337651
FAX (0823) 334517
*At the heart of the town centre, this large hotel with a busy
commercial trade has some very well equipped, attractively
refurbished bedrooms, while others remain more modest. The*
→

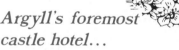

**T**

*restaurant is very popular with locals for its table d'hôte and small à la carte menus, including vegetarian dishes.*
66➔🛏️(4fb)2🛁 CTV in all bedrooms ® T ✱ sB➔🛏️fr£70 dB➔🛏️£85-£95 (room only) 🍴
Lift ℭ 110P CFA *xmas*
V ✿ ⌧ ✴ ✱ Lunch fr£9.50&alc Dinner fr£15.28&alc Last dinner 9.15pm
Credit Cards ① ② ③ ④ ⑤

### ★★64% Corner House
Park St TA1 4DQ ☎(0823)284683 & 272665 FAX (0823) 323464
*Conveniently situated in the town centre, the hotel is privately owned and run, has some modern, spacious bedrooms, a formal dining room and is popular with both business people and tourists.*
33rm(23➔4🛏️)(4fb) CTV in all bedrooms ® T
🏋️ (ex guide dogs) S% sB&Bfr£38 sB&B➔🛏️fr£54 dB&B➔🛏️fr£69.50 🍴
CTV 40P 2🚗 🚗 CFA
♀ English & French V ✿ ⌧ Lunch fr£10alc Dinner fr£15alc Last dinner 9.15pm
Credit Cards ① ③

### ★★64% Falcon
Henlade TA3 5DH (3m E A358) (Exec Hotel) ☎(0823)442502 FAX (0823) 442670
Closed 25 Dec
*This small owner-run hotel in a Victorian house with landscaped gardens, only a mile from junction 25 of the M5, has a friendly relaxed atmosphere. Comfortable bedrooms are equipped with many thoughtful extras and there is a cosy lounge and a restaurant serving well prepared dishes.*
11➔🛏️(2fb)1🛁 in 3 bedrooms CTV in all bedrooms ® T 🏋️
✱ sB&B➔🛏️£35-£45 dB&B➔🛏️£55-£60 🍴
25P 🚗 🚗 CFA ⚓
♀ International V ✿ ⌧ ✂ ✱ Bar Lunch fr£4.50 Dinner £12.50&alc Last dinner 9.30pm
Credit Cards ① ② ③

### TAUNTON DEANE MOTORWAY SERVICE AREA (M5)
Somerset Map **03** ST12 ⊘

🏠 **Roadchef Lodge**
Trull TA1 4BA ☎Taunton(0823)332228 FAX (0823) 338131
Closed 24-26 Dec
*Situated in a service area between junctions 25 and 26 of the southbound M5, this lodge offers excellent value for money, with well equipped comfortable bedrooms, all with en suite facilities. You can eat at the adjacent 24-hour cafeteria or Hickory's Restaurant over the motorway bridge.*
39➔🛏️ in 20 bedrooms CTV in all bedrooms ® T
🏋️ (ex guide dogs) ✱ sB➔🛏️£29 dB➔🛏️£35-£45 (room only)
ℭ 39P 🚗
V ✿ ⌧ ✂
Credit Cards ① ② ③ ④ ⑤

### TAVISTOCK Devon Map **02** SX47

#### ★★★60% The Bedford
Plymouth Rd PL19 8BB (Forte Hotels) ☎(0822)613221 FAX (0822)618034
*This castellated stone building near the town centre is currently undergoing substantial refurbishment, and the finished bedrooms are most comfortable and attractively decorated with smart modern bathrooms. Public areas include a spacious open plan lobby lounge and a redecorated lounge bar.*
31➔🛏️ in 11 bedrooms CTV in all bedrooms ® T ✱
sB➔🛏️£65 dB➔🛏️£80 (room only) 🍴
45P 3🚗 🚗 CFA *xmas*
V ✿ ⌧ ✂ ✱ S% Lunch £8.95&alc High tea £3.25 Dinner £14.95&alc Last dinner 9pm
Credit Cards ① ② ③ ④ ⑤

---

### TAYNUILT Strathclyde *Argyllshire* Map **10** NN03

#### ★★66% Brander Lodge
Bridge of Awe PA35 1HT (Consort) ☎(08662)243 & 225 FAX (08662) 273
*Small, comfortable family run Highland hotel with relaxing, friendly atmosphere.*
20➔🛏️(2fb) CTV in all bedrooms ® T sB&B➔🛏️£29.25-£40.75 dB&B➔🛏️£58.50-£63 🍴
100P 🌸 pool table *xmas*
♀ International V ✿ ⌧ Bar Lunch £6-£15alc Dinner £16-£18&alc Last dinner 8.30pm
Credit Cards ① ② ③ ⑤ ⓔ

#### ★★60% *Polfearn*
PA35 1JQ (Consort) ☎(08662)251
*Situated north of the village on the way to Loch Etive pier, this family-run hotel, with uninterrupted views of the loch and surrounding mountains, is also close to the River Awe. The dinner menu offers good value home cooking and there is also a good range of bar meals.*
16rm(2➔12🛏️)(2fb) ®
CTV 20P
V ✿ ⌧ ✂ Last dinner 9pm
Credit Cards ① ③

---

### TEANGUE
See Skye, Isle of

---

### TEES-SIDE AIRPORT Co Durham Map **08** NZ31

#### ★★★64% St George
Middleton St George DL2 1RH (Mount Charlotte (TS))
☎Darlington(0325)332631 Telex no 587623
FAX (0325) 333851
*Modern hotel within airport complex.*
59➔🛏️(2fb)1🛁 in 8 bedrooms CTV in all bedrooms ® T
ℭ 200P 20🚗 (£2.50 per day) 🌸 squash sauna solarium *xmas*
♀ English & French V ✿ ⌧ ✂
Credit Cards ① ② ③ ⑤

---

### TEIGNMOUTH Devon Map **03** SX97

#### ★★65% Ness House
Marine Dr, Shaldon TQ14 0HP ☎Shaldon(0626)873480 FAX (0626) 873486
*An attractive period house overlooking the bay, tastefully converted and extended to provide character accommodation with modern facilities. Some bedrooms have balconies and glorious views across the estuary to Teignmouth. Guests can enjoy a drink in the lounge bar while making their choice from the extensive à la carte or blackboard menus. Coffees, lunches and teas are very popular with non-residents in the summer season.*
7➔🛏️Annexe5rm(2fb)1🛁 CTV in all bedrooms ® T
🏋️ (ex guide dogs) sB&B£30-£45 sB&B➔🛏️£30-£45 dB&B£55-£70 dB&B➔🛏️£55-£70 🍴
20P 🚗 🌸
♀ French V ✿ ⌧ ✱ Lunch £15-£20alc
Credit Cards ① ② ③

#### ★63% Belvedere
Barnpark Rd TQ14 8PJ ☎(0626)774561
*A white Victorian villa in an elevated position overlooking the town's rooftops to the sea and hills beyond. Many of the traditionally furnished bedrooms enjoy this view, and all except one now have en suite facilities. Public areas include a comfortable lounge, with a coal fire for chilly evenings, a small bar and a well loved garden and patio.*
13rm(12➔5🛏️)(4fb) CTV in all bedrooms ® 🏋️
CTV 10P 1🚗 🌸
V ✿ ⌧
Credit Cards ① ③ ⓔ

★63% **Glenside**
Ringmoor Rd, Shaldon TQ14 0EP (1m S off A379) (Guestaccom)
☎Shaldon(0626)872448
Closed Nov & 3-4 wks during Feb or Mar
*Situated on the Shaldon to Newton Abbot road beside the Teign
Estuary, this well proportioned Georgian house offers comfortable
bedrooms, most with en suite facilites. A cosy bar and adjacent
lounge offers comfortable surroundings where the peaceful
atmosphere can be enjoyed. A small table d'hôte menu offers a
choice of home-cooked food.*
10rm(1⇨6ℝ)(1fb) CTV in all bedrooms Ⓡℝ sB&B£17.50-
£21.30 sB&B⇨ℝ£17.50-£21.30 dB&B£35-£42 dB&B⇨ℝ£35-
£42 Ɽ
10P ⌕
V Bar Lunch £5-£7 Dinner £10-£11 Last dinner 6.30pm

★58% **Bay**
Sea Front, 15 Powerham Ter TQ14 8BL ☎(0626)774123
Closed mid Nov-Mar (ex Xmas)
*A Georgian Grade II listed building opposite the tennis courts and
the seafront. Bedrooms are simply appointed and well equipped
with remote control colour TV, Radio 2, tea and coffee facilities.
Honest home cooking and lots of it is served in the lower ground
floor dining room. The hotel has its own compact car park.*
18rm(5⇨9ℝ)(5fb) CTV in all bedrooms Ⓡ ✳ sB&B£17.50-£21
sB&B⇨ℝ£19.50-£23 dB&B£35-£41 dB&B⇨ℝ£39-£46 Ⱶ
ℂ CTV 16P *xmas*
♡ English & Continental V ♥ ⍩
Credit Cards 1️⃣2️⃣3️⃣5️⃣£

---

TELFORD Shropshire Map **07** SJ60

★★★76% *Madeley Court*
TF7 5DW ☎(0952)680068 FAX (0952) 684275
*A house originating in medieval times, it has now been restored in
Elizabethan style, retaining such features as open fires, panelled
walls and a unique spiral oak staircase. A new accommodation
wing opened in 1991 supplements older, character bedrooms, and
there are 2 restaurants. David Spencer's modern cooking marries
imaginative sauces with good quality fish, meat and game in such
dishes as turbot with cucumber, cream and vermouth, or duck with
honey, ginger and sherry; the well balanced wine list features
many Bordeaux wines. The hotel is approached by a long driveway
off Castlefields Way, just outside Madeley town centre.*
16⇨ℝ CTV in all bedrooms Ⓡ T ✖ (ex guide dogs)
ℂ 110P ♪ ♫
V ♥ ⍩ ✔ Last dinner 10pm
Credit Cards 1️⃣2️⃣3️⃣5️⃣

★★★69% **Telford Moat House**
Forgegate, Telford Centre TF3 4NA (Queens Moat)
☎(0952)291291 Telex no 35588 FAX (0952) 292012
Closed 24 Dec-1 Jan (ex Xmas lunch & NY Eve)
*A modern hotel beside the shopping centre complements spacious,
well equipped rooms and good conference facilities by friendly,
helpful service from a smart staff.*
148⇨ℝ(8fb)✔in 3 bedrooms CTV in all bedrooms Ⓡ T ✳
sB&B⇨ℝ£74.25-£95.15 dB&B⇨ℝ£78.65-£115 Ⱶ
Lift ℂ CTV 300P CFA ⌧ (heated) sauna solarium gymnasium
games room jacuzzi pool table ♫
♡ English & French V ♥ ⍩ ✳ Lunch £10.95-£15.70&alc
Dinner fr£15.70&alc Last dinner 10pm
Credit Cards 1️⃣2️⃣3️⃣4️⃣5️⃣

★★★67% **Holiday Inn**
St Quentin Gate TF3 4EH (Holiday Inns Inc) ☎(0952)292500
Telex no 359126 FAX (0952) 291949
*A modern purpose built hotel close to the centre of Telford,
virtually next to the Racket and Exhibition centre. It has good
conference and function rooms, a business centre and a well
equipped leisure centre. Some bedrooms are somewhat cramped
with excess furniture.*

100⇨ℝ✖in 20 bedrooms CTV in all bedrooms Ⓡ T S10%
sB⇨ℝ£81-£90 dB⇨ℝ£93-£104 (room only) Ⱶ
Lift ℂ 120P CFA ⌧ (heated) ♬ (hard) squash snooker sauna
solarium gymnasium steam room whirlpool spa *xmas*
♡ English & French V ♥ ⍩ ✖ ✳ S10% Lunch £9.95-£12.50
Dinner £15.50-£16.75 Last dinner 10pm
Credit Cards 1️⃣2️⃣3️⃣4️⃣5️⃣

★★★66% **Buckatree Hall**
Wellington TF6 5AL (Best Western) ☎(0952)641821
Telex no 35701 FAX (0952) 247540
*Quite a transformation has occurred at this hotel which has
virtually doubled in size. A new wing of rooms has been built, all
non-smoking, plus new conference rooms and an elegant lounge
bar. Find the hotel by following the signs to Buckatree from
junction 7 of the M54.*
64⇨ℝ(4fb)✖in 7 bedrooms CTV in all bedrooms Ⓡ T
sB&B⇨ℝ£67-£82 dB&B⇨ℝ£77-£92 Ⱶ
Lift ℂ 80P ✿ CFA ♫ *xmas*
♡ International V ♥ ⍩ ✔ ✳ Lunch £10.95 Dinner £10.95&alc
Last dinner 10pm
Credit Cards 1️⃣2️⃣3️⃣5️⃣

**See advertisement on page 689**

★★★65% **Telford Hotel Golf & Country Club**
Great Hay Dr, Sutton Hill TF7 4DT (Queens Moat)
☎(0952)585642 Telex no 35481 FAX (0952) 586602
*This hotel is very popular for its sport and leisure amenities but
also offers facilities for the business person. Snacks are available
throughout the day and the restaurant, with fine views over
Ironbridge, offers a choice of menus.*
86⇨ℝ(4fb)✖in 14 bedrooms CTV in all bedrooms Ⓡ T ✳
sB&B⇨ℝ£74.50-£84.50 dB&B⇨ℝ£84-£94 Ⱶ
ℂ 200P ✿ CFA ⌧ (heated) ▶ 9 squash snooker sauna
solarium gymnasium steam room masseur *xmas*

→

T

♀ International **V** ♦ ⌐ ✻ S% Lunch £9.50-£11&alc Dinner fr£14.30&alc Last dinner 9.45pm
Credit Cards 1 2 3 4 5 ⓔ

★★★60% **Valley**
TF8 7DW ☎(0952)432247
*A Georgian house with lawns at the rear which merge with a park before reaching the banks of the River Severn. Beautiful decorative tiles adorn the hall which leads to Chez Maw restaurant. There is a choice of menus, including an interesting vegetarian selection.*
34➪♠2⊟ CTV in all bedrooms ® **T** ✻ (ex guide dogs) ✻ S%
sB&B➪♠£60-£65 dB&B➪♠£70-£75 ⊟
《100P ✿ CFA
♀ International **V** ♦ ⌐ ✻ Lunch £10-£14.75&alc High tea £4-£6 Dinner £12.75-£14.75&alc Last dinner 9.30pm
Credit Cards 1 2 3 ⓔ

★★65% **White House**
Wellington Rd, Muxton TF2 8NG (off A518) ☎(0952)604276
*This hotel has been extensively altered over the last 12 months and now offers well equipped bedrooms and smart public areas, particularly for the business person, along with 2 acres of lawns and gardens. Muxton is a small village just off the A518 Telford-Stafford road.*
30➪♠(4fb) CTV in all bedrooms ® **T** sB&B➪♠fr£50 dB&B£60 dB&B➪♠fr£60 ⊟
CTV 100P ✿
♀ English & French **V** ♦ ⌐ Lunch fr£8.50&alc Dinner fr£12.50&alc Last dinner 9.30pm
Credit Cards 1 2 3 ⓔ

★★56% **Falcon**
Hoylhead Road, Wellington TF1 2DD ☎(0952)255011
Closed Xmas RS Sun
*There is a fascinating history attached to this traditionally run family inn on the edge of Wellington, and its popular character bar has the advantage of a garden area that is ideal for children to play in.*
13rm(6➪♠)(1fb) CTV in all bedrooms ✻ sB&B£30-£35 sB&B➪♠£35-£41 dB&B£40-£45 dB&B➪♠£45-£50 ⊟
CTV 30P ⊞ nc2yrs
♀ English & Continental **V** ♦ Bar Lunch £1.50-£4.50alc Dinner £10-£15alc Last dinner 9pm
Credit Cards 1 3

★63% **Arleston Inn**
Arleston Ln, Wellington TF1 2LA ☎(0952)501881
*This small, privately owned inn is convenient for Telford and the M54. Accommodation is modern and well equipped, although some rooms are rather compact. Bar areas are cosy and a simply-appointed restaurant serves popular meals.*
6♠ CTV in all bedrooms ® ✻ (ex guide dogs)
40P ✿
**V** Last dinner 10pm
Credit Cards 1 3

⇧**Forte Travelodge**
New Whitchurch Rd(1m NW, on A5223) (Forte)
☎(0952)251244 Central Res (0800) 850950
*Follow the signs to Shawbirch to find this busy Lodge on the edge of Telford at the junction of the A5223/A442/B5063 north-west of the town. A Harvester restaurant and a petrol station are included in the complex.*
40➪♠(40fb) CTV in all bedrooms ® sB➪♠£29.95 dB➪♠£29.95 (room only)
《40P ⊞
Credit Cards 1 2 3

Remember to book early for holiday
and bank holiday times.

**TEMPLECOMBE** Somerset Map **03** ST72

★★59% *Horsington House*
Horsington BA8 0EG (1m N A357) ☎(0963)70721
FAX (0963) 70554
*A country house of honey-coloured stone stands in eight acres of grounds which include facilities for tennis and croquet. Bridge parties are a speciality, in which the proprietors take an active role.*
23➪♠(2fb) CTV in all bedrooms ® **T**
55P ✿ ♪ (hard) croquet putting ⚘
♀ English & Continental **V** ♦ ⌐ Last dinner 9.30pm
Credit Cards 1 2 3

**TEMPLE SOWERBY** Cumbria Map **12** NY62

★★❀74% *Temple Sowerby House*
CA10 1RZ ☎Kirkby Thore(07683)61578
*A very comfortable, personally run hotel with a pleasant rear garden, first built as a farmhouse back in the 1600s, stands on the main A66 at the centre of the village. Here you are assured of a level of care and attention that even includes hot water bottles in the beds during winter! The two lovely lounges provided for guests' use boast open fires in the cooler months and are supplied with books and magazines, while delightfully furnished bedrooms offer good facilities and a charming, almost Victorian style, dining room serves meals of a high standard.*
8➪♠Annexe4➪♠(2fb)2⊟ CTV in all bedrooms ® **T**
30P ⊞ croquet badminton boules ⚘
♀ International **V** ♦ ⌐ ⅄ Last dinner 9pm
Credit Cards 1 3

**TENBY** Dyfed Map **02** SN10

★★❀♨79% *Penally Abbey Country House*
Penally SA70 7PY (Welsh Rarebits) ☎(0834)3033
*Six acres of wooded grounds, which include the ruins of a 14th-century chapel, surround this delightful 200-year-old Flemish-style house which enjoys superb views across the golf links and sand dunes to Carmarthen Bay. The high quality of the bedrooms and public areas reflects the good taste and untiring efforts of the proprietors, who have painstakingly restored and refurbished the housed since acquiring it in 1985. Peace and quiet are assured, and facilities include a small heated indoor swimming pool and a snooker room.*
6➪♠Annexe4➪♠(3fb)7⊟ CTV in all bedrooms ® **T** ✻ ✻
sB&B➪♠£68 dB&B➪♠£110-£124 (incl dinner) ⊟
14P ⊞ ✿ ⊡ (heated) snooker croquet *xmas*
♀ Welsh, British & French ⅄ ✻ Dinner £21.50&alc Last dinner 9pm
Credit Cards 1 3

★★71% **Atlantic**
Esplanade SA70 7DU ☎(0834)2881 & 4176
*Set in attractive Italianate gardens and occupying a superb position on the South Shore, this well run family holiday hotel features good leisure facilities and very comfortable public rooms which include a choice of eating venues; a friendly staff provides helpful service throughout.*
36➪♠(8fb)1⊟⅄in 2 bedrooms CTV in all bedrooms ® **T**
sB&B➪♠£38-£45 dB&B➪♠£56-£90 ⊟
30P ✿ CFA ⊡ (heated) solarium spa bath
♀ French **V** ♦ ⌐ ⅄ S% Sunday Lunch £8.95-£10.50 High tea £4.50-£6 Dinner fr£16 Last dinner 8.30pm
Credit Cards 1 3

See advertisement on page 691

★★68% **Fourcroft**
The Croft SA70 8AP ☎(0834)2886 FAX (0834) 2888
Closed Nov-Etr
*The gardens of this family holiday hotel overlook the popular North Beach and harbour, and it also offers its own excellent pool and leisure facilities. The same proprietors have owned it for many*

*years, and they are very much involved in its day-to-day running, providing well equipped accommodation with friendly, attentive service.*

38⇄🛏(6fb) CTV in all bedrooms ® T S% sB&B⇄🛏£36-£40 dB&B⇄🛏£66-£74 🍴
Lift ( 5P (£1.50 per night) ✿ CFA ⌓ (heated) sauna gymnasium games room spa pool
♡ International V ♥ ⊁
Credit Cards 1 3

### ★★64% *Harbour Heights*
11 The Croft SA70 8AP ☎(0834)2132

*Overlooking the sands of the North Beach, this small, family-run hotel is comfortable and well equipped. Fresh produce is used in the kitchens and the food is good, although the choice of dishes is necessarily fairly small.*

8🛏(4fb) CTV in all bedrooms ® ✖
⅌ ⇙ nc8yrs
♡ English & Continental Last dinner 9.30pm
Credit Cards 1 2 3 5

### ★★63% *Albany*
The Norton SA70 8AB ☎(0834)2698

*A very pleasant resort hotel near the north shore and harbour, and just a short walk from the town centre. Bedrooms are bright and well maintained, there are 3 bars, and a swimming pool outside for good weather. Staff are friendly and helpful, and a good choice of food is available.*

23⇄🛏(2fb) CTV in all bedrooms ®
♡ French V ♥ ⚏ ⊁ Last dinner 9.30pm
Credit Cards 1 2 3

For key to symbols in English see the bookmark.

T

### ★★ 63% *Esplanade*

The Esplanade SA70 7DU ☎(0834)3333

*A modern family-run hotel on the promenade overlooking the sandy south beach, popular with business travellers and holidaymakers alike. Bedrooms are well furnished and equipped. There is a comfortable first-floor residents' lounge, and the open plan bar/restaurant serves a full choice of food.*

15⇨🛏Annexe3⇨🛏(5fb) CTV in all bedrooms ® T

🅟 ⇋

♀ French ♦ ⚗ Last dinner 9.30pm

Credit Cards 1 2 3 5

### ★★ 62% Buckingham

Esplanade SA70 7DU ☎(0834)2622

Closed Dec-Feb RS Mar, Oct & Nov

*Above the sandy South Beach with fine views over Caldey Island, this small family-run hotel has been recently upgraded. There is a comfortable lounge and a small bar, and bedrooms are all neat and well maintained. Service by the Rooke family is very friendly.*

8⇨🛏(2fb)⚡in 4 bedrooms CTV in all bedrooms ® ✱

sB&B⇨🛏£18-£24 dB&B⇨🛏£34-£50 🍴

🅟 ⇋ nc4yrs

V ♦ Lunch £8 Dinner £12 Last dinner 7.45pm

Credit Cards 1 3 £

### ★★ 50% Royal Lion

High St SA70 7ES ☎(0834)2127

Closed Nov-Apr

*This Victorian hotel occupies a fine seafront position with views over the harbour; the comfortable bedrooms are well equipped, and service is friendly.*

31rm(19⇨🛏)(8fb) CTV in all bedrooms ® ✱ sB&B£22.50-£30.65 sB&B⇨🛏£32.50-£40.90 dB&B£35.75-£56.25 dB&B⇨🛏£45.75-£66.50 🍴

Lift CTV 30P

♦ ⚗ ✱ Lunch £5-£7.50 High tea fr80p Dinner fr£12.25 Last dinner 8.30pm

Credit Cards 1 3 5

---

### ★★★ 64% White Lion

High St TN30 6BD (Resort) ☎(05806)5077 FAX (05806) 4157

*This lovely 350-year-old coaching inn retains many of its original features, despite the complete refurbishment which has provided it with every modern amenity. A choice of accommodation includes fine four-posters, spacious executive rooms and some compact doubles, while the Maltings Restaurant is complemented by a small cocktail bar, and conference facilities are available. Service throughout is friendly, helpful and well managed.*

15⇨🛏(2fb)2⚡⚡in 2 bedrooms CTV in all bedrooms ® T ✱ sB&B⇨🛏£51-£56 dB&B⇨🛏£66-£72 🍴

20P

♀ English & Continental V ♦ ⚗ ⚡ ✱ Lunch £7.50-£9.50 Dinner £12.50&alc Last dinner 9.30pm

Credit Cards 1 2 3 5 £

### ★★ 71% Little Silver Country

Ashford Rd, St Michael's TN30 6SP

☎High Halden(0233850)321 FAX (0233850) 665

*Whilst retaining much of its former 'olde worlde' charm, the house has been lovingly renovated and extended to provide a choice of bedrooms, equipped to the highest standard. The beamed sitting room has an open fire at each end, and also extends into a Victorian-style conservatory, which overlooks the beautifully kept lawned gardens. The octagonal-shaped function suite adds yet another dimension to this charming and relaxing, family-run hotel, where the standards of personal service being provided by the resident proprietors is much appreciated by the regular clientèle.*

10⇨🛏(4fb)1⚡ CTV in all bedrooms ® T sB&B⇨🛏£50-£70 dB&B⇨🛏£65-£95

CTV 50P ✿ CFA table tennis badminton ⚙ xmas

---

V ♦ ⚗ ⚡ Lunch £13-£15alc High tea £5-£8alc Dinner £15-£18alc Last dinner 9.30pm

Credit Cards 1 2 3

---

★★★

★★★✿✿✿⚘⚜

**CALCOT MANOR**

Calcot GL8 8YJ (3m W at junc A4135/A46) (Pride of Britain)

☎Leighterton(0666)890391 FAX (0666) 890394

*It may come as a surprise to find such a fine hotel among a collection of Cotswold stone farm buildings, but this is consistent with its understated and unobtrusive style. The proprietors and their small team of staff have perfected the art of hospitality, apparently meeting their guests' needs by instinct rather than formality and creating a completely relaxing atmosphere. Chef Ramon Farthing brings a natural and intuitive skill to the composition of such dishes as a celeriac mousse accompanied by escalope of leeks, asparagus and wild mushrooms, or the delightful duck breast accompanied by the leg prepared in Peking style and served on a rich sherry sauce. Bedrooms have now been refurbished, and although they vary in size and quality each is individually designed and furnished with great attention to detail and comfort; a further three rooms have now been created in the old stables which form a courtyard with the 14th-century tithe barn. An attractive lounge and dining room are extremely comfortable, particularly during the winter months, when log fires burn constantly.*

7⇨🛏Annexe9⇨🛏1⚡ CTV in all bedrooms T 🐕 (ex guide dogs) ✱ sB&B⇨🛏£85-£125 dB&B⇨🛏£97-£143 🍴

40P 3🚗 ⚡ ✿ CFA ⚲ (heated) croquet lawn nc12yrs xmas

♀ English & French ♦ ⚗ ⚡ ✱ Dinner £29-£36 Last dinner 9.30pm

Credit Cards 1 2 3 5

---

### ★★★ 78% Close

8 Long St GL8 8AQ (Small Luxury Hotels) ☎(0666)502272 FAX (0666) 504401

Closed 25-31 Dec

15⇨🛏3⚡ CTV in all bedrooms T 🐕 (ex guide dogs) sB&B⇨🛏£55-£105 dB&B⇨🛏£80-£160 Continental breakfast 🍴

20P 1🚗 ⚡

V ♦ ⚗ ⚡ Lunch £14.50-£16.50alc High tea £2.50-£5.50alc Dinner £28.50-£32.50alc Last dinner 10pm

Credit Cards 1 2 3 5 £

### ★★★ 71% Snooty Fox

Market Place GL8 8DD ☎(0666)502436 FAX (0666) 503479

*In a central position opposite the historic 16th-century market place, the Snooty Fox offers individual bedrooms equipped with homely little extras and the expected modern facilities. The spacious public areas are furnished with antiques and fine prints depicting the long association with the Beaufort Hunt.*

12⇨🛏(1fb)1⚡ CTV in all bedrooms ® T 🐕 (ex guide dogs) sB&B⇨🛏£66 dB&B⇨🛏£84 🍴

🅟 CFA xmas

♀ English & French V ♦ ⚗ Lunch £14.50-£15&alc Dinner fr£18.50&alc Last dinner 9.45pm

Credit Cards 1 2 3 5

---

T

### ★★★ 63% Hare & Hounds

Westonbirt GL8 8QL (Best Western) ☎Westonbirt(066688)233 FAX (066688) 241

*A fine looking hotel of Cotswold stone, in peaceful rural surroundings, set amid 10 acres of well kept gardens and lawns, nevertheless offers easy access to both Bristol and Bath from its position on the A433. Family run, it provides a friendly, informal atmosphere and well equipped, comfortable accommodation; good conference facilities are also available, together with tennis and squash courts.*

22⇌🅟Annexe8⇌🅟(3fb)5🛏 CTV in all bedrooms ® T S% sB&B⇌🅟£57-£67 dB&B⇌🅟£79-£88 🅁

80P 2🚗 ❖ CFA ℘ (hard) squash croquet table tennis *xmas*
♀ English & French V ♥ ⚖ S% Lunch £11.50&alc Dinner £17.75-£19.75&alc Last dinner 9pm
Credit Cards 1 2 3 £

### ★★ 64% Hunters Hall Inn

Kingscote GL8 8X2 ☎Dursley(0453)860393 FAX (0453) 860707
Annexe12⇌🅟(1fb) CTV in all bedrooms ® T
🏋 (ex guide dogs) ✳ sB&B⇌🅟£41-£44 dB&B⇌🅟£49-£54 🅁
120P ❖ *xmas*
V ♥ ⚖ 🏋 Lunch £6-£14 Dinner £13-£15&alc Last dinner 9.30pm
Credit Cards 1 2 3 5 £

---

### ★★★ ❀❀❀74% Puckrup Hall

Puckrup GL20 6EL (3m N A38 ) ☎(0684)296200
FAX (0684) 850788

*A fine country mansion dating from Regency days has been carefully converted into a hotel which meets modern requirements whilst retaining much of its original character and charm. Set in 114 acres of grounds, including carefully tended formal gardens, it provides excellent facilities for both tourists and businessmen; comfortably furnished and well equipped bedrooms with good modern en suite bathrooms offer such caring extras as fresh fruit and flowers, while well proportioned and tastefully furnished public areas include an intimate restaurant serving imaginative food.*

16⇌🅟2🛏 CTV in all bedrooms ® T sB&B⇌🅟£77.50-£99 dB&B⇌🅟£99-£140 🅁

80P 🚗 ❖ CFA ♪ croquet putting shooting *xmas*
♀ English & French V ♥ ⚖ Lunch £13-£17alc Dinner £22.50-£25&alc Last dinner 9.30pm
Credit Cards 1 2 3 5 £

### ★★★ 68% Royal Hop Pole Crest

Church St GL20 5RT (Forte Hotels) ☎(0684)293236
Telex no 437176 FAX (0684) 296680

*Located on the High Street, this former 14th-century coaching inn was largely rebuilt in the Georgian era and following recent refurbishment is now a hotel of charm and character, meeting the needs of the modern traveller. Previous notable guests include Charles Dickens and the hospitality he enjoyed is still evident in the nineties.*

29rm(24⇌🅟)(1fb)1🛏🏋in 6 bedrooms CTV in all bedrooms ® T ✳ S% sB⇌🅟£69 dB⇌🅟£83-£98 (room only) 🅁
🕯 50P ❖ *xmas*
V ♥ ⚖ 🏋 ✳ S% Lunch fr£10.25&alc Dinner fr£15.95&alc Last dinner 9.45pm
Credit Cards 1 2 3 4 5

### ★★★ 65% Tewkesbury Park Golf & Country Club

Lincoln Green Ln GL20 7DN ☎(0684)295405 Telex no 43563
RS No Sat lunch (Garden Restaurant)
*This modern hotel and leisure complex is situated south of the town and is surrounded by grounds containing a golf course, tennis courts and parkland. Indoor facilities include a swimming pool,*

squash courts and health and beauty treatments. Bedrooms are comfortable, public areas are spacious and there is a choice of bars and restaurants.

78⇌🅟(10fb)🏋in 4 bedrooms CTV in all bedrooms ® T 🏋 (ex guide dogs) ✳ S% sB&B⇌🅟£55-£98 dB&B⇌🅟£70-£115 🅁
🕯 150P ❖ CFA ☒ (heated) ▶ 18 ℘ (hard) squash snooker sauna solarium gymnasium health & beauty salon putting green *xmas*
♀ English & French V ♥ ⚖ ✳ S% Lunch fr£11.25 Dinner fr£17 Last dinner 10pm
Credit Cards 1 2 3 4 5 £

### ★★★ 64% Bell

Church St GL20 5SA (Best Western) ☎(0684)293293
FAX (0684) 295938

*This half-timbered building, once a coaching inn, stands directly opposite the Abbey. During the last year it has been extensively refurbished – though retaining the character of its intimate public areas – and bedrooms are all comfortable and well equipped, whatever their size.*

25⇌🅟(2fb)3🛏🏋in 1 bedroom CTV in all bedrooms ® T S% sB&B⇌🅟£62-£75 dB&B⇌🅟£70-£110 🅁
🕯 55P CFA *xmas*
♀ English & French V ♥ ⚖ 🏋 Lunch fr£11.95 Dinner fr£16.95&alc Last dinner 9.30pm
Credit Cards 1 2 3 5 £

### ★★ 62% Tudor House

High St GL20 5BH (Resort) ☎(0684)297755 FAX (0684) 290306
*This charming former inn on the main street of the historic town dates to 1540 and retains many original features, including beams and oak panelling in the public areas. Bedrooms are comfortable and equipped with modern facilities and a new bistro restaurant was added in 1991.*

21⇌🅟(2fb)1🛏 CTV in all bedrooms ® T ✳ sB&B⇌🅟fr£51 dB&B⇌🅟fr£66 🅁
22P 🚗 ❖
♀ English & French V ♥ ⚖ Lunch £3.50-£6.95 Dinner fr£6.95 Last dinner 9.30pm
Credit Cards 1 2 3 5

---

### ★★★ ❀♨ 74% Abingworth Hall

Storrington Rd RH20 3EF ☎West Chiltington(0798)813636
FAX (0798) 813914
Closed 2 wks Jan

*This fine manor house was rebuilt in 1910 in place of an earlier long-established house, it is set in 10 acres of grounds with some lovely views of the south Downs. Philip and Pauline Bulman have recaptured the Hall's former style, relaxed and elegant, through careful design and the selection of quality furnishings. There is a choice of bedrooms with good levels of comfort, and several with very generous bathrooms. Public rooms comprise a wood-panelled drawing room, bar, conservatory-restaurant and breakfast room.*

21⇌🅟 CTV in all bedrooms T 🏋 ✳ sB&B⇌🅟fr£64 dB&B⇌🅟£87-£150 🅁
50P 🚗 ❖ ⌇ (heated) ℘ (hard) croquet lawn nc10yrs *xmas*
♀ English & French V ✳ Lunch fr£17&alc Dinner fr£28&alc Last dinner 9pm
Credit Cards 1 3 4

---

### ★★★ ❀72% Spread Eagle

Cornmarket OX9 2BW ☎(084421)3661 Telex no 83343
FAX (0844) 261380
Closed 28-30 Dec
*This historic and famed hotel in the town centre was owned in the 1920s by the great chef and eccentric John Fothergill, author of*

T

An Innkeeper's Diary. *Today, Fothergill's Restaurant offers a wide choice of well prepared dishes and warm hospitality is provided by the proprietors Mr and Mrs Barrington. Bedrooms are comfortable and very well furnished.*
33⇨🏠(1fb)1🛏 CTV in all bedrooms ® T 🐕 (ex guide dogs)
sB&B⇨🏠£73-£75 dB&B⇨🏠£83.75-£100.75 Continental breakfast 🅟
⟨ 80P CFA *xmas*
♀ English & French V ⍟ ✳ Lunch £15.95-£16.95&alc Dinner £17.95-£18.95&alc Last dinner 10pm
Credit Cards ① ② ③ ⑤ ⓔ

---

THATCHAM Berkshire Map **04** SU56

★★★★63% **Regency Park**
Bowling Green Rd RG13 3RP ☎(0635)71555 due to change to 871555 Telex no 847844 FAX (0635) 71571 due to change to 871571
*An extended house near the centre of Thatcham, with an adjacent conference centre making this hotel particularly popular with business guests. All the bedrooms are well equipped and tastefully decorated and furnished. A choice of menus offers interesting dishes carefully prepared by competent chefs.*
50⇨🏠(12fb) CTV in all bedrooms ® T ✳ sB⇨🏠£82-£92 dB⇨🏠£92-£102 (room only) 🅟
Lift ⟨ 120P 🚌 ✳ CFA ♨ *xmas*
♀ English & Continental V ⍟ ⏛ ✂ ✳ Lunch fr£11.25&alc Dinner £18.50-£19.95&alc Last dinner 10.30pm
Credit Cards ① ② ③ ⑤ ⓔ
**See advertisement under NEWBURY**

A rosette means exceptional standards of cuisine.

---

THAXTED Essex Map **05** TL63

★★60% **Four Seasons**
Walden Rd CM6 2RE ☎(0371)830129 FAX (0371) 830835
*This welcoming former inn on the outskirts of the town, though modernised and extended, contains echoes of the past in the decorative plasterwork of its exterior and the exposed beams inside. Bedrooms vary in size but are all clean and well maintained, the comfortable and spacious bar serves a range of snacks, and there is a small lounge upstairs.*
9rm(8⇨🏠)✂in 2 bedrooms CTV in all bedrooms ® T 🐕 ✳
sB&B⇨🏠£50 dB&B⇨🏠£65 🅟
CTV 100P CFA ✳ nc12yrs
♀ English & French V ⍟ ✂ ✳ Sunday Lunch £10.95 Dinner £10-£15&alc Last dinner 9.30pm
Credit Cards ① ② ③

---

THETFORD Norfolk Map **05** TL88

See also **Brandon (Suffolk)**
★★★61% **The Bell**
King St IP24 2AZ (Forte Hotels) ☎(0842)754455
FAX (0842) 755552
*Attractively located beside the river, yet within the town centre, this comfortable inn still retains some traces of its fifteenth-century origin. Accommodation is currently being refurbished to a good standard and a range of meals, snacks and refreshments is available throughout the day in the choice of bars that complements the restaurant.*
47⇨🏠(1fb)1🛏✂in 11 bedrooms CTV in all bedrooms ® T ✳
S% sB⇨🏠£65 dB⇨🏠£85 (room only) 🅟
⟨ 82P CFA *xmas*
V ⍟ ⏛ ✂ ✳ S% Lunch £7.95-£10.45&alc Dinner £13.95-£15.95&alc Last dinner 9.45pm
Credit Cards ① ② ③ ④ ⑤

### ★★62% Historical Thomas Paine

White Hart St IP24 1AA (Best Western) ☎(0842)755631
Telex no 58298 FAX (0842) 766505

*Reputed to be the birthplace of Thomas Paine, a famous son of
Thetford, this privately owned and run hotel is situated just off the
A11, close to the town centre. Bedrooms vary, most are modestly
furnished but well equipped, and staff are friendly and helpful.*

13⇴ᐟ(1fb)1⌧ CTV in all bedrooms ® T sB&B⇴ᐟ£45-£50
dB&B⇴ᐟ£58-£65 ☐

30P ⌘

V ϑ ℒ ✳ Lunch £9.50-£12.50&alc Dinner £12.50-£14.50&alc
Last dinner 9.30pm

Credit Cards ⬚1 ⬚2 ⬚3 ⬚5

### ★★56% Anchor

Bridge St IP24 3AE ☎(0842)763925

*Set in a good position at the centre of the town, beside the Little
Ouse, this well equipped hotel has its own large car park. Most of
the attractive, cottage-style bedrooms have en suite facilities, the
popular Barnaby's Carvery offers value-for-money meals, and
there is a convivial 'locals' bar.*

17rm(12⇴3ᐟ) CTV in all bedrooms ® T ✖ (ex guide dogs)
60P

V ϑ ℒ ⊬ Last dinner 10pm
Credit Cards ⬚1 ⬚2 ⬚3 ⬚5

---

## THIRSK North Yorkshire Map 08 SE48

### ★★72% Sheppard's

Church Farm, Front St, Sowerby YO7 1JF ☎(0845)523655
FAX (0845) 524720

*Though this charming, family-owned and run hotel stands around
a courtyard within quaint old buildings its very well furnished
bedrooms are provided with good facilities; an excellent choice of
food is available in either the bistro or a cosy restaurant.*

8⇴ᐟ(1fb)1⌧⊬in 2 bedrooms CTV in all bedrooms ® T ✖
sB&B⇴ᐟ£50-£55 dB&B⇴ᐟ£65-£75 ☐

35P ⌘ nc10yrs

♥ International ϑ ℒ ⊬ ✳ Sunday Lunch £9.75 Dinner £16-
£25alc Last dinner 9.30pm

Credit Cards ⬚1 ⬚3

### ★★66% The Golden Fleece

Market Place YO7 1LL ☎(0845)523108 FAX (0845) 523996

*At the heart of James Herriot country, in the 'Darrowby' of the
books, an hotel dating back over 300 years offers well equipped
accommodation (including some en suite rooms) and good service
by caring staff.*

22rm(6⇴)(3fb)2⌧ CTV in all bedrooms ® T
50P

V ϑ ℒ ⊬ Last dinner 9.15pm
Credit Cards ⬚1 ⬚2 ⬚3 ⬚5

### ★★60% Three Tuns Hotel

Market Place YO7 1LH ☎(0845)523124 FAX (0845) 526126

*A three-storey coaching inn situated in the market square.*

11⇴ᐟ(3fb)1⌧ CTV in 10 bedrooms ® T ✳ sB&B⇴ᐟ£38
dB&B⇴ᐟ£58 ☐

50P 2🐾 xmas

V ϑ ℒ ✳ Lunch fr£6.95alc High tea £2.50-£5.50alc Dinner
£8.50 Last dinner 9.30pm

Credit Cards ⬚1 ⬚2 ⬚3 ⬚5

### ★60% Old Red House

Station Rd YO7 4LT ☎(0845)524383

*This simple inn, situated opposite the railway station about a mile
out of town, provides friendly service and good value
accommodation; menus feature a selection of children's meals.*

6⇴ᐟAnnexe6⇴ᐟ(5fb)1⌧⊬in 1 bedroom CTV in 6
bedrooms ® T ✳ sB&B⇴ᐟfr£17 dB&B⇴ᐟfr£28 ☐

30P xmas

V ϑ ℒ Lunch £6.50-£8.50&alc High tea £4.50-£6.50 Dinner
£7-£12&alc Last dinner 10pm

Credit Cards ⬚2 ⬚3 ⬚5

---

## THORNBURY Avon Map 03 ST69

★★★

★★★✿✿ ⓜ

THORNBURY CASTLE

BS12 1HH (Pride of Britain)
☎(0454)281182
FAX (0454) 416188
Closed 2-12 Jan RS 24-29
Dec

*'Not so much a business, more
a love affair', was how his son described owner Maurice
Taylor's involvement with the castle and its history, which
stretches back to 1511. Located on the northern edge of the
town, in the shadow of the church tower, the driveway passes
rows of new vines which can now produce 1,000 bottles of
wine from the Müller Thurgau grape – it's on the hotel wine
list. Uniformed staff give caring, friendly service, even
cleaning shoes left at the bedroom door. This attention to
detail is no less apparent in the high standard of housekeeping
and cleanliness. Each of the bed chambers has had to be fitted
inside massive walls, most are quite spectacular, huge by
modern standards, and crammed with antiques. Many of the
beds have full canopied frames, and there are some fine
ceilings particularly in the later wing. Public rooms include a
cosy library and a baronial-size lounge with deep armchairs,
settees and amazingly comfortable Windsor armchairs. There
are 2 dining rooms for busy times, but the main room is built
into the base of a tower and slit windows show the thickness of
the stone, and with the ancient panelling and lovely
atmosphere this is the perfect setting for the accomplished
cooking of chef Derek Hamlen. There is an excellent wine list
which needs time to study. For those in a hurry it offers a
shortlist of bottles under £15. The proprietor's reserve bin has
been built up over many years and contains rarities from the
1920s.*

18⇴ᐟ8⌧ CTV in all bedrooms T ✖ sB&B⇴ᐟ£75-£80
dB&B⇴ᐟ£90-£190 Continental breakfast ☐

《 40P ⌘ ✿ CFA croquet hot air ballooning archery
nc12yrs xmas

♥ English & French V ϑ ℒ ⊬ ✳ Lunch £17.75 Dinner
£25.50-£29.50 Last dinner 9.30pm

Credit Cards ⬚1 ⬚2 ⬚3 ⬚4 ⬚5

See advertisement under BRISTOL

---

## THORNE South Yorkshire Map 08 SE61

### ★★67% Belmont

Horsefair Green DN8 5EE ☎(0405)812320 Telex no 54480
FAX (0405) 740508

*This friendly hotel in a quiet market town, only half a mile from
the M18, has comfortable, modern public rooms and a restaurant
with a choice of good-value menus, making it popular with locals.
Bedrooms are well furnished and equipped.*

23⇴ᐟ(3fb)1⌧ CTV in all bedrooms ® T sB&B⇴ᐟ£49.50-
£52.50 dB&B⇴ᐟ£62.50-£70.95 ☐

30P CFA xmas

♥ English & French V ϑ ℒ Lunch £9.75-£10.75&alc Dinner
£9.75-£10.75&alc Last dinner 9.30pm

Credit Cards ⬚1 ⬚2 ⬚3 ⬚5 ⬚£

**THORNHILL** Dumfries & Galloway *Dumfriesshire*
Map **11** NX89

### ★★72% Trigony House

Closeburn DG3 5EZ (2m S off A76) (Minotels) ☎(0848)31211

*In an attractive rural location, with direct access from the A76 just south of the town, this tranquil country house offers charming well-appointed bedrooms and inviting public rooms. Resident proprietors and their family provide delightful service and interesting food.*

9⇌↑ CTV in all bedrooms ® **T ✕** (ex guide dogs)
sB&B⇌↑£30.50-£33 dB&B⇌↑£51-£59 ▤

30P ⇎ ✿ nc10yrs

V ✆ Bar Lunch £5-£9.50alc Dinner fr£14.50alc Last dinner 8.30pm

Credit Cards ⬜1⬜ ⬜3⬜ Ⓔ

### ★68% George Hotel

Drumlanrig St DG3 5LU (Exec Hotel) ☎(0848)30326

Closed 25 Dec & 1 Jan

*The hotel has been carefully modernised to preserve its 'village inn' atmosphere and the comfortable lounge bar is now proving popular for its good bar meals.*

8⇌↑(1fb) CTV in all bedrooms ® **T ✱** sB&B⇌↑£25-£30
dB&B⇌↑£37.50-£45

CTV 10P ✦ indoor bowling

V ✆ ✱ Bar Lunch £5.95-£9.95 Dinner £5.95-£9.95&alc Last dinner 8.55pm

Credit Cards ⬜1⬜ ⬜3⬜

---

**THORNLEY** Durham Map **08** NZ33

### ★★64% Crossways

Dunelm Rd DH6 3HT (5m SE of Durham City)
☎Wellfield(0429)821248 FAX (0429) 820034

*This privately owned hotel on the A181 5 miles east of Durham, just south of the village, complements banqueting and conference amenities by well equipped en suite bedrooms which are designed to meet the needs of business travellers; facilities are also provided for disabled guests.*

23⇌↑(9fb)1▤ CTV in all bedrooms ® **T**

℄ CTV 150P ✿ sauna solarium fitness room ♬ ⚙

♡ English & French V ✆ ⚑ ⤶ Last dinner 9.45pm

Credit Cards ⬜1⬜ ⬜2⬜ ⬜3⬜ ⬜5⬜

---

**THORNTHWAITE** Cumbria Map **11** NY22

### ★★⚎67% Thwaite Howe

CA12 5SA ☎Braithwaite(07687)78281

Closed Nov-Feb

*A pleasant Victorian house, set in its own grounds and peacefully located on a hillside, commands fine views of Skiddaw. Pleasingly furnished bedrooms are very well equipped, guests can take their ease in a relaxing lounge, and the 6-course table d'hôte dinner menu is changed daily.*

8⇌ CTV in all bedrooms ® **T** dB&B⇌£64-£78 (incl dinner) ▤

12P ⇎ ✿ nc12yrs

♡ English & French ⤶ Dinner £12 Last dinner 7pm
Ⓔ

### ★★62% Ladstock Country House

CA12 5RZ ☎Braithwaite(07687)78210 & 78249

Closed Jan

*In an elevated position overlooking beautiful Lakeland countryside, this pleasantly furnished country house offers a warm and friendly welcome. There are good public areas and bedrooms are comfortable and well equipped.*

22rm(11⇌7↑)(2fb)3▤ CTV in all bedrooms ® **T**
**✕** (ex guide dogs) ✱ S% sB&B£25-£32 sB&B⇌↑£30-£32
dB&B£38-£60 dB&B⇌↑£48-£60 ▤

---

CTV 50P ✿ CFA *xmas*

V ✆ ⚑ S% Lunch £7.50 High tea £5 Dinner £15 Last dinner 8.30pm

Credit Cards ⬜1⬜ ⬜3⬜

### ★★59% Swan

CA12 5SQ ☎Braithwaite(07687)78256

Closed Nov-Etr

*This former coaching inn, set on a quiet road now that the village has its bypass, provides adequately comfortable lounges and a restaurant with pleasant views over the valley and lake. A good range of food is available in both restaurant and bar.*

14rm(3⇌5↑) CTV in 13 bedrooms S10% sB&B£34-£37.40
dB&B£68-£74.80 dB&B⇌↑£76.70-£83.90 (incl dinner) ▤

CTV 60P 3🚗 (£1.75) ⇎ ✿

♡ English & Continental V ✆ ⚑ ⤶ Bar Lunch £1.35-£11alc Dinner £16.95 Last dinner 8.30pm

Credit Cards ⬜1⬜ ⬜2⬜ ⬜3⬜ Ⓔ

---

**THORNTON CLEVELEYS** Lancashire Map **07** SD34

### ✹✹✹✕The River House

Skippool Creek FY5 5LF (2m E A585)
☎Poulton-Le-Fylde(0253)883497 & 883307
FAX (0253) 892083

*For more years than he cares to remember Bill Scott has run this charming restaurant with enthusiasm and care. The cooking is robust and no-nonsense and the à la carte menu, with its daily variations, offers plenty of choice as does the lengthy wine list. Tuna, scallops and local duck are all likely to feature on the menu. There are also four individually decorated bedrooms.*

Closed Sun & 2 wks in Aug Lunch not served Sat

♡ International 40 seats ✱ Lunch £30-£50alc Dinner £30-£50alc Last lunch 2.30pm Last dinner 9.30pm 20 P

Credit Cards ⬜1⬜ ⬜3⬜

---

**THORNTON HOUGH** Merseyside Map **07** SJ38

### ★★★63% Thornton Hall

Neston Rd L63 1JF ☎051-336 3938 Telex no 628678

*Set in seven acres of well maintained grounds this former residence of a major shipping family has been converted into a comfortable hotel. The main house has fine wood carvings and panelling whilst the majority of bedrooms are contained in a separate, more modern wing which is currently being refurbished to provide a high standard of accommodation.*

9⇌↑Annexe28⇌↑ CTV in all bedrooms ®
**✕** (ex guide dogs)

℄ 100P ✿

♡ English, French & Italian V ✆ Last dinner 9.30pm

Credit Cards ⬜1⬜ ⬜2⬜ ⬜3⬜ ⬜4⬜ ⬜5⬜

---

**THORNTON WATLASS** North Yorkshire Map **08** SE28

### ★63% Buck Inn

HG4 4AH ☎Bedale(0677)422461

*An attractive stone inn overlooking the village green where cricket is played in the summer. Bedrooms are pleasantly furnished and there is a separate lounge. The bars are full of local atmosphere.*

6rm(5⇌↑)(1fb) ® S% sB&B⇌↑£25-£30 dB&B⇌↑£40-£45

CTV 10P ✿ ✦ quoits pool table childrens play area ♬

V ✆ ⚑ Lunch fr£7alc Dinner fr£10alc Last dinner 9.30pm

Credit Cards ⬜1⬜ ⬜2⬜ ⬜3⬜

---

**THORPE (DOVEDALE)** Derbyshire Map **07** SK15

### ★★★67% Peveril of the Peak

DE6 2AW (Forte Hotels) ☎Thorpe Cloud(033529)333
FAX (033529) 507

*Set in lovely Peak District countryside, at the base of Thorpe Cloud, with 11 acres of gardens and grounds, this rambling hotel has been greatly improved by refurbishment to bedrooms and*

→

T

*public areas over the last few years. Public rooms are particularly comfortable and bedrooms now have a more consistent level of modern facilities.*

47⇨⅄in 9 bedrooms CTV in all bedrooms ⓡ T ✻ S%
sB⇨£49 dB⇨£85 (room only) 🏳

《 60P ✿ CFA ♪ (hard) *xmas*
V ⌂ ⚏ ⅄ ✻ S% Lunch £9.45 Dinner £15&alc Last dinner
9.30pm
Credit Cards ①②③⑤

## ★★★63% Izaak Walton
DE6 2AY (1m W on Ilam rd) ☎Thorpe Cloud(033529)555
FAX (033529) 539
*A former farmhouse, dating from the 17th-century and enjoying panoramic views of Dovedale and Thorpe Cloud from its setting in open countryside, has been much extended to create an hotel offering traditional comforts and service. Bedrooms, though sometimes compact, are well equipped and quite comfortably appointed, while a restaurant with views out over the gardens is currently being refurbished.*
34⇨𝄞(2fb)3🛏⅄in 6 bedrooms CTV in all bedrooms ⓡ T
《 80P ✿ ♪
♡ English & French V ⌂ ⚏ ⅄ ✻ S10% Lunch fr£9.90&alc
High tea fr£4.95 Dinner fr£14.85&alc Last dinner 9pm
Credit Cards ①②③⑤

## THRAPSTON Northamptonshire Map 04 SP97

### ⇧Forte Travelodge
Thrapston By-pass(on A14 link road A1/M1) (Forte)
☎Central Res (0800) 850950
*On the A14, the new A1/M1 link road, 8 miles east of Kettering, this new Travelodge provides functional, value-for-money accommodation. Adjacent facilities include a Little Chef, Coffee Stop and picnic area.*
40⇨𝄞(40fb) CTV in all bedrooms ⓡ sB⇨𝄞£29.95
dB⇨𝄞£29.95 (room only)
《 40P 🚗
Credit Cards ①②③

## THREE COCKS Powys Map 03 SO13

### ★★✿70% Three Cocks
LS3 0SL ☎Glasbury(04974)215 due to change to (0497) 847215
Closed Dec & Jan
(Rosette awarded for dinner only)
*Set around a cobbled forecourt, parts of this inn date back to the 15th century. Inviting and relaxing public areas include a pine wood-panelled lounge with comfortable armchairs and sofas, while enjoyable home-cooked meals are served in the more modern dining room overlooking the rear garden. Cheery compact bedrooms are finished with solid oak and attractive fabrics, but there are few modern facilities other than the contemporary bathrooms.*
7rm(5⇨1𝄞)(2fb) ✖ ✻ dB&B⇨𝄞£53 🏳
CTV 40P 🚗 ✿
♡ Continental V ⌂ ✻ Lunch fr£21&alc Dinner fr£21&alc Last
dinner 9pm
Credit Cards ①③

## THRUSSINGTON Leicestershire Map 08 SK61

### ⇧Forte Travelodge
Green Acres Filling Station LE7 8TE (on A46, southbound)
(Forte) ☎Rearsby(0664)424525 Central Res (0800) 850950
*Situated on the southbound side of the A46, about eight miles north of Leicester and surrounded by open countryside, a value-for-money lodge adjacent to a Little Chef restaurant offers accommodation in well furnished bedrooms.*
32⇨𝄞(32fb) CTV in all bedrooms ⓡ sB⇨𝄞£29.95
dB⇨𝄞£29.95 (room only)
《 32P 🚗
Credit Cards ①②③

## THURCROFT South Yorkshire Map 08 SK48

### ★★70% Consort
Brampton Rd s66 9JA (Consort) ☎Rotherham(0709)530022
FAX (0709) 531529
*Situated at the M18/M1 intersection, this is a two-storey modern brick and pantile building. Good levels of service are provided by a very friendly team, and the excellent, well equipped accommodation is comfortable and attractive. There is a good selection of bar snacks and restaurant meals, and a very comfortable lounge. A large banqueting suite has facilities for 300.*
18⇨𝄞(1fb) CTV in all bedrooms ⓡ T ✖ (ex guide dogs) ✻
sB&B⇨𝄞£25-£57 dB&B⇨𝄞£40-£66 🏳
《 90P 🚗 CFA
V ⌂ ⚏ ⅄ ✻ Lunch £7.95-£11.95&alc High tea fr£7.95 Dinner
£7.95-£11.95&alc Last dinner 9.30pm
Credit Cards ①②③ⓕ

**See advertisement under ROTHERHAM**

## THURLASTON Warwickshire Map 04 SP47

### ⇧Forte Travelodge
London Rd CV23 9LG (A45, westbound) (Forte)
☎Dunchurch(0788)521538 Central Res (0800) 850950
*Situated three miles south of Rugby and eight miles from Coventry, this Travelodge offers easy access to the M45.*
40⇨𝄞(40fb) CTV in all bedrooms ⓡ sB⇨𝄞£29.95
dB⇨𝄞£29.95 (room only)
40P 🚗
Credit Cards ①②③

## THURLESTONE Devon Map 03 SX64

### ★★★★65% Thurlestone
TQ7 3NN ☎Kingsbridge(0548)560382 Telex no 42513
FAX (0548) 561069
*A peacefully situated hotel, owned by the same family since the turn of the century and commanding views of Bigbury Bay from its setting in 17 acres of gardens and grounds, offers accommodation in tastefully decorated bedrooms equipped to enhance the comfort of both holiday and commercial users. Public areas carefully positioned to enjoy the views have recently been modernised by the addition of quality furnishings, and the dishes featured on the restaurant's table d'hôte and à la carte menus are based on fresh produce wherever possible. The extensive range of leisure facilities available includes an indoor pool and gym complex, a hairdressing/ beauty salon, badminton and squash courts, and tennis and golf in the grounds.*
68⇨𝄞(13fb) CTV in all bedrooms T ✻ sB&B⇨𝄞£57-£90
dB&B⇨𝄞£113-£168 (incl dinner) 🏳
Lift 《 100P 19🚗 🚗 ✿ ▭ (heated) ≈ (heated) ▶ 9 ♪ (hard)
squash snooker sauna solarium gymnasium games room
badminton spa bath ⚏ *xmas*
♡ English & French V ⌂ ⚏ ⅄ S% Lunch £4.95-£11.50alc
High tea 95p-£3.95alc Dinner £22.50&alc Last dinner 9pm
Credit Cards ①③

## THURSO Highland *Caithness* Map 15 ND16

### ★★62% Pentland
Princes St KW14 7AA ☎(0847)63202 FAX (0847) 62761
*Public areas in this town centre hotel have been tastefully refurbished in the modern style, while the first-floor lounges offer more traditional comforts. Bedrooms, which vary in size, are well equipped and practically appointed.*
53rm(28⇨11𝄞)(4fb) CTV in all bedrooms T ✻ sB&Bfr£19
sB&B⇨𝄞fr£23 dB&Bfr£35 dB&B⇨𝄞fr£42

( ✗ 🖭 CFA
V ✿ ⊡ ✳
Credit Cards 1 3

---

## TICEHURST East Sussex Map 05 TQ63

○ **Dale Hill Golf**
TN5 7DQ ☎(0580)200112
Open
26↪🏠

---

## TIGHNABRUAICH Strathclyde Map 10 NR97

★★68% **Kames**
Kames PA21 2AF (Minotels) ☎(0700)811489
FAX (0700) 811283
*This friendly, family hotel lies on the shore of the Kyles of Bute, and is a popular rendezvous with the yachting fraternity. Its cosy, period-style rooms are a feature and a good range of bar meals augment the dinner menu.*
10↪🏠(3fb) CTV in all bedrooms ® T sB&B↪🏠fr£32 dB&B↪🏠fr£54 🍴
CTV 6P 🖭 ✿ childrens play park sailing water-skiing *xmas*
V ✿ ⊡ ✂ ✳ Bar Lunch £3-£9 High tea £3-£9 Dinner fr£17
Last dinner 9pm
Credit Cards 1 2 3 5 £

---

## TINTAGEL Cornwall & Isles of Scilly Map 02 SX08

★★62% **Bossiney House**
PL34 0AX ☎Camelford(0840)770240 FAX (0840) 770501
Closed Jan-Mar RS Nov-Dec
*With many scenic walks in the area, the family partnership that runs this hotel specialises in holidays for country-minded people. Bedrooms are currently being redecorated and televisions made available (at a nominal charge). The dining room offers simple table d'hôte menus, and a cedarwood lodge in the grounds contains a swimming pool, sauna and solarium.*
17rm(15↪🏠)Annexe1↪(1fb) ® sB&B↪🏠£31.50-£37 dB&B↪🏠£51-£56 🍴
CTV 30P ✿ CFA ⬛ (heated) sauna solarium gymnasium putting green *xmas*
♀ English, French & Portuguese V ✿ ⊡ S% Lunch £5.50-£5.95 Dinner fr£13 Last dinner 9.30pm
Credit Cards 1 2 3 5

★★56% **Atlantic View**
Treknow PL34 0EJ ☎Camelford(0840)770221
*Bedrooms are simply furnished (though some have four-poster beds) and the many lounges are comfortable at this personally-run hotel with lawns and fine sea views.*
9↪🏠(2fb)4🖭 CTV in all bedrooms ® sB&B↪🏠£23-£29 dB&B↪🏠£33-£45 🍴
CTV 20P 🖭 ✿ ⬛ (heated) solarium pool table nc2yrs
♀ English & European V ✿ ⊡ ✂ Lunch £1.50-£6.50 Dinner fr£11.50&alc Last dinner 9pm
Credit Cards 1 3 £

---

## TINTERN Gwent Map 03 SO50

★★★67% **The Beaufort**
NP6 6SF (Jarvis) ☎(0291)689777 FAX (0291) 689727
*A very well run hotel with good modern facilities stands in the beautiful Wye Valley, opposite the ruins of the famous Abbey. Bedrooms are all well appointed, there is a comfortable lounge, and a wide range of food is served in the attractive restaurant and bars.*
24↪🏠(2fb) CTV in all bedrooms ® T ✳ S% sB&B↪🏠fr£67.50 dB&B↪🏠fr£92 🍴
60P ✿ CFA games room *xmas*

---

♀ English & French V ✿ ⊡ ✳ S% Sunday Lunch £6.95-£10.95 Dinner £16.75-£22.25 Last dinner 9pm
Credit Cards 1 2 3 4 5 £

★★64% *Royal George*
NP6 6SF ☎(0291)689205 FAX (0291) 689448
*Standing beside the A466 in the picturesque Wye Valley, not far from the famous Abbey, a family-run hotel whose history as an inn dates back to the seventeenth century now offers well-equipped accommodation, the majority of its rooms being contained in annexes overlooking the delightful gardens.*
2rm(1↪)Annexe14↪(1fb) CTV in all bedrooms ® T
50P ✿
♀ English & French V ✿ ⊡ Last dinner 9.30pm
Credit Cards 1 2 3 5

★★62% **Wye Valley**
NP6 6SP (Consort) ☎(0291)689441 FAX (0291) 689440
*An inn situated beside the A466 at the centre of the village offers comfortable, well equipped en suite bedrooms, a popular restaurant with a good choice of dishes, and friendly, attentive service throughout.*
9↪🏠6🖭 CTV in all bedrooms ® T sB&B↪🏠£35-£45 dB&B↪🏠£48-£58 🍴
60P CFA 🎵 nc12yrs *xmas*
V ✿ ⊡ ✂ Lunch £9.95-£10.50 Dinner £10.95-£11.50 Last dinner 9.30pm
Credit Cards 1 2 3 £

See advertisement on page 699

★★57% **Parva Farmhouse Hotel & Restaurant**
NP6 6SQ ☎(0291)689411 FAX (02912) 79298
*Situated in the wooded Wye valley and near the small parish church, this former 17th-century farmhouse has been converted into a modern, family-run hotel. The comfortable lounge has an* →

*'honesty bar' and the food is enjoyable, though the choice is rather limited.*
9rm(7⇌🏠)(1fb)2🛏 CTV in all bedrooms ® **T** sB&Bfr£30 sB&B⇌🏠fr£35 dB&Bfr£40 dB&B⇌🏠fr£52 🍴
10P
♀ European **V** Dinner £14.50-£16.50&alc Last dinner 8.30pm
Credit Cards 1 3 £

---

TIPTREE Essex Map **05** TL81

### ○Quietwaters Hotel Golf & Country Club
Colchester Rd, Tolleshunt Knights CM9 8HX
☎Maldon(0621)868888 FAX (0621) 868831
Due to have opened Summer 1991
58⇌🏠

---

TITCHFIELD Hampshire Map **04** SU50

### ★★ ⊛67% Abshot Hotel & Country Club
Little Abshot Rd PO14 4LN ☎Locksheath(0489)573936 & 584057 FAX (0489) 575692
*An Edwardian manor house standing in 5.5 acres of garden has recently been tastefully refurbished to create a small, elegant hotel. Well equipped bedrooms with modern facilities are attractively decorated, those facing west being particularly bright, sunny and spacious. Public areas are not large, but the comfortable bar, restaurant and lounge are stylishly appointed; varied, interesting table d'hôte and à la carte menus offer a value-for-money selection of good Anglo-French dishes based on fresh ingredients and fine produce. Guests also have the use of extensive leisure amenities in the adjacent Abshot Country Club, where squash, snooker, gym, swimming pool and health suite are available, together with a large bar area serving snacks.*
13rm(11⇌🏠)(2fb)2🛏 CTV in all bedrooms ® **T** ✳ sB&B£35-£48 sB&B⇌🏠£35-£48 dB&B£76-£98 dB&B⇌🏠£76-£98 🍴
CTV P ✿ 🖃 (heated) ♪ (hard) squash snooker sauna solarium gymnasium ♫ *xmas*
♀ English & French **V** ♥ ♨ ⅙ ✳ Lunch £5-£15&alc Dinner fr£11.95&alc Last dinner 10pm
Credit Cards 1 2 3 5

---

TITCHWELL Norfolk Map **09** TF74

### ★★ ⊛72% Titchwell Manor
PE31 8BB ☎Brancaster(0485)210221 & 210284 Telex no 32376
*Overlooking the salt marshes and sea and close to the RSPB reserve, is this comfortable and warm hotel which has combined modern facilities with a relaxing atmosphere. The Garden Restaurant offers a daily menu featuring skilfully prepared fresh produce, particularly locally caught fish.*
11rm(7⇌🏠)Annexe4⇌🏠(2fb) CTV in all bedrooms ® **T** sB&B£31-£41 sB&B⇌🏠£31-£41 dB&B£62-£82 dB&B⇌🏠£62-£82 🍴
50P 🚗 ✿ CFA *xmas*
♀ European **V** ♥ ♨ ⅙ Lunch fr£8.95 High tea fr£2.95 Dinner £15.95-£21.95 Last dinner 9.30pm
Credit Cards 1 2 3 5

---

TIVERTON Devon Map **03** SS91 ⊖

### ★★★ 60% Tiverton
Blundells Rd EX16 4DB ☎(0884)256120 Telex no 42551 FAX (0884) 258101
*This modern lodge-style hotel near the town centre, yet with easy access to the North Devon Link Road, has spacious well-equipped bedrooms, 45 of them in a new extension and the original 30 currently being refurbished. Open-plan public areas include the Garden restaurant and there are meeting and function rooms available.*
75⇌🏠(75fb) CTV in all bedrooms ® **T** S% sB&B⇌🏠£38-£51 dB&B⇌🏠£64-£90 (incl dinner) 🍴

---

《 130P CFA ♫ *xmas*
♀ English, French & Italian **V** ♥ ♨ ⅙ ✳ Lunch £8.50&alc
Credit Cards 1 2 3 5

### ★★58% Hartnoll
Bolham EX16 7RA (1.5m N on A396) ☎(0884)252777 FAX (0884) 259195
*Just off the North Devon Link Road about a mile from the town centre, this extended Georgian house set in its own gardens has attractively coordinated well equipped bedrooms with good toiletries and extras. There is a comfortable conservatory lounge, a spacious bar serving bar meals and an à la carte restaurant.*
11⇌Annexe5🏠(3fb)1🛏 CTV in all bedrooms ® **T**
100P ✿
♀ English & Continental **V** ♥ ♨ Last dinner 10pm
Credit Cards 1 2 3 5

---

TOBERMORY

See Mull, Isle of

---

TODDINGTON MOTORWAY SERVICE AREA (M1)
Bedfordshire Map **04** SP92

### ⌂Granada Lodge
M1 Motorway LU5 6HR (Granada) ☎(05255)5150 FAX (05255) 5945
*Situated on the M1 southbound carriageway near Luton, with 24-hour services adjacent, the Lodge offers good quality, well equipped accommodation and a high standard of cleanliness.*
43⇌(10fb)⅙in 5 bedrooms CTV in all bedrooms ®
🐕 (ex guide dogs) S% sB⇌fr£31 dB⇌fr£34 (room only) 🍴
《 248P
**V** ♥ ♨ ⅙
Credit Cards 1 2 3 5

**See advertisement under LUTON**

---

TODMORDEN Lancashire Map **07** SD92

### ★★★🏋70% Scaitcliffe Hall
Burnley Rd OL14 7DQ ☎(0706)818888 FAX (0706) 818825
*Set in well tended grounds on the edge of town, this attractive country house dating to 1666 offers comfortable well furnished accommodation and friendly professional service. Bedrooms are well equipped and the restaurant, in the former barn, provides a good standard of cooking.*
13⇌🏠(2fb)1🛏 CTV in all bedrooms ® **T**
《 200P ✿
**V** ♥ ♨
Credit Cards 1 2 3 5

---

TODWICK South Yorkshire Map **08** SK48

### ★★★68% Red Lion
Worksop Rd S31 0DJ (Lansbury) ☎Worksop(0909)771654 Telex no 54120 FAX (0909) 773704
*A former inn on the A57 eastbound, within easy reach of junction 31 of the M1, has been cleverly converted to create a comfortable modern hotel offering well furnished and equipped accommodation, the polite, efficient and generally cheerful service provided by its young staff appealing equally to business travellers and to weekend and leisure guests.*
29⇌🏠1🛏⅙in 9 bedrooms CTV in all bedrooms ® **T**
🐕 (ex guide dogs) sB&B⇌🏠fr£75 dB&B⇌🏠fr£88 🍴
《 90P CFA *xmas*
♀ English & French **V** ♥ ⅙ Lunch fr£8.95 Dinner fr£14.25 Last dinner 10pm
Credit Cards 1 2 3 5

---

For key to symbols in English see the bookmark.

TONBRIDGE Kent Map **05** TQ54 ☺

★★64% **The Rose & Crown**
High St TN9 1DD (Forte Hotels) ☎(0732)357966
FAX (0732)357194
*Traditional décor and a wealth of heavy oak beams characterise this busy hotel – a posting and coaching house dating from the sixteenth century – though its well equipped bedrooms, which are mostly contained in the new wing, are all furnished in the modern style. Attentive, friendly and well managed services are provided and there is a comfortable foyer reception area.*
50rm(49⇄♠)(2fb)1⌷⊁in 20 bedrooms CTV in all bedrooms
® T ✳ S% sB⇄♠£39.50-£49.50 dB⇄♠£39.50-£49.50 (room only) ⊟
《 62P CFA *xmas*
V ♡ ⚏ ⊁ ✳ S% Lunch £9.60-£10.80&alc Dinner £13.60&alc
Last dinner 9.45pm
Credit Cards ①②③④⑤

TONGUE Highland *Sutherland* Map **14** NC55

★★65% **Ben Loyal**
IV27 4XE ☎(084755)216
*This small, friendly, tourist hotel is being steadily improved by the owners. The bedrooms, with private facilities, have recently been refurbished to a good standard and enjoy fine views over the Kyle of Tongue, as do the neat dining room and comfortable lounge. The hotel is warm and well maintained throughout.*
12rm(9⇄♠)1⌷ CTV in all bedrooms ® sB&B£20
sB&B⇄♠£30-£60 dB&B£40 dB&B⇄♠£52-£60 ⊟
19P ✳ ♪ ♫ *xmas*
♀ Scottish & French V ♡ ⚏ ⊁ Lunch fr£11.75 Dinner
£13.50&alc Last dinner 8.30pm
Credit Cards ①③

TOPCLIFFE North Yorkshire Map **08** SE47

★★65% **The Angel Inn**
Long St YO7 3RW ☎Thirsk(0845)577237 FAX (0845) 578000
*Situated at Topcliffe, 4 miles to the south-west of Thirsk, this 17th-century roadside inn retains much of its traditional character. It also offers a new wing of comfortably furnished and well equipped bedrooms and an inviting lounge.*
15⇄♠(2fb) CTV in all bedrooms ® T ✘ (ex guide dogs) ✳
S% sB&B⇄♠fr£30 dB&B⇄♠fr£46 ⊟
100P ✳ ⚫
♡ ⚏ ✳ S% Lunch £9.50 Dinner £9.50&alc Last dinner 9.30pm
Credit Cards ①③

TOPSHAM Devon Map **03** SX98

★★69% **Ebford House**
Exmouth Rd EX3 0QH (1m E on A376) ☎(0392)877658
FAX (0392) 874424
*Conveniently situated for the M5, Exeter and the coast, this elegant Georgian property with a walled garden has comfortable en suite bedrooms well equipped for both commercial and holiday visitors. There is a homely lounge with log fires, lively cellar bar and a choice of bistro or formal restaurant.*
18⇄♠1⌷⊁in 4 bedrooms CTV in all bedrooms ® T
✘ (ex guide dogs) sB&B⇄♠£50-£58 dB&B⇄♠£60-£75 ⊟
45P ⚗ ✳ CFA sauna solarium gymnasium
♀ English & French V ♡ ⚏ ⊁ ✳ Lunch £13.50-£15 Dinner £21-£24 Last dinner 9.30pm
Credit Cards ①②③④

TORBAY

See under **Brixham, Paignton & Torquay**

TORCROSS Devon Map **03** SX84

★66% **Grey Homes**
TQ7 2TH ☎Kingsbridge(0548)580220
Closed Nov-Mar
*This small, comfortable hotel is in an elevated position, overlooking the unique freshwater lake beside the sea, and the little fishing village of Torcross. Built in the 1920s by the grandfather of the present proprietor, guests are assured of a warm welcome. Bedrooms all share the same beautiful views, and are comfortably decorated and furnished. All offer private facilities, and there is a cosy lounge and a separate bar. A limited menu of home-cooked dishes is available in the relaxed atmosphere of the dining room.*
7⇄♠(1fb) CTV in all bedrooms ® ✳ sB&B⇄♠£30.50-£32.50
dB&B⇄♠£51-£55 ⊟
15P 3🚗 (charged) ⚗ ✳ ♪ (hard) nc2yrs
♡ ⚏ ✳ Dinner £11 Last dinner 7.30pm
Credit Cards ①③

TORMARTON Avon Map **03** ST77

★★67% **Compass Inn**
GL9 1JB (Best Western) ☎Chipping Sodbury(0454)218242 &
218577 FAX (0454) 218741
Closed Xmas
*Situated half a mile from the M4, junction 18, this former coaching inn has been restored and extended by the Monyard Family to provide public rooms of character with a good range of eating options and modern, well equipped, en suite bedrooms.*
31⇄♠(7fb)1⌷ CTV in all bedrooms ® T sB&B⇄♠£49.95-£67.50 dB&B⇄♠£64.90-£82.50 ⊟
160P ✳ CFA
V ♡ ⚏ Bar Lunch £3.50-£7alc Dinner £12.50-£17.50alc Last
dinner 9.30pm
Credit Cards ①②③⑤£

699

### TORPOINT Cornwall & Isles of Scilly Map 02 SX45

#### ★64% Whitsand Bay Hotel Golf & Country Club
Portwrinkle PL11 3BU (5m W, off B3247)
☎St Germans(0503)30276
Closed Jan-mid Mar RS Nov-24 Dec

*In a cliff-top location in the small village of Portwrinkle, about 5 miles from the naval base of Torpoint, this popular family and golfing hotel has been owned and managed by the Earle family for 30 years. Bedrooms are steadily being refurbished and offer simple comfort, many with lovely sea views. In addition to cosy, traditional public areas, there is a smartly maintained indoor leisure centre, complete with coffee shop and beauty treatment rooms.*

30rm(28⇨)(10fb) CTV in 10 bedrooms ® ✳ sB&B£17.50-£28 sB&B⇨£20-£28 dB&B⇨£40-£50 ⋓

CTV 60P ❁ CFA ▣ (heated) ▶ 18 sauna solarium gymnasium beauty salon steam room hairdressers ♨ *xmas*
♀ English & Continental V ✆ ♨ ✂ ✳ Sunday Lunch fr£7.50 High tea £4 Dinner £14.50&alc Last dinner 8.30pm
ⓔ

### TORQUAY Devon Map 03 SX96

**See Town Plan Section**

#### ★★★★★58% The Imperial
Park Hill Rd TQ1 2DG (Forte Hotels) ☎(0803)294301
Telex no 42849 FAX (0803) 298293

*A popular resort/conference hotel with fine views of the bay. Some bedrooms have been upgraded and it is hoped that others will be soon, but all are well equipped if a little compact. Public rooms are spacious but in need of refurbishment. The restaurant is in 2 sections and offers a comprehensive set price and à la carte menu of carefully prepared dishes. Excellent indoor and outdoor leisure facilities are available.*

167⇨♠(7fb)✂in 67 bedrooms CTV in all bedrooms T ✳ S%
sB&B⇨♠£76-£86 dB&B⇨♠£162-£262 ⋓
Lift ℂ 150P 30🚗 (£5 per day) ❁ CFA ▣ (heated) ⇌ (heated)
♪ (hard) squash snooker sauna solarium gymnasium health fitness centre croquet putting ♫ ♨ *xmas*
V ✆ ♨ ✂ ✳ S% Lunch £15.50-£16.50&alc Dinner fr£30&alc
Last dinner 9.30pm
Credit Cards ① ② ③ ④ ⑤

#### ★★★★53% Grand
Sea Front TQ2 6NT ☎(0803)296677 FAX (0803) 213462

*This imposing Victorian seafront hotel is undergoing extensive improvements. Public areas are spacious and comfortable and the bedrooms are well equipped.*

112⇨♠(10fb)6🚗 CTV in all bedrooms ® T sB&B⇨♠£47-£79 dB&B⇨♠£94-£158 ⋓
Lift ℂ 35🚗 ❁ CFA ▣ (heated) ⇌ (heated) ♪ (hard) sauna solarium gymnasium jacuzzi hairdressers ♨ *xmas*
V ✆ ♨ Lunch £10.50-£16.80&alc High tea £6.30-£7.88 Dinner £17.33-£19.43&alc Last dinner 9.30pm
Credit Cards ① ③ ⑤

#### ★★★★53% Palace
Babbacombe Rd TQ1 3TG ☎(0803)200200 Telex no 42606 FAX (0803) 299899

*Set in 25 acres of attractive grounds this hotel has excellent sports and leisure facilities including tennis, golf, squash, snooker and two swimming pools. Most bedrooms have recently been refurbished to a good modern standard and public areas are popular with the busy conference trade. Our Inspector found the quality of some of the dishes featured on the menu somewhat disappointing.*

141⇨♠(10fb)6🚗 CTV in all bedrooms ® T ✂ (ex guide dogs)
sB&B⇨♠£55-£93 dB&B⇨♠£110-£186 ⋓
Lift ℂ CTV 100P 40🚗 (£5 per night) ❁ CFA ▣ (heated) ⇌ (heated) ▶ 9 ♪ (hard) squash snooker sauna croquet putting table tennis ♫ ♨ *xmas*

♀ English & French V ✆ ♨ ♨ ✳ Lunch £12.50&alc High tea fr£7.50 Dinner fr£18.50&alc Last dinner 9.15pm
Credit Cards ① ③ ⑤

#### ★★★❁🏊70% Orestone Manor
Rockhouse Ln, Maidencombe TQ1 4SX ☎(0803)328098 & 328099 FAX (0803) 328336

*An hotel in an elevated position overlooking Lyme Bay dates from Georgian times, when it served as a country lodge. Still surrounded by its own gardens and grounds, it provides a warm welcome from resident proprietors and inviting public areas which have recently been modernised; a similar programme of bedroom refurbishment is now under way. A competent chef takes extreme care in the preparation of the interesting dishes that make up the table d'hôte menu, offering such mouth-watering starters as Hot Salmon Mousse Tartlet with Cream and Tarragon Sauce and a choice of desserts which includes Orange Soufflé Pancakes with Grand Marnier and Banana Bavarois.*

19⇨♠(4fb) CTV in all bedrooms ® T S% sB&B⇨♠£26-£64 dB&B⇨♠£52-£138 ⋓
CTV 30P ❁ CFA ⇌ (heated) putting green *xmas*
♀ International V ✆ ♨ ♨ S% Lunch £7.95-£12.50 High tea £5-£6.50 Dinner £19.50-£30&alc Last dinner 9pm
Credit Cards ① ② ③ ⑤ ⓔ

**See advertisement on page 703**

#### ★★★69% Abbey Lawn Hotel
Scarborough Rd TQ2 5UQ ☎(0803)299199 FAX (0803) 291460

*Complete refurbishment has restored this fine hotel to its former Georgian elegance and glory. Public rooms are spacious and richly furnished whilst bedrooms are well equipped. Spotlessly clean throughout the hotel is personally managed with prompt, traditional services.*

56⇨♠ CTV in all bedrooms ® T sB&B⇨♠£38-£60 dB&B⇨♠£76-£105 ⋓
Lift ℂ 50P ❁ CFA ▣ (heated) ⇌ (heated) ♪ (hard & grass )sauna solarium gymnasium nc11yrs *xmas*
♀ English & French V ✆ ♨ ✂ Lunch fr£9.50&alc Dinner fr£16.50&alc Last dinner 9pm
Credit Cards ① ② ③ ⑤

**See advertisement on page 703**

#### ★★★69% Corbyn Head
Torquay Rd, Sea Front, Livermead TQ2 6RH ☎(0803)213611 FAX (0803) 296152

*A modern, well maintained seafront hotel with sea views from many of the bedrooms and all the public areas, including 2 restaurants, a lounge-bar and a further lounge with a dance floor and access to the outdoor heated pool. The bedrooms vary in size but all are well equipped and have been pleasantly decorated with co-ordinating colour schemes.*

51⇨♠(1fb) CTV in all bedrooms ® T sB&B⇨♠£30-£55 dB&B⇨♠£60-£110 ⋓
ℂ 50P CFA ⇌ (heated) ♫ *xmas*
V ✆ ♨ Bar Lunch £3.50-£12.50 High tea £7.50-£10.50 Dinner £16.50-£22.50&alc Last dinner 9pm
Credit Cards ① ② ③ ⑤ ⓔ

**See advertisement on page 703**

#### ★★★68% Homers
Warren Rd TQ2 5TN ☎(0803)213456 FAX (0803) 213458
Closed 2 Jan-7 Feb

*All of the public rooms and most of the well equipped bedrooms at this elegant hotel enjoy panoramic views of Tor Bay. Décor throughout is tasteful and the furnishings have been carefully chosen. Interesting dishes are served in the dining room.*

14rm(13⇨♠)(1fb)1🚗 CTV in all bedrooms T ✳ sB&Bfr£22 sB&B⇨♠£22-£28 dB&B£40-£50 dB&B⇨♠£46-£80 ⋓
CTV 5P 🚗 ❁ nc7yrs *xmas*
♀ European V ✆ ♨ ✂ Dinner £15.85-£25&alc Last dinner 9pm
Credit Cards ① ② ③ ⑤ ⓔ

T

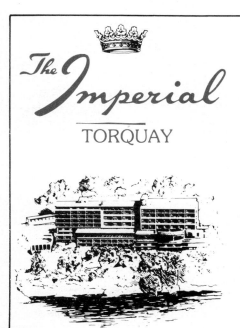
T

# Torquay

### ★★★65% Livermead Cliff
Torbay Rd TQ2 6RQ (Best Western) ☎(0803)299666 & 292881
Telex no 42424 FAX (0803) 294496
*This family-owned establishment stands within easy each of the town centre and local amenities despite an enviable position commanding some breathtaking views from the seafront. Though bedrooms vary in size they are all well equipped to meet the needs of holidaymakers and commercial visitors alike, and public areas refurbished in keeping with the 1990's maintain a high standard of comfort. Table d'hôte and à la carte menus provide a good range of dishes – including home-made desserts – and are complemented by a carefully chosen wine list. Guests are assured of both a warm welcome and friendly, well trained service.*
64⇨↟(21fb)1🛏 CTV in all bedrooms ® T S% sB&B⇨↟£29-£52 dB&B⇨↟£56.50-£102 🍴
Lift (( CTV 60P 12🚗 ❀ CFA ⌒ (heated) ♪ solarium ⚂ xmas
♀ English & Continental V ♥ ⚓ S% Lunch £7.25&alc Dinner £15&alc Last dinner 8.30pm
Credit Cards ① ② ③ ⑤

### ★★★64% *Overmead*
Daddyhole Rd TQ1 2EF (Consort) ☎(0803)297633 & 295666
FAX (0803) 211175
*In a quiet clifftop position commanding glorious sea views, this extended Victorian château offers comfortable bedrooms in a range of sizes, large public lounges and bars, plus conference and leisure facilities. The elegant dining room serves hearty table d'hôte meals.*
55⇨↟(7fb) CTV in all bedrooms ® T
Lift (( 11P ❀ ⌒ (heated) snooker sauna solarium gymnasium ♪
♀ International V ♥ ⚓ Last dinner 9pm
Credit Cards ① ② ③

### ★★★62% Sefton
Babbacombe Downs Rd, Babbacombe TQ1 3LH
☎(0803)328728 & 326591
*Set in an elevated position on the Babbacombe Downs, this modern-fronted property commands a glorious outlook across Lyme Bay. Bedrooms vary in size, but all are brightly decorated, while lounges, dining room and function suite share the same wonderful view. Family owners and their team of staff extend a warm welcome to guests.*
47⇨↟(11fb)1🛏 CTV in all bedrooms ® T ✻ sB&B⇨↟£35-£40 dB&B⇨↟£70-£84 🍴
Lift 40P CFA snooker indoor bowling xmas
V ♥ ⚓ ✻ Lunch £7.50-£12&alc Dinner fr£12&alc Last dinner 9pm
Credit Cards ① ② ③ ⑤

### ★★★61% Belgrave
Seafront TQ2 5HE ☎(0803)296666 FAX (0803) 211308
*Enviably situated on the seafront, and enjoying some glorious views, this hotel offers accommodation of an excellent standard in its 17-bedroom extension; other bedrooms are gradually being upgraded, and all provide good facilities which will appeal to both holidaymakers and commercial users. Public areas are spacious and modern, a simple table d'hôte menu with some à la carte choices being served in the relaxed atmosphere of the dining room.*
68⇨↟(16fb) CTV in all bedrooms ® T sB&B⇨↟£35-£48 dB&B⇨↟£70-£96 🍴
Lift (( 80P 6🚗 (£2) 🚗 ❀ CFA ⌒ (heated) xmas
♀ English & French ♥ ⚓ Bar Lunch £2-£8 Dinner £10-£12 Last dinner 8.30pm
Credit Cards ① ③ ⑤ ⑤

**See advertisement on page 705**

### ★★★59% Kistor
Belgrave Rd TQ2 5HF ☎(0803)212632 FAX (0803) 293219
*This large friendly hotel near the seafront and an easy walk from the town centre provides bedrooms of variable standards but all well equipped. More recently modernised public areas give a choice of lounges and leisure facilities including an indoor pool.*

59⇨↟(16fb)1🛏 CTV in all bedrooms ® T
Lift CTV 45P ❀ 🖃 (heated) sauna solarium gymnasium spa pool games room ♪
♀ English & Continental V ♥ ⚓ ✂
Credit Cards ① ② ③ ⑤

**See advertisement on page 705**

### ★★★57% Toorak
Chestnut Av TQ2 5JS ☎(0803)291444 Telex no 42885
FAX (0803) 291666
*An imposing and recently extended Victorian property set in its own gardens and grounds opposite the River Centre, offers good facilities in all 91 of its bedrooms, though some still await refurbishment. A selection of interesting dishes makes up the restaurant's table d'hôte menu, and guests have the use of a wide range of leisure amenities in adjacent hotels under the same ownership.*
91⇨↟(29fb) CTV in all bedrooms ® T S% sB&B⇨↟£43-£60 dB&B⇨↟£86-£120 (incl dinner) 🍴
Lift (( 90P 🚗 ❀ CFA ⌒ (heated) ♪ (hard) snooker croquet lawn ♪ xmas
♀ English & French V ♥ ⚓ ✻ Sunday Lunch £8.50 Dinner £13.50 Last dinner 8.30pm
Credit Cards ① ② ③ ⑤

### ★★★54% *Devonshire*
Parkhill Rd TQ1 2DY ☎(0803)291123 Telex no 42988
FAX (0803) 291710
*A predominantly holiday hotel, catering mainly for coach and tour parties provides attentive service; public areas include a dining room serving a simple table d'hôte menu. Bedrooms – a number of which are contained in an annexe block – are all well equipped, though some are due for refurbishment.*
47rm(35⇨11↟)Annexe12⇨↟(7fb) CTV in all bedrooms ®  →

## The New Sefton Hotel

Beautifully situated above the beach, this family run hotel boasts 47 delightful en-suite bedrooms, all with tea/coffee making, colour TV, radio and direct dial telephone, most with breathtaking seaviews.

Entertainment during the season

Short mat indoor bowling available
(by arrangement)

Extensive Christmas and New Year programmes

Mini Breaks Oct to May

Ample parking

**Send for our full colour brochure, we think you'll be impressed!**

**THE SEA FRONT
BABBACOMBE DOWNS ROAD, TORQUAY**

**Tel: (0803) 328728/326591**

《 ⌗ CTV 50P ❄ ⌁ (heated) ♪ (hard) snooker horse riding surfing ♫ ♨

♡ English, French, Italian & German ৬ ◻️ Last dinner 8.30pm

Credit Cards ①②③④⑤

See advertisement on page 707

★★★54% *Livermead House*
Torbay Rd TQ2 6QJ ☎(0803)294361 Telex no 42918
FAX (0803) 200758

*Conveniently situated for the town and beaches this hotel has indoor and outdoor leisure facilities, and a range of conference rooms. The compact bedrooms are equipped with good facilities and are suitable for holidaymakers and business guests alike.*

62⇄♪(9fb) CTV in all bedrooms ® T ✖ (ex guide dogs)
Lift 《 90P ❄ ⌁ (heated) ♪ (hard) squash snooker sauna solarium gymnasium

♡ English & French V ৬ ◻️ Last dinner 8.30pm

Credit Cards ①②③⑤

★★69% *Conway Court*
Warren Rd TQ2 5TS ☎(0803)299699
*Friendly holiday hotel with spectacular views across Tor Bay.*
38rm(16⇄19♪)(3fb)4⌗ CTV in all bedrooms ® T
CTV ♪ heated spa pool
৬ ◻️ ✂ Last dinner 8pm
Credit Cards ①②③⑤

★★68% *Oscar's Hotel & Restaurant*
56 Belgrave Rd TQ2 5HY ☎(0803)293563
Closed 12 Nov-17 Dec

*A tall, Victorian, terraced house, tastefully converted, Oscar's is in the Belgravia area of Torquay. Bedrooms are comfortable and the intimate bistro is open from March to October.*

12rm(1⇄8♪)(2fb) CTV in all bedrooms ® T
✖ (ex guide dogs) ✳ sB&B£14.50-£20.50 sB&B⇄♪£16.50-£22.50 dB&B£28-£40 dB&B⇄♪£32-£45 ⊟
CTV 8P ♨

♡ International V ৬ Dinner £7.50-£9.50&alc Last dinner 8pm
Credit Cards ①③④⑤

★★67% *Coppice*
Barrington Rd TQ1 2QJ ☎(0803)297786
Closed Nov-Apr

*The gardens of this attractive detached hotel contain an outdoor pool and ample car parking facilities, while the modernised and extended building provides bright, clean and well equipped public areas; the spacious restaurant's simple table d'hôte menu offers a choice of dishes, and guests are assured of a warm welcome.*

38rm(33⇄3♪)(10fb) CTV in all bedrooms ® T
《 CTV 30P ❄ ⌁ (heated) solarium
৬ Last dinner 8pm

★★67% *Frognel Hall*
Higher Woodfield Rd TQ1 2LD ☎(0803)298339
Closed Dec-Feb RS Xmas & New Year

*A Victorian villa, set in its own grounds with distant views of the sea, has been beautifully restored to preserve the building's original elegance whilst providing both public areas and bedrooms with bright décor in modern style and up-to-date facilities. The simple dishes offered on the restaurant's table d'hôte menu are prepared from the best of fresh ingredients, the atmosphere is relaxed, and guests receive a warm, friendly welcome.*

27rm(16⇄9♪)(4fb) CTV in all bedrooms ® sB&B£15.50-£26.50 sB&B⇄♪£18.50-£29.50 dB&B⇄♪£37-£59 ⊟
Lift CTV 25P ❄ CFA sauna solarium croquet games room exercise equipment *xmas*

♡ English & French V ৬ ◻️ Bar Lunch £1.50-£4.50 Dinner £8.95-£10.95 Last dinner 7.30pm

Credit Cards ①③⑤

★★66% **Burlington**
462-466 Babbacombe Rd TQ1 1HN ☎(0803)294374
FAX (0803) 200189

*A tourist hotel situated on a main road about quarter of a mile from beach and town centre.*

55⇄♪(7fb)1⌗ CTV in all bedrooms ® T ✳ sB&B⇄♪£27-£35 dB&B⇄♪£47-£63 ⊟

《 CTV 20P ❄ ◻️ (heated) sauna solarium pool table spa bath ♫ *xmas*

♡ English, French & Italian V ৬ ◻️ ✂ Sunday Lunch £3-£8 Dinner £8.10-£15&alc Last dinner 8pm

Credit Cards ①③ ⓔ

★★66% **Chelston Tower**
Rawlyn Rd TQ2 6PQ ☎(0803)607351
Closed Jan

*This small, cosy, family-owned hotel in country house style – built in the 1800's as a family home and still quietly set in two acres of woodland and garden – enjoys views over town and bay from its elevated position. Bedrooms vary in size, but all are smart and clean, while public areas are comfortable and service is both prompt and friendly.*

23rm(9⇄4♪)(12fb) T sB&B£19.50-£26 sB&B⇄♪£22.50-£32 dB&B£39-£52 dB&B⇄♪£45-£64
CTV 30P ❄ ⌁ (heated) games room *xmas*
V ৬ ◻️ Dinner £15 Last dinner 7.30pm
Credit Cards ①③

★★66% **Gresham Court**
Babbacombe Rd TQ1 1HG ☎(0803)293007 & 293658
Closed Dec-Feb

*Centrally situated, with easy access to both harbour and town centre, this warmly welcoming hotel has been owned by the same family for more than thirty years. Bedrooms, though simply furnished, are clean and comfortable, while the décor and furnishings of public areas are more modern in style.*

30⇄♪(6fb) CTV in all bedrooms ® sB&B⇄♪£22.50-£26.50 dB&B⇄♪£45-£53
Lift CTV 4P ♫
V ৬ ✂ Bar Lunch £1-£3.50 Dinner £7 Last dinner 8pm
Credit Cards ①③

★★66% **Red House**
Rousdown Rd, Chelston TQ2 6PB ☎(0803)607811
FAX (0803) 200592

*As its name suggests this is an attractive red brick hotel within easy reach of the town and beaches. The accommodation is comfortable and the coffee shop, dining room and lounge are all situated near the hotel's excellent leisure facilities.*

10⇄♪(3fb) CTV in all bedrooms ® S% sB&B⇄♪£22.45-£34 dB&B⇄♪£40.90-£60 ⊟
10P ♨ ❄ CFA ◻️ (heated) ⌁ (heated) sauna solarium gymnasium games room spa pool *xmas*

♡ English & French V ৬ ◻️ ✂ S% Lunch fr£7.95alc High tea £1.90-£3.60alc Dinner £8.80-£9.95&alc Last dinner 8pm
Credit Cards ①③

★★65% **Dunstone**
Lower Warberry Rd TQ1 1QS ☎(0803)293185
Closed Nov-Feb

*An imposing hotel in its own gardens, peacefully situated in an elevated position with some beautiful views over the bay. Bedrooms have been redecorated in cheerful floral schemes with modern furnishings. The lounge and conservatory bar, with access to the patio, retain more of the building's original elegance and the proprietor, Mr Dennys, a professional musician, will likely entertain guests at the grand piano. A table d'hôte menu offers a choice of home-cooked fare in the congenial dining room.*

14rm(13⇄♪)(3fb) CTV in all bedrooms ® T ✖ sB&B£22-£28 sB&B⇄♪£25-£33 dB&B£44-£56 dB&B⇄♪£50-£66 ⊟
CTV 18P ♨ ❄ ⌁ (heated) pool table table tennis badminton
V ৬ ◻️ ✂ ✳ Bar Lunch £2-£4 Dinner £10 Last dinner 7.30pm
Credit Cards ①③

T

# Torquay

## ★★65% Hunsdon Lea

Hunsdon Rd TQ1 1QB ☎(0803)296538
Closed Nov-Etr

*Set in its own gardens in a quiet street away from the town centre, yet offering easy access to it, this hotel offers simply appointed but well equipped bedrooms, comfortable public areas and a heated outdoor pool; the dishes on both à la carte and table d'hôte menus are home-cooked from the best of fresh produce, and resident proprietors welcome guests warmly.*

12rm(7⇨2♠)(3fb) CTV in all bedrooms ® T ⊁ ✱ sB&B£14-£19 dB&B⇨♠£32-£46

CTV 12P ⇔ ➣ (heated) solarium pool table table tennis
V ✿ 및 ⊁ ✱ Bar Lunch £3 Dinner £4.50&alc Last dinner 8pm
£

---

## ★★64% *Albaston House*

27 St Marychurch Rd TQ1 3JF ☎(0803)296758
Closed Dec

*This small, family-run hotel, open all year round, stands within easy reach of both town centre and beaches. Recently refurbished bedrooms are now tastefully decorated, comfortably furnished and equipped with good facilities, while simply appointed public areas include a dining room offering a table d'hôte menu changed weekly. Guests are assured of a warm welcome and friendly service throughout their stay.*

13⇨♠(4fb) CTV in all bedrooms ® T
CTV 12➣ ⇔
⦾ English & French V ✿ 및
Credit Cards [1][3]

---

## ★★63% Roseland

Warren Rd TQ2 5TT ☎(0803)213829 FAX (0803) 291266

*In an elevated setting enjoying breathtaking views across the Bay to Paignton and Brixham. Bedrooms have recently been refurbished and now offer modern facilities and a simple table d'hôte menu is available in the informal restaurant.*

36⇨♠(3fb)3⟊ CTV in all bedrooms ® T ✱ sB&B⇨♠£27-£35 dB&B⇨♠£47-£63 (incl dinner) ⊟
Lift ⟊ *xmas*
⦾ International V ✿ 및 ⊁ Bar Lunch £2-£8 Dinner £10-£16
Last dinner 8pm
Credit Cards [1][3] £

---

## ★★62% Ansteys Lea

Babbacombe Rd, Wellswood TQ1 2QJ ☎(0803)294843
Closed 16 Nov-23 Dec & 29 Dec-Feb

*A large Victorian villa near Babbacombe Beach and Kent's Cavern is family run to provide friendly service and accommodation in simply furnished bedrooms; the attractive well kept garden contains a sheltered, secluded swimming pool and there is a games room in the cellar.*

21⇨♠(2fb) CTV in all bedrooms ® sB&B⇨♠£25-£32
dB&B⇨♠£50-£64 (incl dinner) ⊟
CTV 18P ⇔ ✿ ➣ (heated) ♫ *xmas*
⦾ English & French ✿ 및 Bar Lunch £1.20-£3
Credit Cards [1][3] £

---

## ★★61% *Morningside*

Babbacombe Downs TQ1 3LF ☎(0803)327025

*A friendly, family-run hotel which enjoys views across Lyme Bay from its setting on Babbacombe Downs provides well equipped bedrooms and comfortable public areas, the dining room offering a choice of menus.*

14⇨♠ CTV in all bedrooms ® ⊁
CTV 16P nc10yrs
V ✿ 및
Credit Cards [1][3]

---

## ★★61% Hotel Sydore

Meadfoot Rd TQ1 2JP ☎(0803)294758

*A detached property standing in its own grounds, with easy access to town centre and harbour, provides accommodation in 13 en suite bedrooms (some of which have been redecorated over the last 3 years). Two lounges – one with bar – are individualised by pieces of furniture which, like the many smaller items, have gradually been collected by the proprietor and his family, and a dining room offering table d'hôte menus will also cater for special diets. Guests are assured of a warm welcome and personal service throughout their stay.*

13rm(6⇨6♠)(5fb)1🛏 CTV in all bedrooms ® sB&B⇨♠£17-£30 dB&B⇨♠£34-£50 ⊟
CTV 17P ✿ games room croquet *xmas*
⦾ English & Continental V ✿ 및 ✱ Sunday Lunch fr£6.95&alc
High tea fr75p Dinner fr£6.95&alc Last dinner 8.45pm
Credit Cards [1][3] £

---

## ★★60% Bancourt

Avenue Rd TQ2 5LG ☎(0803)295077

*A large hotel on the main route to the sea front provides accommodation well equipped for both business and holiday visitors, a dining room offering table d'hôte menus, and a spacious ballroom and bar on the lower ground floor; parking is available on the premises.*

46rm(25⇨5♠)(8fb) CTV in all bedrooms ® T ✱ S%
sB&B£20.50-£30.50 sB&B⇨♠£25.50-£33.50 dB&B£41-£61
dB&B⇨♠£51-£67
⟮ CTV 50P ✿ CFA ▢ (heated) snooker games room *xmas*
⦾ English & French ✿ 및 ✱ S% Dinner £11.50 Last dinner
8pm
Credit Cards [1][2][3]

---

## ★★59% Bute Court

Belgrave Rd TQ2 5HQ ☎(0803)293771

*A resort hotel with easy access to the seafront and town centre. The bedrooms, whilst simply furnished, are equipped with colour TVs and direct dial telephones. Entertainment is provided during the season and there is ample car parking.*

48rm(44⇨♠)(10fb) CTV in all bedrooms ® T sB&B£20-£24
sB&B⇨♠£17-£35 dB&B£36-£44 dB&B⇨♠£52-£68 ⊟
Lift ⟮ CTV 37P ✿ CFA ➣ (heated) snooker table tennis darts
♫ ☘ *xmas*
⦾ English & Continental ✿ 및 S% Bar Lunch £1.50-£3.50
Dinner £5-£9 Last dinner 8pm
Credit Cards [1][2][3][5] £

---

## ★★58% Hotel Balmoral

Meadfoot Sea Rd TQ1 2LQ ☎(0803)293381 & 299224

*This family holiday hotel, set in its own small but pleasant grounds and gardens, stands in the quieter part of the town with good views and easy access to Meadfoot Beach. Refurbishment and upgrading of accommodation has followed a recent change of ownership, completed rooms – though a little compact – being attractively decorated, well furnished and equipped with en suite facilities. Public areas include a comfortable, quiet lounge and an informal restaurant serving a simple table d'hôte menu.*

24⇨♠(7fb) CTV in all bedrooms ® T sB&B⇨♠£22-£28
dB&B⇨♠£44-£56 ⊟
18P ✿ CFA *xmas*
⦾ English & French ✿ 및 ⊁ ✱ Lunch £6.50 Dinner £9.50 Last
dinner 8.30pm
Credit Cards [1][2][3]

---

## ★★58% Carlton

Falkland Rd TQ2 5JJ ☎(0803)291166

*Both public areas and bedrooms are undergoing massive refurbishment at this privately owned hotel near the town and English Riviera Centre, new fixtures, fittings and décor providing comfortable and well equipped accommodation.*

32rm(29⇨♠)(19fb) CTV in all bedrooms ® T ⊁
sB&B⇨♠£19-£31 dB&B⇨♠£38-£62

Lift CTV 30P ✿ CFA ⌣ (heated) snooker ♫ *xmas*
V ♥ ⏛ ✂
Credit Cards ①③

### ★★57% Lansdowne
Babbacombe Rd TQ1 1PW ☏(0803)299599 FAX (0803) 290344
*A hotel on the Babbacombe road, near the town centre, is very well geared to the needs of the holidaymaker, offering well equipped bedrooms of various sizes, bright, attractive public areas and friendly service from owners and staff.*
27⌣🐾(9fb) CTV in all bedrooms ® T
CTV 30P ✿ CFA ⌣ (heated) pool table table tennis ♫
♀ English, French & Italian V ♥ ⏛ ✂ Last dinner 8.30pm
Credit Cards ①③

### ★★57% Templestowe
Tor Church Rd TQ2 5UU ☏(0803)299499 FAX (0803) 295101
*This large family owned and managed hotel with easy access to the town centre, offers accommodation in en suite bedrooms which, though simply decorated and furnished, are all well equipped. An à la carte menu of unelaborate dishes is served in the functional restaurant, a wide choice of recreational facilities is available, and there is live entertainment most evenings.*
87⌣🐾(28fb) CTV in all bedrooms ® T sB&B⌣🐾£27-£39 dB&B⌣🐾£54-£78
Lift ☖ CTV 50P ⌣ (heated) ♪ (hard) solarium crazy golf table tennis pool table ♫ ⚘ *xmas*
♀ French V ♥ ⏛ Bar Lunch £2-£4.50 Dinner £7.50&alc Last dinner 8.30pm
Credit Cards ①③

---

🐚 Shell filling stations (7am–11pm) are marked on the town plans.

---

### ★★55% Norcliffe
7 Babbacombe Downs Rd, Babbacombe TQ1 3LF
☏(0803)328456
*This detached Victorian property is located near to the village of Babbacombe, with some sea views. Bedrooms are simply decorated and furnished, yet all offer colour television and direct dial telephones.*
20⌣🐾(2fb)1🛏 CTV in all bedrooms ® T ✳ sB&B⌣🐾£22-£32 dB&B⌣🐾£44-£64 (incl dinner)
Lift 16P CFA *xmas*
♥ ⏛ ✂ Lunch £6.95
Credit Cards ①③④

### ★★52% Vernon Court
Warren Rd TQ2 5TR ☏(0803)292676
Closed Nov-Feb (ex Xmas)
*Beautifully situated in an elevated position, an hotel in process of extension commands glorious views of the bay from both its public areas and some of the simply furnished and decorated bedrooms.*
29rm(14⌣13🐾)(6fb) CTV in all bedrooms ® ✳ sB&B£23.50-£29 sB&B⌣🐾£25.50-£29 dB&B£47-£64 dB&B⌣🐾£47-£64 🅿
CTV 9P *xmas*
♀ English & Continental V ♥ ⏛ ✳ Dinner £10 Last dinner 8pm
Credit Cards ①②③⑤④

### ★70% Fairmount House
Herbert Road, Chelston TQ2 6RW (Guestaccom)
☏(0803)605446
Closed Nov-Feb
*This attractive little hotel is located in a quiet residential area of Torquay. Surrounded by beautifully kept gardens, a warm welcome is assured at this hotel by Maggie and Noel Tolkien, and friendly service is offered. Well equipped bedrooms offer bright décor and co-ordinating colour schemes. The public rooms include a small bar in a conservatory, off the informal dining room where a*
→

*table d'hôte menu is offered, made up of well cooked, interesting dishes.*
8⇨↱(3fb) CTV in all bedrooms ® sB&B⇨↱£23.50-£26.50 dB&B⇨↱£47-£53 ⊟
CTV 9P ♤ *xmas*
♡ English & Continental ♧ ⊻ ⚸ ✻ Sunday Lunch £10.50 Dinner £10.50 Last dinner 7.30pm
Credit Cards [1] [2] [3] (£)

**★68% Westwood**
111 Abbey Rd TQ2 5NP ☎(0803)293818
*Situated near to the centre of the town, and only a short walk away from the harbour and sea front, the Westwood provides clean, comfortable, well equipped bedrooms and attractive public rooms. A simple table d'hôte menu is offered in the relaxed dining room, and the dishes are home cooked and enjoyable. The warm welcome, friendly service and the party atmosphere, created by the caring proprietors and their team of staff, make a stay at this hotel memorable.*
26⇨↱(4fb) CTV in all bedrooms ® ✗ (ex guide dogs) ✻ sB&B⇨↱£15-£19 dB&B⇨↱£30-£38 ⊟
CTV 12P ❊ CFA *xmas*
♡ English & French V ⚸ ✻ Lunch £5-£7&alc
Credit Cards [1] [3] (£)

***★66% Shelley Court***
Croft Rd TQ2 5UD ☎(0803)295642
*An extended Victorian property close to the town centre, overlooking the bay from its own gardens, offers bedrooms which, though compact, are brightly decorated and comfortably furnished. Public areas include a TV lounge, a bar lounge where live entertainment is provided 3 nights a week, and an informal dining room serving table d'hôte meals. Service is friendly throughout.*
29rm(3⇨19↱)(3fb) ® ✗
CTV 20P ❊ ♫
♧ Last dinner 7.30pm
Credit Cards [1]

**★64% Sunleigh**
Livermead Hill TQ2 6QY ☎(0803)607137
Closed Jan-28 Mar & 7 Nov-23 Dec
*Simply furnished but comfortable accommodation is offered by a Victorian hotel set in its own grounds overlooking the bay. The open-plan bar lounge and dining room have recently been refurbished to provide attractive surroundings in which to enjoy a meal chosen from the simple table d'hôte menu, and guests receive a warm welcome from the establishment's resident proprietors.*
20↱(4fb) CTV in all bedrooms ® sB&B↱£25.50-£32 dB&B↱£51-£64 (incl dinner) ⊟
CTV 18P *xmas*
Dinner £9.75 Last dinner 7pm
Credit Cards [1] [2] [3] (£)

**★62% Ashley Rise**
18 Babbacombe Rd, Babbacombe TQ1 3SJ ☎(0803)327282
Closed Dec-Mar ex Xmas
*This family-run hotel near Babbacombe Downs, catering predominantly for the needs of holidaymakers and coach parties, offers simply appointed bedrooms and pleasant public areas which include a table d'hôte restaurant providing some evenings of live entertainment during the season.*
26⇨↱(5fb) CTV in all bedrooms ® ✻ sB&B⇨↱£19-£22 dB&B⇨↱£36-£44
CTV 14P ♫ *xmas*
♧
(£)

A rosette means exceptional standards of cuisine.

**★61% Hotel Fluela**
15-17 Hatfield Rd TQ1 3BW ☎(0803)297512
*This small, family-run hotel has a friendly atmosphere, and the bedrooms, while compact in places, offer good facilities, and the two lounges are comfortably decorated and furnished. A simple choice of home-cooked dinners makes up the table d'hôte menus and the service is friendly and relaxed.*
13⇨↱(3fb) CTV in all bedrooms ® T ✗ (ex guide dogs) dB&B⇨↱£32-£45
CTV 20P ⌗ *xmas*
V ⚸ ✻
Credit Cards [1] [3]

**★58% Sunray**
Aveland Rd, Babbacombe TQ1 3PT ☎(0803)328285
RS Dec-Mar
*Personal service is provided by the owner of a friendly little hotel which offers good-value, basic holiday accommodation.*
22rm(21⇨↱)(3fb) CTV in all bedrooms ® ✻ sB&B⇨↱£14-£18 dB&B⇨↱£28-£36 (incl dinner) ⊟
CTV 15P 1🚗 *xmas*
♡ English, French & Italian ⚸ ✻
Credit Cards [1] [3]

**❀❀❀ ✕✕The Table**
135 Babbacombe Rd TQ1 3SR ☎(0803)324292
*A cosy, intimate restaurant in the centre of Babbacombe, converted from a shop by Jane and Trevor Brooks. Jane is the charming and attentive hostess, while Trevor is the innovative chef, preparing local produce with fresh herbs and robust sauces. His background as a patissier in some of Britain's finest restaurants reveals itself throughout, from the light home-made rolls to the delicious desserts. The wine list is young but carefully compiled, and offers good value for money.*
Closed Mon, 1-16 Feb & 1-16 Sep Lunch not served
♡ British & French 20 seats Dinner £26-£28 Last dinner 10pm ⊁ nc10yrs
Credit Cards [1] [3]

## TORRINGTON, GREAT Devon Map **02** SS42

**❀ ✕Rebecca's**
8 Potacre St EX38 8BH ☎Torrington(0805)22113
*Karl Birk, Mark Jones and Julia Butler have transformed this one-time teashop/restaurant into a more stylish and comfortable establishment, its cottage frontage giving no hint of the very pleasant, modern interior decorated on classical lines in soft pastels with co-ordinating fabrics and quality table appointments. Noteworthy cooking makes excellent use of fresh produce – and in particular of fish from the Cornish port of Newlyn – bringing flair and imagination to its preparation. As a starter, you might enjoy a delicate mousseline of locally caught fish with a sauce of herbs, mayonnaise and Dijon mustard, perhaps following it by the nicely pink breast of Aylesbury duck with a plum and lime sauce, or fluffy poached turbot with a lightly glazed Dijon sauce. Desserts include orange and ginger steamed pudding, raspberry and pear mille feuilles and an infamous chocolate and hazelnut cheesecake, the well balanced wine list is reasonably priced, and excellent, attentive service is unobtrusive.*
Closed Sun, 1st wk Nov & 26-28 Dec Lunch not served Mon Dinner not served Mon (Oct-Mar)
♡ International 36 seats ✻ Lunch £17-£26alc Dinner £17-£26alc Last lunch 2pm Last dinner 10pm ⊁ nc2yrs
Credit Cards [1] [3]

## TOTLAND BAY

See Wight, Isle of

For key to symbols in English see the bookmark.

## TOTNES Devon Map **03** SX86

See also Staverton

**★★61% Royal Seven Stars**

TQ9 5DD ☎(0803)862125 & 863241 FAX (0803) 867925

*Positioned at the foot of this ancient and historic town's main street, an hotel dating back to 1660 offers accommodation in 18 well equipped bedrooms. The Carriage room buffet bar serves snacks throughout the day, while the Brutus Room restaurant (adjacent to the lounge bar) provides a more comprehensive table d'hôte menu; a comfortable and quieter lounge for residents is available on the first floor.*

18rm(12⇌↱)(3fb)2⊟ CTV in all bedrooms ® **T** sB&Bfr£39 sB&B⇌↱fr£49 dB&Bfr£50 dB&B⇌↱£62-£72 ⊟

CTV 20P CFA ♫ *xmas*

☋ English & Continental **V** ♡ ⚡ Lunch £7.50-£8 Dinner £14-£15.50 Last dinner 9.30pm

Credit Cards [1] [3] [5]

## TOWCESTER Northamptonshire Map **04** SP64 ◎

**⌂Forte Travelodge**

East Towcester by pass NN12 0DD (A43 East Towcester by-pass) (Forte) ☎(0327)359105 Central Res (0800) 850950

*A popular lodge on the A43, offering easy access to Northampton (some 9 miles away), offers value for money accommodation in well equipped modern rooms, meals being available from 7am to 10pm in the adjacent Little Chef restaurant.*

33⇌↱(33fb) CTV in all bedrooms ® sB⇌↱£29.95 dB⇌↱£29.95 (room only)

☾ 33P ⊟

Credit Cards [1] [2] [3]

**❀❀ ✕✕ *Vine House***

100 High St, Paulerspury NN12 7NA (3m S A5)
☎Paulerspury(032733)267

*This hotel and restaurant, set in a peaceful, attractive village just off the A5 halfway between Northampton and Milton Keynes, offers an interesting menu featuring a good range of dishes which are skilfully prepared to delight both the eye and palate. Flavours are subtle but clearly identifiable – the mousseline of salmon in a Champagne sauce being particularly praiseworthy – and sweets iclude a crème brûlèe flavoured with jasmine tea and a trio of chocolate desserts that are not to be missed.*

Closed 2 wks before Etr, Xmas-New Year & BHs Lunch not served Sat & Mon

Dinner not served Sun

☋ French **V** 45 seats Last lunch 2pm Last dinner 9.30pm 20 P

Credit Cards [1] [3]

## TREARDDUR BAY Gwynedd Map **06** SH27

**★★★62% *Beach***

LL65 2YT (Best Western) ☎(0407)860332 Telex no 61529
FAX (0407) 861140

*Situated just a few hundred yards from the beach, this privately-owned hotel is ideally suited for the family holidaymaker. The bedrooms are quite well equipped, and the hotel offers a choice of restaurants and bar facilities. There is also a well equipped indoor leisure centre, the facilities of which include a small swimming pool, 2 squash courts and 9 full-sized snooker tables. In short, the hotel offers something for all the family.*

26⇌↱(2fb) CTV in all bedrooms ® **T**

☾ 150P squash snooker sauna solarium gymnasium spa ⌂

☋ English & French **V** ♡ ☕ Last dinner 9.30pm

Credit Cards [1] [2] [3] [5]

**★★★62% *Trearddur Bay***

LL68 2UN ☎(0407)860301 Telex no 61609

*Situated on the seafront, only a few yards from a sandy beach, this popular hotel offers facilities which include a function suite and heated indoor swimming pool. Extensive improvement and refurbishment was carried out in most areas during 1991.*

27rm(20⇌)(7fb) CTV in all bedrooms ®

☾ CTV 300P ✲ ⊡ (heated)

**V** ♡ ☕

Credit Cards [1] [2] [3] [4] [5]

**★★58% *Seacroft***

Ravenspoint Rd LL65 2YU ☎(0407)860348

*This small privately owned hotel is situated close to the beach. The accommodation is simple, but several bedrooms have en suite facilities and 2 are equipped for families with young children.*

6rm(1⇌2↱)(3fb) CTV in all bedrooms ® ✈

CTV 30P ✲

☋ French **V** ♡

## TREBETHERICK Cornwall & Isles of Scilly Map **02** SW97

**★★67% Bodare**

Daymer Bay PL27 6SA ☎(0208)863210

Closed Nov-Feb

14⇌↱Annexe4⇌↱(7fb) ® **T** ✱ sB&B⇌↱£45.28-£50.50 dB&B⇌↱£90.50-£100.10 (incl dinner) ⊟

CTV 25P ⊟ ✲ ♫

**V** ♡ ☕ ✱ Bar Lunch £6 High tea £2.85-£6 Dinner £15 Last dinner 8.30pm

Credit Cards [1] [3]

## TREFRIW Gwynedd Map **06** SH76

**★★71% Hafod House**

LL27 0RQ (Minotels) ☎Llanrwst(0492)640029
FAX (0492) 641351

*Situated in the beautiful Conwy valley, this converted 17th-century farmhouse is personally run by the chef-owner and his wife, and combines warm hospitality, imaginative cuisine and comfortable, well equipped rooms.*

→

7⇨🚻1🛏 CTV in all bedrooms ® T ✖ (ex guide dogs)
sB&B⇨🚻£30 dB&B⇨🚻£60 🅿
20P ✿ nc11yrs *xmas*
🍴 English & French V ✿ ♨ Lunch £4.95-£8.95 Dinner £14.50-
£15.75 Last dinner 9.30pm
Credit Cards 1 2 3 5 ⓔ

## TREMADOG Gwynedd Map 06 SH54

### ★★57% *Madoc*
LL49 9RB ☎Porthmadog(0766)512021
*Stone-built, and dating back to the early 19th century, the hotel
stands in the market square. Furnishings are comfortable, and the
dining room serves good, honest food.*
21rm(1⇨3🚻)(3fb) ®
CTV 12P 4🚗 ♫
V ✿ ♨ Last dinner 9.30pm
Credit Cards 1 3

## TRESAITH Dyfed Map 02 SN25

### ★65% *Bryn Berwyn*
SA43 2JG ☎Aberporth(0239)811126
Closed 24 Dec-29 Jan
7⇨🚻(1fb)1🛏✂in 1 bedroom CTV in all bedrooms ®
✖ (ex guide dogs) ✱ S% sB&B⇨🚻£14.50-£27 dB&B⇨🚻£29-
£52 🅿
CTV 14P 🚗 ✿ pitch & putt
✿ ♨ ✱ S% Lunch £5.50-£6.50&alc High tea £3.50-£6.50&alc
Dinner £8.50-£10.50&alc Last dinner 5.30pm
Credit Cards 1 3

## TRESCO
See Scilly, Isles of

## TREYARNON BAY Cornwall & Isles of Scilly Map 02 SW87

### ★★65% *Waterbeach*
PL28 8JW ☎Padstow(0841)520292 (0841) 521102
Closed Nov-Feb
*A warm welcome awaits guests at this hotel which overlooks bay
and beach from the setting of its own secluded garden. Bedrooms
are well equipped and public areas include a comfortable lounge
and bar as well as the dining room with its imaginative table d'hôte
menu of freshly cooked dishes.*
20rm(7⇨2🚻)(2fb) CTV in all bedrooms ® T ✖ ✱ sB&B£30-
£39 dB&B£60-£72 dB&B⇨🚻£66-£78 (incl dinner)
CTV 20P 🚗 ✿ ♪ (hard) putting
V ✿ ♨ Dinner £12.50 Last dinner 8.15pm
Credit Cards 1 2 3

## TRING Hertfordshire Map 04 SP91

### ★★65% *Rose & Crown*
High St HP23 5AH (Lansbury) ☎(044282)4071 Telex no 826538
FAX (0442) 890735
*This attractive former coaching inn has recently benefited from
much refurbishment, and public rooms now include a cosy lounge
bar with a log fire, a split-level restaurant partly overlooking the
courtyard, and several meeting/function rooms. The bedrooms vary
in size, but they are all decorated and equipped to the same high
standard, and there is extensive parking.*
27⇨🚻(1fb)2🛏✂in 5 bedrooms CTV in all bedrooms ® T
✖ (ex guide dogs) sB&B⇨🚻fr75 dB&B⇨🚻fr88 🅿
◖ 50P CFA *xmas*
🍴 English & Continental V ✿ ✂ Lunch £7.70-£9.95&alc
Dinner fr£14.95 Last dinner 10pm
Credit Cards 1 2 3 5

### ⬆Crows Nest Travel Inn
Tring Hill HP23 4LD ☎(044282)4819
*Well placed for access to main routes, this modern annexe block
alongside a Beefeater restaurant with its own lounge bar provides
well equipped, value for money accommodation.*
30⇨🚻 CTV in all bedrooms ® ✖ (ex guide dogs)
140P
V ✿ ✂ Last dinner 10.30pm
Credit Cards 1 2 3 5

### ○Pendley Manor
Cow Ln HP2 5QY ☎(0442)891891 FAX (0442) 890687
Open
70⇨🚻

## TROON Strathclyde *Ayrshire* Map 10 NS33

### ★★★★❀67% *Marine Highland*
KA10 6HE (Scottish Highland) ☎(0292)314444 Telex no 777595
FAX (0292) 316922
*With Troon's championship golf course on its doorstep this hotel is
popular with golfers, tourists and business people alike. The lively
brasserie, main restaurant and comfortable lounges are
complemented by good leisure facilities and a commendable range
of services.*
72⇨🚻(7fb)1🛏 CTV in all bedrooms ® T sB&B⇨🚻£82-£95
dB&B⇨🚻£123-£133 🅿
Lift ◖ 200P ✿ CFA 📺 (heated) squash snooker sauna solarium
gymnasium shooting fishing golf riding ⚕ *xmas*
🍴 International V ✿ ♨ Lunch £10.20-£11.30&alc Dinner
£17.90-£19.50&alc Last dinner 11pm
Credit Cards 1 2 3 5 ⓔ

### ★★★❀67% *Piersland House*
Craigend Rd KA10 6HD (Consort) ☎(0292)314747
FAX (0292) 315613
15⇨🚻Annexe4⇨🚻(2fb)1🛏 CTV in all bedrooms ® T ✱
sB&B⇨🚻£53-£82 dB&B⇨🚻£82-£105 🅿
◖ 150P ✿ CFA croquet putting *xmas*
🍴 Scottish, English & Contininental V ✿ ✱ Lunch
fr£10.95&alc High tea £4.50-£7.95 Dinner fr£18.50&alc Last
dinner 9.30pm
Credit Cards 1 2 3 5

### ★★62% *Craiglea*
South Beach KA10 6EG ☎(0292)311366
*This long-established family-run hotel looks out to sea across the
South Links and maintains traditional values and courteous
service.*
20rm(10⇨5🚻)(2fb) CTV in all bedrooms ® T sB&B£30-£40
sB&B⇨🚻£35-£45 dB&B£45-£55 dB&B⇨🚻£50-£60 🅿
CTV 14P *xmas*
V ✿ ✱ Lunch £7.50&alc Dinner £12.50&alc Last dinner
8.45pm
Credit Cards 1 2 3 5

### ★★60% *Ardneil*
51 Saint Meddans St KA10 6NU ☎(0292)311611
*A small privately owned commercial hotel close to the station,
providing friendly service and comfortable compact
accommodation. There is a lounge bar and separate cocktail bar,
and a popular mealtime trade with menus emphasising grill dishes.*
9rm(3⇨4🚻)(2fb) CTV in all bedrooms ® ✱ sB&B£30-£35
sB&B⇨🚻£35-£40 dB&B£50-£55 dB&B⇨🚻£55-£60
100P ✿ snooker
V ✿ ♨ Lunch £7.85-£10.95alc High tea £6.95-£7.95alc
Dinner £10.95-£15alc Last dinner 9pm
Credit Cards 1 2 3 ⓔ

**★★60% South Beach**

South Beach Rd KA10 6EG ☎(0292)312033 FAX (0292)318438

*This popular holiday hotel close to the seafront is being steadily upgraded by the owners. The refurbished bedrooms are very attractive, particularly the two studio rooms, and the hotel includes lounge bars and a leisure centre.*

27⇩🎍(6fb) CTV in all bedrooms ® T ✳ sB&B⇩🎍£40-£45 dB&B⇩🎍£55-£65 ☒

⦅ CTV 50P sauna solarium gymnasium jacuzzi beauty therapist ♫ *xmas*

♀ English & French ♡ ⌂ ✳ Bar Lunch £5.50-£9.25 High tea £5.15-£7.50 Dinner £8.50-£12.95 Last dinner 8.30pm

Credit Cards ① ② ③ ⓔ

---

**TROTTON** West Sussex Map **04** SU82

**★★★63% Southdowns**

GU31 5JN (Exec Hotel) ☎Rogate(0730)821521 & 821763 FAX (0730) 821790

*A peaceful rural setting and good leisure facilities make this the ideal venue for both business and pleasure occasions. The recently upgraded accommodation in the original house is supplemented by an extension of uniformly well equipped bedrooms, and a small conservatory lounge has recently been added.*

22⇩(3fb)1 ⊞✂in 4 bedrooms CTV in all bedrooms ® T ✕ sB&B⇩£50-£60 dB&B⇩£65-£90 ☒

CTV 70P ✿ CFA ▭ (heated) ♟ (hard) ♪ sauna solarium croquet exercise equipment *xmas*

V ♡ ⌂ ✂ Lunch £10-£13&alc High tea £5.50 Dinner £16&alc Last dinner 10pm

Credit Cards ① ② ③ ⓔ

**See advertisement under MIDHURST**

---

**TROUTBECK (NEAR WINDERMERE)** Cumbria Map **07** NY40

**★★72% Mortal Man**

LA23 1PL ☎Ambleside(05394)33193

Closed mid Nov-mid Feb

*A delightful historic country inn with a cosy, warm atmosphere and comfortable bedrooms. There are beautiful Lakeland views from the dining room where a high standard of home-cooked food is served.*

12⇩🎍 CTV in all bedrooms ® T S% sB&B⇩🎍£45-£50 dB&B⇩🎍£90-£100 (incl dinner) ☒

20P ⊞ ✿ nc5yrs

V ♡ ⌂ S% Sunday Lunch £11 Dinner £17.50 Last dinner 8pm ⓔ

---

**TROWBRIDGE** Wiltshire Map **03** ST85

**★★60% Polebarn**

Polebarn Rd BA14 7EW ☎(0225)777006 FAX (0225) 754164

*This late Georgian Grade II listed building has an impressive façade and entrance hall, with an intimate bar and restaurant in the basement. Bedrooms vary in size but all are simply decorated and equipped with modern facilities. The husband and wife managers and friendly staff provide helpful service.*

13rm(2⇩10🎍)(1fb) CTV in all bedrooms ® T ✳ sB&B£38-£43 sB&B⇩🎍£38-£43 dB&B£50-£60 dB&B⇩🎍£50-£60 ☒ CTV 10P 2🐎

V ♡ ⌂ ✳ Lunch £2-£8 Dinner fr£11.50 Last dinner 8.45pm

Credit Cards ① ③

**★69% Hilbury Court**

Hilperton Rd BA14 7JW ☎(0225)752949

Closed 24-31 Dec

*Accommodation is clean, very well maintained and equipped with the modern facilities expected by today's business traveller at this hotel, a late Georgian building set in neatly kept gardens on the A361 Trowbridge to Devizes road about half a mile from the town centre. Guests can take their ease in either the comfortable lounge*

→

**T**

*or a small bar, and good home cooking more than compensates for a sometimes restricted range of choice and lack of flexibility in meal times.*
13rm(4⇨3↱)(2fb) CTV in all bedrooms ® T
✈ (ex guide dogs)
CTV 14P ⇎ ✲
V ✿ ☐ Last dinner 7.30pm
Credit Cards [1] [3]

---

**TRURO** Cornwall & Isles of Scilly Map **02** SW84 ◎

**★★★71% Alverton Manor**
Tregolls Rd TR1 1XQ ☏(0872)76633 FAX (0872) 222989
*This cleverly converted convent building sits in an elevated position not far from the city centre. Owned and run by the Costelloe family, assisted by a young team of polite staff, the hotel has retained many of its original features. The prevailing atmosphere is refreshingly short of pretension, and suits the predominently business clientèle. Small conferences, meetings, and local functions form a significant part of the business here, but as these take place mainly in the refurbished chapel, they are unlikely to affect the individual visitor. Public areas are nicely appointed: an elegant and comfortable drawing room with dispense bar and a pleasant restaurant where enjoyable modern cuisine is served. Bedrooms are well equipped and attractively furnished.*
25⇨↱ CTV in all bedrooms T ✈ (ex guide dogs) ✱
sB&B⇨↱£45-£67 dB&B⇨↱£65-£90 ⛿
Lift ☾ 60P ⇎ ✲ CFA snooker nc12yrs *xmas*
☋ English & French V ✿ ☐ ⚡ ✱ Lunch fr£9.95 High tea fr£5.40 Dinner fr£13.50&alc Last dinner 9.45pm
Credit Cards [1] [2] [3] [5] [£]

**★★★65% Brookdale**
Tregolls Rd TR1 1JZ ☏(0872)73513 & 79305 FAX (0872) 72400
Closed Xmas wk
*A small and well managed hotel, pleasantly situated in the centre of Truro. The restaurant offers an imaginative menu and dishes are carefully prepared.*
21⇨↱ CTV in all bedrooms ® T ✈ (ex guide dogs) S10%
sB&B⇨↱£51 dB&B⇨↱£65 ⛿
50P 10🚘
☋ English, French & Italian ✿ ☐ S10% Bar Lunch £2.95-£8.50 Dinner £16 Last dinner 8.45pm
Credit Cards [1] [2] [3] [5]

**★★57% *Carlton***
Falmouth Rd TR1 2HL ☏(0872)72450 FAX (0872) 223938
Closed 21 Dec-5 Jan
*A privately owned and personally managed hotel, centrally positioned and convenient for town, complements bedrooms furnished in a simple, modern style by reasonably spacious public areas; leisure facilities include a small gym, a solarium and a jacuzzi.*
30rm(5⇨22↱)(4fb) CTV in all bedrooms ® T
32P ⇎ sauna solarium gymnasium spa bath
V ✿ ☐ Last dinner 8pm
Credit Cards [1] [3]

**★★52% Royal**
Lemon St TR1 2QB ☏(0872)70345 FAX (0872) 42453
RS Xmas & New Year
*Standing close to the Cathedral this former Georgian coaching inn features well equipped bedrooms, a grill room and two popular bars.*
34⇨↱(4fb) CTV in all bedrooms ® T ✱ sB&B⇨↱£35.50-£39.50 dB&B⇨↱£44.50 ⛿
☾ CTV 34P
☋ International V ✿ ☐ ✱ Bar Lunch £1.60-£3.75 Dinner £9.50&alc Last dinner 9.30pm
Credit Cards [1] [2] [3] [£]

---

**TUNBRIDGE WELLS (ROYAL)** Kent Map **05** TQ53 ◎

**★★★76% Spa**
Mount Ephraim TN4 8XJ (Best Western)
☏Tunbridge Wells(0892)20331 Telex no 957188
FAX (0892) 510575
*An elegant Georgian mansion, set in fourteen acres of landscaped gardens with lakes, owned by the Goring family who maintain high standards throughout. The lounge is particularly noteworthy, with comfortable armchairs and a panelled library area with an open fire. Conference and banqueting facilities and a well equipped leisure centre are additional attractions.*
76⇨↱(9fb) CTV in all bedrooms ® T ✱ S10% sB⇨↱£69-£74 dB⇨↱£84-£97 (room only) ⛿
Lift ☾ 120P ✲ CFA ⊡ (heated) ℘ (hard) sauna solarium gymnasium dance studio jacuzzi jogging track *xmas*
☋ English & French V ✿ ☐ ✱ Lunch fr£15alc Dinner £21.50-£23.50&alc Last dinner 9.30pm
Credit Cards [1] [2] [3] [4] [5] [£]

**★★★67% Pembury Resort**
8 Tonbridge Rd, Pembury TN2 4QL (Resort)
☏Pembury(089282)3567 FAX (089282) 3931
*Conveniently located just off the A21, this new purpose built hotel is based on a combination of old and new architecture, the focal point being the Kentish oasthouse style reception. Bedrooms are attractively decorated in coordinating colour schemes and have all been exceptionally well equipped. There is a range of conference/meeting rooms and an attractive health and leisure club.*
80⇨↱(8fb)⚡in 20 bedrooms CTV in all bedrooms ® T ✱ S% sB⇨↱£60-£70 dB⇨↱£72-£87 (room only) ⛿
☾ 150P CFA ⊡ (heated) sauna solarium spa bath ♫ *xmas*
☋ English & French V ✿ ☐ ⚡ ✱ S% Lunch £11.50&alc Dinner £16.50&alc Last dinner 10pm
Credit Cards [1] [2] [3] [4] [5] [£]

T

T

### ★★ 70% Swan

The Pantiles TN2 5TD ☎(0892)541450 & 27590
FAX (0892) 541465

*In a fine location on The Pantiles, the house dates from the 1600s and has been sympathetically restored. All the bedrooms have been individually designed and decorated to a very high standard. The bar lounge is similarly will appointed and supplements the beamed public bar, TV lounge, Kendals Restaurant and good conference facilities. Chef Clive Stanbridge has created an interesting à la carte menu and produces a good standard of cooking. There is 24-hour service, and car parking is available across the road.*

7⇔🛏(1fb)2🛏 CTV in all bedrooms ® T ✖ ✳ sB&B⇔🛏£50-£64.60 dB&B⇔🛏£80.50-£110 🛏
《 CTV 12P 6🐾 ♫ *xmas*
V ✌ ⚏ ✳ Lunch £10.95-£14&alc
Credit Cards ① ② ③ ⑤

### ★★ 66% Russell

80 London Rd TN1 1DZ (Inter-Hotels)
☎Tunbridge Wells(0892)544833 Telex no 95177
FAX (0892) 515846

*A delightful and well equipped hotel, skilfully and extensively upgraded by the resident proprietors, Mr and Mrs Wilkinson. The bedrooms are particularly well furnished, the very best of them being in the annexe with easy access from the car park. Public rooms are restricted in size but there is a comfortable bar, a small restaurant and 2 meeting rooms. Service is very helpful and there is a 24-hour laundry service.*

21⇔🛏Annexe5⇔🛏(3fb)╳in 10 bedrooms CTV in all bedrooms ® T ✖ (ex guide dogs) sB&B⇔🛏£62-£68 dB&B⇔🛏£76-£84 🛏
《 20P
♀ English & French V ✌ ⚏ ✳ Bar Lunch £3-£8 Dinner £15.50-£17.50&alc Last dinner 9.30pm
Credit Cards ① ② ③ ⑤ ⓔ

### ★★ 62% Royal Wells Inn

Mount Ephraim TN4 8BE (Consort)
☎Tunbridge Wells(0892)511188 FAX (0892) 511908
Closed 25-26 Dec RS 1 Jan & BH Mons

*A long established and family run hotel, recently refurbished, complements comfortable modern bedrooms by an elegant first-floor restaurant and very popular, well used bar, lounge and snack bar which are all managed with the same individuality and character. Conference facilities are available, and there is adequate forecourt car parking.*

25rm(22⇔🛏)2🛏 CTV in all bedrooms ® T S10%
sB&B⇔🛏£60-£70 dB&B⇔🛏£75-£85 🛏
Lift 28P 4🐾 CFA
♀ English & French V ✌ S10% Lunch £13.50-£14.50&alc
Dinner £15.75-£17.50&alc Last dinner 10pm
Credit Cards ① ② ③ ⑤

### ✸ ✖ ✖ Eglantine

65 High St TN1 1XX ☎(0892)24957

*Situated towards one end of the High Street and surrounded by interesting shops, a small, friendly restaurant has been tastefully renovated and decorated in bright, attractive style with a touch of femininity. Chef/patron Susan Richardson offers a limited but farily priced selection of varied and imaginative dishes – noteworthy among them being the very light and subtly flavoured Crab and Sole Mousse with a Butter Sauce; the wine list, like the menu, is reasonably priced though not extensive.*

Closed Mon & 24-28 Dec
Dinner not served Sun
♀ French V 35 seats Lunch £10-£13 Dinner £20 Last lunch 1.45pm Last dinner 9.30pm ✒ ✄
Credit Cards ① ② ③

A rosette means exceptional standards of cuisine.

### ✸✸✸ ✖ ✖ *Thackeray's House*

TN1 1EA ☎Royal Tunbridge Wells(0892)511921

*An elegant town house which was once the home of novelist William Makepeace Thackeray now houses a successful restaurant with downstairs bistro. Chef/proprietor Bruce Wass offers set lunch and dinner menus, these being supplemented in the evening by a short à la carte selection; all menus are changed regularly, making good use of seasonal produce. Such excellent starters as hot turbot and scallop pâté or duck liver and heart terrine with onion marmalade could be followed by a pair of wood pigeon breasts with pear and juniper in a memorable red wine sauce or the lighter fricassée of sole in a mustard seed and chive sauce – and an apricot, ginger and walnut pudding in toffee sauce should not be missed! Cuisine is complemented by an interesting wine list and attentive professional service.*

Closed Sun, Mon & Xmas
♀ English & French V 35 seats Last lunch 2.30pm Last dinner 10pm ✒
Credit Cards ① ③

### ✸✸ ✖ Cheevers

56 High St TN1 1XF ☎(0892)545524

*This small, modern restaurant on the High Street verges on the clinical with its grey and lemon décor, angular wall lights and mirrors, regimented tables and black chairs; service, however, is friendly as well as professional, creating a pleasant atmosphere. Chef/proprietor Tim Cheevers's short but interesting à la carte selection enables the business person to determine the size of his lunch, while a set-price dinner offers excellent value for money in the evenings, menus being changed seasonally though a number of popular dishes are available all year round. Our inspector found a classic crab mousse wrapped in spinach to be rather bland because of overchilling, but the roast guinea fowl – served on a rich Madeira sauce – was moist and flavoursome beneath its crisp exterior, while desserts include a rich, sweet parfait of two chocolates with a bitter, frothy coffee bean sauce and an equally tempting Tarte au Citron. An adequate wine list (including some half bottles), though mostly French, includes some examples from the New World and England.*

Closed Sun, Mon, 1 wk Xmas, 2 wks Etr & 2 wks Summer
34 seats ✳ Lunch £20-£30alc Last lunch 2pm Last dinner 10.30pm ✒
Credit Cards ① ③

### TURNBERRY Strathclyde *Ayrshire* Map **10** NS20

### ★★★★★ 68% Turnberry Hotel and Golf Courses

KA26 9LT ☎(0655)31000 Telex no 777779 FAX (0655) 31706

*A commanding building in well kept grounds overlooking the sea and the world famous golf course, which is a major attraction. There are fine public rooms and, at the moment one restaurant, though a second is nearing completion. The new building will also house an indoor swimming pool and a further 17 bedrooms. Bedrooms in the main building vary in size, some being quite compact, but they are well appointed and equipped. Chef Stewart Cameron offers a varied menu, and dishes are carefully prepared.*

132⇔🛏(7fb)2🛏 CTV in all bedrooms T ✳ sB&B⇔🛏£120-£170 dB&B⇔🛏£130-£195 🛏
Lift 《 200P 🐾 ✿ CFA ▣ (heated) ► 18 ♪ (hard) squash ∪ snooker sauna solarium gymnasium pitch & putt putting ♫ *xmas*
♀ Scottish & French V ✌ ⚏ ✄ ✳ Lunch £16.50-£17.95&alc
Dinner £30&alc Last dinner 9.30pm
Credit Cards ① ② ③ ⑤

### ★★★ 66% Malin Court

KA26 9PB ☎(0655)31457 FAX (0655) 31072

*Just by the famous golf course and within 5 minutes' walk of the coast, this modern slate-roofed hotel is part of a residential home for the elderly, though there is nothing institutional about its attractive comfortable accommodation. Well equipped bedrooms are suited to commercial or leisure guests and the restaurant offers interesting menus.*

8🛏 CTV in all bedrooms ® T sB&B🛏£49.50-£54.95
dB&B🛏£85-£91.90 🅿
Lift ( 50P 🎵 *xmas*
V ✿ ⚸ Lunch £9.95-£10.95&alc High tea £5.25-£6.75 Dinner
£15.30-£16.50&alc Last dinner 9.30pm
Credit Cards ① ② ③ ④ ⑤ ⓔ

### TURNERS HILL West Sussex Map **04** TQ33

★★★❀79% **Alexander House**
East St RH10 4QD (Small Luxury Hotels)
☎Copthorne(0342)714914 & 716333 Telex no 95611
FAX (0342) 717328

*This comfortable character hotel, conveniently located for Gatwick
Airport – to which it runs a chauffered Daimler service – and set in
its own secluded grounds and mature gardens, offers a genuinely
welcoming ambience and the extensive, prompt, professional
service normally associated with establishments of a higher
classification. Bedrooms combining charm with comforts,
individually styled and finished with a profusion of paintings and
objects d'art, contain such thoughtful extras as excellent linen,
bathrobes and quality perfumed toiletries, while classically
furnished lounges, elegantly decorated in ornate style, feature
marble fireplaces and chandeliers. The kitchen – under the
direction of newly promoted Alan Pierce – creates a well balanced
range of modern and classical French cuisine which will appeal to
the majority of palates – starters like the delicate and subtly
flavoured Soufflé Alexander of asparagus and lobster, or Ravioli of
Crab with scallops and fine saffron sauce being followed perhaps
by Saddle of Venison with a game sauce and wild mushrooms or
Magret of Duck served lightly grilled with leek tartlets and
Madeira sauce. Simple vegetables are served al dente and there is
a fine range of home-made puddings. A first class dining room,
equally as attractive as the main restaurant, is available for private
parties.*

→

**T**

14⊸2🛏 CTV in all bedrooms ® T ✖ (ex guide dogs) sB&B⊸fr£110 dB&B⊸fr£195 🅿
Lift ℂ CTV 50P ⇗ ✿ ♪ (hard) ♪ croquet ♫ nc7yrs xmas
♀ English & French V ⊕ ⊿ ✻
Credit Cards ① ② ③ ⑤

---

**TURVEY** Bedfordshire Map **04** SP95

★★61% **Laws**

High St MK43 8DB (Shire) ☎(023064)213 & 655
FAX (023064) 8864

*An attractive stone building with a pretty garden offers en suite bedrooms of good size equipped with modern facilities. Improvements being made by enthusiastic new owners include additional accommodation.*

14rm(12⊸🛁)(3fb)1🛏 CTV in all bedrooms ® T ✻ sB&B£42 sB&B⊸🛁£42 dB&B£55 dB&B⊸🛁£55
ℂ 35P ⇗ ✿ gymnasium ♧ xmas
♀ Continental V ⊕ ⊿ ✻ Lunch £8-£17alc Dinner £18.75-£25alc Last dinner 9.30pm
Credit Cards ① ② ③

---

**TUTBURY** Staffordshire Map **08** SK22

★★★58% **Ye Olde Dog & Partridge**

High St DE13 9LS ☎Burton-on-Trent(0283)813030
FAX (0283) 813178
Closed 25-26 Dec & 1 Jan

*In the centre of the village, this 15th-century inn has a very busy self-service carvery restaurant – reservations are a necessity. Most of the bedrooms are in adjacent Georgian houses and are tastefully decorated with most amenities provided.*

3⊸🛁Annexe14⊸🛁(1fb)3🛏 CTV in all bedrooms ® T sB&B⊸🛁£50-£55 dB&B⊸🛁£60-£70 🅿
ℂ 120P ✿ ♫
♀ English & French V ⊕ ✄ ✻
Credit Cards ① ② ③ ⑤

---

**TUXFORD** Nottinghamshire Map **08** SK77

★★70% **Newcastle Arms**

Market Place NG22 0LA ☎Retford(0777)870208

*A friendly, well run hotel, in the heart of this small town, offering warm, cosy rooms and a choice of bars. The restaurant has earned itself a fine local reputation.*

11⊸🛁(1fb)1🛏 CTV in all bedrooms ® T sB&B⊸🛁£40-£50 dB&B⊸🛁£50-£60 Continental breakfast
50P 2🅿 CFA snooker
♀ French V ⊕ ⊿ ✻ Lunch £8.95-£14.30&alc Dinner £14.30&alc Last dinner 9.30pm
Credit Cards ① ② ③ ⑤ ⓔ

---

**TWICKENHAM** Greater London

See **LONDON** plan **1**B2(page 434)

❀ ✗**Cezanne**

68 Richmond Rd TW1 3BE ☎081-892 3526

*To combat the lean times of 1991 Tim Jefferson has made his pretty little restaurant, close to the town centre, into Cafe Cezanne and now offers snacks as well as full meals. Carefully chosen ingredients are cooked with skill and innovation and choices include pasta, soups (a well-balanced mushroom and cumin), salads, steaks and sauced dishes. A brochette of monkfish with red peppers and bay leaves was particularly tasty; bread, cheeses and coffee are good and service is friendly.*

Closed Sun, 1 wk Xmas & BH's Lunch not served Sat
♀ French V 38 seats ✻ Lunch £11.90-£17.50alc Dinner £11.90-£17.50alc Last lunch 2pm Last dinner 10.30pm ♪
Credit Cards ① ② ③

---

❀❀ ✗**McClements**

12 The Green TW2 5AA ☎081-755 0176 FAX 081-890 1372

*A modest frontage near the village pump on Twickenham green hides a small yet smart and comfortable restaurant offering a short, regularly changing menu in modern style, good ingredients being carefully prepared with imagination and skill. Dishes might include scallops with ginger and soy, chicken mousseline with wild mushrooms, lamb noisettes and kidneys with aubergine charlotte, and sole and lobster with a deliciously pungent sauce; sweets often involve delicate pastry and bavarois. Service is courteous and formal.*

Closed Sun Lunch not served Sat
♀ French V 30 seats ✻ Lunch fr£18.50&alc Dinner fr£18.50&alc Last lunch 2.15pm Last dinner 10.30pm P ✄
Credit Cards ① ② ③ ④

---

**TWO BRIDGES** Devon Map **02** SX67

★★❀♨71% **Prince Hall**

PL20 6SA ☎Princetown(082289)403 FAX (082289) 676
Closed mid Dec-Jan

*This hotel set amidst Dartmoor's splendour has recently been purchased by a French couple who have brought a Gallic influence to bear not only upon the simple, honest food served in the popular restaurant but also on décor and service throughout the establishment. Simplicity, informality and a relaxed atmosphere combine to make this a delightful retreat in which to enjoy the peace and quiet of an ideal location.*

8⊸🛁(1fb)2🛏 CTV in all bedrooms T sB&B⊸🛁£42.50-£47.50 dB&B⊸🛁£85-£95 (incl dinner) 🅿
15P ⇗ ✿
♀ English & French ✄ Dinner £18.50 Last dinner 8.30pm
Credit Cards ① ② ③ ⑤

---

**TYNEMOUTH** Tyne & Wear Map **12** NZ36

★★★61% **Park**

Grand Pde NE30 4JQ ☎091-257 1406 FAX 091-257 1716
RS Xmas & New Year

*A modern functional hotel situated in a prominent position on the seafront.*

49rm(43⊸🛁)(4fb) CTV in all bedrooms ® T sB&B£43 sB&B⊸🛁£48-£65 dB&B⊸🛁£72 🅿
ℂ 400P CFA sauna solarium gymnasium ♫ xmas
♀ English & French V ⊕ ✄ Lunch £8.50-£12.50&alc Dinner £12.50-£15&alc Last dinner 9.30pm
Credit Cards ① ② ③ ⑤ ⓔ

---

**TYNET** Grampian *Banffshire* Map **15** NJ36

★★60% **Mill House**

AB56 2HJ ☎Clochan(05427)233 FAX (05427) 331

*This former meal mill has been converted to create a busy roadside hotel. It offers good value accommodation and the enthusiastic owners have embarked on a phased programme of improvements. A range of special activity packages are available – details on request.*

15⊸🛁(2fb) CTV in all bedrooms ® T sB&B⊸🛁£29-£35 dB&B⊸🛁£46-£50 🅿
CTV 100P CFA ♫
V ⊕ ⊿ ✻ Lunch fr£8.50alc High tea £6.30-£8alc Dinner £9-£14alc Last dinner 9pm
Credit Cards ① ② ③ ⑤ ⓔ

---

**TYWYN** Gwynedd Map **06** SH50

★58% **Greenfield**

High St LL36 9AD ☎(0654)710354
Closed Nov RS Dec-Feb

*Privately owned and run, a small hotel on the edge of the village offers very good value for money in its warm and comfortable accommodation.*

8rm(1⇨) ® ✖ (ex guide dogs) sB&Bfr£14.50 dB&Bfr£29 dB&B⇨fr£34
CTV ♪ ⇼
V ✿ ⬜ Lunch fr£4.95 Dinner fr£6.45&alc Last dinner 9pm

---

## UCKFIELD East Sussex Map 05 TQ42

★★★★❀❀ ≞
**HORSTED PLACE**

Little Horsted TN22 5TS (2m S A26) (Small Luxury Hotels)
☎Isfield(0825)75581
Telex no 95548
FAX (0825) 75459

Closed 1st wk Jan

*This elegant Victorian country house, built in 1850, remained in private hands until recently converted into an hotel attached to the 1,100-acre East Sussex National Golf Club with its two 18-hole golf courses (to which residents have access). Other leisure activities include a croquet lawn, a hard tennis court and a heated swimming pool overlooking the well tended courtyard garden. Spaciously graceful and uncluttered public areas are adorned with fresh flower arrangements as well as pot plants, while log fires warm the hall and three lounges in winter. There are no bars, but duty porters are always available to serve drinks and light refreshments – either in the lounges or in guests' large, comfortable and comprehensively equipped bedrooms, most of which have a separate seating area; the staircase, which was designed by Augustus Pugin and hand carved in oak, is an important feature of the house. The dining room is open for both lunch and dinner, chef Allan Garth presenting fixed-price menus in a style that combines the classical and nouveau. Portions are generous and dishes fairly elaborate – an Assiette of Salmon (composed of smoked, marinated and mousse of salmon complemented by a simple dressing of Greek Yoghurt) might be followed by a moist, flavoursome Saddle of Lamb enriched by a rosemary jus with wild mushrooms sautéed in garlic; vegetables are imaginatively prepared, and the interesting selection of puddings contains an outstanding Chocolate Torte.*

17⇨♠ CTV in all bedrooms T ✖ (ex guide dogs) sB&B⇨♠£125-£315 dB&B⇨♠£125-£315 ⊟
Lift 30P 6⊛ ❀ ⬚ (heated) ▶ 18 ♪ (hard) croquet ♫ nc7yrs *xmas*

♀ English & French V ✿ ⬜ ⅍ Lunch £17.50-£25 Dinner £35 Last dinner 9.15pm
Credit Cards ①②③⑤ ⑥

---

## UDDINGSTON Strathclyde *Lanarkshire* Map 11 NS66

★★62% **Redstones**
8-10 Glasgow Rd G71 7AS ☎(0698)813774 & 814843
FAX (0698) 815319
Closed 25 Dec & 1-2 Jan
*A pleasant family-run commercial hotel with easy access into Glasgow. The dinner menu in the period dining room offers a good choice.*
18rm(16⇨♠)2⇲ CTV in all bedrooms ® T ✖ (ex guide dogs) sB&B£38-£40 sB&B⇨♠£52-£59 dB&B⇨♠£65-£74.50 ⊟
《 CTV 33P ⇼ ❀
♀ Scottish, French & Italian V ✿ Lunch £9.50&alc High tea £6.50-£8.50&alc Dinner £14.95&alc Last dinner 9.30pm
Credit Cards ①②③⑤ ⑥

---

## UIG

See Skye, Isle of

---

## UIST (SOUTH), ISLE OF

See South Uist, Isle of

---

## ULLAPOOL Highland *Ross & Cromarty* Map 14 NH19

★★69% **Ceilidh Place**
West Argyle St IV26 2TV ☎(0854)2103 FAX (0854) 2886
*More an experience than simply a hotel, this charming hostelry successfully combines a well stocked bookshop, an all day coffee shop which also acts as a venue for poetry, folk music and jazz, a bright conservatory-style restaurant serving good fresh food and a tastefully furnished and most comfortable first floor lounge which boasts fine views of Loch Broom and where a range of teas and coffee is available at all hours. Cottage-style bedrooms with beamed walls and ceilings are generally compact but comfortable, those with private bathrooms having telephones. The staff provide a friendly service.*
15rm(8⇨) T ✳ sB&Bfr£30 sB&B⇨£40 dB&B£56 dB&B⇨£76 ⊟
30P ❀ CFA *xmas*
♀ International V ✿ ⬜ ⅍ ✳ Bar Lunch £5-£8alc High tea £7-£9alc Dinner £17.50&alc Last dinner 9pm
Credit Cards ①②③⑤

❀❀❀ ✕✕ **Altnaharrie Inn**
IV26 2SS ☎Dundonnell(085483)230
*This charming, isolated inn with bedrooms can only effectively be reached by the hotel's small launch which leaves the jetty opposite the Shell garage, which is next to the Royal Hotel where one leaves the car. If it rains you'll get wet, and if you want to smoke you have to go outside where the midges will get you. But on a sunny evening looking across the bay smelling the salt air, it is close to heaven. Gunn Eriksen started cooking here by accident not design in 1980.*
→

*Since then she has collected ideas from her Norwegian mother and her art college training. Except for puddings there is no choice, though trouble is taken to find out diners' dislikes. Everyone sits down together at about 8pm for a 5-course meal in the simply furnished dining room, and it's likely to be 10.30pm before you help yourself to coffee in the lounge. At times Gunn's creative cooking scales heights of brilliance, and for the overall experience Altnaharrie is unique, and a stay in the area is recommended to appreciate the delights on view.*

Closed for part of winter Lunch not served (ex to residents)
14 seats Dinner £40-£45 Wine £7.50 Last dinner 7.45pm
℘ nc12yrs ✂

## ULLSWATER

See Glenridding, Patterdale, Pooley Bridge & Watermillock

## ULVERSTON Cumbria Map 07 SD27 ☉

### ★★❀67% Virginia House
Queen St LA12 7AF ☎(0229)54844
*A charming Georgian house with a small enclosed garden to the rear, situated in the town centre, provides accommodation in a warm, friendly atmosphere. Breakfasts are noteworthy, and dinner is particularly recommended, the fixed price evening menu offering excellent value for money with its homemade soups and pâtés, a variety of meat, chicken and fish dishes and delicious sauces.*
7♠(1fb) CTV in all bedrooms ® T ✖ ✱ sB&B♠£29-£34 dB&B♠£39.50-£49
℘ ✚ ❀
♀ International V ✤ ⚖ ✱ Bar Lunch fr£5.75alc Dinner fr£11.95&alc Last dinner 9pm
Credit Cards ①③⑤ⓔ

### ★★62% Sefton House
Queen St LA12 7AF ☎(0229)52190
*A well furnished small hotel near the town centre offering friendly service, well equipped bedrooms and a cosy restaurant serving a good range of dishes.*
14rm(4⇨6♠)(1fb) CTV in all bedrooms ® T
✖ (ex guide dogs) sB&B£29.50-£34 sB&B⇨♠£34-£42.50 dB&B£45-£51 dB&B⇨♠£55-£61.50 ⊟
CTV 15P 3☁ ⇨
V ✤ ⚖ ✱ Lunch £8.50 Dinner fr£15&alc Last dinner 8.30pm
Credit Cards ①③

### ❀❀ ✕Bay Horse Inn & Bistro
LA12 9EL ☎(0229)53972
*Although the approach to this delightful, unpretentious inn is spoilt by the nearby chemical plant, the Bay Horse itself enjoys a waterside setting, overlooking the river estuary and Morecambe Bay which provide an idyllic backdrop for Robert Lyons' cooking. His long experience at Miller Howe with John Tovey has influenced his style and he too has the knack of combining unlikely flavours and ingredients in an assured manner to create successful dishes. An inspection meal included a memorable dish of tender juicy calves' liver topped with avocado and sage, served with a Dubonnet-flavoured orange sauce. Puddings are shamelessly calorific, to speak only of the chocolate walnut fudge pie and the profiteroles (filled with banana cream) and hot chocolate sauce. An alternative to such self-indulgence is the cheese platter, served with home-made biscuits and soda bread. There are two wine lists, one predominantly French, one offering an interesting selection of New World wines, two of which are available by the glass. Service is friendly and prices, despite the automatic addition of a 10 per cent service charge, are most reasonable. At lunch time both bar meals and a simple fixed-price menu are offered.*
Closed Sun & possible closure in Jan & Feb Lunch not served Mon
V 30 seats ✱ Lunch fr£13.90&alc Dinner £17.30-£23alc Last lunch 1.30pm Last dinner 9pm 20 P nc12yrs ✂
Credit Cards ①③

## UPHALL Lothian *West Lothian* Map 11 NT07

### ★★★❀♨65% Houstoun House
EH52 6JS ☎Broxburn(0506)853831 FAX (0506) 854220
Closed 1-3 Jan
*Set in 20 acres of grounds and reached by a tree-lined driveway, this fine, lofty, seventeenth-century tower house on the western edge of the town features a stone staircase leading up from the cellar bar to the dining rooms and on to the period bedrooms beyond; a wing of more modern bedrooms was added some years ago. Fixed-price lunch and dinner menus offering a quality of cuisine synonymous with a country house hotel are a factor in the establishment's popularity both as a retreat and rendezvous for business and corporate clients.*
28⇨♠Annexe2⇨10♨ CTV in all bedrooms ® T ✱ sB&B⇨♠£79-£89 dB&B⇨♠£105-£120 ⊟
《 ⊞ 100P ⇨ ❀ CFA
V ✤ ⚖ ✂ ✱ Lunch £15-£16 Dinner £21-£29 Last dinner 9.30pm
Credit Cards ①②③④⑤ⓔ

## UPHOLLAND Lancashire Map 07 SD50

### ★★62% *Holland Hall*
6 Lafford Ln WN8 0QZ ☎(0695)624426 FAX (0695) 622433
RS 25 Dec & 2 Jan
*Situated just off the main road east of the town centre this hotel has an elegant formal restaurant and a lively pizzeria. Bedrooms vary, the newer rooms are stylish and comfortable with modern bathrooms.*
29⇨♠Annexe5⇨♠(1fb) CTV in all bedrooms ® ✖
《 200P ❀
♀ English, American & French V ✤ ⚖ Last dinner 10pm
Credit Cards ①②③⑤

## UPPER SLAUGHTER Gloucestershire Map 04 SP12

### ★★★♨78% Lords of the Manor
GL54 2JD ☎Cotswold(0451)20243 Telex no 83147 FAX (0451) 20696
*A house dating from 1650 and set in 8 acres of parkland and lake at the heart of beautiful Cotswold countryside has been extended many times, paticularly during the Victorian period. Reception rooms still promote a warm and convivial atmosphere, being comfortable, and thoughtfully furnished to complement the family portraits that still decorate the walls. Tastefully appointed bedrooms retain their charm and character although they have been equipped with many modern facilities. Cuisine is worthy of note, Chef Jenny Coaker providing short menus of light and subtle dishes in modern English style. Starters include a Terrine of Shellfish and Leeks which is well worth trying and a Ravioli with Wild Mushrooms and Tarragon, to be followed perhaps by Steamed Fillet of Brill with Roasted Scallops, Casserole of Rabbit with White Wine or Roast Squat Pigeon on a bed of Buttered Spinach; a limited selection of sweets includes Dark Chocolate Truffle with White Chocolate Sauce and Caramelised Apples with Calvados ice cream. Some good vintage clarets and Burgundies, as well as wines from many other countries, appear on a fine, well balanced and comprehensive list providing some 220 choices. The reputation of Lords of the Manor has justifiably resulted in its nomination as one of the winners of this year's AA 'Courtesy and Care' award (see colour feature on p18).*
29⇨♠3♨ CTV in all bedrooms T ✖ (ex guide dogs) sB&B⇨♠£75-£90 dB&B⇨♠£97.50-£155 ⊟
《 40P ❀ CFA ⚘ croquet xmas
V ✤ ⚖ ✱ Lunch £9.75-£16.25 High tea £2.50-£8.25 Dinner £28.50&alc Last dinner 9.30pm
Credit Cards ①②③⑤ⓔ

**UPPINGHAM** Leicestershire Map **04** SP89

★★★67% **Falcon**

High St LE15 9PY (Inter-Hotels) ☎(0572)823535
FAX (0572) 821620

*The major alterations and refurbishment recently completed at this hotel have created flexible, well furnished public areas and 6 superior bedrooms providing a high degree of quality and comfort; other bedrooms are suitably appointed and maintained, though some singles are compact. A brasserie restaurant is becoming increasingly popular, as are the meals served in the inviting surroundings of the secluded Garden Terrace.*

26⇩🛏(2fb)1🖵 CTV in all bedrooms ® T ✱ sB&B⇩🛏£55-£65 dB&B⇩🛏£65-£75 🍴

⟨ 25P 3🚗 CFA *xmas*

♡ English & French V ♥ ⟠ ✱ Lunch £14.50 High tea £2.50-£5.50 Dinner £14.50 Last dinner 10pm

Credit Cards ①②③⑤ⓔ

★★70% **Garden**

16 High St West LE15 9QD ☎(0572)822352 FAX (0572) 821156

*A lovely old house with walled gardens, set directly opposite the famous Uppingham School and easily reached from the town centre via the one-way system, now operates as a friendly, hospitable hotel whose resident proprietors take a very active interest in their guests' well being. Bedrooms vary in both size and style, but all are equally well equipped and most have en suite facilities. Meals are home-cooked and generously served.*

11⇩🛏(1fb) CTV in all bedrooms ® T ✱ sB&B⇩🛏fr£45 dB&B⇩🛏fr£55 🍴

CTV ✗ 🚿 ♨

♡ English & French V ♥ ⟠ ✱ Lunch £14.95 High tea fr£4.95 Dinner £14.95 Last dinner 10pm

Credit Cards ①②③

★★69% **Lake Isle**

High St East LE15 9PZ ☎(0572)822951

*Tucked away in the High Street, this small hotel offers friendly, informal service, good food and an extensive wine list. Continual upgrading of bedrooms has seen the creation of a good courtyard suite, and further redecoration using colourful soft furnishings.*

10⇩🛏Annexe1rm(1fb) CTV in 10 bedrooms ® T 🍴

4P 1🚗 🚿 *xmas*

♡ English & French V ✱ Lunch £7-£11 Dinner £18.50-£22.50 Last dinner 10pm

Credit Cards ①②③⑤

★65% **Crown**

High St East LE15 9PY ☎Oakham(0572)822302 & 821809

*A 17th-century inn at the centre of this popular village offers attractively refurbished bedrooms which retain their essential character whilst including all modern facilities such as en suite bathrooms. Limited public areas consist simply of lounge bar and restaurant, but they are attractively furnished and have a welcoming atmosphere, the bar being warmed by a log fire; an à la carte menu of traditional English and European dishes is supplemented by bar meals, and a caring, involved proprietor is alert to guests' every need.*

7⇩🛏 CTV in all bedrooms ® T ✱ sB&B⇩🛏£36.50 dB&B⇩🛏£48

15P 🚿

V ♥ ⟠ ✱

Credit Cards ①③

**UPTON UPON SEVERN** Hereford & Worcester
Map **03** SO84

★★★56% **White Lion**

High St WR8 0HJ (Exec Hotel) ☎Upton on Severn(0684)592551
FAX (0684) 592251

Closed 25 Dec RS 26 Dec

*This privately owned, former 16th century coaching inn, has retained many original features, such as beams and sloping floors.*

*Rooms are individually decorated, some in the original building and some in a newer rear wing. An intimate, character restaurant serves a range of traditional dishes.*

10⇩🛏1🖵 CTV in all bedrooms ® T sB&B⇩🛏fr£49.50 dB&B⇩🛏£67.75-£75 🍴

18P 1🚗

♡ English & French V ♥ ⟠ Lunch fr£14.25&alc Dinner fr£14.25&alc Last dinner 9.15pm

Credit Cards ①②③⑤ⓔ

★★63% **Star**

High St WR8 0HQ (Resort) ☎(0684)592300 Telex no 877247
FAX (06846) 2929

*A 17th-century coaching inn by the river has been converted to provide well-equipped accommodation suited to business traveller and tourist alike. The wood-panelled intimate restaurant and convivial lounge bar retain much of their original character and the atmosphere is friendly and informal.*

17⇩🛏(2fb) CTV in all bedrooms ® T ✱ sB&B⇩🛏£22.50-£41 dB&B⇩🛏£45-£56 🍴

8P 2🚗 CFA ♬

V ♥ ⟠ S% Lunch £7.50-£9.50 High tea £3.50-£5 Dinner £11.50-£13 Last dinner 9.30pm

Credit Cards ①③ⓔ

**USK** Gwent Map **03** SO30

★★72% **Glen-yr-Afon**

Pontypool Rd NP5 1SY ☎(02913)2302 & 3202
FAX (02913) 2597

*Situated off the Pontypool road just outside the town, and surrounded by 3 acres of pleasant woods and grassland, this very well run hotel boasts an impressive circular library which is used for dinner parties and small meetings; bar and lounge are very comfortable, while bedrooms are modern and well equipped. A good range of food is served, and staff are friendly and helpful.* →

U

16rm(10✠5♠)(2fb) CTV in all bedrooms ® T ✱ sB&B£30.55-£32.90 sB&B✠♠£35.25-£44.65 dB&B£52.88-£56.40 dB&B✠♠£52.88-£56.40 ♬
《 CTV 100P 1♨ ♨ ✿ croquet *xmas*
V ⚕ ⬩♨ ✂ ✱ Lunch £7-£13.50&alc Dinner £13.50&alc Last dinner 9pm
Credit Cards ①②③

★★ 60% *Three Salmons*
Bridge St NP5 1BQ ☎(02913)2133
Closed 24-26 Dec
*In the busy town centre, this old coaching inn provides good character bars and public rooms. The restaurant is oak-panelled and hung with original 18th-century cartoons, and there are 2 first-floor function/meeting rooms. Bedrooms are well equipped, but now look a bit tired. Two nearby annexe blocks provide additional bedrooms.*
12✠♠ Annexe18rm(14✠2♠)(1fb)2⌗ CTV in 23 bedrooms ® T
40P
⚕
Credit Cards ①②③④

---

UTTOXETER Staffordshire Map 07 SK03 ☺

★★ 66% *Bank House*
Church St ST14 8AG ☎(0889)566922 FAX (0889) 567565
*A busy town-centre hotel with two unusual features – an original bank vault and a fine unsupported staircase – offers a warm atmosphere and filling home-cooked meals.*
16✠♠(2fb)1⌗ CTV in all bedrooms ® T
CTV 16P
V ⚕ ⬩♨ Last dinner 9.45pm
Credit Cards ①②③⑤

⬥Forte Travelodge
Ashbourne Rd ST14 5AA (on A50/A5030) (Forte)
☎(0889)562043 Central Res (0800) 850950
*This lodge at the A50/A5030 junction is particularly popular during the summer months, being only 5 miles from Alton Towers Leisure Park. Meals and snacks are available in the adjacent Little Chef restaurant.*
32✠♠(32fb) CTV in all bedrooms ® sB✠♠£29.95 dB✠♠£29.95 (room only)
《 32P ♨
✱
Credit Cards ①②③

---

UXBRIDGE Greater London Map 04 TQ08

★★★ 62% *Master Brewer*
Western Av UB10 9NX ☎(0895)51199 Telex no 946589 FAX (0895) 810330
(For full entry see Hillingdon)

VALE
See Guernsey under Channel Islands

VENTNOR
See Wight, Isle of

VERYAN Cornwall & Isles of Scilly Map 02 SW93

★★★ 73% *Nare*
Carne Beach TR2 5PF ☎Truro(0872)501279 FAX (0872) 501856
*Excellent service is only one of the pleasing features of this away-from-it-all hotel which is exceptionally well managed by Mr and Mrs Gray who have completely refurbished its accommodation, providing tasteful and elegant furnishings in keeping with the country-house atmosphere. The restaurant menu features many local seafood specialities. Leisure and fitness facilities are good*

*and the hotel is adjacent to National Trust land, with uninterrupted views of Gerrans Bay and Nare Head.*
41rm(39✠3♠)(6fb) CTV in all bedrooms ® T sB&B✠♠£40-£95 dB&B✠♠£80-£160
80P ♨ ✿ ♨ (heated) ♪ (hard) snooker sauna solarium gymnasium boating windsurfing ♨ *xmas*
♀ English & French V ⚕ ⬩♨ Sunday Lunch £11.50 Dinner £22&alc Last dinner 9.30pm
Credit Cards ①③

---

WADEBRIDGE Cornwall & Isles of Scilly Map 02 SW97

★★ 56% *Molesworth Arms*
Molesworth St PL27 7DP ☎(0208)812055 FAX (0208) 814254
*A sixteenth-century coaching inn at the centre of the town complements simply furnished bedrooms with a new cocktail bar and restaurant where friendly, informal staff offer a menu featuring mainly grills.*
14rm(9✠3♠)(2fb)1⌗ CTV in all bedrooms ® T ✱ S% sB&B✠♠fr£32 dB&B✠♠fr£50
CTV 14P CFA ♨
V ⚕ ⬩♨ ✱ S% Sunday Lunch £3.25-£5.65 Dinner £11.95&alc Last dinner 9.30pm
Credit Cards ①③

---

WADHURST East Sussex Map 05 TQ63

★★ ❀♨ 66% Spindlewood Country House Hotel & Restaurant
Wallcrouch TN5 7JG (2.25m SE of Wadhurst on B2099)
☎Ticehurst(0580)200430 FAX (0580) 201132
Closed 4 days Xmas RS Bank Hols
*A country house hotel peacefully located in its own grounds offers traditionally furnished accommodation, most of the rooms being spacious and all of them providing modern facilities. Guests can enjoy a drink in the somewhat dated bar/lounge while perusing chef Harvey Lee Aram's seasonal menu – priced accordingly to the day of the week, Saturday inevitably being the most expensive – where the interesting range of meat, game and poultry dishes are accompanied by a vegetarian option which is changed daily and fresh fish as available. A typical meal might include shredded chicken and apricot terrine (somewhat disappointing in both flavour and texture, but accompanied by a delicious brioche), tender loin of venison served on a red wine jus, and crescents of iced coffee soufflés, coated in coconut, with a light vanilla sauce. Liqueur parfaits and home-made sorbets are a speciality. The wine list includes a few English wines from nearby Lamberhurst as well as a selection from the New World, and a page devoted to half bottles and non-alcoholic beverages has been introduced. Service throughout is attentive though characterless and sometimes lacking supervision.*
9✠♠(1fb) CTV in all bedrooms ® T ✖ (ex guide dogs) sB&B✠♠£48-£51 dB&B✠♠£65.40-£84 ♬
60P ♨ ✿
♀ English & French V ⚕ Lunch £10-£19&alc Dinner £19.20-£25alc Last dinner 9pm
Credit Cards ①③

---

WAKEFIELD West Yorkshire Map 08 SE32 ☺

★★★ 65% Cedar Court
Denby Dale Road, Calder Grove WF4 3QZ ☎(0924)276310 Telex no 557647 FAX (0924) 280221
*A large modern hotel just off the M1 offering a choice of restaurants with varying cuisines and spacious bedrooms with good facilities. Staff are friendly and helpful.*
151✠♠(11fb)✖ in 59 bedrooms CTV in all bedrooms ® T ✱ sB&B✠♠£56.25-£91.50 dB&B✠♠£67.95-£97 ♬
Lift 《 ▦ 350P ✱ CFA
♀ English, French & Italian V ⚕ ⬩♨ ✂ ✱ Lunch £8.95-£11.95&alc Dinner £13.95-£22&alc Last dinner 11pm
Credit Cards ①②③⑤ⓔ

**★★★63% Swallow**
Queens St WF1 1JV (Swallow) ☎(0924)372111 Telex no 557464 FAX (0924) 383648
*A tall modern city centre hotel offering good standards of comfort and service, with well equipped bedrooms and a newly refurbished restaurant serving an interesting range of dishes.*
64⇨↱(4fb)⊁in 17 bedrooms CTV in all bedrooms ® **T** ✱
sB&B⇨↱fr£69.50 dB&B⇨↱fr£86 ⊟
Lift ☾ 40P CFA *xmas*
☋ English & French **V** ♱ ☏ ⊁ ✱ Lunch fr£9.50&alc Dinner fr£14.50 Last dinner 9.45pm
Credit Cards [1] [2] [3] [5] £

**★★★63% Waterton Park**
Walton Hall, The Balk, Walton WF2 6PW (3m SE off B6378) (Consort) ☎(0924)257911 FAX (0924) 240082
*This beautiful Georgian manor house set on an island in a large lake was the home of eccentric 19th-century naturalist Charles Waterton and has been converted into a comfortable well furnished hotel of unusual charm, with excellent leisure facilities and a baronial-style restaurant with a good standard of cooking.*
31⇨↱(1fb)3⊞ CTV in all bedrooms ® **T** ✱ ✱
sB&B⇨↱£74.80-£80 dB&B⇨↱£96.80-£106.80 ⊟
☾ 100P ✲ CFA ⊡ (heated) ♪ squash snooker sauna solarium gymnasium boating jacuzzi beautician masseur *xmas*
☋ English & French **V** ♱ ☏ ✱ Lunch £9.90-£11 High tea fr£6.50 Dinner £15.50-£23 Last dinner 9.30pm
Credit Cards [1] [2] [3] [5] £

**★★★60% Forte Posthouse**
Queen's Dr, Ossett WF5 9BE (Forte Hotels) ☎(0924)276388 Telex no 55407 FAX (0924) 280277
*Spacious and well furnished accommodation is provided by this large modern hotel which stands just off the M1 at junction 40.*
99⇨↱⊁in 49 bedrooms CTV in all bedrooms ® **T** ✱
sB⇨↱£39.50-£49.50 dB⇨↱£39.50-£49.50 (room only) ⊟
→

W

Lift 〔 140P ❀ CFA *xmas*
♀ International **V** ↺ ⬛ ✂ ✳ Lunch fr£9.50&alc High tea fr£5
Dinner fr£13.95&alc Last dinner 10pm
Credit Cards ① ② ③ ⑤

⛫**Granada Lodge**
M1 Service Area, West Bretton WF4 4LQ (Granada)
☎(0924)830569 FAX (0924) 830609
(For full entry see Woolley Edge)

---

**WALKERBURN** Borders *Peeblesshire* Map **11** NT33

★★⚑68% **Tweed Valley Hotel & Restaurant**
Galashiels Rd EH43 6AA (Inter-Hotels) ☎(089687)636
FAX (089687) 639
*This comfortable, traditional hotel stands in its own well tended
gardens, an elevated position providing delightful views over the
river to pine forests. Courteous and attentive service is supervised
by resident proprietors.*
15⇌🛏(2fb)1🖼 CTV in all bedrooms ® **T** sB&B⇌🛏£44
dB&B⇌🛏£68 🏴
35P ❀ ♪ sauna solarium gymnasium shooting stalking ⚓
*xmas*
♀ Scottish, English & French **V** ↺ ⬛ ✂ Lunch £6.50-£8.50
High tea £4.50-£6.50 Dinner £16&alc Last dinner 9.30pm
Credit Cards ① ③ ⓔ

---

**WALL** Northumberland Map **12** NY96

★★58% *Hadrian*
NE46 4EE ☎Humshaugh(043481)232 & 236
*Built largely from stone taken from Hadrian's Wall, this cosy inn
offers simple accommodation, friendly service and a good range of
food.*
11rm(1⇌2🛏)2🖼 CTV in 9 bedrooms ® **T**
CTV 40P 3🐾 ❀ nc14yrs
**V** ↺ ⬛ ✂ Last dinner 10pm
Credit Cards ① ⑤

---

**WALLASEY** Merseyside Map **07** SJ29

★★65% *Grove House*
Grove Rd L45 3HF ☎051-639 3947 & 051-630 4558
FAX 051-630 0028
RS no restaurant BH's
*Bedrooms have been refurbished to a high standard and furnished
with some thoughtful extras at this privately owned hotel which
stands in a residential area close to Wallasey Village. A warm,
friendly atmosphere pervades the public areas, particularly the
wood-panelled restaurant where guests are served a wide choice of
enjoyable dishes.*
17rm(4⇌8🛏)(1fb)1🖼 CTV in all bedrooms ® **T**
✖ (ex guide dogs)
〔 20P 🚗 ❀
♀ English & French **V**
Credit Cards ① ③

**See advertisement under LIVERPOOL**

---

**WALLINGFORD** Oxfordshire Map **04** SU68

★★★68% *George*
High St OX10 0BS (Mount Charlotte (TS)) ☎(0491)36665
Telex no 847468 FAX (0491) 25359
*This traditional timbered hotel dating to Tudor times provides
obliging service and comfortable accommodation, with
characterful cosy bedrooms in the oldest part of the building and
attractively decorated rooms in the newer wing. The beamed public
bar is popular and the restaurant serves some imaginative dishes.*
39⇌🛏(1fb)✂in 9 bedrooms CTV in all bedrooms ® **T** (room
only) 🏴

〔 60P *xmas*
♀ English & French **V** ↺
Credit Cards ① ② ③ ⑤

---

★★★62% **Shillingford Bridge**
Shillingford OX10 8LZ (2m N A329) (Forestdale)
☎Warborough(086732)8567 FAX (086732) 8636
*Beautifully situated on a quarter-mile of river front, with coarse
fishing and private moorings available, this popular conference and
function hotel is gradually refurbishing its well equipped bedrooms
to provide high standards of décor and facilities. The busy bars
and restaurant share river views, and leisure amenities include
squash courts and a swimming pool.*
23⇌🛏Annexe10⇌🛏(3fb)2🖼 CTV in all bedrooms ® **T** ✳
sB&B⇌🛏£63.25 dB&B⇌🛏£85.25 🏴
100P ❀ CFA ⛵ (heated) ♪ squash ♫ *xmas*
♀ International **V** ↺ ⬛ ✂ Lunch £12.50-£13.50&alc Dinner
fr£15.50&alc Last dinner 10pm
Credit Cards ① ② ③ ⑤ ⓔ

---

**WALLSEND** Tyne & Wear Map **12** NZ26

★★★57% *Newcastle Moat House*
Coast Rd NE28 9HP (Queens Moat) ☎091-262 8989 &
091-262 7044 Telex no 53583 FAX 091-263 4172
*Modern and purpose-built, the hotel stands 5 miles from the centre
of Newcastle, at the A1/A1058 junction. Bedrooms, though dated
in style, have every facility, and accommodation should be
enhanced considerably by a planned redevelopment; there is a
small leisure club, and conference/function facilities are good.*
150⇌🛏(8fb)✂in 10 bedrooms CTV in all bedrooms ® **T**
Lift 〔 500P sauna solarium gymnasium steam room
♀ English & Continental **V** ↺ ⬛ ✂ Last dinner 9.45pm
Credit Cards ① ② ③ ⑤

---

**WALSALL** West Midlands Map **07** SP09

See also **Barr, Great**

★★★✿66% **Fairlawns**
178 Little Aston Road, Aldridge WS9 0NU (3m NE off A454)
(Consort) ☎Aldridge(0922)55122 Telex no 339873
FAX (0922) 743120
RS 24 Dec-2 Jan
*Quietly located on the A454, between Walsall and Sutton
Coldfield and convenient for the motorway network, this
considerably extended redbrick house offers modern well-equipped
bedrooms, with particularly comfortable new rooms and suites.
There are extensive conference facilities and a large restaurant
with a good local reputation for well prepared varied dishes and
friendly attentive service.*
36⇌🛏(2fb) CTV in all bedrooms ® **T** sB&B⇌🛏£42.50-
£72.50 dB&B⇌🛏£49.50-£82.50 🏴
〔 80P ❀ CFA
♀ English & French **V** ↺ ⬛ ✳ Lunch £13.50-£15.95&alc
Dinner £19.50&alc Last dinner 10pm
Credit Cards ① ② ③ ④ ⑤ ⓔ

---

★★★66% **Friendly Hotel**
20 Wolverhampton Rd West, Bentley WS2 0BS (junct 10, M6)
(Consort) ☎(0922)724444 Telex no 334854 FAX (0922) 723148
*At junction 10 of the M6, this modern hotel provides comfortable
and well equipped accommodation and open-plan public areas.
There is a popular carvery restaurant and a range of leisure
facilities.*
150⇌🛏(20fb)2🖼✂in 60 bedrooms CTV in all bedrooms ® **T**
sB⇌🛏£53.25-£63.50 dB⇌🛏£70.50-£80.75 (room only) 🏴
〔 140P ❀ CFA ⛵ (heated) sauna solarium gymnasium jacuzzi
♀ English & French **V** ↺ ⬛ ✂ Lunch fr£8.50 Dinner fr£12.75
Last dinner 10pm
Credit Cards ① ② ③ ⑤ ⓔ

★★★62% **Forte Posthouse**

Birmingham Rd WS5 3AB (Forte Hotels) ☎(0922)33555
Telex no 335479 FAX (0922) 612034

*This busy modern hotel on the outskirts of town, with easy access to the M6, has refurbished most of its bedrooms to provide comfortable well equipped accommodation. The Orangerie Restaurant offers a wide choice of meals and there are three bars, one of them with live music.*

98⇌↑(3fb)⊬in 49 bedrooms CTV in all bedrooms ® T ✳ S%
sB⇌↑£39.50-£49.50 dB⇌↑£39.50-£49.50 (room only) ⊟
Lift ₵ CTV 250P CFA pool tables ♫ *xmas*
♈ Continental V ✧ ⵌ ⊬ ✳ S% Lunch £9.95-£10&alc High tea £4.25-£7.50 Dinner £13.95&alc Last dinner 10.30pm
Credit Cards ①②③⑤

★★★58% *Barons Court*

Walsall Rd, Walsall Wood WS9 9AH (3m NE A461) (Best Western) ☎Brownhills(0543)452020 Telex no 333061
FAX (0543) 361276

*Situated on the A461 between Walsall and Lichfield, this mock-Tudor hotel remains busy. Bedrooms are well equipped, many have 4-poster beds and jacuzzis. Public areas are ornate with lots of brass, copper and Cotswold stone. The hotel has a health hydro complete with heart shaped swimming pool.*

100⇌(5fb)23⊟⊬in 6 bedrooms CTV in all bedrooms ® T
Lift ₵ 180P ⊠ (heated) sauna solarium gymnasium health hydro whirlpool ♫
♈ English & French V ✧ ⵌ Last dinner 9.45pm
Credit Cards ①②③④⑤

★★69% **Beverley**

58 Lichfield Rd WS4 2DJ ☎(0922)614967 & 22999
FAX (0922) 724187

*A privately owned and run hotel stands just outside the town on the A461, offering a good standard of accommodation with an*

→

W

*excellent range of modern facilities together with a pool room, sauna, solarium and gymnasium.*

29⇨♠Annexe2⇨♠(2fb)✂in 2 bedrooms CTV in all bedrooms ℝ **T** ✕ (ex guide dogs) ✱ sB&B⇨♠£40-£45 dB&B⇨♠£40-£60 ⊟

⟨ CTV 60P 8🏠 CFA sauna solarium gymnasium

♀ English & French **V** ✿ ⚼ ✂ Lunch £6.95-£8.95 Dinner £10.95&alc Last dinner 9.30pm

Credit Cards ①③ⓔ

### ★★65% Abberley

Bescot Rd WS2 9AD ☎(0922)27413 FAX (0922) 720933

*Conveniently located just off junction 9 of the M6, this family-run hotel in a large Victorian building with ample car parking, offers comfortably furnished well decorated accommodation, with facilities geared to the commercial user.*

28⇨♠(4fb)1❄✂in 4 bedrooms CTV in all bedrooms ℝ **T** S% sB&B⇨♠£42-£46 dB&B⇨♠£55-£59 ⊟

⟨ 29P CFA

♀ English, Asian, Chinese & Vietnamese **V** ✿ ⚼ ✂ S% Lunch £9-£10.50 Dinner £10.50 Last dinner 8.30pm

Credit Cards ①②③ⓔ

### ★★60% Bescot

Bescot Rd WS2 9DG ☎(0922)22447 FAX (0922) 30256

*A well run, privately owned hotel close to junction 9 of the M6. Rooms are modest with good modern facilities and staff create a 'home-from-home' atmosphere for the mainly commercial clientèle.*

13⇨♠(1fb) CTV in all bedrooms ℝ **T** ✕ (ex guide dogs)

⟨ CTV 30P

♀ International **V** ✿ ⚼ Last dinner 9.30pm

Credit Cards ①②③⑤

---

## WALTHAM ABBEY Essex Map 05 TL30

### ★★★★60% Swallow

Old Shire Ln EN9 3LX (Swallow) ☎Lea Valley(0992)717170 Telex no 916596 FAX (0992) 711841

*This hotel and leisure club is particularly well situated for the business traveller, close to junction 26 of the M25. Well appointed bedrooms include honeymoon and executive suites and some have been especially adapted for disabled guests. Public areas are all air-conditioned, and include a brasserie and formal restaurant.*

163⇨(10fb)4❄✂in 60 bedrooms CTV in all bedrooms ℝ **T** S10% sB&B⇨♠£60-£95 dB&B⇨♠£70-£105 ⊟

⟨ ⊞ 240P CFA 🖵 (heated) sauna solarium gymnasium steam room ♫ *xmas*

♀ English & Continental **V** ✿ ⚼ S10% Lunch £13.50&alc High tea £8-£10 Dinner £15.50-£19.50&alc Last dinner 10.30pm

Credit Cards ①②③⑤ⓔ

---

## WALTON UPON THAMES

See **Shepperton & Weybridge**

---

## WANSFORD Cambridgeshire Map 04 TL09

### ★★★66% The Haycock Hotel

PE8 6JA ☎Stamford(0780)782223 Telex no 32710 FAX (0780) 783031

*A 17th-century coaching inn beside the A1 in a peaceful village location. The substantial grounds include formal gardens and ample parking. The courtyard arrangement houses a business centre, a ballroom and some of the bedrooms. Above average accommodation is provided in recently refurbished and upgraded rooms, each individually styled with extensive use of soft furnishings. There is a choice of buttery or restaurant, and services, including early morning tea and shoe cleaning, are provided by a courteous youthful team.*

51⇨♠(4fb)4🖵 CTV in all bedrooms **T** ✱ S% sB&B⇨♠£68-£85 dB&B⇨♠£85-£120 ⊟

⟨ 300P ❄ CFA ♪ petanque outdoor chess ♫ *xmas*

**V** ✿ ⚼ ✂ ✱ Bar Lunch £5.95-£8.75alc High tea £5.95-£8.75alc Last high tea 6pm

Credit Cards ①②③⑤

---

## WANTAGE Oxfordshire Map 04 SU48

### ★★59% Bear

Market Place OX12 8AB (Consort) ☎(02357)66366 Telex no 41363 FAX (02357) 68826

*Most of this hotel is over 400 years old, the most ancient parts dating back to the 12th-century. Set at this centre of the small but busy town, it is following a gradual programme of improvements which had already resulted in prettily decorated bedrooms which, though compact, are very well equipped with modern facilities; traditional public areas have now also been refurbished to a good standard.*

36⇨♠(3fb) CTV in all bedrooms ℝ **T** ✱ S% sB&B⇨♠£29-£54 dB&B⇨♠£58-£70 ⊟

Lift ⟨ ✗ *xmas*

♀ French **V** ✿ ⚼ ✂ ✱ S% Lunch £8.95 Dinner £15.75&alc Last dinner 9.45pm

Credit Cards ①②③⑤ⓔ

**See advertisement under OXFORD**

---

## WARE Hertfordshire Map 05 TL31

### ★★★★ ❀❀❀❀82% Hanbury Manor

Thundridge SG12 0SD (Small Luxury Hotels) ☎(0920)487722 Telex no 817515 FAX (0920) 487692

*Set in 200 acres of lovely countryside, much of it given over to a Jack Nicklaus II designed golf course, this Victorian mansion has been much extended and refurbished since it ceased to be a convent in 1986. The development has many conference and function rooms, including the Garden Court, 200 yds from the house, with 27 bedrooms booked as a unit for conferences. As well as the golf course, leisure facilities include 3 tennis courts, 2 squash courts, a fine indoor pool, 2 snooker tables, hairdressing and a beauty salon. There is a handsome wood-panelled lounge, a library, and 3 restaurants under the direction of Executive Chef Rory Kennedy. In the main restaurant, the Zodiac Room, the influence of Consultant Chef Albert Roux can be seen. Open only for dinner it offers a choice of 3 menus: the Menu Gourmand at £39 for 6 courses; a menu du Chef, £17.50 for 3 courses, and a wide ranging French inspired à la carte menu. Among several fine dishes, the outstanding fillet of Scotch beef with a glacé of red wine, roasted salsify and girolles must be mentioned. And from the starters, another successful dish is the red mullet sautéed with bone marrow and young spinach on a soufflé Suissesse Gavroche. Bedrooms are comfortable, well appointed and mostly of good size; bathrooms are of especially good quality. Although lacking a little skill in some areas, staff are friendly and helpful. Hanbury Manor is an outstanding new hotel in many ways, and it should achieve 5 stars before too long. In the meantime we are delighted to welcome them to the guide and to nominate the AA's Best Newcomer 1991 to 1992 of the South East region.*

71⇨♠Annexe27⇨♠ CTV in all bedrooms **T** ✱ sB&B⇨♠fr£135 dB&B⇨♠£145-£325 ⊟

Lift ⟨ 200P ❄ CFA 🖵 (heated) ▶ 18 ♪ (hard) squash snooker sauna solarium gymnasium beauty treatments *xmas*

♀ English & French **V** ✿ ⚼ ✂ ✱ Lunch fr£14 Dinner fr£14 Last dinner 9.45pm

Credit Cards ①②③⑤

### ★★★63% Ware Moat House

Baldock St SG12 9DR (Queens Moat) ☎(0920)465011 Telex no 817417 FAX (0920) 468016

Closed 25-31 Dec

*This modern hotel just outside the market town and within easy reach of the M25 is popular with business travellers and provides*

very well equipped accommodation. It also has a cosy bar and attractive restaurant with a conservatory extension. Staff are pleasant and helpful.

50rm(43⇄6♠)(1fb)⊁in 6 bedrooms CTV in all bedrooms ® T ✳ sB&B⇄♠fr£74.15 dB&B⇄♠fr£90 🖪
Lift 《 100P CFA ♫
♀ English & Continental V ♦ ♵ ✳ Lunch fr£13.50 Dinner fr£16 Last dinner 9.30pm
Credit Cards ① ② ③ ④ ⑤ ④

---

**WAREHAM** Dorset Map 03 SY98

★★★ ®®78% **Priory**
Church Green BH20 4ND ☎(0929)552772 & 551666
Telex no 41143 FAX (0929) 554519

This interesting 19th-century house, set in renowned gardens and located between the church and the River Frome, offers a sparkling, polished interior with two drawing rooms – one gracious, with open fire and grand piano, while the other is more homely though equally comfortable. A bright, airy dining room in which breakfast and lunch are served provides a complete contrast to the Cellar Restaurant with its bare stone walls and floor. Chef Michael Rust makes good use of fresh local produce and fish in his menus, courteously friendly service from an all-English staff is never intrusive, and the fact that conferences/large parties are not catered for helps to maintain the gentle, relaxing atmosphere of a country house. Accommodation varies in size and price, those in the Boat House being largest and having whirlpool baths, but all rooms are pretty, well equipped and antique-furnished.

15⇄♠Annexe4⇄♠2🖬 CTV in all bedrooms T
✗ (ex guide dogs) ✳ sB&B⇄♠£60-£105 dB&B⇄♠£75-£175 🖪
《 25P 🖨 ✿ ♪ croquet sailing ♫ xmas
V ♦ ♵ ✳ Lunch £11.95-£15.50 Dinner £22.50-£26.50&alc Last dinner 10pm
Credit Cards ① ② ③ ⑤

★★★ ®70% **Springfield Country**
Grange Road, Stoborough BH20 5AL (1.5m S off A351) ☎(0929)552177 & 551785 FAX (0929) 551862

A family-run hotel which has much to offer both holiday-makers and business people stands in 6 acres of carefully tended grounds, its leisure facilities including an outdoor swimming pool and tennis court as well as a large indoor games room with two full-size snooker tables. Cosy bars and lounges are furnished with comfortable armchairs and tables set up to play cards and games, while the two restaurants with its lace cloths, pink napkins, candles, flowers and chandeliers and the larger dining room where dinner dances are sometimes held. The sound menu consists mainly of classical French dishes, the home-made puddings are excellent. Some bedrooms are better furnished than others, though all have good beds and crisp linen, and the friendly service provided by helpful staff helps to create a pleasing, unpretentious atmosphere.

32⇄♠(7fb) CTV in all bedrooms ® T sB&B⇄♠£60-£65 dB&B⇄♠£100-£108 🖪
Lift 《 100P 🖨 ✿ CFA ⊇ (heated) ℘ (hard) snooker solarium table tennis pool table nc2yrs
♀ English & Continental ♦ ♵ ✳ Bar Lunch £1.50-£13alc High tea £2-£6alc Dinner £14&alc Last dinner 9pm
Credit Cards ① ② ③

★★ 69% **Kemps Country House**
East Stoke BH20 6AL ☎Bindon Abbey(0929)462563
FAX (0929) 405287
Closed 26-31 Dec

This small, friendly Victorian hotel offers a choice of accommodation at various prices, spacious modern bedrooms (2 of which have whirlpool baths) being very well decorated and furnished while others – though still comfortable – are more simply appointed; public areas include a bar with open fire and a restaurant which is very popular locally.

---

5rm(1⇄3♠)Annexe10⇄♠(4fb)1🖬 CTV in all bedrooms ® T ✗ sB&B⇄♠£55-£69 dB&B⇄♠£82-£110 🖪
50P 🖨 ✿
♀ English & French V ♦ ⊁ Lunch £8.50-£9.95&alc Dinner £16.95&alc Last dinner 9.30pm
Credit Cards ① ② ③ ④ ⑤

See advertisement on page 727

★★ 54% **Worgret Manor**
BH20 6AB ☎(0929)552957

Quiet Georgian hotel with modern extension.

10rm(5♠)(3fb) CTV in all bedrooms ® ✳ sB&B£32-£36 sB&B♠£36-£40 dB&B£44-£50 dB&B♠£50-£56 🖪
CTV 40P ✿
♀ English & French V ♦ ✳ Lunch £6.50-£8.95&alc Dinner £10.50-£17.75alc Last dinner 9.15pm
Credit Cards ① ③ ④

---

**WARMINSTER** Wiltshire Map 03 ST84

★★★★ ®♨ 67% **Bishopstrow House Hotel**
BA12 9HH (Small Luxury Hotels) ☎(0985)212312
Telex no 444829 FAX (0985) 216769

An imposing Georgian house with mature grounds and gardens and an excellent range of leisure facilities. The introduction of new high quality bedrooms has improved the range of accommodation, although some of the older rooms in the main house and the adjacent stable block are beginning to look inferior by comparison. Public rooms are small but nonetheless comfortable, with fine furnishings to complement the architecture. Young Chef Christopher Suter continues to provide varied and interesting menus with good use of fresh seasonal produce. Service standards continue to improve under the direction of the new management.

→

**W**

32⇄🐾(3fb)1🛏✂in 1 bedroom CTV in all bedrooms T ✳
sB&B⇄🐾fr£95 dB&B⇄🐾£110-£188 Continental breakfast
🛏
《 60P ✿ CFA 🖾 (heated) ⇌ (heated) ♪ (hard) ♪ sauna
solarium clay pigeon shooting archery *xmas*
V ⚘ ⚖ ✳ Lunch £7.50-£15alc Dinner £31-£35alc Last dinner
9pm
Credit Cards [1] [2] [3] [5]

### ⛪Granada Lodge
A36 Bath Rd BA12 7RU (Granada) ☎(0985)219639
FAX (0985) 214380
*Involved and conscientious management makes this lodge beside
the busy A36 a good-value choice for holidaymaker and
businessman alike. Spacious modern bedrooms are well equipped
and exceptionally clean, as is the self- serve/assisted table service
restaurant, and there is a newsagent's shop under the same roof.*
31⇄(10fb)✂in 7 bedrooms CTV in all bedrooms ®
✖ (ex guide dogs) S% sB&B⇄fr£29.50 dB&B⇄£32 (room only) 🛏
《 80P
V ⚘ ⚖ ✂

---

## WARREN ROW Berkshire Map **04** SU88

### ✿✿✖✖The Warrener
RG10 8QS ☎(062882)2803
*Jean-Marie Zimmermann's delightful restaurant, converted from
three cottages in the centre of the village, has a small bar and
pretty pink and white main dining room, with a private dining room
and five charming bedrooms upstairs. The quite short, regularly
changed lunch and dinner menus feature traditional French
cuisine, using good ingredients carefully prepared and cooked to
order. Flavours are clear and dishes imaginatively handled, such
as the delicious cassoulette de fruits de mer with a truffle essence or
the pink and tender roast lamb in pastry with a wild mushroom
stuffing, creamy herb sauce and pungent meat glaze. Desserts are a
speciality : try the warm crème brûlée served with baked peach and
caramel ice cream. Portions are generous and service formal but
unstuffy. Special dishes can be prepared if guests discuss this in
advance with Jean-Marie.*
Closed Sun & 1–9 Jan Lunch not served Sat
♀ French 65 seats Lunch £16–£28&alc Dinner £25&alc Last
lunch 1.45pm Last dinner 10pm 15P
Credit Cards [1] [3] [4]

---

## WARRINGTON Cheshire Map **07** SJ68 ◉

### ★★★63% Fir Grove
Knutsford Old Rd WA4 2LD ☎(0925)67471 FAX (0925) 601092
*A popular hotel 2.5 miles from junction 20 of the M6, following
signs to Warrington on the A50, turning right and right again just
before the swing bridge. Good business-style bedrooms, an à la
carte restaurant, a traditional pub and function rooms are among
the facilities provided here.*
40⇄🐾2🛏 CTV in all bedrooms ® T ✳ S10% sB&B⇄🐾£33-
£55 dB&B⇄🐾£45-£66
《 100P CFA *xmas*
♀ English & French V ⚘ ⚖ ✳ S10% Lunch fr£11&alc Dinner
fr£11&alc Last dinner 10pm
Credit Cards [1] [2] [3] [5]

### ★★71% Old Vicarage Hotel
Stretton Rd WA4 4NS ☎(0925)730706 FAX (0925) 730740
(For full entry see Stretton (Cheshire))

### ★★70% Rockfield
Alexandra Rd, Grappenhall WA4 2EL (1.75m SE off A50)
☎(0925)62898 due to change to 262898
Closed 25-31 Dec
*A charming Edwardian building, with immaculate bedrooms, the
hotel is in a quiet residential area to the south-east of the town, off
the A50 and near to junction 20 of the M6.*

6⇄🐾Annexe7rm(5⇄🐾) CTV in all bedrooms ® T sB&B£35-
£40 sB&B⇄🐾£38-£45 dB&B⇄🐾£45-£55 🛏
CTV 30P ✿ ♫
♀ English, French & Italian V ⚘ ⚖ ✂ Lunch £9.50-£11.50
Dinner £11.50-£12.50&alc Last dinner 9pm
Credit Cards [1] [3] [5] £

### ★★51% Paddington House
514 Old Manchester Rd WA1 3TZ (Exec Hotel) ☎(0925)816767
*A commercial hotel on the outskirts of town, on a slip road off the
A57 to Manchester.*
37⇄🐾(1fb)1🛏 CTV in all bedrooms ®
Lift 《 ⊞ 100P 2🚗 (£5) ✿
♀ French V ⚘ ⚖ Last dinner 9pm
Credit Cards [1] [3]

### ★57% Ribblesdale
Balmoral Rd, Grappenhall WA4 2EB ☎(0925)601197
FAX (0925) 62135
*A small and friendly commercial hotel in a quiet residential area.*
14rm(12⇄) CTV in all bedrooms ® T ✳ S% sB&B⇄£25-£42
dB&B⇄£30-£48
20P 🚗 ✿
♀ French V ⚘ ⚖ ✳ Lunch £10 Dinner £10&alc Last dinner
9pm
Credit Cards [1] [2] [3] £

---

## WARSASH Hampshire Map **04** SU40

### ✿✖Nook and Cranny
Hook Ln, Hook Village SO3 6HH ☎Locks Heath(0489)584129
*Colin Wood and his wife have been running this attractive cottage-
style restaurant for more than four years, delighting their clientele
with dishes inspired by French country cooking. There are table
d'hôte and à la carte menus from which to choose and dishes
enjoyed by our inspector included terrine of duck served with
pickles and tender strips of beef in a creamy, coarse mustard sauce,
served in a puff pastry case with a good selection of gently cooked
seasonal vegetables. Desserts are tempting and the wine list offers
a good choice at affordable prices.*
Closed Sun, Mon, 1 wk Nov, 25-30 Dec & BH's Lunch not
served Sat
♀ French V 50 seats Lunch £11.50 Dinner £18-£22alc Last
lunch 2pm Last dinner 9.45pm 15 P
Credit Cards [1] [3]

---

## WARWICK Warwickshire Map **04** SP26

See also **Barford and** Leamington Spa (Royal)

### ★★66% Warwick Arms
High St CV34 4AJ (Minotels) ☎(0926)492759
FAX (0926) 410587
*Once the property of the Earls of Warwick, this 18th-century inn
has been refurbished over recent years and now offers bedrooms
with good modern facilities and public areas which retain their
character.*
35⇄🐾(4fb)1🛏 CTV in all bedrooms ® T
21P
♀ English & French V ⚘ ⚖ Last dinner 9.30pm
Credit Cards [1] [2] [3] [5]

### ★★57% Lord Leycester
Jury St CV34 4AJ (Consort) ☎(0926)491481 Telex no 41363
FAX (0926) 491561
*Popular with businessmen for its conference and function
facilities – and also because it provides the car parking space which
can so often be a problem in the busy town – this centrally
positioned hotel offers bedrooms which, though in some cases
compact, are continually being upgraded to meet modern
standards.*
52⇄🐾(4fb)1🛏 CTV in all bedrooms ® T ✳ S%
sB&B⇄🐾fr£46 dB&B⇄🐾fr£65

Lift ⟨ 40P CFA
♀ English & French **V** ✿ ⊡ ✳ S% Lunch fr£13.75 Dinner
fr£13.75 Last dinner 8.30pm
Credit Cards ⟦1⟧ ⟦2⟧ ⟦3⟧ ⟦5⟧

**★66% Penderrick**
36 Coten End CV34 4NP ☎(0926)499399 497252
*Situated on the Leamington Spa Road close to the centre, this
large semi-detached Victorian house has been carefully
modernised to provide well equipped bedrooms and comfortable
public areas. Friendly and attentive services are provided by Alan
and Margaret Blackband and their staff.*
7rm(4↖)(2fb) CTV in all bedrooms ® **T** S% sB&B£24.50-£28
dB&B↖£44-£47.50 ⯑
CTV 9P 2🚗 🚲
**V** ✿ ⤩ S% Dinner £12.50-£14 Last dinner 7pm
Credit Cards ⟦1⟧ ⟦2⟧ ⟦3⟧ ⟦5⟧ ⓔ

---

**WASDALE HEAD** Cumbria Map **11** NY10

**★★67% Wasdale Head Inn**
CA20 1EX ☎Wasdale(09467)26229 FAX (09467) 26334
Closed mid Nov-28 Dec & mid Jan-mid Mar
*Beautifully situated amidst spectacular mountain scenery this
comfortable hotel provides well furnished bedrooms and a good
standard of cooking. Service is friendly and helpful.*
10⤳↖(3fb) ® **T** ✳ sB&B⤳↖£48.50-£51.50 dB&B⤳↖£96-
£99 (incl dinner) ⯑
50P 🚲 ✿ ♨
**V** ✿ ⤩ ✳ Bar Lunch £5.45-£8.65alc High tea £5.45-£8.65alc
Dinner £16 Last dinner 7.30pm
Credit Cards ⟦1⟧ ⟦3⟧

---

**WASHINGTON** Tyne & Wear Map **12** NZ35

**★★★68% Washington Moat House**
Stone Cellar Rd, District 12, High Usworth NE37 1PH (Queens
Moat) ☎091-417 2626 Telex no 537143 FAX 091-415 1166
*A modern hotel on the edge of Washington New Town with many
facilities for the sports-minded, including a championship golf
course, leisure pool, gymnasium and squash courts. Bedrooms are
spacious and well appointed, and extensive à la carte and carvery
menus are available in the Lincoln Restaurant.*
106⤳↖(9fb)2⚓⤩in 16 bedrooms CTV in all bedrooms ® **T**
sB⤳↖£70-£90 dB⤳↖£80-£110 (room only) ⯑
⟨ CTV 200P ✿ CFA ▭ (heated) ▶ 18 squash snooker sauna
solarium gymnasium golf driving range hair-dressing salon
♀ English & French **V** ✿ ⊡ ⤩ ✳ Lunch £7.75-£8.75&alc
High tea £7-£12 Dinner £14.25&alc Last dinner 10pm
Credit Cards ⟦1⟧ ⟦2⟧ ⟦3⟧ ⟦5⟧ ⓔ

**★★★61% Forte Posthouse**
Emerson District 5 NE37 1LB (Forte Hotels) ☎091-416 2264
Telex no 537574 FAX 091-415 3371
*Off the A1(M) south of Gateshead, a large well furnished modern
hotel with a comfortable foyer lounge and bar, and friendly staff.*
138⤳↖⤩in 62 bedrooms CTV in all bedrooms ® **T** ✳ S%
sB⤳↖£49.50 dB⤳↖£49.50 (room only) ⯑
Lift ⟨ 198P ✿ CFA ▶ 18 pitch & putt *xmas*
**V** ✿ ⊡ ⤩ ✳ Lunch £9.50-£10.95&alc Dinner fr£13.95&alc
Last dinner 10pm
Credit Cards ⟦1⟧ ⟦2⟧ ⟦3⟧ ⟦4⟧ ⟦5⟧

---

**WASHINGTON SERVICE AREA** Tyne & Wear
Map **12** NZ25

**⌂Granada Lodge**
A1M, Portobello DH3 2SJ (Granada) ☎091-410 0076
FAX 091-410 0057
35⤳↖(10fb)⤩in 6 bedrooms CTV in all bedrooms ®
🦮 (ex guide dogs) S% sB⤳↖fr£31 dB⤳↖fr£34 (room only)
⯑

→

**W**

《118P
V ♿ 🍸 ✂
Credit Cards 1️⃣ 2️⃣ 3️⃣ 5️⃣

## WATCHET Somerset Map 03 ST04

### ★★53% Downfield

16 St Decuman's Rd TA23 0HR ☎(0984)31267
FAX (0984) 34369
*This Victorian house, standing high above the town and commanding splendid views of the harbour and steam railway, is furnished in keeping with its era. Bedrooms are very well equipped, and the restaurant offers various grill menus at a range of prices.*
8rm(6🛏️🐾)(2fb) CTV in all bedrooms ® T ✱ sB&B🛏️🐾£25-£32 dB&B🛏️🐾£35.50-£39
22P ✿ 🐕

♀ English, French & German V ♿ ✱ Lunch £7&alc Dinner £9.50-£13.50alc Last dinner 9.30pm
Credit Cards 1️⃣ 2️⃣ 3️⃣ 5️⃣

## WATERGATE BAY Cornwall & Isles of Scilly Map 02 SW86

### ★★59% Tregurrian

TR8 4AB ☎St Mawgan(0637)860280
Closed Nov-Feb
*A family-run hotel on the edge of the bay, though simply furnished, offers such extra facilities as sauna, solarium and jacuzzi pool; live entertainment is provided during the high season.*
27rm(2🛏️20🐾)(8fb) CTV in all bedrooms ® ✱ sB&B£17-£25 sB&B🛏️🐾£22-£27.50 dB&B£34-£44 dB&B🛏️🐾£40-£56 🏳️
CTV 26P ✿ ⏋ (heated) sauna solarium jacuzzi spa pool games room 🐕
♿ 🍸 ✱
Credit Cards 1️⃣ 3️⃣

## WATERHOUSES Staffordshire Map 07 SK05

### ✸✸ ✕✕ Old Beams Restaurant

Leek Rd ST10 3HW ☎(0538)308254
*On the main road in the centre of the moorland village, this restaurant is in 2 sections, one with beamed ceilings, the other a bright conservatory extension. The atmosphere is warm and friendly, and Ann Wallis supervises the helpful service. Chef/ Patron Nigel Wallis uses his acknowledged skills to produce some well prepared and interesting dishes. A seasonally changed set price menu is offered at lunch and dinner with a few extras added.*
Closed Mon Lunch not served Sat
Dinner not served Sun
♀ English & French 50 seats ✱ Lunch £15.50 Dinner £28 Last lunch 2pm Last dinner 10pm 22 P nc4yrs ✂ 🎵
Credit Cards 1️⃣ 2️⃣ 3️⃣ 5️⃣

## WATERINGBURY Kent Map 05 TQ65

### ★★★68% Wateringbury

Tonbridge Rd ME18 5NS (Lansbury) ☎Maidstone(0622)812632
Telex no 96265 FAX (0622) 812720
*At the centre of the village, on the A26 between Maidstone and Tonbridge, this small, traditional country hotel offers spacious, comfortable and well equipped accommodation which will meet the needs of holidaymaker and businessman alike. Excellently maintained and meticulously clean, it provides both an hospitable welcome and a friendly atmosphere.*
28🛏️1🛋️✂in 3 bedrooms CTV in all bedrooms ® T 🐾 sB&B🛏️frf80 dB&B🛏️frf93 🏳️
《60P sauna *xmas*
♀ European ♿ 🍸 Lunch frf12&alc Dinner frf12&alc Last dinner 10pm
Credit Cards 1️⃣ 2️⃣ 3️⃣ 5️⃣

## WATERMILLOCK Cumbria Map 12 NY42

### ★★★✸ ♨78% Leeming House

CA11 0JJ (Forte Hotels) ☎Pooley Bridge(07684)86622
Telex no 64111 FAX (07684) 86443
*An efficiently run country house hotel set in extensive landscaped gardens on the western shore of Lake Ullswater has recently been sympathetically extended, an attractive conservatory lounge now linking a new wing of exceptionally well appointed bedrooms, many of which have fine lake views; original bedrooms have been refurbished to a similarly high standard. Comfortable sitting rooms with chintzy armchairs and blazing log fires are supplemented by a book-lined library lounge, while the elegant blue dining room set with lace cloths and crystal provides an attractive setting for a carefully prepared and daily changing 6-course dinner; breakfasts, with their home-made preserves, are equally noteworthy. Service – which encompasses early morning tea and evening room service – is quietly efficient throughout.*
40🛏️🐾✂in 9 bedrooms CTV in all bedrooms ® T ✱ S% sB🛏️🐾£85-£90 dB🛏️🐾£115-£145 (room only) 🏳️
《50P 🛋️ ✿ ♪ *xmas*
V ♿ 🍸 ✂ ✱ Lunch £15.75&alc Dinner £32.50 Last dinner 8.45pm
Credit Cards 1️⃣ 2️⃣ 3️⃣ 4️⃣ 5️⃣

### ★★★✸✸ ♨75% Rampsbeck Country House

CA11 0LP ☎Pooley Bridge(07684)86442 & 86688
Closed 6 Jan-24 Feb
(Rosettes awarded for dinner only)
*Beautifully situated overlooking the lake, this delightful country house is caringly run by Mr and Mrs Gibb and offers warm hospitality and comfort. Attractively furnished throughout, it has well designed bedrooms with good facilities, relaxing lounges with log fires and an elegant restaurant serving skilfully cooked dishes that make use of local produce.*
19rm(18🛏️🐾)(1fb) CTV in all bedrooms ® T sB&B🛏️£35-£60 dB&B🛏️£65-£120 🏳️
30P 🛋️ ✿ CFA ♪ croquet lawn nc5yrs *xmas*
♀ English & French V ♿ 🍸 Lunch £16-£23 Dinner £23-£30 Last dinner 8.45pm
Credit Cards 1️⃣ 3️⃣

★★✸ ♨
OLD CHURCH HOTEL
CA11 0JN ☎Pooley Bridge
(07684)86204
FAX (07684) 86368
Closed Dec-Feb
*A small, cosy hotel in a lovely setting on Lake Ullswater.*

*Kevin and Maureen Whitemore are ideal hosts and hospitality and service are of the highest standard. Maureen has applied her skills to the soft furnishings around the hotel which she designed and made herself. The attractive sitting room has a log fire in winter, and there is a second television lounge. Bedrooms are individually decorated and comfortably appointed. A set 5-course dinner is served in the intimate dining room at 8pm. Cooking is plain and uncomplicated, using good basic ingredients. Service is quite formal but attentive and helpful.*
10🛏️ T 🐾 (ex guide dogs) ✱ S% sB&B🛏️£110-£165 dB&B🛏️£150-£210 (incl dinner)
CTV 30P 🛋️ ✿ ♪ boat hire moorings 🐕
♀ English & French ♿ 🍸 ✂ ✱ S% Lunch £7-£15 Dinner £27.50 Last dinner 8pm
Credit Cards 1️⃣

WATERROW Somerset Map **03** ST02

★❀🏠76% **Hurstone Country Hotel & Restaurant**
TA4 2AT ☎Wiveliscombe(0984)23441
*Converted from a 300-year-old farmhouse, this small family-run*
*hotel stands in 65 acres on the edge of the Brendon Hills. The*
*beamed sitting room with its large fireplace and log-burning fire is*
*the ideal place to relax after a day exploring the area. An*
*imaginative table d'hôte menu features carefully prepared fresh*
*produce, and the wine list is extensive for the size of the*
*establishment. Bedrooms are comfortable, attractively furnished*
*and well equipped, and all are south facing with spectacular views.*
*The delightful service and attention given to visitors here has*
*resulted in Hurstone Hotel being awarded one of our 'Courtesy*
*and Care' awards for the South West region for 1991/1992 (see*
*colour feature p 14).*
6rm(5⇨🛏)(1fb)✂in 1 bedroom CTV in 5 bedrooms ® **T** ✱
sB&B⇨🛏£47.50 dB&B⇨🛏£75 🍴
CTV 12P 🚗 ♩ 𝒐𝒃 *xmas*
♡ Continental V ♥ ⚘ ✱ Sunday Lunch £8.75-£9.50 Dinner
£17.50-£18.50 Last dinner 9.30pm
Credit Cards ①②③

WATFORD Hertfordshire Map **04** TQ19 ◎

★★★63%. **Dean Park**
30-40 St Albans Rd WD1 1RN (Queens Moat) ☎(0923)229212
Telex no 8813610 FAX (0923) 54638
Closed 25-31 Dec
*Conveniently placed for access to the motorway network and close*
*to both station and town centre, this large, purpose-built hotel*
*offers well equipped accommodation (though some twin rooms are*
*small). There are two bars, extensive conference facilities and an*
*adjacent NCP car park.*
90⇨🛏(2fb)✂in 18 bedrooms CTV in all bedrooms ® **T**
✈ (ex guide dogs) ✱ sB&B⇨🛏£32-£80 dB&B⇨🛏£44-£90 🍴
Lift ⓒ 12P
♡ French V ♥ ⚘ ✂ ✱ Lunch £8.50-£12&alc Dinner £8.50-
£14.50&alc Last dinner 10pm
Credit Cards ①②③④⑤ ④

★★61% **The White House**
Upton Rd WD1 2EL ☎(0923)37316 Telex no 8955439
FAX (0923) 33109
*A central hotel offering a good choice of accommodation at various*
*prices, from spacious and brand new to smaller, more modest*
*bedrooms in the annexe across the road. The main building has an*
*open plan reception, foyer, lounge and bar area with comfortable*
*seating and a smart but informal dining room.*
62⇨🛏Annexe26⇨🛏(1fb)✂in 5 bedrooms CTV in all
bedrooms ® **T** ✱ sB&B⇨🛏£49-£120 dB&B⇨🛏£78-£130 🍴
Lift ⓒ CTV 40P
♡ English & French V ♥ ⚘ ✱ Lunch £14.95-£19.95&alc High
tea £4.85-£8alc Dinner £14.95-£19.95&alc Last dinner 9.45pm
Credit Cards ①②③⑤

**See advertisement on page 731**

WATTON Norfolk Map **05** TF90

★★67% **Clarence House**
78 High St IP25 6AH (Exec Hotel) ☎(0953)884252 & 884487
FAX (0953) 881323
*A small, family-run hotel at the centre of the little market town*
*offers friendly, attentive service, modestly appointed but well*
*equipped bedrooms and public areas which combine comfort and a*
*homely atmosphere.*
6⇨🛏(1fb) CTV in all bedrooms ® **T** S% sB&B⇨🛏fr£38
dB&B⇨🛏fr£50 🍴
7P 🚗 *xmas*
♡ English & French V ♥ ⚘ ✱ Lunch fr£11 Dinner £13.45-
£16.45 Last dinner 9pm
Credit Cards ①②③⑤

**W**

## WEEDON Northamptonshire Map **04** SP65

### ★★★69% **Crossroads**

NN7 4PX (Best Western) ☎(0327)40354 FAX (0327) 40849
Closed 24-26 Dec

*At the heart of England where the A5 and A45 cross, this welcoming family-run hotel has a deceptive modern exterior. The interior abounds with antiques and memorabilia, and individually styled rooms are comfortable and thoughtfully equipped, with many little extras.*

10➪Annexe40➪(3fb)3⌧ CTV in all bedrooms ® T
✻ (ex guide dogs) sB&B➪£40-£90 dB&B➪£50-£99 ▯
100P ✿ CFA ⌂ (heated) ♪ (hard)
V ✿ ⚏ Lunch £17-£25alc High tea £5-£10alc Dinner £17-£25alc Last dinner 10.15pm
Credit Cards ①②③⑤

### ★★66% *Heart Of England*

Daventry Rd NN7 4QD ☎(0327)40335
*Rooms are attractively furnished and well equipped in an hotel which dates back to the eighteenth century; today it offers convenient access to junction 16 of the M1 from its town centre position beside the A45. Good levels of hospitality and service are maintained by a particularly friendly staff, and a selection of grill meals is available in the Gables Restaurant.*

12rm(1➪1✿)1⌧ CTV in all bedrooms ® ✻ (ex guide dogs)
70P ⇜ ✿
V ✿ ⚏ Last dinner 10pm
Credit Cards ①②③⑤

### ★★★61% *Globe*

High St NN7 4QD (Inter-Hotels) ☎(0327)40336
FAX (0327) 349058

*A privately owned country inn situated at the crossroads of the A5 and A45, close to junction 16 of the M1. Accommodation is well equipped, though a couple of the single rooms are compact, and are equally suitable for business guests or tourists. Improvements continue, and the restaurant and bar have recently been upgraded.*

14➪✿(1fb) CTV in all bedrooms ® T
CTV 40P ♫
☷ Mainly grills V ✿ ⚏ Last dinner 10pm
Credit Cards ①②③⑤

## WELLINGBOROUGH Northamptonshire Map **04** SP86 ◉

### ★★★57% **Hind**

Sheep St NN8 1BY (Queens Moat) ☎(0933)222827
FAX (0933) 441921

*Dating from the early 1600s, this coaching inn is reputed to have accommodated Oliver Cromwell before the battle of Naseby. In the centre of the town, easily accessible from the M1 and A45, car parking can be difficult. The accommodation was completely refurbished during 1990 to provide modern, well equipped guest rooms. The Commons Room Restaurant offers both table d'hôte and à la carte menus, but meals can disappoint.*

34➪✿(2fb)1⌧ CTV in all bedrooms ® T sB&B➪✿£50-£70
dB&B➪✿£65-£87 ▯
℄ 13P 3⇜ CFA
☷ English & Continental V ✿ ⚏ ✗ Lunch £9.95-£10.95&alc
Dinner £11.95-£12.95&alc Last dinner 10pm
Credit Cards ①②③④⑤ ⓔ

### ★★61% **Columbia**

19 Northampton Rd NN8 3HG (Consort) ☎(0933)229333
FAX (0933) 440418
Closed 24-27 Dec

*A popular privately-owned hotel close to the town centre, accommodation here is well equipped and ideal for commercial guests. Public areas are open-plan and include a small restaurant where an extensive range of dishes is available. Staff are friendly and helpful and create an amiable atmosphere.*

29➪✿(1fb) CTV in all bedrooms ® T ✻ (ex guide dogs) ✱
sB&B➪✿£30-£48 dB&B➪✿£45-£58 ▯

18P CFA
☷ English & French V ✿ ⚏ ✱ Lunch £7.75-£8.75&alc Dinner
£10.75-£13.75&alc Last dinner 9.30pm
Credit Cards ①②③

### ★★59% **High View**

156 Midland Rd NN8 1NG ☎(0933)278733 FAX (0933) 225948
*This hotel is conveniently situated for the town centre and the railway station. Proprietors Mr and Mrs Hunter play an active role in providing a personal service to guests. Accommodation is well equipped and maintained, with an additional 3 rooms in a nearby house. Public areas include a simply appointed dining room on the lower ground floor overlooking the garden.*

14➪✿Annexe3rm(2fb) CTV in all bedrooms ® T sB&B£24
sB&B➪✿£27-£44 dB&B£34 dB&B➪✿£45-£50 ▯
CTV 8P 1⇜ ✿
V ✿ ✗ S% Lunch fr£8.10alc Dinner fr£8.10alc Last dinner
8.30pm
Credit Cards ①②③⑤ ⓔ

### ○Forte Travelodge

Higham Rd, Little Irchester NN8 2DB (on A45, westbound)
(Forte) ☎Central Res (0800) 850950
Due to have opened Winter 1991
40➪✿

## WELLINGTON

See Telford

## WELLINGTON **Somerset** Map **02** ST12

### ★★59% **Beambridge**

Sampford Arundel TA21 0HB ☎Greenham(0823)672223
*A small fully licensed family-run hotel about 1.5 miles west of Wellington on the A38. Bedrooms are comfortable and well equipped, and the restaurant offers an à la carte menu featuring grills and a few house specialities. The bars are favoured by locals and an extensive range of bar meals is available. The function room is also popular.*

10rm(9➪✿)Annexe8rm1⌧ CTV in 10 bedrooms ® T ✱
sB&B£15-£26.50 sB&B➪✿£26.50 dB&B➪✿£41.50
CTV 100P
V ✿ ⚏ ✱ Lunch £6.75-£13.80alc High tea £3 Dinner £6.75-£13.80alc Last dinner 9pm
Credit Cards ①③

## WELLS **Somerset** Map **03** ST54

Telephone numbers are liable to change during the currency of this guide.

### ★★★61% **Swan**

Sadler St BA5 2RX (Best Western) ☎(0749)78877 due to change
to 678877 Telex no 449658 FAX (0749) 77647 due to change to
677647

*A 15th-century coaching inn with superb views of the west front of the cathedral features well equipped, spacious bedrooms, many furnished with antiques and some have four poster beds. Lounge and bar are warmed by open fires, meals served in the cosy dining room are complemented by a good wine list, and service is both friendly and efficient.*

32➪✿(2fb)⌧ CTV in all bedrooms ® T ✱ sB&B➪✿£56-£65 dB&B➪✿⚏✿£76.50-£90 ▯
30P CFA squash *xmas*
V ✿ ⚏ Lunch £10.95-£11.95&alc Dinner £14.50-£15.50&alc
Last dinner 9.30pm
Credit Cards ①②③⑤

### ★★66% *Crown*

Market Place BA5 2RP ☎(0749)73457
*Service is relaxed and friendly at the Crown, located in the market square of this small cathedral city. Bedrooms have been refurbished with style, retaining many period features. The lounge has also been upgraded, and the Penn Eating House and Bar*

→

W

*provides value-for-money meals. Formal service is available in the hotel's restaurant where table d'hôte and à la carte menus feature house specialities.*

15⇨♪4🎤 CTV in 21 bedrooms ®

15P squash

V ♥ �‍ Last dinner 10pm

Credit Cards ① ② ③ ④ ⑤

### ★★ 64% The Star

18 High St BA5 2SQ (Resort) ☎(0749)73055 & 670500
FAX (0749) 72654

12⇨♪(2fb)1🎤 CTV in all bedrooms ® T ♨ (ex guide dogs)
✱ sB&B⇨♪£41 dB&B⇨♪£56 🍴

𝆏 xmas

♁ English & Cosmopolitan V ♥ �‍ ✂ ✱ Lunch fr£3.95alc
High tea fr£3alc Dinner fr£9alc Last dinner 10.30pm

Credit Cards ① ② ③

### ★ 57% Ancient Gate House

Sadler St BA5 2RR ☎(0749)72029

Closed 24-26 Dec

*A hotel with plenty of character situated close to the cathedral. Accommodation is basic but is in the process of being upgraded. The Italian cooking is of a good standard and service is friendly and efficient.*

9rm(1⇨5♪)(1fb)6🎤 CTV in all bedrooms ® T ✱ sB&B£30-£35 sB&B⇨♪£35-£40 dB&B£45-£50 dB&B⇨♪£50-£55 🍴

𝆏

♁ English & Italian V ♥ ✱ Lunch £4.50-£5.50&alc Dinner £12.50-£13.75&alc Last dinner 10.30pm

Credit Cards ① ② ③ ⑤

### WELLS-NEXT-THE-SEA Norfolk Map 09 TF94

### ★ 57% Crown

The Buttlands NR23 1EX (Minotels) ☎Fakenham(0328)710209

*A high standard of French provincial cuisine, the dishes featured in its daily-changing menu using only fresh local produce, can be enjoyed in this restaurant at the heart of Wells. The building, despite its Georgian façade, has its origins in Tudor times, and the comfortable bar areas are still warmed by open log fires, while the town's association with Nelson is reflected in naval prints depicting him. Accommodation, though modest, is both warm and comfortable, informal service being attentive and friendly, so that the hotel offers an ideal base both for commercial clients and for holidaymakers exploring the area.*

15rm(4⇨5♪)(3fb) CTV in all bedrooms ® sB&B£34-£43
sB&B⇨♪£50 dB&B£54 dB&B⇨♪£62 🍴

CTV 10P 🚲 xmas

♁ English & Continental V ♥ �‍ ✂ Lunch fr£14.50&alc High tea fr£3.50 Dinner fr£14.50&alc Last dinner 9.30pm

Credit Cards ① ② ③ ⑤

### ❀❀❀✕ Moorings

6 Freeman St NR23 1BA ☎Fakenham(0328)710949

*Locally caught seafood is a speciality of this charming little restaurant that stands close to the harbour of this small Norfolk fishing town. Dishes are predominantly provincial French – mussels, oysters, sea-trout and dogfish are well-flavoured, with a lavish use of herbs. Vegetarians are particularly well catered for, with dishes such as eggs and broccoli with mustard and cheese sauce or Chinese vegetables with beancurd. The wine list is extensive and modestly priced.*

Closed Tue, Wed, 2 wks early Jun & late Nov-mid Dec Lunch not served Thu

♁ English & French V 40 seats ✱ Lunch £12-£15 Dinner £15-£20 Last lunch 1.45pm Last dinner 8.45pm 𝆏 ✂

For key to symbols in English see the bookmark.

### WELSH HOOK Dyfed Map 02 SM92

### ❀✕✕ Stone Hall

SA62 5NS ☎Letterston(0348)840212 FAX (0348) 840815

*Stone Hall stands near the hamlet of Welsh Hook between Haverfordwest and Fishguard. The charming restaurant in the 600-year-old part of the house serves imaginative food prepared by a talented young chef whose experience was gained in Nice and Brittany.*

Closed Mon & First 2 wks Dec Lunch not served (ex by prior arrangement only)

♁ French V 34 seats Dinner £13-£14.50&alc Last dinner 9.30pm 50 P

Credit Cards ① ② ③

### WELSHPOOL Powys Map 07 SJ20

### ★★⚑73% Golfa Hall

Llanfair Rd SY21 9AF ☎(0938)553399 FAX (0938) 554777

*Set in an elevated position amid several acres of parkland and gardens, this small but very pleasant hotel lies off the A458 just 1.5 miles west of the town. Exceptionally comfortable lounge facilites complement fully equipped modern bedrooms, and a well chosen à la carte menu offers enjoyable food.*

10⇨♪(3fb) TV available ® T ✱ sB&B⇨♪fr£37
dB&B⇨♪£47-£57 🍴

50P 🚲 ✿ CFA clay pigeon shooting

♁ English & Continental V ♥ �‍ ✂ ✱ Lunch £10-£15alc Dinner £10-£15alc Last dinner 8.30pm

Credit Cards ① ② ③ ⑤ ⓔ

### ★★ 64% Royal Oak

SY21 7DG (Consort) ☎(0938)552217 Telex no 57515
FAX (0938) 552217

*Dating from the mid 18th century, and right in the heart of this busy mid Wales market-town, this hotel provides a popular function suite and a good choice of bars and lounges. Many bedrooms have recently been modernised, and a good choice of food is available in the timbered restaurant.*

24⇨♪(3fb)1🎤 CTV in all bedrooms ® T ♨ (ex guide dogs)
sB&B⇨♪£38-£40 dB&B⇨♪£65-£70 🍴

CTV 60P 🚗 CFA

♁ English, French & Italian V ♥ �‍ Lunch fr£9 Dinner fr£12 Last dinner 9pm

Credit Cards ① ② ③ ⓔ

### WELWYN GARDEN CITY Hertfordshire Map 04 TL21

### ★★★ 61% Crest

Homestead Ln AL7 4LX (Forte Hotels) ☎(0707)324336
Telex no 261523 FAX (0707) 326447

*In a quiet residential area a short drive from the centre, this small hotel is popular with business travellers and provides well equipped bedrooms and friendly service.*

58⇨♪✱in 13 bedrooms CTV in all bedrooms ® ✱
sB⇨♪£73 dB⇨♪£87 (room only) 🍴

Lift ( 80P ✿ CFA xmas

V ♥ ✂ ✱ Lunch £9.95&alc Dinner £16.30&alc Last dinner 9.45pm

Credit Cards ① ② ③ ④ ⑤

### WEMBLEY Greater London

See **LONDON plan** 1B4(page 434)

### ❀✕ Woodlands

402A High Rd HA9 7AB ☎081-902 9869 FAX 081-908 0253

*This comfortable, friendly restaurant in a busy shopping road offers some deliciously reviving Southern Indian vegetarian cuisine, clear in flavour and texture and skilfully spiced to differing degrees of heat. The Rava Masala crisp semolina and onion pancake comes with a sharp lentil dressing, the light potato bonda with a pungent coconut chutney, and the fluffy bhatura bread puts many a*

**W**

*Yorkshire Pudding to shame! In contrast to these spicy flavours, try an almond and saffron milkshake.*
Closed 25-26 Dec
♥ South Indian V 55 seats Last lunch 2.30pm Last dinner 10.30pm 2 P
Credit Cards 1 2 3 5

---

WENTBRIDGE (NEAR PONTEFRACT) West Yorkshire Map **08** SE41 ☉

★★★👥67% **Wentbridge House**
WF8 3JJ (Select) ☎Pontefract(0977)620444 FAX (0977) 620148
Closed Xmas night
*This is a pleasant country house dating back to the 18th century and set in 15 acres of grounds. It is well furnished in all areas and conveniently situated just off the A1 in the village of Wentbridge.*
12⇌🛏1🖵 CTV in all bedrooms ® T 🐾 (ex guide dogs) S%
sB&B⇌🛏£66-£93.50 dB&B⇌🛏£78-£108 🍴
100P 🐴 ✿
♥ English & French V ♥ Lunch £15.50-£19.50&alc Dinner £30-£35alc Last dinner 9.30pm
Credit Cards 1 2 3 5

---

WEST BAY

See **Bridport**

---

WEST BEXINGTON Dorset Map **03** SY58

★★67% **Manor**
Beach Rd DT6 9DF ☎Burton Bradstock(0308)897616
FAX (0308) 897035
*This lovely old stone house enjoys good views from its position close to the sea. Bedrooms in cottage style have antique furniture and bright floral fabrics, and two lounges – warmed by log fires during the colder months – feature deep armchairs and a notable* →

**W**

*collection of horse racing pictures. As well as the formal bar which caters for the needs of walkers and holidaying families, spilling over into the conservatory and large garden during the summer. Resident proprietors and local staff provide warm hospitality throughout.*

13⇨🅿(1fb) CTV in all bedrooms Ⓡ T ✗ sB&B⇨🅵£39-£44 dB&B⇨🅵£64-£69 ⋐

28P ✿ CFA

V ♥ ⚏ Lunch £14 Dinner £17.95 Last dinner 10pm
Credit Cards ①②③⑤

**See advertisement under BRIDPORT**

---

WEST BROMWICH West Midlands Map **07** SP09 ◉

See also Barr, Great

★★★62% **West Bromwich Moat House**
Birmingham Rd B70 6RS (Queens Moat) ☎021-553 6111
Telex no 336232 FAX 021-525 7403
*A purpose-built group hotel, conveniently situated at junction 1 of the M5, offers extensive conference facilities and well equipped accommodation, while Rafferty's Restaurant complements its à la carte menu with a popular carvery operation.*
180⇨🅵(115fb)⚤in 17 bedrooms CTV in all bedrooms Ⓡ T ✱
sB⇨🅵£55-£65 dB⇨🅵£65-£75 (room only) ⋐
Lift ⟨▦ 200P CFA *xmas*
♀ English & French V ♥ ⚏ ✱ Lunch fr£11.50 Dinner fr£13.50 Last dinner 10pm
Credit Cards ①②③⑤ⓔ

★★★60% **Great Barr Hotel & Conference Centre**
Pear Tree Dr, off Newton Rd B43 6HS ☎021-357 1141
Telex no 336406 FAX 021-357 7557
(For full entry see Barr, Great)

---

WEST CHILTINGTON West Sussex Map **04** TQ01

★★★63% **Roundabout**
Monkmead Ln RH20 2PF (1.75m S) (Best Western)
☎(0798)813838 FAX (0798) 812962
*Tudor-style public areas, furnished in dark oak and tapestry-hung, offer the comfort of Parker Knoll armchairs in a relaxing atmosphere; the small lounge is complemented by a candlelit restaurant and bar warmed by a log fire in winter. Bedrooms in two Tudor cottages and a spacious annexe supplement main building accommodation, several of the well equipped rooms having four poster beds. Competently supervised service is attentively helpful, and the hotel enjoys a pleasant setting in carefully tended gardens.*
23⇨🅵(4fb)4⌧ CTV in all bedrooms Ⓡ T S10%
sB&B⇨🅵£64.75-£69.75 dB&B⇨🅵£79.50-£83.50 ⋐
46P ✿ CFA nc3yrs *xmas*
♀ English & French V ♥ ⚏ ⚥ S10% Lunch £11.55-£12.55&alc Dinner £18-£18.75&alc Last dinner 9pm
Credit Cards ①②③④⑤

---

WESTCLIFF-ON-SEA

See Southend-on-Sea

---

WESTERHAM Kent Map **05** TQ45

★★★63% **Kings Arms**
Market Square TN16 1AN ☎(0959)62990 FAX (0959) 61240
*Bedrooms are individually decorated, spacious and well equipped at this elegant Georgian coaching inn in the town centre; public areas are undergoing refurbishment, and in the attractive surroundings of the recently completed restaurant guests are assured of attentive service and an interesting selection from table d'hôte and à la carte menus.*
16⇨🅵(2fb)1⌧⚤in 3 bedrooms CTV in all bedrooms Ⓡ T ✗ (ex guide dogs) sB&B⇨🅵fr£60 dB&B⇨🅵fr£75 ⋐
30P 4🚗 CFA ⚙

V ♥ ⚏ ✱ Lunch £14.50-£17.50&alc Dinner £14.50-£17.50&alc Last dinner 10pm
Credit Cards ①②③⑤ⓔ

---

WESTGATE ON SEA Kent Map **05** TR37

★★55% **Ivyside**
25 Sea Rd CT8 8SB ☎Thanet(0843)31082 FAX (0843) 31082
*A seafront hotel providing functional and varied accommodation especially designed for families with children features games rooms, play areas and good indoor leisure facilities; it is also popular with local residents, friendly service being supervised by the second generation of the proprietor's family.*
67rm(65⇨🅵)(58fb) CTV in all bedrooms Ⓡ T ✗ (ex guide dogs) sB&B⇨🅵£25-£39 dB&B⇨🅵£50-£78
《 CTV 30P ✿ CFA ▱ (heated) ⚊ (heated) squash snooker sauna solarium gymnasium spa pool steam room table tennis ⚙ *xmas*
♀ English & French V ♥ ⚏ ✱ Lunch £6-£8 High tea £5 Dinner £9.50&alc Last dinner 8.30pm
Credit Cards ①③

---

WESTHILL Grampian *Aberdeenshire* Map **15** NJ80

★★★61% **Westhill**
AB32 6TT (Consort) ☎Aberdeen(0224)740388 Telex no 739925 FAX (0224) 744354
*Just off the A944, 6 miles west of Aberdeen, this modern commercial hotel which is also popular for the local functions, offers a choice of bars and an à la carte restaurant plus some leisure facilities. Bedrooms are practical and well equipped.*
38⇨🅵Annexe14⇨🅵(2fb) CTV in all bedrooms Ⓡ T ✱ S%
sB&B⇨🅵£50-£55 dB&B⇨🅵£60-£70
Lift 《 ▦ 350P CFA sauna solarium gymnasium ♫ *xmas*
♀ International V ♥ ✱
Credit Cards ①②③⑤

**See advertisement under ABERDEEN**

---

WESTLETON Suffolk Map **05** TM46

★★72% **The Crown at Westleton**
IP17 3AD ☎(072873)273
Closed 25-26 Dec
*This delightful village inn, constantly being extended and upgraded, offers varied but for the most part well furnished and comprehensively equipped accommodation. The public bar – simply styled to retain its rustic charm – is supplemented by a comfortable lounge, and further improvements should by now have provided a good reception area and the larger kitchens necessary to cope with the demands of the popular bar meal and restaurant business.*
7rm(3⇨)Annexe7⇨🅵(3fb)2⌧ CTV in all bedrooms Ⓡ 30P
V ♥ ⚤ Last dinner 9.30pm
Credit Cards ①②③⑤

---

WEST LULWORTH Dorset Map **03** SY88

★★62% **Cromwell House**
BH20 5RJ ☎(092941)253 FAX (092941) 566
*An hotel which commands splendid coastal and country views from its elevated position two hundred metres from the famous cove offers comfortable, well furnished bedrooms and a cosy bar where guests can enjoy an aperitif before dinner; young owners and a loyal team of staff create a happy, relaxed atmosphere.*
14⇨🅵(1fb)1⌧ CTV in all bedrooms Ⓡ T sB&B⇨🅵£29.50-£36.50 dB&B⇨🅵£61-£65 (incl dinner) ⋐
CTV 14P 1🚗 ✿ CFA ⚊ (heated) solarium *xmas*
V ♥ ⚏ Lunch £6.95-£7.50 High tea £4-£6 Dinner £10-£12.50&alc Last dinner 8.30pm
Credit Cards ①②③ⓔ

★★ 61% **Gatton House**

BH20 5RU ☎(092941)252
Closed 21 Dec-Feb

*A small hotel which commands splendid views over surrounding countryside from its position high on a hill is run on friendly lines by its resident proprietors, featuring a comfortable lounge bar with real log fire and a bright, airy dining room which offers a short table d'hôte menu of fresh British dishes.*

8⇨🏠(1fb)⌿in 1 bedroom CTV in all bedrooms ®
sB&B⇨🏠£25-£30 dB&B⇨🏠£49-£53 🏴
CTV 11P 🚗
♀ English & French ❖ ⚏ ⌿ Dinner £13.50-£15.50 Last dinner 7.30pm
Credit Cards ① ③ ⓔ

★ 65% **Shirley**

Main Rd BH20 5RL ☎(092941)358
Closed early Nov-Feb

*The hotel has been in the hands of the same proprietors for twenty years, and their good-natured, natural hospitality creates an informal atmosphere which make it ideal for the holidaymaker. Bedrooms, though small in many cases, are fully equipped with modern facilities, books and games are available in the comfortable lounge, and the garden contains a sheltered pool and giant chess set.*

19⇨🏠(2fb) CTV in all bedrooms ® T ⚹ sB&B⇨🏠£18-£24.50 dB&B⇨🏠£36-£49 🏴
20P 🚗 ⊐ (heated) giant chess pool table
V ⌿ Dinner £9&alc Last dinner 8pm
Credit Cards ① ② ③

---

WESTON-ON-THE-GREEN Oxfordshire Map **04** SP51

★★★ 68% **Weston Manor**

OX6 8QL (Best Western) ☎Bletchington(0869)50621
Telex no 83409 FAX (0869) 50901

*An impressive 14th-century manor house with elegant public areas decorated in medieval style – the beautiful oak-panelled restaurant has a minstrel's gallery. Bedrooms are tastefully decorated and the hotel also has good leisure facilities.*

17⇨🏠Annexe20⇨🏠(3fb)2🏠 CTV in all bedrooms ® T
✕ (ex guide dogs) sB&B⇨🏠£75-£85 dB&B⇨🏠£95-£120 🏴
❪ 150P ❁ CFA ⊐ (heated) croquet *xmas*
♀ English & French V ❖ ⚏ ✳ Lunch £14.50-£16.95&alc High tea £5-£7.50 Dinner £19.75-£21.75&alc Last dinner 9.30pm
Credit Cards ① ② ③ ⑤

---

WESTON-SUPER-MARE Avon Map **03** ST36 ⊙

★★★ 64% **The Grand Atlantic**

Beach Rd BS23 1BA (Forte Hotels) ☎(0934)626543
FAX (0934) 415048

*In a prominent promenade position close to the Tropicana Centre, this large Victorian hotel is being steadily refurbished and provides well equipped bedrooms, spacious public areas and well tended gardens with an outdoor swimming pool and tennis court.*

76⇨🏠(5fb)⌿in 12 bedrooms CTV in all bedrooms ® T ⚹
sB⇨🏠fr£60 dB⇨🏠£80-£110 (room only) 🏴
Lift ❪ 150P ❁ CFA ⊐ (heated) ♪ (hard) pool table 🎱 *xmas*
V ❖ ⚏ ⌿ ⚹ Lunch fr£9.66 Dinner fr£17.95 Last dinner 9.30pm
Credit Cards ① ② ③ ⑤

★★★ ❀63% **Commodore**

Beach Rd, Sand Bay, Kewstoke BS22 9UZ (Exec Hotel)
☎(0934)415778 FAX (0934) 636483

*A constantly improving modern hotel standing on the sands at Kewstoke, 2 miles from Weston, offers compact but very well equipped bedrooms and bright, open-plan public areas including a choice of bars. The restaurant offers a wide range of skilfully cooked dishes by Paul Evans and his brother Nigel, from traditional grills, steaks and favourites such as prawn cocktail and* →

**W**

*sherry trifle to more modern choices: venison with red wine and pear sauce; oatmeal basket with chocolate and hazelnut ice cream.*
12⇨🏠Annexe7rm(4🏠)(1fb) CTV in all bedrooms ® T ✠ (ex guide dogs) sB&B⇨🏠£50 dB&B⇨🏠£65 🍴
85P ✿ CFA ♫ ♨
☺ English & French **V** ✿ ♨ ⚓ Lunch £8.75-£10.75&alc High tea £3.50-£5 Dinner £11-£15&alc Last dinner 9.30pm
Credit Cards ①②③⑤ⓔ

### ★★★53% Royal Pier
Birnbeck Rd BS23 2EJ (Best Western) ☎(0934)626644
FAX (0934) 624169
*Friendly services and spacious public areas are attractive features of this holiday hotel which commands views of the bay from its position near Birnbeck Pier; bedrooms vary in quality but are currently being upgraded to a higher standard.*
40rm(38⇨🏠)(4fb) CTV in all bedrooms ® T ✠ ✱
sB&B⇨🏠£49.50-£55.50 dB&B⇨🏠£76.50-£86.50 🍴
Lift ⦅ CTV 70P CFA pool table table tennis *xmas*
☺ European **V** ✿ ♨ ✱ Lunch £9.50-£11&alc Dinner £12.95-£14.50&alc Last dinner 9.15pm
Credit Cards ①②③⑤ⓔ

### ★★69% Rozel
Madeira Cove BS23 2BU ☎(0934)415268
*A friendly, family-run hotel with some fine sea views offers bedrooms which have a good selection of modern facilities, most of them being spacious and some featuring their own small balconies. Guests enjoy the use of an outdoor heated swimming pool.*
46⇨🏠(15fb) CTV in all bedrooms ® T sB&B⇨🏠£47-£59 dB&B⇨🏠£69-£85 🍴
Lift ⦅ 30P 50🚗 ✿ CFA 🏊 (heated) ♫ *xmas*
☺ English & French **V** ✿ ♨ ✱ Sunday Lunch £9-£12 Dinner £12.95-£12.95 Last dinner 8.30pm
Credit Cards ①②③⑤ⓔ

### ★★64% Beachlands
17 Uphill Rd North BS23 4NG ☎(0934)621401
FAX (0934) 621966
*A family-run hotel which is situated in a mainly residential area, overlooking the golf course, offers modern, well-equipped bedrooms, spacious open-plan public areas and particularly friendly, attentive services.*
18⇨🏠(5fb) CTV in all bedrooms ® T sB&B⇨🏠£28.50-£33.50 dB&B⇨🏠£57-£67 🍴
CTV 15P 🚗 CFA
☺ English & French **V** ✿ ♨ ⚓ ✱ Bar Lunch fr£3.90 High tea fr£3.50 Dinner fr£11.50 Last dinner 8.30pm
Credit Cards ①②③⑤

### ★★62% Old Manor Inn
Queensway, Worle BS22 9LP ☎(0934)515143
FAX (0934) 521738
*On the site of a former monastery, the hotel offers functional accommodation. The lively skittle bar is popular with the locals, and a lounge bar is also available. Leisure facilities include a sauna, solarium and multi-gym.*
Annexe21⇨🏠(4fb) CTV in all bedrooms ® T ✠ ✱ S%
sB&B⇨🏠fr£32.50 dB&B⇨🏠fr£45 🍴
75P ✿ CFA sauna solarium gymnasium skittle alley games room
**V** ✿ ⚓ ✱ S% Lunch £9.20-£18.50alc Dinner £9.20-£18.50alc Last dinner 10pm
Credit Cards ①②③⑤

### ★★60% Berni Royal
South Pde BS23 1JN (Chef & Brewer) ☎(0934)623601
FAX (0934) 415135
*Situated close to the Promenade, this Victorian hotel has been modernised to provide well equipped, en suite bedrooms, popular bars and a grill restaurant.*

37⇨🏠2🏠 CTV in all bedrooms ® T ✠ (ex guide dogs) sB&B⇨🏠£51-£62 dB&B⇨🏠£73 🍴
Lift ⦅ 150P ✿ CFA
☺ International **V** ✿ ♨ ⚓ Bar Lunch £2.95-£5.50alc
Credit Cards ①②③⑤

---

## WEST RUNTON Norfolk Map 09 TG14

### ★★★65% Links Country Park Hotel & Golf Club
Sandy Ln NR27 9QH ☎(026375)691 FAX (026375) 8264
*An hotel with a Tudor-style façade, surrounded by pastureland and its own golf course, occupies a prominent position behind the village which, together with its range of commercial facilities, attracts all type of custom. It strives to keep up with modern requirements by constant refurbishment, and although planned improvements are not yet complete, public areas are now fully air conditioned.*
30⇨🏠Annexe10⇨🏠(16fb) CTV in all bedrooms ® T
sB&B⇨🏠£63-£83 dB&B⇨🏠£126-£166 (incl dinner) 🍴
Lift ⦅ 150P ✿ CFA ⊡ (heated) ⚑ 9 ♪ (hard) sauna solarium *xmas*
☺ English & French **V** ✿ ♨ Bar Lunch £5-£14.25alc High tea £2.45-£5alc Dinner £16.95-£18.95&alc Last dinner 9.30pm
Credit Cards ①③

---

## WEST THURROCK Essex Map 05 TQ57

### ○Granada Lodge
RM16 3BG (off A1306 Arterial Rd) (Granada)
☎Central Res (0800) 555300
Due to open Spring 1992
44⇨🏠

---

## WESTWARD HO! Devon Map 02 SS42

### ★★62% Culloden House
Fosketh Hill EX39 1JA ☎Bideford(0237)479421
Closed Nov-Feb
*In an elevated position commanding glorious views across the bay, this friendly family-run Victorian residence has a comfortable feel and provides comfortable attractive public areas and simple modern bedrooms.*
9rm(2⇨5🏠)(2fb) CTV in all bedrooms sB&B£25-£30
sB&B⇨🏠£25-£35 dB&B£50-£58 dB&B⇨🏠£50-£58
CTV 9P 🚗 ✿
**V** ✿ ♨ Bar Lunch £3-£6alc Dinner £10-£15 Last dinner 8.45pm
Credit Cards ①②③⑤ⓔ

---

## WEST WITTON North Yorkshire Map 07 SE08

### ★★68% Wensleydale Heifer Inn
DL8 4LS (Consort) ☎Wensleydale(0969)22322
FAX (0969) 24183
*Situated on the main road, the A684, through beautiful Wensleydale, this 17th-century inn provides accommodation in the main building and in 2 adjacent houses – 'The Old Reading Room' and 'East View House'. All rooms are attractively decorated, comfortable and are very well equipped. A cosy, chintzy lounge with an open fire, original beams and a similar bar provide the traditional ambience of the coaching inn. Freshly cooked and interesting food is the highlight of a stay here, served in the elegant candlelit dining room. The hotel is family owned, with a young, pleasant staff.*
9⇨🏠Annexe10⇨🏠(1fb)3🛏 CTV in all bedrooms ® T
sB&B⇨🏠£45 dB&B⇨🏠£62 🍴
25P CFA *xmas*
**V** ✿ ♨ Sunday Lunch £10.95 Dinner £19.95 Last dinner 9.30pm
Credit Cards ①②③⑤ⓔ

## WETHERAL Cumbria Map **12** NY45

★★★ 66% **Crown**
CA4 8ES (Shire) ☎(0228)561888 FAX (0228) 561637
*Situated in a quiet picturesque village this former inn has been modernised and extended to provide comfortable accommodation for the visiting holidaymaker and businessman alike. Leisure and conference facilities are available.*
49⇰(6fb)1📺✂in 13 bedrooms CTV in all bedrooms ® **T** ✳
S% sB&B⇰£84-£104 dB&B⇰£100-£120 ⌸
⟪ 80P ✿ CFA ⬓ (heated) squash snooker sauna solarium gymnasium spa pool *xmas*
♋ English & French **V** ♿ ◻ ✂ ✳
Credit Cards 1 2 3 5

## WETHERBY West Yorkshire Map **08** SE44

★★★❀♨ **WOOD HALL**

Trip Ln, Linton LS22 4JA
☎(0937)587271
FAX (0937) 584353

*A mile-long drive brings guests to this imposing Georgian mansion which looks out over sweeping lawns and parkland to the River Wharfe at the heart of the Yorkshire Dales. Its position is secluded, and an atmosphere of tranquility pervades its elegant and stylish rooms, from the series of dining rooms to the comfortable drawing room, the library and wood-panelled cocktail bar where drinks are* →

**W**

*served from a converted grand piano. Bedrooms are all individually furnished and superbly comfortable, with large fluffy towels and high quality toiletries a most welcome feature of the spotless bathrooms. A team of attentive and obliging staff bring a note of informality that creates a most pleasant and relaxing atmosphere. In the kitchens, chef Simon Wood draws on an American-inspired cuisine to produce enjoyable meals of a lighter and more modern style than is often associated with country house hotels: for instance a hot spinach and chestnut pithivier with a sauce of carrot and coriander, and a rich lemon tart with lightly caramelised top.*

16⇨👤 Annexe6⇨👤1🛏⊬in 4 bedrooms CTV in all bedrooms T ✱ sB&B⇨👤£98-£133 dB&B⇨👤£108-£143 🍴

《 CTV 70P ✿ CFA ✔ snooker *xmas*

♥ British & French ✤ ⚓ ⊬ ✱ Lunch £12.95-£14.95 Dinner £19.95 Last dinner 9.30pm

Credit Cards ① ② ③ ④ ⑤

---

★★★ 72% *Linton Spring Country House*

Sickling Hall Rd LS22 4AF ☎(0937)585353 FAX (0937) 67579
Closed 1-8 Jan

*Standing in extensive mature grounds about 2 miles west of the town centre, this well furnished comfortable country house has a relaxing atmosphere. The wood-panelled bedrooms are exceptionally well equipped, with many little extras, and the attractive restaurant provides well prepared food served by professional friendly staff.*

12rm(10⇨👤)2🛏 CTV in all bedrooms T ✖ (ex guide dogs)
《 55P 🚗 ✿ nc5yrs
V ✤ Last dinner 9.30pm
Credit Cards ① ② ③ ⑤

---

★★★ 57% **Wetherby Resort**

Leeds Rd LS22 5HE (junc A1/A58) (Resort) ☎(0937)583881
Telex no 556428 FAX (0937) 580062

*This popular commercial-style hotel situated just off the A1 to the south of the town, offers good all-round furnishings and comforts.*

72⇨👤(2fb)⊬in 8 bedrooms CTV in all bedrooms ® T ✱
sB⇨👤£66 dB⇨👤£80 (room only) 🍴
《 150P ✿ CFA *xmas*
V ✤ ⚓ ⊬✱ Lunch fr£8.50 High tea £6 Dinner £13.50&alc
Last dinner 9.45pm
Credit Cards ① ② ③ ⑤ ⓔ

---

❀❀❀✕✕*Dicken's*

The Green CM7 4BS ☎Great Dunmow(0371)850723

*Chef patron John Dicken, a head chef in the Channel Islands for five years, has brought to this restaurant professional cooking skills and a flair for distinctive menu composition, with imaginative French recipes. Foie Gras terrine with home-made brioche, ravioli or crab with coriander, fillet of beef with wild mushroom sauté, supreme of salmon with herbs and fricassée of chicken with wild morel and home-made noodles have all been recommended by our Inspectors. Maria Dicken provides very attentive and friendly service.*

Closed Mon & 3 wks Feb Lunch not served Sat
Dinner not served Sun
♥ English & French V 45 seats Last lunch 2pm Last dinner 9.30pm 11 P
Credit Cards ① ③

---

Hotels with red star ratings are
especially high quality.

---

★★ 59% **Maltings**

NR25 7SY (Consort) ☎(026370)731 Telex no 57515

*A coastal inn of traditional flintstone offering well equipped accommodation, comfortable public lounges and restaurant. Family owned it has a pleasant atmosphere. The Retreat buttery is presently being converted into a conference/banqueting room.*

11⇨👤Annexe9⇨👤(5fb)2🛏 CTV in all bedrooms S%
sB&B⇨👤£41-£44 dB&B⇨👤£61-£65 🍴
150P ✿ CFA *xmas*
♥ International V ✤ ⚓ S% Lunch fr£7.50&alc Dinner £16.50-£17.50&alc Last dinner 9.30pm
Credit Cards ① ② ③ ⑤

---

See LONDON plan 1*A1*(page 434)

★★★ 61% **Ship Thistle**

Monument Green KT13 8BQ (Mount Charlotte (TS))
☎(0932)848364 Telex no 894271 FAX (0932) 857153

*A popular town centre hotel providing comfortable, well equipped, modern bedrooms. There is a tastefully appointed restaurant, cosy cocktail bar/lounge and a busy public bar opening out onto an attractive courtyard in summer.*

39⇨👤 CTV in all bedrooms ® T (room only) 🍴
《 50P 20🚗 ✿
♥ International ✤ ⚓ ⊬
Credit Cards ① ② ③ ④ ⑤

---

★★ 63% **Crown**

51-52 St Thomas St DT4 8EQ ☎(0305)760800
FAX (0305) 760300
Closed 25-26 Dec

*Centrally situated on the town's complicated one-way system, a busy coaching hotel of imposing appearance offers good value accommodation with comfortable bedrooms and simple fare.*

77⇨👤(10fb) CTV in all bedrooms ® ✖ (ex guide dogs) ✱
sB&B⇨👤£26-£32 dB&B⇨👤£48-£55 🍴
Lift 《 CTV 8🚗 CFA
V ✤ Sunday Lunch £4.25-£7.50alc Dinner fr£7.50 Last dinner 8pm
Credit Cards ① ② ③ ⑤ ⓔ

---

★★ 63% **Hotel Rex**

29 The Esplanade DT4 8DN ☎(0305)760400
FAX (0305) 760300
Closed Xmas

*A recently expanded hotel, very well placed for access to shops, sea front and ferry, offers simply furnished but well equipped bedrooms and comfortable, attractively decorated public areas.*

31⇨👤(5fb)🛏 CTV in all bedrooms ® T sB&B⇨👤£36-£42 dB&B⇨👤£64-£70 🍴
Lift 《 CTV 6🚗 (£1 per night) CFA
♥ International V ✤ ⚓ Bar Lunch £1.50-£4.50alc Dinner £7-£8&alc Last dinner 10.30pm
Credit Cards ① ② ③ ⓔ

---

★★ 63% **Streamside**

29 Preston Rd DT3 6PX ☎Preston(0305)833121
FAX (0305) 832043

*This attractive hotel, with its flower-filled tubs and hanging baskets, offers bedrooms which, though small and simply furnished, are freshly painted; the lounge is spacious, and an intimate restaurant provides an alternative to the popular dining room.*

15rm(8⇨👤1👤)(4fb) CTV in all bedrooms ® T sB&B£29-£40 sB&B⇨👤£30-£45 dB&B£39-£55 dB&B⇨👤£40-£65 🍴
35P ✿ CFA games room

---

♨ English & French **V** ✆ ⌧ Lunch £8.75-£10 Dinner £8.75-£10&alc Last dinner 9pm
Credit Cards ① ② ③ ⑤ ⓔ

**★★**62% **Glenburn**
42 Preston Rd DT3 6PZ (3m NE A353) ☎Preston(0305)832353
Closed 25 Dec-1 Jan
*Welcoming and energetic proprietors, Mr and Mrs Cotton, have created a cosy home from home here, and while bedrooms are simply furnished they are clean and well kept. The extensive menu provides British and classical dishes, particularly popular when dinner dances are held.*
13rm(5⇨7♠)(1fb) CTV in all bedrooms ® ✖ ➡
30P ⇔ ❀ CFA nc3yrs
♨ English & French **V** ✆ ⌧ ✱ Sunday Lunch fr£6.75 High tea fr£2.50 Dinner fr£11&alc Last dinner 8.30pm
Credit Cards ① ③ ⓔ

**★★★**57% **Hotel Prince Regent**
139 The Esplanade DT4 7NR (Consort) ☎(0305)771313
Closed 24 Dec-3 Jan
*A holiday hotel which enjoys a delightful setting on the seafront provides accommodation which, though simple and inexpensive, is well equipped with modern facilities. The smartly decorated restaurant with its à la carte and table d'hôte menus is augmented during the summer months by an all-day bar and coffee shop.*
50rm(37⇨8♠)(25fb) CTV in all bedrooms ® **T** ✖ (ex guide dogs) sB&B£39.50-£44 sB&B⇨♠£49.50-£54 dB&B£57.50-£64 dB&B⇨♠£68-£75 ➡
Lift ( 5P 14🚗 CFA
♨ English & French **V** ✆ ✖ ✱ Bar Lunch £1.50-£10alc Dinner £11.75-£13.25&alc Last dinner 8.30pm
Credit Cards ① ② ③ ⑤

**★**62% **Alexandra**
27/28 The Esplanade DT4 8DN ☎(0305)785767
*This friendly and relaxing hotel has been attractively upgraded, with the public areas and first and second floor bedrooms receiving attention. The bar lounge is spacious and comfortable and wholesome, simple meals are served in the dining room.*
20rm(5⇨9♠)(4fb) CTV in 14 bedrooms ® ✱ sB&B£17.50-£25 sB&B⇨♠£19.50-£27.50 dB&B⇨♠£38-£60 ➡
7P *xmas*
**V** ✆ ⌧ ✱ Sunday Lunch £6.50-£7.50 Dinner £6.50-£7.50 Last dinner 7pm
Credit Cards ① ③

❀ ✕**Perry's**
The Harbourside, 4 Trinity Rd DT4 8TJ ☎(0305)785799
Closed 24 & 26 Dec Lunch not served
V 70 seats ✱ Dinner £13.95&alc Last dinner 10.30pm 🎜
Credit Cards ① ③

**★★**63% **The Haven**
Grantham Rd NG13 9EU ☎(0949)50800 FAX (0949) 51454
*A family-run hostelry on the A52 offering modern well equipped bedrooms. There is a choice of eating in the à la carte restaurant or the pine-furnished bar dining area where substantial snacks are served.*
33⇨♠(5fb)3🛏 CTV in all bedrooms ® **T** sB&B⇨♠£30-£40 dB&B⇨♠£45-£55
70P ⇔ ❀ CFA
**V** ✆ ⌧ Lunch £5-£10&alc High tea £4-£6 Dinner £5-£10&alc Last dinner 9.45pm
Credit Cards ① ② ③

A rosette means exceptional standards of cuisine.

⬦**Forte Travelodge**
London Rd(off A40) (Forte)
☎(0867)75705 Central Res (0800) 850950
*Quietly tucked away behind a Harvester Restaurant, this lodge on the A418 (A40) Oxford road 3 miles from the M40 offers modern, neatly presented and very clean bedrooms; the adjacent steak house restaurant also serves breakfast, and a 24-hour reception means that even late arrivals can be accommodated. Comfortable surroundings and fixed-price menus make a meal here good value for money.*
24⇨♠(24fb) CTV in all bedrooms ® sB⇨♠£29.95 dB⇨♠£29.95 (room only)
( 24P ⇔
Credit Cards ① ② ③

**★★**⚑70% **Raleigh Manor**
TA24 7BB ☎Timberscombe(0643)841484
Closed Nov-Feb
*The comfortable family home of the resident proprietors stands in over an acre of grounds and gardens overlooking Snowdrop Valley, and on a clear day the island of Steep Holme. Seven bedrooms with coordinating fabrics and antique furnishings offer comfortable and spotlessly clean accommodation. There is a choice of lounge with log fires, and interesting home-cooked dishes are available on the table d'hôte menu served in the dining room.*
7⇨♠1❔ CTV in all bedrooms ® ✱ sB&B⇨♠£35.50-£38.50 dB&B⇨♠£71-£77 (incl dinner)
8P ⇔ ❀
**V** ✆ ⌧ ✕ ✱ Dinner £14 Last dinner 8pm
Credit Cards ① ③

★★

Situated 2 miles from busy town centre yet only short walk from beach and coastal paths.
15 bedrooms all equipped with direct dial telephone, colour TV, radio and hot drinks tray. Most rooms ensuite.
À la carte restaurant open every evening. Bar lunches and traditional Sunday menu available.
Ample car parking. Delightful rear garden. Games room.

**Streamside Restaurant and Hotel**
Preston Road, Weymouth,
Dorset DT3 6PX
Telephone (0305) 833121
*Proprietor:* John Alderman FHCIMA

**W**

## WHICKHAM Tyne & Wear Map **12** NZ26

See also Newcastle upon Tyne

**★★68% Gibside Arms**

Front St NE16 4JG ☎091-488 9292 FAX 091-488 8000

*A hotel offering comfortable modern accommodation, interesting menus and friendly service.*

45⇨↑(2fb) CTV in all bedrooms ® T ✖ (ex guide dogs)
sB&B⇨↑fr£58 dB&B⇨↑fr£73 ♬
Lift ( 18P 10🍴 ♫ *xmas*
♀ English & French V ♥ ⚗ ✱ Sunday Lunch £4.95-£7.95
Dinner fr£12.50&alc Last dinner 10pm
Credit Cards ①②③⑤ ⓔ

## WHIMPLE Devon Map **03** SY09

★★❀❀ ♨ **WOODHAYES**
EX5 2TD ☎(0404)822237

*The Rendle family's welcome is very warm at their small Georgian country house set in apple-orchard countryside on the edge of the village. (Tucked away from busy roads but close to the A30 and M5.) An impressive entrance lobby with flowers and fine pictures leads to 2 small, comfortably furnished lounges. Katherine Rendle, a keen and accomplished self-taught cook, offers an interesting 7-course menu at dinner, served in the intimate dining room. There are 6 bedrooms with some nice pieces of period furniture, all are well equipped with modern facilities, and bathrooms are a good size. Leisure facilities include a tennis court and croquet.*

6rm(5⇨) CTV in all bedrooms T ✖ S% sB&B⇨£75
dB&B⇨£110 (incl dinner) ♬
20P 2🍴 🍴 ✱ ♪ (grass) croquet nc12yrs *xmas*
♀ English & French V ✱ Lunch £14 Dinner £22.50 Last dinner 9.30pm
Credit Cards ①②③⑤

## WHITBY North Yorkshire Map **08** NZ81

**★★68% Saxonville**

Ladysmith Av, (Off Argyle Road) YO21 3HX ☎(0947)602631
Closed mid Oct-mid May

*A pleasant and friendly family-run hotel, offering good food and value for money.*

24⇨↑(2fb) CTV in all bedrooms ® T ✖ (ex guide dogs) S%
sB&B⇨↑fr£33 dB&B⇨↑fr£66
20P CFA
V ♥ S% Bar Lunch fr£1 Dinner fr£13.50&alc Last dinner 8.30pm
Credit Cards ①②③ ⓔ

**★★67% *Sneaton Hall***

Beacon Way, Sneaton YO22 5HP (3m S B1416) ☎(0947)605929

*Friendly service and a relaxing atmosphere are provided by a family-run hotel in an attractive location close to coast and town.*

8⇨↑(2fb) CTV in all bedrooms ®
30P 🍴
V ♥ ⚗ Last dinner 8.30pm
Credit Cards ①③

**★★65% *Larpool Hall Country House***

Larpool Ln YO22 4ND ☎(0947)602737

*This elegant Georgian mansion house is rich in local history. It stands in 10 acres of beautiful gardens and woodland and offers lovely views all round. Well furnished in all areas, it offers good comforts and peaceful surroundings. Very attentive service is provided by the resident owner, and a good standard of cooking is served in the pleasant dining room.*

10⇨↑(1fb)1🛏 CTV in all bedrooms ® T ✖ (ex guide dogs)
CTV 40P ✱
♀ English & Continental V ♥ ⚗ ✔ Last dinner 9pm
Credit Cards ①③

**★★65% White House**

Upgang Lane, West Cliff YO21 3JJ ☎(0947)600469

*Situated just off the A174, next to the Golf Club, and commanding fine views over Sandsend Bay, this family-run hotel provides comfortable accommodation and a friendly ambience.*

12rm(7⇨4↑)(3fb) CTV in all bedrooms ® T sB&B⇨£18.50
sB&B⇨↑£23.50-£25.50 dB&B£37 dB&B⇨↑£47-£50 ♬
CTV 50P ✱ *xmas*
♀ English & French V ♥ ✱ Sunday Lunch £6.50 Dinner
£10.50&alc Last dinner 10pm
Credit Cards ①③

**★★64% *Old West Cliff***

42 Crescent Av YO21 3EQ ☎(0947)603292

*A small family-owned and run hotel close to both sea and Crescent Gardens has recently undergone extensive refurbishment to provide accommodation of a good standard. Its cosy basement restaurant offers an extensive choice of dishes while service is friendly and attentive throughout.*

12⇨↑(6fb) CTV in all bedrooms ®
CTV ♪ 🍴
V ♥ ⚗ ✔ Last dinner 8pm
Credit Cards ①②③

**★★64% Stakesby Manor**

Manor Close, High Stakesby YO21 1HL ☎(0947)602773
FAX (0947) 602140

*Set between coast and countryside in well tended gardens, this establishment provides bedrooms with good facilities. Well prepared food is served in the oak-panelled dining room with à la carte and table d'hôte menus as well as bar meals.*

8⇨↑ CTV in all bedrooms ® T ✖ (ex guide dogs) ✱
sB&B⇨↑£38 dB&B⇨↑£56-£58 ♬
40P 🍴 ✱ ⚗
♀ International V ♥ ⚗ ✱ Lunch £12.50&alc Dinner
£12.50&alc Last dinner 9.30pm
Credit Cards ①②③ ⓔ

## WHITCHURCH Shropshire Map **07** SJ54

**★★★62% Terrick Hall Country**

Hill Valley SY13 4JZ (off A49 NE of town centre) ☎(0948)3031

*A country house style of hotel that has strong links with the adjacent golf course. It is set in four acres of grounds with an ornamental pool and hard tennis court.*

10⇨↑Annexe7⇨↑(7fb) CTV in all bedrooms ® T ✱
sB&B⇨↑£38 dB&B⇨↑£52-£58 ♬
CTV 50P ✱ CFA ▶ 18 ♪ (hard) squash snooker sauna
♀ International V ♥ ⚗ ✱ Lunch £10.50&alc Dinner
£10.50&alc Last dinner 9pm
Credit Cards ①②③⑤

**★★★56% Dodington Lodge**

Dodington SY13 1EN (Inter-Hotels) ☎(0948)2539

*This roadside hotel situated at the junction of the A41 and A49 is also popular with the locals who make full use of the small function room for wedding receptions and private meetings.*

10rm(9⇨↑)(2fb)1🛏 CTV in all bedrooms ® T ✱
sB&B⇨↑fr£39.50 dB&B⇨↑fr£49.50 ♬

W

70P ✤ CFA *xmas*
V ♥ ⚏ ✳ Lunch fr£10.50 Dinner fr£10.50 Last dinner 9.30pm
Credit Cards 1 3

★★59% **Redbrook Hunting Lodge**
Wrexham Rd SY13 3ET (Inter-Hotels)
☎Redbrook Maelor(094873)204 & 533
*A privately owned hotel which was once a hunting lodge offers
unpretentious but reasonably well equipped accommodation which
is suitable for both tourists and commercial users. Set at the A495/
A525 junction 2.5 miles west of Whitchurch, it stands close to the
Clwyd/Shropshire border.*
13⇥↑(3fb)2▦ CTV in all bedrooms ⓡ T ⋇ (ex guide dogs)
sB&B⇥↑fr£44 dB&B⇥↑fr£60.50 ⊟
100P ✤
♵ English & French V ♥ ⚏ ✳ Lunch fr£7 Dinner fr£9.50&alc
Last dinner 9pm
Credit Cards 1 2 3 ⑤

**WHITEBRIDGE** Highland *Inverness-shire* Map **14** NH41

★★❀❀▟▖ KNOCKIE LODGE

IV1 2UP (Pride of Britain)
☎Gorthleck(04563)276
FAX (04563) 389

Closed 30 Oct-29 Apr
*A shallow bowl high in the
mountains, hidden from view
and protected from the
elements, is the setting for Knockie Lodge and nearby Loch* →

W

*Nan Lann ; and a short walk will provide an eagle's eye view of Loch Ness far below. Ian and Brenda Milward came here in the early 80s with the intention of running a comfortable, relaxing, country house hotel. It is very much their home and guests quickly find that they are the personal guests of the Milwards. Bedrooms vary widely in shape and size, many have sloping ceilings yet offer wonderful views over loch or mountain. A fine drawing room is complemented by a smaller sitting room, full of maps and local guides for the essential work of planning your activities. Next door is the billiard room which must have the finest view of any such room in Britain. There is a set dinner, but the menu is provided early enough to be changed if necessary, and the quality of the food is exceptionally good.*

10⇨🌢 T sB&B⇨🌢fr£75 dB&B⇨🌢£118-£182 (incl dinner)

20P 🚗 ❀ ✔ snooker sailing nc10yrs

✳ Dinner fr£23 Last dinner 8pm

Credit Cards 1 2 3 5

---

### ★★63% Whitebridge
IV1 2UN ☎Gorthleck(04563)226
Closed 21 Dec-Feb

*A friendly atmosphere prevails at this small family-run Highland hotel. Popular with holidaymakers and sporting enthusiasts, it provides traditional services and good value accommodation.*
12rm(10⇨🌢)(3fb) CTV in all bedrooms ® sB&B£25-£30 sB&B⇨🌢£25-£30 dB&B£40-£50 dB&B⇨🌢£40-£50

30P 2🏚 (50p) 🚗 ❀ ✔

✿ 🍽 Bar Lunch £6-£12&alc Dinner fr£12.50 Last dinner 9pm
Credit Cards 1 2 3 5 ①

---

## WHITEBROOK Gwent Map 03 SO50

### ★★❀70% Crown at Whitebrook
NP5 4TX (Exec Hotel) ☎Monmouth(0600)860254
FAX (0600) 860607
Closed 3 wks Jan

*This delightful small country hotel, caringly run by Roger and Sandra Bates, has well-equipped pretty bedrooms and a very comfortable lounge bar. The restaurant has an excellent local reputation and combines Welsh ingredients with a French influence.*
12⇨🌢1🖤 CTV in all bedrooms ® T sB&B⇨🌢£66 dB&B⇨🌢£112 (incl dinner) 🏁

40P 🚗 ❀

🍴 French V ✠ Lunch £13.95-£24 Dinner £24 Last dinner 9.30pm
Credit Cards 1 2 3 4 5 ①

---

## WHITEHAVEN Cumbria Map 11 NX91

### ○Howgate
Howgate CA28 6PL ☎(0946)66286
Due to have opened Sep 1991
20⇨🌢

---

## WHITING BAY

See Arran, Isle of

---

## WHITLEY BAY Tyne & Wear Map 12 NZ37

### ★★66% Windsor
South Pde NE25 8UT ☎091-252 3317 FAX 091-297 0272
Closed 25 Dec

*A friendly hotel with well equipped bedrooms, many of which have been recently upgraded. Situated midway between the sea and the town, ideal for pleasure or business purposes, the hotel offers facilities for business meeting and conferences.*

45⇨🌢(14fb) CTV in all bedrooms ® T sB&B⇨🌢£35-£55 dB&B⇨🌢£48-£60 🏁

Lift ( CTV 25P 2🏚 CFA xmas

🍴 European V ✿ 🍽 Sunday Lunch £10 High tea £6-£8 Dinner £10-£12.50&alc Last dinner 9.30pm

Credit Cards 1 2 3 5 ①

---

### ★★63% Holmedale
106 Park Av NE26 1DN ☎091-251 3903 & 091-253 1162
FAX 091-253 0053

*Not far from the town or the sea, this family-run hotel offers an informal, relaxing atmosphere. All the bedrooms have en suite facilities and are well equipped.*
18rm(7⇨9🌢)(3fb)1🖤 CTV in all bedrooms ® T
CTV 10P pool table

🍴 English & Continental Last dinner 8pm
Credit Cards 1 2 3 5

---

### ★61% Park Lodge Hotel
160-164 Park Av NE26 1AO ☎091-253 0288 & 091-252 6879
FAX 091-297 1006

*Attractively decorated bedrooms and a very friendly atmosphere are provided by this small hotel situated close to the seafront. Ideal for business users seeking warmth and relaxation, it enjoys many of the facilities normally confined to larger establishments.*
16rm(12⇨🌢)(1fb) CTV in all bedrooms ® T
✠ (ex guide dogs) sB&Bfr£25 sB&B⇨🌢£35-£40 dB&B⇨🌢£58-£60

CTV 8P 🚗 snooker solarium gymnasium nc
✿ 🍽 ✠ ✳ Dinner £12-£16 Last dinner 9.30pm
Credit Cards 1 2 3 5

---

### ★56% Cavendish
51 Esplanade NE26 2AS ☎091-253 3010
*Simple seaside hotel managed by proprietor and his family.*
11rm(5⇨1🌢)(2fb) CTV in all bedrooms ® ✳ sB&Bfr£19 sB&B⇨🌢fr£26 dB&Bfr£34 dB&B⇨🌢fr£42

CTV 12P

V ✳ Sunday Lunch £6.95 Dinner £8.75&alc Last dinner 9.30pm
Credit Cards 1 3

---

## WHITTINGTON Shropshire Map 07 SJ33

### ★63% Ye Olde Boot Inn
SY11 4DG (Frederic Robinson) ☎Oswestry(0691)662250

*A bustling country inn with a busy bar and restaurant, reservations are necessary at weekends for the generously served meals. The rooms are quite spacious and some have views of the castle ruins and moat, home to many wildfowl.*
6⇨🌢(2fb) CTV in all bedrooms ®
100P

V ✿ 🍽 Last dinner 10pm
Credit Cards 1 3

---

## WICK Highland *Caithness* Map 15 ND35

### ★★58% *Mackay's*
Union St KW1 5ED ☎(0955)2323
Closed 1-2 Jan

*On the south bank of the River Wick, convenient for the town centre, this family-run commercial hotel is also popular for local functions. It has a friendly atmosphere, a choice of tastefully refurbished bars, and well equipped but somewhat functional bedrooms.*
26rm(23⇨1🌢)(4fb) CTV in all bedrooms ® T
Lift ( CTV 12P 🚗
V ✿ ✠
Credit Cards 1 3

---

**W**

**WICKHAM** Hampshire Map **04** SU51 ⊙

★★ 🏵🏵73% **Old House**
The Square PO17 5JG ☎(0329)833049 FAX (0329) 833672
Closed 10 days Xmas, 2 wks Etr & 2 wks Jul/Aug RS Mon-Sat
*The Old House Hotel is an attractive Georgian town house overlooking the village square which has been run by the same proprietors for the last twenty years. Its comfortably furnished public areas adorned with fresh flowers combine with bedrooms individually decorated and furnished with style and taste to make guests feel that they are being entertained in a private house. The restaurant provides an ideal venue for either business meal or family celebration, offering a short à la carte menu, which changes weekly and bases imaginative dishes in French regional style on the freshest of ingredients – including fish from nearby Portsmouth in such specialities as L'Assiette de Poisson Frais au Beurre de Pamplemousse Rose. The wine list is short but well balanced, and service is relaxed and friendly.*
9🖙🌤Annexe3🖙🌤(1fb) CTV in all bedrooms ® T 🛏 S10%
sB&B🖙🌤£80-£85 dB&B🖙🌤£90-£110
12P 🖼 ♨
♀ French V S10% Lunch fr£28alc Dinner fr£28alc Last dinner 9.30pm
Credit Cards 1 2 3 5 £

**WIDNES** Cheshire Map **07** SJ58

★★66% **Hill Crest**
75 Cronton Ln WA8 9AR ☎051-424 1616 Telex no 627098
FAX 051-495 1348
*This well run commercial hotel offers well equipped bedrooms and friendly service. There are two attractive bars which complement the popular 'Palms' restaurant. The hotel is on the A5080 Widnes to Huyton road.*
57🖙🌤(1fb)3🖼 CTV in all bedrooms ® T ✳
sB&B🖙🌤£49.50-£65 dB&B🖙🌤£60-£74
Lift ( 200P CFA ♫ *xmas*
♀ Continental V ✧ ⚏ Lunch £10.50-£11.95&alc Dinner
£10.50-£11.95&alc Last dinner 10pm
Credit Cards 1 2 3 5

**WIGAN** Greater Manchester Map **07** SD50

★★★69% **Kilhey Court Hotel**
Chorley Rd WN1 2XN (Best Western) ☎Standish(0257)472100
Telex no 67460 FAX (0257) 422401
(For full entry see Standish)

★★★64% **Almond Brook Moat House**
Almond Brook Rd WN6 0SR (Queens Moat)
☎Standish(0257)425588 Telex no 677662 FAX (0257) 427327
(For full entry see Standish)

★★★60% **Bellingham**
149 Wigan Ln WN1 2NB ☎(0942)43893 FAX (0942) 821027
*On the A49 beside Haig Hall Country Park, one mile north of the town centre, this Victorian terraced property has been extended and refurbished to provide comfortable well equipped bedrooms. Public areas include an attractive restaurant, and service throughout is friendly and willing.*
30🖙🌤(4fb)✂in 4 bedrooms CTV in all bedrooms ® T
🛏 (ex guide dogs) ✳ sB&B🖙🌤£35-£47 dB&B🖙🌤£45-£60 ⊟
Lift ( CTV 45P CFA
♀ English & French V ✧ ⚏ ✂ ✳ Lunch £5.95-£14.95&alc
Dinner £11.95-£14.95&alc Last dinner 9.45pm
Credit Cards 1 2 3 5 £

★★64% **Bel-Air**
236 Wigan Ln WM1 2NU ☎(0942)41410 FAX (0942) 43967
*Situated beside the A49 in a residential area on the northern outskirts of the town, this friendly small hotel offers pleasant accommodation, with an attractive restaurant, cosy lounge bar and individually decorated bedrooms.*
→

12⇄�(3fb)1🛏 CTV in all bedrooms Ⓡ **T**
CTV 12P
🍽 English & Continental **V** ☼ ☑
Credit Cards ① ③

## ★★ 61% *Brocket Arms*
Mesnes Rd WN1 2DD ☎(0942)46283 Telex no 628117
*A privately owned commercial hotel to the north of the town centre offering a good standard of accommodation, including a comfortable lounge bar and small restaurant.*
27⇄climb CTV in all bedrooms Ⓡ ✈
《 60P
**V** ☼ Last dinner 9.30pm
Credit Cards ① ② ③ ⑤

## ○Oak
WN1 3SS ☎(0942)826888
Due to have opened Jun 1991
88⇄climb

---

---

### BEMBRIDGE Map **04** SZ68

## ★★ 57% *Birdham*
1 Steyne Rd PO35 5UH ☎Isle of Wight(0983)872875
Closed 24-26 Dec
*A small comfortable hotel dating to the 1890s, popular with the local villagers. Bright bedrooms have modern facilities and public areas include 2 busy bars, lounges, dining room and breakfast room. Both the à la carte and bar menus offer a good choice.*
14rm(12⇄)(5fb)⚥ in 4 bedrooms CTV in all bedrooms Ⓡ
sB&B£15 sB&B⇄£25 dB&B£30 dB&B⇄£45
《 CTV 100P ✽ pool table petanque darts
🍽 Continental **V** ☼ ⚥ S% Lunch £8.50&alc Dinner £7-£12&alc Last dinner 9.30pm

---

### BONCHURCH See Ventnor

---

### CHALE Map **04** SZ47

## ★ 69% **Clarendon Hotel & Wight Mouse Inn**
PO38 2HA ☎Isle of Wight(0983)730431
*The Clarendon Hotel provides an exciting and lively atmosphere for guests. The dining area within the hotel has been extended and improvements have been made throughout. Bedrooms are individually furnished with style and taste and the service is relaxed and friendly. Wholesome food is on offer from a table d'hôte and extensive à la carte menu. Children are catered for extremely well here.*
14rm(4⇄6climb)(9fb) CTV in all bedrooms Ⓡ ✽ sB&B£15-£27
sB&B⇄climb£20-£33 dB&B£30-£54 dB&B⇄climb£40-£66 🏠
200P ✽ CFA petanque ♫ ♒
🍽 European **V** ☼ ☑ ✽ Lunch £4-£10alc High tea £3-£8alc
Dinner £10-£16&alc Last dinner 10pm
Credit Cards ① ⑤

---

### COWES Map **04** SZ49

## ★★★ 67% **New Holmwood**
Queens Rd, Egypt Point PO31 8BW
☎Isle of Wight(0983)292508 FAX (0983) 295020
*Completely refurbished in 1991, this hotel now offers high quality accommodation. Spacious oak furnished bedrooms with vast beds include four sea-facing luxury rooms. Public rooms also overlook the Solent and include a terrace where brunch is served in summer. The shorter winter set menu is supplemented by an à la carte menu in summer, offering a wide choice of dishes.*
25⇄climb CTV in all bedrooms Ⓡ **T** ✽ sB&B⇄climbfr£60
dB&B⇄climbfr£70 🏠
17P CFA ⌿ (heated) *xmas*

🍽 French **V** ☼ ☑ ⚥ Lunch £10.50-£25 Dinner £16-£25 Last dinner 9.30pm
Credit Cards ① ② ③ ⑤

## ★★ 62%, *Cowes*
260 Artic Rd PO31 7PJ ☎Isle of Wight(0983)291541
Telex no 86284
Closed 27 Dec-1 Jan
*A small, well-run hotel facing the River Medina and local wharfs complements modern, well equipped bedrooms with a very popular restaurant and bar; service is extensive, friendly and personally managed by the proprietors.*
15⇄climb(4fb) CTV in all bedrooms
《 24P ♒ ✽ sauna
🍽 English & French **V** ☼ ☑ Last dinner 9.30pm
Credit Cards ① ② ③ ⑤

## ★★ 55% *Fountain*
High St PO31 7AN ☎Isle of Wight(0983)292397
*Located in West Cowes, alongside the Cowes Ferry and Hydrofoil Terminal and the Quay, this popular coaching inn is ideally placed for business travellers. Accommodation comprises well-equipped, modern bedrooms, the popular Henekey Restaurant and the lively Quayside Bar. Car parking can be difficult.*
20⇄ CTV in all bedrooms Ⓡ **T** ✈ (ex guide dogs)
⚥ ♒
🍽 European **V** ☼ ☑ Last dinner 10.30pm
Credit Cards ① ② ③ ④ ⑤

---

## ❀ ✗Sullivan's
10 Bath Rd, The Parade PO31 7QN ☎Isle of Wight(0983)297021
(Rosette awarded for lunch only)
*Michael and Susan Sullivan's small, simple back-street restaurant resembles a fisherman's cottage – and, indeed, a fisherman may well arrive during lunch to deliver the fresh fish which will feature at dinner. An honest and inexpensive menu offers such well balanced and full flavoured dishes as sautéed pheasant served with a rich red wine sauce flavoured with bacon, mushrooms and onions; this might be followed by a tempting crème brûlée with a light, smooth centre and crisp topping and the meal will be accompanied by a short but carefully selected wine list with a wide price range, a reasonable selection of half bottles and some interesting new World wines. Chef Michael (formerly of Café des Amis du Vin in Covent Garden) has slowly built up a loyal clientèle who his wife cares for front-of-house while he produces the food.*
Lunch not served in winter (ex by prior arrangement only)
🍽 French 42 seats ✽ Lunch £8.95-£16.50&alc Last lunch 3pm
Last dinner 11pm ⚥
Credit Cards ① ③

---

### FRESHWATER Map **04** SZ38

## ★★★57% *Albion*
PO40 9RA ☎Isle of Wight(0983)753631 FAX (0983) 755295
*This large, sprawling hotel enjoys a prime position, set on the sea shore overlooking the bay. Public areas have been recently refurbished and are now smartly presented and comfortable. Bedrooms, rather dated in areas, are gradually being upgraded, but are generally spacious and bright. Staff are friendly and hospitable and the hotel continues to attract regularly returning guests.*
42rm(39⇄climb)(28fb) CTV in all bedrooms Ⓡ **T**
《 CTV 75P ♒
🍽 International **V** ☼ ☑ Last dinner 9pm
Credit Cards ① ② ③ ⑤

Hotels with red star ratings are
especially high quality.

## RYDE  Map **04** SZ59

**★★★64%  *Hotel Ryde Castle***
The Esplanade PO33 1JA ☎Isle of Wight(0983)63755
Telex no 869466 FAX (0983) 616436
*This unusual and comfortable hotel, in a castellated building
facing the seafront, is furnished in keeping with the castle theme.
Some bedrooms have 4-poster beds, plus many modern facilities;
the new residents' lounge is hung with tapestries; and the
restaurant with an interesting menu of English and French dishes
is decorated to resemble the interior of a galleon. Business facilities
are also available.*
17⇔🛏🖵7🖪✂in 1 bedroom CTV in all bedrooms ® T
75P 🚗
🍽 English & French V 🕁 🖵 Last dinner 10pm
Credit Cards ① ② ③ ⑤

**★★67%  Biskra House Beach**
17 Saint Thomas's St PO33 2DL ☎Isle of Wight(0983)67913
*This family-owned hotel, which offers easy access to the beach
from its convenient location close to the esplanade, provides a good
choice of facilities in its comfortably furnished, well decorated,
modernised bedrooms. Well presented public areas include a
basement dining room with flagstone floor and bright gingham
cloths which serves an Italian-style menu popular with guests and
locals alike.*
9⇔🖪🖵 CTV in all bedrooms ® T sB&B⇔🖪£29.50-£31.50
dB&B⇔🖪£47.50-£57.50 🍴
14P 🚗 CFA
🍽 Italian V 🕁 🖵 Lunch £5-£6&alc Dinner £13.50&alc Last
dinner 10.30pm
Credit Cards ① ③ ⑥

**See advertisement on page 747**

**W**

# Wight, Isle of

**★★64% Yelf's**
Union St PO33 2LG ☎Isle of Wight(0983)64062
FAX (0983) 63937

*A popular commercial hotel in the town centre provides a varied choice of bedrooms, an agreeable restaurant and a busy bar and lounge; service is well-managed and friendly throughout.*
21⇌♪(2fb) CTV in all bedrooms ® T sB&B⇌♪£30-£50 dB&B⇌♪£40-£65 ☐
♪ ⇔ CFA *xmas*
V ♥ ⚩ ⚼ ✱ Lunch £7.25-£8.15 Dinner £10.50&alc Last dinner 9pm
Credit Cards ①②③⑤ ⓔ

ST LAWRENCE Map **04** SZ57

**★★64% *Rocklands***
PO38 1XH ☎Ventnor(0983)852964
Closed Nov-Apr

*Built in 1842, this quietly situated hotel stands in its own well kept grounds. Traditional in style, Rocklands is gradually being upgraded, and public rooms are spacious and comfortably appointed. Chef/Patron Mr Exposite produces adequate fare and the amiable Manager, Brenda Robertson-Walker, is a charming hostess, attuned to guests' needs.*
16⇌♪Annexe5rm(4⇌♪)(9fb)1⇔ CTV in all bedrooms ✖ (ex guide dogs)
CTV 18P ✿ ⚬ (heated) snooker sauna solarium croquet ◊
⚩ English & Continental V ♥ ⚩ Last dinner 8.15pm

**★71% The Lawyers Rest Country House**
Undercliff Dr PO38 1XF ☎Isle of Wight(0983)852610
Closed Nov RS Dec-Feb

*This elegant hotel, built in 1840 and occupying a superb elevated setting with views far across the bay, offers prettily decorated bedrooms which are gradually being refurbished to a high standard. Public areas – including a cosy drawing room where guests adjourn for coffee and often chat until late into the night – are pervaded by a warm, relaxed atmosphere. Simple but enjoyable home-made meals are complemented by an excellent wine list, and terraced gardens full of exotic plants provide a pleasant venue for lunches and afternoon teas during the summer months.*
8⇌♪ sB&B⇌♪£44.06 dB&B⇌♪£77.56-£88.12 (incl dinner) ☐
13P ⇔ ✿ CFA nc10yrs *xmas*
⚩ International V ♥ ⚩ ⚼ Lunch £7-£12alc Dinner £14.50-£17 Last dinner 7pm
Credit Cards ①②③④

SANDOWN Map **04** SZ58

**★★★57% Melville Hall**
Melville St PO36 9DH ☎Isle of Wight(0983)406526
FAX (0983) 407093

*Set in a semi-rural residential area, with a trim lawn at the front and a swimming pool behind, Melville Hall is run very much as a resort hotel, providing evening entertainment on occasion. Accommodation is in well equipped bedrooms with modern fitted furniture.*
33⇌♪(11fb) CTV in all bedrooms ® T ✖ (ex guide dogs)
sB&B⇌♪£27-£37 dB&B⇌♪£54-£74 (incl dinner) ☐
⚭ 30P ✿ CFA ⚬ (heated) 9 hole putting ♪ *xmas*
⚩ English & Continental V ♥ ⚩ Sunday Lunch fr£5.50 Dinner fr£8&alc Last dinner 9.30pm
Credit Cards ①②③⑤ ⓔ

The AA's star rating scheme is the market leader in hotel classification.

SEAVIEW Map **04** SZ69

**★★❀❀74% Seaview**
High St PO34 5EX ☎Isle of Wight(0983)612711
FAX (0983) 613729

*A very special atmosphere permeates this charming seaside hotel; the bedrooms are individually decorated and furnished with imagination and flair, and its Pump Bar bustles with locals who cherish the Seaview and all it stands for. The restaurant offers an imaginative but unpretentious cuisine based on the best of local produce and seafood, the menu changing every six or eight weeks to take advantage of seasonal availability, and always including a vegetarian selection. Popular choices include such dishes as Hot Crab Ramekin, Flaked Smoked Haddock au Gratin, French Breast of Duck with Plum Sauce, and Fillet of Beef with Mustard Sauce, while dessert-lovers will enjoy the White Chocolate Pot with Rum, or Meringues with Blackcurrant Coulis. An extensive range of bar meals is also available in two al fresco eating areas.*
16⇌♪(2fb) CTV in all bedrooms T ✱ sB&B⇌♪fr£43.50 dB&B⇌♪fr£65 ☐
12P ⇔ *xmas*
⚩ English & French V ♥ ⚩ ⚼ ✱ Lunch £7.95-£15.85alc Dinner fr£15.85alc Last dinner 9.30pm
Credit Cards ①②③

SHANKLIN Map **04** SZ58

**★★★61% Cliff Tops**
Park Rd PO37 6BB ☎Isle of Wight(0983)863262
FAX (0983) 867139

*A well known hotel, open all year round and enjoying magnificent sea views from its elevated location, has direct lift access to the beach below. Planned refurbishment will soon bring bedrooms up to the good standard of the smart public areas which include both a popular carvery operation and the table d'hôte menus, and the quieter, more relaxed setting of Asquith's Restaurant. Extensive and well maintained leisure facilities are particularly noteworthy, not least for the willing advice on health and fitness provided by friendly professional staff.*
88⇌♪(8fb) CTV in all bedrooms ® T sB&B⇌♪£65.50-£75 dB&B⇌♪£94-£110 ☐
Lift ⚭ 30P CFA ☒ (heated) snooker sauna solarium gymnasium steam room beautician hairdresser *xmas*
⚩ French V ♥ ⚩ ✱ Lunch £7.50-£9.50 Dinner £13.35&alc Last dinner 10pm
Credit Cards ①②③⑤ ⓔ

**★★★59% Holliers**
Church Rd, Old Village PO37 6NU ☎Isle of Wight(0983)862764
FAX (0983) 867134

*Overlooking several thatched buildings from its position in the old village, this former coaching inn dating from the 18th century provides good accommodation and informally friendly service. The pleasant restaurant offers an extensive value-for-money fixed-price menu supplemented by grill dishes, and guests can relax in either the Holliers Wine Bar or a bustling public bar; compact leisure facilities are also available.*
37⇌♪(7fb)⇔ CTV in all bedrooms ® T ✖ (ex guide dogs)
✱ sB&B⇌♪£30-£33 dB&B⇌♪£60-£66 ☐
40P ✿ CFA ☒ (heated) ⚬ (heated) sauna solarium multigym *xmas*
V ♥ ⚩ Bar Lunch fr£2.50 Dinner fr£9.75 Last dinner 8.30pm
Credit Cards ①②③ ⓔ

**★★68% Fernbank**
Highfield Rd PO37 6PP ☎Isle of Wight(0983)862790
Closed Xmas

*Set in an acre of well-tended, sheltered gardens enjoying country and woodland views from its peaceful location yet handy for the old village, the hotel offers friendly, relaxed service and good leisure facilities. The restaurant's table d'hôte menu is augmented by an à la carte dinner selection (except after 8pm on Sundays and Tuesdays).*

19⇨📞Annexe3⇨📞(7fb)1🛏 CTV in all bedrooms ® T
sB&B⇨📞£31.50-£41.50 dB&B⇨📞£63-£83 (incl dinner) 🍴
22P ❄ ⬚ (heated) sauna solarium pool table whirlpool bath
nc7yrs
♀ English, French & Italian V ♦ ⚪ ✂ ✳ Lunch £8.50-£10
Dinner £10-£12&alc Last dinner 10.30pm
Credit Cards ①③ⓔ

**★★66% Keats Green**
3 Queens Rd PO37 6AN 🕿Isle of Wight(0983)862742
Closed mid Oct-Etr
*A friendly hotel situated directly on Keats Green enjoying
panoramic views across the bay. The proprietors are involved in the
day-to-day running of the place and staff are eager and helpful.
Bedrooms are smartly presented following continued upgrading
and improvement, furnished in a modern, comfortable manner and
well equipped. Coach parties can dominate during the low season.*
34rm(23⇨10📞)(3fb) CTV in all bedrooms ® T ✳
sB&B⇨📞£24-£32 dB&B⇨📞£48-£64 (incl dinner) 🍴
34P ❄ ⬚ (heated)
♦ ✳ Lunch £5 Dinner £10 Last dinner 7.45pm
Credit Cards ①③ⓔ

**★★64% Luccombe Hall**
Luccombe Rd PO37 6RL (Exec Hotel)
🕿Isle of Wight(0983)862719 FAX (0983) 867482
RS 1-12 Jan
*An hotel overlooking the sea and Culver Down from a quiet
residential lane just outside the town centre complements
comfortably furnished and equipped bedrooms with modern
facilities by reasonably spacious public areas, good indoor leisure
facilities and a popular outdoor pool.*
30⇨📞(14fb)1🛏 CTV in all bedrooms ® T ✳ sB&B⇨📞£28-
£37 dB&B⇨📞£56-£74 (incl dinner) 🍴
CTV 30P ❄ ⬚ (heated) ⊇ (heated) 𝒫 (grass) squash sauna
solarium gymnasium games room *xmas*
♀ English & Continental ♦ ⚪ ✂ Bar Lunch £1.50-£4.60alc
Credit Cards ①③

**★★64% Shanklin Manor House**
Manor Rd, Old Village PO37 6QX 🕿Isle of Wight(0983)862777
*This privately owned and particularly well sited stone manor
house, quietly set in 4 acres of well tended gardens, offers a style of
service and hospitality which will appeal particularly to the leisure
user. Public areas are comfortable, and the whole establishment
incorporates a wide range of facilities whilst still retaining its
Victorian splendour.*
33⇨📞(12fb)1🛏 CTV in all bedrooms ® T 🐾 (ex guide dogs)
✳ sB&B⇨📞£30.50-£37.50 dB&B⇨📞£61-£75 🍴
50P ❄ CFA ⬚ (heated) ⊇ (heated) 𝒫 (hard) sauna solarium
gymnasium spa bath putting croquet jacuzzi nc6mths ✿ *xmas*
♀ English & French ♦ ⚪ ✂ ✳ Bar Lunch £2.25-£6 Dinner
£12.50 Last dinner 8.30pm
Credit Cards ①③ⓔ

**★★61% Melbourne Ardenlea**
Queen's Rd PO37 6AP 🕿Isle of Wight(0983)862283
Closed Nov-Feb RS Mar & late Oct
*An old-fashioned family-run hotel which offers good value for
money and is popular with families and larger parties. Bedrooms
are simple and functional but well equipped with modern facilities.
There is an indoor leisure complex and live entertainment is offered
most evenings.*
51⇨📞(9fb) CTV in all bedrooms ® T sB&B⇨📞£21-£36
dB&B⇨📞£42-£72
Lift CTV 28P ❄ ⬚ (heated) sauna solarium games room spa
bath ♫
♀ English & French V Bar Lunch £1-£5 Dinner £9-£11&alc
Last dinner 8pm
Credit Cards ①③ⓔ

## TOTLAND BAY Map 04 SZ38

**★★63% *Sentry Mead***
Madeira Rd PO39 0BJ 🕿Isle of Wight(0983)753212
*This small comfortable hotel has steadily improved in standards
under the caring owners Mr and Mrs Hodgson. Bright airy
bedrooms of varying size are well furnished and have good modern
facilities, public areas are pleasant and there are plans to add a sun
terrace and improve car parking facilities.*
12rm(8⇨2📞)(4fb) CTV in all bedrooms ®
CTV 10P 🌂 ❄ putting
♀ European ♦ ⚪ Last dinner 8pm
Credit Cards ②

## VENTNOR Map 04 SZ57

**★★★64% Ventnor Towers**
Madeira Rd PO38 1QT (Consort) 🕿Isle of Wight(0983)852277
Telex no 8951182 FAX (0983) 855536
*Set proudly on the cliff side, with sea views from most of its rooms,
this turreted Victorian mansion is run by 2 generations of
dedicated and professional hoteliers whose commitment to the
upgrading of the hotel is matched by the warmth of the welcome
that they extend to their guests. Simple, comfortable bedrooms
show a high standard of housekeeping, while day rooms are bright
and traditional in style. Excellent outdoor sporting facilities are
available.*
27rm(26⇨📞)(27fb)1🛏 CTV in all bedrooms ® T
sB&B⇨📞£32-£38 dB&B⇨📞£48-£68 🍴
CTV 40P 1🚗 ❄ CFA ⊇ (heated) ▶ 9 𝒫 (hard) croquet
games room ♫ *xmas*
♀ English & French V ♦ ⚪ ✂ Lunch £7.50 Dinner
£11.95&alc Last dinner 8.30pm
Credit Cards ①②③⑤ⓔ

**W**

### ★★71% **Madeira Hall Country House Hotel and Restaurant**
Trinity Rd PO38 1NS ☎Isle of Wight(0983)852624
FAX (0983) 854906

*This handsome Grade II listed building was once the home of a Miss Dick on whom Dickens based the character of Miss Havisham in Great Expectations – and rumour has it that it was the author himself who jilted her on their wedding day! Very smartly presented bedrooms have been equipped with modern facilities, all offering comfort and a high standard of furnishing and décor, though one or two are smaller than the others. Attractive and well furnished public areas pervaded by a warm, welcoming atmosphere include a restaurant servicing an interesting à la carte menu of dishes based on good fresh produce, and resident proprietors provide amiable hospitality.*

8⇨📺(2fb)3🛏⅟ᴍin all bedrooms CTV in all bedrooms ® T
🛏 (ex guide dogs) ✳ sB&B⇨📺£36–£41 dB&B⇨📺£72–£86
(incl dinner) 🍴
20P 🚗 ✿ ≏ (heated) putting green bowls green nc7yrs
V ♥ ⊻ ⅟ ✳ Lunch £7–£20alc Dinner £15–£20alc Last dinner 8.45pm
Credit Cards 1 2 3 4

### ★★65% **Burlington**
Bellevue Rd PO38 1DB ☎Isle of Wight(0983)852113
Closed Nov-Feb

23⇨📺(8fb)1🛏 CTV in all bedrooms ® T 🛏 ✳
sB&B⇨📺£26.50–£31 dB&B⇨📺£53–£64 (incl dinner) 🍴
CTV 20P ✿ ≏ (heated) nc3yrs
♥ ⊻ ✳ Bar Lunch £1.20–£4 Dinner £9.50 Last dinner 8.30pm
Credit Cards 1 3

### ★★63% **Highfield**
Leeson Rd, Bonchurch PO38 1PU
☎Isle of Wight(0983)852800 & 854611
Closed Nov-Feb

*On the hillside overlooking the bay, with views out to sea, this hotel dates back 160 years and has been comfortably renovated by the resident proprietors. The bedrooms are freshly decorated with pretty papered prints and furnished in a cosy style. Each is well equipped with modern facilities. Public areas are neatly presented, and while Mrs Flaherty does the cooking her husband is in charge front of house and enjoys chatting to guests. Both are friendly, welcoming hosts.*

12⇨📺(1fb)2🛏 CTV in all bedrooms ® T sB&B⇨📺£35.50–£41
dB&B⇨📺£59–£72 (incl dinner)
12P 🚗 ✿ nc5yrs
♥ English & French V ♥ ⊻ ⅟ ✳ Lunch £6.95–£8.50 High tea
£5–£6 Dinner £11.95–£14.95&alc Last dinner 7.30pm
Credit Cards 1 3 ⓔ

**See advertisement under BONCHURCH**

---

**WOOTTON** Map **04** SZ58

### ✿✿✿✕**Lugley's**
Staplers Rd PO33 4RW ☎Isle of Wight(0983)882202

*A cosy restaurant in a country cottage, with a warm, intimate atmosphere. Chef/Proprietor Angela Hewitt continues to provide cooking in an individual style. Dishes are painstakingly prepared and produce the best flavours from good fresh ingredients.*
Closed Sun (in winter), Lunch not served (ex by prior arrangement only)
16 seats ✳ Lunch £12.95 Dinner fr£19.95&alc Last lunch 1.30pm Last dinner 9.30pm 10 P nc5yrs

---

**WIGTON** Cumbria Map **11** NY24

### ★★61% **Greenhill Lodge**
Red Dial CA7 8LS (2m S off A595) ☎(06973)43304
*This mansion house set beside the A595 at Red Dial, built in the 18th century and now converted into a comfortable hotel, offers accommodation with good facilities and a carvery room and bar serving a wide range of food.*

---

7⇨📺2🛏 CTV in all bedrooms ® T sB&B⇨📺£31-£35
dB&B⇨📺£45-£50 🍴
100P ✿ nc xmas
♥ International V ♥ ✳ Lunch £6.75 Dinner £15 Last dinner 9pm
Credit Cards 1 3 ⓔ

### ★★59% *Wheyrigg Hall*
Wheyrigg CA7 0DH (4m NW on B5302)
☎Abbeytown(06973)61242 FAX (06973) 61020

*A converted and extended farmhouse situated in open countryside on the B5302, 4 miles northwest of the town. Bedrooms are well furnished and meals are available all day.*
6rm(2⇨3📺)(2fb) CTV in all bedrooms ® 🛏
60P ✿
V ♥ ⊻ Last dinner 9pm
Credit Cards 1 2 3

---

**WILLERBY** Humberside Map **08** TA03

### ★★★73% **Grange Park**
Main St HU10 6EA (Best Western) ☎Hull(0482)656488
Telex no 592773 FAX (0482) 655848

*This modern hotel complex caters for business clientele and holidaymakers alike, with modern, well appointed bedrooms and a good choice of eating options with the formal L'Eau Vive Restaurant or the more relaxed Cedars Bar and Restaurant. Guests have the use of the extensive indoor leisure and health club facilities, and for business people, a good range of conference and banqueting rooms is available.*

109⇨📺4🛏 CTV in all bedrooms ® T sB⇨📺£56-£89
dB⇨📺£78-£99 (room only) 🍴
Lift (⊞ CTV 600P ✿ CFA ≏ (heated) sauna solarium
gymnasium hairdressing beauty clinic ♫ xmas
♥ English, French & Italian V ♥ ⊻ ✳ Dinner fr£14.95 Last dinner 10.30pm
Credit Cards 1 2 3 5 ⓔ

**See advertisement under HULL**

### ★★★70% **Willerby Manor**
Well Ln HU10 6ER ☎Hull(0482)652616 Telex no 592629
FAX (0482) 653901

*The public rooms of this hotel have been given a comfortable and stylish touch after a recent refurbishment. The bedrooms are similarly well appointed and comfortable. A choice of restaurants is available; Raffaele's provides an informal setting for Italian cuisine, and for entertaining, there is the good French Lafite restaurant.*

36⇨📺(2fb)2🛏 CTV in all bedrooms ® T
《 250P ✿ CFA
♥ French V ♥ ⊻ Last dinner 9.45pm
Credit Cards 1 2 3

**See advertisement under HULL**

---

**WILLITON** Somerset Map **03** ST04

### ★★✿✿72% **White House**
Long St TA4 4QW ☎(0984)32306 & 32777
Closed Dec-16 May
(Rosettes awarded for dinner only)

*This Georgian house on the A39 is reminiscent of the Mediterranean with its whitewashed and shuttered façade, bountiful fig tree in the courtyard and palm trees in front. Only open for a short season, it provides bedrooms which, like the stone and bark walled bar and stylish lounge, have been decorated in attractive personal style by long-established owners. It is because of the reputation of its restaurant, however, that most people visit this establishment, the set-price 5-course menu offering a choice of 4 honest and unpretentious – though imaginative – dishes at each stage after the soup starter. Such favourites as a smooth duck liver pâté flavoured with thyme and Armagnac and local quail baked pink with apricots are complemented by a superb wine list containing many fine, mature French wines from different regions and also examples from Italy, Spain and the New World. Service throughout is informal, friendly and attentive.*

8rm(5⇨3🛏)Annexe4⇨3(1fb) CTV in all bedrooms T sB&B£33-£35 sB&B⇨3🛏£37-£45 dB&B£57-£60 dB&B⇨3🛏£66-£75 🅿 15P 🚗

♀ English & French ⅙ ✳ Dinner £27-£29 Last dinner 8.30pm £

---

### WILMCOTE Warwickshire Map **04** SP15

**★★60% Swan House**

The Green CV37 9XJ ☎Stratford-upon-Avon(0789) 267030 FAX (0789) 204875
Closed 24-28 Dec

*Standing just three miles from Stratford in the little village of Wilmcote, overlooking its green and Mary Arden's House, the hotel provides accommodation in simply furnished bedrooms with en suite facilities. The lounge bar is popular with tourists and locals alike, and there is a separate snooker room with full-size table.*

12⇨3🛏(1fb)1🖥 CTV in all bedrooms ® ✈ (ex guide dogs) 40P ❀ snooker ♫

♀ English & French V ✿ ♨ Last dinner 9.30pm

Credit Cards ①②③

**See advertisement under STRATFORD-UPON-AVON**

---

### WILMSLOW Cheshire Map **07** SJ88 ⊙

See also Manchester Airport

**★★★⊛⊛⊛71% Stanneylands**

Stanneylands Rd SK9 4EY ☎(0625)525225 FAX (0625) 537282 RS 1 Jan & Good Fri

*An extended but unspoiled residence in Manchester's commuter belt stands amid 4.5-acre grounds which contain a small lake, home to ornamental waterfowl and surrounded by trees and shrubs. Personally owned and managed, the hotel and restaurant is a popular choice for business entertaining through the week. Chef Steven Kitchen produces a menu that reveals a sound command of techniques, his skill being demonstrated in the fixed-price speciality menu 'Tastes and Textures', and in the à la carte menu, supplemented by 'Today's Markets'. Our inspector enjoyed two layers of light, buttery flaky pastry sandwiching a creamy smoked haddock mousse that formed the centre of a 'Bouquet of Asparagus partnered by a Mille Feuilles of Arbroath Smokies', served with cucumber sauce. Vegetables get a certain amount of dressing up, but flavours haven't been sacrificed in the process. Desserts have included a fine summer pudding, served with a cassis sauce and a ball of clotted cream. The wine list has no great surprises, but there is a good range and good choice of half bottles. Booking is a necessity here.*

33⇨🛏2🖥 CTV in all bedrooms ✈ S% sB⇨3🛏£40-£80 dB⇨3🛏£60-£100 (room only) 🅿

✆ 80P 🚗 ❀ CFA

V ✿ ♨ ✳

Credit Cards ①②③⑤

**See advertisement under MANCHESTER AIRPORT**

---

### WIMBORNE MINSTER Dorset Map **04** SZ09

**★★★61% The King's Head**

The Square BH21 1JA (Forte Hotels) ☎(0202)880101 FAX (0202) 881667

*An old coaching inn set right on the town square now provides some smart, well decorated bedrooms and a comfortable lounge with extensive service; though other public areas are less attractive, guests can enjoy meals selected from a range of table d'hôte and à la carte menus in a pleasant, spacious dining room.*

27⇨3🛏(1fb)1🖥 CTV in all bedrooms ® T ✳ S% sB⇨3🛏£65 dB⇨3🛏£80 (room only) 🅿

Lift 25P CFA *xmas*

V ✿ ♨ ⅙

Credit Cards ①②③④⑤

---

**★★58% Coach House Inn**

Tricketts Cross BH22 9NW (Consort) ☎Ferndown(0202)861222 FAX (0202) 894130
(For full entry see Ferndown)

---

### ⊛✕✕Les Bouviers

Oakley Hill, Merley BH21 1RJ ☎Wimborne(0202)889555

*Attractively decorated in sage green and dusky pink, this friendly restaurant has won considerable popularity in the town. The carte is supplemented by a daily 'menu gourmand' and occasional special events. Dishes enjoyed on an inspection visit included a courgette and coriander mousse with Noilly Prat sauce, followed by sautéed venison with rum and bananas. Vegetables were fresh and simply cooked. The wine list is mostly French, with a choice of half a dozen wines available in quarter litres.*

Closed Sun & last 2wks Jan Lunch not served Sat

♀ French V 40 seats Lunch £7.95-£10.45 Dinner fr£17.75&alc Last lunch 2.15pm Last dinner 10pm 12 P ⅙

Credit Cards ②③④

---

### WINCANTON Somerset Map **03** ST72

**★★🏌59% Holbrook House**

Holbrook BA9 8BS ☎(0963)32377
Closed 31 Dec

*Extensive outdoor leisure facilities at this hotel include a swimming pool, tennis courts, squash and croquet. Inside, the rather old fashioned décor and unhurried pace give the impression of stepping back in time; lounges are comfortable and there are some spacious bedrooms.*

20rm(8⇨8🛏)(2fb) TV available ® T ✈ (ex guide dogs) ✳ sB&B⇨3🛏£39.50-£47.50 dB&B⇨3🛏£72 🅿

CTV 30P 4🚗 ❀ CFA ⚘ (heated) ♬ (hard & grass )squash croquet table tennis ⚑ *xmas*

V ✿ ✳ Lunch £8.50&alc High tea £6&alc Dinner £15&alc Last dinner 8.30pm

Credit Cards ①②③£

**See advertisement on page 751**

---

### WINCHESTER Hampshire Map **04** SU42 ⊙

**★★★★⊛🏌71% Lainston House**

Sparsholt SO21 2LT (3m NW off A272) (Small Luxury Hotels) ☎(0962)863588 Telex no 477375 FAX (0962) 72672
(Rosette awarded for dinner only)

*This gracious William and Mary style house is situated in 63 acres of peaceful countryside just 3 miles from Winchester. Bedrooms are tastefully decorated and made comfortable with excellent beds and Swiss linen. The bar has magnificent cedar panelling, while the lounge has good pictures and fresh flowers. The dining room comprises 2 panelled rooms, and Chef Friedrich Litty provides a short menu of British dishes using fresh, often local, produce. There is a good choice of fish and 2 vegetarian dishes, and the food can be robust in flavour and hearty in portion. Service is quietly friendly, creating a relaxing atmosphere amid very refined surroundings.*

32rm(30⇨1🛏)(1fb) CTV in all bedrooms T sB⇨3🛏fr£99 dB⇨3🛏fr£120 (room only) 🅿

✆ 150P 🚗 ❀ ♪ croquet clay pigeon shooting ⚑ *xmas*

♀ English & French V ✿ ♨ Lunch £7.80-£26alc Dinner £30-£40alc Last dinner 10pm

Credit Cards ①②③④⑤

**See advertisement on page 753**

---

For key to symbols in English see the bookmark.

**★★★★**62% **Forte Crest**
Paternoster Row SO23 9LQ (Forte Hotels) ☎(0962)861611
Telex no 47419 FAX (0962) 841503

*A functional, purpose-built hotel, its style in stark contrast to the
adequately equipped but rather mixed bedrooms, the larger among
them overlooking the cathedral, others facing the service entrance
to the High Street. It has undergone a complete refurbishment over
the last 12 months and is smart and bright. The main restaurant,
looking out on the cathedral, offers a club house menu, while the
terrace restaurant is less formal. A new business centre is available
to guests.*

94⇔🛏⊱in 61 bedrooms CTV in all bedrooms ® T ✳ S%
sB⇔🛏£85 dB⇔🛏£95-£105 (room only) 🍴
Lift ( 60P CFA *xmas*
V ♥ ⚏ ✳ ⊱ S% Lunch £12.50-£13.95&alc Dinner
fr17.50&alc Last dinner 11pm
Credit Cards ① ② ③ ④ ⑤

**★★★**68% **Winchester Moat House**
Worthy Ln SO23 7AB (Queens Moat)(Consort) ☎(0962)868102
Telex no 47383 FAX (0962) 840862

*This modern hotel, a healthy walk from the town centre, provides
spacious, well equipped bedrooms and a comfortable bar/lounge
adjoining the pleasant restaurant, with table d'hôte and à la carte
menus. Service is provided by friendly young staff.*

72⇔🛏 (6fb)⊱in 20 bedrooms CTV in all bedrooms ® T S%
sB⇔🛏£55-£76.50 dB⇔🛏£84-£86 (room only) 🍴
( 72P CFA 🏊 (heated) sauna solarium gymnasium steam
room jacuzzi plunge pool *xmas*
♀ English & French V ♥ ⚏ ⊱ Lunch £13-£15&alc Dinner
£17-£18.50&alc Last dinner 9.45pm
Credit Cards ① ② ③ ⑤ ⓔ

**★★★**63% **Marwell Resort**
Colden Common SO21 1JY (Resort) ☎(0962) 777681
FAX (0962) 777625
60⇔🛏

For full entry see **Marwell**

**★★★**61% *Royal*
Saint Peter St SO23 8BS (Best Western) ☎(0962)840840
Telex no 477071 FAX (0962) 841582

*Despite its central situation this hotel is a haven of peace, set in a
well kept garden and adorned with colourful hanging baskets.
Comfortable, well coordinated rooms are availabe in both the
original building and a modern, purpose-built extension, meals are
taken in an attractive conservatory-style restaurant and there is a
car parking space at both the front and rear of the building.*

59⇔🛏(4fb)1🚪 CTV in all bedrooms ®
( 60P ❖ fly fishing
♀ English & French ♥ ⚏ Last dinner 9.30pm
Credit Cards ① ② ③ ⑤

---

**WINDERMERE** Cumbria Map **07** SD49

**See Town Plan Section.**

**★★★★**56% **The Old England**
Church St, Bowness LA23 3DF (Forte Hotels) ☎(05394)42444
Telex no 65194 FAX (05394) 43432

*This long established lakeside hotel is gradually being improved
under the direction of a dedicated management team, who ensure
that guests are well looked after. Bedrooms vary in size but many
enjoy fine views of Lake Windermere, and there is an inviting
lounge in which to relax. Leisure facilities include a heated outdoor
pool and billiard room.*

82⇔🛏(59fb)⊱in 11 bedrooms CTV in all bedrooms ® T ✳
S% sB⇔🛏£75-£80 dB⇔🛏£95-£105 (room only) 🍴
Lift ( ⊞ CTV 82P ❖ CFA 🏊 (heated) snooker sauna solarium
golf driving net *xmas*
V ♥ ⚏ ✳ ⊱ S% Lunch £8.95-£10.50&alc Dinner £16.95-
£20.95&alc Last dinner 9.45pm
Credit Cards ① ② ③ ④ ⑤

**★★★**❀ **♨**74% **Linthwaite**
Crook Rd, Bowness LA23 3JA ☎(05394)88600
FAX (05394) 88601
(Rosette awarded for dinner only)

*A delightful country house hotel set in 14 acres of woodland and
gardens overlooking Windermere, offering one of the finest views of
the English Lakes. Public rooms include comfortable lounges, a
conservatory and a dining room, with fine silver and china, where
excellent modern British cuisine is served. Bedrooms are stylish
and very well equipped. Although secluded, Linthwaite is not
difficult to find : from the M6, junction 36, follow the A591 Kendal
bypass for about 8 miles to a large roundabout, then take the
B5284 signed Crook. About half a mile past Windermere Golf
Club, on the left, the drive to the hotel is signed.*

18⇔🛏(3🚪)⊱in all bedrooms CTV in all bedrooms ® T
🐕 (ex guide dogs) ✳ sB&B⇔🛏£43-£88 dB&B⇔🛏£86-£126
🍴
30P 🚐 ❖ CFA ✔ putting green nc8yrs
V ♥ ⚏ ⊱ S% Bar Lunch £1.95-£5.95 Dinner £24 Last dinner
9pm
Credit Cards ① ② ③ ⑤ ⓔ

**★★★**70% **Wild Boar**
Crook LA23 3NF (2.5m S of Windermere on B5284 Crook road)
(Best Western) ☎(05394) 45225 Telex no 65464

*Staff are very keen to please, and a good standard of cooking is
provided in the attractive restaurant of this well furnished and
comfortable country hotel.*

36⇔🛏(3fb)4🚪⊱in 6 bedrooms CTV in all bedrooms ® T S%
sB&B⇔🛏£47-£55 dB&B⇔🛏£94-£110 🍴
60P ❖ CFA free boat launching facilities *xmas*
♀ English & French V ♥ ⚏ ⊱ ✳ Lunch fr£7.40 Dinner
fr£18.95 Last dinner 8.45pm
Credit Cards ① ② ③ ④ ⑤

**★★★**♨66% **Langdale Chase**
LA23 1LW ☎(05394)32201 FAX (05394) 32604

*Guests can enjoy extensive views of lake and mountain, as well as a
high standard of cuisine, in the lovely dining room of this beautiful
country house hotel ; extensive, comfortable lounge facilities are
available, and superb grounds and gardens stretch down to the
shores of Lake Windermere.*

24⇔🛏Annexe7⇔🛏(1fb)2🚪 CTV in all bedrooms ® T ✳
sB&B⇔🛏£44-£56.50 dB&B⇔🛏£88-£113 🍴
( 36P 🚐 ❖ ♪ (grass) croquet rowing boats putting *xmas*
♀ English & French ♥ ⚏ ✳ S% Lunch £9.50 Dinner £19.95
Last dinner 8.45pm
Credit Cards ① ② ③ ⑤

**★★★**❀64% **Burn How Garden House Hotel**
Back Belsfield Rd, Bowness LA23 3HH ☎(05394) 46226
(Rosette awarded for dinner only)

*Delightfully situated amid secluded gardens in an elevated position
at Bowness, the hotel offers accommodation in family garden
chalets, in the now modernised original Victorian house or in a
purpose-built wing with sun balconies and 4-poster beds ; a good
standard of cooking is provided in the charming restaurant.*

Annexe26⇔🛏(10fb)4🚪 CTV in all bedrooms ® T
🐕 (ex guide dogs) sB&B⇔🛏£39-£46 dB&B⇔🛏£58-£72 🍴
30P ❖ sauna solarium gymnasium water sports ⚓ *xmas*
♀ English & French V ♥ ⊱ Bar Lunch £2.50-£7.50 Dinner
£16.50&alc Last dinner 9pm
Credit Cards ① ② ③

See advertisement on page 755

**★★★**64% *Burnside*
Kendal Road, Bowness LA23 3EP ☎(05394)42211
Telex no 65430 FAX (05394) 43824

*This large, stone Victorian building stands in an elevated position,
commanding views of Lake Windermere. Well furnished
throughout, it features a very good leisure centre and a choice of
several eating options.*

**W**

45⇄(11fb)4🏠 CTV in all bedrooms ® **T**
Lift 80P ✿ ⊠ (heated) squash snooker sauna solarium
gymnasium watersports steam room badminton ♫
**V** ✿ ⚓ ⅍ Last dinner 9.45pm
Credit Cards ①②③⑤

★★★64% **Low Wood**
LA23 1LP (3m N A591) (Best Western) ☎(05394)33338
Telex no 65273 FAX (05394) 34072
*This large and recently refurbished and extended hotel stands on
the shore of Lake Windermere. Extensive leisure amenities include
a water ski and windsurfing school. The hotel also has conference
facilities.*
99⇄⋔(10fb)3🏠 CTV in all bedrooms ® **T** ✻ sB&B⇄⋔£60-
£90 dB&B⇄⋔£120-£160 🍴
Lift ( 200P ✿ CFA⊠ (heated) ♪ squash snooker sauna
solarium gymnasium water skiing sub aqua diving windsurfing
*xmas*
⊕ International **V** ✿ ⚓ ⅍ ✳ Lunch fr£9.50&alc High tea £7-
£18alc Dinner fr£19&alc Last dinner 10pm
Credit Cards ①②③⑤ⓔ

★★★63% **The Belsfield**
Kendal Rd, Bowness LA23 3EL (Forte Hotels) ☎(05394)42448
Telex no 65238 FAX (05394) 46397
*This large and elegant Victorian house overlooking Lake
Windermere offers good-quality accommodation. Public areas are
comfortable and well furnished, while bedrooms have all modern
amenities. Leisure facilities include a popular indoor pool.*
64⇄⋔(8fb)2🏠⅍in 6 bedrooms CTV in all bedrooms ® **T** ✻
S% sB⇄⋔£70 dB⇄⋔£90-£133 (room only) 🍴
Lift ( 100P ✿ CFA⊠ (heated) ♟ (grass) snooker sauna
solarium mini golf putting green ♫ *xmas*
⊕ French **V** ✿ ⚓ ⅍ ✳ S% Sunday Lunch £9.50 High tea £5-
£15 Dinner £13.95&alc Last dinner 9.30pm
Credit Cards ①②③⑤

**W**

# Windermere

## ★★★60% Hydro

Helm Rd, Bowness LA23 3BA (Mount Charlotte (TS))
☎(05394)44455 Telex no 65196 FAX (05394) 88000

*A large hotel in an elevated position just off the town centre, with views over lake and fells, offers individually furnished, well appointed bedrooms and friendly service.*

96⇄📺(9fb) CTV in all bedrooms ℝ 🖳
Lift ℂ 140P *xmas*

V ⇩

Credit Cards ①②③⑤

★★

★★❀❀ ⚑ HOLBECK GHYLL
COUNTRY HOUSE

Holbeck Ln LA23 1LU
☎(05394)32375
FAX (05394) 34743

Closed Jan

*Set high in the hills overlooking Lake Windermere, this small hotel continues to improve under the enthusiastic direction of owners David and Patricia Nicholson. Winners of our Courtesy and Care award in 1990, the greatest asset of this hotel is the staff, particularly Sarah, a senior member who sets a fine example to her other young colleagues with a combination of courtesy, care and competence. Particularly pleasing is the lack of fuss or pretence. Immaculately clean bedrooms vary considerably in size and comfort, the best rooms being at the front of the hotel. All the rooms have every modern facility and good private bathrooms. Lounge areas are particularly comfortable, with open fires on winter evenings enhancing further the excellent cream teas. Dinner is served in the pleasant wood-panelled dining room. Chef Leslie Anderson offers a wide ranging fixed-price 5-course dinner, featuring British based food. Good soups, an excellent red mullet with butter sauce, tomato and basil; several game dishes, and plain roasts with all the trimmings can be recommended, together with many of the cream-based desserts on open display.*

14⇄📺(1fb)1⚑ CTV in all bedrooms ℝ T
20P ⇘ ❀ putting green
♀ English & French V ⇩ ⚋ ⅄ Last dinner 8.45pm
Credit Cards ①③

**See advertisement under AMBLESIDE**

★★

★★❀❀❀ MILLER HOWE

Rayrigg Rd LA23 1EY
☎(05394) 42536
FAX (05394) 45664

Closed early Dec-early Mar

*Hospitality is the hallmark of this charming hotel, peacefully located in a superb setting. In addition to the comfortable lounges there is now a conservatory extension with a panoramic view of the lake. Many fine paintings, china and antiques, together with some attractive floral displays, contribute to the ambience of the house. Although compact, the bedrooms are comfortable and well equipped, with pleasing décor and quality furnishings. A set-price 5-course menu is served at 8pm in the intimate split-level dining room. John Tovey, his Head Chef, Ian Dutton, and their team produce a meal of high quality and change their menu daily. Except for puddings, only one choice is*

*offered, but the cooking belies the simplicity of the menu. For starters perhaps the Babotie pasta, comprising curried minced lamb with nuts and apricots, topped with a rich brandy cream sauce. Then Miller Howe devilled mushrooms in puff pastry served with quail eggs and salad is followed by home-made soup. For main course, sugar baked Lakeland ham on mustard, cheese, watercress and pineapple ring with rich madeira gravy, or roast local loin of pork stuffed with hazelnuts, Dijon mustard and rosemary on a rhubarb purée with rich gravy. Exciting puddings include shortbread rounds filled with raspberries on butterscotch sauce, or orange and ginger steamed sponge with vanilla pod custard. The wine list concentrates on wines from the New World, and an interesting selection is offered at reasonable prices.*

13⇄📺1⚑ TV available sB&B⇄📺£70-£120
dB&B⇄📺£140-£240 (incl dinner) 🖳
40P ⇘ ❀ nc12yrs
V ⇩ ⚋ ⅄ ✱ Dinner £30 Last dinner 8.30pm
Credit Cards ①②③⑤

## ★★❀75% Cedar Manor Hotel & Restaurant

Ambleside Rd LA23 1AX (Exec Hotel) ☎(05394) 43192

*Friendly service is provided by resident proprietors at this attractive hotel set in its own delightful garden on the A591. Bedrooms are pleasantly furnished and have good facilities, and a good standard of cooking is served in the attractive dining room.*

10⇄📺Annexe2⇄📺(4fb)1⚑ CTV in all bedrooms ℝ T
sB&B⇄📺£35-£55 dB&B⇄📺£62-£90 (incl dinner) 🖳
15P ⇘ ❀ *xmas*
♀ English, French & Italian V ⇩ ⚋ ⅄ Dinner £15.50-£18
Last dinner 8.30pm
Credit Cards ①③£

## ★★74% Hillthwaite House

Thornbarrow Rd LA23 2DF ☎(05394)43636 & 46691

*A very attractive, family-owned hotel, set in its own grounds and occupying an elevated position, offers a good standard of comfort in its well furnished bedrooms and good lounges; guests also have the use of an indoor swimming pool. Caring service is provided by a friendly staff.*

25⇄📺(2fb)8⚑ CTV in all bedrooms ℝ
26P ⇘ ❀ ☐ (heated) sauna solarium
♀ English & French V ⇩ ⚋ Last dinner 9pm
Credit Cards ①②③

## ★★⚑74% Lindeth Fell

Upper Storrs Park Rd, Bowness LA23 3JP ☎(05394)43286 & 44287

Closed mid Nov-mid Mar

*A charming country house set in beautiful grounds high above the lake, offering warm hospitality from resident owners Mr and Mrs P A Kennedy. Well furnished bedrooms have good facilities and there are comfortable lounges with log fires and a dining room serving good English cooking.*

14⇄📺(2fb) CTV in all bedrooms ℝ T ✖ sB&B⇄📺£48.50-£54 dB&B⇄📺£90-£108 (incl dinner)
20P ⇘ ❀ ♗ (grass) ♪ croquet putting nc7yrs
⇩ ⚋ Dinner £21 Last dinner 8.30pm
Credit Cards ①③

## ★★68% Bordriggs Country House

Longtail Hill, Bowness LA23 3LD ☎(05394) 43567
FAX (05394) 46949

*Guests are given a warm welcome by Judith and Roger Stones at this small family-run hotel, set in well kept gardens in a secluded location. Comfortable bedrooms have good facilities and there is a relaxing lounge.*

→

# LAINSTON HOUSE HOTEL

★ ★ ★ ★ ❁

Standing in 63 acres of superb downland countryside, this graceful William and Mary country house has been lovingly converted into an excellent hotel, retaining all the elegance and warmth of the original manor. Stylish, individually designed bedrooms invite relaxation, and the main reception rooms are elegantly and comfortably furnished. Freshly prepared food, excellent service and superb views over the lawns combine to make the restaurant one of the most popular in Hampshire. The hotel has facilities for small informal meetings, or larger gatherings in the superbly restored 17th-century barn. The charming grounds hold many surprises — a 12th-century chapel, complete with ghost, an 18th-century herb garden, a dovecote and a croquet lawn. Historic Winchester and the Royal Winchester Golf Course are a short distance away, whilst Romsey Abbey, Salisbury and the New Forest are within easy reach. The hotel has its own stretch of the River Test which is available to guests and provides excellent trout fishing. Other facilities available locally include riding and shooting.

*Directions:* Lainston House is well signposted off the A272 Winchester-Stockbridge road, at Sparsholt 2½ miles from Winchester.

W

**Sparsholt, Winchester, Hants SO21 2LT**
**Tel: 0962 863588   Fax: 0962 72672   Telex: 477375**

## Windermere

9🚻🛏Annexe2🚻🛏(2fb)1🛁in all bedrooms CTV in all bedrooms **T** ✕ (ex guide dogs) sB&B🚻🛏fr£28 dB&B🚻🛏fr£50 🆓
《 20P 🚭 ❄ ☄ 🛁 (heated) croquet badminton nc10yrs
♀ English & Continental **V** ✂ Dinner £14.50 Last dinner 7.30pm
ⓔ

### ★★ 68% *Crag Brow*

Helm Rd LA23 3BU ☎(05394)44080
*Quietly situated, with views of the surrounding fells, this charming hotel has a licensed restaurant (which is open to non-residents) and offers a wide choice of delectable dishes from table d'hôte and à la carte menus.*
11🚻🛏(3fb) CTV in all bedrooms ⓡ **T** ✕ (ex guide dogs)
30P ❄ free membership to leisure club
♀ English, French & Italian **V** ♥ ✂ Last dinner 9.30pm
Credit Cards 1 3

### ★★ 68% Hideaway

Phoenix Way LA23 1DB ☎(05394)43070
*A pleasant, stone-built house set in a quiet area yet convenient for the town centre, offers comfortable accommodation and friendly atmosphere.*
11rm(4🚻🛏6🛏)Annexe5🚻🛏(3fb)6🛁 CTV in all bedrooms ⓡ
sB&B🚻🛏£31-£44 dB&B🚻🛏£36-£50 (incl dinner) 🆓
16P 🚭 ❄ 🛁 *xmas*
♀ English & Continental **V** ♥ ✂ ✂

### ★★ 67% Quarry Garth Country House Hotel & Restaurant

Troutbeck Bridge LA23 1LF ☎(05394)88282 FAX (05394) 46584
*Eight acres of carefully tended gardens and grounds surround this pleasant country house hotel located midway between Windermere and Ambleside. Well furnished and equipped throughout, it offers warm, comfortable lounges, cosy bedrooms and good service from attentive staff.*
10🚻🛏(2fb) CTV in all bedrooms ⓡ **T** ✳ sB&B🚻🛏£35-£60 dB&B🚻🛏£70-£120 (incl dinner) 🆓
35P 🚭 ❄ ♩ *xmas*
♀ English & Continental **V** ♥ ✂ ✳ Sunday Lunch £10.75
Dinner £18.50 Last dinner 9pm
Credit Cards 1 2 3 5

### ★★ 66% Ravensworth

Ambleside Rd LA23 1BA ☎(05394)43747
*A well furnished, friendly hotel set beside the main road to Ambleside and close to the town centre. Bedrooms have good facilities.*
9🚻🛏Annexe5🚻🛏(1fb)4🛁 CTV in all bedrooms ⓡ **T**
sB&B🚻🛏£27.50-£32.50 dB&B🚻🛏£50-£65 🆓
17P 🚭 ❄ CFA ♪ (hard) *xmas*
♀ French **V** ♥ ✂ Dinner £11.75-£13.25alc Last dinner 8.30pm
Credit Cards 1 3 ⓔ

### ★★♨ 65% *Belmont Manor*

LA23 1LN ☎(05394)33316
*Set in 7 acres of beautiful grounds and gardens, this small country house on the A591 midway between Windermere and Ambleside has modern well equipped bedrooms with full en suite facilities, plus a honeymoon suite with 4-poster bed and circular bath. A 5-course dinner is served in the attractive dining room.*
13🚻🛏(2fb)1🛁 CTV in all bedrooms ⓡ **T** ✕ (ex guide dogs)
100P ❄ ♫
**V** ♥ ✂ ✂

### ★★ 63% Royal

Queens Square, Bowness-on-Windermere LA23 3DB
☎(05394)43045 Telex no 65273 FAX (05394) 42498
*In the centre of Bowness close to the lake, this hotel is one of the oldest in the Lake District, with many famous past guests. It is comfortably furnished throughout, with an attractive lounge, well-equipped bedrooms and a pleasant restaurant.*

29🚻🛏(4fb)1🛁 CTV in all bedrooms ⓡ **T** ✳ S%
sB&B🚻🛏£32.25-£40.50 dB&B🚻🛏£64.50-£81 🆓
16P 5🛄 (£1.50) ❄ CFA sub-aqua diving water skiing pool table ⚙
♀ English & French **V** ♥ ✂ ✂ ✳ S% Lunch £7.50-£14.30
High tea £5.50-£7.50 Dinner £14.30&alc Last dinner 9pm
Credit Cards 1 2 3 4 5 ⓔ

### ★★ 58% The Knoll

Lake Rd, Bowness LA23 2JF ☎(05394) 43756
Closed Dec-Feb
*This 19th-century local stone house commands fine lake and mountain views from a setting in its own grounds close to the centre of Bowness. Small, privately owned and quietly run, it provides modest accommodation in traditional style.*
12rm(9🚻🛏)(4fb) CTV in all bedrooms ⓡ **T** ✕ sB&B£35 sB&B🚻🛏£40 dB&B🚻🛏£80 (incl dinner) 🆓
CTV 20P ❄ nc3yrs
**V** ♥ ✂ ✂ Dinner fr£12.50 Last dinner 7.30pm
Credit Cards 1 3 ⓔ

### ★ 63% Willowsmere

Ambleside Rd LA23 1ES ☎(05394)43575
Closed Dec-Feb
*A traditional Lakeland hotel managed by its enthusiastic young proprietors offers comfortably spacious lounges and an interesting, freshly prepared dinner menu which changes daily.*
13🚻🛏(7fb) ⓡ ✳ sB&B🚻🛏£24-£26 dB&B🚻🛏£48-£56
CTV 20P 🚭
♀ English & Austrian ♥ ✂ ✂ ✳ Dinner £15 Last dinner 7pm
Credit Cards 1 2 3 5 ⓔ

A rosette means exceptional standards of cuisine.

# WILLOWSMERE HOTEL ★

### Ambleside Road, Windermere, Cumbria LA23 1ES
### Tel. (05394) 43575

Willowsmere is situated on the main road Windermere – Ambleside (A591) and is an excellent centre from which to tour the whole Lake District.

Near to the Lake (Millerground) for Boating, Fishing, Swimming, Picnics (Public heated swimming pool ¾ mile). Orrest Head and Troutbeck Valley for walking. All bedrooms with private facilities. Tea & Coffee.

Sheltered Private Garden. Central Heating in all rooms. Colour television in one Lounge. Large Free Car Park.

Noted for excellent catering. Residential licence.

Under the Personal Supervision of Resident proprietors.
**Heather & Alan Cook & Family**

W

### ❋✕ *Porthole Eating House*
3 Ash St, Bowness LA23 3EB ☎(05394)42793

*A small Italian-style restaurant with an informal ambience, discreetly positioned in a quiet street near the lakeside, augments its à la carte menu with a daily selection which includes both classical Italian dishes like Fettuccini Al Pesto and such English cuisine as a lamb speciality created by one of the chefs. The wine list is outstanding, featuring many unusual examples at competitive prices, and service is both friendly and attentive.*

Closed Tue & mid Dec-mid Feb Lunch not served
♀ English, French & Italian **V** 36 seats Last dinner 11pm ⚓
Credit Cards ①②③⑤

### ❋✕ *Rogers*
4 High St LA23 1AF ☎(05394) 44954
(Rosette awarded for dinner only)

*This attractive intimate restaurant is easy to find, being almost opposite the railway station. Roger Pergl-Wilson and his wife Alena have made it into a most inviting place for those who enjoy both French and English cuisine. The 4-course table d'hôte menu offers no choices, but the à la carte offers a wide variety of dishes, including soups, spinach mousse with goat's cheese and tomato sauce and quenelles of Arbroath Smokies as starters, followed by roast rack of lamb with herb crust, or Lobster Thermidor, or calves' liver with sage and marsala sauce. Puddings may include treacle tart with cinammon ice cream, brown sugar meringues with bananas and coffee cream, and crème brulée.*

Closed Sun (ex BH's) & 2 wks in Jan, Feb & Mar Lunch not served (ex by prior arrangement only)
♀ English & French 42 seats Dinner £14-£16&alc Last lunch 1.30pm Last dinner 9.45pm ⚓
Credit Cards ①②③⑤

---

**WINDSOR** Berkshire Map **04** SU97

See also **Datchet**

### ★★★★ ❋❋73% **Oakley Court**
Windsor Road, Water Oakley SL4 5UR (2m W A308) (Queens Moat)(Small Luxury Hotels) ☎Maidenhead(0628)74141
Telex no 849958 FAX (0628) 37011

*Beautifully set in 35 acres of landscaped gardens on the bank of the Thames, this impressive 19th-century mansion has been thoughtfully extended to provide excellent additional accommodation in the Garden and River wings, while already spacious and comfortable bedrooms are due for further upgrading to provide even more facilities. The relaxing public rooms which feature fine wood panelling and ornamental ceilings are furnished to a high standard, and the Oakley Restaurant serves a good selection of interesting, thoughtfully prepared dishes. Helpful staff give unpretentious service.*

65⇨🛏Annexe27⇨🛏5🛌⚓in 4 bedrooms CTV in all bedrooms ® **T** ✠ (ex guide dogs) ✳ S% sB⇨🛏£107-£350 dB⇨🛏£126-£350 (room only) 🅿
《120P ❁ CFA ▶ 9 ⚒ snooker croquet lawn punting boating xmas
♀ English & French **V** ♉ 🕮 ✱ Lunch £18.25&alc High tea £8.50-£9.50 Dinner £28.25&alc Last dinner 10pm
Credit Cards ①②③⑤ £

### ★★★ ❋68% **The Castle**
High St SL4 1LJ (Forte Hotels) ☎(0753)851011 Telex no 849220
FAX (0753) 830244

*The elegant, balconied Georgian frontage of this hotel overlooks the High Street, almost opposite the castle. Guests are welcomed at reception with friendly efficiency and can relax in public areas which include a comfortable town-house lounge/foyer and a good choice of eating options – the popular brasserie and stylishly decorated restaurant offering well prepared and presented dishes to suit both simple and more sophisticated tastes. Bedrooms vary in size, outlook and quietness, but all are smart and well appointed; extensive room service is available.*

103⇨🛏(40fb)4🛌⚓in 41 bedrooms CTV in all bedrooms ® **T** ✱ S% sB⇨🛏£90 dB⇨🛏£110-£130 (room only) 🅿

Lift 《 116P 40🚗 CFA ♫ *xmas*
**V** ♉ 🕮 ✠ ✱ S% Lunch £14.95-£18&alc High tea £4.50-£7 Dinner £20.40&alc Last dinner 10pm
Credit Cards ①②③④⑤

### ★★67% *Aurora Garden*
14 Bolton Av SL4 3JF ☎(0753)868686 FAX (0753) 831394

*A small, quality hotel, in a quiet part of town close to Windsor Great Park's Long Walk, which has benefited from recent upgrading and refurbishment. It has a bright, garden conservatory restaurant, and modern bedrooms equipped with an extensive range of facilities for the modern traveller.*

14⇨🛏(1fb) CTV in all bedrooms ® **T**
20P ❁
♀ English & French **V** ♉ 🕮 Last dinner 9pm
Credit Cards ①②③⑤

### ★★64% *Royal Adelaide*
46 Kings Rd SL4 2AG ☎(0753)863916 FAX (0753) 830682

*A comfortable, relaxed atmosphere pervades this 3-storey Georgian hotel a short stroll from the town centre. Both standard and executive bedrooms are available, the latter having better quality furnishings and smart modern bathrooms, but all are equally well equipped and maintained. Public areas have been attractively decorated, and service is both friendly and helpful.*

39⇨🛏(1fb) CTV in all bedrooms ® **T** ✱ sB&B⇨🛏£65-£75 dB&B⇨🛏£85-£95 🅿
《30P CFA
♀ English & French **V** ♉ ✱ Bar Lunch £3-£10 Dinner £10.75-£18&alc Last dinner 9.30pm
Credit Cards ①②③⑤

### ★★60% **Ye Harte & Garter**
High St SL4 1LR (Chef & Brewer) ☎(0753)863426
FAX (0753) 830527

*Facing Windsor Castle, this rambling Victorian building was once 2 Tudor inns. On the ground floor is a popular Berni restaurant with a menu featuring steaks and grills. Bedrooms are on 4 floors above and vary in size, view and style, but are generally comfortable and well equipped and maintained.*

50rm(36⇨7🛏)(8fb) CTV in all bedrooms ® **T**
✠ (ex guide dogs) sB&B£54-£65 sB&B⇨🛏£66-£71 dB&B£83 dB&B⇨🛏£89 🅿
Lift 《 ⚓ CFA
♀ International **V** ♉ 🕮 ✠ Bar Lunch £2.95-£5.50alc
Credit Cards ①②③⑤

### ★60% *Union Inn*
17 Crump Hill SL4 2QY ☎(0753)861955 FAX (0753) 831378

*First-time visitors to this attractively extended farmhouse are advised to ask for directions when booking, as it stands in a rural setting in Old Windsor. Life revolves around the busy, characterful bar and a restaurant with beams, exposed brickwork and a woodburning stove, while well equipped bedrooms enhanced by pine furniture and matching fabrics are contained on the first floor. No meals are served on Sunday evening.*

12⇨🛏 CTV in all bedrooms ® **T** ✠ (ex guide dogs)
32P 🚌
♀ English & French **V** ♉ 🕮 Last dinner 10.15pm
Credit Cards ①②③

---

**WINSFORD** Somerset Map **03** SS93

### ★★75% **Royal Oak Inn**
Exmoor National Park TA24 7JE (Best Western) ☎(064385)455
FAX (064385) 388

*A picturesque thatched inn in the centre of this much visited Exmoor village. Bedrooms in the main building are pleasantly decorated and furnished and have original features, including some low doorways. There is a luxury bedroom available for special occasions with additional accommodation available in a separate cottage. Lounges are particularly comfortable, and a huge inglenook fireplace is a feature of one of the 2 bars. Short table*

→

756

**W**

W

*d'hôte and à la carte menus are available in the dining room, and there is an extensive range of bar meals. Activity holidays include riding, fishing and clay pigeon shooting.*

8⇄Annexe6⇄(1fb) CTV in all bedrooms ® T sB&B⇄£69.50-£84.50 dB&B⇄£109-£139 (incl dinner) 🏽

20P 3🐎 ♪ hunting shooting *xmas*

V ♥ ⚏ ✱ Lunch £12.50-£15 Dinner £20-£22.50 Last dinner 9.30pm

Credit Cards ①②③⑤ⓔ

---

## WINTERBOURNE Avon Map 03 ST68

★★★❀67% **The Grange Resort**

Northwoods BS17 1RP (2m NW of village B4427) (Resort) ☎(0454)777333 FAX (0454) 777447

*Standing in 18 acres of grounds, this constantly improving hotel offers a country atmosphere coupled with good modern facilities including an indoor swimming pool and a conference suite. Chef Richard Barker creates French influenced imaginative food using excellent local produce. Situated one mile from M5 junction 16 on the B4427.*

52⇄��✂in 20 bedrooms CTV in all bedrooms ® T ✱ sB⇄🏽£66-£76 dB⇄🏽£77-£87 (room only) 🏽

⊄100P ✿ CFA ⊠ (heated) sauna solarium gymnasium ballooning clay pigeon shooting ♫ *xmas*

♀ English & Continental V ♥ ⚏ ✱ Lunch £13.50&alc Dinner £17&alc Last dinner 9.30pm

Credit Cards ①②③⑤ⓔ

---

## WINTERBOURNE ABBAS Dorset Map 03 SY69

★★❀64% *Whitefriars*

Copyhold Ln DT2 9LT ☎Martinstown(0305)889206

*Skilfully prepared meals based on good, fresh produce, spacious, well equipped and tastefully appointed bedrooms and a warm, relaxing atmosphere are the attraction of this charming hotel.*

7⇄🏽 CTV in all bedrooms ® T

16P 🚘 ✿ nc12yrs

V ♥ ⚏ Last dinner 9.30pm

Credit Cards ①②③⑤

---

## WINTERINGHAM Humberside Map 08 SE92

❀❀❀ ✕✕✕**Winteringham Fields**

DN15 9PE ☎Scunthorpe(0724)733096 FAX (0724) 733898

*Humberside is not noted for its culinary establishments and the Schwabs must be congratulated for creating what is by any standards a very fine restaurant, which is without equal for very many miles. The carefully restored manor house is in the centre of the charming village. It has a series of low ceilinged rooms with beams, open fires and assorted bric-à-brac. The restaurant is quite formal, with comfortable upholstered chairs and finely laid tables. Annie Schwab is the charming hostess and well groomed staff provide very professional and attentive service. The competent kitchen brigade, under the direction of Chef/Patron Germain Schwab, produce some excellent food. First class produce – fish from Grimsby and locally grown vegetables – are sympathetically handled and cooked to bring out the full flavour. The cooking is modern in its lightness, but the technique is firmly rooted in the classical style.*

Closed Sun, 1st 2wks in Jan & 1st wk Aug Lunch not served Sat & Mon

♀ French & Swiss V 36 seats Last lunch 1.30pm Last dinner 9.30pm 14 P ✂

Credit Cards ①③

---

## WISBECH Cambridgeshire Map 05 TF40

★★65% **Crown Lodge**

Downham Rd, Outwell PE14 8SE ☎(0945)773391 & 772206

*Clever conversion has created a small hotel and leisure centre from a former garage and car showroom on the A1122, close to its junction with the A1101, 5 miles southeast of Wisbech. All 6 well equipped modern bedrooms offer en suite facilities, there is a small Grill Room restaurant with adjoining bar, and leisure facilities include a good gymnasium, two squash courts, two full-size snooker tables and two solariums.*

6⇄🏽 CTV in all bedrooms ® T ⌌ (ex guide dogs) sB&B⇄🏽£31-£35 dB&B⇄🏽£37-£40

65P 🚘 squash snooker sauna solarium gymnasium

♀ International V ♥ ⚏ ✱ Lunch £4.95-£10&alc Dinner £6.95-£12.50&alc Last dinner 10pm

Credit Cards ①③⑤ⓔ

★★64% **Queens**

South Brink PE13 1JJ ☎(0945)583933 Telex no 329197 FAX (0945) 474250

*One of a splendid row of Georgian buildings in the town centre, adjacent to the River Nene, this hotel which has been steadily improved over the years, creates the atmosphere of a Town House in its warm, inviting and comfortable public areas. En suite bedrooms are clean and comfortable, and car parking is available to the rear.*

12⇄🏽Annexe6⇄(3fb)2🌀 CTV in all bedrooms ® T ✱ sB&B⇄🏽£39-£49.50 dB&B⇄🏽£49-£60 🏽

40P ✿ CFA

♀ English & French V ♥ ⚏ ✱ Lunch fr£9.95&alc Dinner fr£9.95&alc Last dinner 10pm

Credit Cards ①②③⑤

★★61% *Orchard House*

5 North Brink PE13 1JR ☎(0945)474559 FAX (0945) 474497

*Behind the Georgian façade of this town-centre building overlooking the River Nene lies a modern and cheerfully run small hotel; accommodation, though modest, offers en suite facilities, while public areas include a choice of restaurants and a small, comfortable lounge.*

18⇄🏽(1fb) CTV in all bedrooms ® T

⊄CTV 6P 4🐎

♀ English & French V ♥ ⚏ Last dinner 10pm

Credit Cards ①③

---

## WISHAW West Midlands Map 07 SP19

★★★★68% **The Belfry**

Lichfield Rd B76 9PR (A446) (De Vere) ☎Curdworth(0675)470301 FAX (0675) 470178

*Close to Birmingham and the National Exhibition Centre, this impressive luxury hotel and leisure complex set in 370 acres of parkland is perhaps best known for its world-class golf course. Major alterations over recent years have provided public areas with every comfort and facility for a wide range of guests and refurbishment of the Jacklin bedroom wing in 1991 will bring all the bedroom blocks up to comparable high standard. Extensive facilities include a health and leisure resort, a night club and a conference centre.*

219⇄(34fb)2🌀✂in 48 bedrooms CTV in all bedrooms ® T ⌌ (ex guide dogs) ✱ sB&B⇄£50-£150 dB&B⇄£60-£170 🏽

Lift ⊄1500P ✿ CFA ⊠ (heated) ▶ 18 ♪ (hard) squash snooker sauna solarium gymnasium archery clay pigeon shooting ⚭ *xmas*

♀ French V ♥ ⚏

Credit Cards ①②③⑤

---

Remember to book early for holiday and bank holiday times.

◉ Shell filling stations (7am–11pm) are marked on the town plans.

**★★★ 50% Moxhull Hall**
Holly Ln B76 9PD (Exec Hotel) ☎021-329 2056 Telex no 333779
*This fine, red-brick house, standing in eight acres of garden and woodland just off the A446, is popular with local families for its leisurely atmosphere and French-style bistro.*
21⇨📞(2fb)1🗏 CTV in all bedrooms ® T sB&B⇨📞£45-£50 dB&B⇨📞£55-£70 🗏
60P ✿ CFA croquet
♀ English & French V ♥ ✳ Lunch £8.95-£9.95&alc Dinner fr£9.95&alc Last dinner 10pm
Credit Cards ①②③⑤

---

**WITHAM** Essex Map **05** TL81

**★★★ 64% Rivenhall Resort**
Rivenhall End CM8 3BH (Resort) ☎(0376)516969
FAX (0376) 513674
*A popular hotel halfway between Chelmsford and Colchester with direct access to the A12. The bedrooms, mostly situated in blocks around the main building are well equipped and comfortable. The wood panelled bar and restaurant offers a choice of table d'hôte and à la carte menus which include traditional roasts. An extensive leisure complex in a recently converted barn houses a smart conference room, indoor pool, squash, mini-gym and beauty room.*
6⇨📞Annexe48⇨📞(3fb)✂in 14 bedrooms CTV in all bedrooms ® T ✳ S% sB⇨📞£51-£61 dB⇨📞£62-£72 (room only) 🗏
《 200P ✿ ▣ (heated) squash sauna solarium gymnasium
♀ English & French V ♥ 𝓛 ✳ S% Lunch £6.30-£11.50 Dinner £14 Last dinner 9.30pm
Credit Cards ①②③⑤

**★★ 59% White Hart**
Newland St CM8 2AF ☎(0376)512245
*At the time of inspection, upgrading was planned for the public areas of this hotel. Bedrooms are compact but nicely appointed and equipped. There is an informal atmosphere, and the staff provide an attentive service. The restaurant enjoys a busy non-resident trade. Located in the busy town centre of Witham, the White Hart is effectively two different operations under one roof; the carvery restaurant in a characterful beamed dining room downstairs; upstair the compact, well equipped bedrooms.*
18⇨📞(1fb)1🗏 CTV in all bedrooms ® T 🏕 (ex guide dogs) 43P
♀ International V ♥ ✂ Last dinner 10pm
Credit Cards ①②③⑤

---

**WITHERSLACK** Cumbria Map **07** SD48

★

**★ ✿🏕 OLD VICARAGE COUNTRY HOUSE**

LA11 6RS ☎(044852)381
Telex no 668230
FAX (044852) 373
*A charming country house in a peaceful setting away from main road traffic. The two-family partnership of Jill and Roger Burrington-Brown and Irene and Stanley Reeve assures a high level of hospitality and a warm, friendly atmosphere. Bedrooms, which vary in size, have been thoughtfully decorated and furnished. Public areas are limited, but cosy and comfortable, with a dining room in 3 sections providing a degree of privacy. Chef Stanley Reeve offers a 6-course set price menu which changes daily. His cooking is simple and sound in a mainly English style. The wine list is exceptional for a small hotel, there are some fine*

*clarets and Burgundies, with a selection of New World wines and a good price range to suit all pockets.*
7⇨📞Annexe5⇨📞1🗏 CTV in all bedrooms ® T ✳ sB&B⇨📞£41-£98 dB&B⇨📞£66-£144 🗏
25P 🚗 ✿ 𝓡 (hard) xmas
✂ ✳ Dinner £26 Last dinner 8pm
Credit Cards ①②③①

---

**WITHYPOOL** Somerset Map **03** SS83

**★★ ✸71% Royal Oak Inn**
TA24 7QP ☎Exford(064383)506 Telex no 46529
FAX (064383) 659
Closed 25 & 26 Dec
*This small and friendly village inn, popular with locals and with visitors to the moor, has two cosy bars with beams and inglenook fireplaces and individually furnished very well equipped bedrooms. The intimate restaurant is highly reputed in the area and both the table d'hôte and à la carte menus feature interesting dishes such as cheesey chicken, all cooked to order using locally produced fresh vegetables, meat and fish; mouthwatering sweets include creamy coffee and rum syllabub and strawberry pavlova. The wine list is well balanced and there is also an extensive bar menu.*
8rm(3⇨3📞)(1fb)1🗏 CTV in all bedrooms ® T ✳ sB&B£30-£39 sB&B⇨📞£39 dB&B£50 dB&B⇨📞£60-£64
20P 🚗 ♪ clay pigeon shooting nc10yrs xmas
♀ English & French V ♥ 𝓛
Credit Cards ①②③⑤

For key to symbols in English see the bookmark.

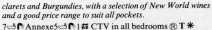

W

★★👤69% **Westerclose Country House**

TA24 7QR 🕿Exford(064383)302

*This hotel, built as a hunting lodge some 60 years ago, overlooks the Exmoor village from 9-acre gardens and paddocks. Guests can take their ease in two comfortable lounges and a Victorian-style conservatory bar, while the carefully prepared and served dishes featured on the dining room's table d'hôte menu make good use of local recipes and ingredients. Bedrooms, which vary in size, include 2 spacious suites on the first floor and 5 cottage-style rooms on the second.*

10⇨🇵(1fb)1🛏 CTV in all bedrooms ® ✳ sB&B⇨🇵£28
dB&B⇨🇵£56-£63 🇵
CTV 15P 🚗 ✿ ✔ ∪ *xmas*
V ✿ ⚓ ✔ ✳ Lunch £11&alc High tea £2-£4.50 Dinner
£21&alc Last dinner 9.30pm
Credit Cards 1 2 3 £

---

## WITNEY Oxfordshire Map **04** SP30

★★★67% **Witney Lodge**

Ducklington Ln OX8 7TS (Consort) 🕿(0993)779777
Telex no 83459 FAX (0993) 703467

*A modern privately owned hotel on the edge of town with easy access to major road networks. The 74 bedrooms offer good facilities for commercial or holiday visitors. A recently opened leisure complex provides an indoor heated pool and gymnasium. The Buttercross Restaurant has a relaxed style of operation and a choice of menus is available for lunch and dinner.*

74⇨(10fb)✔in 8 bedrooms CTV in all bedrooms ® T
✖ (ex guide dogs) ✳ S% sB&B⇨🇵£42-£64 dB&B⇨🇵£52-£72
Continental breakfast 🇵
《 ▦ 120P CFA ⬓ (heated) snooker sauna solarium
gymnasium whirlpool spa *xmas*
V ✿ ⚓ ✔ ✳ S% Lunch £8.50-£10.20&alc High tea fr£3.50
Dinner £9.75-£10.20&alc Last dinner 10pm
Credit Cards 1 2 3 £

---

## WIVELISCOMBE Somerset Map **03** ST02

See also Waterrow

★★

★★❀❀ **LANGLEY HOUSE**

Langley Marsh TA4 2UF (1m
N on unclass rd)
🕿(0984)23318
FAX (0984) 24573

*A charming Georgian house
in well kept grounds where
Peter and Anne Wilson
continue to maintain a very
high standard of comfort and hospitality. Two lounges, with lovely floral displays, are attractively appointed, and the intimate dining room is the setting for Peter Wilson's 5-course menu. Dishes are prepared with skill and care and guests will not be disappointed with the food. An interesting wine list is available, and wines are well chosen and reasonably priced. Charming bedrooms are individually decorated and furnished, all have colour TV, radio, mineral water, fresh flowers and many other thoughtful touches.*

8⇨🇵(1fb)1🛏 CTV in all bedrooms T ✳ S%
sB&B⇨🇵£52.50-£64 dB&B⇨🇵£79-£99.50 🇵
16P 4🚗 (£2.50) 🚗 ✿ croquet 🚲 *xmas*
✿ ⚓ ✔ ✳ S% Dinner £23.50-£26.50 Last dinner 9pm
Credit Cards 1 2 3

---

## WOBURN Bedfordshire Map **04** SP93

★★67% **The Bell Inn**

34 Bedford St MK17 9OD (Best Western) 🕿(0525)290280
FAX (0525) 290017

*The hotel comprises two buildings facing each other across the narrow High Street. The older part houses the pub and beamed restaurant, where a wide range of snacks and meals are served (don't miss the sweet trolley). Above are 6 original rooms and opposite, in a converted Georgian house, is the reception and a small residents' lounge and bar. The majority of the bedrooms are here, all attractively decorated and well maintained, the best are those styled 'executive', they are larger and face the back – the road can be noisy.*

21⇨🇵Annexe6rm(3⇨1🇵)(2fb) CTV in all bedrooms ® T
✖ (ex guide dogs) ✳ sB&B⇨🇵£60-£72.50 dB&B⇨🇵£72.50-
£82 🇵
《 50P 🚗 CFA
♈ English & French V ✿ ✳ Lunch £18.95&alc Dinner
£18.95&alc Last dinner 9.30pm
Credit Cards 1 2 3 5 £

❀❀ ✖✖✖ *Paris House*

Woburn Park MK17 9QP 🕿(0525)290692 FAX (0525) 290471

*A restaurant enjoying a most distinctive and attractive setting within the Woburn estate, overlooking pasture land grazed by Père David deer, is contained in a black and white timbered house originally built in 1878 for the Paris Exhibition. Chef de Cuisine Peter Chandler creates a friendly, welcoming atmosphere in which guests enjoy imaginative dishes in classical French style accompanied by a well chosen wine list introducing many lesser known products.*

Closed Mon & Feb
Dinner not served Sun
♈ French V 50 seats Last lunch 2pm Last dinner 10pm 30 P
Credit Cards 1 2 3 5

❀ ✖✖ *Shalbon*

13 Bedford St MK17 9QB 🕿(0525)290035 & 290071
Closed 25-26 Dec
♈ Indian V Lunch fr£12alc Dinner fr£12alc Last lunch 2.30pm
Last dinner 11pm P
Credit Cards 1 2 3 5

---

## WOKINGHAM Berkshire Map **04** SU86

★★★★63% **Stakis St Anne's Manor**

London Rd RG11 1ST (Stakis) 🕿Reading(0734)772550
Telex no 847342 FAX (0734) 772526

*Set amidst 25 acres of private gardens and grounds, this 19th-century hotel has been sympathetically extended and provides comfortable modern accommodation. There are two restaurants, one offering a carvery and set price menu, the other a more serious à la carte choice. Service is professional and efficient. Although lounge facilities are limited, the bedrooms are spacious. There are good leisure and conference facilities.*

130⇨🇵(30fb)1🛏✔in 10 bedrooms CTV in all bedrooms ® T
sB⇨🇵£110.25-£120.75 dB⇨🇵£128.10-£138.60 (room only)
🇵
Lift 《 ▦ CTV 170P ✿ CFA ⬓ (heated) ♪ (hard) sauna
solarium gymnasium jogging track spa bath steam room *xmas*
♈ English & French V ✿ ⚓ ✔
Credit Cards 1 2 3 4 5

★★★66% **Reading Moat House**

Mill Ln, Sindlesham RG11 5DF (Queens Moat)
🕿Reading(0734)351035 Telex no 846360 FAX (0734) 666530

*A modern hotel adjoining an historic 19th-century mill house in an attractive setting beside the River Loddon nevertheless offers easy access to junction 10 of the M4/A329(M). Well equipped bedrooms furnished in a modern style have 24-hour room service (though it lacks substance), while comfortable public areas include*

**W**

*a small leisure centre, a pub within the old mill, a choice of restaurants and a popular night club.*

96⇌(10fb) CTV in all bedrooms ® **T** S% sB⇌£105-£112 dB⇌£114-£121 (room only) ⊟

Lift ( 350P ✿ CFA sauna gymnasium jacuzzi steam room ♀ International **V** ♦ ⊈ ✱ S% Lunch fr£14.25 Dinner fr£16.50&alc Last dinner 10.30pm

Credit Cards [1] [2] [3] [5] [£]

★★60% *Cantley House*

Milton Rd RG11 5QG ☎(0734)789912 FAX (0734) 774294

*A converted late Victorian manor house, standing in rural surroundings just off the A321 to the north of the town centre, offers accommodation which is well equipped though generally compact; an attractive 17th-century timbered barn adjoining the hotel has been converted into a restaurant, and a team of young staff provides friendly, relaxed service throughout.*

29⇌🅿(2fb)1⊟ CTV in all bedrooms ® **T**

( 70P ✿ ♪ (hard) croquet ♫

♀ English & French **V** ♦ Last dinner 10pm

Credit Cards [1] [2] [3] [5]

---

**WOLVERHAMPTON** West Midlands Map **07** SO99 ◉

See also Himley

★★★60% **Park Hall**

Park Drive, Goldthorn Park WV4 5AJ (2m S off A459) (Jarvis) ☎(0902)331121 Telex no 333546 FAX (0902) 344760

*An 18th-century house, much extended, now offers bedrooms with a good range of modern facilities and a restaurant whose carvery operation and friendly staff make it popular with non-residents as well as residents. The hotel is not easy to find, tucked away as it is in a residential area just off the A459, and it is advisable to ask for directions when booking.*

57⇌🅿(20fb)⅓in 4 bedrooms CTV in all bedrooms ® **T** ✱ sB⇌🅿£26-£64.50 dB⇌🅿£36-£74.50 (room only) ⊟

( 408P ✿ CFA xmas

♀ English & French **V** ♦ ⊈ ✱ Lunch fr£10&alc High tea fr£6.50 Dinner fr£11.50&alc Last dinner 9.45pm

Credit Cards [1] [2] [3] [4] [5]

★★★59% **Mount**

Mount Road, Tettenhall Wood WV6 8HL (2.5m W off A454) (Jarvis) ☎(0902)752055 FAX (0902) 745263

*Set in 4.5 acres of landscaped gardens and located in a rural area, the hotel is nevertheless near enough to the centre of Wolverhampton to be popular with business people.*

49⇌🅿(11fb)⅓in 4 bedrooms CTV in all bedrooms ® **T** ✱ sB⇌🅿fr£74.50 dB⇌🅿fr£85 (room only) ⊟

( 250P ✿ CFA xmas

♀ English & French **V** ♦ ⊈ ✱ Lunch £10.50-£11 Dinner £15&alc Last dinner 9.45pm

Credit Cards [1] [2] [3] [4] [5]

---

**WOOBURN COMMON** Buckinghamshire Map **04** SU98

★★65% *Chequers Inn*

Kiln Ln HP10 0JQ (1m W unclass towards Bourne End) ☎Bourne End(06285)29575 FAX (0628) 850124

*A 17th-century village inn in a quiet rural location, yet within easy reach of major motorways and only 24 miles from central London. While Chequers provides modern facilities, many original features have been retained. Bedrooms are pleasantly furnished with antique pine pieces. The busy bar is popular with locals as is the restaurant which offers interesting à la carte and table d'hôte menus. Food is freshly prepared from quality produce.*

17⇌🅿1⊟ CTV in all bedrooms ® **T** ✖ (ex guide dogs) 60P

♀ English & French **V** ♦ Last dinner 9pm

Credit Cards [1] [2] [3]

**See advertisement under BEACONSFIELD**

**W**

## WOODBRIDGE Suffolk Map 05 TM24 ☺

### ★★★♨ 73% Seckford Hall

IP13 6NU ☎(0394)385678 Telex no 987446 FAX (0394) 380610
Closed 25 Dec

*A 16th-century house, set in 34 acres of beautiful gardens and parkland that contains a lake stocked with trout, stands 200 yards to the left of the A12 as you approach Woodbridge from the Ipswich direction. Privately owned, and retaining such original features as carved and beamed ceilings, oak wall-panels and enormous stone fireplaces, it offers comfortable, well-equipped bedrooms and elegant lounges with some period furniture; recent improvements have added modern family rooms and a swimming pool. International and traditional cuisine is of a consistent standard, and a caring staff provides charming service.*

24➾↑Annexe10➾↑(4fb)5❒ CTV in all bedrooms ® T ✳ S10% sB&B➾↑fr£72 dB&B➾↑£85-£125 ☄
( 200P ✿ CFA ❒ (heated) ▶ 9 ♪ solarium gymnasium spa bath
♀ International V ♥ ♨ S% Lunch £11.50&alc High tea £5.50 Dinner £18-£35alc Last dinner 9.30pm
Credit Cards 1 2 3 5

### ★★ 62% The Crown

2 Thoro'fare IP12 1AD (Forte Hotels) ☎(0394)384242
FAX (0394) 387192

*Ideally situated for the town's centre, quays and waterfront, this former coaching inn retains such traces of its 16th-century origins as the oak beamed restaurant with open fireplace which provides a pleasant setting both for morning coffee and for meals; the menu's varied selection of freshly prepared dishes is served by a delightfully informal but courteous young team of staff.*

20➾↑(2fb)⊬in 4 bedrooms CTV in all bedrooms ® T ✳ S% sB➾↑£60 dB➾↑£70 (room only) ☄
( 40P CFA *xmas*
♀ English & French V ♥ ♨ ⊬ ✳ S% Sunday Lunch £10.23 Dinner £13&alc Last dinner 9pm
Credit Cards 1 2 3 4 5

### ❀✗ The Captain's Table

3 Quay St IP12 1BX ☎(0394)383145

*This well established restaurant, situated between the town and quay, is simply furnished and decorated with marine memorabilia; service is competent and informal. A la carte, table d'hôte and bar menus, complemented by a reasonably priced wine list, feature a full range of fresh fish dishes (with token meat and vegetarian choices), locally caught fish being simply prepared and presented for the most part – though fresh salmon in aspic and lobster thermidor are included.*

Closed Sun & Mon 22 seats P

## WOODFORD BRIDGE Devon Map 02 SS31

### ★★★ 52% Woodford Bridge

Milton Damerel EX22 7LL ☎Milton Damerel(040926)481
FAX (040926) 585

*A 15th-century thatched building, with a thoughtfully planned extension, set in peaceful rural surroundings. Standards of accommodation are modest, but the process of upgrading should be completed in 1991. There are 2 restaurants, a carvery which is open 7 days a week, and a more formal restaurant with restricted opening times in winter. Services are of an acceptable standard, and staff are friendly and helpful.*

12➾↑(1fb) CTV in all bedrooms ® T ✖ (ex guide dogs) ✳ sB&B➾↑£45-£55 dB&B➾↑£70 ☄
( 100P ✿ CFA ❒ (heated) ♪ squash sauna solarium gymnasium table tennis badminton ♫ *xmas*
♀ English & French V ♥ ♨ ⊬ ✳ Lunch £5.95 Dinner £14.95-£16.95 Last dinner 9pm
Credit Cards 1 2 3 5

## WOODFORD GREEN Greater London

See **LONDON plan 1** *F5*(page 435)

### ★★★ 68% Woodford Moat House

Oak Hill IG8 9NY (Queens Moat) ☎081-505 4511
Telex no 264428 FAX 081-506 0941

*This busy purpose-built conference and function hotel is peacefully located on the edge of Epping Forest. There is a spacious lobby, comfortable cocktail bar and pleasant wood-panelled restaurant. Bedrooms are in various wings and all are attractively decorated, spacious and well equipped.*

99➾↑ CTV in all bedrooms ® T ✖ (ex guide dogs) sB&B➾↑£79.50-£82.50 dB&B➾↑£89.50-£92.50 ☄
Lift ( 150P CFA
♀ English & French V ♥ ♨ Lunch £14.80-£15.80&alc Dinner £14.80-£15.80&alc Last dinner 10.15pm
Credit Cards 1 2 3 5 ⓔ

## WOODHALL SPA Lincolnshire Map 08 TF16

### ★★★ 66% Petwood House

Stixwould Rd LN10 6QF (Best Western) ☎(0526)52411
FAX (0526) 53473

*This house is set in quiet surroundings of 30 acres of gardens and mature woodland; formerly the house of Sir Archibald Wiesall, and laterly the officers' mess of the famous 'Dambuster' 617 Squadron during World War II. The hotel is currently undergoing a refurbishment programme to enhance and restore public rooms. The bedrooms are modern, with a good range of facilities and are generally spacious.*

46➾↑(5fb)3❀⊬in 6 bedrooms CTV in all bedrooms ® T ✖ (ex guide dogs) sB&B➾↑£74-£85 dB&B➾↑£85-£95 ☄
Lift ( 80P ✿ CFA snooker croquet bowls boules putting green ♫ *xmas*
♀ English & European V ♥ ♨ ⊬ Lunch £11.50&alc Dinner £14.50&alc Last dinner 9.30pm
Credit Cards 1 2 3 5 ⓔ

## WOODLANDS Hampshire Map 04 SU31

### ★★ 61% Busketts Lawn

174 Woodlands Rd SO4 2GL ☎Ashurst(0703)292272 & 292077
FAX (0703) 292487

*This small relaxing hotel, set in 2 acres of well kept gardens on the edge of the New Forest, has been run by Con, Linda and Damian Hayes for the last 22 years. Simply furnished bedrooms are comfortable and well equipped, food is generous and the atmosphere friendly and informal.*

14➾↑(3fb)1❀ CTV in all bedrooms ® T ✳ sB&B➾↑£30-£33.50 dB&B➾↑£60-£67 ☄
CTV 50P ✿ CFA ⊿ (heated) putting croquet football *xmas*
♀ English & Continental V ♥ ♨ S% Lunch £9.50-£12.50 High tea £5 Dinner £13-£17 Last dinner 8.30pm
Credit Cards 1 2 3 5

**See advertisement under SOUTHAMPTON**

## WOODSTOCK Oxfordshire Map 04 SP41

### ★★★ ❀❀63% Bear

Park St OX7 1SZ (Forte Hotels) ☎(0993)811511
Telex no 837921 FAX (0993) 813380

*This well known, historic inn in the centre of the village has preserved its original character, with dark beams, solid old furniture, copper and pewter ornaments and oil paintings in the public rooms, with a 16th-century staircase, complete with creaking boards, giving access to the roomy, comfortable bedrooms in the main building (some bedrooms are in converted outbuildings around the courtyard). The dining room is full of character, and chef Ian Rhodes, winner of the 1990 Young Chef of the Year Award, offers a menu which preserves a nice balance between the traditional and the modern. Among the appetising dishes noted on our inspection visit were fish soup consisting of an intense broth*

*with sensitively cooked mussels and prawns; juicy snails under a puff-pastry hat with a piquant Pernod sauce, and a moist, marinated guinea fowl with a herb, mushroom and Madeira cream sauce. The menus change periodically.*
33⇆🇳Annexe12⇆🇳(1fb)7🖵✂️in 14 bedrooms CTV in all bedrooms ® T ✳ S% sB⇆🇳£69-£80 dB⇆🇳£79-£110 (room only) 🇭
《 CTV 30P CFA *xmas*
V ✆ 🍷 ✂️ ✳ S% Lunch £14.50&alc Dinner £19.95&alc Last dinner 9.30pm
Credit Cards ①②③④⑤

★★🏵🏵75% **Feathers**
Market St OX7 1SX ☎(0993)812291 FAX (0993) 813158
*The Feathers Hotel is an attractive 17th-century three-storey building with courtyard garden in the centre of Woodstock. Elegance and comfort are major features here, log fires blaze in winter, and bedrooms are nicely furnished, with many thoughtful extras such as mineral waters, magazines, bath gels and shampoos provided. New owners have redecorated the restaurant in warm colours and strong fabrics, and have appointed David Lewis executive chef. The excellent menu features starters such as duck liver parfait and crab and Madeira essence, carefully cooked main courses with good sauces, and puddings ranging from a delicate lemon mousse to sticky toffee pudding.*
17⇆🇳 CTV in all bedrooms T ✳ sB&B⇆🇳£80-£95 dB&B⇆🇳£95-£150 Continental breakfast 🇭
🅿 🖨 *xmas*
V ✆ 🍷 Lunch £17.50-£18.50&alc Dinner £21-£22&alc Last dinner 9.45pm
Credit Cards ①②③⑤

A rosette means exceptional standards of cuisine.

---

WOODY BAY Devon Map 03 SS64

★★77% **Woody Bay**
EX31 4QX ☎Parracombe(05983)264
Closed early Jan-mid Feb RS mid Feb-mid Mar & Nov-Dec
*Set in a magnificent spot overlooking the bay on the edge of Exmoor National Park, this spacious Victorian house offers comfortable bedrooms – many with sea views, a cosy chintzy lounge and imaginative cooking. An interesting feature here is a small sanctuary for injured owls.*
14rm(13⇆🇳)(1fb)2🖵 ® sB&B£26-£38 dB&B⇆🇳£46-£82 🇭
15P 🖨 ❀ ♫ nc8yrs *xmas*
♈ English & French V ✆ 🍷 Bar Lunch £5-£10alc Dinner £16.50-£17&alc Last dinner 8.30pm
Credit Cards ①③

---

WOOFFERTON Shropshire Map 07 SO56

⬦**Forte Travelodge**
(on A49) (Forte) ☎(058472)695 Central Res (0800) 850950
*Situated on the A49 at the A456/B4362 junction, four miles from the town, this lodge offers functional value-for-money accommodation. Meals are available at the adjacent Little Chef.*
32⇆🇳(32fb) CTV in all bedrooms ® sB⇆🇳£29.95 dB⇆🇳£29.95 (room only)
《 32P 🖨
Credit Cards ①②③

---

WOOLACOMBE Devon Map 02 SS44

★★★68% **Watersmeet**
Mortehoe EX34 7EB ☎(0271)870333 FAX (0271) 870890
Closed Dec-mid Feb
*Beautifully situated on the headland of Mortehoe, this hotel has undergone extensive refurbishment to provide individually designed bedrooms which offer a good combination of quality and*
→

---

**W**

comfort. Relaxing public areas include a restaurant with fine panoramic views.

25rm(23⇌3♠)(3fb)1☞ CTV in all bedrooms T ✹ S%
sB&B⇌3♠£45-£74 dB&B⇌3♠£90-£140 (incl dinner) ☐
20P 10☎ ⇪ ❋ CFA ⌲ (heated) ♪ (grass) clay pigeon shooting
♀ English & French V ✿ ♨ ✂ S% Dinner £12.50-£22alc Last dinner 8.30pm
Credit Cards ①②③⑤

### ★★★59% Woolacombe Bay
South St EX34 7BN (Best Western) ☎(0271)870388
Telex no 46761
Closed Jan
Set on the edge of the central village, its 6-acre grounds adjacent to the sands, this hotel provides accommodation in a range of categories which includes some self-catering apartments. The gracious dining room is complemented by Maxwell's Carvery and a public bar, and excellent leisure facilities are available both indoors and out.
59⇌3♠(26fb)1☞ CTV in all bedrooms ® T ✹ (ex guide dogs)
sB&B⇌3♠£52-£103 dB&B⇌3♠£104-£206 (incl dinner) ☐
Lift ℂ CTV 100P ⇪ ❋ CFA ▣(heated) ⌲ (heated) ▸ 9 ♪ (hard) squash sauna solarium gymnasium spa bath masseur short mat bowling ♫ xmas
♀ English & French V ✿ ♨ ✂ Sunday Lunch £8.50 High tea £6.60 Dinner £17&alc Last dinner 9.45pm
Credit Cards ①②③⑤

### ★★68% Little Beach
The Esplanade EX34 7DJ ☎Barnstaple(0271)870398
Closed Nov-Feb
Enjoying a prime position overlooking the bay, the hotel provides well equipped, modern bedrooms and spacious public areas enhanced by good antiques; meals are imaginative and service is friendly throughout.
10rm(4⇌4♠) CTV in all bedrooms ® T sB&B£25.50-£28.25
sB&B⇌♠£25.50-£28.25 dB&B⇌♠£43.50-£69 ☐
8P ⇪ nc7yrs
♀ English & Continental
Credit Cards ①③

### ★★65% Whin Bay
Bay View Rd EX34 7DQ ☎(0271)870475
Maggie and Martin Smith extend a warm welcome to guests at their hotel which enjoys panoramic views across Woolacombe Bay. There is a lively bar and children have a good choice of videos to watch in the lounge. Interesting dishes make up the table d'hôte menu.
16rm(4⇌11♠)(5fb) CTV in all bedrooms ® T
CTV 16P
V ✿ ♨
Credit Cards ①②③

### ★★64% Devon Beach
The Esplanade EX34 7DJ ☎(0271)870449
Closed mid Oct-Etr
This personally-run holiday hotel features a wonderful sun terrace overlooking the sea, some of the sea-facing bedrooms also having balconies. Spacious public areas include a non-smoking lounge and a dining room offering a six-course table d'hôte dinner (with an extensive buffet available on Wednesday evenings during the main season).
36rm(24⇌3)(21fb) CTV in all bedrooms ® ✲ sB&B£30-£35.50
dB&B£60-£75 (incl dinner)
28P 3☎ (£4 per day) CFA ▣(heated) solarium
♀ English, French & Italian ✿ ♨ ✂ Lunch £6-£8 Dinner £10-£14 Last dinner 8.15pm
Credit Cards ①③

### ★★60% Atlantic
Sunnyside Rd EX34 7DG ☎(0271)870469 FAX (0271) 870223
Closed Nov-Feb
Comfortable, friendly, privately owned holiday hotel, overlooking village and bay.
16rm(9⇌3♠)(10fb)✂in 4 bedrooms CTV in all bedrooms ®
CTV 16P ❋ table tennis pool table
♀ English & Continental V ✿ ♨ ✂ Last dinner 7.30pm

### ★70% Crossways
The Esplanade EX34 7DJ ☎(0271)870395
Closed last Sat in Oct-1st Sat in Mar
This cosy hotel which stands in a fine, elevated position overlooking the bay, has been refurbished to a good standard. Public areas include a comfortable themed bar and a quality lounge with fine sea views, while bedrooms, though small, are tastefully decorated and well equipped (some having very good en suite facilities). Guests enjoy good home cooking and the services of particularly friendly and attentive hosts.
9rm(5♠)(5fb) CTV in all bedrooms ® sB&B£15.50-£27
sB&B♠£17.50-£27 dB&B£31-£43 dB&B♠£35-£43 ☐
9P ⇪
✿ ✂

---

## WOOLER Northumberland Map 12 NT92

### ★★55% Tankerville Arms
Cottage Rd NE71 6AD (Minotels) ☎(0668)81581
Closed 22-28 Dec
Reasonable accommodation and polite, friendly service are provided by an old coaching inn standing beside the main road. A good range of both bar and restaurant meals is available.
14rm(6⇌3♠)(1fb) CTV in 9 bedrooms ® sB&B£25
sB&B⇌♠£35 dB&B£42 dB&B⇌♠£58-£65 Continental breakfast ☐
CTV 100P ❋ CFA ⚓
V ✿ ✂ ✳ Sunday Lunch £7.50 High tea £6.50 Dinner £14.75 Last dinner 9pm
Credit Cards ①③

---

## WOOLLEY EDGE MOTORWAY SERVICE AREA (M1)
West Yorkshire Map 08 SE31

### ⌂Granada Lodge
M1 Service Area, West Bretton WF4 4LQ (between junct 38/39, adj to service area) (Granada) ☎Wakefield(0924)830569
FAX (0924) 830609
Situated in the service area between junctions 38 and 39 of the northbound M1 and offering spacious bedrooms with good facilities. Meals are available at the adjacent Country Kitchen restaurant.
31⇌3♠(4fb)✂in 7 bedrooms CTV in all bedrooms ®
✹ (ex guide dogs) S% sB⇌♠fr£31 dB⇌♠fr£34 (room only) ☐
ℂ 168P
V ✿ ♨ ✂
Credit Cards ①②③⑤

---

## WOOTTON

See Wight, Isle of

---

## WORCESTER Hereford & Worcester Map 03 SO85 ●

### ★★★70% Fownes
City Walls Rd WR1 2AP ☎(0905)613151 Telex no 335021
FAX (0905) 23742
Situated beside the canal on the inner ring road and convenient for the city centre shops and cathedral, this hotel has been skilfully converted from Fownes glove factory. Comfortable well equipped bedrooms are attractively decorated and furnished and the appealing public rooms include a restaurant and all-day brasserie.

61⇨🐾(4fb) CTV in all bedrooms ® **T** ✖ (ex guide dogs) ✳
sB⇨🐾£71-£130 dB⇨🐾£85-£130 (room only) 🍴
Lift ℭ 94P CFA sauna gymnasium ♫
🍷 English & French V ⇔ ꞏ𝒫 ✳ Lunch £8.95-£11.25&alc
Dinner £10.50-£14.95&alc Last dinner 9.45pm
Credit Cards ①②③⑤ⓔ

### ★★★61% Star
Foregate St WR1 1EA (Crown & Raven) ☎(0905)24308
Telex no 335075 FAX (0905) 23440
*This popular, busy hotel with its own car park stands within the city centre. Public areas include two bars and both a restaurant and coffee shop, but some bedrooms are so compact as to lack comfort, despite recent refurbishment.*
46⇨🐾(2fb) CTV in all bedrooms ® **T**
Lift ℭ 55P
🍷 English & French V ⇔ ꞏ𝒫 Last dinner 10pm
Credit Cards ①②③

### ★★★57% The Giffard
High St WR1 2QR (Forte Hotels) ☎(0905)726262
Telex no 338869 FAX (0905) 723458
*A modern hotel above a shopping precinct, by a NCP on a small roundabout opposite the cathedral. Bedrooms are compact singles or larger twins/doubles. All are due to undergo a refurbishment programme. Best choices are the higher floors as they offer a splendid roofscape view across the city to the Malverns.*
103⇨🐾(2fb)⚲in 16 bedrooms CTV in all bedrooms ® **T** ✳
S% sB⇨🐾£60 dB⇨🐾£75-£95 (room only) 🍴
Lift ℭ P (£5) CFA snooker *xmas*
🍷 English & International V ⇔ ꞏ𝒫 ⚲ ✳ S% Lunch £7.25&alc
High tea £1.25-£4 Dinner £14&alc Last dinner 10pm
Credit Cards ①②③④⑤

**W**

### ★★65% Loch Ryan Hotel

119 Sidbury Rd WR5 2DH ☎(0905)351143

*A fully restored Georgian house at the edge of town on the London road which leads to junction 7 of the M5. Recent refurbishment work has greatly improved the bedrooms which are quite spacious. To the rear of the hotel is a secluded walled garden, reached by a series of staircases, where children can play safely.*

10⇌🛏(1fb) CTV in all bedrooms ® ✖ sB&B⇌🛏£35-£40 dB&B⇌🛏£50-£60 🏦

CTV 🅿 ✿ ⏚

V 🕭 ⏢ ✔ Lunch £11.50-£13.50alc Dinner £11.50-£13.50alc Last dinner 8pm

Credit Cards ①②③⑤ ⓔ

### ★★62% Diglis Hotel

Riverside, Severn St WR1 2NF ☎(0905)353518

RS 25 Dec night

*A comfortable and friendly hotel in an old house on the banks of the River Severn, close to the cathedral. Bedrooms have good facilities and there are two cosy bars and an upstairs residents' lounge.*

14rm(3⇌)(1fb) CTV in all bedrooms ® ✳ sB&B£32.50-£42.50 sB&B⇌fr£37.50 dB&Bfr£52.50 dB&B⇌fr£62.50 🏦

CTV 60P ✿ CFA ➴

♀ English & French V 🕭 ⏢ ✳ Bar Lunch £1.35-£4.50 Dinner £8.95 Last dinner 9.45pm

Credit Cards ①③

### ★★60% Ye Olde Talbot

Friar St WR1 2NA (Lansbury) ☎(0905)23573 Telex no 333315 FAX (0905) 612760

*This former coaching inn in the city centre partly dates to the 13th-century and offers comfortable accommodation well equipped with modern facilities to meet the needs of business travellers. The cosy dining room offers a simple grill-style menu though our inspectors felt more care could be taken in the preparation and presentation of meals.*

29⇌🛏(6fb)1🖭✔in 3 bedrooms CTV in all bedrooms ® T ✖ (ex guide dogs) ✳ sB&B⇌🛏£27-£60 dB&B⇌🛏£54-£72 🏦 ⓒ8🐾 CFA

♀ English & Continental V 🕭 ⏢ ✳ ✖ Lunch £5.75-£18alc High tea £3-£5alc Dinner £9-£18alc Last dinner 10pm

Credit Cards ①②③⑤ ⓔ

### ★56% Park House

12 Droitwich Rd WR3 7LJ (Guestaccom) ☎(0905)21816 FAX (0905) 612178

*This private hotel, situated on the A38 close to its junction with the A445 and only a short drive from the city centre, is run on a casual, informal basis by its resident proprietors; dating from the late Victorian era, it provides varying standards of accommodation and compact public areas.*

7rm(4🛏)(1fb) CTV in all bedrooms ®

CTV 10P 🖭

V 🕭 ⏢ Last dinner 7.30pm

### ✿✿ ✖✖ Brown's

The Old Cornmill, South Quay WR1 2JN ☎(0905)26263

*Housed in a converted corn mill near the River Severn and only a short walk from the city centre, this restaurant features a fixed-price menu offering a good choice which usually includes one or two 'specials' each day; such dishes as poached pear with a watercress sauce and Roquefort mousse, salmon with a sorrel sauce and gooseberry fool are particularly noteworthy.*

Closed Xmas wk & BH Mon's Lunch not served Sat Dinner not served Sun

♀ English & French 70 seats Last lunch 1.45pm Last dinner 9.45pm 🎗 nc10yrs

Credit Cards ①②③⑤

### WORFIELD Shropshire Map 07 SO79

### ★★★✿✿ 🍴68% Old Vicarage

WV15 5JZ ☎(07464)497 Telex no 35438 FAX (07464) 552

*This Edwardian former parsonage is hidden away in a peaceful hamlet, yet is easily accessible from the A442 and A545. Christine and Peter Iles have carefully restored the property, combining modern comfort with original character. Bedrooms offer an excellent range of facilities. Coach house rooms are particularly spacious, and one has been carefully designed for disabled guests. Chef John Williams presents innovative menus, and the best fresh ingredients are skilfully prepared. Both proprietors and staff work hard to ensure guests' comfort, providing good, old-fashioned levels of hospitality.*

10⇌🛏Annexe4⇌🛏(1fb)1🖭✔in 6 bedrooms CTV in all bedrooms ® T ✳ sB&B⇌🛏£61.50-£72.50 dB&B⇌🛏£76.50-£84.50 🏦

CTV 30P 🖭 ✿ CFA *xmas*

V 🕭 ⏢ ✔ Lunch £16.50 High tea £3.50 Dinner fr£16.50 Last dinner 9pm

Credit Cards ①②③⑤

### WORKINGTON Cumbria Map 11 NX92

### ★★★68% Washington Central

Washington St CA14 3AW ☎(0900)65772 FAX (0900) 68770 Closed 1 Jan

*This modern very well furnished hotel in the town centre offers every comfort, with well equipped bedrooms and cosy lounges and bars. The restaurant and all-day coffee shop provide a good standard of cooking and staff are friendly and helpful.*

40⇌🛏(4fb) CTV in all bedrooms ® T ✖ (ex guide dogs) ✳ sB&B⇌🛏£46-£57 dB&B⇌🛏£67.50-£75 🏦

Lift ⓒ 50P CFA ♫

V 🕭 ⏢ ✔ ✳ Lunch fr£9 Dinner fr£12.95&alc Last dinner 9.30pm

Credit Cards ①②③

### ★★★62% The Hunday Manor

Hunday CA14 4JF ☎(0900)61798 FAX (0900) 601202

14⇌🛏 CTV in all bedrooms ® T ✳ sB&B⇌🛏fr£46.50 dB&B⇌🛏fr£61.50 (incl dinner) 🏦

60P 🖭 ✿ ♪ (grass)

♀ English & Continental V 🕭 ✳ Lunch fr£6.95alc Dinner £5-£20alc Last dinner 10pm

Credit Cards ①②③⑤

### ★★57% Crossbarrow Motel

Little Clifton CA14 1XS (3m E on A595) ☎(0900)61443

*Situated in open countryside on the A595 near the A66 junction, this friendly motel comprises a main house with cosy public areas and purpose-built functional bedroom blocks to the rear.*

Annexe27⇌🛏 CTV in all bedrooms ® T

50P ✿ ⏚

V 🕭 ⏢ Last dinner 8.30pm

Credit Cards ①③

### WORKSOP Nottinghamshire Map 08 SK57

### ★★74% Lion

112 Bridge St S80 1HT ☎(0909)477925 FAX (0909) 479038

*Car parking is available behind this town-centre coaching inn near the market place (ask directions on booking); redevelopment and extension of the original 16th-century building has created a small hotel offering modern accommodation and high levels of service. Bedrooms are generally spacious – the Executive being particularly roomy – and all are well equipped with good bathrooms. A Fitness Room is available for the exclusive use of residents.*

30⇌🛏(3fb) CTV in all bedrooms ® T ✳ sB&B⇌🛏£40-£45 dB&B⇌🛏£50-£60 🏦

ⓒ ⊞ sauna solarium gymnasium

♥ French **V** ✿ ♨ ✳ Lunch fr£6.95 Dinner fr£14.50&alc Last dinner 10pm
Credit Cards [1][2][3][5]

### ★★ 61% Regancy
Carlton Rd S80 1PS ☎(0909)474108 FAX (0909) 479398
*A busy family run commercial hotel on the edge of town adjacent to a railway line. The hotel has a popular restaurant where friendly local staff serve reasonably priced meals.*
13rm(7🖕)(1fb) CTV in all bedrooms ® **T** ✳ sB&B£21-£26 sB&B🖕£26 dB&B£32-£42 dB&B🖕£42
CTV 25P 5🍴 🚗 sauna solarium gymnasium
**V** ✳ Lunch £4.50&alc Dinner £6.50-£7.50&alc Last dinner 8pm
Credit Cards [1][2][3][5]

### ⛫ Forte Travelodge
Dunkeries Mill(on A57) (Forte) ☎Central Res (0800) 850950
*Conveniently situated on the outskirts of town, on the roundabout junction of the A60/A57, with access only from St Annes Drive on the same roundabout, the Lodge is adjacent to a Little Chef Restaurant.*
40🛏🖕(40fb) CTV in all bedrooms ® sB🛏🖕£29.95 dB🛏🖕£29.95 (room only)
( 40P 🚗
Credit Cards [1][2][3]

### ○ Clumber Park
Clumber Park S80 3PA (Lansbury) ☎Mansfield(0623)835333
Open
48🛏🖕

---

## WORMIT Fife Map 11 NO32

### ★★ 58% The Sandford
DD6 8RG ☎Newport-on-Tay(0382)541802 FAX (0382) 542136
*Located 3 miles south of the Tay Road Bridge, this well-established hotel is popular with both businessmen and tourists. The public rooms have a homely atmosphere and the practical modern bedrooms are well equipped.*
16🛏🖕(3fb) CTV in all bedrooms ® **T** S10% sB&B🛏🖕fr£70 dB&B🛏🖕£85-£115 🅿
CTV 50P ✿ ♬ (hard) ✈ shooting *xmas*
♥ Scottish & Continental **V** ✿ ♨ ✳ Lunch £8.50-£11.75 High tea £5.40-£9.25 Dinner £19.35-£21.75 Last dinner 9.30pm
Credit Cards [1][2][3][5] ⓔ

---

## WORSLEY Greater Manchester Map 07 SD70

### ★★★ 57% Novotel Manchester West
Worsley Brow M28 4YA (adjacent to M62 junc 13)
☎061-799 3535 Telex no 669586 FAX 061-703 8207
*Conveniently placed for the motorway network, this purpose-built hotel offers clean functional accommodation and is a popular venue for business conferences. The restaurant, part of an open-plan area, operates from 6am to midnight.*
119🛏🖕(119fb)½in 20 bedrooms CTV in all bedrooms ® **T**
Lift 133P ✿ CFA ⌇ (heated)
♥ English & French **V** ✿ ♨ ½ Last dinner mdnt
Credit Cards [1][2][3][5]

---

## WORTHING West Sussex Map 04 TQ10

Telephone numbers are liable to change during the currency of this guide.

### ★★★ 67% Beach
Marine Pde BN11 3QJ ☎(0903)34001 FAX (0903) 34567
*In an excellent seafront position, this welcoming family-run hotel has traditionally furnished well equipped bedrooms with bathrooms that have recently been completely refurbished. A spacious comfortable lounge offers a full service.*
80🛏🖕(8fb) CTV in all bedrooms ® **T** ✖ sB&B🛏🖕£46-£52.75 dB&B🛏🖕£69.50-£79.50 🅿

Lift ( 55P 🚗 CFA nc8yrs *xmas*
**V** ✿ ♨ Lunch fr£11.75&alc Dinner fr£16.50&alc Last dinner 8.45pm
Credit Cards [1][2][3][4][5]

### ★★★ 58% Chatsworth
Steyne BN11 3DU ☎(0903)36103 due to change to 236103 FAX (0903) 823726
*A Georgian hotel overlooking Steyne Gardens and the sea. Bedrooms may look rather dated but are well equipped, and there are leisure facilities and a range of meeting rooms that cater well for the conference user.*
107🛏🖕(5fb) CTV in all bedrooms ® **T** sB&B🛏🖕£62 dB&B🛏🖕£77 🅿
Lift ( 🚗 CFA snooker games room *xmas*
♥ English & Continental **V** ½ Lunch £10&alc Dinner £15&alc Last dinner 8.30pm
Credit Cards [1][2][3][5] ⓔ

### ★★★ 57% Kingsway
Marine Pde BN11 3QQ ☎(0903)37542 due to change to 237542 FAX (0903) 204173
*The seafront position and the personal supervision of the Howlett family make this hotel a popular choice. Bedrooms are constantly being upgraded and offer reasonable comfort. There is a choice of 2 cosy lounges, a small bar with a buttery menu, and the restaurant which provides a choice of carvery or à la carte menus. There is a small car park at the side.*
28🛏🖕(1fb) CTV in all bedrooms ® **T** sB&B🛏🖕£43.50-£55 dB&B🛏🖕£57.40-£65 🅿
Lift ( 12P 🚗 CFA *xmas*
♥ English & French **V** ✿ ♨ Lunch fr£4.60&alc Dinner fr£13.95&alc Last dinner 9pm
Credit Cards [1][2][3][5] ⓔ

**W**

**★★64% Cavendish**
115/116 Marine Pde BN11 3QG (Minotels) ☎(0903)36767
FAX (0903) 823840
*Ideally placed on the seafront within easy reach of the town centre, this welcoming family-run hotel has been completely refurbished and provides very well equipped bedrooms, those on the front being particularly spacious. Cooking standards are reliable and skilful, and conference facilities are also available.*
17rm(14⇌🚿)(1fb) CTV in all bedrooms ® T
✗ (ex guide dogs) sB&Bfr£24.75 sB&B⇌🚿£39 dB&B⇌🚿£65
▤
☾ CTV 4P ⛟ CFA
☋ English & Continental V ♧ ✱ Lunch fr£7.75 Dinner fr£9.50
Last dinner 9pm
Credit Cards [1] [2] [3] [5] £

**★★62% Windsor House**
14/20 Windsor Rd BN11 2LX ☎(0903)39655 FAX (0903) 210763
*A personally run hotel situated in a peaceful residential area, yet only 100 yards from the beach, which has been extensively refurbished to provide a range of bright, comfortable and well equipped bedrooms with en suite facilities, and improvements are continuing. Public areas include a comfortable bar, foyer lounge and carvery restaurant, and there is a small garden area to the rear.*
30⇌🚿(7fb)1⊞✗in 4 bedrooms CTV in all bedrooms ® T
✗ (ex guide dogs) sB&B⇌🚿£42.50-£46 dB&B⇌🚿£69-£90 ▤
CTV 18P CFA *xmas*
☋ English & French V ♧ ☐ Sunday Lunch fr£12.95 High tea fr£3.50 Dinner £11.50-£13.50&alc Last dinner 9.30pm
Credit Cards [1] [3] [5] £

**★★59% *Ardington***
Steyne Gardens BN11 3DZ ☎(0903)30451
Closed Xmas
*This family-run commercial hotel conveniently close to the Promenade comprises a choice of well equipped modern bedrooms (the best of which have recently been upgraded), a comfortable bar lounge, several conference/meeting rooms and a restaurant where the proprietors' involvement maintains good standards. Room service is available.*
55rm(22⇌22🚿)(4fb) CTV in all bedrooms ® T
☾ 16P
☋ International ♧ ☐ Last dinner 8.30pm
Credit Cards [1] [2] [3] [5]

## WREXHAM Clwyd Map 07 SJ34

See also Marchwiel and Marford

**★★★64% *Llwyn Onn Hall***
Cefn Rd LL13 0NY (Welsh Rarebits) ☎(0978)261225
*Though only a mile south-east of the town centre, this privately owned hotel – built in the early 18th century as a gentleman's residence – stands in extensive grounds surrounded by peaceful countryside. Its well equipped bedrooms are equally suitable for tourists and business visitors to the nearby industrial estate.*
13⇌🚿1⊞ CTV in all bedrooms T
70P
V ♧ ☐ Last dinner 9pm
Credit Cards [1] [2] [3] [5]

**★★★63% *Wynnstay Arms***
High Street/Yorke St LL13 8LP (Consort) ☎(0978)291010
Telex no 61674 FAX (0978) 362138
*Behind this centrally-located establishment's Georgian façade lies a large, busy and modern hotel whose attractive public areas and well equipped bedrooms are popular with both holidaymakers and business clients.*
75⇌🚿(8fb)✗in 4 bedrooms CTV in all bedrooms ® T
Lift ☾ CTV 50P 20🚘
V ♧ ☐ ✗ Last dinner 9.45pm
Credit Cards [1] [2] [3] [5]

**⌂ Forte Travelodge**
Wrexham By Pass, Rhostyllen LL14 4EJ (4m S, at A483/A5152 roundabout) (Forte) ☎(0978)365705
Central Res (0800) 850950
*A purpose-built hotel conveniently situated at the A438/A5152 junction, 3 miles south of the town, offers well equipped modern accommodation which includes one room designed for disabled guests; meals are provided at an adjacent Little Chef restaurant.*
32⇌🚿(32fb) CTV in all bedrooms ® sB⇌🚿£29.95
dB⇌🚿£29.95 (room only)
☾ 31P ⛟
Credit Cards [1] [2] [3]

## WRIGHTINGTON Lancashire Map 07 SD51

**★★★65% Wrightington Hotel & Restaurant**
Moss Ln WN6 9PB (Mount Charlotte (TS))
☎Standish(0257)425803 FAX (0257) 425830
*Set in rural surroundings just off junction 27 of the M6, this well furnished hotel has extensive leisure facilities plus conference and banqueting rooms. Bedrooms, particularly those in the new wing, are very well equipped.*
47⇌(4fb) CTV in all bedrooms ® T ▤
☾ 80P CFA ▭ (heated) squash sauna solarium gymnasium
☋ International V ♧ ☐ ✱ Lunch £8.45-£9.95&alc High tea fr£2.50 Dinner £12.95-£13.50&alc Last dinner 10pm
Credit Cards [1] [2] [3] [5]

**❀❀ ✕✕✕ High Moor**
Highmoor Ln WN6 9QA (junct 27 off M6, take B5239)
☎Appley Bridge(02575)2364
(Rosettes awarded for dinner only)
*Off the beaten track but within easy reach of the M6, Highmoor is a character, cottage-style restaurant, with exposed beams and a cosy lounge. Imaginative dishes are offered on an à la carte menu, including delights such as scallop tart with stir-fried vegetables and ginger and oyster sauce as a starter, followed by boned and roasted guinea fowl with a stuffing of cabbage, mushrooms, smoked bacon and juniper with a port wine sauce. The sweets are attractively presented and include a combination of lemon crème brûlée, orange cream caramel and grapefruit salad, served together; or white chocolate parfait with apricot sauce. Coffee and petits fours conclude the meal.*
Lunch not served Mon-Sat
☋ English & French V 80 seats Sunday Lunch fr£10.75 Dinner £19-£27alc Last lunch 1.45pm Last dinner 9.45pm 35 P
Credit Cards [1] [2] [3] [5]

## WROTHAM Kent Map 05 TQ65

**★★★64% Forte Posthouse Maidstone/Sevenoaks**
London Rd, Wrotham Heath TN15 7RS (Forte Hotels)
☎Borough Green(0732)883311 Telex no 957309
FAX (0732) 885850
*This attractive, purpose-built hotel bordered by National Trust land stands conveniently close to junction 24 of the M26. Guests can relax in spacious lounges of considerable comfort and a pleasant bar area – or perhaps make use of the busy leisure club's facilities to work off the carvery or simple à la carte meals enjoyed in Trader's Restaurant – while bedrooms are well appointed and usefully equipped.*
119⇌🚿(16fb)✗in 35 bedrooms CTV in all bedrooms ® T ✱
S% sB⇌🚿£39.50-£49.50 dB⇌🚿£39.50-£49.50 (room only) ▤
☾ 110P CFA ▭ (heated) sauna solarium gymnasium health & fitness centre *xmas*
V ♧ ☐ ✗ ✱ S% Lunch £9.50-£13.95&alc Dinner £13.95&alc
Last dinner 11pm
Credit Cards [1] [2] [3] [4] [5]

For key to symbols in English see the bookmark.

W

WROXHAM Norfolk Map **09** TG31

★★★63% **Broads**

Station Rd NR12 8UR ☎Norwich(0603)782869
FAX (0603) 784066

*A centrally situated hotel run by the Bales family who extend a
warm welcome to their guests. Popular with both commercial
visitors and holidaymakers the hotel provides comfortable
accommodation and a variety of well-cooked dishes.*

21 ⇨🛏 Annexe7 ⇨🛏 (1fb) CTV in all bedrooms ® **T**
sB&B ⇨🛏 fr£34 dB&B ⇨🛏 £45-£55 🏥

40P ♫ *xmas*

♡ English & French **V** ♥ ⚲ ✱ Lunch £7-£10.50 Dinner £9-
£10.50&alc Last dinner 9.30pm

Credit Cards ① ② ③ ⑤ ⑥

★★62% **Hotel Wroxham**

Hoveton NR12 8AJ ☎(0603)782061 FAX (0603) 784279

*This is an hotel in an enviable setting right on the Broads, at the
heart of a town popular with boating enthusiasts, and offering quite
serviceable but well equipped bedrooms, a restaurant which
supplements its reasonably priced table d'hôte menu with an à la
carte selection of dishes, and a bar serving meals and snacks;
public areas which accommodate the extremely busy seasonal
trade are adapted to commercial use out of season.*

18rm(14 ⇨🛏)(2fb) CTV in all bedrooms ® **T** ✱ sB&B£30-£48
sB&B ⇨🛏 £48-£58 dB&B£44-£68 dB&B ⇨🛏 £58-£68 🏥

CTV 55P CFA ⏌ boating facilities ♫ *xmas*

♡ English & French **V** ♥ ⚲ ✱ Lunch £4.25-£7.25&alc
High tea £3.60 Dinner £9.50&alc Last dinner 9.30pm

Credit Cards ① ② ③ ⑤

★62% **Kings Head**

Station Rd NR12 8UR (Chef & Brewer) ☎(0603)782429

6 ⇨🛏(2fb) CTV in all bedrooms ® **T** ✘ (ex guide dogs)
sB&B ⇨🛏 £43 dB&B ⇨🛏 £51 🏥

50P CFA

♡ International **V** ♥ ⚲ ✱ Bar Lunch £2.95-£5.50alc

Credit Cards ① ② ③ ⑤

WROXTON Oxfordshire Map **04** SP44

★★★71% **Wroxton House**

OX15 6QB (Best Western) ☎Banbury(0295)730482 & 730777
FAX (0295) 730800

*A part-thatched 17th-century property built in attractive local
stone and situated just 2 miles northwest of Banbury, between
Oxford and Stratford-on-Avon, Wroxton House provides
accommodation in smartly designed and well equipped bedrooms,
those in the main building retaining such original features as huge
open fireplaces, exposed stone walls and a wealth of beams. A good
mix of new and old is also achieved in the comfortably appointed
public areas with their open fires and partially flagstoned floors;
they include a bright, airy conservatory-style lounge/foyer and a
formal dining room providing a range of dishes which are skilfully
prepared from good fresh local produce with seasonal vegetables
and herbs. Staff with a professional air are friendly, helpful and
pleasant.*

28 ⇨🛏 Annexe3 🛏 1 🛏 CTV in all bedrooms ® **T** ✱
sB&B ⇨🛏 £55-£75 dB&B ⇨🛏 £65-£95 🏥

《 40P 🚗 ✿ CFA *xmas*

♡ English & Continental **V** ♥ ⚲ ✱ ✱ Lunch £15.50&alc
Dinner £15.50&alc Last dinner 9.30pm

Credit Cards ① ② ③ ⑤ ⑥

**See advertisement under BANBURY**

**W**

**WYKEHAM (NEAR SCARBOROUGH)** North Yorkshire
Map **08** SE98

### ★★65% Downe Arms
YO13 9QB ☎Scarborough(0723)862471 Telex no 527192
FAX (0723) 864329
*Attractive accommodation, an informally friendly atmosphere and good value menus are among the attractions of this charming old inn.*
10⇥♠(2fb) CTV in all bedrooms ® T ✱ sB&B⇥♠£25.75
dB&B⇥♠£51.50 ⊟
CTV 150P 2☎ ❊ shooting *xmas*
♀ English & French V ♥ ⚑ ✱ Sunday Lunch £7.95-£8.50
Dinner £12.75-£13.75 Last dinner 9pm
Credit Cards ①②③⑤

---

**WYMONDHAM** Norfolk Map **05** TG10

### ★★65% Abbey
Church St NR18 0PH (Best Western) ☎(0953)602148
FAX (0953) 606247
*Quietly situated by the Abbey a few minutes walk from the town centre, this recently refurbished hotel provides all modern comforts and facilities while retaining some historic features. There is a cosy bar and lounge, and staff are attentive to the needs of commercial or leisure users.*
25⇥♠Annexe1rm(3fb) CTV in all bedrooms ® T
sB&B⇥♠£43-£54 dB&B⇥♠£63-£74 ⊟
Lift ⊄ 3P CFA *xmas*
V ♥ ⚑ Lunch £7-£8 Dinner £13-£13.50&alc Last dinner 9.30pm
Credit Cards ①②③⑤ ⓔ

### ★★64% *Sinclair*
28 Market St NR18 0BB ☎(0953)606721 FAX (0953) 601361
*A friendly, family-run hotel with comfortable and well equipped bedrooms. In the centre of the town, the Sinclair has the advantage of its own small rear car park and a public car park next door.*
20⇥♠(2fb)1🛏⚋in 12 bedrooms CTV in all bedrooms ® T ✼
8P ❊ sauna
V ♥ ⚑ Last dinner 9.30pm
Credit Cards ①②③

---

**WYRE PIDDLE** Hereford & Worcester Map **03** SO94

### ★★62% *Avonside*
Main Rd WR10 2JB (2m NE on B4084) ☎Pershore(0386)552654
*A small, family-run hotel in the village of Wyre Piddle, close to Pershore. Rooms are very well equipped with modern facilities and the comfortable lounge overlooks the River Avon. The hotel has an outdoor swimming pool.*
7⇥♠(3fb) CTV in all bedrooms ® T ✼
10P 🚗 ❊ ⚌ (heated) ✔ nc7 yrs
♀ English & French Last dinner 7.30pm
Credit Cards ①③

---

**YARCOMBE** Devon Map **03** ST20

### ★★69% The Belfry Hotel
EX14 9BD (Minotels) ☎Upottery(040486)234 & 588
FAX (040486) 579
*Built in 1872 as the village school, and still retaining some original features, this hotel beside the A30 on the edge of the village offers easy access to Honiton, Chard and the whole of East Devon. Recently refurbished, it provides accommodation in 6 comfortably appointed and well equipped en suite rooms; compact, intimate public areas include a wood-panelled dining room with open fire and bar featuring a choice of table d'hôte and à la carte menus. Friendly proprietors are on hand to welcome guests and provide personal service.*
6⇥♠(1fb) CTV in all bedrooms ® T ✼ (ex guide dogs)
sB&B⇥♠£42-£44 dB&B⇥♠£64-£68 ⊟

10P 🚗 nc12yrs *xmas*
♀ English & French V ♥ ⚑ ✔ ✱ Lunch £9.50&alc Dinner £15.95-£21.45 Last dinner 8.45pm
Credit Cards ①②③⑤ ⓔ

---

**YARMOUTH, GREAT** Norfolk Map **05** TG50

### ★★★71% *Cliff*
Gorleston NR31 6DH (2m S A12) (Best Western)
☎Great Yarmouth(0493)662179 Telex no 975608
FAX (0493) 653617
*Overlooking sea and estuary from a prominent position adjacent to beaches, yet offering easy access to the town centre, this unpretentious hotel features spaciously comfortable and tastefully furnished public rooms with a choice of bars. Accommodation is varied, new and very attractive rooms (which will include a suite) supplementing older ones which have, for the most part, been refurbished. An involved proprietor and loyal team of staff provide both an instant welcome and a genuinely friendly atmosphere.*
30⇥♠(5fb)🛏⚋in 2 bedrooms CTV in all bedrooms T
⊄ 70P ❊ ⚋
V ♥ ⚑ ✔ Last dinner 9.30pm
Credit Cards ①②③⑤

### ★★★66% Carlton
Marine Pde NR30 3JE (Consort)
☎Great Yarmouth(0493)855234 Telex no 975642
FAX (0493) 852220
*The Carlton Hotel has just completed a total refurbishment and now offers comfortable public rooms, and modern accommodation that is particularly well equipped. A good range of services – a blend of the formal and informal – are readily provided in a polite and efficient manner, suitable for both the holidaymaker and business guest.*
95⇥♠(10fb)4🛏 CTV in all bedrooms ® T sB&B⇥♠£56.10
dB&B⇥♠£78.65-£90.20 ⊟
Lift ⊄ CTV 30P 30☎ (£3) CFA hairdressing salon *xmas*
V ♥ ⚑ Sunday Lunch £7.90 Dinner £17.90&alc Last dinner 9.30pm
Credit Cards ①②③④⑤

### ★★★ ❀62% Imperial
North Dr NR30 1EQ ☎Great Yarmouth(0493)851113
FAX (0493) 852229
*An imposing Victorian hotel overlooking the sea on North Beach, the quieter side of this popular resort. The recently refurbished public areas are a vast improvement and now include stylish lounge areas. The Mobbs family combine competent service with friendly hospitality, and always strive to improve. The Rambouillet Restaurant continues to provide well prepared fresh dishes with a choice of 3 menus, which are good value and suit all tastes. Accommodation, while modest, is modern and well equipped.*
39⇥♠(4fb) CTV in all bedrooms ® T ✱ sB&B⇥♠fr£51
dB&B⇥♠fr£65.30 ⊟
Lift ⊄ CTV 50P CFA *xmas*
♀ English & French V ♥ ⚑ ✱ Lunch fr£10.50 Dinner fr£15.50 Last dinner 10pm
Credit Cards ①②③④⑤

### ★★★60% Meridian Dolphin
Albert Square NR30 3JH ☎Great Yarmouth(0493)855070
Telex no 975037 FAX (0493) 853798
*Informally run by a friendly and competent team, and offering attractively furnished, well equipped accommodation, the hotel is quietly situated despite its proximity to the main sea front attractions.*
49⇥♠(3fb) CTV in all bedrooms ® T ✱ S% sB&B⇥♠£49-£75 dB&B⇥♠£65-£85 ⊟
⊄ CTV 12P 12☎ ❊ CFA ⚋ (heated) sauna gymnasium whirlpool *xmas*
♀ English & French V ♥ ⚑ ✱ Bar Lunch £1.50-£7.50 Dinner fr£10.25&alc Last dinner 9.30pm
Credit Cards ①②③⑤ ⓔ

★★64% **Burlington**
11 North Dr NR30 1EG ☎Great Yarmouth(0493)844568 &
842095
Closed Jan-Feb RS Dec
*This traditional, family-owned, resort hotel stands at the quieter*
*end of the sea front; bedrooms are steadily being improved to offer*
*good modern facilities, and some have fine sea views. Leisure*
*amenities include a swimming pool, steam room and solarium.*
27rm(25⇨♠)(9fb)⊬in 5 bedrooms CTV in all bedrooms ® T
✠ (ex guide dogs) sB&B£25-£35 sB&B⇨♠£37.50-£50
dB&B⇨♠£55-£70 ⊟
Lift CTV 40P CFA ⊠ (heated) sauna solarium gymnasium
jacuzzi turkish steam room *xmas*
♀ English & French V ♥ ⏛ ✱ Sunday Lunch £8-£9 Dinner
£10-£15 Last dinner 8pm
Credit Cards ①②③ⓔ

★★★64% **Regency**
5 North Dr NR30 1ED ☎(0493)843759 FAX (0493) 330411
13⇨♠(1fb) CTV in all bedrooms ® T ✠ ✱ sB&B⇨♠£29-
£30 dB&B⇨♠frf46
CTV 10P 🚗 nc10yrs *xmas*
⊬ ✱ Dinner £8.50&alc
Credit Cards ①②③⑤

---

★★❀❀73% **Royal Oak**
The Square RG16 0UF ☎Hermitage(0635)201325
FAX (0635) 201926
*The opportunity to purchase the inn she had previously managed*
*was a dream come true for new proprietor Julie Huff. It is set*
*among a row of cottages in the square of this pretty village between*
*Newbury and Reading, with easy access to the M4. Five bedrooms*
*have been well decorated and finished, and great attention has*
*been given to guests' comfort. Thoughtful extras such as*
*magazines, mineral waters, toothpicks and quality toiletries are*
*provided in addition to the usual facilities. The bar has a friendly*
*and relaxed atmosphere which extends to the cosy lounge where a*
*log fire blazes during colder months; in good weather the walled*
*garden is popular. The intimate restaurant is the setting for the*
*imaginative cooking of Chef Dominique Orizot whose interesting*
*menus are also available in the bar. Delicious starters include a*
*subtly flavoured hot cheese soufflé served with a creamy wild*
*mushroom sauce. A main dish of duck breast cooked nicely pink*
*was served with a rich sauce of calvados and apple and a selection*
*of fresh vegetables. The mouthwatering desserts are a real treat,*
*particularly a chocolate charlotte of mousse surrounded by sponge*
*and served with an orange sauce and candied orange peel.*
5rm(3⇨) CTV in all bedrooms T ✱ sB&B⇨♠£60-£70
dB&B⇨♠£70-£80 ⊟
40P 🚗 ❀
♀ English & French V ♥ ⏛ ✱ Lunch £20-£30alc Dinner £25-
£30alc Last dinner 10pm
Credit Cards ①②③④⑤

---

★★★69% **Moorland Links**
PL20 6DA (Forestdale) ☎(0822)852245 Telex no 45616
FAX (0822) 855004
Closed 24 Dec-2 Jan
*Set in nine acres of grounds with breathtaking views across the*
*Tamar Valley this hotel provides attractive public areas and*
*tastefully decorated bedrooms. Conference facilities are also*
*available.*
30⇨♠✠⊬in 5 bedrooms CTV in all bedrooms ® T ✱
sB&B⇨♠£41-£62 dB&B⇨♠£52-£77.50 ⊟

⟨ 120P ❀ CFA ♪ (hard)
♀ English & French V ♥ ⏛ ⊬ ✱ Lunch £10.25&alc Dinner
fr£18.50&alc Last dinner 10pm
Credit Cards ①②③⑤ⓔ

---

★★★64% **The Manor**
Hendford BA20 1TG (Forte Hotels) ☎(0935)23116
FAX (0935) 706607
*A town-centre hotel, parts of which date back to the 17th century,*
*has recently refurbished its comfortable lounge and bar areas. The*
*Eliot Restaurant supplements imaginative table d'hôte menus with*
*a short à la carte selection of dishes, bedrooms in a variety of styles*
*and sizes are all well equipped, and staff are friendly and obliging.*
*To reach the hotel, follow signs for town centre and Octagon*
*Theatre.*
20⇨♠Annexe21⇨♠(2fb)1⊞⊬in 11 bedrooms CTV in all
bedrooms ® T ✱ sB⇨♠£42-£70 dB⇨♠£55-£85 (room only)
⊟
⟨ 41P CFA *xmas*
V ♥ ⏛ ⊬ ✱ Lunch £8.95&alc Dinner £13.95&alc Last dinner
10pm
Credit Cards ①②③⑤

---

★★★64% **Yeovil Court**
West Coker Rd BA20 2NE ☎(093586)3746 FAX (093586) 3990
*This attractive modern hotel, set beside the Chard-Crewkerne road*
*at the edge of the town, offers a friendly, informal atmosphere.*
*Though some rooms are compact, the well equipped*
*accommodation includes three annexe bedrooms with their own*
*lounge areas, while Suite D is split-level, with a half tester bed*
*under the rafters. A spacious restaurant serves a well balanced à la*
*carte menu, and the bar area is relaxing and comfortable.*
15⇨♠Annexe3⇨♠(4fb) CTV in all bedrooms ® T ✱
sB&B⇨♠£49-£60 dB&B⇨♠£59-£85 ⊟

→

**Y**

75P ✤ CFA *xmas*

♈ English & French **V** ✿ ⚑ ✳ Lunch £7.50-£9.50&alc Dinner £9-£16.50alc Last dinner 10pm

Credit Cards ①②③⑤ⓔ

★★★57% *Four Acres*

West Coker BA22 9AJ (3m W A30) ☎West Coker(093586)2555 Telex no 46666

*An 18th-century stone house, set back from the A30 Yeovil to Crewkerne road in its own gardens, supplements the individually furnished and decorated accommodation in its main building with a modern wing of identically coordinated bedrooms. The spacious Bingham Restaurant offers an imaginative à la carte menu.*

20rm(16⇆3♠)Annexe5⇆ CTV in all bedrooms ®

✝ (ex guide dogs)

40P 5🛏 ⚐ ✤ pool table

♈ French **V** ✿ ⚑ Last dinner 9.30pm

Credit Cards ①②③⑤

★❀❀77% **Little Barwick House**

Barwick Village BA22 9TD ☎(0935)23902

Closed 22 Dec-6 Jan

*Christopher and Veronica Colley provide a warm welcome for guests in their well kept and comfortable Georgian listed dower house. The 6 spacious en suite bedrooms are nicely appointed, and thoughtful touches include mineral water and fresh flowers. Fine cuisine is a feature here, and Veronica Colley has gained widespread commendation for her interesting 4-course dinners, carefully prepared from good fresh ingredients. She makes extensive use of fish, game and other local produce, and a realistically priced wine list complements the menu. Our inspector enjoyed tender and succulent lamb cutlets, served with a creamy sauce with julienne of cucumber and chopped fresh mint. An endless pot of coffee with chocolate fudge completes the enjoyable and satisfying meals.*

6⇆♠ CTV in all bedrooms ® **T** ✳ S% sB&B⇆♠fr£45 dB&B⇆♠£69-£103 ⊟

P ⚐ ✤

♈ English & French **V** ✂ ✳ Dinner £19.90-£21.90 Last dinner 9pm

Credit Cards ①②③

★60% **Preston**

64 Preston Rd BA20 2DL ☎(0935)74400 FAX (0935) 410142

*A small, convivial hotel, family-owned and run, is situated on the Taunton Road at the edge of the town and offers good parking.*

7rm(2⇆3♠)Annexe8⇆♠(2fb) CTV in all bedrooms ® **T** ✳ sB&B£33-£38 sB&B⇆♠£33-£38 dB&B£49 dB&B⇆♠£49 19P

♈ English & French **V** ✿ ⚑ ✂ ✳ Lunch fr£7.50alc Dinner fr£10&alc Last dinner 9pm

Credit Cards ①②③⑤ⓔ

---

**YORK** North Yorkshire Map **08** SE65 ◉

See also Pocklington

★★★★63% **Viking**

North St YO1 1JF (Queens Moat) ☎(0904)659822 Telex no 57937 FAX (0904) 641793

*Conveniently situated close to the city centre on the banks of the River Ouse, this modern high-rise hotel is ideally placed for visitors to this historic town. Many of the bedrooms and both restaurants overlook the river towards the famous minster.*

188⇆♠(7fb)✂in 6 bedrooms CTV in all bedrooms ® **T** ✝ (ex guide dogs) sB&B⇆♠£78-£95 dB&B⇆♠£95-£115 ⊟

Lift ⓒ 15P 70🛏 (£5 per night) CFA sauna solarium gymnasium spa bath golf driving range ♫ *xmas*

♈ International **V** ✿ ⚑ ✂ Lunch £9-£10 Dinner £12.50-£13.50&alc Last dinner 9.45pm

Credit Cards ①②③⑤ⓔ

★★★★62% **Holiday Inn**

Tower St YO1 1SB (Holiday Inns Inc) ☎(0904)648111 Telex no 57566 FAX (0904) 610317

*A modern well furnished hotel in the centre of the city offering bedrooms with good facilities and comfortable but not over spacious public areas. A good standard of cooking is provided in the restaurant and there is also an informal brasserie.*

128⇆♠(10fb)✂in 26 bedrooms CTV in all bedrooms ® **T** sB⇆♠£92-£102 dB⇆♠£107-£117 (room only) ⊟

Lift ⓒ 47🛏 CFA

♈ English & French **V** ✿ ⚑ ✂ Lunch £10.95-£12.95&alc Dinner £16.25-£17.95&alc Last dinner 10.30pm

Credit Cards ①②③④⑤

★★★⚑ BILBROUGH MANOR COUNTRY HOUSE

YO2 3PH ☎Tadcaster(0937)834002 FAX (0937) 834724 (For full entry see Bilbrough)

★★★★❀ THE GRANGE

Clifton YO3 6AA ☎(0904)644744 FAX (0904) 612453

*This Regency town house set close to the ancient city centre has been beautifully restored to create a privately owned hotel which provides comfortable and very well appointed accommodation. Individually decorated bedrooms, a range of lounges with open fires, cosy bars and an elegant hall and foyer combine to create a restful country house atmosphere; the very high standard of cuisine featured in the restaurant is* →

Y

competently served by a friendly young staff, while the
Brasserie, which is open all day, gives the opportunity to enjoy
snacks and light meals in a more informal setting.

29⇨🛊2🎝 CTV in all bedrooms T ✳ S% sB&B⇨🛊£82
dB&B⇨🛊£95-£128 🆓

《 26P CFA xmas

♀ English & French V ♥ ⚏ ✳ Lunch £12.50&alc Dinner
£20&alc Last dinner 10pm

Credit Cards 1 2 3 5 £

★★★

★★★❀❀
**MIDDLETHORPE HALL**

Bishopthorpe Rd YO2 1QB
(Small Luxury Hotels)
☎(0904)641241
Telex no 837108
FAX (0904) 620176

A skilfully restored William
III country house, a mile and
a half from the city centre, overlooking York racecourse. The
atmosphere is warm and friendly, with willing, helpful staff,
and new manager Andrew Bridgford ensures that high
standards are maintained. There are some fine public rooms,
none more so than the elegant drawing room, the walls decked
with many portraits. There are 2 restaurants, a grill room in
the basement which is only open in season, and the main
restaurant, divided between 2 rooms, both of which are small
so tables are a little cramped. Set price and à la carte menus
are available, and chef Kevin Francksen cooks with flair and
imagination. Many of the bedrooms are in the converted
stables in the courtyard, all are well appointed with some fine
furniture and offer the comfort and character one would
expect.

30⇨🛊1🎝 CTV in all bedrooms ® T ✻ S10% sB⇨🛊£83-
£99 dB⇨🛊£115-£189 (room only) 🆓

Lift 《 70P ✿ CFA croquet nc8yrs xmas

V ♥ ⚏ ✳ S10% Lunch £14.90-£16.90 Dinner fr£29.25&alc
Last dinner 9.45pm

Credit Cards 1 2 3 5

---

★★★72% **Dean Court**
Duncombe Place YO1 2EF (Best Western) ☎(0904)625082
Telex no 57584 FAX (0904) 620305

A well furnished hotel in the shadow of the famous York Minster
makes the ideal base from which to explore the city. Lounges are
comfortable and attractive – fresh flowers and books adding to the
pleasant atmosphere – while a wide choice of dishes is available in
either the restaurant or all-day coffee shop ; attractively furnished
and decorated en suite bedrooms offer good facilities, and friendly
staff are particularly helpful throughout.

40⇨🛊 CTV in all bedrooms ® T ✻ ✳ sB&B⇨🛊£50-£68
dB&B⇨🛊£92-£122 🆓

Lift 《 25P 🚲 xmas

♀ English & French V ♥ ⚏ ✳ Lunch £11.20-£12.50&alc High
tea £7-£12 Dinner £17.35-£20 Last dinner 9.30pm

Credit Cards 1 2 3 4 5

---

★★★72% **Swallow Chase**
Tadcaster Rd YO2 2QQ (Swallow) ☎(0904)701000
Telex no 57582 FAX (0904) 702308

A delightfully furnished and comfortable hotel overlooking the
race course just outside the city, which complements bedrooms
equipped with good facilities by comfortable lounges and a choice
of dining styles. Service is friendly yet professional, and guests

have the use of a leisure club including pool, sauna, solarium and
gymnasium.

112⇨🛊(14fb)⚥in 40 bedrooms CTV in all bedrooms ® T
sB&B⇨🛊£78-£85 dB&B⇨🛊£90-£110 🆓

Lift 《 200P ✿ CFA ⊡ (heated) sauna solarium gymnasium
putting green golf practise net croquet xmas

♀ English & French V ♥ ⚏ ✳ S% Lunch £13-£14&alc
High tea £5.50-£6.50 Dinner £18.50-£19.50&alc Last dinner
10pm

Credit Cards 1 2 3 5

---

★★★71% **Ambassador**
125 The Mount YO2 2DA ☎(0904)641316

Conveniently situated near both city centre and racecourse, this
recently refurbished hotel offers spacious, comfortable bedrooms
which are all very well appointed ; individually styled public areas
are tastefully furnished and decorated, and the table d'hôte menu
represents good value for money. The establishment's most
appealing feature, however, is the courteous and attentive service
provided by a happy young staff.

19⇨🛊(2fb) CTV in all bedrooms ® T ✳ sB&B⇨🛊£77-£90
dB&B⇨🛊£90-£110 🆓

Lift ⊞ 30P 🚲 ✿ 🎝 xmas

V ♥ ⚏ ✳ Sunday Lunch £7.50&alc

Credit Cards 1 3

---

★★★❀68% *York Pavilion*
45 Main St, Fulford YO1 4PJ (Best Western) ☎(0904)622099
Telex no 57305 FAX (0904) 626939

In the old village of Fulford but only 2 miles from the city centre,
this elegant Georgian property has a friendly country house
atmosphere, with comfortable, attractively furnished public areas
and well equipped bedrooms – traditional in style in the house and
more modern in the stable annexe. The elegant restaurant provides
a high standard of cooking.

11⇨🛊Annexe10⇨🛊(3fb) CTV in all bedrooms ® T
✻ (ex guide dogs)

46P 🚲

V ♥ ⚏ Last dinner 9.30pm

Credit Cards 1 2 3 5

---

★★★67% **Mount Royal**
The Mount YO2 2DA ☎(0904)628856 Telex no 611171
FAX (0904) 57414
Closed 22-30 Dec

Situated between the race course and the city centre, this friendly
family-run hotel has been sympathetically created from 2 William
IV houses. Comfortable public areas include an intimate cocktail
bar and spacious restaurant. Attractive well furnished bedrooms
include 4 modern rooms with small terraces giving access to the
gardens and swimming-pool.

22⇨🛊(2fb)3🎝 CTV in all bedrooms ® T ✳
sB&B⇨🛊£62.50-£82.50 dB&B⇨🛊£70-£95 🆓

《 CTV 12P ✿ ⊡ (heated) snooker sauna solarium gymnasium

♀ International V ✳ Dinner £21.95 Last dinner 9.30pm

Credit Cards 1 2 3 5

---

★★★64% **Forte Posthouse**
Tadcaster Rd YO2 2QF (Forte Hotels) ☎(0904)707921
Telex no 57798 FAX (0904) 702804

Well equipped accommodation is provided by a large, purpose-
built hotel standing close to the racecourse on the A1036 southern
approach to the city centre. Public areas include a pleasant,
spacious, open-plan lounge/bar area and a restaurant where the à
la carte menu is supplemented by a good-value carvery operation
with assisted service.

139⇨🛊⚥in 69 bedrooms CTV in all bedrooms ® T ✳
dB⇨🛊£39.50-£49.50 (room only) 🆓

Lift 《 180P ✿ CFA ♨ xmas

♀ International V ♥ ⚏ ⚥ ✳ S% Lunch fr£10.95&alc Dinner
£13.95&alc Last dinner 10.30pm

Credit Cards 1 2 3 4 5

### ★★★63% Monkbar
Monkbar YO3 7PF ☎(0904)638086 FAX (0904) 629195
*Recently refurbished to a good standard, this hotel is situated close to the Minster and offers comfortable accommodation, some rooms have jacuzzi and mini-bars. The restaurant serves a steak and grill menu.*
47⇩♠(3fb)4⊞ CTV in all bedrooms ® T ✳
sB&B⇩♠£60.50-£70.50 dB&B⇩♠£80-£90 ⊟
Lift ℂ 50P CFA *xmas*
V ✿ ⚏ ✔ ✳ Lunch £6.25-£8.25 Dinner £9.50-£13.95 Last dinner 10pm
Credit Cards ①②③⑤

### ★★★62% Novotel
Fishergate YO1 4AD ☎(0904)611660 Telex no 57556
FAX (0904) 610925
*A modern purpose-built hotel located on the river's edge, just off the A19 on the southern side of the city. Bedrooms are spacious and well equipped, whilst the restaurant enjoys views of the river. An indoor swimming pool and terrace area are under construction.*
124⇩♠(124fb)✔in 31 bedrooms CTV in all bedrooms ® T ✳
sB⇩♠fr£59 dB⇩♠fr£71.50 (room only) ⊟
Lift ℂ 150P CFA ⌷ (heated) *xmas*
♀ English & French V ✿ ⚏ ✔ ✳ Lunch fr£13.50&alc Dinner fr£13.95&alc Last dinner mdnt
Credit Cards ①②③⑤

### ★★❀74% Kilima
129 Holgate Rd YO2 4DE (Inter-Hotels) ☎(0904)658844 & 625787 Telex no 57928 FAX (0904) 612083
*Standing beside the A59 only a short walk from the city centre, this converted rectory offers 15 bedrooms which, though compact, are well equipped with every modern amenity, including en suite facilities. The original cellars have been developed to provide an attractive restaurant in which guests can enjoy freshly prepared meals, and a very comfortable lounge overlooks the rear patio and garden.*
15⇩♠(1fb)3⊞ CTV in all bedrooms ® T ✳ sB&B⇩♠£41-£45 dB&B⇩♠£63.40-£70 ⊟
20P ⇗ *xmas*
♀ English & French V ✿ ⚏ ✔ ✳ Lunch £10.50 Dinner £16.25&alc Last dinner 9.30pm
Credit Cards ①②③⑤ £

### ★★70% Heworth Court
76-78 Heworth Green YO3 7TQ ☎(0904)425156 & 425126
FAX (0904) 415290
*On the east side of York, about 10 minutes' walk from the city walls, this hotel provides individually designed and well equipped bedrooms which range from spacious, traditional style to compact modern in the main building, in an adjoining courtyard and in a new block 200 yards away. Public areas include a cosy lounge, a welcoming bar and a lamplit restaurant where friendly staff serve imaginative meals, which, like everything else about this family-run establishment, represent value for money.*
17⇩♠Annexe10⇩♠(7fb)✔in 1 bedroom CTV in all bedrooms ® T ✘ sB&B⇩♠fr£40.50 dB&B⇩♠fr£58 ⊟
CTV 27P 1🏵 ⇗ CFA *xmas*
♀ English & Continental V ✿ ⚏ Lunch fr£13.75&alc High tea fr£1.10&alc Dinner fr£13.75&alc Last dinner 9.30pm
Credit Cards ①②③⑤ £

### ★★69% Beechwood Close
19 Shipton Rd, Clifton YO3 6RE (Minotels) ☎(0904)658378
FAX (0904) 647124
Closed 25 Dec
*Managed by resident proprietors, with the assistance of friendly staff, this comfortable hotel offers neat, well appointed bedrooms and a choice of substantial bar and restaurant meals.*
14⇩♠(2fb) CTV in all bedrooms ® T ✘ sB&B⇩♠£36.30-£40 dB&B⇩♠£59.50-£65 ⊟
CTV 36P ⇗

→

**Y**

V ✿ ⚏ Lunch £6.50 High tea £4.50-£7 Dinner £11.75-£13 Last dinner 9pm
Credit Cards ①②③ ⓔ

★★68% **Town House**
100-104 Holgate Rd YO2 4BB ☎(0904)636171
FAX (0904) 623044
Closed 24-31 Dec
*On the A59, close to the city centre and railway station, this family owned hotel has been sympathetically converted from a Victorian terrace to offer comfortable, inviting lounges and well equipped bedrooms.*
23rm(21⇨ℕ)(3fb) CTV in all bedrooms ® T sB&Bfr£28 sB&B⇨ℕ£40-£48 dB&Bfr£48 dB&B⇨ℕ£70 ⊟
25P CFA
♀ European V ✿ ⚏ Bar Lunch £2-£6alc High tea £3.50-£6.50alc Dinner £11.50&alc Last dinner 9.15pm
Credit Cards ①③ ⓔ

★★65% **Hudsons**
60 Bootham YO3 7BZ ☎(0904)621267 FAX (0904) 654719
*Ideally situated close to the city centre and offering good parking facilities, the hotel has been converted from 2 Victorian houses and retains the atmosphere of that period. Bedrooms are well furnished, and meals are taken either in the restaurant or in a basement bistro.*
30⇨ℕ(3fb)1⊞ CTV in all bedrooms ® T ✖ (ex guide dogs)
sB&B⇨ℕ£39-£45 dB&B⇨ℕ£69-£75 ⊟
Lift 34P CFA pool table *xmas*
♀ English & French V ✿ ⚏ Bar Lunch £7&alc Dinner £12-£14&alc Last dinner 9.30pm
Credit Cards ①②③⑤

★★64% **Cottage**
3 Clifton Green YO3 6LH ☎(0904)643711 FAX (0904) 611230
Closed 24-26 Dec
*Pleasantly located overlooking Clifton Green and close to the town centre, this privately owned hotel offers attractive accommodation and friendly service.*
16⇨ℕAnnexe4⇨ℕ(3fb) CTV in all bedrooms ® T ✖ (ex guide dogs)
12P
V ✿ Last dinner 9pm
Credit Cards ①②③⑤

★★64% **Disraeli's**
140 Acomb Rd YO2 4HA ☎(0904)781181
Closed 25 Dec-1 Jan
*A traditional hotel managed by the resident proprietor, working alongside a friendly team to ensure courteous service. Restaurant and bar meals are available at dinner, and the interesting, good value menus have earned a good reputation locally.*
12rm(8⇨ℕ)(4fb) CTV in all bedrooms ® T ✖ (ex guide dogs)
sB&B⇨ℕ£42-£47 dB&B⇨ℕ£62-£69 ⊟
CTV 40P ⚑ ✿ ♧
♀ Cosmopolitan V ✿ ⚏ Sunday Lunch £6.25-£7 Dinner £11.25-£16 Last dinner 9.30pm
Credit Cards ①②③

★★64% **Holgate Bridge**
106-108 Holgate Rd YO2 4BB ☎(0904)635971
FAX (0904) 670049
Closed 24-26 Dec
*A friendly little hotel in a row of town houses a short walk from the city centre offers comfortable modern bedrooms, a conservatory-style lounge and a cosy basement restaurant serving a good range and standard of food.*
14rm(11⇨ℕ)(4fb)1⊞ CTV in all bedrooms ® T sB&B£21 sB&B⇨ℕ£32-£37 dB&B£35-£36 dB&B⇨ℕ£47-£52 ⊟

A rosette means exceptional standards of cuisine.

14P
V Bar Lunch £1.75-£7.50alc Dinner £10&alc Last dinner 9pm
Credit Cards ①②③ ⓔ

See advertisement on page 779

★★63% **Abbots' Mews**
6 Marygate Ln, Bootham YO3 7DE ☎(0904)634866
Telex no 57777 FAX (0904) 612848
*The hotel, a Victorian coachman's cottage, is close to the Museum Gardens just a short walk from the city centre. The well equipped bedrooms are situated in buildings adjacent to the main hotel.*
12ℕAnnexe41⇨ℕ(9fb) CTV in all bedrooms ® T ✖
sB&B⇨ℕ£38-£50 dB&B⇨ℕ£66-£90 ⊟
30P CFA *xmas*
♀ International V ✿ ⚏ Lunch fr£7.45 Dinner £12.50-£14 Last dinner 9.30pm
Credit Cards ①②③⑤ ⓔ

See advertisement on page 779

★★63% **Savages**
15 St Peters Grove YO3 6AQ ☎(0904)610818
FAX (0904) 627729
Closed 25 Dec
*This pleasant, well maintained Victorian house stands in a peaceful residential cul de sac off the A19, approximately 2 miles from the ring road yet within walking distance of the city centre. Bedrooms vary in size, but all are comfortably furnished and well equipped, while public areas retain a number of Victorian features. Informal service is provided by a friendly young staff.*
18rm(7⇨9ℕ)(3fb) CTV in all bedrooms ® T
✖ (ex guide dogs) S% sB&Bfr£28 sB&B⇨ℕfr£32 dB&B⇨ℕfr£64 ⊟
CTV 16P
V ✿ ⚏ ✖ ⚏ ✱ Lunch fr£7.50 Dinner fr£11.50&alc Last dinner 9pm
Credit Cards ①②③⑤ ⓔ

See advertisement on page 779

Y

**★★62% Alhambra Court**
31 St Mary's, Bootham YO3 7DD ☎(0904)628474
*Conveniently located in a quiet road close to the town centre, the hotel offers comfortable lounges, an attractive restaurant and bar, and inviting, well appointed bedrooms, along with a spacious car park.*
25⇌↱(5fb)1⊞ CTV in all bedrooms ® T sB&B⇌↱£31.50-£36.50 dB&B⇌↱£49-£57 ⊟
Lift CTV 25P *xmas*
☋ English & French ✱ Dinner £10.50-£12.50&alc Last dinner 9pm
Credit Cards 1 3

**★★62% Ashcroft**
294 Bishopthorpe Rd YO2 1LH (Minotels) ☎(0904)659286
FAX (0904) 640107
Closed Xmas & New Year
*Close to the town centre, set in gardens which stretch down to the river the Ashcroft offers modern, well appointed bedrooms and comfortable lounges.*
11⇌↱Annexe4⇌↱(3fb) CTV in all bedrooms ® T ✱
sB&B⇌↱fr£36 dB&B⇌↱fr£62 ⊟
CTV 40P ✲ CFA
V ♉ ⊥ ✱ Lunch fr£6.50alc High tea fr£6.50alc Dinner fr£10.50&alc Last dinner 8pm
Credit Cards 1 2 3 5

**★★62% Knavesmire Manor**
302 Tadcaster Rd YO2 2HE ☎(0904)702941 FAX (0904) 709274
*A one-time home of the Rowntree family, this late Georgian house overlooking the racecourse offers pleasant public areas including an attractive oak-panelled bar and a comfortable lounge. Bedrooms vary in shape, size and style from modest 2nd-floor rooms to motel chalet rooms in the garden.*
13rm(8⇌1↱)Annexe9↱(2fb)1⊞ CTV in all bedrooms ® T
sB&B£25-£39 sB&B⇌↱£39.50-£52 dB&B£39-£49
dB&B⇌↱£49-£72 ⊟
Lift 26P 1⌂ CFA ▧ (heated) sauna *xmas*
V ♉ ⊥
Credit Cards 1 2 3 5 £

**★★61% Lady Anne Middletons Hotel**
Skeldergate YO1 1DS ☎(0904)632257 & 630456
FAX (0904) 613043
Closed 24-27 Dec
*A rambling hotel with great character offering spacious, bright conservatory-style lounges. There is an assortment of bedrooms, some rather compact but all well appointed. Service is very informal and friendly.*
40⇌↱Annexe26rm(17⇌↱)3⊞ CTV in 57 bedrooms ® T
✗ (ex guide dogs) sB&B⇌↱£53 dB&B⇌↱£65 ⊟
☾ CTV 56P ✲ CFA ▧ ⩳ sauna solarium gymnasium jacuzzi
V ♉ ⊥ Dinner £12.95-£14.95alc Last dinner 9pm
Credit Cards 1 2 3 £

**★★58% The Sheppard**
63 The Mount YO2 2AX ☎(0904)643716 & 620500
*This small family-run hotel, close to the city centre, serves a good choice of food in the basement restaurant. Bedrooms have good facilities, though some are rather compact.*
20rm(16⇌)(3fb)1⊞⅍in 2 bedrooms CTV in all bedrooms ®
✗ (ex guide dogs) ⊟
10P 6⌂ (£2 per night) *xmas*
☋ English & French V ♉ ⊥ ⅍ ✱ Sunday Lunch £8.25 Dinner £15-£25 Last dinner 9.15pm
Credit Cards 1 3 £

**★66% *Fairmount***
230 Tadcaster Road, Mount Vale YO2 2ES ☎(0904)638298
*Friendly service, comfortable accommodation and interesting menus are offered at this city hotel, pleasantly located opposite the racecourse.*
10rm(4⇌4↱)(4fb) CTV in all bedrooms ®
7P 3⌂
☋ International V ♉ ⊥ Last dinner 9pm
Credit Cards 1 3

**See advertisement on page 780**

**★65% Clifton Bridge**
Water End, Clifton YO3 6LL ☎(0904)610510
FAX (0904) 640208
Closed 24-31 Dec
*An hotel situated close to the town centre, in a quiet residential area just off the A19, provides very good modern bedrooms, a comfortable lounge and bar, and value-for-money dinner menus.*
14⇌↱(1fb) CTV in all bedrooms ® T sB&B⇌↱£35-£40
dB&B⇌↱£50-£60 ⊟
12P 2⌂ ⌂
☋ English & French V ♉ ⊥ ⅍ Dinner £6.50-£9&alc Last dinner 8pm
Credit Cards 1 2 3 £

**See advertisement on page 780**

**★65% Newington**
147 Mount Vale YO2 2DJ ☎(0904)625173 Telex no 65430
FAX (0904) 679937
*Four town houses have been suitably converted to form this hotel on the A1036 (south) approach road into the city.*
25⇌↱Annexe15⇌↱(3fb)2⊞ CTV in all bedrooms ® T ✗
sB&B⇌↱£30-£42 dB&B⇌↱£52-£62 ⊟
Lift 40P CFA ▧ (heated) sauna solarium *xmas*

→

# York

V ♥ Bar Lunch £2-£4.50 Dinner £12.50-£15 Last dinner 9.30pm
Credit Cards 1 2 3 £

○Fairfield Manor
Shipton Rd, Skelton YO3 6XW (Consort) ☎(0904)625621
Telex no 57476 FAX (0904) 612725
Due to open Spring 1992
90 ⇌ ↑

※✕19 Grape Lane
19 Grape Ln YO1 2HU ☎(0904)636366
*Situated in the centre of the city, close to the Minster and main shopping centre, this restaurant is in a beautiful timbered house, and it has a wealth of character and original features. Service is attentive, yet informal, and tables are provided on 2 floors – the top floor being for smoking guests. Food is refreshingly unpretentious, and it is competently cooked using the very best fresh ingredients in traditional dishes with imaginative touches. Delightful home-made sweets such as treacle tart and sticky toffee pudding are very much recommended by one of our inspectors. Fish terrines and soups are full of flavour, and sauces have a good depth of flavour. It is very good value for money, and there is an honest, relaxed and friendly atmosphere.*
Closed Sun, Mon, 1st 2 wks Feb & last 2 wks Sep
V 34 seats ✳ Lunch £6-£16alc Dinner £17.95&alc Last lunch 2pm Last dinner 10.30pm ♪ nc5yrs ✎
Credit Cards 1 3

※※※✕Melton's
7 Scarcroft Rd YO2 1ND ☎(0904)634341 FAX (0904) 629233
*This small, stylish restaurant just outside the city walls offers relaxed, good value dining from the short but interesting à la carte menu. Michael Hjort gained experience within the Roux empire in London before retiring to his native city. His cooking style is careful, accurate and straightforward, with no unnecessary frills. Daily specials supplement the regular menus, and there are special events, including seafood every Tuesday. The inspection meal began with home-made pasta with a tomato and basil sauce, followed by some excellent monkfish with saffron sauce (though the carrot timbale was not a strong enough flavour to satisfy). No extra charge is made for coffee or mineral water and the service, supervised by Lucy Hjort is relaxed and friendly.*
Closed Sun, Mon, 24 Dec-13 Jan, 17 Apr & 31 Aug-7 Sep
♀ English & French V 28 seats ✳ Lunch £13.50-£14alc Dinner £13-£24alc Last lunch 2pm Last dinner 9.45pm ♪
Credit Cards 1 3

※✕Le Petit Hotel & Restaurant
103 The Mount YO2 2AX ☎(0904)647339
*This is indeed a small hotel, with 6 en suite bedrooms furnished to a very high standard, but its reputation has been gained for the classic regional French cuisine served in its two elegant dining rooms. You can mix choices from the menu campagnard and à la carte menu, which change every 5 weeks and feature such delicious dishes as Basque fish soup and grilled duck breast with pear sauce. The delectable desserts are made daily.*
Closed Sun
Lunch by arrangement only
♀ French V 40 seats ✳ Dinner £16.80&alc Last dinner 10.15pm ♪ nc8yrs
Credit Cards 1 2 3

Hotels with red star ratings are
especially high quality.

# Useful Information
## (NORTHERN IRELAND AND THE REPUBLIC OF IRELAND)

In most instances, the details for establishments in the Irish section are outlined in the 'Using the guide' section on page 50, including 'How we classify hotels and restaurants'; 'Sample directory entry'; and 'Useful information'.

### PRICES
In the Republic of Ireland prices are quoted in Punts, indicated by the symbol IR£. The rates of exchange between pounds sterling and Punts is liable to fluctuate.

In the Republic of Ireland, as part of the registration scheme operated by Bord Fáilte, establishments must display tariffs; these are usually shown in bedrooms or reception. The application of VAT and service charges varies, but all prices quoted must be inclusive of VAT.

### TELEPHONE NUMBERS
The area codes shown against the numbers in the Republic of Ireland are applicable within the Republic only. Similarly, the area codes shown for entries in Great Britain and Northern Ireland cannot be used directly from the Republic of Ireland. Check your telephone directory for details.

### FIRE PRECAUTIONS
Northern Ireland: The Fire Precautions Act 1971 does not apply here. The Fire Services (NI) Order 1984 covers hotels and boarding houses providing sleeping accommodation for more than six persons, which must have a fire certificate issued by the Northern Ireland Fire Authority. Properties that sleep less must satisfy the Authority that they have adequate exits.

Republic of Ireland: AA officials inspect emergency notices, fire-fighting machinery and fire exits, although fire safety regulations are a matter for local authority fire services. You are strongly urged to read and understand emergency notices for your own and other people's safety.

### LICENSING REGULATIONS
Northern Ireland: public houses open 11.30–23.00 Monday–Saturday, 12.30–14.30 and 19.00–22.00 Sunday. Also Christmas Day 12.30–22.00. Hotels can serve residents seven days a week without restriction. On Sundays non-residents may be served 12.00–14.30 and 19.00–22.00, and on Christmas Day 12.30–22.00.

Children under 18 are not allowed in the bar area of licensed premises, neither can they buy or consume liquor in hotels.

Republic of Ireland: general licensing hours under present legislation are 10.30–23.00 Monday–Saturday in winter and 10.30–23.30 in summer. On Sundays and St Patrick's Day 12.30–14.00 and 16.00–23.00. No service on Christmas Day and Good Friday.

### Classification and awards
For this first year of the inclusion of Northern Ireland and the Republic of Ireland to the guide we are not including percentages and rosette awards in the Republic.

You will, however, find black star ratings, country house awards and the prestigious red star awards, full details of which you will find on p50 in 'How we classify'.

This year's top Irish hotels are:
Sea View, **Ballylickey, Co Cork**; Cashel House, **Cashel, Co Galway**; Marlfield House, **Gorey, Co Wexford**; Park Hotel, **Kenmare, Co Kerry**; Kelly's, **Rosslare, Co Wexford**.

## A   Directory — Northern Ireland and Republic of Ireland

### ABBEYFEALE Co Limerick Map 01 B2 ⊙

**★Leen's**
☎Listowel(068)31121
Closed 24-31 Dec
13rm(3⇨3♠)(1fb) ✠ (ex guide dogs)
CTV ♪ ♫ ♨
V ✿ ♨ Last high tea 8.30pm
Credit Cards 1 3

### ADARE Co Limerick Map 01 B3

**★★★★♨Adare Manor**
(Small Luxury Hotels) ☎(061)396566 Telex no 70733
FAX (061) 396124
*A magnificent manor house, for long the home of the Earls of
Dunraven, recently converted into a luxury hotel. Set in 840 acres
of formal gardens, park and woodlands on the broad River
Maigue, the house reflects all the grandeur and character of its
past combined with all the facilities of a quality modern hotel. An
18-hole golf course is under construction to add to the already
superb facilities.*
28⇨♠Annexe36⇨♠ CTV in all bedrooms T
✠ (ex guide dogs) S% sB⇨♠IR£100-IR£180 dB⇨♠IR£100-
IR£230 (room only) ♬
Lift ℂ CTV 70P ❊ CFA ▨ (heated) ♪ sauna gymnasium clay
pigeon shooting ♫ ♨ *xmas*
♡ Irish, English & French V ✿ ♨ Lunch IR£15&alc Dinner
IR£27&alc Last dinner 10pm
Credit Cards 1 2 3 4 5

**★★★Dunraven Arms**
☎(061)396209 Telex no 70202 FAX (061) 396541
45⇨♠(1fb)🗲♫ CTV in all bedrooms ✳ S12.5% sB⇨♠IR£35-
IR£55 dB⇨♠IR£50-IR£77.50 (room only) ♬
ℂ CTV 300P ❊ CFA
♡ Irish & French V ✿ ♨
Credit Cards 1 2 3 4 5

### AHERLOW Co Tipperary Map 01 B3

**★★★Aherlow House**
☎Tipperary(062)56147 FAX (061) 355405
RS 13 Jan-5 Mar & 2 Nov-10 Dec
10⇨♠(2fb) CTV in all bedrooms T ✠ (ex guide dogs)
sB⇨♠IR£26-IR£29 dB⇨♠IR£40-IR£44 (room only) ♬
ℂ CTV 200P 3🏌 ❊ CFA ♨
V ✿ ♨ 🗲 Lunch IR£9-IR£9.50 Dinner IR£17-IR£18 Last
dinner 9.30pm
Credit Cards 1 2 3 5

**★★Glen**
☎(062)56146
24⇨♠(4fb)🗲in 2 bedrooms CTV in all bedrooms T
ℂ CTV P ❊ ♫ ♨
Credit Cards 1 2 3 5

### ARDMORE Co Waterford Map 01 C2

**★Cliff House**
☎Youghal(024)94106 FAX (024) 94496
Closed Oct-Apr
21rm(2⇨11♠)(2fb) ® ✠ (ex guide dogs) S% sB&BIR£20.75-
IR£26 sB&B⇨♠IR£24.75-IR£30 dB&B⇨♠IR£47.50-IR£58
CTV 30P 🚗 ❊
V ✿ ♨ S% Sunday Lunch IR£9.50 Dinner IR£16.95 Last
dinner 9pm
Credit Cards 1 2 3 5

### ASHFORD Co Wicklow Map 01 D3

**★Cullenmore**
☎Wicklow(0404)40422 & 40187 FAX (0404) 47744
14⇨♠(4fb) CTV in all bedrooms ® T ✠ (ex guide dogs) ✳
sB&B⇨♠IR£23-IR£28 dB&B⇨♠IR£21-IR£25 ♬
CTV 200P ❊ CFA Pool
♡ Irish & French V ✿ ♨ 🗲 ✳ Lunch IR£6-IR£9 Dinner
IR£12-IR£13 Last dinner 11pm
Credit Cards 1 2 3 5

### ATHLONE Co Westmeath Map 01 C4 ⊙

**★★★Prince Of Wales**
☎(0902)72626 Telex no 53068 FAX (0902) 75658
RS 25-29 Dec
72⇨♠(2fb)🗲in 4 bedrooms CTV in all bedrooms ® T
✠ (ex guide dogs) sB&B⇨♠IR£35-IR£70 dB&B⇨♠IR£60-
IR£95 ♬
ℂ 35P CFA
♡ French V ✿ ♨ 🗲 Lunch IR£7-IR£14 High tea IR£3-
IR£9alc Dinner IR£17-IR£19&alc Last dinner 9.30pm
Credit Cards 1 2 3 4 5

**★★Royal Hoey**
☎(0902)72924
RS 25-28 Dec
45rm(12⇨15♠)(7fb) CTV in 29 bedrooms ® T
✠ (ex guide dogs)
Lift ℂ ⊞ CTV P ❊ ♫ ♨

### BALLINA Co Mayo Map 01 B4 ⊙

**★★★Downhill**
☎(096)21033 Telex no 40796 FAX (096) 21338
Closed 24-25 Dec
51⇨♠(13fb) CTV in all bedrooms ® T ✠ (ex guide dogs)
sB&B⇨♠IR£34.50-IR£41 dB&B⇨♠IR£62-IR£79 ♬
ℂ CTV 300P ❊ CFA ▨ (heated) ℘ (hard) squash snooker
sauna solarium gymnasium sunbed jacuzzi ♫ ♨ *xmas*
♡ French V ✿ ♨ ✳ Lunch IR£8-IR£10.50 High tea IR£7-
IR£16.50 Dinner IR£13-IR£17 Last dinner 9pm
Credit Cards 1 2 3 4 5

### BALLINASLOE Co Galway Map 01 B4 ⊙

**★★★Hayden's**
☎(0905)42347 FAX (0905) 42895
RS 24-26 Dec
55⇨♠(7fb) CTV in all bedrooms T ✳ sB⇨♠IR£22-IR£24
dB⇨♠IR£39-IR£42 (room only) ♬
Lift ℂ CTV 100P CFA ♫
♡ International V ✿ ♨ 🗲 ✳ Lunch IR£7.85-IR£10.50 High
tea IR£9.75-IR£17alc Dinner IR£14-IR£16.50 Last dinner
9.15pm
Credit Cards 1 2 3 5

Red star hotels are each
highlighted by a pink
tinted panel.

### BALLYBOFEY Co Donegal Map 01 C5 ⊖

**★★★Kee's**
Stranolar(1m NE on N15) ☎Letterkenny(074)31917
Closed 24-25 Dec
27⇌🏠(8fb) CTV in all bedrooms ®
90P ♨
♿ ⚗ Last dinner 9.15pm
Credit Cards ①②③⑤

### BALLYBUNION Co Kerry Map 01 A3 ⊖

**★★Marine**
☎Listowel(068)27522 & 27139 FAX (068) 27666
Closed Dec-Etr
13⇌🏠 CTV in 8 bedrooms ® T 🐾 (ex guide dogs)
sB&B⇌🏠IR£38.95 dB&B⇌🏠IR£53.90
《 CTV 100P 🚗 CFA ♫
♀ Irish & French V ♿ ⚗
Credit Cards ① ③

### BALLYCONNELL Co Cavan Map 01 C4

○**Slieve Russell**
☎(049)26444 FAX (049) 26474
Open
140⇌🏠

### BALLYCOTTON Co Cork Map 01 B2

**★Bay View**
☎Cork(021)646714 FAX (021) 646824
18rm(5⇌3🏠)(2fb) T 🐾 (ex guide dogs)
CTV 25P 3🛏 ❄ ⚑ 18 ℘ (hard) Free golf course to residents ♫ ♨
V ♿ ⚗ Last dinner 9pm
Credit Cards ② ③

### BALLYGALLY Co Antrim Map 01 D5

**★★★57% Ballygally Castle**
274 Coast Rd BT40 2QZ (HG) ☎Larne(0574)83212
FAX (0574) 83681
*A comfortable hotel built around a 17th-century castle overlooking
the sea on the beautiful Antrim coast. Bedrooms have good
facilities and staff are friendly and helpful.*
30⇌🏠(1fb) CTV in all bedrooms ® T
《 ⊞ 100P ❄ ⚑ 18 ℘ (hard) ♪ ♫ ♨
♀ French Last dinner 9.30pm
Credit Cards ①②③⑤

### BALLYLICKEY Co Cork Map 01 A2

**★★**

**★★🛥 SEA VIEW**
☎Bantry(027)50073 &
50462 FAX (027) 51555
Closed Nov-Mar
*A delightful country house
with well tended gardens, set
back from the main Bantry/
Cork road, overlooking
Bantry Bay. There are cosy lounges with turf fires, and
comfortable, pleasantly redecorated bedrooms. Catering for
the fishing and golfing enthusiast, the hotel is also a good
touring base for west Cork and Kerry.*
17⇌🏠Annexe5rm(4fb) T ✻ S10% sB&B⇌🏠IR£30-
IR£50 dB&B⇌🏠IR£50-IR£80

CTV 30P 🚗 ❄
V ♿ ⚗ ✻ Sunday Lunch IR£9-IR£11 Dinner IR£18.50-
IR£20 Last dinner 9.30pm
Credit Cards ①②③⑤

### BALLYLIFFEN Co Donegal Map 01 C6

**★★Strand**
☎(077)76107
Closed 24-25 Dec
12⇌🏠(4fb) CTV in all bedrooms ® T 🐾 (ex guide dogs)
CTV 30P 🚗 ❄ ⚑ 18 ♫ ♨
♀ English V ♿ ⚗ Last dinner 9.30pm
Credit Cards ① ③

### BALLYMENA Co Antrim Map 01 D5 ⊖

**★★★62% Adair Arms**
Ballymoney Rd BT43 5 (HG) ☎(0266)653674
FAX (0266) 40436
Closed 25 Dec
*The spacious public areas of this traditional town-centre hotel have
recently been refurbished to a very high standard, and most of the
well equipped bedrooms have also been redecorated and partly
refurnished. Private car parking is provided at the rear of the
building.*
39⇌🏠 CTV in all bedrooms ® T 🐾 (ex guide dogs) 🏳
《 50P
♀ English & French V ♿ ⚗ ✻ Lunch fr£9 High tea fr£4.50
Dinner fr£13 Last dinner 9.30pm
Credit Cards ①②③⑤

### BALLYNAHINCH Co Galway Map 01 D5 ⊖

**★★★🛥Ballynahinch Castle**
☎(095)31006 & 31086 FAX (095) 31085
28⇌🏠8🚗 CTV in 8 bedrooms T 🐾 (ex guide dogs)
sB&B⇌🏠IR£53-IR£73 dB&B⇌🏠IR£76-IR£112 🏳
CTV 45P ❄ CFA ℘ (hard) ♪ xmas
♀ Irish & French V ♿ ⚗ ⚭ ✻ Dinner IR£23 Last dinner
8.30pm
Credit Cards ①②③⑤

### BALLYSHANNON Co Donegal Map 01 B5 ⊖

**★★Dorrians Imperial**
☎(072)51147 FAX (072) 51001
Closed 24-31 Dec RS Good Friday & Xmas day
26⇌🏠(6fb) CTV in all bedrooms T 🐾 (ex guide dogs) ✻
sB&B⇌🏠IR£25-IR£32 dB&B⇌🏠IR£42-IR£52 🏳
CTV 10P CFA
V ♿ ⚗ ✻ Lunch IR£7.50-IR£8.50 Dinner IR£13-IR£15 Last
dinner 8.30pm
Credit Cards ① ③

### BALLYVAUGHAN Co Clare Map 01 B3

**★★★🛥Gregans Castle**
☎(065)77005 FAX (065) 77111
Closed late Oct-9 Apr
*Situated at the foot of Corkscrew Hill with dramatic views over
Galway Bay, the hotel is situated in a terrain rich with
archaeological monuments. The unique grey limestone of the
Burren, a geologist's and botanist's dream, belies the warmth of the
interior. Hosts Peter and Moira Haden offer a warm welcome, and
a wealth of information about the area. A high level of personal
service and hospitality have earned them special commendations in
recent years, and the emphasis here is on good food using fresh
local produce.*
22⇌🏠3🚗 T 🐾 🏳

→

CTV 22P 🚲 ❀ croquet lawn
♡ Irish & French **V** ⚹ ⚗
Credit Cards [1] [3]

**★★Hyland's**
☎(065)77037 & 77015 FAX (065) 77131
Closed Nov-Etr
12↪🏠(3fb) CTV in 2 bedrooms-® **T** ✈ ✱
sB&B↪🏠IR£27.50-IR£33 dB&B↪🏠IR£46.20-IR£55 🍴
CTV P ❀ CFA ♫ ๘
**V** ⚹ ⚗ ✱ Bar Lunch IR£3.50-IR£13.50 Dinner IR£17-
IR£18&alc Last dinner 9.30pm
Credit Cards [1] [3]

---

**BANTRY** Co Cork Map **01** A2 ⊖

**★★★Westlodge**
☎(027)50360 Telex no 91880 FAX (027) 50438
Closed 20-27 Dec
90↪🏠(20fb) CTV in all bedrooms **T** ✈ (ex guide dogs)
sB&B↪🏠IR£32-IR£42 dB&B↪🏠IR£65-IR£75 🍴
《 ▦ CTV 400P ❀ CFA ▣ (heated) ⋀ (hard) squash snooker
sauna solarium gymnasium jacuzzi ๘
**V** ⚹ ⚗ ✱ S12.5% Lunch IR£7.95-IR£8.50 High tea IR£7.50-
IR£8.50 Dinner IR£18-IR£20 Last dinner 9pm
Credit Cards [1] [2] [3] [4] [5]

---

**BELFAST** Map **01** D5 ⊖

**★★★66% Stormont**
587 Upper Newtonards Rd BT4 3LP (HG) ☎(0232)658621
Telex no 748198 Storm G FAX 480240
Closed 25 Dec
*Overlooking the grounds of Stormont Castle, 4 miles from the city
centre, this busy hotel has spacious comfortable public areas, with
a choice of restaurants and extensive function and meeting
facilities. Bedrooms are well equipped if functionally furnished;
those by the Newtonards Road can be noisy.*
67↪🏠 CTV in all bedrooms ® **T** ✈ (ex guide dogs) ✱
sB&B↪🏠£74 dB&B↪🏠£96 🍴
Lift 《 600P CFA
♡ French **V** ⚹ ⚗ ✱ Lunch £8.50-£10 High tea £6-£8 Dinner
£14.95&alc Last dinner 10pm
Credit Cards [1] [2] [3] [5]

**★★★60% Plaza**
15 Brunswick St ☎(0232)333555
80↪🏠(2fb)⚟in 14 bedrooms CTV in all bedrooms ® **T** ✱ S%
sB↪🏠£69 dB↪🏠£79-£89 (room only) 🍴
Lift 《 CTV ⋀ *xmas*
♡ International **V** ⚹ ⚗ ✱ Lunch £8-£20alc High tea £8-£20alc
Dinner £8-£20alc Last dinner 10.30pm
Credit Cards [1] [2] [3] [5]

**⊛⊛⊛ ✕✕Roscoff**
7 Lesley House, Shaftesbury Square BT2 7DB ☎(0232)331532
*Roscoff is our much praised Best Restaurant award winner 1991/
1992 for Northern Ireland. Pale cream walls, canvas hangings and
Kentia palms give a cool elegance to a stylish modern restaurant
whose popularity makes it advisable to book in advance. Here
chef/patron Paul Rankin combines quality ingredients with
thought and flair to create table d'hôte and à la carte menus from
which you might enjoy a meal beginning with Chicken Ravioli with
Pancetta, Garlic and Rosemary Oil, followed by tender
Medallions of Veal with Artichoke and Basil, and completed by a
wickedly rich Hot Chocolate Soufflé. The accompanying wine list
is both well chosen and extensive, and sympathetic service is
friendly and attentive. (See colour feature on p40.)*
Closed Sun, 25-26 Dec, 1 Jan, Easter Mon & Tue, Mayday, 12
& 13 Jul Lunch not served Sat
♡ French **V** 75 seats ✱ Lunch £10.95&alc Dinner £15.95&alc
Last lunch 2pm Last dinner 10.30pm P ⚟
Credit Cards [1] [2] [3] [5]

---

**BIRR** Co Offaly Map **01** C3 ⊖

**★★County Arms**
☎(0509)20791 20193 FAX (0509) 21234
18↪🏠(4fb) CTV in all bedrooms ® ✈ (ex guide dogs)
《 150P ❀ squash sauna ๘
**V** ⚹ ⚗ Last dinner 9pm
Credit Cards [1] [2] [3] [4] [5]

---

**BLARNEY** Co Cork Map **01** B2

**★★★Blarney Park**
☎(021)385281 Telex no 75022 FAX (021) 381506
76↪🏠(20fb)⚟in 2 bedrooms CTV in all bedrooms **T**
✈ (ex guide dogs) S% sB&B↪🏠IR£45-IR£60
dB&B↪🏠IR£70-IR£80 🍴
《 100P ❀ CFA ▣ (heated) ⋀ (hard) sauna gymnasium steam
room childrens pool ♫ ๘ *xmas*
**V** ⚹ ⚗ ⚟ Lunch IR£9.50 Dinner IR£16&alc Last dinner
9.30pm
Credit Cards [1] [2] [3] [5]

---

**BLESSINGTON** Co Wicklow Map **01** C3

**★★★Downshire House**
☎Naas(045)65199 FAX (0454) 65335
Closed 31 Dec-6 Jan
14↪🏠Annexe11↪🏠 CTV in all bedrooms ® **T**
✈ (ex guide dogs) sB↪🏠IR£29 dB↪🏠IR£45 (room only)
《 CTV 30P ❀ CFA ⋀ (hard) table tennis croquet
**V** ⚹ ⚗ ⚟ Lunch IR£8-IR£12 High tea IR£8.30-IR£17.50alc
Dinner IR£15-IR£19 Last dinner 9.30pm
Credit Cards [1] [3]

---

**BORRIS-IN-OSSORY** Co Laois Map **01** C3

**★★Leix County**
☎(0505)41213
19↪🏠(2fb) CTV in all bedrooms ✈ (ex guide dogs)
▦ CTV CFA
⚹ ⚗
Credit Cards [1] [2] [3]

---

**BOYLE** Co Roscommon Map **01** B4 ⊖

**★★Royal**
(Minotels) ☎(079)62016 FAX (079) 62016
Closed Xmas
16↪🏠(5fb) CTV in all bedrooms ® **T** ✱ sB&B↪🏠IR£28.50-
IR£30.50 dB&B↪🏠IR£50-IR£56 🍴
《 CTV 120P CFA ⚑ 9
♡ Irish, French & Italian. **V** ⚹ ⚗ ⚟ ✱ Lunch IR£7.50-
IR£8.75 Dinner IR£13-IR£14.75&alc Last dinner 9pm
Credit Cards [1] [2] [3] [4] [5]

---

**BRAY** Co Wicklow Map **01** B4 ⊖

**★★Royal**
Main St ☎862935 Telex no 33502 FAX 867373
70↪🏠Annexe70↪🏠(9fb) CTV in 70 bedrooms ✈
Lift 《 ▦ CTV 180P ๘
♡ Irish & European **V** ⚹ ⚗ ⚟ Last dinner 11pm
Credit Cards [1] [2] [3] [5]

A rosette means exceptional standards of cuisine.

**BUNRATTY** Co Clare Map **01** B3

**★★★Fitzpatrick Shannon Shamrock**
☎Shannon(061)361177 Telex no 72114 FAX (061) 61252
RS 25 Dec
115⇨♪♠(6fb) CTV in all bedrooms **T ✕** (ex guide dogs)
sB⇨♠IR£55-IR£67 dB⇨♠IR£70-IR£93 (room only) ⊟
《 CTV 150P ✿ CFA 🖾 (heated) sauna steam room *xmas*
♀ European **V** ✿ ♨ ✻ Lunch frIR£9.95 Dinner frIR£17 Last
dinner 9.30pm
Credit Cards ①②③④⑤

**CAHERDANIEL** Co Kerry Map **01** A2

**★★Derrynane**
(Best Western) ☎(0667)5136 FAX (0667) 5160
Closed Nov-14 Mar
62⇨♪(16fb) **T** ✻ sB&B⇨IR£30-IR£35 dB&B⇨IR£50-IR£60
⊟
《 CTV P ✿ CFA ⇌ (heated) ♪ (hard) ♪ snooker ♫
♀ International **V** ✿ ♨ ✻ Lunch IR£8 Dinner IR£15.75 Last
dinner 9.30pm
Credit Cards ①②③④⑤

**CAHIR** Co Tipperary Map **01** C2

**★★Kilcoran Lodge**
☎(052)41288 & 41465 FAX (052) 41994
18⇨Annexe5rm(5fb) CTV in all bedrooms ⑧ **T** ✻
sB&B⇨IR£35-IR£45 dB&B⇨IR£60-IR£80 ⊟
《 100P ✿ CFA 🖾 (heated) sauna solarium gymnasium jacuzzi
*xmas*
♀ Irish & French **V** ✿ ♨ ✻ Lunch IR£10-IR£15&alc High tea
IR£7 Dinner IR£15-IR£20&alc Last dinner 9.15pm
Credit Cards ①②③⑤

**CARLOW** Co Carlow Map **01** C3 ◉

**★★★Royal**
☎(0503)31621
Closed 25 Dec
34⇨♠(3fb)1🛏 CTV in all bedrooms ⑧ **T ✕** (ex guide dogs)
✻ sB&B⇨♠frIR£30 dB&B⇨♠frIR£54 ⊟
《 CTV 50P CFA ♫ ◊
♀ Continental **V** ✿ ♨ ✕ ✻ Lunch IR£5&alc High tea
IR£8.95&alc Dinner IR£14&alc Last dinner 10pm
Credit Cards ①②③⑤

**CARNLOUGH** Co Antrim Map **01** D5

**★★71%** *Londonderry Arms*
BT44 0EU ☎(0574)885255 FAX (0574) 885263
*Situated in the centre of the fishing village, this long-established*
*well run hotel is full of character. Comfortably furnished*
*throughout, it offers a choice of lounges and bars, with friendly and*
*efficient service provided by smartly dressed staff. We are very*
*pleased to say that our 'Courtesy and Care' award for 1991/1992*
*for Northern Ireland has been won by the Londonderry Arms (see*
*colour feature on p20).*
15⇨♠(3fb)
▦CTV 18P ♫
**V** ✿ ♨ Last dinner 9pm
Credit Cards ①②③⑤

**CARRICKFERGUS** Co Antrim Map **01** D5 ◉

**★55%** *Dobbins Inn*
6-8 High St BT38 7AF ☎(09603)51905
Closed 25 & 26 Dec
*In the centre of the town not far from the castle, this small family-*
*run commercial hotel dates from the 16th century and offers*
*modest but characterful accommodation and friendly service.*

13⇨♠(2fb) CTV in all bedrooms ⑧ **T** S% sB&B⇨♠£38
dB&B⇨♠£62 ⊟
《 CTV ♪ ♫
♀ English & French **V** ✿ ♨ ✻ Lunch £7-£8 High tea £4-£8
Dinner £7-£12alc Last dinner 9.15pm
Credit Cards ①②③⑤ ⓔ

**CASHEL** Co Galway Map **01** A4

**★★★**

**★★★🏆 CASHEL HOUSE**
(Relais et Châteaux)
☎Clifden(095)31001
Telex no 50812
FAX (095) 31077
Closed 16 Nov-14 Feb ex
Xmas
*This converted country*
*residence at the head of Cashel Bay, owned and managed by*
*Dermot and Kay McEvilly, is set in 50 acres of flowering*
*shrubs, woodland walks and an award-winning garden. The*
*accommodation is excellent and is comfortably furnished, and*
*lounges are tastefully decorated and have turf fires. Bedrooms*
*offer peace and tranquillity and luxury suites are also*
*available. Cashel itself is a small, quiet village on the edge of*
*the Atlantic Ocean and at the foot of Cashel Hill.*
32rm(31⇨♠)(4fb)1🛏 CTV in all bedrooms **T** ✻
sB&B⇨♠IR£46-IR£56 dB&B⇨♠IR£92-IR£112 ⊟
CTV 40P 🐎 ✿ ♪ (hard) ♪ ∪ nc5yrs *xmas*
**V** ✿ ♨ ✻ Dinner IR£23.50-IR£25 Last dinner 9pm
Credit Cards ①②③④

**★★★Zetland House**
☎(095)31111 FAX (095) 31117
Closed 2 Nov-14 Apr
19⇨♠(2fb) **T** S10% sB&B⇨♠IR£45-IR£61
dB&B⇨♠IR£80-IR£95 ⊟
CTV 20P 🐎 ✿ CFA ♪ (hard) ♪ snooker
♀ International **V** ✿ ♨ S10% Lunch IR£5-IR£16alc
Credit Cards ①②③⑤

**CASHEL** Co Tipperary Map **01** C3 ◉

**★★★★🏆Cashel Palace**
☎Tipperary(062)61411 Telex no 70638 FAX (062) 61521
RS 25-26 Dec
20⇨2🛏 CTV in all bedrooms ✕ (ex guide dogs) sB⇨IR£75-
IR£155 dB⇨IR£90-IR£175 (room only) ⊟
《 100P ✿ CFA ♪
♀ Irish & French **V** ✿ ♨ Bar Lunch IR£11-IR£25.50alc
Dinner IR£18-IR£30 Last dinner 10pm
Credit Cards ①②③⑤

**CASTLEBALDWIN** Co Sligo Map **01** B4

**★★★🏆Cromleach Lodge Country House**
Ballindoon ☎Sligo(071)65155 FAX (071) 65455
Closed 25-26 Dec & 7-31 Jan
10⇨♠✕in 5 bedrooms CTV in all bedrooms ⑧ **T ✕** ✻
sB&B⇨♠IR£74.80 dB&B⇨♠IR£105.60 ⊟
25P 🐎 ✿ CFA ♪
♀ French **V** ✿ ♨ ✕ ✻ Lunch IR£15.95 Dinner IR£24.95-
IR£27.95 Last dinner 9pm
Credit Cards ①②③

**C**

---

★★★**Breaffy House**
(Best Western) ☎(094)22033
Closed 23-26 Dec
40⇨(3fb) CTV in all bedrooms Ⓡ T ✻ sB&B⇨ﬨIR£40-IR£43
dB&B⇨ﬨIR£64-IR£70 ᕰ
Lift ℂ CTV 100P ✿ CFA pool table croquet crazy golf
♈ Irish & French V ✿ ♨ ✔ ✻ Lunch IR£8.50 Dinner IR£15
Last dinner 9pm
Credit Cards ⒈ ⒉ ⒊ ⒌

★★**Welcome Inn**
☎(094)22288 & 22054 FAX (094) 21766
43⇨ﬨ(5fb)2⊟ CTV in all bedrooms T 🐾 (ex guide dogs)
sB&B⇨ﬨIR£25-IR£32 dB&B⇨ﬨIR£45-IR£60
ℂ CTV 100P CFA ♫
♈ Irish & French V ✿ ♨ ✔ Lunch IR£8-IR£10 Dinner
IR£13-IR£16 Last dinner 9.15pm
Credit Cards ⒈ ⒉ ⒊

---

★★★**Castle Oaks House**
☎Limerick(061)377666 FAX (061) 377717
Closed 25 Dec
11⇨ﬨ(6fb) CTV in all bedrooms T 🐾 (ex guide dogs)
sB&B⇨ﬨIR£42-IR£54 dB&B⇨ﬨIR£66-IR£80 ᕰ
ℂ 200P 200🐎 ✿ CFA ♪ ♫
♈ French V ✿ ♨ ✔ S10% Lunch IR£8.50-IR£8.95 Dinner
IR£14-IR£16&alc Last dinner 9.30pm
Credit Cards ⒈ ⒉ ⒊ ⒋ ⒌

---

★★★**Abbeyglen Castle**
☎(095)21201 FAX (095) 21797
Closed 10 Jan-10 Feb
40⇨ﬨ CTV in all bedrooms T S% sB&B⇨ﬨIR£81-
IR£103.50 dB&B⇨ﬨIR£108-IR£130.50 (incl dinner)
CTV 40P ✿ ⇌ (heated) ▶ 9 ♪ (hard) snooker sauna solarium
♫ xmas
♈ French ✿ ♨ ✻ Bar Lunch IR£5.50-IR£15alc Dinner
IR£15.70-IR£20.20alc Last dinner 9.15pm
Credit Cards ⒈ ⒉ ⒊ ⒋ ⒌

★★★**Ardagh**
Ardbear Bay ☎(095)21384 FAX (095) 21314
Closed 1wk before Etr & Nov
21⇨ﬨ(2fb) CTV in all bedrooms Ⓡ T 🐾 S10%
sB&B⇨ﬨIR£37.95-IR£44 dB&B⇨ﬨIR£53.90-IR£66
35P 🚗
✿ ♨ S10% Dinner IR£15.50-IR£19.80 Last dinner 9.30pm
Credit Cards ⒈ ⒉ ⒊ ⒌

★★★⚑**Rock Glen**
☎(095)21035 & 21431 FAX (095) 21737
Closed Nov-Feb
29⇨ﬨ(5fb) CTV in all bedrooms Ⓡ T 🐾 (ex guide dogs)
S12.5% sB&B⇨ﬨfrIR£45 dB&B⇨ﬨfrIR£80 ᕰ
CTV 50P ✿ CFA ♪ (hard) snooker ⚘
V ✿ ♨ S12.5% Dinner IR£20-IR£22.50 Last dinner 9pm
Credit Cards ⒈ ⒉ ⒊ ⒌

---

★★★**Clonmel Arms**
Sarsfield Rd ☎(052)21233 FAX (052) 21526
34rm(26⇨ﬨ)(4fb) CTV in all bedrooms Ⓡ sBIR£22
sB⇨ﬨIR£42 dB⇨ﬨIR£54 (room only) ᕰ
Lift ℂ CTV ♪

♈ Irish & French V ✿ ♨ ✻ Lunch IR£8.75-IR£9 Dinner
frIR£14.95 Last dinner 10pm
Credit Cards ⒈ ⒉ ⒋ ⒌

★★★**Minella**
☎(052)22388 & 22717 FAX (052) 24381
43⇨ﬨ(18fb)✔in 6 bedrooms CTV in all bedrooms Ⓡ T ✻
sB&B⇨ﬨIR£30-IR£45 dB&B⇨ﬨIR£50-IR£100 ᕰ
ℂ CTV 200P ✿ CFA
V ✿ ♨ ✻ Lunch IR£11-IR£15 High tea frIR£3 Dinner IR£17-
IR£22 Last dinner 9.30pm
Credit Cards ⒈ ⒉ ⒊ ⒌

---

★★★★**Jurys**
Western Rd ☎(021)276622 Telex no 76073 FAX (021) 274477
Closed Xmas
185⇨ﬨ(36fb)✔in 2 bedrooms CTV in all bedrooms Ⓡ T
🐾 (ex guide dogs) ✻ sB⇨ﬨIR£78 dB⇨ﬨIR£93 (room only)
ᕰ
Lift ℂ 400P CFA ▱ (heated) ⇌ (heated) ♪ (hard) squash
sauna gymnasium jacuzzi ♫
♈ French V ✿ ♨ ✻ Lunch IR£7.70-IR£11.65&alc High tea
IR£1-IR£6.70 Dinner IR£14.50&alc Last dinner 11pm
Credit Cards ⒈ ⒉ ⒊ ⒋ ⒌

★★★**Fitzpatrick Silver Springs**
Tivoli ☎(021)507533 Telex no 76111 FAX (021) 507641
Closed 25 Dec
109⇨ﬨ(50fb)✔in 4 bedrooms CTV in all bedrooms T
🐾 (ex guide dogs) S% sB⇨ﬨIR£61-IR£72 dB⇨ﬨIR£75-
IR£92 (room only) ᕰ
Lift ℂ 450P ✿ CFA ▱ (heated) ▶ 9 ♪ (hard) squash snooker
sauna solarium gymnasium ♫ ⚘
♈ International V ✿ ♨ ✔ ✻ Lunch IR£9.50-IR£11&alc
Dinner IR£15-IR£16.50&alc Last dinner 9.30pm
Credit Cards ⒈ ⒉ ⒊ ⒌

★★★**Rochestown Park**
☎(021)892233 FAX (021) 892178
*Peacefully situated, on the south side of the city, the hotel is set in*
*magnificent gardens. Close to the airport and ferries, this is an*
*ideal touring base.*
39⇨ﬨ(5fb) CTV in all bedrooms Ⓡ T sB&B⇨ﬨIR£30-
IR£50 dB&B⇨ﬨIR£50-IR£70
Lift ℂ CTV 75P ✿ CFA xmas
♈ Irish & French V ✿ ♨ ✔ Lunch IR£9.20-IR£10 High tea
IR£7-IR£7.50 Dinner IR£15-IR£20 Last dinner 10pm
Credit Cards ⒈ ⒉ ⒊ ⒋ ⒌

★★**Vienna Woods**
Glanmire ☎(021)821146 FAX (021) 821120
20⇨ﬨ(2fb) CTV in all bedrooms Ⓡ T ✻ sB&B⇨ﬨIR£25-
IR£32 dB&B⇨ﬨIR£40-IR£44
CTV P ✿ CFA
♈ English & French V ✿ ♨ ✔ S10% Sunday Lunch IR£7.50
Dinner IR£10-IR£17&alc Last dinner 9.30pm
Credit Cards ⒈ ⒉ ⒊ ⒌

---

★★**Courtmacsherry**
☎Bandon(023)46198
Closed Oct-Mar
15rm(9⇨ﬨ)(1fb) CTV in all bedrooms T S% sB&BIR£25-IR£30
dB&BIR£45-IR£55 dB&B⇨ﬨIR£50-IR£60 ᕰ
CTV 60P ✿ CFA ♪ (hard & grass) Ս
♈ International V ✿ ♨ ✔ S% Sunday Lunch IR£9.50-
IR£10.50 Dinner IR£16.50-IR£18 Last dinner 9pm
Credit Cards ⒈ ⒊

---

**C**

COURTOWN HARBOUR Co Wexford Map **01** D3

★★*Bay View*
☎(055)25307
Closed Nov-Feb
16rm(6🛏)(12fb) ✖ (ex guide dogs)
CTV 30P ♪ (hard) squash ჿ
✤ ₪ Last dinner 9pm
Credit Cards ①③

★★**Courtown**
(Minotels) ☎Gorey(055)25210 & 25108 FAX (055) 25304
Closed Dec-Etr
21⇔🛏(4fb) CTV in all bedrooms T ✖ (ex guide dogs) ✳ S10%
sB&B⇔🛏IR£25-IR£33 🏳
《 CTV 10P CFA 🖬 (heated) ≏ (heated) ▶ 18 ♪ (hard &
grass)✔ squash ∪ snooker sauna
♀ Irish, English & French V ✤ ₪ Lunch IR£10-IR£12&alc
Dinner IR£17.50-IR£19&alc Last dinner 9.30pm
Credit Cards ①②③⑤

CRAWFORDSBURN Co Down Map **01** D5

★★★68% **Old Inn**
15 Main St BT19 1JH ☎Helens Bay(0247)853255 FAX 852711
Closed 25-29 Dec
*A charming hotel on the B20 20 miles east of Belfast, said to be
one of the oldest hostelries in Ireland, complements attractive and
well equipped bedrooms with public areas full of character. The
landscaped garden at its rear makes it an ideal setting for wedding
receptions.*
32⇔🛏2🖸 CTV in all bedrooms ® T ✖ ✳ sB&B⇔🛏£37-£62
dB&B⇔🛏£52-£77 🏳
《 CTV 65P ✤ CFA
V ✤ ✳ Lunch £11-£17alc High tea £7-£13 Dinner £12&alc Last
dinner 9.30pm
Credit Cards ①②③⑤

CUSHENDALL Co Antrim Map **01** D6

★★58% **Thornlea**
6 Coast Rd BT44 0RU ☎Cushendal(02667)71223 FAX 71362
*On the edge of the village next to the golf course, this hotel offers
sound accommodation, friendly service and a wide choice of food.*
13⇔🛏 CTV in all bedrooms ® sB&B⇔🛏£21
dB&B⇔🛏£38.50 🏳
CTV 25P CFA ♫
V ✤ ₪ ✳ Lunch £6.50-£7.95 High tea £6 Dinner £10-£15alc
Last dinner 9.15pm
Credit Cards ①②③⑤

DINGLE Co Kerry Map **01** A2 ◉

★★★**Benner's**
Main St ☎(066)51638 FAX (066) 51412
25⇔🛏(2fb)2🖸⅍in 4 bedrooms CTV in all bedrooms T
✖ (ex guide dogs) S10% sB&B⇔🛏IR£27-IR£38
dB&B⇔🛏IR£48-IR£64 🏳
《 20P ✤ CFA ♪ (hard) ♫ xmas
V ✤ ₪ ⅍ ✳ Lunch IR£9 Dinner IR£15-IR£18&alc Last
dinner 9.30pm
Credit Cards ①②③⑤

★★★**Skellig**
☎(066)51144 FAX (066) 51501
Closed mid Nov-mid Mar
75⇔🛏 TV available T ✖ (ex guide dogs) S10%
《 CTV P 🖬 (heated) ♪ (hard) snooker sauna solarium ♫
♀ French ✤ ₪

DONEGAL Co Donegal Map **01** B2 ◉

★★★**Abbey**
The Diamond ☎(073)21014
49⇔🛏(7fb) CTV in all bedrooms T ✳ S10% sB&B⇔🛏IR£28-
IR£33 dB&B⇔🛏IR£55-IR£65 🏳
Lift 《 ⊞ CTV 70P ✤ ♪ (hard & grass)✔ squash ∪ snooker
sauna solarium gymnasium ♫
♀ International V ✤ ₪ ✳ Lunch IR£8.50-IR£10 High tea
IR£6-IR£15&alc Dinner IR£10-IR£15&alc Last dinner
9.30pm
Credit Cards ①②③④⑤

★★★**Harvey's Point Country**
Lough Eske ☎(073)22208 FAX (073) 22352
20⇔🛏Annexe12🛏4🖸 CTV in 20 bedrooms ® T S10%
sB&B⇔🛏IR£40-IR£55 dB&B⇔🛏IR£60-IR£90 🏳
200P CFA ♪ (hard) ✔ ♫ xmas
♀ French ✤ ₪ ✳ Sunday Lunch IR£8.95 Dinner
IR£12.95&alc Last dinner 9.45pm
Credit Cards ①②③

★★★**The Hyland Central**
The Diamond(Best Western) ☎Donegal Town(073)21027 &
21090 Telex no 40522 FAX (073) 22295
Closed 25-27 Dec
72⇔🛏(2fb) CTV in all bedrooms ® T ✖ (ex guide dogs)
sB&B⇔🛏IR£45-IR£55 dB&B⇔🛏IR£70-IR£90 🏳
Lift 《 CTV 18P CFA 🖬 (heated) ▶ 18 ♪ (hard) squash ∪
sauna solarium gymnasium xmas
V ✤ ₪
Credit Cards ①②③

DROGHEDA Co Louth Map **01** D4

★★★**Boyne Valley**
☎(041)37737 FAX (041) 39188
35⇔🛏(4fb) CTV in all bedrooms ® T ✳ S%
sB&B⇔🛏IR£25-IR£45 dB&B⇔🛏IR£48-IR£70
《 CTV 200P ✤ CFA ▶ 18 xmas
♀ Continental V ✤ ₪ ✳ S% Lunch IR£7-IR£9&alc High tea
IR£4-IR£7 Dinner frIR£17&alc Last dinner 10pm
Credit Cards ①②③⑤

DUBLIN Co Dublin Map **01** D4

★★★★**Burlington**
Lesson St ☎(01)605222 Telex no 93815 FAX (01) 608496
500⇔🛏 CTV in all bedrooms T ✖ (ex guide dogs)
sB⇔🛏IR£70-IR£75 dB⇔🛏IR£86-IR£92 (room only) 🏳
Lift 《 450P CFA xmas
♀ French & Irish V ✤ ₪ ⅍ ✳ Lunch IR£7.20-IR£14.60 High
tea IR£3.75-IR£6alc Dinner IR£14-IR£28alc Last dinner
11.45pm
Credit Cards ①②③④⑤

★★★★**Conrad**
Earlsfort Ter ☎(01)765555 Telex no 91872 FAX (01) 765424
190⇔🛏⅍in 36 bedrooms CTV in all bedrooms T ✖ ✳
sB⇔🛏IR£120 dB⇔🛏IR£150 (room only) 🏳
Lift 《 ⊞ 80🍴 ♪ xmas
♀ Irish & Continental V ✤ ₪ ⅍ ✳ Lunch frIR£10.95 Dinner
frIR£10.95 Last dinner 10.45pm
Credit Cards ①②③⑤

★★★★**Jurys**
Ballsbridge ☎(01)605000 Telex no 93723 FAX (01) 605540
300⇔🛏Annexe100⇔🛏⅍in 59 bedrooms CTV in all
bedrooms T ✖ (ex guide dogs) ✳ sB⇔🛏IR£95-IR£135
dB⇔🛏IR£110-IR£165 (room only) 🏳
Lift 《 320P CFA 🖬 (heated) ≏ (heated) whirlpool xmas

→

♀ International **V** ✆ ⚓ ⅄ ✳ Lunch IR£14-IR£15.50&alc Dinner IR£16.50-IR£19.50&alc Last dinner 10.15pm
Credit Cards ①②③⑤

### ★★★Ashling
Parkgate St(Best Western) ☎(01)772324 Telex no 32802 FAX (01) 793783
Closed 24-26 Dec
56⇆🏠(3fb) CTV in all bedrooms **T** ✖ (ex guide dogs)
sB&B⇆🏠frIR£48.50 dB&B⇆🏠frIR£70 🍴
Lift ⦗ CTV 70P 8🚗 CFA
♀ International **V** ✆ ⚓ ⅄ ✳ S10% Lunch frIR£8.80&alc High tea frIR£5alc Dinner frIR£14.50 Last dinner 9.45pm
Credit Cards ①②③④⑤

### ★★★Central
1-5 Exchequer St ☎(01)6797302 FAX (01) 6797303
*A city centre hotel, refurbished and reopened after a long closure. There are modernised en suite bedrooms of a high standard, and smart public rooms off a chequered marble lobby. The hotel has a good food service.*
70⇆🏠(8fb)1 🏠⅄in 9 bedrooms CTV in all bedrooms ® **T** ✖ (ex guide dogs) ✳ sB&B⇆🏠IR£57.37-IR£68.62 dB&B⇆🏠IR£81-IR£103.50 🍴
Lift ⦗ 🚗 (charged) CFA
**V** ✆ ⚓ ⅄ ✳ Lunch IR£10 High tea IR£10 Dinner IR£18&alc Last dinner 11pm
Credit Cards ①②③⑤

### ★★★Green Isle
Clondalkin ☎(01)593406 Telex no 90280 FAX (01) 592178
50⇆🏠Annexe34rm CTV in all bedrooms **T** ✖ (ex guide dogs) ✳ sB⇆🏠IR£40-IR£44 dB⇆🏠IR£62-IR£66 (room only)
⦗ 400P ✿ CFA ▶ 18 ♫ (hard) ♪ squash ◡ snooker sauna solarium gymnasium ♫
**V** ✆ ⚓ S15% Lunch IR£7-IR£10&alc Dinner IR£12-IR£15&alc Last dinner 10.30pm
Credit Cards ①②③⑤

### ★★★Marine
Sutton ☎(01)322613 FAX (01) 390442
Closed 24-26 Dec
*On the north shore of Dublin Bay with attractive gardens and seashore walks, the Marine Hotel is convenient for Dublin Airport and the car ferry, catering for tourists and the business sector.*
27⇆ CTV in all bedrooms ® **T** ✖ sB&B⇆IR£46-IR£48 dB&B⇆IR£75-IR£80 🍴
⦗ 150P 🏢 ✿ CFA ▭ (heated) sauna
♀ International **V** ✆ ⚓ ✳ Lunch IR£9.70-IR£10.25alc Dinner frIR£16.90alc Last dinner 10.15pm
Credit Cards ①②③⑤

### ★★★Hotel Montrose
Stillorgan Rd ☎(01)2693311 Telex no 91207 FAX (01) 2691164
190⇆🏠(6fb) CTV in all bedrooms **T** ✖ (ex guide dogs)
sB⇆🏠IR£40-IR£44 dB⇆🏠IR£62-IR£66 (room only) 🍴
Lift ⦗ 150P CFA sauna *xmas*
♀ Irish **V** ✆ ⚓ ⅄ ✳ S15% Lunch IR£7-IR£11&alc Dinner IR£9-IR£11.50&alc Last dinner 10.30pm
Credit Cards ①②③④⑤

### ★★★Skylon
Drumcondra Rd ☎(01)379121 Telex no 90790 FAX (01) 372778
82⇆🏠(4fb) CTV in all bedrooms **T** ✖ (ex guide dogs) S15% sB⇆🏠IR£40-IR£44 dB⇆🏠IR£62-IR£66 (room only) 🍴
Lift ⦗ 100P CFA *xmas*
**V** ✆ ⚓ ✳ Lunch IR£6.70-IR£9.30&alc Dinner IR£7-IR£10&alc Last dinner 10.30pm
Credit Cards ①②③④⑤

### ★★★Tara Tower
Merrion Rd ☎(01)2694666 Telex no 90790 FAX (01) 2691027
100⇆ CTV in all bedrooms ® **T** ✖ (ex guide dogs)
sB⇆IR£40-IR£44 dB⇆IR£62 (room only) 🍴
Lift ⦗ CTV 300P *xmas*
**V** ⚓ Lunch IR£7.50-IR£10&alc Dinner IR£9-IR£11.50&alc Last dinner 9.30pm
Credit Cards ①②③④⑤

### ★★Longfield's
Fitzwilliam St ☎(01)761367 FAX (01)761542
Closed 25-31 Dec
*An intimate townhouse hotel, newly opened, close to the city centre. Particular emphasis is placed on personalised service, good food and a relaxed, comfortable atmosphere. Extensive improvements are planned for the near future to increase the overall standards of comfort and amenities.*
26⇆🏠 CTV in all bedrooms **T** ✖ (ex guide dogs)
sB&B⇆🏠£85 dB&B⇆🏠£99
Lift ⦗ **V** ✆ ⚓ Lunch £11-£15alc Dinner £22.50 Last dinner 10pm
Credit cards ①②③⑤

### ○Stephen's Hall
14/17 Lower Leeson St ☎(01)610585 FAX (01) 610606
37⇆🏠

---

**DUNDALK** Co Louth Map **01 D4**

### ★★★Ballymascanlon House
☎(042)71124 Telex no 34735 FAX (042) 71598
Closed 24-26 Dec
36⇆(11fb) CTV in all bedrooms ® **T** S10% sB&B⇆IR£41-IR£48 dB&B⇆IR£66-IR£71 🍴
⦗ CTV 250P ✿ CFA ▭ (heated) ▶ 9 ♫ (hard) squash snooker sauna solarium gymnasium ♫ *xmas*
♀ Irish & French ✆ ⚓ ⅄ Lunch IR£9.35-IR£10&alc High tea IR£10-IR£11 Dinner IR£16.50-IR£17.50 Last dinner 9.30pm
Credit Cards ①②③④⑤

### ★★★Imperial
(Best Western) ☎(042)32241 Telex no 43735 FAX (042) 37909
Closed 25 Dec
47⇆(47fb) CTV in 31 bedrooms **T** ✳ S10% sB&B⇆IR£33-IR£35 dB&B⇆IR£45-IR£48
Lift ⦗ CTV 100P CFA
**V** ✆ ⚓ ⅄ ✳ S12.5% Lunch IR£7.50-IR£10.25 Dinner IR£10.50-IR£12 Last dinner 9.30pm
Credit Cards ①②③

---

**DUNDRUM** Co Tipperary Map **01 B3**

### ★★★⬙Dundrum House
☎Tipperary(062)71116 Telex no 70255 FAX (062) 71366
55⇆🏠(6fb)8🏢 **T** ✖ (ex guide dogs)
Lift ⦗ CTV 300P ✿ ♫ (hard) ♪ snooker 🐎
♀ Irish & Continental **V** ✆ ⚓ Last dinner 9.30pm
Credit Cards ①②③⑤

### ★★⬙Rectory House
☎Tipperary(062)71266 Telex no 93348
11⇆🏠(5fb) CTV in 7 bedrooms **T** ✖ (ex guide dogs)
▦ CTV 300P ✿ 🐎
♀ Irish & French ✆ ⚓ ⅄ Last dinner 9.30pm
Credit Cards ①②③⑤

The AA's star rating scheme is the
market leader in hotel
classification.

**DUNFANAGHY** Co Donegal Map **01** C6

### ★★Arnold's
☎Letterkenny(074)36208 & 36142 FAX (074) 36352
Closed Nov-Mar
34⇛(10fb) CTV in all bedrooms T ✹ (ex guide dogs) ➡
CTV 60P ❊ CFA ♗ (hard) ♪
V ♥ ♨ ⊁
Credit Cards ❘1❘❘2❘❘3❘❘5❘

### ★★Carrig Rua
(Minotels) ☎(074)36133 & 36277
Closed Nov-Etr
22⇛(6fb) CTV in all bedrooms ✹ (ex guide dogs) ✳
sB&B⇛IR£22-IR£24 dB&B⇛IR£44-IR£48 ➡
20P
V ♥ ♨ Lunch IR£8-IR£10 Dinner IR£15.50-IR£17.50 Last
dinner 8.15pm
Credit Cards ❘1❘❘2❘❘3❘

**DUNGARVAN** Co Waterford Map **01** C2 ◷

### ★★*Lawlors*
☎(058)41122 FAX (058) 41000
77⇛(7fb) CTV in all bedrooms T
Lift ℭ CTV ♗ ♨
V ♥ ♨ Last dinner 10pm
Credit Cards ❘1❘❘2❘❘3❘

**DUN LAOGHAIRE** Co Dublin Map **01** B1

### ★★★Hotel Victor
Rochestown Av(Best Western) ☎(01)2853555 & 2853102
Telex no 93366 FAX (01) 2853914
Closed 25 Dec
64⇛♘(8fb) CTV in all bedrooms T ✹ (ex guide dogs) ✳
sB&B⇛♘IR£35-IR£45 dB&B⇛♘IR£66-IR£80 ➡
Lift ℭ ⊞ CTV P ❊ CFA ♨
♒ Irish & French V ♥ ♨ ⊁ Lunch IR£7.50-IR£9 High tea
IR£7-IR£8 Dinner IR£14.50-IR£16.50 Last dinner 9.30pm
Credit Cards ❘1❘❘2❘❘3❘❘4❘❘5❘

**DUNMORE EAST** Co Waterford Map **01** C2 ◷

### ★★Haven
☎Waterford(051)83150 & 83540
Closed Nov-Feb
14⇛♘(3fb) CTV in all bedrooms T ✳ sB&B⇛♘IR£25-
IR£30 dB&B⇛♘IR£50-IR£60
CTV 40P ❊ CFA sauna solarium
V ♥
Credit Cards ❘1❘❘2❘❘3❘

### ★*Candlelight Inn*
☎Waterford(051)83215 FAX (051) 83289
Closed 25 Dec
11⇛♘(4fb) CTV in all bedrooms T ✹ (ex guide dogs)
CTV 9P ⚑ ❊ ⌣ (heated) ♗ (hard) squash ♨
V ♥ Last dinner 10pm
Credit Cards ❘1❘❘2❘❘3❘

**EMO** Co Laois Map **01** C3

### ★★★*Hotel Montague*
☎Portlaise(0502)26154 Telex no 60036 FAX (0502) 21976
Closed Jan-14 Mar
80⇛♘(4fb) CTV in all bedrooms T ✹ (ex guide dogs)
ℭ P ♨
♒ International V ♥ ♨ Last dinner 9.30pm
Credit Cards ❘1❘❘2❘❘3❘❘5❘

**ENNIS** Co Clare Map **01** B3 ◷

### ★★★Auburn Lodge
Galway Rd ☎Limerick(065)21247 Telex no 71077
FAX (065) 21202
75⇛♘(40fb)⊁in 15 bedrooms CTV in all bedrooms ⓡ T ✹ ✳
sB&B⇛♘IR£25-IR£38 dB&B⇛♘IR£40-IR£65 ➡
ℭ CTV 400P ❊ CFA squash snooker sauna ♬ *xmas*
♒ Irish & Continental V ♥ ♨ ⊁ Lunch IR£8.50 High tea
IR£6-IR£9&alc Dinner IR£11.50-IR£15&alc Last dinner
9.30pm
Credit Cards ❘1❘❘2❘❘3❘❘5❘

### ★★★*West County Inn*
☎(065)28421 Telex no 70794 FAX (065) 28801
(14fb) CTV in 110 bedrooms T
Lift ℭ CTV 400P 50☂ snooker sauna solarium gymnasium ♬
♨
♒ Irish & French V ♥ ♨ ⊁ Last dinner 9.30pm
Credit Cards ❘1❘❘2❘❘3❘❘5❘

### ★★Queen's
Abbey St ☎(065)28963 FAX (065) 28628
30⇛♘(20fb) CTV in all bedrooms ⓡ T ✳ sB&B⇛♘IR£25-
IR£35 dB&B⇛♘IR£40-IR£60 ➡
ℭ CTV ♗ CFA
♒ Irish & Continental V ♥ ♨ ⊁ Lunch IR£5-IR£8 High tea
IR£5-IR£8alc Dinner IR£10-IR£14&alc Last dinner 9.30pm
Credit Cards ❘1❘❘2❘❘3❘❘5❘

**ENNISCORTHY** Co Wexford Map **01** C3 ◷

### ★★Murphy-Flood's
☎(054)33413 Telex no 80464 FAX (054) 27398
Closed 25 Dec
21rm(5⇛13♘)(2fb) CTV in all bedrooms ⓡ T
✹ (ex guide dogs) sB&B⇛♘IR£23-IR£29
dB&B⇛♘IR£39-IR£49 ➡
ℭ CTV ♗
V ♥ ♨ ✳ Lunch IR£8.50-IR£10 High tea IR£7-IR£14 Dinner
IR£13-IR£16 Last dinner 9.30pm
Credit Cards ❘1❘❘2❘❘3❘❘4❘❘5❘

**ENNISKILLEN** Co Fermanagh Map **01** C5 ◷

### ★★★52% Killyhevlin
BT74 6H (Consort) ☎(0232)323481 FAX 324726
*This distinctive white-painted hotel stands just off the A4 2 miles*
*south of the town, beautifully situated on the shores of Lough*
*Erne; lawns lead down to the water's edge, and many rooms have*
*balconies with fine views towards distant hills.*
22⇛♘Annexe26rm(17fb) CTV in 22 bedrooms ⓡ T
✹ (ex guide dogs) sB&B⇛♘£50-£55 dB&B⇛♘£70-£75 ➡
ℭ CTV 500P ❊ CFA ♬
♒ International V ♥ ♨ ✳ Lunch £10.50-£20alc High tea £6-
£10&alc Dinner £14-£25alc Last dinner 9.15pm
Credit Cards ❘1❘❘2❘❘3❘❘5❘

### ★66% Railway
☎(0365)22084
Closed 25 Dec
*This friendly well managed commercial hotel now provides*
*attractively decorated accommodation. Some bedrooms are rather*
*compact but all are well equipped and the restaurant serves well*
*prepared meals.*
18⇛♘(4fb) CTV in 14 bedrooms ⓡ
ℭ CTV ▶ ♬ ♨
V ♥ ♨ Last dinner 9.15pm
Credit Cards ❘1❘❘3❘

**FURBO** Co Galway Map **01** B3 ❂

**★★★Connemara Coast**
☎Galway(091)92108 Telex no 50905 FAX (091) 92065
112⇌⌐(30fb) CTV in all bedrooms **T** ✗ (ex guide dogs) S10%
sB&B⇌⌐IR£45-IR£59 dB&B⇌⌐IR£70-IR£90 ⊟
☾ CTV 100P ❁ CFA ≋ ♫ *xmas*
♉ Irish & French **V** ♧ ☕ ✻ Bar Lunch IR£5-IR£9 Dinner IR£16.50-IR£17 Last dinner 9.30pm
Credit Cards [1] [2] [3] [4] [5]

**GALWAY** Co Galway Map **01** B3 ❂

**★★★★*Great Southern***
Eyre Square ☎(091)64041 Telex no 50164 FAX (091) 66704
120⇌⌐(10fb) CTV in all bedrooms ® **T** ✗ (ex guide dogs)
Lift ☾ ₱ ⊡ (heated) sauna ⌂
**V** ♧ ☕ ⚟ Last dinner 10pm
Credit Cards [1] [2] [3] [5]

**★★★Ardilaun House**
Taylor's Hill ☎(091)21433 Telex no 50013 FAX (091) 21546
Closed 23-31 Dec
91⇌⌐(19fb) CTV in all bedrooms **T** ✻ sB&B⇌⌐IR£35-IR£55 dB&B⇌⌐IR£56-IR£90
Lift ☾ CTV P CFA snooker sauna gymnasium
**V** ♧ ☕ ⚟ ✻ Lunch IR£8-IR£9 Dinner IR£15-IR£19.50 Last dinner 9.30pm
Credit Cards [1] [2] [3] [5]

**★★★Corrib Great Southern**
Dublin Rd ☎(091)55281 Telex no 50044 FAX (091) 51390
*A recently refurbished 5-storey hotel catering for both tourists and business guests. The hotel is conveniently situated just off the main Dublin/Galway road on the eastern side of the city, and friendly staff ensure a warm welcome.*
178⇌⌐(10fb)⚟in 5 bedrooms CTV in all bedrooms **T** ✗ (ex guide dogs) ⊟
Lift ☾ 350P ❁ CFA ⊡ (heated) ⚲ snooker table tennis jacuzzi *xmas*
♉ French ♧ ☕ ⚟ ✻ Lunch IR£9-IR£11 Dinner IR£17-IR£20&alc Last dinner 8.50pm
Credit Cards [1] [2] [3] [4] [5]

**★★★Galway Ryan**
Dublin Rd ☎(091)53181 Telex no 50149 FAX (091) 53187
96⇌⌐(96fb) CTV in all bedrooms **T** ✗ ✻ sB⇌⌐IR£45-IR£60 dB⇌⌐IR£70-IR£90 (room only) ⊟
Lift ☾ 100P ❁ ♫ *xmas*
**V** ♧ ☕ ✻ Bar Lunch IR£5-IR£10 High tea IR£8-IR£12 Dinner IR£15-IR£20&alc Last dinner 9pm
Credit Cards [1] [2] [3] [5]

**★★*Anno Santo***
Salthill ☎(091)23011
Closed 21-31 Dec
14⇌⌐ CTV in all bedrooms ® **T** ✗
CTV 12P ⌂
♧ ☕ ⚟ Last dinner 8.30pm
Credit Cards [1] [2] [3] [5]

**★★Lochlurgain**
22 Monksfield, Upper Salthill ☎(091)22122 FAX (091) 22399
Closed 2 Nov-13 Mar
13⇌⌐(3fb) CTV in all bedrooms **T** ✗ (ex guide dogs) ✻
sB&B⇌⌐IR£32.95-IR£42.50 dB&B⇌⌐IR£49.50-IR£65 ⊟
CTV 8P ⛟
♉ English & French ♧ ☕ ✻ Lunch IR£10 Dinner IR£11-IR£17.25 Last dinner 8pm
Credit Cards [1] [2] [3] [5]

**★*Atlanta***
☎(091)62241
RS Dining room closed after b/fast on Sun.
20rm(4⌐)(2fb) ✗
CTV 35P ⛟ ⌂

**GARRETTSTOWN** Co Cork Map **01** B2

**★★Coakley's Atlantic**
(Minotels) ☎Cork(021)778215 FAX (021) 778215
RS Jan-16 Mar
22⇌⌐(2fb) ✗ (ex guide dogs) ⊟
☾ CTV 60P ❁ CFA ⌂
**V** ♧ ☕ ⚟ ✻ Lunch frIR£9.75 High tea frIR£4.50 Dinner frIR£15 Last dinner 8.45pm
Credit Cards [1] [2] [3] [5]

**GARRYVOE** Co Cork Map **01** B2

**★★*Garryvoe***
☎Castlemartyr(021)646718 FAX (021) 646824
Closed 25 Dec
21rm(11⇌4⌐)(3fb) CTV in 12 bedrooms **T** ✗ (ex guide dogs)
CTV 20P ⛟ ❁ ⚑ 18 ⚲ (hard) table tennis ⌂
♧ ☕ Last dinner 8.45pm
Credit Cards [1] [2] [3] [4] [5]

**GLENDALOUGH** Co Wicklow Map **01** D3

**★★*The Glendalough***
☎Wicklow(0404)5135 FAX (0404) 5142
Closed Nov-15 Mar
17⇌⌐ **T** ✗ (ex guide dogs)
Lift CTV 100P ⚓ ⌂
♉ French **V** ♧ ☕ ⚟ Last dinner 8.45pm
Credit Cards [1] [2] [3] [4] [5]

**GLOUNTHAUNE** Co Cork Map **01** B2

**★★Ashbourne House**
☎Cork(021)353319 & 353310 FAX (021) 354338
26⇌⌐(3fb) CTV in all bedrooms ® **T** sB&B⇌⌐IR£36-IR£37 dB&B⇌⌐IR£62-IR£64 ⊟
CTV 100P ❁ CFA ≋ (heated) ⚲ (hard) sauna *xmas*
♉ French **V** ♧ ☕ Lunch IR£7-IR£12alc Dinner IR£17-IR£17.50&alc Last dinner 10pm
Credit Cards [1] [2] [3] [4] [5]

**GOREY** Co Wexford Map **01** D3 ❂

**★★★**

**★★★ ♛ MARLFIELD HOUSE**
(Relais et Châteaux)
☎(055)21124
Telex no 80757
FAX (055) 21572
Closed 10-31 Jan
*This lovely old Regency house stands in 35 acres of ground, allowing ample room for guests to stroll about and enjoy the wooded walks. The house was once the Dower House on the estate of the Earls of Courtown; it has been tastefully decorated and furnished in a style befitting its grand origins. An extension has been added to make a semi-circular marble entrance hall and bedrooms have been beautifully furnished with period furnishings and fireplaces.*

19⇨🐾(5fb)6⊞⊁in all bedrooms CTV in all bedrooms T
✠ sB&B⇨🐾IR£65-IR£120 dB&B⇨🐾IR£115-IR£150
⊞ ✿ CFA ♀ (grass) sauna
♀ Irish & French V ⍤ ₤ ✳ Lunch IR£17 Dinner IR£28
Last dinner 9pm
Credit Cards ①②③⑤

---

## GORTAHORK Co Donegal Map 01 B6

★★ *McFadden's*
☎(074)35267
Closed 25 Dec
20rm(5⇨8🐾)(6fb) CTV in 13 bedrooms ®
CTV 20P ✿ snooker table tennis ♨
♀ French ⍤ ₤
Credit Cards ①②③④⑤

---

## GOUGANE BARRA Co Cork Map 01 B2

★★Gougane Barra
☎(026)47069 & 47223 FAX (026) 47226
15 Apr-7 Oct
25rm(24⇨) CTV in 24 bedrooms T ✠ (ex guide dogs) ✳ S10%
sB⇨IR£24-IR£28 dB⇨IR£34-IR£42 (room only)
CTV 25P ⊞ ♪ nc5yrs
♀ Irish & French V ⍤ ₤ ⊁ ✳ S% Lunch IR£7 High tea IR£5-
IR£10alc Dinner IR£15-IR£16 Last dinner 8.30pm
Credit Cards ①②③⑤

---

## HEADFORD Co Galway Map 01 B4

★*Angler's Rest*
☎(093)35528
Closed 23 Dec-Jan
14rm(5⇨4🐾)(2fb) CTV in 8 bedrooms T
CTV 50P ♀ (hard & grass) squash ∪ ♨
⍤ ₤
Credit Cards ①②③

---

## HOLYWOOD Co Down Map 01 D5 ○

★★★★❀70% *Culloden*
BT18 0EX (HG) ☎(02317)5223 Telex no 74617
FAX (02317) 6777
Closed 24 & 25 Dec
*Its reputation as the province's finest hotel does not allow this
former bishop's palace, now much extended, to stand still. A
swimming pool and leisure complex have recently been added,
while good traditional standards continue to be maintained.
Bedrooms are modern and particularly spacious, and the popular
restaurant provides fine food and attentive service.*
91🐾4⊞ CTV in all bedrooms ® T
Lift ⟨ 500P ✿ ⊠ (heated) ♀ (hard) squash snooker sauna
solarium gymnasium putting and croquet ♨
V ⍤ ₤ Last dinner 9.30pm
Credit Cards ①②③⑤

---

## HOWTH Co Dublin Map 01 D4 ○

★★★Howth Lodge
(Best Western) ☎Dublin(01)321010 FAX (01) 322268
Closed 24-27 Dec
17🐾(2fb) CTV in all bedrooms ® T ✠ (ex guide dogs) S10%
sB🐾IR£45-IR£50 dB🐾IR£60-IR£70 (room only) 🍴
⟨ 200P ⊞ ✿ CFA ⊠ (heated) sauna solarium gymnasium
♀ Irish & French V ⍤ ₤ ⊁ S10% Lunch IR£9-IR£12 Dinner
IR£15-IR£18&alc Last dinner 9.30pm
Credit Cards ①②③④⑤
**See advertisement in colour supplement**

---

## INCHIGEELAGH Co Cork Map 01 B2

★Creedon's
☎(026)49012
16rm(8⇨🐾) ✠ ✳ sB&BfrIR£14 sB&B⇨🐾frIR£15
dB&BfrIR£26 dB&B⇨🐾frIR£29
CTV 4P
✳ Dinner frIR£11
Credit Cards ③

---

## INISHANNON Co Cork Map 01 B2 ○

★★Inishannon House
☎(021)775121 FAX (021) 775609
13⇨🐾(2fb)1⊞ CTV in all bedrooms T ✳ sB&B⇨🐾IR£40-
IR£90 dB&B⇨🐾IR£50-IR£100 🍴
P ✿ CFA ♪ *xmas*
♀ French V ⍤ ₤ ✳ Lunch IR£9.95-IR£16&alc Dinner
IR£17.50-IR£19.50&alc Last dinner 9.30pm
Credit Cards ①②③⑤

---

## IRVINESTOWN Co Fermanagh Map 01 C5

★★★63% Mahons
BT74 1GS ☎(03656)21656 Telex no 748105 FAX (03656) 21945
Closed 25 Dec
*A friendly long-established family-run hotel, with modestly
furnished but well equipped bedrooms and characterful public
areas filled with bric-a-brac and objets d'art.*
18⇨🐾(4fb)2⊞ ✿ CTV in all bedrooms T sB&B⇨🐾£23.50
dB&B⇨🐾£45 🍴
CTV 30P 10🚗 CFA solarium ♫
V ⍤ ₤ ⊁ Lunch fr£7 Dinner fr£10.50 Last dinner 9pm
Credit Cards ①③£

---

## JULIANSTOWN Co Meath Map 01 D4

★★Glenside
☎Drogheda(041)29049
14⇨🐾(6fb) CTV in all bedrooms T ✠ (ex guide dogs)
100P ♨
♀ French V ⍤ ₤ Last dinner 10pm
Credit Cards ①②③⑤

---

## KENMARE Co Kerry Map 01 A2

★★★★

★★★★★🏨 PARK
☎Killarney(064)41200
Telex no 73905
FAX (064) 41402
Closed 4 Jan-Etr & 18 Nov-
23 Dec
*On the edge of the Ring of
Kerry, in a lovely setting*

*beside the Kenmare River with its mountain backdrop, this
hotel has beautiful terraced gardens and walkways. The
award-winning restaurant, with river and mountain views,
offers fine food. Fish dishes are a speciality. Personal service
is a feature of the hotel and a warm welcome is assured.*
48⇨🐾(2fb) CTV in all bedrooms T ✠ sB&B⇨🐾IR£100-
IR£117 dB&B⇨🐾IR£168-IR£200 🍴
Lift ⟨ CTV 60P ✿ ▶ 9 ♀ (hard) snooker *xmas*
⍤ ₤ Lunch IR£16.50&alc Dinner IR£35&alc Last dinner
9pm
Credit Cards ①③④

**★★★★ Sheen Falls Lodge**
Kenmare, Co Kerry ☎Killarney(064)41600 Telex no 73820
FAX (064) 41386
Closed beginning Jan-mid Mar
*In a superb location beside the rapids on Sheen River before it joins Kenmare Bay. The hotel is surrounded by 300 acres of lawns and semi-tropical gardens, and offers views of woodland, water and distant mountains. Fishing rights on the river, famed for its salmon and sea trout, are available in season to guests. There is a fully equipped conference centre.*
40🛁🚿(11fb) CTV in all bedrooms T ✘ (ex guide dogs)
sB&B🛁🚿IR£135-IR£155 dB&B🛁🚿IR£190-IR£350 ⊟
Lift ☾ 50P ✤ CFA ℘ (hard) ♩ U snooker sauna solarium gymnasium jacuzzi croquet table tennis steamroom ♫ ⌂ *xmas*
V ✿ ☕ ⚔ Sunday Lunch IR£15.50 High tea IR£13.75-IR£18.50alc Dinner IR£35&alc Last dinner 9.30pm
Credit Cards [1] [2] [3] [4] [5]

**★ Lansdowne Arms**
☎(064)41368 FAX (064) 41114
22🛁🚿 CTV in all bedrooms ® T ✘ ✱ sB&B🛁🚿frIR£30
dB&B🛁🚿frIR£50 Continental breakfast ⊟
☾ CTV CFA
V ✿ ☕

KILKEE Co Clare Map **01** A3

**★ Halpin's**
Erin St ☎(065)56032 FAX (065) 56317
Closed Oct-Apr
11rm(7🛁🚿) T ✱ sB&BIR£16-IR£20 sB&B🛁🚿IR£18-IR£20
dB&BIR£30-IR£34 dB&B🛁🚿IR£34-IR£40
☾ ⊞ CTV P ▶ 9
V ✿ ☕ ⚔
Credit Cards [1] [2] [3] [4] [5]

KILKENNY Co Kilkenny Map **01** C3

**★★★ Hotel Kilkenny**
College Rd ☎(056)62000 FAX (056) 65984
*A modern hotel with an extensive range of facilities, including conference and leisure amenities. There are good public rooms and comfortable, well equipped bedrooms and bathrooms.*
60🛁🚿(20fb) CTV in all bedrooms T ✱ S12.5%
sB&B🛁🚿IR£36-IR£42 dB&B🛁🚿IR£60-IR£75 ⊟
☾ 250P ✤ CFA ▭ (heated) ℘ (hard) sauna solarium gymnasium turbo jacuzzi ♫ *xmas*
♁ French V ✿ ☕ ⚔ ✱ Lunch IR£8.25-IR£10&alc Dinner IR£14.50-IR£17&alc Last dinner 9.30pm
Credit Cards [1] [2] [3]

**★★★ Newpark**
☎(056)22122 FAX (056) 61111
60🛁🚿(18fb) CTV in all bedrooms ® T ✘ (ex guide dogs) ✱
sB🛁🚿IR£32-IR£38 dB🛁🚿IR£53 (room only) ⊟
☾ CTV 350P ✤ CFA ▭ (heated) ℘ (hard) sauna solarium gymnasium jacuzzi plunge pool *xmas*
V ✿ ☕ ✱ Lunch IR£8-IR£9.50&alc High tea IR£2.95-IR£10
Dinner IR£13.95-IR£15 Last dinner 10.15pm
Credit Cards [1] [2] [3] [4] [5]

**★★ Club House**
(Minotels) ☎(056)21994
27rm(22🛁🚿) CTV in all bedrooms ✱ S10% sB&BIR£25.50-IR£30.50 sB&B🛁🚿IR£33.50-IR£40.50 dB&BIR£45-IR£50
dB&B🛁🚿IR£52.50-IR£60 ⊟
☾ CTV 80P CFA squash sauna solarium gymnasium
V ✿ ☕ ⚔ S10% Lunch IR£5-IR£8.50alc High tea IR£6.50-IR£12.50alc Dinner IR£10.85-IR£13.50 Last dinner 9.30pm
Credit Cards [1] [2] [3] [4] [5]

KILLARNEY Co Kerry Map **01** A2

**★★★★ Aghadoe Heights**
☎(064)31766 Telex no 73942 FAX (064) 31345
61🛁🚿(5fb) CTV in all bedrooms T ✘ (ex guide dogs)
sB&B🛁🚿IR£60-IR£85 dB&B🛁🚿IR£90-IR£130 ⊟
☾ 180P ✤ CFA ▶ 18 ℘ (hard) ♩
♁ French V ✿ ☕ ⚔ ✱ Lunch IR£15.50&alc High tea IR£2.50-IR£11.50alc Dinner IR£25.50&alc Last dinner 9.30pm
Credit Cards [1] [2] [3] [5]

**★★★★ *Great Southern***
☎(064)31262 Telex no 73998 FAX (064) 31642
Closed 3 Jan-Feb
180🛁(20fb) CTV in all bedrooms T
Lift ☾ 150P ✤ ▭ (heated) ℘ (hard) snooker sauna gymnasium ⌂
♁ French & International V ✿ ☕ Last dinner 9.30pm
Credit Cards [1] [2] [3] [4] [5]

**★★★ Gleneagle**
☎(064)31870 Telex no 73923 FAX (064) 32646
177🛁🚿(6fb) CTV in all bedrooms T ✘ (ex guide dogs) ✱
S12.5% sB&B🛁🚿IR£42-IR£52 dB&B🛁🚿IR£54-IR£74 ⊟
Lift ☾ CTV 500P ✤ CFA ▭ (heated) ▶ 36 ℘ (hard) ♩ squash snooker sauna gymnasium table tennis steam room *xmas*
V ✿ ☕ ✱ S12.5% Lunch IR£8 Dinner IR£16.50 Last dinner 8.30pm
Credit Cards [1] [2] [3] [5]

**★★★ International**
(Best Western) ☎(064)31816 Telex no 73825 FAX (064) 31837
Closed Nov-Feb
92🛁🚿(14fb) CTV in all bedrooms ® T sB🛁🚿IR£30-IR£39
dB🛁🚿IR£36-IR£54 (room only) ⊟
Lift ☾ CTV ₱ CFA ♫
V ✿ Lunch frIR£8.50
Credit Cards [1] [2] [3] [5]

**★★★ Killarney Ryan**
☎(064)31555 Telex no 73950 FAX (064) 32438
Closed Nov-Feb
168🛁🚿(168fb) CTV in all bedrooms T ✘ ✱ sB🛁🚿IR£45-IR£60 dB🛁🚿IR£70-IR£90 (room only) ⊟
Lift ☾ 150P ✤ CFA ▭ (heated) ℘ (hard) sauna pitch & putt ♫
V ✿ ☕ ⚔ High tea IR£8-IR£12 Dinner IR£13-IR£15&alc
Last dinner 9pm
Credit Cards [1] [2] [3] [5]

**★★★ Lake**
Muckross Rd ☎(064)31035 FAX (064) 31902
Closed Dec-Feb
65🛁🚿(10fb) CTV in all bedrooms T ✘ (ex guide dogs) ✱
sB&B🛁🚿IR£30-IR£52 dB&B🛁🚿IR£50-IR£74 ⊟
☾ ⊞ CTV 120P ✤ ℘ (hard) ♩ ⌂
V ✿ ☕ S% Lunch IR£6.50-IR£8 Dinner IR£11-IR£16.50 Last dinner 9pm
Credit Cards [1] [3]

**★★★ *Torc Great Southern***
☎(064)31611 Telex no 73807
Closed 11 Oct-14 Mar
96🛁(15fb) CTV in all bedrooms T
☾ 100P ✤ ▭ (heated) ℘ (hard) sauna ⌂
Credit Cards [1] [2] [3] [5]

**★★ *Arbutus***
☎Tralee(064) 31037 FAX (064) 34033
35🛁🚿(2fb) CTV in all bedrooms ® T ✘ (ex guide dogs)

( ⊞ CTV ✗ ♨
♿ ⚼ Last dinner 8pm
Credit Cards ① ③ ⑤

### ★★ *Castlerosse*
☎(064)31144 Telex no 73910 FAX (064) 31031
Closed 31 Oct-Mar
67⇨♠(6fb) TV available **T**
( CTV 200P ✿ ♠ 18 ♪ (hard) ♪ ○ snooker sauna
gymnasium pitch & putt ♨
♿ ⚼ Last dinner 9pm
Credit Cards ① ③ ④ ⑤

### ★★ Dromhall
Muckross Rd(Minotels) ☎(064)31431 & 31894
FAX (064) 34242
Closed 31 Oct-Etr
59⇨♠(7fb) CTV in all bedrooms **T** ✷ sB&B⇨♠IR£25-
IR£32 dB&B⇨♠IR£44-IR£58 🛏
( ⊞ CTV 50P
**V** ♿ ⚼ ✷ Dinner IR£13-IR£15 Last dinner 8.30pm
Credit Cards ① ② ③

---

### ★★★ Court
☎Dublin(01)2851622 Telex no 33244 FAX (01) 2852085
Closed 25-26 Dec
86⇨♠(29fb)✗in 8 bedrooms CTV in all bedrooms ® **T**
S12.5% sB&B⇨♠IR£40-IR£45 dB&B⇨♠IR£56-IR£66 🛏
Lift ( 200P ✿ CFA snooker
♀ International **V** ♿ ⚼ ⚼ Lunch frIR£10&alc High tea IR£5-
IR£15alc Dinner frIR£16.50&alc Last dinner 10.30pm
Credit Cards ① ② ③ ⑤

### ★★★ Fitzpatrick Castle
☎Dublin(01)2840700 Telex no 30353 FAX (01) 2850207
92⇨♠(6fb)26🖃 CTV in all bedrooms **T** ✠ sB⇨♠IR£61.01-IR£79
dB⇨♠IR£81-IR£112 (room only) 🛏
Lift ( 300P ✿ CFA ⊡ (heated) ♪ (hard) squash sauna
solarium gymnasium beauty & hairdressing salon *xmas*
♀ International **V** ♿ ⚼ ⚼ Lunch IR£11.50 Dinner
IR£17.50&alc Last dinner 10.30pm
Credit Cards ① ② ③ ④ ⑤

---

### ★★ *Inis Cathaig*
☎(065)51036
16⇨ TV available **T**
CTV P ♨
♀ Continental **V** ♿ ⚼
Credit Cards ① ② ③ ④

---

### ★★ *Trident*
Worlds End ☎Cork(021)772301 Telex no 75892
FAX (021) 774173
40⇨ CTV in all bedrooms **T** ✠ (ex guide dogs)
( CTV 40P ♪ ♨
**V** ♿ ⚼ Last dinner 10pm
Credit Cards ① ② ③ ⑤

---

### ★★★ *Aberdeen Arms*
☎(065)81100 Telex no 70132
Closed mid Oct-Etr
48⇨♠
( 50P
Credit Cards ① ② ③ ⑤

---

### ★★★ Jurys
Ennis Rd ☎(061)327777 Telex no 70766 FAX (061) 326400
Closed 24-25 Dec

*Set in 4 acres of grounds with landscaped gardens beside the River*
*Shannon, this hotel is an oasis in the city centre for business people*
*and tourists alike. The recently added leisure centre is proving very*
*popular, and the personal service complements the improvements*
*that have been made to the hotel.*

95⇨♠(32fb) CTV in all bedrooms **T** ✠ (ex guide dogs) S10%
sB⇨♠IR£63 dB⇨♠IR£75 (room only) 🛏
( 180P ✿ CFA ⊡ (heated) sauna gymnasium plunge pool
childrens pool steam room ♪ ♨
♀ French **V** ♿ ⚼ ⚼ S10% Lunch IR£8.50&alc Dinner IR£10-
IR£20&alc Last dinner 10.30pm
Credit Cards ① ② ③ ⑤

### ★★★ *Limerick Inn*
Ennis Rd ☎(061)51544 Telex no 70621 FAX (061) 326281
Closed 25 Dec
153⇨ CTV in all bedrooms ® **T** ✠ (ex guide dogs)
Lift ( CTV 1000P ✿ ⊡ (heated) ♪ (hard) snooker sauna
solarium gymnasium ♨
♀ International **V** ♿ ⚼ ⚼ Last dinner 9.45pm
Credit Cards ① ② ③ ④ ⑤

### ★★★ Limerick Ryan
Ennis Rd ☎(061)53922 Telex no 70720 FAX (061) 326333
184⇨♠(184fb) CTV in all bedrooms **T** ✠ ✷ sB⇨♠IR£45-
IR£60 dB⇨♠IR£70-IR£90 (room only) 🛏
Lift ( 100P CFA ♪ *xmas*
**V** ♿ ⚼ ⚼ ✷ Bar Lunch IR£5-IR£10 High tea IR£8-IR£12
Dinner IR£15-IR£20&alc Last dinner 9.15pm
Credit Cards ① ② ③ ⑤

### ★★★ *New Green Hills*
Caherdavin ☎(061)53033 Telex no 70246 FAX (061) 53307
55⇨♠(3fb) CTV in all bedrooms ® **T** ✠
( CTV 150P ✿ ♨
**V** ♿ ⚼ ⚼ Last dinner 10pm
Credit Cards ① ② ③ ④ ⑤

### ★★★ *Two Mile Inn*
Ennis Rd ☎(061)53122 Telex no 70157 FAX (061) 53783
Closed 25 Dec
125⇨(2fb) CTV in all bedrooms **T** ✠ (ex guide dogs)
( ⊞ CTV 300P ✿ ♨
♀ International **V** ♿ ⚼ ⚼ Last dinner 9.30pm
Credit Cards ① ② ③ ④ ⑤

### ★★ *Royal George*
O'Connell St ☎(061)44566 FAX (061) 317171
Closed 25 Dec
58⇨ CTV in all bedrooms **T**
Lift ( CTV 50P ♨
♀ English & Continental **V** ♿ ⚼ ⚼ Last dinner 9.30pm
Credit Cards ① ② ③ ④ ⑤

---

### ★★ *Liscannor Golf*
☎(065)81186
Closed 15 Oct-15 Apr RS 15-30 Apr & 1-14 Oct
30⇨♠ ✠ (ex guide dogs)
( ⊞ CTV 50P ♠ 18 ♨
**V** ♿ ⚼ Last dinner 9.15pm
Credit Cards ① ② ③ ⑤

For key to symbols in English see the bookmark.

**K**

---

**LISDOONVARNA**Co Clare Map **01** B3

### ★★Lynch's
☎(065)74010
Closed 10 Oct-14 May
15rm(7⇨6♟)(3fb) ✳ sB&BfrIR£16 sB&B⇨♟frIR£18
dB&BfrIR£32 dB&B⇨♟frIR£36
《 ▦ CTV 10P 4🚗
V ۞ ⚏
Credit Cards ⒈ ⒊

### ★★Spa View
☎Ennis(065)74026
RS Mid Oct-Mid Mar
11⇨♟ T ✹ ✳ sB&B⇨♟frIR£30 dB&B⇨♟frIR£46
CTV 40P 2🚗 ⛱ 🎾 (hard)
♀ Irish, English & French ۞ ⚏ ✳ Dinner IR£16.50-IR£19
Last dinner 8.30pm
Credit Cards ⒈ ⒉ ⒊ ⒌

---

**LISMORE**Co Waterford Map **01** C2

### ★★★⚤Ballyrafter House
☎Dungarvan(058)54002
Closed Oct-Mar
12rm(4⇨) ⓡ ✹ (ex guide dogs) ✳ S10% sB&BIR£21
sB&B⇨IR£24 dB&BIR£36 dB&B⇨IR£40
CTV 40P 2🚗 ⛱ ✿ ⚘
♀ Irish & Italian V ۞ ⚏ ✳ Sunday Lunch IR£7.50-IR£10alc
Dinner IR£12-IR£14alc Last dinner 8.30pm
Credit Cards ⒈ ⒊ ⒌

---

**LISNASKEA**Co Fermanagh Map **01** C5 ◎

### ★★ 51%Ortine
☎(03657)21206 FAX (03657) 21100
Closed 25 & 26 Dec
*This modernised hotel in the town centre has a popular lounge bar and offers extensive function facilities, though bedrooms remain modest.*
18⇨♟(4fb) CTV in all bedrooms T ✹ (ex guide dogs)
sB&B⇨♟£27-£30 dB&B⇨♟£39.50-£45 🍴
《 CTV 50P 1🚗 CFA
V ۞ ⚏
Credit Cards ⒈ ⒊ ⓔ

---

**LONDONDERRY**Co Londonderry Map **01** C5 ◎

### ★★★ 66%Everglades
Prehen Rd BT47 2PA (Consort) ☎(0504)46722 Telex no 748005
FAX (0504) 49200
*A modern hotel on the A5 to the south of the town, offering well equipped comfortably furnished bedrooms. Pleasant staff provide a good level of services, though public areas are tending to look rather worn.*
52⇨♟(1fb)1🛏 CTV in all bedrooms ⓡ T ✹ (ex guide dogs)
✳ sB&B♟fr£55 dB&B♟fr£65 (room only) 🍴
Lift 《 ▦ CTV 250P ✿ CFA ♫ *xmas*
♀ International V ۞ ⚏ ⅙ ✳ Lunch fr£7.75 High tea fr£5.50
Dinner fr£11.50 Last dinner 9.45pm
Credit Cards ⒈ ⒉ ⒊ ⒌ ⓔ

---

**LUCAN**Co Dublin Map **01** D4 ◎

### ★★★Finnstown House
Newcastle Rd ☎(01)6280644 FAX (01) 6281088
25⇨♟(10fb) CTV in all bedrooms ⓡ T sB&B⇨♟IR£69
dB&B⇨♟IR£95 🍴
《 CTV 90P ✿ CFA ⬆ (heated) ▶ 9 🎾 (hard) sauna solarium
gymnasium table tennis croquet lawn ♫ *xmas*

♀ International V ۞ ⚏ ✳ Lunch frIR£13 Dinner frIR£17
Last dinner 9.30pm
Credit Cards ⒈ ⒉ ⒊ ⒌

### ★★★Lucan Spa
☎Dublin(01)6280494 FAX (01) 6280841
RS 2-3 Jan
25⇨♟(10fb) CTV in all bedrooms ⓡ T
《 CTV 90P ⛱ ✿ ▶ 9 🎾 (hard) sauna solarium gymnasium
table tennis croquet. ⚘
♀ French & international V ۞ ⚏ Last dinner 9.30pm
Credit Cards ⒈ ⒉ ⒊ ⒌

---

**MACROOM**Co Cork Map **01** B2 ◎

### ★★Castle
☎(026)41074 FAX (026) 41505
26⇨♟(5fb) CTV in all bedrooms ⓡ T ✹ sB&B⇨♟IR£25-
IR£30 dB&B⇨♟IR£45-IR£52 🍴
CTV 6P squash gymnasium ♫
V ۞ ⚏ Lunch IR£9-IR£11 High tea IR£9-IR£20alc Dinner
IR£10-IR£20 Last dinner 9pm
Credit Cards ⒈ ⒉ ⒊ ⒋ ⒌

### ★★Victoria
☎(026)41082 FAX (026) 42148
Closed 25-29 Dec
11⇨♟(7fb) ⓡ T
CTV 🅿 ♫ ⚘
♀ Irish, French & Italian V ۞ ⚏ Last dinner 9pm
Credit Cards ⒈ ⒉ ⒊ ⒌

---

**MALAHIDE**Co Dublin Map **01** D4

### ★★★Grand
☎(01)450633 Telex no 31446 FAX (01) 450987
Closed 25-26 Dec
*A fine old hotel with an imposing pillared entrance and lobby. A smart modern extension houses comfortable rooms, many with good sea views. There is a separate cabaret venue and busy conference centre to the rear.*
100⇨♟(20fb) CTV in all bedrooms T ✹ (ex guide dogs)
S12.5% sB&B⇨♟IR£47.25-IR£53 dB&B⇨♟IR£83.25-
IR£92.25 🍴
Lift 《 CTV 600P ✿ CFA
♀ European V ۞ ⚏ S12.5% Lunch IR£10.15-IR£12 Dinner
IR£18.50-IR£20 Last dinner 10.15pm
Credit Cards ⒈ ⒉ ⒊ ⒌

---

**MALIN**Co Donegal Map **01** C6

### ★Malin
☎(077)70606
12rm(2⇨) CTV in all bedrooms T ✹
CTV 100P ♫ ⚘
♀ English V ۞ ⚏ Last dinner 9.30pm
Credit Cards ⒈ ⒊ ⒌

---

**MALLOW**Co Cork Map **01** B2 ◎

### ★★★⚤Longueville House
(Relais et Châteaux) ☎(022)47156 & 47306 FAX (022) 47459
Closed 23 Dec-28 Feb
17⇨♟3🛏 CTV in all bedrooms T ✹ sB&B⇨♟IR£40-IR£60
dB&B⇨♟IR£80-IR£150 🍴
CTV 50P 3🚗 ⛱ 🎾 ✦ snooker nc8yrs
♀ Irish & French V ۞ ⚏ Lunch frIR£14 Dinner frIR£22 Last
dinner 9.30pm
Credit Cards ⒈ ⒉ ⒊ ⒋

**MOVILLE** Co Donegal Map **01** C6

**★★** *McNamara's*
☎(077)82010
Closed 24-26 Dec
15rm(5⇨📺)(3fb)
CTV 𝄞 ঌ
V ✆ ⚲ Last dinner 9.30pm
Credit Cards 1 2 3 4

**★** *Foyle*
☎(077)82025
20rm(2⇨2📺)(4fb) ® ✖ (ex guide dogs)
⊞ CTV 𝄞 ✿ ঌ
V ✆ ⚲ Last dinner 9pm

**NEWCASTLE** Co Down Map **01** D5

**★★★**60% **Slieve Donard**
(HG) ☎(03967)23681 FAX (03967) 24830
*This large, red brick, late Victorian house with its own beach
overlooks the sea from grounds at the foot of the beautiful
Mountains of Mourne. Many bedrooms have been upgraded to a
very good standard, and a continual programme of improvement
operates throughout the hotel. Facilities include all-weather tennis
courts, a well equipped gymnasium and a luxurious indoor
swimming pool.*
120⇨(20fb) CTV in all bedrooms ® T ✳ sB&B⇨£70
dB&B⇨£112 🅱
Lift 《 ⊞ CTV 500P ✿ CFA ⌧ (heated) ▶ 27 ♪ (hard)
solarium gymnasium jacuzzi *xmas*
♀ English & French V ✆ ⚲ ✳ Lunch £12.95 Dinner £16 Last
dinner 9.30pm
Credit Cards 1 2 3 5

**★★⚘**64% *Enniskeen*
98 Bryansfold Rd BT33 0LF ☎(03967)22392 FAX (03967) 24084
23rd Mar – 11th Nov
*This friendly, family-run, country house hotel, enjoying views of
the Mountains of Mourne and Dundrum Bay from its setting in 10
acres of grounds and gardens just outside the town, provides the
ideal base from which to tour the area.*
12⇨📺(1fb)⚥in 2 bedrooms CTV in all bedrooms ® T ✖
CTV 45P ✿ ♪ (grass) ঌ
V ✆ ⚲ Last dinner 8.30pm
Credit Cards 1 3

**NEWCASTLE WEST** Co Limerick Map **01** B3

**★** *River Room Motel*
☎Limerick(069)62244
15⇨📺(1fb) CTV in all bedrooms T ✖
⊞ CTV P ✿ ♫ ঌ
V ✆ ⚲ ⚥ Last dinner 8.45pm
Credit Cards 1 2 3 5

**NEWMARKET-ON-FERGUS** Co Clare Map **01** B3 ☺

**★★★** *Clare Inn*
☎(061)71161 Telex no 72085
121⇨📺
《 150P ⌧ (heated) ▶
Credit Cards 1 2 3 4 5

**NEWPORT** Co Mayo Map **01** A4 ☺

**★★★⚘** **Newport House**
☎(098)41222 & 41154 FAX (098) 41613
Closed Oct-18 Mar
*Not only have we pleasure in including hotels from all over Ireland
in our 1992 guide, but also we are delighted to award our first
'Courtesy and Care' award to an hotel in Eire to Kieran and*

*Thelma Thompson's Newport House Hotel. A warm and
hospitable welcome awaits the arriving guest at Newport House,
with complimentary afternoon tea to make one feel at home. Fine
food and comfortable accommodation are the hallmarks of this
beautiful old country mansion on on edge of Newport village, and
old fashioned service at its best. Renowned for its fishing, the hotel
has extensive fishing rights on surrounding lakes and rivers. The
Thompsons are genial hosts and join the chat among the guests in
the evening. Much of the food is from the fishery, garden or farm
and is carefully cooked and presented in elegant surroundings.
(See colour feature on p20.)*
24⇨📺Annexe10⇨📺(2fb)2⚅ T S% sB&B⇨📺IR£48-IR£61
dB&B⇨📺IR£80-IR£106
《⊞P ✿ ♪ ঌ
♀ French V ✆ ⚲ S% Lunch IR£12-IR£18 Dinner IR£27 Last
dinner 9.30pm
Credit Cards 1 2 3 5

**NEW ROSS** Co Wexford Map **01** C3 ☺

**★★** **The Old Rectory**
Rosbercon ☎(051)21719 FAX (051) 22974
*A comfortable small family-run hotel overlooking the River
Barrow and the historic town of New Ross. It is a peaceful place
with well tended gardens, and makes a good base for visiting some
lovely spots in the area.*
13rm(3⇨9📺)(3fb)⚥in 2 bedrooms CTV in all bedrooms ® T
✖ S% sB&BIR£25-IR£30 sB&B⇨📺IR£25-IR£30
dB&BIR£40-IR£50 dB&B⇨📺IR£40-IR£50
CTV 80P ✿ *xmas*
♀ French V ✆ ⚲ ⚥ S% Lunch IR£7.95 High tea IR£7.95
Dinner IR£14.95&alc Last dinner 9.30pm
Credit Cards 1 3 5

---

★★★59% **Chimney Corner**
630 Antrim Rd BT36 8RF ☎Belfast(0232)844925
Telex no 748158 FAX (0232) 844352
Closed 12-24 Jul & 19-31 Dec
*Situated beside the A6, midway between Belfast and the Airport, this busy commercial hotel has grown from a 19th century inn, and offers compact but well equipped modern bedrooms. There are extensive function facilities and a choice of eating venues.*
63⇄🏠⚡️in 10 bedrooms CTV in all bedrooms ® T
🐕 (ex guide dogs) sB&B⇄🏠fr£70 dB&B⇄🏠fr£85
《 CTV 300P CFA ♬ (hard) sauna ♬ *xmas*
♀ British & French V ♥ ✔ ✳ Lunch fr£10 Dinner fr£15 Last dinner 9.30pm
Credit Cards ①②③④⑤

---

★★63% **Royal Arms**
51 High St BT78 1BA (Consort) ☎(0662)243262 FAX 245011
Closed 25 Dec
*This long-established family-run commercial hotel in the town centre has been refurbished to provide pleasant well equipped bedrooms and attractive public areas of some character. Extensive function facilities are available and staff are friendly and helpful.*
21⇄🏠1🚪 CTV in all bedrooms ® T sB&B⇄🏠fr£29.75 dB&B⇄🏠fr£55.50 🅿
《 CTV 200P 🅿 18 ♪ ⚲ snooker ♬
V ♥ ⚡️ Lunch fr£5.50&alc High tea fr£6 Dinner fr£9.50 Last dinner 9.30pm
Credit Cards ①③ ⑥

---

★★★**Connemara Gateway**
☎Galway(091)82328 Telex no 50905 FAX (091) 82332
62⇄🏠(24fb) CTV in all bedrooms ® T 🐕 (ex guide dogs) ✳ S10% sB&B⇄🏠IR£38-IR£53.75 dB&B⇄🏠IR£72.50-IR£83.50 🅿
CTV 80P ❄ CFA🏊 (heated) ♬ (hard) sauna solarium croquet table tennis
♀ Irish & French V ♥ ⚡️ ✳ Bar Lunch IR£2.50-IR£8alc Dinner IR£16.50-IR£17.50&alc Last dinner 9.15pm
Credit Cards ①③④⑤

★★**Corrib**
(Minotels) ☎(091)82329 FAX (091) 82522
Closed Jan-Feb
18⇄🏠Annexe8⇄🏠 CTV in 9 bedrooms ® T
🐕 (ex guide dogs) sB&B⇄🏠IR£23-IR£32 dB&B⇄🏠IR£44-IR£53 🅿
CTV 30P ❄
⚡️ Dinner IR£15.95
Credit Cards ①②③④

---

★★★★**Great Southern**
☎(064)45122 Telex no 73899
Closed 2 Jan-12 Mar
25⇄🏠Annexe59⇄🏠(6fb) CTV in all bedrooms T
🐕 (ex guide dogs) ✳ sB&B⇄🏠IR£68.50-IR£79.50 dB&B⇄🏠IR£118-IR£140 🅿
《60P ❄ CFA🏊 (heated) 🅿 9 ♬ (hard) ♪ ⚲ snooker sauna
♬ ♋ *xmas*
V ♥ ⚡️ ✔ ✳ Dinner IR£19-IR£24&alc Last dinner 8.45pm
Credit Cards ①②③⑤

---

A rosette means exceptional standards of cuisine.

---

★★68% **Bayview**
2 Bayhead Rd BT57 8RZ ☎Bushmills(02657)31453 FAX 32360
*Overlooking the harbour on the beautiful north Antrim coast and within easy reach of the Giant's Causeway, this well-furnished hotel offers comfortable accommodation with friendly service and good home cooking.*
16⇄🏠 CTV in all bedrooms ® T 🐕 (ex guide dogs) ✳ sB&B⇄🏠fr£35 dB&B⇄🏠fr£56 🅿
《 CTV 50P CFA 🖼 (heated) snooker sauna solarium ♬ ♋ *xmas*
V ♥ ⚡️ ✳ Lunch £7.50 High tea £4.50-£9 Dinner £5-£14 Last dinner 10pm
Credit Cards ①③

★★60% **Beach House**
The Sea Front BT57 8RT ☎(02657)31214 FAX 31664
*Conveniently situated for the beach, this resort hotel offers generally spacious if rather functional accommodation. Bedrooms are equipped with modern facilities and many enjoy sea views.*
32⇄🏠(17fb) CTV in all bedrooms ® T 🐕 (ex guide dogs)
《 CTV 40P CFA table tennis pool table
♀ French V ♥ ⚡️ ✔ ✳ Lunch £7.50 High tea £5-£9alc Dinner £11-£13 Last dinner 9pm
Credit Cards ①③

---

★★★**Killeshin**
Dublin Rd ☎(0502)21663 Telex no 60036
44⇄🏠
《 P
Credit Cards ①②③④⑤

---

❀❀❀ ✕✕**Ramore**
The Harbour BT56 8DF ☎(0265)824313
*An attractive restaurant, delightfully located to overlook the harbour, strongly features fresh local fish in a selection of interesting and inventive dishes which are temptingly presented in a modern style. Smartly dressed staff provide friendly and very attentive service.*
Closed Mon, Sun & 1st 2 wks Feb Lunch not served
♀ French V 60 seats Bar Lunch £2.50-£5.25alc Dinner £18-£24alc Last dinner 10pm 10 P nc5yrs
Credit Cards ①③

---

★★**Westpark**
☎(0509)41121 & 41112 FAX (0509) 41357
Closed Oct-Mar
29⇄🏠(1fb) CTV in all bedrooms T 🐕 (ex guide dogs) ✳ sB&B⇄🏠IR£25.30-IR£29.70 dB&B⇄🏠IR£44-IR£52 🅿
《 CTV 400P ❄ CFA ♋
♥ ⚡️ ✔
Credit Cards ①②③④⑤

---

★★**Curryhills House**
☎(045)68150 FAX (045) 68805
Closed 23-30 Dec
10⇄🏠(10fb) ® T ✳ S10% sB&B⇄🏠IR£26.40-IR£37 dB&B⇄🏠IR£40-IR£55 🅿
⊞ TV 50P ❄ CFA ♬ ♋
♥ ✔ ✳ S10% Sunday Lunch IR£8.90 Dinner IR£16.50&alc Last dinner 11pm
Credit Cards ①③

---

N

## RATHMULLAN Co Donegal Map 01 C6

### ★*Pier*
☎(074)58178
Closed Oct-1 Mar
16rm(11⇨🏠)

## RATHNEW Co Wicklow Map 01 D3

### ★★★🏤Tinakilly House
☎(0404)69274 FAX (0404) 67806
29⇨🏠5🛏 CTV in all bedrooms ® T ✝ (ex guide dogs) S%
sB&B⇨🏠IR£75-IR£80 dB&B⇨🏠IR£90-IR£200
60P ✿ CFA ♪ (hard) *xmas*
♺ ⚏ ✄ S% Lunch frIR£17 Dinner frIR£27 Last dinner 9pm
Credit Cards 1️⃣ 2️⃣ 3️⃣ 4️⃣ 5️⃣

### ★★ *Hunter's*
☎(0404)40106
RS 25 Dec
18rm(10⇨🏠)
50P
Credit Cards 1️⃣ 2️⃣ 3️⃣ 5️⃣

## RECESS Co Galway Map 01 A4

### ★★★🏤Lough Inagh Lodge
Inagh Valley ☎Clifden(095)34706 & 34694 FAX (095) 34708
Closed Nov-Mar
*This 19th-century shooting lodge has been skilfully restored and
upgraded into a luxurious hotel. It is in a superb location, fronted
by a good fishing lake and with lovely mountain views. Large
lounges with blazing fires and a cosy oak-lined bar offer great
warmth and comfort. The spacious high-ceilinged bedrooms are
beautifully furnished with comfort much in mind. Food and
presentation are excellent, and over all a friendly informal
atmosphere prevails. (Best Newcomer award winner 1991/1992
see p38.)*
12⇨🏠2🛏 CTV in all bedrooms T ✝ (ex guide dogs)
dB&B⇨🏠IR£76-IR£112
⊞16P ♨ CFA ♪
♀ Irish & French V ♺ ⚏ ✄ ✱ Bar Lunch IR£2-IR£6 Dinner
IR£12.50-IR£23alc Last dinner 9pm
Credit Cards 1️⃣ 2️⃣ 3️⃣

## RENVYLE Co Galway Map 01 A4

### ★★★Renvyle House
☎(095)43511 FAX (095) 43515
Closed 7 Jan-14 Mar
65⇨🏠 CTV in all bedrooms T S12.5% sB&B⇨🏠IR£46-
IR£62 dB&B⇨🏠IR£67.75-IR£89.25 🛏
( CTV 100P ✿ CFA 🏊 (heated) ► 9 ♪ (hard) ✔ ∪ snooker
sauna solarium croquet boating lawn bowls bicycle hire ♨
*xmas*
♀ International ♺ ⚏ ✄ ✱ S12.5% Lunch IR£10-IR£20alc
Dinner IR£22 Last dinner 9pm
Credit Cards 1️⃣ 2️⃣ 3️⃣ 5️⃣

## ROSCOMMON Co Roscommon Map 01 B4 ⊙

### ★★★Abbey
☎(0903)26240 & 26505 FAX (0903) 25305
RS 25 Dec
20⇨🏠 CTV in all bedrooms ® T ✝ sB&B⇨🏠IR£32-
IR£42.50 dB&B⇨🏠IR£45-IR£50 🛏
( CTV 45P ✿ CFA
♀ French ✱ Lunch IR£7-IR£10.50 High tea IR£7.50-IR£12
Dinner IR£15-IR£17.50 Last dinner 9.30pm
Credit Cards 1️⃣ 2️⃣ 3️⃣ 5️⃣

## ROSCREA Co Tipperary Map 01 C3 ⊙

### ★*Pathé*
☎(0505)21622 & 21301 FAX (0505) 21813
Closed 25-26 Dec
20rm(9⇨🏠)(2fb) CTV in 10 bedrooms T ✝ (ex guide dogs) ✱
sB&BIR£18.50-IR£22 sB&B⇨🏠IR£20-IR£25 dB&BIR£28-
IR£30 dB&B⇨🏠IR£30-IR£36 🛏
10P
♺ ⚏ ✄
Credit Cards 1️⃣ 2️⃣ 3️⃣ 5️⃣

## ROSSCAHILL Co Galway Map 01 B4

### ★★★Ross Lake House
(Minotels) ☎(091)80109 & 80154 FAX (091) 80184
13⇨🏠 T ✝ (ex guide dogs) ✱ sB&B⇨🏠IR£32.45-IR£39.60
dB&B⇨🏠IR£49-IR£63.80
CTV 100P ✿ CFA ♪ (hard) *xmas*
V ♺ ⚏ ✱ Lunch IR£9 Dinner IR£17 Last dinner 9pm
Credit Cards 1️⃣ 2️⃣ 3️⃣ 4️⃣ 5️⃣

## ROSSLARE Co Wexford Map 01 D2 ⊙

★★★

### ★★★ KELLY'S STRAND
☎(053)32114
FAX (053) 32222

Closed mid Dec-late Feb

*Since 1895, successive
generations of the Kelly
family have extended and
improved the original
building, creating a truly fine hotel concentrating on family
holidays all year round. There is plenty for those who want an
activity holiday or those who wish to rest and relax. With its
extensive recreational facilities, guests can keep themselves
busy or simply relax – either in one of the many comfortable
lounges or by playing a leisurely game of giant outdoor chess
and draughts in the sun. Entertainment is provided nightly in
the hotel's own ballroom. One of the more lasting impressions
gained here is of the hospitality offered by the Kellys who
cater in every possible way for their guests. Menus are varied
and generous and reflect care in preparation. Fresh local fish
and shellfish are very popular.*
Annexe96⇨🏠(15fb) CTV in all bedrooms T ✝ ✱
sB&B⇨🏠IR£35-IR£38 dB&B⇨🏠IR£64-IR£70 🛏
Lift ( CTV ♨ ✿ CFA 🏊 (heated) 🏊 ♪ (hard) squash
snooker sauna solarium gymnasium
♀ English & French ♺ ⚏ ✄ ✱ Lunch IR£9.50-IR£11.50
Dinner IR£18.95-IR£19.95 Last dinner 9pm
Credit Cards 1️⃣ 3️⃣

### ★★★Cedars
☎(053)32124 FAX (053) 32243
Closed 11 Oct-10 Mar
34⇨🏠(34fb) CTV in all bedrooms ® T ✝ (ex guide dogs)
S12.5% sB&B⇨🏠IR£35-IR£40 dB&B⇨🏠IR£70-IR£80 🛏
( ⊞ CTV 150P ✿ CFA sauna solarium gymnasium ♪ ♨ *xmas*
V ♺ ⚏ ✄ S12.5% Sunday Lunch IR£7.95-IR£8.95 Dinner
IR£16.95&alc Last dinner 9.45pm
Credit Cards 1️⃣ 3️⃣ 4️⃣

For key to symbols in English see the bookmark.

R

## ROSSLARE HARBOUR Co Wexford Map **01** D2

**★★★Great Southern**
☎Wexford(053)33233 Telex no 80788 FAX (053) 33543
Closed 4 Jan-9 Mar
99⇌↱(28fb) CTV in all bedrooms **T** ✱ sB⇌↱frIR£45 dB⇌↱frIR£60.75 (room only) ⊟
☾ CTV 100P CFA ⊡ (heated) ♪ (hard) snooker sauna gymnasium steam room ♤ *xmas*
**V** ♡ ⊻ ⊁ ✱ S12.5% Sunday Lunch frIR£8.75 Dinner IR£18 Last dinner 9pm
Credit Cards [1] [2] [3] [5]

**★★★Hotel Rosslare**
☎(053)33110 & 33312 FAX (053) 33386
Closed 25 Dec
25rm(22⇌↱)(7fb) CTV in all bedrooms **T** ✱ sB&BIR£19-IR£26 sB&B⇌↱IR£31.75-IR£39 dB&BIR£38-IR£52 dB&B⇌↱IR£53.50-IR£78 ⊟
☾ ⊞ 50P CFA squash snooker sauna
♉ International **V** ♡ ⊻ ⊁ ✱ Lunch IR£6.75-IR£13alc Dinner IR£11.50-IR£15.75&alc Last dinner 8.45pm
Credit Cards [1] [2] [3] [5]

## ROSSNOWLAGH Co Donegal Map **01** B5

**★★★Sand House**
☎Sligo(072)51777 FAX (072) 52100
Closed early Oct-Etr
42⇌↱(6fb)3⊟ **T** ✱ sB&B⇌↱IR£30-IR£53 dB&B⇌↱IR£60-IR£95 ⊟
CTV 40P 2⌂ ✲ CFA ♪ (hard) croquet miniature golf
♉ Irish & French ♡ ⊻ ⊁ ✱ Lunch IR£10.50 Dinner IR£17.50-IR£18.50 Last dinner 9pm
Credit Cards [1] [2] [3] [5]

## SALTHILL

See Galway

## SLANE Co Meath Map **01** C4 ◉

**★★Conyngham Arms**
☎Drogheda(041)24155 FAX (041) 24205
Closed Good Friday & Xmas
16rm(15⇌↱)(4fb)1⊟ CTV in all bedrooms **T** ✗ (ex guide dogs) S% sB&B⇌↱IR£23-IR£30 dB&B⇌↱IR£42-IR£62 ⊟
12P 12⌂ ✲ CFA
♉ Irish & French **V** ♡ ⊻ ⊁ Sunday Lunch IR£9.50-IR£10.50 High tea IR£8.90-IR£10alc Dinner IR£10.50-IR£20alc Last dinner 9.45pm
Credit Cards [1] [2] [3] [5]

## SLIGO Co Sligo Map **01** B5 ◉

**★★★Ballincar House**
Rosses Point Rd ☎(071)45361 FAX (071) 44198
Closed 23-28 Dec
*A converted country house set in spacious mature gardens, with views of the rose garden from the dining room. The hotel has good food, friendly service and pleasant staff, and is ideal for both tourist and commercial users.*
26⇌↱ CTV in all bedrooms **T** ✗ (ex guide dogs) S10% sB&B⇌↱IR£45-IR£55 dB&B⇌↱IR£70-IR£90
☾ CTV 60P ✲ CFA ♪ (hard) snooker sauna
**V** ♡ ⊻ ⊁ ✱ Bar Lunch IR£8.50-IR£9.50 High tea IR£8-IR£12 Dinner IR£17.50-IR£19 Last dinner 9.15pm
Credit Cards [1] [2] [3] [5]

**★★★Sligo Park**
Pearse Rd ☎(071)60291 FAX (071) 69556
89⇌↱ CTV in all bedrooms **T** sB⇌↱IR£45-IR£50 dB⇌↱IR£65-IR£75 (room only) ⊟
☾ ⊞ CTV P ✲ CFA ⊡ (heated) ♪ (hard) snooker sauna gymnasium jacuzzi steamroom plunge pool ♫ *xmas*
♉ Irish & French **V** ♡ ⊻ ⊁ ✱ Lunch IR£8.50-IR£9 Dinner IR£16.90-IR£17.50&alc Last dinner 9.15pm
Credit Cards [1] [2] [3] [5]

**★★Silver Swan**
☎(071)43231 FAX 42232
Closed 25 & 26 Dec
27⇌↱ CTV in all bedrooms ® **T** ✗ (ex guide dogs) S10% sB&B⇌↱IR£30-IR£38 dB&B⇌↱IR£46-IR£70
☾ 40P CFA
**V** ♡ ⊻ ⊁ ✱ Bar Lunch IR£1.50-IR£5alc
Credit Cards [1] [2] [3] [5]

## SPIDDAL Co Galway Map **01** B3 ◉

**★★*Bridge House***
Connemara ☎(091)83118
Closed 23 Dec-Jan
14rm(11⇌↱)
☾ 20P 2⌂
Credit Cards [1] [2] [3] [5]

**★★Park Lodge**
☎(091)83159 FAX (091) 83494
Closed Oct-May
23⇌↱(4fb) **T** ✗ ✱ sB&B⇌↱IR£28-IR£32 dB&B⇌↱IR£40-IR£44
CTV 50P ✲ CFA
✱ Dinner frIR£15
Credit Cards [1] [2] [3] [5]

## STRABANE Co Tyrone Map **01** C5 ◉

**★★★62% Fir Trees**
Melmount Rd BT82 9JT (HG) ☎(0504)382382 FAX 885932
*A modern hotel with white walls and a red tiled roof, standing beside the A5 just south of the town, offers accommodation in rooms which, though compact, are well equipped and scheduled for upgrading in the near future. Ample public areas are matched by good parking amenities, facilities are available for banquets, conferences or small meetings, and friendly staff provide helpful service.*
26⇌↱(1fb) CTV in all bedrooms ® **T** ✱ S% sB&B⇌↱£42 dB&B⇌↱£60 ⊟
☾ ⊞ CTV 100P ✲ CFA ▶ 18 ♩ U ♫
♉ French **V** ♡ ⊻ ✱ Lunch £6.95 High tea £5.95-£6.75 Dinner £12.95&alc Last dinner 9.15pm
Credit Cards [1] [2] [3] [5]

## STRAFFAN Co Kildare Map **01** C4

**○The Kildare Hotel & Country Club**
☎(01)6273333 FAX (01) 6273312
Due to have opened mid Jul 1991
42⇌↱

## TIPPERARY Co Tipperary Map **01** B3 ◉

**★Royal**
Bridge St ☎(062)51204 & 51285
Closed 25 Dec & Good Friday
16⇌↱(3fb) CTV in 5 bedrooms ✗ sB&B⇌↱IR£20 dB&B⇌↱IR£40
CTV 200P CFA
♡ ⊻ ✱ Lunch IR£7-IR£7.50 Dinner frIR£8.50 Last dinner 8.45pm
Credit Cards [1] [2] [3]

TRALEE Co Kerry Map **01** A2 ⊕

**★★★The Brandon**
☎(066)23333 Telex no 73130 FAX (066) 25019
160⇔🏠(2fb) CTV in all bedrooms **T** S% sB&B⇔🏠IR£35-IR£42 dB&B⇔🏠IR£70-IR£110 🕮
Lift ℂ 200P CFA 🖾 (heated) sauna solarium gymnasium ♬
✳ Lunch IR£7.50&alc Dinner IR£12-IR£15&alc Last dinner 9.30pm
Credit Cards ①②③④⑤

**★★★Earl Of Desmond**
Killarney Rd ☎(066)21299 Telex no 73064 FAX (066) 21976
Closed 22 Nov-Feb
52⇔🏠 CTV in all bedrooms **T** ✾ (ex guide dogs) S%
sB&B⇔🏠IR£35-IR£48 dB&B⇔🏠IR£50-IR£80 🕮
ℂ🎹 CTV 400P ✿ CFA ♟ (hard) ♪ ♨
**V** ✆ ♨ ⊬ S% Sunday Lunch IR£8.50-IR£10 Dinner IR£13-IR£28 Last dinner 9.30pm
Credit Cards ①②③④⑤

**★★Grand**
Denny St ☎(066)21499 FAX (066) 22877
48rm(42⇔🏠) CTV in all bedrooms **T** ✾ S% sB&BIR£32-IR£36 sB&B⇔🏠IR£32-IR£36 dB&B⇔🏠IR£48-IR£56 dB&B⇔🏠IR£48-IR£56 🕮
ℂ🎹 CTV CFA
**V** ✆ ♨ Lunch IR£5-IR£6 High tea IR£6-IR£8 Dinner IR£12-IR£14&alc Last dinner 9.30pm
Credit Cards ①②③

WARINGSTOWN Co Armagh Map **01** D5 ⊕

**⊛✕ ✕ Grange**
Main St BT66 7QH ☎(0762)881989
*This very attractive building – once a Cromwellian planter's home – now houses a delightfully furnished restaurant with an intimate atmosphere. A good standard of cookery makes full use of local produce, while service successfully combines friendliness and professionalism.*
P

WATERFORD Co Waterford Map **01** C2 ⊕

**★★★★🏌Waterford Castle**
The Island ☎(051)78203 Telex no 80332 FAX (051) 79316
19⇔🏠4🛏 CTV in all bedrooms **T** ✾ (ex guide dogs) 🕮
Lift ℂ 60P ⊞ ✿ CFA 🖾 (heated) ♟ (hard) snooker gymnasium clay pigeon shooting ♨ *xmas*
**V** ✆ ♨ ⊬ Lunch IR£15.50&alc Dinner IR£28.50&alc Last dinner 10pm
Credit Cards ①②③⑤

**★★★Granville**
The Quay(Best Western) ☎(051)55111 FAX (051) 70307
Closed 25-26 Dec
74⇔🏠(35fb) CTV in all bedrooms **T** ✾ (ex guide dogs) ✳
sB&B⇔🏠IR£42.50-IR£54 dB&B⇔🏠IR£69-IR£92.50 🕮
Lift ℂ CFA sauna gymnasium ♬
⚒ International **V** ✆ ♨ ⊬ S% Lunch IR£6.25-IR£8.95 High tea IR£6.25-IR£7 Dinner IR£15-IR£16.50 Last dinner 10.30pm
Credit Cards ①②③④⑤

A rosette means exceptional standards of cuisine.

**★★★Jurys**
Ferrybank ☎(051)32111 Telex no 80684 FAX (051) 32863
98⇔🏠(20fb)⊬in 4 bedrooms CTV in all bedrooms ® **T** ✳
sB⇔🏠IR£53 dB⇔🏠IR£73 (room only) 🕮
Lift ℂ 300P ✿ CFA 🖾 (heated) ♟ (hard) sauna solarium gymnasium steam room plunge pool ♬ *xmas*
⚒ International **V** ✆ ♨ ⊬ ✳ Lunch IR£9.90 Dinner IR£16&alc Last dinner 9.15pm
Credit Cards ①②③④⑤

**★★★Tower**
The Mall ☎(051)75801 Telex no 80699 FAX (051) 70129
Closed 24-26 Dec
125⇔🏠(12fb) CTV in all bedrooms **T** ✳ sB⇔🏠IR£37.50-IR£43.50 dB⇔🏠IR£62-IR£70 (room only) 🕮
Lift ℂ ♟ CFA 🖾 (heated) sauna solarium gymnasium jacuzzi steam room ♬
⊬
Credit Cards ①②③⑤

**★★Bridge**
The Quay ☎(051)77222 Telex no 80141
67⇔🏠
Lift ℂ
Credit Cards ①②③④⑤

**★★Dooley's**
30 The Quay ☎(051)73531 FAX (051) 70262
Closed 25-27 Dec
37rm(34⇔🏠) CTV in all bedrooms ® **T** ✾ ✳
sB&B⇔🏠IR£31-IR£33 dB&B⇔🏠IR£46-IR£57
CTV ♟ CFA
⚒ International **V** ✆ ♨ ⊬ ✳ Lunch IR£8.50 High tea IR£6.50-IR£9 Dinner IR£13.50&alc Last dinner 9.30pm
Credit Cards ①②③⑤

WESTPORT Co Mayo Map **01** A4

**★★★Hotel Westport**
☎(098)25122 FAX (098) 26739
Closed 24 & 25 Dec
49⇔🏠(5fb) CTV in all bedrooms **T** ✾ (ex guide dogs)
sB&B⇔🏠IR£28-IR£46 dB&B⇔🏠IR£40-IR£66 🕮
ℂ CTV 100P ✿ CFA
**V** ⊬ Lunch IR£5-IR£7 Dinner IR£10-IR£14&alc Last dinner 9pm
Credit Cards ①②③⑤

**★★The Olde Railway**
The Mall ☎(098)25166 & 25605 Telex no 80464
FAX (098) 25090
27rm(25⇔🏠)(2fb)2🛏 CTV in all bedrooms **T** ✾ (ex guide dogs) ✳ sB&B⇔🏠IR£30-IR£45 dB&B⇔🏠IR£50-IR£75 🕮
ℂ 50P 4🚗 ✿ CFA clay pigeon shooting
**V** ✆ ♨ ⊬ S% Sunday Lunch IR£7.50-IR£8.95 Dinner IR£13.50-IR£15&alc Last dinner 9.30pm
Credit Cards ①②③⑤

WEXFORD Co Wexford Map **01** D2 ⊕

**★★★Ferrycarrig**
Ferrycarrig ☎(053)22999 FAX (053) 41982
40⇔🏠(3fb) CTV in all bedrooms **T** S%
sB&B⇔🏠IR£35-IR£48 dB&B⇔🏠IR£63-IR£86 🕮
Lift ℂ 40P ✿ CFA ♟ (hard) ♬ *xmas*
⚒ Irish & French **V** ✆ ♨ ⊬ ✳ Lunch IR£12.50-IR£13.50 Dinner IR£22.50-IR£24&alc Last dinner 9.45pm
Credit Cards ①②③⑤

**T**

### ★★★Talbot

Trinity St ☎Waterford(053)22566 Telex no 80658
FAX (053) 23377
RS 25 Dec
100⇨🟤(12fb)⊬in 10 bedrooms CTV in all bedrooms ® T
🏋 (ex guide dogs) ✳ sB⇨🟤IR£35-IR£45 dB⇨🟤IR£55-
IR£65 (room only)
Lift ℂ 60P CFA ▭ ⌔ squash snooker sauna gymnasium
games room beautician *xmas*
V ✪ 🌮 ⊬ ✳ Lunch frIR£7 Dinner IR£13-IR£18 Last dinner
8.45pm
Credit Cards 1 2 3 4 5

### ★★★White's

George's St(Best Western) ☎(053)22311 Telex no 80630
FAX (053) 45000
Closed 24-26 Dec
76⇨🟤Annexe6⇨🟤(1fb)2🛏 CTV in all bedrooms ® T
🏋 (ex guide dogs) S12.5% sB&B⇨🟤IR£40-IR£48
dB&B⇨🟤IR£60-IR£87.50 🛏
Lift ℂ 100P CFA 🎵
🍽 International V ✪ 🌮 ⊬ Lunch IR£9-IR£14 High tea
IR£4.15-IR£7.15alc Dinner IR£11.50-IR£24.95alc Last dinner
9.30pm
Credit Cards 1 2 3 4 5

A rosette means exceptional standards of cuisine.

### ★★Wexford Lodge

(Minotels) ☎(053)23611 FAX (053) 23342
19⇨🟤(5fb) CTV in all bedrooms ® T 🏋 (ex guide dogs) ✳
sB&B⇨🟤IR£25-IR£27.50 dB&B⇨🟤IR£50-IR£55
CTV 30P 🚗 CFA
🍽 French V ✪ 🌮 ⊬ ✳ Sunday Lunch frIR£7.50 Dinner
frIR£8.95 Last dinner 9pm
Credit Cards 1 2 3 5

**WOODENBRIDGE** Co Wicklow Map **01** D3 ⊕

### ★★Woodenbridge Inn

☎(0402)35146 FAX (0402) 35573
11⇨🟤(2fb)1🛏 CTV in all bedrooms T 🏋 (ex guide dogs) ✳
S% sB&B⇨🟤IR£24-IR£36 dB&B⇨🟤IR£44-IR£56 🛏
200P ✿ CFA
✪ 🌮 ⊬ ✳ Bar Lunch IR£4-IR£9&alc
Credit Cards 1 2 3

**YOUGHAL** Co Cork Map **01** C2 ⊕

### ★★Devonshire Arms

Pearse Square ☎(024)92827 & 92409 FAX (024) 92900
Closed Xmas
10⇨🟤(3fb) CTV in all bedrooms T 🏋 (ex guide dogs) S10%
sB&B⇨🟤IR£27-IR£29 dB&B⇨🟤IR£50-IR£55
20P ✿ CFA 🎵
🍽 Irish & French V ✪ 🌮 S10% Lunch frIR£8.50 High tea
frIR£8 Dinner IR£18-IR£24&alc Last dinner 8.30pm
Credit Cards 1 2 3 5

W

# Country
# HOUSE HOTELS

The following list includes country houses in England; the Channel Islands; Northern Ireland; the Republic of Ireland; Scotland; Scottish islands and Wales.

**ENGLAND**

**AVON**
**Hinton Charterhouse**
✸✸ ★★★ ♨ 77% Homewood Park
**Hunstrete**
✸✸★★★ ♨ Hunstrete House
**Rangeworthy**
★★ ♨ 68% Rangeworthy Court
**Thornbury**
✸✸ ★★★ ♨ Thornbury Castle

**BEDFORDSHIRE**
**Flitwick**
✸✸✸ ★★★ ♨ 72% Flitwick Manor

**BUCKINGHAMSHIRE**
**Aylesbury**
✸✸ ★★★ ♨ Hartwell House
**Taplow**
✸✸ ★★★★★ ♨ Cliveden

**CHESHIRE**
**Chester**
✸✸ ★★★ ♨ 78% Crabwall Manor
**Nantwich**
★★★ ♨ 78% Rookery Hall
**Sandiway**
✸✸ ★★★ ♨ 79% Nunsmere Hall Country House
**Tarporley**
★★ ♨ 64% The Willington Hall

**CLEVELAND**
**Easington**
✸ ★★★ ♨ 69% Grinkle Park

**CO DURHAM**
**Darlington**
★★★ ♨ 67% Headlam Hall

**CORNWALL & ISLES OF SCILLY**
**Falmouth**
★★★ ♨ 76% Penmere Manor
**Helston**
★★ ♨ 70% Nansloe Manor
**Lamorna Cove**
★★★ ♨ 60% Lamorna Cove
**Liskeard**
★★ ♨ 60% Country Castle
✸✸✸ ★★ ♨ Well House
**Mawnan Smith**
★★★ ♨ 73% Meudon
**Penzance**
★★★ ♨ 60% Higher Faugan
**Portscatho**
★★ ♨ 61% Roseland House
**St Agnes**
★★ ♨ 61% Rose in Vale

**St Austell**
✸ ★★ ♨ 75% Boscundle Manor
**St Wenn**
✸✸ ★★ ♨ Wenn Manor
**Talland Bay**
★★★ ♨ 72% Talland Bay

**CUMBRIA**
**Alston**
★★ ♨ 78% Lovelady Shield
**Ambleside**
★★ ♨ 66% Crow How
★★ ♨ 72% Nanny Brow
**Appleby-in-Westmorland**
✸ ★★★ ♨ 70% Appleby Manor
**Bassenthwaite**
★★★★ ♨ 60% Armathwaite Hall
✸ ★★ ♨ 69% Overwater Hall
**Brampton**
✸✸ ★★ ♨ Farlam Hall
**Coniston**
★ ♨ 72% Old Rectory
**Crosby on Eden**
✸ ★★★ ♨ 70% Crosby Lodge
**Elterwater**
★★ ♨ 68% Eltermere
**Grange-over-Sands**
★★ ♨ 66% Graythwaite Manor
**Grasmere**
✸ ★★★ ♨ Michael's Nook
**Hawkshead**
✸ ★★ ♨ 73% Field Head House
★★ ♨ 73% Highfield House
**Howtown**
✸✸✸ ★★★ ♨ Sharrow Bay
**Keswick**
✸ ★★ ♨ 74% Dale Head Hall
★★ ♨ 68% Lyzzick Hall
★★ ♨ 59% Red House
**Thornthwaite**
★★ ♨ 67% Thwaite House
**Watermillock**
✸ ★★★ ♨ 78% Leeming House
✸ ★★ ♨ Old Church
✸✸ ★★★ ♨ 75%
Rampsbeck
**Windermere**
★★ ♨ 65% Belmont Manor
✸✸ ★★ ♨ Holbeck Ghyll
★★★ ♨ 66% Langdale Chase
★★ 74% Lindeth Fell
✸ ★★★ ♨ 74% Linthwaite
**Witherslack**
✸ ★ ♨ Old Vicarage

**DERBYSHIRE**
**Ashbourne**
✸ ★★ ♨ 74% Callow Hall
**Ashford-in-the-Water**
★★★ ♨ 69% Riverside
**Matlock**
★★ ♨ 65% Red House
✸ ★★★ ♨ 73% Riber Hall
**Rowsley**
★★ ♨ 71% East Lodge

**DEVON**
**Ashburton**
✸ ★★ ♨ 73% Holne Chase
**Barnstaple**
✸ ★★ ♨ 69% Downrew House
✸ ★ ♨ Halmpstone Manor
**Burrington**
✸ ★★★ ♨ 69% Northcote Manor
**Chagford**
✸ ★★★ ♨ Gidleigh Park
✸ ★★★ ♨ 75% Mill End
**Chittlehambolt**
★★★ ♨ 74% Highbullen
**Clawton**
★★ ♨ 70% Court Barn
**Gittisham**
✸ ★★★ ♨ 68% Combe House
**Hawkchurch**
★★★ ♨ 71% Fairwater Head
**Haytor**
★★★ ♨ 73% Bel Alp House
**Honiton**
★★★ ♨ 63% Deer Park
**Kingsbridge**
★★★ ♨ 76% Buckland-Tout-Saints
**Lewdown**
✸ ★★ ♨ Lewtrenchard Manor
**Lydford**
★★ ♨ 67% Lydford House
**Lynton**
★ ♨ 66% Combe Park
★★ ♨ 65% Hewitts
**Martinhoe**
✸ ★★ ♨ 70% Old Rectory
**Mary Tavy**
★★ ♨ 62% Moorland Hall
**Moretonhampstead**
★★ ♨ 64% Glebe House
**North Huish**
✸✸✸ ★★ ♨ Brookdale House
**Sidmouth**
★★ ♨ 70% Brownlands
**South Brent**
✸ ★★ ♨ 74% Glazebrook House

**South Molton**
★★ ♨ 73% Marsh Hall
✸✸✸ ★★ ♨ Whitechapel Manor
**Stoke Gabriel**
★★★ ♨ 71% Gabriel Court
**Torquay**
✸ ★★★ ♨ 70% Oreston Manor House
**Two Bridges**
✸ ★★ ♨ 71% Prince Hall
**Whimple**
✸✸ ★★ ♨ Woodhayes

**DORSET**
**Gillingham**
✸✸ ★★ ♨ Stock Hill House
**Studland**
★★ ♨ 63% Manor House

**EAST SUSSEX**
**Battle**
✸ ★★ ♨ Netherfield Place
**Uckfield**
✸ ★★ ♨ Horsted Place
**Wadhurst**
✸ ★★ 66% Spindlewood

**ESSEX**
**Dedham**
★★★ ♨ Maison Talbooth

**GLOUCESTERSHIRE**
**Bibury**
★★ ♨ 67% Bibury Court
**Buckland**
✸✸ ★★★ ♨ Buckland Manor
**Charingworth**
✸✸ ★★★ ♨ 79% Charingworth Manor
**Cheltenham**
✸✸ ★★★ ♨ Greenway
**Stroud**
★★★ ♨ 65% Burleigh Court
**Tetbury**
✸✸✸ ★★★ ♨ Calcot Manor
**Upper Slaughter**
✸✸ ★★★ ♨ 78% Lords of the Manor

**HAMPSHIRE**
**Brockenhurst**
★★ ♨ 70% Whitley Ridge
**Hurstbourne Tarrant**
✸ ★★ ♨ 74% Esseborne Manor
**Lymington**
★★★ ♨ 73% Passford House
**Lyndhurst**
✸ ★★★ ♨ 70% Parkhill
**New Milton**
✸✸✸ ★★★★ ♨ Chewton Glen

# COUNTRY HOUSE HOTELS

**Rotherwick**
★★★★ ⚜ 80% Tylney Hall
**Winchester**
❀ ★★★★ ⚜ 71% Lainston House

**HEREFORD & WORCESTER**
**Abberley**
❀ ★★★ ⚜ 77% Elms
**Broadway**
❀❀ ★★ ⚜ 71% Collin House
**Chaddesley Corbett**
❀❀ ★★★ ⚜ 75% Brockencote Hall
**Hereford**
★★ ⚜ 64% Netherwood
**Ledbury**
❀❀❀ ★★ ⚜ 72% Hope End
**Leominster**
❀ ★ ⚜ Marsh Country House
**Malvern**
★★★ ⚜ 65% Cottage in the Wood
★★ ⚜ 72% Holdfast Cottage
**Pencraig**
★★ ⚜ 62% Pencraig Court
**Ross-on-Wye**
★★ ⚜ 71% Glewstone Court
★★★ ⚜ 65% Pengethley Manor
★★ ⚜ 75% Peterstow

**HUMBERSIDE**
**Driffield**
★★ ⚜ 57% Wold House
**Little Weighton**
★★★ ⚜ 63% Rowley Manor

**KENT**
**Ashford**
❀ ★★★★★ ⚜ Eastwell Manor
**Cranbrook**
★★ ⚜ 69% Kennel Holt

**LANCASHIRE**
**Garstang**
★★ ⚜ 72% The Pickerings

**LEICESTERSHIRE**
**Melton Mowbray**
❀ ★★★★ ⚜ Stapleford Park
**Oakham**
❀❀❀ ★★★ ⚜ Hambleton Hall

**LINCOLNSHIRE**
**Lincoln**
★★★ ⚜ 68% Washingborough Hall

**NORFOLK**
**Bunwell**
★★ ⚜ 64% Bunwell Manor
**Cawston**
❀ ★ ⚜ 66% Grey Gables
**Felmingham**
★★ ⚜ 72% Felmingham Hall
**Grimston**
❀❀ ★★★ ⚜ Congham Hall

**NORTH YORKSHIRE**
**Aldwark**
★★★ ⚜ 78% Aldwark Manor
**Appleton le Moors**
★★ ⚜ 73% Dweldapilton Hall

**Arncliffe**
★★ ⚜ 74% Amerdale House
**Ayton, Great**
❀ ★★★ ⚜ 74% Ayton Hall
**Bilbrough**
★★★ ⚜ Bilbrough Manor
**Crathorne**
★★★★ ⚜ 63% Crathorne Hall
**Hackness**
★★★ ⚜ 68% Hackness Grange
**Hawes**
★★ ⚜ 69% Stone House
**Lastingham**
★★ ⚜ 75% Lastingham Grange
**Malton**
★★★ ⚜ 70% Burythorpe House
**Markington**
★★★ ⚜ 76% Hob Green
**Masham**
★★ ⚜ 74% Jervauix Hall
**Monk Fryston**
★★★ ⚜ 68% Monk Fryston Hall
**Scarborough**
★★★ ⚜ 64% Wrea Head

**NORTHUMBERLAND**
**Allendale**
❀ ★★ ⚜ 70% Bishopfield
**Belford**
★★ ⚜ 77% Waren House
**Cornhill-on-Tweed**
★★★ ⚜ 62% Tillmouth Park
**Powburn**
★★ ⚜ 75% Breamish House

**NOTTINGHAMSHIRE**
**Nottingham**
❀ ★ ⚜ 70% Langar Hall

**OXFORDSHIRE**
**Chadlington**
❀ ★★ ⚜ 79% The Manor
**Horton-cum-Studley**
❀❀ ★★★ ⚜ 67% Studley Priory
**Milton, Great**
❀❀❀❀ ★★★ ⚜ Le Manoir aux Quat' Saisons

**SHROPSHIRE**
**Market Drayton**
❀ ★★★ ⚜ 71% Goldstone Hall
**Oswestry**
★★ ⚜ 55% Sweeney Hall
**Shrewsbury**
❀ ★★★ ⚜ 73% Albright Hussey
**Worfield**
❀❀ ★★★ ⚜ 68% Old Vicarage

**SOMERSET**
**Dulverton**
❀ ★★ ⚜ Ashwick House
★★★ ⚜ 72% Carnarvon Arms

**Holford**
★★ ⚜ 69% Combe House
**Lympsham**
★★ ⚜ 64% Batch Farm Country House
**Minehead**
❀ ★★ ⚜ 72% Periton Park
**Shipdam**
❀ ★★ ⚜ 67% Daneswood House
**Simonsbath**
★★ ⚜ 72% Simonsbath House
**Ston Easton**
❀ ★★★ ⚜ Ston Easton Park
**Waterrow**
❀ ★ ⚜ 76% Hurstone Country Hotel & Restaurant
**Wheddon Cross**
★★ ⚜ 70% Raleigh Manor
**Wincanton**
★★ ⚜ 59% Holbrook House
**Withypool**
★★ ⚜ 69% Westerclose

**SUFFOLK**
**Bury St Edmunds**
❀ ★★★ ⚜ 75% Ravenwood Hall
**Hintlesham**
❀❀ ★★★ ⚜ Hintlesham Hall
**Woodbridge**
★★★ ⚜ 73% Seckford Hall

**SURREY**
**Bagshot**
❀❀❀ ★★★★ ⚜ 72% Pennyhill Park

**WARWICKSHIRE**
**Billesley**
❀❀❀ ★★★ ⚜ 76% Billesley Manor
**Leamington Spa**
❀❀❀ ★★★ ⚜ Mallory Court

**WEST MIDLANDS**
**Hockley Heath**
❀❀❀ ★★★ ⚜ 77% Nuthurst Grange

**WEST SUSSEX**
**Amberley**
❀❀ ★★★ ⚜ 77% Amberley Castle
**Arundel**
★ ⚜ 62% Burpham
**Climping**
★★★ ⚜ 67% Bailiffscourt
**East Grinstead**
❀❀ ★★★ ⚜ Gravetye Manor
**Lower Beeding**
❀❀ ★★★★ ⚜ 70% South Lodge
**Thakeham**
❀ ★★★ ⚜ 74% Abingworth Hall

**WEST YORKSHIRE**
**Todmorden**
★★★ ⚜ 70% Scaitcliffe Hall

**Wentbridge**
★★★ ⚜ 67% Wentbridge House
**Wetherby**
❀ ★★★ ⚜ Wood Hall

**WILTSHIRE**
**Bradford on Avon**
❀❀ ★★★ ⚜ 75% Woolley Grange
**Castle Combe**
❀❀ ★★★★ ⚜ 76% Manor House
**Limpley Stoke**
★★★ ⚜ 69% Cliffe
**Malmesbury**
★★★ ⚜ 76% Whatley Manor
**Melksham**
❀❀❀ ★★★ ⚜ 74% Beechfield House
**Warminster**
❀ ★★★★ ⚜ 67% Bishopstrow House

## CHANNEL ISLANDS

**JERSEY**
**Rozel Bay**
❀ ★★★ ⚜ 75% Château la Chaire
**St Saviour**
❀❀ ★★★★ ⚜ Longueville Manor

## NORTHERN IRELAND

**DOWN**
**Newcastle**
★★ ⚜ Enniskeen

## REPUBLIC OF IRELAND

**CLARE**
**Ballyvaughan**
★★★ ⚜ Gregans Castle
**CORK**
**Ballylickey**
★★ ⚜ Sea View
**Mallow**
★★★ ⚜ Longueville House
**GALWAY**
**Ballynahinch**
★★★ ⚜ Ballynahinch Castle
**Cashel**
★★★ ⚜ Cashel House
**Clifden**
★★★ ⚜ Rock Glen
**Recess**
★★★ ⚜ Lough Inagh Lodge
**KERRY**
**Kenmare**
★★★★ ⚜ Sheen Falls Lodge
★★★ ⚜ Park
**LIMERICK**
**Adare**
★★★★ ⚜ Adare Manor
**MAYO**
**Newport**
★★★ ⚜ Newport House

**SLIGO**
**Castlebaldwin**
★★★ ♨ Cromleach Lodge
Country House
**TIPPERARY**
**Cashel**
★★★★ ♨ Cashel Palace
**Dundrum**
★★★ ♨ Dundrum House
★★ ♨ Rectory House
**WATERFORD**
**Lismore**
★★★ ♨ Ballyrafter House
**Waterford**
★★★★ ♨ Waterford Castle
**WEXFORD**
**Gorey**
★★★ ♨ Marlfield House
**WICKLOW**
**Rathnew**
★★★ ♨ Tinakilly House

## SCOTLAND

**BORDERS**
**Greenlaw**
★★ ♨ 63% Purves Hall
**Kelso**
❀❀ ★★★ ♨ 77% Sunlaws
House
**Peebles**
★★ ♨ 76% Cringletie House
★★ ♨ 67% Venlaw Castle
**Walkerburn**
★★ ♨ 68% Tweed Valley
**CENTRAL**
**Alloa**
❀❀ ★★★ ♨ 79% The Gean
House
**Callander**
❀ ★★★ ♨ 69% Roman
Camp
**Dunblane**
❀❀ ★★★ ♨ Cromlix House
**DUMFRIES & GALLOWAY**
**Auchencairn**
★★★ ♨ 70% Balcary Bay
**Clarencefield**
★★ ♨ 67% Comlongen Castle
**Crossmichael**
★★ ♨ 59% Culgruff House
**Newton Stewart**
★★★ ♨ 64% Kirroughtree
**Portpatrick**
❀❀❀ ★★ ♨ Knockinaam
Lodge
**Port William**
★★★ ♨ 63% Corsemaizie
House
**Rockcliffe**
★★★ ♨ 68% Baron's Craig
**FIFE**
**Markinch**
★★★★ ♨ 73% Balbirnie
House
**GRAMPIAN**
**Banchory**
❀ ★★★ ♨ Banchory Lodge

★★★★ ♨ 71% Invery
House
★★★ ♨ 75% Raemoir
**Huntly**
★★ ♨ 56% Castle
**Kildrummy**
❀ ★★★ ♨ 78% Kildrummy
Castle
**Rothes**
★★★ ♨ 64% Rothes Glen
**HIGHLAND**
**Achnasheen**
★★ ♨ 70% Ledgowan Lodge
**Arisaig**
❀ ★★★ ♨ Arisaig House
**Cannich**
❀ ★★ ♨ 69% Cozac Lodge
**Dulnain Bridge**
★★ ♨ 67% Muckrach Lodge
**Fort William**
❀❀ ★★★★ ♨ Inverlochy
Castle
**Invergarry**
★★ ♨ 63% Glengarry Castle
**Inverness**
❀ ★★★ ♨ 78% Bunchrew
House
★★ ★ ♨ Dunain Park
**Kentallen**
❀ ★★ ♨ 73% Ardsheal House
**Whitebridge**
❀❀ ★★ ♨ Knockie Lodge
**LOTHIAN**
**Gullane**
❀ ★★★ ♨ Greywalls
**Humbie**
★★★ ♨ 66% Johnstounburn
House
**Uphall**
❀ ★★★ ♨ 65% Houstoun
House
**STRATHCLYDE**
**Appin**
❀ ★★★ ♨ 73% Invercreran
**Biggar**
❀ ★★★ ♨ 75% Shieldhill
★★ ♨ 68% Wyndales House
**Dolphinton**
★★★ ♨ 65% Dolphinton
House
**Eriska**
❀ ★★★ ♨ Isle of Eriska
**Kilchrenan**
❀ ★★★ ♨ 73% Ardanaiseig
★★★ ♨ 64% Taychreggan
**Kilwinning**
★★★ ♨ 69% Montgreenan
Mansion House
**Langbank**
❀❀ ★★★ ♨ 72% Gleddoch
House
**Maybole**
❀ ★★★ ♨ Ladyburn
**Oban**
★ ♨ 67% Foxholes
**Skelmorlie**
★★★ ♨ 60% Manor Park
**Stewarton**
❀ ★★★ ♨ 75% Chapeltoun
House

**TAYSIDE**
**Aberfeldy**
❀ ★★ ♨ Farleyer House
❀❀ ★ ♨ 73% Guinach House
**Alyth**
★★ ♨ 62% Lands of Loyal
**Auchterarder**
❀❀ ★★★ ♨ 76%
Auchterarder House
★★★ ♨ 68% Duchally House
**Auchterhouse**
❀ ★★★ ♨ 71% Old Mansion
House
**Blairgowrie**
★★★ ♨ 65% Altamount House
★★★ ♨ 77% Kinloch House
**Dunkeld**
❀❀ ★★★ ♨ 81% Kinnaird
House
**Glamis**
★★★ ♨ 71% Castleton
House
**Glenshee**
★★ ♨ 64% Dalmunzie House
**Kinclaven**
★★★ ♨ 77% Ballathie House
**Letham**
★★★ ♨ 66% Idvies House
**Perth**
❀❀ ★★★ ♨ 78%
Murrayshall
**Pitlochry**
★★★ ♨ 69% Pine Trees

## SCOTTISH ISLANDS

**SHETLANDS**
**Brae**
★★★ ♨ 67% Busta House
**SKYE**
**Isle Ornsay**
❀❀ ★★ ♨ 69% Kinloch
Lodge
**Skeabost Bridge**
★★★ ♨ 66% Skeabost House

## WALES

**CLWYD**
**Llandrillo**
★★ ♨ 76% Tyddyn Llan
Country House Hotel &
Restaurant
**Llangollen**
★★★ ♨ 64% Bryn Howel
**Northop**
❀ ★★★ ♨ 79% Soughton
Hall
**Wrexham**
★★★ ♨ 64% Llwyn Onn Hall
**DYFED**
**Aberystwyth**
❀ ★★★ ♨ 66% Conrah
**Crugybar**
★★ ♨ 70% Glanrannel Park
**Egwysfach**
❀ ★★★ ♨ 72% Ynishir Hall
**Lampeter**
★★★ ♨ 66% Falcondale
Country House

**Lamphey**
❀ ★★★ ♨ 65% Court
**St Davids**
❀ ★★★ ♨ 64% Warpool
Court
**Tenby**
❀ ★★ ♨ 79% Penally Abbey
**GWYNEDD**
**Aberdovey**
★★★ ♨ 65% Plan Penhelig
**Abersoch**
★★★ ♨ 65% Porth Tocyn
**Beddgelert**
★★★ ♨ 64% Bryn Eglwys
★ ♨ 69% Sygun Fawr
**Betws-y-Coed**
★★★ ♨ 64% Craig-y-
Dderwyn
★★★ ♨ 64% Plas Hall
**Criccieth**
★★★ ♨ 66% Bron Eifion
★★ ♨ 65% Mynydd
Ednyfed
**Dolgellau**
❀ ★★★ ♨ 70% Domelynllyn
Hall
**Llanbedr**
★★ ♨ 60% Cae Nest Hall
**Llandudno**
❀ ★★★ ♨ Bodysgallen Hall
**Llangefni**
❀ ★★★ ♨ 81% Tre-Ysgawen
Hall
**Llanrwst**
★★★ ♨ 64% Plas Maenan
**Pwllheli**
❀❀❀ ★★ ♨ 75% Plas
Bodegroes Restaurant
**Rowen**
★★★ ♨ 63% Tir-y-Coed
**Talsarnau**
❀ ★★ ♨ Maes y Neuadd
**POWYS**
**Builth Wells**
★★★ ♨ 64% Caer Beris
Manor
**Crickhowell**
★★ ♨ 70% Gliffaes
**Llanfyllin**
★★ ♨ 72% Bodfach Hall
**Llangammarch Wells**
❀ ★★★ ♨ 76% Lake
**Llanwddyn**
★★★ ♨ 71% Lake Vyrnwy
**Llyswen**
❀ ★★★★ ♨ 74% Llangoed
Hall
**Welshpool**
★★ ♨ 73% Golfa Hall
**SOUTH GLAMORGAN**
**Barry**
❀ ★★★ ♨ 76% Egerton Grey
Country House
**WEST GLAMORGAN**
**Reynoldston**
★★ ♨ 70% Fairyhill

# AA LODGES

Lodges are primarily designed for overnight stops at a very reasonable price per room. They are usually adjacent to a motorway or roadside restaurant, and are fairly standard in quality and in the facilities they offer, and they are well insulated. They have good, functional bedroooms each with a sofa which converts to two extra beds, as well as a double bed, all for the double rate of approximately £30 a night and so are ideal for a family of four. In addition, each room has en suite facilities, colour television and tea and coffee making facilities.

Usually there are rooms available which are specially designed for wheelchair-bound visitors. We list below 126 AA lodges in England, Scotland and Wales.

| TOWN | COUNTY | NAME | LOCATION |
|---|---|---|---|
| Acle | Norfolk | Forte Travelodge | Junc A47 & Acle bypass |
| Adlington | Cheshire | Forte Travelodge | A523 |
| Alwalton | Cambridgeshire | Forte Travelodge | A1, southbound |
| Amesbury | Wiltshire | Forte Travelodge | Junc A345 & A303, eastbound |
| Aust Motorway Service Area | Avon | Rank Motor Lodge | M4, junc 21 |
| Baldock | Hertfordshire | Forte Travelodge | A1, southbound |
| Barnsdale Bar | South Yorkshire | Forte Travelodge | A1, southbound |
| Barnsley | South Yorkshire | Forte Travelodge | Stairfoot roundabout A633/A635 |
| Barton Mills | Suffolk | Forte Travelodge | A11 |
| Barton Stacey | Hampshire | Forte Travelodge | A303 |
| Barton-under-Needwood | Staffordshire | Forte Travelodge (northbound) | A38, northbound |
| Barton-under-Needwood | Staffordshire | Forte Travelodge (southbound) | A38, southbound |
| Basildon | Essex | Watermill Travel Inn | A132, NE of town |
| Basildon | Essex | Campanile | A127 |
| Basingstoke | Hampshire | Forte Travelodge | Off A30 |
| Bebington | Merseyside | Forte Travelodge | A41, northbound |
| Birch Motorway Service Area | Greater Manchester | Granada Lodge | M62, junc 18–19 |
| Birmingham | West Midlands | Campanile | Off A38, SW of city centre |
| Blyth | Nottinghamshire | Granada Lodge | Junc A1M/A614 |
| Blyth | Nottinghamshire | Forte Travelodge | A1, southbound |
| Burnley | Lancashire | Forte Travelodge | Junc A671/A679 |
| Burtonwood Motorway Service Area | Cheshire | Forte Travelodge | Between junc 7 & 9 M62, westbound |
| Cannock | Staffordshire | Longford House Travel Inn | A5, off M6 junc 12 |
| Carcroft | South Yorkshire | Forte Travelodge | A1, N of Doncaster |
| Cardiff | South Glamorgan | Campanile | Pentwyn, M4 junc 29, off A48 |
| Cardiff | South Glamorgan | Forte Travelodge | 4m Ne of city centre, off A48(M) |
| Cardiff | South Glamorgan | Rank Motor Lodge | M4, junc 33 |
| Chesterfield | Derbyshire | Forte Travelodge | A61, Inner Ring Road |
| Colsterworth | Lincolnshire | Granada Lodge | A1, S of Grantham |
| Colsterworth | Lincolnshire | Forte Travelodge | At roundabout of junc A1/A151 |
| Coventry | West Midlands | Campanile | A46, E of city |
| Crewe | Cheshire | Forte Travelodge | 5m E, at junc 16 M6/A500 |
| Crianlarich | Central | Benmore Lodge Hotel | A85 |
| Cross Hands | Dyfed | Forte Travelodge | A48, eastbound |
| Desborough | Northamptonshire | Forte Travelodge | A6, southbound |
| Doncaster | South Yorkshire | Campanile Hotel | A638, near racecourse |
| Dorking | Surrey | Forte Travelodge | 0.5m E, on A25 |
| Droitwich | Hereford & Worcester | Forte Travelodge | 2m N, on A38 |
| Dudley | West Midlands | Forte Travelodge | 3m W, on A461 |
| Dumbarton | Strathclyde | Forte Travelodge | 1m E, on A82, westbound |
| East Horndon | Essex | Forte Travelodge | A127, eastbound |
| Eastleigh | Hampshire | Forte Travelodge | Off A335 |
| Edinburgh | Lothian | Forte Travelodge | 6m S, A720 Ring Rd South |

| TOWN | COUNTY | NAME | LOCATION |
|---|---|---|---|
| Farthing Corner Motorway Service Area | Kent | Rank Motor Lodge | Between junc 4 & 5 M2 |
| Felling | Tyne & Wear | Forte Travelodge | A194 |
| Fenstanton | Cambridgeshire | Forte Travelodge | A604, SE of Huntingdon |
| Ferrybridge Service Area | West Yorkshire | Granada Lodge | A1/M62 junc 33 |
| Five Oaks | West Sussex | Forte Travelodge | A29, northbound |
| Fontwell | West Sussex | Forte Travelodge | A27 |
| Forton Motorway Service Area | Lancashire | Rank Motor Lodge | Between junc 32 & 33 |
| Four Marks | Hampshire | Forte Travelodge | A31, northbound |
| Frankley Motorway Service Area | West Midlands | Granada Lodge | 3m SE at M5 service area |
| Gordano Motorway Service Area | Avon | Forte Travelodge | M5 junc 19, West of Bristol |
| Grantham | Lincolnshire | Forte Travelodge | 4m N on A1 |
| Gretna | Dumfries & Galloway | Forte Travelodge | A74, northbound |
| Hailsham | East Sussex | Forte Travelodge | A22 |
| Halkyn | Clwyd | Forte Travelodge | A55, westbound |
| Hamilton Motorway Service Area | Strathclyde | Roadchef Lodge | M74, northbound junc 5–6 |
| Heston Motorway Service Area | Greater London | Granada Lodge | M4 junc 2–3 |
| Hilton Park Motorway Service Area | West Midlands | Rank Motor Lodge | M6 between junc 10a & 11 |
| Hockliffe | Bedfordshire | Forte Travelodge | 3m N, on A5 |
| Hull | Humberside | Campanile | A1079 S of town centre |
| Ilminster | Somerset | Forte Travelodge | A303 |
| Kinross | Tayside | Granada Lodge | A977, off junc 6 of M90 |
| Knutsford | Cheshire | Forte Travelodge | A556, northbound |
| Leigh Delamere Motorway Service Area | Wiltshire | Granada Lodge | M4 junc 17–18 |
| Llandegai | Gwynedd | Rank Motor Lodge | A55, E of Bangor |
| Lolworth | Cambridgeshire | Forte Travelodge | A604 |
| Long Sutton | Lincolnshire | Forte Travelodge | A17 |
| Markfield | Leicestershire | Granada Lodge | M1/A50 junc 22, NW of Leicester |
| Markham Moor | Nottinghamshire | Forte Travelodge | A1, Leicester northbound |
| Marston Moretaine | Bedfordshire | Forte Travelodge | A421, northbound |
| Morcott | Leicestershire | Forte Travelodge | A47, eastbound |
| Morden | Greater London | Forte Travelodge | A24 |
| Musselburgh | Lothian | Granada Lodge | A1, E of Edinburgh |
| Newark-on-Trent | Nottinghamshire | Forte Travelodge | 3m N, on A1, southbound |
| Northampton | Northamptonshire | Forte Travelodge | A45, towards M1 junc 16 |
| Northop Hall | Clwyd | Forte Travelodge | A55, eastbound |
| Nuneaton | Warwickshire | Griff House Travel Inn | A444, N of M6 junc 3 |
| Nuneaton | Warwickshire | Longshoot Toby Hotel | A5/A47, E of town |
| Nuneaton | Warwickshire | Forte Travelodge | 2m S, on A444 |
| Okehampton | Devon | Forte Travelodge | 4m W, on A30 |
| Oldbury | West Midlands | Forte Travelodge | A4123, northbound |
| Oswestry | Shropshire | Forte Travelodge | Junc A5/A483 |
| Pencoed | Mid Glamorgan | Forte Travelodge | A473 |
| Penrith | Cumbria | Forte Travelodge | A66 |
| Plymouth | Devon | Hotel Campanile | A38, N of city centre |
| Podimore | Somerset | Forte Travelodge | A303, S of junc with A37 |
| Reading | Berkshire | Forte Travelodge | A33, southbound |
| Redditch | Hereford & Worcester | Campanile | Off M42, junc 3 |
| Rugeley | Staffordshire | Forte Travelodge | A51/B5013 |
| Rushden | Northamptonshire | Forte Travelodge | A45 |
| Saltash | Cornwall & Isles of Scilly | Granada Lodge | A38, W of Plymouth |
| Sampford Peverell | Devon | Forte Travelodge | Junc 27, M5 |
| Sarn Park Motorway Service Area | Mid Glamorgan | Forte Travelodge | Junc 36, M4 |
| Scotch Corner | North Yorkshire | Rank Motor Lodge | A1/A66, NE of Richmond |
| Scotch Corner | North Yorkshire | Forte Travelodge | 0.5m S on A1 |
| Sedgemoor Motorway Service Area | Somerset | Forte Travelodge | Junc 22 M5, northbound |
| Sheffield | South Yorkshire | Comfort Inn | Town centre, near Crucible Theatre |
| Skipton | North Yorkshire | Forte Travelodge | A65/A59 roundabout |
| Sleaford | Lincolnshire | Forte Travelodge | 1m N, at roundabout A17/A15 |
| South Mimms | Hertfordshire | Forte Travelodge | Junc 23, M25 |
| South Witham | Lincolnshire | Forte Travelodge | A1, northbound |
| Southwaite Motorway Service Area | Cumbria | Granada Lodge | M6 |

# AA LODGES

| TOWN | COUNTY | NAME | LOCATION |
|------|--------|------|----------|
| Stirling | Central | Granada Lodge | Junc M9/M80 |
| Stowmarket | Suffolk | Forte Travelodge | A45 |
| Sutton Coldfield | West Midlands | Forte Travelodge | 2m S, on B4531 |
| Sutton Scotney | Hampshire | Forte Travelodge | A34, north side |
| Sutton Scotney | Hampshire | Forte Travelodge | A34, south side |
| Tamworth | Staffordshire | Granada Lodge | A5/M42 junc 10 |
| Taunton Deane Motorway Service Area | Somerset | Roadchef Lodge | M5 services junc 25-26 |
| Telford | Shropshire | Forte Travelodge | 1m NW, on A5223 |
| Thrapston | Northamptonshire | Forte Travelodge | A14 link road A1/M1 |
| Thrussington | Leicestershire | Forte Travelodge | A46, southbound |
| Thurlaston | Warwickshire | Forte Travelodge | A45, westbound |
| Toddington Motorway Service Area | Bedfordshire | Granada Lodge | M1 services, junc 11–12 |
| Towcester | Northamptonshire | Forte Travelodge | A43 East Towcester bypass |
| Tring | Hertfordshire | Crows Nest Travel Inn | Junc A41(M)/A4011, N of town |
| Uttoxeter | Staffordshire | Forte Travelodge | A50/A5030 |
| Warminster | Wiltshire | Granada Lodge | A36, NW of town |
| Washington Service Area | Tyne & Wear | Granada Lodge | A1(M) services |
| Wheatley | Oxfordshire | Forte Travelodge | Off A40 |
| Woofferton | Shropshire | Forte Travelodge | A49 |
| Woolley Edge Motorway Service Area | West Yorkshire | Granada Lodge | Between junc 38/39, adj to service area |
| Worksop | Nottinghamshire | Forte Travelodge | A57 |
| Wrexham | Clwyd | Forte Travelodge | 4m S A483/A5152 roundabout |

# *Index of*
# *TOWN PLANS*

# *Key To*
# *TOWN PLANS*

| | |
|---|---|
| - - -<br>- - - | Roads with restricted access |
| † | Churches |
| $\boxed{i}$ | Tourist Information Centre |
| **AA** | AA Centre |
| **P** | Car parking |
| ⬤ | Shell filling station, open 7am–11pm<br>(some 24 hours) throughout the year with<br>leaded and unleaded petrol, and diesel |
| ⑤ | Hotel and restaurant |
| ★ | Red star hotel |
| 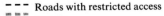 | Distance to hotels from edge of plan |

**Aberdeen**

1 Caledonian Thistle ★★★
2 Copthorne ★★★
3 New Marcliffe ★★★
4 Skean Dhu Altens ★★★★

# Aberdeen

© The Automobile Association 1991

(5/91)

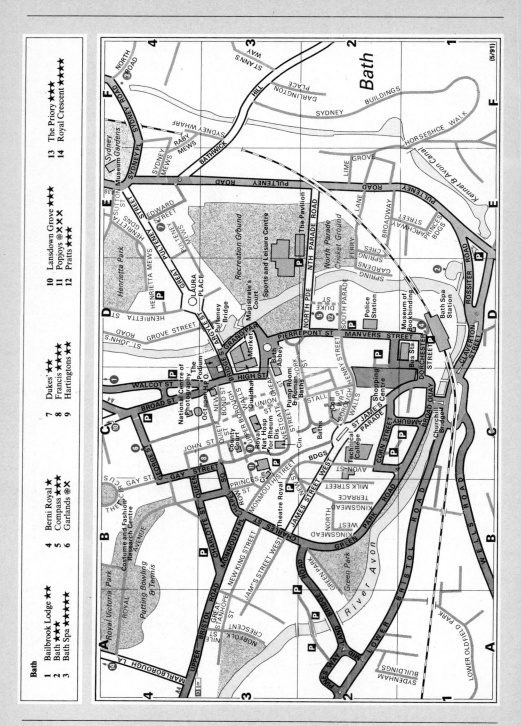

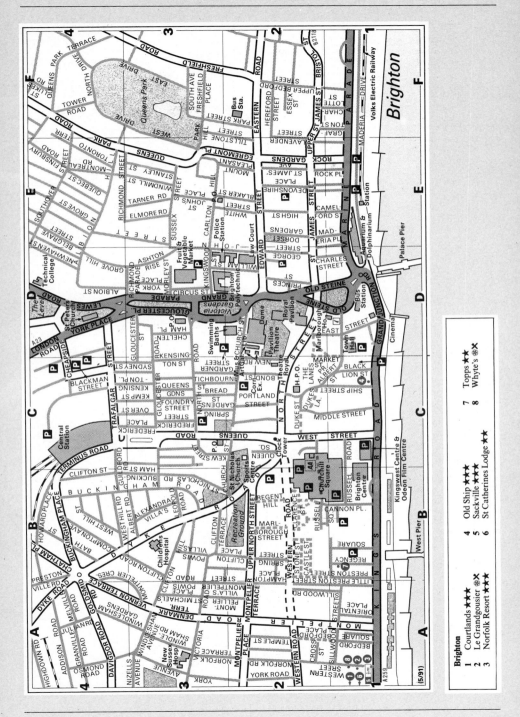

Brighton

Volks Electric Railway

**Brighton**

| | |
|---|---|
| 1 Courtlands ★★★ | 4 Old Ship ★★★ |
| 2 Le Grandgousier ◈✕ | 5 Sackville ★★★ |
| 3 Norfolk Resort ★★★ | 6 St Catherines Lodge ★★ |
| | 7 Topps ★★ |
| | 8 Whyte's ◈✕ |

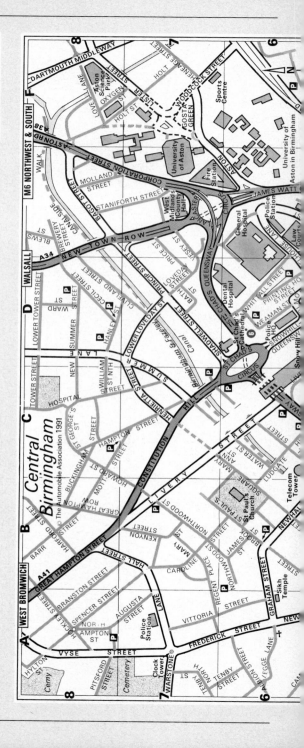

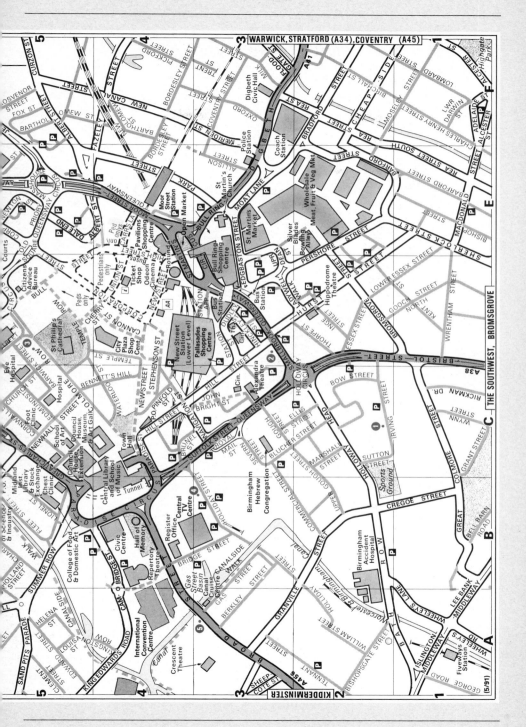

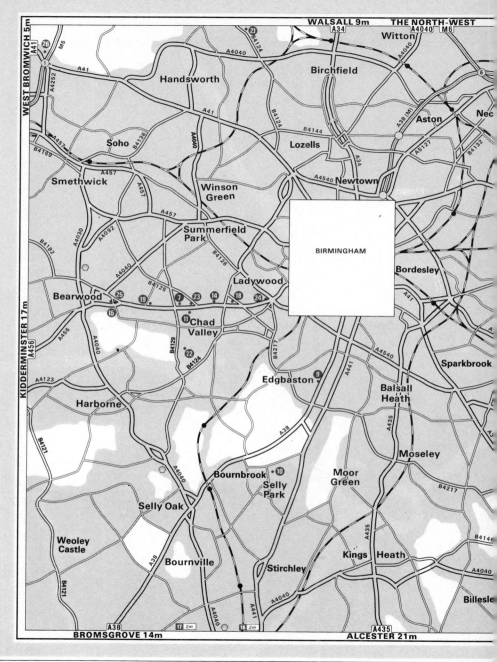

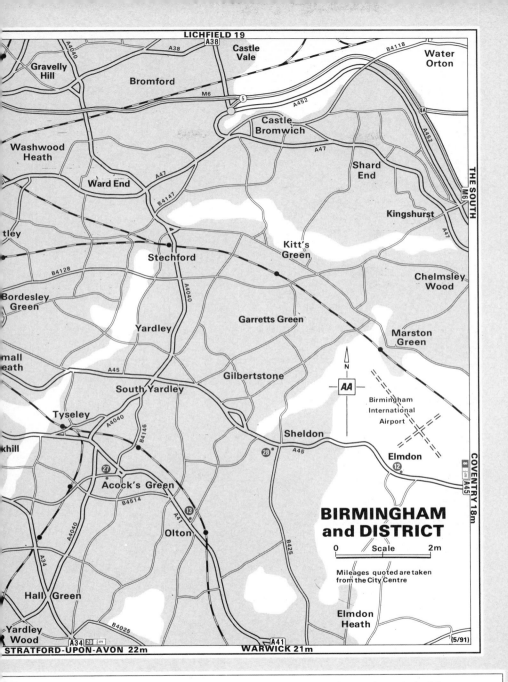

# BIRMINGHAM and DISTRICT

LICHFIELD 19

Castle Vale

Gravelly Hill

Bromford

Water Orton

Washwood Heath

Castle Bromwich

Shard End

Ward End

Kingshurst

tley

Kitt's Green

Chelmsley Wood

Stechford

Bordesley Green

Yardley

Garretts Green

Marston Green

mall eath

Gilbertstone

South Yardley

Birmingham International Airport

Tyseley

Sheldon

khill

Elmdon

Acock's Green

Olton

Hall Green

Elmdon Heath

Yardley Wood

STRATFORD-UPON-AVON 22m

WARWICK 21m

Scale 0 — 2m

Mileages quoted are taken from the City Centre

(5/91)

THE SOUTH

COVENTRY 18m

| 16 | Norwood ★★ |
| 17 | Plough & Harrow ★★★★ |
| 18 | Portland ★★ |
| 19 | Saracens Head ★★ (See under Solihull) |
| 20 | Sheriden House ★★ |
| 21 | Sloan's ⊛⊛⊛⊛ ✗ ✗ ✗ |
| 22 | Strathallan Thistle ★★★ |
| 23 | Swallow ⊛⊛⊛★★★★ |
| 24 | Westbourne Lodge ★★ |
| 25 | West Bromwich Moat House ★★★ (See under West Bromwich) |
| 26 | Westley Arms ★★★ |
| 27 | Wheatsheaf ★★ |

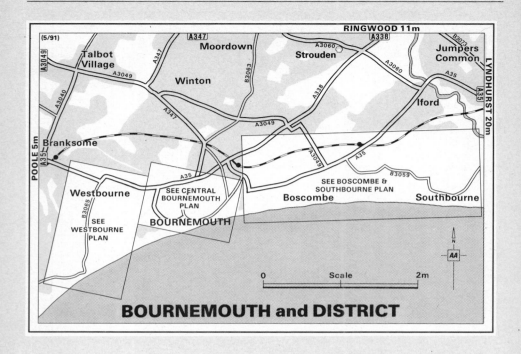

**BOURNEMOUTH and DISTRICT**

RINGWOOD 11m

(5/91)

Talbot Village
Moordown
Strouden
Jumpers Common

Winton

Iford

Branksome

POOLE 5m

LYNDHURST 20m

Westbourne
SEE CENTRAL BOURNEMOUTH PLAN
SEE WESTBOURNE PLAN
BOURNEMOUTH
SEE BOSCOMBE & SOUTHBOURNE PLAN
Boscombe
Southbourne

0        Scale        2m

---

**Bournemouth Central**

| | |
|---|---|
| **1** Arlington ★★ | **22** Marsham Court ★★★ |
| **2** Belvedere ★★★ | **23** New Durley Dean ★★★ |
| **3** Boltons ★★ | **24** Norfolk Royale ★★★★ |
| **4** Bournemouth Heathlands ★★★ | **25** Pavillion ★★★ |
| **5** Bournemouth Highcliff ★★★★ | **26** Hotel Piccadilly ★★★ |
| **6** Burley Court ★★★ | **27** Queens ★★★ |
| **7** Cadogan ★★★ | **28** Hotel Riviera (West Cliff Gardens) ★★ |
| **8** The Connaught ★★ | **29** Royal Bath ❀★★★★★ |
| **9** County ★★ | **30** Royal Exeter ★★ |
| **10** Durley Chine ★★ | **31** Russell Court ★★ |
| **11** Durley Grange ★★ | **32** St George ★★ |
| **12** Durley Hall ★★★ | **33** Silver How ★ |
| **13** Durlston Court ★★★ | **34** Sophisticats ❀✕✕ |
| **14** East Anglia ★★★ | **35** Sun Court ★★ |
| **15** East Cliff Court ★★★ | **36** Trouville ★★★ |
| **16** Embassy ★★★ | **37** Ullswater ★★ |
| **17** Forte Posthouse ★★★ | **38** Wessex ★★★ |
| **18** Gresham Court ★★ | **39** West Cliff Hall ★★ |
| **19** Grosvenor ★★★ | **40** Whitehall ★★ |
| **20** Lynden Court ★ | **41** Winterbourne ★★ |
| **21** Mansfield ★★ | **42** Woodcroft Tower ★★ |

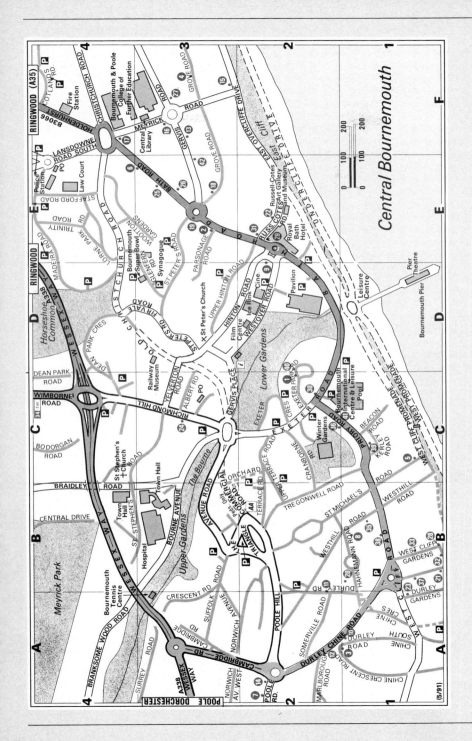

# Central Bournemouth

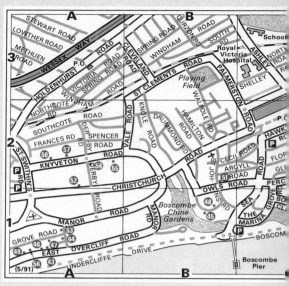

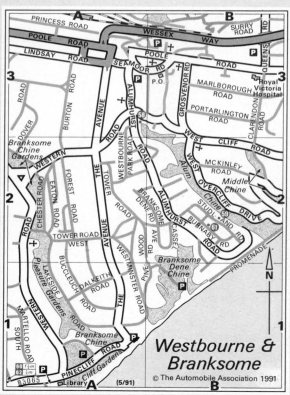

Westbourne &
Branksome

© The Automobile Association 1991

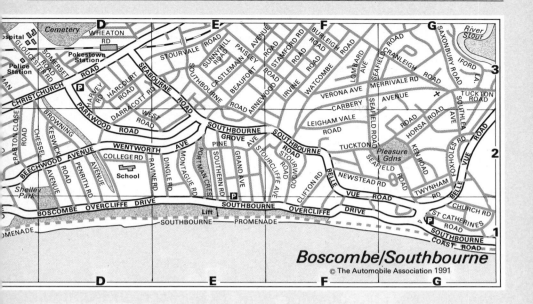

Boscombe/Southbourne

© The Automobile Association 1991

**Boscombe & Southbourne**

43  Bay View Court ★★★
44  Chesterwood ★★★
45  Chine ★★★
46  Cliffeside ★★★
47  Cottonwood ★★
48  Hotel Courtlands ★★★
49  Cumberland ★★★
50  Elstead ★★★
51  Fircroft ★★
52  Hartford Court ★★
53  Hinton Firs ★★★
54  Langtry Manor ★★★
55  Moat House ★★★
56  Suncliff ★★★
57  Taurus Park ★

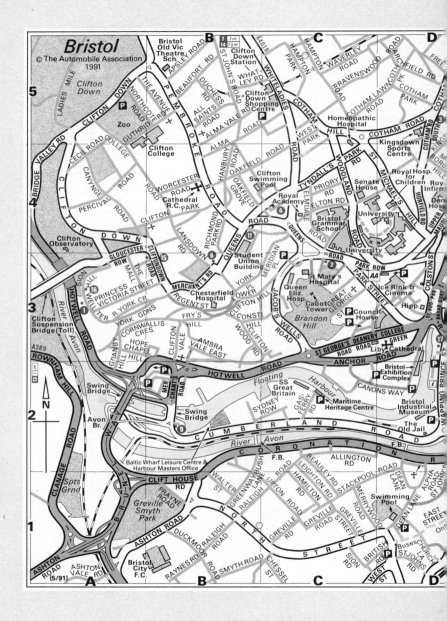

Bristol
© The Automobile Association 1991

**Bristol**

1   Avon Gorge ★★★
2   Berkeley Square ★★★
3   Bistro Twenty One ❀❀ ✕
4   Clifton ★★
5   Forte Crest ★★★
6   Glenroy ★★
7   Henbury Lodge ★★★
8   Holiday Inn ★★★★
9   Howards ❀ ✕
10  Marwicks ❀❀ ✕ ✕
11  Orient Rendezvous ❀ ✕ ✕
12  Parkside ★★
13  Redwood Lodge & Country Club ★★★
14  Restaurant Lettonie ❀❀❀ ✕ ✕
15  Rodney ❀ ★★
16  St Vincent's Rocks ★★★
17  Unicorn ★★★

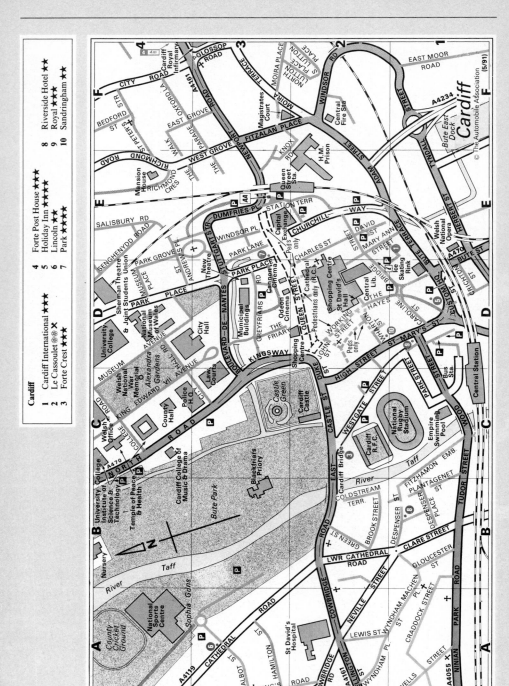

Cardiff

1 Cardiff International ★★★ ✕
2 Le Cassoulet ❀❀❀ ✕
3 Forte Crest ★★★

4 Forte Post House ★★★
5 Holiday Inn ★★★★
6 Lincoln ★★
7 Park ★★★★

8 Riverside Hotel ★★
9 Royal ★★★
10 Sandringham ★★

© The Automobile Association

Cardiff

A4234 (5/91)

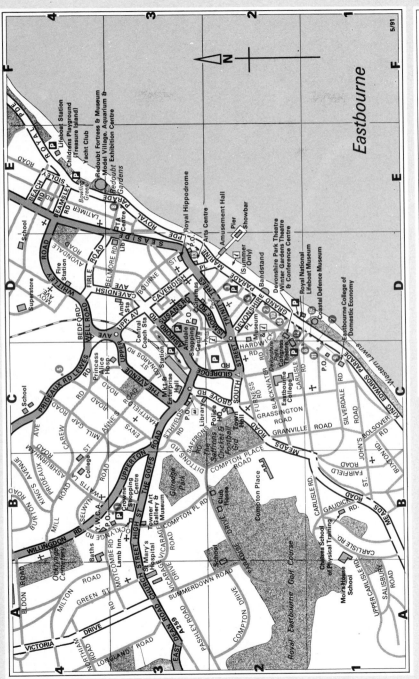

Eastbourne

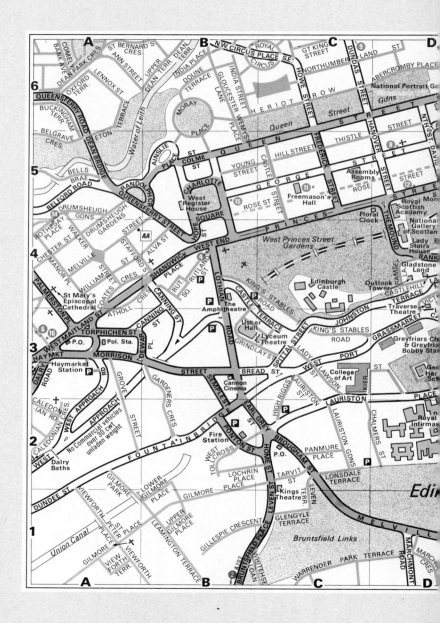

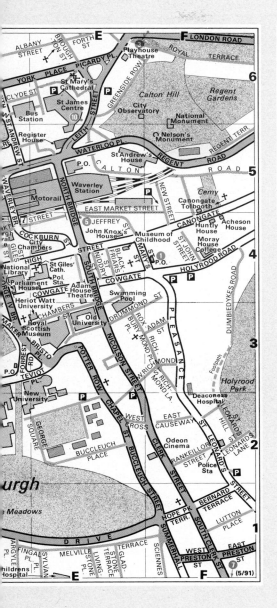

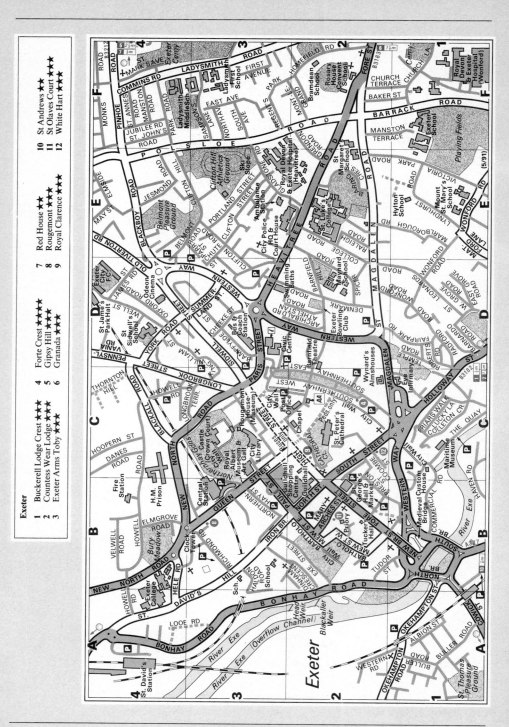

Exeter

| 1 | Buckerell Lodge Crest ★★★ | 4 | Forte Crest ★★★★ | 7 | Red House ★★ | 10 | St Andrews ★★ |
| 2 | Countess Wear Lodge ★★★ | 5 | Gipsy Hill ★★★ | 8 | Rougemont ★★★ | 11 | St Olaves Court ★★★ |
| 3 | Exeter Arms Toby ★★★ | 6 | Granada ★★★ | 9 | Royal Clarence ★★★ | 12 | White Hart ★★★ |

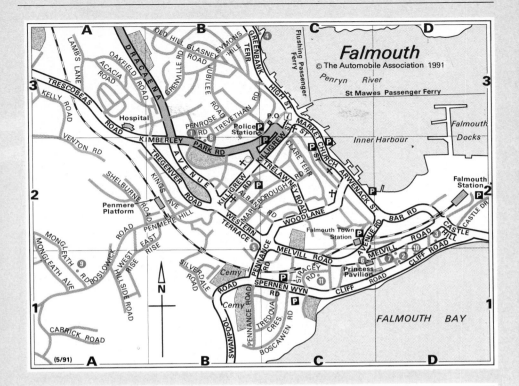

# Falmouth

© The Automobile Association 1991

**Falmouth**

| | | | | | |
|---|---|---|---|---|---|
| 1 | Broadmead ★★ | 5 | Green Lawns ★★★ | 9 | Penmere Manor ★★★⚐ |
| 2 | Carthion ★★ | 6 | Gyllyngdune Manor ★★★ | 10 | Royal Duchy ★★★ |
| 3 | Falmouth ★★★ | 7 | Lerryn ★★ | 11 | St Michaels ★★★ |
| 4 | Greenbank ★★★ | 8 | Park Grove ★★ | | |

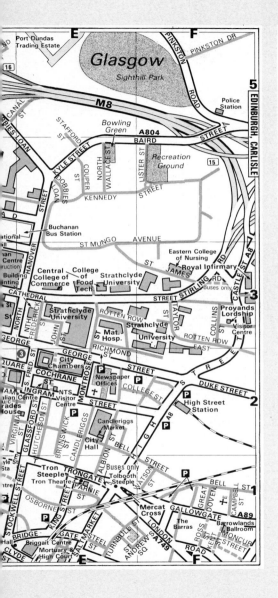

**Glasgow**

1 Buttery ✿ ✗ ✗
2 Central ★★★
3 Copthorne ★★★
4 Forte Crest ★★★★
5 Glasgow Crest ★★★
6 Holiday Inn Glasgow ★★★★
7 Hospitality Inn ★★★★
8 Kelvin Park Lorne ★★★
9 Killermont House Restaurant ✿✿ ✗ ✗
10 Mitchells ✿ ✗
11 Rogano ✿✿ ✗ ✗
12 Stakis Ingram ★★★
13 Swallow ★★★

Inverness

| | | | | |
|---|---|---|---|---|
| **Inverness** | 4 | Culloden House ★★★★ | 12 | Mercury ★★★ |
| 1 Beaufort ★★ | 5 | Cummings ★★ | 13 | Loch Ness House ★★ |
| 2 Caledonian ★★★ | 8 | Dunain Park ※★★★⚑ | 14 | Palace ★★★ |
| 3 Craigmonie ★★★ | 9 | Glen Mhor ★★ | 15 | Redcliffe ★ |
| | 11 | Kingsmills ★★★★ | | |

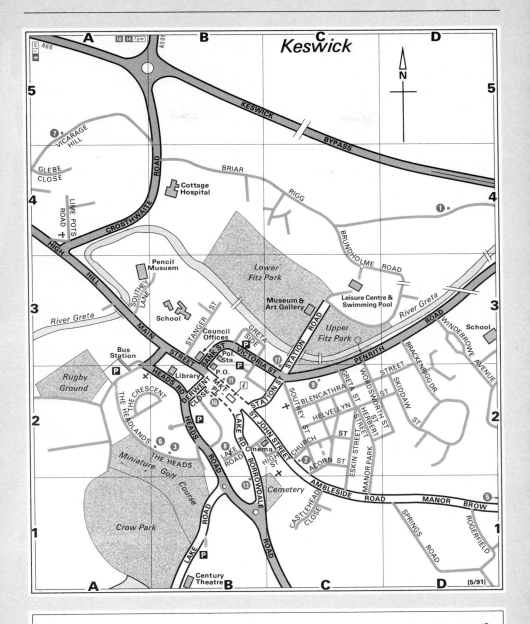

# Keswick

| | | | | | |
|---|---|---|---|---|---|
| **Keswick** | | | | | |
| **1** | Brundholme Country House ❀★★★ | **5** | Grange Country House ★★ | **10** | Lyzzick Hall Country House ★★🏖 |
| **2** | Chaucer House ★★ | **6** | Highfield ★ | **11** | Queen's ★★ |
| **3** | Crow Park ★★ | **7** | Lairbeck ★★ | **13** | Priorholm ★ |
| **4** | Derwentwater ★★★ | **8** | Latrigg Lodge ★ | **14** | Red House ★★★🏖 |
| | | **9** | Linnett Hill ★ | **16** | Skiddaw ★★ |
| | | | | **17** | Walpole ★★ |

(5/91)

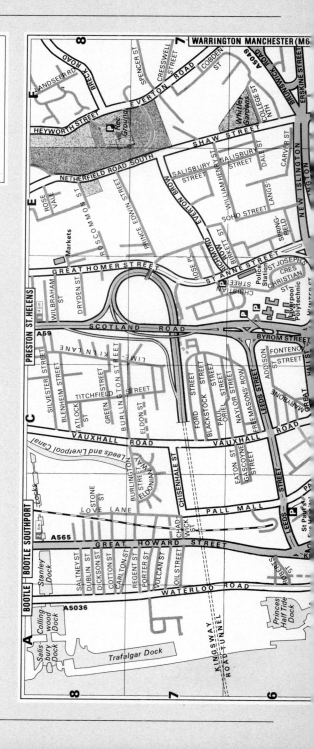

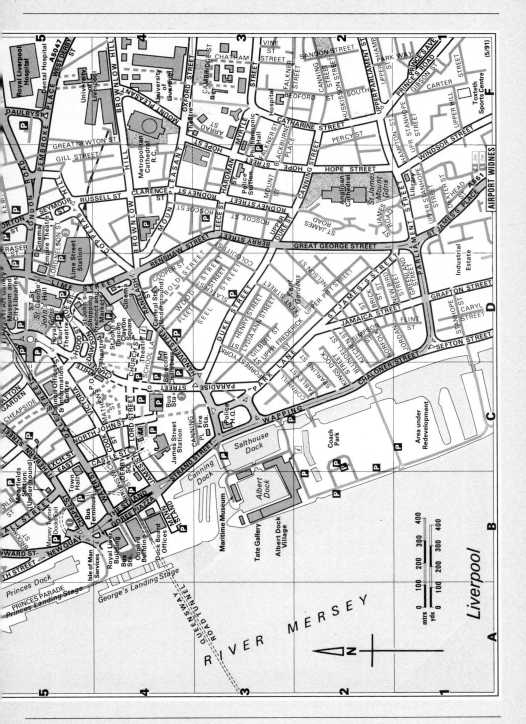

Liverpool

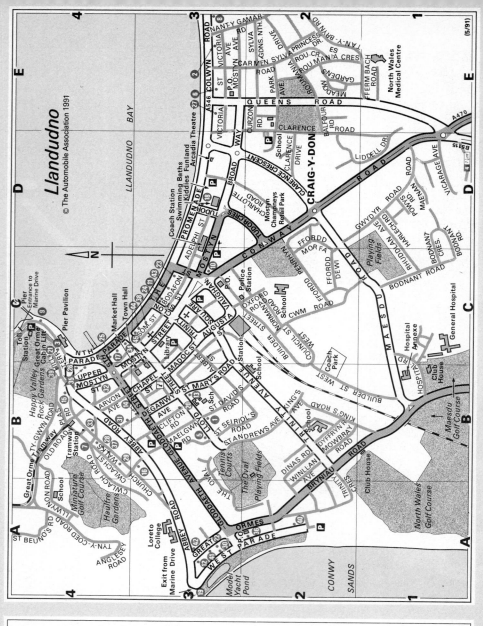

# Llandudno

© The Automobile Association 1991

(5/91)

834

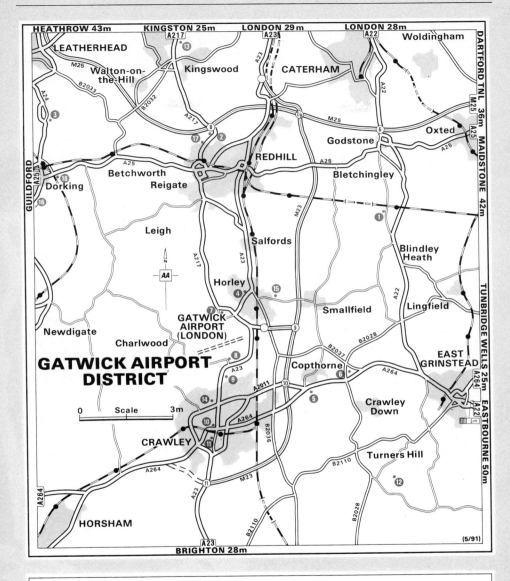

**Gatwick Airport & District**

1 La Bonne Auberge ❀❀✕✕✕ (See under South Godstone)
2 Bridge House ★★★ (See under Reigate)
3 Burford Bridge ★★★★ (See under Dorking)
4 Chequers Thistle ★★★
5 Copthorne ★★★★
6 Copthorne Effingham Park ★★★★
7 Forte Crest ★★★
8 Gatwick Concorde ★★★
9 Gatwick Manor ★★

10 George ★★★
11 Goffs Park ★★★
12 Gravetye Manor ❀❀★★★🎖 (See under East Grinstead)
13 Heathside ★★ (See under Burgh Heath)
14 Holiday Inn ★★★
15 Langshott Manor ❀★
16 Partners West Street ❀❀✕✕
17 Reigate Manor ★★★ (See under Reigate)
18 Travelodge ⌂
19 The White Horse ★★★ (See under Dorking)
20 Woodbury House ❀★★★ (See under East Grinstead)

835

**Heathrow Airport**

1    Ariel ★★★
2    Berkeley Arms ★★★
3    Excelsior ★★★★
4    Forte Crest ★★★
5    Heathrow Penta ★★★★
6    Holiday Inn ★★★★
7    Hotel Ibis Heathrow ★★
8    Master Robert ★★★ (See under Hounslow)
9    Sterling ★★★★
10   Thames Lodge ★★★ (See under Staines)

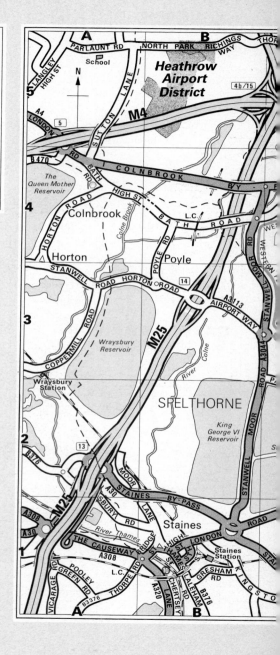

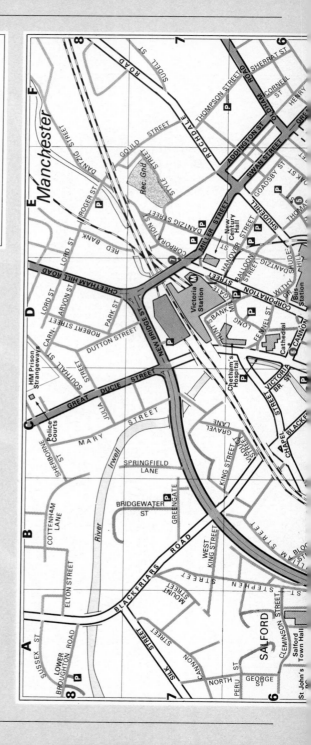

**Manchester**

1 Charterhouse ★★★★
2 Forte Post House ★★★
3 Holiday Inn Crowne Plaza ★★★★
4 Little Yang Sing ❀✕
5 Market ❀✕
6 Mitre ★★
7 Parkers ★★★
8 Hotel Piccadilly ★★★★
9 Portland Thistle ★★★★
10 Ramada Renaissance ★★★★
11 Willow Bank ★★★
12 Woodlands ❀✕✕
13 Yang Sing ❀❀✕✕

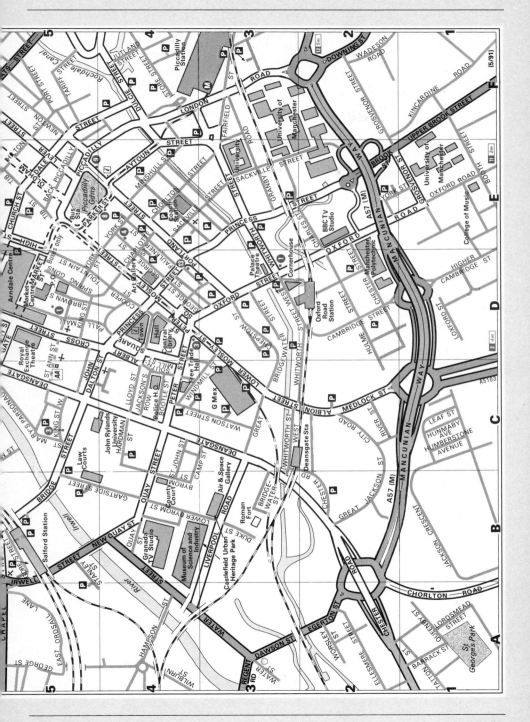

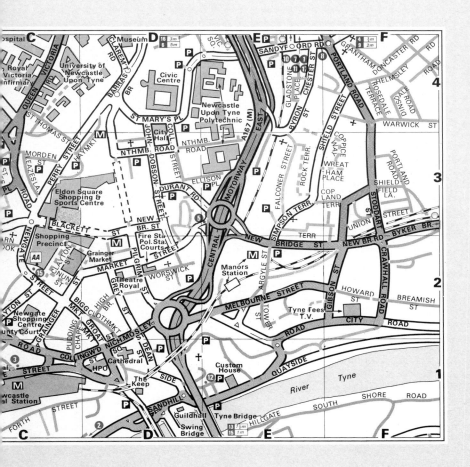

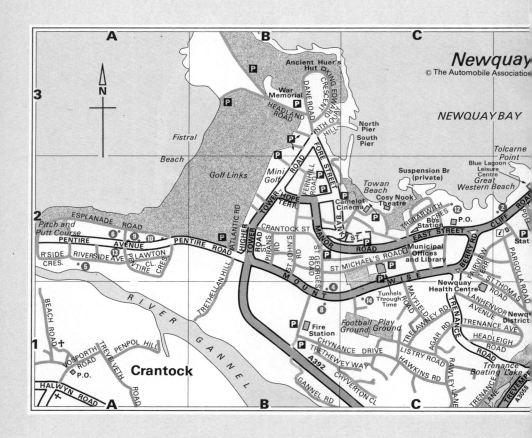

**Newquay**

1 Barrowfield ★★★
2 Beachcroft ★★
3 Hotel Bristol ★★★
4 Cedars ★★
5 Corisande Manor ★★
6 Euro ★★★
7 Kilbirnie ★★★
8 Lowenva ★
9 Hotel Mordros ★★★
10 Philema ★★
11 Porth Veor Manor House ★★
12 Trebarwith ★★★
13 Tremont ★★
14 Trevone ★
15 Whipsiderry ★★

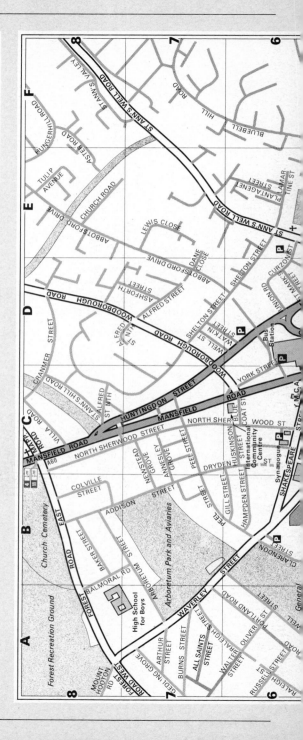

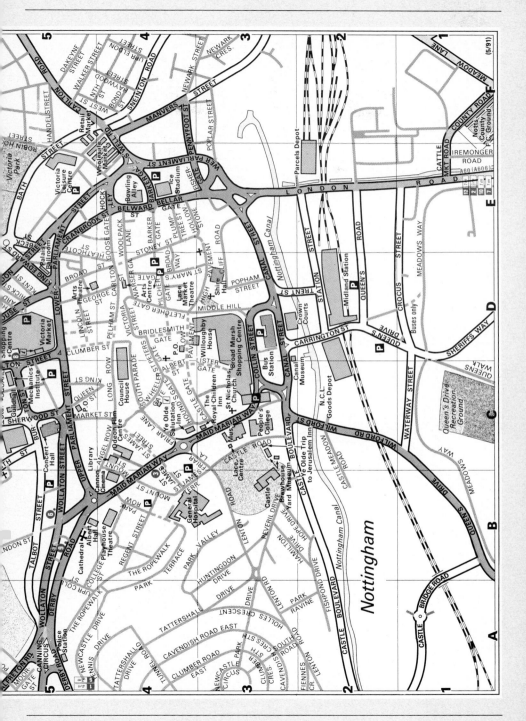

Nottingham

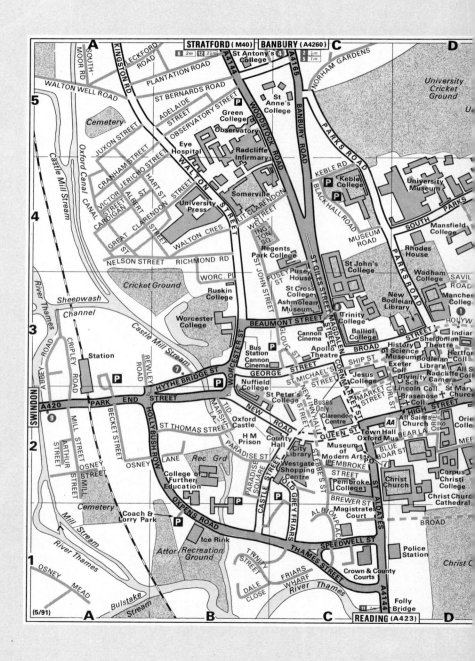

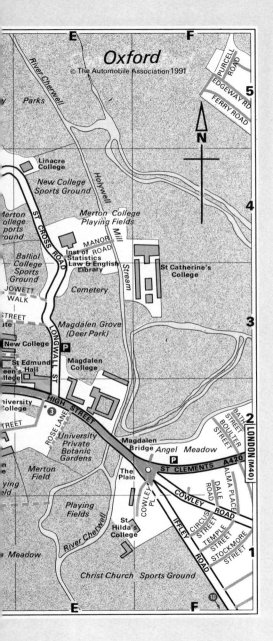

## Oxford

© The Automobile Association 1991

**Oxford**

| | |
|---|---|
| 1 | Bath Place ⊛✕✕ |
| 2 | Cotswold Lodge ★★★ |
| 3 | Eastgate ★★★ |
| 4 | 15 North Parade ⊛✕ |
| 5 | Linton Lodge ★★★ |
| 6 | Oxford Moat House ★★★ |
| 7 | Paddyfield ⊛✕✕ |
| 8 | Randolph ★★★★ |
| 9 | River ★ |
| 10 | The Trees ★★ |
| 11 | Victoria ★★ |
| 12 | Welcome Lodge ★★ |

**Plymouth**

1 Camelot ★★
2 Campanile ⌂
3 Chez Nous ❀❀ ✕
4 New Continental ★★★
5 Copthorne ★★★★
6 Drake ★
7 Duke of Cornwall ★★★
8 Forte Crest ★★★
9 Grosvenor ★★
10 Plymouth Moat House ★★★★
11 Imperial ★
12 Invicta ★★
13 Novotel Plymouth ★★★
14 Strathmore ★★★
15 Victoria Court ★

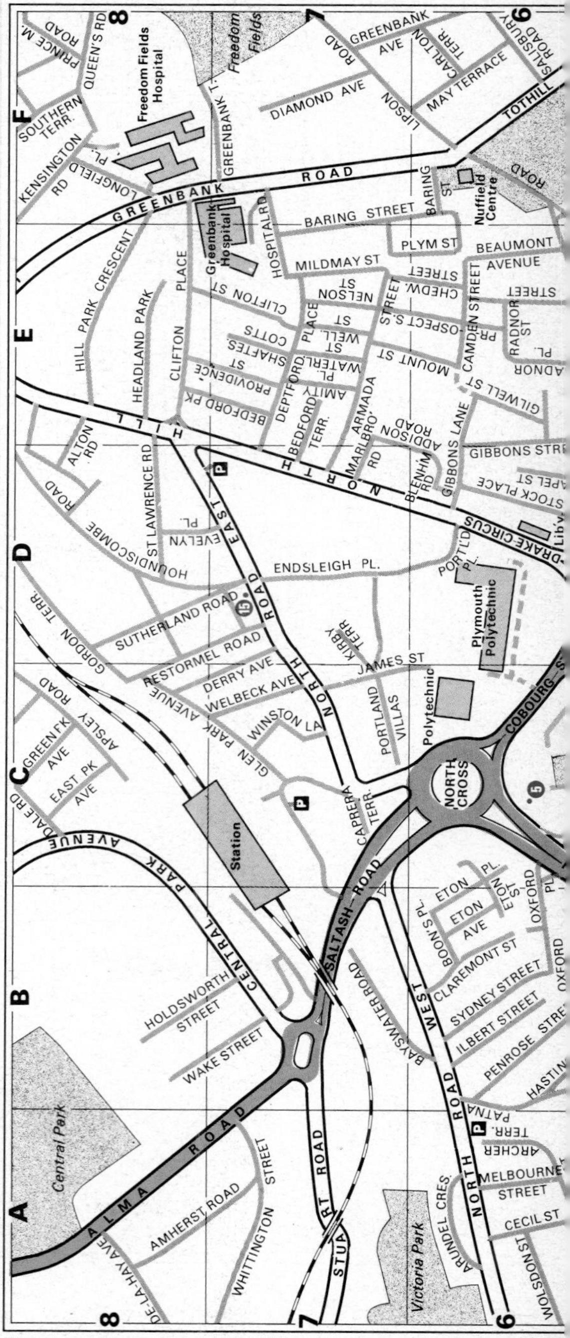

PRINCE M
QUEEN'S RD.
Freedom Fields
Freedom Fields Hospital
SOUTHERN TERR.
PRINCE M
KENSINGTON RD
LONGFIELD PL.
GREENBANK T.
GREENBANK ROAD
GREENBANK AVE
CARLTON
MAY TERRACE
DIAMOND AVE
LIPSON
TOTHILL
SALISBURY ROAD
GREENBANK ROAD
Greenbank Hospital
HOSPITAL RD
BARING
BARING STREET
Nuffield Centre
RD
ROAD
HILL PARK CRESCENT
HEADLAND PARK
CLIFTON PLACE
CLIFTON ST
PLYM ST
MILDMAY ST
CHEDW. STREET
NELSON ST
PROSPECT S.
BEAUMONT AVENUE
CAMDEN STREET
RADNOR PL.
ADNOR
ALTON RD
ST LAWRENCE RD
PROVIDENCE PL
ST SHAFTES COTTS
WELL ST
AMITY PL
MOUNT ST
GILWELL ST
BEDFORD PK
BEDFORD TERR.
ADDISON ROAD
MARLBRO
ARMADA ST
GIBBONS LANE
GIBBONS STRE
HILL
NORTH
BLENH
BENH
PORTLD PL
STOCK PLACE
APEL ST
DRAKE CIRCUS
EVELYN PL.
ENDSLEIGH PL.
EAST
ROAD
Plymouth Polytechnic
SUTHERLAND ROAD
GORDON TERR.
RESTORMEL ROAD
DERRY AVE
WELBECK AVE
KIRBY TERR
JAMES ST
Polytechnic
PORTLAND VILLAS
GREEN PK AVE
EAST PK AVE
APSLEY ROAD
GLEN PARK AVENUE
WINSTON LA
HILTON
CABRERA TERR.
NORTH CROSS
COBOURG S
Station
P
P
ETON PL
BOON'S PL.
ETON AVE
ETON ST
OXFORD
OXFORD
HOLDSWORTH STREET
CENTRAL PARK AVENUE
SALTASH ROAD
WEST
CLAREMONT ST
SYDNEY STREET
ILBERT STREET
PENROSE STRE
HASTIN
WAKE STREET
BAXWATER ROAD
NORTH ROAD
Central Park
ALMA ROAD
AMHERST ROAD
WHITTINGTON STREET
STUART ROAD
PATNA
ARCHER TERR.
P
MELBOURNE STREET
CECIL ST
Victoria Park
ARUNDEL CRES.
WOLSON ST
DE-LA-HAY AVE

*Plymouth*

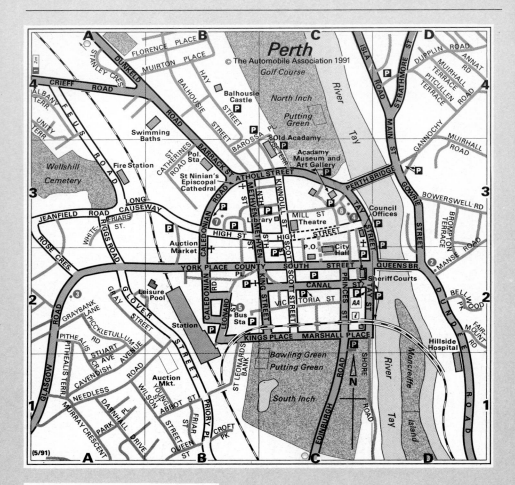

**Perth**

1 Huntingtower ★★★
2 Isle of Skye Toby ★★★
3 Lovat ★★★
4 Number Thirty Three ⊕ ✕ ✕
5 Queens ★★★
6 Royal George ★★★
7 Stakis City Mills ★★★

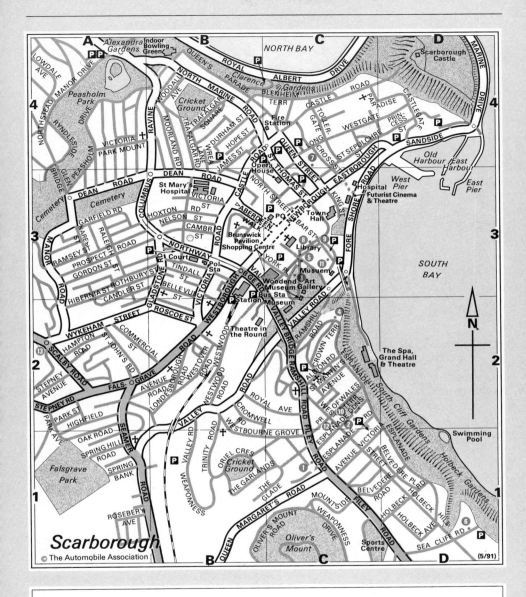

Scarborough
© The Automobile Association

(5/91)

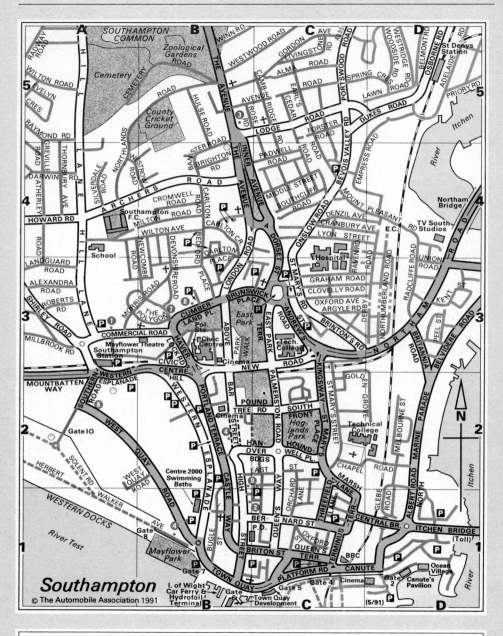

# Southampton

© The Automobile Association 1991

(5/91)

**Southampton**

| | | | | | |
|---|---|---|---|---|---|
| 1 | Browns Brasserie ⊛ ✕ ✕ | 4 | Forte Post House ★★★ | 7 | Polygon ★★★ |
| 2 | Dolphin ★★★ | 5 | Golden Palace ⊛ ✕ | 8 | Southampton Park ★★★ |
| 3 | Elizabeth House ★★ | 6 | Novotel Southampton ★★★ | 9 | Star ★★ |

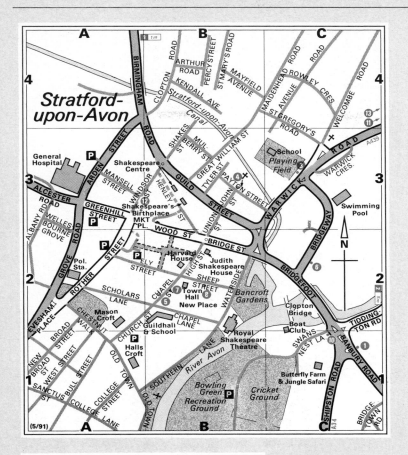

**Stratford-upon-Avon**

1   Alveston Manor ★★★
2   Charlecote Pheasant ★★★ (listed under Charlecote)
3   The Coach House ★★
4   Dukes ★★★
5   Falcon ★★★
6   Moat House International ★★★★
7   Shakespeare ★★★★
8   Stratford House ★★
9   Swan House ★★
10   Swan's Nest ★★★
11   Welcombe ★★★★
12   White Swan ★★★
13   Windmill Park Hotel & Country Club ★★★

**Torquay**

1 Abbey Lawn ★★★
2 Albaston ★★
3 Hotel Balmoral ★★
4 Bancourt ★★
5 Belgrave ★★★
6 Burlington ★★★
7 Bute Court ★★

8 Carlton ★★
9 Chelston Towers ★★
10 Conway Court ★★
11 Corbyn Head ★★★
12 Devonshire ★★★
13 Dunstone ★★
14 Frognel Hall ★★
15 Grand ★★★
16 Gresham Court ★★

17 Homers ★★★
18 Hunsdon Lea ★★
19 Imperial ★★★★★
20 Kistor ★★★
21 Lansdowne ★
23 Livermead Cliff ★★★
24 Livermead House ★★★
26 Oscar's Hotel & Restaurant ★★

27 Rainbow House ★★★
28 Red House ★★
30 Roseland ★★
32 Shelley Court ★
33 Hotel Sydore ★★
34 Templestowe ★★
35 Toorak ★★
36 Vernon Court ★★

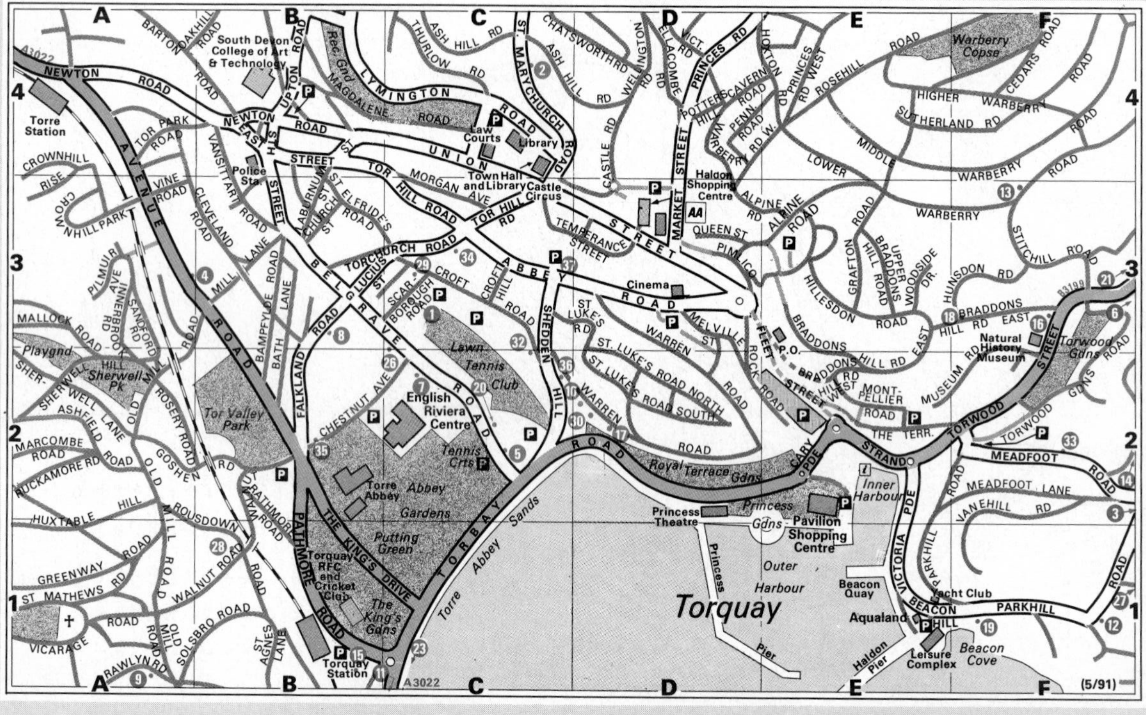

Torquay

(5/91)

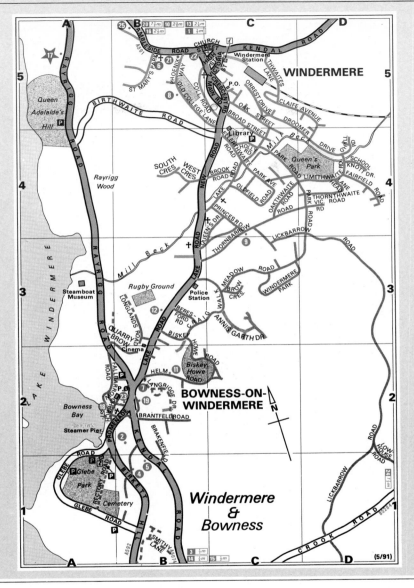

**WINDERMERE**

*Windermere & Bowness*

**Windermere & Bowness**

1  Belmont Manor ★★🏠♨
2  Belsfield ★★★
3  Bordriggs Country House ★★
4  Burn How Garden House Hotel,
   Motel and Rest ⊛★★★
5  Burnside ★★★
6  Cedar Manor ⊛★★
7  Crag Brow Cottage ★★

8  Hideaway ★★
9  Hillthwaite House ★★
10 Holbeck Ghyll ⊛⊛★★★♨
11 Hydro ★★★
12 Knoll ★★
13 Langdale Chase ★★★★♨
14 Lindeth Fell ★★★♨
15 Linthwaite ★★★♨
16 Low Wood ★★★
17 Miller Howe ⊛⊛⊛★★

18 The Old England ★★★★
19 Porthole Eating House ⊛ ✗
20 Quarry Garth Country House
   Hotel & Restaurant ★★
21 Ravensworth ★★
22 Rogers ⊛ ✗
23 Royal ★★
24 Wild Boar ★★★
25 Willowsmere ★

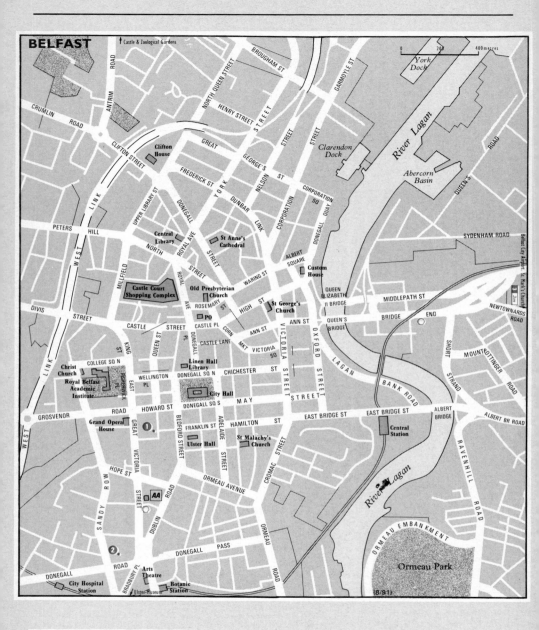

**BELFAST**

Castle & Zoological Gardens

York Dock

River Lagan

CRUMLIN ROAD

ANTRIM ROAD

BROUGHAM ST

GARMOYLE ST

QUEEN'S ROAD

CLIFTON STREET

Clifton House

GREAT GEORGE'S ST

NORTH QUEEN STREET

HENRY STREET

STREET

NELSON STREET

STREET

Clarendon Dock

Abercorn Basin

PETERS HILL

WEST LINK

FREDERICK ST

YORK STREET

DUNBAR LINK

CORPORATION SQ

CORPORATION STREET

DONEGALL QUAY

SYDENHAM ROAD

Belfast City Airport, St. Mark's Church

Central Library

St Anne's Cathedral

ALBERT SQUARE

Custom House

UPPER LIBRARY ST

DONEGALL STREET

ROYAL AVE

NORTH STREET

ROYAL AVE

MILLFIELD

Castle Court Shopping Complex

Old Presbyterian Church

ROSEMARY ST

PO

WARING ST

HIGH ST

ST GEORGE'S Church

ANN ST

QUEEN ELIZABETH II BRIDGE

MIDDLEPATH ST

QUEEN'S BRIDGE

LAGAN BRIDGE

END

NEWTOWNARDS ROAD

3m

DIVIS STREET

CASTLE STREET

QUEEN ST

DONEGALL PL

CASTLE PL

CASTLE LANE

CORN MKT

VICTORIA SQ

VICTORIA STREET

OXFORD STREET

BANK ROAD

SHORT STRAND

MOUNTPOTTINGER ROAD

WEST LINK

KING ST

COLLEGE SQ N

ASHERWICK PL

EAST

WELLINGTON PL

Linen Hall Library

DONEGALL SQ N

CHICHESTER ST

City Hall

DONEGALL SQ S

MAY STREET

Christ Church

Royal Belfast Academic Institute

GROSVENOR ROAD

HOWARD ST

BEDFORD STREET

FRANKLIN ST

ADELAIDE STREET

HAMILTON ST

EAST BRIDGE ST

EAST BRIDGE ST

ALBERT BRIDGE

ALBERT BR ROAD

Grand Opera House

**1.**

GREAT VICTORIA STREET

Ulster Hall

St Malachy's Church

CROMAC STREET

Central Station

River Lagan

RAVENHILL ROAD

WEST

SANDY ROW

HOPE ST

ORMEAU AVENUE

ORMEAU ROAD

AA

DUBLIN ROAD

**2.**

DONEGALL PASS

ORMEAU EMBANKMENT

DONEGALL ROAD

BRADBURY PL

Arts Theatre

Botanic Station

Ormeau Park

City Hospital Station

Ulster Museum

(8/91)

---

**Belfast**

1  Plaza ★★★
2  Roscoff ❀❀❀ ✕✕
3  Stormont ★★★

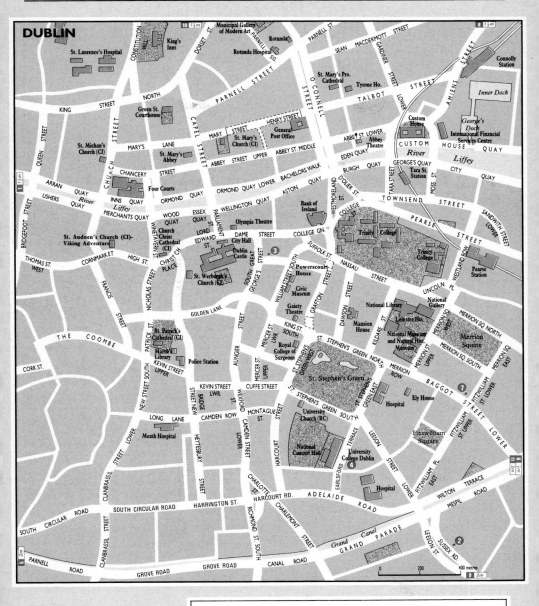

**DUBLIN**

**Dublin**

| | | | |
|---|---|---|---|
| 1 | Ashling ★★★ | 7 | Longfield's ★★ |
| 2 | Burlington ★★★★ | 8 | Marine ★★★ |
| 3 | Central ★★★ | 9 | Hotel Montrose ★★★ |
| 4 | Conrad ★★★★ | 10 | Skylon ★★★ |
| 5 | Green Isle ★★★ | 11 | Tara Tower ★★★ |
| 6 | Jurys ★★★★ | | |

# HOTEL GROUPS

**Key to abbreviations and central reservation telephone numbers (where applicable)**

Special corporate rates are available at hotel companies marked with an *, to those business travellers who have a company account with the AA Business Travel Service.

Bookings may be made via the AA Business Travel Centres listed below

| Company | Abbreviations | Telephone |
|---|---|---|
| Berni Chef & Brewer | Berni and Chef & Brewer | |
| *Best Western | Best Western | 081-541 0033 |
| Brend Hotels Ltd | Brend | Barnstaple (0271) 44496 |
| *Consort Hotels Ltd | Consort | York (0904) 643151 |
| *Commonwealth Holiday Inns of Canada Ltd | Holiday Inns | 071-722 7755 |
| Crown & Raven | Crown & Raven | |
| De Vere Hotels Ltd | De Vere | Warrington (0925) 65050 |
| Exec Hotels | Exec Hotel | |
| Forestdale Hotels Ltd | Forestdale | |
| Forte Hotels | Forte Posthouse | Freephone 0800 404040 |
| | Forte Crest | Freephone 0800 404040 |
| Frederic Robinson Ltd | Frederic Robinson | |
| Granada Motorway Services Ltd | Granada | Freephone 0800 555300 |
| Greenall Whitley Hotels Ltd | GW Hotels | Warrington (0925) 65050 |
| Guestaccom | Guestaccom | |
| Jarvis Hotels | Jarvis | (0345) 581237 |
| Leading Hotels of the World | | Freephone 0800 181123 |
| for Berkeley, Claridges, Connaught, Savoy, Hyde Park, London; Royal Crescent, Bath, Avon; Lygon Arms, Broadway, Worcs; Grosvenor, Chester; Chewton Glen, New Milton, Hants | | |
| Inter-Hotels | Inter-Hotels | (0608) 642211 |
| Minotels | Minotels | Blackpool (0253) 594185 |
| *Mount Charlotte Thistle Hotels Ltd | Mount Charlotte (TS) | Freephone (0800) 700400 |
| *Novotel International | Novotel | 071-724 1000 |
| Porterhouse Restaurants Ltd | Porterhouse | |
| Pride of Britain Ltd | Pride of Britain | Andover (026476) 444 |
| *Queens Moat House Ltd | Queens Moat | Romford (0708) 766677 |
| *Rank Organisation Ltd | Rank | 071-262 2893 |
| Relais et Châteaux Hotels | Relais et Châteaux | |
| Scottish Highland Hotels | Scottish Highland | 041-332 6538 |
| Shire Inns Ltd | Shire | |
| Small Luxury Hotels of the World | Small Luxury Hotels | Freephone (0800) 282 124 |
| *Stakis Hotels & Inns | Stakis | 041-332 4343 |
| *Swallow Hotels Ltd | Swallow | 091-529 4666 |
| Toby Restaurants Ltd | Toby | |
| Whitbread Group of Hotels PLC | Lansbury | (0582) 396922 |
| | Country Club Hotels | (0582) 396922 |
| | Travel Inn | (0582) 396922 |

**Automobile Association**
Bookings for hotels belonging to groups marked * can only be made if your company has an account with AA Business Travel Service. Business Travel Centres are located throughout the UK and are listed below with telephone numbers.

| | | | | | |
|---|---|---|---|---|---|
| Aberdeen | (0224) 645138 | Guildford | (0483) 574070 | Twickenham | 081-891 6211 |
| Basingstoke | (0256) 493881 | Halesowen | 021-501 7779 | Manchester | 061-488 7499 |
| Bristol | (0272) 308373 | Haymarket | 071-930 6854 | Northampton | (0604) 231911 |
| Chester | (0244) 350541 | Leeds | (0532) 46022 | Reading | (0734) 580663 |
| Edinburgh | 031-225 7677 | Stanmore | 081-954 6270 | Wolverhampton | (0902) 712345 |
| Glasgow | 041-221 4373 | | | | |

# REPORT FORM

To the Editor
**Hotels and Restaurants in Britain and Ireland 1992**
AA Publishing
Fanum House
Basingstoke
Hampshire RG21 2EA

Name of hotel or
restaurant _____

Address _____

_____

_____

Date visited _____

Your comment on our current report:

Your report:

Signed _____

Name and address (block capitals please) _____

_____

_____

# *REPORT FORM*

To the Editor
**Hotels and Restaurants in Britain and Ireland 1992**
AA Publishing
Fanum House
Basingstoke
Hampshire RG21 2EA


Name of hotel or
restaurant _____

Address _____

_____

_____

Date visited _____

Your comment on our current report:




Your report:








Signed _____

Name and address (block capitals please) _____

_____

_____

# REPORT FORM

To the Editor
**Hotels and Restaurants in Britain and Ireland 1992**
AA Publishing
Fanum House
Basingstoke
Hampshire RG21 2EA


Name of hotel or
restaurant _____

Address _____

_____

_____

Date visited _____

Your comment on our current report:




Your report:










Signed _____

Name and address (block capitals please) _____

_____

_____

# REPORT FORM

To the Editor
**Hotels and Restaurants in Britain and Ireland 1992**
AA Publishing
Fanum House
Basingstoke
Hampshire RG21 2EA


Name of hotel or
restaurant _____

Address _____

_____

_____

Date visited _____

Your comment on our current report:




Your report:













Signed _____

Name and address (block capitals please) _____

_____

_____

# AA
# BUDGET GUIDE
# BRITAIN

In this new series, the AA's Budget Guide Britain breaks entirely fresh ground. Practical budgeting advice on planning your holiday is combined with a voyage of discovery.

The book covers eight regions, from the Scottish Highlands in the north to the Cornish penninsula in the far South-west. Insider information reveals unusual places to visit as well as familiar tourist attractions such as the Shakespeare country of the Midlands and the Georgian elegance of Bath.

Good value accomodation and eating out, money-saving tips, getting around by bus and train, local specialities and events, specially drawn location maps - all these and more are included in this wide-ranging guide which gives you all the information you need to plan and enjoy a stay in Britain.

*Available at good bookshops and AA shops.*

*Another great guide from the AA*

# KEY TO ATLAS

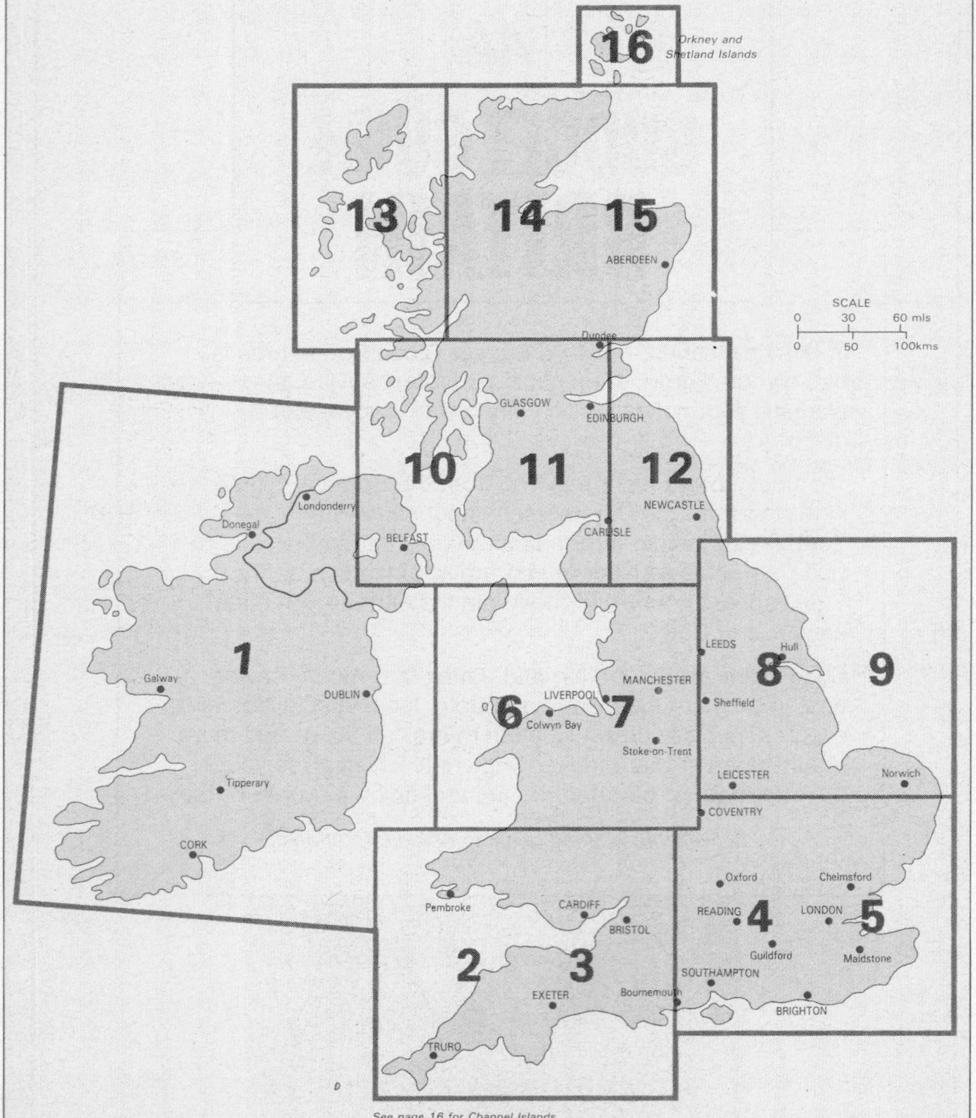

**16** Orkney and Shetland Islands

**13**

**14**

**15** Aberdeen

SCALE
0    30    60 mls
0    50    100kms

Dundee

**10** Londonderry
Donegal
BELFAST

**11** GLASGOW
EDINBURGH

**12** NEWCASTLE
CARLISLE

**1** Galway
DUBLIN
Tipperary
CORK

**6** LIVERPOOL
Colwyn Bay

**7** MANCHESTER
Sheffield
Stoke-on-Trent

**8** LEEDS
Hull

**9** Norwich

LEICESTER
COVENTRY

**2** Pembroke

**3** CARDIFF
BRISTOL
EXETER
TRURO
Bournemouth

Oxford
READING **4**
Guildford
SOUTHAMPTON

LONDON **5**
Chelmsford
Maidstone
BRIGHTON

See page 16 for Channel Islands

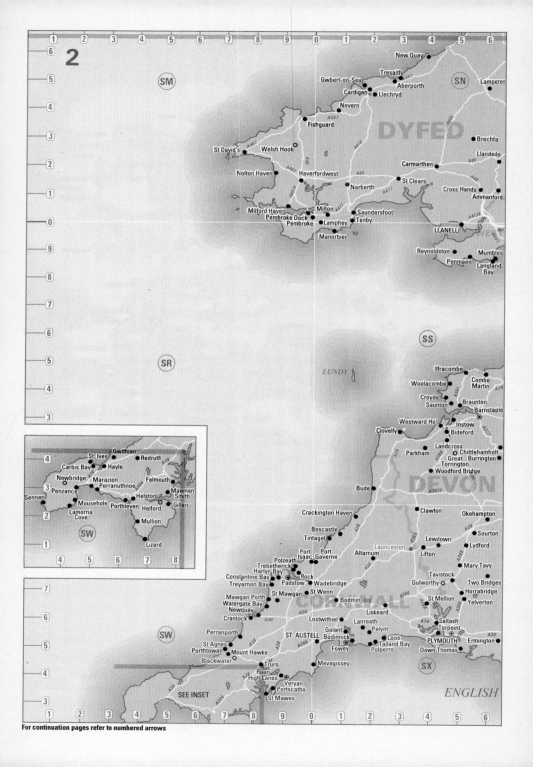

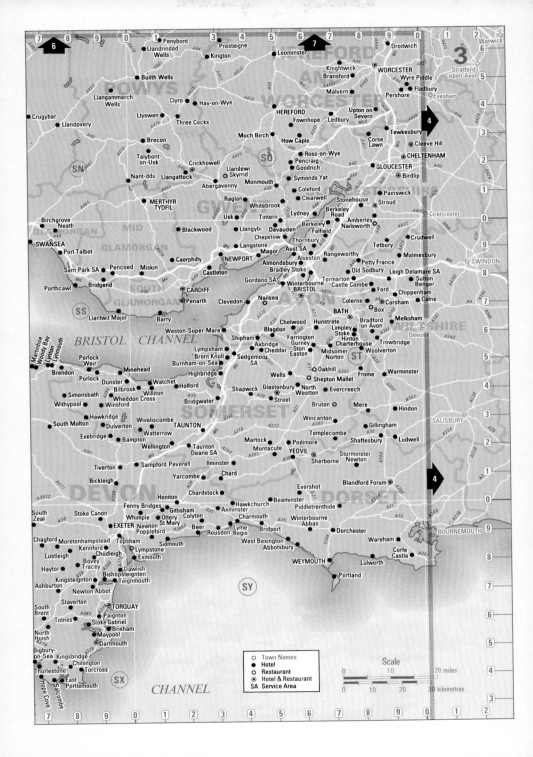

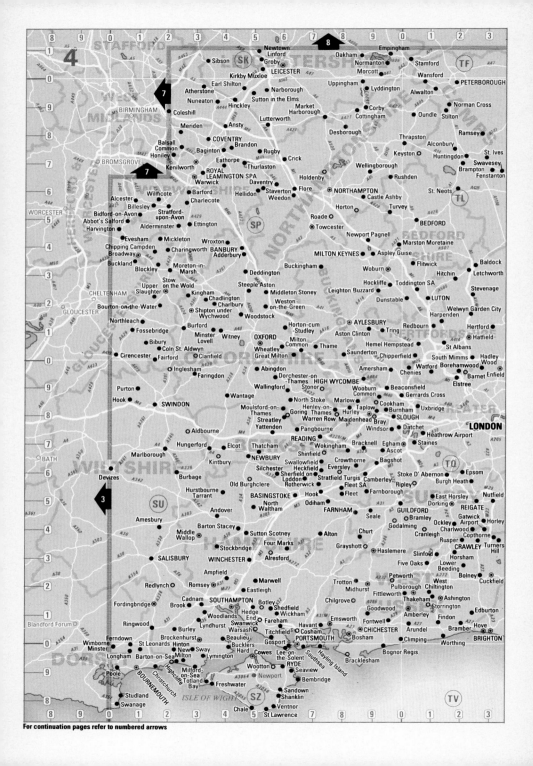

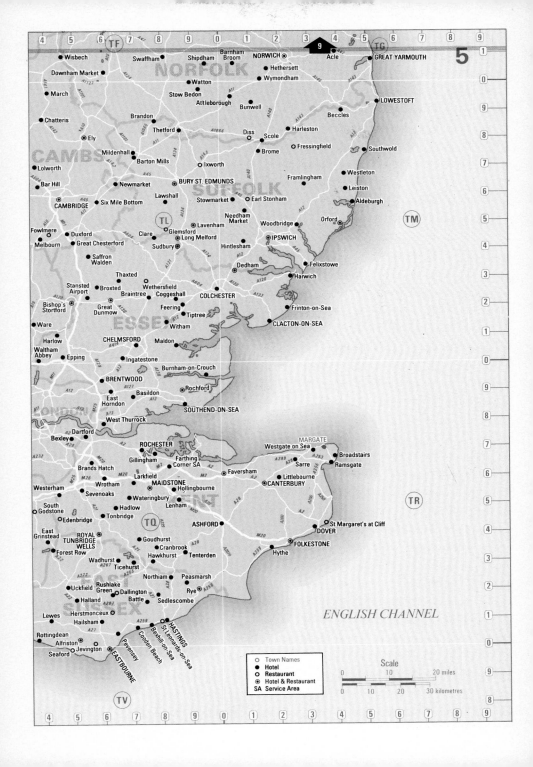

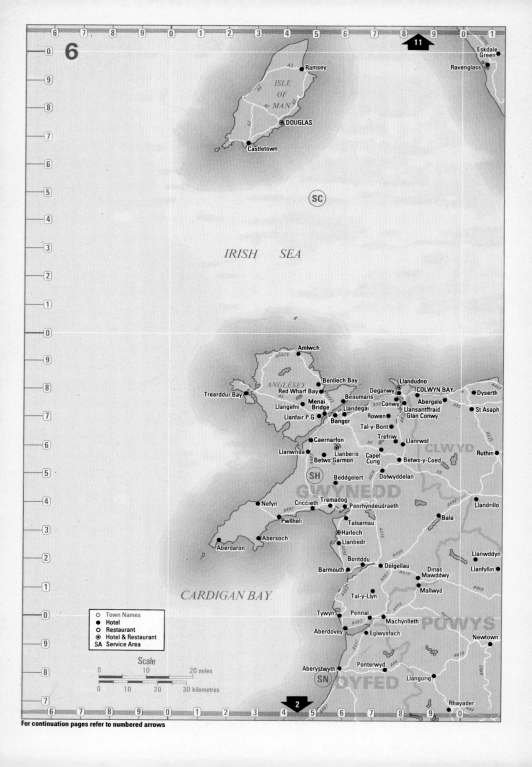

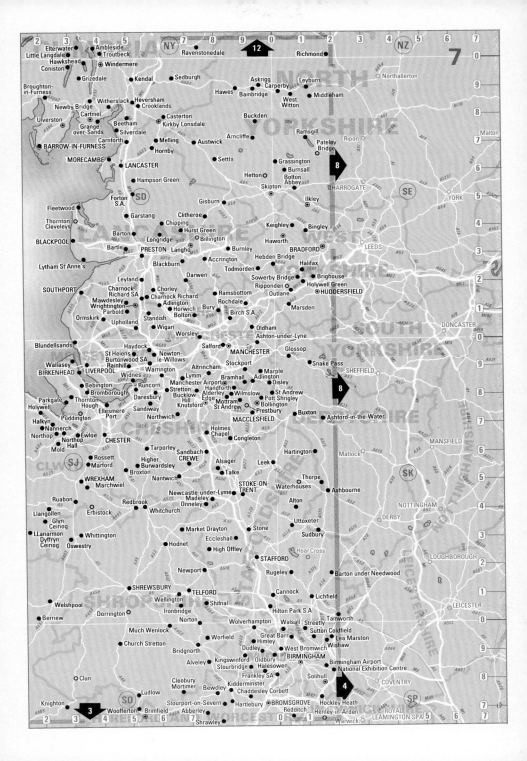

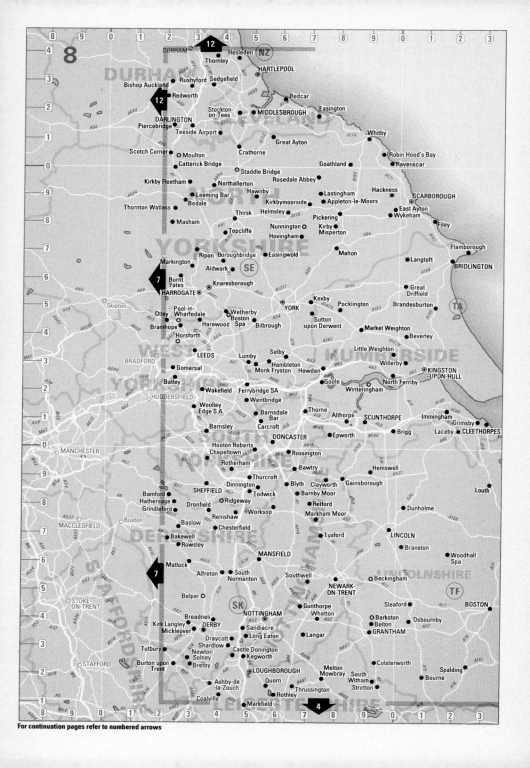

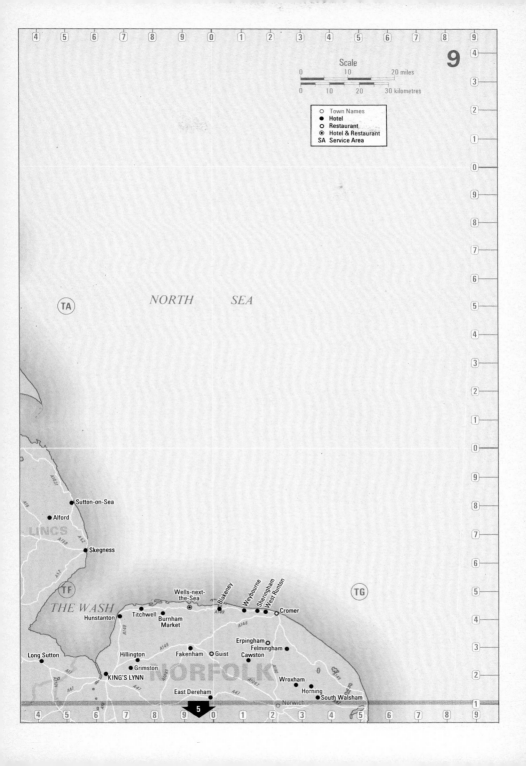

**9**

Scale

| 0 | 10 | 20 miles |

| 0 | 10 | 20 | 30 kilometres |

○ Town Names
● Hotel
○ Restaurant
◉ Hotel & Restaurant
SA Service Area

*NORTH    SEA*

(TA)

● Sutton-on-Sea

● Alford

**LINCS**

● Skegness

(TF)

*THE WASH*

(TG)

Wells-next-the-Sea

● Blakeney
● Weybourne
● Sheringham
● West Runton
○ Cromer

● Titchwell
Hunstanton ●
● Burnham Market

● Erpingham
Felmingham ●
● Hillington   ● Fakenham   ○ Guist   Cawston ●

Long Sutton ●

● Grimston
**KING'S LYNN** ●

**NORFOLK**

● Wroxham
● Horning
East Dereham ●   ● South Walsham

○ Norwich

▼ **5**

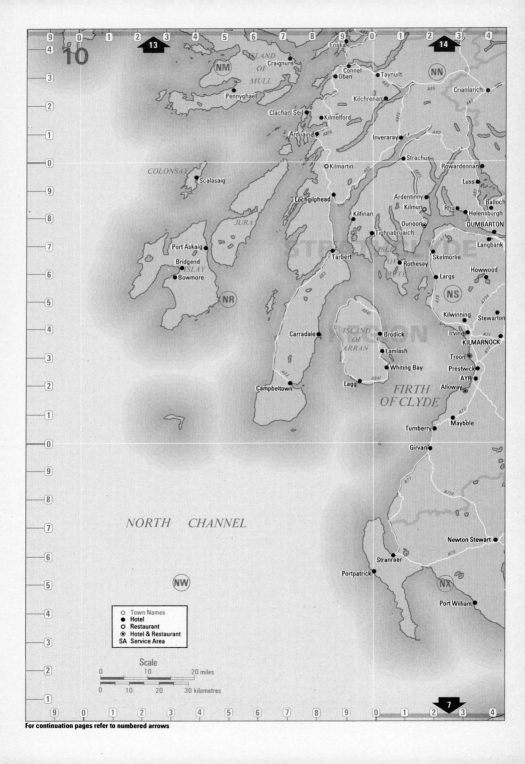

**13**

**14**

Eriska

ISLAND OF MULL

NM

Craignure

Connel
Oban

Taynuilt

NN

Crianlarich

Pennyghael

Kilchrenan

A85

Clachan-Seil
Kilmelford

Inveraray

Arduaine
A816

Rowardennan

COLONSAY

Kilmartin

Strachur

Scalasaig

Ardentinny

Luss

Balloch

Lochgilphead

Kilmun
Dunoon

Rhu

Helensburgh

DUMBARTON

JURA

Kilfinan

Tighnabruaich

Langbank

Port Askaig

ISLAY
Bridgend

Bowmore

NR

Tarbert

Rothesay

Skelmorlie

Largs

Howwood

NS

Kilwinning

Stewarton

Carradale

ISLAND OF ARRAN

Brodick

Irvine

KILMARNOCK

Lamlash

Whiting Bay

Troon

Prestwick
AYR

Campbeltown

Lagg

FIRTH OF CLYDE

Alloway

Turnberry

Maybole

Girvan

NORTH    CHANNEL

Newton Stewart

NW

Stranraer

Portpatrick

NX

Port William

○ Town Names
● Hotel
○ Restaurant
◉ Hotel & Restaurant
SA Service Area

**Scale**

| 0 | 10 | 20 miles |

| 0 | 10 | 20 | 30 kilometres |

**7**

**For continuation pages refer to numbered arrows**

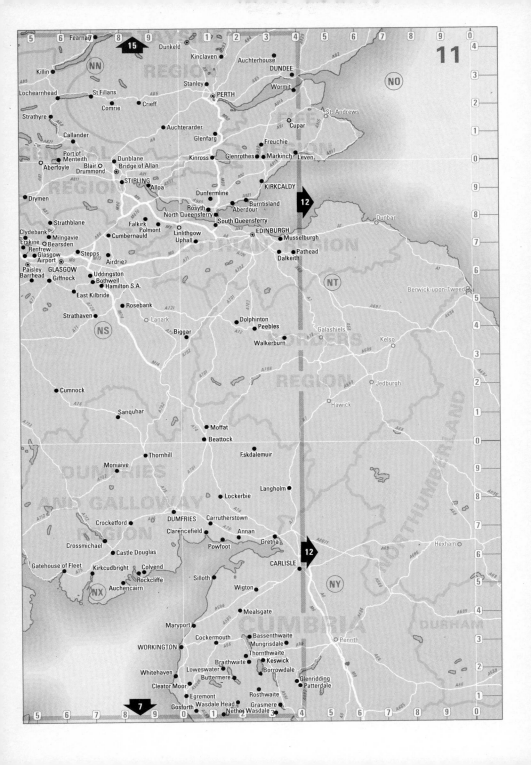

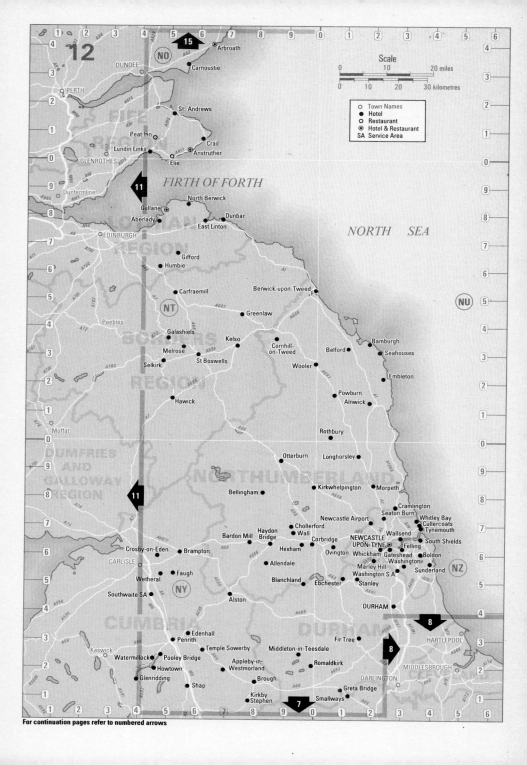

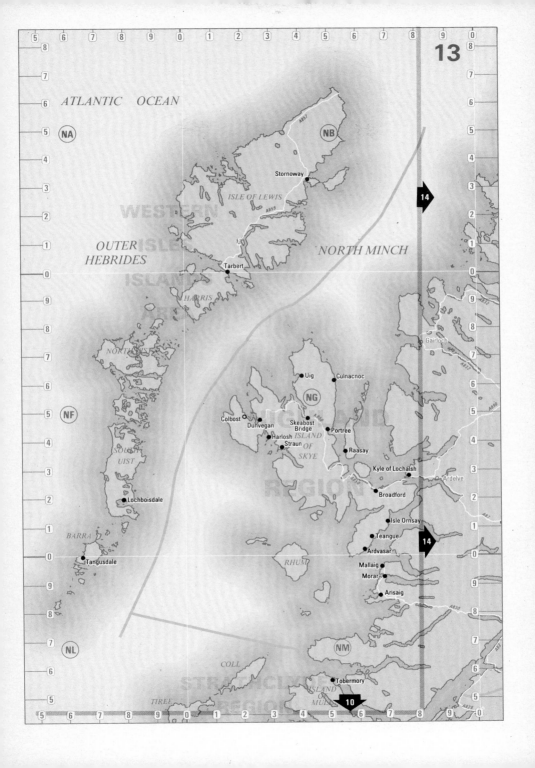

ATLANTIC    OCEAN

NA

NB

A857

Stornoway

ISLE OF LEWIS

14

A859

WESTERN

OUTER
HEBRIDES

OUTER ISLE

NORTH MINCH

ISLANDS

Tarbert

HARRIS

NORTH UIST

Gairloch

A87

NF

Uig

Culnacnoc

NG

Colbost

HIGHLAND

Dunvegan    Skeabost
Bridge

Portree

SOUTH
UIST

Harlosh  ISLAND

Straun  OF

SKYE

Raasay

Kyle of Lochalsh

Ardelve

REGION

A87

Lochboisdale

Broadford

BARRA

Isle Ornsay

Teangue

14

Tangusdale

Ardvasar

RHUM

Mallaig

Morar

Arisaig

A830

NL

NM

COLL

Tobermory

STRATHCLYDE

TIREE

ISLAND
OF MULL

10

A828

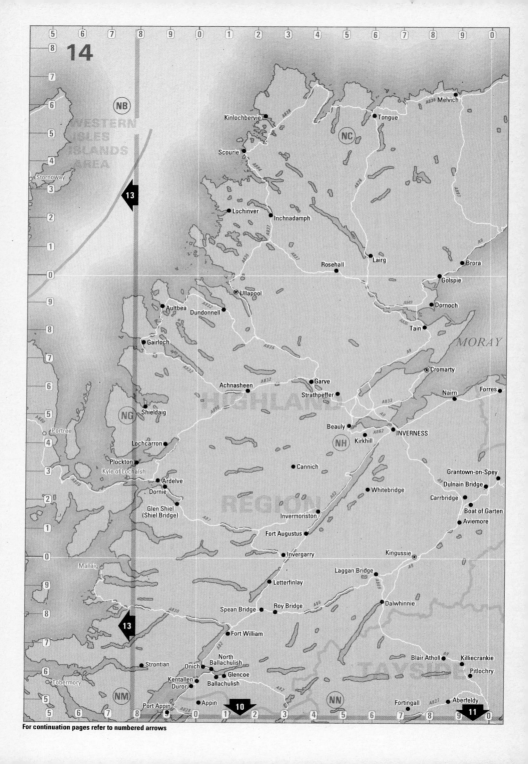

WESTERN ISLES ISLANDS AREA

NB

NC

Stornoway

13

Kinlochbervie

Tongue

Melvich

Scourie

Lochinver

Inchnadamph

Rosehall

Lairg

Brora

Golspie

Dornoch

Ullapool

Aultbea

Dundonnell

Tain

MORAY

Gairloch

Cromarty

Garve

Achnasheen

Strathpeffer

Nairn

Forres

HIGHLAND

Shieldaig

NG

Portree

Beauly

INVERNESS

Lochcarron

Kirkhill

NH

Plockton

Kyle of Lochalsh

Cannich

Grantown-on-Spey

Ardelve

Dulnain Bridge

Dornie

Whitebridge

Carrbridge

Glen Shiel
(Shiel Bridge)

Invermoriston

Boat of Garten

Aviemore

REGION

Fort Augustus

Kingussie

Invergarry

Malaig

Laggan Bridge

Letterfinlay

Dalwhinnie

13

Spean Bridge

Roy Bridge

NM

Fort William

Strontian

North
Ballachulish

Blair Atholl

Killiecrankie

TAYSIDE

Onich

Glencoe

Pitlochry

Kentallen

Duror

Ballachulish

Tobermory

NN

Fortingall

Aberfeldy

Port Appin

Appin

10

NM

11

For continuation pages refer to numbered arrows

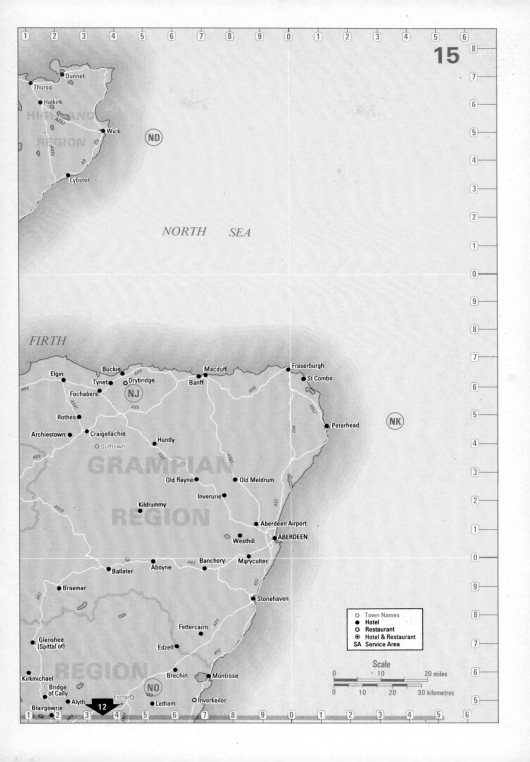

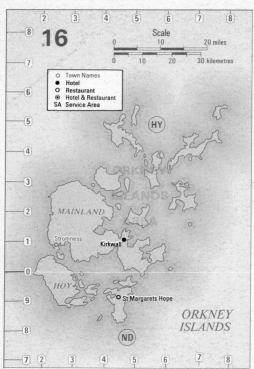
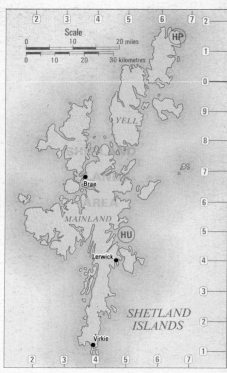
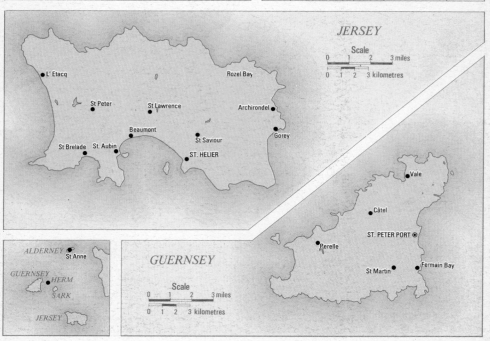